#54409864

NORTH CAROLINA TEACHER'S EDITION

PRENTICE HALL MATHEMATICS

GEOMETRY

Laurie E. Bass

Randall I. Charles

Art Johnson

Dan Kennedy

PEARSON

Prentice
Hall

Needham, Massachusetts
Upper Saddle River, New Jersey

NORTH CAROLINA

Dorling Kindersley (DK) is an international publishing company that specializes in the creation of high-quality, illustrated information books for children and adults. Dorling Kindersley's unique graphic presentation style is used in this program to motivate students in learning about real-world applications of mathematics. DK is part of the Pearson family of companies.

ISBN 0-13-180864-8

1 2 3 4 5 6 7 8 9 10   07 06 05 04 03

North Carolina Geometry Standard Course of Study Handbook

North Carolina Standard Course of Study Correlation

This correlation identifies sections on which the North Carolina Standard Course of Study objectives are addressed in this book. With the help of this chart you can find solid, fully developed instruction on any standard

Standard	Prentice Hall Geometry Lessons
Number & Operations	
1.01 Use the trigonometric ratios to model and solve problems involving right triangles.	9-1, 9-2, 9-3, 9-4, 9-5
1.02 Use length, area, and volume of geometric figures to solve problems. Include arc length, area of sectors of circles; lateral area, surface area, and volume of three-dimensional figures; and perimeter, area, and volume of composite figures.	1-6, 1-7, 7-1, 7-4, 7-5, 7-6, 7-7, 8-1, 10-3, 10-4, 10-5, 10-6, 10-7, 10-8
1.03 Use length, area, and volume to model and solve problems involving probability.	7-8
Geometry	
2.01 Use logic and deductive reasoning to draw conclusions and solve problems.	1-1, 2-1, 2-2, 2-3, 2-4, 5-4
2.02 Apply properties, definitions, and theorems of angles and lines to solve problems and write proofs.	1-2, 1-3, 1-4, 1-5, 2-5, 3-1, 3-2, 3-5, 3-6, 3-7, 11-6
2.03 Apply properties, definitions, and theorems of two-dimensional figures to solve problems and write proofs:	
a) Triangles.	3-3, 4-2, 4-3, 4-4, 4-5, 4-6, 4-7, 5-1, 5-2, 5-3, 5-5, 7-2, 7-3, 8-2, 8-3, 8-4, 8-5, 8-6
b) Quadrilaterals.	6-1, 6-2, 6-3, 6-4, 6-5, 6-6, 6-7, 8-2, 8-6
c) Other polygons.	3-4, 4-1, 8-2, 8-6
d) Circles.	8-2, 11-1, 11-2, 11-3, 11-4, 11-5
2.04 Develop and apply properties of solids to solve problems.	10-1, 10-2, 10-3, 10-4, 10-5, 10-6, 10-7, 10-8
3.01 Describe the transformation (translation, reflection, rotation, dilation) of polygons in the coordinate plane in simple algebraic terms.	12-1, 12-2, 12-3, 12-4, 12-6, 12-7
3.02 Use matrix operations (addition, subtraction, multiplication, scalar multiplication) to describe the transformation of polygons in the coordinate plane.	12-2, 12-7

North Carolina Standard Course of Study Year-at-a-Glance

The following chart provides an overview of where within Prentice Hall Geometry each objective in the North Carolina Standard Course of Study is introduced, developed, and concluded.

Standard	PRENTICE HALL GEOMETRY CHAPTERS											
	1	2	3	4	5	6	7	8	9	10	11	12
Number & Operations												
1.01 Use the trigonometric ratios to model and solve problems involving right triangles.									I,D,C			
1.02 Use length, area, and volume of geometric figures to solve problems. Include arc length, area of sectors of circles; lateral area, surface area, and volume of three-dimensional figures; and perimeter, area, and volume of composite figures.	I						D	D		D,C		
1.03 Use length, area, and volume to model and solve problems involving probability.							I,D,C					
Geometry												
2.01 Use logic and deductive reasoning to draw conclusions and solve problems.	I	D			C							
2.02 Apply properties, definitions, and theorems of angles and lines to solve problems and write proofs.	I	D	D								C	
2.03 Apply properties, definitions, and theorems of two-dimensional figures to solve problems and write proofs:												
a) Triangles.			I	D	D,C							
b) Quadrilaterals.						I,D	C					
c) Other polygons.			I	D				C				
d) Circles.								I		D,C		
2.04 Develop and apply properties of solids to solve problems.									I,D,C			
Algebra												
3.01 Describe the transformation (translation, reflection, rotation, dilation) of polygons in the coordinate plane in simple algebraic terms.												I,D,C
3.02 Use matrix operations (addition, subtraction, multiplication, scalar multiplication) to describe the transformation of polygons in the coordinate plane.												I,D,C

I = introduced   D = developed   C = concluded

North Carolina Standard Course of Study Lesson-by-Lesson Correlation

This chart provides pacing suggestions based on the objectives of the North Carolina Standard Course of Study for Geometry. It is designed to help you maximize your coverage of the objectives.

Chapter 1 Tools of Geometry		North Carolina Course of Study	Pacing	
			Traditional	Block
1-1	Patterns and Inductive Reasoning	2.01	2 days	1 day
1-2	Points, Lines, and Planes	2.02	2 days	1 day
1-3	Segments, Rays, Parallel Lines and Planes	2.02	2 days	1 day
1-4	Measuring Segments and Angles	2.02	2 days	1 day
1-5	Basic Constructions	2.02	2 days	1 day
1-6	The Coordinate Plane	1.02	3 days	1 day
1-7	Perimeter, Circumference, and Area	1.02	2 days	1 day
Testing and Additional Activities			3 days	2 days

Chapter 2 Reasoning and Proof		North Carolina Course of Study	Pacing	
			Traditional	Block
2-1	Conditional Statements	2.01	2 days	1 day
2-2	Biconditionals and Definitions	2.01	2 days	1 day
2-3	Deductive Reasoning	2.01	2 days	1 day
2-4	Reasoning in Algebra	2.01	2 days	1 day
2-5	Proving Angles Congruent	2.02	3 days	1 day
Testing and Additional Activities			3 days	2 days

Chapter 3 Parallel and Perpendicular Lines		North Carolina Course of Study	Pacing	
			Traditional	Block
3-1	Properties of Parallel Lines	2.02	2 days	1 day
3-2	Proving Lines Parallel	2.02	2 days	1 day
3-3	Parallel Lines and the Triangle Angle-Sum Theorem	2.03	2 days	1 day
3-4	The Polygon Angle-Sum Theorems	2.03	2 days	1 day
3-5	Lines in the Coordinate Plane	2.02	3 days	1 day
3-6	Slopes of Parallel and Perpendicular Lines	2.02	2 days	1 day
3-7	Constructing Parallel and Perpendicular Lines	2.02	2 days	1 day
Testing and Additional Activities			3 days	2 days

Chapter 4 Congruent Triangles		North Carolina Course of Study	Pacing	
			Traditional	Block
4-1	Congruent Figures	2.03	1 day	1 day
4-2	Triangle Congruence by SSS and SAS	2.03	1 1/2 days	1 day
4-3	Triangle Congruence by ASA and AAS	2.03	1 1/2 days	1 day
4-4	Using Congruent Triangles: CPCTC	2.03	1 day	1 day
4-5	Isosceles and Equilateral Triangles	2.03	1 1/2 days	1 day
4-6	Congruence in Right Triangles	2.03	1 1/2 days	1 day
4-7	Using Corresponding Parts of Congruent Triangles	2.03	2 days	1 day
Testing and Additional Activities			3 days	2 days

Chapter 5 Relationships Within Triangles		North Carolina Course of Study	Pacing	
			Traditional	Block
5-1	Midsegments of Triangles	2.03	2 days	1 day
5-2	Bisectors in Triangles	2.03	2 days	1 day
5-3	Concurrent Lines, Medians, and Altitudes	2.03	2 days	1 day
5-4	Inverses, Contrapositives, and Indirect Reasoning	2.01	2 days	1 day
5-5	Inequalities in Triangles	2.03	2 days	1 day
Testing and Additional Activities			3 days	2 days

Chapter 6 Quadrilaterals		North Carolina Course of Study	Pacing	
			Traditional	Block
6-1	Classifying Quadrilaterals	2.03	2 days	1 day
6-2	Properties of Parallelograms	2.03	2 days	1 day
6-3	Proving That a Quadrilateral is a Parallelogram	2.03	2 days	1 day
6-4	Special Parallelograms	2.03	1 day	1 day
6-5	Trapezoids and Kites	2.03	2 days	1 day
6-6	Placing Figures in the Coordinate Plane	2.03	2 days	1 day
6-7	Proofs Using Coordinate Geometry	2.03	2 days	1 day
Testing and Additional Activities			3 days	2 days

Chapter 7 Area		North Carolina Course of Study	Pacing	
			Traditional	Block
7-1	Areas of Parallelograms and Triangles	1.02	2 days	1 day
7-2	The Pythagorean Theorem and Its Converse	2.03	2 days	1 day
7-3	Special Right Triangles	2.03	2 days	1 day
7-4	Areas of Trapezoids, Rhombuses, and Kites	1.02	2 days	1 day
7-5	Areas of Regular Polygons	1.02	1 day	1 day
7-6	Circles and Arcs	1.02	2 days	1 day
7-7	Areas of Circles and Sectors	1.02	2 days	1 day
7-8	Geometric Probability	1.03	2 days	1 day
Testing and Additional Activities			3 days	2 days

Chapter 8 Similarity		North Carolina Course of Study	Pacing	
			Traditional	Block
8-1	Ratios and Proportions	1.02	2 days	1 day
8-2	Similar Polygons	2.03	2 days	1 day
8-3	Proving Triangles Similar	2.03	3 days	1 1/2 days
8-4	Similarity in Right Triangles	2.03	2 days	1 day
8-5	Proportions in Triangles	2.03	3 days	1 1/2 days
8-6	Perimeters and Areas of Similar Figures	2.03	2 days	1 day
Testing and Additional Activities			3 days	2 days

Chapter 9 Right Triangle Trigonometry	North Carolina Course of Study	Pacing	
		Traditional	Block
9-1 The Tangent Ratio	1.01	2 days	1 day
9-2 Sine and Cosine Ratios	1.01	2 days	1 day
9-3 Angles of Elevation and Depression	1.01	2 days	1 day
9-4 Vectors	1.01	3 days	1 1/2 days
9-5 Trigonometry and Area	1.01	3 days	1 1/2 days
Testing and Additional Activities		3 days	2 days

Chapter 10 Surface Area and Volume	North Carolina Course of Study	Pacing	
		Traditional	Block
10-1 Space Figures and Nets	2.04	2 days	1 day
10-2 Space Figures and Drawings	2.04	2 days	1 day
10-3 Surface Areas of Prisms and Cylinders	1.02, 2.04	2 days	1 day
10-4 Surface Areas of Pyramids and Cones	1.02, 2.04	2 days	1 day
10-5 Volumes of Prisms and Cylinders	1.02, 2.04	2 days	1 day
10-6 Volumes of Pyramids and Cones	1.02, 2.04	2 days	1 day
10-7 Surface Areas and Volumes of Spheres	1.02, 2.04	2 days	1 day
10-8 Areas and Volumes of Similar Solids	1.02, 2.04	2 days	1 day
Testing and Additional Activities		3 days	2 days

Chapter 11 Circles	North Carolina Course of Study	Pacing	
		Traditional	Block
11-1 Tangent Lines	2.03	3 days	1 day
11-2 Chords and Arcs	2.03	2 days	1 day
11-3 Inscribed Angles	2.03	3 days	1 day
11-4 Angle Measures and Segment Lengths	2.03	2 days	1 day
11-5 Circles in the Coordinate Plane	2.03	2 days	1 day
11-6 Locus: A Set of Points	2.02	2 days	1 day
Testing and Additional Activities		3 days	2 days

Chapter 12 Transformations	North Carolina Course of Study	Pacing	
		Traditional	Block
12-1 Reflections	3.01	2 days	1 day
12-2 Translations	3.01, 3.02	3 days	1 day
12-3 Rotations	3.01	2 days	1 day
12-4 Compositions of Reflections	3.01	2 days	1 day
12-5 Symmetry		1 day	1 day
12-6 Tessellations	3.01	2 days	1 day
12-7 Dilations	3.01, 3.02	3 days	1 day
Testing and Additional Activities		3 days	2 days

North Carolina Course of Study

Use these pages to acquaint yourself with the North Carolina Geometry Standard Course of Study at this grade level with respect to where previous standards have brought the student and where this year's standards will lead their studies going forward.

Number & Operations

Progression

Prior Years
Students focused on exploring the Pythagorean Theorem and similar and congruent triangles. They also learned to work with exponents and how to find the square root of a number.

This Year
They will expand their understanding to include determining and using trigonometric ratios of right triangles. They will use this understanding to solve a variety of problems, such as the height of a building or distance to a landmark.

Going Forward
Using trigonometric ratios will expand to include using these ratios to find areas of other polygons.

1.01 Use the trigonometric ratios to model and solve problems involving right triangles.

In the 15th century, Copernicus used trigonometric ratios to study the orbits of planets when they formed a right triangle with Earth and the sun. Earth is 1 AU (astronomical unit) from the sun. How far is Mercury from the sun if the angle of this triangle that has Earth at its vertex is 22.3°?

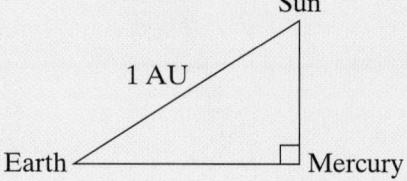

Answer: $\sin 22.3° = 0.38 = \frac{x}{1}$, so Mercury is about 0.38 AU from the sun.

Most of the Egyptian pyramids form a 52° angle with the ground. If a crumbling pyramid was found to have a base length of 70 m, how tall was the original pyramid, to the nearest meter?

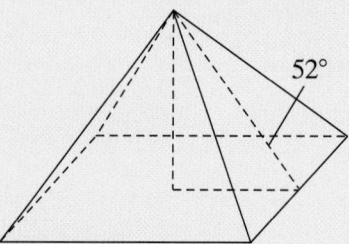

A 22 m
B 45 m
C 28 m
D 90 m

Answer: B

Progression

Prior Years
Students have learned the properties of two-dimensional and three-dimensional figures. Students have also focused on using measurements of length to calculate the area of plane figures and the volume of cylinders and prisms.

This Year
Students will extend their knowledge to understand the properties of circles and the relationships between a circle and geometric figures interacting with a circle. They will expand their understanding to include finding length, area, and volume of more complicated geometric figures.

Going Forward
Finding length, area, and volume will expand to include finding area and volume of similar solids.

1.02 Use length, area, and volume of geometric figures to solve problems. Include arc length, area of sectors of circles, lateral area, surface area, and volume of three-dimensional figures; and perimeter, area, and volume of composite figures.

Math Background
There are a number of basic formulas for area and volume of two-dimensional and three-dimensional geometric figures. Most students will be familiar with several area formulas, notably for rectangles, triangles, and circles. But additional formulas for trapezoids and rhombuses, for example, may need reinforcing as you expand or manipulate basic area formulas to develop volume formulas that may not be intuitive.

Students can also use exercise understanding that "width" in one formula may be interchangeable with "base" in another. They may also need reinforcement with the differences in terms. For example, the base of a triangle has a measured length while the base of a pyramid has a measured area.

Continued exercise and reinforcement of the formulas will help students to be more comfortable and confident using them.

A circle graph shows types of trash in a typical American city. The section of the graph that shows the amount of paper thrown away has an angle of 137°. If the circumference of the graph is 32 cm, what is the length of the arc for this part of the graph, to the nearest centimeter?

A   12 cm
B   20 cm
C   32 cm
D   84 cm

Answer: A

A building used for storing road salt is shaped like a cone and has a door near the top for filling it with salt. If the diameter of the building is 10 m and its height is 8.0 m, how much salt can the building hold, to the nearest whole unit?

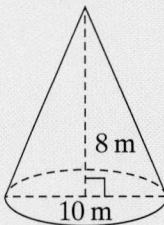

Answer: 209 m³

NC11

Progression

Prior Years	This Year	Going Forward
Students learned the fundamental concepts of probability. They learned to find probability by comparing the number of favorable outcomes to the number of possible outcomes.	They will apply what they know about geometric properties and quantities to compare favorable geometric outcomes to the number of possible outcomes, for example, the likelihood of hitting a certain portion of a target.	Finding geometric probability will expand to include finding geometric probability of multiple events.

1.03 Use length, area, and volume to model and solve problems involving probability.

Math Background

In Algebra we address probability more extensively than in geometry. However, the use of geometric models for probability can be very intriguing to students, especially if the students find the geometric models intuitively appealing.

Just as with formulas, it remains important to also reinforce the basic concept of probability of an event as the likelihood of that event occurring. This is measured by the ratio of favorable outcomes (of the event occurring) to the total possible outcomes.

A plastic metric ruler is 30 cm long. A drop of paint falls on the ruler. What is the probability that the paint lands between the 15-cm mark and the 18-cm mark?

A $\frac{1}{2}$ B $\frac{3}{5}$

C $\frac{1}{10}$ D $\frac{9}{10}$

Answer: C

A dartboard has a diameter of 48 cm. In the center, it has a red circle with a diameter of 10 cm. Surrounding the red circle, is a green circle with a diameter of 30 cm. The rest of the dartboard is yellow. What is the probability that a dart thrown will land in the green area?

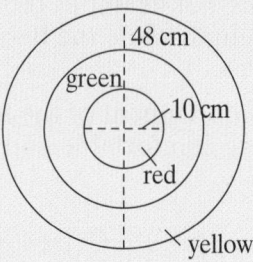

Answer: $P = \dfrac{A_{green}}{A_{total}}$

$\approx \dfrac{628}{1809}$

Progression

Prior Years	This Year	Going Forward
Students focused on thinking logically on an intuitive basis. They also have learned the basic tenets of inductive and deductive reasoning.	They will expand their understanding to include learning and applying different methods of deductive reasoning, such as two-column proof and paragraph proof. They will use deductive reasoning and their understanding of geometric concepts to reach logical conclusions.	Deductive reasoning will expand to include geometric proofs and algebraic proofs.

2.01 Use logic and deductive reasoning to draw conclusions and solve problems.

Math Background

Students have exercised logic and reasoning in everything from common board games to writing research papers. Within geometry, reasoning deductively or logically from given statements to a conclusion can strengthen those same skills for students.

Whether using conditional statements or proofs, it is important to reason correctly as students continue to exercise the basic tools of geometry: definitions, postulates, and theorems. Similar to the justifications students use in everyday life, the validity of their arguments are only as good as their logic and the truth of their statements.

You know that if the roads are icy, the temperature must be less than or equal to the freezing point of water. Using deductive reasoning, which of the following is true?

A It's 20°F, so the roads must be icy.
B The roads are icy, so it must be less than or equal to 32°F.
C The roads are not icy, so it must be warmer than 32°F.
D Ice on the roads has no relation to temperature.

Answer: B

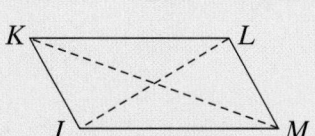

Given: $\overline{KJ} \parallel \overline{LM}$
$\overline{KJ} \cong \overline{LM}$

Prove: $JKLM$ is a parallelogram.

Justify each step.

Answer: If one pair of opposite sides of a quadrilateral is both congruent and parallel, then the quadrilateral is a parallelogram.

Progression

Prior Years
Students have learned fundamental geometric principles and relationships relating to lines and angles. Students focused on using properties of rational numbers to solve problems.

This Year
They will expand and apply their understanding of geometric figures and their properties to understanding postulates and theorems. They will use this information to form logical arguments to prove a geometric statement is true.

Going Forward
Solving problems and writing proofs will expand to include areas other than geometry.

2.02 Apply properties, definitions, and theorems of angles and lines to solve problems and write proofs.

Math Background
Regardless of whether students become more proficient with one form of a proof over another, the logic and completeness of the proof remain the high priorities. Again, the strength of such logic and completeness is reliant upon students comfort with their tools: definitions, properties, and theorems.

Exercise with students the theorems that seem most intuitive and those that do not. Examples, counterexamples, and constructions will prove valuable in such exercises.

For a set of intersecting lines:

$\angle A \cong \angle B$ and $\angle A \cong \angle C$.

What property can you use to prove the following?

$\angle B \cong \angle C$

A   identity
B   reflexive
C   symmetric
D   transitive

Answer: D

Two lines intersect, forming a 48° angle. Using the definition of a supplementary angle, find the measures of the other three angles formed.

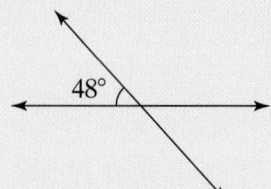

48°

Answer: Two of the angles are 132°, and one angle is 48°.

Progression

Prior Years	This Year	Going Forward
Students classified triangles by angle and side measurements. They constructed triangles given angle and side measures. They explored congruent and similar figures and used similar triangles in indirect measurement.	They will develop and prove theorems for triangles. They will use conjectures, postulates, and theorems to form logical arguments to prove triangles are congruent or similar. They will also use this information to find dimensions and properties of triangles to solve problems.	Solving problems and writing proofs will expand to include other figures in geometry and other areas of mathematics. Properties of triangles will be used in many real-world applications, including architectural design and vectors used in physics.

2.03 Apply properties, definitions, and theorems of two-dimensional figures to solve problems and write proofs:

a) Triangles.

Math Background

Students may remember the terms *congruent triangles* (corresponding angle measures and side lengths are equal) and *similar triangles* (corresponding angle measures are equal and corresponding side lengths are in proportion). Some students may have difficulty determining if triangles are congruent or similar when they have been flipped or rotated. Therefore, a review of naming congruent triangles may be helpful.

Some of the theorems and postulates that relate to similarity and congruence may be familiar, for example, when students use the Side-Side-Side Postulate to identify congruent triangles. Exercises using them in formal proofs will reinforce both the theorems themselves and the principles involved in writing proofs.

Encourage students to use the complete name when referring to theorems and postulates to reinforce their understanding of the theorems and their meaning (for example, students should say "side-angle-side" when using SAS to prove triangles congruent). Practice using different forms of proof—paragraph, two-column, and flow chart—will also give students a broad understanding of proof that focuses on the justification of steps rather than a specific form.

 In $\triangle ABC$ L and M are midpoints. Find $\overline{AC}$ and $\overline{LM}$.

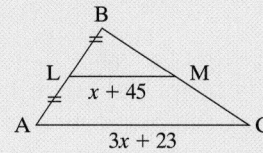

Assume that $LM = \frac{1}{2} AC$.

$3x + 23 = 2(x + 45)$

$x = 67$

Therefore,

$AC = 3(67) + 23 = 224$

$LM = 67 + 45 = 112$

 A quilt contains different triangles. One triangle has a side of 25 cm, another side of 20 cm, with the angle between them being 60°. Another triangle also has a side of 25 cm, another side of 20 cm, with the angle between them being 60°. Which of the following postulates proves that the triangles are congruent?

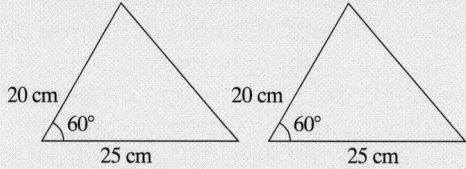

A SSS   B ASA   C SAS   D AAS

Answer: C

Progression

Prior Years	This Year	Going Forward
Students have identified and classified quadrilaterals when given information about sides and angles. They have used formulas for perimeter and the area of various quadrilaterals and have related quadrilaterals to triangles.	Students will continue to explore properties of quadrilaterals. They will develop proofs and theorems using definitions of types of quadrilaterals and the properties of parallel lines, and geometric figures. They will explore how diagonals of a quadrilateral are related to its sides and angles, and they will use proofs and theorems to classify quadrilaterals when side and angle measures are not given.	Students will encounter quadrilaterals in many real-world situations. They will expand their proof-writing skills to algebraic proofs, and they will use the geometric properties of quadrilaterals to create and manipulate algebraic expressions.

b) Quadrilaterals.

Math Background

Understanding the hierarchy of special quadrilaterals is important to understanding the properties and applications of each type of special quadrilateral. That is knowing that all squares are rectangles, that all rectangles are parallelograms, and so on.

Students have worked within the basics of these frameworks in the past but the expansion of both special types of quadrilaterals and their properties requires additional exercise of both the "old" and the "new" concepts. Working with both the similarities and differences between the quadrilaterals can strengthen that understanding.

A key concept in identifying and describing quadrilaterals is the relationship between different types of quadrilaterals. For example, a square is a rhombus with four right angles. Thus, all squares are rhombuses, but not all rhombuses are squares. Students should practice identifying quadrilaterals using the definitions they may already know and the relationship of a figure to other figures that have been identified.

It is important that students do not confuse a property of a special quadrilateral with the definition of the shape. For example, although the diagonals of a rhombus are perpendicular, the information that the diagonals of a quadrilateral are perpendicular is not sufficient to identify the figure. The quadrilateral may be a rhombus, but it may also be a kite. Familiarity with different examples of quadrilaterals and the proofs of theorems will help students recognize which properties are sufficient to name a quadrilateral.

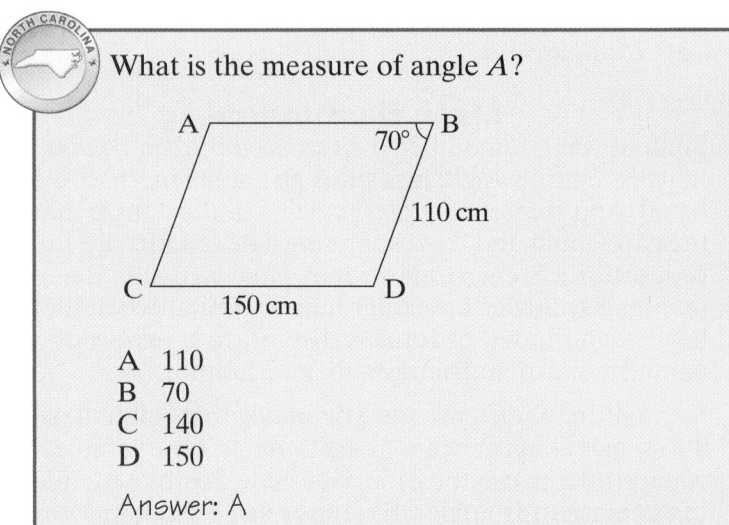

What is the measure of angle *A*?

A 110
B 70
C 140
D 150

Answer: A

You are building a rectangular shed to be used for your outdoor tools. You want to be sure that the building is completely rectangular, but you don't have a tool that will measure the corner angles. Explain how you could use geometry and a piece of string to be sure your building is rectangular.

Answer: Use the string to make sure the diagonals are the same length, which means that it's a rectangle. You can't use the string to check the lengths of the walls because they could be the correct lengths and form a non-rectangular parallelogram.

Progression

Prior Years	This Year	Going Forward
Students identified polygons based on the number of sides in a figure. They used angle and side measures to classify polygons as *regular* or *irregular*. They used simple polygons, such as triangles and trapezoids, to evaluate quantities (such as area) in complex polygons.	Students will explore convex and concave polygons. They will develop theorems relating to interior and exterior angles of polygons, and they will continue to apply their knowledge of triangles and quadrilaterals to polygons. They will explore how parallel lines and diagonals relate to polygons, and they will work with tessellations.	Polygons in the form of triangles, quadrilaterals, and *n*-gons appear in real-world applications, which range from landscaping and architecture to art and design. Polygons can also be used to simplify volume and surface area problems that relate maximum volume and minimum material.

c) Other polygons.

Math Background

Students may know some of the more formal names of different polygons: pentagons, octagons, and decagons for examples. Relating many of the words through the prefixes of these names can also help to strengthen their understanding. These prefixes appear all around us.

There is the Pentagon in Washington and the pentathalon in track and field competition. We also have the octopus and a decade. Again, just strengthening students' understanding of their basic geometric tools can help them better utilize those tools in attaining their goal or solutions in proofs or problems.

As students begin to work with various polygons, they may find it helpful to review what they have learned about triangles and quadrilaterals. For example, work with a hexagon may be simplified if it is treated as a group of six triangles. Encourage students to describe polygons in terms of figures that are familiar. To reinforce properties of polygons, it may be useful to construct polygons on coordinate grids to demonstrate measurements and relationships.

Find the sum of the measure of the angles of a 20-gon.

A 3,600
B 7,200
C 3,240
D 2,880

Answer: C

A small garden is built in the shape of a regular hexagon. Each side is 8 ft long, and its apothem is 9.7 ft. To the nearest tenth, find the area of the garden.

Answer: 232.8 ft^2

Progression

d) Circles.

Math Background

Angles, arcs, chords, secants, and tangents are all distinct yet related terms. They relate to circles.

Segments intersecting a circle to form tangents or chords, also distinguish arcs. The arcs in turn have central angles of measure originating from the center of the circle. It can all be very logical or disorienting for students. Either way, exercise and distinction between patterns and differences can strengthen comprehension.

Students may tend to confuse *arc length* (a fraction of a circle's circumference) and the *measure of an arc* (a degree measure). Encourage students to use precise language when describing arcs and to make the distinction between the two quantities. In notation, the measure of arc AB is written $m\overarc{AB}$. Students should recognize the similarity of the notation to the notation for the measure of an angle A, $m\angle A$. Students should be comfortable with arc length and the measure of an arc before moving on to work with sectors (wedges in a circle) and segments (formed by a chord in a circle).

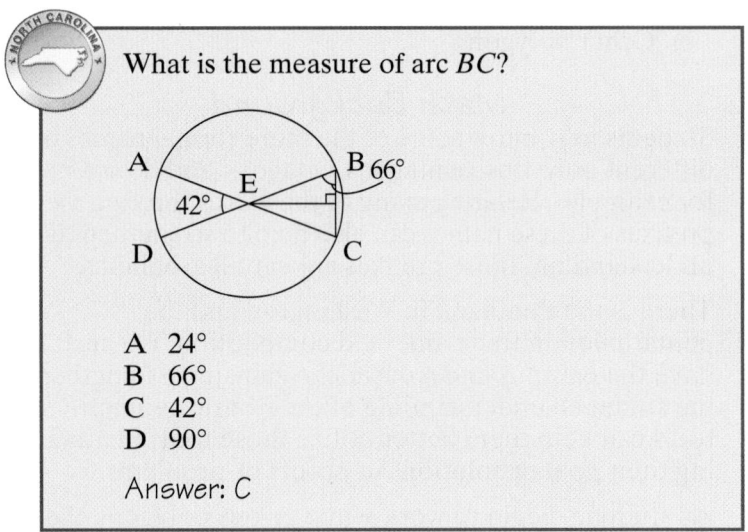

What is the measure of arc BC?

A 24°
B 66°
C 42°
D 90°

Answer: C

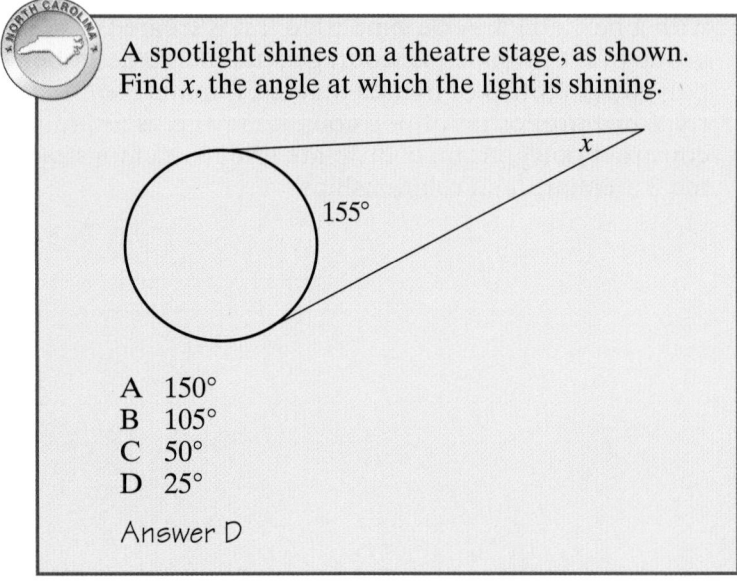

A spotlight shines on a theatre stage, as shown. Find x, the angle at which the light is shining.

A 150°
B 105°
C 50°
D 25°

Answer D

Progression

Prior Years	This Year	Going Forward
Students learned to recognize and create three-dimensional figures. Students learned to use formulas to find surface area and volume of solids.	Students will apply their understanding of solids and their properties to build visualization skills. They will also work with more complicated three-dimensional figures and additional properties of three-dimensional figures, such as cross section and lateral surface area.	Using properties of solids will expand to include creation of solids using models such as computer simulations.

2.04 Develop and apply properties of solids to solve problems.

Math Background

Visualizing how a two-dimensional drawing relates to a three-dimensional figure is key to understanding surface area and volume formulas. Students may have difficulty visualizing the three-dimensional figure described by a *net,* or pattern, and drawing nets for three-dimensional figures. Folding nets to create prisms, cones, and other solids can help students recognize the relationship between their two-dimensional patterns and the figures they describe.

As students become comfortable with the various two-dimensional representations of solid figures, they will begin to recognize the relationship between the bases and lateral area (the product of height and "distance around"). As they develop formulas for surface area, remind students to return to their two-dimensional nets to understand how the formulas work.

The *cross section* of a figure can be thought of as a slice of the solid. Encourage students to find more than one cross section of a figure; for example, one cross section of a cube is a square, while a slice made at a corner produces a rectangle. When describing volume, students may think of solids as a "stack" of cross sections. This will help students understand Cavalieri's Principle (two figures with the same height and same cross-sectional area at every level have the same volume).

A silo is 14 m tall and has a diameter of 4 m. How much grain can the silo hold? A theorem states that the volume of a cylinder is the product of the area of its base and its height.

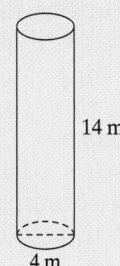

14 m

4 m

A 56 m^3 B 176 m^3 C 616 m^3 D 704 m^3

Answer: B

A theorem states that the lateral area of a right cone is one-half the circumference of the base times the height along the slant. If paper cones used for snow cones are 10 cm across the top and have a slant height of 12 cm, how much paper does it take to make one cone, to the nearest whole number?

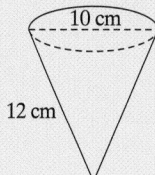

10 cm

12 cm

Answer: 188 cm^2

Progression

Prior Years	This Year	Going Forward
Students have learned to plot points on a coordinate plane. They have also learned the fundamental aspects of congruence by reproducing identical figures in the coordinate plane.	Students will learn to describe a figure based on the location of points on a coordinate plane. They will apply their understanding to include how to translate (slide), rotate, dilate (expand or contract), and reflect figures in the coordinate plane.	Transformation of figures will expand to include changes in the size and shape of a figure.

3.01 Describe the transformation (translation, reflection, rotation, dilation) of polygons in the coordinate plane in simple algebraic terms.

Math Background

As students begin exploring transformations, they may find it useful to describe transformations with more familiar terms. Using tiles and drawings, they can see how a *translation* (slide), *reflection* (flip), *rotation* (turn), and *reflection* (flip) affect a figure. *Dilations* (enlargements and reductions) are easily studied using geometry software. As students become familiar with basic transformations, encourage them to explore combinations of transformations.

The introduction of matrices and vectors to describe translations will be new to most students. Some students will be familiar with arrow notation (translations described in the form $(x, y) \rightarrow (x + n, y + m)$, where n describes horizontal change and m describes vertical change). It may be helpful to relate the translation vector $\langle n, m \rangle$ to the arrow notation form. As students begin to work with matrices, have them label the rows and columns to help them distinguish the matrix for a figure (which contains the coordinates of the vertices) and a translation matrix (which contains the translation vector).

A rectangle that has vertices at $(1, 1), (1, 4), (3, 1)$ and $(3, 4)$ undergoes a translation. The point that was at $(1, 1)$ is now at $(6, 5)$. Which one of these points is one of the vertices of the translated rectangle?

A (5, 8)   B (8, 6)
C (5, 6)   D (8, 5)

Answer: D

The vertices of a triangle are at points $(1, 3), (4, 5),$ and $(3, 1)$. The triangle is reflected over the vertical line at $x = 5$. What points describe the reflected triangle?

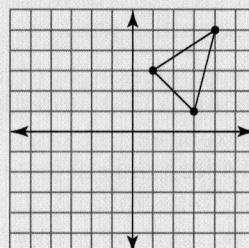

Answer: First, draw the original triangle on a grid.

Next, draw a vertical line at $x = 5$.

Then, reflect the triangle over the line and find that the vertices of the reflected triangle are at $(9, 3), (6, 5),$ and $(7, 1)$

Progression

Prior Years	This Year	Going Forward
Students have learned to use a matrix to organize data. Students focused on finding the results of a transformation on a coordinate plane by using a grid.	Students will learn to use matrices to organize x- and y-coordinate data for a figure on a coordinate plane, They will learn to use matrix operations to move or dilate an object.	Using matrices will expand to include more complicated transformations.

3.02 Use matrix operations (addition, subtraction, multiplication, scalar multiplication) to describe the transformation of polygons in the coordinate plane.

Math Background

Similar to probability models, matrices are not unique to algebra but are typically exercised more in algebra. Furthermore, students need just as much review, if not more so, with these tools while using them again, than with other tools they may use throughout the year.

Review the naming of a two-by-three matrix. Some students may know that it is a matrix with two rows and three columns while other students incorrectly guess it has two columns and three rows.

Regardless, matrices can simplify work with transformations, which may be enough motivation for some students to sharpen their skills with matrices.

The rectangle with vertices at points $(2, 1)$, $(4, 1)$, $(2, 6)$, and $(4, 6)$ is translated on the coordinate plane. The point that was at $(4, 1)$ is now at $(8, 3)$ Use matrices to find the other vertices of the translated rectangle.

Answer: Find the vector that describes the translation:

Horizontal change: $8 - 4 = 4$

Vertical change: $3 - 1 = 2$

The vector is $\langle 4, 2 \rangle$.

Then write a matrix for the original rectangle and one for the vector, and add them:

$$\begin{bmatrix} 2 & 2 & 4 & 4 \\ 1 & 1 & 6 & 6 \end{bmatrix} + \begin{bmatrix} 4 & 4 & 4 & 4 \\ 2 & 2 & 2 & 2 \end{bmatrix} = \begin{bmatrix} 6 & 8 & 6 & 8 \\ 3 & 3 & 8 & 8 \end{bmatrix}$$

The vertices of the translated rectangle are $(6, 3)$, $(8, 3)$, $(6, 8)$, and $(8, 8)$.

A triangle with vertices at $(3, 0)$, $(6, 6)$, and $(9, 6)$ undergoes a dilation with a scale factor of 3. Use scalar multiplication of a matrix to find the vertices of the dilated triangle.

A $(1, 0)$, $(2, 2)$, and $(3, 2)$
B $(3, 0)$, $(6, 6)$, and $(9, 6)$
C $(9, 0)$, $(18, 18)$, and $(27, 18)$
D $(6, 0)$, $(9, 6)$, and $(3, 6)$

Answer: C

North Carolina
Geometry
Standard Course of
Study Handbook

North Carolina High School Standard Course of Study, Geometry

These pages introduce you to the state standards which you will be learning this year. You will see the wording from the state documents, a short explanation of what the standard means to you, as well as an example of how the standard might be tested. Don't worry if you don't understand the concepts and the vocabulary yet. This book will guide you through all of the standards using skills and concepts that you *do* know.

Student's Guide

North Carolina Course of Study

Here is a complete list of the objectives of the North Carolina Standard Mathematics Course of Study for Geometry. These are provided so that you will know what you are expected to learn this year.

Following each objective is an example of how you might see that objective tested. These test questions will become more meaningful to you as the year unfolds. You might want to check back to this section of the book from time to time to check that you understand how to answer the questions.

NUMBER & OPERATION

1.01 Use the trigonometric ratios to model and solve problems involving right triangles.

What It Means to You

Suppose you have a right triangle (a triangle with a 90° angle) and you determine the ratio of two of the sides of this triangle with respect to one of the angles. For example, you have △*ABC* as shown below.

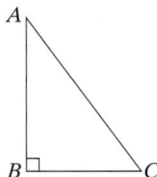

If you find the ratio of the length of the side opposite ∠*A* (*BC*) to the length of the side next to ∠*A* (*AB*) you will find what is known as the *tangent* ratio. This ratio is one of three that relate the lengths of sides of a right triangle. These ratios are known as the *trigonometric ratios*.

Trigonometric ratios show the relationship between the lengths of two sides of a right triangle for a particular angle in the triangle. For example, the *sine* of an angle is the length of the side opposite the angle divided by the length of the hypotenuse (the side opposite the right angle).

You will learn to find the sine, as well as the two other trigonometric ratios, cosine and tangent, when given the measure of the angle. You will learn to find the measure of the angle when given a trigonometric ratio.

You will also learn to use these ratios to solve problems. You will learn to apply this learning, such as determining the height of an object or building. And, as you will see, the trigonometric ratios will have other applications in areas such as astronomy, navigation, and surveying.

Where You'll Learn This

You will study this in chapter 9.

In the 15th century, Copernicus used trigonometric ratios to study the orbits of planets when they formed a right triangle with Earth and the sun. Earth is 1 AU (astronomical unit) from the sun. How far is Venus from the sun if the angle of this triangle, which has Earth at its vertex, is 46°?

Answer: The measure of an angle of a right triangle and the length of the hypotenuse is given. To find the length of the opposite leg, write an equation using the sine of the angle:

$\sin 46° = \frac{x}{1}$

Then, use a calculator to find sin 46°:

$\sin 46° \approx 0.72$

$0.72 \approx \frac{x}{1}$, so Venus is about 0.72 AU from the sun.

1.02 Use length, area, and volume of geometric figures to solve problems. Include arc length, area of sectors of circles, lateral area, surface area, and volume of three-dimensional figures; and perimeter, area, and volume of composite figures.

What It Means to You

To solve problems involving two- or three-dimensional geometric figures requires measurements of those figures. You have measured parts of geometric figures and have used these measurements to find out other properties of the figure. For example, to find the distance around the rectangle, its perimeter, you can measure the sides of a rectangle and add the measures. Perimeter is one example of a geometric property of two-dimensional figures (figures with length and width). You will also learn to find the area of two-dimensional figures. For example, the area of a triangle is half the product of a base and the corresponding height ($A = \frac{1}{2}bh$).

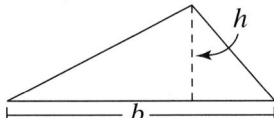

Three-dimensional figures have the added dimension of height or depth. As you will see, you can apply what you learn about two-dimensional figures to explore the properties of three-dimensional figures. For instance, you can use what you know about area of a two-dimensional figure to determine the surface area (the sum of all the surfaces of a three-dimensional figure) by adding the area of each of the faces of the three-dimensional figure.

You will learn to use length measurements to calculate the many properties of two- and three-dimensional geometric figures.

Where You'll Learn This

You will study this in chapters 1, 7, 8, and 10.

A circle graph shows types of trash in a typical U.S. city. The section of the graph that shows the amount of paper thrown away has an angle of 137°. If the circumference of the graph is 32 cm, what is the length of the arc for this part of the graph, to the nearest centimeter?

A 12 cm
B 20 cm
C 32 cm
D 84 cm

Answer: A

Ravi wants to frame a piece of art shaped as a right triangle. Its hypotenuse is 20 in, and one leg is 16 in. Its area is 96 in². How many inches of frame does he need?

A 12 in
B 22 in
C 48 in
D 96 in

Answer: C

1.03 Use length, area, and volume to model and solve problems involving probability.

What It Means to You

When you think about probability, you think of comparing the number of favorable outcomes to the number of possible outcomes. For example, the probability of tossing a 4 on a 6-sided number cube is $\frac{1}{6}$.

Suppose you spill a drop of ink on your ruler. What is the probability that the drop hits the ruler between 1 and 4? You could set up a ratio comparing the likelihood of the drop landing between 1 and 4 (the favorable outcome, or segment) and the rest of the length of the ruler.

$$P(1 \text{ to } 4) = \frac{\text{length of favorable outcome}}{\text{length of entire ruler}} = \frac{3}{12} = \frac{1}{4}$$

As you can see, geometric probability takes probability one step further in that points represent outcomes. You will learn to compare favorable length, area, or volume to possible length, area, or volume to determine geometric probability.

Where You'll Learn This

You will study this in chapter 7.

A dartboard has a diameter of 48 cm. In the center, it has a red circle with a diameter of 10 cm. Surrounding the red circle, it has a green circle that extends out 15 cm from the center. The rest of the dartboard is yellow. What is the probability that a dart thrown will land in the green area?

Answer: First, find the area of the red circle:

$$A_{red} = \pi r^2 = \pi(5 \text{ cm})^2 \approx 79 \text{ cm}^2.$$

Then, find the green area:

$$A_{green} \approx \pi(15 \text{ cm})^2 - 79 \text{ cm}^2 \approx 628 \text{ cm}^2.$$

Next, find the area of the entire dartboard:

$$A_{total} = \pi(24 \text{ cm})^2 \approx 1809 \text{ cm}^2.$$

Use these areas to find the geometric probability:

$$P = \frac{A_{green}}{A_{total}} \approx \frac{628}{1809}$$

North Carolina Fact

Did you know that the first X-ray photograph was taken in Davidson, North Carolina in 1896? Dr. Henry Louis Smith is credited with this scientific achievement.

GEOMETRY

2.01 Use logic and deductive reasoning to draw conclusions and solve problems.

What It Means to You

In math, you can use logic to solve a problem. You are given that $2x + 4 = 10$, and wish to prove that $x = 3$. To do so you would go through a series of steps and justify each with a mathematical property. The first step would be to subtract 4 from each side, and say you used the Subtraction Property of Equality to justify the step (the result is $2x = 6$). Next, you would divide each side by 2. You would justify this step by saying you used the Division Property of Equality (with the result that $x = 3$).

Deductive reasoning is the process of logical reasoning and using given statements to reach a conclusion. You use and come in contact with deductive reasoning daily. For example, you know that if a car is out of gas, it will not start. You can conclude from this that if your car has no gas, it will not start. Can you conclude that the reverse is true? No, you cannot. If your car does not start, many different things might be wrong. You cannot assume that it has no gas.

In geometry, you will use a form of logical reasoning, known as a proof, to prove that a geometric statement is true. Constructing and using proof is an example of deductive reasoning. There are many different kinds of proofs. Every proof is based on evidence, which is given as definitions or theorems. Proofs can be written in a paragraph, two-column, or even a flow-chart format.

Throughout the year, you will make observations, combine these with true statements, or theorems, and reach conclusions about geometric figures or properties. You will learn to evaluate the truth of given statements and use these statements and deductive reasoning to reach logical conclusions.

Where You'll Learn This

You will study this in chapters 1, 2, and 5.

You know that if the roads are icy, the temperature must be less than or equal to the freezing point of water. Using deductive reasoning, which of the following is true?

A It is 20°F, so the roads must be icy.
B The roads are icy, so it must be less than or equal to 32°F.
C The roads are not icy, so it must be warmer than 32°F.
D Ice on the roads has no relation to temperature.

Answer: B

Given: $\overline{KJ} \parallel \overline{LM}$

$$\overline{KJ} \cong \overline{LM}$$

Prove: *JKLM* is a parallelogram.

Justify each step.

Answer: If one pair of opposite sides of a quadrilateral is both congruent and parallel, then the quadrilateral is a parallelogram.

Student's Guide

2.02 Apply properties, definitions, and theorems of angles and lines to solve problems and write proofs.

What It Means to You

The study of geometry starts with some simple ideas and builds upon them. These simple ideas include terms such as *line* or *plane*. A line is a series of points that extends in two directions without end. A plane is a flat surface that has no thickness. Many geometric figures are formed by a part of a line called a *ray* (part of a line with an endpoint and all points of the line on one side of the endpoint). An *angle* is formed by two rays with the same endpoint.

As you get deeper into your study of geometry you will study the properties of lines and angles. For example, look at the two angles below:

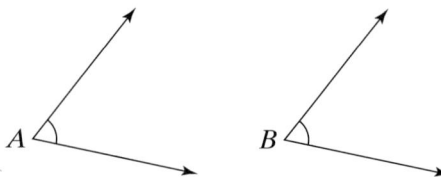

Are they exactly alike or congruent? How can you be sure? You cannot rely on appearances alone.

In geometry you will use logical thinking and deductive reasoning to reach conclusions. To reach these conclusions, however, reasoning must be based on statements that are assumed to be true. You will use the tools of deductive reasoning, properties, definitions, and theorems to help you reach a conclusion. These tools are statements that are true, or they have been found to be true so many times that it is assumed that they are true.

You will learn to use true statements about lines and angles to reach a conclusion.

Where You'll Learn This

You will study this in chapters 1, 2, 3, and 11.

For a set of intersecting lines:

$\angle A \cong \angle B$ and $\angle A \cong \angle C$.

What property can you use to prove the following?

$\angle B \cong \angle C$

A   identity
B   reflexive
C   symmetric
D   transitive

Answer: D

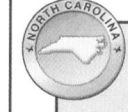

Lines *x* and *y* are parallel. Find the measure of $\angle b$.

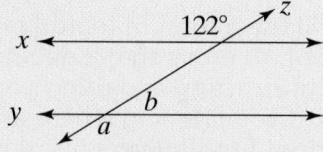

A   32°
B   122°
C   180°
D   58°

Answer: D

2.03 Apply properties, definitions, and theorems of two-dimensional figures
to solve problems and write proofs:
a) Triangles.

What It Means to You

If your friend draws a shape, tells you it has three sides, and asks you to close your eyes and guess what it is, you would probably guess a triangle. If your friend gives you additional information, such as one of the angles measures 90°, you would know you have a particular type of triangle known as a right triangle.

As you will see, triangles have many parts and properties. By understanding the relationships between these parts and properties you can prove that two triangles are exactly alike, or congruent.

The two triangles below are exactly alike, or congruent. Two figures are congruent if the measures of the corresponding sides and angles are equal.

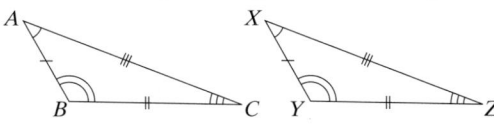

Can you prove they are congruent? Just as logic and deductive reasoning can be used to write proofs and solve problems involving lines and angles, they can be used to write proofs and solve problems for two-dimensional figures, such as triangles.

Just as properties, definitions, and theorems can be assumed to be true statements used for reasoning in regards to lines and angles, you can assume the ones that apply to two-dimensional figures are true. You will learn to use true statements to solve problems and write proofs for two-dimensional figures.

Where You'll Learn This

You will study this in chapters 4, 5, 7, 8, 9, 10, and 11.

North Carolina Fact

With more than 112,000 seats, Charlotte Motor Speedway is the largest outdoor sports stadium in the United States.

A quilt contains different triangles. One triangle has a side of 25 cm, another side of 20 cm, with a 60° angle between them. Another triangle also has a side of 25 cm, another side of 20 cm, with a 60° angle between them. Which of the following postulates proves that the triangles are congruent?

A   side-side-side (SSS)
B   angle-side-angle (ASA)
C   side-angle-side (SAS)
D   angle-angle-side (AAS)

Answer: C

b) Quadrilaterals.

What It Means to You

Cheese is a dairy product, and it is also made from milk. In the same way, polygons fit into categories. For example, a square and a rectangle are two types of four-sided figures known as *quadrilaterals*. While a square and a rectangle are quadrilaterals, they are also a special type of quadrilateral known as a parallelogram (quadrilaterals with a pairs of parallel sides).

Quadrilaterals are four-sided geometric figures. The figures below are just a few examples of the many types of quadrilaterals

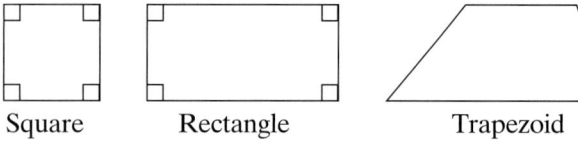

Square   Rectangle   Trapezoid

A parallelogram is just one type of quadrilateral. However, parallelograms have many unique properties, such as opposite sides and angles being congruent. Trapezoids and kites are other types of quadrilaterals, but their opposite sides and angles are not congruent.

Quadrilaterals have many properties. For example, you learned that you can find the area of a rectangle using the formula $A = \ell w$. You will learn new formulas to find the areas of other quadrilaterals. You will relate these formulas to the properties of quadrilaterals.

You will explore the properties of quadrilaterals, especially special quadrilaterals, such as the ones shown above. As you will see, you can use these properties and logic and deductive reasoning to write proofs and solve problems involving quadrilaterals.

Where You'll Learn This

You will study this in chapter 6.

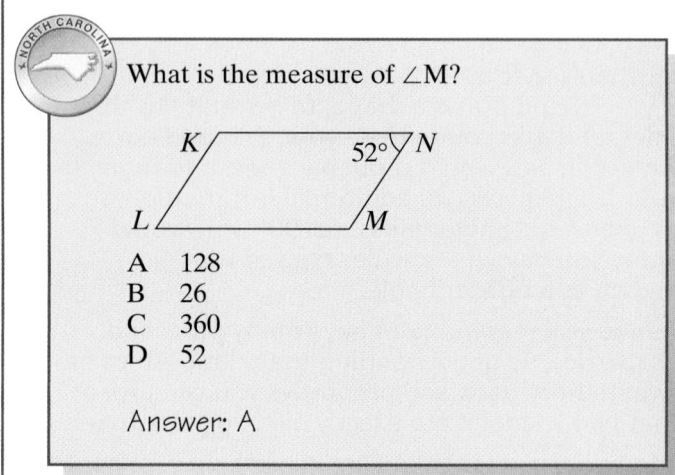

What is the measure of ∠M?

A   128
B   26
C   360
D   52

Answer: A

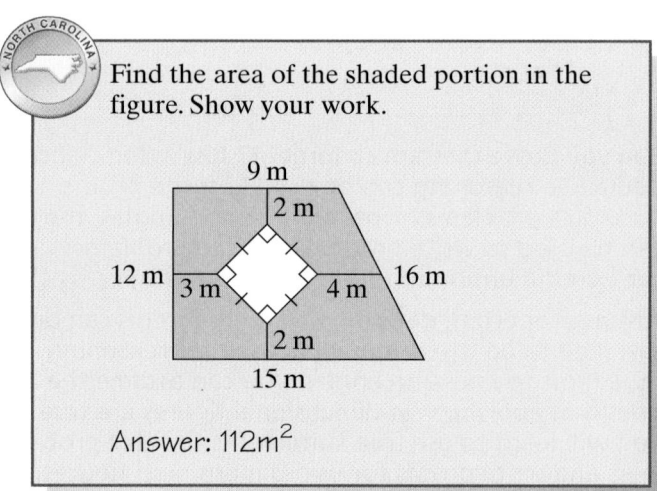

Find the area of the shaded portion in the figure. Show your work.

Answer: 112m²

c) Other polygons.

What It Means to You

As you drive down a road or highway you have probably seen the following sign.

The shape of a stop sign is one type of geometric figure. It is a polygon. The figures below are some of the other types of polygons you have seen.

 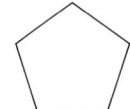

Hexagon   Pentagon

As you may have noticed, a polygon is a two-dimensional figure with at least three sides.

You have measured the length of the sides of certain polygons. Using these measures you have found the areas (the square units a figure encloses) and perimeters (the sum of the lengths of all sides) of rectangles, squares, and triangles. To help you find these values you learned different formulas.

You will learn about the different types of polygons, the properties they share, and the unique properties of each. You will use their properties in logical arguments to prove a statement true.

 What is the sum of the measure of the interior angles of a polygon with 20 sides?

Use the following formula to determine the sum of the angles:

Sum = $(n - 2)180$; where n is the number of sides.

Knowing that $n = 20$, plug that into the equation.

Multiply and the result is 3,240.

Answer: 3,240°

 What is the measure of each exterior angle of a stop sign?

A   180°
B   135°
C   120°
D   45°

Answer: D

North Carolina Fact

The haze that gives the Great Smokey Mountains their name is not really smoke. It is a kind of natural air pollution produced by the local evergreen trees.

Student's Guide

d) Circles.

What It Means to You

The spokes of a bicycle wheel emerge from the center of the wheel. Every circle has a center. You can use a compass to draw a circle by first laying down a point for the center of the circle. You will learn how to draw a circle even if you do not know the center point.

You have learned some important properties of circles. The circle below shows some of these properties.

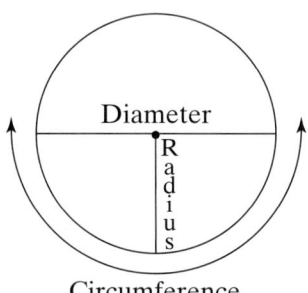

For example you know that the distance around a circle is the circumference, and a line drawn across a circle through the center is the diameter. You also know the ratio of circumference to diameter is a number known as pi (π).

Just as you will learn about the relationships between the angles and sides in a right triangle, you will learn about the relationships between angles, arcs, and lines that pass through circles. You will also learn about the theorems that describe these relationships. You will come to see that the relationships are true for every circle. As a result, you can use these properties to solve problems in other areas, such as architecture and space science.

You will learn other properties of circles, as well as properties of lines and angles that intercept a circle. You will use logic and deductive reasoning to write proofs and solve problems with circles.

Where You'll Learn This

You will study this in chapter 11.

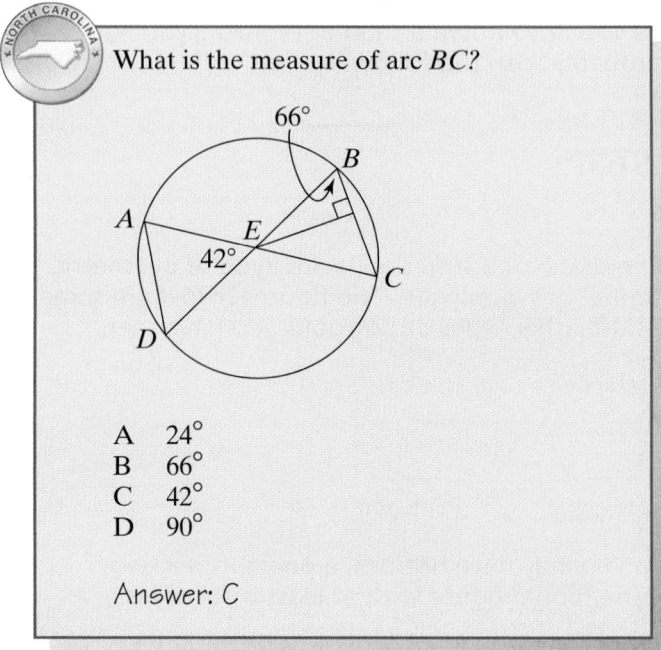

What is the measure of arc *BC*?

A   24°
B   66°
C   42°
D   90°

Answer: C

The radius of a circle is 15 cm and a chord of the same circle is 6 cm. Measuring along the radius that is perpendicular to the chord, what is the distance of the chord from the center of the circle to the nearest tenth?

A   3 cm
B   14.7 cm
C   7.5 cm
D   20.3 cm

Answer: B

2.04 Develop and apply properties of solids to solve problems.

What It Means to You

A basketball and a shoebox are just two examples of three-dimensional figures, or solids. Unlike two-dimensional figures that have only length and width, solids have length, width, and depth. The properties of solids include volume, lateral surface area, and total surface area.

Suppose you want to know how much juice will fill a pitcher. You might calculate volume. If you want to wrap a gift box, you might calculate the amount of space around the box to find how much wrapping paper you will need. This is called surface area. To find these quantities you can use a formula that shows you the relationship between the quantity and certain measures of the solid.

As with two-dimensional figures, you can view three-dimensional figures in terms of similarity and congruence. Even if two figures appear to be exactly alike, you must prove they are exactly alike. For example, if the sides of two triangles are all the same length and their angles are all the same measure, they are exactly alike, or *congruent.* Sometimes they might have the same shape but not the same size, in which case they are *similar.* You will learn about similar relationships in solid figures.

As with two-dimensional figures, theorems provide formulas for calculating these properties. You will learn about the properties of solid figures and use them to solve problems.

Where You'll Learn This

You will study this in chapter 10.

A theorem states that the lateral area of a right cone is one-half the circumference of the base times the height along the slant. If paper cones used for snow cones are 12 cm across the top and have a slant height of 14 cm, how much paper does it take to make one?

Answer: First, find the circumference of the base:

$C = \pi d = (12 \text{ cm})\pi \approx 38 \text{ cm}.$

Then, calculate the lateral area:

$LA \approx \frac{1}{2}(38 \text{ cm})(14 \text{ cm}) \approx 266 \text{ cm}^2.$

A family is choosing ice-cream cones for their favorite flavors. The volume of the children's size cone is $128\pi \text{ cm}^3$ and of the adult size is $250\pi \text{ cm}^3$. The cones are similar. Find their ratio. Show your work.

Answer: 4 : 5

Student's Guide

ALGEBRA

3.01 Describe the transformation (translation, reflection, rotation, dilation) of polygons in the coordinate plane in simple algebraic terms.

What It Means to You

In playing chess, you move a piece from one position to another. In one sense, you are performing a *transformation.*

In geometry, a *transformation* is a change in the position, shape, or size of a figure on a coordinate plane. There are different types of transformations. Some transformations involve moving a figure from one place to another.

One such type of transformation is a *translation,* which means sliding a figure from one place to another. In a translation all the points of a figure have moved the same distance in the same direction.

In a geometric *reflection,* a figure is flipped over a line. The resulting figure is the mirror image of the original figure. A reflection is not unlike a reflection you see in a mirror. Just like in a mirror, a figure that has undergone a geometric reflection appears to be backwards. This appearance is the result of the figure and its image having opposite orientations.

A *rotation* turns a figure around a point. A *dilation* differs from the other transformations in that it is any change in size. To describe a rotation you need to know the center of rotation, the angle of rotation, and if the rotation is clockwise or counterclockwise.

A dilation includes both enlargements and reductions; shape does not change. This means that angles do not change, either. In a dilation, the figure and the resulting image are similar figures. Every dilation must have a scale factor, which describes the change in size from the original figure to the new figure.

You will learn to transform figures and describe these different types of transformations.

Where You'll Learn This
You will study this in chapter 12.

The vertices of a quadrilateral are at points $(1,3), (4,5), (5,2),$ and $(3,1)$. The quadrilateral is reflected over the vertical line at $x = 5$. What points describe the reflected quadrilateral?

Answer: First, draw the original quadrilateral on a grid.

Next, draw a vertical line at $x = 5$.

Then, reflect the quadrilateral over the line. The vertices of the reflected quadrilateral are at $(9, 3), (6, 5), (5, 2),$ and $(7, 1)$.

Reflect $\triangle ABC$ about the line $x = 4$.

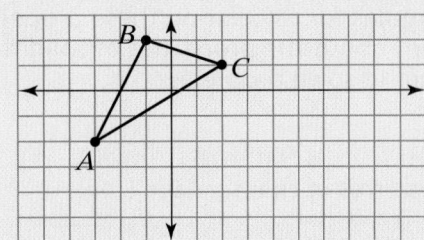

Answer: $A'(11, -2), B'(9, 2), C'(6, 1)$

3.02 Use matrix operations (addition, subtraction, multiplication, scalar multiplication) to describe the transformation of polygons in the coordinate plane.

What It Means to You

You have created data tables to organize and analyze data. A matrix is similar to a data table because it uses rows and columns to organize data.

You can use matrices in geometry to plot the location of a figure and to find the location of a figure that has undergone a transformation. For example, if you know the vector that describes a translation, you can write a translation matrix. You would then add it to the matrix of the points of the original figure, to find the vertices of the translated figure.

For example, you can use a matrix to describe the location on a coordinate grid of a $\triangle ABC$ with the vertices located as follows: A(−1, −1), B(2, −5), and C(3, 2).

$$
\begin{array}{c}
\quad A \quad B \quad C \\
\begin{array}{l} x\text{-coordinate} \\ y\text{-coordinate} \end{array}
\begin{bmatrix} -1 & 2 & 3 \\ -1 & -5 & 2 \end{bmatrix}
\end{array}
$$

If you know how much you translate the image, you can use matrix addition to determine the new coordinates. Suppose you translate the figure under ⟨2, 3⟩. You would add this translation as a matrix that you would then add to the original coordinates.

With resulting coordinates:

$$
\begin{array}{ccc} A & B & C \\ \begin{bmatrix} -1 & 2 & 3 \\ -1 & -5 & 2 \end{bmatrix} \end{array}
+
\begin{array}{ccc} A & B & C \\ \begin{bmatrix} 2 & 2 & 2 \\ 3 & 3 & 3 \end{bmatrix} \end{array}
=
\begin{array}{ccc} A' & B' & C' \\ \begin{bmatrix} 1 & 4 & 5 \\ 2 & -2 & 5 \end{bmatrix} \end{array}
$$

You will learn to use matrices to describe the polygon that results from the transformation of a polygon in the coordinate plane.

Where You'll Learn This

You will study this in chapter 12.

The rectangle with vertices at points $(2, 1)$, $(4, 1)$, $(2, 6)$, and $(4, 6)$ is translated on the coordinate plane. The point that was at $(4, 1)$ is now at $(8, 3)$. Use matrices to find the other vertices of the translated rectangle.

Answer: Find the vector that describes the translation.

Horizontal change: $8 - 4 = 4$

Vertical change: $3 - 1 = 2$

The vector is $\langle 4, 2 \rangle$.

Next, write a matrix for the original rectangle and one for the vector, and add them:

$$
\begin{bmatrix} 2 & 4 & 2 & 4 \\ 1 & 1 & 6 & 6 \end{bmatrix}
+
\begin{bmatrix} 4 & 4 & 4 & 4 \\ 2 & 2 & 2 & 2 \end{bmatrix}
=
\begin{bmatrix} 6 & 8 & 6 & 8 \\ 3 & 3 & 8 & 8 \end{bmatrix}
$$

The vertices of the translated rectangle are $(6, 3)$, $(8, 3)$, $(6, 8)$, and $(8, 8)$.

Student's Guide

North Carolina Mathematics Formulas

The following information is for your reference in solving some of the problems of the test.

Area of a Trapezoid $A = \frac{1}{2}h(b_1 + b_2)$

Area of an Equilateral Triangle $A = \frac{s^2}{4}\sqrt{3}$

Distance $= \sqrt{(x_2 - x_1)^2 + (y_2 - y_1)^2}$

Midpoint $M = \left(\frac{x_1 + x_2}{2}, \frac{y_1 + y_2}{2}\right)$

Circle $(x - h)^2 + (y - k)^2 = r^2$

Cylinder
    Lateral Area (right) $L = 2\pi rh$
    Total Area (right) $T = 2\pi r(h + r)$
    Volume $V = \pi r^2 h$

Sphere
    Surface Area $A = 4\pi r^2$
    Volume $V = \frac{4}{3}\pi r^3$

Cone, where l is the slant height
    Lateral Area (right) $L = \pi rl$
    Total Area (right) $T = \pi r(l + r)$
    Volume $V = \frac{1}{3}\pi r^2 h$

Trig Ratios $\sin x = \dfrac{\text{opposite side}}{\text{hypotenuse}}$

$\cos x = \dfrac{\text{adjacent side}}{\text{hypotenuse}}$

$\tan x = \dfrac{\text{opposite side}}{\text{adjacent side}}$

Probability $P(A \text{ and } B) = P(A) \cdot P(B)$
$P(A \text{ or } B) = P(A) + P(B)$

$$P(n, r) = \frac{n!}{(n - r)!}$$

$$C(n, r) = \frac{n!}{(n - r)!r!}$$

Prism, where p is the perimeter of the base and B is the area of the base

Lateral Area (right)	$L = ph$
Total Area (right)	$T = L + 2B$
Volume	$V = Bh$

Pyramid, where p is the perimeter of the base, B is the area of the base, and l is the slant height.

Lateral Area (regular)	$L = \frac{1}{2}lp$
Total Area (regular)	$T = L + B$
Volume	$V = \frac{1}{3}Bh$

Other Formulas

$$C = \tfrac{5}{9}(F - 32) \qquad F = \tfrac{9}{5}C + 32$$

Simple interest $A = prt$

Compound Interest $A = p(1 + r)^2$

Student's Guide

Teacher's Edition Contents

Teacher Handbook

Student Edition with Teacher Notes

Prentice Hall Mathematics

A comprehensive program
for North Carolina
Grades 6-12

From middle school math
to high school algebra
and geometry, Prentice Hall
has the solutions you need
to guarantee math success
for all students.

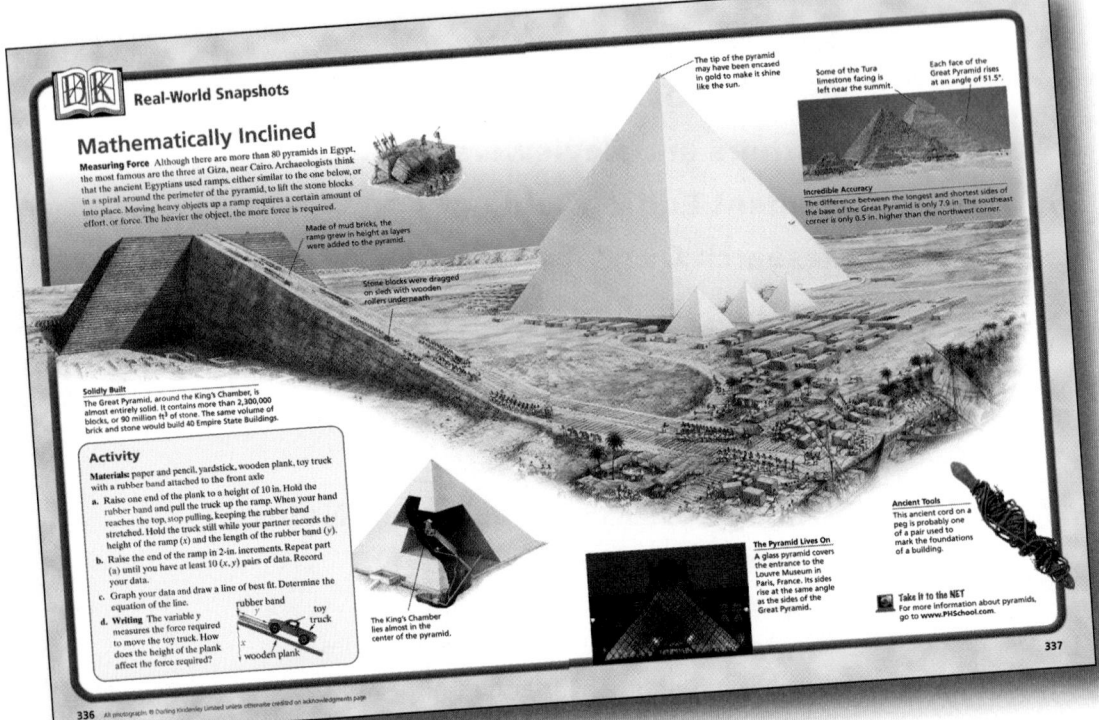

Reach Them ▶

Comprehensive Content Connects to Their World

Our comprehensive scope and sequence of content addresses the North Carolina Standard Course of Study, NAEP, and teacher expectations. Abundant real-world connections reinforce math applications, while unique *Dorling Kindersley Real-World Snapshots* bring math to life.

Empower Them ▶

Give Every North Carolina Student the Opportunity to Succeed

The *Instant Check System™* enables students to check their understanding at key points during instruction. No other program provides such an easy-to-use way to measure students' progress.
Leveled exercise sets allow you to easily craft just the right assignments for your classes. Plus, we've built in homework helpers along the way.

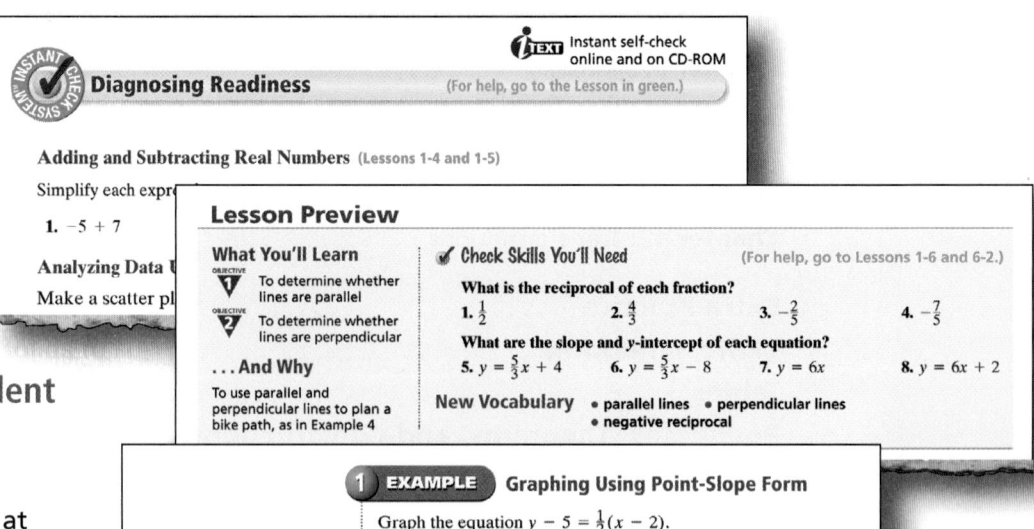

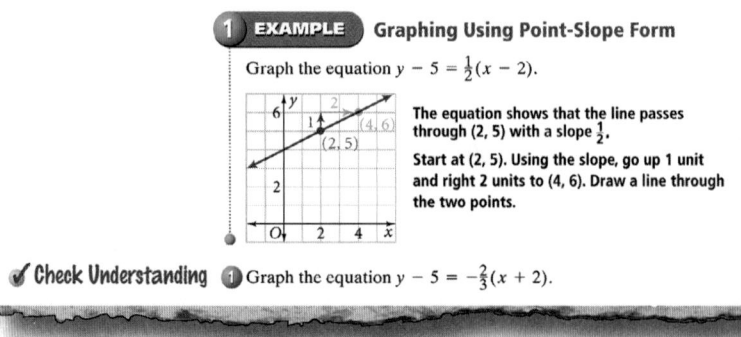

1 EXAMPLE Graphing Using Point-Slope Form

Graph the equation $y - 5 = \frac{1}{2}(x - 2)$.

The equation shows that the line passes through (2, 5) with a slope $\frac{1}{2}$.

Start at (2, 5). Using the slope, go up 1 unit and right 2 units to (4, 6). Draw a line through the two points.

✓ **Check Understanding** ① Graph the equation $y - 5 = -\frac{2}{3}(x + 2)$.

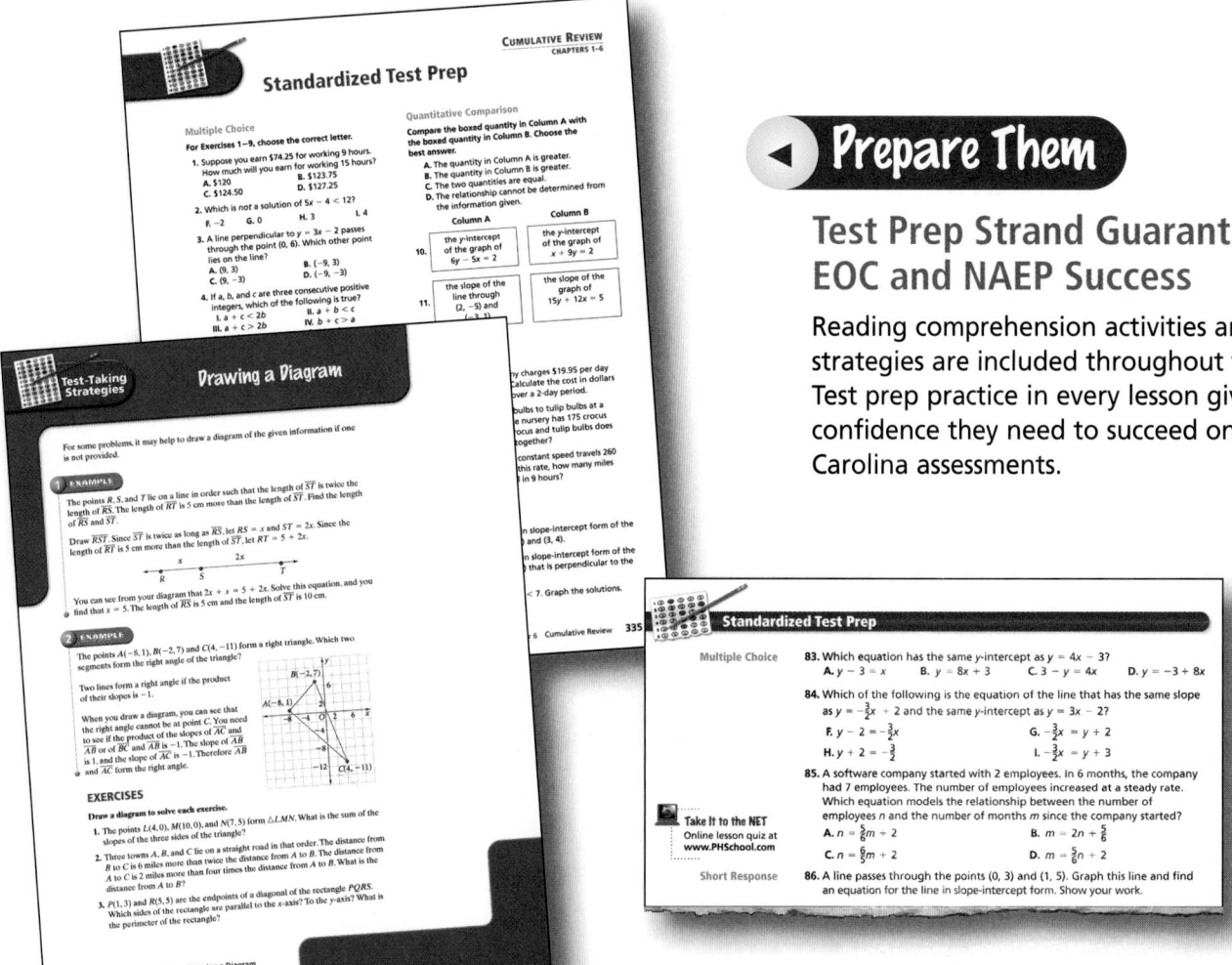

◀ Prepare Them

Test Prep Strand Guarantees EOC and NAEP Success

Reading comprehension activities and test-taking strategies are included throughout the program. Test prep practice in every lesson gives students the confidence they need to succeed on the North Carolina assessments.

◀ And Get the Support You Deserve

Outstanding Teacher Time Savers Allow for Effective Instruction

Our comprehensive *Presentation Assistant Plus!* provides all the material you need to teach every lesson step-by-step from beginning to end, while the unique *PH SuccessNet* unlocks a whole new set of online solutions for teaching success.

OVER 700 transparencies per Grade Level!

Prentice Hall Mathematics

Comprehensive content with a scope and sequence that helps you meet the North Carolina Standard Course of Study while focusing on specific student needs

Content Standards

Careful consideration of the North Carolina Standard Course of Study and the National Assessment of Educational Progress 2005 Guidelines was made prior to developing the scope and sequence of content for each text. In addition, North Carolina teacher input concerning content issues helped to determine the final content coverage of the entire program. Consequently, with *Prentice Hall Mathematics*, you can be assured that new content standards are covered along with the content North Carolina teachers know is important.

Strand Coverage

Important mathematics strands such as number theory, algebra, geometry, measurement, data analysis, statistics, and probability are thoroughly developed as appropriate to each level. Each text from *Pre-Algebra* through *Algebra 2* provides excellent coverage of the topics indicated for that level while other strands are reviewed and reinforced to help students make important connections

Reading and Math

Reading Math lessons are included throughout the program to help students to become more active in the learning process. Reading math vocabulary is carefully developed, and students learn a variety of techniques to help them more effectively read their textbook and mathematical text in general. Reading and Math Literacy Masters are also available.

Alternate Course Planning Guides

A Basic Algebra Planning Guide and an Informal Geometry Planning Guide help you structure alternative courses to meet the needs of less able students. In addition, Connections to Precalculus Masters accompany *Algebra 2* to help you highlight key skills that will ensure success for all your students who continue their study of mathematics.

Tables of Contents

Complete North Carolina Resources

 North Carolina Student Edition
iText—Interactive text online and on CD-ROM
North Carolina Teacher's Edition
Teaching Resources
- Grab & Go Chapter Support Files
  - Practice
  - Reteaching
  - Enrichment
  - Chapter Projects
  - Checkpoint Quizzes
  - Chapter Tests
  - Alternative Assessment
  - Cumulative Review
- Cumulative Assessment
- Solution Key

Reaching All Students

Practice Workbook
Reading and Math Literacy Masters
Guided Problem-Solving Masters
Hands-on Activities
Technology Activities
Prentice Hall MathNotes Folders
Skills Intervention Kit

 Coming Soon— Online Intervention

Teacher Time Savers

Presentation Assistant Plus!
- Additional Examples on Transparencies
- Daily Skills Check and Lesson Quiz Transparencies
- Problem of the Day Transparencies
- Student Edition Answers on Transparencies
- Classroom Aid Transparencies
- Prentice Hall Presentation Pro CD-ROM

Assessment and Test Prep

Prentice Hall Assessment System
- North Carolina Computer Test Generator CD-ROM
- Algebra Readiness Tests
- Assessment Resources
  - Checkpoint Quizzes
  - Chapter Tests, Forms A & B
  - Alternative Assessment
  - Cumulative Assessment
- North Carolina Content Diagnostic Tests
- Skills and Concepts Review
- North Carolina EOC and NAEP Preparation Workbook with Teacher's Guide
- Test-Taking Strategies with Transparencies

Spanish Support

Student Edition, Spanish Version
Spanish Practice Workbook
Spanish Reading and Math Literacy Masters
Spanish Assessment Resources

Technology

iText—Interactive text online and on CD-ROM
Prentice Hall Presentation Pro CD-ROM
North Carolina Resource Pro® with Planning Express® CD-ROM
North Carolina Computer Test Generator CD-ROM
PH SuccessNet Teacher Center Web Site
PHSchool.com Textbook Site

**Take a virtual tour of the program at
PHSchool.com/northcarolina**

Authors

Series Authors

Dan Kennedy, Ph.D., is a classroom teacher and the Lupton Distinguished Professor of Mathematics at the Baylor School in Chattanooga, Tennessee. A frequent speaker at professional meetings on the subject of mathematics education reform, Dr. Kennedy has conducted more than 50 workshops and institutes for high school teachers. He is co-author of textbooks in calculus and precalculus, and from 1990 to 1994 he chaired the College Board's AP Calculus Development Committee. He is a 1992 Tandy Technology Scholar and a 1995 Presidential Award winner.

Randall I. Charles, Ph.D., is Professor Emeritus in the Department of Mathematics and Computer Science at San Jose State University, San Jose, California. He began his career as a high school mathematics teacher, and he was a mathematics supervisor for five years. Dr. Charles has been a member of several NCTM committees and is a former Vice President of the National Council of Supervisors of Mathematics. Much of his writing and research has been in the area of problem solving. He has authored more than 75 mathematics textbooks for kindergarten through college.

Dorling Kindersley (DK) is an international publishing company that specializes in the creation of high-quality, illustrated information books for children and adults. Dorling Kindersley's unique graphic presentation style is used in this program to motivate students in learning about real-world applications of mathematics. DK is part of the Pearson family of companies.

ISBN 0-13-062560-4

3 4 5 6 7 8 9 10   07 06 05 04 03

Geometry Authors

Laurie E. Bass is a classroom teacher at Fieldston, the grades 7–12 division of the Ethical Culture Fieldston School in Riverdale, New York. Ms. Bass has a wide base of teaching experience, ranging from grades 6 and 7 through Advanced Placement Calculus. She was the recipient of a 2000 Honorable Mention for the RadioShack National Teacher Awards. She also has been a contributing writer of a number of publications, including software-based activities for the Algebra 1 classroom. Among her areas of special interests are cooperative learning for high school students and geometry exploration on the computer.

Art Johnson, Ed.D., is a mathematics educator with 32 years of public school teaching experience. Dr. Johnson is a frequent speaker and workshop leader, and the recipient of a number of awards, including the Tandy Prize for Teaching Excellence in 1995 and a 1992 Presidential Award for Excellence in Mathematics Teaching. He was profiled by the Disney Corporation in the American Teacher of the Year Program. Dr. Johnson is currently a professor of mathematics education at Boston University.

Algebra 1 and Algebra 2 Authors

Allan E. Bellman
Lecturer/Supervisor in the
    School of Education at the
    University of California
Davis, California

Willam G. Handlin, Sr.
Department Chairman of
    Technology Applications
Spring Woods High School
Houston, Texas

Sadie Chavis Bragg, Ed.D
Professor of Mathematics
    and Vice President of
    Academic Affairs
Borough of Manhattan
    Community College of the
    City University of New York
New York, New York

Reviewers

North Carolina Math Program Advisors

Kelly S. Crisp
Mathematics Teacher
Buncombe County Schools
Arden, North Carolina

Don McGurrin
Educational Math
Consultant
Clayton, North Carolina

Sheila S. Brookshire
Mathematics Teacher
AC Reynolds Middle School
Asheville, North Carolina

Cynthia Hanner Davis
Mathematics Teacher
Northeast High School
Greensboro, North Carolina

Judy Porter
Leesville Road High School
Raleigh, North Carolina

Dr. Ann R. Crawford
University of North Carolina
   at Wilmington
Wilmington, North Carolina

Algebra 1 Reviewers

Mary Lou Beasley
Southside Fundamental
   Middle School
St. Petersburg, Florida

Jane E. Damaske
Lakeshore Public Schools
Stevensville, Michigan

**Ann Marie Palmieri-
   Monahan**
Director of Mathematics
Bayonne Board of Education
Bayonne, New Jersey

Blanche Smith Brownley
Washington, D.C., Public
   Schools
Washington, D.C.

Stacy A. Ego
Warren Central High School
Indianapolis, Indiana

Marie Schalke
Woodlawn Middle School
Long Grove, Illinois

Joseph Caruso
Somerville High School
Somerville, Massachusetts

Earl R. Jones
Formerly, Kansas City
   Public Schools
Kansas City, Missouri

Julie Welling
LaPorte High School
LaPorte, Indiana

Belinda Craig
Highland West Junior High
   School
Moore, Oklahoma

Jeanne Lorenson
James H. Blake High School
Silver Spring, Maryland

Sharon Zguzenski
Naugatuck High School
Naugatuck, Connecticut

John T. Mace
Hibbett Middle School
Florence, Alabama

Geometry Reviewers

Marian Avery
Great Valley High School
Malvern, Pennsylvania

Mary Emma Bunch
Farragut High School
Knoxville, Tennessee

Karen A. Cannon
K–12 Mathematics Coordinator
Rockwood School District
Eureka, Missouri

Johnnie Ebbert
Department Chairman
DeLand High School
DeLand, Florida

Russ Forrer
Math Department Chairman
East Aurora High School
Aurora, Illinois

Andrea Kopco
Midpark High School
Middleburg Heights, Ohio

Gordon E. Maroney III
Camden Fairview High School
Camden, Arkansas

Charlotte Phillips
Math Coordinator
Wichita USD 259
Wichita, Kansas

Richard P. Strausz
Farmington Public Schools
Farmington, Michigan

Jane Tanner
Jefferson County International
Baccalaureate School
Birmingham, Alabama

Karen D. Vaughan
Pitt County Schools
Greenville, North Carolina

Robin Washam
Math Specialist
Puget Sound Educational
   Service District
Burien, Washington

Algebra 2 Reviewers

Josiane Fouarge
Landry High School
New Orleans, Louisiana

Susan Hvizdos
Math Department Chair
Wheeling Park High School
Wheeling, West Virginia

Kathleen Kohler
Kearny High School
Kearny, New Jersey

Julia Kolb
Leesville Road High School
Raleigh, North Carolina

Deborah R. Kula
Sacred Hearts Academy
Honolulu, Hawaii

Betty Mayberry
Gallatin High School
Gallatin, Tennessee

John L. Pitt
Formerly, Prince William
   County Schools
Manassas, Virginia

Margaret Plouvier
Billings West High School
Billings, Montana

Sandra Sikorski
Berea High School
Berea, Ohio

Tim Visser
Grandview High School
Cherry Creek School District
Aurora, Colorado

Mathematics Content Consultants

Courtney Lewis
Prentice Hall Senior National Consultant
Baltimore, Maryland

Deana Cerroni
Prentice Hall National Consultant
Las Vegas, Nevada

Kim Margel
Prentice Hall National Consultant
Scottsdale, Arizona

Sandra Mosteller
Prentice Hall National Consultant
Anderson, South Carolina

Rita Corbett
Prentice Hall Consultant
Elgin, Illinois

Cathy Davies
Prentice Hall Consultant
Laguna Niguel, California

Sally Marsh
Prentice Hall Consultant
Baltimore, Maryland

Addie Martin
Prentice Hall Consultant
Upper Marlboro, Maryland

Rose Primiani
Prentice Hall Consultant
Brick, New Jersey

Loretta Rector
Prentice Hall Consultant
Foresthill, California

Charlotte Samuels
Prentice Hall Consultant
Lafayette Hill, Pennsylvania

Margaret Thomas
Prentice Hall Consultant
Indianapolis, Indiana

Contents in Brief

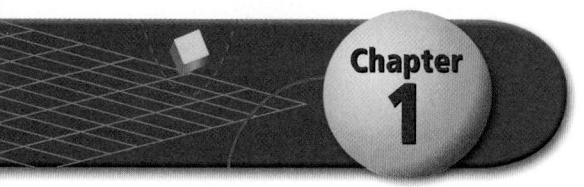

Tools of Geometry

Contents **vii**

Chapter 2

Reasoning and Proof

Student Support

Parallel and Perpendicular Lines

Chapter 4

Congruent Triangles

Relationships Within Triangles

Table of Contents

Chapter 6

Quadrilaterals

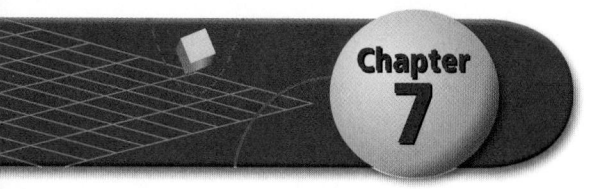

Chapter 7

Area

Table of Contents

Chapter 8

Similarity

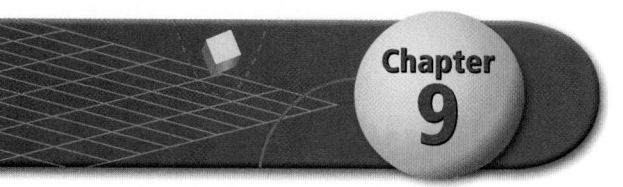

Chapter 9

Right Triangle Trigonometry

Table of Contents

Chapter 10

Surface Area and Volume

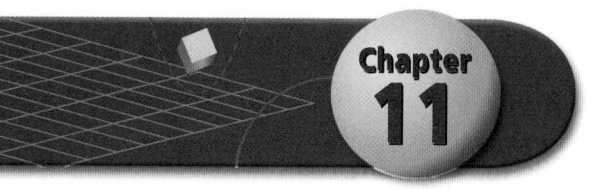

Chapter 11

Circles

Assessment

Student Support

Table of Contents

Chapter 12

Transformations

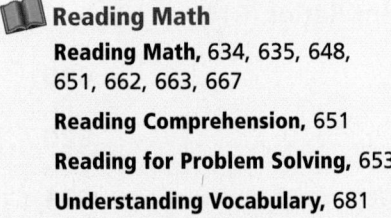

Take It to the Net

Throughout this book you will find links to the Prentice Hall Web site for *Geometry*. Use the Web Code provided with each link to gain direct access to online material.

For a complete list of online features, use Web Code afk-0099

Here's how to **Take It to the Net**:
• Go to **PHSchool.com**.
• Enter the Web Code.
• Click Go!

Lesson Quiz Web Codes

There is an online quiz for each lesson. Access these quizzes with Web Codes afa-0101 through afa-1209 for Lesson 1-1 through Lesson 12-9. *See page 8.*

88 Lesson Quizzes
Web Code format: afa-0204
02 = Chapter 2   04 = Lesson 4

Chapter Resource Web Codes

Chapter	Vocabulary Quizzes *See page 61.*	Chapter Tests *See page 64.*	Dorling Kindersley Real-World Snapshots *See pages 110–111.*	Chapter Projects
1	afj-0151	afe-0152		afd-0161
2	afj-0251	afe-0252	afe-0253	afd-0261
3	afj-0351	afe-0352		afd-0361
4	afj-0451	afe-0452	afe-0453	afd-0461
5	afj-0551	afe-0552		afd-0561
6	afj-0651	afe-0652	afe-0653	afd-0661
7	afj-0751	afe-0752		afd-0761
8	afj-0851	afe-0852	afe-0853	afd-0861
9	afj-0951	afe-0952		afd-0961
10	afj-1051	afe-1052	afe-1053	afd-1061
11	afj-1151	afe-1152		afd-1161
12	afj-1251	afe-1252	afe-1253	afd-1261
End-of-Course		afe-1254		

Additional Resource Web Codes

Data Updates Use Web Code afg-2041 to get up-to-date government data for use in examples and exercises. *See page 389.*

Geometry at Work For information about each Geometry at Work feature, use Web Code afb-2031. *See page 40.*

A Point in Time For information about each A Point in Time feature, use Web Code afe-2032. *See page 88.*

Graphing Calculator Procedures There are 27 procedures available online. Use Web Code afe-2100 for an index of all the procedures, or Web Codes afe-2101 through afe-2127 to access individual procedures. *See page 57.*

Prentice Hall Mathematics programs are research-based and proven to work

The stakes for mathematics educators are high. You are expected to raise student achievement. Prentice Hall understands your dedicated efforts and gives you the confidence to meet this challenge. In developing Prentice Hall programs, the use of research studies is a central, guiding construct. Research on *Prentice Hall Mathematics* indicated key elements of a textbook program that ensure student success: constant review within instruction, support for reading and writing in mathematics, and an ongoing assessment strand. This research was conducted in three phases:

Phase ❶: Exploratory Needs Assessment

Phase ❷: Formative, Prototype Development and Field Testing

Phase ❸: Summative, Validation Research

❶ Exploratory Needs Assessment

Along with periodic surveys concerning curriculum issues and challenges, we conducted specific product development research, which included discussions with teachers and advisory panels, focus groups, and quantitative surveys. We explored the specific needs of teachers, students, and other educators regarding each book we developed in *Prentice Hall Mathematics*.

In conjunction with Prentice Hall authors, secondary research was done to explore educational research about learning. This research was incorporated into our instructional strategy and pedagogy to make a more effective mathematics program.

❷ Formative, Prototype Development and Field Testing

During this phase of research, we worked to develop prototype materials for each course in *Prentice Hall Mathematics*. Then we tested the materials, including field testing with students and teachers, and qualitative and quantitative evaluations of different kinds. We received solid feedback about our lesson structure in our early prototype testing. Results were channeled back into the program development for improvement. For example, teachers commented positively on motivational quality and richness of the mathematics in the Dorling Kindersley features.

❸ Summative, Validation Research

Finally, we conducted and continue to conduct longer-term research based on scientific, experimental designs under actual classroom conditions. This research identifies what works and what can be improved in the next revision of *Prentice Hall Mathematics*. We also continue to monitor the program in the market. We talk to our users about what works, and then we begin the cycle over again. Highlights of this research follow in the next section.

Prentice Hall Research Time Line

Market Needs Assessment
(Quantitative & Qualitative)
- Teacher Interviews
- Classroom Observations
- Mail Surveys
- Conference Participation

Formative Research
(Quantitative & Qualitative)
- Field Testing of Prototypes
- Classroom Observations
- Teacher Reviews
- Supervisor Reviews
- Educator Advisory Panels
- Prentice Hall Sales Force Input

Summative Research
(Experimental and Quasi-Experimental Study Designs & Qualitative Research)
- Pre-Publication Learner Verification Research
- Post-Publication Validation Studies
- Classroom Observations
- Evaluation of In-Market Results on Standardized Tests

Prentice Hall Math programs get results!

Standardized Test End-of-Year Results
(adjusted for differences in pre-test levels)

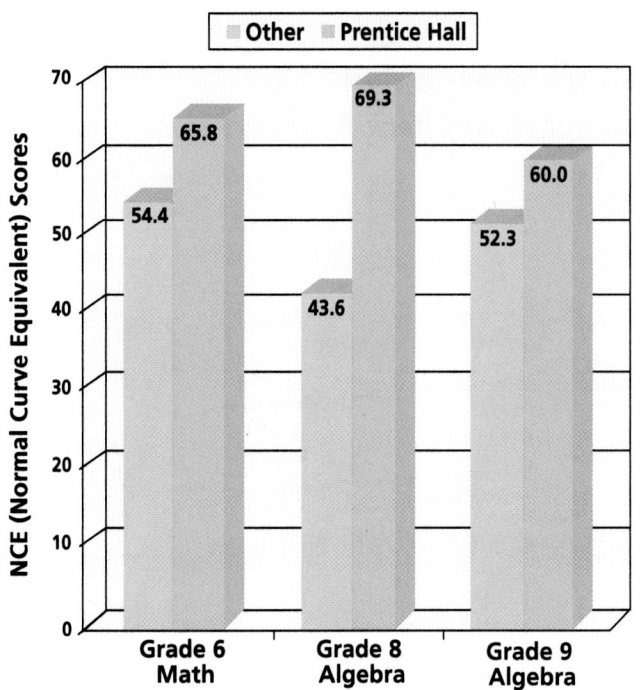

Prentice Hall mathematics programs are continually researched to determine "what works." Our programs are regularly revised to keep the best of what has worked in prior editions, and to improve them to meet changing market and curriculum needs. For example . . .

In a year-long study conducted in six states, students using Prentice Hall mathematics programs at grades 6, 8 (algebra), and 9 (algebra) outscored students using other math programs on a nationally normed standardized test.

The study followed a scientific, experimental design with two classes per school. The classes selected were of similar ability levels, and the assignment of the Prentice Hall program was done randomly. A total of eight schools (a mix of rural, suburban, and urban) participated, with 350 students involved in the study.

Classes were tested at the beginning of the school year using the TerraNova™ CTBS Basic Battery, and they were re-tested at the end of the school year. The final results, shown in the graph at the left, have been adjusted (via ANCOVA) to eliminate any contribution of higher or lower starting points on the pre-test to the observed post-test score.

All tests were scored by CTB/McGraw-Hill, the publisher of the TerraNova™ exam. Statistical analyses were conducted by an independent statistician from Pulse Analytics, Inc.

Additional studies of program effectiveness are under way, and many districts have demonstrated math improvement since adopting Prentice Hall mathematics programs.

Detailed results of this study can be obtained at **www.PHSchool.com**.

A unique progress-monitoring system that gives every student the opportunity to excel

What Research Indicates: Students' learning progresses to higher levels of understanding only if they have mastered a foundational understanding of preliminary concepts. If students are not functioning at a particular level of understanding, they are not ready to move on. Review plays a key role in promoting retention. Research clearly indicates that review should be systematically planned and incorporated into instruction. Before a new chapter or topic is begun, an inventory can help you ascertain whether any prerequisite knowledge is missing. Review should be continuous for students to attain mastery.

(Suydam, Marilyn N. *The Role of Review in Mathematical Instruction.* Columbus, Ohio: ERIC Clearinghouse for Science, Mathematics, and Environmental Education.)

Prentice Hall's Response: *Prentice Hall Mathematics* provides a unique **Instant Check System™** that is built right into the text to assess mastery and diagnose weaknesses before, during, and after each lesson's instruction. This ongoing monitoring strand allows students to check their understanding of skills before moving on to the next topic. If students have misconceptions or need to reinforce their skills, the green type throughout the text clearly indicates where they can go for help. All the answers for the *Instant Check System™* questions are available at the back of the student edition so students can check their work.

✓ Diagnosing Readiness

At the beginning of every chapter, students complete the *Diagnosing Readiness* exercises to see what prerequisite skills they may need to review before they begin the chapter. The Teacher's Edition prescribes specific *Examples* and *Exercises* that students can do for intervention.

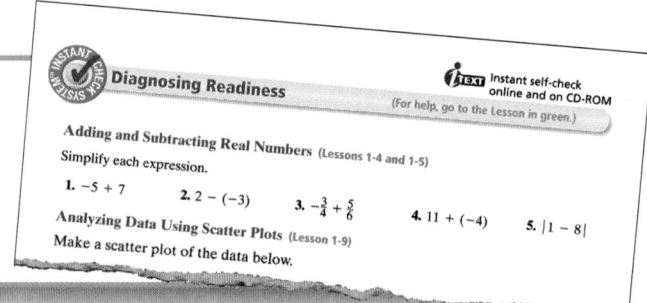

✓ Check Skills You'll Need

To begin each lesson, students complete the *Check Skills You'll Need* exercises to make sure they have the skills needed to successfully learn the concepts in the lesson. These questions with worked-out solutions are conveniently available as transparencies and on CD-ROM.

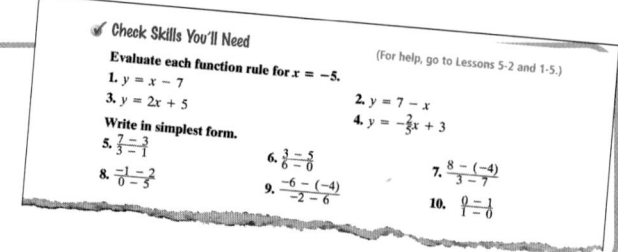

"If students do not have the proper level of understanding, they cannot further their knowledge of concepts and relationships in mathematics. Both the Instant Check System and the Diagnosing Readiness feature help teachers assess how well students have achieved understanding of related skills before having them move on to subsequent concepts."

—Art Johnson, Prentice Hall Mathematics program author

✓ Check Understanding

Every lesson includes numerous *Examples*, each followed by *Check Understanding* questions that students can do on their own. As skills and concepts are introduced, these questions focus students on the mathematics being presented and allow them to assess their understanding. More importantly, these questions will raise misconceptions that students have so that you may immediately address them.

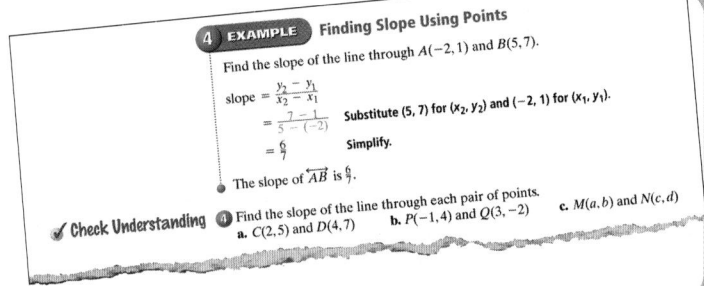

Leveled Exercises

The abundant *Exercises* in every lesson are organized by level to provide ample opportunity for students of all abilities to master the concepts. The *A: Practice by Example* exercises directly relate to the *Examples* in the lesson. The *B: Apply Your Skills* and *C: Challenge* exercises provide richer skill and application problems to extend students' thinking.

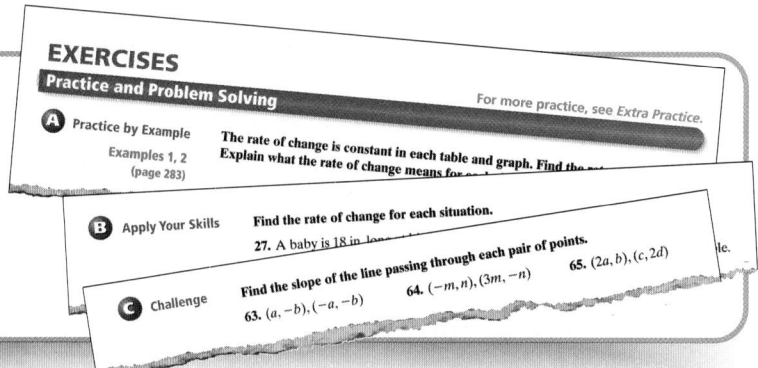

✓ Checkpoint Quizzes

Two *Checkpoint Quizzes* in every chapter provide students with opportunities for ongoing assessment. Each quiz provides a cumulative review of skills within specific lessons. Alternate versions are available in the Teaching Resources and online.

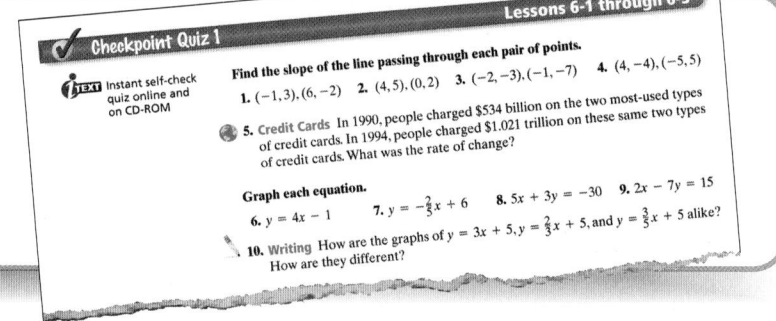

Prentice Hall Mathematics *iText* with Self-Grading Assessments

The *iText* provides the complete Student Edition online and on CD-ROM. The unique *Instant Check System™* is made interactive in the *iText* to allow students ongoing opportunities for checking their learning. Also, the click of a button lets students go back to a lesson or Example for additional help. Students get instant feedback so they know whether they're on track and where to go to get help.

Reading and Writing throughout build communication skills

What Research Indicates: Reading mathematics requires the same skills as reading in other content areas—decoding and comprehending what is read, analyzing and evaluating the content based on one's prior knowledge, and making inferences and generating conclusions. Mathematics text demands that readers also use additional, content-specific reading skills, for example, reading graphs. Students need to learn to focus on significant details, explanations, and the underlying logic in texts where there are more concepts per word, per sentence, and per paragraph than in any other kind of text.

(Barton, Mary Lee & Heidema, Clare. *Teaching Reading in Mathematics:* A Supplement to Teaching Reading in the Content Areas Teacher's Manual, 2nd Ed. Aurora, Colorado: Mid-continent Research for Education and Learning.)

The development of a student's power to use mathematics also involves learning the signs, symbols, and terms of mathematics. This is best accomplished in problem-solving situations in which students have an opportunity to read, write, and discuss ideas so that the use of the language of mathematics becomes natural. As students communicate their ideas, they learn to clarify, refine, and consolidate their thinking.

(*Curriculum and Evaluation Standards for School Mathematics*. Reston, Virginia: The National Council of Teachers of Mathematics, Inc.)

Prentice Hall's Response: *Prentice Hall Mathematics* provides a consistent emphasis on mathematics literacy with a special focus on reading and writing in mathematics. This program integrates even more ways for you to develop your students' ability to read and write mathematically so that they are successful in this course and on state tests.

Reading Math

The *Reading Math* tips within lessons help students to read and understand the language of mathematics. The *Reading Math* features help students read more effectively, so that they can write, speak, and think mathematically. Reading to Analyze Errors, Reading Math Vocabulary, and Reading an Example are just a few of the strategies included.

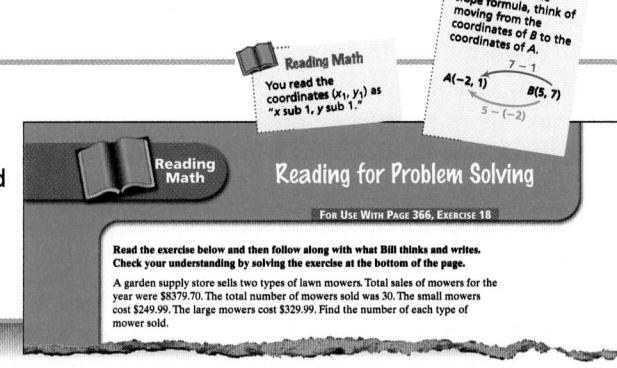

Writing in Math

Every lesson incorporates *Writing* exercises that help students learn to explain, describe, or compare in a mathematical situation. Special emphasis is also given to writing as it relates to Critical Thinking, Reasoning, and Error Analysis. Instruction in writing answers to rubric-scored questions helps students communicate successfully on today's tests.

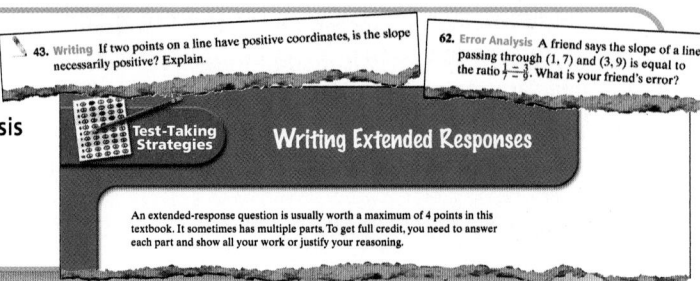

> "Success in subsequent mathematics courses and on standardized tests depends greatly on a student's ability to communicate in mathematics. The emphasis on reading and writing in *Prentice Hall Mathematics* through the Reading Tips and Reading Math features and through the Writing in Math opportunities enables all students to develop their communication skills."
>
> —Randy Charles, *Prentice Hall Mathematics* program author

Understanding Vocabulary

Prentice Hall Mathematics carefully develops the skill of reading math vocabulary. New vocabulary is conveniently listed at the beginning of each chapter and each lesson. Each new term is highlighted in yellow. The Chapter Review includes exercises that help students to correctly use the vocabulary presented in the chapter. The **i TEXT** reinforces students' vocabulary skills with an online vocabulary quiz for every chapter and an audio version of all glossary terms.

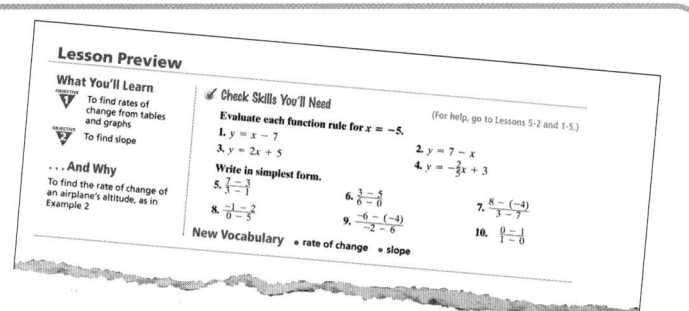

Reading and Math Literacy Masters

These unique blackline masters supplement the coverage of reading and math in the textbook. Students learn a variety of techniques to master mathematics vocabulary and symbols, read for problem solving, and increase comprehension.

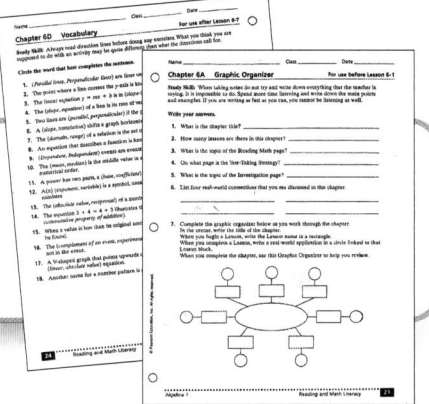

Reading for problem solving through Real-World Connections

Prentice Hall Mathematics incorporates abundant real-world connections within *Examples* and *Exercises* to provide a problem-solving context for applications of mathematics. Dorling Kindersley Real-World Snapshots bring math to life, with activities in which students gather data they need by reading graphic displays and captions.

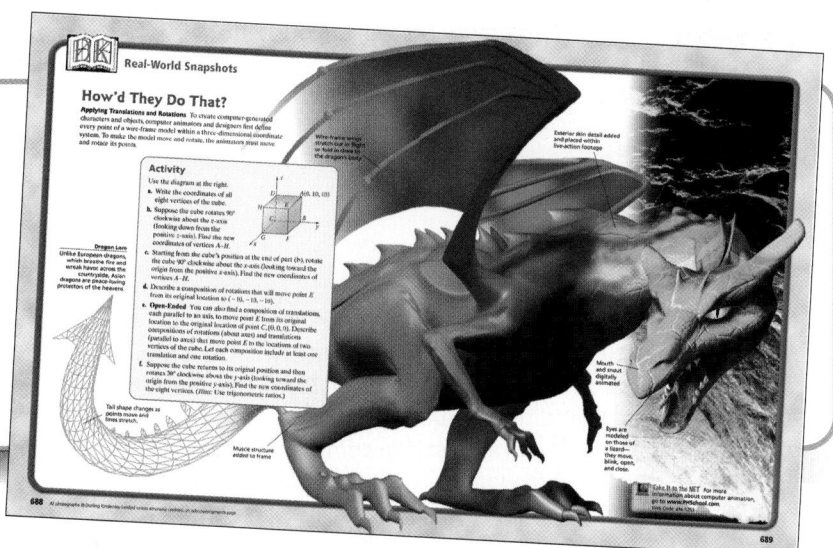

Ongoing assessment and test preparation guarantee testing success

What Research Indicates: We assess students most fairly when we assess often and with a variety of different answers. Research also shows that assessment needs to measure and describe a student's growth and achievement in all domains of mathematics and at three levels of thinking. Because of this, there should be questions at all levels of thinking, of varying degrees of difficulty, and in all content domains.

(Shafer, Mary C. & Foster, Sherian. "The Changing Faces of Assessment." *Principled Practice in Mathematics and Science Education,* Volume 1, No. 2.)

Prentice Hall's Response: *Prentice Hall Mathematics* provides an ongoing assessment strand that begins within the lesson instruction and continues throughout the program components. The program exposes students to questions of varying difficulty and at different levels of thinking in the daily *Check Understanding* questions and in the leveled *Exercises*.

A variety of question formats, including those found on today's standardized tests, is built into the Student Edition to assess student learning and prepare students for high-stakes tests. The ability to demonstrate knowledge in short-answer and open-ended formats increases opportunities for students to be successful on today's tests and in gaining admission to higher schooling and to the workplace.

✓ Check Understanding

Check Understanding questions after worked-out *Examples* allow students to assess their progress on a daily basis. These questions often emphasize the processes of explaining or reasoning—mirroring the types of questions that students will encounter on today's tests. You can use these questions to address any misconceptions or weaknesses before moving on to new topics.

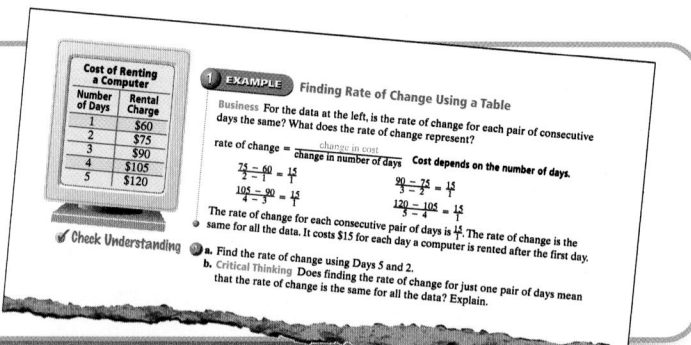

Quizzes and Tests—In Print and Online

You can assess student progress at key points with the *Lesson Quizzes, Checkpoint Quizzes,* and *Chapter Tests.* The Teaching Resources provides additional quizzes and tests, as well as alternative assessments. Online self-grading quizzes and tests are available on the Prentice Hall Web site at **www.PHSchool.com**.

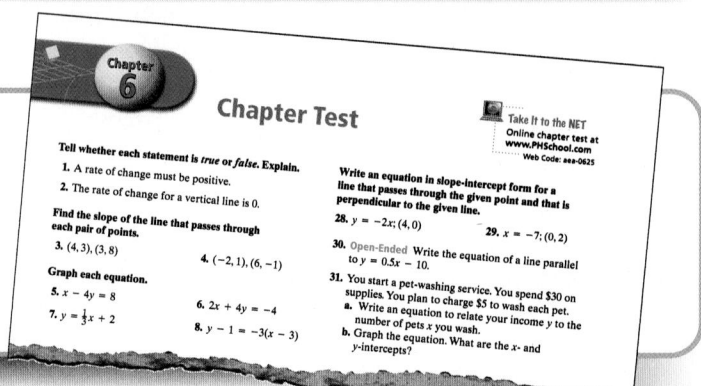

> "Assessment is an integral part of a mathematics program. *Prentice Hall Mathematics* provides a strong formative and summative assessment strand. The formative assessment features—before and during instruction—offer a variety of modalities that speak to different kinds of learners. The summative assessment features—after instruction—further prepare students for success on today's tests."
>
> —Sadie Chavis Bragg, *Prentice Hall Mathematics* program author

Standardized Test Prep Exercises

Standardized Test Prep exercises in every lesson give students daily practice with the types of test item formats that they will encounter on state tests. You can also provide students with the *Standardized Test Prep* page at the end of each chapter.

The daily exercises and the test prep pages include these most common test item formats:

- Multiple Choice
- Gridded Response
- Short Response
- Quantitative Comparison
- Reading Comprehension
- Extended Response

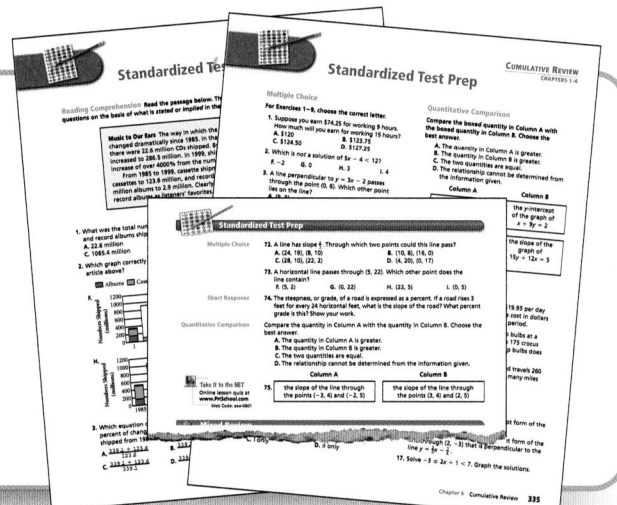

Test-Taking Strategies

Test-Taking Strategies in every chapter teach students strategies to be successful and give them practice in the skills they need to pass state tests and standardized national exams. Several lessons focus on helping students answer rubric-based questions.

The *Test-Taking Strategies With Transparencies* provide instruction on overheads and include additional practice sheets for the strategies taught in each chapter.

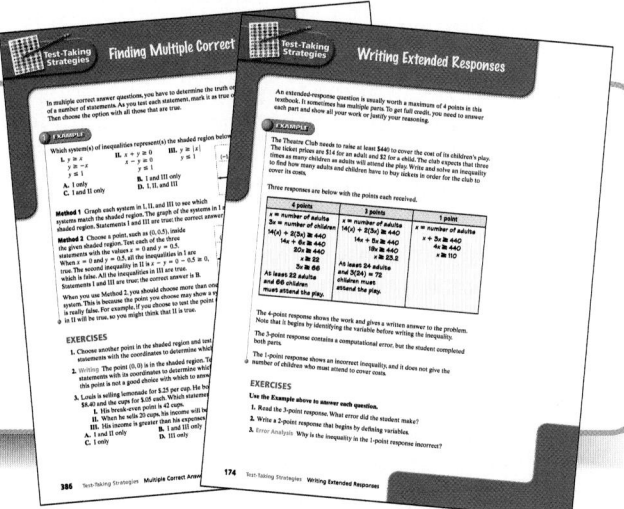

Prentice Hall Assessment System

An innovative *Assessment System* gives you everything you need to assess student progress on the content covered in the course, and to prepare students for high-stakes testing. The system contains the program Assessment Resources and the Computer Test Generator CD-ROM with unlimited questions and ready-to-use Chapter Tests.

In addition, you can diagnose student knowledge with *Content Diagnostic Tests*, prescribe intervention with the *Skills and Concept Review*, and have students practice for standardized assessments with the *Test Preparation* booklet. A *Teacher's Guide* gives you correlations and answers. Also included is the *Test-Taking Strategies With Transparencies* described above.

Mathematical Strands

Overview and Background

Number and Operations

NCTM Standard for Grades 9–12

- Understand numbers, ways of representing numbers, relationships among numbers, and number systems
- Understand meanings of operations and how they relate to one another
- Compute fluently and make reasonable estimates

Key Content in Prentice Hall
Algebra 1, Geometry, Algebra 2

- Represent and compute with rational numbers and real numbers (A1: Ch 1, 11; A2: Ch 1, 7)
- Understand the properties and operations of matrices, vectors, and complex numbers (A1: Ch 1; G: Ch 9; A2: Ch 4, 5)
- Justify relationships within number systems and compare properties of number systems (A1: Ch 1; A2: Ch 1, 4, 5)
- Judge the effects of multiplying, dividing, computing powers, and computing roots on the magnitude of quantities (A1: Ch 8; A2: Ch 7)
- Use counting techniques, including permutations and combinations (A1: Ch 12; A2: Ch 6)
- Judge reasonableness of numerical computations (throughout A1, G, A2)

Background and Progression

Students usually enter an Algebra 1 course having some facility with integers, fractions, and decimals. They have worked with square roots and used the Pythagorean Theorem.

In *Algebra 1,* students build an understanding of real numbers by using symbolic, graphic, and numeric representations as they solve equations and inequalities. Work with rational and radical expressions, equations, and functions builds a wide base of experience with rational and irrational numbers. Matrices are introduced.

In *Geometry,* students' understanding of the properties of real numbers becomes a base for building reasoned geometric arguments. In this year, students first study vectors.

In *Algebra 2,* students study matrices and complex numbers—number systems that do not share all the properties of real numbers (for example, multiplication of matrices is not commutative, and complex numbers cannot be arranged in order).

Data Analysis and Probability

NCTM Standard for Grades 9–12

- Formulate questions that can be addressed with data and collect, organize, and display relevant data to answer them
- Select and use appropriate statistical methods to analyze data
- Develop and evaluate inferences and predictions that are based on data
- Understand and apply basic concepts of probability

Key Content in Prentice Hall
Algebra 1, Geometry, Algebra 2

- Construct and interpret histograms, box plots, and scatterplots (A1: Ch 6; A2: Ch 12)
- Compute statistics, including mean, median, mode, range, and standard deviation (A1: Ch 2; A2: Ch 12)
- Identify trends in bivariate data and find functions that model the data (A1: Ch 6, 10; A2: Ch 2, 5, 6, 8)
- Construct sampling distributions and use them for informal inference about the population (A2: Ch 12)
- Compute probabilities of simple and compound events, geometric probabilities, and conditional probabilities (A1: Ch 4; G: Ch 7; A2: Ch 1, 9, 12)

Background and Progression

In the middle grades, students have gathered, displayed, and interpreted many types of data, including one-variable (for example, test scores), two-variable (height vs. age), and data related to categories (numbers of students who like various foods). They can distinguish appropriate uses of bar, line, and circle graphs, and can find simple probabilities.

In *Algebra 1,* students work with scatter plots and functions to model two-variable, or bivariate, data. They compute probabilities for simple and compound events.

In *Geometry,* students maintain skills, with probability exercises found throughout the text, and are introduced to geometric probability.

In *Algebra 2,* students begin a study of histograms (probability distributions based on experimental results) and theoretical distributions, including binomial (based on two possible outcomes) and normal (representing many real-life random variables, such as adult heights). Students also use tree diagrams to analyze conditional probabilities.

 *For more **Math Background** on every lesson, see page B before each chapter and see each lesson's teaching notes.*

Algebra

NCTM Standard for Grades 9–12

- Understand patterns, relations, and functions
- Represent and analyze mathematical situations and structures using algebraic symbols
- Use mathematical models to represent and understand quantitative relationships
- Analyze change in various contexts

Key Content in Prentice Hall
Algebra 1, Geometry, Algebra 2

- Use various representations of functions and choose types to model quantitative relationships (throughout A1, A2)
- Analyze functions of one variable, including rates of change, intercepts, zeros, and asymptotes (A1: Ch 5, 6, 8, 10; A2: Ch 2, 5–9, 11, 13)
- Combine, compose, and invert common functions (A2: Ch 7, 8, 13, 14)
- Interpret functions of two variables and use parametric forms (A2: Ch 3, 10)
- Understand properties of different types of functions, including linear, quadratic, exponential, polynomial, rational, radical, logarithmic, and periodic functions (A1: Ch 6, 8, 10–12; A2: Ch 2, 5–9, 11, 13)
- Use symbolic algebra to represent and explain mathematical relationships (throughout A1, A2)
- Write equivalent forms of and solve equations, inequalities, and systems (throughout A1, G, A2)

Background and Progression

Today's middle school students are comfortable with tables, graphs, verbal rules, and variables in the representation of simple relationships. Many know how to solve linear equations.

In *Algebra 1,* students use tables, graphs, verbal rules, and symbolic rules to describe linear, quadratic, and exponential functions. They choose a best model for data from among these functions. Rate of change is studied in the context of direct variation, linear equations, and arithmetic and geometric sequences. Students learn how to write equivalent forms of polynomial, radical, and rational expressions.

In *Geometry,* Algebra 1 skills are reinforced with applications involving both linear and quadratic relationships.

In *Algebra 2,* students use multiple representations in studying polynomial, rational, radical, logarithmic, and periodic functions. Using technology, students study residuals as an indicator of the most appropriate model for data. Students first see functions of two variables in the concrete context of linear programming. Trigonometric functions are presented first in the unit circle, and then applied to solving triangles.

Geometry

NCTM Standard for Grades 9–12

- Analyze characteristics and properties of two- and three-dimensional geometric shapes and develop mathematical arguments about geometric relationships
- Specify locations and describe spatial relationships using coordinate geometry and other representational systems
- Apply transformations and use symmetry to analyze mathematical situations
- Use visualization, spatial reasoning, and geometric modeling to solve problems

Key Content in Prentice Hall
Algebra 1, Geometry, Algebra 2

- Analyze properties of plane and space figures. Solve problems involving them, and real-world applications in general (throughout G)
- Explore congruence and similarity (throughout G)
- Use deductive reasoning to establish the validity of conjectures, to prove theorems, and to critique arguments (G: Ch 2–12)
- Use coordinates to analyze shapes, solve problems, and prove relationships (G: Ch 3, 6, 12; A2: Ch 10)
- Understand and represent transformations in the plane using sketches, coordinates, vectors, functions, and matrices (G: Ch 12; A2: Ch 2, 4, 5, 7–10, 13)
- Visualize, draw, and construct plane and space figures, from different perspectives (G: Ch 1, 10; A2: Ch 3, 10)
- Use geometric models to solve problems in other areas of mathematics (A1: Ch 4; G: Ch 7, 9; A2: Ch 14)

Background and Progression

In the middle grades, students have explored various plane and space figures to identify and compare properties. This includes working with similarity, congruence, tessellations, symmetry, slides, flips, turns, and simple figures in the coordinate plane.

In *Algebra 1,* students begin to use geometric models with proportions, percent, and probability. They also explore ways to describe translations of familiar functions in both words and symbols.

In *Geometry,* all key strand content is covered. The first two chapters establish the tools of geometry—methods of reasoning, construction, the coordinate plane, and types of measurement. Subsequent chapters focus on properties and applications of lines, triangles, quadrilaterals, similarity, right triangle trigonometry, circles, and transformations.

In *Algebra 2,* students apply principles of translating in the coordinate plane to functions and conic sections. Geometric models for trigonometric relationships are also utilized.

 *For more **Math Background** on every lesson, see page B before each chapter and see each lesson's teaching notes.*

Mathematical Strands

Measurement

NCTM Standard for Grades 9–12

- Understand measurable attributes of objects and the units, systems, and processes of measurement
- Apply appropriate techniques, tools, and formulas to determine measurements

Key Content in Prentice Hall
Algebra 1, Geometry, Algebra 2

- Make decisions about appropriate units and scales in problems involving measurement (A1: Ch 6; G: Ch 8, 10; A2: Ch 1, 13, 14)
- Understand and use formulas for area, surface area, and volume (A1: Ch 2; G: Ch 7, 10; A2: Ch 6, 7)
- Apply concepts of successive approximation, upper and lower bounds, and limits (G: Ch 10; A2: Ch 11, 12)
- Use unit analysis (A1: Ch 4; G: Ch 7)

Background and Progression

Middle school students have usually experienced direct measurements (such as length, mass, and volume), indirect measurements (based on similar triangles), and derived measurements (such as rates). They are familiar with precision and accuracy in measurement, and have developed and used formulas for the perimeters, areas, and volumes of simple figures.

In *Algebra 1,* students make decisions about appropriate scales with graphical representations of data. They use formulas for the perimeters and areas of figures to find missing measures, and use unit analysis (sometimes called dimensional analysis) to help set up proportions and other equations.

In *Geometry,* students justify formulas for perimeter and area and apply them to composite and irregular plane shapes. Students use cross sections to develop formulas for the volumes of prisms, cylinders, pyramids, and cones. The approximation techniques used to help justify the formulas for the surface area and volume of a sphere anticipate calculus. Through work with arc length and the areas of circles and parts of circles, students become comfortable with exact measures (which are irrational and expressed in terms of π) and rational approximations of these measures.

In *Algebra 2,* students use polynomials to express the areas and volumes of figures, and polynomial equations to find missing measures. With geometric sequences they explore successive approximations and the concept of a limit. Various statistical measures lead to the concepts of statistical error and standard deviation. In their study of trigonometry, students learn how to use the parallel measuring scales of degrees and radians, and when to choose one over the other. In "solving" triangles (finding the measures of all sides and angles, and the area), they use trigonometric relationships to make indirect measurements.

Problem Solving

NCTM Standard for Grades 9–12

- Build new mathematical knowledge through problem solving
- Solve problems that arise in mathematics and in other contexts
- Apply and adapt a variety of appropriate strategies to solve problems
- Monitor and reflect on the process of mathematical problem solving

Key Processes in Prentice Hall
Algebra 1, Geometry, Algebra 2

- Solve problems taken from the student's current and future world (Real-World Connection Examples throughout each text)
- Use a variety of appropriate methods to solve problems (Examples showing two methods throughout each text)
- Construct an appropriate expression, equation, or function to solve a problem (Examples using the "Relate-Define-Write" model throughout A1 and A2)
- Use various problem solving strategies as appropriate (reviewed in the Skills Handbook of each text)
- Build understanding of new topics through problem solving (Investigations and Reading for Problem Solving throughout each text)
- Reflect on the process of problem solving (Checks for Reasonableness, Writing, Critical Thinking, Reasoning, and Error Analysis exercises throughout each text)

Background and Progression

The Prentice Hall Mathematics Program for the middle grades contains a rich problem solving strand, including lessons each year covering ten problem solving strategies.

In *Algebra 1, Geometry,* and *Algebra 2,* the strategies are reviewed in the Skills Handbook. In each text, students practice the critical skill of expressing mathematical relationships from real-world problems with symbolic models. Each text contains numerous real-world examples, many of which use the "Relate-Define-Write" format to guide the student in choosing and writing a correct model.

Where possible, examples show more than one method for solving a problem. Many examples include a check for reasonableness. Investigations found throughout each text allow students to form their understanding of a new math topic through guided discovery. The Reading for Problem Solving pages model the thinking of an inquiring student.

Writing, Critical Thinking, Reasoning, and Error Analysis exercises allow students to analyze and verbalize their own understanding of the problem solving process.

 *For more **Math Background** on every lesson, see page B before each chapter and see each lesson's teaching notes.*

Reasoning and Proof

NCTM Standard for Grades 9–12

- Recognize reasoning and proof as fundamental aspects of mathematics
- Make and investigate mathematical conjectures
- Develop and evaluate mathematical arguments and proofs
- Select and use various types of reasoning and methods of proof

Key Processes in Prentice Hall
Algebra 1, Geometry, Algebra 2

- Use inductive reasoning to make and investigate conjectures (Make a Conjecture exercises and Investigation pages throughout each text)
- Develop deductive proof in various formats, including paragraph, flow, two-column, indirect, and coordinate proof (A1: Ch 1; G: Ch 2–12; A2: Ch 6, 14)
- Apply appropriate reasoning to analyze mathematical statements (Checks for Reasonableness, Writing, Critical Thinking, Reasoning, and Error Analysis exercises throughout each text)
- Study and write proofs of geometric theorems (G: Ch 2–12)
- Study and write proofs of algebraic theorems, properties, and equivalences (A1: Ch 1; A2: Ch 6, 8, 14)
- Explain work and justify conclusions (Writing, Critical Thinking, Reasoning, Error Analysis, Short Response, and Extended Response exercises throughout each text)

Background and Progression

In middle grades, students identify the use of Commutative, Associative, Identity, Inverse, and Distributive properties. They use these properties and the Properties of equality to justify steps in solving equations. Students also differentiate deductive and inductive reasoning.

In *Algebra 1,* students solve equations using the properties of real numbers and of equality to justify their steps. These justifications are extended to simple algebraic proofs.

In *Geometry,* students develop an understanding of the structure and concepts of Euclidean plane geometry, building naturally on the step-by-step processes of algebra. They prove theorems in more than one way using paragraph proofs, flow proofs, and two-column proofs.

In *Algebra 2,* students further their understanding and ability to prove concepts not only by deduction but also by using mathematical induction.

Communication

NCTM Standard for Grades 9–12

- Organize and consolidate their mathematical thinking through communication
- Communicate their mathematical thinking coherently and clearly to peers, teachers, and others
- Analyze and evaluate the mathematical thinking and strategies of others
- Use the language of mathematics to express mathematical ideas precisely

Key Processes in Prentice Hall
Algebra 1, Geometry, Algebra 2

- Write about mathematical concepts by summarizing, comparing, analyzing, and explaining (Writing, Critical Thinking, Reasoning, Short Response, and Extended Response exercises throughout each text)
- Understand the language and notations of mathematics (Reading Math notes and Reading for Problem Solving pages throughout each text and Understanding Vocabulary exercises in each Chapter Review)
- Use appropriate notation to express mathematical relationships in real-world contexts (Examples using the "Relate-Define-Write" model throughout A1 and A2, Reading Comprehension exercises, and the Reading for Problem Solving pages in each text)
- Analyze sample work to find errors (Error Analysis exercises throughout each text)

Background and Progression

The Prentice Hall Mathematics Program for the middle grades gives students numerous opportunities to explain and justify their reasoning.

The *Algebra 1, Geometry,* and *Algebra 2* textbooks continue this rich communication strand. In-lesson Investigations and Investigation pages have students develop critical concepts, which students are encouraged first to summarize and then to use in exercises.

The Reading for Problem Solving pages focus on a variety of topics to help students read more effectively, so that they can write, speak, and think mathematically. The Reading Math hints in lessons help students use the language and notation of mathematics correctly and relate new mathematical vocabulary to English terms they already know.

Students are given instruction on answering Short Response questions with two-point rubrics and Extended Response questions with four-point rubrics. Throughout each text, students get ample opportunity to answer rubric-based exercises.

 *For more **Math Background** on every lesson, see page B before each chapter and see each lesson's teaching notes.*

A1: *Algebra 1*; G: *Geometry*; A2: *Algebra 2*

Connections

NCTM Standard for Grades 9–12

- Recognize and use connections among mathematical ideas
- Understand how mathematical ideas interconnect and build on one another to produce a coherent whole
- Recognize and apply mathematics in contexts outside of mathematics

Key Processes in Prentice Hall
Algebra 1, Geometry, Algebra 2

- Solve problems in more than one way (A1 and A2: Examples showing two methods; G: Alternative proofs)
- Solve problems arising from real-world contexts (Real-World Connection Examples, Real-World Snapshots, and application and Reading Comprehension exercises throughout each text)
- Use algebraic concepts such as the coordinate plane, slope, vectors, matrices with transformations, and properties of geometric figures (A1: Ch 5; G: Ch 3, 5, 6, 9, 11,12; A2: Ch 4, 10)
- Use algebraic equations to solve measurement problems in geometry (throughout G)
- Use geometric concepts with probability, systems of equations, functions, and quadratic relations (A1: Ch 7, 10–12; G: Ch 7; A2: Ch 2, 3, 5–13)

Background and Progression

In middle grades, students make connections between geometric and algebraic concepts through graphing geometric figures in the coordinate plane and using slope to investigate the concepts of parallelism and perpendicularity.

In *Algebra 1,* students use algebra to develop formulas for geometric measurement and to describe statistical relationships (lines of best fit). Critical Thinking exercises have students make connections between previously learned material and lesson content. Students understand geometric relationships using slope, midpoint, and distance formulas.

In *Geometry,* students use algebra to interpret and apply geometric relationships. Students take an alternative look at many geometric facts by revisiting them in the coordinate plane.

In *Algebra 2,* students use matrices to describe transformations in the coordinate plane. They extend algebra-geometry connections to reinforce the structure and processes involving functions and conic sections.

Representation

NCTM Standard for Grades 9–12

- Create and use representations to organize, record, and communicate mathematical ideas
- Select, apply, and translate among mathematical representations to solve problems
- Use representations to model and interpret physical, social, and mathematical phenomena

Key Processes in Prentice Hall
Algebra 1, Geometry, Algebra 2

- Organize mathematical information in order to make and support conjectures (Investigations throughout each text)
- Use tables, graphs, verbal rules, and symbolic rules interchangeably as appropriate (A1: Ch 5–8, 10-12; A2: Ch 1, 3, 5, 6, 8–10, 12, 13)
- Choose an appropriate algebraic function model for two-variable measurement data (A1: Ch 10; A2: Ch 2, 5, 8)
- Solve real-world problems by creating a mathematical model to represent the essential mathematics involved (Examples using the "Relate-Define-Write" model in A1 and A2, application exercises, Reading Comprehension exercises, and Real-World Snapshots throughout each text)

Background and Progression

In the middle grades, students have experiences using tables, rules, and graphs to describe functional relationships. They also use tables in problem solving situations to organize real-world data.

In *Algebra 1,* students gain facility in graphing these families of functions: linear, quadratic, exponential, and rational functions. Using tables and graphs, students determine which function best models a given set of data.

In *Geometry,* students learn to recognize, apply, and interpret geometric principles in real-world settings, and frequently use coordinate methods to take another look at these principles.

In *Algebra 2,* students extend their knowledge of the families of functions to polynomial, logarithmic, and trigonometric functions. They also use three-variable equations to model problem situations.

 *For more **Math Background** on every lesson, see page B before each chapter and see each lesson's teaching notes.*

Pacing Options for Geometry

Pacing Guide

This chart is provided merely as a guide to help you customize your course. To accommodate flexible scheduling, most lessons are subdivided into objectives. Within the lessons of the Student Edition, these objectives are indicated in red by the symbol ▼. The Assignment Guide for each lesson indicates which exercises in the Student Edition correspond to each objective of the lesson.

Detailed Chapter Pacing Options precede each chapter and give you lesson-by-lesson pacing suggestions for that specific chapter.

CHAPTER	Traditional (45-minute class periods)	Two-Year (45-minute class periods)	Block (90-minute class periods)	Two-Year Block (90-minute class periods)
1	16 days	32 days	7 days	16 days
2	10 days	20 days	5 days	10 days
3	14 days	28 days	7 days	14 days
4	10 days	20 days	7 days	10 days
5	9 days	18 days	5 days	9 days
6	10 days	20 days	7 days	10 days
7	16 days	32 days	8 days	16 days
8	10 days	20 days	6 days	10 days
9	12 days	24 days	5 days	12 days
10	17 days	34 days	9 days	17 days
11	16 days	32 days	6 days	16 days
12	20 days	40 days	8 days	20 days
Total	160 days	320 days	80 days	160 days

Differentiated Scope of Course

I = Informal Course   C = Core Course   A = Advanced Course

Chapter 1 Tools of Geometry	I	C	A
1-1: Patterns and Inductive Reasoning	✓	✓	✓
1-2: Points, Lines, and Planes	✓	✓	✓
1-3: Segments, Rays, Parallel Lines, and Planes	✓	✓	✓
• Algebra 1 Review: Solving Linear Equations	✓	✓	
1-4: Measuring Segments and Angles	✓	✓	✓
1-5: Basic Constructions	✓	✓	✓
• Technology: Exploring Constructions	✓	✓	✓
• Investigation: Distance in the Coordinate Plane	✓	✓	
1-6: The Coordinate Plane	✓	✓	✓
1-7: Perimeter, Circumference, and Area	✓	✓	✓
• Technology: Comparing Perimeters and Areas		✓	✓

Chapter 2 Reasoning and Proof	I	C	A
2-1: Conditional Statements	✓	✓	✓
2-2: Biconditionals and Definitions	✓	✓	✓
2-3: Deductive Reasoning	✓	✓	✓
2-4: Reasoning in Algebra	✓	✓	✓
2-5: Proving Angles Congruent	✓	✓	✓

Chapter 3 Parallel and Perpendicular Lines	I	C	A
• Technology: Parallel Lines and Related Angles	✓	✓	✓
3-1: Properties of Parallel Lines	✓	✓	✓
3-2: Proving Lines Parallel	✓	✓	✓
3-3: Parallel Lines and the Triangle Angle-Sum Theorem	✓	✓	✓
• Extension: Exploring Spherical Geometry		✓	✓
• Technology: Exterior Angles of Polygons	✓	✓	✓
3-4: The Polygon Angle-Sum Theorems	✓	✓	✓
• Algebra 1 Review: Slope	✓	✓	
3-5: Lines in the Coordinate Plane	✓	✓	✓
3-6: Slopes of Parallel and Perpendicular Lines	✓	✓	✓
3-7: Constructing Parallel and Perpendicular Lines	✓	✓	
• Technology: Using Tables and Lists		✓	✓

Chapter 4 Congruent Triangles	I	C	A
4-1: Congruent Figures	✓	✓	✓
4-2: Triangle Congruence by SSS and SAS	✓	✓	✓
4-3: Triangle Congruence by ASA and AAS	✓	✓	✓
• Technology: Exploring AAA and SSA		✓	✓
4-4: Using Congruent Triangles: CPCTC	✓	✓	✓
• Algebra 1 Review: Systems of Linear Equations	✓	✓	
4-5: Isosceles and Equilateral Triangles	✓	✓	✓
4-6: Congruence in Right Triangles	✓	✓	✓
4-7: Using Corresponding Parts of Congruent Triangles		✓	✓
• Extension: Writing Flow Proofs			✓

Chapter 5 Relationships Within Triangles	I	C	A
• Technology: Investigating Midsegments	✓	✓	✓
5-1: Midsegments of Triangles	✓	✓	✓
5-2: Bisectors in Triangles	✓	✓	✓
• Technology: Special Segments in Triangles	✓	✓	✓
5-3: Concurrent Lines, Medians, and Altitudes	✓	✓	✓
5-4: Inverses, Contrapositives, and Indirect Reasoning		✓	✓
• Algebra 1 Review: Solving Inequalities	✓	✓	
5-5: Inequalities in Triangles	✓	✓	✓

Chapter 6 Quadrilaterals	I	C	A
6-1: Classifying Quadrilaterals	✓	✓	✓
6-2: Properties of Parallelograms	✓	✓	✓
6-3: Proving That a Quadrilateral Is a Parallelogram	✓	✓	✓
• Technology: Diagonals of Parallelograms	✓	✓	✓
6-4: Special Parallelograms	✓	✓	✓
• Technology: Quadrilaterals in Quadrilaterals	✓	✓	✓
6-5: Trapezoids and Kites	✓	✓	✓
6-6: Placing Figures in the Coordinate Plane		✓	✓
6-7: Proofs Using Coordinate Geometry		✓	✓

Chapter 7 Area	I	C	A
7-1: Areas of Parallelograms and Triangles	✓	✓	✓
• Algebra 1 Review: Simplifying Radicals	✓	✓	
• Investigation: The Pythagorean Theorem		✓	✓
7-2: The Pythagorean Theorem and Its Converse	✓	✓	✓
7-3: Special Right Triangles	✓	✓	✓
7-4: Areas of Trapezoids, Rhombuses, and Kites	✓	✓	✓
7-5: Areas of Regular Polygons	✓	✓	✓
7-6: Circles and Arcs	✓	✓	✓
• Algebra 1 Review: Dimensional Analysis	✓	✓	
7-7: Areas of Circles and Sectors	✓	✓	✓
• Technology: Exploring Area and Circumference		✓	✓
7-8: Geometric Probability		✓	✓

Chapter 8 Similarity	I	C	A
8-1: Ratios and Proportions	✓	✓	
• Algebra 1 Review: Solving Quadratic Equations		✓	
8-2: Similar Polygons	✓	✓	✓
• Extension: Fractals		✓	✓
8-3: Proving Triangles Similar	✓	✓	✓
8-4: Similarity in Right Triangles	✓	✓	✓
• Technology: Exploring Proportions in Triangles	✓	✓	✓
8-5: Proportions in Triangles	✓	✓	✓
8-6: Perimeters and Areas of Similar Figures	✓	✓	✓

Chapter 9 Right Triangle Trigonometry	I	C	A
9-1: The Tangent Ratio	✓	✓	✓
• Technology: Exploring Trigonometric Ratios	✓	✓	✓
9-2: Sine and Cosine Ratios	✓	✓	✓
9-3: Angles of Elevation and Depression	✓	✓	✓
9-4: Vectors			✓
9-5: Trigonometry and Area			✓

Chapter 10 Surface Area and Volume	I	C	A
10-1: Space Figures and Nets	✓	✓	✓
• Extension: Perspective Drawing			✓
10-2: Space Figures and Drawings	✓	✓	✓
• Algebra 1 Review: Literal Equations		✓	
10-3: Surface Areas of Prisms and Cylinders	✓	✓	✓
• Technology: Exploring Surface Area		✓	✓
10-4: Surface Areas of Pyramids and Cones	✓	✓	✓
10-5: Volumes of Prisms and Cylinders	✓	✓	✓
10-6: Volumes of Pyramids and Cones	✓	✓	✓
10-7: Surface Areas and Volumes of Spheres	✓	✓	✓
• Technology: Exploring Similar Solids			✓
10-8: Areas and Volumes of Similar Solids		✓	✓

Chapter 11 Circles	I	C	A
11-1: Tangent Lines	✓	✓	✓
11-2: Chords and Arcs	✓	✓	✓
11-3: Inscribed Angles	✓	✓	✓
• Technology: Exploring Chords and Secants		✓	✓
11-4: Angle Measures and Segment Lengths		✓	✓
• Extension: Tangent Lines, Tangent Ratios			✓
11-5: Circles in the Coordinate Plane	✓	✓	✓
11-6: Locus: A Set of Points		✓	✓

Chapter 12 Transformations	I	C	A
12-1: Reflections	✓	✓	✓
• Algebra 1 Review: Matrices		✓	
12-2: Translations	✓	✓	✓
12-3: Rotations	✓	✓	✓
12-4: Compositions of Reflections			✓
• Technology: Kaleidoscopes		✓	✓
12-5: Symmetry	✓	✓	✓
12-6: Tessellations	✓	✓	✓
12-7: Dilations		✓	✓

Using Your Book for Success

Welcome to Prentice Hall *Geometry*. There are many features built into the daily lessons of this text that will help you learn the important skills and concepts you will need to be successful in this course. Look through the following pages for some study tips that you will find useful as you complete each lesson.

Instant Check System™
An *Instant Check System™*, built into the text and marked with a ✓, allows you to check your understanding of skills before moving on to the next topic.

✓ Diagnosing Readiness
Complete the *Diagnosing Readiness* exercises to see what topics you may need to review before you begin the chapter.

✓ Check Skills You'll Need
Complete the *Check Skills You'll Need* exercises to make sure you have the skills needed to successfully learn the concepts in the lesson.

New Vocabulary
New Vocabulary is listed for each lesson so you can pre-read the text. As each term is introduced, it is highlighted in yellow.

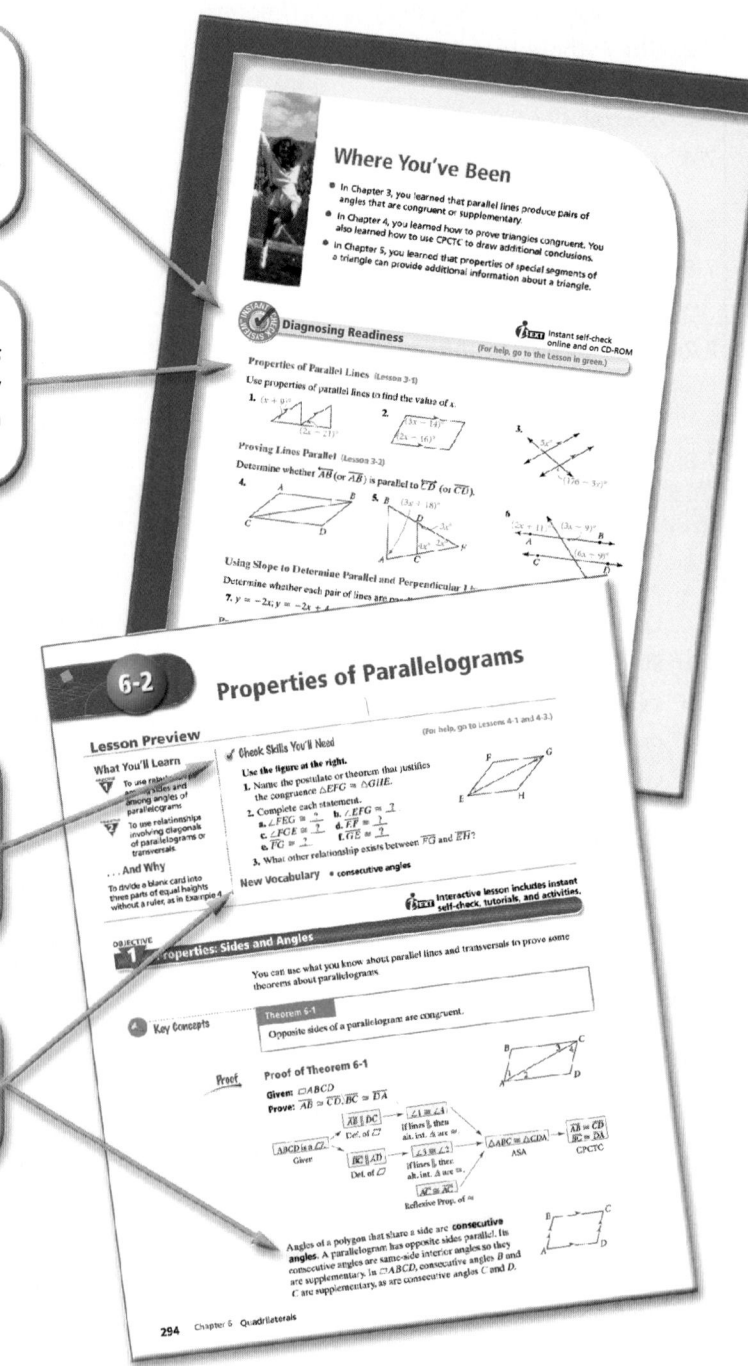

Reading Math

The *Reading Math* hints help you to use mathematical notation correctly, understand new mathematical vocabulary, and translate mathematical symbols into everyday English so you can talk about what you've learned.

✓ Check Understanding

Every lesson includes numerous *Examples,* each followed by a *Check Understanding* question that you can do on your own to see if you understand the skill being introduced. Check your progress with the answers at the back of the book.

Need Help?

Need Help? notes provide a quick review of a concept you need to understand the topic being presented. Look for the green labels throughout the text that tells you where to "Go" for help.

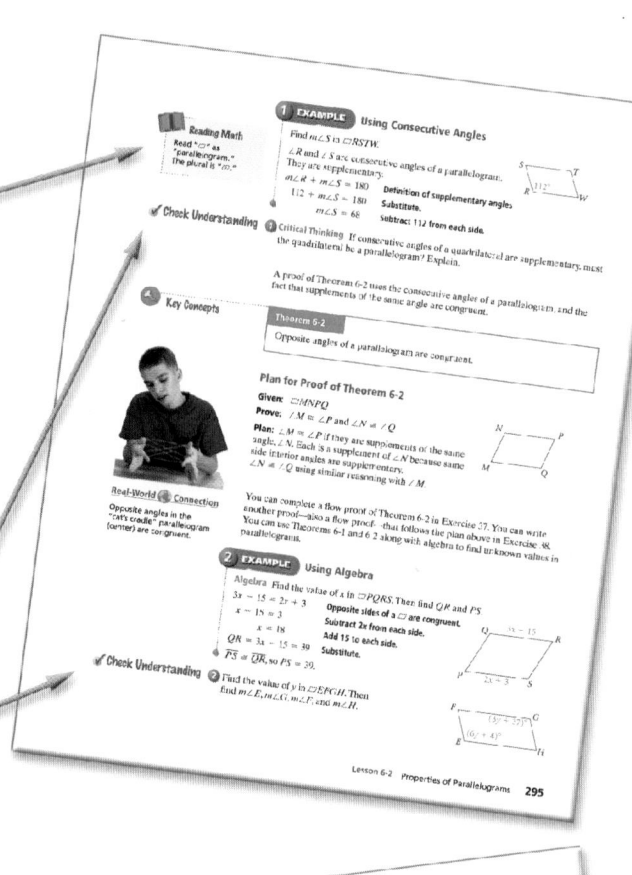

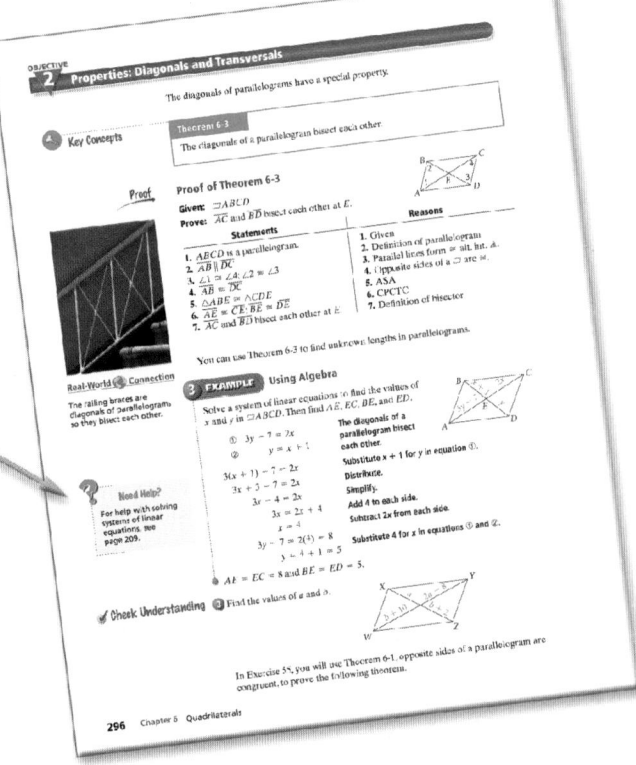

Exercises
There are numerous *Exercises* in each lesson that give you the practice you need to master the concepts of the lesson. Each practice set includes the following sections.

A: Practice by Example
The *A: Practice by Example* exercises refer you back to the Examples in the lesson, in case you need help with completing these exercises.

B: Apply Your Skills
The *B: Apply Your Skills* exercises combine skills from earlier lessons to offer you richer skill exercises and multi-step application problems.

C: Challenge
The *C: Challenge* exercises give you an opportunity to solve problems that extend and stretch your thinking.

Standardized Test Prep
Standardized Test Prep exercises give you daily practice with the types of test question formats that you will encounter on state and national tests.

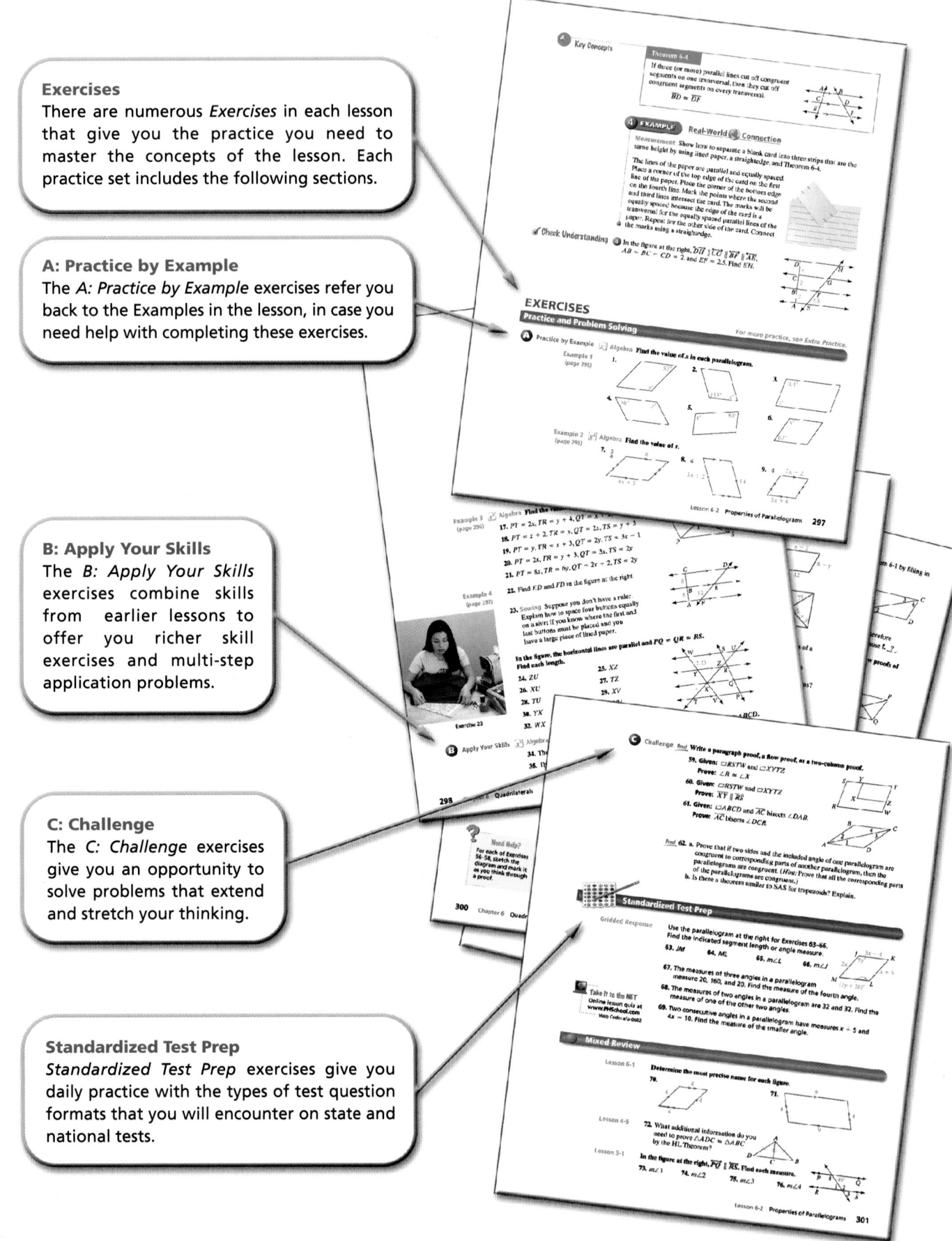

Test-Taking Strategies
Test-Taking Strategies in every chapter teach you strategies to be successful and give you practice in the skills you need to pass state tests and standardized national exams.

Standardized Test Prep
Standardized Test Prep pages in every chapter give you more opportunities to prepare for the tests you will have to take.

Test Item Formats
The *Standardized Test Prep* exercises in your book give you the practice you need to answer all types of test questions.
- *Multiple Choice*
- *Quantitative Comparison*
- *Gridded Response*, for which you write your answer in a grid
- *Short Response*, which are scored using a rubric
- *Extended Response*, which are scored using a rubric
- *Reading Comprehension*

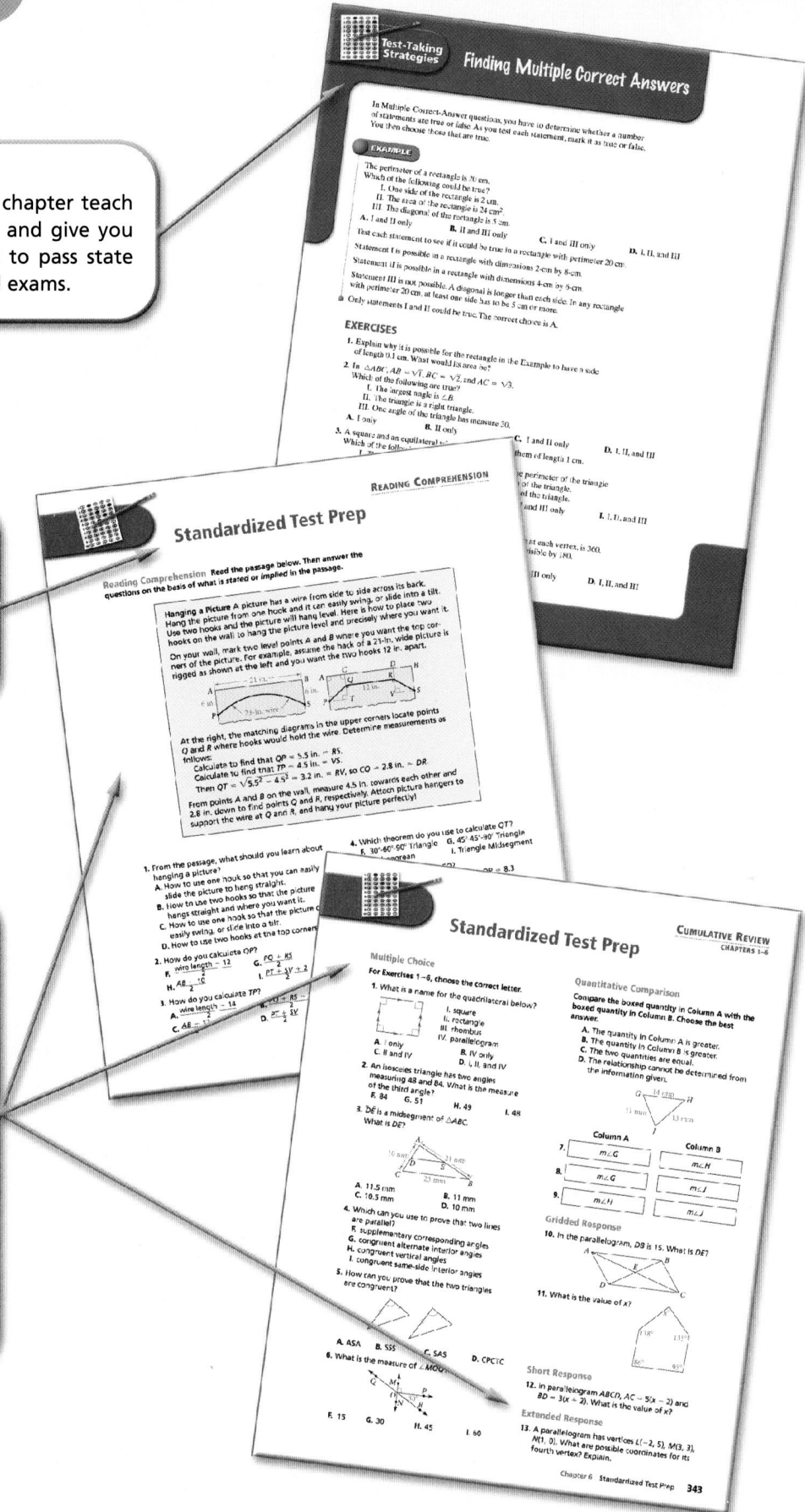

Student's Guide

In addition to the Reading Math hints shown on page xxi, your *Geometry* text provides even more ways for you to develop your ability to read mathematically so that you are successful in this course and on state tests.

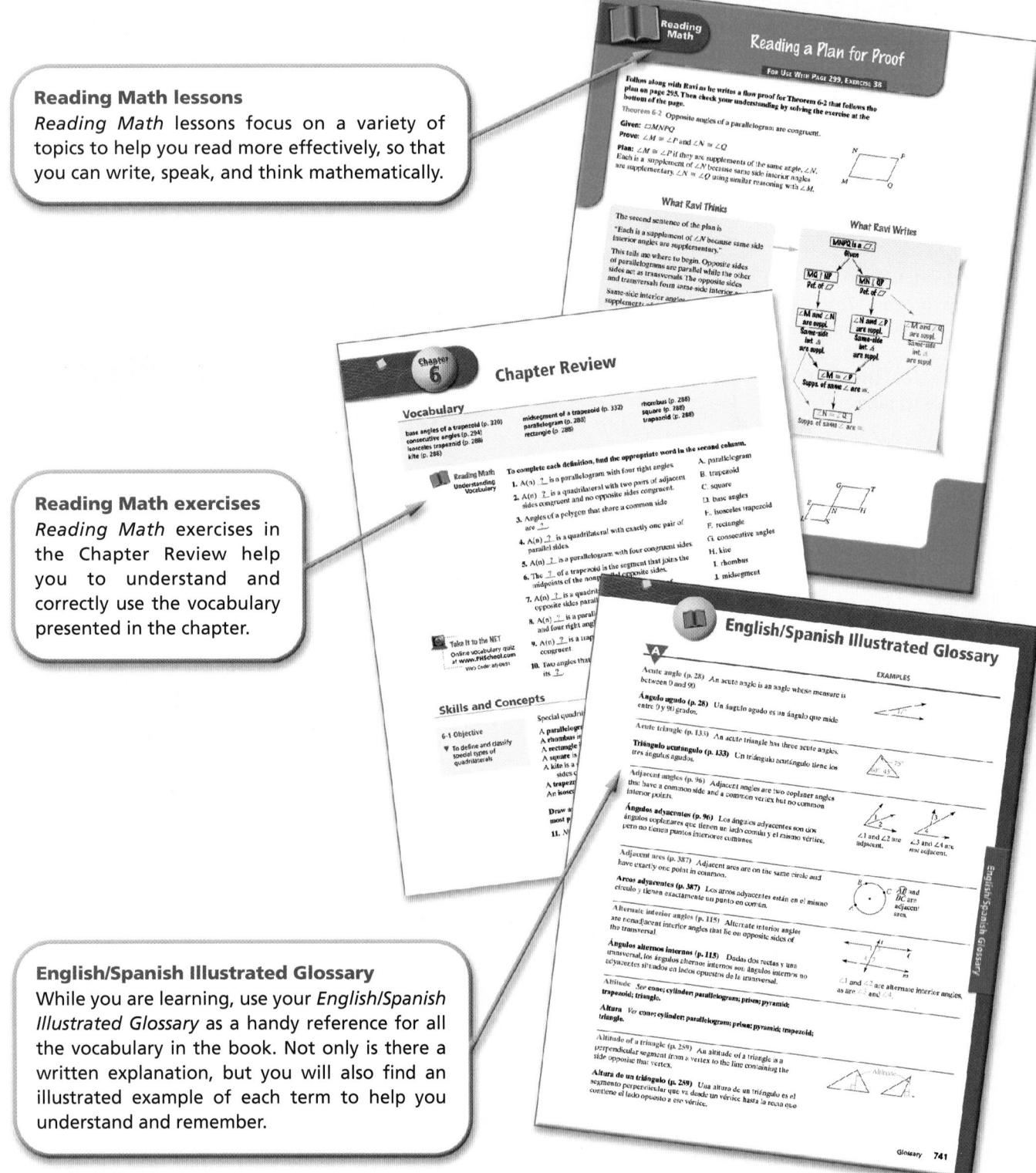

Reading Math lessons
Reading Math lessons focus on a variety of topics to help you read more effectively, so that you can write, speak, and think mathematically.

Reading Math exercises
Reading Math exercises in the Chapter Review help you to understand and correctly use the vocabulary presented in the chapter.

English/Spanish Illustrated Glossary
While you are learning, use your *English/Spanish Illustrated Glossary* as a handy reference for all the vocabulary in the book. Not only is there a written explanation, but you will also find an illustrated example of each term to help you understand and remember.

Dorling Kindersley (DK) Real-World Snapshots

Dorling Kindersley (DK) is an international publishing company that specializes in the creation of high-quality, illustrated information books for children and adults. DK is part of the Pearson family of companies.

Real-World Snapshots
The *Real-World Snapshots* feature applies the exciting and unique graphic presentation style found in Dorling Kindersley books to show you how mathematics is used in real life.

Activities
Using data from these pages and data that you gather, complete the hands-on *Activities* to apply the mathematics you are learning in real-world situations.

Take It to the Net
Enter the Web Code for online information you can use to learn more about the topic of the feature.

Chapter 1

Tools of Geometry

Chapter at a Glance

North Carolina Objectives

1-1	Patterns and Inductive Reasoning	2.01
NCTM 1, 6, 7, 8, 9, 10	∇ Using Inductive Reasoning	

1-2	Points, Lines, and Planes	2.02
NCTM 3, 6, 7, 8, 9, 10	∇ Basic Terms of Geometry ∇ Basic Postulates of Geometry	

1-3	Segments, Rays, Parallel Lines and Planes	2.02
NCTM 3, 6, 8, 9, 10	∇ Identifying Segments and Rays ∇ Recognizing Parallel Figures	

1-4	Measuring Segments and Angles	2.02
NCTM 1, 2, 3, 4, 6, 7, 8, 9, 10	∇ Finding Segment Lengths ∇ Finding Angle Measures	

1-5	Basic Constructions	2.02
NCTM 3, 4, 6, 8, 9, 10	∇ Constructing Segments and Angles ∇ Constructing Bisectors	

1-6	The Coordinate Plane	1.02
NCTM 1, 2, 3, 4, 6, 8, 9, 10	∇ Finding Distance on the Coordinate Plane ∇ Finding the Midpoint of a Segment	

1-7	Perimeter, Circumference, and Area	1.02
NCTM 1, 2, 3, 4, 6, 8, 9, 10	∇ Finding Perimeter and Circumference ∇ Finding Area	

NCTM STANDARDS 2000

1	Number and Operations	6	Problem Solving
2	Algebra	7	Reasoning and Proof
3	Geometry	8	Communication
4	Measurement	9	Connections
5	Data Analysis and Probability	10	Representation

Pacing Options

This chart suggests pacing only for the lessons and their parts. It is provided as a possible guide. It will help you determine how much time you have in your schedule to cover other components, such as the features, Chapter Review and Chapter Test.

Day	Traditional 45 min.	Two-Year 45 min.	Block 90 min.
1	1-1 ∇	1-1 ∇	1-1 ∇
2	1-2 ∇	1-1 ∇	1-2 ∇ ∇
3	1-2 ∇	1-2 ∇	1-3 ∇ ∇
4	1-3 ∇	1-2 ∇	1-4 ∇ ∇
5	1-3 ∇	1-3 ∇	1-5 ∇ ∇
6	1-4 ∇	1-3 ∇	1-6 ∇ ∇
7	1-4 ∇	1-4 ∇	1-7 ∇ ∇
8	1-5 ∇	1-4 ∇	
9	1-5 ∇	1-4 ∇	
10	1-6 ∇	1-5 ∇	
11	1-6 ∇	1-5 ∇	
12	1-7 ∇	1-5 ∇	
13	1-7 ∇	1-6 ∇	
14		1-6 ∇	
15		1-7 ∇	
16		1-7 ∇	
17		1-7 ∇	
18			
19			
20			
21			
22			

NAEP Correlation (National Assessment of Educational Progress 2000 Mathematics Objectives)

1-1	1-2	1-3	1-4	1-5	1-6	1-7
G7, A1, A7A	G1b	G1B	N4b, M1, M2	G1A	A3c, G9A	N4b, M4a, A5b

N = Number Sense, Properties, and Operations; **M** = Measurement; **G** = Geometry and Spatial Sense; **D** = Data Analysis, Statistics, and Probability; **A** = Algebra and Functions

Math Background

Chapter Overview

Using inductive reasoning to formulate conjectures will promote an intuitive understanding of principles that are later presented as postulates and theorems.

Coordinate geometry will be used throughout the course to solve problems and complete proofs. The concepts of perimeter, circumference, and area reviewed here will be studied in more detail in later chapters.

Students are asked to identify various figures and to express the relationships presented in postulates. Memorizing definitions and postulates may be counterproductive if students are able only to repeat them but are unable to apply them to problem situations. Concept recognition and application are the key skills.

Patterns and Inductive Reasoning   1-1

Conjectures are plausible conclusions that accommodate all known data, but they need not be true. Conjectures also may be developed using historical data, as in Exercise 52. Inductive reasoning forms a conjecture, or hypothesis, from a finite number of true facts. Deductive reasoning uses logic to prove hypotheses using an agreed set of axioms and undefined terms. (See Lesson 2-3.)

Points, Lines, and Planes   1-2

Undefined terms are needed to avoid circular definitions. They serve as building blocks for subsequent definitions.

It is important to emphasize the description of a *point* as having no length or width because the concepts of line, plane, segment, and so on build on it. Help students who think that lines named by two points are composed of only two points to internalize that an infinite number of points make up a line. Planes represented by drawings (often parallelograms) may cause students to think that planes are limited in size. Emphasize that planes are unbounded flat surfaces with no edges.

Segments, Rays, Parallel Lines and Planes   1-3

"Betweenness" in the definition of *segment* and "interior of an angle" are difficult to define. Although visual and intuitive understanding suffices for now, students interested in formal geometry should further explore these concepts.

Students can easily compare a ray in geometry to a ray of light from the sun. The ray

may be difficult for some students to name because the order of letters from left to right on the ray differs from the order under the ray symbol ($\overrightarrow{BA}$).

Parallel lines differ from skew lines in that parallel lines are coplanar, but skew lines are not.

Measuring Segments and Angles   1-4

The term "congruent" describes the relationship between segments, angles, triangles, or other figures having the same size and shape. All congruence statements refer to sets of points, while = statements refer to measurements.

Basic Constructions   1-5

A segment in a plane has an infinite number of bisectors but only one perpendicular bisector. In space, there are infinitely many perpendicular bisectors of a segment; for example, lines through the teeth of a gear in the center of its axle or the wheel spokes of a gyroscope and its axis.

Euclidean constructions require a straightedge. To help students avoid using ruler markings, have them turn their rulers over. Three famous construction problems tantalized ancient Greek geometers: trisecting an angle, constructing a cube with double the original volume, and constructing a square whose area is that of a given circle. No solutions could be found. It was many years before mathematicians proved that no solutions exist.

The Coordinate Plane   1-6

This lesson demonstrates the close connection between geometry and algebra and introduces tools that will be used throughout subsequent chapters.

Perimeter, Circumference, and Area   1-7

Some students may think that 3.14 or $\frac{22}{7}$ is the exact value of the irrational number π rather than an approximation. Help them appreciate that any answer involving a circumference or a circle's area expressed in terms of π is exact.

An alternate strategy for finding the area of an irregular figure (such as in Exercises 37–39) is to enclose the figure in a larger, more regular, figure, find that area, and subtract the unwanted area(s).

 # Ongoing Assessment and Intervention

Tools for Monitoring Student Progress

The Prentice Hall *Geometry* program provides you with many options for assessment in the Student Edition, the Teacher's Edition and the teaching resources. From these options, you may choose instructional materials and techniques that are appropriate for your students and support your district's curriculum requirements.

Instant Check System™ in Chapter 1

Allows students to check their own learning before, during, and after each lesson.

Diagnosing Readiness before the chapter (p. 2)

Check Skills You'll Need exercises in each lesson (pp. 4, 10, 17, 25, 34, 43, 51)

Check Understanding questions with each Example (pp. 4, 5, 6, 11, 13, 17, 18, 19, 26, 27, 28, 29, 34, 35, 36, 37, 44, 45, 50, 52, 53, 54)

Checkpoint Quiz (pp. 23 and 49)

Test Prep in Chapter 1

Teaches students strategies and gives them practice with all the test item formats they will encounter on state tests and standardized national exams.

Standardized Test Prep exercises in each lesson (pp. 9, 16, 22, 33, 39, 48, 58)

Test-Taking Strategies (p. 60: Writing Gridded Responses)

Standardized Test Prep (p. 65: Reading Comprehension)

 PRENTICE HALL
ASSESSMENT SYSTEM

All your assessment needs in one place!

Program Assessment

Assess student progress throughout the *Geometry* text with blackline masters and CD-ROM.

Assessment Resources

- Checkpoint Quizzes 1 & 2
- Chapter Test, Forms A & B
- Chapter Alternative Assessment

Spanish versions available. Tests for Informal Geometry also available.

 Computer Test Generator

- Unlimited questions of varying difficulty for every lesson objective.
- Create your own practice sheets, quizzes, and tests, or use the pre-made Chapter Tests.
- Diagnose readiness with questions on prerequisite skills.
- Prepare students by making tests based on standardized test objectives.
- Access Algebra 1, Geometry, and Algebra 2 content—all on one CD-ROM.

Test Preparation

A three-step approach to preparing students for high stakes, national, and state exams.

❶ **Diagnose & Prescribe**

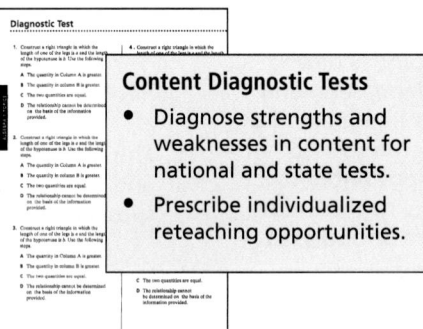

Content Diagnostic Tests

- Diagnose strengths and weaknesses in content for national and state tests.
- Prescribe individualized reteaching opportunities.

❷ **Review & Reteach**

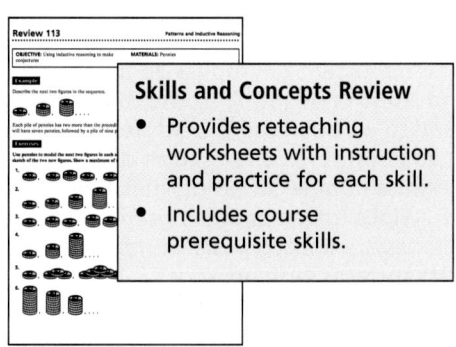

Skills and Concepts Review

- Provides reteaching worksheets with instruction and practice for each skill.
- Includes course prerequisite skills.

❸ **Practice & Assess**

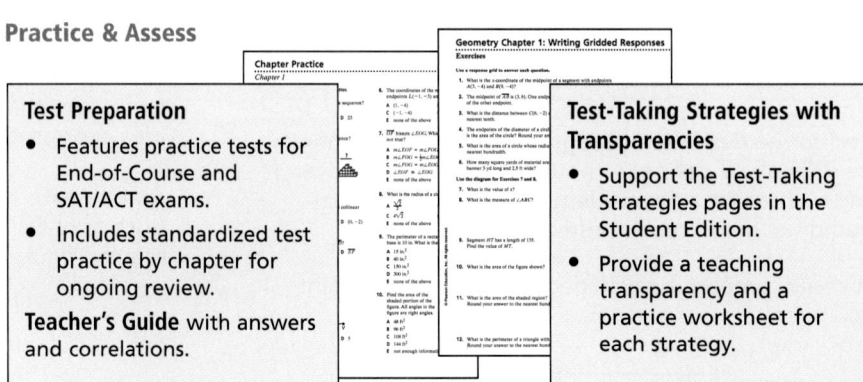

Test Preparation

- Features practice tests for End-of-Course and SAT/ACT exams.
- Includes standardized test practice by chapter for ongoing review.

Teacher's Guide with answers and correlations.

Test-Taking Strategies with Transparencies

- Support the Test-Taking Strategies pages in the Student Edition.
- Provide a teaching transparency and a practice worksheet for each strategy.

Reaching All Students

Support in the Student Text and Additional Resources

The textbook, the iText, and other technology components provide numerous opportunities to reach students of various ability levels and learning styles. Each Teacher's Edition lesson suggests how you can help *all* your students be successful and understand the mathematics in Chapter 1.

Below Level

Student Edition
- Diagnosing Readiness*: p. 2
- Check Skills You'll Need*: pp. 4, 10, 17, 25, 34, 43, 51

Reteaching
Chapter 1 Support File: pp. 8–14

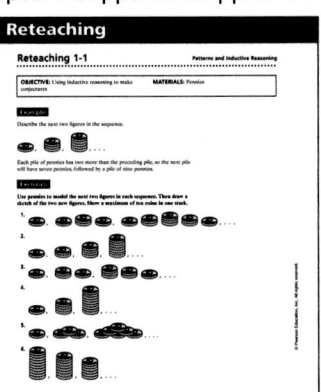

Informal Geometry Planning Guide
Chapter 1 Lesson Plans: pp. 1–7
Chapter 1 Tests: pp. 79–82

* Can be used with all ability levels to ensure mastery of prerequisite skills.

Advanced Learners

Student Edition
- Challenge exercises: pp. 9, 15, 21, 32, 39, 47, 57

Enrichment
Chapter 1 Support File: pp. 15–21

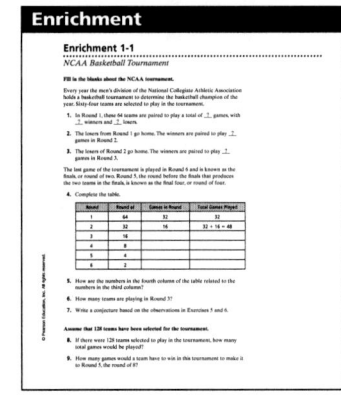

Reading and Math Literacy

Student Edition
- Vocabulary: pp. 3, 61, *plus* in every Lesson Preview
- Reading Math: pp. 11, 12, 18, 20, 25, 27, 28, 44, 50, 53, 61
- Illustrated Glossary: pp. 741–777

Reading and Math Literacy Masters
Chapter 1: pp. 1–4

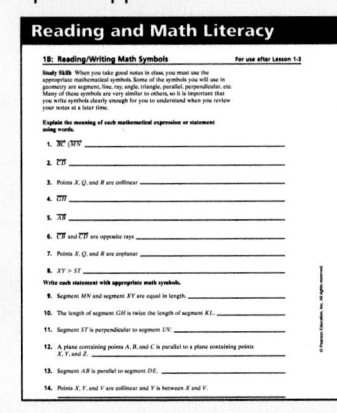

English Learners

Student Edition
- English/Spanish Illustrated Glossary: pp. 741–777

Workbook and Masters
Spanish Practice Workbook: pp. 1–7
Spanish Reading and Math Literacy Masters: pp. 1–4

Learning Styles

Student Edition
- Investigation: pp. 10, 42, 51
- Technology: pp. 7, 33, 41, 44, 50, 53, 57, 59
- Writing: pp. 7, 15, 21, 23, 32, 39, 47, 56, 64

Activity Masters
Hands-On Activities: 1, 2, 3

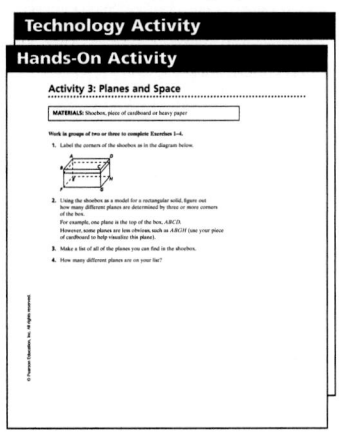

Program Resources

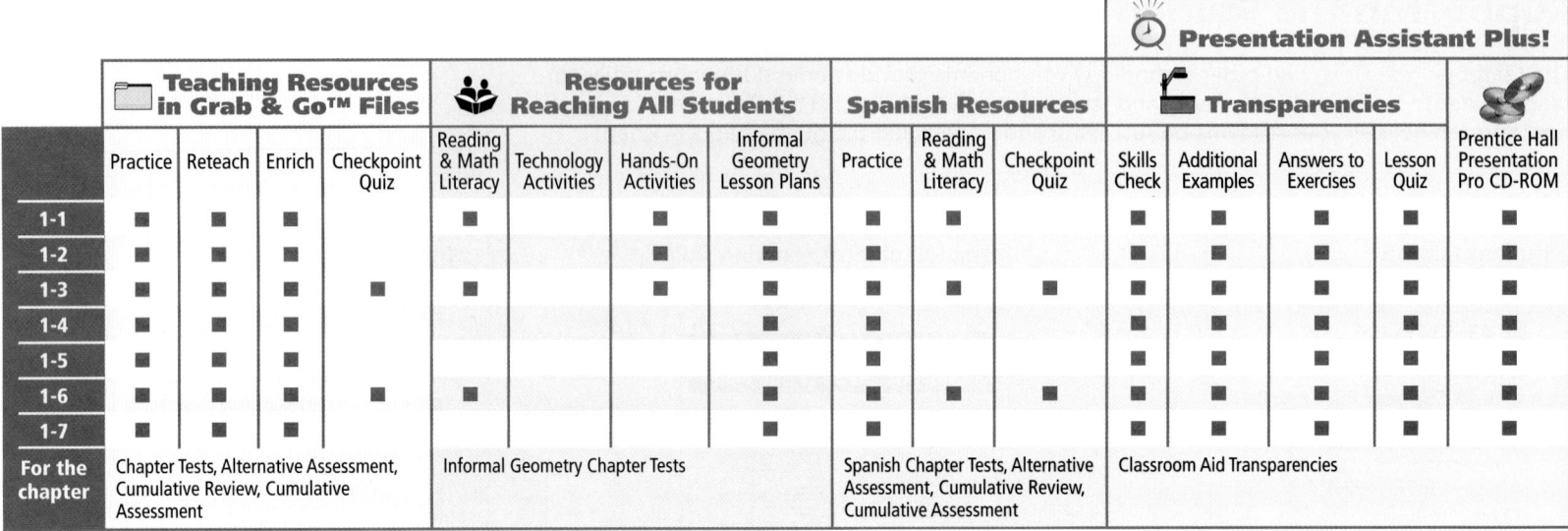

	Teaching Resources in Grab & Go™ Files				Resources for Reaching All Students				Spanish Resources			Transparencies				Presentation Assistant Plus!
	Practice	Reteach	Enrich	Checkpoint Quiz	Reading & Math Literacy	Technology Activities	Hands-On Activities	Informal Geometry Lesson Plans	Practice	Reading & Math Literacy	Checkpoint Quiz	Skills Check	Additional Examples	Answers to Exercises	Lesson Quiz	Prentice Hall Presentation Pro CD-ROM
1-1	■	■	■		■		■	■	■	■		■	■	■	■	■
1-2	■	■	■					■	■			■	■	■	■	■
1-3	■	■	■	■	■		■	■	■	■	■	■	■	■	■	■
1-4	■	■	■					■	■			■	■	■	■	■
1-5		■	■					■				■	■	■	■	■
1-6	■	■	■	■	■			■	■		■	■	■	■	■	■
1-7		■						■				■	■	■	■	■
For the chapter	Chapter Tests, Alternative Assessment, Cumulative Review, Cumulative Assessment				Informal Geometry Chapter Tests				Spanish Chapter Tests, Alternative Assessment, Cumulative Review, Cumulative Assessment			Classroom Aid Transparencies				

Also available for use with the chapter:

 *see page 2C.*

- Practice Workbook
- Solution Key

- For teacher support and access to student Web site materials, use Web Code afk-5500.
- For additional online and technology resources, see below.

  ## Technology

 Online and on CD-ROM

Complete Interactive Student Text online and on CD-ROM—with instant feedback assessment, tutorial help, dynamic activities, instructional and real-world videos, audio, and additional practice.

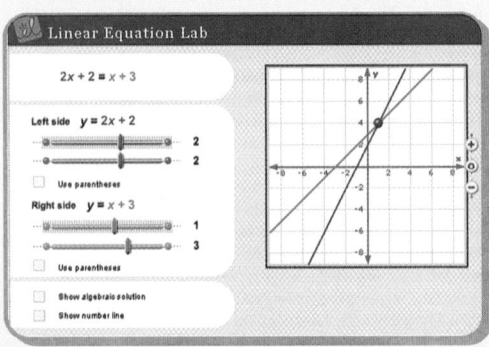

www.PHSchool.com
For Students

Use **Web Codes** for easy access to online activities, chapter projects, self-grading lesson quizzes and chapter tests, vocabulary quizzes, updated data sources, graphing calculator procedures, and more.

 **For Teachers**

Online lesson planning with built-in state correlations, all the teaching resources, complete reference library, your own calendar and Teacher Web page, professional development, and more.

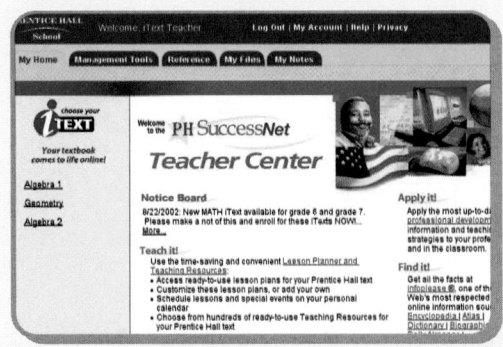

Presentation Assistant Plus!

The Prentice Hall *Presentation Assistant Plus!* provides you with the material you need to teach a lesson from beginning to end. Two easy-to-use formats—Transparencies and CD-ROM—allow you to present a lesson the way you are most comfortable.

 ## Transparencies

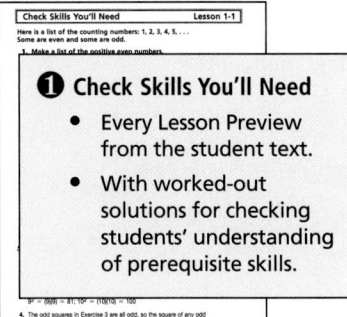

❶ Check Skills You'll Need
- Every Lesson Preview from the student text.
- With worked-out solutions for checking students' understanding of prerequisite skills.

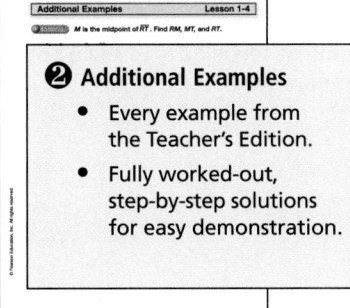

❷ Additional Examples
- Every example from the Teacher's Edition.
- Fully worked-out, step-by-step solutions for easy demonstration.

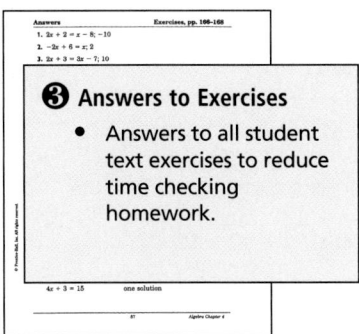

❸ Answers to Exercises
- Answers to all student text exercises to reduce time checking homework.

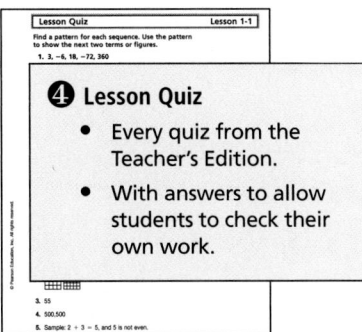

❹ Lesson Quiz
- Every quiz from the Teacher's Edition.
- With answers to allow students to check their own work.

 Throughout the Teacher's Edition, this symbol indicates material that is available on transparency in the Presentation Assistant Plus!

 ## Prentice Hall Presentation Pro CD-ROM

- Includes all Transparencies.
- Conveniently organized by lesson so you can easily ❶ Introduce, ❷ Teach, ❸ Check Homework, and ❹ Assess each lesson.
- Animated examples allow step-by-step instruction at your own pace.
- Easy to edit so you can create custom presentations.

Teaching Chapter 1 Using Presentation Assistant Plus!

	❶ Introduce	❷ Teach	❸ Check Homework	❹ Assess
	Check Skills You'll Need	Additional Examples	Student Edition Answers	Lesson Quiz
1-1	p. 1	pp. 1–2	✔	p. 76
1-2	p. 2	pp. 2–4	✔	p. 77
1-3	p. 3	pp. 4–5	✔	p. 78
1-4	p. 4	pp. 6–8	✔	p. 79
1-5	p. 5	pp. 9–13	✔	p. 80
1-6	p. 6	pp. 14–15	✔	p. 81
1-7	p. 7	pp. 16–19	✔	p. 82

 ### Prentice Hall Presentation Pro

CD-ROM with dynamic PowerPoint® presentations for every lesson. Helps you introduce and develop concepts, check homework, and assess progress. Part of Presentation Assistant Plus! *(See above.)*

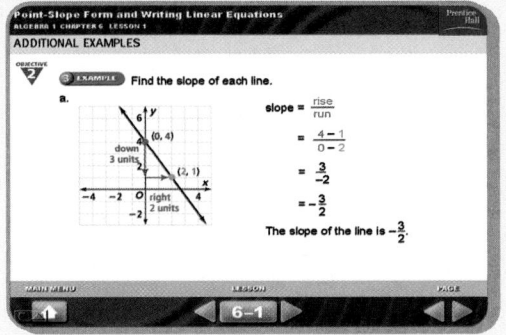

 ### Computer Test Generator

CD-ROM to create practice sheets and tests for course objectives and standardized tests. Includes Instant Chapter Tests™, online testing, and student reports. Part of the PH Assessment System. *(See page 2C.)*

 ### Resource Pro® with Planning Express®

CD-ROM with a lesson planning tool that allows you to import state and local objectives. Includes electronic versions of all the teaching resources.

Tools of Geometry

 Diagnosing Readiness

Students will find answers to these exercises in the back of their textbooks.

For intervention, direct students to:

Squaring Numbers
Skills Handbook, p. 715

Simplifying Expressions
Skills Handbook: p. 716

Evaluating Expressions
Skills Handbook: p. 716

Finding Absolute Value
Skills Handbook: p. 719

Solving Equations
Skills Handbook: p. 720

Where You've Been

In previous courses, you learned

- to apply your knowledge of arithmetic to the study of algebra. You also learned about the real number system, including operations on rational and irrational numbers.

- to write algebraic expressions, and equations to represent relationships.

- to use a variety of techniques to solve equations and inequalities with one or more variables.

 **i TEXT** Instant self-check online and on CD-ROM

Diagnosing Readiness

(For help, go to the Skills Handbook.)

Squaring Numbers (Skills Handbook page 715)

Simplify.

1. 3^2 9
2. 4^2 16
3. 11^2 121

Simplifying Expressions (Skills Handbook page 716)

Simplify each expression. Use 3.14 for π.

4. $2 \cdot 7.5 + 2 \cdot 11$ 37
5. $\pi(5)^2$ 78.5
6. $\sqrt{5^2 + 12^2}$ 13

Evaluating Expressions

Evaluate the following expressions for $a = 4$ and $b = -2$.

7. $\frac{a + b}{2}$ 1
8. $\frac{a - 7}{3 - b}$ $-\frac{3}{5}$
9. $\sqrt{(7 - a)^2 + (2 - b)^2}$ 5

Finding Absolute Value (Skills Handbook page 719)

Simplify each absolute value expression.

10. $|-8|$ 8
11. $|2 - 6|$ 4
12. $|-5 - (-8)|$ 3

Solving Equations (Skills Handbook page 720)

x^2 **Algebra** Solve each equation.

13. $2x + 7 = 13$ 3
14. $5x - 12 = 2x + 6$ 6
15. $2(x + 3) - 1 = 7x$ 1

Tools of Geometry

Where You're Going

- In this chapter, you will learn how to make plausible conclusions based on patterns you observe.
- You will learn the foundation blocks for the structure of geometry.
- These foundations will provide you with ways to measure segments and angles.
- You will also learn to use constructions and the coordinate plane to represent geometric figures.

 Real-World Connection Applying what you learn, you will do activities involving parallel lines and planes on pages 18 and 19.

LESSONS

Key Vocabulary

- acute angle (p. 28)
- angle bisector (p. 36)
- collinear points (p. 11)
- congruent angles (p. 29)
- congruent segments (p. 25)
- conjecture (p. 5)
- coordinate (p. 25)
- coplanar (p. 11)
- counterexample (p. 5)
- inductive reasoning (p. 4)
- obtuse angle (p. 28)
- parallel lines (p. 18)
- parallel planes (p. 18)
- perpendicular bisector (p. 35)
- perpendicular lines (p. 35)
- plane (p. 11)
- postulate (p. 12)
- ray (p. 17)
- right angle (p. 28)
- segment (p. 17)
- skew lines (p. 18)
- straight angle (p. 28)

Chapter 1 Overview

Students begin their study of geometry by learning to reason inductively. They will use the undefined terms *point, line,* and *plane* in postulates about segments, rays, lines, planes, and angles. Students will learn how to measure segments and angles and how to use a compass and straightedge to construct geometric figures. Finally, they will find distance on the coordinate plane algebraically and calculate the circumference, perimeter, and area of geometric figures.

Reading Math
Reading an Example, p. 50

Vocabulary
A complete list of terms, plus vocabulary exercises, appears in the Chapter Review, p. 61.

Illustrated Glossary
Examples for each vocabulary term, plus definitions in both English and Spanish, appear starting on p. 741.

Test-Taking Strategies
Writing Gridded-Responses, p. 60

Real-World Connections
Some of the applications you will find in this chapter are navigation (1-2), diamond cutting (1-3), optics (1-5), and travel (1-6).

www.PHSchool.com
Internet support for this chapter includes:
- Self-grading Vocabulary and Chapter 1 Tests
- Chapter Project
- Chapter Planner
- Ch. 1 Resources

Plus **iTEXT**

3

1. Plan

Lesson Preview

✔ **Check Skills You'll Need**

For help use
Skills Handbook, p. 715.

Lesson Resources

📁 **Teaching Resources**
Practice, Reteaching, Enrichment

👥 **Reaching All Students**
Practice Workbook 1-1
Spanish Practice Workbook 1-1
Reading and Math Literacy 1A
Spanish Reading & Literacy 1A
Hands-On Activities 1
Informal Geometry Planning
    Guide 1-1

🕐 **Presentation Assistant Plus!**
Transparencies
• Check Skills You'll Need 1-1
• Additional Examples 1-1
• Student Edition Answers 1-1
• Lesson Quiz 1-1
PH Presentation Pro CD 1-1

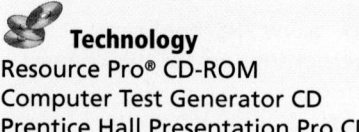
PRENTICE HALL
ASSESSMENT SYSTEM

Computer Test Generator CD

💿 **Technology**
Resource Pro® CD-ROM
Computer Test Generator CD
Prentice Hall Presentation Pro CD

🖥 **www.PHSchool.com**
Student Site
• Teacher Web Code: afk-5500
• Self-grading Lesson Quiz
Teacher Center
• Lesson Planner
• Resources

Plus 𝒊TEXT

1-1 Patterns and Inductive Reasoning

North Carolina Objectives

2.01 Use logic and deductive reasoning to draw conclusions and solve problems.

Lesson Preview

What You'll Learn

OBJECTIVE 1
To use inductive reasoning to make conjectures

. . . And Why

To predict future sales for a skateboard business, as in Example 4

✔ **Check Skills You'll Need** (For help, go to the Skills Handbook page 715.)

Here is a list of the counting numbers: 1, 2, 3, 4, 5, . . .
Some are even and some are odd.

1. Make a list of the positive even numbers. 2, 4, 6, 8, 10, . . .
2. Make a list of the positive odd numbers. 1, 3, 5, 7, 9, . . .
3. Copy and extend this list to show the first 10 perfect squares.
    $1^2 = 1, 2^2 = 4, 3^2 = 9, 4^2 = 16, . . .$
4. Which do you think describes the square of any odd number?
    It is odd.   It is even. It is odd.

3. $1^2 = 1$
   $2^2 = 4$
   $3^2 = 9$
   $4^2 = 16$
   $5^2 = 25$
   $6^2 = 36$
   $7^2 = 49$
   $8^2 = 64$
   $9^2 = 81$
   $10^2 = 100$

New Vocabulary • inductive reasoning • conjecture • counterexample

---

𝒊TEXT **Interactive lesson includes instant self-check, tutorials, and activities.**

OBJECTIVE
1 Using Inductive Reasoning

Real-World 🌐 Connection

You can predict growth of the chambered nautilus shell by studying patterns in its cross sections.

Inductive reasoning is reasoning that is based on patterns you observe. If you observe a pattern in a sequence, you can use inductive reasoning to tell what the next terms in the sequence will be.

1 EXAMPLE Finding and Using a Pattern

Find a pattern for each sequence. Use the pattern to show the next two terms in the sequence.

a. 3, 6, 12, 24, . . .

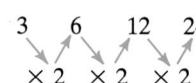
$\times 2 \quad \times 2 \quad \times 2$

Each term is twice the preceding term. The next two terms are
$2 \times 24 = 48$ and $2 \times 48 = 96$.

b.

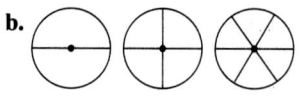

Each circle has one more segment through the center to form equal parts. The next two figures:

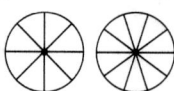

✔ **Check Understanding** ① Write the next two terms in each sequence.
a. 1, 2, 4, 7, 11, 16, 22, . . . 29, 37
b. Monday, Tuesday, Wednesday, . . . Thursday, Friday
c. Answers may vary. Sample:

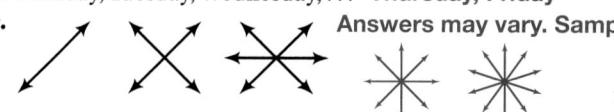

Ongoing Assessment and Intervention

Before the Lesson Diagnose prerequisite skills using:	**During the Lesson** Monitor progress using:	**After the Lesson** Assess knowledge using:
• Check Skills You'll Need	• Check Understanding • Additional Examples • Standardized Test Prep	• Lesson Quiz • Computer Test Generator CD

A conclusion you reach using inductive reasoning is called a **conjecture.**

② EXAMPLE Using Inductive Reasoning

Make a conjecture about the sum of the first 30 odd numbers.

Find the first few sums. Notice that each sum is a perfect square.

$$1 = 1 = 1^2$$
$$1 + 3 = 4 = 2^2$$
$$1 + 3 + 5 = 9 = 3^2$$
$$1 + 3 + 5 + 7 = 16 = 4^2$$

The perfect squares form a pattern.

Using inductive reasoning, you can conclude that the sum of the first 30 odd numbers is 30^2, or 900.

✓ **Check Understanding** ② Make a conjecture about the sum of the first 35 odd numbers. Use your calculator to verify your conjecture. **The sum of the first 35 odd numbers is 35^2, or 1225.**

Not all conjectures turn out to be true. You can prove that a conjecture is false by finding one counterexample. A **counterexample** to a conjecture is an example for which the conjecture is incorrect.

③ EXAMPLE Testing a Conjecture

When points on a circle are joined by as many segments as possible, nonoverlapping regions are formed inside the circle as shown below.

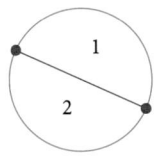 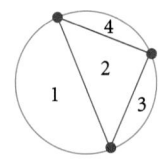 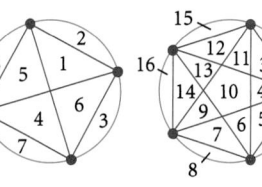

The table at the right shows the number of regions for 2, 3, 4, and 5 points. You might conjecture that the number of regions doubles at each stage. Find a counterexample to show that this conjecture is false.

Make a diagram showing a circle with 6 points. This diagram shows that only 31 regions are possible. You have found a counterexample that shows your "doubling" conjecture is false.

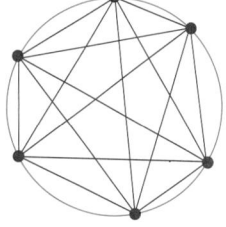

Points	Regions
2	2
3	4
4	8
5	16

✓ **Check Understanding** ③ **Critical Thinking** Some products have 5 as a factor, as shown. Make two conjectures based on these products, one that you believe is true and one that you know is false.
Answers may vary. Sample: true; the product of 5 and any odd number is odd. False; the product of 5 and any number ends in 5.

$5 \times 7 = 35$	$5 \times 13 = 65$
$5 \times 3 = 15$	$5 \times 9 = 45$
$5 \times 11 = 55$	$5 \times 25 = 125$

👥 **Reaching All Students**

| **Below Level** Have students recreate the geometric patterns in Examples 1 and 3 to reinforce using a pattern. | **Advanced Learners** Have students explore the pattern in Example 2 geometrically by placing 3, then 5, then 7 squares on the top and right sides of the previous square. | **English Learners** See note on page 7. **Visual Learners** See note on page 6. |

2. Teach

Math Background

Inductive reasoning assumes that an observed pattern will continue. This may or may not be true. For example, "$x = x \cdot x$" is true for $x = 0$ and $x = 1$, but then the pattern fails. Inductive reasoning can lead to conjectures that seem likely but are unproven. A single counterexample is enough to disprove a conjecture.

OBJECTIVE
① Teaching Notes

② EXAMPLE Teaching Tip

Point out that the number that is squared equals the number of terms that are added.

Additional Examples

① Find a pattern for the sequence. Use the pattern to show the next two terms in the sequence.
384, 192, 96, 48, ... **Each term is half the preceding term; 24, 12.**

② Make a conjecture about the sum of the cubes of the first 25 counting numbers. **The sum equals $(1 + 2 + 3 + ... + 25)^2$.**

③ The first three odd prime numbers are 3, 5, and 7. Make and test a conjecture about the fourth odd prime number. **Sample: The fourth odd prime number is 9. The conjecture is false.**

④ The price of overnight shipping was $8.00 in 2000, $9.50 in 2001, and $11.00 in 2002. Make a conjecture about the price in 2003. **Sample: The price will be $12.50.**

Closure

Explain how you can use a conjecture to help solve a problem. **Sample: A conjecture can be tested to see whether it is a solution.**

5

Assignment Guide

1 Objective
- Ⓐ Ⓑ Core 1–53
- Ⓒ Extension 54, 55

Standardized Test Prep 56–59

Mixed Review 60–70

Exercises 7, 8 You may want to provide a hint that the letters are the first letters in a sequence of words.

Visual Learners
Exercise 18 Encourage students to draw the first three figures shown to help them see the pattern unfold.

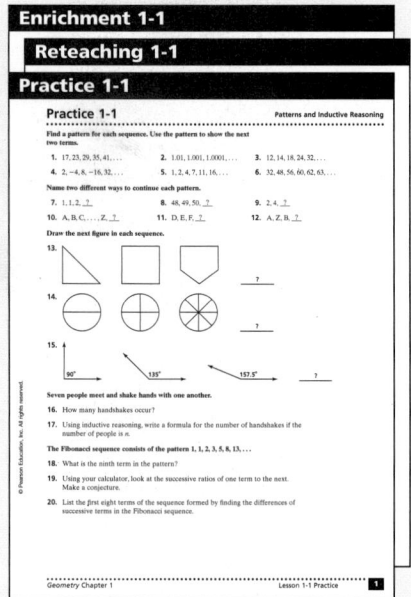

4 EXAMPLE Real-World 🌐 Connection

Business Sales A skateboard shop finds that over a period of five consecutive months, sales of small-wheeled skateboards decreased.

Use inductive reasoning. Make a conjecture about the number of small-wheeled skateboards the shop will sell in June.

The graph shows that sales of small-wheeled skateboards is decreasing by about 3 skateboards each month. By inductive reasoning you might conclude that the shop will sell 42 skateboards in June.

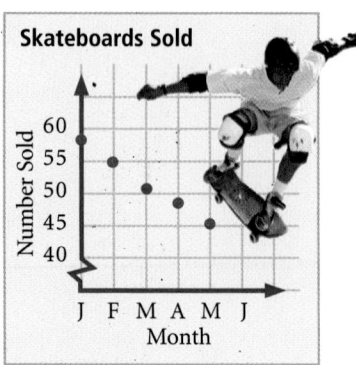

Skateboards Sold

✓ **Check Understanding** ④ **a.** Make a conjecture about the number of small-wheeled skateboards the shop will sell in July.   **39 skateboards**
b. Critical Thinking How confident would you be in using the graph to make a conjecture about sales in December? Explain.
Not confident; December is too far away.

EXERCISES
For more practice, see *Extra Practice*.

Practice and Problem Solving

Ⓐ **Practice by Example**

Example 1
(page 4)

Find a pattern for each sequence. Use the pattern to show the next two terms.

1. 5, 10, 20, 40, . . . **80, 160** **2.** 3, 33, 333, 3333, . . . **3.** 1, −1, 2, −2, 3, . . . **−3, 4**

4. 1, $\frac{1}{2}$, $\frac{1}{4}$, $\frac{1}{8}$, . . . **$\frac{1}{16}$, $\frac{1}{32}$** **5.** 15, 12, 9, 6, . . . **3, 0** **6.** 81, 27, 9, 3, . . . **1, $\frac{1}{3}$**

2. 33,333; 333,333

7. O, T, T, F, F, S, S, E, . . . **N, T 8.** J, F, M, A, M, . . . **J, J** **9.** 1, 2, 6, 24, 120, . . .

9. 720, 5040

10. 2, 4, 8, 16, 32, . . . **64, 128 11.** 1, $\frac{1}{4}$, $\frac{1}{9}$, $\frac{1}{16}$, $\frac{1}{25}$, . . . **$\frac{1}{36}$, $\frac{1}{49}$ 12.** 1, $\frac{1}{2}$, $\frac{1}{3}$, $\frac{1}{4}$, . . . **$\frac{1}{5}$, $\frac{1}{6}$**

13. George, John, Thomas, James, . . . **14.** Martha, Abigail, Martha, Dolley, . . .
James, John   **Elizabeth, Louisa**
15. George, Thomas, Abe, Alexander, . . . **16.** Aquarius, Pisces, Aries, Taurus, . . .
Andrew, Ulysses   **Gemini, Cancer**

Draw the next figure in each sequence.

17.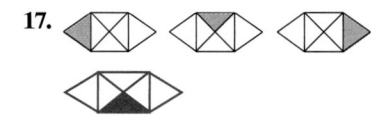

18.

Example 2
(page 5)

Use the table and inductive reasoning. Make a conjecture about each value.

19. the sum of the first 6 positive even numbers   **19–22.**
20. the sum of the first 30 positive even numbers   **See margin.**

2	= 2 = 1 · 2
2 + 4	= 6 = 2 · 3
2 + 4 + 6	= 12 = 3 · 4
2 + 4 + 6 + 8	= 20 = 4 · 5
2 + 4 + 6 + 8 + 10	= 30 = 5 · 6

21. the sum of the first 100 positive even numbers

22. Use the pattern in Example 2 to make a conjecture about the sum of the first 100 odd numbers.

19. The sum of the first 6 positive even numbers is 6 · 7, or 42.

20. The sum of the first 30 positive even numbers is 30 · 31, or 930.

21. The sum of the first 100 positive even numbers is 100 · 101, or 10,100.

22. The sum of the first 100 odd numbers is 100², or 10,000.

25–28. Answers may vary. Samples are given.

25. 8 + (−5) = 3 and 3 ≯ 8

26. $\frac{1}{3} \cdot \frac{1}{2} \not> \frac{1}{3}$ and $\frac{1}{3} \cdot \frac{1}{2} \not> \frac{1}{2}$

27. −6 − (−4) ≮ −6 and −6 − (−4) ≮ −4

28. $\frac{1}{2} \div \frac{1}{3} = \frac{3}{2}$ and $\frac{3}{2}$ is improper.

Predict the next term in each sequence. Use your calculator to verify your answer.

23. 12345679 × 9 = 111111111
12345679 × 18 = 222222222
12345679 × 27 = 333333333
12345679 × 36 = 444444444
12345679 × 45 = ▪ **555,555,555**

24. 1 × 1 = 1
11 × 11 = 121
111 × 111 = 12321
1111 × 1111 = 1234321
11111 × 11111 = ▪ **123,454,321**

Example 3 (page 5)

Find one counterexample to show that each conjecture is false. **25–28. See margin, p. 6.**

25. The sum of two numbers is greater than either number.

26. The product of two positive numbers is greater than either number.

27. The difference of two integers is less than either integer.

28. The quotient of two proper fractions is a proper fraction.

Example 4 (page 6)

29. **Weather** The speed with which a cricket chirps is affected by the temperature. If you hear 20 cricket chirps in 14 seconds, what is the temperature? **75°F**

Chirps per 14 Seconds

5 chirps	45°F
10 chirps	55°F
15 chirps	65°F

30. 40 push-ups; answers may vary. Sample: No, Dino may reach a limit to the number of push-ups he can do in his allotted time for exercises.

30. **Physical Fitness** Dino works out regularly. When he first started exercising, he could do 10 push-ups. After the first month he could do 14 push-ups. After the second month he could do 19, and after the third month he could do 25. Predict the number of push-ups Dino will be able to do after the fifth month of working out. How confident are you of your prediction? Explain. **See left.**

B Apply Your Skills

33. 0.0001, 0.00001

34. 201, 202

Find a pattern for each sequence. Use the pattern to show the next two terms.

31. 1, 3, 7, 13, 21, . . . **31, 43**
32. 1, 2, 5, 6, 9, . . . **10, 13**
33. 0.1, 0.01, 0.001, . . .
34. 2, 6, 7, 21, 22, 66, 67, . . .
35. 1, 3, 7, 15, 31, . . . **63, 127**
36. $0, \frac{1}{2}, \frac{3}{4}, \frac{7}{8}, \frac{15}{16}, \ldots$ $\mathbf{\frac{31}{32}, \frac{63}{64}}$
37. M, V, E, M, . . . **J, S**
38. AL, AK, AZ, AR, . . . **CA, CO**
39. H, He, Li, Be, . . . **B, C**

40. **Writing** Choose two of the sequences in Exercises 31–36 and describe the patterns. **See margin.**

41. Draw two parallel lines on your paper. Locate four points on the paper, each an equal distance from both lines. Describe the figure you get if you continue to locate points, each an equal distance from both lines. **See margin.**

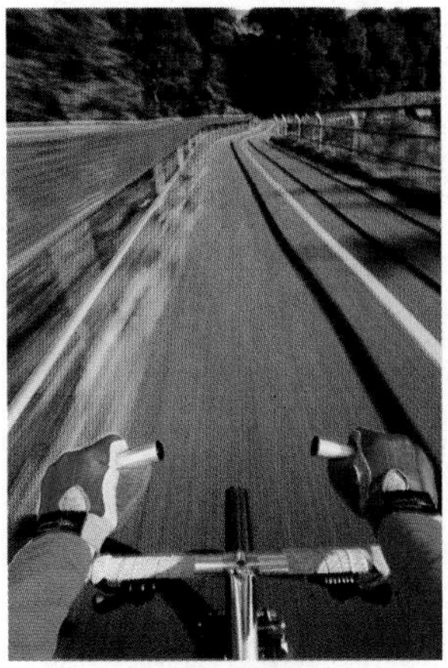

Real-World Connection

Points along the yellow line are equal distances from both sides of the bike trail (Exercise 41).

Draw the next figure in each sequence. **42–45. See margin.**

42.
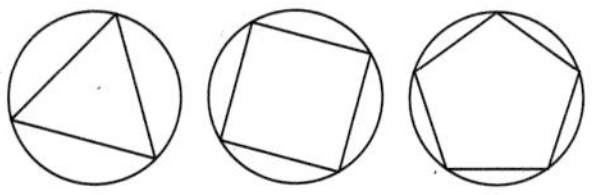

43.
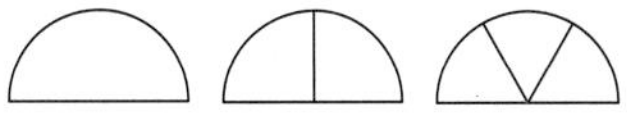

44.
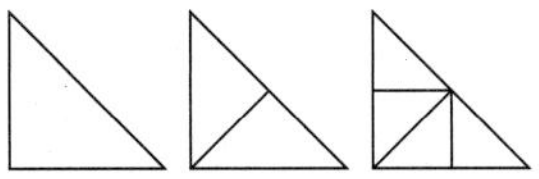

45.
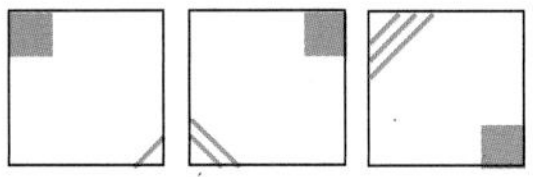

46. Use inductive reasoning. Find the perimeter when 100 triangles are put together in the pattern shown. Assume that all triangle sides are 1 cm long. **102 cm**

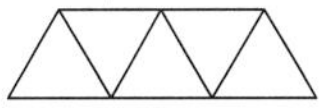

Error Prevention

Exercise 30 Because the problem contains many words, urge students to organize the data in a table. Then point out that the problem asks for the number of push-ups the *fifth* month, not the *next* month.

Exercise 41 You may need to define *parallel* for some students. In addition, students may think the answer is a segment instead of a line. Discuss ways to distinguish segments from lines. The formal treatment of the distance from a point to a line occurs in Chapter 5.

English Learners

Exercises 42–45 These problems rely solely on visual cues. They may prove helpful in assessing ELL students' abilities to use inductive reasoning.

Exercise 46 Students may find it difficult to apply inductive reasoning to this problem. Encourage them to make a table that relates the number of triangles to the perimeter.

Exercise 51 Students may need to review how to use ordered pairs to make a line graph.

Exercise 53 Students may find that the pattern is not as simple as they originally thought. Use this exercise to illustrate that straightforward conjectures may be incorrect.

40. Answers may vary. Sample: In Exercise 31, each number increases by increasing multiples of 2. In Exercise 33, to get the next term, divide by 10.

41.
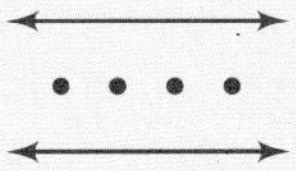

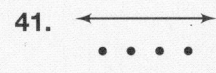

You would get a third line between and parallel to the first two lines.

42.
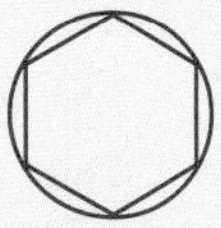

43.
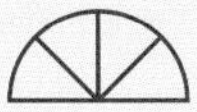

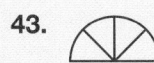

44.
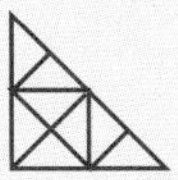

45.
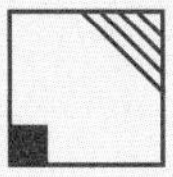

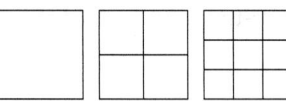
Find a pattern for each sequence. Use the pattern to show the next two terms or figures.

1. 3, −6, 18, −72, 360 −2160; 15,120

2.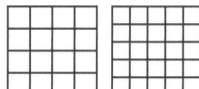

Use the table and inductive reasoning. Make a conjecture about each value.

1	= 1	= $\frac{1 \cdot 2}{2}$
1 + 2	= 3	= $\frac{2 \cdot 3}{2}$
1 + 2 + 3	= 6	= $\frac{3 \cdot 4}{2}$
1 + 2 + 3 + 4	= 10	= $\frac{4 \cdot 5}{2}$

3. the sum of the first 10 counting numbers **55**

4. the sum of the first 1000 counting numbers **500,500**

Show that the conjecture is false by finding one counterexample.

5. The sum of two prime numbers is an even number. **Sample: 2 + 3 = 5, and 5 is not even.**

Alternative Assessment

Have each student write two conjectures, one true and one false; exchange conjectures with a partner; and determine whether the partner's conjectures are true or false. Have partners compare their findings.

---

47. Answers may vary. Samples are given.
   a. Women may soon outrun men in running competitions.
   b. The conclusion was based on continuing the trend shown in past records.
   c. The conclusions are based on fairly recent records for women, and those rates of improvement may not continue. The conclusion about the marathon is most suspect because records date only from 1955.

49. Answers may vary. Sample: 1, 3, 9, 27, 81, . . . 1, 3, 5, 7, 9, . . .

Need Help?

For Exercise 51, you may want to review "Coordinates of a point" in the Glossary.

53a. Leap years are years that are divisible by 4.
   b. 2020, 2100, and 2400
   c. Leap years are years divisible by 4, except the final year of a century which must be divisible by 400. So, 2100 will not be a leap year, but 2400 will be.

---

47. **Math in the Media** Read this exerpt from a news article.

> **Top female runners** have been improving about twice as quickly as the fastest men, a new study says. If this pattern continues, women may soon outrun men in competition!
>
> The study is based on world records collected at 10-year intervals, starting in 1905 for men and in the 1920s for women. If the trend continues, the top female and male runners in races ranging from 200 m to 1500 m might attain the same speeds sometime between 2015 and 2055.
>
> Women's marathon records date from 1955 but their rapid fall suggests that the women's record will equal that of men even more quickly, perhaps by 2005.

   a. What conclusion was reached in the study? **a–c. See left.**
   b. How was inductive reasoning used to reach the conclusion?
   c. Explain why the conclusion that women may soon be outrunning men may be incorrect. For which race is the conclusion most suspect? For what reason?

48. **Communications** The table shows the number of commercial radio stations in the United States for a 50-year period. **See**
   a. Make a line graph of the data. **back of book.**
   b. Use the graph and inductive reasoning to make a conjecture about the number of radio stations in the United States in the year 2010. **about 12,000 radio stations**
   c. How confident are you about your conjecture? Explain. **See back of book.**

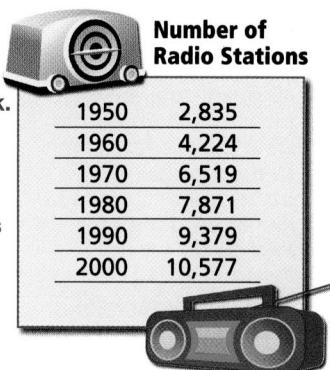

Number of Radio Stations

1950	2,835
1960	4,224
1970	6,519
1980	7,871
1990	9,379
2000	10,577

SOURCE: Federal Communications Commission

49. **Open-Ended** Write two different number-pattern sequences that begin with the same two numbers. **See left.**

50. **Error Analysis** For each of the past four years, Paulo has grown 2 in. every year. He is now 16 years old and is 5 ft 10 in. tall. He figures that when he is 22 years old he will be 6 ft 10 in. tall. What would you tell Paulo about his conjecture? **See margin.**

51. **Coordinate Geometry** You are given x- and y-coordinates for 14 points.
   $A(1,5)$ $B(2,2)$ $C(2,8)$ $D(3,1)$ $E(3,9)$ $F(6,0)$ $G(6,10)$
   $H(7,-1)$ $I(7,11)$ $J(9,1)$ $K(9,9)$ $L(10,2)$ $M(10,8)$ $N(11,5)$
   a. Graph each point. **See margin.**
   b. Most of the points fit a pattern. Which points do not? **H and I**
   c. Describe the figure that fits the pattern. **a circle**

52. **History** Leonardo of Pisa (about 1175–1258), also known as Fibonacci (fee buh NAH chee), was born in Italy and educated in North Africa. He was one of the first Europeans known to use modern numerals instead of Roman numerals. The special sequence 1, 1, 2, 3, 5, 8, 13, . . . is known as the Fibonacci sequence. Find the next three terms of this sequence. **21, 34, 55**

53. **Time Measurement** Leap years have 366 days. **a–b. See left.**
   a. The years 1984, 1988, 1992, 1996, and 2000 are consecutive leap years. Look for a pattern in their dates. Then, make a conjecture about leap years.
   b. Of the years 2010, 2020, 2100, and 2400, which do you think will be leap years?
   c. **Research** Find out whether your conjecture for part (a) and your answer for part (b) are correct. How are leap years determined? **See left.**

pages 6–9 Exercises

50. His conjecture is probably false because most people's growth slows by 18 until they stop growing somewhere between 18 and 22 years.

51. a.
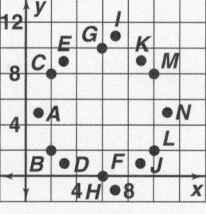

C Challenge  54. **History** When he was in the third grade, German mathematician Karl Gauss (1777–1855) took ten seconds to sum the integers from 1 to 100. Now it's your turn. Find a fast way to sum the integers from 1 to 100; from 1 to n. (*Hint:* Use patterns.) **See margin.**

55a. 1, 3, 6, 10, 15, 21

x^2 55. **a. Algebra** Write the first six terms of the sequence that starts with 1, and for which the difference between consecutive terms is first 2, and then 3, 4, 5, and 6.

b. Evaluate $\frac{n^2 + n}{2}$ for $n = 1, 2, 3, 4, 5,$ and 6. Compare the sequence you get with your answer for part (a). **They are the same.**

c. Examine the diagram at the right and explain how it illustrates a value of $\frac{n^2 + n}{2}$. **See margin.**

d. Draw a similar diagram to represent $\frac{n^2 + n}{2}$ for $n = 5.$ **See margin.**

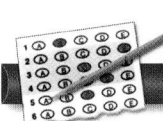

Standardized Test Prep

Multiple Choice 56. The sum of the numbers from 1 to 10 is 55. The sum of the numbers from 11 to 20 is 155. The sum of the numbers from 21 to 30 is 255. Based on this pattern, what is the sum of numbers from 91 to 100? **B**

A. 855   B. 955   C. 1055   D. 1155

57. Which of the following conjectures is false? **I**
F. The product of two even numbers is even.
G. The sum of two even numbers is even.
H. The product of two odd numbers is odd.
I. The sum of two odd numbers is odd.

58. [2] a. 25, 36, 49
    b. n^2
[1] one part correct

Short Response 58. a. How many dots would be in each of the next three figures? **a–b. See left.**
b. Write an expression for the number of dots in the nth figure.

A   B   C   D

Extended Response 59. a. Describe the pattern. List the next two equations in the pattern.
b. Guess what the product of 181 and 11 is. Test your conjecture.
c. State whether the pattern can continue forever. Explain. **a–c. See margin.**

$(101)(11) = 1111$
$(111)(11) = 1221$
$(121)(11) = 1331$
$(131)(11) = 1441$
$(141)(11) = 1551$

 Take It to the NET
Online lesson quiz at
www.PHSchool.com
Web Code: afa-0101

Mixed Review

Previous Course Graph each point. 60–67. See margin.

60. $Y(-5, -8)$ 61. $B(7, -10)$ 62. $M(9, 12)$ 63. $Q(-3, 2)$

64. $G(-6, 0)$ 65. $F(-4, -5)$ 66. $C(-7, 10)$ 67. $N(0, -5)$

Classify the points in Exercises 60–67 as described below.

68. in Quadrant IV **B**   69. on the y-axis **N**   70. on the x-axis **G**

54. **Answers may vary.**
Sample:
$100 + 99 + 98 + \ldots + 3 + 2 + 1$
$\underline{1 + 2 + 3 + \ldots + 98 + 99 + 100}$
$101 + 101 + 101 + \ldots + 101 + 101 + 101$
The sum of the first 100 numbers is $\frac{100 \cdot 101}{2}$, or 5050.
The sum of the first n numbers is $\frac{n(n + 1)}{2}$.

Resources
For additional practice with a variety of test item formats:
• Standardized Test Prep, p. 65
• Test-Taking Strategies, p. 60
• Test-Taking Strategies with Transparencies

Exercise 57 Any true conjecture cannot be the correct answer to this problem. Students may eliminate any answer choice that must be true.

55. c. The diagram shows the product of n and $n + 1$ divided by 2 when $n = 3$. The result is 6.

d.
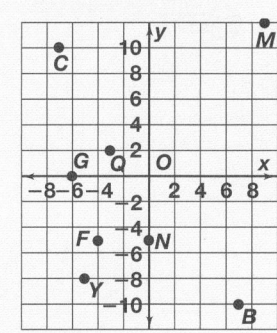

59. [4] a. The product of 11 and a three-digit number that begins and ends in 1 is a four-digit number that begins and ends in 1 and has middle digits that are each one greater than the middle digit of the three-digit number.
$(151)(11) = 1661$
$(161)(11) = 1771$

b. 1991

c. No; $(191)(11) = 2101$

[3] minor error in explanation

[2] incorrect description in part (a)

[1] correct products for $(151)(11)$, $(161)(11)$, and $(181)(11)$

60–67.

9

1. Plan

Lesson Preview

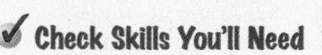
✔ **Check Skills You'll Need**

For help use
Skills Handbook, p. 722

Lesson Resources

📁 **Teaching Resources**
Practice, Reteaching, Enrichment

👥 **Reaching All Students**
Practice Workbook 1-2
Spanish Practice Workbook 1-2
Hands-On Activities 2
Informal Geometry Planning
   Guide 1-2

🕐 **Presentation Assistant Plus!**
Transparencies
• Check Skills You'll Need 1-2
• Additional Examples 1-2
• Student Edition Answers 1-2
• Lesson Quiz 1-2
PH Presentation Pro CD 1-2

PRENTICE HALL
ASSESSMENT SYSTEM

Computer Test Generator CD

💿 **Technology**
Resource Pro® CD-ROM
Computer Test Generator CD
Prentice Hall Presentation Pro CD

🖥 **www.PHSchool.com**
Student Site
• Teacher Web Code: afk-5500
• Self-grading Lesson Quiz
Teacher Center
• Lesson Planner
• Resources

Plus **iTEXT**

1-2

Points, Lines, and Planes

North Carolina Objectives

2.02 Apply properties, definitions, and theorems of angles and lines to solve problems and write proofs.

Lesson Preview

What You'll Learn

OBJECTIVE
1
To understand basic terms of geometry

OBJECTIVE
2
To understand basic postulates of geometry

. . . And Why

To explain why a photographer uses a tripod, as in Exercise 45

✔ **Check Skills You'll Need**   (For help, go to the Skills Handbook page 722.)

x^2 **Algebra** **Solve each system of equations.**

1. $y = x + 5$ **(1, 6)**
   $y = -x + 7$

2. $y = 2x - 4$ **(3, 2)**
   $y = 4x - 10$

3. $y = 2x$ **(5, 10)**
   $y = -x + 15$

4. Copy the diagram of the four points $A, B, C,$ and D. Draw as many different lines as you can to connect pairs of points. See margin, p. 11.

                               $A\bullet$
                                       $\bullet B$
                       $C\bullet$
                           $\bullet D$

New Vocabulary   • point   • space   • line   • collinear points   • plane
                            • coplanar   • postulate   • axiom

---

OBJECTIVE
1   **Basic Terms of Geometry**

🔲 **iTEXT** **Interactive lesson includes instant self-check, tutorials, and activities.**

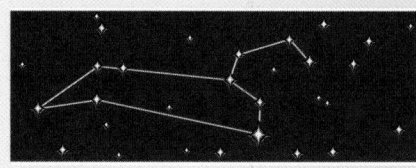

Investigation: How Many Lines Can You Draw?

Many constellations are named for animals and mythological figures. It takes some imagination to join the points representing the stars to get a recognizable figure such as Leo the Lion. How many lines can you draw connecting the 10 points in Leo the Lion?

• Make a table and look for a pattern to help you find out.

1. Mark three points on a circle. Now connect the three points with as many (straight) lines as possible. How many lines can you draw? **3 lines**

2. Mark four points on another circle. How many lines can you draw to connect the four points? **6 lines**

3. Repeat this procedure for five points on a circle and then for six points. How many lines can you draw to connect the points? **10 lines, 15 lines**

4. Use inductive reasoning to tell how many lines you can draw to connect the ten points of the constellation Leo the Lion. **45 lines**

In geometry, some words such as *point*, *line*, and *plane* are undefined. In order to define these words you need to use words that need further defining. It is important however, to have general descriptions of their meanings.

INSTANT CHECK SYSTEM ✔ **Ongoing Assessment and Intervention**

Before the Lesson	During the Lesson	After the Lesson
Diagnose prerequisite skills using:	**Monitor progress using:**	**Assess knowledge using:**
• Check Skills You'll Need	• Check Understanding	• Lesson Quiz
	• Additional Examples	• Computer Test Generator CD
	• Standardized Test Prep	

You can think of a **point** as a location. A point has no size. It is represented by a small dot and is named by a capital letter. A geometric figure is a set of points. **Space** is defined as the set of all points.

Reading Math

$\overleftrightarrow{AB}$ and $\overleftrightarrow{BA}$ name the same line.

You can think of a **line** as a series of points that extends in two opposite directions without end. You can name a line by any two points on the line, such as $\overleftrightarrow{AB}$ (read "line AB"). Another way to name a line is with a single lowercase letter, such as line t (see above). Points that lie on the same line are **collinear points.**

1 EXAMPLE Identifying Collinear Points

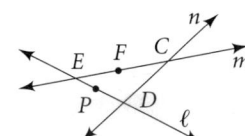

a. Are points E, F, and C collinear? If so, name the line on which they lie.

Points E, F, and C are collinear. They lie on line m.

b. Are points E, F, and D collinear? If so, name the line on which they lie.

Points E, F, and D are not collinear.

✓ **Check Understanding** **1 a.** Are points F, P, and C collinear? **no**
b. Name line m in three other ways. **Answers may vary. Sample:** $\overleftrightarrow{EF}$, $\overleftrightarrow{FC}$, $\overleftrightarrow{CE}$
c. Critical Thinking Why do you think arrowheads are used when drawing a line or naming a line such as $\overleftrightarrow{EF}$? **Arrowheads are used to show that the line extends in opposite directions without end.**

A **plane** is a flat surface that has no thickness. A plane contains many lines and extends without end in the directions of all its lines. You can name a plane by either a single capital letter or by at least three of its noncollinear points. Points and lines in the same plane are **coplanar.**

Plane P Plane ABC

2 EXAMPLE Naming a Plane

Each surface of the ice cube represents part of a plane. Name the plane represented by the front of the ice cube.

You can name the plane represented by the front of the ice cube using at least three noncollinear points in the plane. Some names are plane AEF, plane AEB, and plane $ABFE$.

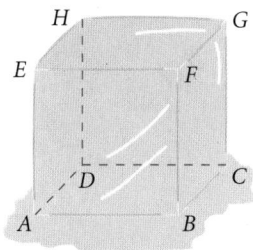

✓ **Check Understanding** **2** List three different names for the plane represented by the top of the ice cube.
Answers may vary. Sample: *HEF, HEFG, FGH*

Reaching All Students

Below Level Encourage students to use pencils and sheets of paper to model Postulates 1-1, 1-2, and 1-3. Students may cut partially through each sheet and join the sheets to model Postulate 1-3.	**Advanced Learners** In Example 4, have students find the number of different planes named by any three vertices of the cube.	**English Learners** See note on page 14. **Inclusion** See note on page 11.

---

2. Teach

Math Background

The formal study of geometry requires simple ideas and statements that can be accepted as true without proof. The undefined terms *point, line,* and *plane* provide the simple ideas. Basic postulates about points, lines and planes can be accepted without proof. These form the building blocks for the first theorems that students can prove.

OBJECTIVE
1 Teaching Notes

Investigation (Optional)
Some students may count lines in both "directions." Point out that each line should be counted only once.

2 EXAMPLE Inclusion

Pair students with visual difficulties with visual learners to identify and name planes.

Additional Examples

1 In the figure below, name three points that are collinear and three points that are not collinear. **Y, Z, and W are collinear; X, Y, and Z and X, W, and Z are not collinear.**

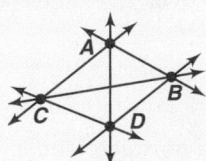

2 Name the plane shown in two different ways. **Sample: plane RST, plane RSTU**

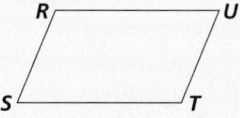

page 10   Check Skills You'll Need

4.

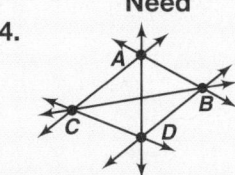

Teaching Tip
The word *noncollinear* in Postulate 1-4 may confuse students. Discuss how the prefix *non-* indicates *not*. So, noncollinear points do not lie on a line.

Tactile Learners
Have students use index cards to illustrate Postulates 1-3 and 1-4.

 3 EXAMPLE **Math Tip**

The drawing of a plane is necessarily finite. Remind students that the intersection is a line, not a segment, and that they should use a line symbol above the letters.

 Additional Examples

3 Use the diagram from Example 3. What is the intersection of plane *HGC* and plane *AED*? $\overleftrightarrow{HD}$

4 Shade the plane that contains *X*, *Y*, and *Z*.

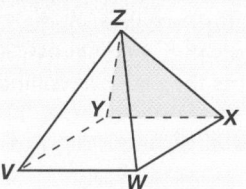

Closure

Explain how a postulate and a conjecture are alike and how they are different. **Sample: You accept a postulate as true without proof, but you try to determine whether a conjecture is true or false.**

A **postulate** or **axiom** is an accepted statement of fact.

You have used some of the following geometry postulates in algebra. For example, you used Postulate 1-1 when you graphed an equation such as $y = -2x + 8$. You plotted two points and then drew the line through those two points.

 Key Concepts

 Reading Math

There is exactly one means "there is one and there is no more than one."

Postulate 1-1
Through any two points there is exactly one line. Line *t* is the only line that passes through points *A* and *B*. 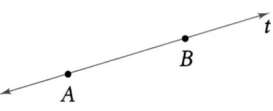

In algebra, one way to solve a system of two equations is to graph the two equations. As the graphs of

$$y = -2x + 8$$
$$y = 3x - 7$$

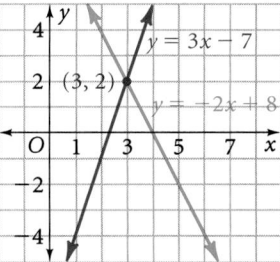

show, the two lines intersect at a single point, $(3, 2)$. The solution to the system of equations is $(3, 2)$.

This illustrates Postulate 1-2.

 Key Concepts

Postulate 1-2
If two lines intersect, then they intersect in exactly one point. $\overleftrightarrow{AE}$ and $\overleftrightarrow{BD}$ intersect at *C*. 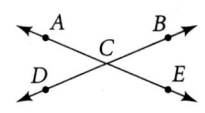

There is a similar postulate about the intersection of planes.

Key Concepts

Postulate 1-3
If two planes intersect, then they intersect in exactly one line. Plane *RST* and plane *STW* intersect in $\overleftrightarrow{ST}$. 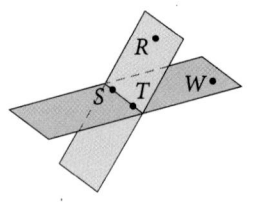

When you know two points in the intersection of two planes, Postulates 1-1 and 1-3 tell you that the line through those points is the line of intersection of the planes.

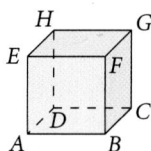

3 EXAMPLE Finding the Intersection of Two Planes

What is the intersection of plane *HGFE* and plane *BCGF*?

Plane *HGFE* and plane *BCGF*, intersect in $\overleftrightarrow{GF}$.

✔ **Check Understanding** ③ Name two planes that intersect in $\overleftrightarrow{BF}$.
ABF and CBF

A three-legged stand will always be stable. As long as the feet of the stand don't lie in one line, the feet of the three legs will lie exactly in one plane.

This illustrates Postulate 1-4.

🔑 **Key Concepts**

Postulate 1-4
Through any three noncollinear points there is exactly one plane.

4 EXAMPLE Using Postulate 1-4

a. Shade the plane that contains *A*, *B*, and *C*.

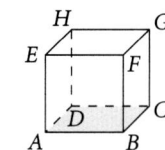

b. Shade the plane that contains *E*, *H*, and *C*.

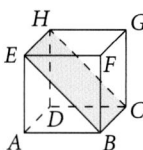

✔ **Check Understanding** ④ **a.** Name another point that is in the same plane as points *A*, *B*, and *C*. **D**
b. Name another point that is coplanar with points *E*, *H*, and *C*. **B**

EXERCISES

For more practice, see *Extra Practice*.

Practice and Problem Solving

Ⓐ **Practice by Example**

Example 1
(page 11)

3. yes; line *n*

5. yes; line *n*

9. Answers may vary.
Sample: $\overleftrightarrow{AE}$, $\overleftrightarrow{EC}$, $\overleftrightarrow{GA}$

Are the three points collinear? If so, name the line on which they lie.

1. *A, D, E* no   **2.** *B, C, D* yes; line *n*

3. *B, C, F*   **4.** *A, E, C* yes; line *m*

5. *F, B, D*   **6.** *F, A, E* no

7. *G, F, C* no   **8.** *A, G, C* yes; line *m*

9. Name line *m* in three other ways.

10. Name line *n* in three other ways.
Answers may vary. Sample: $\overleftrightarrow{BF}$, $\overleftrightarrow{CD}$, $\overleftrightarrow{DF}$

Assignment Guide

▼① **Objective**
   Ⓐ Ⓑ **Core** 1–16, 48–59, 67–69, 73–78
   Ⓒ **Extension** 79, 82–84

▼② **Objective**
   Ⓐ Ⓑ **Core** 17–47, 60–66, 70–72
   Ⓒ **Extension** 80, 81

Standardized Test Prep 85–89

Mixed Review 90–96

Error Prevention
Exercises 9, 10 Check that students use a line symbol and not a segment or ray symbol as they name lines.

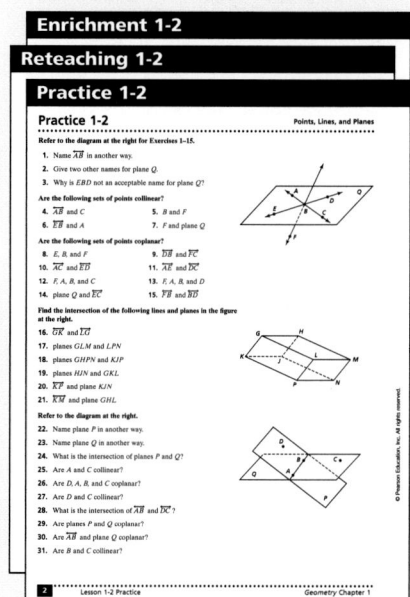

Exercises 38–43 These exercises introduce the term *noncoplanar*. Discuss with students how they can derive its meaning from what they already know about the terms *collinear* and *noncollinear*.

Exercises 48–51 Discuss the exercises for which students think that drawing a figure for the description is not possible. Have students explain their reasoning. This is a good way to clarify the ideas that form the basis of a formal proof.

English Learners

Exercises 60–65 These exercises reinforce the vocabulary and postulates in the lesson. Have students work with partners to discuss any unclear terms. Emphasize the mathematical importance of the phrase *exactly one* in Exercise 61. Also point out in Exercise 65 that *two lines* means *two distinct lines*.

Careers

Exercise 70 Ask: *What fact about Earth's surface complicates the work of a surveyor who uses lines and planes?* Earth is a sphere and not flat, so distances are measured along curves.

pages 13–16   Exercises

44. Answers may vary.
Sample: The plane of the ceiling and the plane of a wall intersect in a line.

45. Through any three noncollinear points there is exactly one plane. The ends of the legs of the tripod represent three noncollinear points, so they rest in one plane. Therefore, the tripod won't wobble.

47. Answers may vary.
Sample:

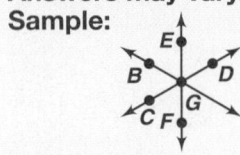

48.

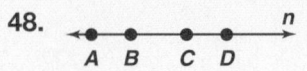

Example 2 (page 11)

Name the plane represented by each surface of the box.

11. the bottom **ABCD**   12. the top **EFHG**

13. the front **ABHF**   14. the back **EDCG**

15. the left side **EFAD**   16. the right side **BCGH**

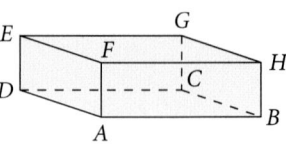

Example 3 (page 13)

Use the figure at the right for Exercises 17–37.

First, name the intersection of each pair of planes.

17. $\overleftrightarrow{RS}$ 17. planes QRS and RSW 18. planes UXV and WVS $\overleftrightarrow{VW}$

19. planes XWV and UVR 20. planes TXW and TQU $\overleftrightarrow{XT}$
$\overleftrightarrow{UV}$

Name two planes that intersect in the given line.

21. $\overleftrightarrow{QU}$ 22. $\overleftrightarrow{TS}$ 23. $\overleftrightarrow{XT}$ 24. $\overleftrightarrow{VW}$ Exercises 17–37
QUX and **QUV**   **XTS** and **QTS**   **UXT** and **WXT**   **UVW** and **RVW**

Example 4 (page 13)

Copy the figure. Shade the plane that contains the given points.

25. R, V, W 26. U, V, W 27. U, X, S 28. T, U, X 29. T, V, R
25–29. See back of book.

Name another point in each plane.

30. plane RVW 31. plane UVW 32. plane UXS 33. plane TUX 34. plane TVR
S   **X**   **R**   **Q**   **X**

Is the given point coplanar with the other three points?

35. point Q with V, W, S 36. point U with T, V, S 37. point W with X, V, R
no   yes   no

B Apply Your Skills

Postulate 1-4 states that any three noncollinear points lie in one plane. Find the plane containing the first three points listed, then decide whether the fourth point is in that plane. Write *coplanar* or *noncoplanar* to describe the points.

38. Z, S, Y, C coplanar   39. S, U, V, Y coplanar

40. X, Y, Z, U noncoplanar 41. X, S, V, U coplanar

42. X, Z, S, V noncoplanar 43. S, V, C, Y noncoplanar

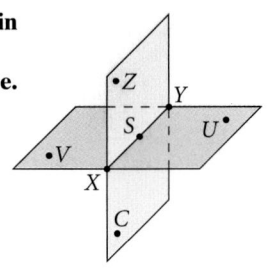

44. Describe two intersecting planes in your classroom. Describe their intersection.
See margin.

45. **Photography** Photographers and surveyors use a tripod, or three-legged stand, for their instruments. Use one of the postulates to explain why. **See margin.**

46. Which postulate is sometimes stated as "Two points determine a line"?
Postulate 1-1: Through any two points there is exactly one line.

47. **Open-Ended** Draw a figure with points $B, C, D, E, F,$ and G that shows $\overleftrightarrow{CD}$, $\overleftrightarrow{BG}$, and $\overleftrightarrow{EF}$, with one of the points on all three lines. **See margin.**

If possible, draw a figure to fit each description. Otherwise write *not possible*.
48–51. See margin.

48. four points that are collinear   49. two points that are noncollinear

50. three points that are noncollinear   51. three points that are noncoplanar

52–59. See back of book.

Coordinate Geometry Graph the points and state whether they are collinear.

52. $(0,0), (0,2), (0,4)$ 53. $(0,0), (3,0), (5,0)$ 54. $(0,0), (0,2), (3,0)$

55. $(2,-2), (2,2), (2,3)$ 56. $(3,-3), (2,-3), (-3,1)$ 57. $(2,2), (-2,-2), (3,2)$

58. $(2,-2), (-2,-2), (3,-2)$ 59. $(-3,3), (-3,2), (-3,-1)$

Real-World Connection

Careers The photographer uses a tripod to help assure a clear picture.

49. not possible

50. A•   •B

    C•

51. not possible

67.
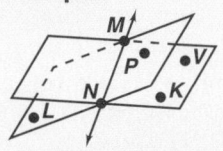 Post. 1-4: Through three noncollinear points there is exactly one plane.

68. Answers may vary.
Sample:

14

Use always, sometimes, or never to make a true statement.

60. Intersecting lines are ? coplanar. **always**

61. Two planes ? intersect in exactly one point. **never**

62. Three points are ? coplanar. **always**

63. A plane containing two points of a line ? contains the entire line. **always**

64. Four points are ? coplanar. **sometimes**

65. Two lines ? meet in more than one point. **never**

Need Help?

In Exercise 66, segments of the given lines are shown in the diagram.

66. How many planes contain each line and point?
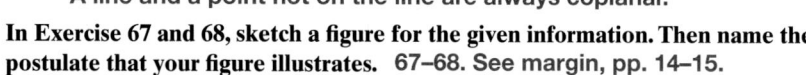
  a. $\overleftrightarrow{EF}$ and point G **1**   **b.** $\overleftrightarrow{PH}$ and point E **1**
  c. $\overleftrightarrow{FG}$ and point P **1**   **d.** $\overleftrightarrow{EP}$ and point G **1**
  e. Make a Conjecture What do you think is true of a line and a point not on the line?
  A line and a point not on the line are always coplanar.

In Exercise 67 and 68, sketch a figure for the given information. Then name the postulate that your figure illustrates. 67–68. See margin, pp. 14–15.

67. The noncollinear points A, B, and C are all contained in plane N.

68. Planes LNP and MVK intersect in $\overleftrightarrow{NM}$.

69. Optical Illusions The diagram (right) is an optical illusion. Which three points are collinear: A, B, and C or A, B, and D? Are you sure? Use a straightedge to check your answer.
A, B, and D
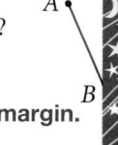

Writing Use postulates to explain each situation. 70–72. See margin.

70. A land surveyor can always find a straight line from the point where she stands to any other point she can see.

71. A carpenter knows that a line can represent the intersection of two flat walls.

72. A furniture maker knows that a three-legged table is always steady, but a four-legged table will sometimes wobble.

73–77. See back of book. 78. See margin.
Coordinate Geometry Graph the points and state whether they are collinear.

73. $(1, 1), (4, 4), (-3, -3)$ **74.** $(2, 4), (4, 6), (0, 2)$ **75.** $(0, 0), (-5, 1), (6, -2)$

76. $(0, 0), (8, 10), (4, 6)$ **77.** $(0, 0), (0, 3), (0, -10)$ **78.** $(-2, -6), (1, -2), (4, 1)$

Challenge

79. How many planes contain the same three collinear points? Explain. **See left.**

80. Navigation Rescue teams use Postulates 1-1 and 1-2 to determine the location of a distress signal. In the diagram, a ship at point A receives a signal from the northeast. A ship at point B receives the same signal from due west. Trace the diagram and find the location of the distress signal. Explain how the two postulates help locate the distress signal.
See margin.

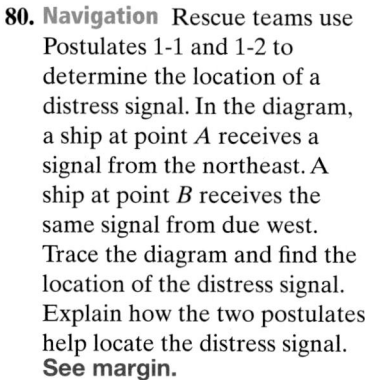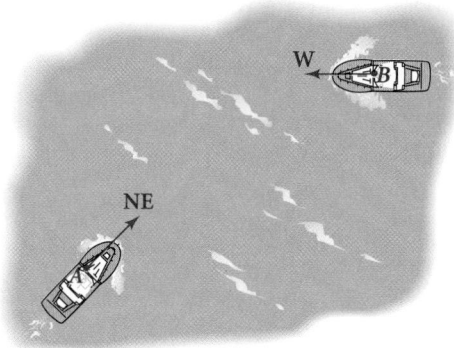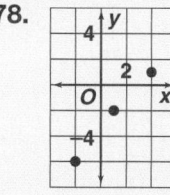

79. Infinitely many; explanations may vary. Sample: Infinitely many planes can intersect in one line.

Post. 1-3: If two planes intersect, then they intersect in exactly one line.

70. Post. 1-1: Through any two points there is exactly one line.

71. Post. 1-3: If two planes intersect, then they intersect in exactly one line.

72. The end of one leg might not be coplanar with the ends of the other three legs. (Post. 1-4)

78.
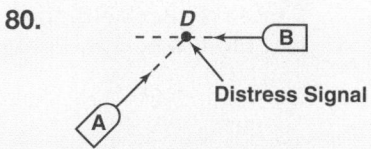
no

Lesson Quiz 1-2

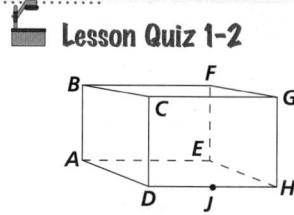

Use the diagram above.

1. Name three collinear points. **D, J, and H**

2. Name two different planes that contain points C and G. **planes $BCGF$ and $CGHD$**

3. Name the intersection of plane AED and plane HEG. **$\overrightarrow{HE}$**

4. How many planes contain the points A, F, and H? **1**

5. Show that this conjecture is false by finding one counterexample: *Two planes always intersect in exactly one line.* **Sample: Planes $AEHD$ and $BFGC$ never intersect.**

Alternative Assessment

Have students write Postulate 1-4, illustrate it, and explain it in their own words. Then have them explain how changing the word *three* to *four* or the word *plane* to *line* makes the postulate unreasonable.

80.

By Post. 1-1, points D and B determine a line and points A and D determine a line. The distress signal is on both lines and, by Post. 1-2, there can be only one distress signal.

15

Resources

For additional practice with a variety of test item formats:
- Standardized Test Prep, p. 65
- Test-Taking Strategies, p. 60
- Test-Taking Strategies with Transparencies

Exercise 87 When a multiple-choice problem asks for *the least number,* students should first check the smallest number in the answer choices.

---

81. **a.** Since the plane is flat, the line would have to curve so as to contain the 2 points and not lie in the plane; but lines are straight.

  b. One plane; Points *A*, *B*, and *C* are noncollinear. By Post. 1-4, they are coplanar. Then, by part (a), $\overleftrightarrow{AB}$ and $\overleftrightarrow{BC}$ are coplanar.

89. [2] **a.** *ABD, ABC, ACD, BCD*

  b. $\overleftrightarrow{AD}, \overleftrightarrow{BD}, \overleftrightarrow{CD}$

  [1] one part correct

90.

n	Last digit of 3^n
1	3
2	9
3	7
4	1
5	3
6	9
7	7
8	1

$$4\overline{)45}^{\,11R1}$$

The pattern 3, 9, 7, 1 repeats 11 times for $n = 1$ to 44. For $n = 45$, the last digit is 3.

---

81. a. Open-Ended Suppose two points are in plane *P*. Explain why it makes sense that the line containing the points would be in the same plane. **See margin.**

  b. Suppose two lines intersect. How many planes do you think contain both lines? You may use the diagram and your answer in part (a) to explain your answer. **See margin.**

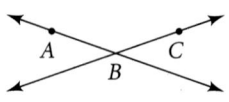

Probability Points are picked at random from *A*, *B*, *C*, and *D*, which are arranged as shown. Find the probability that the indicated number of points meet the given condition.

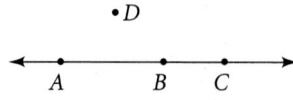

82. 2 points, collinear **1**   **83.** 3 points, collinear $\frac{1}{4}$ **84.** 3 points, coplanar **1**

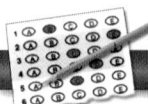

Standardized Test Prep

Multiple Choice

85. In the figure at the right, which points are collinear with *C* and *H*? **A**
  A. *B, F*
  B. *E, F, G*
  C. *A, D, G, I*
  D. *A, D, E, H*

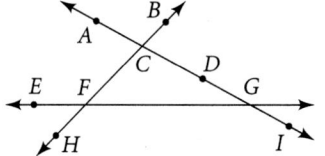

86. A solid chunk of cheese is to be cut into 4 pieces. What is the least number of slices needed? **I**
  F. 5   **G.** 4   **H.** 3   **I.** 2

Take It to the NET
Online lesson quiz at
www.PHSchool.com
Web Code: afa-0102

87. Ronald is making a table. What is the least number of legs that the table should have so that it will not wobble? **B**
  A. 4   **B.** 3   **C.** 2   **D.** 1

88. At most, how many lines can contain pairs of the points *P*, *Q*, and *R*? **H**
  F. 1   **G.** 2
  H. 3   **I.** 4

Short Response

89. Use the figure at the right. **a–b. See margin.**
  a. Name all the planes that form the figure.
  b. Name all the lines that intersect at *D*.

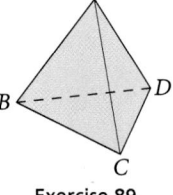

Exercise 89

Mixed Review

Lesson 1-1

90. Reasoning What is the last digit of 3^{45}? To answer, make a table, look for a pattern, and use inductive reasoning. Explain the pattern. **See margin.**

Find a pattern for each sequence. Use the pattern to show the next two terms.

91. A, C, E, G, … **I, K**

92. 2, 6, 12, 20, 30, … **42, 56**

93. 4, 16, 64, 256, … **1024, 4096**

94. 100, 95, 85, 70, 50, … **25, −5**

Previous Course $\boxed{x^2}$ **Algebra Evaluate each expression for the given values.**

95. $a^2 + b^2$ for $a = 3$ and $b = -5$ **34**   **96.** $\frac{1}{2}bh$ for $b = 8$ and $h = 11$ **44**

Segments, Rays, Parallel Lines and Planes

 North Carolina Objectives   2.02 Apply properties, definitions, and theorems of angles and lines to solve problems and write proofs.

Lesson Preview

What You'll Learn

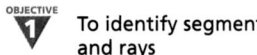

OBJECTIVE 1 To identify segments and rays

OBJECTIVE 2 To recognize parallel lines

...And Why

To identify compass directions that can be represented by opposite rays, as in Exercise 49

✔ **Check Skills You'll Need**   (For help, go to Lesson 1-2.)

Judging by appearances, will the lines intersect?

1. 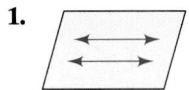 no   **2.** 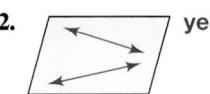 yes   **3.** 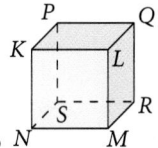 no

Name the plane represented by each surface of the box.

4. the bottom *NMR*   **5.** the top *PQL*

6. the front *NKL*   **7.** the back *PQR*

8. the left side *PKN*   **9.** the right side *LQR*

New Vocabulary
- segment
- ray
- opposite rays
- parallel lines
- skew lines
- parallel planes

OBJECTIVE 1

Identifying Segments and Rays

🖳 Interactive lesson includes instant self-check, tutorials, and activities.

Real-World 🌐 Connection

A sunbeam models a ray. The sun is its endpoint.

Many geometric figures, such as squares and angles, are formed by parts of lines called segments or rays. A **segment** is the part of a line consisting of two endpoints and all points between them.

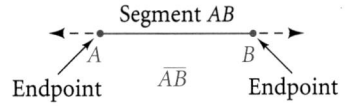

A **ray** is the part of a line consisting of one endpoint and all the points of the line on one side of the endpoint.

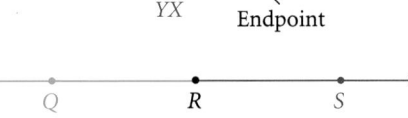

Opposite rays are two collinear rays with the same endpoint. Opposite rays always form a line.

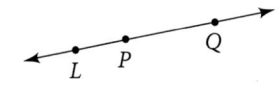

$\overrightarrow{RQ}$ and $\overrightarrow{RS}$ are opposite rays.

1 EXAMPLE **Naming Segments and Rays**

Name the segments and rays in the figure at the right.
- The three segments are $\overline{LP}, \overline{PQ},$ and $\overline{LQ}$.
- The four rays are $\overrightarrow{LP}$ or $\overrightarrow{LQ}, \overrightarrow{PQ}, \overrightarrow{PL},$ and $\overrightarrow{QP}$ or $\overrightarrow{QL}$.

✔ **Check Understanding** **1 Critical Thinking** $\overrightarrow{LP}$ and $\overrightarrow{PL}$ form a line. Are they opposite rays? Explain. No, they do not have the same endpoint.

⏱ **Ongoing Assessment and Intervention**

Before the Lesson	During the Lesson	After the Lesson
Diagnose prerequisite skills using:	**Monitor progress using:**	**Assess knowledge using:**
• Check Skills You'll Need	• Check Understanding	• Lesson Quiz
	• Additional Examples	• Computer Test Generator CD
	• Standardized Test Prep	• Chapter Checkpoint 1 (p. 23)

Lesson Preview

✔ **Check Skills You'll Need** 🖳

Basic Postulates of Geometry
Lesson 1-2: Examples 3, 4
Exercises 17–37
Extra Practice, p. 690

Lesson Resources

📁 **Teaching Resources**
Practice, Reteaching, Enrichment
Checkpoint Quiz 1

👥 **Reaching All Students**
Practice Workbook 1-3
Spanish Practice Workbook 1-3
Reading and Math Literacy 1B
Spanish Reading & Literacy 1B
Spanish Checkpoint Quiz 1
Hands-On Activities 3
Informal Geometry Planning
  Guide 1-3

⏱ **Presentation Assistant Plus!**
Transparencies
- Check Skills You'll Need 1-3
- Additional Examples 1-3
- Student Edition Answers 1-3
- Lesson Quiz 1-3
PH Presentation Pro CD 1-3

PRENTICE HALL ASSESSMENT *SYSTEM*

Checkpoint Quiz 1
Computer Test Generator CD

💿 **Technology**
Resource Pro® CD-ROM
Computer Test Generator CD
Prentice Hall Presentation Pro CD

🖥 **www.PHSchool.com**
Student Site
- Teacher Web Code: afk-5500
- Self-grading Lesson Quiz
Teacher Center
- Lesson Planner
- Resources

Plus 🖳

2. Teach

Math Background

The undefined terms *point*, *line*, and *plane* form the basis for the definitions of ray, segment, and parallel planes. Together these terms form the beginning vocabulary for the study of geometry. Euclid used this approach in Book 1 of *The Elements*.

OBJECTIVE 1 Teaching Notes

Teaching Tip
Point out that the first letter naming a ray is always its endpoint. The second letter is any other point on the ray. Emphasize that opposite rays are two *distinct* collinear rays with only their endpoints in common.

1 EXAMPLE Visual Learners

Remind students to associate the notations for line, segment, and ray with the actual figures.

Additional Examples

1 Name the segments and rays in the figure.

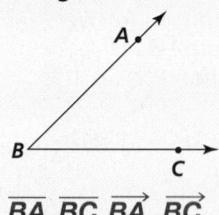

$\overline{BA}, \overline{BC}, \overrightarrow{BA}, \overrightarrow{BC}$

OBJECTIVE 2 Teaching Notes

2 EXAMPLE Tactile Learners

Some students may have trouble visualizing skew lines from the figure shown. Provide physical models for these students.

OBJECTIVE 2 Recognizing Parallel Figures

Lines that do not intersect may or may not be coplanar.

Parallel lines are coplanar lines that do not intersect. **Skew lines** are noncoplanar; therefore, they are not parallel and do not intersect.

Reading Math

You read $\overleftrightarrow{AB} \parallel \overleftrightarrow{EF}$ as line *AB* is parallel to line *EF*.

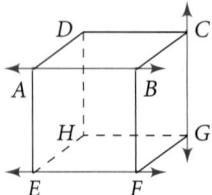

$\overleftrightarrow{AB} \parallel \overleftrightarrow{EF}$
$\overleftrightarrow{AB}$ and $\overleftrightarrow{CG}$ are skew.

Segments or rays are parallel if they lie in parallel lines. They are skew if they lie in skew lines. $\overline{AB}$ and $\overline{CG}$ are skew because $\overleftrightarrow{AB}$ and $\overleftrightarrow{CG}$ are skew.

2 EXAMPLE Identifying Parallel and Skew Segments

a. Name all labeled segments that are parallel to $\overline{DC}$.

$\overline{AB}, \overline{GH}$, and $\overline{JI}$ are parallel to $\overline{DC}$.

b. Name all labeled segments that are skew to $\overline{DC}$.

$\overline{NJ}, \overline{GJ}$, and $\overline{HI}$ are skew to $\overline{DC}$.

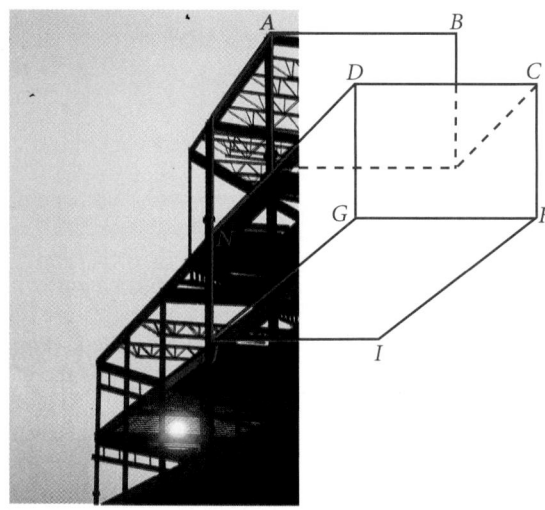

✓ Check Understanding **2** Use the diagram in Example 2.
a. Name all labeled segments that are parallel to $\overline{GJ}$. $\overline{HI}, \overline{DN}$
b. Name all labeled segments that are skew to $\overline{GJ}$. $\overline{AB}, \overline{CD}, \overline{CH}$
c. Name another pair of parallel segments; of skew segments. $\overline{DN}, \overline{HI}; \overline{DN}, \overline{HC}$

Parallel planes are planes that do not intersect.

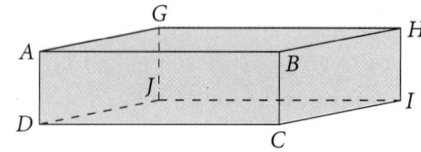

Plane *ABCD* ∥ Plane *GHIJ*

👥 Reaching All Students

| **Below Level** Remind students that the different notations for *line*, *line segment*, and *ray* readily identify and distinguish them. | **Advanced Learners** Have students justify the statement, "Skew lines are noncoplanar; therefore they are not parallel and do not intersect." They may need to reason indirectly. | **English Learners** See note on page 21. **Visual Learners** See note on page 18. |

3 **EXAMPLE** Identifying Parallel Planes

The planes of the front and back are parallel. Name two other pairs of parallel planes in the figure.

Plane *ABHG* ∥ plane *DCIJ*; plane *ADJ* ∥ plane *BCI*.

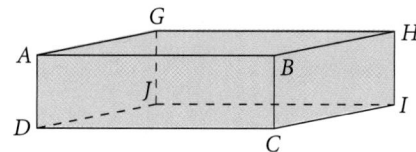

✔ **Check Understanding**

3a. *PSWT* ∥ *RQVU*,
  PRUT ∥ *SQVW*,
  PSQR ∥ *TWVU*

3 Use the diagram at the right to name the figures.
  a. three pairs of parallel planes
  b. a line that is parallel to $\overrightarrow{PQ}$ $\overleftrightarrow{TV}$
  c. a line that is parallel to plane *QRUV*
  Answers may vary. Sample: $\overleftrightarrow{PS}$

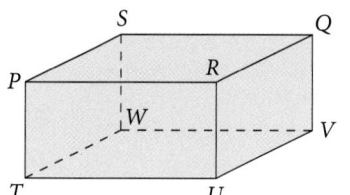

EXERCISES

For more practice, see *Extra Practice.*

Practice and Problem Solving

A Practice by Example

Example 1
(page 17)

Sketch each of the following. 1–4. See margin.

1. $\overline{AB}$ **2.** $\overrightarrow{AB}$ **3.** $\overrightarrow{BA}$ **4.** $\overleftrightarrow{BA}$

Use the figure at the right for Exercises 5–10.
  5. Name all the labeled segments. $\overline{RS}, \overline{RT}, \overline{RW}, \overline{ST}, \overline{SW}, \overline{TW}$
  6. Name all the labeled rays. $\overrightarrow{RS}, \overrightarrow{ST}, \overrightarrow{TW}, \overrightarrow{WT}, \overrightarrow{TS}, \overrightarrow{SR}$

  7. a. Name a pair of opposite rays with *T* as an endpoint. $\overrightarrow{TS}$ or $\overrightarrow{TR}, \overrightarrow{TW}$
  b. Name another pair of opposite rays. $\overrightarrow{SR}, \overrightarrow{ST}$

Exercises 5–10

Copy the line pictured above. On your copy mark a different point, *Y*. How many of each type of figure are there with *Y* as an endpoint? Name them.

  8. segments **9.** rays 8–9. See margin.

  10. Critical Thinking Are there any new rays you can name (see Exercise 6) using *R, S, T,* or *W* as the endpoint and *Y* as the second point? If *yes,* name them. Answers may vary. Check students' work.

Example 2
(page 18)

In the diagram, name all segments shown that are parallel to the given segment.

  11. $\overline{AC}$ $\overline{DF}$ **12.** $\overline{EF}$ $\overline{BC}$ **13.** $\overline{AD}$ $\overline{BE}, \overline{CF}$

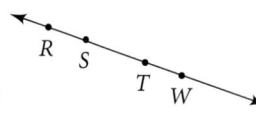

In the diagram, name all segments shown that are skew to the given segment.

  14. $\overline{AC}$ $\overline{DE}, \overline{EF}, \overline{BE}$ **15.** $\overline{EF}$ $\overline{AD}, \overline{AB}, \overline{AC}$ **16.** $\overline{AD}$ $\overline{BC}, \overline{EF}$

Exercises 11–20

18–20. Answers may vary. Samples are given.

Example 3
(page 19)

Use the diagram above and name a pair of figures to match each description.

  17. parallel planes *ABC* ∥ *DEF* **18.** parallel lines $\overleftrightarrow{BE}$ ∥ $\overleftrightarrow{AD}$ **19.** skew lines $\overleftrightarrow{CF}, \overleftrightarrow{DE}$

  20. a line and a plane that are parallel *DEF,* $\overleftrightarrow{BC}$

---

2 Use the figure from Example 3. Name all segments that are parallel to $\overline{AD}$. Name all that are skew to $\overline{AD}$. parallel: $\overline{GJ}, \overline{HI}, \overline{BC}$; skew: $\overline{GH}, \overline{JI}, \overline{BH}, \overline{CI}$

3 Identify a pair of parallel planes in your classroom.
Sample: floor and ceiling

Closure

How are parallel and skew lines alike? How are they different? Both parallel and skew lines never intersect; parallel lines are coplanar, whereas skew lines are not.

pages 19–23 Exercises

1. ·————·
   A   B

2. ·————▸
   A   B

3. ·————▸
   B   A

4. ◂—·———·—▸
      A   B

8. 4; $\overline{RY}, \overline{SY}, \overline{TY}, \overline{WY}$

9. Answers may vary. Sample: 2; $\overrightarrow{YS}$ or $\overrightarrow{YR}, \overrightarrow{YT}$ or $\overrightarrow{YW}$

Error Prevention

Exercise 6 Students may think that $\overrightarrow{TR}$ and $\overrightarrow{SW}$ are opposite rays. Ask: *How many points do opposite rays have in common?* **exactly 1** *What is it?* **the endpoint of both rays**

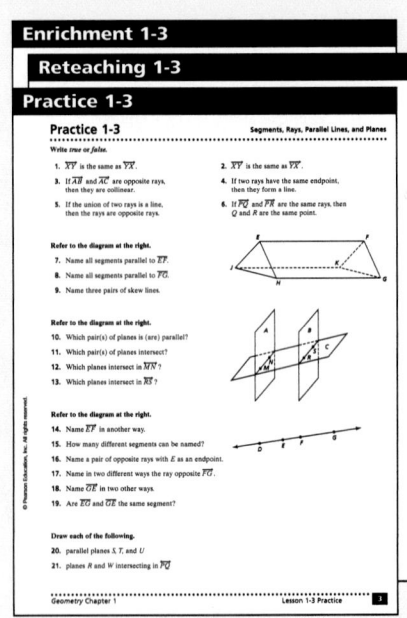

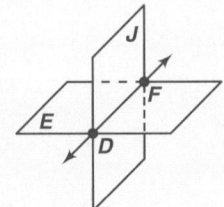

pages 19–23   Exercises

36.

20

---

22. Answers may vary.
Sample: $\overleftrightarrow{CD}$, $\overleftrightarrow{AB}$

23. $\overleftrightarrow{BG}$, $\overleftrightarrow{DH}$, $\overleftrightarrow{CL}$

B **Apply Your Skills**

30. False; they intersect above pt. *A*.

33. Yes; both name the segment with endpoints *X* and *Y*.

34. No; the two rays have different endpoints.

35. Yes; both are the line through pts. *X* and *Y*.

Reading Math

"Always," "sometimes," and "never" refer to all possible cases, not to intervals of time.

Use the figure at the right to name the following.

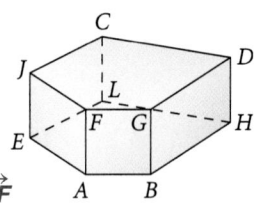

21. all lines that are parallel to $\overleftrightarrow{AB}$ $\overleftrightarrow{FG}$

22. two lines that are skew to $\overleftrightarrow{EJ}$

23. all lines that are parallel to plane *JFAE*

24. the intersection of plane *FAB* and plane *FAE* $\overleftrightarrow{AF}$

In Exercises 25–32, describe the statement as true or false. If *false*, explain.

25. $\overleftrightarrow{CB} \parallel \overleftrightarrow{HG}$ true

26. $\overleftrightarrow{ED} \parallel \overleftrightarrow{HG}$ False; they are skew.

27. plane *AED* $\parallel$ plane *FGH* true

28. plane *ABH* $\parallel$ plane *CDF* False; they intersect above $\overline{CG}$.

29. $\overleftrightarrow{AB}$ and $\overleftrightarrow{HG}$ are skew lines. true

30. $\overleftrightarrow{AE}$ and $\overleftrightarrow{BC}$ are skew lines. See left.

31. $\overleftrightarrow{CG}$ and $\overleftrightarrow{AI}$ are skew lines. False; they are $\parallel$.

32. $\overleftrightarrow{CF}$ and $\overleftrightarrow{AJ}$ are skew lines. False; they are $\parallel$.

Are the two figures the same? Explain.   33–35. See left.

33. $\overline{XY}$ and $\overline{YX}$

34. $\overrightarrow{XY}$ and $\overrightarrow{YX}$

35. $\overleftrightarrow{XY}$ and $\overleftrightarrow{YX}$

36. The following steps show how to draw planes *A* and *B* intersecting in $\overleftrightarrow{FG}$.

Step 1   Step 2   Step 3

Use similar steps to draw plane *DFE* and plane *DFJ* intersecting in $\overleftrightarrow{DF}$.
See margin.

Complete Exercises 37–47 with *always*, *sometimes*, or *never* to make a true statement.

37. Two parallel lines are ? (always) coplanar.   38. Two skew lines are ? (never) coplanar.

39. Two opposite rays ? (always) form a line.   40. $\overrightarrow{TQ}$ and $\overrightarrow{QT}$ are ? (always) the same line.

41. $\overrightarrow{GH}$ and $\overrightarrow{HG}$ are ? (never) the same ray.   42. $\overrightarrow{JK}$ and $\overrightarrow{JL}$ are ? (sometimes) the same ray.

43. $\overline{AX}$ and $\overline{XA}$ are ? the same segment.   **always**

44. Two lines in the same plane are ? parallel.   **sometimes**

45. Two planes that do not intersect are ? parallel.   **always**

46. Two lines that lie in parallel planes are ? parallel.   **sometimes**

47. Two lines in intersecting planes are ? skew.   **sometimes**

48. **Coordinate Geometry** $\overrightarrow{AB}$ has endpoint $A(2, 3)$ and contains $B(4, 6)$. Give possible coordinates for point *C* so that $\overrightarrow{AB}$ and $\overrightarrow{AC}$ are opposite rays. Graph your answer.
Answers may vary. Sample: (0, 0); check students' graphs.

---

49. a. Answers may vary.
Sample: northeast and southwest

b. Answers may vary.
Sample: northwest and southeast, east and west

50. Two lines can be parallel, skew, or intersecting in one point. Samples: Train tracks–parallel; vapor trail of a northbound jet

and an eastbound jet at different altitudes–skew; streets that cross–intersecting

49. Directional Compass On a directional compass, the directions north and south can be represented by opposite rays.
  a. Name two other compass directions that can be represented by opposite rays.
  b. What other pairs of opposite directions, if any, can you find? **a–b. See margin, p. 20.**

50. Open-Ended Summarize the three ways in which two lines may be related. Give examples from the real world that illustrate the relationships. **See margin, p. 20.**

51. Answers may vary. Sample: Skew lines cannot be contained in one plane. Therefore, they have "escaped" a plane.

51. Writing The term *skew* is a Middle English word meaning "to escape." Explain how this meaning might be appropriate for skew lines. **See left.**

Describe each figure using geometric terms. **53–54. See margin.**

52.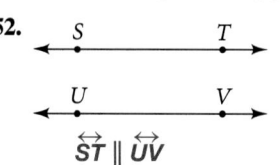
$$\overleftrightarrow{ST} \parallel \overleftrightarrow{UV}$$

53.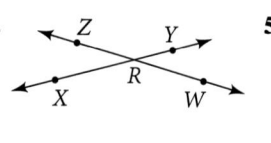

54.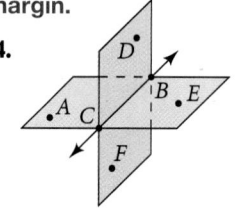

55. Critical Thinking Suppose two parallel planes A and B are each intersected by a third plane C.
  a. Make a conjecture about the intersection of planes A and C and the intersection of planes B and C. **The lines of intersection are parallel.**
  b. Find examples in your classroom. **See margin.**

C Challenge 🌐 **56. Chemistry** In diamond, each carbon atom bonds to four other carbon atoms in a three-dimensional network. In graphite, each carbon atom bonds to three carbon atoms in the same plane. The "sheets" or planes of graphite are parallel. Find out how these structures affect the properties of diamond and graphite. **See margin.**

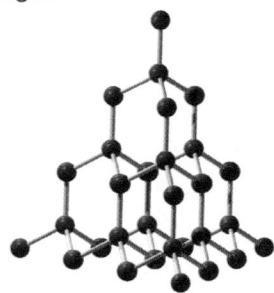 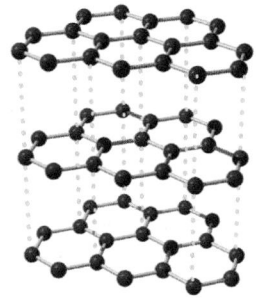

Real-World 🌐 Connection

Careers Because of the diamond's atomic structure, a diamond cutter can split a diamond in four directions parallel to the octahedral crystal faces.

57. a. Draw a line. Draw points E and F on the line. How many different segments do points E and F determine? Name the segments. **See margin.**
  b. Draw another line. Draw points E, F, and G on the line. How many segments do points E, F, and G determine? Name them. **See margin.**
  c. Continue to draw lines, labeling one more point each time. Make a table showing the number of points and the number of segments determined. Look for and describe a pattern in the data. **See margin.**
  d. Use your pattern to find how many segments are determined if you label 10 points on a line. **45 segments**
  e. If you label n points on a line, how many segments can you name?
$$\frac{n(n-1)}{2}$$

53. Answers may vary. Sample: $\overleftrightarrow{XY}$ and $\overleftrightarrow{ZW}$ intersect at R.

54. Planes *ABC* and *DCBF* intersect in $\overleftrightarrow{BC}$.

55. b. Examples may vary. Sample: The floor and ceiling are parallel. A wall intersects both. The lines of intersection are parallel.

56. Answers may vary. Sample: The diamond structure makes it tough, strong, hard, and durable. The graphite structure makes it soft and slippery.

Tactile Learners
Exercises 25–32 Have students use physical models to help them answer these exercises.

English Learners
Exercises 37–47 These exercises reinforce the meaning of the new vocabulary in the lesson as well as the use of the terms *always, sometimes,* and *never* in mathematical reasoning. You may want students to work with partners to discuss the new terms and their meanings.

Auditory Learners
Exercises 52–54 These exercises are open-ended. Discuss them as a class to help students gain insights from other students' ideas. Let several students suggest possible answers for each exercise.

Connection to Chemistry
Exercise 56 When atoms combine, the geometric structure of the atoms determines the physical properties of a substance. Chemists understand or investigate this relationship when they work with substances.

57. a.

one segment; $\overline{EF}$

b.

3 segments; $\overline{EF}$, $\overline{EG}$, $\overline{FG}$

C.

Number of points	Number of segments
2	1
3	3
4	6
5	10
6	15

Answers may vary. Sample: For each "new" point, the number of new segments equals the number of "old" points.

21

Lesson Quiz 1-3

Use the figure below for Exercises 1–3.

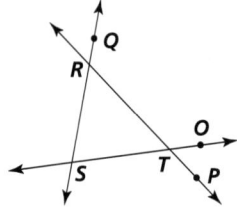

1. Name the segments that form the triangle.
   $\overline{RS}, \overline{TR}, \overline{ST}$

2. Name the rays that have point *T* as their endpoint.
   $\overrightarrow{TO}, \overrightarrow{TP}, \overrightarrow{TR}, \overrightarrow{TS}$

3. Explain how you can tell that no lines in the figure are parallel or skew.
   The three pairs of lines intersect, so they cannot be parallel or skew.

Use the figure below for Exercises 4 and 5.

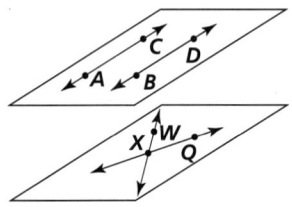

4. Name a pair of parallel planes. **plane *ABCD* ‖ plane *XWQ***

5. Name a line that is skew to $\overleftrightarrow{XW}$. $\overleftrightarrow{AC}$ **or** $\overleftrightarrow{BD}$

Alternative Assessment

Provide each student with a model of a rectangular solid, such as an empty cereal box. Have students describe how to find each of the following on the model: intersecting lines, parallel lines, skew lines, parallel planes, and intersecting planes.

Use the figure at the right for Exercises 58 and 59.

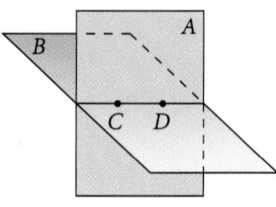

58. Do planes *A* and *B* have other lines in common that are parallel to $\overleftrightarrow{CD}$? Explain. **See margin.**

59. **Visualization** Are there planes that intersect planes *A* and *B* in lines parallel to $\overleftrightarrow{CD}$? Draw a sketch to support your answer. **See margin.**

The figure at the right is a pyramid.

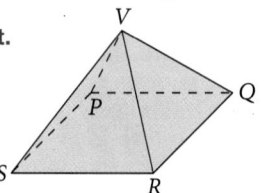

60. **Answers may vary. Sample:** $\overleftrightarrow{VR}, \overleftrightarrow{QR}, \overleftrightarrow{SR}$

60. Name three lines that intersect at one point. **See left.**

61. What line could be parallel to $\overleftrightarrow{PS}$? $\overleftrightarrow{QR}$

62. **Visualization** Consider a plane through *V* that is parallel to plane *PQRS*. Can a line in that plane be parallel to $\overleftrightarrow{SR}$? Can it intersect $\overleftrightarrow{SR}$? Can it be skew to $\overleftrightarrow{SR}$? Explain each answer.
    Yes; no; yes; explanations may vary.

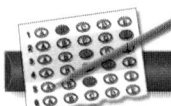

Standardized Test Prep

Use the figure at the right for Exercises 63–65.

A B C D E

Multiple Choice

63. How many labeled segments are in the figure? **D**
    A. 1   B. 4   C. 6   D. 10

64. Which ray is opposite $\overrightarrow{BC}$? **H**
    F. $\overrightarrow{BE}$ G. $\overrightarrow{BD}$ H. $\overrightarrow{BA}$ I. $\overrightarrow{AB}$

65. What is another name for $\overrightarrow{CA}$? **B**
    A. $\overrightarrow{AC}$ B. $\overrightarrow{CB}$ C. $\overrightarrow{CE}$ D. $\overrightarrow{DC}$

66. Which figure could be the intersection of two planes? **F**
    F. line   G. ray   H. point   I. segment

Quantitative Comparison

Compare the boxed quantity in Column A with the boxed quantity in Column B. Choose the best answer.
A. The quantity in Column A is greater.
B. The quantity in Column B is greater.
C. The two quantities are equal.
D. The relationship cannot be determined from the information given.

Column A	Column B
B 67. the next number in the sequence 1, 3, 5, 7, . . .	the next number in the sequence 2, −4, 6, −8, . . .
C 68. the number of lines determined by two points	the number of points determined by two intersecting lines
D 69. the number of segments that can be named using points *A*, *B*, and *C*	the number of lines determined by three points, *A*, *B*, and *C*

Take It to the NET
Online lesson quiz at **www.PHSchool.com**
Web Code: afa-0103

pages 19–23   Exercises

58. **No; two different planes cannot intersect in more than one line.**

59. **yes; plane *P*, for example**

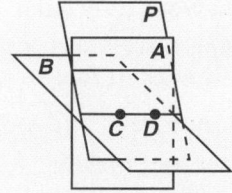

Short Response

70. a. Use the diagram to explain how parallel lines and skew lines are alike and how parallel lines and skew lines are different. **a–b. See margin.**

b. Does the diagram suggest other lines that are parallel to $\overleftrightarrow{JM}$, besides $\overleftrightarrow{KL}$, $\overleftrightarrow{QR}$, and $\overleftrightarrow{PS}$? Explain.

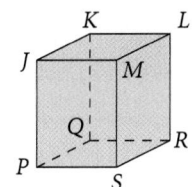

Resources
For additional practice with a variety of test item formats:
• Standardized Test Prep, p. 65
• Test-Taking Strategies, p. 60
• Test-Taking Strategies with Transparencies

Mixed Review

Lesson 1-2

71–78. Answers may vary. Samples are given.
Use the diagram for Exercises 71–78 and name each geometric figure.

71. a line $\overleftrightarrow{EF}$ **72.** a point **A**

73. the intersection of $\overline{DC}$ and $\overleftrightarrow{CG}$ **C**

74. two planes that intersect in $\overleftrightarrow{EF}$ **AEF** and **HEF**

75. the plane represented by the top of the box **ABH**

76. the plane represented by the front of the box **EHG**

77. the intersection of planes EFG and DFG $\overleftrightarrow{FG}$

78. another point in plane CGH **B**

Draw the following. 79–81. See margin.

79. $\overleftrightarrow{TR}$ **80.** $\overline{PQ}$ **81.** $\overrightarrow{NV}$

Lesson 1-1

Find the next two terms in each sequence.

82. $1, 1.08, 1.16, 1.24, 1.32, \dots$ **1.4, 1.48**   **83.** $-1, -2, -4, -7, -11, -16, \dots$ **−22, −29**

84. $AB, BC, CD, DE, EF, \dots$ **FG, GH**   **85.** $A, D, G, J, M, \dots$ **P, S**

86. Reasoning Raven conjectured: "If you subtract a number from a given number, the result is always less than the given number." Is her conjecture true? Explain. **No; whenever you subtract a negative number, the answer is greater than the given number. Also, if you subtract 0, the answer stays the same.**

Connection to Probability

Exercise 63 Another way to solve this problem is to find the number of combinations possible for 5 letters taken 2 at a time.

Exercise 66 This problem is answered by using Postulate 1-3 from Lesson 1-2: *If two planes intersect, then they intersect in exactly one line.*

✓ Chapter Checkpoint 1

To check understanding of Lessons 1-1 to 1-3:

Checkpoint Quiz 1 (p. 23)

Teaching Resources
Checkpoint Quiz 1 (also in Prentice Hall Assessment System)

Reaching All Students
Reading and Math Literacy 1B

Spanish versions available

✓ Checkpoint Quiz 1   Lessons 1-1 through 1-3

  Instant self-check quiz online and on CD-ROM

3. For 1: Add 2.5. For 2: Extend the decimal to one more place with a digit that is 1 more than the one to its left.

Find the next two terms in each sequence.

1. $19, 21.5, 24, 26.5, \dots$ **29, 31.5**   **2.** $3.4, 3.45, 3.456, 3.4567, \dots$ **3.45678, 3.456789**

3. Writing Describe the pattern of each sequence in Exercises 1 and 2. **See left.**

Use the diagram for Exercises 4–10. In Exercises 4–7, do the points appear to be coplanar? If *yes*, name the plane. If *no*, explain. 4–7. See margin.

4. Points A, E, F, and B **5.** Points D, C, E, and F

6. Points H, G, F, and B **7.** Points A, E, B, and C

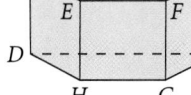

8. Name all the segments parallel to $\overline{HG}$. **CD, AB, EF**

9. Answers may vary.
Sample: $\overleftrightarrow{AE}$ and $\overleftrightarrow{BC}$

9. Name a pair of skew lines. **See left.**

10. What is the intersection of plane $EFGH$ and $\overleftrightarrow{DH}$? **H**

page 23   Checkpoint Quiz 1

4. yes, plane *AEF*

5. yes, plane *DCEF*

6. No; *H*, *G*, and *F* are in the front plane, *B* is not.

7. No; *A*, *E*, and *B* are in the top plane, *C* is not.

70. [2] **a.** Alike: They do not intersect. Different: Parallel lines are coplanar and skew lines lie in different planes.

b. No; of the 8 other lines shown, 4 intersect $\overleftrightarrow{JM}$ and 4 are skew to $\overleftrightarrow{JM}$.

[1] one likeness, one difference

79. ←•———————•→
        T R

80. •———————•
        P Q

81. •———————→
        N V

Algebra 1 Review

Solving Linear Equations

Solving Linear Equations

Students will practice solving linear equations to prepare for solving for segment lengths and for angle measurements in Lesson 1-4.

Resources

Technology

Geometry Resource Pro® CD-Rom: Algebra Review Resources
Computer Test Generator CD-Rom, Chapter 0, Integer, Decimal and Fraction Operations

Teaching Notes

1 EXAMPLE   Error Prevention

Discuss with the class why subtraction of a term in parentheses is equivalent to adding the product of −1 and the term. This will help students avoid future errors in subtracting negative terms imbedded within parentheses.

2 EXAMPLE   Tactile Learners

Have students model the problem using a pan balance.

Alternative Method

Ask students to solve the problem by subtracting $7x$ instead of $4x$ from each side. Lead them to understand that both methods work.

Sometimes you need to combine like terms to solve a linear equation.

1 EXAMPLE

Solve $(5x + 8) - (2x - 9) = 38$.

$$(5x + 8) - (2x - 9) = 38$$
$$(5x + 8) + (-1)(2x - 9) = 38 \qquad -(2x - 9) = (-1)(2x - 9)$$
$$(5x + 8) + (-1)2x + (-1)(-9) = 38 \qquad \text{Use the Distributive Property.}$$
$$5x + 8 - 2x + 9 = 38 \qquad \text{Simplify.}$$
$$3x + 17 = 38 \qquad \text{Combine like terms.}$$
$$3x = 21 \qquad \text{Subtract 17 from each side.}$$
$$x = 7 \qquad \text{Divide each side by 3.}$$

To solve an equation with the variable on *both* sides, first convert the equation to one with the variable on *only one* side.

2 EXAMPLE

Solve $4x - 9 = 7x - 15$.

$$4x - 9 = 7x - 15$$
$$-9 = 3x - 15 \qquad \text{Subtract 4x from each side.}$$
$$6 = 3x \qquad \text{Add 15 to each side.}$$
$$2 = x \qquad \text{Divide each side by 3.}$$

EXERCISES

Solve.

1. $10n + 12 = 14n - 12$ **6**

2. $(4w - 28) + (11w + 13) = 180$ **13**

3. $(7a + 3) + (-a - 5) = -16$ $-\frac{7}{3}$ or $-2\frac{1}{3}$

4. $7y + 44 = 12y + 11$ **6.6**

5. $(7t - 21) + (t + 4) = 15$ **4**

6. $8x - 4 - 2x = -10$ **−1**

7. $(8t + 30) + (-2t - 16) = -22$ **−6**

8. $6x + 17 = 9x + 2$ **5**

9. $(3y - 5) + (5y + 20) = 135$ **15**

10. $(11x - 37) + (5x + 59) = 54$ **2**

11. $3x - 35 = 9x - 59$ **4**

12. $9x - 3 = 8x - 7$ **−4**

13. $(5w + 24) + (2w + 13) = 156$ **17**

14. $(3x + 10) - 5x = 6x - 50$ **7.5**

15. $8y + 12 = 2y - 18$ **−5**

16. $7t - 8t + 4 = 5t - 2$ **1**

17. $13c + 40 = 9c - 20 + c$ **−20**

18. $(6a - 54) - (5a + 27) = 23$ **104**

19. $(2 + 4y) - (y + 9) = 26$ **11**

20. $(12c + 35) - (5c - 11) = -2$ $-\frac{48}{7}$ or $-6\frac{6}{7}$

Measuring Segments and Angles

 North Carolina Objectives

2.02 Apply properties, definitions, and theorems of angles and lines to solve problems and write proofs.

Lesson Preview

What You'll Learn

 OBJECTIVE 1 To find the lengths of segments

 OBJECTIVE 2 To find the measures of angles

... And Why

To find distance using a highway number line, as in Exercise 36

 **Check Skills You'll Need** (For help, go to the Skills Handbook pages 719 and 720.)

Simplify each absolute value expression.

1. $|-6|$ 6
2. $|3.5|$ 3.5
3. $|7 - 10|$ 3
4. $|-4 - 2|$ 6
5. $|-2 - (-4)|$ 2
6. $|-3 + 12|$ 9

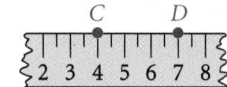 **Algebra Solve each equation.**

7. $x + 2x - 6 = 6$ 4
8. $3x + 9 + 5x = 81$ 9
9. $w - 2 = -4 + 7w$ $\frac{1}{3}$

New Vocabulary
- coordinate
- congruent segments
- midpoint
- angle
- acute angle
- right angle
- obtuse angle
- straight angle
- congruent angles

Lesson Preview

 **Check Skills You'll Need**

For help use
Skills Handbook, pp. 719, 720

Lesson Resources

 **Teaching Resources**
Practice, Reteaching, Enrichment

Reaching All Students
Practice Workbook 1-4
Spanish Practice Workbook 1-4
Informal Geometry Planning
  Guide 1-4

Presentation Assistant Plus!
Transparencies
- Check Skills You'll Need 1-4
- Additional Examples 1-4
- Student Edition Answers 1-4
- Lesson Quiz 1-4
PH Presentation Pro CD 1-4

ASSESSMENT SYSTEM

Computer Test Generator CD

Technology
Resource Pro® CD-ROM
Computer Test Generator CD
Prentice Hall Presentation Pro CD

 www.PHSchool.com
Student Site
- Teacher Web Code: afk-5500
- Self-grading Lesson Quiz
Teacher Center
- Lesson Planner
- Resources

Plus

 OBJECTIVE 1

Finding Segment Lengths

The distance between points C and D on the ruler is 3. You can use the Ruler Postulate to find the distance between points on a number line.

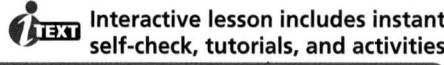

 Key Concepts

Postulate 1-5	Ruler Postulate

The points of a line can be put into one-to-one correspondence with the real numbers so that the distance between any two points is the absolute value of the difference of the corresponding numbers.

the length of $\overline{AB}$
$$AB = |a - b|$$
coordinate of A **coordinate** of B

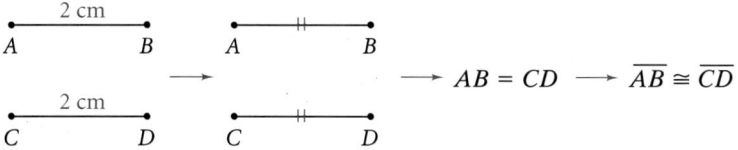

Reading Math

The congruence symbol ($\cong$) shows that two figures are equal (=) in size and similar ($\sim$) in shape.

Two segments with the same length are **congruent** ($\cong$) **segments.** In other words, if $AB = CD$, then $\overline{AB} \cong \overline{CD}$. You can use these statements interchangeably.

As illustrated above, segments can be marked alike to show they are congruent.

 ## Ongoing Assessment and Intervention

Before the Lesson
Diagnose prerequisite skills using:
- Check Skills You'll Need

During the Lesson
Monitor progress using:
- Check Understanding
- Additional Examples
- Standardized Test Prep

After the Lesson
Assess knowledge using:
- Lesson Quiz
- Computer Test Generator CD

Professional Development

Math Background

A one-to-one correspondence, as used in the Ruler Postulate, is one way to show that two sets are equivalent when their elements cannot be counted. The Ruler and Protractor Postulates are abstract descriptions of how the two measurement tools work. Although he did not list it as a postulate, Euclid implicitly used the Segment Addition Postulate in his proofs.

OBJECTIVE

1 Teaching Notes

Teaching Tip
The Ruler Postulate may seem more complicated to students than it is. Have them rephrase it in their own words, relating the postulate to the way rulers are used.

Error Prevention
The statements $\overline{AB} \cong \overline{CD}$ and $AB = CD$ are interchangeable. However, point out that $\overline{AB} = \overline{CD}$ is never correct. The equal sign only compares numbers, never geometric figures.

1 EXAMPLE Alternative Method

Students may count along the number line to find the lengths. This will help them better understand the Ruler Postulate.

2 EXAMPLE

Point out that *between* in the Segment Addition Postulate is an undefined term. Discuss with students what points are between collinear points.

---

1 EXAMPLE Comparing Segment Lengths

Find *AB* and *BC*.

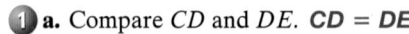

$AB = |-8 - (-5)| = |-3| = 3$
$BC = |-5 - (-2)| = |-3| = 3$
● $AB = BC$ or $\overline{AB} \cong \overline{BC}$

✔ **Check Understanding** **1 a.** Compare *CD* and *DE*. **CD = DE**
 b. Critical Thinking To find *AB* in Example 1, suppose you subtract -8 from -5. Do you get the same result? Why? **yes; $|-5 - (-8)| = |3| = 3$**

Examine the lengths of $\overline{AB}$ and $\overline{BC}$ in Example 1. Notice that $AB + BC = 6$. Notice that $AC = 6$. This suggests the following postulate.

🔑 **Key Concepts**

Postulate 1-6	Segment Addition Postulate

If three points *A*, *B*, and *C* are collinear and *B* is between *A* and *C*, then $AB + BC = AC$.

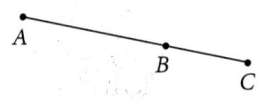

2 EXAMPLE Using the Segment Addition Postulate

Algebra If $DT = 60$, find the value of *x*. Then find *DS* and *ST*.

$$DS + ST = DT \quad \text{Segment Addition Postulate}$$
$$(2x - 8) + (3x - 12) = 60 \quad \text{Substitute.}$$
$$5x - 20 = 60 \quad \text{Simplify.}$$
$$5x = 80 \quad \text{Add 20 to each side.}$$
$$x = 16 \quad \text{Divide each side by 5.}$$
$$DS = 2x - 8 = 2(16) - 8 = 24 \quad \text{Substitute 16 for } x.$$
● $ST = 3x - 12 = 3(16) - 12 = 36$

✔ **Check Understanding** **2** $EG = 100$. Find the value of *x*. Then find *EF* and *FG*.
15; EF = 40, FG = 60

A **midpoint** of a segment is a point that divides a segment into two congruent segments. A midpoint, or any line, ray, or other segment through a midpoint, is said to *bisect* the segment.

$$\overline{AB} \cong \overline{BC}$$

👥 Reaching All Students

Below Level Have students use rulers and protractors to examine and demonstrate the postulates in this lesson.	**Advanced Learners** Have students investigate "one-to-one correspondence" as it applies to algebraic functions.	**English Learners** See note on page 31. **Visual Learners** See note on page 28.

3 EXAMPLE Finding Lengths

Algebra *C* is the midpoint of $\overline{AB}$. Find *AC*, *CB*, and *AB*.

$$\overset{2x+1}{\underset{A \qquad\qquad C}{\rule{4cm}{0.4pt}}} \overset{3x-4}{\underset{\qquad\qquad B}{}}$$

$AC = CB$	**Definition of midpoint**
$2x + 1 = 3x - 4$	**Substitute.**
$2x + 5 = 3x$	**Add 4 to each side.**
$5 = x$	**Subtract 2x from each side.**
$AC = 2x + 1 = 2(5) + 1 = 11$	**Substitute 5 for x.**
$CB = 3x - 4 = 3(5) - 4 = 11$	

● *AC* and *CB* are both 11, which is half of 22, the length of $\overline{AB}$.

✓ **Check Understanding** **3** *Z* is the midpoint of $\overline{XY}$, and *XY* = 27. Find *XZ*. **13.5**

OBJECTIVE
2 Finding Angle Measures

Reading Math
You may also refer to the angle suggested by the two segments $\overline{BT}$ and $\overline{BQ}$ as ∠*TBQ*.

An **angle** (∠) is formed by two rays with the same endpoint. The rays are the *sides* of the angle. The endpoint is the *vertex* of the angle. The sides of the angle shown here are $\overrightarrow{BT}$ and $\overrightarrow{BQ}$. The vertex is *B*. You could name this angle ∠*B*, ∠*TBQ*, ∠*QBT*, or ∠1.

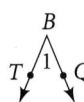

4 EXAMPLE Naming Angles

Name ∠1 in two other ways.

● ∠*AEC* and ∠*CEA* are other names for ∠1.

✓ **Check Understanding** **4 a.** Name ∠*CED* two other ways. **∠2, ∠*DEC***
b. Critical Thinking Would it be correct to name any of the angles ∠*E*? Explain.
No; 3 ∠ have *E* for a vertex, so you need more info. in the name to distinguish them from one another.

One way to measure an angle is in degrees. To indicate the size or degree measure of an angle, write a lowercase *m* in front of the angle symbol. The degree measure of angle *A* is 80. You show this by writing *m*∠*A* = 80.

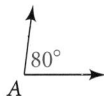

27

---

1 Find which two of the segments $\overline{XY}$, $\overline{ZY}$, and $\overline{ZW}$ are congruent.

XY = *ZW* and *XZ* = *YW*

2 If *AB* = 25, find the value of *x*. Then find *AN* and *NB*.

$$\overset{2x-6}{\underset{A \qquad N}{\rule{3cm}{0.4pt}}} \overset{x+7}{\underset{\qquad B}{}}$$

x = 8; *AN* = 10, *NB* = 15

3 *M* is the midpoint of $\overline{RT}$. Find *RM*, *MT*, and *RT*.

$$\overset{5x+9}{\underset{R \qquad M}{\rule{3cm}{0.4pt}}} \overset{8x-36}{\underset{\qquad T}{}}$$

RM = 84, *MT* = 84,
RT = 168

OBJECTIVE
2 Teaching Notes

4 EXAMPLE Error Prevention

Discuss as a class why it is inappropriate to name ∠1 as ∠*E*. Ask: *How could this cause confusion?* There are three angles whose vertex is *E*. Explain also that the measure of an angle does not need a degree symbol.

Math Tip
Ask: *How is the Protractor Postulate like the Ruler Postulate?* Both pair numbers in a one-to-one correspondence with geometric objects and use absolute value to determine measurements.

Auditory Learners
Have students take turns with a partner explaining the Protractor Postulate in their own words.

Connection to Algebra

Review the meaning of the inequality symbol.

Visual Learners

Draw the figures for the Angle Addition Postulate on the board. Have students place other points in the interior of ∠AOC to reinforce the concept of interior.

Additional Examples

④ Name the angle below in four ways.

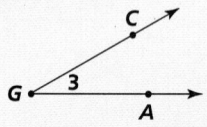

∠3, ∠G, ∠AGC, ∠CGA

⑤ Find the measure of each angle. Classify each as *acute, right, obtuse,* or *straight.*

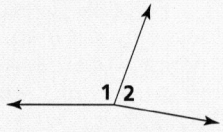

$m\angle 1 = 110$, obtuse;
$m\angle 2 = 80$, acute

⑥ Suppose that $m\angle 1 = 42$ and $m\angle ABC = 88$. Find $m\angle 2$.

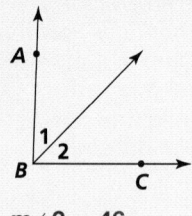

$m\angle 2 = 46$

Closure

Explain how two of the postulates in this lesson can help you measure segments and angles. Sample: Segment Add. Post. states that the sum of all the parts of a segment equals the whole segment. Angle Add. Post. states that an angle can be divided into two angles, the sum of whose measures equals the measure of the whole angle.

Key Concepts

Postulate 1-7	Protractor Postulate

Let $\overrightarrow{OA}$ and $\overrightarrow{OB}$ be opposite rays in a plane. $\overrightarrow{OA}$, $\overrightarrow{OB}$, and all the rays with endpoint O that can be drawn on one side of $\overleftrightarrow{AB}$ can be paired with the real numbers from 0 to 180 so that

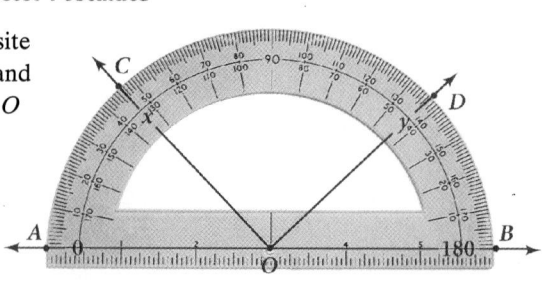

a. $\overrightarrow{OA}$ is paired with 0 and $\overrightarrow{OB}$ is paired with 180.

b. If $\overrightarrow{OC}$ is paired with x and $\overrightarrow{OD}$ is paired with y, then $m\angle COD = |x - y|$.

Reading Math

This symbol indicates a right angle.

You can classify angles according to their measures.

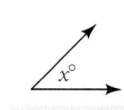

acute angle
$0 < x < 90$

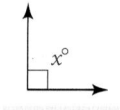

right angle
$x = 90$

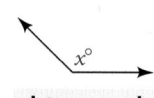

obtuse angle
$90 < x < 180$

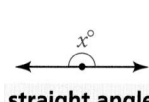

straight angle
$x = 180$

⑤ **EXAMPLE** Measuring and Classifying Angles

Find the measure of each angle. Classify each as *acute, right, obtuse,* or *straight.*

a.

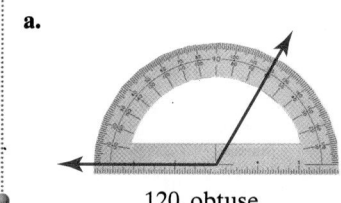

120, obtuse

b.

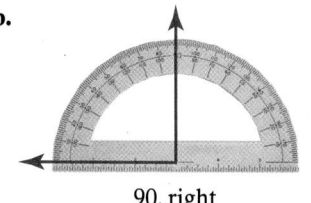

90, right

✓ **Check Understanding**

⑤ Find the measure of each angle. Classify each as *acute, right, obtuse,* or *straight.*

a. 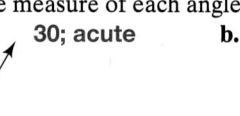 30; acute

b. 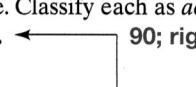 90; right

c. 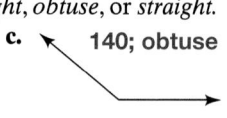 140; obtuse

The Angle Addition Postulate is similar to the Segment Addition Postulate.

Key Concepts

Postulate 1-8	Angle Addition Postulate

If point B is in the interior of $\angle AOC$, then $m\angle AOB + m\angle BOC = m\angle AOC$.

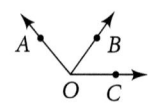

If $\angle AOC$ is a straight angle, then $m\angle AOB + m\angle BOC = 180$.

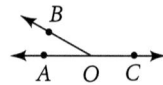

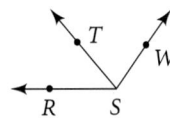 **EXAMPLE** Using the Angle Addition Postulate

What is $m\angle TSW$ if $m\angle RST = 50$ and $m\angle RSW = 125$?

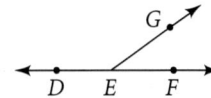

$$m\angle RST + m\angle TSW = m\angle RSW \qquad \text{Angle Addition Postulate}$$
$$50 + m\angle TSW = 125 \qquad \text{Substitute.}$$
$$m\angle TSW = 75 \qquad \text{Subtract 50 from each side.}$$

✔ **Check Understanding** ⑥ If $m\angle DEG = 145$, find $m\angle GEF$. **35**

Angles with the same measure are **congruent angles.** In other words, if $m\angle 1 = m\angle 2$, then $\angle 1 \cong \angle 2$. You can use these statements interchangeably.

Angles can be marked alike to show that they are congruent, as in this photograph of the Air Force Thunderbirds precision flying team.

EXERCISES

For more practice, see *Extra Practice.*

Practice and Problem Solving

 **Practice by Example**

Find the length of each segment. Tell whether the segments are congruent.

1. $\overline{AC}$ and $\overline{BD}$ **9, 9; yes**
2. $\overline{BD}$ and $\overline{CE}$ **9, 6; no**
3. $\overline{AD}$ and $\overline{BE}$ **11, 13; no**
4. $\overline{BC}$ and $\overline{CE}$ **7, 6; no**

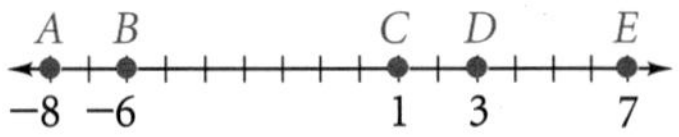

A number line showing points A B at -8, -6 and C D at 1, 3 and E at 7.

Example 1
(page 26)

On a number line, the coordinates of X, Y, Z, and W are -7, -3, 1, and 5, respectively. Compare the lengths of the two segments.

5. $\overline{XY}$ and $\overline{ZW}$
   $XY = ZW$
6. $\overline{ZX}$ and $\overline{WY}$
   $ZX = WY$
7. $\overline{YZ}$ and $\overline{XW}$
   $YZ < XW$

Example 2
(page 26)

Use the figure at the right for Exercises 8–11.

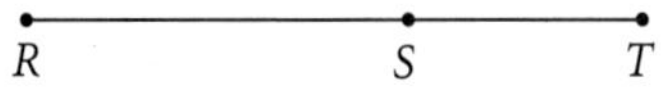

8. If $RS = 15$ and $ST = 9$, then $RT = \blacksquare$. **24**

9. If $ST = 15$ and $RT = 40$, then $RS = \blacksquare$. **25**

A segment with points R, S, T.

$\boxed{x^2}$ 10. a. **Algebra** If $RS = 3x + 1$, $ST = 2x - 2$, and $RT = 64$, find the value of x.
   b. Find RS and ST.   **10a. 13**   **10b. $RS = 40$, $ST = 24$**

$\boxed{x^2}$ 11. a. **Algebra** If $RS = 8y + 4$, $ST = 4y + 8$, and $RT = 15y - 9$, find the value of y. **7**
   b. Find RS, ST, and RT.   **$RS = 60$, $ST = 36$, $RT = 96$**

Assignment Guide

 **Objective**
Ⓐ Ⓑ **Core** 1–15, 29–46, 49, 71, 72
Ⓒ **Extension** 79

 **Objective**
Ⓐ Ⓑ **Core** 16–28, 47, 48, 50–70, 73–78
Ⓒ **Extension** 80, 81

Standardized Test Prep 82–86

Mixed Review 87–97

Visual Learners
Exercises 5–7 Have students draw a number line to represent each problem.

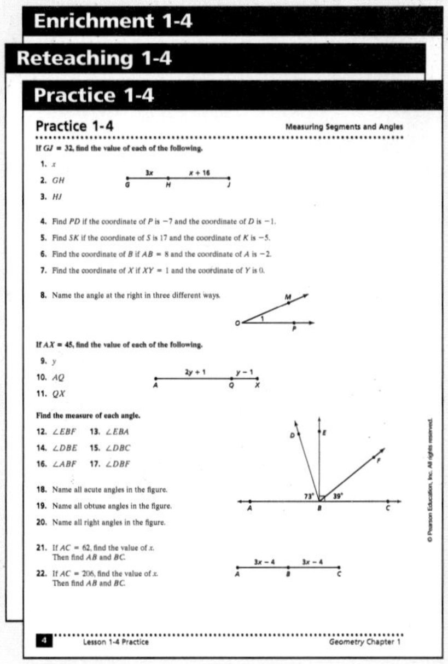

Enrichment 1-4

Reteaching 1-4

Practice 1-4

Practice 1-4 — Measuring Segments and Angles

If $GI = 32$, find the value of each of the following.
1. x
2. GH
3. HI

4. Find PD if the coordinate of P is -7 and the coordinate of D is -1.
5. Find SK if the coordinate of S is 17 and the coordinate of K is -5.
6. Find the coordinate of B if $AB = 8$ and A is -2.
7. Find the coordinate of X if $XY = 1$ and the coordinate of Y is 0.

8. Name the angle at the right in three different ways.

If $AX = 45$, find the value of each of the following.
9. y
10. AQ
11. QX

Find the measure of each angle.
12. $\angle EBF$ 13. $\angle EBA$
14. $\angle DBE$ 15. $\angle DBC$
16. $\angle ABF$ 17. $\angle DBF$

18. Name all acute angles in the figure.
19. Name all obtuse angles in the figure.
20. Name all right angles in the figure.

21. If $AC = 62$, find the value of x. Then find AB and BC.
22. If $AC = 20t$, find the value of x. Then find AB and BC.

Lesson 1-4 Practice   Geometry Chapter 1

29

Error Prevention

Exercises 13–15 Students may think they are finished after they solve for *x*. Remind them to read the directions carefully.

Exercises 20–23 Check that students label the vertex with the middle letter of each angle's name.

Tactile Learners

Exercises 24–26 Using a corner of paper to model a 90° angle makes classifying acute and obtuse angles visually apparent. For students who have little experience with protractors, demonstrate again how to line up an angle on a protractor to measure it.

Exercise 28 Because the measure of only one angle is given, students may think that the Angle Addition Postulate cannot be used here. Ask: *If ∠JFE is a straight angle, what is its degree measure?* **180**

Exercises 30–32 Each exercise asks for a coordinate. Students may think they are asked to name a point on the diagram by a letter, instead of giving a number.

Example 3 x^2 **12. Algebra** *A* is the midpoint of $\overline{XY}$.
(page 27)
  a Find *XA*. **9**
  b Find *AY* and *XY*. **9; 18**

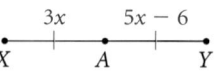

x^2 **Algebra In Exercises 13–15, use the figure and find *PT*.**

13. $PT = 5x + 3$ and $TQ = 7x - 9$ **33**

14. $PT = 4x - 6$ and $TQ = 3x + 4$ **34**

15. $PT = 7x - 24$ and $TQ = 6x - 2$ **130**

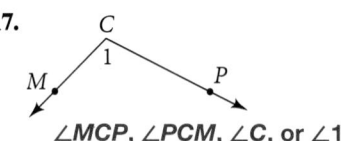

Example 4 **Name each angle in three ways.**
(page 27)

16. 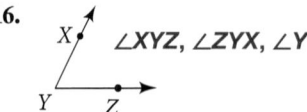 ∠XYZ, ∠ZYX, ∠Y

17.

∠MCP, ∠PCM, ∠C, or ∠1

Use the figure at the right. Name the indicated angle in two different ways.

18. ∠1 **∠ABC, ∠CBA**   **19.** ∠2
  ∠CBD, ∠DBC

Example 5 **Draw and label a figure to fit each description.**
(page 28)   **20–23. See margin.**

20. an obtuse angle, ∠*RST*   **21.** an acute acute, ∠*BCD*

22. a straight angle, ∠*EFG*   **23.** a right angle, ∠*GHI*

Measure and classify each angle.

24. 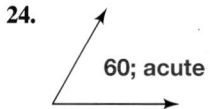 60; acute   **25.**  90; right   **26.**  135; obtuse

Example 6 **27.** Find $m\angle CBD$ if $m\angle ABC = 45$ **28.** Find $m\angle GFJ$ if $m\angle EFG = 110$. **70**
(page 29)   and $m\angle ABD = 79$. **34**

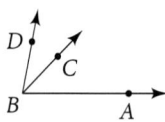

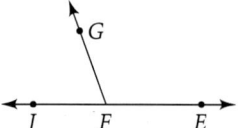

B **Apply Your Skills**   **Use the figure at the right for Exercises 29–32.**

29. Find the midpoint of $\overline{AB}$. **Q**

30. What is the coordinate of the midpoint of $\overline{QB}$? **6**

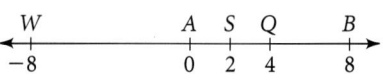

31. What is the coordinate of the midpoint of $\overline{WA}$? **−4**

32. What is the coordinate of the midpoint of the segment formed by the two points you found in Exercises 30 and 31? **1**

Suppose the coordinate of *A* is 0 and *AR* = 5 and *AT* = 7 in the figure above. What are the possible coordinates of the midpoint of the given segment?

33. $\overline{AR}$ **−2.5, 2.5**   **34.** $\overline{AT}$ **−3.5, 3.5**   **35.** $\overline{RT}$ **−6, −1, 1, 6**

30   Chapter 1   Tools of Geometry

pages 29–33   **Exercises**

20–23. Drawings may vary.

20.

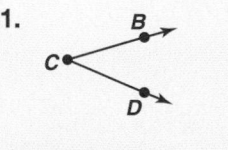

21.

22.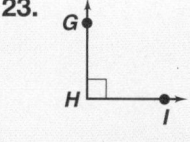

23.

36. Mileage Highways and the mile markers along their sides suggest a number line. You can find the distance between mile markers in the same way that you find distance on a number line.

    a. Michael sees mile marker 237 when he enters the highway and mile marker 159 when he exits. How far did he travel? **78 mi**

    b. Open-Ended Give another real example of finding distance using a number line. **Answers may vary. Sample: measuring with a ruler**

Visualization **Without using your ruler, sketch a segment with the given length. Then use your ruler to see how well you did.** **37–41. Check students' work.**

37. 3 cm   **38.** 3 in.   **39.** 6 in.   **40.** 10 cm   **41.** 65 mm

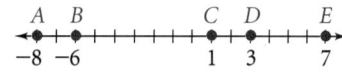

Exercises 42–46

In Exercises 42–45, describe the statement as *true* or *false*. Explain. **42–45. See margin.**

42. $\overline{AB} \cong \overline{CD}$ **43.** $BD < CD$

44. $AC + BD = AD$ **45.** $AC + CD = AD$

46. Suppose $EG = 5$. Find the possible coordinate(s) of point G.
    2, 12

In the diagram, $m\angle ACB = 65$. Find each of the following.

47. $m\angle BCD$ **115**   **48.** $m\angle ECD$ **65**

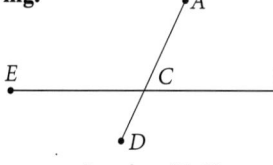

49. Coordinate Geometry $A(3, 0)$ is an endpoint of $\overline{AB}$. If $AB = 12$, give four possible coordinates for point B. **See margin.**

Exercises 47–48

Visualization **Without using your protractor, sketch an angle with the given measure. Then use your protractor to see how well you did.** **50–54. Check students' work.**

50. 45   **51.** 60   **52.** 90   **53.** 120   **54.** 135

55. Skiing Use a protractor on the photograph to measure the angle formed by the two skis. **about 42°**

Open-Ended **Name two times of the morning when the hands of a clock form each type of angle.**
56–58. Answers may vary. Samples are given.
56. right   **57.** obtuse   **58.** straight
     3:00, 9:00   5:00, 7:00   6:00, 12:32

Estimation **Estimate the measure of the angle formed by the hands of a clock at each time.**

59. 6:00 **180**   **60.** 7:00 **150**   **61.** 11:00 **30**

62. 4:40 **100**   **63.** 5:20 **40**   **64.** 10:40 **80**

Use this figure for Exercises 65–69.

65. If $m\angle MQV = 90$ and $m\angle VQP = 35$, what is $m\angle MQP$? **125**

66. If $m\angle MVQ = 55$, what is $m\angle QVP$? **125**

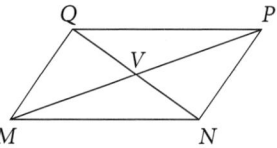

Judging by appearance in the diagram above, name each of the following.
67–69. Answers may vary. Samples are given.
67. two acute angles   **68.** two obtuse angles   **69.** two right angles
    $\angle QVM$ and $\angle VPN$ $\angle MNP$ and $\angle MVN$ $\angle MQV$ and $\angle PNQ$

Need Help?

For Exercise 43 you are to decide whether the distance *BD is less than* the distance *CD*.

Diversity

Exercise 36 Some students may be unfamiliar with mile markers. Have other students explain where they have seen them and how they are used.

Exercise 44 Solve this exercise together as a class, as it highlights that the Segment Addition Postulate does not apply to overlapping segments.

Visual Learners

Exercises 37–41, 50–54 These exercises provide excellent practice of visual estimation skills.

Exercises 47, 48 These exercises anticipate the Vertical Angles Theorem, which is proved in Lesson 2-5.

Connection to Coordinate Geometry

Exercise 49 Have students draw a coordinate grid or use graph paper to help them solve the exercise.

English Learners

Exercise 80 A golf *tee* and the drink *tea* are homonyms because they sound the same but have different spellings.

---

42. true; *AB* = 2, *CD* = 2

43. false; *BD* = 9, *CD* = 2

44. false; *AC* = 9, *BD* = 9, *AD* = 11, and 9 + 9 ≠ 11

45. true; *AC* = 9, *CD* = 2, *AD* = 11, and 9 + 2 = 11

49. Answers may vary. Sample: (15, 0), (−9, 0), (3, 12), (3, −12)

Lesson Quiz 1-4

Use the figure below for Exercises 1–3.

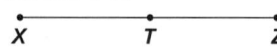

X   T   Z

1. If $XT = 12$ and $XZ = 21$, then $TZ = \blacksquare$. **9**

2. If $XZ = 3x$, $XT = x + 3$, and $TZ = 13$, find XZ. **24**

3. Suppose that T is the midpoint of $\overline{XZ}$. If $XT = 2x + 11$ and $XZ = 5x + 8$, find the value of x. **14**

Use the figure below for Exercises 4–6.

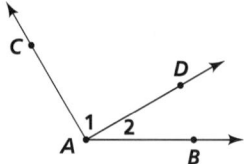

4. Name $\angle 2$ two different ways. **∠DAB, ∠BAD**

5. Measure and classify $\angle 1$, $\angle 2$, and $\angle BAC$. **90, right; 30, acute; 120, obtuse**

6. Which postulate relates the measures of $\angle 1$, $\angle 2$, and $\angle BAC$? **Angle Addition Postulate**

Alternative Assessment

Have students draw diagrams to illustrate the Segment Addition Postulate and the Angle Addition Postulate. Then have them write examples that use each postulate to find a missing measurement when two of the three measurements are known.

pages 29–33   Exercises

73. a. Answers may vary. Sample: The two rays come together at a sharp point.

    b. Answers may vary. Sample: Molly had an *acute* pain in her knee.

32

70c. Answers may vary. Sample: The sum of the $\angle$ measures should be 180.

71. $y = 15$; $AC = 24$, $DC = 12$

72. $ED = 10$, $DB = 10$, $EB = 20$

Real-World 🌐 Connection

Japanese flower arranging makes precise use of angles to create a mood.

Challenge

80. a–c. Check students' work.

---

x^2 **70. a. Algebra** Solve for x if $m\angle RQS = 2x + 4$ and $m\angle TQS = 6x + 20$. **19.5**
    b. What is $m\angle RQS$? $m\angle TQS$? **43; 137**
    c. Show how you can check your answer. **See left.**

x^2 **Algebra Use the diagram at the right for Exercises 71 and 72.**

71. If $AD = 12$ and $AC = 4y - 36$, find the value of y. Then find AC and DC.

72. If $ED = x + 4$ and $DB = 3x - 8$, find ED, DB, and EB.

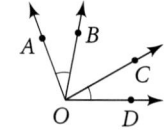

✏️ 73. **Writing** The word *acute* can mean "sharp" in conversational English.
    a. Explain why this meaning describes an acute angle.
    b. Use "acute" in a sentence. **a–b. See margin.**

74. **Flower Arranging** In Japanese flower arranging, you match a stem that is vertical with 0. You match other stems with numbers from 0 to 90, in both directions from the vertical. What numbers would the flowers shown be paired with on a standard protractor?
45, 75, and 165, or 135, 105, and 15

x^2 **Algebra Use the diagram, below right, for Exercises 75–78. Solve for x. Find the angle measures to check your work. 75–78. See margin.**

75. $m\angle AOC = 7x - 2$, $m\angle AOB = 2x + 8$, $m\angle BOC = 3x + 14$

76. $m\angle AOB = 4x - 2$, $m\angle BOC = 5x + 10$, $m\angle COD = 2x + 14$

77. $m\angle AOB = 28$, $m\angle BOC = 3x - 2$, $m\angle AOD = 6x$

78. $m\angle AOB = 4x + 3$, $m\angle BOC = 7x$, $m\angle AOD = 16x - 1$

79. C is the midpoint of $\overline{AB}$, D is the midpoint of $\overline{AC}$, E is the midpoint of $\overline{AD}$, F is the midpoint of $\overline{ED}$, G is the midpoint of $\overline{EF}$, and H is the midpoint of $\overline{DB}$. If $DC = 16$, find GH. **30**

🌐 80. **Golf** Copy the diagram.
    a. Estimate the angle in degrees from the tee hole to the hole marked by the flag. Then estimate the distance in centimeters or millimeters from the tee to the hole.
    b. Use a protractor and ruler to plot each estimate. This is stroke 1. Add a penalty stroke if you land in the water.
    c. Continue until you are at most 5mm from the hole marked by the flag. What is your score?

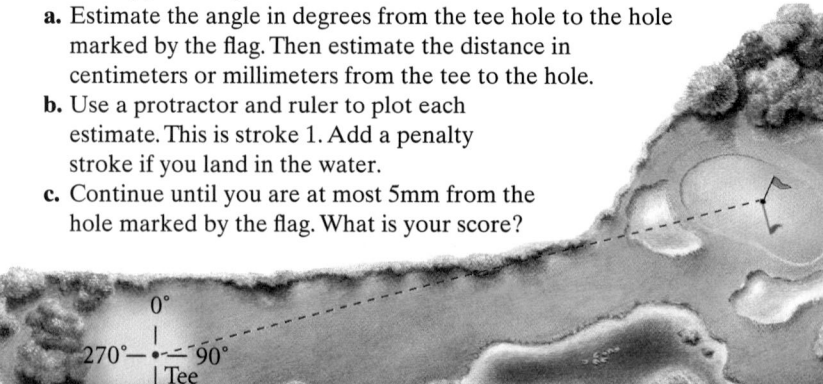

75. 12; $m\angle AOC = 82$, $m\angle AOB = 32$, $m\angle BOC = 50$

76. 8; $m\angle AOB = 30$, $m\angle BOC = 50$, $m\angle COD = 30$

77. 18; $m\angle AOB = 28$, $m\angle BOC = 52$, $m\angle AOD = 108$

78. 7; $m\angle AOB = 31$, $m\angle BOC = 49$, $m\angle AOD = 111$

81. Technology Leon constructed an angle. Then he constructed a ray from the vertex of the angle to a point in the interior of the angle. He measured all the angles formed. Then he moved the interior ray. What postulate do the two pictures support? **Angle Add. Post.**

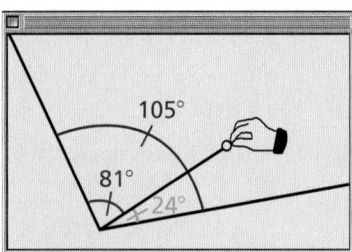 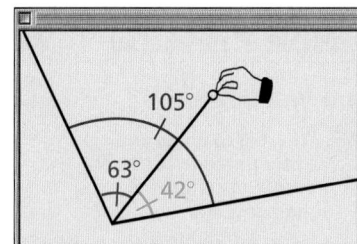

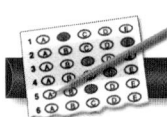

Standardized Test Prep

Multiple Choice

82. If $KC = 31$, what is KN? **C**
    A. 43   **B.** 62
    C. 74   **D.** 82

$$2x + 10 \qquad 4x + 1$$
$$K \qquad\qquad C \qquad\qquad N$$
Exercises 82–84

83. If $KN = 29$, what is CN? **F**
    F. 13   **G.** 14.5   **H.** 15.5   **I.** 16

84. If C is the midpoint of $\overline{KN}$, what is KC? **D**
    A. 4.5   **B.** 9   **C.** 18   **D.** 19

85. When 15 is subtracted from the measure of an angle, the result is the measure of a right angle. What is the measure of the original angle? **H**
    F. 75   **G.** 85   **H.** 105   **I.** 115

Short Response

86. You are given that $m\angle ABD + m\angle DBC = m\angle ABC$.
    a. Draw a diagram to show the above. **a–b. See margin.**
    b. If $m\angle ABD = 12$ and $\angle ABC$ is obtuse, what are the least and greatest whole number measures possible for $\angle DBC$? Explain.

Mixed Review

Lesson 1-3

Complete each statement with *always*, *sometimes*, or *never* to make a true statement.

87. Skew lines are __?__ coplanar. **never**   **88.** Skew lines __?__ intersect. **never**

89. Opposite rays __?__ form a line. **always** **90.** Parallel planes __?__ intersect. **never**

Lesson 1-2

91. Three points are __?__ coplanar. **always**

92. Two points are __?__ collinear. **always**

93. The intersection of two planes is __?__ a line. **always**

94. Intersecting lines are __?__ parallel. **never**

Lesson 1-1

Find the next two terms in each sequence.

95. $5, 10, 15, 20, \ldots$ **96.** $5, 25, 125, 625, \ldots$ **97.** $14, 18, 22, 26, \ldots$
    25, 30   **3125; 15,625**   **30, 34**

📁 **Resources**
For additional practice with a variety of test item formats:
• Standardized Test Prep, p. 65
• Test-Taking Strategies, p. 60
• Test-Taking Strategies with Transparencies

Exercise 85 Work backward from the measure of a right angle to find the measure of the original angle.

Exercise 86 Students should remember that the measure of an obtuse angle is greater than 90, less than 180, and not 90. For example, the least whole-number degree measure of an obtuse angle is 91.

86. [2] **a.**

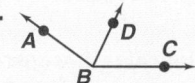

    b. An obtuse ∠ measures between 90 and 180 degrees; the least and greatest whole number values are 91 and 179 degrees. Part of ∠ABC is 12°. So the least and greatest ∠ measures for ∠DBC are 79 and 167.

[1] one part correct

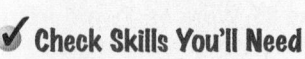
Lesson Preview

✔ Check Skills You'll Need 📖

Finding Segment Lengths
Lesson 1-3: Example 1
Exercises 1–6
Extra Practice, p. 690

Finding Angle Measures
Lesson 1-4: Examples 4 and 5
Exercises 16–26
Extra Practice, p. 690

Lesson Resources

📁 Teaching Resources
Practice, Reteaching, Enrichment

🎓 Reaching All Students
Practice Workbook 1-5
Spanish Practice Workbook 1-5
Informal Geometry Planning
    Guide 1-5

⏱ Presentation Assistant Plus!
Transparencies
• Check Skills You'll Need 1-5
• Additional Examples 1-5
• Student Edition Answers 1-5
• Lesson Quiz 1-5
PH Presentation Pro CD 1-5

PRENTICE HALL
ASSESSMENT *SYSTEM*

Computer Test Generator CD

💿 Technology
Resource Pro® CD-ROM
Computer Test Generator CD
Prentice Hall Presentation Pro CD

🖥 www.PHSchool.com
Student Site
• Teacher Web Code: afk-5500
• Self-grading Lesson Quiz
Teacher Center
• Lesson Planner
• Resources

Plus 🅘**TEXT**

Basic Constructions

North Carolina Objectives 〜

2.02 · Apply properties, definitions, and theorems of angles and lines to solve problems and write proofs.

Lesson Preview

What You'll Learn

OBJECTIVE **1**
To use a compass and a straightedge to construct congruent segments and congruent angles

OBJECTIVE **2**
To use a compass and a sraightedge to bisect segments and angles

. . . And Why

To construct the bisector of an angle to illustrate angles of incidence and reflection, as in Exercise 18

✔ Check Skills You'll Need   (For help, go to Lessons 1-3 and 1-4.)

In Exercises 1–6, sketch each figure. 1–6. See back of book.
1. $\overline{CD}$ 2. $\overrightarrow{GH}$ 3. $\overleftrightarrow{AB}$
4. line m 5. acute $\angle ABC$ 6. $\overline{XY} \parallel \overline{ST}$

7. $DE = 20$. Point C is the midpoint of $\overline{DE}$. Find CE. **10**

8. Use a protractor to draw a 60° angle. **8–9. See back of book.**

9. Use a protractor to draw a 120° angle.

New Vocabulary   • construction • straightedge • compass
• perpendicular lines • perpendicular bisector
• angle bisector

  Interactive lesson includes instant self-check, tutorials, and activities.

OBJECTIVE
1   **Constructing Segments and Angles**

Need Help?

You may use a ruler as a straightedge, but you may not use its markings.

In a **construction** you use a straightedge and a compass to draw a geometric figure. A **straightedge** is a ruler with no markings on it. A **compass** is a geometric tool used to draw circles and parts of circles called arcs.

Four basic constructions involve constructing congruent segments, congruent angles, and bisectors of segments and angles.

1 **EXAMPLE**   **Constructing Congruent Segments**

Construct a segment congruent to a given segment.

Given: $\overline{AB}$

Construct: $\overline{CD}$ so that $\overline{CD} \cong \overline{AB}$

Step 1
Draw a ray with endpoint C.

Step 2
Open the compass to the length of $\overline{AB}$.

Step 3
With the same compass setting, put the compass point on point C. Draw an arc that intersects the ray. Label the point of intersection D.

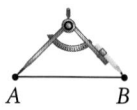

● $\overline{CD} \cong \overline{AB}$

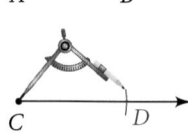

✔ Check Understanding ①
Use a straightedge to draw $\overline{XY}$. Then construct $\overline{RS}$ so that $RS = 2XY$. **See margin, p. 35.**

 Ongoing Assessment and Intervention

Before the Lesson	**During the Lesson**	**After the Lesson**
Diagnose prerequisite skills using:	**Monitor progress using:**	**Assess knowledge using:**
• Check Skills You'll Need	• Check Understanding	• Lesson Quiz
	• Additional Examples	• Computer Test Generator CD
	• Standardized Test Prep	

2 EXAMPLE · Constructing Congruent Angles

Construct an angle congruent to a given angle.

Given: ∠A
Construct: ∠S so that ∠S ≅ ∠A

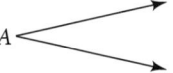

? Need Help?

In Step 2, make your arc big enough to swing the compass easily, but small enough to intersect both sides.

Step 1
Draw a ray with endpoint S.

Step 2
With the compass point on point A, draw an arc that intersects the sides of ∠A. Label the points of intersection B and C.

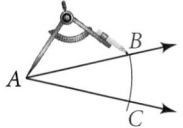

Step 3
With the same compass setting, put the compass point on point S. Draw an arc and label its point of intersection with the ray as R.

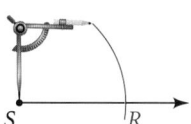

Step 4
Open the compass to the length BC. Keeping the same compass setting, put the compass point on R. Draw an arc to locate point T.

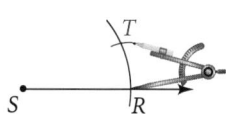

Step 5
Draw $\overrightarrow{ST}$.

● ∠S ≅ ∠A

✓ **Check Understanding** ② Construct ∠F with m∠F = 2m∠B.

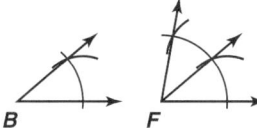 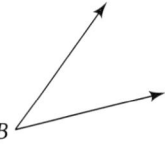

Real-World 🌐 Connection

Perpendicular hands signal "Time out."

Perpendicular lines are two lines that intersect to form right angles. The symbol ⊥ means "is perpendicular to." In the diagram at the right, $\overleftrightarrow{AB} \perp \overleftrightarrow{CD}$ and $\overleftrightarrow{CD} \perp \overleftrightarrow{AB}$.

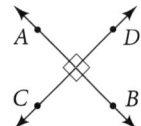

A **perpendicular bisector** of a segment is a line, segment, or ray that is perpendicular to the segment at its midpoint, thereby bisecting the segment into two congruent segments.

As you will learn in Chapter 5, there is just one line that is the perpendicular bisector of a segment in a given plane. Here is a way to construct the perpendicular bisector.

👥 **Reaching All Students**

Below Level Demonstrate the construction steps in Examples 1, 2, 3, and 5 by using a large demonstration compass. Then ask student volunteers to demonstrate the constructions.	**Advanced Learners** Have students investigate ancient and modern attempts to trisect an angle.	**Inclusion** See note on page 35. **Visual Learners** See note on page 38.

---

2. Teach

Math Background

Construction methods are justified by postulates such as Euclid's Fourth Postulate, that a circle can be drawn with any center and any positive radius, and by, for example, triangle congruency theorems. Compass-and-straightedge constructions provide a hands-on introduction to these postulates and theorems.

OBJECTIVE
▼ Teaching Notes

Inclusion

If students have problems using a compass and straightedge, have them work in pairs to share the construction steps.

① EXAMPLE · Error Prevention

Have students make sure that their compasses are not so loose that they slip during use and make an incorrect arc. Point out that some compasses can be tightened.

📐 Additional Examples

① Construct $\overline{TW}$ congruent to $\overline{KM}$.

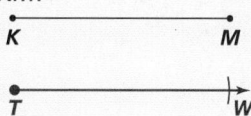

② Construct ∠Y so that ∠Y ≅ ∠G.

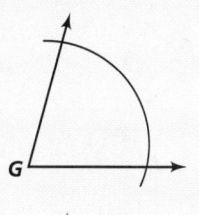
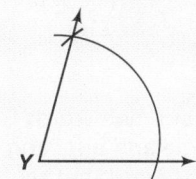

Teaching Tip
Point out that the symbol for *perpendicular* resembles perpendicular lines. Ask: *What other symbol resembles what it represents?* Sample: the symbol for *parallel*

3 EXAMPLE **Connection to Language Arts**

The word *bisector* contains the prefix *bi-*, which means *two*.

4 EXAMPLE

Point out that segments and lines can be angle bisectors.

Additional Examples

3 Open the compass less than $\frac{1}{2}AB$ in step 1 of Example 3. Explain why the construction is not possible. **Sample: When the opening is less than $\frac{1}{2}AB$, the arcs drawn in steps 1 and 2 do not intersect. So, the perpendicular bisector cannot be drawn.**

4 $\overrightarrow{WR}$ bisects $\angle AWB$. $m\angle AWR = x$ and $m\angle BWR = 4x - 48$. Find $m\angle AWB$. **32**

5 Construct $\overrightarrow{MX}$, the bisector of $\angle M$.

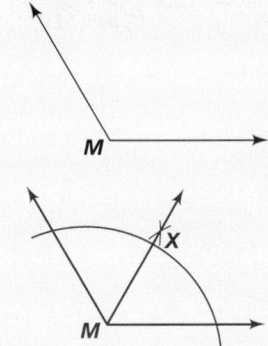

Closure

Write steps in your own words for bisecting an angle and bisecting a segment. Use drawings that show the arcs in each step. **Check students' work.**

Real-World 🌐 Connection

Careers Architects use construction tools to work with their designs.

---

3 EXAMPLE **Constructing the Perpendicular Bisector**

Construct the perpendicular bisector of a segment.

Given: $\overline{AB}$
Construct: $\overleftrightarrow{XY}$ so that $\overleftrightarrow{XY} \perp \overline{AB}$ at the midpoint M of $\overline{AB}$.

Step 1
Put the compass point on point A and draw a long arc as shown. Be sure the opening is greater than $\frac{1}{2}AB$.

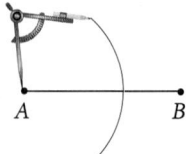

Step 2
With the same compass setting, put the compass point on point B and draw another long arc. Label the points where the two arcs intersect as X and Y.

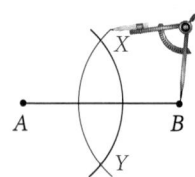

Step 3
Draw $\overleftrightarrow{XY}$. The point of intersection of $\overline{AB}$ and $\overleftrightarrow{XY}$ is M, the midpoint of $\overline{AB}$.

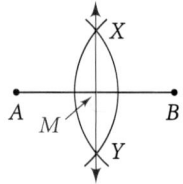

$\overleftrightarrow{XY} \perp \overline{AB}$ at the midpoint of $\overline{AB}$, so $\overleftrightarrow{XY}$ is the perpendicular bisector of $\overline{AB}$.

✓**Check Understanding** **3** Draw $\overline{ST}$. Construct its perpendicular bisector.

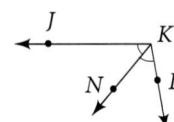

An **angle bisector** is a ray that divides an angle into two congruent coplanar angles. Its endpoint is at the angle vertex. Within the ray, a segment with the same endpoint is also an angle bisector. You may say that the ray or segment *bisects* the angle.

4 EXAMPLE **Finding Angle Measures**

Algebra $\overrightarrow{KN}$ bisects $\angle JKL$ so that $m\angle JKN = 5x - 25$ and $m\angle NKL = 3x + 5$. Solve for x and find $m\angle JKN$.

$m\angle JKN = m\angle NKL$	Definition of angle bisector
$5x - 25 = 3x + 5$	Substitute.
$5x = 3x + 30$	Add 25 to each side.
$2x = 30$	Subtract $3x$ from each side.
$x = 15$	Divide each side by 2.
$m\angle JKN = 5x - 25 = 5(15) - 25 = 50$	Substitute 15 for x.

$m\angle JKN = 50$

✓**Check Understanding** **4** Find $m\angle NKL$ and $m\angle JKL$. **50; 100**

36 Chapter 1 Tools of Geometry

pages 34–37 **Check Understanding**

1.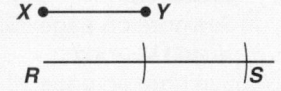

5. a.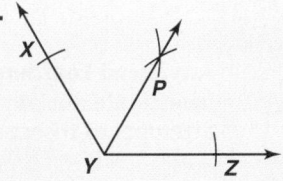

pages 37–40 **Exercises**

1.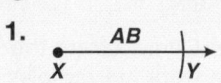

2.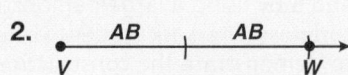

5 EXAMPLE **Constructing the Angle Bisector**

Construct the bisector of an angle.

Given: ∠A

Construct: $\overrightarrow{AX}$, the bisector of ∠A

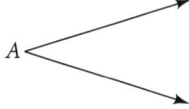

Step 1

Put the compass point on vertex A. Draw an arc that intersects the sides of ∠A. Label the points of intersection B and C.

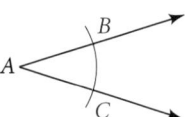

Step 2

Put the compass point on point C and draw an arc. With the same compass setting, draw an arc using point B. Be sure the arcs intersect. Label the point where the two arcs intersect as X.

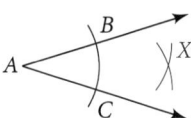

Step 3

Draw $\overrightarrow{AX}$.

$\overrightarrow{AX}$ is the bisector of ∠CAB.

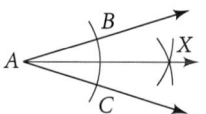

✓ **Check Understanding** **5 a.** Draw obtuse ∠XYZ. Then construct its bisector $\overrightarrow{YP}$. **See margin, p. 36.**
b. Explain how you can use your protractor to check your construction.
Measure ∠XYP and ∠PYZ to see that they are ≅.

EXERCISES

For more practice, see *Extra Practice*.

Practice and Problem Solving

Ⓐ Practice by Example

Example 1
(page 34)

In Exercises 1–8, draw a diagram similar to the given one. Then do the construction. Check your work with a ruler or a protractor. **1–8. See margin, pp. 36–37.**

1. Construct $\overline{XY}$ congruent to $\overline{AB}$.

A ———————————— B

2. Construct $\overline{VW}$ so that $VW = 2AB$.

3. Construct $\overline{DE}$ so that $DE = TR + PS$.

4. Construct $\overline{QJ}$ so that $QJ = TR - PS$.

T ——————— R P ——— S

Example 2
(page 35)

5. Construct ∠D so that ∠D ≅ ∠C.

6. Construct ∠F so that $m∠F = 2m∠C$.

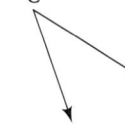

Example 3
(page 36)

7. Construct the perpendicular bisector of $\overline{AB}$.

8. Construct the perpendicular bisector of $\overline{TR}$.

Example 4
(page 36)

x^2 **9. Algebra** $\overrightarrow{GH}$ bisects ∠FGI.
a. Solve for x and find $m∠FGH$. **11; 30**
b. Find $m∠HGI$. **30**
c. Find $m∠FGI$. **60**

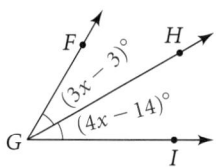

Lesson 1-5 Basic Constructions **37**

3. Practice

Assignment Guide

▼**1** Objective
Ⓐ Ⓑ **Core** 1–6, 22–24, 29–32
Ⓒ **Extension** 34

▼**2** Objective
Ⓐ Ⓑ **Core** 7–21, 25–28, 33
Ⓒ **Extension** 35, 36

Standardized Test Prep 37–40

Mixed Review 41–50

Technology Tip
Have students investigate what software can model compass and straightedge constructions. Some programs use a mouse and pointer to model the action of compass, straightedge, and pencil.

Exercises 2–4 If necessary, discuss ways that students can copy the segment lengths.

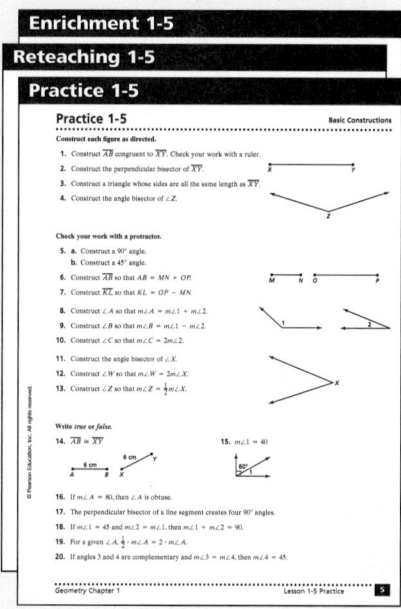

3.
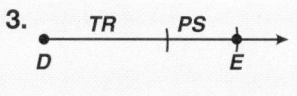

4.
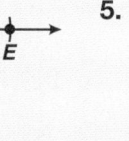

5.
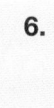

6.
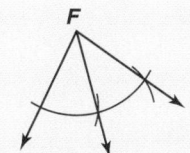

7.

8.
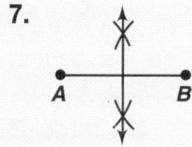

13.
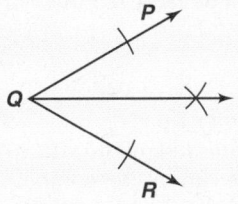

14.
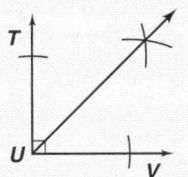

15.
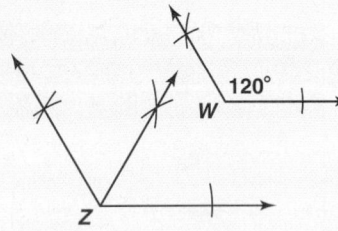

16. Find a segment on $\overleftrightarrow{XY}$ so that you can construct $\overleftrightarrow{YZ}$ as its ⊥ bisector.

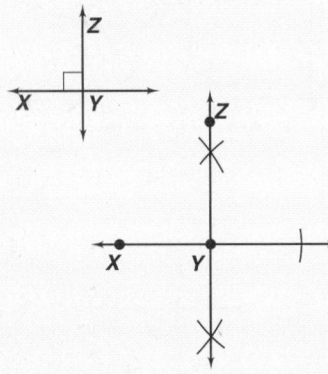

$\boxed{x^2}$ **Algebra** For Exercises 10–12, $\overrightarrow{BX}$ bisects $\angle ABC$. Solve for x and find $m\angle ABC$.

10. $m\angle ABX = 5x, m\angle XBC = 3x + 10$ **5; 50**

11. $m\angle ABC = 4x - 12, m\angle ABX = 24$ **15; 48**

12. $m\angle ABX = 4x - 16, m\angle CBX = 2x + 6$ **11; 56**

Example 5
(page 37)

13. Draw acute $\angle PQR$. Then construct its bisector. **See margin.**

14. Draw right $\angle TUV$. Then construct its bisector. **See margin.**

B **Apply Your Skills**

15. Use your protractor and draw $\angle W$ with $m\angle W = 120$. Construct $\angle Z \cong \angle W$. Then construct the bisector of $\angle Z$. **See margin.**

Sketch the figure described. Explain how to construct it. Then do the construction.

16. $\overleftrightarrow{XY} \perp \overleftrightarrow{YZ}$ **16–17. See margin.**

17. $\overrightarrow{ST}$ bisecting right $\angle PSQ$

18. **Optics** A beam of light and a mirror can be used to study the behavior of light. Light that strikes the mirror is reflected so that the angle of reflection and the angle of incidence are congruent. In the diagram, $\overline{BC}$ is perpendicular to the mirror and $\angle ABC$ has a measure of 41°.
   a. Name the angle of reflection and find its measure. **$\angle CBD$; 41**
   b. Find $m\angle ABD$. **82**
   c. Find $m\angle ABE$ and $m\angle DBF$. **49; 49**

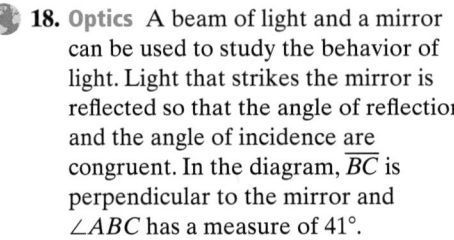
Angle of incidence   Angle of reflection
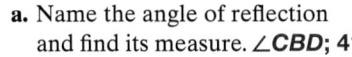

19. Use a straightedge and protractor. **a–b. See back of book.**
   a. Draw a mirror and a light beam striking the mirror and reflecting from it.
   b. Construct the bisector of the angle formed by the incoming and reflected light beams. Label the angles of incidence and reflection.

PEANUTS® by Charles M. Schulz

20. **Open-Ended** Snoopy can draw squares with his compass. You can only draw circles. You can, however, construct a square. Explain how to do this. Use sketches if needed. Then do the construction. **See back of book.**

21. Answer these questions about a segment in a plane. Explain each answer.
   a. How many midpoints does the segment have? **See back of book.**
   b. How many bisectors does it have? How many lines in the plane are its perpendicular bisectors? **b–c. See left.**
   c. How many lines in space are its perpendicular bisectors?

21b. Infinitely many; there's only 1 midpt. but there exist infinitely many lines through the midpoint. A segment has exactly one ⊥ bisecting line because there can be only one line ⊥ to a segment at its midpt.

c. There are an infinite number of lines in space that are ⊥ to a segment at its midpt. The lines are coplanar.

For Exercises 22–24, copy $\angle 1$ and $\angle 2$. **22–24. See back of book.**

22. Construct $\angle B$ so that $m\angle B = m\angle 1 + m\angle 2$.

23. Construct $\angle C$ so that $m\angle C = m\angle 1 - m\angle 2$.

24. Construct $\angle D$ so that $m\angle D = 2m\angle 2$.

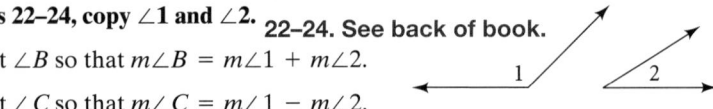

17. Find a segment on $\overleftrightarrow{SQ}$ so that you can construct $\overleftrightarrow{SP}$ as its ⊥ bisector. Then bisect $\angle PSQ$.

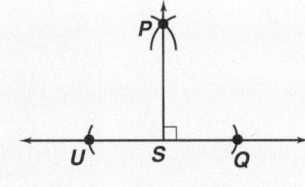
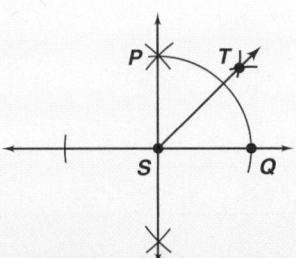

25. They are both correct. If you mult. each side of Lani's eq. by 2, the result is Denyse's eq.

25. Reasoning When $\overrightarrow{BX}$ bisects $\angle ABC$, $\angle ABX \cong \angle CBX$. Lani claims there is always a related equation, $m\angle ABX = \frac{1}{2}m\angle ABC$. Denyse claims the related equation is $2m\angle ABX = m\angle ABC$. Which equation is correct? Explain.

26. Writing Describe how to construct the midpoint of a segment.
See back of book.

27. Construct a 45° angle. **See below left.**

28. a. Draw a large triangle with three acute angles. Construct the bisectors of the three angles. What appears to be true about the three angle bisectors?
b. Repeat the constructions with a triangle that has one obtuse angle.
c. Make a Conjecture What appears to be true about the three angle bisectors of any triangle? **a–c. See back of book.**

Need Help?

In Exercise 28a, your construction may suggest something but be slightly off. If so, test your conjecture very carefully in part (b).

Use a ruler to draw segments of 2 cm, 4 cm and 5 cm. Then construct each triangle, if possible. If not possible, explain. **29–30. See back of book.**

29. with 4-cm, 4-cm, and 5-cm sides   **30.** with 2-cm, 5-cm, and 5-cm sides

27.

31. with 2-cm, 2-cm, and 5-cm sides   **32.** with 2-cm, 2-cm, and 4-cm sides
31–32. Impossible; the short segments are not long enough to form a △.

33. a. Draw a segment, $\overline{XY}$. Construct a triangle with sides congruent to $\overline{XY}$.
b. Measure the angles of the triangle. **a–c. See margin.**
c. Writing Describe how to construct a 60° angle; a 30° angle.

34. Art You can create daisy designs with a compass.
a. Construct a circle. Keeping the same compass setting, put the compass point on the circle and construct an arc within the circle. The endpoints of the arc should be on the circle. **a–c. See back**
b. Keeping the same compass setting, put the **of book.** compass point on each endpoint of the first arc and draw two new arcs.
c. Continue to make arcs around the circle using the endpoints of previously drawn arcs until you get a six-petal daisy.

C Challenge

35. a. Use your compass to draw a circle. **a–c. See back of book.** Locate three points A, B, and C on the circle.
b. Construct the perpendicular bisectors of $\overline{AB}$ and $\overline{BC}$.
c. Critical Thinking Label the intersection of the two perpendicular bisectors as point O. Make a conjecture about point O.

36. Study the figures. Complete the definition of a line perpendicular to a plane:

A line is perpendicular to a plane if it is __?__ to every line in the plane that __?__.
⊥; the line intersects

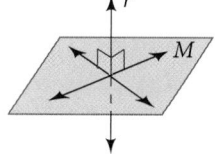
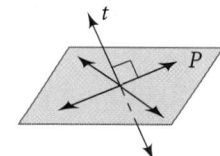

Line $r \perp$ plane M.   Line t is not $\perp$ plane P.

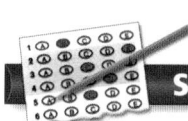

Standardized Test Prep

Multiple Choice

37. What must you do to construct the midpoint of a segment? **D**
A. Measure half its length.   **B.** Measure twice its length.
C. Construct an angle bisector.   **D.** Construct a perpendicular bisector.

33. a.

b. They are all 60°.

c. Answers may vary. Sample: Mark a pt., A. Swing a long arc from A. From a pt. P on the arc, swing another arc the same size that intersects the arc at a second pt., Q. Draw $\angle PAQ$. To construct a 30° ∠, bisect the 60° ∠.

Lesson Quiz 1-5

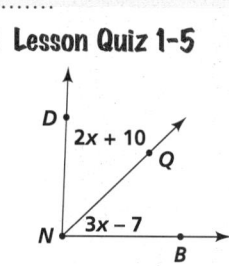

Use the figure above. For problems 1–4, check students' work.

1. Construct $\overline{AC}$ so that $\overline{AC} \cong \overline{NB}$.

2. Construct the perpendicular bisector of $\overline{AC}$.

3. Construct $\angle RST$ so that $\angle RST \cong \angle QNB$.

4. Construct the bisector of $\angle RST$. $\overrightarrow{NQ}$ bisects $\angle DNB$.

5. Find x. **17**

6. Find $m\angle DNB$. **88**

Alternative Assessment

Have each student construct a right triangle using the methods learned in this lesson. Students should write a set of steps that other students could use to complete the construction.

Standardized Test Prep

Resources
For additional practice with a variety of test item formats:
• Standardized Test Prep, p. 65
• Test-Taking Strategies, p. 60
• Test-Taking Strategies with Transparencies

Exercises 37, 38 If students attempt each construction choice, they can determine the correct answer more quickly.

38. Which of these is the first step in constructing a congruent segment? **F**
  F. Draw a ray.   G. Draw a line.
  H. Label two points.   I. Measure the segment.

39. Explain how to do each construction using a compass and a straightedge.
  a. Draw an acute angle, ∠ABC. Construct an angle congruent to ∠ABC.
  b. Construct an angle whose measure is twice that of ∠ABC.

40. Explain how to do each construction using a compass and a straightedge.
  a. Divide a segment into two congruent segments.   **a–c. See margin.**
  b. Divide a segment into four congruent segments.
  c. Construct a segment that is 1.25 times as long as a given segment.

Take It to the NET
Online lesson quiz at
www.PHSchool.com
Web Code: afa-0105

Mixed Review

pages 37–40   Exercises

39. [2] a. Draw $\overrightarrow{XY}$. With the compass pt. on *B* swing an arc that intersects $\overrightarrow{BA}$ and $\overrightarrow{BC}$. Label the intersections *P* and *Q*, respectively. With the compass point on *X*, swing a ≅ arc intersecting $\overrightarrow{XY}$. Label the intersection *K*. Open the compass to *PQ*. With compass pt. on *K*, swing an arc to intersect the first arc. Label the intersection *R*. Draw $\overrightarrow{XR}$.

  b. With the compass open to *XK*, put compass point on *X* and swing an arc intersecting $\overrightarrow{XR}$. With the compass on *R* and open to *KR*, swing an arc to intersect the first arc. Label the intersection *T*. Draw $\overrightarrow{XT}$.

  [1] one part correct

40. [4] a. Construct its ⊥ bisector.

  b. Construct the ⊥ bisector. Then construct the ⊥ bisector of two new segments.

40

Lesson 1-4   **Use the number line at the right. Find the length of each segment.**

41. $\overline{AC}$ 6   **42.** $\overline{AD}$ 10

43. $\overline{CD}$ 4   **44.** $\overline{BC}$ 3

$$\begin{array}{ccccccccccccc} A & & B & & C & & & D \\ \bullet & & \bullet & & \bullet & & & \bullet \end{array}$$
−7 −6 −5 −4 −3 −2 −1 0 1 2 3 4

45.
72°

45. Use a protractor to draw a 72° angle. **See left.**

46. ∠DEF is a straight angle. m∠DEG = 80. Find m∠GEF. **100**

47. m∠TUV = 100 and m∠VUW = 80. Find possible values of m∠TUW.
   20 and 180

Lesson 1-3   **48.** Draw $\overleftrightarrow{RS}$. $\overset{\bullet}{R} \quad \overset{\bullet}{S}$

Use your drawing from Exercise 48. Answer and explain.

49. Are $\overrightarrow{RS}$ and $\overrightarrow{SR}$ opposite rays?
No; they do not have the same endpt.

50. Are $\overline{RS}$ and $\overline{SR}$ the same segment?
Yes; they both represent a segment with endpts. *R* and *S*.

Geometry at Work

······· Cabinetmaker

Cabinetmakers not only make cabinets but all types of wooden furniture. The artistry of cabinetmaking can be seen in the beauty and uniqueness of the finest doors, shelves, and tables. The craft is in knowing which types of wood and tools to use, and how to use them.

  The carpenter's square is one of the most useful of the cabinetmaker's tools. It can be applied to a variety of measuring tasks. The figure shows how to use a carpenter's square to bisect ∠O.

Take It to the NET For more information about cabinetmaking, go to www.PHSchool.com.
Web Code: afb-2031

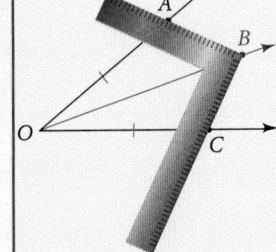

First, mark equal lengths *OA* and *OC* on the sides of the angle. Then position the square so that *BA* = *BC* to locate point *B*. Finally, draw $\overrightarrow{OB}$. $\overrightarrow{OB}$ bisects ∠O.

  c. Draw $\overleftrightarrow{AB}$. Do constructions as in parts a and b. Open the compass to the length of the shortest segment in part b. With the

pt. of the compass on *B*, swing an arc in the opp. direction from *A* intersecting $\overleftrightarrow{AB}$ at *C. AC* = 1.25 (*AB*).

  [3] explanations are not thorough

  [2] two explanations correct

  [1] part (a) correct

 **Technology**

Exploring Constructions

 **Technology**

Exploring Constructions

Students will use the Draw and Construct tools of geometry software and investigate the differences between the tools.

Resources

Students may use any geometry software program to explore Draw and Construct tools.

Teaching Notes

Exploring with Draw and Construct tools allows students to apply what they are learning about points, segments, rays, lines, and angles. In particular, when students watch perpendicular and angle bisectors change as they drag points on a screen, it creates a powerful impression of the relationships involved.

Inclusion

Students with motor difficulties may have difficulties using a computer mouse in this lesson. Have students work in pairs.

English Learners

After students have completed the activities, have them read again the opening paragraph as a summary. Then ask students to write their own summaries of the difference between Draw and Construct tools.

Points, lines, and figures are created in geometry software using Draw tools or Construct tools. A figure created by Draw has no constraints. When the figure is manipulated, it moves or changes size freely. A figure created by Construct is dependent upon an existing object. When you manipulate the existing object, the constructed object similarly moves or resizes.

In this activity you will explore the difference between Draw and Construct. Before you begin, familiarize yourself with the tools of your software.

Draw and Construct
- Draw $\overline{AB}$ and Construct the perpendicular bisector $\overleftrightarrow{DC}$.
- Draw $\overline{EF}$ and Construct G, any point on $\overline{EF}$. Draw $\overleftrightarrow{HG}$. Find EG, GF, and $m\angle HGF$. Try to drag G so that $EG = GF$. Try to drag H so that $m\angle HGF = 90$. Were you able to draw the perpendicular bisector of $\overline{EF}$? Explain.

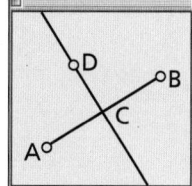 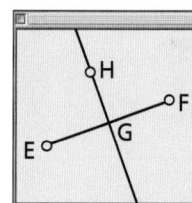

Investigate
- Drag A and B. Observe AC, CB, and $m\angle DCB$. Is $\overleftrightarrow{DC}$ always the perpendicular bisector of $\overline{AB}$ no matter how you manipulate the figure?
- Drag E and F. Observe EG, GF, and $m\angle HGF$. How is the relationship between $\overline{EF}$ and $\overleftrightarrow{HG}$ different from the relationship between $\overline{AB}$ and $\overleftrightarrow{DC}$?

EXERCISES

1. a. Write a description of the general difference between Draw and Construct. **See margin.**
   b. Use your description to explain why the relationship between $\overline{EF}$ and $\overleftrightarrow{HG}$ differs from the relationship between $\overline{AB}$ and $\overleftrightarrow{DC}$. **Construction is exact and drawing is not.**

2. a. Draw $\angle JKL$. **2a–b. Check students' work.**
   b. Construct its angle bisector, $\overrightarrow{KM}$.
   c. Manipulate the figure and observe the different angle measures. Is $\overrightarrow{KM}$ always the angle bisector of $\angle JKL$? **yes**

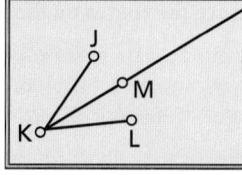

3a. Check students' work.

3. a. Draw $\angle NOP$. Draw $\overrightarrow{OQ}$ in the interior of $\angle NOP$. Drag Q until $m\angle NOQ = m\angle QOP$.
   b. Manipulate the figure and observe the different angle measures. Is $\overrightarrow{OQ}$ always the angle bisector of $\angle NOP$? **no**

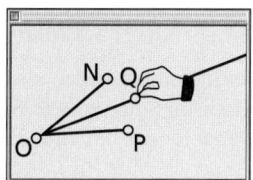

---

page 41   Technology

1. Answers may vary. Samples are given.

   a. With "Draw" you can change measures by moving pts. The tools allow you to *draw* objects with very few constraints. A *construction* attaches some type of geometric prop. to the object being created. It will remain true no matter how the figure is manipulated.

Investigation — **Distance in the Coordinate Plane**

Distance in the Coordinate Plane

The Distance Formula is presented in Lesson 1-6 to calculate the shortest path between two points in a coordinate plane. In the real world, distances cannot always be measured along the shortest path. Here, students will explore what this means on the streets of New York City.

Teaching Notes

Diversity
Ask students whether they know of any other cities where streets are arranged in a rectangular grid. **Sample: Chicago, IL; Washington, D.C.; Calgary, ONT**

Connection to History
The way a city's streets are laid out reveals its history. For example, some streets at the southern tip of New York City meet at odd angles and end one or two blocks after they begin. New York City was first settled by the Dutch at this southern tip, and streets were built as the population grew, with no master plan to lay streets out in a rectangular grid. In fact, some of the streets, such as Broadway, follow original Native American paths.

Much of Manhattan is laid out in a rectangular grid, as shown in this map. In general, the streets are parallel running east and west. The avenues are parallel running north and south.

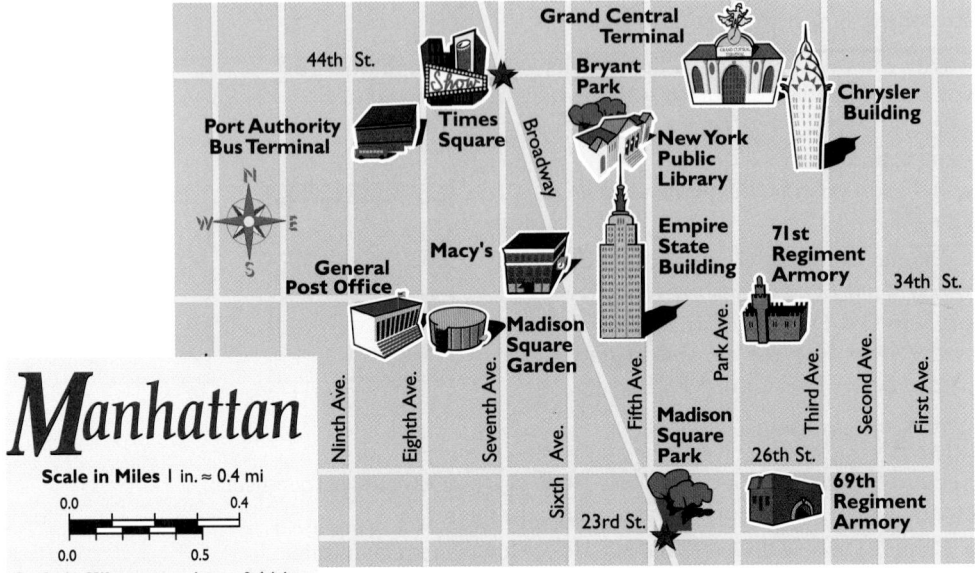

Yvonne's family is at the corner of 44th Street and 7th Avenue. They plan to walk to Madison Square Park at 23rd Street and 5th Avenue. There are several possible routes they can take.

EXERCISES

Use tracing paper to trace the routes on the map. Answer the following questions.

1. Yvonne's father wants to walk east on 44th Street until they reach 5th Avenue. He then plans to walk south on 5th Avenue to Madison Square Park. About how long is his route? **1.4 mi or 2.3 km**

2. Yvonne's mother wants to walk south on 7th Avenue until they reach 23rd Street. She then plans to walk east on 23rd Street to Madison Square Park. About how long is her route? **1.4 mi or 2.3 km**

3. Yvonne notices on the map that Broadway cuts across the grid of streets and leads directly to Madison Square Park. She suggests walking all the way on Broadway. About how long is her route? **$1\frac{1}{8}$ mi or 1.8 km**

4. Whose route is the shortest? Explain. **Yvonne's route; it's the most direct.**

5. Whose route is the longest? Explain. **Yvonne's father's route and her mother's route tie for the longest route. They walked the sides of a rectangle.**

ALGEBRA

The Coordinate Plane

1.02 Use length, area, and volume of geometric figures to solve problems.

 North Carolina Objectives

Lesson Preview

What You'll Learn

OBJECTIVE **1**
To find the distance between two points in the coordinate plane

OBJECTIVE **2**
To find the coordinates of the midpoint of a segment in the coordinate plane

. . . And Why

To find the distance between two points on a map, as in Example 2

 Check Skills You'll Need (For help, go to the Skills Handbook pages 715 and 716.)

Find the square root of each number. Round to the nearest tenth if necessary.

1. 25 5

2. 17 4.1

3. 123 11.1

x^2 **Algebra** Evaluate each expression for $m = -3$ and $n = 7$.

4. $(m - n)^2$ 100

5. $(n - m)^2$ 100

6. $m^2 + n^2$ 58

x^2 **Algebra** Evaluate each expression for $a = 6$ and $b = -8$.

7. $(a - b)^2$ 196

8. $\sqrt{a^2 + b^2}$ 10

9. $\frac{a + b}{2}$ −1

 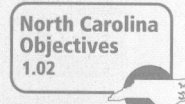
Lesson Preview

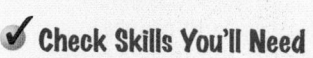 **Check Skills You'll Need**

For help use
Skills Handbook, pp. 715, 716

Lesson Resources

📁 **Teaching Resources**
Practice, Reteaching, Enrichment
Checkpoint Quiz 2

Reaching All Students
Practice Workbook 1-6
Spanish Practice Workbook 1-6
Reading and Math Literacy 1C
Spanish Reading and Literacy 1C
Spanish Checkpoint Quiz 2
Informal Geometry Planning
   Guide 1-6

Presentation Assistant Plus!
Transparencies
• Check Skills You'll Need 1-6
• Additional Examples 1-6
• Student Edition Answers 1-6
• Lesson Quiz 1-6
PH Presentation Pro CD 1-6

ASSESSMENT SYSTEM
(PRENTICE HALL)

Checkpoint Quiz 2
Computer Test Generator CD

Technology
Resource Pro® CD-ROM
Computer Test Generator CD
Prentice Hall Presentation Pro CD

💻 **www.PHSchool.com**
Student Site
• Teacher Web Code: afk-5500
• Self-grading Lesson Quiz
Teacher Center
• Lesson Planner
• Resources

Plus

 Interactive lesson includes instant self-check, tutorials, and activities.

OBJECTIVE
1   **Finding Distance on the Coordinate Plane**

You can think of a point as a dot, and a line as a series of points. In coordinate geometry you describe a point by an ordered pair (x, y), called the *coordinates of the point*.

Need Help?
To help review terms shown here, see "Coordinate plane" in the Glossary.

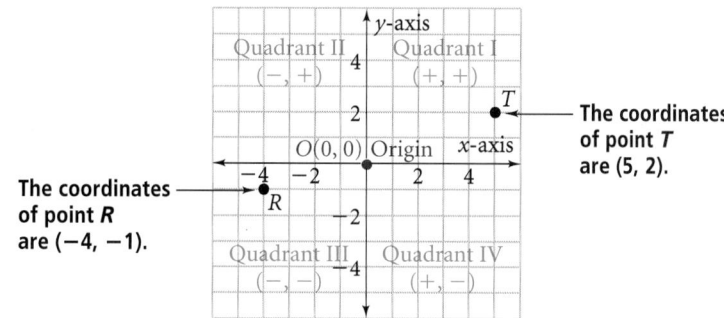

The coordinates of point *T* are (5, 2).

The coordinates of point *R* are (−4, −1).

You can use the Ruler Postulate to find the distance between two points if the points are on a horizontal line or a vertical line. To find the distance between two points that are not on a horizontal or vertical line, you can use the Distance Formula.

 Key Concepts

Formula	The Distance Formula

The distance d between two points $A(x_1, y_1)$ and $B(x_2, y_2)$ is
$$d = \sqrt{(x_2 - x_1)^2 + (y_2 - y_1)^2}.$$

You will verify this formula in Chapter 7.

 Ongoing Assessment and Intervention

Before the Lesson
Diagnose prerequisite skills using:
• Check Skills You'll Need

During the Lesson
Monitor progress using:
• Check Understanding
• Additional Examples
• Standardized Test Prep

After the Lesson
Assess knowledge using:
• Lesson Quiz
• Computer Test Generator CD
• Chapter Checkpoint 2 (p. 49)

2. Teach

Math Background

This lesson covers important geometric concepts in an algebraic context. The Distance Formula, an extension of the Ruler Postulate to points in a two-dimensional coordinate system, is an application of the Pythagorean Theorem. The Midpoint Formula follows from the Ruler Postulate and the Side-Splitter Theorem.

OBJECTIVE 1 Teaching Notes

Math Tip
Point out that the term *coordinate* describing one number on a one-dimensional number line in Lesson 1-4 is expanded in this lesson to describe an ordered pair of two numbers on a two-dimensional coordinate plane.

① EXAMPLE Teaching Tip

Have students sketch the relative positions of the points in the example. Have them draw a horizontal line through $R(-4, -1)$ and a vertical line through $T(5, 2)$ and draw segment RT to form a right triangle. Ask: *What rule relates the legs to the hypotenuse of a right triangle?* **Pythagorean Theorem**

② EXAMPLE Error Prevention

Remind students to enclose negative numbers in parentheses when they substitute them into the Distance Formula. Have them double-check their work.

Careers
Mapmakers must report distances accurately. Their work is complicated by the fact that Earth's surface is not a Euclidean plane.

Reading Math
For help with reading Example 1, see p. 50.

① EXAMPLE Finding Distance

Find the distance between $T(5, 2)$ and $R(-4, -1)$ to the nearest tenth.

Let $(5, 2)$ be (x_1, y_1) and $(-4, -1)$ be (x_2, y_2).

$d = \sqrt{(x_2 - x_1)^2 + (y_2 - y_1)^2}$	Use the Distance Formula.
$d = \sqrt{(-4 - 5)^2 + (-1 - 2)^2}$	Substitute.
$d = \sqrt{(-9)^2 + (-3)^2}$	Simplify.
$d = \sqrt{81 + 9} = \sqrt{90}$	
$90 \boxed{\sqrt{}} \; \mathbf{9.4868330}$	Use a calculator.

● To the nearest tenth, $TR = 9.5$.

✓ Check Understanding ❶ **a.** $\overline{AB}$ has endpoints $A(1, -3)$ and $B(-4, 4)$. Find AB to the nearest tenth. **8.6**
b. Critical Thinking In Example 1, suppose you let $(-4, -1)$ be (x_1, y_1) and $(5, 2)$ be (x_2, y_2). Do you get the same result? Why? **Yes; the differences are opposites, and the square of a number and the square of its opposite are the same.**

② EXAMPLE Real-World Connection

Travel Each morning Juanita takes the "Blue Line" subway from Oak Station to Jackson Station. As the map at the left shows, Oak Station is 1 mile west and 2 miles south of City Plaza. Jackson Station is 2 miles east and 4 miles north of City Plaza. Find the distance Juanita travels between Oak Station and Jackson Station.

Let Oak$(-1, -2)$ be (x_1, y_1) and Jackson $(2, 4)$ be (x_2, y_2).

$d = \sqrt{(x_2 - x_1)^2 + (y_2 - y_1)^2}$	Use the Distance Formula.
$d = \sqrt{(2 - (-1))^2 + (4 - (-2))^2}$	Substitute.
$d = \sqrt{3^2 + 6^2}$	Simplify.
$d = \sqrt{9 + 36} = \sqrt{45}$	
$45 \boxed{\sqrt{}} \; \mathbf{6.7082039}$	Use a calculator.

● Juanita travels about 6.7 miles between Oak Station and Jackson Station.

✓ Check Understanding ❷ **a.** Find the distance between Elm Station and Symphony Station. **about 8.9 mi**
b. Maple Station is located 6 miles west and 2 miles north of City Plaza. Find the distance between Cedar Station and Maple Station. **about 3.2 mi**

OBJECTIVE 2 Finding the Midpoint of a Segment

To find the coordinate of the midpoint of a segment on a number line, find the *average* or *mean* of the coordinates of the endpoints. The coordinate of the midpoint of a segment with endpoints a and b is $\frac{a + b}{2}$.

You can extend this process (see next page) to find the coordinates of the midpoint of a segment in the coordinate plane.

👥 Reaching All Students

Below Level Use an overhead projector and right triangles on graph paper to relate the distance formula and the Pythagorean Theorem.	**Advanced Learners** Encourage students to try to derive the Midpoint Formula algebraically by using the Distance Formula.	**Visual Learners** See note on page 45. **Error Prevention** See note on page 44.

Real-World Connection

A well-made seesaw balances (without riders) at its midpoint.

Study the diagram of ___ with endpoints $T(4, 3)$ and $S(8, 5)$. $\overline{TR}$ is a horizontal segment and $\overline{SR}$ is a vertical segment. The coordinates of R are $(8, 3)$.

The coordinates of M, the midpoint of $\overline{TR}$, are $(6, 3)$. The coordinates of N, the midpoint of $\overline{SR}$, are $(8, 4)$. A vertical line through M and a horizontal line through N meet at P, the midpoint of $\overline{TS}$.

The coordinates of P are $(6, 4)$.

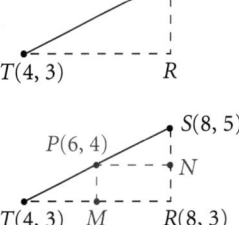

Thus, you find the coordinates of the midpoint of a segment by averaging the x-coordinates and averaging the y-coordinates of the endpoints.

Key Concepts

Formula	The Midpoint Formula

The coordinates of the midpoint M of $\overline{AB}$ with endpoints $A(x_1, y_1)$ and $B(x_2, y_2)$ are the following:

$$M\left(\frac{x_1 + x_2}{2}, \frac{y_1 + y_2}{2}\right)$$

3 EXAMPLE Finding the Midpoint

Algebra $\overline{QS}$ has endpoints $Q(3, 5)$ and $S(7, -9)$. Find the coordinates of its midpoint M.

Let $(3, 5)$ be (x_1, y_1) and $(7, -9)$ be (x_2, y_2).

x-coordinate of $M = \dfrac{x_1 + x_2}{2} = \dfrac{3 + 7}{2} = \dfrac{10}{2} = 5$

y-coordinate of $M = \dfrac{y_1 + y_2}{2} = \dfrac{5 + (-9)}{2} = \dfrac{-4}{2} = -2$

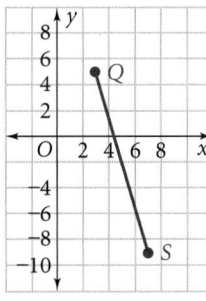

The coordinates of midpoint M are $(5, -2)$.

✓ Check Understanding 3 Find the coordinates of the midpoint of $\overline{XY}$ with endpoints $X(2, -5)$ and $Y(6, 13)$.
(4, 4)

4 EXAMPLE Finding an Endpoint

Algebra The midpoint of $\overline{AB}$ is $M(3, 4)$. One endpoint is $A(-3, -2)$. Find the coordinates of the other endpoint B.

Use the Midpoint Formula. Let the coordinates of B be (x_2, y_2).

$3 = \dfrac{-3 + x_2}{2}$ ← Midpoint Formula → $4 = \dfrac{-2 + y_2}{2}$

$6 = -3 + x_2$ ← Multiply each side by 2. → $8 = -2 + y_2$

$9 = x_2$ $\qquad\qquad\qquad\qquad\qquad 10 = y_2$

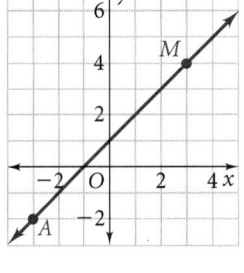

The coordinates of B are $(9, 10)$.

✓ Check Understanding 4 The midpoint of $\overline{XY}$ has coordinates $(4, -6)$. X has coordinates $(2, -3)$. Find the coordinates of Y. **(6, −9)**

Additional Examples

1 Find the distance between $R(-2, 6)$ and $S(6, -2)$ to the nearest tenth. **11.3**

2 Use the diagram from Example 2. How far is the subway ride from Oak to Symphony? Round to the nearest tenth. **4.5 mi**

OBJECTIVE 2 Teaching Notes

3 EXAMPLE Visual Learners

Have students use graph paper to find the midpoints M, N, and P at the top of page 45.

4 EXAMPLE Connection to Algebra

If necessary, review how to solve linear equations before beginning Example 4.

Teaching Tip
Discuss with the class how the Distance and Midpoint Formulas provide ways to solve geometry problems without having to use a drawing.

Additional Examples

3 $\overline{AB}$ has endpoints $(8, 9)$ and $(-6, -3)$. Find the coordinates of its midpoint M. **(1, 3)**

4 The midpoint of $\overline{DG}$ is $M(-1, 5)$. One endpoint is $D(1, 4)$. Find the coordinates of the other endpoint G. **(−3, 6)**

Closure

Use a coordinate plane to draw an obtuse triangle whose vertices have whole number coordinates. Then find the length and midpoint of each side. **Check students' work.**

Assignment Guide

 **Objective**

Ⓐ Ⓑ **Core** 1–17, 43, 47–58

Ⓒ **Extension** 60–63

 **Objective**

Ⓐ Ⓑ **Core** 18–42, 44–46

Ⓒ **Extension** 59

Standardized Test Prep 64–69

Mixed Review 70–78

Error Prevention

Exercises 1–9 Remind students to substitute the four coordinates correctly into the Distance Formula. If students substitute incorrectly, have them write x_1, y_1, x_2, and y_2 above the given coordinates.

Exercise 23 If necessary, review the arithmetic of mixed numbers.

Exercise 41 Ask: *Why is the point (0, 0) called "the origin"?*
Sample: It is a starting point for numbering coordinates on the coordinate plane.

Ⓐ **Practice by Example**

Example 1
(page 44)

Find the distance between the points to the nearest tenth.

1. $J(2, -1), K(2, 5)$ **6**
2. $L(10, 14), M(-8, 14)$ **18**
3. $N(-1, -11), P(-1, -3)$ **8**
4. $A(0, 3), B(0, 12)$ **9**
5. $C(12, 6), D(-8, 18)$ **23.3**
6. $E(6, -2), F(-2, 4)$ **10**
7. $Q(12, -12), T(5, 12)$ **25**
8. $R(0, 5), S(12, 3)$ **12.2**
9. $X(-3, -4), Y(5, 5)$ **12.0**

Example 2
(page 44)

Use the map in Example 2 on page 44. Find the distance between the stations.

10. North and South **9 mi**
11. Oak and Symphony **about 4.5 mi**
12. City Plaza and Cedar **about 3.2 mi**

Use the map at the right. Find the distances between the stations to the nearest tenth.

13. Station A and Station B **6.4**
14. Station B and Station C located at (5, 8) **15.8**
15. Station B and Station D located at (1, 10) **15.8**
16. Station E at (2, 12) and Station F at (5, 16) **5.0**
17. List the stations B, C, D, E, and F in the order of least to greatest distance from Station A. **B, C, D, E, F**

Example 3
(page 45)

x^2 **Algebra** **Find the coordinates of the midpoint of $\overline{HX}$.**

18. $H(0, 0), X(8, 4)$ **(4, 2)**
19. $H(-1, 3), X(7, -1)$ **(3, 1)**
20. $H(13, 8), X(-6, -6)$ **(3.5, 1)**
21. $H(7, 10), X(5, -8)$ **(6, 1)**
22. $H(-6.3, 5.2), X(1.8, -1)$ **(-2.25, 2.1)**
23. $H\left(5\frac{1}{2}, -4\frac{3}{4}\right), X\left(2\frac{1}{4}, -1\frac{1}{4}\right)$ $\left(3\frac{7}{8}, -3\right)$

Example 4
(page 45)

x^2 **Algebra** **The coordinates of point T are given. The midpoint of $\overline{ST}$ has coordinates (5, -8). Find the coordinates of point S.**

24. $T(0, 4)$ **(10, -20)**
25. $T(5, -15)$ **(5, -1)**
26. $T(10, 18)$ **(0, -34)**
27. $T(-2, 8)$ **(12, -24)**
28. $T(1, 12)$ **(9, -28)**
29. $T(4.5, -2.5)$ **(5.5, -13.5)**

An endpoint and a midpoint are given. Find the coordinates of the other endpoint.

30. endpoint (2, 6), midpoint (5, 12) **(8, 18)**
31. endpoint (2, 3), midpoint (3, -4) **(4, -11)**

Ⓑ **Apply Your Skills**

Find (a) PQ to the nearest tenth and (b) the coordinates of the midpoint of $\overline{PQ}$.

32. 5.0; (4.5, 4)
33. 5.8; (1.5, 0.5)
34. 7.1; (-1.5, 0.5)
35. 5.4; (-2.5, 3)
36. 10; (1, -4)
37. 2.8; (-4, -4)

32. $P(3, 2), Q(6, 6)$
33. $P(0, -2), Q(3, 3)$
34. $P(-4, -2), Q(1, 3)$
35. $P(-5, 2), Q(0, 4)$
36. $P(-3, -1), Q(5, -7)$
37. $P(-5, -3), Q(-3, -5)$
38. $P(-4, -5), Q(-1, 1)$ **6.7; (-2.5, -2)**
39. $P(2, 3), Q(4, -2)$ **5.4; (3, 0.5)**
40. $P(4, 2), Q(3, 0)$ **2.2; (3.5, 1)**

41. The midpoint of $\overline{TS}$ is the origin. Point T is located in Quadrant II. What quadrant contains point S? **IV**

42. Graph the points $A(2, 1), B(6, -1), C(8, 7)$, and $D(4, 9)$. Draw quadrilateral $ABCD$. Use the Midpoint Formula to find the midpoints of $\overline{AC}$ and $\overline{BD}$. What appears to be true? **See back of book.**

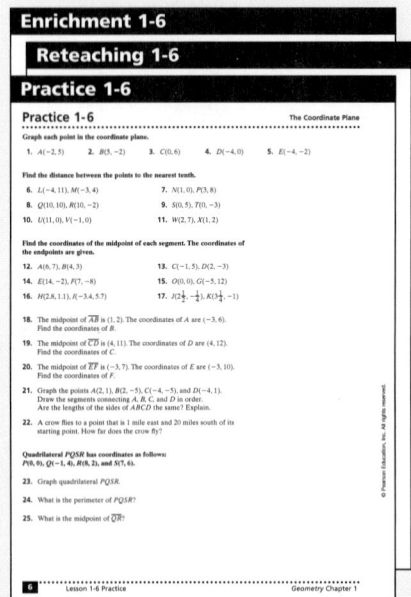

43. The coordinates of S, T, V, and W are given below. Graph the points and draw segments to join them in order. Draw $\overline{WS}$. Are the lengths of the four sides of quadrilateral $STVW$ the same? Show your work. **See margin.**

$S(-6, 2)$ $\qquad$ $T(-3, 5)$ $\qquad$ $V(-6, 6)$ $\qquad$ $W(-9, 5)$

For each graph, find (a) AB to the nearest tenth and (b) the coordinates of the midpoint of $\overline{AB}$.

44.
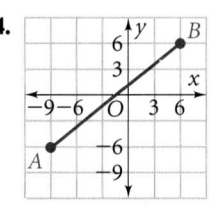
19.2 units; (−1.5, 0)

45.
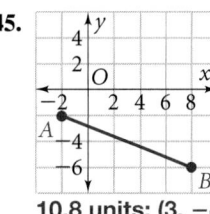
10.8 units; (3, −4)

46.
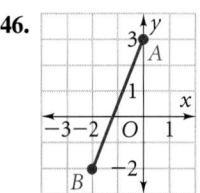
5.4 units; (−1, 0.5)

48. 165 units; The dist. *TV* is less than the dist. *TU*, so the airplane should fly from *T* to *V* to *U* for the shortest route.

Real-World Connection

Teens average about 7 hours on the phone each week.

47. Navigation A boat at $X(5, -2)$ needs to travel to $Y(-6, 9)$ or $Z(17, -3)$. Which point is closer? What is the distance to the closer point? **Z; about 12 units**

48. Writing An airplane at $T(80, 20)$ needs to fly to both $U(20, 60)$ and $V(110, 85)$. What is the shortest possible distance for the trip? Explain. **See above left.**

Communications The cell phone screen at the right shows coordinates of six cities from a grid placed on North America by a long-distance carrier. The carrier finds distance by the Distance Formula. Each grid unit equals $\sqrt{0.1}$ mile. Find the distance between each pair of cities to the nearest mile.

San Francisco	(8495, 8720)
Chicago	(5985, 3439)
New Orleans	(8448, 2625)
Denver	(7490, 5881)
Houston	(8936, 3542)
Boston	(4422, 1241)

SOURCE: Peter H. Dana

49. Houston and Chicago **934 mi**

50. Denver and New Orleans **1073 mi**

51. Boston and San Francisco **2693 mi**

52. New Orleans and Houston **328 mi**

Graph $X(-2, 1)$, $Y(2, 3)$, $A(-1, 4)$, $B(0, 2)$, and $C(4, 2)$. For each point described below, give two sets of possible coordinates if they exist. Otherwise, write *exactly one point* and give the coordinates, or *not possible* and explain. 53–56. Answers may vary. Samples are given.

53. point D so that $\overleftrightarrow{AD} \parallel \overleftrightarrow{XY}$ (3, 6), (0, 4.5)

54. E so that $\overleftrightarrow{EC} \parallel \overleftrightarrow{XY}$ (0, 0), (8, 4)

55. point F so that $\overleftrightarrow{FB} \perp \overleftrightarrow{XY}$ (1, 0), (−1, 4)

56. point G so that $\overleftrightarrow{GC} \perp \overleftrightarrow{XY}$ (0, 10), (5, 0)

57. point H so that $\overleftrightarrow{HX} \parallel \overleftrightarrow{AY}$, and $\overleftrightarrow{HA} \parallel \overleftrightarrow{XY}$ exactly one pt., E (−5, 2)

58. point J so that $\overleftrightarrow{JB} \perp \overleftrightarrow{XY}$, and $\overleftrightarrow{JC} \perp \overleftrightarrow{CY}$ exactly one pt., J (2, − 2)

59. Open-Ended In a coordinate plane, draw any $\overline{AB}$. Draw another segment that is both congruent and parallel to $\overline{AB}$. Label the new segment $\overline{CD}$ in such a way that $ABCD$ is a quadrilateral. **a–f. See margin.**
  a. Find BC and AD. What do you notice?
  b. Write a conjecture that generalizes the result you found in part (a).
  c. Find the midpoint of $\overline{AC}$ and the midpoint of $\overline{BD}$. What do you notice?
  d. Write a conjecture that generalizes the result you found in part (c).
  e. Find the midpoint E of $\overline{AD}$ and the midpoint F of $\overline{BC}$. Find EF and AB. What do you notice?
  f. Write a conjecture that generalizes the result you found in part (e).

Alternative Method

Exercises 44–46 After students solve the exercises, ask: *Can you exchange points (x_1, y_1) and (x_2, y_2) and still have the correct lengths and midpoints?* Help students recognize that order doesn't affect the squares of the differences in the Distance Formula and that the sums in the Midpoint Formula are the same because of the Commutative Property of Addition.

Exercises 53–56 Students work informally with the properties of parallel and perpendicular lines in a coordinate plane. In Chapter 3, these properties will be formally treated.

59. a–f. Answers may vary. Samples are given.

  a. $BC = AD$

  b. If two opp. sides of a quad. are both $\parallel$ and $\cong$, then the other two opp. sides are $\cong$.

  c. The midpts. are the same.

  d. If one pair of opp. sides of a quad. are both $\parallel$ and $\cong$, then its diagonals bisect each other.

  e. $EF = AB$

  f. If a pair of opp. sides of a quad. are both $\parallel$ and $\cong$, then the segment joining the midpts. of the other two sides has the same length as each of the first pair of sides.

pages 46–49 Exercises

43.
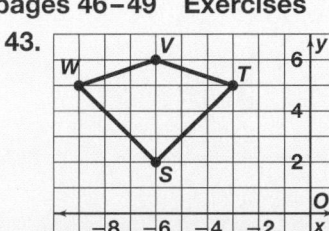

$ST = \sqrt{(5-2)^2 + (-3-(-6))^2} = \sqrt{9+9} = 3\sqrt{2} \approx 4.2$

$TV = \sqrt{(6-5)^2 + (-6-(-3))^2} = \sqrt{1+9} = \sqrt{10} \approx 3.2$

$VW = \sqrt{(5-6)^2 + (-9-(-6))^2} = \sqrt{1+9} = \sqrt{10} \approx 3.2$

$SW = \sqrt{(5-2)^2 + (-9-(-6))^2} = \sqrt{9+9} = 3\sqrt{2} \approx 4.2$

No, but $ST = SW$ and $TV = VW$.

47

4. Assess

Exercise 60

Lesson Quiz 1-6

A has coordinates (3, 8).
B has coordinates (0, −4).
C has coordinates (−5, −6).

1. Find the distance between *A* and *B* to the nearest tenth. **12.4**

2. Find *BC* to the nearest tenth. **5.4**

3. Find the midpoint *M* of $\overline{AC}$ to the nearest tenth. **(−1, 1)**

4. *B* is the midpoint of $\overline{AD}$. Find the coordinates of endpoint *D*. **(−3, −16)**

5. An airplane flies from Stanton to Mercury in a straight flight path. Mercury is 300 miles east and 400 miles south of Stanton. How many miles is the flight? **500 mi**

6. Toni rides 2 miles north, then 5 miles west, and then 14 miles south. At the end of her ride, how far is Toni from her starting point, measured in a straight line? **13 mi**

Alternative Assessment

Have each student graph two points in a coordinate plane and then exchange graphs with a partner. Each partner should calculate the length and the midpoint of the segment whose endpoints are the two graphed points.

Standardized Test Prep

Resources

For additional practice with a variety of test item formats:
- Standardized Test Prep, p. 65
- Test-Taking Strategies, p. 60
- Test-Taking Strategies with Transparencies

Exercise 64 Students may want to sketch a coordinate plane to help solve the exercise.

48

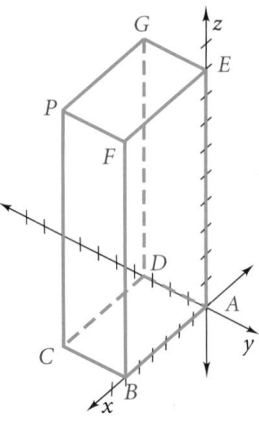

Geometry in 3 Dimensions You can use three coordinates (*x, y, z*) to locate points in three dimensions. Point *P* has coordinates (6, −3.5, 9).

60. Give the coordinates of points *A, B, C, D, E, F,* and *G*. **See margin.**

61. Draw three axes like those shown. Then graph *R*(4, 5, 9). **See margin.**

Distance in 3 Dimensions In a three-dimensional coordinate system, the distance between two points (x_1, y_1, z_1) and (x_2, y_2, z_2) can be found using this extension of the Distance Formula.

$$d = \sqrt{(x_2 - x_1)^2 + (y_2 - y_1)^2 + (z_2 - z_1)^2}$$

Find the distance between each pair of points to the nearest tenth.

62. *P*(2, 3, 4), *B*(−2, 4, 9) **6.5 units**   63. *Q*(0, 12, 15), *Y*(−8, 20, 12) **11.7 units**

Standardized Test Prep

Multiple Choice

64. What are the coordinates of the point that is halfway between (4, 1) and (−22, 8)? **B**
   A. (−9, 3.5)   B. (−9, 4.5)   C. (−18, 9)   D. (13, 4.5)

65. Which point lies the farthest from the origin? **I**
   F. (0, −7)   G. (5, 1)   H. (−4, −3)   I. (−3, 8)

Quantitative Comparison

Compare the boxed quantity in Column A with the boxed quantity in Column B. Choose the best answer.
   A. The quantity in Column A is greater.
   B. The quantity in Column B is greater.
   C. The two quantities are equal.
   D. The relationship cannot be determined from the information given.

Column A	Column B
A 66. distance from (2, −3) to (0, 19)	distance from (−12, 6) to (−4, −10)
C 67. distance from (−31, −17) to (−23, −16)	distance from (8, 0) to (0, −1)

A segment has endpoints at (14, −5) and (6, 14).

A 68. the *x*-coordinate of the midpoint of the segment	the *y*-coordinate of the midpoint of the segment

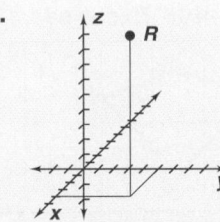

Take It to the NET
Online lesson quiz at
www.PHSchool.com
Web Code: afa-0106

Short Response

69. a. Points *P*(−4, 6), *Q*(2, 4), and *R* are collinear. One of the points is the midpoint of the segment formed by the other two points. What are the possible coordinates of *R*? **a–b. See margin, p. 49.**
   b. *RQ* = $\sqrt{160}$. Does this information affect your answer to part (a)? Explain.

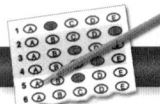

---

pages 46–49   Exercises
60. **A** (0, 0, 0)
    B (6, 0, 0)
    C (6, −3.5, 0)
    D (0, −3.5, 0)
    E (0, 0, 9)
    F (6, 0, 9)
    G (0, −3.5, 9)

61.

Lesson 1-5   **Use a straightedge and compass.   70–73. See margin.**

70. Draw $\overline{AB}$. Construct $\overline{PQ}$ so that $PQ = 2AB$.

71. Draw $\overline{LK}$. Construct the perpendicular bisector of $\overline{LK}$.

72. Draw an obtuse $\angle B$. Construct $\angle C$ so that $m\angle C = m\angle B$.

73. Draw an acute $\angle RTS$. Construct the bisector of $\angle RTS$.

Lesson 1-4 x^2 **74. Algebra** The length of $\overline{AC}$ is 45. If $AB = x + 8$ and $BC = 3x - 3$, find the value of x.   **10**

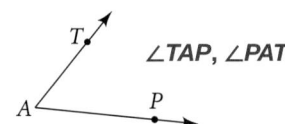

75. Find AB if the coordinate of A is 5 and the coordinate of B is -5.   **10**

x^2 **76. Algebra** C is the midpoint of $\overline{EF}$. Find EF.   **48**

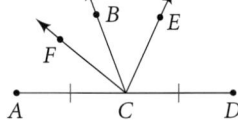

77. Name $\angle A$ two other ways.

∠TAP, ∠PAT

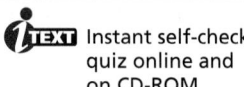

78. $m\angle PQR = 60$. What is $m\angle RQS$?

150

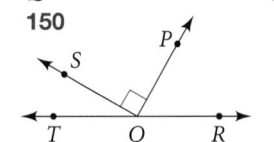

i TEXT Instant self-check quiz online and on CD-ROM

Use the figure for Exercises 1–3.

1. If $AC = 4x + 5$ and $DC = 3x + 8$, find AC.   **17**

2. If $m\angle BCE = 45$ and $m\angle ECD = 65$, find $m\angle BCD$.   **110**

3. If $m\angle FCA = 40$, find $m\angle FCD$.   **140**

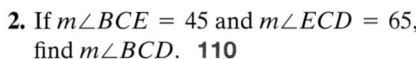

4. $\overleftrightarrow{AX}$ is the perpendicular bisector of $\overline{QS}$ at M.
  a. What is $m\angle AMS$?   **90**
  b. If $QM = 30$, what is QS?   **60**

5. $\overrightarrow{PT}$ is the bisector of $\angle APR$. Name two congruent angles. $\angle APT \cong \angle RPT$

6. $\overrightarrow{OR}$ is the bisector of right $\angle TOS$. Find $m\angle TOR$.   **45**

Use a straightedge to draw three figures like the ones shown at the right. Then do each construction. 7–8. See margin.

7. Construct $\overline{FG}$ so that $FG = CD + RT$.

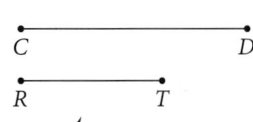

8. Construct $\angle HSK$ so that $m\angle HSK = \frac{1}{2}m\angle LSK$.

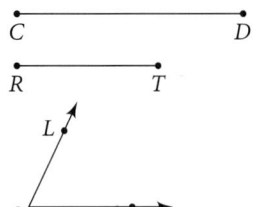

$\overline{AB}$ has endpoints $A(-4, 5)$ and $B(6, -2)$.

9. Find AB to the nearest tenth.   **12.2 units**

10. Find the coordinates of the midpoint of $\overline{AB}$.   **(1, 1.5)**

Lesson 1-6   The Coordinate Plane   **49**

Exercises 66–68 Tell students: *Comparing quantities is common on standardized tests such as the SAT. Whenever a problem asks you to compare quantities, spend a little time making sure that you fully understand the answer choices.*

✔ **Chapter Checkpoint 2**

To check understanding of Lessons 1-4 to 1-6:

Checkpoint Quiz 2 (p. 49)

📁 **Teaching Resources**
Checkpoint Quiz 2 (also in Core Resources and Prentice Hall Assessment System)

👥 **Reaching All Students**
Reading and Math Literacy 1C

Spanish versions available

72.

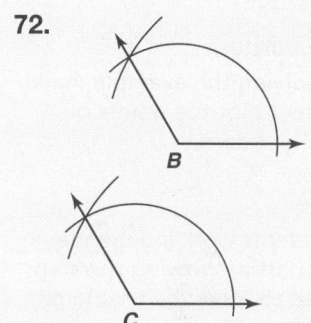

73.

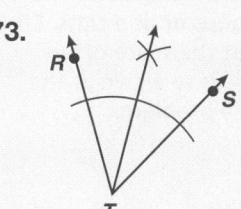

p. 49 Checkpoint Quiz 2

7.

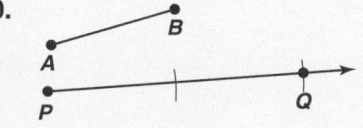

8.

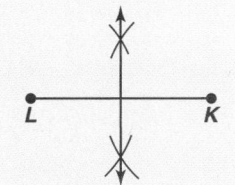

69. [2] a. $(-10, 8), (-1, 5), (8, 2)$
  b. Yes, R must be $(-10, 8)$ so that $RQ = \sqrt{160}$.
[1] part (a) correct or plausible explanation for part (b)

70.

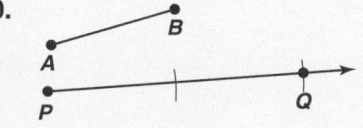

71.

49

Reading an Example

Mathematics texts use examples in their expository sections to illustrate concepts and to teach techniques. A student's success in transferring theory into practice is predicated on fully understanding the textbook examples. Learning how to read examples is directly related to success in mathematics.

Teaching Notes

Read the example as a class. Point out that the left-hand column illustrates what is typically found in the student text and the right-hand column explains details about the solution and the way solutions are presented in this text.

Visual Learners

Before solving the example, have a volunteer plot the points on a grid on the board.

Exercise

Have students work independently to solve part a, showing the steps they used to solve the problem. Then have students discuss part b in small groups or as a class. Elicit the fact that there are often different ways to arrive at the solution of a problem.

In this text, every lesson has two or more worked-out examples. Examples show you how to use the concepts taught in each lesson. In each example, a problem is stated, then solved. Each step in the solution is in the left-hand column, and an explanation of each step is in **bold** at the right.

Before you read an example, be sure to read the material that comes before it. There you will often find important information about the concept illustrated by the example.

EXAMPLE **Finding Distance**

Find the distance between $T(5, 2)$ and $R(-4, -1)$ to the nearest tenth.

This is the statement of the problem.

Let $(5, 2)$ be (x_1, y_1) and $(-4, -1)$ be (x_2, y_2).

This is the first step in the solution. It assigns the numbers in the example to the variables in the Distance Formula.

$d = \sqrt{(x_2 - x_1)^2 + (y_2 - y_1)^2}$ **Use the Distance Formula.**

This is the next step. The text in **bold** explains what is being done.

$d = \sqrt{(-4 - 5)^2 + (-1 - 2)^2}$ **Substitute.**

Variables and their corresponding values are shown in color to help you see the substitutions.

$d = \sqrt{(-9)^2 + (-3)^2}$ **Simplify.**

$d = \sqrt{81 + 9} = \sqrt{90}$

Check the calculations yourself to verify that the expression is simplified correctly.

90 $\boxed{\sqrt{}}$ **9.4868330**   **Use a calculator.**

The input and the keystroke for one type of calculator is given, followed by the calculator output. Try it yourself on your calculator, using, of course, the keystroke(s) appropriate for it.

To the nearest tenth, $TR = 9.5$.

The solution is written as a sentence.

EXERCISE

You will see this Check after every example. The Check Understanding exercise will help you check your understanding of the mathematics in each example. Try the one on page 44 under Example 1, as shown below.

a. $\overline{AB}$ has endpoints $A(1, -3)$ and $B(-4, 4)$. Find AB to the nearest tenth. **8.6**

b. Critical Thinking In Example 1, suppose you let $(-4, -1)$ be (x_1, y_1) and $(5, 2)$ be (x_2, y_2). Do you get the same result? Why?
Yes; the differences are opposites, and the square of a number and the square of its opp. are the same.

Perimeter, Circumference, and Area

1.02 Use length, area, and volume of geometric figures to solve problems.

 North Carolina Objectives

Lesson Preview

What You'll Learn

 OBJECTIVE 1
To find perimeters of rectangles and squares, and circumferences of circles

 OBJECTIVE 2
To find areas of rectangles, squares, and circles

. . . And Why

To find the amount of fencing material needed to build a fence, as in Example 1

✔ **Check Skills You'll Need**   (For help, go to Skills Handbook page 719 and Lesson 1-6.)

Simplify each absolute value.

1. $|4 - 8|$ **4**   2. $|10 - (-5)|$ **15**   3. $|-2 - 6|$ **8**

Find the distance between the points to the nearest tenth.

4. $A(2, 3), B(5, 9)$ **6.7**   5. $K(-1, -3), L(0, 0)$ **3.2**

6. $W(4, -7), Z(10, -2)$ **7.8**   7. $C(-5, 2), D(-7, 6)$ **4.5**

8. $M(-1, -10), P(-12, -3)$ **13.0**   9. $Q(-8, -4), R(-3, -10)$ **7.8**

OBJECTIVE 1 **Finding Perimeter and Circumference**

 iTEXT Interactive lesson includes instant self-check, tutorials, and activities.

? Need Help?

You can think of the *perimeter* of a polygon as the distance around it and the *area* as the number of square units it encloses.

Investigation: Finding Perimeter and Area

Draw each figure on centimeter grid paper.

- a rectangle with length 5 cm and width 3 cm
- a rectangle with length 8 cm and height 2 cm
- a rectangle with each side 4 cm

1. To find the perimeter of each rectangle, find the sum of the lengths of the sides. Record the perimeter of each rectangle. **1–2. See margin.**

2. To find the area of each rectangle, count the number of square centimeters in its interior. Record the area of each rectangle.

3. Do rectangles with equal perimeters have the same area? **no**

4. Do rectangles with the same area have the same perimeter? **no**

The perimeter P of a polygon is the sum of the lengths of its sides. The area A of a polygon is the number of square units it encloses. For special figures such as squares, rectangles, and circles, you can use formulas for perimeter (called circumference in circles) and area.

Some formulas for perimeter and area are given in the chart at the top of the next page. You will also find the chart on pages 726 and 727 to be useful at times.

⚡ Ongoing Assessment and Intervention

Before the Lesson **Diagnose prerequisite skills using:** • Check Skills You'll Need	**During the Lesson** **Monitor progress using:** • Check Understanding • Additional Examples • Standardized Test Prep	**After the Lesson** **Assess knowledge using:** • Lesson Quiz • Computer Test Generator CD

1. Plan

Lesson Preview

✔ **Check Skills You'll Need**

For help use
Skills Handbook, p. 719

Finding Distance
Lesson 1–6: Example 1, Exercises 1–9, Extra Practice, p. 690

Lesson Resources

📁 **Teaching Resources**
Practice, Reteaching, Enrichment

👥 **Reaching All Students**
Practice Workbook 1-7
Spanish Practice Workbook 1-7
Informal Geometry Planning
   Guide 1-7

 Presentation Assistant Plus!
Transparencies
• Check Skills You'll Need 1-7
• Additional Examples 1-7
• Student Edition Answers 1-7
• Lesson Quiz 1-7
PH Presentation Pro CD 1-7

PRENTICE HALL ASSESSMENT SYSTEM

Computer Test Generator CD

 Technology
Resource Pro® CD-ROM
Computer Test Generator CD
Prentice Hall Presentation Pro CD

💻 **www.PHSchool.com**
Student Site
• Teacher Web Code: afk-5500
• Self-grading Lesson Quiz
Teacher Center
• Lesson Planner
• Resources

Plus  **iTEXT**

page 51   Investigation

1. 5 cm by 3 cm → 16 cm
    8 cm by 2 cm → 20 cm
    4 cm by 4 cm → 16 cm

2. 5 cm by 3 cm → 15 cm²
    8 cm by 2 cm → 16 cm²
    4 cm by 4 cm → 16 cm²

2. Teach

Math Background

Strictly speaking, a polygon has no area because it is composed only of segments. A polygonal region is the union of a polygon and its interior. You can use Euclidean geometry to derive formulas for the areas of polygonal regions, but you need calculus to find the areas of some nonpolygonal regions.

OBJECTIVE

① Teaching Notes

Investigation (Optional)
Encourage students to use the term *counterexample* in Exercises 3 and 4.

① EXAMPLE Error Prevention

Students may think they need to add 3 ft only once to each dimension. Discuss why 3 ft is added twice to each dimension. Have students examine a window frame to help clarify each new length and width.

② EXAMPLE Teaching Tip

The calculator value for π is used for all the examples and exercises in this lesson.

Additional Examples

① Margaret's garden is a square 12 ft on each side. She wants a 1-ft-wide path around the entire garden. What will the outside perimeter of the path be? **56 ft**

② $\odot G$ has a radius of 6.5 cm. Find the circumference of $\odot G$ in terms of π. Then find the circumference to the nearest tenth. **13π; about 40.8 cm**

③ Quadrilateral *ABCD* has vertices *A*(0, 0), *B*(9, 12), *C*(11, 12), and *D*(2, 0). Find the perimeter. **34**

 Key Concepts

Summary	Perimeter and Area

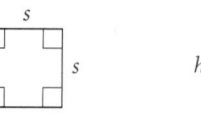

Square with side length *s*

Perimeter $P = 4s$

Area $A = s^2$

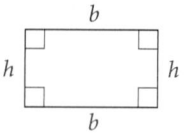

Rectangle with base *b* and height *h*

Perimeter $P = 2b + 2h$

Area $A = bh$

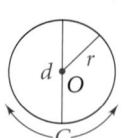

Circle with radius *r* and diameter *d*

Circumference $C = \pi d$, or $C = 2\pi r$

Area $= \pi r^2$

The units of measurement for perimeter and circumference include inches, feet, yards, miles, centimeters, meters, and kilometers. When measuring area, use square units such as square inches (in.^{2}), square centimeters (cm^2), square meters (m^2), and square miles (mi^2).

① EXAMPLE Real-World Connection

Fencing Your pool is 15 ft wide and 20 ft long with a 3-ft wide deck surrounding it. You want to build a fence around the deck. How much fencing will you need?

To find the perimeter of the pool with the deck, first find the width and length of the pool with the deck.

Width of pool and deck $= 15 + 3 + 3 = 21$

Length of pool and deck $= 20 + 3 + 3 = 26$

Perimeter of a rectangle $= 2b + 2h$ Use the formula for the perimeter of a rectangle.

$P = 2(21) + 2(26)$ Substitute.

$P = 42 + 52$ Simplify.

$P = 94$

You will need 94 ft of fencing.

? Need Help?
For a rectangle, "length" and "width" are sometimes used in place of "base" and "height."

✓ Check Understanding **①** Suppose you want to frame a picture that is 6 in. by 7 in. with a $\frac{1}{2}$-in. wide frame.
a. Find the perimeter of the picture. **26 in.**
b. Find the perimeter of the outside edge of the frame. **30 in.**

Notice that the formulas for a circle involve π. Since the number π is irrational,

$$\pi = 3.1415926\ldots,$$

you cannot write it as a terminating decimal. For an approximate answer, you can use 3.14 or $\frac{22}{7}$ $\left(3.14 \approx \frac{22}{7}\right)$ for π. You can also use the rounded decimal you get by pressing $\boxed{\pi}$ on your calculator. For an exact answer leave the result in terms of π.

👥 Reaching All Students

Below Level Review the difference between rational and irrational numbers before discussing why π is irrational.	**Advanced Learners** After students find the perimeter in Example 1, have them find the area of the deck.	**English Learners** See note on page 56. **Visual Learners** See note on page 55.

2 EXAMPLE Finding Circumference

Find the circumference of ⊙A in terms of π. Then find the circumference to the nearest tenth.

$C = \pi d$

$C = 12\pi$ **This is the exact answer.**

12 ⊠ π 🟰 37.699112 **Use a calculator.**

$C \approx 37.7$

● The circumference of the circle is 12π in., or about 37.7 in.

✔ **Check Understanding** **2 a.** Find the circumference of a circle with a radius of 18 m in terms of π. **36π m**

         b. Find the circumference of a circle with a diameter of 18 m to the nearest tenth. **56.5 m**

3 EXAMPLE Finding Perimeter in the Coordinate Plane

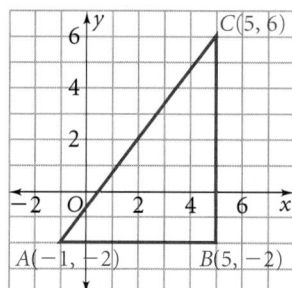

Algebra Find the perimeter of $\triangle ABC$.

Find the length of each side. Add the lengths to find the perimeter.

$AB = |5 - (-1)| = 6$

$BC = |6 - (-2)| = 8$ **Use the Ruler Postulate.**

$AC = \sqrt{(5 - (-1))^2 + (6 - (-2))^2}$ **Use the Distance Formula.**

$ = \sqrt{6^2 + 8^2} = \sqrt{100} = 10$

$AB + BC + AC = 6 + 8 + 10 = 24$

● The perimeter of $\triangle ABC$ is 24 units.

✔ **Check Understanding** **3** Graph quadrilateral $KLMN$ with vertices $K(-3, -3), L(1, -3), M(1, 4),$ and $N(-3, 1)$. Find the perimeter of $KLMN$. **See margin.**

OBJECTIVE

2 Finding Area

To find area, you should use the same unit for both dimensions.

4 EXAMPLE Finding Area of a Rectangle

You are designing a rectangular banner for the front of the museum. The banner will be 4 ft wide and 7 yd high. How much material do you need?

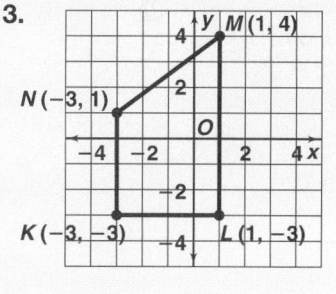

$7 \text{ yd} = 21 \text{ ft}$ **Change yards to feet using 1 yd = 3 ft.**

$\text{Area} = bh$ **Use the formula for area of a rectangle.**

$A = 4(21)$ **Substitute 4 for b and 21 for h.**

$A = 84$

● The area of the banner is 84 square feet (ft²). You need at least 84 ft² of material.

✔ **Check Understanding** **4** Find the area of the banner in Example 4 by first changing all units to yards. Compare your answer to the one in Example 4. How do they compare? **$9\frac{1}{3}$ yd²; $9\frac{1}{3}$ is one-ninth of 84.**

Lesson 1-7   Perimeter, Circumference, and Area   **53**

OBJECTIVE

2 Teaching Notes

5 EXAMPLE Teaching Tip

Students may think that finding area in terms of π is less accurate than using an approximation for π, when the opposite is true. At this point, encourage students to find area both in terms of π and by using an approximation for π.

6 EXAMPLE Math Tip

Use the figure from Example 6 to remind students that Postulate 1-10, *The area of a region is the sum of the areas of its nonoverlapping parts,* does not apply to perimeter.

Auditory Learners

Have students discuss ways to remember the formulas in this lesson. Encourage suggestions from the class.

Additional Examples

4 To make a project, you need a rectangular piece of fabric 36 in. wide and 4 ft long. How many square feet of fabric do you need? **12 ft²**

page 53 Check Understanding

3.

20 units

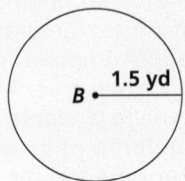
5 Find the area of ⊙B in terms of π.

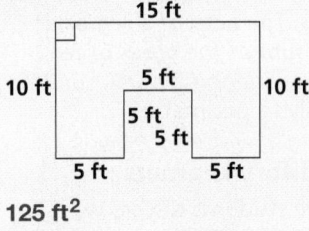

2.25π yd²

6 Find the area of the figure below.

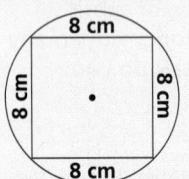

125 ft²

Closure

Find the area and perimeter of the square. Find the area and circumference of the circle in terms of π.

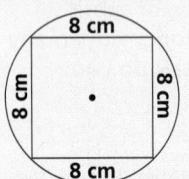

square: 64 cm²; 32 cm; circle: 32π cm²; 8√2π cm

---

5 EXAMPLE **Finding Area of a Circle**

The diameter of a circle is 10 in. Find the area in terms of π.

radius = $\frac{10}{2}$ or 5 $r = \frac{d}{2}$

Area = πr^2 Use the formula for area of a circle.

$A = \pi(5)^2$ Substitute 5 for r.

$A = 25\pi$

● The area of the circle is 25π in.²

✓ **Check Understanding** **5** The diameter of a circle is 5 ft.
  a. Find the area in terms of π. $\frac{25}{4}\pi$ ft²
  b. Find the area to the nearest tenth.   **19.6 ft²**

The following postulates are useful in finding areas of figures with irregular shapes.

🔑 **Key Concepts**

Postulate 1-9

If two figures are congruent, then their areas are equal.

Postulate 1-10

The area of a region is the sum of the areas of its nonoverlapping parts.

Example 6 applies Postulate 1-10 by summing the areas of the parts of a figure.

6 EXAMPLE **Finding Area of an Irregular Shape**

Find the area of the figure at the right.

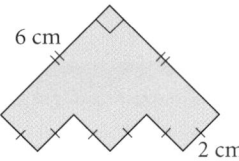

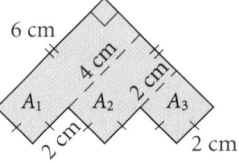

Separate the figure into rectangles.

Area = bh Use the formula for the area of a rectangle.

$A_1 = 6 \cdot 2 = 12$ Find the area of each rectangle.

$A_2 = 4 \cdot 2 = 8$

$A_3 = 2 \cdot 2 = 4$

Total Area = $12 + 8 + 4 = 24$ Add the areas.

● The area of the figure is 24 cm².

✓ **Check Understanding** **6** Copy the figure in Example 6. Separate it in a different way. Find the area.
  See margin.

page 54 Check Understanding

6.

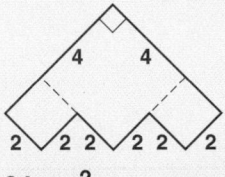

24 cm²

EXERCISES

For more practice, see *Extra Practice*.

Practice and Problem Solving

A **Practice by Example**

Example 1
(page 52)

Find the perimeter of each figure.

1.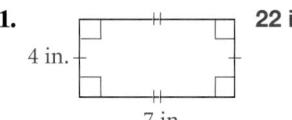

2.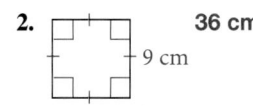

Find the perimeter of each rectangle with the given base and height.

3. 21 in., 7 in. **56 in.**   **4.** 16 cm, 23 cm **78 cm**   **5.** 24 m, 36 m **120 m**

6. Framing A rectangular certificate 8 in. by 10 in. will have a frame $1\frac{1}{2}$ in. wide surrounding it. What is the perimeter of the outside edge of the frame? **48 in.**

7. Fencing A garden that is 5 ft by 6 ft has a walkway 2 ft wide around it. Find the amount of fencing needed to surround the walkway. **38 ft**

Example 2
(page 53)

Find the circumference of each circle in terms of π.

8.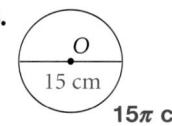
15π cm

9.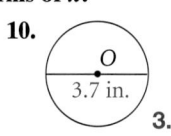
10π ft

10.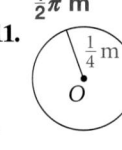
3.7π in.

11. $\frac{1}{2}\pi$ m

Find the circumference of the circle to the nearest tenth.

12. $r = 9$ in.
56.5 in.

13. $d = 7.3$ m
22.9 m

14. $d = \frac{1}{2}$ yd
1.6 yd

15. $r = 56$ cm
351.9 cm

Example 3
(page 53)

Draw each figure in the coordinate plane. Find the perimeter. See back of book.

16. $X(0, 2), Y(4, -1), Z(-2, -1)$

17. $A(-4, -1), B(4, 5), C(4, -2)$

18. $L(0, 1), M(3, 5), N(5, 5), P(5, 1)$

19. $S(-5, 3), T(7, -2), U(7, -6), V(-5, -6)$

Example 4
(page 53)

Find the area of each rectangle with the given base and height. 20–25. See margin.

20. 4 ft, 4 in.

21. 30 in., 4 yd

22. 2 ft 3 in., 6 in.

23. 40 cm, 2 m

24. 3 m, 190 cm

25. 240 cm, 5 m

26. Find the area of a section of road pavement that is 20 ft wide and 100 yd long.
6000 ft² or $666\frac{2}{3}$ yd²

Example 5
(page 54)

Find the area of each circle in terms of π.

27.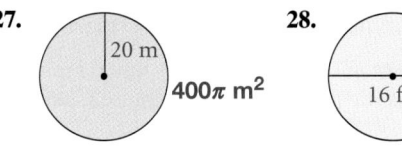
400π m²

28.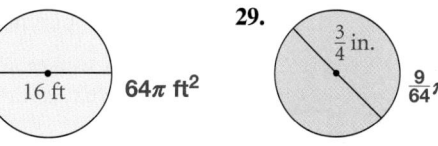
64π ft²

29. $\frac{9}{64}\pi$ in.²

30.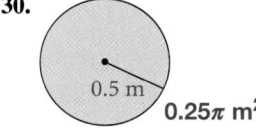
0.25π m²

31.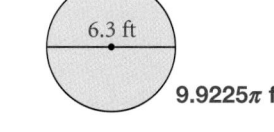
9.9225π ft²

32.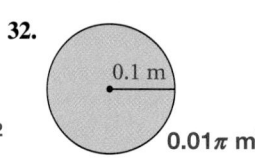
0.01π m²

pages 55–58 **Exercises**

20. $1\frac{1}{3}$ ft² or 192 in.²

21. 4320 in.² or $3\frac{1}{3}$ yd²

22. $1\frac{1}{8}$ ft² or 162 in.²

23. 8000 cm² or 0.8 m²

24. 5.7 m² or 57,000 cm²

25. 120,000 cm² or 12 m²

---

3. Practice

Assignment Guide

1 Objective
 **Core** 1–19, 56
Extension 72

2 Objective
 **Core** 20–55, 57–65
Extension 66–71

Standardized Test Prep 73–77

Mixed Review 78–90

Visual Learners

Exercises 6, 7 Encourage students to draw the rectangles, write the applicable formula next to each drawing, and label their drawings with the appropriate units.

Exercises 20–26 Use these exercises to highlight the importance of using the same units when working with measurements.

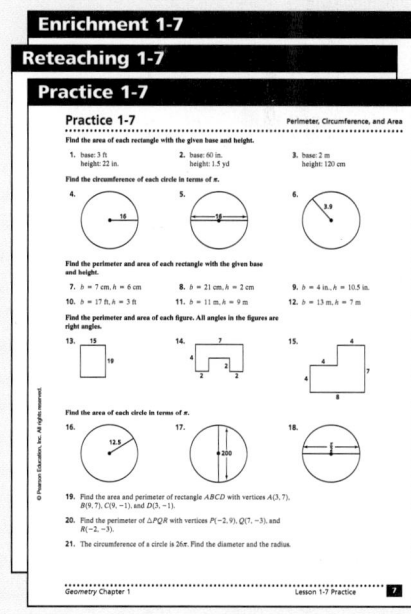

Alternative Method

Exercises 37–40 Each figure can be separated in several ways. After students find the areas, have them share with a partner how they separated the figures.

Error Prevention

Exercise 59 Point out that students must first find the radius of the circle before finding its diameter.

Diversity

Exercise 62 Some students may be unfamiliar with weather-stripping. Invite a student to explain its use.

Exercise 66 If necessary, review the procedure for making tables on a graphing calculator.

Exercise 71 Students may have difficulty if they try to find just two squares for this exercise. Have students read the directions carefully.

English Learners

Exercise 72 Point out that the prefix *semi-* means *half*. Ask: *What do two halves make?* one whole

Example 6
(page 54)

41c. There are 144 square inches in one square foot. A square whose sides are 12 in. long and a square whose sides are 1 ft long are the same size.

B Apply Your Skills

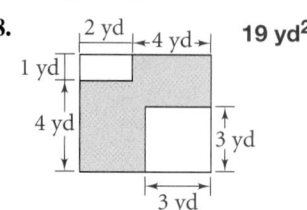

El Castillo
Chichen Itza, Mexico

Real-World Connection

Postulate 1-10 can help you estimate the area of the "footprint," of El Castillo.

Find the area of each circle to the nearest tenth.

33. $r = 7$ ft
153.9 ft^2

34. $d = 8.3$ m
54.1 m^2

35. $d = 24$ cm
452.4 cm^2

36. $r = 12$ in.
452.4 in.^{2}

Find the area of the shaded region. All angles are right angles.

37. 310 m^2
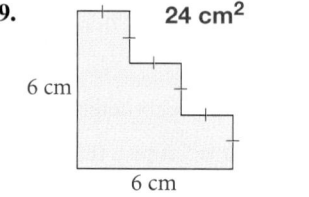

38. 19 yd^2
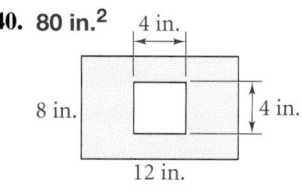

39. 24 cm^2

40. 80 in.^{2}
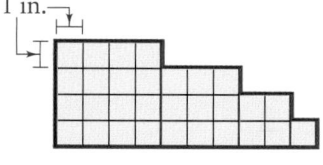

41. a. What is the area of a square whose sides are 12 in. long? **144 in.^{2}**
b. What is the area of a square whose sides are 1 ft long? **1 ft^2**
c. Reasoning How many square inches are in a square foot? Explain. **See left.**

42. a. Count squares to find the area of the polygon outlined in blue. **30 squares**
b. Use a formula to find the area of each square outlined in red. **16; 9; 4; 1**
c. How does the sum of your results in part (b) compare to your result in part (a)? Which postulate does this support? **They are =. Post. 1-10**

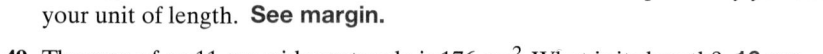

1 in.

43. Estimation On a postcard from Mexico, Ky sketched the "footprint" of the pyramid known as El Castillo in the ancient Mayan city Chichen Itza. He said he estimated the three different lengths on each side to be 22 m, 6 m, and 11 m. Use those estimates to estimate the area of El Castillo's footprint. **3289 m^2**

44–47. Answers may vary. Check students' work. Samples are given.
Estimation Estimate the perimeter and area of each object.

44. the front cover of this book 38 in.; 90 in.^{2}

45. the front cover of your notebook 39 in.; 93.5 in.^{2}

46. a classroom bulletin board
12 ft; 8 ft^2

47. the top of your desk
8 ft; 3.75 ft^2

48. Writing Choose one exercise from Exercises 44–47 and explain why you chose your unit of length. **See margin.**

49. The area of an 11-cm wide rectangle is 176 cm^2. What is its length? **16 cm**

50. The perimeter of a rectangle is 40 cm and the base is 12 cm. What is its area? **96 cm^2**

51. A square and a rectangle have equal area. The rectangle is 64 cm by 81 cm. What is the perimeter of the square? **288 cm**

52. a. Critical Thinking Can you use the formula for the perimeter of a rectangle to find the perimeter of any square? Explain. **See margin.**
b. Can you use the formula for the perimeter of a square to find the perimeter of any rectangle? Explain. **See margin.**
c. Use the formula for the perimeter of a square to write a formula for the area of a square in terms of its perimeter. $A = \left(\frac{P}{4}\right)^2$ or $A = \frac{P^2}{16}$

56 Chapter 1 Tools of Geometry

48. Answers may vary. Sample: For Exercise 46, you use feet because the bulletin board is too big for inches.

You do not use yards because your estimated lengths in feet were not divisible by 3.

b. Answers may vary. Sample: No, not all rectangles are squares.

52. a. Yes; every square is a rectangle.

Real-World **Connection**

Four 6 in.-by-6 in. tiles will cover 1 ft^2.

53. Tiling The students in the Art Club are tiling a wall that is 8 ft by 16 ft at the entrance to the community center. They are using tiles that are 6 in. by 6 in. to create a multi-colored design. How many tiles do the students need? **512 tiles**

$\boxed{x^2}$ **Algebra** Draw each rectangle in the coordinate plane. Find its perimeter and area.

54. $A(-3, 2), B(-2, 2), C(-2, -2), D(-3, -2)$ **54–55. See back of book.**

55. $A(-2, -6), B(-2, -3), C(3, -3), D(3, -6)$

Coordinate Geometry On graph paper, draw polygon $ABCDEFGH$ with vertices $A(1, 1)$, $B(10, 1)$, $C(10, 8)$, $D(7, 8)$, $E(7, 5)$, $F(4, 5)$, $G(4, 8)$, and $H(1, 8)$.

56. Find the perimeter of the polygon. **38 units**

57. Divide the polygon into rectangles. Find the area of the polygon. **54 units^2**

58. Biology In the Pacific Northwest, a red fox has a circular home range with a radius of about 718 meters. To the nearest thousand square meters, what is the area of the home range of a red fox? **1,620,000 m^2**

59. A circle has area 225π m^2. What is the diameter of the circle? **30 m**

$\boxed{x^2}$ **60. Algebra** A rectangle has a base of x units. The area is $(4x^2 - 2x)$ square units. What is the height of the rectangle in terms of x? **$(4x - 2)$ units**

Home Maintenance To determine how much of each item to buy, tell whether you need to know area or perimeter. Explain your choice. **61–64. See margin.**

61. wallpaper for a bedroom

62. weatherstripping for a door

63. fence for a garden

64. paint for a basement floor

65. Coordinate Geometry The endpoints of a diameter of a circle are $A(2, 1)$ and $B(5, 5)$. Find the area of the circle in terms of π. **6.25π units^2**

C Challenge

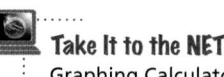

Take It to the NET
Graphing Calculator procedures online at **www.PHSchool.com**
Web Code: afe-2104

66. Graphing Calculator You want to build a rectangular corral by using the side of a barn for one side and 100 ft of fencing for the other three sides.
   a. Create a table on your graphing calculator listing integer values for the base and the corresponding values of the height and area.
   b. Make a graph using your table values. Graph the base on the horizontal axis and area on the vertical axis. **a–b. See back of book.**
   c. What are the dimensions of the corral with the greatest area? **25 ft by 50 ft**

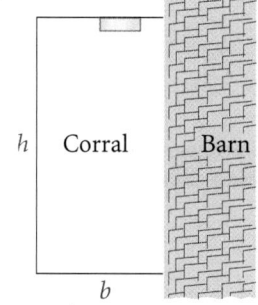

67. How many circles with the given radius are needed for the sum of their areas to equal the area of a circle with the second given radius?
   a. 1 in., 3 in. **9**   **b.** 2 in., 6 in. **9**   **c.** 3 in., 9 in. **9**
   d. Make a Conjecture How many circles with a radius of n in. are needed for the sum of their areas to equal the area of a circle with a radius of $3n$ in.? **9**

$\boxed{x^2}$ **Algebra** Find the area of each figure.

68. a rectangle with side lengths of $\frac{2a}{5b}$ units and $\frac{3b}{8}$ units $\frac{3a}{20}$ **units^2**

69. a square with perimeter $10n$ units $\frac{25n^2}{4}$ **units^2**

70. a square with side lengths of $(3m - 4n)$ units $(9m^2 - 24mn + 16n^2)$ **units^2**

Lesson 1-7 Perimeter, Circumference, and Area   **57**

61. **Area; the wall is a surface.**

62. **Perimeter; weatherstripping must fit the edges of the door.**

63. **Perimeter; the fence must fit the perimeter of the garden.**

64. **Area; the floor is a surface.**

4. Assess

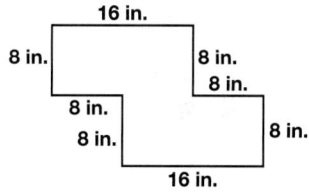

Lesson Quiz 1-7

A rectangle is 9 ft long and 40 in. wide.

1. Find the perimeter in inches. **296 in.**

2. Find the area in square feet. **30 ft^2**

3. The diameter of a circle is 18 cm. Find the area in terms of π. **81π cm^2**

4. Find the perimeter of a triangle whose vertices are $X(-6, 2)$, $Y(8, 2)$, and $Z(3, 14)$. **42 units**

5. Find the area of the figure below. All angles are right angles. **256 in.^{2}**

16 in.

8 in.

8 in.

8 in.

8 in.

8 in.

8 in.

16 in.

Alternative Assessment

Have students draw and label a rectangle and a circle, each having an area between 20 and 25 in.^{2} They should include with each drawing a written explanation of how each area can be verified.

A sheet of blank grids is available in the Test-Taking Strategies with Transparencies booklet. Give this sheet to students for practice with filling in the grids.

📁 **Resources**

For additional practice with a variety of test item formats:
- Standardized Test Prep, p. 65
- Test-Taking Strategies, p. 60
- Test-Taking Strategies with Transparencies

Exercises 75–77 Students should be careful that the tiles cover the floor with no gaps or overlapping. Remind them to write the dimensions of both the floor and the tiles using the same unit of measurement.

71. Answers may vary.
Sample: one
8 in.-by-8 in. square
+ one 5 in.-by-5 in.
square + two
4 in.-by-4 in. squares

71. Open-Ended The area of a 5 in.-by-5 in. square is the same as the sum of the areas of a 3 in.-by-3 in. square and a 4 in.-by-4 in. square. Find two or more squares whose total area is the same as the area of an 11 in.-by-11 in. square. **See left.**

🌐 **72. Track** An athletic field is a rectangle, 100 yards by 40 yards, with a semicircle at each of the short sides. A running track 10 yards wide surrounds the field. Find the perimeter of the outside of the running track to the nearest tenth of a yard. **388.5 yd**

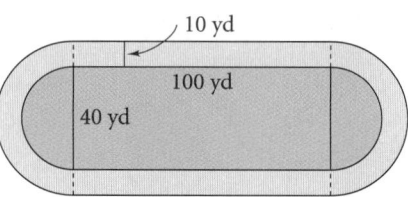

10 yd
100 yd
40 yd

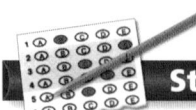

Standardized Test Prep

Gridded Response

For Exercises 73 and 74, a rectangular garden has a rectangular walkway around it. The width of the walkway is 8 ft.

73. How many feet greater than the perimeter of the garden is the outside perimeter of the walkway? **64**

74. If the garden is a square with a perimeter of 260 ft, what is the area of the walkway in square feet? **2336**

Take It to the NET
Online lesson quiz at
www.PHSchool.com
Web Code: afa-0107

75. You need to tile a 12 ft-by-15 ft floor. The color you want allows you the choices found in the table at the right. How many dollars would it cost to tile the floor with 12 in.-by-12 in. tiles? **540**

Size of Tiles	Cost
12″ × 12″	$3/ft^2
11″ × 11″	$3/ft^2
10″ × 12″	$4/ft^2
6″ × 8″	$4.50/ft^2

76. How many tiles would cover the 12 ft-by-15 ft floor if you choose the 10 in.-by-12 in. tiles? **216**

77. How many dollars would it cost to cover the 12 ft-by-15 ft floor with the tiles that are 6 in. by 8 in.? **810**

Mixed Review

Lesson 1-6

78. The midpoint of $\overline{CD}$ has coordinates $(5, 6)$. Point C has coordinates $(-5, -1)$. Find the coordinates of point D. **(15, 13)**

Find (a) AB to the nearest tenth and (b) the coordinates of the midpoint of $\overline{AB}$.

79. $A(4, 1)$, $B(7, 9)$
8.5 units; (5.5, 5)

80. $A(0, 3)$, $B(3, 8)$
5.8 units; (1.5, 5.5)

81. $A(9, 2)$, $B(-3, 9)$
13.9 units; (3, 5.5)

82. $A(0, 1)$, $B(-4, 6)$
6.4 units; (-2, 3.5)

83. $A(4, 10)$, $B(-2, 3)$
9.2 units; (1, 6.5)

84. $A(-1, 1)$, $B(-4, -5)$
6.7 units; (-2.5, -2)

Lesson 1-5

$\overleftrightarrow{BG}$ is the perpendicular bisector of $\overline{WR}$ at point I.

85. What is $m\angle BIR$? **90**

86. Name two congruent segments. $\overline{WI} \cong \overline{RI}$

87. $\overline{WR}$ has length 124. What is the length of $\overline{IR}$? **62 units**

Lesson 1-4

For the given coordinates, find PQ.

88. P: 12, Q: -6
18 units

89. P: 3, Q: 9
6 units

90. P: -23, Q: 10
33 units

Comparing Perimeters and Areas

FOR USE WITH LESSON 1-7

You can use a graphing calculator or spreadsheet technology to find maximum and minimum values for area and perimeter problems.

You have 32 yards of fencing. You want to make a rectangular pen for the calf you are raising as a 4-H project. What dimensions will give the maximum area? What is the maximum area?

Take It to the NET
Graphing Calculator procedures online at
www.PHSchool.com
Web Code: afe-2104

Investigate
Draw some possible rectangular pens and find their areas.

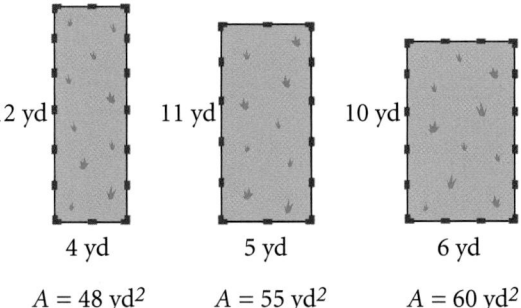

12 yd	11 yd	10 yd
4 yd	5 yd	6 yd
$A = 48$ yd^2	$A = 55$ yd^2	$A = 60$ yd^2

Create a graphing calculator table to find area. Let X represent values for the base. The height then is $16 - X$, and the area is $X(16 - X)$. Enter $Y1 = 16 - X$ and $Y2 = X(16 - X)$. Set the table so that X starts at 1 and changes by 1.

Scroll down the table. Area is maximum when X (or b) is 8. When $b = 8, h = 8$ and $A = 64$.

You can confirm this result by graphing $Y1 = X(16 - X)$. Trace on the graph to find the maximum area.

A square pen with sides of 8 yd will give maximum area for your calf. The maximum area is 64 yd^2.

X	Y₁	Y₂
4	12	48
5	11	55
6	10	60
7	9	63
8	8	64
9	7	63
10	6	60

X=4

Y2=X(16-X)

X=8   Y=64

X min = 0	Y min = 0
X max = 18	Y max = 70
X scl = 2	Y scl = 7

EXERCISES

1. **Make a Conjecture** For a fixed perimeter, what rectangular shape will result in a maximum area? **square**

2. Consider that the pen is not restricted to polygon shapes. Determine the area of a circular pen if the circumference is 32 yd. How does this result compare with the maximum square area of 64 yd^2 found in the investigation? **about 81.5 yd^2; the circular pen has greater area.**

3. You want to make a rectangular garden with an area of 900 ft^2. You want to use a minimum amount of fencing to keep the cost low.
   a. List some possible dimensions for the rectangular garden. Find the perimeter of each rectangle.
      3a. Answers may vary. Sample: 25 ft-by-36 ft; $P = 122$ ft
      30 ft-by-30 ft; $P = 120$ ft
   b. Create a graphing calculator table. Use integer values of the base b, and the corresponding values of the height h, to find values for P, the perimeter. **10 ft-by-90 ft; $P = 200$ ft** What dimensions will give you a garden with the minimum perimeter?
      30 ft-by-30 ft square

Comparing Perimeters and Areas

Students will use graphing calculators or spreadsheets to explore the relationship between perimeters and areas of rectangles.

Resources

Students may use any graphing calculator or any spreadsheet program to complete this investigation.

Teaching Notes

Constructing a table and graphing the parabola $y = x(16 - x)$ can provide students with organized, visual ways to help them understand the complex relationship between perimeter and area.

English Learners
Discuss as a class the meanings of *maximum* and *minimum*. Have students point out ways the words are used outside mathematics class, such as "maximum security" and "minimum wage."

Connection to Calculus
In a calculus course, you would use the same equation, $y = x(16 - x)$, to solve this problem. For the solution, you would find and solve another function called the *derivative*.

Exercise 2 Remind students to use the formula for the circumference of a circle $C = 2\pi r$ to solve for r when $C = 32$. Then ask: *How can you now find the area?* Substitute the value for r in the equation $A = \pi r^2$.

Test-Taking Strategies

Writing Gridded Responses

Many assessment tests now require students to answer gridded-response problems in addition to the more traditional multiple-choice problems with which they are already familiar. This feature helps students understand how to approach these problems.

Resources

PRENTICE HALL
ASSESSMENT SYSTEM

Test-Taking Strategies with Transparencies
- Transparency 1
- Practice sheet p. 13
- Blank sheet of Grids, p. vi

Teaching Notes

The answer to a gridded-response problem often can be written in two or more ways, as shown in Examples 1 and 2.

Inclusion

Students with motor difficulties may find it hard to write the answer in the space allowed and fill in the bubbles. Explain that special administrations of assessment tests are sometimes provided for these students.

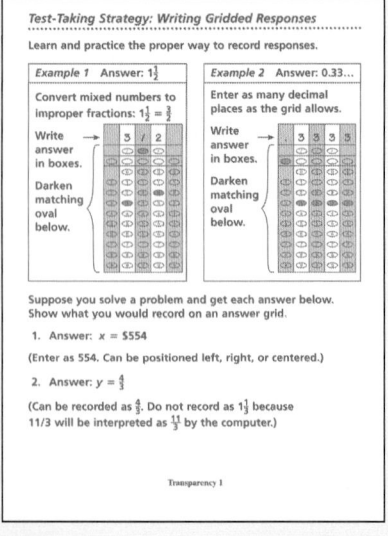

Test-Taking Strategies with Transparencies

Test-Taking Strategies

Writing Gridded Responses

Some tests include gridded-response questions. You find a numerical answer. Then you write the answer at the top of the grid and fill in the corresponding bubbles below. You have to be sure that you use the grid correctly.

1 EXAMPLE

What is the x-coordinate of the midpoint of the segment with endpoints $H(5, 1)$ and $K(12, 2)$?

By the Midpoint Formula, you can find that the coordinates of the midpoint are $\left(\frac{17}{2}, \frac{3}{2}\right)$.

The answer to the question is $\frac{17}{2}$.

You can write the answer as 17/2 or 8.5.

The grids at the right show two ways to enter the answer.

Certain tests may have specific directions for entering answers in grids.

If your answer doesn't fit, then you may have misread the directions or the problem itself, or you made a calculation error. Go back and check.

2 EXAMPLE

What is the distance between the points $A(0, 0.14)$ and $B(0.1, 0.2)$? Round your answer to the nearest hundredth.

The answer is 0.12. You grid this as .12 or as 0.12.

EXERCISES

Write what you would grid for each answer.

1. What is the y-coordinate of the midpoint of a segment with endpoints $C(0, -1)$ and $D(-6, 12)$? **11/2**

2. What is the diameter, in centimeters, of a circle with circumference 0.5π cm? **0.5**

3. What is the distance between $L(0, 0)$ and $M(0.3, 0.4)$? **0.5**

4. The endpoints of a diameter of a circle are $R(3, 5)$ and $T(12, 5)$. What is the area of the circle? Round your answer to the nearest hundredth. **63.62**

5. What is the radius of a circle whose area is 10π cm^2? Round your answer to the nearest hundredth of a centimeter. **3.16**

Chapter Review

Vocabulary

acute angle (p. 28)
angle (p. 27)
angle bisector (p. 36)
axiom (p. 12)
collinear points (p. 11)
compass (p. 34)
congruent angles (p. 29)
congruent segments (p. 25)
conjecture (p. 5)
construction (p. 34)
coordinate (p. 25)

coplanar (p. 11)
counterexample (p. 5)
inductive reasoning (p. 4)
line (p. 11)
midpoint (p. 26)
obtuse angle (p. 28)
opposite rays (p. 17)
parallel lines (p. 18)
parallel planes (p. 18)
perpendicular bisector (p. 35)
perpendicular lines (p. 35)

plane (p. 11)
point (p. 11)
postulate (p. 12)
ray (p. 17)
right angle (p. 28)
segment (p. 17)
skew lines (p. 18)
space (p. 11)
straight angle (p. 28)
straightedge (p. 34)

Resources

Student Edition
Extra Practice Ch. 7, p. 690
English/Spanish Glossary, p. 741
Postulates and Theorems, p. 732
Table of Symbols, p. 726

 **Reaching All Students**
Reading and Math Literacy 1D
Spanish Reading and Literacy 1D

 PRENTICE HALL
ASSESSMENT *SYSTEM*

Standardized Test Prep
• Ch. 1 practice in standardized
test formats

 **www.PHSchool.com**
Student Site
• Self-grading Vocabulary Test
Teacher Center
• Resources

Plus

 **Reading Math**
Understanding
Vocabulary

Choose the correct term to complete each sentence.

1. Figures that are in the same plane are ? . **coplanar**

2. A(n) ? is the part of a line consisting of two endpoints and all points between them. **segment**

3. Two segments with the same length are ? . **congruent**

4. A(n) ? of a segment is the point that divides the segment into two congruent segments. **midpoint**

5. angle bisector
5. A(n) ? is a ray that divides an angle into two congruent angles.

6. A conclusion based upon inductive reasoning is sometimes called a(n) ? .
conjecture

7. A(n) ? is an accepted statement of fact. **postulate or axiom**

8. ? are coplanar lines that do not intersect. **Parallel lines**

9. A(n) ? is an angle whose measure is between 90 and 180. **obtuse angle**

10. A(n) ? of a segment is a line, segment, or ray that is perpendicular to a segment at its midpoint. **perpendicular bisector**

 **Take It to the NET**
Online vocabulary quiz
at **www.PHSchool.com**
Web Code: ajf-0151

Skills and Concepts

1-1 Objectives

▼ To use inductive reasoning to make conjectures

You use **inductive reasoning** when you make conclusions based on patterns you observe. A **conjecture** describes a conclusion reached using inductive reasoning. A **counterexample** to a conjecture is an example for which the conjecture is incorrect.

Find a pattern for each sequence. Describe the pattern and use it to show the next two terms. 11–16. See margin.

11. $40, 35, 30, 25, \ldots$

12. $5, -5, 5, -5, \ldots$

13. $34, 27, 20, 13, 6, \ldots$

14. $6, 24, 96, 384, \ldots$

15. $2, 4, 8, 16, 32, \ldots$

16. $1, 2, 5, 6, 9, \ldots$

17.

17. Draw the next figure in the sequence.
See left.

pages 61–63   Chapter Review

11. subtract 5; 20, 15

12. Answers may vary.
Sample: mult. by −1;
5, −5

13. subtr.7; −1, −8

14. mult. by 4; 1536, 6144

15. mult. by 2; 64, 128

16. alternate adding 1 and 3;
10, 13

1-2 and 1-3 Objectives

▼ To understand basic terms and postulates of geometry

▼ To identify segments and rays

▼ To recognize parallel lines

Points that lie on the same line are **collinear points.** Points and lines in the same plane are **coplanar. Segments** and **rays** are parts of lines.

Lines that are coplanar and do not intersect are **parallel lines.** Lines in space that are not parallel and do not intersect are **skew.** Planes that do not intersect are **parallel planes.**

A **postulate** or **axiom** is an accepted statement of fact.

18–23. Answers may vary. Samples are given.

Use the figure at the right for Exercises 18–23.

18. Name two intersecting lines. **$\overleftrightarrow{AQ}$ and $\overleftrightarrow{QR}$**

19. Name a pair of skew lines. **$\overleftrightarrow{AQ}$ and $\overleftrightarrow{BC}$**

20. Name three noncollinear points. **A, Q, R**

21. Name four noncoplanar points. **A, Q, R, S**

22. Name a pair of parallel planes. **AQTD and BRSC**

23. Name three lines that intersect at D.
$\overleftrightarrow{AD}$, $\overleftrightarrow{TD}$, $\overleftrightarrow{CD}$

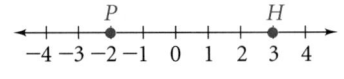

Complete with *always, sometimes,* or *never* to make a true statement.

24. always

24. A line and a point are __?__ coplanar.

25. Two segments are __?__ coplanar. **sometimes**

26. Skew lines are __?__ coplanar. **never**

27. Parallel lines are __?__ skew. **never**

28. Two points are __?__ collinear. **always**

29. Parallel lines are __?__ coplanar. **always**

1-4 Objectives

▼ To find the lengths of segments

▼ To find the measures of angles

Segments with the same length are **congruent segments.** The **midpoint** of a segment divides a segment into two congruent segments.

Two rays with the same endpoint form an **angle.** Angles are sometimes measured in degrees. Angles can be classified as acute, right, obtuse, or straight. Angles with the same measure are **congruent angles.**

30. Find two possible coordinates of Q so that $PQ = 5$. **−7, 3**

31. Find the coordinate of the midpoint of $\overline{PH}$. **0.5**

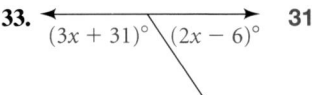

x^2 **Algebra Find the value of each variable.**

32.
$$3m + 5 \quad 4m - 10 \qquad \mathbf{15}$$

A   B   C

33. $(3x + 31)° \quad (2x - 6)°$ **31**

34. Name the congruent segments.

A B   C D   E
−6 −4 −2   0   2   4   6

$\overline{AB} \cong \overline{CD}$
$\overline{AC} \cong \overline{BD} \cong \overline{CE}$
$\overline{BC} \cong \overline{DE}$

35. Name $\angle 1$ and $\angle 2$ two other ways.

∠1: **∠WXY, ∠YXW**
∠2: **∠YXZ, ∠ZXY**

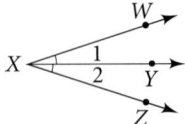

1-5 Objectives

▼ To use a compass and a straightedge to construct congruent segments and congruent angles

▼ To use a compass and a straightedge to bisect segments and angles

Construction is the process of making geometric figures using a **compass** and a **straightedge.** Four basic constructions involve constructing congruent segments, congruent angles, and bisectors of segments and angles.

Perpendicular lines intersect at right angles. A **perpendicular bisector** of a segment is perpendicular to the segment at its midpoint, and bisects it into two congruent segments. An **angle bisector** is a ray that divides an angle into two congruent angles.

36. Use a protractor to draw a 64° angle. Then construct an angle congruent to your 64° angle. **See margin.**

37. Use a ruler and draw $\overline{PQ}$.
   a. Construct $\overline{AB} \cong \overline{PQ}$.   **a–b. See margin.** $P \bullet\!\!-\!\!-\!\!-\!\!-\!\!-\!\!-\!\!\bullet Q$
   b. Construct the perpendicular bisector of $\overline{AB}$.

1-6 Objectives

▼ To find the distance between two points in the coordinate plane

▼ To find the coordinates of the midpoint of a segment in the coordinate plane

The x-axis and the y-axis intersect at the origin $(0, 0)$ and determine a coordinate plane. You can find the coordinates of the midpoint M of $\overline{AB}$ with endpoints $A(x_1, y_1)$ and $B(x_2, y_2)$ using the **Midpoint Formula.**

$$M = \left(\frac{x_1 + x_2}{2}, \frac{y_1 + y_2}{2} \right)$$

You can find the distance d between points $A(x_1, y_1)$ and $B(x_2, y_2)$ using the **Distance Formula.**

$$d = \sqrt{(x_2 - x_1)^2 + (y_2 - y_1)^2}$$

Find the distance between the points to the nearest tenth.

38. $A(-1, 5), B(0, 4)$ **39.** $C(-1, -1), D(6, 2)$ **40.** $E(-7, 0), F(5, 8)$
   1.4 units   **7.6 units**   **14.4 units**

$\overline{GH}$ has endpoints $G(-3, 2)$ and $H(3, -2)$.

41. Find the coordinates of the midpoint of $\overline{GH}$.   **(0, 0)**

42. Find GH to the nearest tenth.   **7.2 units**

1-7 Objectives

▼ To find perimeters of rectangles and squares, and circumferences of circles

▼ To find areas of rectangles, squares, and circles

The perimeter P of a polygon is the sum of the lengths of its sides. The area A of a polygon is the number of square units it encloses.

Formulas: Square   Rectangle   Circle
             $P = 4s$ $P = 2b + 2h$ $C = \pi d$ or $C = 2\pi r$
             $A = s^2$ $A = bh$ $A = \pi r^2$

Find the perimeter and the area of each figure.

43.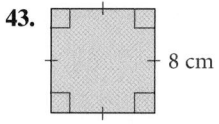
8 cm
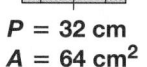
P = 32 cm
A = 64 cm²

44.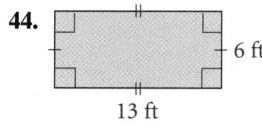
6 ft
13 ft
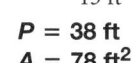
P = 38 ft
A = 78 ft²

45.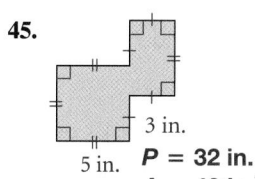
3 in.
5 in.
P = 32 in.
A = 40 in.²

Find the circumference and the area of each circle to the nearest hundredth.

46. $r = 3$ in.   **47.** $d = 15$ m   **48.** $r = 26$ m
C = 18.85 in.   **C = 47.12 m,**   **C = 163.36 m, A = 2123.72 m²**
A = 28.27 in.²   **A = 176.71 m²**

Chapter 1   Chapter Review   **63**

pages 61–63   Chapter Review

36.

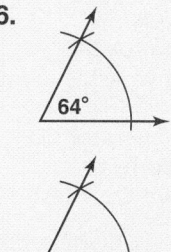
64°

37. a–b.

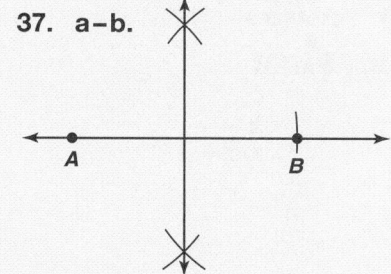
A   B

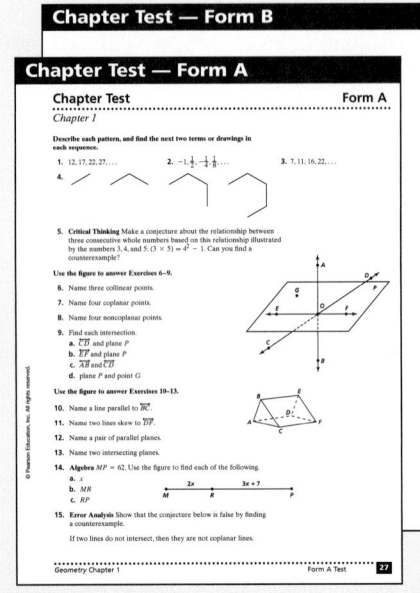

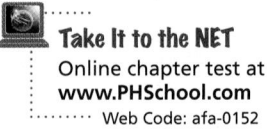
Take It to the NET
Online chapter test at
www.PHSchool.com
Web Code: afa-0152

Describe each pattern and find the next two terms of each sequence. **1–3. See margin.**

1. $8, -4, 2, -1, \ldots$

2. $0, 2, 4, 6, 8, \ldots$

3.
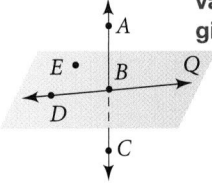

4. **Open-Ended** Write two different sequences whose first three terms are $1, 2, 4$. Describe each pattern. **See margin.**

Use the figure for Exercises 5–9. **6–7. Answers may vary. Samples are given.**

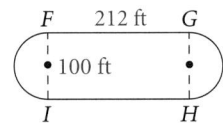

5. Name three collinear points. **A, B, C**

6. Name four coplanar points. **A, B, C, D**

7. Name four noncoplanar points. **A, B, D, E**

8. What is the intersection of $\overleftrightarrow{AC}$ and plane Q? **B**

9. How many planes contain each line and each point?
   a. $\overleftrightarrow{BD}$ and point A **1**   b. $\overleftrightarrow{AB}$ and point C
   c. $\overleftrightarrow{BE}$ and point C **1**   d. $\overleftrightarrow{BD}$ and point E **1**
   9b. infinitely many

10. **Track** The running track is a rectangle with a half circle on each end. If $\overline{FI}$ and $\overline{GH}$ are diameters, find the area inside the track to the nearest tenth. **29,054.0 ft²**

F   212 ft   G
• 100 ft •
I   H

Complete with always, sometimes, or never to make each statement true.

11. $\overrightarrow{LJ}$ and $\overrightarrow{TJ}$ are ___?___ opposite rays. **never**

12. Four points are ___?___ coplanar. **sometimes**

13. Skew lines are ___?___ coplanar. **never**

14. Two segments that lie in parallel lines are ___?___ parallel. **always**

15. The intersection of two planes is ___?___ a point. **never**

x^2 16. **Algebra** $JK = 48$. Find the value of x. **10**

J   H   K
  $4x - 15$ $2x + 3$

x^2 17. **Algebra** $M(x, y)$ is the midpoint of $\overline{CD}$ with endpoints $C(5, 9)$ and $D(17, 29)$.
   a. Find the values of x and y. **(11, 19)**
   b. Show $MC = MD$. **MC = MD = $\sqrt{136}$**

18. To the nearest tenth, find the perimeter of $\triangle ABC$ with vertices $A(-2, -2)$, $B(0, 5)$, and $C(3, -1)$. **19.1 units**

For the given dimensions, find the area of each figure to the nearest hundredth.

19. rectangle   20. square   21. circle
   $b = 4$ m $s = 3.5$ in. $d = 9$ cm
   $h = 2$ cm   **12.25 in.²**   **63.62 cm²**
   800 cm² or 0.08 m²

x^2 **Algebra** Find the value of each variable in Exercises 22 and 23.

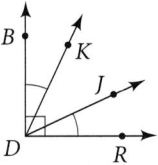

22. $m\angle BDK = 3x + 4$, $m\angle JDR = 5x - 10$ **7**

23. $m\angle BDJ = 7y + 2$, $m\angle JDR = 2y + 7$ **9**

24. **Writing** Why is it useful to have more than one way of naming an angle? **See margin, p. 65.**

25. Draw an obtuse $\angle ABC$. Use a compass and straightedge to bisect the angle. **See margin, p. 65.**

Use the figure to complete Exercises 26–30.

26. $\overline{VW}$ is the ___?___ of $\overline{AY}$. **⊥ bisector**

27. $EW + EV = $ ___?___ **VW**

28. If $EY = 3.5$, then $AY = $ ___?___. **7**

29. $\frac{1}{2}$ ___?___ $= AE$ **AY**

30. ___?___ is the midpoint of ___?___. **E; $\overline{AY}$**

31. **Carpeting** How many square yards of carpet are needed to carpet a room that is 15 ft long and 20 ft wide? **$33\frac{1}{3}$ yd²**

---

page 64   Chapter Test

1. **Div. each preceding term by -2; $\frac{1}{2}$, $-\frac{1}{4}$**

2. **Add 2 to the preceding term; 10, 12**

3. **Rotate the U clockwise one-quarter turn. Alphabet is backwards;**
   O N

4. **Answers may vary. Sample:**

$1, 2, 4, 8, 16, 32, \ldots$
$1, 2, 4, 7, 11, 16, \ldots$
In the first seq. double each term. In the second seq., add consecutive counting numbers.

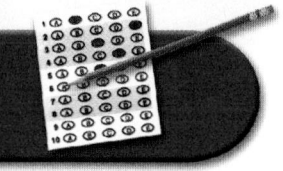

Standardized Test Prep

Reading Comprehension Read the passage below, then answer the questions on the basis of what is *stated* or *implied* in the passage.

Instructions for Building the Rainbow Toy Chest

Use $\frac{3}{4}$-in.-thick plywood.
- Cut the top and bottom 18 in. by 42 in.
  Paint the top red and the bottom violet.

Use $\frac{1}{2}$-in.-thick plywood.
- Cut the two sides 18 in. by 60 in.
  Paint: left side brown, right side white.
- Cut the three shelves 15 in. by 41 in.
  Paint: top orange, middle yellow, bottom green.
- Cut the two dividers 24 in. by 15 in.
  Paint: left blue, right indigo.

Use particleboard.
- Cut the back 41 in. by 60 in. Paint the back gray.

Assemble the painted pieces using nails and glue.

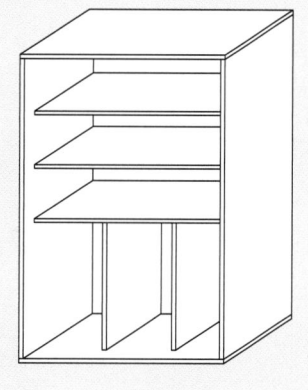

---

1. How many pieces must be cut to make the chest? **D**
A. 5   B. 7   C. 9   D. 10

2. What is the shape of each piece? **G**
F. square   G. rectangular
H. round   I. cannot be determined

3. Which uses thicker wood, a divider or the top? **B**
A. divider   B. top
C. same thickness   D. cannot be determined

Assume that the toy chest has been assembled.

4. Take the top of the bookshelf as the first horizontal surface and count downward. What is the color of the fourth surface down? **H**
F. white   G. yellow   H. green   I. blue

5. Which corners are NOT coplanar? **B**
A. the four corners of the right side
B. the two top corners of the left side and the two front corners of the bottom
C. the two top corners of the right side and the two bottom corners of the left side
D. the two front corners of the top and the two back corners of the bottom

6. Where do the violet board and the particleboard meet? **I**
F. the front edge of the violet board
G. the back edge of the left side
H. the right edge of the bottom
I. the bottom edge of the back

7. Which edge is skew to the front edge of the orange board? **B**
A. the left edge of the orange board
B. the top edge of the white board
C. the back edge of the yellow board
D. the front edge of the middle shelf

8. What are the colors of two boards that are NOT perpendicular? **H**
F. blue and gray   G. indigo and violet
H. blue and white   I. yellow and brown

9. How tall is the toy chest? $61\frac{1}{2}$ in.

10. What is the area of the top? 756 in.²

11. What is the perimeter of the front? 207 in.

12. The back edge of each shelf touches the back of the chest. How far "recessed" is the front edge of a shelf from the front edge of a side? $2\frac{1}{4}$ in.

---

24. Answers may vary. Sample: Some ways of naming an ∠ can help identify a side or vertex.

25.

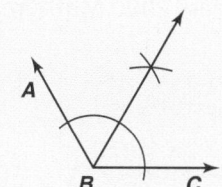

Students must be able to extract information from reading passages, answer multiple-choice questions, and construct responses in order to be successful on current state and national assessments.

To answer the questions, students apply skills and concepts from this chapter and previous chapters.
Multiple Choice: Items 1–8
Extended Response: Items 9–12

Resources

📁 **Teaching Resources**
Cumulative Review

👥 **Reaching All Students**
Spanish Cumulative Review

PRENTICE HALL ASSESSMENT SYSTEM

Standardized Test Prep
- Ch. 7 Standardized Test Practice
Assessment Masters
- Cumulative Review
Computer Test Generator CD
- Standardized Test Practice

💻 **www.PHSchool.com**
- Standardized Test Practice
- Resources

Plus 🄸TEXT

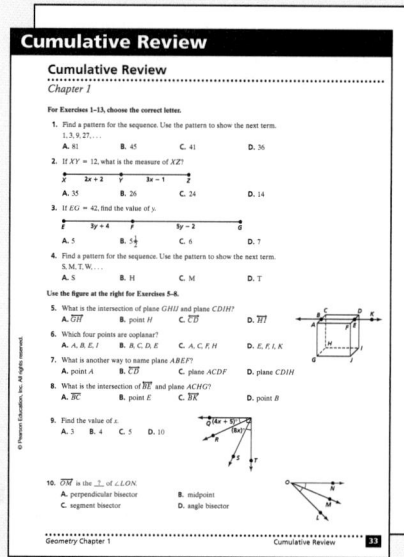

Chapter 2

Reasoning and Proof

Chapter at a Glance

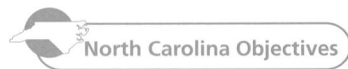
North Carolina Objectives

2-1	**Conditional Statements**	2.01

NCTM
2, 3, 6, 7, 8, 9, 10
- ▼ Conditional Statements
- ▼ Converses

2-2	**Biconditionals and Definitions**	2.01

NCTM
3, 6, 7, 8, 9, 10
- ▼ Writing Biconditionals
- ▼ Recognizing Good Definitions

2-3	**Deductive Reasoning**	2.01

NCTM
3, 6, 7, 8, 9, 10
- ▼ Using the Law of Detachment
- ▼ Using the Law of Syllogism

2-4	**Reasoning in Algebra**	2.01

NCTM
2, 3, 6, 7, 8, 9, 10
- ▼ Connecting Reasoning in Algebra and Geometry

2-5	**Proving Angles Congruent**	2.02

NCTM
3, 6, 7, 8, 9, 10
- ▼ Identifying Angle Pairs
- ▼ Theorems About Angles

NCTM STANDARDS 2000

1	Number and Operations	6	Problem Solving
2	Algebra	7	Reasoning and Proof
3	Geometry	8	Communication
4	Measurement	9	Connections
5	Data Analysis and Probability	10	Representation

Pacing Options

This chart suggests pacing only for the lessons and their parts. It is provided as a possible guide. It will help you determine how much time you have in your schedule to cover other components, such as the features, Chapter Review and Chapter Test.

Day	Traditional 45 min.	Two-Year 45 min.	Block 90 min.
1	2-1 ▼	2-1 ▼	2-1 ▼ ▼
2	2-1 ▼	2-1 ▼	2-2 ▼ ▼
3	2-2 ▼	2-1 ▼	2-3 ▼ ▼
4	2-2 ▼	2-1 ▼	2-4 ▼
5	2-3 ▼	2-2 ▼	2-5 ▼ ▼
6	2-3 ▼	2-2 ▼	
7	2-4 ▼	2-2 ▼	
8	2-5 ▼	2-3 ▼	
9	2-5 ▼	2-3 ▼	
10		2-3 ▼	
11		2-3 ▼	
12		2-4 ▼	
13		2-5 ▼	
14		2-5 ▼	
15		2-5 ▼	
16			
17			
18			
19			
20			
21			
22			
23			

NAEP Correlation (National Assessment of Educational Progress 2000 Mathematics Objectives)

2-1	2-2	2-3	2-4	2-5
A7a	A7b	A7b, c	A7b	G4a, A2

N = Number Sense, Properties, and Operations; **M** = Measurement; **G** = Geometry and Spatial Sense; **D** = Data Analysis, Statistics, and Probability; **A** = Algebra and Functions

Math Background

Chapter Overview

Most of this chapter emphasizes hypotheses and conclusions in deductive reasoning. Students will apply the basic rules of deduction to solve algebraic equations, justifying each step. The chapter culminates in simple paragraph proofs involving intuitively obvious theorems about angle relationships. This chapter sets the stage for subsequent proofs by presenting proofs as convincing arguments, similar to the justifications students regularly employ in everyday life. This fosters a healthy view of proofs as a tool for building a system of geometry by means of definitions, postulates, and theorems, but not as the most important aspect of geometry.

Conditional Statements   2-1

Point out to students that many of the decisions they make are predicated on *if-then* statements such as "If I do well in math class, then my parents will be happy." The definitions, postulates, and theorems in subsequent chapters are more easily understood and applied when thought of as conditional statements.

The hypothesis is sometimes called the "antecedent" and the conclusion the "consequent." This terminology avoids confusing the mathematical meaning of "hypothesis" (the antecedent clause of a conditional) with its scientific meaning (a theory or guess). It is critical to stress to students that converse statements may or may not be true, regardless of the truth of the original conditional statement. Venn diagrams provide a powerful and intuitive tool for establishing the truth of some *if-then* statements. Emphasize that proving a conditional statement false requires only a single counterexample, in contrast with proving a conditional statement true.

Biconditionals and Definitions   2-2

Definitions in mathematics must be biconditional statements. For example, *a right angle is an angle of measure 90,* is a definition. It is equivalent to the two statements "if an angle is a right angle, its measure is 90" and "if the measure of an angle is 90, the angle is a right angle." Students often benefit from trying to define everyday objects and situations. Group discussions of their definitions will help clarify the relationship between a conditional statement and its converse. Just as some students are reluctant to write "$3 = x$," some have difficulty using both conditional statements of a definition. Emphasize the biconditional aspect of all geometric definitions because students will need to use both conditional statements in exercises and proofs.

Deductive Reasoning   2-3

Students have used deduction in activities ranging from logic puzzles to guessing the culprit in mystery stories. Among different types of reasoning, deductive reasoning stands out because conclusions reached by it are logically consistent. With other forms of reasoning, such as inductive reasoning or analogy, conclusions have only a probability of holding.

This lesson focuses on two rules of formal logic. The Law of Detachment uses a conditional statement (if p then q) and given information "detached" from it (p), to draw a conclusion. The Law of Syllogism is sometimes called the Law of Transitivity. A true conditional statement's conclusion becomes the hypothesis for another true conditional, until the desired conclusion is reached.

Reasoning in Algebra   2-4

Because many students first encounter mathematical proofs in geometry, they may view proofs as unique to geometry. This lesson associates solving simple algebraic equations with proofs. Most of the properties used to justify each step are named for the operations involved, so remembering each property's name should not be difficult for students.

You may wish to review why the concepts of congruence and equality are both necessary in geometry. Not all relationships satisfy the reflexive, symmetric, and transitive properties of an equivalence relationship. Examples of this are the relationships "$<$" (transitive only), "$\leq$" (reflexive and transitive), and "is the sibling of" (symmetric and transitive).

Proving Angles Congruent   2-5

You may wish to point out to students that one of the most important applications of the Angle Addition Postulate in this course is to identify adjacent supplementary angles.

It is important to stress that proofs are simply convincing logical arguments in which the specified conclusion necessarily follows from the known facts. In a sense, proofs are problems in which the answer is already known and the focus is on demonstrating how the answer is derived, using principles of deductive reasoning and related definitions, postulates, and theorems.

These first proofs are in paragraph form, the form in which most students think through a justification or an explanation. Students should be discouraged from memorizing proofs, so that they focus on thinking logically. They should identify the uses of the Laws of Detachment and Syllogism in a particular proof to prepare them to follow the logical arguments of any proof and begin to frame their own proofs.

 # Ongoing Assessment and Intervention

Tools for Monitoring Student Progress

The Prentice Hall *Geometry* program provides you with many options for assessment in the Student Edition, the Teacher's Edition and the teaching resources. From these options, you may choose instructional materials and techniques that are appropriate for your students and support your district's curriculum requirements.

Instant Check System™ in Chapter 2

Allows students to check their own learning before, during, and after each lesson.

Diagnosing Readiness before the chapter (p. 66)

Check Skills You'll Need exercises in each lesson (pp. 68, 75, 82, 89, 96)

Check Understanding questions with each Example (pp. 68, 69, 70, 75, 76, 77, 82, 83, 84, 90, 91, 95, 97, 98, 99)

Checkpoint Quiz (p. 88)

Test Prep in Chapter 2

Teaches students strategies and gives them practice with all the test item formats they will encounter on state tests and standardized national exams.

Standardized Test Prep exercises in each lesson (pp. 74, 81, 87, 94, 103)

Test-Taking Strategies (p. 104: Writing Short Responses)

Standardized Test Prep (p. 109: Cumulative Review)

Program Assessment

Assess student progress throughout the *Geometry* text with blackline masters and CD-ROM.

Assessment Resources

- Checkpoint Quiz 1
- Chapter Test, Forms A & B
- Chapter Alternative Assessment

Spanish versions available. Tests for Informal Geometry also available.

 Computer Test Generator

- Unlimited questions of varying difficulty for every lesson objective.
- Create your own practice sheets, quizzes, and tests, or use the pre-made Chapter Tests.
- Diagnose readiness with questions on prerequisite skills.
- Prepare students by making tests based on standardized test objectives.
- Access Algebra 1, Geometry, and Algebra 2 content—all on one CD-ROM.

Test Preparation

A three-step approach to preparing students for high stakes, national, and state exams.

① Diagnose & Prescribe

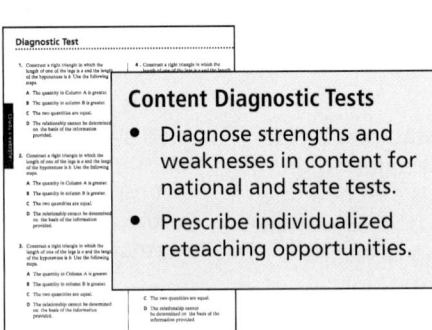

Content Diagnostic Tests
- Diagnose strengths and weaknesses in content for national and state tests.
- Prescribe individualized reteaching opportunities.

② Review & Reteach

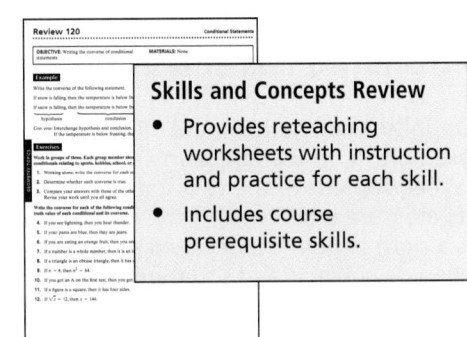

Skills and Concepts Review
- Provides reteaching worksheets with instruction and practice for each skill.
- Includes course prerequisite skills.

③ Practice & Assess

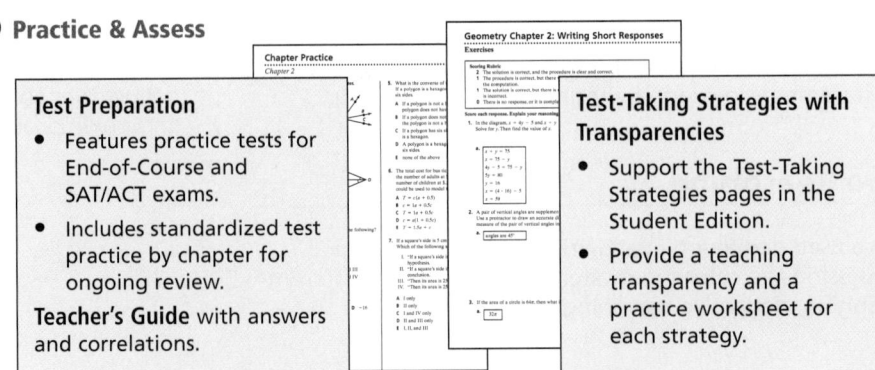

Test Preparation
- Features practice tests for End-of-Course and SAT/ACT exams.
- Includes standardized test practice by chapter for ongoing review.

Teacher's Guide with answers and correlations.

Test-Taking Strategies with Transparencies
- Support the Test-Taking Strategies pages in the Student Edition.
- Provide a teaching transparency and a practice worksheet for each strategy.

All your assessment needs in one place!

 # Reaching All Students

Support in the Student Text and Additional Resources

The textbook, the iText, and other technology components provide numerous opportunities to reach students of various ability levels and learning styles. Each Teacher's Edition lesson suggests how you can help *all* your students be successful and understand the mathematics in Chapter 2.

Below Level

Student Edition
- Diagnosing Readiness*: p. 66
- Check Skills You'll Need*: pp. 68, 75, 82, 89, 96

Reteaching
Chapter 2 Support File: pp. 6–10

Informal Geometry Planning Guide
Chapter 2 Lesson Plans: pp. 8–12
Chapter 2 Tests: pp. 83–86

* Can be used with all ability levels to ensure mastery of prerequisite skills.

Advanced Learners

Student Edition
- Challenge exercises: pp. 74, 80, 86, 93, 102

Enrichment
Chapter 2 Support File: pp. 11–15

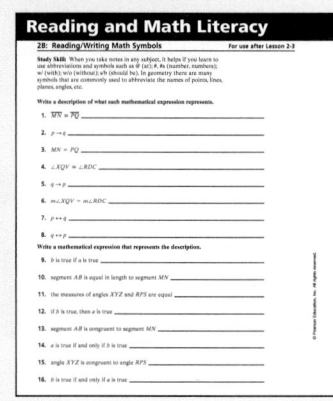 ### Reading and Math Literacy

Student Edition
- Vocabulary: pp. 67, 105, *plus* in every Lesson Preview
- Reading Math: pp. 71, 75, 80, 83, 93, 95, 105
- Illustrated Glossary: pp. 741–777

Reading and Math Literacy Masters
Chapter 2: pp. 5–8

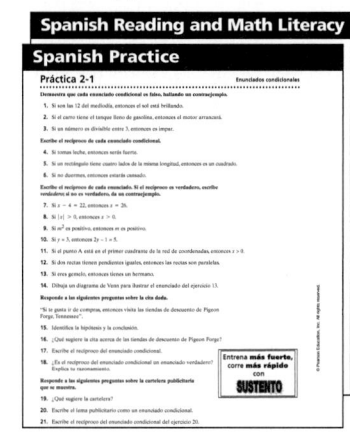 ### English Learners

Student Edition
- English/Spanish Illustrated Glossary: pp. 741–777

Workbook and Masters
Spanish Practice Workbook: pp. 8–12
Spanish Reading and Math Literacy Masters: pp. 5–8

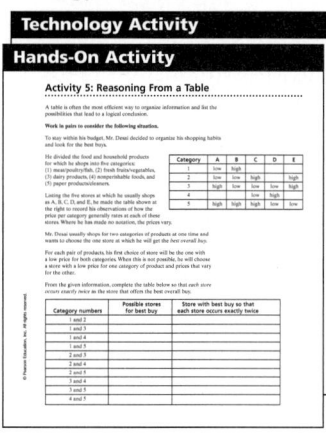 ### Learning Styles

Student Edition
- Investigation: pp. 76, 98
- Writing: pp. 73, 78, 79, 86, 92, 101, 108
- DK Activities: pp. 110–111

Activity Masters
Hands-On Activities: 4, 5, 6
Technology Activities: 39

Program Resources

	Teaching Resources in Grab & Go™ Files				Resources for Reaching All Students				Spanish Resources			Transparencies				Presentation Assistant Plus!
	Practice	Reteach	Enrich	Checkpoint Quiz	Reading & Math Literacy	Technology Activities	Hands-On Activities	Informal Geometry Lesson Plans	Practice	Reading & Math Literacy	Checkpoint Quiz	Skills Check	Additional Examples	Answers to Exercises	Lesson Quiz	Prentice Hall Presentation Pro CD-ROM
2-1	■	■	■		■		■	■	■	■		■	■	■	■	■
2-2	■	■	■					■	■			■	■	■	■	■
2-3	■	■	■	■	■		■	■	■		■	■	■	■	■	■
2-4	■	■	■					■	■			■	■	■	■	■
2-5	■	■	■		■	■	■	■	■	■		■	■	■	■	■
For the chapter	Chapter Tests, Alternative Assessment, Cumulative Review, Cumulative Assessment				Informal Geometry Chapter Tests				Spanish Chapter Tests, Alternative Assessment, Cumulative Review, Cumulative Assessment			Classroom Aid Transparencies				

Also available for use with the chapter:

 PRENTICE HALL ASSESSMENT SYSTEM *see page 66C.*

- Practice Workbook
- Solution Key

- For teacher support and access to student Web site materials, use Web Code afk-5500.
- For additional online and technology resources, see below.

  ## Technology

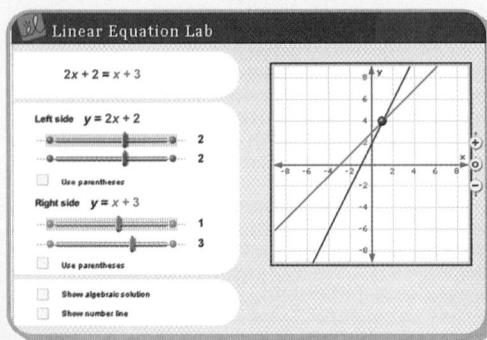
iTEXT Online and on CD-ROM

Complete Interactive Student Text online and on CD-ROM—with instant feedback assessment, tutorial help, dynamic activities, instructional and real-world videos, audio, and additional practice.

www.PHSchool.com For Students

Use **Web Codes** for easy access to online activities, chapter projects, self-grading lesson quizzes and chapter tests, vocabulary quizzes, updated data sources, graphing calculator procedures, and more.

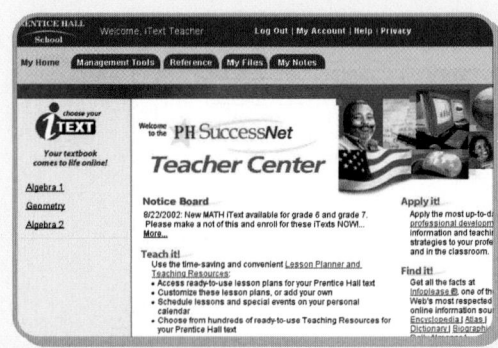
PH SuccessNet For Teachers

Online lesson planning with built-in state correlations, all the teaching resources, complete reference library, your own calendar and Teacher Web page, professional development, and more.

Presentation Assistant Plus!

The Prentice Hall *Presentation Assistant Plus!* provides you with the material you need to teach a lesson from beginning to end. Two easy-to-use formats—Transparencies and CD-ROM—allow you to present a lesson the way you are most comfortable.

 ## Transparencies

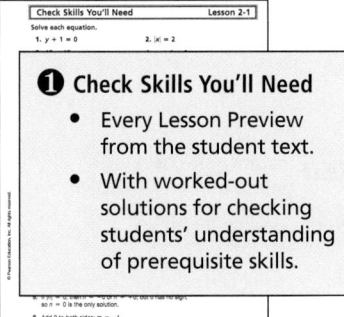

❶ Check Skills You'll Need
- Every Lesson Preview from the student text.
- With worked-out solutions for checking students' understanding of prerequisite skills.

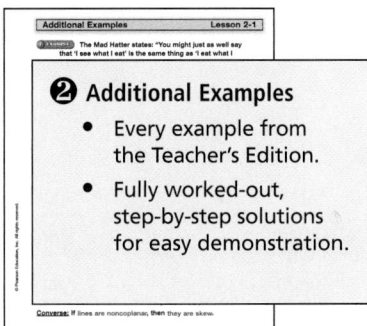

❷ Additional Examples
- Every example from the Teacher's Edition.
- Fully worked-out, step-by-step solutions for easy demonstration.

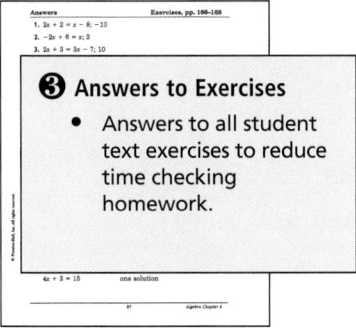

❸ Answers to Exercises
- Answers to all student text exercises to reduce time checking homework.

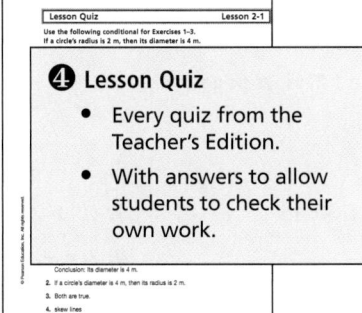

❹ Lesson Quiz
- Every quiz from the Teacher's Edition.
- With answers to allow students to check their own work.

 Throughout the Teacher's Edition, this symbol indicates material that is available on transparency in the Presentation Assistant Plus!

 ## Prentice Hall Presentation Pro CD-ROM

- Includes all Transparencies.
- Conveniently organized by lesson so you can easily ❶ Introduce, ❷ Teach, ❸ Check Homework, and ❹ Assess each lesson.
- Animated examples allow step-by-step instruction at your own pace.
- Easy to edit so you can create custom presentations.

Teaching Chapter 2 Using Presentation Assistant Plus!

	❶ Introduce	❷ Teach	❸ Check Homework	❹ Assess
	Check Skills You'll Need	Additional Examples	Student Edition Answers	Lesson Quiz
2-1	p. 8	pp. 20–22	✔	p. 83
2-2	p. 9	pp. 22–23	✔	p. 84
2-3	p. 10	pp. 23–25	✔	p. 85
2-4	p. 11	pp. 25–26	✔	p. 86
2-5	p. 12	pp. 27–29	✔	p. 87

 ### Prentice Hall Presentation Pro

CD-ROM with dynamic PowerPoint® presentations for every lesson. Helps you introduce and develop concepts, check homework, and assess progress. Part of Presentation Assistant Plus! *(See above.)*

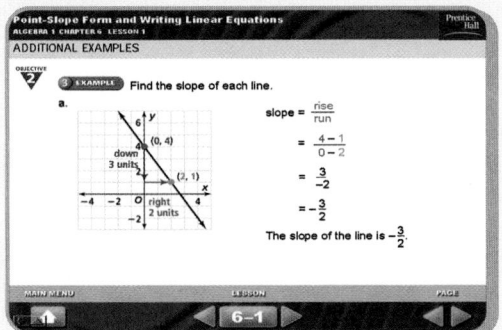

 ### Computer Test Generator

CD-ROM to create practice sheets and tests for course objectives and standardized tests. Includes Instant Chapter Tests™, online testing, and student reports. Part of the PH Assessment System. *(See page 66C.)*

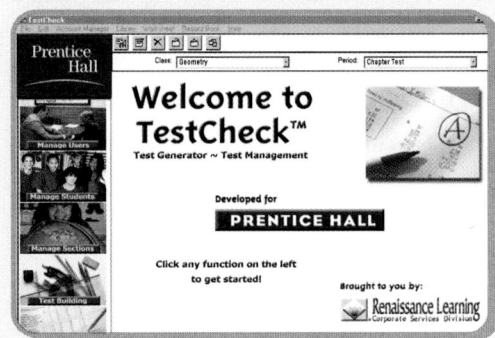

 ### Resource Pro® with Planning Express®

CD-ROM with a lesson planning tool that allows you to import state and local objectives. Includes electronic versions of all the teaching resources.

Chapter 2

Reasoning and Proof

 Diagnosing Readiness

Students will find answers to these exercises in the back of their textbooks.

For intervention, direct students to:

Solving Equations
Algebra 1 Review, p. 24

Evaluating Expressions
Skills Handbook: p. 716

Segments and Angles
Lesson 1–4: Examples 3, 4, 6
Exercises 12–19, 27, 28
Extra Practice, p. 690

Where You've Been

In Chapter 1, you learned

- many of the basic terms and assumptions used in geometry.

- to measure angles and segments, do basic constructions, and use the coordinate plane to find the midpoint of a segment and the distance between two points.

- to find the area of and the distance around rectangles and circles.

 **Instant self-check**
online and on CD-ROM

INSTANT CHECK SYSTEM **Diagnosing Readiness**   (For help, go to the Lesson in green.)

Evaluating Expressions (Skills Handbook page 716)

x^2 **Algebra** Evaluate each expression for the given value of x.

1. $9x - 13$ for $x = 7$ **50**   **2.** $90 - 3x$ for $x = 31$ **−3**   **3.** $\frac{1}{2}x + 14$ for $x = 23$ **$25\frac{1}{2}$**

Solving Equations (Algebra 1 Review, page 24)

x^2 **Algebra** Solve each equation.

4. $2x - 17 = 4$ **10.5**

5. $3x + 8 = 53$ **15**

6. $(10x + 5) + (6x - 1) = 180$ **11**

7. $(x + 21) + (2x + 9) = 90$ **20**

8. $3x + 4 = 2x - 1$ **−5**

9. $3(x + 8) = 12$ **−4**

10. $2(x + 4) = x + 13$ **5**

11. $7x + 5 = 5x + 17$ **6**

12. $14x = 2(5x + 14)$ **7**

13. $2(3x - 4) + 10 = 5(x + 4)$ **18**

Segments and Angles (Lesson 1-4)

Use the figure at the right.

14. Name $\angle 1$ in two other ways. **$\angle ACD$, $\angle DCA$**

15. Name the vertex of $\angle 2$. **C**

16. If D is the midpoint of $\overline{AB}$, find x. **3**

17. If $m\angle ADC$ and $m\angle BDC$ have a sum of 180, name the straight angle. **$\angle ADB$ or $\angle BDA$**

18. If $\angle 1 \cong \angle 2$, name the bisector of $\angle ACB$. **$\overrightarrow{CD}$**

19. If $m\angle 2 = 45$ and $\angle ACB$ is a right angle, find $m\angle 1$. **45**

20. If $\angle ACB$ is a right angle, $m\angle 1 = 4x$ and $m\angle 2 = 2x + 18$, find $m\angle 1$ and $m\angle 2$. **48, 42**

(figure: triangle with vertices A top, C bottom-left, B bottom-right; point D on segment AB; A to D labeled $x + 8$; D to B labeled $2x + 5$; angles 1 and 2 at C)

Reasoning and Proof

Key Vocabulary

- adjacent angles (p. 96)
- biconditional (p. 75)
- complementary angles (p. 96)
- conclusion (p. 68)
- conditional (p. 68)
- converse (p. 69)
- deductive reasoning (p. 82)
- hypothesis (p. 68)
- Law of Detachment (p. 82)
- Law of Syllogism (p. 83)
- hypothesis (p. 68)
- reflexive (p. 91)
- supplementary angles (p. 96)
- symmetric (p. 91)
- theorem (p. 98)
- transitive (p. 91)
- truth value (p. 69)
- vertical angles (p. 96)

Where You're Going

- In this chapter, you will learn how to write special types of statements known as conditionals, biconditionals, and definitions.

- You will use such statements and deductive reasoning to conclude that other statements are true.

- Understanding how deductive reasoning works, you will apply it to form conclusions using algebra.

- You will also use it to study elementary proofs and form your first significant conclusions about geometric relationships.

Real-World Snapshots Applying what you learn, you will do activities involving food on pages 110 and 111.

Chapter 2 Overview

Students will apply postulates from Chapter 1, deductive reasoning, and laws of logic to write paragraph proofs. After learning about conditionals, converses, and biconditionals, students will evaluate logical arguments using the Law of Detachment and the Law of Syllogism. They will use algebraic properties to justify each step in solving algebraic equations. Finally, students will prove several theorems about angles.

📖 **Reading Math**
Reading for Problem Solving, p. 95

📖 **Vocabulary**
A complete list of terms, plus vocabulary exercises, appears in the Chapter Review, p. 105.

📖 **Illustrated Glossary**
Examples for each vocabulary term, plus definitions in both English and Spanish, appear starting on p. 741.

▦ **Test-Taking Strategies**
Writing Short Responses, p. 104

DK **Real-World Snapshots**
See pages 110–111 for a real-world application of area and volume that utilizes Dorling Kindersley's (DK) unique graphic presentation.

🌐 **Real-World Connections**
Some of the applications you will find in this chapter are advertising (2-1), the American Manual Alphabet (2-2), and auto maintenance (2-3).

💻 **www.PHSchool.com**
Internet support for this chapter includes:
- Self-grading Vocabulary and Chapter 2 Tests
- Chapter Project
- Chapter Planner
- Ch. 2 Resources

Plus 🅘 **TEXT**

1. Plan

Lesson Preview

✔ **Check Skills You'll Need**

For help use
Skills Handbook, p. 720

Lesson Resources

📁 **Teaching Resources**
Practice, Reteaching, Enrichment

👥 **Reaching All Students**
Practice Workbook 2-1
Spanish Practice Workbook 2-1
Reading and Math Literacy 2A
Spanish Reading & Literacy 2A
Hands-On Activities 4
Informal Geometry Planning
   Guide 2-1

⏱ **Presentation Assistant Plus!**
Transparencies
• Check Skills You'll Need 2-1
• Additional Examples 2-1
• Student Edition Answers 2-1
• Lesson Quiz 2-1
PH Presentation Pro CD 2-1

(PRENTICE HALL ASSESSMENT SYSTEM)

Computer Test Generator CD

🖱 **Technology**
Resource Pro® CD-ROM
Computer Test Generator CD
Prentice Hall Presentation Pro CD

💻 **www.PHSchool.com**
Student Site
• Teacher Web Code: afk-5500
• Self-grading Lesson Quiz
Teacher Center
• Lesson Planner
• Resources

Plus

2-1

Conditional Statements

2.01   Use logic and deductive reasoning to draw conclusions and solve problems.

North Carolina Objectives

Lesson Preview

What You'll Learn

OBJECTIVE 1
To recognize conditional statements

OBJECTIVE 2
To write converses of conditional statements

. . . And Why

To help you read critically, as in Example 7

✔ Check Skills You'll Need   (For help, go to the Skills Handbook pages 719 and 720.)

x^2 **Algebra** Solve each equation.

1. $y + 1 = 0$ -1 **2.** $|x| = 2$ $-2, 2$ **3.** $17 = 15 + z$ 2

4. $x + 4 = 0$ -4 **5.** $|n| = 0$ 0 **6.** $m - 9 = -10$ -1

New Vocabulary   • conditional   • hypothesis   • conclusion
                       • truth value   • converse

OBJECTIVE

1 **Conditional Statements**

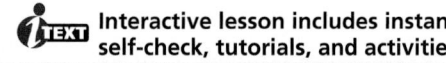
iTEXT Interactive lesson includes instant self-check, tutorials, and activities.

You have heard *if-then* statements such as this one:
   If you are not completely satisfied, then your money will be refunded.
Another name for an *if-then* statement is a **conditional.** Every conditional has two parts. The part following *if* is the **hypothesis,** and the part following *then* is the **conclusion.**

1 EXAMPLE **Identifying the Hypothesis and the Conclusion**

Identify the hypothesis and the conclusion of this conditional statement:
   If today is the first day of fall, then the month is September.

Hypothesis: Today is the first day of fall.
● Conclusion: The month is September.

✔ **Check Understanding** **1** Identify the hypothesis and the conclusion of this conditional statement:
   If $y - 3 = 5$, then $y = 8$.   **Hypothesis:** $y - 3 = 5$
                                 Conclusion: $y = 8$

You can write many sentences as conditionals.

2 EXAMPLE **Writing a Conditional**

Write each sentence as a conditional.

a. A rectangle has four right angles.
   If a figure is a rectangle, then it has four right angles.

b. A tiger is an animal.
●   If something is a tiger, then it is an animal.

✔ **Check Understanding** **2** Write each sentence as a conditional.
a. An integer that ends with 0 is divisible by 5. If an integer ends with 0, then it is divisible by 5.
b. A square has four congruent sides.
   If a figure is a square, then it has 4 congruent sides.

68   Chapter 2 Reasoning and Proof

(INSTANT CHECK SYSTEM) **Ongoing Assessment and Intervention**

Before the Lesson	**During the Lesson**	**After the Lesson**
Diagnose prerequisite skills using:	**Monitor progress using:**	**Assess knowledge using:**
• Check Skills You'll Need	• Check Understanding	• Lesson Quiz
	• Additional Examples	• Computer Test Generator CD
	• Standardized Test Prep	

A conditional can have a **truth value** of *true* or *false*. To show that a conditional is true, show that every time the hypothesis is true, the conclusion is also true. To show that a conditional is false, you need to find only one counterexample for which the hypothesis is true and the conclusion is false.

3 EXAMPLE Finding a Counterexample

Show that this conditional is false by finding a counterexample:
    If it is February, then there are only 28 days in the month.

To show that this conditional is false, you need to find one counterexample that makes the hypothesis true and the conclusion false.

February in the year 2008 is a counterexample. Because 2008 is a leap year, the month of February has 29 days.

● The conditional is false because February 2008 is a counterexample.

✓ **Check Understanding** ③ Show that this conditional is false by finding a counterexample:
    If the name of a state contains the word *New*, then the state borders an ocean.
The conditional is false because New Mexico is a counterexample.

You can use a Venn diagram to better understand true conditional statements.

4 EXAMPLE Using a Venn Diagram

Draw a Venn diagram to illustrate this conditional:
    If you live in Chicago, then you live in Illinois.

The set of things that satisfy the hypothesis lies
● inside the set of things that satisfy the conclusion.

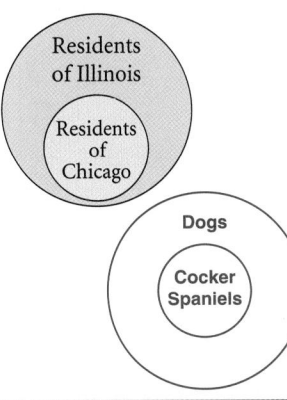

✓ **Check Understanding** ④ Draw a Venn diagram to illustrate this conditional:
    If something is a cocker spaniel, then it is a dog.

OBJECTIVE
2 Converses

The **converse** of a conditional switches the hypothesis and the conclusion.

5 EXAMPLE Writing the Converse of a Conditional

Write the converse of the following conditional.

<u>Conditional</u>
If two lines intersect to form right angles, **then** they are perpendicular.

<u>Converse</u>
● If two lines are perpendicular, **then** they intersect to form right angles.

✓ **Check Understanding** ⑤ Write the converse of the following conditional.
    If two lines are not parallel and do not intersect, then they are skew.
If two lines are skew, then they are not parallel and do not intersect.

Lesson 2-1 Conditional Statements   **69**

👥 Reaching All Students

| **Below Level** Have students determine the truth value of the converse of each sentence in Example 2. | **Advanced Learners** The terms *sufficient* and *necessary* describe the hypothesis and conclusion, respectively, of a conditional. Have students give examples to explain why these terms are appropriate. | **English Learners** See note on page 70. **Visual Learners** See note on page 69. |

---

2. Teach

Math Background

The truth value of a conditional statement is a function of the truth values of its hypothesis and its conclusion. The only way a conditional can be false is if its hypothesis is true and its conclusion is false. This fact forms the basis for using a counterexample to disprove a conjecture.

OBJECTIVE
1 Teaching Notes

Visual Learners
Have students make a class poster to display the new terms used in this lesson and their definitions.

3 EXAMPLE Math Tip

When a hypothesis is false, there can be no counterexample. In such a case, the conditional is said to be *vacuously true*. Ask: *If an elephant can fly, then 2 + 2 = 5. True or false?* It is *vacuously true* because no counterexample can be found.

🔖 Additional Examples

❶ Identify the hypothesis and the conclusion: If two lines are parallel, then the lines are coplanar. **Hypothesis: Two lines are parallel. Conclusion: The lines are coplanar.**

❷ Write the statement as a conditional: An acute angle measures less than 90. **If an angle is acute, then it measures less than 90.**

❸ Find a counterexample to show that this conditional is false: If $x^2 \geq 0$, then $x \geq 0$. **Sample: $x = -1$**

❹ Use the Venn diagram from Example 4. What does it mean to be inside the large circle but outside the small circle? **living in Illinois, but outside Chicago**

69

5 **EXAMPLE** English Learners

Point out that when a converse is written, the wording of the hypothesis and conclusion may change slightly. Ask: *How is that true in Example 5?* Only the phrase *two lines* remains in the hypothesis, and only *they* remains in the conclusion.

6 **EXAMPLE** Connection to Logic

The formal study of logic considers errors in reasoning called *fallacies*. The converse of a true conditional statement may or may not be true. To conclude that the converse is automatically true is to commit a fallacy.

Additional Examples

5 Write the converse of the conditional: If $x = 9$, then $x + 3 = 12$. If $x + 3 = 12$, then $x = 9$.

6 Write the converse of the conditional, and determine the truth value of each: If $a^2 = 25$, then $a = 5$. If $a = 5$, then $a^2 = 25$; conditional is false; converse is true.

7 Provide a counterexample to show that one of the Hatter's statements is false. Sample: I see a car on the road, but I do not eat the car, so "I eat what I see" is false.

Closure

Write the statement "All dogs are mammals" as a conditional statement. Then write its converse. Determine the truth value of each statement. If something is a dog, then it is a mammal. (true) If something is a mammal, then it is a dog. (false)

In Example 5, both the original conditional and its converse are true. It is possible for a conditional and its converse to have different truth values.

6 **EXAMPLE** Finding the Truth Value of a Converse

Consider this true conditional statement. Write the converse and determine its truth value.

Conditional
If a figure is a square, then it has four sides.

Converse
If a figure has four sides, then it is a square.

The converse is *not* true. You can use any rectangle that is not a square as a counterexample to show that the converse is false.

✓ **Check Understanding**

6b. If $|x| = 2$, then $x = 2$. The conditional is true and the converse is false.

6 Write the converse of each conditional statement. Determine the truth value of the conditional and its converse. (*Hint:* One of these conditionals is *not* true.)
a. If two lines do not intersect, then they are parallel. **If two lines are parallel, then they do not intersect. The conditional is false and the converse is true.**
b. If $x = 2$, then $|x| = 2$.

7 **EXAMPLE** Real-World 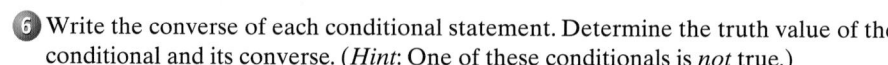 Connection

This is an illustration by John Tenniel for *Alice's Adventures in Wonderland.*

Literature In Lewis Carroll's *Alice's Adventures in Wonderland*, the Mad Hatter states: "Why you might just as well say that 'I see what I eat' is the same thing as 'I eat what I see'!" Explain why the Mad Hatter is wrong.

The statement "I see what I eat" can be rewritten as a conditional.
"If I eat it, then I see it."

The statement "I eat what I see," can be rewritten as a conditional.
"If I see it, then I eat it."

The two statements are converses of each other. A statement and its converse do not always have the same meaning or the same truth value. The Mad Hatter is wrong to suggest that you can use one just as well as the other.

✓ **Check Understanding**

7 In *Alice's Adventures in Wonderland*, the Dormouse states:
"...that 'I breathe when I sleep' is the same thing as 'I sleep when I breathe'!" Use conditionals to explain why this statement is wrong. **See below.**

You can use symbolic form to represent a conditional and its converse. In symbolic form, the letter p stands for the hypothesis and the letter q stands for the conclusion.

Key Concepts

Summary	Conditional Statements and Converses		
Statement	**Example**	**Symbolic Form**	**You Read It**
Conditional	If an angle is a straight angle, then its measure is 180.	$p \to q$	If p, then q.
Converse	If the measure of an angle is 180, then it is a straight angle.	$q \to p$	If q, then p.

7. Answers may vary. Sample: The statement "I breathe when I sleep" can be rewritten as "If I sleep, then I breathe." The statement "I sleep when I breathe" can be rewritten as "If I breathe, then I sleep." The two statements are converses, and do not have the same meaning.

EXERCISES

Practice and Problem Solving

For more practice, see *Extra Practice*.

 Practice by Example

Example 1
(page 68)

1. Hypothesis: You send in the proof-of-purchase. Conclusion: They send you a get-well card.

1. Identify the hypothesis and the conclusion in the cartoon. **See left.**

FRANK AND ERNEST   By BOB THAVES

 Reading Math

Some conditionals may omit *then*. You can insert it mentally if you wish.

Identify the hypothesis and conclusion of each conditional. 2–6. See margin.

2. If you want to be fit, then get plenty of exercise.

x^2 **3. Algebra** If $x + 20 = 32$, then $x = 12$.

4. "If you can see the magic in a fairy tale, you can face the future."
— Danielle Steel, novelist

5. "If somebody throws a brick at me, I can catch it and throw it back."
— Harry S Truman

6. "If you can accept defeat and open your pay envelope without feeling guilty, you're stealing." — George Allen, former NFL coach

7. Hypothesis: My fans think that I can do everything I say I can do.
Conclusion: They're crazier than I am.

8. Hypothesis: I could paint that flower in a huge scale.
Conclusion: You could not ignore its beauty.

7. "If my fans think that I can do everything I say I can do, then they're crazier than I am."— Muhammad Ali
7–8. See left.

8. ". . . if I could paint that flower in a huge scale, you could not ignore its beauty." — Georgia O'Keeffe, artist

Example 2
(page 68)

Write each sentence as a conditional.

9. Glass objects are fragile. **If an object is glass, then it is fragile.**

x^2 **10. Algebra** $3x - 7 = 14$ implies that $3x = 21$. **If $3x - 7 = 14$, then $3x = 21$.**

11. Whole numbers that have 2 as a factor are even. **If a whole number has 2 as a factor, then it is even.**

12. If something is an obtuse angle, then it has a measure greater than 90.

12. All obtuse angles have measure greater than 90. **See left.**

13. Good weather makes a picnic enjoyable.
If the weather is good, then a picnic is enjoyable.

14. Two skew lines do not lie in the same plane.
If two lines are skew, then they do not lie in the same plane.

Lesson 2-1 Conditional Statements **71**

Assignment Guide

1 Objective
Ⓐ Ⓑ **Core** 1–22, 33–35, 40–42
Ⓒ **Extension** 59–61

2 Objective
Ⓐ Ⓑ **Core** 23–32, 36–39, 43–58
Ⓒ **Extension** 62, 63

Standardized Test Prep 64–67

Mixed Review 68–78

Visual Learners

Exercises 1–8 Students look for the words *if* and *then* when asked to identify the hypothesis and conclusion. Discuss as a group how to proceed when the word *then* is not in a conditional statement, as in Exercises 1, 4, 5, 6, and 8.

Connection to Language Arts

Exercise 10 Point out that in mathematics the word *implies* indicates a conditional statement.

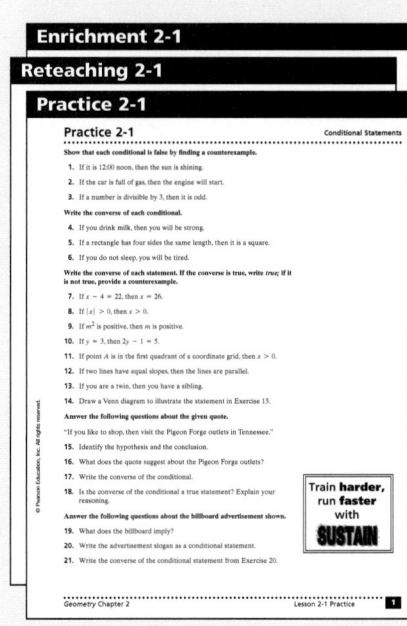

Enrichment 2-1
Reteaching 2-1
Practice 2-1

---

pages 71–74   **Exercises**

2. Hypothesis: You want to be fit. Conclusion: Get plenty of exercise.

3. Hypothesis: $x + 20 = 32$ Conclusion: $x = 12$

4. Hypothesis: You can see the magic in a fairy tale. Conclusion: You can face the future.

5. Hypothesis: Somebody throws a brick at me. Conclusion: I can catch it and throw it back.

6. Hypothesis: You can accept defeat and open your pay envelope without feeling guilty. Conclusion: You're stealing.

Diversity

Exercise 18 Some students may not be familiar with baseball or other sports that use a ball and bat, such as cricket. Ask knowledgeable students to explain how to use these items.

Error Prevention

Exercise 22 Remind students to rewrite the statement as a conditional first.

Exercise 57 This is Postulate 1-1 from Lesson 1-2.

Exercise 58 This is Postulate 1-4 from Lesson 1-2.

pages 71–74 Exercises

19.

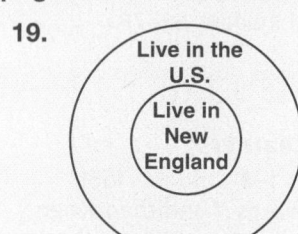

20.

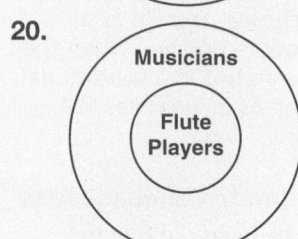

21.

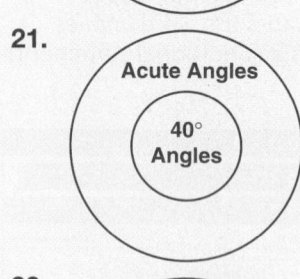

22.

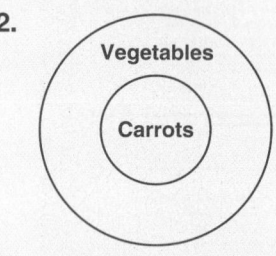

27. Converse: If you have a passport, then you travel from the U.S. to Kenya. The original conditional is true and the converse is false.

Example 3
(page 69)

Show that each conditional is false by finding a counterexample.

15. If it is not a weekday, then it is Saturday. **Sunday**

16. Odd integers less than 10 are prime. **Answers may vary. Sample: 9**

17. If you live in a country that borders the United States, then you live in Canada. **Mexico**

18. If you play a sport with a ball and a bat, then you play baseball. **Answers may vary. Sample: softball**

Example 4
(page 69)

Draw a Venn diagram to illustrate each statement. 19–22. See margin.

19. If you live in New England, then you live in the United States.

20. If you play the flute, then you are a musician.

21. If an angle has measure 40, then it is acute.

22. Carrots are vegetables.

Example 5
(page 69)

Write the converse of each conditional statement.

23. If you eat your vegetables, then you grow. **If you grow, then you eat your vegetables.**

24. If a triangle is a right triangle, then it has a 90° angle. **If a triangle has a 90° angle, then it is a right triangle.**

25. If two segments are congruent, then they have the same length. **If two segments have the same length, then they are congruent.**

26. If you do not work, you do not get paid. **If you do not get paid, then you do not work.**

Examples 6 and 7
(page 70)

Write the converse of each conditional statement. Determine the truth values of the original conditional and its converse. 27–32. See margin pp. 72-73.

27. If you travel from the United States to Kenya, then you have a passport.

28. Coordinate Geometry If a point is in the first quadrant, then its coordinates are positive.

29. Chemistry If a substance is water, then its chemical formula is H_2O.

30. Probability If the probability that an event will occur is 1, then the event is certain to occur.

31. If you are in Indiana, then you are in Indianapolis.

32. If two angles have measure 90, then the angles are congruent.

B **Apply Your Skills**

33. If a person is an Olympian, then that person is an athlete.

36a. If x^2 is an integer divisible by 3, then x is an integer divisible by 3.

b. The converse is false. Counterexample: If $x^2 = 3$, then $x = \sqrt{3}$ and $\sqrt{3}$ is not an integer divisible by 3.

Write a conditional statement that each Venn diagram illustrates.

33. 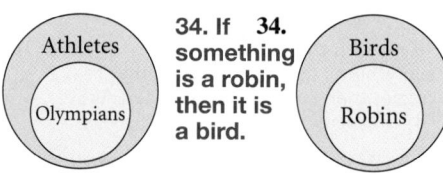 **34. If something is a robin, then it is a bird.**

35.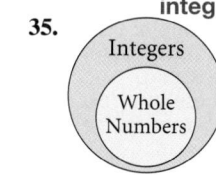

35. If something is a whole number, then it is an integer.

36. Error Analysis Ellen claims that both this conditional and its converse are true.
If x is an integer divisible by 3, then x^2 is an integer divisible by 3.
  a. Write the converse of the conditional. **a–b. See left.**
  b. Only one of the statements is true. Determine which statement is false and provide a counterexample to support your answer.

Open-Ended Write a conditional statement and its converse (different from others in this lesson) as described below.

37. Both are true. If $x = 1$, then $2x = 2$.

38. One is true; one is false. If $x = 2$, then $x^2 = 4$.

39. Both are false. If $x = 3$, then $x^2 = 6$.

---

28. Converse: If the coordinates of a point are positive, then it is in the first quadrant. Both statements are true.

29. Converse: If the chemical formula for a substance is H_2O, then it is water. Both statements are true.

30. Converse: If an event is certain to occur, then the probability of the event is 1. Both statements are true.

31. Converse: If you are in Indianapolis, then you are in Indiana. The original statement is false and the converse is true.

Jeanette Rankin was one of nine women among 435 members of Congress at the start of World War II.

45. If $|x| = 6$, then $x = -6$; 6.

46. If $x^2 > 0$, then $x < 0$; 5.

47. If $x^2 = 4$, then $x = 2$; −2.

50. If a figure is a square, then it has four congruent angles; true.

51. If a figure has four congruent angles, then it is a square; false; a rectangle that is not a square.

52. Answers may vary. Sample: If you had bought Treadmaster tires, you would not have had a flat tire.

Need Help?

Try identifying the conclusion first.

Write each statement as a conditional.

40. "We're half the people; we should be half the Congress."— Jeanette Rankin, former U.S. Congresswoman, calling for more women in office
If we're half the people, then we should be half the Congress.

41. "A great work is made out of a combination of obedience and liberty."
— Nadia Boulanger, orchestra conductor and musical mentor
If a work is great, then it is made out of a combination of obedience and liberty.

42. "A problem well stated is a problem half solved."
— Charles F. Kettering, inventor
If a problem is well stated, then it is half solved.

x^2 **Algebra** **Write the converse of each statement. If the converse is true, write *true*; if not true, provide a counterexample.**

If $-y$ is positive, then y is negative; true.

43. If $x - 3 = 15$, then $x = 18$.
If $x = 18$, then $x - 3 = 15$; true.

44. If y is negative, then $-y$ is positive.

45. If $x = -6$, then $|x| = 6$. **See left.**

46. If $x < 0$, then $x^2 > 0$. **See left.**

47. If $x = 2$, then $x^2 = 4$. **See left.**

48. If $x < 0$, then $x^3 < 0$.
If $x^3 < 0$, then $x < 0$; true.

49. Advertising Al sees an ad that states, "You want to look good at the beach this summer. Join GoodFit Health Club." Al figures, "I am going to join GoodFit Health Club, so that I will look good at the beach."
   a. Write the statement in the ad as a conditional. **a–c. See margin.**
   b. Write Al's statement as a conditional.
   c. Writing Explain why the statement in the ad does not have the same meaning as Al's statement.

Reading Math **Let p represent the statement "A figure is a square."**
Let q represent the statement "A figure has four congruent angles." Write the words for the symbolic statement shown. Determine the truth value of the statement. If it is false, provide a counterexample. **50–51. See left.**

50. $p \rightarrow q$

51. $q \rightarrow p$

Advertising **Advertisements often suggest conditional statements. For example, an ad might imply that if you buy a product, you will be popular.**

52. What conditional is implied in the ad at the right?

53. Open-Ended Find an ad in which a conditional is used or implied. **Check students' work.**

Write each postulate as a conditional statement. **54–58. See margin.**

54. Two intersecting lines meet in exactly one point.

55. Two intersecting planes meet in exactly one line.

56. Two congruent figures have equal areas.

57. Through any two points there is exactly one line.

58. Through any three noncollinear points there is exactly one plane.

For a few extra bucks, you could've had **TREADMASTERS.**

⬤ TREADMASTER TIRES

c. Answers may vary. Sample: Al's statement means that joining the club will make him look good. The ad statement does not guarantee that he will look good.

54–58. Answers may vary. Samples are given.

54. If two lines intersect, then they meet in exactly one point.

55. If two planes intersect, then they meet in exactly one line.

56. If two figures are congruent, then they have equal areas.

57. If two points are given, then there is exactly one line through them.

58. If three noncollinear points are given, then there is exactly one plane that contains them.

32. Converse: If two angles are congruent, then they have measure 90. The original statement is true and the converse is false.

49. **a.** If you want to look good at the beach this summer, then join GoodFit Health Club.

b. If I join GoodFit Health Club, then I will look good at the beach this summer.

C Challenge

59. All integers that are divisible by 8 are divisible by 2.

60. No triangles are squares. (or No squares are triangles.)

61. Some students are musicians. (or Some musicians are students.)

Write a statement beginning with *All, Some,* or *No* to match each Venn diagram.

59.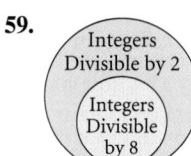

60.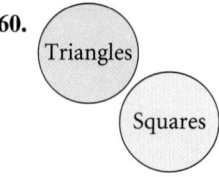

61.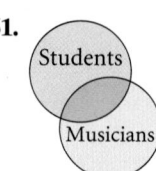

62. **Critical Thinking** You can write many statements that begin with *All* or *No* as conditionals. Give an example of each. (*Hint:* See Exercises 59–61.) **See margin.**

63. Let *a* represent an integer. Consider the five statements *r, s, t, u,* and *v*:
    r: a is even.   *s:* a is odd.   *t:* $2a$ is even.   *u:* $2a$ is odd.   *v:* $2a + 1$ is odd.
    How many statements of the form $p \rightarrow q$ can you make from these five statements? Decide whether each of the statements is true or false. **See back of book.**

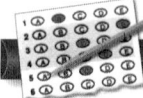

Standardized Test Prep

Multiple Choice

64. Which is the hypothesis of the following statement?   **A**
    If $4 < k < 6$, then $-4 > -k > -6$.
    A. $4 < k < 6$ **B.** $4 > k > 6$ **C.** $-4 > -k > -6$ **D.** $-4 < -k < -6$

65. Which is the converse of this statement?   **I**
    If you can sing, then you can go with Sarah.
    F. You can't sing, then you can't go with Sarah.
    G. If you can't go with Sarah, then you can sing.
    H. If you can't sing, then you can go with Sarah.
    I. If you can go with Sarah, then you can sing.

66. Which statement has a true converse?   **D**
    A. If a vehicle is a car, then it has four wheels.
    B. If you go to Asia from the United States, then you cross an ocean.
    C. If you own a dog, then your pet is furry.
    D. If you can stand up, then you can walk.

Short Response

67. Write the converse of the following statement. Determine its truth value.
    If Marta is five years old, then she is too young to vote.   **See margin.**

Mixed Review

Lesson 1-7   **Find the perimeter of each rectangle with the given base and height.**

68. 6 in., 12 in.   69. 3.5 cm, 7 cm   70. $1\frac{3}{4}$ yd, 18 in.   71. 11 m, 60 cm
    36 in.   **21 cm**   **$4\frac{1}{2}$ yd or 162 in.**   **23.2 m or 2320 cm**

72. Find the area of a circle with diameter 10 in. Leave your answer in terms of π.
    25π in.^{2}

Lesson 1-6   **Find the distance between the points. Round each answer to the nearest tenth.**

73. $A(1, 2), B(4, -2)$ **5**   74. $M(-5, 1), N(0, 5)$ **6.4**   75. $R(0, -6), T(2, 3)$ **9.2**

Lesson 1-1   **Find the pattern for each sequence. Use the pattern to show the next two terms.**

78. Write the previous letter of the alphabet; *J, I.*

76. $4, 2, 1, \frac{1}{2}, \ldots$ Divide the previous term by 2; $\frac{1}{4}, \frac{1}{8}$.

77. $5, 2, -1, -4, \ldots$ Subtract 3 from the previous term; $-7, -10$.

78. N, M, L, K, ... See left.

2-2

Biconditionals and Definitions

North Carolina Objectives

2.01 Use logic and deductive reasoning to draw conclusions and solve problems.

Lesson Preview

What You'll Learn

 OBJECTIVE 1
To write biconditionals

 OBJECTIVE 2
To recognize good definitions

. . . And Why

To evaluate definitions of letters used in the American Manual Alphabet, as in Exercises 36–40

5. If we go on a picnic, then the sun shines.

 Check Skills You'll Need   (For help, go to Lesson 2-1.)

Identify the hypothesis and the conclusion of each conditional statement.

1. If $x > 10$, then $x > 5$. **Hypothesis: $x > 10$ Conclusion: $x > 5$**

2. If you live in Milwaukee, then you live in Wisconsin.
 Hypothesis: You live in Milwaukee. Conclusion: You live in Wisconsin.
Write each statement as a conditional.

3. Squares have four sides.   4. All butterflies have wings.
If a figure is a square, then it has four sides.   **If something is a butterfly,**
Write the converse of each statement.   **then it has wings.**

5. If the sun shines, then we go on a picnic. **See left.**

6. If two lines are skew, then they do not intersect.   **If two lines do not**
                                      intersect, then they are skew.
7. If $x = -3$, then $x^3 = -27$.
If $x^3 = -27$, then $x = -3$.

New Vocabulary   • biconditional

---

1. Plan

Lesson Preview

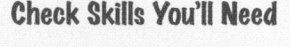 **Check Skills You'll Need**

Conditional Statements
Lesson 2-1: Examples 1, 2
Exercises 1–14
Extra Practice, p. 691

Converses
Lesson 2-1: Example 5
Exercises 23–26
Extra Practice, p. 691

Lesson Resources

Teaching Resources
Practice, Reteaching, Enrichment

Reaching All Students
Practice Workbook 2-2
Spanish Practice Workbook 2-2
Informal Geometry Planning
  Guide 2-2

Presentation Assistant Plus!
Transparencies
• Check Skills You'll Need 2-2
• Additional Examples 2-2
• Student Edition Answers 2-2
• Lesson Quiz 2-2
PH Presentation Pro CD 2-2

ASSESSMENT SYSTEM

Computer Test Generator CD

Technology
Resource Pro® CD-ROM
Computer Test Generator CD
Prentice Hall Presentation Pro CD

 www.PHSchool.com
Student Site
• Teacher Web Code: afk-5500
• Self-grading Lesson Quiz
Teacher Center
• Lesson Planner
• Resources

Plus

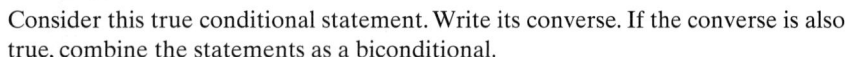

OBJECTIVE

1 Writing Biconditionals

 Interactive lesson includes instant self-check, tutorials, and activities.

When a conditional and its converse are true, you can combine them as a true **biconditional.** This is the statement you get by connecting the conditional and its converse with the word *and.* You can write a biconditional more concisely, however, by joining the two parts of each conditional with the phrase *if and only if.*

Reading Math

Connect the conditional and its converse with *and.* Then compare with the *if and only if* form.

---

1 EXAMPLE   Writing a Biconditional

Consider this true conditional statement. Write its converse. If the converse is also true, combine the statements as a biconditional.

<u>Conditional</u>
If two angles have the same measure, then the angles are congruent.

<u>Converse</u>
If two angles are congruent, then the angles have the same measure.
The converse is also true.

Since both the conditional and its converse are true, you can combine them in a true biconditional by using the phrase *if and only if.*

<u>Biconditional</u>
Two angles have the same measure if and only if the angles are congruent.

✔ **Check Understanding**

1. If three points lie on the same line, then they are collinear. The converse is also true. Three points are collinear if and only if they lie on the same line.

1 Consider this true conditional statement. Write its converse. If the converse is also true, combine the statements as a biconditional. **See left.**

<u>Conditional</u>
If three points are collinear, then they lie on the same line.

Lesson 2-2 Biconditionals and Definitions   **75**

 Ongoing Assessment and Intervention

Before the Lesson
Diagnose prerequisite skills using:
• Check Skills You'll Need

During the Lesson
Monitor progress using:
• Check Understanding
• Additional Examples
• Standardized Test Prep

After the Lesson
Assess knowledge using:
• Lesson Quiz
• Computer Test Generator CD

Math Background

Whenever a theorem is investigated or proved in geometry, the converse also should be examined. When both a theorem and its converse are true, they can be written as a biconditional. The strict requirement in mathematics that definitions be biconditional is not always followed outside mathematics.

OBJECTIVE

1 Teaching Notes

1 EXAMPLE **Teaching Tip**

Ask: *What word with the prefix bi- have you used in this class?* the word *bisect*

2 EXAMPLE **Connection to Language Arts**

Discuss the phrase *if and only if*. Ask students to use each part of the phrase separately in a sentence not related to mathematics. Point out that a statement such as "I play soccer only if it is Saturday" is equivalent to "If I play soccer, then it is Saturday" but is not equivalent to "If it is Saturday, then I play soccer."

Additional Examples

1 Consider this true conditional statement. Write its converse. If the converse is also true, combine the statements as a biconditional. If $x = 5$, then $x + 15 = 20$.
If $x + 15 = 20$, then $x = 5$; $x = 5$ if and only if $x + 15 = 20$.

2 Write the two statements that form this biconditional. Lines are skew if and only if they are noncoplanar. If lines are skew, then they are noncoplanar. If lines are noncoplanar, then they are skew.

---

2. If a number is prime, then it has only two distinct factors, 1 and itself. If a number has only two distinct factors, 1 and itself, then it is prime.

 Check Understanding

You can write a biconditional as two conditionals that are converses of each other.

2 EXAMPLE **Separating a Biconditional Into Parts**

Algebra Write two statements that form this biconditional about whole numbers:
A number is divisible by 3 if and only if the sum of its digits is divisible by 3.

Here are the two statements. They are converses of each other.

If a number is divisible by 3, then the sum of its digits is divisible by 3.

If the sum of a number's digits is divisible by 3, then the number is divisible by 3.

2 Write two statements that form this biconditional about integers greater than 1: A number is prime if and only if it has only two distinct factors, 1 and itself. **See left.**

Key Concepts

Summary	Biconditional Statements

A biconditional combines $p \rightarrow q$ and $q \rightarrow p$ as $p \leftrightarrow q$.

Statement	Example	Symbolic Form	You Read It
Biconditional	An angle is a straight angle if and only if its measure is 180.	$p \leftrightarrow q$	p if and only if q.

OBJECTIVE

2 Recognizing Good Definitions

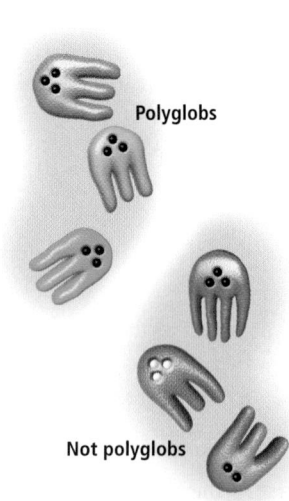

Investigation: Writing a Definition

Polyglobs

Not polyglobs

1. Use the examples at the left to identify the figures above that are *polyglobs*. **Figure B is a polyglob.**

2. Write a definition of a *polyglob* by describing what a *polyglob* is. **Answers may vary. Sample: A polyglob has three fingers and three solid dots.**

Reaching All Students

Below Level	Advanced Learners	Inclusion
Have students write the two conditionals that make up the definition in Example 4, and then discuss the truth value of each.	Have students look up three words in a dictionary and explain why the definitions do or do not obey the rules at the top of page 77.	See note on page 79. **Visual Learners** See note on page 79.

In geometry you start with undefined terms such as point, line, and plane whose meanings you understand intuitively. Then you use those terms to define other terms such as collinear points.

A good definition is a statement that can help you identify or classify an object. A good definition has several important components.

✔ A good definition uses clearly understood terms. The terms should be commonly understood or already defined.

✔ A good definition is precise. Good definitions avoid words such as *large*, *sort of*, and *some*.

✔ A good definition is reversible. That means that you can write a good definition as a true biconditional.

3 EXAMPLE **Writing a Definition as a Biconditional**

Show that this definition of *perpendicular lines* is reversible. Then write it as a true biconditional.

<u>Definition</u>
Perpendicular lines are two lines that intersect to form right angles.

<u>Conditional</u>
If two lines are perpendicular, then they intersect to form right angles.

<u>Converse</u>
If two lines intersect to form right angles, then they are perpendicular.

The two conditionals—converses of each other—are true, so the definition can be written as a true biconditional.

<u>Biconditional</u>
Two lines are perpendicular if and only if they intersect to form right angles.

✔ Check Understanding

3 Show that this definition of *right angle* is reversible. Then write it as a true biconditional.

<u>Definition</u>
A right angle is an angle whose measure is 90. **See left.**

3. Conditional: If an angle is a right angle, then its measure is 90. Converse: If an angle has measure 90, then it is a right angle. The two statements are true. An angle is a right angle if and only if its measure is 90.

One way to show that a statement is *not* a good definition is to find a counterexample.

? Need Help?

Think about the Venn diagram for "An airplane is a vehicle that flies."

4 EXAMPLE **Real-World** 🌐 **Connection**

Language Arts Is the given statement a good definition? Explain.
a. An airplane is a vehicle that flies.

The statement is not a good definition because it is not reversible. A helicopter is a counterexample. A helicopter is a vehicle that flies, but a helicopter is not an airplane.

b. A triangle has sharp corners.
The statement is not a good definition because it uses the imprecise word *sharp*, and it is not reversible.

✔ Check Understanding

4 Is the following statement a good definition? Explain.
A square is a figure with four right angles.
It is not a good definition because a rectangle has four right angles and is not necessarily a square.

Lesson 2-2 Biconditionals and Definitions **77**

Assignment Guide

1 Objective
Ⓐ Ⓑ **Core** 1–12, 32–35, 41–46
Ⓒ **Extension** 47

2 Objective
Ⓐ Ⓑ **Core** 13–31, 36–40
Ⓒ **Extension** 48, 49

Standardized Test Prep 50–54

Mixed Review 55–69

Exercises 1–6 Remind students that only one counterexample is needed to prove a statement false.

Error Prevention
Exercise 21 If students think this is a good definition, ask: *What other property do parallel lines have?* They are coplanar. Remind students of the importance of looking for counterexamples.

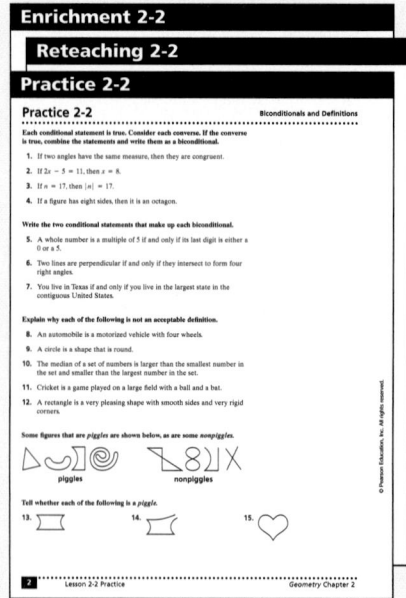

EXERCISES
For more practice, see *Extra Practice*.

Practice and Problem Solving

Ⓐ **Practice by Example**

Example 1
(page 75)

Each conditional statement below is true. Write its converse. If the converse is also true, combine the statements as a biconditional. 1–4. See back of book.

1. If two segments have the same length, then they are congruent.

x^2 **2. Algebra** If $x = 12$, then $2x - 5 = 19$.

3. If a number is divisible by 20, then it is even.

x^2 **4. Algebra** If $x = 3$, then $|x| = 3$.

5. In the United States, if it is July 4th, then it is Independence Day.

x^2 **6. Algebra** If $x = -10$, then $x^2 = 100$.   **5–6. See margin.**

Example 2
(page 76)

Write the two statements that form each biconditional. 7–8. See margin.

7. A line bisects a segment if and only if the line intersects the segment only at its midpoint.

8. An integer is divisible by 100 if and only if its last two digits are zeros.

9–12. See margin p. 79.

9. You live in Washington, D. C., if and only if you live in the capital of the United States.

10. Two lines are parallel if and only if they are coplanar and do not intersect.

11. Two angles are congruent if and only if they have the same measure.

x^2 **12. Algebra** $x^2 = 144$ if and only if $x = 12$ or $x = -12$.

Example 3
(page 77)

Test each statement below to see if it is reversible. If so, write it as a true biconditional. If not, write *not reversible*.

13. A line, segment, or ray is a perpendicular bisector of a segment if and only if it is perpendicular to the segment at its midpoint.

13. A perpendicular bisector of a segment is a line, segment, or ray that is perpendicular to a segment at its midpoint. **See left.**

14. Parallel planes are planes that do not intersect.
Planes are parallel if and only if they do not intersect.

15. A Tarheel is a person who was born in North Carolina.
not reversible

16. A rectangle is a four-sided figure with at least one right angle.
not reversible

17. A midpoint of a segment is a point that divides a segment into two congruent segments. **A point is a midpoint of a segment if and only if it divides the segment into two congruent segments.**

Example 4
(page 77)

Is each statement below a good definition? If not, explain. 18–23. See margin p. 79.

18. A cat is an animal with whiskers.

19. A dog is a good pet.

20. A segment is part of a line.

21. Parallel lines do not intersect.

22. A square is a figure with two pairs of parallel sides.

23. An angle bisector is a ray that divides an angle into two congruent angles.

Ⓑ **Apply Your Skills**

24. No; a straight angle has a measure that is greater than 90, but it is not an obtuse angle.

24. Language Arts Is the following a good definition? Explain.
An obtuse angle is an angle whose measure is greater than 90. **See left.**

25. Open-Ended Choose a definition from a dictionary or from a glossary. Explain what makes the statement a good definition. **See margin p. 79.**

26. Writing Write a definition of *a line parallel to a plane.*
A line is parallel to a plane if and only if it does not intersect the plane.

78   Chapter 2   Reasoning and Proof

pages 78–80   Exercises

5. In the United States, if it is Independence Day, then it is July 4th. It is true. In the United States,

it is Independence Day if and only if it is July 4th.

6. If $x^2 = 100$, then $x = -10$. It is false since x can also equal 10.

7. If a line bisects a segment, then the line intersects the segment only at its midpoint. If a line intersects a segment only at its midpoint, then it bisects the segment.

8. If an integer is divisible by 100, then its last two digits are zeros. If an integer's last two digits are zeros, then it is divisible by 100.

Need Help?

For Exercise 27, complete this sentence: Two angles are a linear pair if and only if. . .

27. Writing Use the figures below to write a good definition of *linear pair*. Answers may vary. Sample: Two angles are a linear pair if and only if they share a side and a vertex and are supplementary.

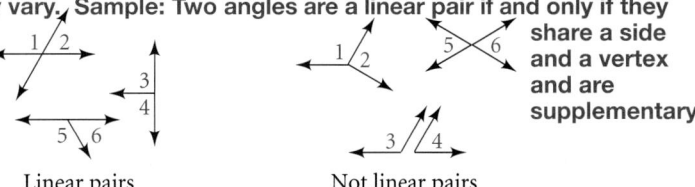

Linear pairs   Not linear pairs

Do angles 1 and 2 form a linear pair? Explain. (*Hint:* See Exercise 27.)

28.   29.   30.   31.

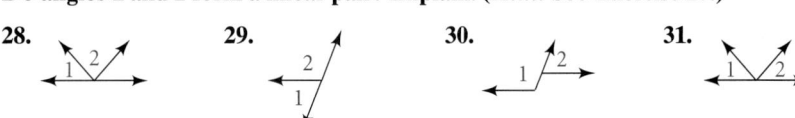

28. No; ∠1 and ∠2 are not suppl.

29. Yes; ∠1 and ∠2 share a side and a vertex, and are suppl.

30. No; ∠1 and ∠2 do not share a vertex.

31. No; ∠1 and ∠2 do not share a side, and are not suppl.

x^2 **Algebra** Each conditional statement is true. If the converse is true, write a biconditional. If not, provide a counterexample to show that the converse is false.

32–35. See margin.

32. If $x = 19$, then $2x - 3 = 35$.   **33.** If $x = 3$, then $x^2 = 9$.

34. If $x > 0$, then $|x| > 0$.   **35.** If $x = 5$, then $x^3 = 125$.

The American Manual Alphabet For Exercises 36–40, use the chart below. Decide whether the description of each letter is a good definition. If not, provide a counterexample by giving another letter that could fit the definition.

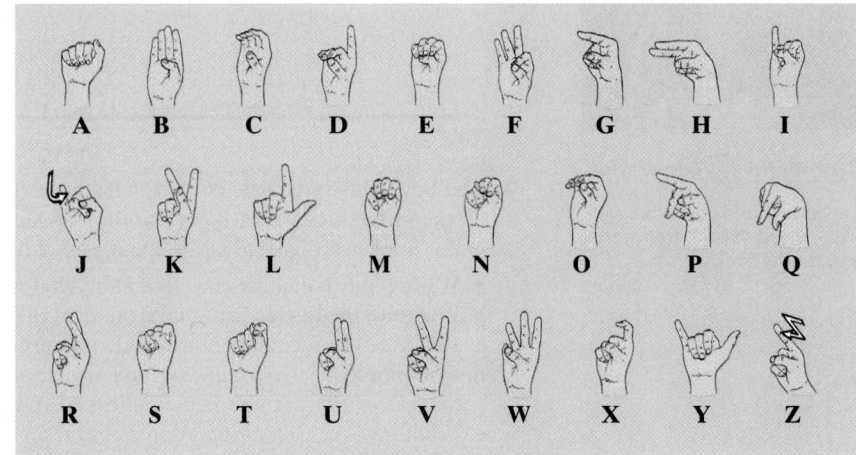

36. The letter D is formed by pointing straight up with the finger beside the thumb and folding the other fingers and the thumb so that they all touch. **good definition**

37. The letter K is formed by making a V with the two fingers beside the thumb. ***V* is a counterexample.**

38. You have formed the letter Y if and only if the thumb and one finger are pointing up and the other fingers are folded into the palm of your hand. ***L* is a counterexample.**

39. You have formed the letter I if and only if the smallest finger is sticking up and the other fingers are folded into the palm of your hand with your thumb folded over them, and your hand is held still. **good definition**

40. You form the letter B by holding all four fingers tightly together and pointing them straight up while your thumb is folded into the palm of your hand. **good definition**

Real-World Connection

The five letters above form a word to think about.

9. If you live in Washington, D.C., then you live in the capital of the United States. If you live in the capital of the United States, then you live in Washington, D.C.

10. If two lines are parallel, then they are coplanar and do not intersect. If two lines are coplanar and do not intersect, then they are parallel.

11. If two angles are congruent, then they have the same measure. If two angles have the same measure, then they are congruent.

Inclusion

Exercises 36–40 If any students are adept at the American Manual Alphabet, have them demonstrate it for the rest of the class.

Exercise 47 Point out that once a row or column contains two *X*'s, the remaining box identifies the instrument the musician plays.

Visual Learners

Exercise 48 Seeing that a biconditional becomes a single circle in a Venn diagram can deepen students' understanding and make abstract ideas concrete.

12. If $x^2 = 144$, then $x = 12$ or $x = -12$. If $x = 12$ or $x = -12$, then $x^2 = 144$.

18–23. Answers may vary. Samples are given.

18. No; it is not reversible; a mouse is a counterexample.

19. No; it is not reversible; a cat is a counterexample.

20. No; it is not precise; a ray or pt. could be part of a line.

21. No; it is not reversible; skew lines are not parallel.

22. No; it is not reversible; stop sign is a counterexample.

23. good definition

25. Answers may vary. Sample: An acute angle is an angle whose measure is between 0 and 90. The terms are clearly understood. It is precise and it is reversible.

32. $2x - 3 = 35$ if and only if $x = 19$.

33. The converse is false. $x = -3$ is a counterexample.

34. The converse is false. Any $x < 0$ is a counterexample.

35. $x^3 = 125$ if and only if $x = 5$.

Lesson Quiz 2-2

1. Write the converse of the statement.
   If it rains, then the car gets wet. **If the car gets wet, then it rains.**

2. Write the statement above and its converse as a biconditional. **It rains if and only if the car gets wet.**

3. Write the two conditional statements that make up the biconditional.
   Lines are skew if and only if they are noncoplanar. **If lines are skew, then they are noncoplanar; if lines are noncoplanar, then they are skew.**

Is each statement a good definition? If not, find a counterexample.

4. The midpoint of a line segment is the point that divides the segment into two congruent segments. **yes**

5. A line segment is a part of a line. **No; the statement is not reversible; a ray.**

Alternative Assessment

Have students work with partners. Assign partners the task of writing good definitions for the terms *hat* and *automobile*. Then discuss the definitions as a class, encouraging students to critique and defend the definitions.

pages 78–81   Exercises

44. If ∠A is an acute angle, then ∠A has measure between 0 and 90.

45. If ∠A has measure between 0 and 90, then ∠A is an acute angle.

46. ∠A is an acute angle if and only if ∠A has measure between 0 and 90.

Reading Math

The expression *vice versa* is a synonym for *conversely*.

Real-World Connection

Careers Music educators are well-versed in both traditional and modern music.

49. **Answers may vary. Sample:** If the two hats in front of Alan were blue, he would know he was wearing red. Ben can tell from Alan's response that there are 1 or 2 red hats in front of Alan. Since Ben can't tell his hat color, Cal's hat must be red.

Write each statement as a biconditional.

41. Congruent angles are angles with equal measure. **Angles are congruent if and only if they have equal measure.**

42. When the sum of the digits of an integer is divisible by 9, the integer is divisible by 9 and vice versa. **The sum of the digits of an integer is divisible by 9, if and only if the integer is divisible by 9.**

43. The whole numbers are the nonnegative integers. **A number is a whole number if and only if it is a nonnegative integer.**

Reading Math Let p be the statement "∠A is an acute angle." Let q be the statement "∠A has measure between 0 and 90." Substitute for p and q and write each statement the way you would read it. **44–46. See margin.**

44. $p \rightarrow q$ 45. $q \rightarrow p$ 46. $p \leftrightarrow q$

47. **Reasoning** In a band, Amy, Bob, and Carla are the drummer, guitarist, and keyboard player. Use the clues to find the instrument that each one plays.

Carla and the drummer wear different-colored shirts.
The keyboard player is older than Bob.
Amy, the youngest band member, lives next door to the guitarist.

You can solve this type of logic puzzle by eliminating possibilities. Copy the grid below. Put an X in a box once you eliminate it as a possibility.

Instrument	Amy	Bob	Carla
Drums		x	x
Guitar	x		x
Keyboard	x	x	

Amy plays the drums. Bob plays the guitar. Carla plays the keyboard.

48. You have illustrated true conditional statements with Venn diagrams. You can do the same thing with true biconditionals. Consider the following statement.
   An integer is divisible by 10 if and only if its last digit is 0. **a–f. See margin pp. 80–81.**
   a. Write the two conditional statements that make up this biconditional.
   b. Illustrate the first conditional from part (a) with a Venn diagram.
   c. Illustrate the second conditional from part (a) with a Venn diagram.
   d. Combine your two Venn diagrams from parts (b) and (c) to form a Venn diagram representing the biconditional statement.
   e. What must be true of the Venn diagram for any true biconditional statement?
   f. **Reasoning** How does your conclusion in part (e) help to explain why a good definition can be written as a biconditional?

49. **Reasoning** Alan, Ben, and Cal are seated as shown with their eyes closed. Diane places a hat on each of their heads from a box they know contains 3 red and 2 blue hats. They open their eyes and look forward.

Alan says, "I cannot deduce what color hat I'm wearing."
Hearing that, Ben says, "I cannot deduce what color I'm wearing, either."
Cal then says, "I know what color I'm wearing!"

How does Cal know the color of his hat? **See left.**

48. a. **If an integer is divisible by 10, then its last digit is 0. If an integer's last digit is 0, then it is divisible by 10.**

b–c.

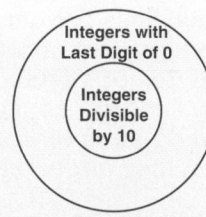

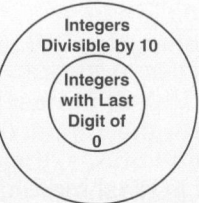

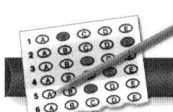

Resources
For additional practice with a variety of test item formats:
- Standardized Test Prep, p. 109
- Test-Taking Strategies, p. 104
- Test-Taking Strategies with Transparencies

Multiple Choice

50. Which statement is a good definition? **C**
   A. Skew lines are lines that do not intersect.
   B. Parallel lines are lines that do not intersect.
   C. A square is a rectangle with four congruent sides.
   D. Right angles are angles formed by two intersecting lines.

Exercise 50 Encourage students to use counterexamples to eliminate incorrect answer choices.

51. Which statement is NOT true? **G**
   F. If two lines are parallel, then they lie in one plane and do not intersect.
   G. Two lines lie in one plane if and only if the lines are parallel.
   H. If two coplanar lines do not intersect, then the lines are parallel.
   I. Two lines lie in one plane and do not intersect if and only if the two lines are parallel.

Take It to the NET
Online lesson quiz at
www.PHSchool.com
Web Code: afa-0202

52. Which statement is NOT true? **B**
   A. If $x = 1$, then $x^2 = 1$.
   B. If $x^2 = 1$, then $x = 1$.
   C. If $x = -1$, then $x^2 = 1$.
   D. $x^2 = 1$ if and only if $x = 1$ or $x = -1$.

Short Response

53. Write the two conditionals that form this biconditional: **See margin.**
You can go to the movies if and only if you do your homework.

53. [2] If you can go to the movies, then you did your homework. If you do your homework, then you can go to the movies.
[1] just one of the conditionals

Extended Response

54. Here is a true conditional statement:
If a person is 18 years old, that person is old enough to vote.
   a. Write the converse. **a–c. See margin.**
   b. Determine whether the converse is true or false.
   c. If the converse is false, give a counterexample to show that it is false. If the converse is true, combine the original statement and its converse by writing a biconditional.

54. [4] a. If a person is old enough to vote, then that person is 18 years old.
   b. false
   c. A 20-year-old is a counterexample. A 20-year-old is old enough to vote, but is not 18 years old.
(OR equivalent conditionals)
[3] predominantly correct but with one error
[2] at least one correct answer, and some appropriate information for one other part
[1] some correct information

Mixed Review

Lesson 2-1

Write each statement as a conditional.

55. Whole numbers that end in zero are even.
If a whole number ends in 0, then it is even.
56. When $x = -5$, $x^2 = 25$.
If $x = -5$, then $x^2 = 25$.
57. Sunday is a weekend day.
If a day is Sunday, then it is a weekend day.
58. All prime numbers greater than 2 are odd.
If a prime number is greater than 2, then it is odd.

Lesson 1-5

59. Draw a segment $\overline{XY}$. Construct a bisector of $\overline{XY}$. **See margin.**

60. Draw an acute angle, $\angle 1$. Construct an angle congruent to $\angle 1$. **See margin.**

61. Draw an obtuse angle, $\angle CAD$. Construct the bisector of $\angle CAD$. **See back of book.**

59.
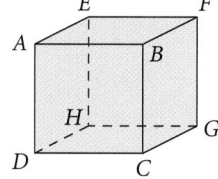
Line ℓ bisects $\overline{XY}$.

60.
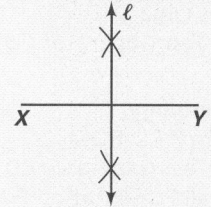
$\angle 2 \cong \angle 1$

Lesson 1-2

Use the figure at the right to name each of the following.
62–69. Answers may vary. Samples are given.

62. $\overleftrightarrow{AB}$ and $\overleftrightarrow{BC}$
63. $\overleftrightarrow{AB}$ and $\overleftrightarrow{CG}$
64. $\overleftrightarrow{AB}$ and $\overleftrightarrow{CD}$

62. two intersecting lines
63. two skew lines
64. two parallel lines
65. two parallel planes
   ABC, EFG
66. three coplanar points
   A, B, C
67. two intersecting planes
   AEF, BFG
68. a plane that contains H
   EFG
69. the intersection of two planes $\overleftrightarrow{BC}$

d.
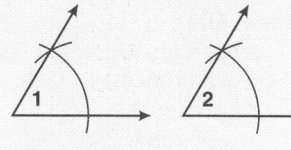
Integers Divisible by 10 — Integers with Last Digit of 0

e. Answers may vary. Sample: The two circles coincide.

f. Answers may vary. Sample: A good definition may be written as a biconditional because either of the coinciding circles of its Venn diagram can be the hypothesis of a conditional, and the other can be the conclusion.

1. Plan

Lesson Preview

✓ **Check Skills You'll Need**

Conditional Statements
Lesson 2-1: Example 2
Exercises 9–14
Extra Practice, p. 691

Converses
Lesson 2-1: Example 5
Exercises 23–26
Extra Practice, p. 691

Lesson Resources

📁 **Teaching Resources**
Practice, Reteaching, Enrichment
Checkpoint Quiz 1

👥 **Reaching All Students**
Practice Workbook 2-3
Reading and Math Literacy 2B
Spanish Reading & Literacy 2B
Spanish Checkpoint Quiz 1
Hands-On Activities 5
Informal Geometry Planning
  Guide 2-3

⏱ **Presentation Assistant Plus!**
Transparencies
• Check Skills You'll Need 2-3
• Additional Examples 2-3
• Student Edition Answers 2-3
• Lesson Quiz 2-3
PH Presentation Pro CD 2-3

PRENTICE HALL
ASSESSMENT SYSTEM

Checkpoint Quiz 1
Computer Test Generator CD

💿 **Technology**
Resource Pro® CD-ROM
Computer Test Generator CD
Prentice Hall Presentation Pro CD

💻 **www.PHSchool.com**
Student Site
• Teacher Web Code: afk-5500
• Self-grading Lesson Quiz
Teacher Center
• Lesson Planner
• Resources

Plus 🔲 **TEXT**

2-3

Deductive Reasoning

2.01   Use logic and deductive reasoning to draw conclusions and solve problems.

North Carolina Objectives

Lesson Preview

What You'll Learn

OBJECTIVE 1
To use the Law of Detachment

OBJECTIVE 2
To use the Law of Syllogism

...And Why

To use deductive reasoning to conclude that the Nile River is the longest river in the world, as in Example 5

✓ Check Skills You'll Need

(For help, go to Lesson 2-1.)

Write the converse of each statement. 1–2. See back of book.

1. If you don't sleep enough, then your grades suffer.

2. If you want to arrive on time, then you must start early.

Write each statement as a conditional.

3. Leap years have 366 days. **If a year is a leap year, then it has 366 days.**

4. Students who do not complete their homework will have lower grades.

5. Two lines that are perpendicular meet to form right angles. **4–5. See back of book.**

6. Every sixteen-year-old is a teenager.
If a person is 16 years old, then that person is a teenager.

New Vocabulary • deductive reasoning   • Law of Detachment
                   • Law of Syllogism

Interactive lesson includes instant self-check, tutorials, and activities.

OBJECTIVE
1 Using the Law of Detachment

Real-World 🌐 Connection

Careers An auto mechanic uses deductive reasoning as in Example 1.

In Chapter 1 you learned that inductive reasoning is based on observing what has happened and then making a conjecture about what will happen. In this lesson, you will study deductive reasoning.

Deductive reasoning (or logical reasoning) is the process of reasoning logically from given statements to a conclusion. If the given statements are true, deductive reasoning produces a true conclusion.

Many people use deductive reasoning in their jobs. A physician diagnosing a patient's illness uses deductive reasoning. A carpenter uses deductive reasoning to determine what materials are needed at a work site.

1 EXAMPLE   **Real-World 🌐 Connection**

Auto Maintenance An auto mechanic knows that if a car has a dead battery, the car will not start. A mechanic begins work on a car and finds the battery is dead. What conclusion can she make?

● The mechanic can conclude that the car will not start.

✓ **Check Understanding** ❶ **Critical Thinking** Suppose that a mechanic begins work on a car and finds that the car will not start. Can the mechanic conclude that the car has a dead battery? Explain. **No, there could be other things wrong with the car, such as a faulty starter.**

In Example 1 the mechanic is using a law of deductive reasoning called the **Law of Detachment.**

Ongoing Assessment and Intervention

Before the Lesson	**During the Lesson**	**After the Lesson**
Diagnose prerequisite skills using:	**Monitor progress using:**	**Assess knowledge using:**
• Check Skills You'll Need	• Check Understanding	• Lesson Quiz
	• Additional Examples	• Computer Test Generator CD
	• Standardized Test Prep	• Chapter Checkpoint 1 (p. 88)

Key Concepts

📖 **Reading Math**

You can read $p \rightarrow q$ as "p implies q."

Property	Law of Detachment
	If a conditional is true and its hypothesis is true, then its conclusion is true.
	In symbolic form:
	If $p \rightarrow q$ is a true statement and p is true, then q is true.

2 EXAMPLE **Using the Law of Detachment**

For the given true statements, what can you conclude?

Given: If M is the midpoint of a segment, then it divides the segment into two congruent segments.
M is the midpoint of $\overline{AB}$.

You are given that a conditional and its hypothesis are true. By the Law of Detachment, you can conclude that M divides $\overline{AB}$ into two congruent segments, or $\overline{AM} \cong \overline{MB}$.

✓ **Check Understanding** **2** If a baseball player is a pitcher, then that player should not pitch a complete game two days in a row. Vladimir Nuñez is a pitcher. On Monday, he pitches a complete game. What can you conclude? **Answers may vary. Sample: Vladimir Nuñez should not pitch a complete game on Tuesday.**

3 EXAMPLE **Real-World Connection**

Does the following argument illustrate the Law of Detachment?

Given: If it is snowing, then the temperature is less than or equal to 32°F.
The temperature is 20°F.

You conclude: It must be snowing.

You are given that a conditional and its conclusion are true.
You cannot apply the Law of Detachment and conclude that the hypothesis is true.
You cannot come to any conclusion about whether it is snowing from the information given.

✓ **Check Understanding** **3** If possible, use the Law of Detachment to draw a conclusion. If it is not possible to use this law, explain why.

Given: If a road is icy, then driving conditions are hazardous.
Driving conditions are hazardous.
Not possible: you do not know that the hypothesis is true.

OBJECTIVE
2 **Using the Law of Syllogism**

Another law of deductive reasoning is the Law of Syllogism. The **Law of Syllogism** allows you to state a conclusion from two true conditional statements when the conclusion of one statement is the hypothesis of the other statement.

 Key Concepts

Property	Law of Syllogism
	If $p \rightarrow q$ and $q \rightarrow r$ are true statements, then $p \rightarrow r$ is a true statement.

Lesson 2-3 Deductive Reasoning **83**

 Reaching All Students

Below Level The wordiness of Examples 4 and 5 is typical of complex arguments. Show students how to substitute letters for hypotheses and conclusions, as in the properties.	**Advanced Learners** Use Example 3 as a springboard for students to research other logical fallacies.	**English Learners** See note on page 84. **Auditory Learners** See note on page 84.

2. Teach

Professional Development

Math Background

Deductive reasoning is a process of reasoning logically from given facts to a conclusion. The Law of Detachment is found in almost every line of two-column proofs, where q is the "conclusion" and $p \rightarrow q$ is the "justification" for q. It is p, the given, that is sometimes lost when thinking about each line.

OBJECTIVE
1 **Teaching Notes**

2 EXAMPLE **Teaching Tip**

Discuss the use of the word *Given* before the two statements. Point out that in mathematics, the statements following *Given* are considered true. Ask: *What do you call statements that are assumed to be true without proof?* axioms, postulates

3 EXAMPLE **Connection to Logic**

The error illustrated is sometimes called the *fallacy of the converse*. Explain that a fallacy is an error in logical thinking. Ask: *Why is this error a "fallacy of the converse"?* The fallacy is concluding that the converse is true because the conditional is true.

Additional Examples

1 A gardener knows that if it rains, the garden will be watered. It is raining. What conclusion can he make? **The garden will be watered.**

2 For the given statements, what can you conclude?

Given: If $\angle A$ is acute, $m\angle A < 90$. $\angle A$ is acute. **$m\angle A < 90$**

3 Does the following argument illustrate the Law of Detachment?

Given: If you make a field goal in basketball, you score two points. Jenna scored two points in basketball.

You conclude: Jenna made a field goal. **no**

83

English Learners

The Law of Syllogism uses many words to explain a complex relationship. Discuss how the symbolic form summarizes it clearly and succinctly. Have students explain how the two forms are related.

5 EXAMPLE **Auditory Learners**

Many students are not familiar with written logical arguments, although they hear and speak them. Students will benefit from your reading the example aloud. Then have them reproduce the argument verbally before reading the example for themselves.

Careers

Trial lawyers must present logical arguments to win their cases.

🖥 **Additional Examples**

4 **Use the Law of Syllogism to draw a conclusion from the following true statements:**

If a quadrilateral is a square, then it contains four right angles.
If a quadrilateral contains four right angles, then it is a rectangle.
If a quadrilateral is a square, then it is a rectangle.

5 **Use the Laws of Detachment and Syllogism to draw a possible conclusion.**

If the circus is in town, then there are tents at the fairground.
If there are tents at the fairground, then Paul is working as a night watchman.
The circus is in town. **Paul is working as a night watchman.**

Closure

Use either law from this lesson to draw a conclusion from the two statements. Explain which law you used.
If it rains, then Jan stays inside.
If Jan stays inside, then she does not get wet.
The Law of Syllogism lets you conclude: If it rains, then Jan does not get wet.

84

❓ ······
Need Help?

2 is a repeated factor of 12 because it appears more than once in the prime factorization of 12.

$12 = 2 \cdot 2 \cdot 3$

✔ **Check Understanding**

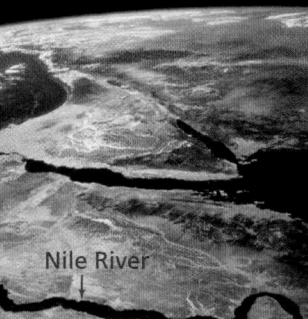

Nile River
↓

Real-World 🌎 **Connection**

Over 99% of Egypt's people live close to the Nile River.

✔ **Check Understanding**

---

4 EXAMPLE **Using the Law of Syllogism**

Algebra Use the Law of Syllogism to draw a conclusion from the following true statements.

If a number is prime, then it does not have repeated factors.
If a number does not have repeated factors, then it is not a perfect square.

You have two true conditionals where the conclusion of one is the hypothesis of the other. You can use the Law of Syllogism to draw the following conclusion:
● If a number is prime, then it is not a perfect square.

4 If possible, state a conclusion using the Law of Syllogism. If it is not possible to use this law, explain why.
   a. If a number ends in 0, then it is divisible by 10.   **If a number ends in 0,**
      If a number is divisible by 10, then it is divisible by 5.   **then it is divisible by 5.**
   b. If a number ends in 6, then it is divisible by 2.
      If a number ends in 4, then it is divisible by 2.
      Not possible; the conclusion of one statement is not the hypothesis of the other statement.

You can use both the Law of Detachment and the Law of Syllogism to draw conclusions.

5 EXAMPLE **Real-World** 🌎 **Connection**

Geography Use the Law of Detachment and the Law of Syllogism to draw conclusions from the following true statements.

If a river is more than 4000 mi long, then it is longer than the Amazon.
If a river is longer than the Amazon, then it is the longest river in the world.
The Nile is 4132 mi long.

You can use the first two statements and the Law of Syllogism to conclude:
If a river is more than 4000 mi long, then it is the longest river in the world.

With this, the fact that the Nile is 4132 mi long, and the Law of Detachment, you can also conclude:
● The Nile is the longest river in the world.

5 Use the Law of Detachment and the Law of Syllogism to draw conclusions.
The Volga River is in Europe.
If a river is less than 2300 mi long, it is not one of the world's ten longest rivers.
If a river is in Europe, then it is less than 2300 mi long.
The Volga River is less than 2300 miles long.
The Volga River is not one of the world's ten longest rivers.

EXERCISES

For more practice, see *Extra Practice*.

Practice and Problem Solving

A **Practice by Example**   **Use the Law of Detachment to draw a conclusion.**

Examples 1 and 2
(pages 82 and 83)

1. If a student gets an A on a final exam, then the student will pass the course.
   Felicia gets an A on the music theory final exam.   **Felicia will pass the music theory course.**

2. If a student wants to go to college, then the student must study hard.
   Rashid wants to go to the University of North Carolina.
   Rashid must study hard.

84   Chapter 2   Reasoning and Proof

---

pages 84–87   **Exercises**

14–15. Answers may vary. Samples are given.

14. If an Alaskan mountain is over 20,300 ft high, then it is the highest in the United States. Alaska's Mt. McKinley is the highest in the United States.

15. If you live in Little Rock, then you live in the 25th state to enter the Union. Levon lives in the 25th state to enter the Union.

16. Must be true; by (E) and (A), it is breakfast time. Then by (D), Julio drinks juice.

3. If two lines are parallel, then they do not intersect.
Line ℓ is parallel to line *m*. **Line ℓ and line *m* do not intersect.**

4. If there is lightning, then it is not safe to be out in the open.
Marla sees lightning from the soccer field. **It is not safe for Marla to be out in the open.**

Example 3
(page 83)

If possible, use the Law of Detachment to draw a conclusion. If not possible, write *not possible.*

5. If a figure is a rectangle, then it has two pairs of parallel sides.
Figure *ABCD* is a rectangle. **Figure *ABCD* has two pairs of parallel sides.**

x^2 **6. Algebra** If *n* is a prime number greater than 2, then n^2 is an odd number.
9^2 is an odd number. **not possible**

7. If three points are on the same line, then they are collinear.
Points *X*, *Y*, and *Z* are on line *m*. **Points *X*, *Y*, and *Z* are collinear.**

8. If an angle is obtuse, then it is not acute.
∠*XYZ* is not obtuse. **not possible**

9. If you are a Golden Gopher, you've attended the University of Minnesota.
(See photo.) **Nadine Muzerall attended the University of Minnesota.**

Real-World 🌎 Connection

Hockey wing Nadine Muzerall is a Golden Gopher (Exercise 9).

Use the Law of Syllogism to draw a conclusion. 10–13. See left.

Example 4
(page 84)

10. If an animal is a red wolf, then it is endangered.

11. If two planes are not parallel, then they intersect in a line.

12. If you read a good book, then your time is well spent.

13. If you are studying botany, then you are studying a science.

10. Zoology If an animal is a red wolf, then its scientific name is *Canis rufus*.
If an animal is named *Canis rufus*, then it is endangered.

11. If two planes intersect, then they intersect in a line.
If two planes are not parallel, then they intersect.

12. If you read a good book, then you enjoy yourself.
If you enjoy yourself, then your time is well spent.

13. If you are studying biology, then you are studying a science.
If you are studying botany, then you are studying biology.

Example 5
(page 84)

Geography Use the Law of Detachment and the Law of Syllogism to draw conclusions from the following statements. 14–15. See margin p. 84.

14. If a mountain is the highest in Alaska, then it is the highest in the United States.
If an Alaskan mountain is over 20,300 ft high, then it is the highest in Alaska.
Alaska's Mount McKinley is 20,320 ft high.

15. If you live in Little Rock, then you live in Arkansas.
Levon lives in Little Rock.
If you live in Arkansas, then you live in the 25th state to enter the Union.

B **Apply Your Skills**

For Exercises 16–21, assume that the following statements are true.

    A. If Maria drinks juice, then it is breakfast time.
    B. If it is lunchtime, then Kira drinks milk and nothing else.
    C. If it is mealtime, then Curtis drinks water and nothing else.
    D. If it is breakfast time, then Julio drinks juice and nothing else.
    E. Maria drinks juice.

Use only the information given above. For each statement, write *must be true, may be true,* **or** *is not true.* **Explain your reasoning. 16–21. See margin pp. 84–85.**

16. Julio drinks juice.   **17.** Curtis drinks water.   **18.** Kira drinks milk.

19. Curtis drinks juice.   **20.** Maria drinks water.   **21.** Julio drinks milk.

Lesson 2-3 Deductive Reasoning   **85**

17. Must be true; by (E) and (A), it is breakfast time. Then by (C), Curtis drinks water.

18. May be true; by (E) and (A), it is breakfast time. We don't know what Kira drinks at breakfast time.

19. Is not true; by (E) and (A), it is breakfast time. By (C), Curtis drinks water and nothing else.

20. May be true; by (E), Maria drinks juice. We don't know if she also drinks water.

21. Is not true; by (A) and (E), it is breakfast time. By (D), Julio drinks juice and nothing else.

3. Practice

Assignment Guide

 **Objective**
A **B** Core 1–9, 22–26

 **Objective**
A **B** Core 10–21, 27–32
C Extension 33

Standardized Test Prep 34–37

Mixed Review 38–44

Error Prevention

Exercise 6 Spend some time discussing as a class why the Law of Detachment does not apply to Exercise 6. Ask students to state why a conclusion would not make sense and to provide counterexamples.

Exercise 8 Because this exercise shows a fallacy not seen before in this lesson, students may think it shows valid reasoning. Discuss counterexamples.

Alternative Method

Exercises 10–13 Have students write each statement symbolically after defining which statements the letters *p*, *q*, and *r* represent. Then have them write each conclusion *p* → *r* in words.

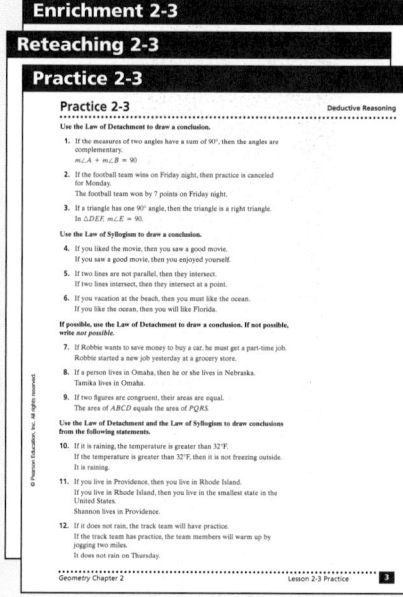

Enrichment 2-3
Reteaching 2-3
Practice 2-3

Exercises 16–21 The list of statements assumed to be true may seem daunting to students. Before they begin the exercises, ask: *How many of the given statements are conditionals, and how many are simple statements?* **four conditionals and one simple statement** Point out that the simple statement makes the hypothesis of conditional statement A true.

Exercise 32 Students must use indirect reasoning to conclude that Anita and Beth did not go. Discuss as a class how students reasoned through this exercise. Point out that this type of reasoning becomes increasingly important as students continue studying mathematics.

Math Tip

Exercise 33 This exercise establishes the logical rule that when a statement is true, its *contrapositive* is also true. Symbolically, if $p \to q$ is a true statement, then $\sim q \to \sim p$ is a true statement.

Real-World 🌐 Connection

Average ocean temperature in Key West is about 80°F, a good snorkeling temperature.

26. Answers may vary. Sample: If a student wears a hat to school, then the student must take it off indoors. Amy wears a hat to school. Then Amy must take off the hat indoors.

28. No; guys with beards cannot park on Monday.

30. No; there is no parking Tuesday from 6:49 A.M. to 9:11 A.M.

For each of the following, write the first statement as a conditional. If possible, use the Law of Detachment to make a conclusion. If not possible, write *not possible*.

22. All national parks are interesting. **If something is a national park, then it is** Mammoth Cave is a national park. **interesting; Mammoth Cave is interesting.**

23. **Weather** The temperature is always above 32°F in Key West, Florida. The temperature is 62°F. **If you are in Key West, Florida, then the temperature is always above 32°F; not possible.**

24. Every high school student likes music. Ling likes music. **If you are a high school student, then you like music; not possible.**

25. All squares are rectangles. *ABCD* is a square. **If a figure is a square, then it is a rectangle; *ABCD* is a rectangle.**

✏ 26. **Writing** Give an example of a rule used in your school that could be written as a conditional. Explain how the Law of Detachment is used in applying that rule. **See left.**

For Exercises 27–31, use the cartoon and deductive reasoning to answer *yes* or *no*. If *no*, explain.

27. Is a person with a red car allowed to park here on Tuesday at 10:00 A.M.? **No; red cars can never park.**

28. Is a man with a beard allowed to park here on Monday at 10:30 A.M.? **See left.**

29. Is a woman with a wig allowed to park here on Saturday at 10:00 A.M.? **yes**

30. Is a person with a blue car allowed to park here on Tuesday at 9:05 A.M.? **See left.**

31. Is a person with a convertible with leather seats allowed to park here on Sunday at 6:00 P.M.? **yes**

32. **Reasoning** Assume that the following statements are true.
If Anita goes to the concert, Beth will go.
If Beth goes to the concert, Aisha will go.
If Aisha goes to the concert, Ramon will go.
Only two of the four students went to the concert. Who were they? **Aisha and Ramon**

Ⓒ Challenge

33a.

Gills
Fish
Turtles

33. **Critical Thinking** Consider the following given statements and conclusion.

Given: If an animal is a fish, then it has gills. A turtle does not have gills.
You conclude: A turtle is not a fish.

This argument does not use the Law of Syllogism or the Law of Detachment, but it does use good deductive reasoning.

a. Draw a Venn diagram to illustrate the given information. **See left.**
b. Use the Venn diagram to help explain why the argument uses good reasoning. **Turtles are not in the circle of animals with gills, so a turtle is not a fish.**

86 Chapter 2 Reasoning and Proof

pages 84–87 Exercises
36.[2] a. Bert
b. Andrea, Bert, and Carl; if Darla were reading *King Lear,* all four people would be reading it.

[1] one part correct

37. [4] a. Harold; Clara and Mark won't eat sandwiches, so Harold had the sandwich. Since Harold had the sandwich, he also had the milk.

b. Salad; because Mark won't eat salad or bread, he had the soup. Since he had the soup, he had

Multiple Choice

34. What conclusion can you draw from the following two statements? **D**

If a person does not get enough sleep, that person will be tired.
Evan does not get enough sleep.

  A. Evan will get enough sleep.   **B.** Evan will not be tired.
  C. Evan should get enough sleep.   **D.** Evan will be tired.

35. What conclusion can you draw from the following two statements? **F**

If you have a job, then you have an income.
If you have an income, then you must pay taxes.

  F. If you have a job, then you must pay taxes.
  G. If you don't have a job, then you don't pay taxes.
  H. If you pay taxes, then you have a job.
  I. If you have a job, then you don't have to pay taxes.

Short Response

36. Carl reads anything Andrea chooses to read. Bert reads what Carl chooses to read and Carl reads what Bert chooses. Andrea reads whatever Darla chooses to read. **a–b. See margin p. 86.**
  a. Carl is reading *Hamlet*. Who else, if anyone, must also be reading *Hamlet*?
  b. Exactly three people are reading *King Lear*. Who are they? Explain.

Extended Response

37. Harold, Clara, and Mark each chose a different lunch from three categories: soup, salad, and sandwiches. Each ordered a different drink. Clara will not eat sandwiches. Mark won't eat salad or bread. The person who had the soup also had the iced tea. The person who had the sandwich also had the milk. **a–b. See margin pp. 86–87.**
  a. Who drank the milk? How do you know?
  b. One person ordered mineral water. What food did the water go with? Explain.

Take It to the NET
Online lesson quiz at
www.PHSchool.com
  Web Code: afa-0203

Lesson Quiz 2-3

Use the three statements below.

A. If games are canceled, then Maria reads a book.
B. If it snows, then games are canceled.
C. It is snowing.

1. Using only statements A and B, what can you conclude? **If it snows, then Maria reads a book.**

2. Using only statements B and C, what can you conclude? **Games are canceled.**

3. Using statements A, B and C, what can you conclude? **Maria is reading a book.**

4. Suppose both statement B and "games are canceled" are true. Can you conclude that statement C is true? Explain. **No; sample: you cannot apply the Law of Detachment.**

Mixed Review

Lesson 2-2

Is each statement a good definition? If not, find a counterexample.

38. No; counterexamples may vary. Sample: two rays that do not intersect do not form an angle.

38. An angle is a figure formed by two rays. **See left.**

39. A ray is an angle bisector if and only if it divides an angle into two congruent angles. **good definition**

Lesson 2-1

Show that each conditional is false by finding a counterexample.

40. Geography If the name of a state contains the word *North*, then the state borders Canada. **North Carolina**

x^2 **41. Algebra** If you square a fraction, then the result is always greater than the original fraction. **Answers may vary. Sample:** $\frac{1}{2}$

Lesson 1-3

Complete with *always*, *sometimes*, or *never* to make a true statement.

42. Two lines that do not intersect are ? parallel. **sometimes**

43. Two lines that intersect are ? skew. **never**

44. Two segments that intersect are ? coplanar. **always**

Lesson 2-3 Deductive Reasoning   **87**

Alternative Assessment

Have each student follow these two rules to write a logic puzzle.
• The puzzle must contain at least three statements.
• The puzzle must be solvable using the Law of Detachment and the Law of Syllogism.
Have students exchange puzzles and solve. **Check students' work.**

Standardized Test Prep

Resources
For additional practice with a variety of test item formats:
• Standardized Test Prep, p. 109
• Test-Taking Strategies, p. 104
• Test-Taking Strategies with Transparencies

the iced tea. We know from part (a) that Harold had the sandwich and milk. Thus Clara had the salad and mineral water.

[3] correct answers with poor explanations

[2] only one correct answer with poor explanations

[1] one correct answer with no explanations

Chapter Checkpoint 1

To check understanding of Lessons 2-1 to 2-3:

Checkpoint Quiz 1 (p. 88)

📁 **Teaching Resources**
Checkpoint Quiz 1 (*also in Prentice Hall Assessment System*)

👥 **Reaching All Students**
Reading and Math Literacy 2B

Spanish versions available

Checkpoint Quiz 1   Lessons 2-1 through 2-3

iTEXT Instant self-check quiz online and on CD-ROM

1. Identify the hypothesis and the conclusion of this conditional statement:
   If $x > 5$, then $x^2 > 25$.   **Hypothesis: $x > 5$ Conclusion: $x^2 > 25$**

2. Write this statement as a conditional: Roses are beautiful flowers.
   If something is a rose, then it is a beautiful flower.

For Exercises 3 and 4, use this conditional statement:
If an integer ends with 0, then the integer is divisible by 2.

3. Write the converse of the statement. **If an integer is divisible by 2, then the integer ends with 0.**

4. Find a counterexample to show that the converse is *not* true.
   Answers may vary. Sample: 42 is divisible by 2, but it does not end with 0.

5. Write the two conditionals that make up this biconditional:
   An angle is an acute angle if and only if its measure is between 0 and 90.
   See left.

6. Rewrite this definition as a biconditional: **Points are collinear if and only if they lie on the same line.**
   Points that lie on the same line are collinear.

7. Find a counterexample to show that the following statement is *not* a good definition:
   A computer is a machine with a keyboard and a memory. **Answers may vary. Sample: A graphing calculator has a keyboard and a memory.**

Use the Law of Detachment or the Law of Syllogism to draw a conclusion from each pair of statements. If not possible, write *not possible*.

8. If a student is on the basketball team, then that student has passing grades.
   Theresa is on the basketball team. **Theresa has passing grades.**

9. If a student studies geometry, the student studies mathematics.
   If a student studies mathematics, the student's mind is expanded.
   If a student studies geometry, then the student's mind is expanded.

10. If you miss the bus, then you will be late for school.
    You are late for school. **not possible**

5. If an angle is an acute angle, then its measure is between 0 and 90. If an angle's measure is between 0 and 90, then it is an acute angle.

A P●int in Time

1500 1600 1700 1800 1900 2000

Hercule Poirot as played by David Suchet, 1989–1997.

Most people are not detectives, but as a young woman, the English writer Agatha Christie (1890–1976) correctly deduced that many people would like to be. In 1920 she published her first book, a detective novel entitled *The Mysterious Affair at Styles* in which she introduced the eccentric and ultra-logical Belgian detective Hercule Poirot. In this and in many subsequent novels, Poirot solves mysteries not with guns or car chases but with logical reasoning.

💻 **Take It to the NET** For more information about Agatha Christie, go to **www.PHSchool.com**.
Web Code: afe-2032

88   Chapter 2   Reasoning and Proof

2-4

Reasoning in Algebra

North Carolina Objectives

2.01 Use logic and deductive reasoning to draw conclusions and solve problems.

Lesson Preview

What You'll Learn

OBJECTIVE **1** To connect reasoning in algebra and geometry

. . . And Why

To justify steps in a logical argument, as in Example 1

✓ **Check Skills You'll Need**   (For help, go to Lesson 1-4.)

For Exercises 1–5, use the figure at the right.

1. Name ∠1 in two other ways. **∠AOB, ∠BOA**
2. Name the vertex of ∠2. **O**
3. If ∠1 ≅ ∠2, name the bisector of ∠AOC. **$\overrightarrow{OB}$**
4. If $m\angle AOC = 90$ and $m\angle 1 = 45$, find $m\angle 2$. **45**
5. If $m\angle AOC = 90$, name two perpendicular rays. **$\overrightarrow{OA}$ and $\overrightarrow{OC}$**

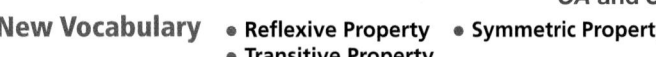

New Vocabulary • **Reflexive Property** • **Symmetric Property**
  • **Transitive Property**

OBJECTIVE **1**

Connecting Reasoning in Algebra and Geometry

Interactive lesson includes instant self-check, tutorials, and activities.

In geometry you accept postulates and properties as true. You use deductive reasoning to prove other statements. Some of the properties that you accept as true are the properties of equality from algebra. They are listed below in terms of any numbers a, b, and c.

🔑 **Key Concepts**

Summary	Properties of Equality
Addition Property	If $a = b$, then $a + c = b + c$.
Subtraction Property	If $a = b$, then $a - c = b - c$.
Multiplication Property	If $a = b$, then $a \cdot c = b \cdot c$.
Division Property	If $a = b$ and $c \neq 0$, then $\frac{a}{c} = \frac{b}{c}$.
Reflexive Property	$a = a$
Symmetric Property	If $a = b$, then $b = a$.
Transitive Property	If $a = b$ and $b = c$, then $a = c$.
Substitution Property	If $a = b$, then b can replace a in any expression.

You also assume that other properties from algebra are true.

🔑 **Key Concepts**

Property	The Distributive Property
	$a(b + c) = ab + ac$

2-4

North Carolina Objectives 2.01

1. Plan

Lesson Preview

✓ **Check Skills You'll Need**

Finding Angle Measures
Lesson 1-4: Examples 4, 6
Exercises 16–19, 27, 28
Extra Practice, p. 690

Lesson Resources

📁 **Teaching Resources**
Practice, Reteaching, Enrichment

👥 **Reaching All Students**
Practice Workbook 2-4
Spanish Practice Workbook 2-4
Informal Geometry Planning
   Guide 2-4

⏱ **Presentation Assistant Plus!**
Transparencies
• Check Skills You'll Need 2-4
• Additional Examples 2-4
• Student Edition Answers 2-4
• Lesson Quiz 2-4
PH Presentation Pro CD 2-4

ASSESSMENT SYSTEM

Computer Test Generator CD

🔧 **Technology**
Resource Pro® CD-ROM
Computer Test Generator CD
Prentice Hall Presentation Pro CD

www.PHSchool.com
Student Site
• Teacher Web Code: afk-5500
• Self-grading Lesson Quiz
Teacher Center
• Lesson Planner
• Resources

Plus

Ongoing Assessment and Intervention

Before the Lesson
Diagnose prerequisite skills using:
• Check Skills You'll Need

During the Lesson
Monitor progress using:
• Check Understanding
• Additional Examples
• Standardized Test Prep

After the Lesson
Assess knowledge using:
• Lesson Quiz
• Computer Test Generator CD

2. Teach

Professional Development

Math Background

There are three types of properties in mathematics: *assumed, defining,* and *deduced.* Assumed properties are actual postulates. Defining properties are in definitions. Deduced properties are concluded from theorems. Simplifying expressions and solving equations both represent a series of justified steps. A proof with a given and only one justified conclusion is often called a *one-step proof.*

OBJECTIVE

 Teaching Notes

1 EXAMPLE Alternative Method

The reason given for writing $x + 2x$ as $3x$ is "Simplify." Write $x + 2x = 1x + 2x = (1 + 2)x = 3x$ on the board to show the class how the Distributive Property was used to simplify the sum. Ask: *Which equation shows the Distributive Property?*
$1x + 2x = (1 + 2)x$

2 EXAMPLE Teaching Tip

Ask: *What is the key difference between Example 1 and Example 2?* Example 1 uses the Angle Add. Post., and Example 2 uses the Segment Add. Post. Point out that students will use both postulates.

Error Prevention

Because the properties discussed in this lesson apply to both equality and congruence, students may erroneously extend them to comparative relations such as *greater than* and *less than.* Ask: *Do the Reflexive, Symmetric, and Transitive Properties apply to the relations "greater than" and "less than"?* only the Transitive Property

3 EXAMPLE English Learners

Discuss as a class how students can determine when to name a property of equality and when to name a property of congruence.

90

You use deductive reasoning every time you solve an equation. You can justify each statement that you make with a postulate, a property, or a definition. When you solve problems involving angle measures, you can use the Angle Addition Postulate.

1 EXAMPLE Justifying Steps in Solving an Equation

Algebra Solve for x and justify each step.

Given: $m\angle AOC = 139$

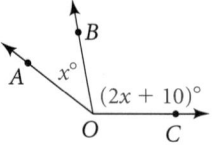

 Need Help?
To review the Angle Addition Postulate, go to p. 28.

$m\angle AOB + m\angle BOC = m\angle AOC$	**Angle Addition Postulate**
$x + 2x + 10 = 139$	**Substitution Property**
$3x + 10 = 139$	**Simplify.**
$3x = 129$	**Subtraction Property of Equality**
$x = 43$	**Division Property of Equality**

✓ **Check Understanding** ❶ Fill in each missing reason.

Given: $\overrightarrow{LM}$ bisects $\angle KLN$.

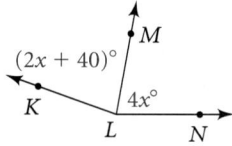

$\overrightarrow{LM}$ bisects $\angle KLN$.	**Given**	
$m\angle MLN = m\angle KLM$	**Definition of angle bisector**	
$4x = 2x + 40$	_?_	**Substitution Prop.**
$2x = 40$	_?_	**Subtraction Prop. of Equality**
$x = 20$	_?_	**Division Prop. of Equality**

You can use the Segment Addition Postulate to justify statements about lengths of segments.

2 EXAMPLE Justifying Steps in Solving an Equation

Algebra Solve for y and justify each step.

Given: $AC = 21$

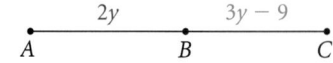

Need Help?
To review the Segment Addition Postulate, go to p. 26.

$AB + BC = AC$	**Segment Addition Postulate**
$2y + (3y - 9) = 21$	**Substitution Property**
$5y - 9 = 21$	**Simplify.**
$5y = 30$	**Addition Property of Equality**
$y = 6$	**Division Property of Equality**

✓ **Check Understanding** ❷ Find AB and BC by substituting $y = 6$ in the expressions in the diagram above. Check that $AB + BC = 21$. **$AB = 12$; $BC = 9$; $AB + BC = 12 + 9 = 21$**

The Reflexive, Symmetric, and Transitive Properties of Equality have corresponding properties of congruence. You can use properties of congruence to justify statements.

👥 Reaching All Students

Below Level Solve several equations on the board in which the Transitive and Substitution Properties justify steps. Ask students to name the property used. In some cases, both properties may apply.	**Advanced Learners** Have students determine which of the properties of equality apply to the relations $\geq$ and $\leq$.	**English Learners** See note on page 90. **Visual Learners** See note on page 92.

Key Concepts

Summary	Properties of Congruence
Reflexive Property	$\overline{AB} \cong \overline{AB}$ $\angle A \cong \angle A$
Symmetric Property	If $\overline{AB} \cong \overline{CD}$, then $\overline{CD} \cong \overline{AB}$. If $\angle A \cong \angle B$, then $\angle B \cong \angle A$.
Transitive Property	If $\overline{AB} \cong \overline{CD}$ and $\overline{CD} \cong \overline{EF}$, then $\overline{AB} \cong \overline{EF}$. If $\angle A \cong \angle B$ and $\angle B \cong \angle C$, then $\angle A \cong \angle C$.

3 EXAMPLE Using Properties of Equality and Congruence

Name the property of equality or congruence that justifies each statement.

a. $\angle K \cong \angle K$
Reflexive Property of Congruence

b. If $2x - 8 = 10$, then $2x = 18$.
Addition Property of Equality

c. If $\overline{RS} \cong \overline{TW}$ and $\overline{TW} \cong \overline{PQ}$, then $\overline{RS} \cong \overline{PQ}$.
Transitive Property of Congruence

d. If $m\angle A = m\angle B$, then $m\angle B = m\angle A$.
Symmetric Property of Equality

✓ **Check Understanding** **3** Name the property of equality or congruence illustrated.
a. $\overline{XY} \cong \overline{XY}$ **Reflexive Prop. of ≅**
b. If $m\angle A = 45$ and $45 = m\angle B$, then $m\angle A = m\angle B$. **Transitive or Substitution Prop. of Equality**

EXERCISES

For more practice, see *Extra Practice*.

Practice and Problem Solving

A **Practice by Example** x^2 **Algebra** Fill in the reason that justifies each step.

Examples 1 and 2
(page 90)

1a. Angle Addition Post.
b. Substitution Prop.

1. Solve for x.

$m\angle CDE + m\angle EDF = 180$ **a.** _?_
$x + (3x + 20) = 180$ **b.** _?_
$4x + 20 = 180$ **c.** _?_ **Simplify.**
$4x = 160$ **d.** _?_ **Subtraction Prop. of Equality**
$x = 40$ **e.** _?_ **Div. Prop. of Equality**

a–b. See left.

2. Solve for n.
Given: $XY = 42$

$XZ + ZY = XY$ **a.** _?_ **Segment Addition Post.**
$3(n + 4) + 3n = 42$ **b.** _?_ **Substitution Prop.**
$3n + 12 + 3n = 42$ **c.** _?_ **Distributive Prop.**
$6n + 12 = 42$ **d.** _?_ **Simplify.**
$6n = 30$ **e.** _?_ **Subtraction Prop. of Equality**
$n = 5$ **f.** _?_ **Division Prop. of Equality**

---

1 Justify each step used to solve $5x - 12 = 32 + x$ for x.
1. $5x = 44 + x$ Addition Property of Equality
2. $4x = 44$ Subtraction Property of Equality
3. $x = 11$ Division Property of Equality

2 Suppose points A, B, and C are collinear with point B between points A and C. Solve for x if $AB = 4 + 2x$, $BC = 15 - x$, and $AC = 21$. Justify each step.
$AB + BC = AC$
   (Seg. Add. Post.),
$(4 + 2x) + (15 - x) = 21$
   (Subst. Prop. of Equality),
$19 + x = 21$ (Simplify),
$x = 2$ (Subtr. Prop. of Equality)

3 Name the property that justifies each statement.
a. If $x = y$ and $y + 4 = 3x$, then $x + 4 = 3x$. **Substitution Property of Equality**
b. If $x + 4 = 3x$, then $4 = 2x$. **Subtraction Property of Equality**
c. If $\angle P \cong \angle Q$, $\angle Q \cong \angle R$, and $\angle R \cong \angle S$, then $\angle P \cong \angle S$. **Transitive Property of Congruence**

Closure

Joy and Hue solve the equation $3x = 18$. Each writes $x = 6$. Joy names the Division Property of Equality to justify the step. Hue names the Multiplication Property of Equality to justify the step. Explain why both Joy and Hue are correct. **Division by 3 is the same as multiplication by $\frac{1}{3}$.**

3. Practice

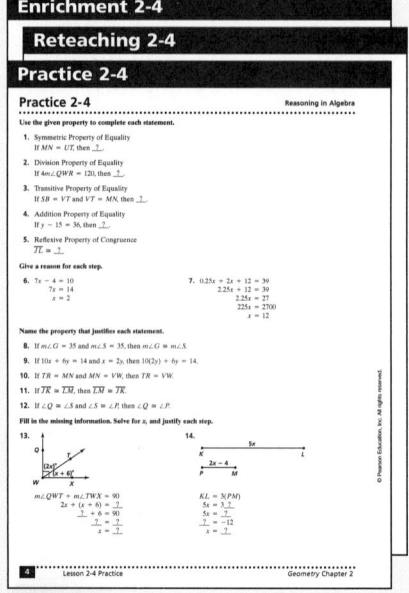

Assignment Guide

1 Objective

A B Core 1–30

C Extension 31–37

Standardized Test Prep 38–42

Mixed Review 43–53

Visual Learners

Exercise 1 Before they read the steps, have students examine the diagram and think of a method to find *x*. Practicing this approach will help them work with proofs later.

Error Prevention

Exercise 2 Students often confuse the Transitive and Substitution Properties. In some situations either property could be cited as justification. Here, the Substitution Property of Equality justifies the second step because terms in an equation are replaced with their equivalents.

Exercises 5–15 The properties in this lesson are familiar to students, but their names may not be. Display a poster that names and describes the properties for students' reference as they work through the exercises.

Enrichment 2-4

Reteaching 2-4

Practice 2-4

92

4a. Distr. Prop.
 b. Subtr. Prop. of =
 c. Div. Prop. of =

Example 3
(page 91)

B Apply Your Skills

25. Answers may vary.
Sample: $\overline{LR}$ and $\overline{RL}$ are different ways to name the same segment and $\angle CBA$ and $\angle ABC$ are different ways to name the same $\angle$.

?

Need Help?

For Exercise 25, you may want to review naming segments and angles (pp. 18 and 27).

---

x^2 **Algebra** Give a reason for each step.

3. $\frac{1}{2}x - 5 = 10$ Given

$2\left(\frac{1}{2}x - 5\right) = 20$ **a.** __?__ Mult. Prop. of =

$x - 10 = 20$ **b.** __?__ Distr. Prop.

$x = 30$ **c.** __?__ Add. Prop. of =

4. $5(x + 3) = -4$ Given

$5x + 15 = -4$ **a.** __?__

$5x = -19$ **b.** __?__

$x = -\frac{19}{5}$ **c.** __?__

a–c. See left.

Name the property that justifies each statement.

5. $\angle Z \cong \angle Z$ **Reflexive Prop. of ≅**

6. $2(3x + 5) = 6x + 10$ **Distr. Prop.**

7. If $12x = 84$, then $x = 7$. **Div. Prop. of =**

8. If $\overline{ST} \cong \overline{QR}$, then $\overline{QR} \cong \overline{ST}$.
Symmetric Prop. of ≅

9. If $m\angle A = 15$, then $3m\angle A = 45$.
Mult. Prop. of =

10. $XY = XY$
Reflexive Prop. of =

11. If $3x + 14 = 80$, then $3x = 66$.
Subtr. Prop. of =

12. If $KL = MN$, then $MN = KL$.
Symmetric Prop. of =

13. If $2x + y = 5$ and $x = y$, then $2x + x = 5$.
Subst. Prop.

14. If $AB - BC = 12$, then $AB = 12 + BC$.
Add. Prop. of =

15. If $\angle 1 \cong \angle 2$ and $\angle 2 \cong \angle 3$, then $\angle 1 \cong \angle 3$.
Trans. Prop. of ≅

Use the given property to complete each statement.

16. Addition Property of Equality
If $2x - 5 = 10$, then $2x =$ __?__. **15**

17. Subtraction Property of Equality
If $5x + 6 = 21$, then __?__ $= 15$. **5x**

18. Symmetric Property of Equality
If $AB = YU$, then __?__. **YU = AB**

19. Symmetric Property of Congruence
If $\angle H \cong \angle K$, then __?__ $\cong \angle H$. **∠K**

20. Reflexive Property of Congruence
$\angle PQR \cong$ __?__   **∠PQR**

21. Distributive Property
$3(x - 1) = 3x -$ __?__   **3**

22. Substitution Property
If $LM = 7$ and $EF + LM = NP$, then __?__ $= NP$. **EF + 7**

23. Transitive Property of Congruence
If $\angle XYZ \cong \angle AOB$ and $\angle AOB \cong \angle WYT$, then __?__. **∠XYZ ≅ ∠WYT**

24. Multiplication Property of Equality
If $\frac{1}{3}TR = UW$, then __?__. **TR = 3UW**

25. **Writing** Jero claims that the statements $\overline{LR} \cong \overline{RL}$ and $\angle CBA \cong \angle ABC$ are both true by the Reflexive Property of Congruence. Explain why Jero is correct.
See left.

26. Use what you know about transitive properties to complete the following:

The Transitive Property of Falling Dominoes:

If domino A causes domino B to fall, and domino B causes domino C to fall, then domino A causes domino __?__ to fall. **C**

27. Algebra Fill in the reason that justifies each step.

Given: C is the midpoint of $\overline{AD}$.

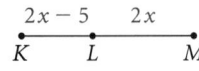

C is the midpoint of $\overline{AD}$.	**a.** ?	Given
$AC = CD$	**b.** ?	Def. of midpoint
$4x = 2x + 12$	**c.** ?	Subst. Prop. of $=$
$2x = 12$	**d.** ?	Subtr. Prop. of $=$
$x = 6$	**e.** ?	Division Prop. of $=$

Reading Math

For help with reading and solving Exercise 28, see p. 95.

 28. Algebra In the figure at the right, $KM = 35$.
a. Solve for x. Justify each step. **See margin.**
b. Find the length of $\overline{KL}$. **15**

29. Algebra In the figure at the right, $m\angle GFI = 128$.
a. Solve for x. Justify each step. **See margin.**
b. Find $m\angle EFI$. **40**

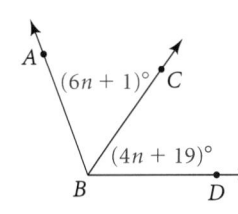

30a. Given
b. Def. of $\angle$ Bisector
c. Subst. Prop.
d. Subtr. Prop. of $=$
e. Div. Prop. of $=$

30. Algebra Fill in the reason that justifies each step. **See left.**

Given: $\overrightarrow{BC}$ bisects $\angle ABD$.

$\overrightarrow{BC}$ bisects $\angle ABD$.	**a.** ?
$m\angle ABC = m\angle CBD$	**b.** ?
$6n + 1 = 4n + 19$	**c.** ?
$2n = 18$	**d.** ?
$n = 9$	**e.** ?

C Challenge

31. Error Analysis The steps below "show" that $1 = 2$. Find the error.
In the fifth step, each side is divided by $(b - a)$.
Given: $a = b$ But $b - a = 0$ and division by 0 is not defined.

$a = b$	Given
$ab = b^2$	Multiplication Property of Equality
$ab - a^2 = b^2 - a^2$	Subtraction Property of Equality
$a(b - a) = (b + a)(b - a)$	Distributive Property
$a = b + a$	Division Property of Equality
$a = a + a$	Substitution Property
$a = 2a$	Simplify.
$1 = 2$	Division Property of Equality

Real-World Connection

President Calvin Coolidge, advice columnist Ann Landers, and musician Bill Withers were all born on the Fourth of July. Each one of them "has the same birthday as" either one of the others.

Relationships You know that the relationships "is equal to" and "is congruent to" are reflexive, symmetric, and transitive. In a later chapter, you will see that this is also true for the relationship "is similar to." Consider the following relationships among people. State whether each relationship is reflexive, symmetric, transitive, or none of these.

Sample: The relationship "is younger than" is transitive. If Sue is younger than Fred and Fred is younger than Alana, then Sue is younger than Alana. The relationship "is younger than" is not reflexive because Sue is not younger than herself. It is also not symmetric because if Sue is younger than Fred, Fred is not younger than Sue.

32. has the same birthday as **reflexive, symmetric, transitive**

33. is taller than **transitive**

34. lives in the same state as **reflexive, symmetric, transitive**

35. lives in a different state than **symmetric**

36. is the same height as **reflexive, symmetric, transitive**

37. is a descendant of **transitive**

Lesson 2-4 Reasoning in Algebra **93**

pages 91–94 Exercises

28. a.

$KL + LM = KM$	Segment Add. Post.
$2x - 5 + 2x = 35$	Subst. Prop.
$4x - 5 = 35$	Simplify.
$4x = 40$	Add. Prop. of $=$
$x = 10$	Div. Prop. of $=$

29. a.

$m\angle GFE + m\angle EFI = m\angle GFI$	$\angle$ Addition Post.
$9x - 2 + 4x = 128$	Subst. Prop.
$13x - 2 = 128$	Simplify.
$13x = 130$	Add. Prop. of $=$
$x = 10$	Div. Prop. of $=$

Lesson Quiz 2-4

Name the justification for each statement.

1. $ab = ab$ Reflexive Prop. of Eq.

2. If $m\angle ABC + 40 = 85$, then $m\angle ABC = 45$. Subtraction Prop. of Eq.

3. If $k = m$ and $k + w = 12$, then $m + w = 12$. Substitution Prop. of Eq.

4. If B is a point in the interior of $\angle AOC$, then $m\angle AOB + m\angle BOC = m\angle AOC$. Angle Add. Post.

5. Fill in the missing information.

Given: $AC = 36$

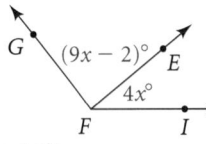

a. $AB + BC = AC$ **i.** ? Segment Add. Post.

b. $3x + 2x + 1 = 36$ **ii.** ? Substitution Prop. of Eq.

c. ?   **iii.** Simplify.
$5x + 1 = 36$

d. $5x = 35$ **iv.** ? Subtraction Prop. of Eq.

e. $x = $?   **v.** ?
7;   Division Prop. of Eq.

Alternative Assessment

Have students work in pairs. Each student should write a linear equation that can be solved for x. Then have partners exchange equations and solve, justifying each step.

93

Standardized Test Prep

Resources

For additional practice with a variety of test item formats:
• Standardized Test Prep, p. 109
• Test-Taking Strategies, p. 104
• Test-Taking Strategies with Transparencies

Exercise 40 When students compare quantities, the most difficult problems are often those for which "cannot be determined from the information given" is the correct answer. Use this exercise to show students how to find examples in which the quantity in either column might be greater. Whenever examples can be found for greater quantities in both columns, the correct answer must be "cannot be determined."

pages 91–94 Exercises

42. [2] a. $2y + 15 + y = 120$
Subst. Prop.
$3y + 15 = 120$
Simplify.

b. $3y = 105$ Subtr. Prop. of Equality

$y = 35$ Div. Prop. of Equality

$x = 2y + 15$

$x = 2(35) + 15$

$x = 85$

[1] solved for y only, OR no work shown

Multiple Choice

38. Which property justifies this statement? **D**
    If $4x = 16$, then $16 = 4x$.
    A. Multiplication Property of Equality
    B. Transitive Property of Equality
    C. Reflexive Property of Equality
    D. Symmetric Property of Equality

Quantitative Comparison

Compare the boxed quantity in Column A with the boxed quantity in Column B. Choose the best answer.
A. The quantity in Column A is greater.
B. The quantity in Column B is greater.
C. The two quantities are equal.
D. The relationship cannot be determined from the information given.

	Column A	Column B
B 39.	area of a circle with diameter 6 cm	area of a circle with radius 6 cm
D 40.	perimeter of a square with 4-in. sides	perimeter of a rectangle with a pair of 4-in. sides
A 41.	area of a rectangle with base 12 cm and height 5 cm	area of a square with 6 cm sides

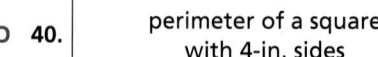

Take It to the NET
Online lesson quiz at
www.PHSchool.com
Web Code: afa-0204

Short Response

42. In the diagram, $x = 2y + 15$ and $x + y = 120$. See margin.
    a. Use a Property of Equality to explain why $3y + 15 = 120$.
    b. Solve for y. Justify each step. Then find the value of x.

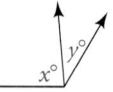

Mixed Review

Lesson 2-3

Reasoning Use logical reasoning to draw a conclusion.

43. If a student is having difficulty in class, then that student's teacher is concerned. Elena is having difficulty in history class.   **Elena's teacher is concerned.**

44. If a person has a job, then that person is earning money.
    If a person is earning money, then that person can save money each week.
    If a person has a job, then that person can save money each week.

Lesson 1-4

Use the diagram at the right and find each measure.

45. $m\angle AOC$ **80**   46. $m\angle AOD$ **125**

47. $m\angle DOB$ **65**   48. $m\angle BOE$ **90**

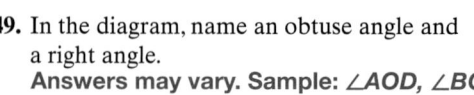

49. In the diagram, name an obtuse angle and a right angle.
    Answers may vary. Sample: $\angle AOD$, $\angle BOE$

Lesson 1-1

Find the next two terms in each sequence.

50. $19, 21.5, 24, 26.5$ **29, 31.5**

51. $3.4, 3.45, 3.456, 3.4567$ **3.45678, 3.456789**

52. $-2, 6, -18, 54$ **−162, 486**

53. $8, -4, 2, -1$ $\frac{1}{2}, -\frac{1}{4}$

Reading for Problem Solving

Read the problem below and then follow along with what Larissa thinks as she solves the problem. Check your understanding by solving the exercise at the bottom of the page.

x^2 **Algebra** In the figure at the right, $KM = 35$.
  a. Solve for x. Justify each step.
  b. Find the length of $\overline{KL}$.

$\overset{2x-5 \qquad 2x}{\underset{K \qquad L \qquad M}{\bullet \qquad \bullet \qquad \bullet}}$

What Larissa Thinks

What information am I given?

Points K, L, and M are collinear. I can use the Segment Addition Postulate to write an equation.

Now I will substitute for KL, LM, and KM. I get an equation that I can solve for x.

I simplify the left side.

I add 5 to each side.

I divide each side by 4.

Part (b) asks me to find KL.
The diagram shows that $KL = 2x - 5$.
I know $x = 10$, so I'll substitute to find KL.

Now, I'll write my answer.

What Larissa Writes

Given: KM = 35, KL = 2x − 5,
LM = 2x

1. KL + LM = KM   1. Segment Addition Postulate

2. (2x − 5) + 2x = 35   2. Substitute.

3. 4x − 5 = 35   3. Simplify.

4. 4x = 40   4. Addition Property of Equality

5. x = 10   5. Division Property of Equality

KL = 2x − 5
    = 2(10) − 5
    = 20 − 5 = 15

The length of $\overline{KL}$ is 15.

Reading for Problem Solving

Students must be able to analyze problem situations and to translate their problem-solving ideas into step-by-step solutions. This feature shows how a student's logical thought process translates into problem solving.

Teaching Notes

After students read the problem, have them compare "What Larissa Thinks" with "What Larissa Writes" for each step. Point out that what Larissa writes formalizes what she thinks. Also point out that the steps in the second column demonstrate a two-column proof.

Auditory Learners

Before students read the solution, ask them to propose their own methods of solution in a class discussion. Elicit as many different approaches as students can suggest.

Exercise

Have students work independently to solve the problem, showing the steps they used. Then have volunteers share with the class what they were thinking as they wrote each step.

EXERCISE

x^2 **Algebra** $\angle 1$ and $\angle 2$ are supplementary; $m\angle 1 = 4y + 15$ and $m\angle 2 = 7y - 11$.
  a. Solve for y. Justify each step.
  b. Find $m\angle 2$.   **101**

a. 1. $m\angle 1 + m\angle 2 = 180$ (Def. of suppl.)
    2. $4y + 15 + 7y - 11 = 180$ (Subst.)
    3. $11y + 4 = 180$ (Simplify.)
    4. $11y = 176$ (Subtr. Prop. of =)
    5. $y = 16$ (Div. Prop. of =)

1. Plan

Lesson Preview

✓ **Check Skills You'll Need**

Measuring Angles
Lesson 1-4: Example 6,
Exercises 27 and 28
Extra Practice, p. 690

Lesson Resources

📁 **Teaching Resources**
Practice, Reteaching, Enrichment

👥 **Reaching All Students**
Practice Workbook 2-5
Spanish Practice Workbook 2-5
Reading and Math Literacy 2C
Spanish Reading & Literacy 2C
Technology Activities 9
Hands-On Activities 6
Informal Geometry Planning
  Guide 2-5

⏰ **Presentation Assistant Plus!**
Transparencies
• Check Skills You'll Need 2-5
• Additional Examples 2-5
• Student Edition Answers 2-5
• Lesson Quiz 2-5
PH Presentation Pro CD 2-5

PRENTICE HALL
ASSESSMENT SYSTEM

Computer Test Generator CD

💿 **Technology**
Resource Pro® CD-ROM
Computer Test Generator CD
Prentice Hall Presentation Pro CD

🖥 **www.PHSchool.com**
Student Site
• Teacher Web Code: afk-5500
• Self-grading Lesson Quiz
Teacher Center
• Lesson Planner
• Resources

Plus **iTEXT**

2-5

Proving Angles Congruent

2.02 Apply properties, definitions, and theorems of angles and lines to solve problems and write proofs.

 North Carolina Objectives

Lesson Preview

What You'll Learn

OBJECTIVE 1
To identify angle pairs

OBJECTIVE 2
To prove and apply theorems about angles

. . . And Why

To find the measures of angles formed by the legs of a director's chair, as in Exercise 36

✓ **Check Skills You'll Need** (For help, go to Lesson 1-4.)

x^2 **Algebra Find the value of each variable.**

1. 50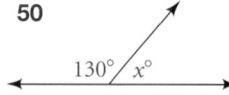

2. 90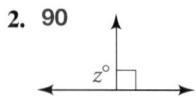

3. 35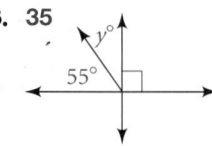

Fill in each blank.

4. Perpendicular lines are two lines that intersect to form ___?___. **right angles**

5. An angle is formed by two rays with the same endpoint. The endpoint is called the ___?___ of the angle. **vertex**

New Vocabulary • vertical angles • adjacent angles • complementary angles • supplementary angles • theorem • paragraph proof

---

OBJECTIVE 1 **Identifying Angle Pairs**

iTEXT Interactive lesson includes instant self-check, tutorials, and activities.

In this lesson, you will learn about important angle pairs that have special names.

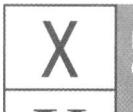 Helvetica Condensed

 Times Roman

 Eurostile Extended

 MarkerFelt Thin

In each font, a capital X suggests vertical angles.

vertical angles

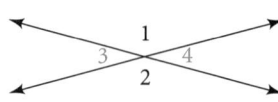

two angles whose sides form two pairs of opposite rays

adjacent angles

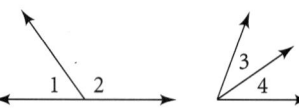

two coplanar angles with a common side, a common vertex, and no common interior points

complementary angles

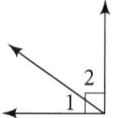

two angles whose measures have sum 90

Each angle is called the *complement* of the other.

supplementary angles

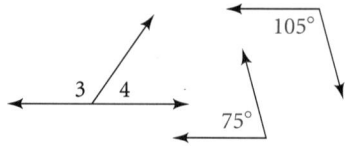

two angles whose measures have sum 180

Each angle is called the *supplement* of the other.

96 Chapter 2 Reasoning and Proof

Ongoing Assessment and Intervention

Before the Lesson Diagnose prerequisite skills using:	**During the Lesson** Monitor progress using:	**After the Lesson** Assess knowledge using:
• Check Skills You'll Need	• Check Understanding • Additional Examples • Standardized Test Prep	• Lesson Quiz • Computer Test Generator CD

① EXAMPLE **Identifying Angle Pairs**

In the diagram identify pairs of numbered angles that are related as follows:

a. complementary
∠2 and ∠3

b. supplementary
∠4 and ∠5; ∠3 and ∠4

c. vertical
∠3 and ∠5

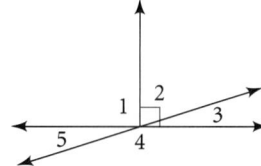

✔ **Check Understanding** **① a.** Name two pairs of adjacent angles in the photo below. **Answers may vary.**
b. If m∠EFD = 27, find m∠AFD. **153**

Sample: ∠AFB and ∠BFC; ∠BFD and ∠DFE

When entering the roadway, turn and look for oncoming traffic regardless of what you see in the rear-view mirror.

Whether you draw a diagram or use a given diagram, you can make some conclusions directly from the diagrams. You *can* conclude that angles are

* adjacent angles
* adjacent supplementary angles
* vertical angles

Unless there are marks that give this information, you *cannot* assume

* angles or segments are congruent
* an angle is a right angle
* lines are parallel or perpendicular

② EXAMPLE **Making Conclusions From a Diagram**

What can you conclude from the information in the diagram?

* ∠1 ≅ ∠2, by the markings.
* ∠2 and ∠3, for example, are adjacent angles.
* ∠4 and ∠5, for example, are adjacent supplementary angles,
  or m∠4 + m∠5 = 180 by the Angle Addition Postulate.
* ∠1 and ∠4, for example, are vertical angles.

2a. Yes; the congruent segments are marked.
b. No; there are no markings.
c. No; there are no markings.
d. No; there are no markings.

✔ **Check Understanding** **②** Can you make each conclusion from the information in the diagram? Explain.
a. $\overline{TW} \cong \overline{WV}$ **b.** $\overline{PW} \cong \overline{WQ}$ **a–d. See left.**
c. $\overline{TV} \perp \overline{PQ}$ **d.** $\overline{TV}$ bisects $\overline{PQ}$.
e. W is the midpoint of $\overline{TV}$. **Yes; the congruent segments are marked.**

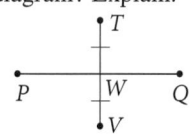

Professional Development

Math Background

Inductive reasoning can lead to conjectures, but only deductive reasoning can establish truth conclusively. Proving a theorem by logically progressing from a given condition to a necessary conclusion is a fundamental mathematical activity.

OBJECTIVE
▼① **Teaching Notes**

Teaching Tip
After students read the definition of vertical angles, ask: *What is another way to define vertical angles?* opposite angles formed by two intersecting lines

Error Prevention
Students sometimes confuse complementary and supplementary angles. One way to keep them straight is to remember that *c* comes before *s* in the alphabet, just as 90 comes before 180.

① EXAMPLE **Connection to Language Arts**

Students are familiar with the word *compliment*. Point out that the word in this lesson has an *e* instead of an *i*. Ask students to find examples where the words *complement* and *supplement* are not used in a mathematical context.

② EXAMPLE **Math Tip**

By drawing conclusions directly from a diagram, you need less information in the Given list of a proof. Point out to students that learning to draw accurate conclusions from a diagram will make proofs easier.

Investigation (Optional)
Provide patty paper (which is also used to separate frozen hamburger patties) for students to fold for this investigation.

👥 Reaching All Students

Below Level Have students use protractors to verify the Vertical Angles Theorem. Actually measuring the angles also will reinforce the underlying algebraic argument in the proof in Example 3.	**Advanced Learners** Use the definition of *adjacent angles* to help students refine their understanding of a good definition.	**Tactile Learners** See note on page 98.

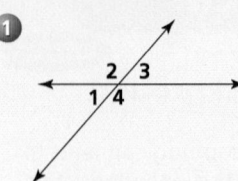

1

Name all pairs of angles in the diagram that are
a. vertical
∠1 and ∠3; ∠2 and ∠4
b. supplementary ∠1 and ∠2;
∠2 and ∠3; ∠3 and ∠4;
∠4 and ∠1
c. complementary none

2 Use the diagram from Example 2. Which of the following can you conclude: ∠3 is a right angle, ∠1 and ∠5 are adjacent, ∠3 ≅ ∠5? ∠1 and ∠5 are adjacent.

OBJECTIVE

2 Teaching Notes

Technology Tip
Students can explore the Vertical Angles Theorem with geometry software.

Tactile Learners
Have students copy the diagrams for the Vertical Angles and Congruent Supplements Theorems to reinforce each Given and the conclusions that follow.

3 EXAMPLE Alternative Method

Work as a class to write the paragraph proof in two columns, justifying each step in the right column as in Lesson 2-4.

4 EXAMPLE Teaching Tip

Ask: *How is this method like writing a paragraph proof? How is it different?* **Sample: You work step-by-step, building on what you know; you can quickly see the list of steps.**

Investigation: Vertical Angles

- Draw two intersecting lines. Number the angles as shown.

- Fold the sides of ∠1 onto ∠2.

- Fold the sides of ∠3 onto ∠4.

- Make a conjecture about vertical angles. **Vertical angles are congruent.**

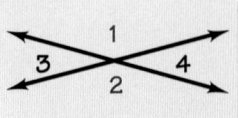

You can use deductive reasoning to show that a conjecture is true. The set of steps you take is called a proof. The statement that you prove true is a **theorem.** The Investigation above leads to a conjecture that becomes the following theorem.

 Key Concepts

Theorem 2-1	**Vertical Angles Theorem**

Vertical angles are congruent.

∠1 ≅ ∠2 and ∠3 ≅ ∠4

In the proof of a theorem, a "Given" list shows you what you know from the hypothesis of the theorem. You prove the conclusion of the theorem. A diagram records the given information visually.

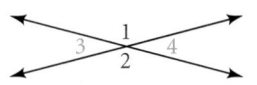

what you know ↘ Given: ～～～
what you must show ↗ Prove: ～～～
diagram that ← shows what you know

There are many forms of proofs. A **paragraph proof** is written as sentences in a paragraph. Here is a paragraph proof of Theorem 2-1.

Proof **3 EXAMPLE Proving Theorem 2-1**

Study what is Given, what you Prove, and the diagram. Write a paragraph proof.

Given: ∠1 and ∠2 are   ← what you know →
            vertical angles.

Prove: ∠1 ≅ ∠2   ← what you show

3. No; no; the size of the angles does not affect the proof or the truth value of the theorem.

Paragraph Proof: By the Angle Addition Postulate, $m\angle 1 + m\angle 3 = 180$ and $m\angle 2 + m\angle 3 = 180$. By substitution, $m\angle 1 + m\angle 3 = m\angle 2 + m\angle 3$. Subtract $m\angle 3$ from each side. You get $m\angle 1 = m\angle 2$, or $\angle 1 \cong \angle 2$.

✓ **Check Understanding** **3** **Critical Thinking** Does the size of the angles in the diagram affect the proof? Would the proof change if ∠1 and ∠2 were acute rather than obtuse? Explain. **See left.**

98   Chapter 2   Reasoning and Proof

You can use the Vertical Angles Theorem to solve for variables and find the measures of angles.

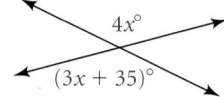

4 EXAMPLE   Using the Vertical Angles Theorem

Algebra Find the value of x.

$4x = 3x + 35$ **Vertical angles are congruent.**

$x = 35$ **Subtract 3x from each side.**

✓ **Check Understanding** **4 a.** Find the measures of the labeled pair of vertical angles in the diagram above. **140**
b. Find the measures of the other pair of vertical angles. **40**
c. Check to see that adjacent angles are supplementary. **140 + 40 = 180**

The Vertical Angles Theorem is actually a special case of the following theorem. A proof of this theorem is shown below. You can write a proof of another form of this theorem in Exercise 55.

 Key Concepts

Theorem 2-2	Congruent Supplements Theorem

If two angles are supplements of the same angle (or of congruent angles), then the two angles are congruent.

Proof

Proof of Theorem 2-2

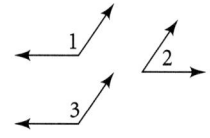

Given: ∠1 and ∠2 are supplementary.
∠3 and ∠2 are supplementary.

Prove: ∠1 ≅ ∠3

Proof: By the definition of supplementary angles, $m\angle 1 + m\angle 2 = 180$ and $m\angle 3 + m\angle 2 = 180$. By substitution, $m\angle 1 + m\angle 2 = m\angle 3 + m\angle 2$. Subtract $m\angle 2$ from each side. You get $m\angle 1 = m\angle 3$, or $\angle 1 \cong \angle 3$.

Theorem 2-3 is like the Congruent Supplements Theorem. You can demonstrate its proof in Exercises 19 and 56.

 Key Concepts

Theorem 2-3	Congruent Complements Theorem

If two angles are complements of the same angle (or of congruent angles), then the two angles are congruent.

Theorem 2-4

All right angles are congruent.

Theorem 2-5

If two angles are congruent and supplementary, then each is a right angle.

You can complete proofs of Theorems 2-4 and 2-5 in Exercises 31 and 35, respectively.

3 In the paragraph proof of Example 3, which property justifies the step "Subtract $m\angle 3$ from both sides"? Subtraction Prop. of Eq.

4 Find the value of x. 52

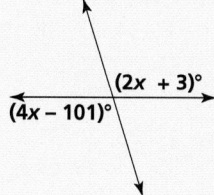

$(2x + 3)°$
$(4x - 101)°$

Closure

Point out two things that are incorrect in the diagram. Explain your reasoning.

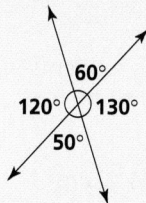

60°
120° 130°
50°

Pairs of vertical angles do not have the same measure; the Vertical Angles Theorem says they are congruent. One pair of supplementary angles has a sum of 170, and another pair has a sum of 190; supplementary angles have a sum of 180.

Assignment Guide

▼ **1 Objective**

Ⓐ Ⓑ **Core** 1–18, 27, 32–34, 37, 38

▼ **2 Objective**

Ⓐ Ⓑ **Core** 19–26, 28–31, 35, 36, 39–54

Ⓒ **Extension** 55–59

Standardized Test Prep 60–66

Mixed Review 67–74

Error Prevention

Exercise 2 Point out to students that two conditions must be met in this exercise.

Exercises 10, 11 Ask: *Why are three letters used to name the angles in Exercise 11, but only one letter is used in Exercise 10?* Vertex *J* and vertex *D* each apply to only one angle, but many angles share vertex *A*.

Exercise 19 When they finish the proof, have students compare their justifications to those of the Vertical Angles Theorem proof.

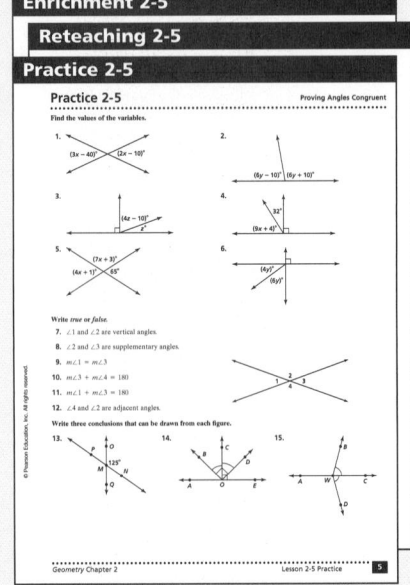

EXERCISES

For more practice, see *Extra Practice.*

Practice and Problem Solving

Ⓐ **Practice by Example**

Example 1
(page 97)

Name an angle or angles in the diagram described by each of the following.

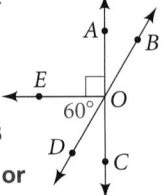

1. supplementary to ∠AOD ∠AOB or ∠DOC

2. adjacent and congruent to ∠AOE ∠EOC

3. supplementary to ∠EOA ∠EOC

4. complementary to ∠EOD ∠DOC or ∠AOB

5. a pair of vertical angles ∠AOB and ∠DOC or ∠BOC and ∠AOD

In the diagram above, find the measure of each of the following angles.

6. ∠EOC 90   **7.** ∠DOC 30   **8.** ∠BOC 150   **9.** ∠AOB 30

Example 2
(page 97)

12. Yes; you can conclude that the angles are adjacent and supplementary from the diagram.

14. Yes; you can conclude that angles are supplementary from the diagram.

17. Yes; you can conclude that the angles are vertical from the diagram.

Can you make each conclusion from the information in the diagram? Explain.

10. ∠J ≅ ∠D Yes; the markings show they are congruent.

11. ∠JAC ≅ ∠DAC No; there are no markings.

12. ∠JAE and ∠EAF are adjacent and supplementary. **See left.**

13. m∠JCA = m∠DCA No; there are no markings.

14. m∠JCA + m∠ACD = 180 **See left.**

15. AJ ≅ AD Yes; there are markings.

16. *C* is the midpoint of JD. No; there are no markings.

17. ∠EAF and ∠JAD are vertical angles. **See left.**

18. AC bisects ∠JAD. No; there are no markings.

Example 3
(page 98)

19. Developing Proof Complete this proof of one form of Theorem 2-3 by filling in the blanks.

If two angles are complements of the same angle, then the two angles are congruent.

Given: ∠1 and ∠2 are complementary.
∠3 and ∠2 are complementary.

Prove: ∠1 ≅ ∠3

Proof: By the definition of complementary angles,
m∠1 + m∠2 = **a.** _?_ **90** and m∠3 + m∠2 = **b.** _?_. 90
Then m∠1 + m∠2 = m∠3 + m∠2 by **c.** _?_. substitution
Subtract m∠2 from each side. You get m∠1 = **d.** _?_. m∠3

Example 4
(page 99)

x^2 **Algebra** **Find the value of each variable.**

20.
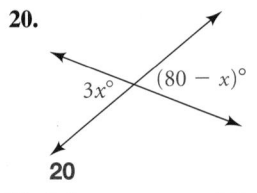
$3x°$ $(80 - x)°$
20

21.
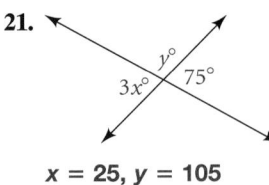
$3x°$ $y°$ $75°$
x = 25, y = 105

22.
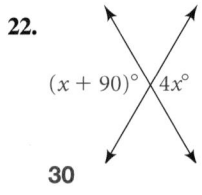
$(x + 90)°$ $4x°$
30

Find the measures of the labeled angles in each exercise.

23. Exercise 20
60, 60

24. Exercise 21
75, 105

25. Exercise 22
120, 120

 **B** **Apply Your Skills**

26. Writing How is a theorem different from a postulate? **Answers may vary. Sample: A theorem is proven and a postulate is assumed to be true.**

27. Open-Ended Give an example of vertical angles in your home.
Answers may vary. Sample: scissors

28. Reasoning Explain why this statement is true:
If $m\angle 1 + m\angle 2 = 180$ and $m\angle 3 + m\angle 2 = 180$, then $\angle 1 \cong \angle 3$. **See margin.**

x^2 **Algebra** Find the value of each variable and the measure of each labeled angle.

29.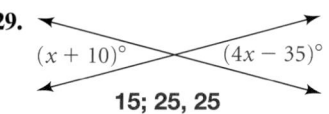
$(x + 10)°$ $(4x - 35)°$
15; 25, 25

30. $x = 14, y = 15; 50, 50, 130$
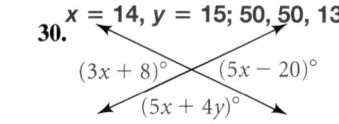
$(3x + 8)°$ $(5x - 20)°$
$(5x + 4y)°$

31. Developing Proof Complete this proof of Theorem 2-4 by filling in the blanks.

All right angles are congruent.

Given: $\angle X$ and $\angle Y$ are right angles.

Prove: $\angle X \cong \angle Y$

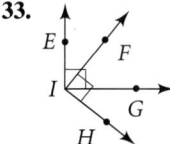 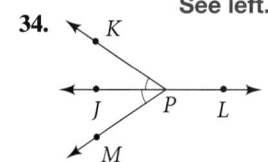
X   Y

Proof: By the definition of **a.** _?_ , $m\angle X = 90$ and $m\angle Y = 90$. **right angle**
By the Substitution Property, $m\angle X =$ **b.** _?_ , or $\angle X \cong \angle Y$. **$m\angle Y$**

Name two pairs of congruent angles in each figure. Justify your answers. **32–34. See left.**

32.

32. $\angle DOB \cong \angle AOC$ and $\angle DOA \cong \angle BOC$ since they are vertical angles.

33. $\angle EIG \cong \angle FIH$ since all right angles are congruent; $\angle EIF \cong \angle HIG$ since they are complements of the same angle.

34. $\angle KPJ \cong \angle MPJ$ since they are marked congruent; $\angle KPL \cong \angle MPL$ since they are supplements of congruent angles.

33.

34.

35. Developing Proof Complete this proof of Theorem 2-5 by filling in the blanks.

If two angles are congruent and supplementary,
then each is a right angle.

Given: $\angle W$ and $\angle V$ are congruent and supplementary.

Prove: $\angle W$ and $\angle V$ are right angles.

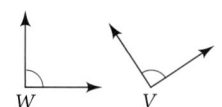
W   V

Proof: $\angle W$ and $\angle V$ are congruent, so $m\angle W = m\angle$ **a.** _?_ . **V**
$\angle W$ and $\angle V$ are supplementary so $m\angle W + m\angle V =$ **b.** _?_ . **180**
Substituting $m\angle W$ for $m\angle V$, you get $m\angle W + m\angle W = 180$, or $2m\angle W = 180$.
By the **c.** _?_ Property of Equality, $m\angle W = 90$. **Division**
Since $\angle W \cong \angle V$, $m\angle V = 90$, too. Then both angles are **d.** _?_ angles. **right**

36. Design The two back legs of the director's chair pictured at the left meet in a 72° angle. Find the measure of each angle formed by the two back legs. **See margin.**

37. Coordinate Geometry $\angle AOX$ contains points $A(1, 3)$, $O(0, 0)$, and $X(4, 0)$.
a. Find the coordinates of a point B so that $\angle BOA$ and $\angle AOX$ are adjacent complementary angles. **a–b. See margin.**
b. Find the coordinates of a point C so that $\overrightarrow{OC}$ is a side of a different angle that is adjacent and complementary to $\angle AOX$.

38. Coordinate Geometry $\angle DOE$ contains points $D(2, 3)$, $O(0, 0)$, and $E(5, 1)$.
Find the coordinates of a point F so that $\overrightarrow{OF}$ is a side of an angle that is adjacent and supplementary to $\angle DOE$. **Answers may vary. Sample: $(-5, -1)$**

Exercise 36

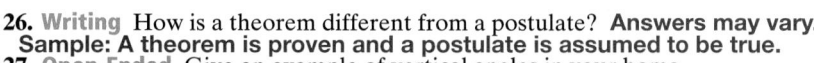

Exercise 26 When students are finished, ask: *How is a theorem similar to a postulate?* **Sample: Both are true statements about geometric figures.** Point out that students will use both postulates and theorems that are already proved to prove each new theorem.

Connection to Architecture

Exercise 27 Ask: *What angles are used frequently in house and building design?* **Sample: right angle, straight angle** Have students discuss where these angles appear.

Exercises 32–34 Have partners explain their reasoning to each other. Point out that being able to explain your reasoning carefully is like writing a good proof in geometry.

Exercises 55, 56 Do these exercises as a class activity. Students may refer back to the proofs in the lesson for ideas, if necessary.

Connection to Algebra

Exercises 57–59 Students must set up and solve a system of two equations.

pages 100–103 Exercises

28. If $m\angle 1 + m\angle 2 = 180$, and $m\angle 2 + m\angle 3 = 180$, then $m\angle 1 + m\angle 2 = m\angle 2 + m\angle 3$ by subst. Subtr. $m\angle 2$ from each side $m\angle 1 = m\angle 3$ or $\angle 1 \cong \angle 3$.

36. The two acute $\angle$s have measure 72. The two obtuse $\angle$s have measure 108.

37. a. Answers may vary. *B* can be any point on the positive *y*-axis. Sample: (0, 5).

b. Answers may vary. Sample: (3, −1)

101

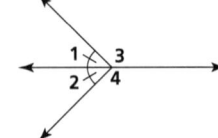

1. Name a pair of adjacent angles. **Samples: ∠1 and ∠2, ∠2 and ∠4, ∠4 and ∠3, ∠3 and ∠1**

2. Name a pair of supplementary angles. **Samples: ∠1 and ∠3, ∠2 and ∠4**

3. Can you conclude that there are vertical angles in the diagram? Explain. **No; no angle pairs are formed by opposite rays.**

4. Can you conclude that there are complementary angles in the diagram? Explain. **No; no angle is marked with a right angle symbol or labeled 90°.**

5. Suppose $m\angle 1 = 3x + 6$ and $m\angle 2 = 5x - 20$. Find x. **13**

6. What theorem allows you to conclude that ∠3 and ∠4 are congruent? **Congruent Supplements Theorem (Theorem 2-2)**

Exercise 43

x^2 **Algebra** Find the value of each variable and the measure of each labeled angle.

39. **9; 36**
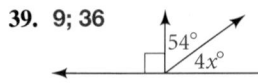

40. **10; 105, 75**
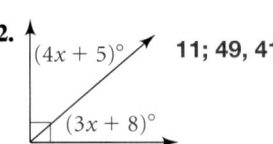

41. **18; 54, 36**
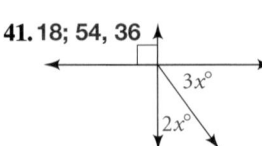

42. **11; 49, 41**
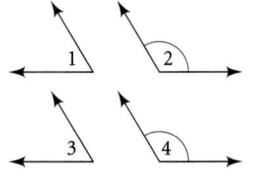

🌐 43. **Sports** In the photograph, the wheels of the racing wheelchair are tilted so that ∠1 ≅ ∠2. What theorem can you use to justify the statement ∠3 ≅ ∠4? **Supplements of ≅ ∕s are ≅.**

Critical Thinking If possible, find the measures of the angles described. If it is not possible, explain why.

44. congruent adjacent supplementary angles **90, 90**

45. congruent adjacent complementary angles **45, 45**

46. congruent vertical angles **Not possible; a pair of vertical angles can have any measure greater than 0 or less than 180.**

x^2 **Algebra** Find the measure of each angle.
$m\angle A = 72, m\angle B = 18$

47. ∠A and ∠B are complementary. $m\angle A = 3x + 12$ and $m\angle B = 2x - 22$.

48. ∠A and ∠B are supplementary. $m\angle A = 3x + 12$ and $m\angle B = 2x - 22$.

48. $m\angle A = 126, m\angle B = 54$

49. ∠A is twice as large as its complement, ∠B. **$m\angle A = 60, m\angle B = 30$**

50. ∠A is half as large as its complement, ∠B. **$m\angle A = 30, m\angle B = 60$**

51. ∠A is twice as large as its supplement, ∠B. **$m\angle A = 120, m\angle B = 60$**

52. ∠A is half as large as twice its supplement, ∠B. **$m\angle A = 90, m\angle B = 90$**

53. The measure of ∠B, the supplement of ∠A, is four times the measure of ∠C, the complement of ∠A. **$m\angle A = 60, m\angle B = 120, m\angle C = 30$**

54. The measure of ∠B, the complement of ∠A, is one-sixth the measure of ∠C, the supplement of ∠A. **$m\angle A = 72, m\angle B = 18, m\angle C = 108$**

🅒 **Challenge** Proof **55.** Write a paragraph proof for this form of Theorem 2-2. **See margin.**

If two angles are supplements of congruent angles, then the two angles are congruent.

Given: ∠1 and ∠2 are supplementary.
∠3 and ∠4 are supplementary.
∠2 ≅ ∠4

Prove: ∠1 ≅ ∠3

Proof **56.** Write a paragraph proof for this form of Theorem 2-3. **See margin.**

If two angles are complements of congruent angles, then the two angles are congruent.

Given: ∠1 and ∠2 are complementary.
∠3 and ∠4 are complementary.
∠2 ≅ ∠4

Prove: ∠1 ≅ ∠3

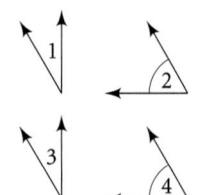

102 Chapter 2 Reasoning and Proof

pages 100–103 **Exercises**

55. **By the def. of suppl. ∕s, $m\angle 1 + m\angle 2 = 180$ and $m\angle 3 + m\angle 4 = 180$. By the Subst. Prop. $m\angle 1 + m\angle 2 = m\angle 3 + m\angle 4$. It is given that ∠2 ≅ ∠4,** so $m\angle 2 = m\angle 4$. Then by the Subtr. Prop. of =, $m\angle 1 = m\angle 3$, or ∠1 ≅ ∠3.

56. **By the def. of compl. ∕s, $m\angle 1 + m\angle 2 = 90$ and $m\angle 3 + m\angle 4 = 90$. By** the Subst. Prop. of =, $m\angle 1 + m\angle 2 = m\angle 3 + m\angle 4$. It is given that ∠2 ≅ ∠4, so $m\angle 2 = m\angle 4$. Then by the Subtr. Prop. of =, $m\angle 1 = m\angle 3$ or ∠1 ≅ ∠3.

x^2 **Algebra** Find the value of each variable and the measure of each labeled angle.

57.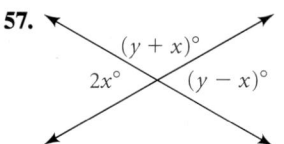

$x = 30, y = 90;$
60, 120, 60

58.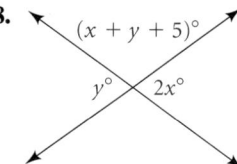

$x = 35, y = 70;$
70, 110, 70

59.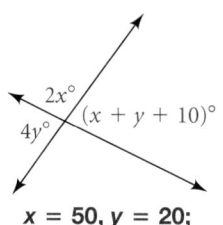

$x = 50, y = 20;$
80, 100, 80

Standardized Test Prep

Standardized Test Prep

A sheet of blank grids is available in the Test-Taking Strategies with Transparencies booklet. Give this sheet to students for practice with filling in the grids.

📁 **Resources**
For additional practice with a variety of test item formats:
• Standardized Test Prep, p. 109
• Test-Taking Strategies, p. 104
• Test-Taking Strategies with Transparencies

Gridded Response

Find the measure of each angle.

60. an angle with measure 8 less than the measure of its complement **41**

61. one angle of a pair of complementary vertical angles **45**

62. an angle with measure three times the measure of its supplement **135**

Exercise 62 Students can write and solve an equation in x to find the measure of the angle.

💻 **Take It to the NET**
Online lesson quiz at
www.PHSchool.com
Web Code: afa-0205

Use the diagram at the right to find the measure of each of the following angles.

63. ∠1 **20**

64. ∠2 **90**

65. ∠3 **70**

66. ∠4 **110**

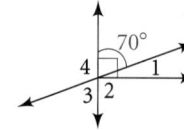

Mixed Review

Lesson 2-4

Use the given property to complete each statement.

67. Subtraction Property of Equality
If $3x + 7 = 19$, then $3x = $ _?_ . **12**

68. Reflexive Property of Congruence
$\overline{AB} \cong$ _?_ **$\overline{AB}$**

69. Substitution Property
If $MN = 3$ and $MN + NP = 15$, then _?_ . **3 + NP = 15**

Lesson 2-3

Use deductive reasoning to draw a conclusion. If not possible, write *not possible*.

70. If two lines intersect, then they are coplanar.
Lines m and n are coplanar. **not possible**

71. If two angles are vertical angles, then they are congruent.
∠1 and ∠2 are vertical angles. **∠1 and ∠2 are congruent.**

Lesson 2-2

Each conditional statement below is true. Write its converse. If the converse is also true, combine the statements as a biconditional.

72. If $y = 25$, then
$y + 7 = 32$.
$y + 7 = 32$ if and
only if $y = 25$.

72. If $y + 7 = 32$, then $y = 25$.

73. If you live south of the equator, then you live in Australia.

73. If you live in Australia, then you live south of the equator.

74. If $n > 0$, then $n^2 > 0$. **If $n^2 > 0$, then $n > 0$.**

Writing Short Responses

Some assessment tests now require students to answer short-response questions. This feature helps students understand the rationale behind the way such questions are scored and the importance of giving a complete, clear answer to earn full credit.

Resources

PRENTICE HALL
ASSESSMENT SYSTEM

Test-Taking Strategies with Transparencies
• Transparency 2
• Practice sheet p. 14

Teaching Notes

An answer without explanation in a short-response problem does not earn full credit. The requirement of an explanation or elaboration in a short-response problem should motivate students to understand the key mathematical concepts before they take assessment tests.

English Learners

Students new to English may encounter special difficulties when asked to write explanations. Point out that much mathematical terminology is new to all students.

Test-Taking Strategies with Transparencies

Test-Taking Strategy: Writing Short Responses

Della went to the carnival at the county fair. The admission to the carnival was $5.00 and the rides were $1.25 each. Della spent $20 at the carnival. Write and solve an equation to find out how many rides Della rode at the carnival.

Scoring Guide

2 The equation and solution are correct, AND all work is shown.

1 An incorrect equation is used, but the procedure for solving the equation is incorrect.

1 The correct equation or solution is given, but no work is shown.

0 No response, OR completely incorrect response with no work shown.

Answer earning 2 points	
$5 + 1.25x = 20$ $1.25x = 15$ $x = 12$ Della rode 12 rides.	In the 2-point response, the student used the correct equation, found the correct answer, AND showed all the work.
Answer earning 1 point	
$1.25x = 20$ $x = 16$ Della rode 16 rides	In this 1-point response, an incorrect equation is used, but the procedure is correct for the used equation.
Answer earning 1 point	
Della rode 12 rides.	In this 1-point response, the correct solution is given, but no work is shown.
Answer earning 0 points	
15 rides	In the 0-point response, the solution is incorrect, AND no work is shown.

Transparency 2

104

Short-response questions are usually worth 2 points. To get full credit you must demonstrate a thorough understanding and knowledge of mathematical concepts and techniques.

EXAMPLE

Name a pair of adjacent angles in the diagram at the right. Use the definition of adjacent angles to explain why your angles are adjacent.

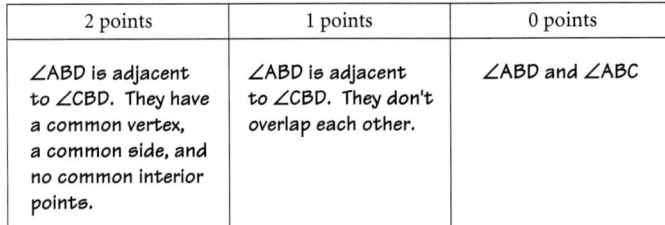

To respond correctly to this problem you have to know that adjacent angles are coplanar angles with a common vertex, a common side, and no common interior points. You have to pick a pair of angles that are adjacent and then use the definition to explain why your angles are adjacent.

2 points	1 points	0 points
∠ABD is adjacent to ∠CBD. They have a common vertex, a common side, and no common interior points.	∠ABD is adjacent to ∠CBD. They don't overlap each other.	∠ABD and ∠ABC

A 2-point response has a correct pair of adjacent angles and an explanation that uses the definition. This 1-point response has a correct pair but an incomplete definition. (An incorrect pair with an explanation that uses the definition is also worth 1 point.) The 0-point response has an incorrect pair and no explanation.

EXERCISES

1–3. Check students' work.

Score each response to the exercise in the Example above. Explain your reasoning.

1.
∠DBC and ∠ABD are adjacent because they are next to each other and don't overlap.

2.
∠BAD and ∠BCD They aren't next to each other.

3.
∠DBA and ∠DBC Adjacent angles share a vertex and a side and have no interior points in common.

Write a 2-point response to each exercise. Refer to the diagram in the Example.

4. Name a pair of supplementary angles. Use the definition of supplementary angles to explain why your angles are supplementary. **See margin.**

5. ∠ABD and ∠BDC are complementary, $m\angle ABD = 6x$, and $m\angle BDC = 2x + 2$. Use the definition of complementary to explain what x must be. **See margin.**

page 104   **Test-Taking Strategies**

4–5. **Answers may vary. Samples are given.**

4. ∠ABD and ∠DBC are suppl. They form a linear pair.

5. $m\angle ABD + m\angle BDC = 90$
$6x + 2x + 2 = 90$
$8x = 88$
$x = 11$

Chapter Review

Vocabulary

adjacent angles (p. 96)
biconditional (p. 75)
complementary angles (p. 96)
conclusion (p. 68)
conditional (p. 68)
converse (p. 69)

deductive reasoning (p. 82)
hypothesis (p. 68)
Law of Detachment (p. 82)
Law of Syllogism (p. 83)
paragraph proof (p. 98)
Reflexive Property (pp. 89 and 91)

supplementary angles (p. 96)
Symmetric Property (pp. 89 and 91)
theorem (p. 98)
Transitive Property (pp. 89 and 91)
truth value (p. 69)
vertical angles (p. 96)

Resources

Student Edition
Extra Practice Ch. 2, p. 691
English/Spanish Glossary, p. 741
Postulates and Theorems, p. 732
Table of Symbols, p. 725

 Reading Math
Understanding
Vocabulary

Choose the correct vocabulary term to complete each sentence.

1. The statement "∠A ≅ ∠A" is an example of the __?__ Property of Congruence. **Reflexive**

2. In a conditional statement, the part that directly follows *if* is the __?__. **hypothesis**

3. Two coplanar angles with a common side, a common vertex, and no common interior points are __?__. **adjacent**

4. "If ∠A ≅ ∠B and ∠B ≅ ∠C, then ∠A ≅ ∠C" is an example of the __?__ Property of Congruence. **Transitive**

5. If the sum of the measures of two angles is 90, the angles are __?__. **complementary**

6. When a conditional and its converse are true, they may be written as a single true statement called a __?__. **biconditional**

7. Two angles whose sides are opposite rays are __?__. **vertical angles**

8. The __?__ of a conditional switches the hypothesis and the conclusion. **converse**

9. "If ∠A ≅ ∠B, then ∠B ≅ ∠A" is an example of the __?__ Property of Congruence. **Symmetric**

10. If the sum of the measures of two angles is 180, the angles are __?__. **supplementary**

Reaching All Students
Reading and Math Literacy 2D
Spanish Reading and Literacy 2D

ASSESSMENT SYSTEM

Standardized Test Prep Workbook
• Ch. 2 practice in standardized test formats

www.PHSchool.com
Student Site
• Self-grading Vocabulary Test
Teacher Center
• Resources

Plus **iTEXT**

Take It to the NET
Online vocabulary quiz
at www.PHSchool.com
Web Code: afg-0251

Skills and Concepts

2-1 and 2-2 Objectives

▼ To recognize conditional statements

▼ To write converses of conditional statements

▼ To write biconditionals

▼ To recognize good definitions

An *if-then statement* is a **conditional.** The part following *if* is the **hypothesis.** The part following *then* is the **conclusion.** You find the truth value of a conditional by determining whether it is true or false. The symbolic form of a conditional is $p \rightarrow q$.

The **converse** of a conditional switches the hypothesis and the conclusion. The symbolic form of a converse is $q \rightarrow p$.

When a conditional and its converse are true, you can combine them as a true **biconditional.** To write a biconditional, you join the two parts of each conditional with the phrase *if and only if.* The symbolic form of a biconditional is $p \leftrightarrow q$.

For Exercises 11–13, (a) write the converse and (b) determine the truth value of the conditional and its converse. (c) If both statements are true, write a biconditional.

11. If you are a teenager, then you are younger than 20. **11–13. See margin.**

12. If an angle is obtuse, then its measure is greater than 90 and less than 180.

13. If a figure is a square, then it has four sides.

Spanish Reading & Math Literacy 2D

pages 105–107 Chapter Review

11. a. If you are younger than 20, then you are a teenager.

   b. conditional: true, converse: false

12. a. If an angle has measure greater than 90 and less than 180, then it is obtuse.

   b. conditional: true, converse: true

   c. An angle is obtuse if and only if it has measure greater than 90 and less than 180.

13. a. If a figure has four sides, then it is a square.

   b. conditional: true, converse: false

14. Write the following sentence as a conditional: All flowers are beautiful.
If something is a flower, then it is beautiful.
A good definition is precise. A good definition uses terms that have been previously defined or are commonly accepted.

15. Rico defines a *book* as something you read. Explain why this is not a good definition. **Rico's definition is not reversible. A magazine is a counter-example. You read a magazine, but it is not a book.**

16. Write this definition as a biconditional:

An *oxymoron* is a phrase that contains contradictory terms.
A phrase is an oxymoron if and only if it contains contradictory terms.

17. Write this biconditional as two statements, a conditional and its converse:

Two angles are complementary if and only if the sum of their measures is 90.
If two angles are complementary, then the sum of their measures is 90. If the sum of the measures of two angles is 90, then the angles are complementary.

2-3 Objectives

▼ To use the Law of Detachment

▼ To use the Law of Syllogism

Deductive reasoning is the process of reasoning logically from given statements to a conclusion. If the given statements are true, deductive reasoning produces a true conclusion.

The following are two important laws of deductive reasoning:
Law of Detachment: If $p \rightarrow q$ is a true statement and p is true, then q is true.
Law of Syllogism: If $p \rightarrow q$ and $q \rightarrow r$ are true statements, then $p \rightarrow r$ is true.

Use the Law of Detachment to make a conclusion.

18. If you practice table tennis every day, you will become a better player. Lucy practices table tennis every day. **Lucy will become a better player.**

19. Line ℓ and line m are perpendicular. If two lines are perpendicular, they intersect to form right angles. **Lines ℓ and m intersect to form right angles.**

20. If two angles are supplementary, then the sum of their measures is 180. $\angle 1$ and $\angle 2$ are supplementary. **The sum of the measures of $\angle 1$ and $\angle 2$ is 180.**

Use the Law of Syllogism to make a conclusion.

21. If Kate studies, she will get good grades. If Kate gets good grades, she will graduate. **If Kate studies, then she will graduate.**

22. If a, then b. If b, then c. **If a, then c.**

23. If the weather is wet, the Huskies will not play soccer. If the Huskies do not play soccer, Nathan can stop at the ice cream shop.
If the weather is wet, then Nathan can stop at the ice cream shop.

2-4 Objective

▼ To connect reasoning in algebra and geometry

In algebra, you use deductive reasoning and properties to solve equations. In geometry, each statement in a deductive argument is justified by a property, definition, or postulate. Some of the properties you need are listed below.

Properties of Equality

Addition Property	If $a = b$, then $a + c = b + c$.
Subtraction Property	If $a = b$, then $a - c = b - c$.
Multiplication Property	If $a = b$, then $a \cdot c = b \cdot c$.
Division Property	If $a = b$ and $c \neq 0$, then $\frac{a}{c} \neq \frac{b}{c}$.
Substitution Property	If $a = b$, then b can replace a in any expression.
Distributive Property	$a(b + c) = ab + ac$

Properties of Congruence

Reflexive Property $\overline{AB} \cong \overline{AB}$

                      $\angle A \cong \angle A$

Symmetric Property   If $\overline{AB} \cong \overline{CD}$, then $\overline{CD} \cong \overline{AB}$.

                      If $\angle A \cong \angle B$, then $\angle B \cong \angle A$.

Transitive Property   If $\overline{AB} \cong \overline{CD}$ and $\overline{CD} \cong \overline{EF}$, then $\overline{AB} \cong \overline{EF}$.

                      If $\angle A \cong \angle B$ and $\angle B \cong \angle C$, then $\angle A \cong \angle C$.

$\boxed{x^2}$ **24. Algebra** Fill in the reason that justifies each step.

Given: $QS = 42$

$QR + RS = QS$	**a.** _?_	Segment Addition Postulate
$x + 3 + 2x = 42$	**b.** _?_	Substitution Property
$3x + 3 = 42$	**c.** _?_	Simplify.
$3x = 39$	**d.** _?_	Subtraction Property of Equality
$x = 13$	**e.** _?_	Division Property of Equality

Use the given property to complete each statement.

25. Addition Property of Equality
If $x = 5$, then $x + 3 = $ _?_. **8**

26. Division Property of Equality   **BY**
If $2(AX) = 2(BY)$, then $AX = $ _?_.

27. Reflexive Property of Equality
$m\angle Y = $ _?_ $m\angle Y$

28. Symmetric Property of Equality
If $XY = RS$, then _?_. **RS = XY**

29. Transitive Property of Equality
If $x = 5$ and $5 = y$, then $x = $ _?_. **y**

30. Distributive Property
$2(4x + 5) = 8x + $ _?_ **10**

31. Distributive Property
$3p - 6q = 3($_?_$)$ **p − 2q**

32. Reflexive Property of Congruence
$\overline{NM} \cong $ _?_ **$\overline{NM}$**

2-5 Objectives

▼ To identify angle pairs

▼ To prove and apply theorems about angles

36. $m\angle KJD + m\angle DJH = m\angle KJH$ by the Angle Add. Post.; $m\angle KJD = m\angle DJH$ by the markings; $\overrightarrow{JD}$ bisects $\angle KJH$ by the definition of angle bisector.

38. $\angle 1 \cong \angle 4$ by the markings; $\angle 1 \cong \angle 2$ and $\angle 3 \cong \angle 4$ because vert. angles are $\cong$; $\angle 2 \cong \angle 3$ by the Trans. Prop. of $\cong$.

Special relationships exist between some angle pairs. For example, **vertical angles** are congruent. The sum of the measures of **complementary angles** is 90. The sum of the measures of **supplementary angles** is 180.

$\boxed{x^2}$ **Algebra**   **Find the value of each variable.**

33.
18
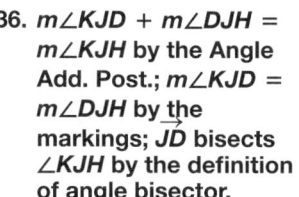

34.
31
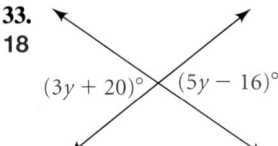

35.
20
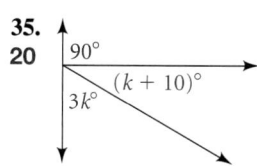

What can you conclude from each diagram? Justify your answers.

36.
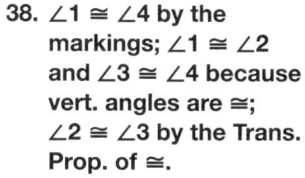

See left.

37.
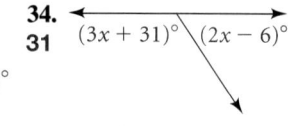

37. $AB = CD$ by the markings; $AC = BD$ by the Add. Prop of = and the Seg. Add. Post.

38.
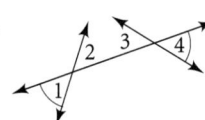

See left.

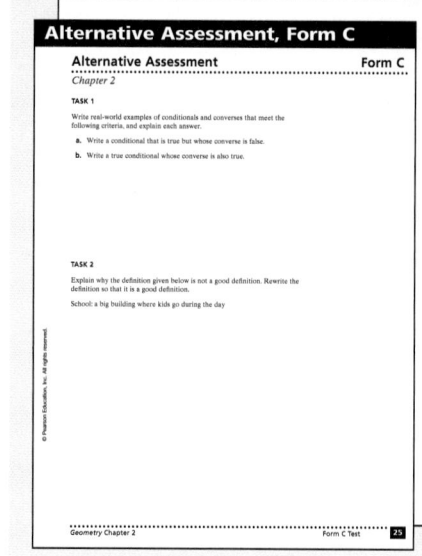

Resources

Teaching Resources

Ch. 2 Test, Forms A & B
Ch. 2 Alternative Assessment,
   Form C

Reaching All Students

Spanish Ch. 2 Test, Forms A & B
Spanish Ch. 2 Alternative
   Assessment, Form C
Informal Geometry Ch. 2 Test,
   Forms D & E

PRENTICE HALL
ASSESSMENT SYSTEM

Assessment Masters
• Ch. 2 Test, Forms A & B
• Ch. 2 Alternative Assessment,
   Form C
Computer Test Generator CD
• Ch. 2 pre-made Test
• Make your own Ch. 2 test

www.PHSchool.com

Student Site
• Self-grading Chapter 2 Test
Teacher Center
• Resources

Plus **iTEXT**

Chapter Test — Form B

Chapter Test — Form A

Chapter Test   Form A
Chapter 2

Chapter
2

Chapter Test

Take It to the NET
Online chapter test at
www.PHSchool.com
Web Code: afa-0252

1. Identify the hypothesis and conclusion:
   If $x + 9 = 11$, then $x = 2$. **Hypothesis: $x + 9 = 11$**
   Conclusion: $x = 2$

2. Write this statement as a conditional.
   All babies are cute.
   If something is a baby, then it is cute.

3. Find a counterexample to show that this statement is *not* true.
   If two angles are complementary, then they are not congruent. **Counterexample: two 45° angles are complementary and congruent.**

For each statement, (a) write the converse and (b) decide whether the converse is true or false.
                                 4–6. See margin.

4. If a figure is a rectangle, then it has two right angles.

5. If two lines intersect, then they lie in the same plane.

6. If it is snowing in South Carolina, then it is not summer.

Writing **Explain why each statement is *not* a good definition.**
                                 7–9. See margin.

7. A pencil is a writing instrument.

8. Complementary angles are angles that form a right angle.

9. Vertical angles are angles that are congruent.

For Exercises 10–14, name the property that justifies each statement.
                   Trans. Prop. of = or Subst. Prop.
10. If $UV = KL$ and $KL = 6$, then $UV = 6$.

11. If $m\angle 1 + m\angle 2 = m\angle 4 + m\angle 2$, then $m\angle 1 = m\angle 4$. **Subtr. Prop. of =**

12. $\angle ABC \cong \angle ABC$ **Reflexive Prop. of $\cong$**

13. If $\frac{1}{2}m\angle D = 45$, then $m\angle D = 90$. **Mult. Prop. of =**

14. If $\angle DEF \cong \angle HJK$, then $\angle HJK \cong \angle DEF$. **Symmetric Prop. of $\cong$**

15. Find the measure of each angle.
    a. $\angle CDM$ **135** b. $\angle KDM$ **135**
    c. $\angle JDK$ **180** d. $\angle JDM$ **45**
    e. $\angle CDB$ **180** f. $\angle CDK$ **90**

16. The measure of an angle is $2z$. What is the measure of its supplement? **$180 - 2z$**

17. The measure of an angle is 52 more than the measure of its complement. What is the measure of the angle? **71**

Give two conclusions you can make from each diagram. Justify your conclusions. **18–19. See back of book.**

18.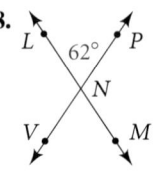

19.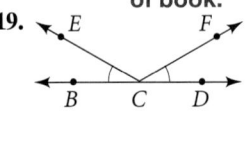

20. Rewrite this biconditional as two conditionals.
    A fish is a bluegill if and only if it is a bluish, freshwater sunfish. **See back of book.**

21. Complete this statement.
    If two angles are complements of congruent angles, the angles are __?__. **congruent**

For Exercises 22–26, use the Law of Detachment and the Law of Syllogism to make any possible conclusion. Write *not possible* if you cannot make any conclusion.

22. People who live in glass houses shouldn't throw stones. Lindsay shouldn't throw stones.
    not possible

23. James wants to be a chemical engineer. If a student wants to be a chemical engineer, that student must graduate from college.
    James must graduate from college.

24. $p \rightarrow q$ and $q \rightarrow r$ are true statements. **$p \rightarrow r$ is true.**

25. $p \rightarrow q$ and p are true statements. **q is true.**

26. $p \rightarrow q$ and q are true statements. **not possible**

27. **Developing Proof** Complete this proof by filling in the blanks.
    Given: $\angle FED$ and $\angle DEW$ are complementary.
    Prove: $\angle FEW$ is a right angle.

    Proof: By the definition of complementary angles,
    $m\angle FED + m\angle DEW = $ **a.** __?__. **90**   27b–d. See below.
    $m\angle FED + m\angle DEW = m\angle FEW$ by the **b.** __?__.
    $90 = m\angle FEW$ by the **c.** __?__ Property of Equality.
    Then, $\angle FEW$ is a right angle, by the **d.** __?__.
    b. Angle Add. Post.   c. Subst. Prop.
    d. def. of right $\angle$

---

page 108   Chapter Test

4. a. If a figure has two right angles, then it is a rectangle.
   b. false

5. a. If two lines lie in the same plane, then they intersect.
   b. false

6. a. If it is not summer, then it is snowing in South Carolina.

b. false

7. The definition is not reversible. A pen is a counterexample.

8. The definition is not true.

Two nonadjacent angles may be complementary.

9. The definiton is not precise. Any two angles can be congruent.

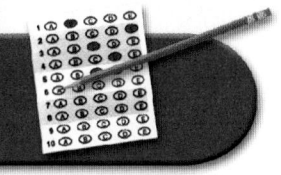

Standardized Test Prep

Multiple Choice

For Exercises 1–10, choose the correct letter.

1. What is the converse of the statement, "If a strawberry is red, then it is ripe"? **B**
   A. If a strawberry is not red, then it is not ripe.
   B. If a strawberry is ripe, then it is red.
   C. A strawberry is ripe if and only if it is red.
   D. If a strawberry is red, then it is ripe.

2. Which is the intersection of two planes? **G**
   F. a point   G. a line
   H. a plane   I. a ray

3. Which property justifies this statement? **A**
   If $4AB = 8CD$, then $AB = 2CD$.
   A. Division Property of Equality
   B. Reflexive Property of Equality
   C. Substitution Property of Equality
   D. Distributive Property

4. Which point lies the farthest from the origin? **G**
   F. $(0, -7)$ G. $(-3, 8)$
   H. $(-4, -3)$ I. $(5, 1)$

5. What is the length of the segment with endpoints $A(1, 7)$ and $B(-3, -1)$? **C**
   A. $\sqrt{40}$ B. 8   C. $\sqrt{80}$ D. 40

6. What is the next number in the pattern? **H**
   $1, -4, 9, -16,$
   F. -35 G. -25 H. 25   I. 35

7. If the measure of an angle is 78 less than the measure of its complement, what is the measure of the angle? **A**
   A. 6   B. 12   C. 51   D. 84

8. $\angle A$ and $\angle B$ are supplementary and vertical angles. What is $m\angle B$? **G**
   F. 45   G. 90   H. 135   I. 180

9. What is the midpoint of a segment with endpoints $(0, -4)$ and $(-4, 7)$? **C**
   A. $(-4, \frac{3}{2})$ B. $(-2, 3)$
   C. $(-2, \frac{3}{2})$ D. $(2, -3)$

10. The measure of an angle is 12 less than twice the measure of its supplement. What is the measure of the angle? **I**
    F. 28   G. 34   H. 64   I. 116

Quantitative Comparison

Compare the boxed quantity in Column A with the boxed quantity in Column B. Choose the best answer.

A. The quantity in Column A is greater.
B. The quantity in Column B is greater.
C. The two quantities are equal.
D. The relationship cannot be determined from the information given.

Column A	Column B
Perimeter of square $RSTV = 12x$	

C 11.

VT	$3x$

$\angle A$ is the complement of $\angle B$.

D 12.

$m\angle A$	$m\angle B$

B 13.

$m\angle A + m\angle B$	180

B 14.

$m\angle B$	90

B 15.

$m\angle A$	measure of the supplement of $\angle B$

Gridded Response

16. The area of a circle is 10π cm². What is the circle's diameter? Round to the nearest hundredth of a centimeter. **6.32**

17. The measure of an angle is one third the measure of its supplement. What is the measure of the angle? **45**

Short Response

18. $\overline{AB}$ has endpoints $A(3, 6)$ and $B(9, -2)$ and midpoint M. Justify each response. **See margin.**
    a. Find the coordinates of M.
    b. Find AB.

Extended Response

19. Construct a right triangle. Then construct the bisectors of two of its angles. **See back of book.**

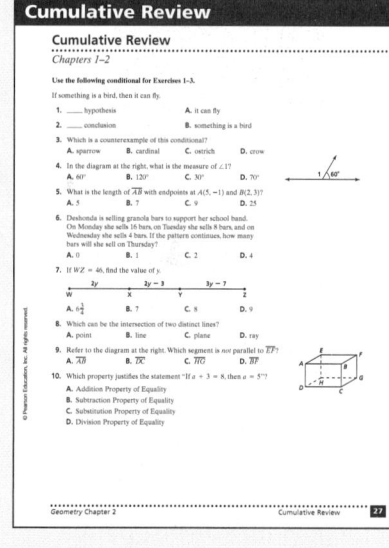

page 111   **Standardized Test Prep**

18. [2] a. (6, 2)
        b. 10
    [1] one answer correct

Item	1	2	3	4	5	6	7	8	9	10	11	12	13	14	15	16	17	18	19
Lesson	2-1	1-2	2-4	2-5	1-6	1-1	2-5	2-5	1-6	2-5	2-5	2-5	2-5	2-5	2-5	1-5	2-5	1-7	1-5

The Delicious Side of Division

In these activities students apply their knowledge of area and volume and devise ways to compare the areas of objects that have different shapes.

Connecting to Prior Knowledge

Have students describe their own experiences with baking and cooking. As they provide examples, ask whether they used arithmetic or geometry.

Teaching Notes

As students work through the activities, they may want to refer to formulas for the areas of different shapes. Ask volunteers to write formulas on the board that might be helpful. For example, the area of a triangle $A = \frac{1}{2}bh$, where b is any base and h is the corresponding height.

Tactile Learners

If possible, demonstrate the use of a mortar and pestle to grind peppercorns or another spice. Then let students use the mortar and pestle themselves.

Teaching Tip

Have students work in pairs or in small groups to complete the activities. Have each team read through both activities before beginning to work. If time is limited, allow each team to choose one of the two activities to complete.

110

Real-World Snapshots

The Delicious Side of Division

Applying Reasoning Splitting dessert evenly among brothers and sisters sometimes causes arguments. In some families, one child divides the dessert and another has first choice among the pieces. This encourages the divider to be very, very careful!

Activity 1

Dividing a square cake into an even number of pieces that are alike can be relatively simple. Dividing a square cake into seven same-size pieces is more challenging.

One method is to divide the perimeter of the cake by 7. Then mark the perimeter in seven equal lengths. (Some lengths may go around a corner.) Cut segments from the center of the cake to the marks on the perimeter. This splits the cake into the seven same-size pieces.

Show why this method works.

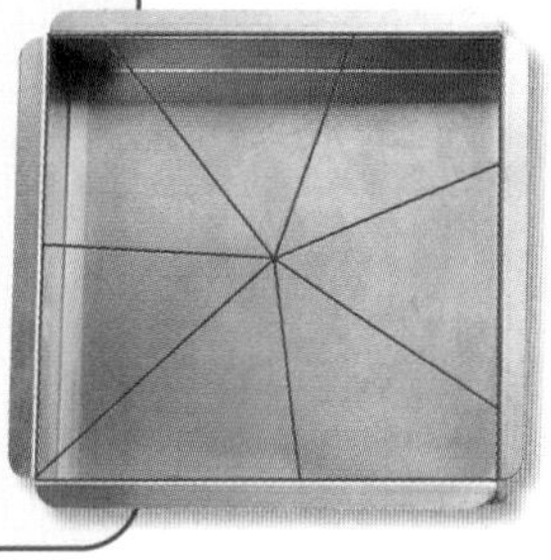

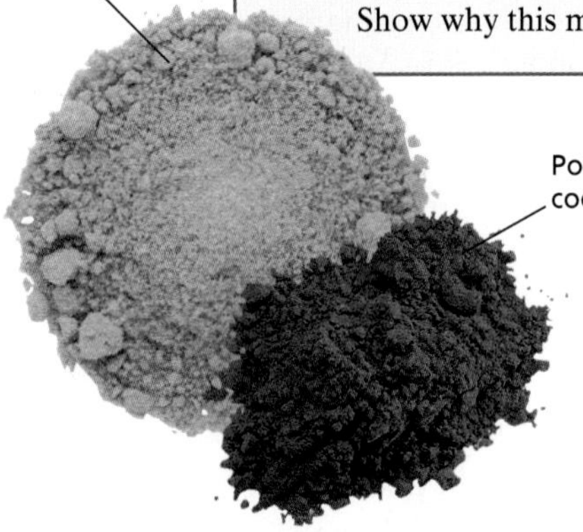

Ground mace

Powdered cocoa

Cooking with Spices

Mace comes from the kernel of an apricot-like fruit that grows mainly in Indonesia. Cocoa comes from the fruit of the cacao tree. Finely ground, both spices add flavor to baked goods.

110

pages 110–111   Real-World Snapshots

Activity 1
Let s = the length of a side of the cake. The perimeter is $4s$ and the length of each piece is $\frac{4s}{7}$.

The area of each triangular piece of cake is $\frac{1}{2}\left(\frac{4s}{7}\right)\left(\frac{s}{2}\right) = \frac{s^2}{7}$. For pieces that include a corner, let $\frac{4s}{7} = a + b$, the two lengths from the corner. The total area of two triangles with bases a and b is $\frac{1}{2}a\left(\frac{s}{2}\right) + \frac{1}{2}b\left(\frac{s}{2}\right) = \frac{1}{2}(a + b)\left(\frac{s}{2}\right) = \frac{1}{2}\left(\frac{4s}{7}\right)\left(\frac{s}{2}\right) = \frac{s^2}{7}$.

Hence, every piece has area $\frac{s^2}{7}$.

Activity 2

Use the photo of the pizza.

a. Estimate the area of the pizza slice. Support your answer by drawing a diagram.

b. Suppose you are told to divide a round pizza fairly, but without cutting through the center. Draw diagrams to show how you might creatively cut the pizza into 2, 4, 6, or 8 equal-size pieces.

12 in.

Cooking with Herbs
A bundle of bay leaves, rosemary, and parsley adds flavor to soups, stews, and pizza sauce.

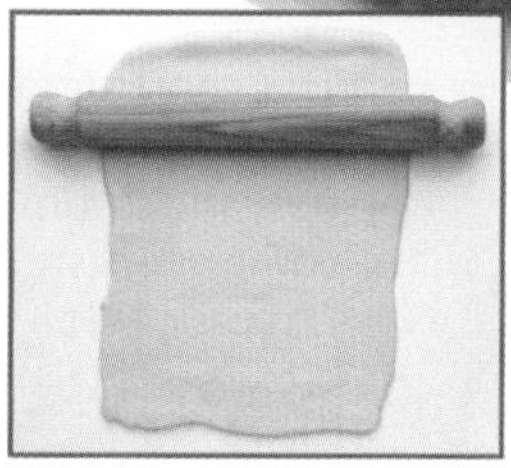

The Geometry of Pizza
Pizza comes in many shapes. In the United States, pizza is usually round and cut into wedges, although some pizza parlors make rectangular pizzas that they cut into squares.

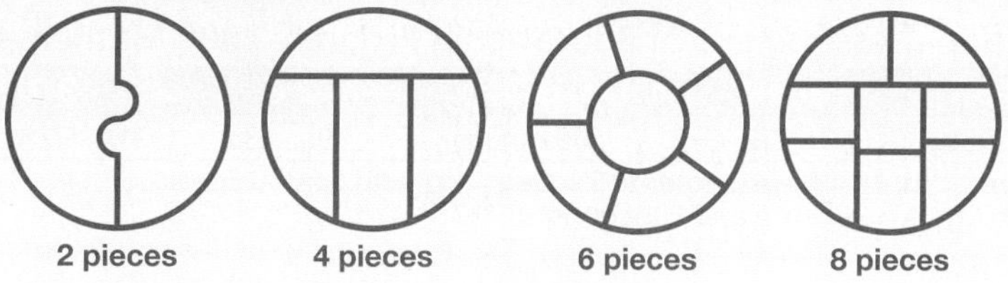

Cooking Utensils
A cook in Ancient Rome would use a mortar and pestle for grinding, a metal grater for shredding, and metal pans and wooden spoons for cooking. Two thousand years later, many cooks still use these same tools.

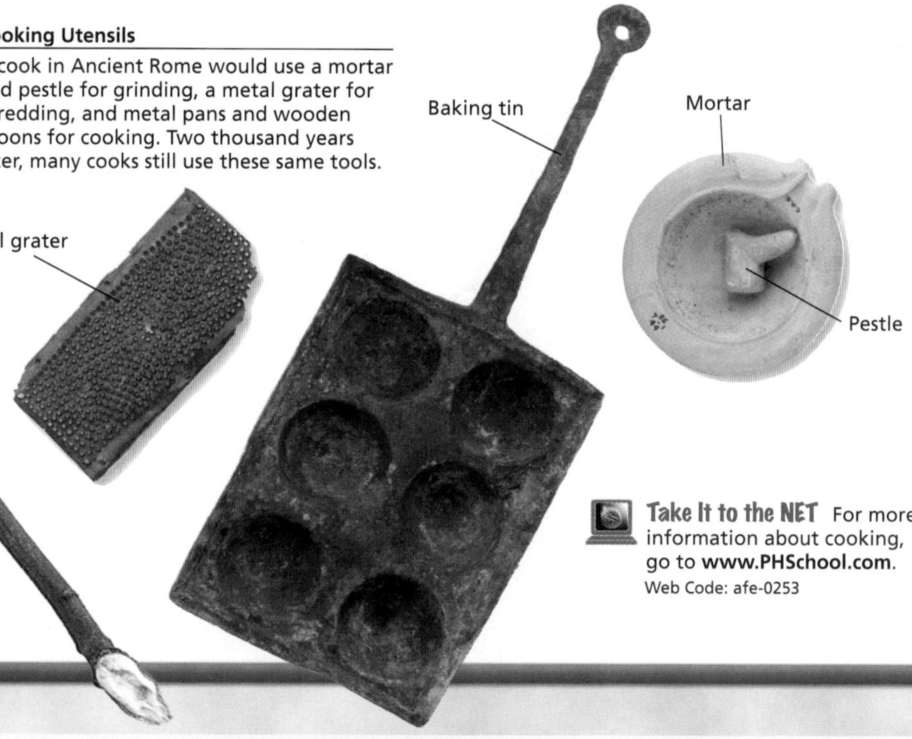

Metal grater

Baking tin

Mortar

Pestle

Take It to the NET For more information about cooking, go to **www.PHSchool.com**.
Web Code: afe-0253

111

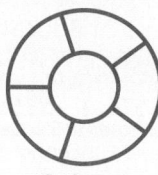
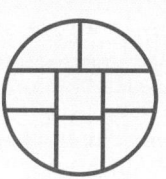
111

Parallel and Perpendicular Lines

Chapter at a Glance

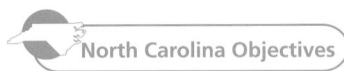
North Carolina Objectives

3-1 Properties of Parallel Lines	2.02

NCTM 2, 3, 4, 6, 7, 8, 9, 10
- ▼ Identifying Angles
- ▽ Properties of Parallel Lines

3-2 Proving Lines Parallel	2.02

NCTM 2, 3, 6, 7, 8, 9, 10
- ▼ Using a Transversal
- ▽ Relating Parallel and Perpendicular Lines

3-3 Parallel Lines and the Triangle Angle-Sum Theorem	2.03a

NCTM 2, 3, 4, 6, 7, 8, 9, 10
- ▼ Finding Angle Measures in Triangles
- ▽ Using Exterior Angles of Triangles

3-4 The Polygon Angle-Sum Theorems	2.03c

NCTM 2, 3, 6, 7, 8, 9, 10
- ▼ Classifying Polygons
- ▽ Polygon Angle Sums

3-5 Lines in the Coordinate Plane	2.02

NCTM 2, 3, 6, 8, 9, 10
- ▼ Graphing Lines
- ▽ Writing Equations of Lines

3-6 Slopes of Parallel and Perpendicular Lines	2.02

NCTM 2, 3, 6, 8, 9, 10
- ▼ Slope and Parallel Lines
- ▽ Slope and Perpendicular Lines

3-7 Constructing Parallel and Perpendicular Lines	2.02

NCTM 3, 6, 8, 9, 10
- ▼ Constructing Parallel Lines
- ▽ Constructing Perpendicular Lines

NCTM STANDARDS 2000

1	Number and Operations	6	Problem Solving
2	Algebra	7	Reasoning and Proof
3	Geometry	8	Communication
4	Measurement	9	Connections
5	Data Analysis and Probability	10	Representation

Pacing Options

This chart suggests pacing only for the lessons and their parts. It is provided as a possible guide. It will help you determine how much time you have in your schedule to cover other components, such as the features, Chapter Review and Chapter Test.

Day	Traditional 45 min.	Two-Year 45 min.	Block 90 min.
1	3-1 ▼▽	3-1 ▼	3-1 ▼▽
2	3-2 ▼	3-1 ▽	3-2 ▼▽
3	3-2 ▽	3-1 ▽	3-3 ▼▽
4	3-3 ▼	3-2 ▼	3-4 ▼▽
5	3-3 ▽	3-2 ▽	3-5 ▼▽
6	3-4 ▼	3-3 ▼	3-6 ▼▽
7	3-4 ▽	3-3 ▽	3-7 ▼▽
8	3-5 ▼	3-4 ▼	
9	3-5 ▽	3-4 ▼	
10	3-6 ▼	3-4 ▽	
11	3-6 ▽	3-5 ▼	
12	3-7 ▼▽	3-5 ▽	
13		3-6 ▼	
14		3-6 ▽	
15		3-6 ▽	
16		3-7 ▼	
17		3-7 ▽	
18		3-7 ▽	
19			
20			
21			
22			

NAEP Correlation (National Assessment of Educational Progress 2000 Mathematics Objectives)

3-1	3-2	3-3	3-4	3-5	3-6	3-7
G4a	G4a, G8	G2, A5b	N3d, G2, G7B	69a, A3a	69a, A3c	G1A, G2A, A3c

N = Number Sense, Properties, and Operations; **M** = Measurement; **G** = Geometry and Spatial Sense; **D** = Data Analysis, Statistics, and Probability; **A** = Algebra and Functions

Math Background

Chapter Overview

This chapter contains theorems about parallel lines and angle measures. Two-column proofs and flow proofs are introduced as additional forms of mathematical proof. It is important that students attempt to write proofs in all three forms. Proof format is not critical, but the logic and completeness of a proof does matter. By the end of this chapter, most students should be able to complete a simple proof in any of these three forms.

Properties of Parallel Lines   3-1

For a pair of lines, *interior* means *between the lines* and *exterior* means *not between the lines.* For a pair of lines cut by a transversal, *alternate* means *on opposite sides of the transversal* and *corresponding* means *in the same position with respect to the intersections.* English learners may find it helpful to use the words in other contexts, such as the *interior* of houses, frames, or courtyards; *alternate* plans or sides of a street; and *corresponding* positions of buildings on street corners.

Because the postulate and theorems all begin "If a transversal intersects two parallel lines," some students may ignore the hypothesis and remember only the conclusions. Clarify that "parallel lines" are a necessary condition for the postulate and theorems in this lesson.

Point out that planning a proof requires listing the statements that must be made and justified. Students who have difficulty deciding on this list should be encouraged to list all the postulates, definitions, and theorems that relate to the given information and desired conclusion so that they can more easily identify the path to follow.

Proving Lines Parallel   3-2

This lesson presents the converses of the postulate and theorems in Lesson 3-1 and introduces flow proofs. Emphasize that a theorem is true only if it can be proved, not simply if an example supports it, and that not every theorem has a true converse. For example, consider the Vertical Angles Theorem; its converse (*If two angles are congruent, the angles are vertical angles*) is clearly untrue.

Parallel Lines and the Triangle Angle-Sum Theorem   3-3

It does not matter which side of an angle is extended to form an exterior angle. The two exterior angles produced by extending both sides are vertical angles, so they are congruent.

Exercise 38 asks whether every equilateral triangle is isosceles or whether every isosceles triangle is equilateral. Clarifying that only the second relationship is true will benefit students when they study the hierarchy of quadrilaterals in Chapter 6.

The Polygon Angle-Sum Theorems   3-4

Students are probably familiar with most of the formal names for various polygons. Few will be familiar with the concepts *convex* or *concave,* but the visual explanation is fairly intuitive. Some students may be able to connect the concepts to experiences with convex and concave mirrors at a carnival. One term that should not be glossed over is *regular,* as in *regular polygon.* Students tend to assume that all polygons are regular because that is how they are often represented. The Angle-Sum Theorems apply to all polygons, but unless a polygon is regular, other information must be supplied in order to determine the measures of its angles.

Ask students who try to name a polygon by listing the vertices in random order to identify the only polygon that can be correctly named with its vertices in any order (triangle). The Polygon Exterior Angle-Sum Theorem will seem nonintuitive to some students because more sides in a polygon mean more angles, so students may reason that more angles should result in a larger angle sum. Discuss this with students to help them realize that exterior angle size decreases as the number of polygon sides increases.

Lines in the Coordinate Plane and Slopes of Parallel and Perpendicular Lines   3-5, 3-6

Some students will still have trouble identifying the equations of vertical and horizontal lines. For $x = 2$, many will envision a line that is horizontal because the x-axis is horizontal and this equation involves only x. Similar thinking will lead students to picture a vertical line for $y = 3$. Ask these students to name five different points with x-coordinate 2 and then to plot and connect them.

The two-point form for the equation of a line is the point-slope form with the rise-over-run quotient substituted for m.

Remind students that, in this text, parallel lines must be distinct; a line is not parallel to itself. So the relation *is parallel to* is not reflexive.

Slopes of perpendicular lines are described as two numbers whose product is −1. They also may be thought of as negative reciprocals. In either case, the slopes of vertical and horizontal lines are exceptions.

Constructing Parallel and Perpendicular Lines   3-7

Constructions are easier for students if they recall the geometry behind the procedures. Constructing parallel lines depends on constructing a congruent angle and using the Converse of the Corresponding Angles Postulate. Constructing a perpendicular through a point on a line involves constructing a segment on the line with the point as its midpoint and then constructing the perpendicular bisector of that segment. Constructing a line perpendicular to line t through a point Q not on the line is an extension of this construction. Students will be better able to justify these constructions when they have studied congruent triangles in Chapter 4.

112B

Ongoing Assessment and Intervention

Tools for Monitoring Student Progress

The Prentice Hall *Geometry* program provides you with many options for assessment in the Student Edition, the Teacher's Edition and the teaching resources. From these options, you may choose instructional materials and techniques that are appropriate for your students and support your district's curriculum requirements.

Instant Check System™ in Chapter 3

Allows students to check their own learning before, during, and after each lesson.

Diagnosing Readiness before the chapter (p. 112)

Check Skills You'll Need exercises in each lesson (pp. 115, 122, 131, 143, 152, 158, 165)

Check Understanding questions with each Example (pp. 115, 116, 117, 118, 123, 124, 125, 130, 132, 133, 134, 143, 144, 145, 146, 152, 153, 154, 158, 159, 160, 161, 165, 166, 167)

Checkpoint Quiz (pp. 139 and 164)

Test Prep in Chapter 3

Teaches students strategies and gives them practice with all the test item formats they will encounter on state tests and standardized national exams.

Standardized Test Prep exercises in each lesson (pp. 121, 129, 138, 150, 157, 164, 170)

Test-Taking Strategies (p. 172: Writing Extended Responses)

Standardized Test Prep (p. 177: Reading Comprehension)

All your assessment needs in one place!

Program Assessment

Assess student progress throughout the *Geometry* text with blackline masters and CD-ROM.

Assessment Resources

- Checkpoint Quizzes 1 & 2
- Chapter Test, Forms A & B
- Chapter Alternative Assessment

Spanish versions available. Tests for Informal Geometry also available.

Computer Test Generator

- Unlimited questions of varying difficulty for every lesson objective.
- Create your own practice sheets, quizzes, and tests, or use the pre-made Chapter Tests.
- Diagnose readiness with questions on prerequisite skills.
- Prepare students by making tests based on standardized test objectives.
- Access Algebra 1, Geometry, and Algebra 2 content—all on one CD-ROM.

Test Preparation

A three-step approach to preparing students for high stakes, national, and state exams.

❶ Diagnose & Prescribe

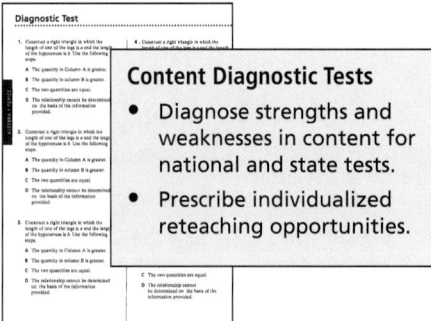

Content Diagnostic Tests
- Diagnose strengths and weaknesses in content for national and state tests.
- Prescribe individualized reteaching opportunities.

❷ Review & Reteach

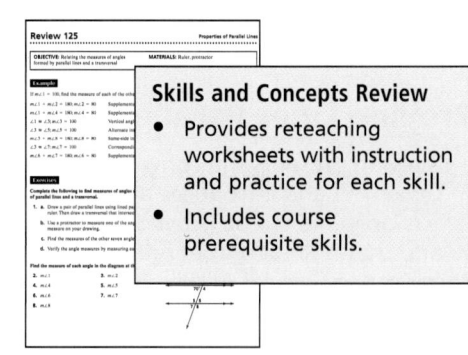

Skills and Concepts Review
- Provides reteaching worksheets with instruction and practice for each skill.
- Includes course prerequisite skills.

❸ Practice & Assess

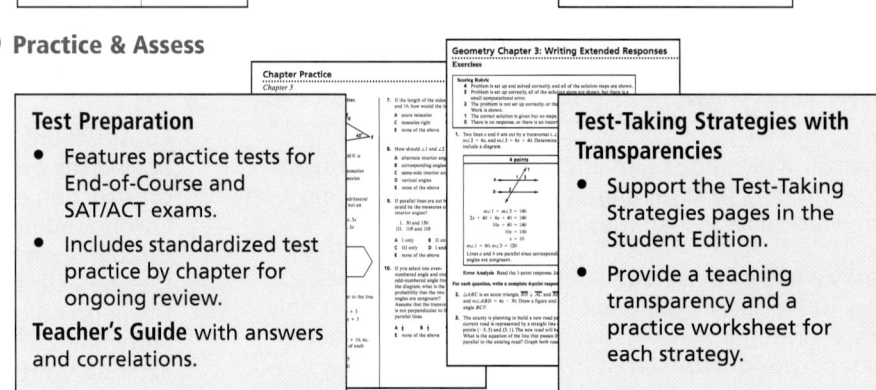

Test Preparation
- Features practice tests for End-of-Course and SAT/ACT exams.
- Includes standardized test practice by chapter for ongoing review.

Teacher's Guide with answers and correlations.

Test-Taking Strategies with Transparencies
- Support the Test-Taking Strategies pages in the Student Edition.
- Provide a teaching transparency and a practice worksheet for each strategy.

 # Reaching All Students

Support in the Student Text and Additional Resources

The textbook, the iText, and other technology components provide numerous opportunities to reach students of various ability levels and learning styles. Each Teacher's Edition lesson suggests how you can help *all* your students be successful and understand the mathematics in Chapter 3.

Below Level

Student Edition
- Diagnosing Readiness*: p. 112
- Check Skills You'll Need*: pp. 115, 122, 131, 143, 152, 158, 165

Reteaching
Chapter 3 Support File: pp. 8–14

Informal Geometry Planning Guide
Chapter 3 Lesson Plans: pp. 13–19
Chapter 3 Tests: pp. 87–90

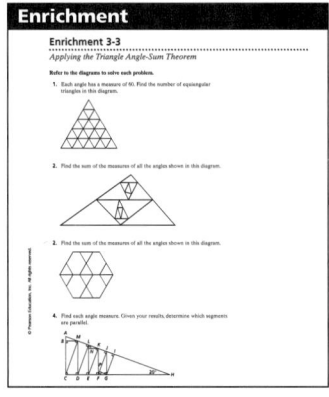

* Can be used with all ability levels to ensure mastery of prerequisite skills.

Advanced Learners

Student Edition
- Challenge exercises: pp. 120, 128, 138, 149, 156, 163, 169
- Extension: pp. 140–141

Enrichment
Chapter 3 Support File: pp. 15–21

Reading and Math Literacy

Student Edition
- Vocabulary: pp. 113, 173, *plus* in every Lesson Preview
- Reading Math: pp. 115, 117, 127, 130, 133, 136, 145, 153, 173
- Illustrated Glossary: pp. 741–777

Reading and Math Literacy Masters
Chapter 3: pp. 9–12

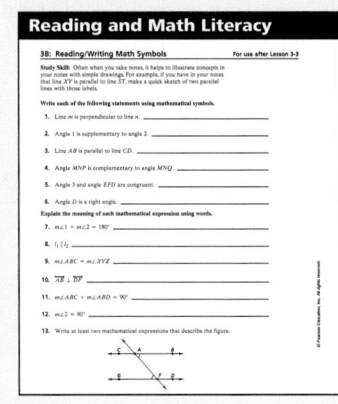

English Learners

Student Edition
- English/Spanish Illustrated Glossary: pp. 741–777

Workbook and Masters
Spanish Practice Workbook: pp. 13–19
Spanish Reading and Math Literacy Masters: pp. 9–12

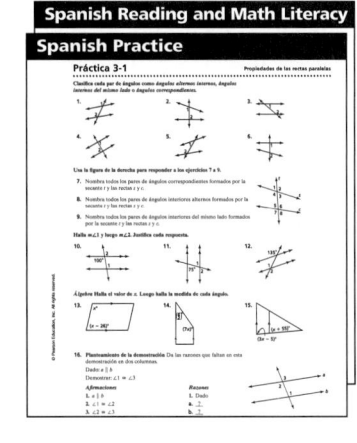

Learning Styles

Student Edition
- Investigation: pp. 131, 145
- Technology: pp. 114, 142, 149, 156, 163, 171
- Writing: pp. 120, 127, 136, 149, 156, 162, 168, 169, 174, 175, 176

Activity Masters
Hands-On Activities: 7, 8, 9
Technology Activities: 40

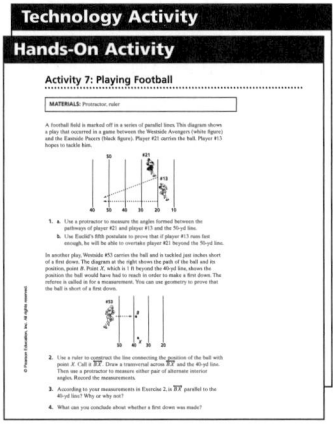

Program Resources

	Teaching Resources in Grab & Go™ Files				Resources for Reaching All Students				Spanish Resources			Transparencies				Prentice Hall Presentation Pro CD-ROM
	Practice	Reteach	Enrich	Checkpoint Quiz	Reading & Math Literacy	Technology Activities	Hands-On Activities	Informal Geometry Lesson Plans	Practice	Reading & Math Literacy	Checkpoint Quiz	Skills Check	Additional Examples	Answers to Exercises	Lesson Quiz	
3-1	■	■	■		■			■	■			■	■	■	■	■
3-2	■	■	■				■	■				■	■	■	■	■
3-3	■	■	■	■	■	■	■	■	■	■	■	■	■	■	■	■
3-4	■	■	■				■	■				■	■	■	■	■
3-5	■	■	■					■				■	■	■	■	■
3-6	■	■	■	■	■			■	■		■	■	■	■	■	■
3-7	■	■	■					■				■	■	■	■	■
For the chapter	Chapter Tests, Alternative Assessment, Cumulative Review, Cumulative Assessment				Informal Geometry Chapter Tests				Spanish Chapter Tests, Alternative Assessment, Cumulative Review, Cumulative Assessment			Classroom Aid Transparencies				

Also available for use with the chapter:

 *see page 112C.*

- Practice Workbook
- Solution Key

- For teacher support and access to student Web site materials, use Web Code afk-5500.
- For additional online and technology resources, see below.

Technology

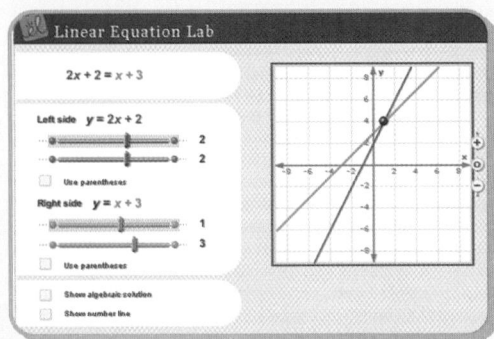

iTEXT — Online and on CD-ROM

Complete Interactive Student Text online and on CD-ROM—with instant feedback assessment, tutorial help, dynamic activities, instructional and real-world videos, audio, and additional practice.

www.PHSchool.com — For Students

Use **Web Codes** for easy access to online activities, chapter projects, self-grading lesson quizzes and chapter tests, vocabulary quizzes, updated data sources, graphing calculator procedures, and more.

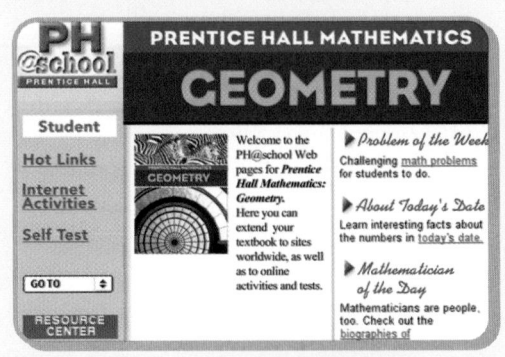

PH SuccessNet — For Teachers

Online lesson planning with built-in state correlations, all the teaching resources, complete reference library, your own calendar and Teacher Web page, professional development, and more.

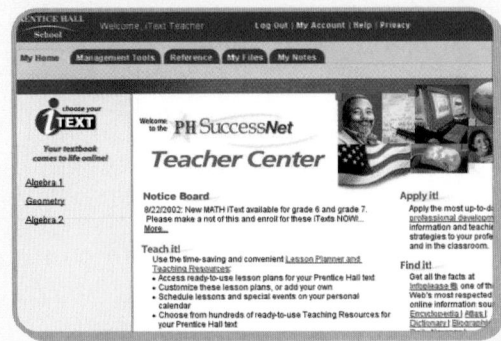

Presentation Assistant Plus!

The Prentice Hall *Presentation Assistant Plus!* provides you with the material you need to teach a lesson from beginning to end. Two easy-to-use formats—Transparencies and CD-ROM—allow you to present a lesson the way you are most comfortable.

Transparencies

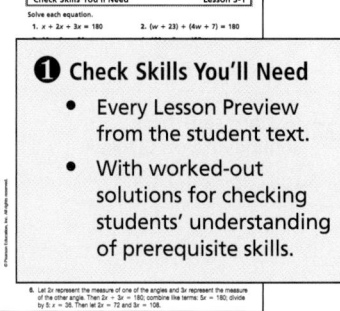

❶ Check Skills You'll Need
- Every Lesson Preview from the student text.
- With worked-out solutions for checking students' understanding of prerequisite skills.

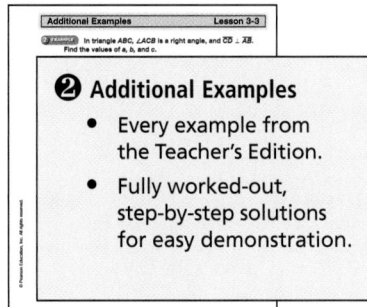

❷ Additional Examples
- Every example from the Teacher's Edition.
- Fully worked-out, step-by-step solutions for easy demonstration.

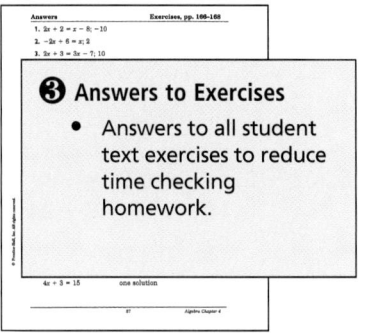

❸ Answers to Exercises
- Answers to all student text exercises to reduce time checking homework.

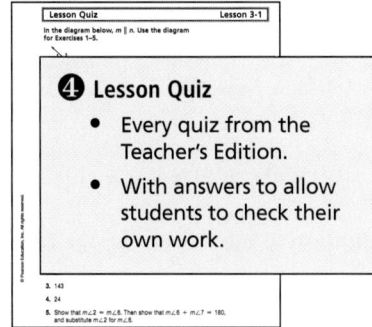

❹ Lesson Quiz
- Every quiz from the Teacher's Edition.
- With answers to allow students to check their own work.

 Throughout the Teacher's Edition, this symbol indicates material that is available on transparency in the Presentation Assistant Plus!

Prentice Hall Presentation Pro CD-ROM

- Includes all Transparencies.
- Conveniently organized by lesson so you can easily ❶ Introduce, ❷ Teach, ❸ Check Homework, and ❹ Assess each lesson.
- Animated examples allow step-by-step instruction at your own pace.
- Easy to edit so you can create custom presentations.

Teaching Chapter 3 Using Presentation Assistant Plus!

	❶ Introduce	❷ Teach	❸ Check Homework	❹ Assess
	Check Skills You'll Need	Additional Examples	Student Edition Answers	Lesson Quiz
3-1	p. 13	pp. 30–31	✔	p. 88
3-2	p. 14	pp. 32–34	✔	p. 89
3-3	p. 15	pp. 34–37	✔	p. 90
3-4	p. 16	pp. 38–41	✔	p. 91
3-5	p. 17	pp. 41–44	✔	p. 92
3-6	p. 18	pp. 45–48	✔	p. 93
3-7	p. 19	pp. 49–52	✔	p. 94

Prentice Hall Presentation Pro

CD-ROM with dynamic PowerPoint® presentations for every lesson. Helps you introduce and develop concepts, check homework, and assess progress. Part of Presentation Assistant Plus! *(See above.)*

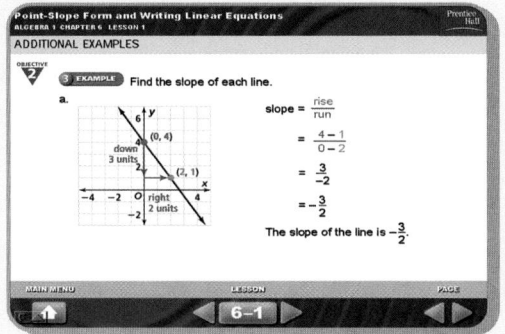

Computer Test Generator

CD-ROM to create practice sheets and tests for course objectives and standardized tests. Includes Instant Chapter Tests™, online testing, and student reports. Part of the PH Assessment System. *(See page 112C.)*

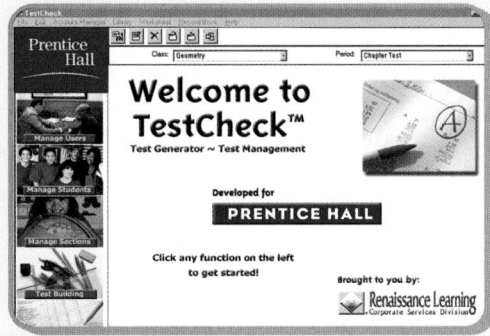

Resource Pro® with Planning Express®

CD-ROM with a lesson planning tool that allows you to import state and local objectives. Includes electronic versions of all the teaching resources.

Chapter 3

Parallel and Perpendicular Lines

 Diagnosing Readiness

Students will find answers to these exercises in the back of their textbooks.

For intervention, direct students to:

Solving Equations
Algebra 1 Review, p. 24

Evaluating Algebraic Expressions
Skills Handbook: p. 716

Graphing Lines
Skills Handbook: p. 713

Slope of a Line
Skills Handbook: p. 720

9. Sample:

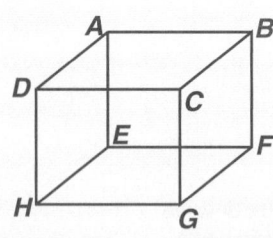

$\overleftrightarrow{AB}$ and $\overleftrightarrow{GH}$; $\overleftrightarrow{AE}$ and $\overleftrightarrow{EF}$

Where You've Been

- In Chapter 1, you learned that two coplanar lines that do not intersect are parallel.

- In Chapters 1 and 2, you learned how to measure angles, recognize congruent angles, and identify angles whose measures have sum 180.

- In Chapter 2, you learned how to use deductive reasoning to draw conclusions.

 **Instant self-check** online and on CD-ROM

Diagnosing Readiness   (For help, go to the Lesson in green.)

Evaluating Algebraic Expressions (Skills Handbook page 716)

x^2 **Algebra** Evaluate each expression for the given value of n.

1. $\frac{360}{n}$; $n = 5$ **72**   2. $(n - 2)180$; $n = 9$ **1260**   3. $(n - 2)180$; $n = 17$ **2700**

Solving Equations (Algebra 1 Review page 24)

x^2 **Algebra** Solve each equation.

4. $3x + 11 = 7x - 5$ **4**   5. $(2x + 5) + (3x - 10) = 70$ **15**   6. $(3x + 2) - (2x - 3) = -19$ **−24**

Writing and Solving an Equation (Skills Handbook page 720)

Write an equation and solve the problem.

7. The sum of the measures of three angles is 180. One measure is twice the size of each of the other two. Find the measure of each angle. $2x + x + x = 180$; **45, 45, 90**

8. The sum of the measures of three angles is 180. One measure is half the size of each of the other two. Find the measure of each angle. $\frac{1}{2}x + x + x = 180$; **36, 72, 72**

Drawing Parallel and Perpendicular Lines (Lesson 1-3)

9. Draw a picture of a rectangular box and label its eight corners A through H. Name two lines in your picture that appear to be parallel. Name two lines that appear to be perpendicular. **Answers may vary. See margin.**

Drawing and Measuring Angles (Lesson 1-4)

Use a straightedge and draw the given type of angle as best you can. Estimate its measure, and then find its measure with a protractor. **10–12. Check students' work.**

10. acute   11. right   12. obtuse

Parallel and Perpendicular Lines

Where You're Going

- In this chapter, you will use deductive reasoning to make conclusions about parallel and perpendicular lines.

- You will use parallel lines to learn about angle measures in triangles and other polygons.

- You will also learn ways to think about parallel and perpendicular lines in a coordinate plane.

 Real-World Connection Applying what you learn, you will make conclusions about airport runways on pages 116 and 177.

LESSONS

Key Vocabulary

- alternate interior angles (p. 115)
- concave polygon (p. 144)
- convex polygon (p. 144)
- corresponding angles (p. 115)
- equiangular triangle (p. 133)
- equilateral triangle (p. 133)
- exterior angle of a polygon (p. 133)
- flow proof (p. 123)
- isosceles triangle (p. 133)
- polygon (p. 143)
- regular polygon (p. 146)
- remote interior angles (p. 133)
- same-side interior angles (p. 115)
- scalene triangle (p. 133)
- transversal (p. 115)

Chapter 3 Overview

Students will build on their knowledge of angles to prove and use properties of parallel lines. They will use these properties to prove that the sum of the measures of the angles in a triangle is 180, and to find the formula for the sum of the angle measures in a polygon having *n* sides. Students will learn the relationship that different forms of linear equations have with the slopes of parallel and perpendicular lines. Finally, students will construct parallel and perpendicular lines, and quadrilaterals.

Reading Math
Reading for Developing Proof, p. 130

Vocabulary
A complete list of terms, plus vocabulary exercises, appears in the Chapter Review, p. 173.

Illustrated Glossary
Examples for each vocabulary term, plus definitions in both English and Spanish, appear starting on p. 741.

Test-Taking Strategies
Writing Extended Responses, p. 172

Real-World Connections
Some of the applications you will find in this chapter are engineering (3-1), woodworking (3-2), packaging (3-4), soccer (3-6), and paper folding (3-7).

www.PHSchool.com
Internet support for this chapter includes:
- Self-grading Vocabulary and Chapter 3 Tests
- Chapter Project
- Chapter Planner
- Ch. 3 Resources

Plus

113

Technology Parallel Lines and Related Angles

FOR USE WITH LESSON 3-1

Parallel Lines and Related Angles

Students will use geometry software to investigate the relationships among the eight angles formed by parallel lines and a transversal. By manipulating the lines and measuring angles, they will discover the postulates and theorems that will be presented formally in Lessons 3-1 and 3-2.

Resources

Students may use any geometry software program to explore parallel lines and related angles.

Teaching Notes

Using software enables students to manipulate lines and measure angles. They can observe that parallel lines and a transversal always have special angle relationships and that when alternate angles are congruent or same-side interior angles are supplementary, the lines must be parallel.

Tactile Learners

Students may see how many of the activities they can complete on paper using a protractor and a straightedge.

Error Prevention

Students who take a shortcut and draw lines that appear parallel may not observe the angle relationships desired here. In most software programs, it is easy to draw horizontal and vertical lines. Suggest that students use parallel horizontal lines or parallel vertical lines.

Construct

Use geometry software to construct two parallel lines. Check that the lines remain parallel as you manipulate them. Construct a point on each line. Then construct the line through these two points. This line is called a transversal.

Investigate

Measure each of the eight angles formed by the parallel lines and the transversal. Record the measurements. Manipulate the lines and record the new measurements. What relationships do you notice?

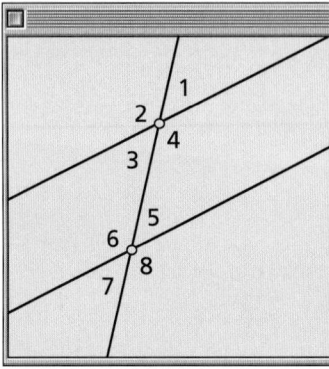

EXERCISES

1. When a transversal intersects two parallel lines, what are the relationships among the angles formed? Make as many conjectures as possible.

Extend

2. Use your software to construct three or more parallel lines. Construct a line that intersects all three lines. **a-b. See below.**
   a. What relationships exist among the angles formed?
   b. How many different angle measures are there?

3. Construct two parallel lines and a transversal perpendicular to one of the parallel lines. What angle does it make with the second parallel line?
   a right ∠

4. Using geometry software, construct two lines and a transversal, making sure that the two lines are *not* parallel. Locate two angles that are on alternate sides of the transversal and in the interior region between the other two lines. Manipulate the lines so that these angles have the same measure.
   a. Make a conjecture as to the relationship between the two lines.
   b. How is this conjecture different from the conjecture(s) you made in Exercise 1? **The other conjecture is the converse.**

5. Again, draw two lines and a transversal, making sure that the two lines are *not* parallel. Locate two angles that are on the same side of the transversal and in the interior region between the two lines. Manipulate the lines so that these angles are supplementary.
   a. Make a conjecture as to the relationship between the two lines.
   b. How is this conjecture different from the conjecture(s) you made in Exercise 1? **The other conjecture is the converse.**

   2a. Many of the ∡ are ≅ to each other.
   b. There are only two measures for all the ∡ formed.

∠2 ≅ ∠4 ≅ ∠6 ≅ ∠8; ∠1 ≅ ∠3 ≅ ∠5 ≅ ∠7; **when a transversal intersects two parallel lines, the ∡ formed have one of two measures; ∡ between ∥ lines on the opp. sides of the transversal are ≅; ∡ between the ∥ lines on the same side of the transversal are suppl.**

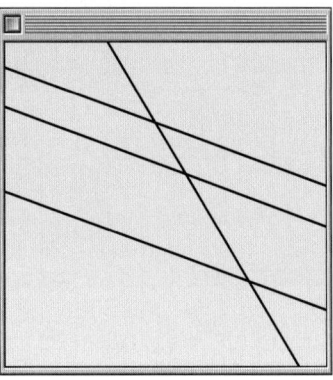

4a. If the ∡ between the lines on alt. sides of the transversal are ≅, then the lines are ∥.

5a. If the same-side int. ∡ are suppl., then the lines are ∥.

Properties of Parallel Lines

North Carolina Objectives

2.02 Apply properties, definitions, and theorems of angles and lines to solve problems and write proofs.

Lesson Preview

What You'll Learn

OBJECTIVE 1
To identify angles formed by two lines and a transversal

OBJECTIVE 2
To prove and use properties of parallel lines

...And Why

To describe angles formed by an airport runway that crosses two parallel runways, as in Example 2

✓ **Check Skills You'll Need** (For help, go to page 24 or Skills Handbook page 720.)

 Algebra Solve each equation.

1. $x + 2x + 3x = 180$ **30**

2. $(w + 23) + (4w + 7) = 180$ **30**

3. $90 = 2y - 30$ **60**

4. $180 - 5y = 135$ **9**

Write an equation and solve the problem.

5. The sum of $m\angle 1$ and twice its complement is 146. Find $m\angle 1$.
$m\angle 1 + 2(90 - m\angle 1) = 146; m\angle 1 = 34$

6. The measures of two supplementary angles are in the ratio 2 : 3. Find their measures. **72 and 108**

New Vocabulary
- transversal
- alternate interior angles
- same-side interior angles
- corresponding angles
- two-column proof

 Interactive lesson includes instant self-check, tutorials, and activities.

OBJECTIVE

1 **Identifying Angles**

A **transversal** is a line that intersects two coplanar lines at two distinct points. The diagram shows the eight angles formed by a transversal t and two lines ℓ and m.

Pairs of the eight angles have special names as suggested by their positions.

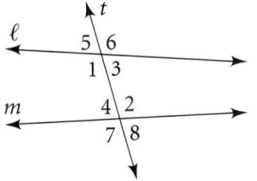

 Reading Math

Corresponding objects are related in a special way. Here, corresponding angles are angles that are in similar positions on the same side of a transversal.

$\angle 1$ and $\angle 2$ are **alternate interior angles.**

$\angle 1$ and $\angle 4$ are **same-side interior angles.**

$\angle 1$ and $\angle 7$ are **corresponding angles.**

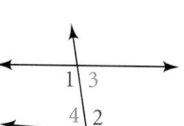

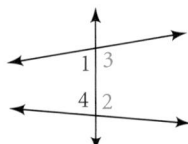

1 EXAMPLE **Identifying Angles**

Use the diagrams above. Name another pair of alternate interior angles and another pair of same-side interior angles.

● $\angle 3$ and $\angle 4$ are alternate interior angles. $\angle 2$ and $\angle 3$ are same-side interior angles.

✓ **Check Understanding** ① Name three other pairs of corresponding angles in the diagrams above.
∠5 and ∠4, ∠6 and ∠2, ∠3 and ∠8

Ongoing Assessment and Intervention

Before the Lesson
Diagnose prerequisite skills using:
- Check Skills You'll Need

During the Lesson
Monitor progress using:
- Check Understanding
- Additional Examples
- Standardized Test Prep

After the Lesson
Assess knowledge using:
- Lesson Quiz
- Computer Test Generator CD

---

1. Plan

Lesson Preview

✓ **Check Skills You'll Need**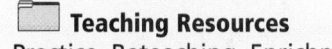

Solving Linear Equations
Algebra Review, page 24
Examples 1, 2, Exercises 1–22

For help use
Skills Handbook, p. 720

Lesson Resources

📁 **Teaching Resources**
Practice, Reteaching, Enrichment

👥 **Reaching All Students**
Practice Workbook 3-1
Spanish Practice Workbook 3-1
Reading and Math Literacy 3A
Spanish Reading & Literacy 3A
Informal Geometry Planning Guide 3-1

⏱ **Presentation Assistant Plus!**
Transparencies
- Check Skills You'll Need 3-1
- Additional Examples 3-1
- Student Edition Answers 3-1
- Lesson Quiz 3-1
PH Presentation Pro CD 3-1

 PRENTICE HALL ASSESSMENT SYSTEM

Computer Test Generator CD

💿 **Technology**
Resource Pro® CD-ROM
Computer Test Generator CD
Prentice Hall Presentation Pro CD

💻 **www.PHSchool.com**
Student Site
- Teacher Web Code: afk-5500
- Self-grading Lesson Quiz
Teacher Center
- Lesson Planner
- Resources

Plus

115

2. Teach

Math Background

The Corresponding Angles Postulate is a variation of Euclid's famous Parallel Postulate, which subsequent mathematicians vainly hoped could be proved as a theorem. In the nineteenth century, altering the postulate enabled the invention of hyperbolic and elliptic geometries. Any geometry that obeys the Parallel Postulate is now known as a Euclidean geometry.

OBJECTIVE
1 Teaching Notes

Tactile Learners

Provide straws for students to use to model parallel lines and transversals, and provide protractors to test the postulate and theorems in this lesson.

1 EXAMPLE English Learners

Have partners discuss the vocabulary in the example. Encourage them to use the words *alternate, corresponding, interior,* and *exterior* in nonmathematical contexts.

Additional Examples

1

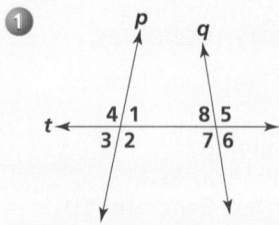

Use the diagram above. Identify which angle forms a pair of same-side interior angles with ∠1. Identify which angle forms a pair of corresponding angles with ∠1.
∠8; ∠5

2 Use the diagram from Example 2. Compare ∠2 and the vertical angle of ∠1. Classify them as alternate interior angles, same-side interior angles, or corresponding angles. **alternate interior angles**

---

2 EXAMPLE Real-World Connection

Aviation In the diagram of Lafayette Regional Airport, the black segments are runways and the gray areas are taxiways and terminal buildings. Classify ∠1 and ∠2 as alternate interior angles, same-side interior angles, or corresponding angles.

● ∠1 and ∠2 are corresponding angles.

✔ **Check Understanding** **2** Classify ∠2 and ∠3 as alternate interior angles, same-side interior angles, or corresponding angles. **same-side int. ∠s**

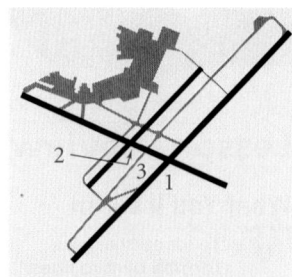

**Lafayette Regional Airport
Lafayette, Louisiana**

OBJECTIVE
2 Properties of Parallel Lines

In the photograph, the vapor trail of the high-flying aircraft suggests a transversal of the parallel trails of the low-flying aircraft.

The same-size angles that appear to be formed by the vapor trails suggest the postulate and theorems below.

Key Concepts

Postulate 3-1	Corresponding Angles Postulate

If a transversal intersects two parallel lines, then corresponding angles are congruent.

∠1 ≅ ∠2

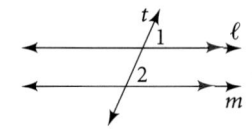

Key Concepts

Theorem 3-1	Alternate Interior Angles Theorem

If a transversal intersects two parallel lines, then alternate interior angles are congruent.

∠1 ≅ ∠3

Theorem 3-2	Same-Side Interior Angles Theorem

If a transversal intersects two parallel lines, then same-side interior angles are supplementary.

$m\angle 1 + m\angle 2 = 180$

116 Chapter 3 Parallel and Perpendicular Lines

👥 Reaching All Students

Below Level Students can fold and cut a sheet of paper along a line not parallel to an edge and then match angles to confirm Theorem 3-1.	**Advanced Learners** Ask students to explain how to find the other 15 angle measures in Example 4 when a different angle measure is given.	**English Learners** See note on page 116. **Visual Learners** See note on page 117.

You can display the steps that prove a theorem in a **two-column proof.**

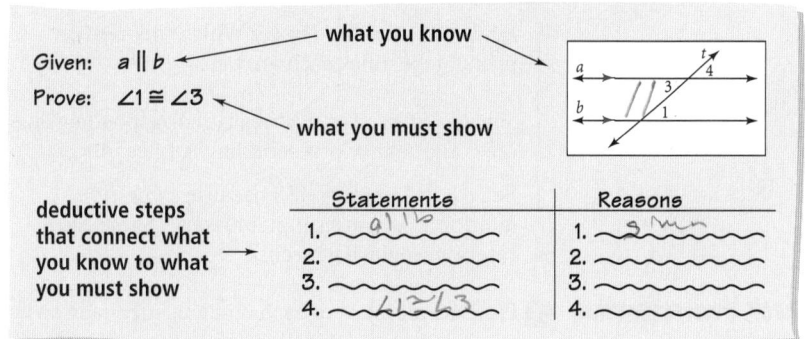

Two-Column Proof of Theorem 3-1

If a transversal intersects two parallel lines, then alternate interior angles are congruent.

Given: $a \parallel b$

Prove: $\angle 1 \cong \angle 3$

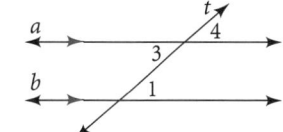

Statements	Reasons
1. $a \parallel b$	1. Given
2. $\angle 1 \cong \angle 4$	2. If lines are $\parallel$, then corresponding angles are congruent.
3. $\angle 4 \cong \angle 3$	3. Vertical angles are congruent.
4. $\angle 1 \cong \angle 3$	4. Transitive Property of Congruence

To write a proof, you may find it helpful to first write a plan for the proof. In a plan, you write key statements that connect what you prove to what is given.

Proof ③ **EXAMPLE** Planning a Proof

Developing Proof For Theorem 3-2 below, study what is given, what you are to prove, and the diagram. Then write a plan for a proof.

If two lines are parallel and cut by a transversal, then same-side interior angles are supplementary.

3. 1. $a \parallel b$ (Given)
   2. $m\angle 3 + m\angle 2 = 180$
     (Angle Add. Post.)
   3. $m\angle 1 = m\angle 3$
     (Corr. ⦦ Post.)
   4. $m\angle 1 + m\angle 2 = 180$
     (Substitute.)
   5. $\angle 1$ and $\angle 2$ are supp.
     (Def. of Supp. ⦦)

Given: $a \parallel b$

Prove: $\angle 1$ and $\angle 2$ are supplementary.

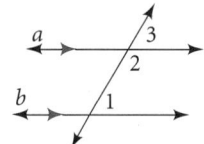

Plan: To prove that $m\angle 1 + m\angle 2 = 180$, show that $m\angle 3 + m\angle 2 = 180$. Then show that $m\angle 1 = m\angle 3$ and substitute $m\angle 1$ for $m\angle 3$.

✔ **Check Understanding** ③ Use the plan to write a two-column proof. **See left.**

When you see two parallel lines and a transversal, and you know the measure of one angle, you can find the measures of all the angles. This is illustrated in Example 4.

OBJECTIVE
2 Teaching Notes

Error Prevention

Students may try to apply the Corresponding Angles Postulate, Alternate Interior Angles Theorem, and Same-Side Interior Angles Theorem when lines are not parallel. Emphasize that the postulate and theorems apply only when a transversal intersects *parallel* lines.

Teaching Tip

Provide this summary of the steps to follow in a two-column proof.
- Draw and label a diagram.
- State the Given and the Prove in terms of the diagram.
- Develop a Plan for Proof.
- Write each step in the left column and the reason for each step in the right column.

3 EXAMPLE Alternative Method

After students study the Plan for Proof, point out that working backward can help them plan a proof.

4 EXAMPLE Technology Tip

You might want to use geometry software and the postulate and theorems in this lesson to find the measures of the angles.

Visual Learners

Suggest that students draw a diagram of parallel lines and a transversal, use numbers to label the eight angles formed, and color-code the angles to indicate which are congruent.

3 Study the Plan for Proof from Example 3. Which theorem or postulate gives the reason that $m\angle 3 + m\angle 2 = 180$? **Angle Add. Post.**

4

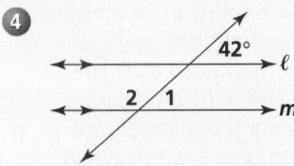

In the diagram above, $\ell \parallel m$. Find $m\angle 1$ and then $m\angle 2$. $m\angle 1 = 42$; $m\angle 2 = 138$

5

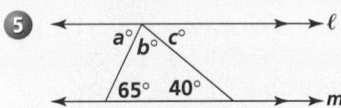

In the diagram above, $\ell \parallel m$. Find the values of a, b, and c. $a = 65$, $b = 75$, $c = 40$

Closure

In the diagram below, $a \parallel b$. Find all the angles that have equal measures.

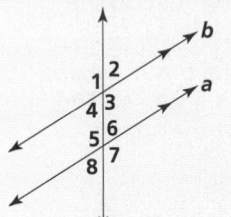

$m\angle 1 = m\angle 3 = m\angle 5 = m\angle 7$;
$m\angle 2 = m\angle 4 = m\angle 6 = m\angle 8$

---

4 **EXAMPLE** Finding Measures of Angles

Find $m\angle 1$, and then $m\angle 2$. Which theorem or postulate justifies each answer?

Since $a \parallel b$, $m\angle 1 = 50$ because corresponding angles are congruent (Corresponding Angles Postulate).

Since $c \parallel d$, $m\angle 2 = 130$ because same-side interior angles are supplementary (Same-Side Interior Angles Theorem).

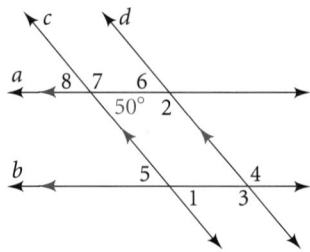

✓ **Check Understanding** **4** Find the measure of each angle. Justify each answer.
 a. $\angle 3$ b. $\angle 4$ c. $\angle 5$ 50; alt. int. ⓢ are ≅.
 d. $\angle 6$ e. $\angle 7$ f. $\angle 8$ 50; corr. ⓢ are ≅ or vert. ⓢ are ≅.
 4a. 130; corr. ⓢ are ≅.   b. 130; vert. ⓢ are ≅.
 d. 50; alt. int. ⓢ are ≅.   e. 130; same-side int. ⓢ are supp.
 Sometimes you can use algebra to find angle measures.

5 **EXAMPLE** Using Algebra to Find Angle Measures

Algebra Find the values of x and y.

$x = 70$ Corresponding angles of parallel lines are ≅.
$70 + 50 + y = 180$ Angle Addition Postulate
$y = 60$ Subtraction Property of Equality

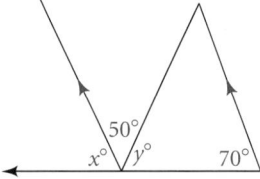

✓ **Check Understanding** **5** Find the values of x and y. Then find the measures of the angles.
$x = 45$, $y = 115$; 90, 90, 115, 65

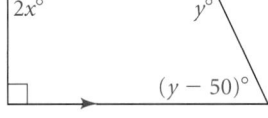

EXERCISES

For more practice, see *Extra Practice*.

Practice and Problem Solving

A **Practice by Example**

Examples 1, 2 (pages 115, 116)

1. $\overleftrightarrow{PQ}$ and $\overleftrightarrow{SR}$ with transversal $\overleftrightarrow{SQ}$; alt. int. ⓢ

2. $\overleftrightarrow{PS}$ and $\overleftrightarrow{QR}$ with transversal $\overleftrightarrow{SQ}$; alt. int. ⓢ

3. $\overleftrightarrow{PS}$ and $\overleftrightarrow{QR}$ with transversal $\overleftrightarrow{PQ}$; same-side int. ⓢ

4. $\overleftrightarrow{PS}$ and $\overleftrightarrow{QR}$ with transversal $\overleftrightarrow{SR}$; corr. ⓢ

Name the two lines and the transversal that form each pair of angles. Then classify the pair of angles.

1. $\angle 2$ and $\angle 3$
2. $\angle 1$ and $\angle 4$
3. $\angle SPQ$ and $\angle PQR$
4. $\angle 5$ and $\angle PSR$

Classify each pair of angles labeled in the same color as *alternate interior angles*, *same-side interior angles*, or *corresponding angles*. 5–7. See margin.

5.   6.   7.

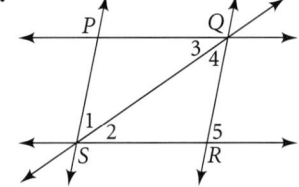

pages 118–121   Exercises

5. $\angle 1$ and $\angle 2$: corr. ⓢ
 $\angle 3$ and $\angle 4$: alt. int. ⓢ
 $\angle 5$ and $\angle 6$: corr. ⓢ

6. $\angle 1$ and $\angle 2$: same-side int. ⓢ
 $\angle 3$ and $\angle 4$: corr. ⓢ
 $\angle 5$ and $\angle 6$: corr. ⓢ

7. $\angle 1$ and $\angle 2$: corr. ⓢ
 $\angle 3$ and $\angle 4$: same-side int. ⓢ
 $\angle 5$ and $\angle 6$: alt. int. ⓢ

8. The boards securing this barn door suggest two parallel lines and a transversal. Classify $\angle 1$ and $\angle 2$ as alternate interior angles, same-side interior angles, or corresponding angles. **alt. int. $\angle$s**

Example 3
(page 117)

9. Developing Proof Complete the plan for a proof of the following statement.

If two lines are parallel and one of them is perpendicular to a transversal, then so is the other.

Given: $\ell \parallel m, \ell \perp t$

Prove: $m \perp t$

Plan: To prove $m \perp t$, show that **a.** $\angle\underline{\ ?\ }$ is a right angle. $\angle 2$ is a right angle if it is congruent to **b.** $\angle\underline{\ ?\ }$. **1**
$\angle 2 \cong \angle 1$ because $\ell \parallel m$ and **c.** $\underline{\ ?\ }$ angles are congruent.
2 (above a.)   **corr.** (below c.)

10. Developing Proof Supply the missing reasons in this two-column proof.

In a plane, if a line is perpendicular to one of two parallel lines, then it is perpendicular to the other.

Given: $k \perp r, r \parallel s$

Prove: $k \perp s$

Statements	Reasons
1. $k \perp r$	**1.** Given
2. $\angle 1$ is a right angle.	**a.** $\underline{\ ?\ }$ Def. of $\perp$
3. $m\angle 1 = 90$	**b.** $\underline{\ ?\ }$ Def. of right $\angle$
4. $r \parallel s$	**4.** Given
5. $m\angle 2 = m\angle 1$	**c.** $\underline{\ ?\ }$ Corr. $\angle$s of parallel lines are $\cong$.
6. $m\angle 2 = 90$	**d.** $\underline{\ ?\ }$ Subst.
7. $\angle 2$ is a right angle.	**e.** $\underline{\ ?\ }$ Def. of right $\angle$
8. $k \perp s$	**f.** $\underline{\ ?\ }$ Def. of $\perp$

Example 4
(page 118)

Find $m\angle 1$, and then $m\angle 2$. Justify each answer.   11–13. See margin.

11.
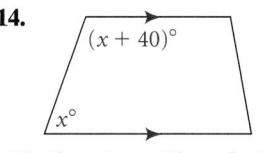

12.
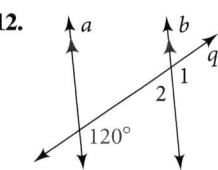

13.
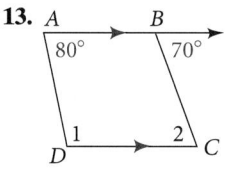

Example 5
(page 118)

$\boxed{x^2}$ **Algebra Find the value of x. Then find the measure of each labeled angle.**

14.
$(x + 40)°$
$x°$
70; the $\angle$s are 70 and 110.

15.
$(3x - 10)°$
$(x + 40)°$
25; the $\angle$s are both 65.

16.
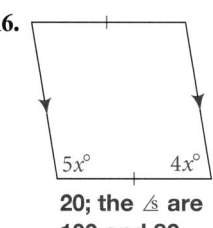
$5x°$ $4x°$
20; the $\angle$s are 100 and 80.

Lesson 3-1 Properties of Parallel Lines   **119**

11. $m\angle 1 = 75$ because corr. $\angle$s of $\parallel$ lines are $\cong$; $m\angle 2 = 105$ because same-side int. $\angle$s of $\parallel$ lines are suppl.

12. $m\angle 1 = 120$ because corr. $\angle$s of $\parallel$ lines are $\cong$; $m\angle 2 = 60$ because same-side int. $\angle$s of $\parallel$ lines are suppl.

13. $m\angle 1 = 100$ because same-side int. $\angle$s of $\parallel$ lines are suppl.; $m\angle 2 = 70$ because alt. int. $\angle$s of $\parallel$ lines have = measure.

---

3. Practice

Assignment Guide

1 Objective
   Ⓐ Ⓑ **Core** 1–8, 19–22, 26, 28

2 Objective
   Ⓐ Ⓑ **Core** 9–18, 23–25, 27, 29–31
   Ⓒ **Extension** 32–36

Standardized Test Prep 37–41

Mixed Review 42–50

Exercises 1, 2 Go over these exercises as a large group to make sure that students understand which lines form the angles.

Exercise 10 Point out to students the similarity of this exercise to the paragraph proofs in Lesson 2-4.

Connection to Discrete Math
Exercises 19–22 These exercises use the concept of combinations.

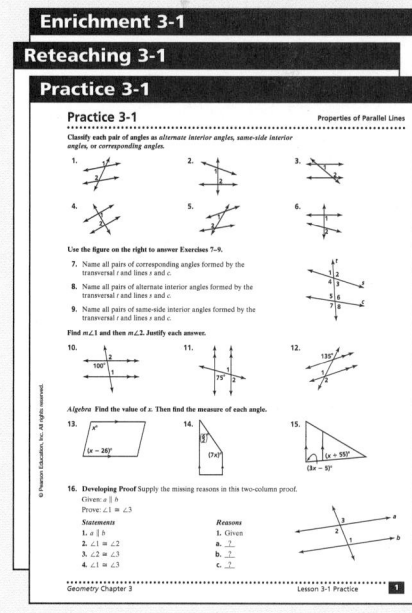

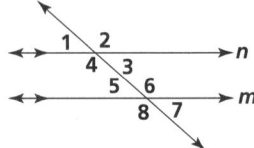

Lesson Quiz 3-1

In the diagram below, $m \parallel n$.
Use the diagram for
Exercises 1–5.

1. Complete: _____ and
   $\angle 4$ are alternate interior
   angles. **∠6**

2. Complete: _____
   and $\angle 8$ are corresponding
   angles. **∠4**

3. Suppose that $m\angle 3 = 37$.
   Find $m\angle 6$. **143**

4. Suppose that $m\angle 1 = x + 12$
   and $m\angle 5 = 3x - 36$.
   Find x. **24**

5. If a transversal intersects
   two parallel lines, then
   same-side exterior angles
   are supplementary. Write
   a Plan for Proof.
   Given: $m \parallel n$
   Prove: $\angle 2$ and $\angle 7$ are
   supplementary. **Show that**
   $m\angle 2 = m\angle 6$. **Then show**
   that $m\angle 6 + m\angle 7 = 180$,
   and substitute $m\angle 2$ **for**
   $m\angle 6$.

Alternative Assessment

Have each student draw a
diagram of two lines cut by a
transversal. Then have students
use their diagrams to write
answers to these exercises.
● Define *alternate interior*
  angles, corresponding angles,
  and *same-side interior angles*
  in your own words.
● Summarize what you know
  about these angles when the
  transversal cuts parallel lines.

B Apply Your Skills

17. In the figure at the right, $f \parallel g$ and $m \parallel n$.
    Find the measure of each numbered angle.
    See margin.
18. Two pairs of parallel segments form the
    "pound sign" on your telephone keypad. To find
    the measures of all the angles in the pound sign,
    how many angles must you measure? Explain. **See margin.**

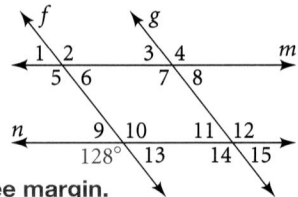

Two lines and a transversal form how many pairs of the following?

19. alternate interior angles **two**
20. corresponding angles **four**
21. same-side interior angles **two**
22. vertical angles **four**

Need Help?
In Exercise 24, turn
your book so the other
two parallel lines
appear horizontal.

x^2 **Algebra** Find the values of the variables.

23.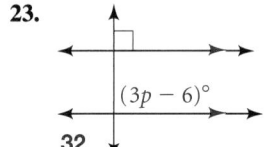

    32

24.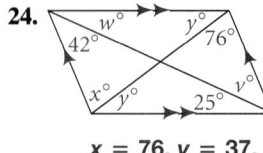

    $x = 76, y = 37,$
    $v = 42, w = 25$

25.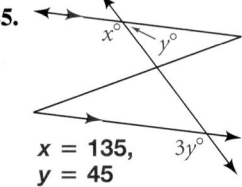

    $x = 135,$
    $y = 45$

26. **Error Analysis** The diagram at the right
    contains contradictory information. What is it?
    Why is it contradictory? **See margin p. 121.**

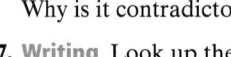

27. **Writing** Look up the meaning of the prefix
    trans. Explain how the meaning of the prefix
    relates to the word *transversal*. **Trans means across or over.**
    A transversal cuts across other lines.
28. **Open-Ended** The letter Z illustrates alternate interior angles. Find at least two
    other letters that illustrate the pairs of angles presented in this lesson. Draw the
    letters, mark the angles, and describe them. **See margin p. 121.**

29. **History** About 220 B.C., Eratosthenes estimated
    the circumference of Earth. He achieved this
    remarkable feat by using two locations in Egypt.
    He assumed that Earth is a sphere and that the
    sun's rays are parallel. He used the measures of
    $\angle 1$ and $\angle 2$ in his estimation. **alt. int. ⦨**
    a. Classify $\angle 1$ and $\angle 2$ as alternate interior,
       same-side interior, or corresponding angles.
    b. How did Eratosthenes know that $\angle 1 \cong \angle 2$?
       He knew that alt. int. ⦨ of parallel lines are ≅.
30. **Engineering** Engineers are laying pipe below ground on opposite sides of the
    street as shown here. To join the pipe, workers on each side of the street work
    towards the middle.
    a. If one team lays pipe at the angle shown,
       what should the other team use for $m\angle 1$? **57**
    b. Are these two angles alternate interior,
       same-side interior, or corresponding angles?
       same-side int. ⦨

C Challenge

31. **Critical Thinking** $\angle 4$ and $\angle 5$ are same-side
    exterior angles. **a-b. See margin p. 121.**
    a. Make a conjecture about same-side exterior angles
       formed by two parallel lines and a transversal.
    Proof b. Prove your conjecture or show a counterexample.

pages 118–121 **Exercises**
17. $m\angle 1 = m\angle 3 = m\angle 6 =$
     $m\angle 8 = m\angle 9 = m\angle 11 =$
     $m\angle 13 = m\angle 15 = 52;$
     $m\angle 2 = m\angle 4 = m\angle 5 =$
     $m\angle 7 = m\angle 10 =$
     $m\angle 12 = m\angle 14 = 128$

18. **You must find the**
     measure of one ∠. All ⦨
     that are vert., corr., or
     alt. int. to that ∠ will
     have that measure. All
     other ⦨ will be the suppl.
     of that measure.

32. 1. $a \parallel b$ (Given)
   2. $\angle 1 \cong \angle 2$
      (Vertical $\angle s$ are $\cong$.)
   3. $\angle 2 \cong \angle 3$
      (Corr. $\angle s$ are $\cong$.)
   4. $\angle 1 \cong \angle 3$
      (Trans. Property)

32. Developing Proof $\angle 1$ and $\angle 3$ are alternate exterior angles. Follow the plan for a proof and write a two-column proof of the following statement.   **See left.**

If a transversal intersects two parallel lines, then alternate exterior angles are congruent.

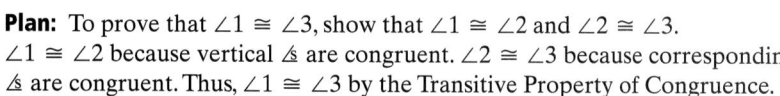

Given: $a \parallel b$

Prove: $\angle 1 \cong \angle 3$

Plan: To prove that $\angle 1 \cong \angle 3$, show that $\angle 1 \cong \angle 2$ and $\angle 2 \cong \angle 3$. $\angle 1 \cong \angle 2$ because vertical $\angle s$ are congruent. $\angle 2 \cong \angle 3$ because corresponding $\angle s$ are congruent. Thus, $\angle 1 \cong \angle 3$ by the Transitive Property of Congruence.

33. Never; the two planes do not intersect.
34. Sometimes; if they are $\parallel$.

Line m is in plane A and line n is in plane B. Planes A and B are parallel. Complete each statement with *sometimes, always,* or *never*. Justify each answer.

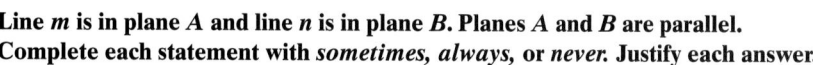

33. Lines m and n ___?___ intersect.

34. Lines m and n are ___?___ coplanar.
   See left.

35. Lines m and n are ___?___ parallel.
   Sometimes; they may be skew.

36. Lines m and n are ___?___ skew.
   Sometimes; they may be $\parallel$.

Standardized Test Prep

A fence on a hill uses vertical posts L and M to hold parallel rails N and P. Use the diagram for Exercises 37–41.

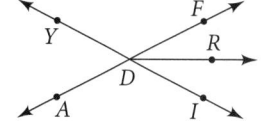

Multiple Choice

37. $\angle 10$ and $\angle 14$ are alternate interior angles. Which is the transversal? **D**
   A. L   **B.** M
   C. N   **D.** P

38. If $m\angle 1 = 115$, what is $m\angle 16$? **G**
   F. 35   **G.** 65   **H.** 85   **I.** 115

Take It to the NET
Online lesson quiz at
www.PHSchool.com
Web Code: afa-0301

39. If $m\angle 10 = x - 24$, what is $m\angle 7$? **D**
   A. $156 + x$ **B.** $204 + x$ **C.** $156 - x$ **D.** $204 - x$

40. If $m\angle 1 = 6x$ and $m\angle 12 = 4x$, what is $m\angle 5$? **I**
   F. 54   **G.** 60   **H.** 72   **I.** 108

Short Response

41. a. Describe a plan for showing that $\angle 1 \cong \angle 5$. **a–b. See margin.**
   b. Explain why $\angle 1 \cong \angle 5$. Justify each step.

Mixed Review

Lesson 2-5

Find the measure of each angle if $m\angle YDF = 121$ and $\overrightarrow{DR}$ bisects $\angle FDI$.

42. $\angle IDA$ **43.** $\angle YDA$ **44.** $\angle RDI$
   121   59   29.5

Lesson 1-6

Coordinate Geometry Find the coordinates of the midpoint of $\overline{AB}$.

45. $A(0, 9), B(1, 5)$ **46.** $A(-3, 8), B(2, -1)$ **47.** $A(10, -1), B(-4, 7)$
   (0.5, 7)   **(−0.5, 3.5)**   **(3, 3)**

Lesson 1-1

Find a pattern for each sequence. Use the pattern to show the next two terms.

48. $4, 8, 12, 16, \ldots$ **49.** $1, -2, 4, -8, \ldots$ **50.** $23, 16, 9, 2, \ldots$
   Add 4; 20, 24.   **Multiply by −2; 16, −32.**   **Subtract 7; −5, −12.**

Standardized Test Prep

📁 **Resources**

For additional practice with a variety of test item formats:
- Standardized Test Prep, p. 177
- Test-Taking Strategies, p. 172
- Test-Taking Strategies with Transparencies

Exercises 37–41 Whenever a problem indicates that lines are parallel, students should copy the diagram and mark the lines as parallel to remind them to use the postulates and theorems that apply to parallel lines.

28. Answers may vary.

1	Sample: *E*
2	illustrates corr. $\angle s$
3	($\angle 1$ and $\angle 3$, $\angle 2$ and
4	$\angle 4$) and same-side int. $\angle s$ ($\angle 1$ and $\angle 2$, $\angle 3$ and $\angle 4$);

| 1 | 2 | *I* illustrates alt. int. $\angle s$ ($\angle 1$ and $\angle 4$, $\angle 2$ |
| 3 | 4 | and $\angle 3$) and same-side int. $\angle s$ ($\angle 1$ and $\angle 3$, $\angle 2$ and $\angle 4$). |

31. a. If two lines are $\parallel$ and cut by a transversal, then same-side ext. $\angle s$ are suppl.

   b. Given: $a \parallel b$
      Prove: $\angle 4$ and $\angle 5$ are suppl.

   1. $a \parallel b$ (Given) 2. $m\angle 5 + m\angle 6 = 180$ ($\angle$ Add. Post.) 3. $\angle 4 \cong \angle 6$ (Corr. $\angle s$ are $\cong$) 4. $m\angle 5 + m\angle 4 = 180$ (Subst.) 5. $\angle 4$ and $\angle 5$ are suppl. (Def. of suppl.)

41. [2] **a.** First show that $\angle 1 \cong \angle 7$. Then show that $\angle 7 \cong \angle 5$. Finally, show that $\angle 1 \cong \angle 5$ (OR other valid solution plan).

   b. $\angle 1 \cong \angle 7$ because vert. $\angle s$ are $\cong$. $\angle 7 \cong \angle 5$ because corr. $\angle s$ of $\parallel$ lines are $\cong$. Finally, by the Transitive Prop. of $\cong$, $\angle 1 \cong \angle 5$.

   [1] incorrect sequence of steps OR incorrect logical argument

26. The $\angle s$ labeled are corr. $\angle s$ and should be $\cong$. If you solve $2x - 60 = 60 - 2x$, you get $x = 30$. This would be impossible since the diagram shows they are positive $\angle s$ and $2x - 60$ and $60 - 2x$ would equal 0.

1. Plan

Lesson Preview

✓ **Check Skills You'll Need**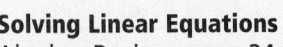

Solving Linear Equations
Algebra Review, page 24
Examples 1, 2, Exercises 1–22

Converses
Lesson 2-1: Examples 5, 6
Exercises 23–32
Extra Practice, p. 691

Lesson Resources

📁 **Teaching Resources**
Practice, Reteaching, Enrichment

📖 **Reaching All Students**
Practice Workbook 3-2
Spanish Practice Workbook 3-2
Hands-On Activities 7
Informal Geometry Planning
  Guide 3-2

⏰ **Presentation Assistant Plus!**
Transparencies
• Check Skills You'll Need 3-2
• Additional Examples 3-2
• Student Edition Answers 3-2
• Lesson Quiz 3-2
PH Presentation Pro CD 3-2

ASSESSMENT SYSTEM

Computer Test Generator CD

💻 **Technology**
Resource Pro® CD-ROM
Computer Test Generator CD
Prentice Hall Presentation Pro CD

🖥 **www.PHSchool.com**
Student Site
• Teacher Web Code: afk-5500
• Self-grading Lesson Quiz
Teacher Center
• Lesson Planner
• Resources

Plus

Proving Lines Parallel

2.02 Apply properties, definitions, and theorems of angles and lines to solve problems and write proofs.

Lesson Preview

What You'll Learn

OBJECTIVE 1 To use a transversal in proving lines parallel

OBJECTIVE 2 To relate parallel and perpendicular lines

. . . And Why

To show why opposite sides of a picture frame are parallel, as in Example 5

✓ Check Skills You'll Need

(For help, go to page 24 and Lesson 2-1.)

x^2 **Algebra** Solve each equation.

1. $2x + 5 = 27$ **11**

2. $8a - 12 = 20$ **4**

3. $x - 30 + 4x + 80 = 180$ **26**

4. $9x - 7 = 3x + 29$ **6**

Write the converse of each conditional statement. Determine the truth value of the converse. 5–6. See back of book.

5. If a triangle is a right triangle, then it has a 90° angle.

6. If two angles are vertical angles, then they are congruent.

7. If two angles are same-side interior angles, then they are supplementary.
If two ∠s are supp., then they are same-side int. ∠s; false.

New Vocabulary • flow proof

OBJECTIVE 1

Using a Transversal

🔑 **Key Concepts**

On window blinds like those shown here, you move the tilt bar to let in or shut out the light.

When you move the bar, the slats tilt at the same angle. This keeps them parallel and illustrates the converse of the Corresponding Angles Postulate.

Postulate 3-2	**Converse of the Corresponding Angles Postulate**

If two lines and a transversal form corresponding angles that are congruent, then the two lines are parallel.

$\ell \parallel m$

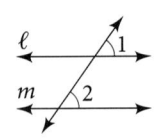

In Lesson 3-1, you proved two theorems based on the Corresponding Angles Postulate. You can also prove theorems that are based on its converse. In fact, Theorems 3-3 and 3-4 happen to be converses of the two theorems from Lesson 3-1, Theorems 3-1 and 3-2.

122 Chapter 3 Parallel and Perpendicular Lines

⚡ **Ongoing Assessment and Intervention**

Before the Lesson Diagnose prerequisite skills using:	**During the Lesson** Monitor progress using:	**After the Lesson** Assess knowledge using:
• Check Skills You'll Need	• Check Understanding • Additional Examples • Standardized Test Prep	• Lesson Quiz • Computer Test Generator CD

Key Concepts

Theorem 3-3	**Converse of the Alternate Interior Angles Theorem**

If two lines and a transversal form alternate interior angles that are congruent, then the two lines are parallel.

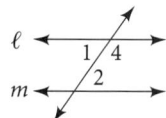

If ∠1 ≅ ∠2, then ℓ ∥ m.

Theorem 3-4	**Converse of the Same-Side Interior Angles Theorem**

If two lines and a transversal form same-side interior angles that are supplementary, then the two lines are parallel.

If ∠2 and ∠4 are supplementary, then ℓ ∥ m.

You have seen two forms of proof—paragraph and two-column. In a third form, called **flow proof,** arrows show the logical connections between the statements. Reasons are written below the statements.

Proof **1 EXAMPLE** **Proving Theorem 3-3**

Developing Proof For Theorem 3-3, study what is given, what you are to prove, and the diagram. Then write a flow proof.

If two lines and a transversal form alternate interior angles that are congruent, then the two lines are parallel.

Given: ∠1 ≅ ∠2
Prove: ℓ ∥ m

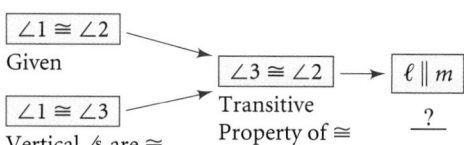

✓ Check Understanding **1** Supply the missing reason in Example 1.
If corr. ∡ are ≅, then the lines are ∥.

You will write a flow proof of Theorem 3-4 in Exercise 47. Theorems 3-4, 3-3, and Postulate 3-2 now provide you with three ways to prove that two lines are parallel.

2 EXAMPLE **Using Theorem 3-4**

Developing Proof Which lines, if any, must be parallel if ∠1 ≅ ∠2? Justify your answer with a theorem or postulate.

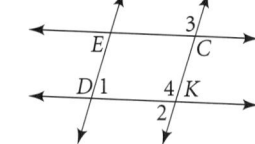

$\overleftrightarrow{DE} \parallel \overleftrightarrow{KC}$ by Theorem 3-3, the Converse of the Alternate Interior Angles Theorem: If alternate interior angles are congruent, then the lines are parallel.

✓ Check Understanding **2** Which lines, if any, must be parallel if ∠3 ≅ ∠4? Explain.
$\overleftrightarrow{EC} \parallel \overleftrightarrow{DK}$; Conv. of Corr. ∡ Post.

👥 **Reaching All Students**

Below Level Begin Example 1 by substituting values for ∠1 and ∠2. Generalize the proof only after it is understood for specific values.	**Advanced Learners** Ask students to write the postulates and theorems in Lessons 3-1 and 3-2 as biconditionals.	**Visual Learners** See note on page 125. **Tactile Learners** See note on page 127.

Math Background

Euclid's discussion of parallelism in *The Elements* introduced the topics in this text in a different order and proved the converse of the Corresponding Angles Postulate as a theorem. Thus the only postulate that required acceptance without proof for proving lines parallel was the Corresponding Angles Postulate.

OBJECTIVE
▼ 1 **Teaching Notes**

Error Prevention
Students may incorrectly use a conditional statement to justify an answer when its converse should be used. Discuss as a class how to determine which to use.

1 EXAMPLE **Alternative Method**

To check students' understanding, have the class prove the Converse of the Corresponding Angles Postulate using the Converse of the Alternate Interior Angles Theorem as a postulate.

2 EXAMPLE **Teaching Tip**

Whenever possible, mark the congruent angles on a diagram on the board to help students relate angles and parallel lines.

OBJECTIVE
2 **Teaching Notes**

Math Tip
After students understand Theorem 3-5, ask: *Is the relationship "is parallel to" reflexive, symmetric, and/or transitive?* **symmetric and transitive**

Visual Learners
Have students demonstrate Theorems 3-5 and 3-6 with classroom objects.

5 EXAMPLE **Diversity**

Show pictures of a miter box and a backsaw from a tool catalog to help explain the terms to students who are unfamiliar with them.

Additional Examples

1 Write the flow proof of the Alternate Interior Angles Theorem in Example 1 as a paragraph proof. **By the Vertical Angles Thm., ∠3 ≅ ∠1. By the Transitive Prop. of ≅, ∠3 ≅ ∠2. Because ∠3 and ∠2 are ≅ corr. ∠s, by the Converse of the Corresponding Angles Post., ℓ ∥ m.**

2 Use the diagram from Example 2. Which lines, if any, must be parallel if ∠3 and ∠2 are supplementary? $\overleftrightarrow{EC} \parallel \overleftrightarrow{DK}$

3 Use the diagram from Example 3. Which angle would you use with ∠1 to prove the theorem *In a plane, if two lines are perpendicular to the same line, then they are parallel to each other* (Theorem 3-6) using the Converse of the Alternate Interior Angles Theorem instead of the Converse of the Corresponding Angles Postulate? **the vertical angle of ∠2**

4 Find the value of x for which ℓ ∥ m. **40**

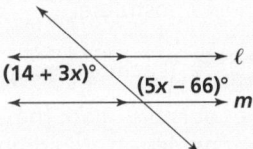

5 Suppose that the top and bottom pieces of a picture frame are cut to make 60° angles with exterior sides of the frame. The two sides should be cut at what angle to ensure that opposite sides of the frame will be parallel? **30°**

Closure

Name three methods this lesson gives to prove that two lines are parallel. **Show that corresponding angles are congruent, alternate interior angles are congruent, or same-side interior angles are supplementary.**

The two diagrams suggest ways to draw parallel lines. You can draw them (a) parallel to a given line, or (b) perpendicular to a given line. Theorems 3-5 and 3-6 guarantee that the lines you draw are indeed parallel.

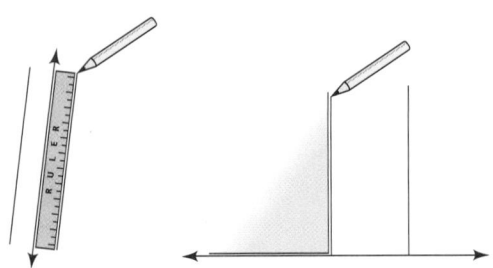

Key Concepts

Theorem 3-5

If two lines are parallel to the same line, then they are parallel to each other.

$a \parallel b$

Theorem 3-6

In a plane, if two lines are perpendicular to the same line, then they are parallel to each other.

$m \parallel n$

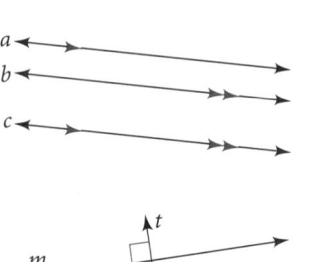

Theorem 3-6 includes the phrase *in a plane*. On the other hand, Theorem 3-5 is true for any three such lines, whether they are coplanar (Exercise 26) or noncoplanar.

Need Help?

Three lines that meet in the corner of a room show why Theorem 3-6 is not true in space.

3 EXAMPLE Proof of Theorem 3-6

Developing Proof Study what is given, what you are to prove, and the diagram. Then write a paragraph proof.

Given: $r \perp t, s \perp t$

Prove: $r \parallel s$

Proof: ∠1 and ∠2 are right angles by the definition of perpendicular, so they are congruent. Since corresponding angles are congruent, $r \parallel s$.

✓ **Check Understanding** **3 Critical Thinking** In a plane, if two lines form congruent angles with a third line, must the lines be parallel? **no**

You may need algebra to find values in problems with parallel lines.

4 EXAMPLE Using Algebra

Algebra Find the value of x for which ℓ ∥ m.

The two angles are corresponding angles. ℓ ∥ m when $2x + 6 = 40$.

$2x + 6 = 40$

$2x = 34$ **Subtract 6 from each side.**

$x = 17$ **Divide each side by 2.**

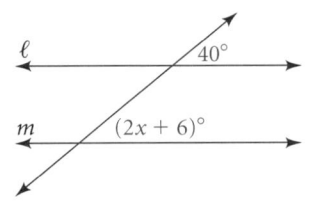

pages 125–129 Exercises

4. *a* ∥ *b*; if two lines and a transversal form same-side int. ∠s that are suppl., then the lines are ∥.

5. *a* ∥ *b*; if two lines and a transversal form same-side int. ∠s that are suppl., then the lines are ∥.

✔ **Check Understanding** ④ Find the value of x for which $a \parallel b$. Explain how you can check your answer. **18; 7 · 18 − 8 = 118, and 62 + 118 = 180.**

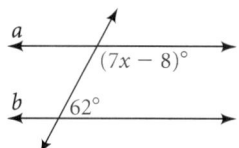

⑤ **EXAMPLE** Real-World 🌎 Connection

Woodworking To make a frame for a painting, a miter box and a backsaw are used to cut the framing at 45° angles. Explain why cutting the framing at this angle ensures that opposite sides of the frame will be parallel.

Two adjacent 45° angles form a 90° angle. Two 90° angles are supplementary. By the Converse of the Same-Side Interior Angles Theorem, opposite sides of the frame are parallel.

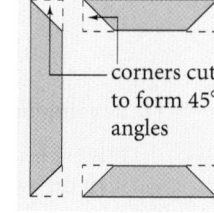

corners cut to form 45° angles

✔ **Check Understanding** ⑤ Explain how you would use the Converse of the Same-Side Interior Angles Theorem to justify the following statement:

In a plane, two lines perpendicular to the same line are parallel. **By def. of ⊥, all ∡ formed are 90°. So, the sum of the measures of each pair of same-side int. ∡ is 180, making them suppl. By the Conv. of the Same-Side Int. ∡ Thm., the lines are ∥.**

EXERCISES

For more practice, see *Extra Practice*.

Practice and Problem Solving

A Practice by Example

Example 2
(page 123)

3. $\overline{JO} \parallel \overline{LM}$; if two lines and a transversal form same-side int. ∡ that are suppl., then the lines are ∥.

Developing Proof **Which lines or segments are parallel? Justify your answer with a theorem or postulate.**

1.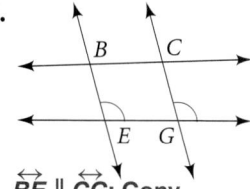
$\overleftrightarrow{BE} \parallel \overleftrightarrow{CG}$; Conv. of Corr. ∡ Post.

2.
$\overline{CA} \parallel \overline{HR}$; Conv. of Corr. ∡ Post.

3.
$m\angle J + m\angle L = 180$
See left.

Developing Proof **Using the given information, which lines, if any, can you conclude are parallel? Justify each conclusion with a theorem or postulate.**

4–15. See margin pp. 124–125.

4. ∠2 is supplementary to ∠3.

5. ∠6 is supplementary to ∠7.

6. ∠4 is supplementary to ∠8.

7. $m\angle 7 = 70, m\angle 9 = 110$

8. ∠1 ≅ ∠3

9. ∠9 ≅ ∠12

10. ∠3 ≅ ∠6

11. ∠2 ≅ ∠10

12. ∠1 ≅ ∠6

13. ∠8 ≅ ∠6

14. ∠11 ≅ ∠7

15. ∠5 ≅ ∠10

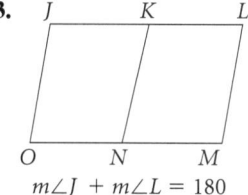

6. none

7. none

8. $a \parallel b$; Conv. of Corr. ∡ Post.

9. none

10. $a \parallel b$; Conv. of Alt. Int. ∡ Thm.

11. $\ell \parallel m$; Conv. of Corr. ∡ Post.

12. none

13. $a \parallel b$; Conv. of Corr. ∡ Post.

14. none

15. $\ell \parallel m$; Conv. of Alt. Int. ∡ Thm.

Lesson 3-2 Proving Lines Parallel **125**

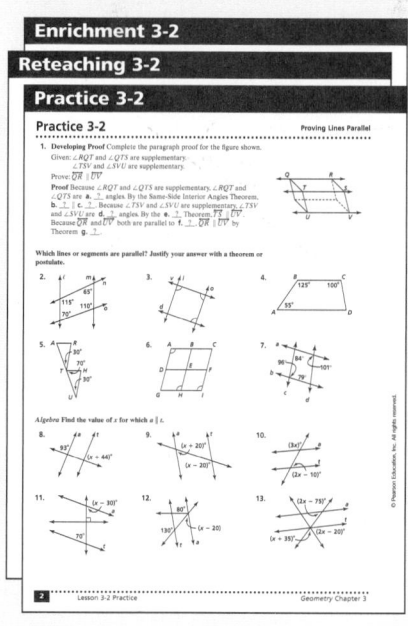

Exercise 16 Have students use the flow proof in Example 1 as a model.

Exercise 17 Have students use the paragraph proof in Example 3 as a model.

Exercise 19 Ask: *What is the relationship between the two labeled angles?* alternate interior angles

Error Prevention

Exercises 21–23 Point out that diagrams and word problems sometimes contain information that is not needed. Ask: *What information in each diagram is not needed to solve for the value of x?* the perpendicular line in Exercise 21; the angle marked $27x°$ in Exercise 22; the angle marked $5x°$ in Exercise 23

Real-World Connection

The ladder rungs are perpendicular to each side. Therefore, the rungs are parallel to each other.

Examples 1, 3
(pages 123, 124)

16. Developing Proof Complete this flow proof of Theorem 3-6.

In a plane, if two lines are perpendicular to the same line, then they are parallel to each other.

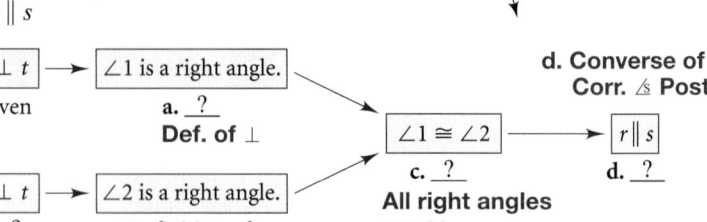

Given: $r \perp t, s \perp t$
Prove: $r \parallel s$

```
r ⊥ t  →  ∠1 is a right angle.                        d. Converse of
Given        a. __?__                                     Corr. ∠ Post.
             Def. of ⊥
                                      ∠1 ≅ ∠2  →  r ∥ s
s ⊥ t  →  ∠2 is a right angle.          c. __?__        d. __?__
 b. __?__      Definition of         All right angles
 Given      perpendicular lines      are ≅.
```

17. Developing Proof Complete this paragraph proof of Theorem 3-4.

If two lines and a transversal form supplementary same-side interior angles, then the two lines are parallel.

Given: $\angle 1$ and $\angle 2$ are supplementary.
Prove: $\ell \parallel m$

Proof: $\angle 2$ is a supplement of **a.** __?__ and $\angle 3$ is
b. $\angle 1$ a supplement of **b.** __?__. Since supplements of
the same angle are congruent, **c.** __?__ ≅ **d.** __?__. **c.** $\angle 2$ **d.** $\angle 3$
Since $\angle 2$ and $\angle 3$ are also corresponding angles, $\ell \parallel m$ by the **e.** __?__ Postulate.
Converse of Corr. ∠

Example 4
(page 124)

x^2 **Algebra** Find the value of x for which $\ell \parallel m$.

18. 30
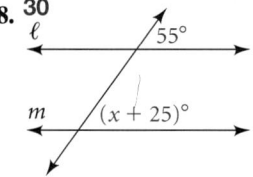

19. 50
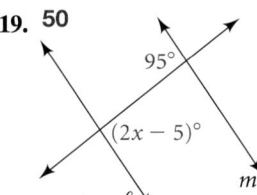

20. 59
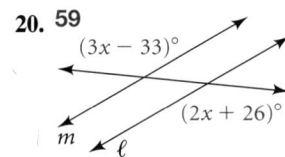

21. 31
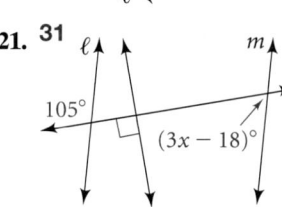

22. 5
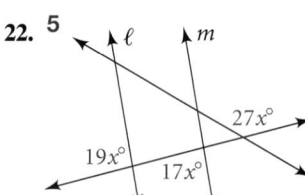

23. 20
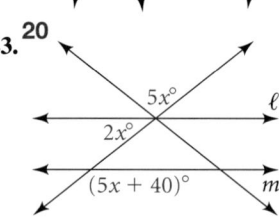

Example 5
(page 125)

24. The top and bottom of a frame are cut from the narrower piece of wood. The sides are cut from the wider piece of wood. Explain why the opposite sides of the frame will be parallel. **See margin.**

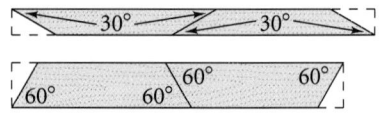

126 Chapter 3 Parallel and Perpendicular Lines

pages 125–129 **Exercises**

24. When the frame is put together, each ∠ of the frame is a right ∠. Two right ∠ are suppl. By the Conv. of the Same-Side

Int. ∠ Thm., opp. sides of the frame are ∥.

25. The corr. ∠ are ≅, so the lines are ∥ by the Conv. of Corr. ∠ Post.

25. Drafting An artist uses the drawing tool in the diagram at the right. The artist draws a line, slides the triangle along the flat surface, and draws another line. Explain why the drawn lines must be parallel. **See margin p. 126.**

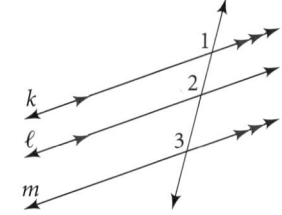

Flat surface   30°-60°-90° triangle

B Apply Your Skills

Proof **26. Developing Proof** Copy and complete the paragraph proof of Theorem 3-5 for three coplanar lines.

Reading Math

For help with reading and solving Exercise 26, see p. 130.

If two lines are parallel to the same line, then they are parallel to each other.

Given: $\ell \parallel k$ and $m \parallel k$

Prove: $\ell \parallel m$

Proof: $\ell \parallel k$ means that $\angle 2 \cong \angle 1$ by the **a.** ? Postulate. $m \parallel k$ means that **b.** ? $\cong$ **c.** ? for the same reason. By the Transitive Property of Congruence, $\angle 2 \cong \angle 3$. By the **d.** ? Postulate, $\ell \parallel m$.

corr. $\angle$s the a.
$\angle 1, \angle 3$ (any order)
Converse of Corr. $\angle$s

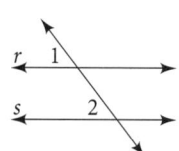

$\boxed{x^2}$ **Algebra** Determine the value of x for which $r \parallel s$. Then find $m\angle 1$ and $m\angle 2$.

27. $m\angle 1 = 80 - x, m\angle 2 = 90 - 2x$
10; $m\angle 1 = m\angle 2 = 70$
28. $m\angle 1 = 60 - 2x, m\angle 2 = 70 - 4x$
5; $m\angle 1 = m\angle 2 = 50$
29. $m\angle 1 = 40 - 4x, m\angle 2 = 50 - 8x$
2.5; $m\angle 1 = m\angle 2 = 30$
30. $m\angle 1 = 20 - 8x, m\angle 2 = 30 - 16x$
1.25; $m\angle 1 = m\angle 2 = 10$

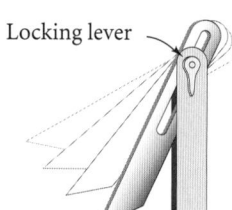

31. Carpentry A T-bevel is a tool used by carpenters to draw congruent angles. By loosening the locking lever, the carpenter can adjust the angle. Explain how the carpenter knows that two lines drawn using the T-bevel are parallel.
The corr. $\angle$s he draws are $\cong$.

Locking lever

Which sides of quadrilateral *PLAN* must be parallel? Explain.

32. $m\angle P = 72, m\angle L = 108, m\angle A = 72, m\angle N = 108$
$\overline{PL} \parallel \overline{NA}$ and $\overline{PN} \parallel \overline{LA}$ by Conv. of Same-Side Int. $\angle$s Thm.
33. $m\angle P = 59, m\angle L = 37, m\angle A = 143, m\angle N = 121$
$\overline{PL} \parallel \overline{NA}$ by Conv. of Same-Side Int. $\angle$s Thm.
34. $m\angle P = 67, m\angle L = 120, m\angle A = 73, m\angle N = 100$
none
35. $m\angle P = 56, m\angle L = 124, m\angle A = 124, m\angle N = 5$
$\overline{PN} \parallel \overline{LA}$ by Conv. of Same-Side Int. $\angle$s Thm.

36. Writing Theorem 3-6: In a plane, two lines perpendicular to the same line are parallel. Use the rectangular solid at the right to explain why the words *in a plane* are needed.
See margin.

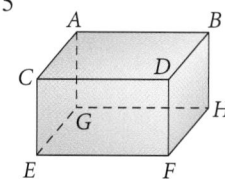

Critical Thinking The Reflexive, Symmetric, and Transitive Properties for Congruence ($\cong$) are listed on page 91.   37–38. See margin.

37. Write reflexive, symmetric, and transitive statements for "is parallel to" ($\parallel$). State whether each statement is true or false and justify your answer.

38. Repeat Exercise 37 for "is perpendicular to" ($\perp$).

36. Answers may vary. Sample: In the diagram, $\overline{AB} \perp \overline{BH}$ and $\overline{AB} \perp \overline{BD}$, but $\overline{BH} \nparallel \overline{BD}$. They intersect.

37. Reflexive: $a \parallel a$; false; any line intersects itself. **Symmetric:** If $a \parallel b$, then $b \parallel a$; true; b and a are coplanar and do not intersect.

Transitive: In general if $a \parallel b$, and $b \parallel c$, then $a \parallel c$; however, when $a \parallel b$ and $b \parallel a$, it does not follow that $a \parallel a$.

38. Reflexive: $a \perp a$; false; $\perp$ lines are two lines that intersect to form right $\angle$s. **Symmetric:** If $a \perp b$, then $b \perp a$; true; b and a intersect to form right $\angle$s. **Transitive:** If $a \perp b$, and $b \perp c$, then $a \perp c$; false; in a plane, two lines $\perp$ to the same line are $\parallel$.

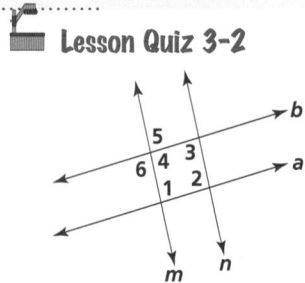

Lesson Quiz 3-2

Using the diagram above and the given information, which lines, if any, are parallel? Justify your answer with a theorem or postulate.

1. ∠6 ≅ ∠3 *m ∥ n* by Converse of Corresponding Angles Post.

2. ∠1 and ∠4 are supplementary. *a ∥ b* by Converse of Same-Side Interior Angles Th.

3. ∠2 ≅ ∠4 No lines must be parallel.

Suppose that *m∠1 = 3x + 10, m∠2 = 3x + 14,* and *m∠6 = x + 58* in the diagram above.

4. Find the value of *x* for which *a ∥ b*. 24

5. Find the value of *x* for which *m ∥ n*. 26

Alternative Assessment

Have partners work with protractors and rulers. Have one student draw a quadrilateral with *two* pairs of parallel sides and 120°, 120°, 60°, and 60° angles. Have the other student draw a quadrilateral with *one* pair of parallel sides and 120°, 120°, 60°, and 60° angles. Students should explain how they know the sides are parallel.

pages 125–129 Exercises

Exercise 39

 **Challenge**

45. It is given that ℓ ∥ m, so ∠4 ≅ ∠8 by Corr. ∠s Post. It is also given that ∠12 ≅ ∠8, so ∠4 ≅ ∠12 by Trans. Prop. of ≅. So, *j ∥ k* by the Conv. of Corr. ∠s Post.

Need Help?

To show ∠1 and ∠3 are supplementary in Exercise 47, use the Angle Addition Postulate.

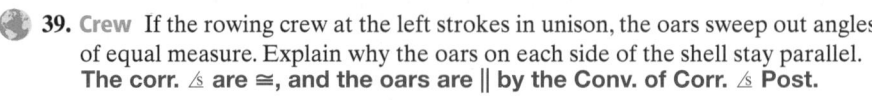

39. **Crew** If the rowing crew at the left strokes in unison, the oars sweep out angles of equal measure. Explain why the oars on each side of the shell stay parallel. The corr. ∠s are ≅, and the oars are ∥ by the Conv. of Corr. ∠s Post.

Open-Ended In each exercise, information is given about the figure below. State another fact about ∠1, ∠2, ∠3, or ∠4 that will guarantee two lines are parallel. Tell which lines will be parallel and why. 40–43. See margin.

40. ∠1 ≅ ∠3

41. *m∠8 = 70, m∠9 = 110*

42. ∠5 ≅ ∠11

43. ∠11 and ∠12 are supplementary.

44. **Reasoning** If ∠1 ≅ ∠7 in the diagram, what two theorems or postulates can you use to show that ℓ ∥ m? Vert. ∠s Thm. and Conv. of Corr. ∠s Post.

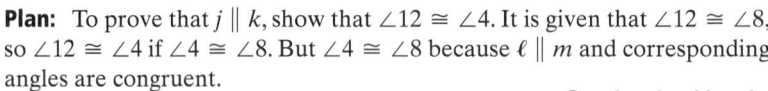

Developing Proof For Exercises 45 and 46, use the diagram at the right and this plan for a proof.

Given: ℓ ∥ m, ∠12 ≅ ∠8

Prove: *j ∥ k*

Plan: To prove that *j ∥ k*, show that ∠12 ≅ ∠4. It is given that ∠12 ≅ ∠8, so ∠12 ≅ ∠4 if ∠4 ≅ ∠8. But ∠4 ≅ ∠8 because ℓ ∥ m and corresponding angles are congruent. **See back of book.**

45. Write a paragraph proof. **See left.**   46. Write a flow proof.

47. **Developing Proof** Rewrite this paragraph proof of Theorem 3-4 as a flow proof. If two lines and a transversal form supplementary same-side interior angles, then the two lines are parallel. **See back of book.**

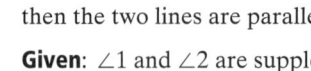

Given: ∠1 and ∠2 are supplementary.

Prove: ℓ ∥ m

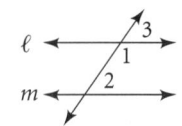

Proof: It is given that ∠1 and ∠2 are supplementary. ∠1 and ∠3 are also supplementary, so ∠2 ≅ ∠3. Since ∠2 and ∠3 are corresponding angles, ℓ ∥ m.

Proof For Exercises 48 and 49, write a flow proof.

48. **Given:** *a ∥ b, ∠1 ≅ ∠2*
    Prove: ℓ ∥ m **See back of book.**

49. **Given:** ℓ ∥ m, ∠1 is supplementary to ∠3.
    Prove: *a ∥ b* **See back of book.**

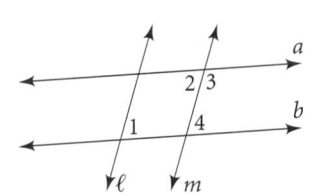

Proof 50. Prove the following statement is true by following the steps below:

If a transversal intersects two parallel lines, then the bisectors of two corresponding angles are parallel.

a. Draw and label a diagram on paper.   a–e. See back of book.
b. State what is given and mark the diagram to keep track of the information.
c. State what you are to prove.
d. Write a plan for proof.
e. Follow your plan and write the proof.

40. **Answers may vary. Sample:** ∠3 ≅ ∠9; *j ∥ k* by Conv. of the Alt. Int. ∠s Thm.

41. **Answers may vary. Sample:** ∠3 ≅ ∠9; *j ∥ k* by Conv. of the Alt. Int. ∠s Thm. and ℓ ∥ m by Conv. of Same-Side Int. ∠s Thm.

42. **Answers may vary. Sample:** ∠3 ≅ ∠11; ℓ ∥ m by Conv. of the Alt. Int. ∠s Thm. and *j ∥ k* by Conv. of Corr. ∠s Post.

43. **Answers may vary. Sample:** ∠3 and ∠12 are suppl.; *j ∥ k* by the Conv. of Corr. ∠s Post.

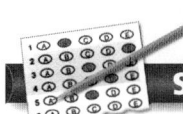
Multiple Choice

51. If *a*, *b*, *c*, and *d* are coplanar lines and $a \parallel b$, $b \perp c$, and $c \parallel d$, then which statement must be true? **C**
   A. $d \perp c$ **B.** $c \parallel a$ **C.** $d \perp a$ **D.** $d \parallel b$

Use the diagram for Exercises 52–54.

52. For what value of *x* is $c \parallel d$? **F**
   F. 21   **G.** 23
   H. 43   **I.** 53

53. If $c \parallel d$, what is $m\angle 1$? **B**
   A. 24   **B.** 44
   C. 136   **D.** 146

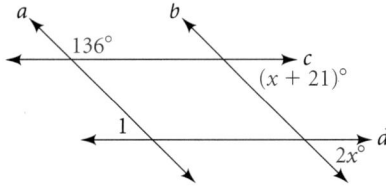

Short Response

54. Suppose $a \parallel b$ in the diagram above. **a–b. See margin.**
   a. Write and solve an equation to find the value of *x*.
   b. Write and solve an equation to find whether $c \parallel d$. Explain your answer.

Extended Response

Take It to the NET
Online lesson quiz at
www.PHSchool.com
Web Code: afa-0302

55. Two lines, *a* and *b*, are cut by a transversal *t*. $\angle 1$ and $\angle 2$ are any pair of corresponding angles. $\angle 1$ and $\angle 3$ are adjacent angles. $m\angle 1 = 2x - 38$, $m\angle 2 = x$, and $m\angle 3 = 6x + 18$. **a–b. See back of book.**
   a. Draw and label a diagram for the figure described.
   b. Determine whether lines *a* and *b* are parallel. Justify your answer.

Mixed Review

Lesson 3-1

Find $m\angle 1$, and then $m\angle 2$. Justify each answer.

56. $m\angle 1 = 70$ since it is a supp. of the $110°$ $\angle$. $m\angle 2 = 110$ since same-side int. $\angle\!\!\!\angle$ are supp.

56.
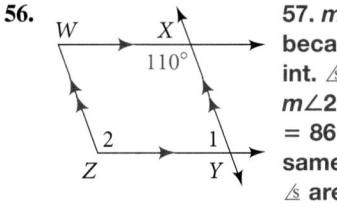

57. $m\angle 1 = 66$ **57.** because alt. int. $\angle\!\!\!\angle$ are $\cong$. $m\angle 2 = 180 - 94 = 86$ because same-side int. $\angle\!\!\!\angle$ are supp.

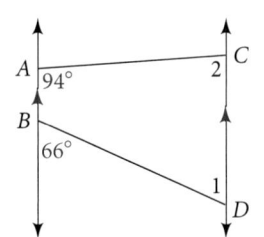

Lesson 2-1

Write the converse of each conditional statement. Determine the truth values of the original conditional and its converse. 58–62. See margin.

58. If you are in Nebraska, you are west of the Mississippi River.

59. If a circle has a diameter of 8 cm, then it has a radius of 4 cm.

60. If a line intersects a pair of parallel lines, then same-side interior angles are supplementary.

61. If you add *ed* to a verb, you form the past tense of a verb.

62. If it is raining, then there are clouds in the sky.

Lesson 1-7

Find the area of each circle. Round to the nearest tenth.

63. $r = 8$ in. — 201.1 in.^{2} **64.** $d = 6$ cm — 28.3 cm^2 **65.** $d = 9$ ft — 63.6 ft^2 **66.** $r = 5$ in. — 78.5 in.^{2}
67. $d = 2.8$ m — 6.2 m^2 **68.** $r = 1.2$ m — 4.5 m^2 **69.** $d = 4.75$ ft — 17.7 ft^2 **70.** $r = 0.6$ m — 0.3 m^2

Lesson 3-2   Proving Lines Parallel   **129**

58. If you are west of the Mississippi River, then you are in Nebraska. Original statement is true, converse is false.

59. If a circle has a radius of 4 cm, then it has a diameter of 8 cm. Both are true.

60. If same-side int. $\angle\!\!\!\angle$ are supp., then a line intersects a pair of $\parallel$ lines. Both are true.

61. If you form the past tense of a verb, then you add *ed* to the verb. Original statement is false, converse is false.

62. If there are clouds in the sky, then it is raining. Orginal statement is true, converse is false.

54. **[2] a.** $136 + (x + 21) = 180$ so $x = 23$ (OR equivalent equation resulting in $x = 23$).   **b.** $x + 21 = 2x$ so $x = 21$. Lines *c* and *d* are not $\parallel$ because *x* cannot $= $ both 21 and 23 (OR equivalent explanation).   **[1]** incorrect equations OR incorrect solutions

 **Reading Math**

Reading for Developing Proof

Reading for Developing Proof

Completing a proof fully and correctly requires connecting steps logically and justifying each step. Here, the process of proof is analyzed using Theorem 3-5.

Teaching Notes

Proofs may be new to your students. A good introduction is to analyze a proof with missing parts and to recreate the reasoning behind each step. Comparing "What Collin Thinks" and "What Collin Writes" allows students to see the logical development of each answer.

Tactile Learners

Have students use three large rulers on a desk to model lines *k, l,* and *m.*

Teaching Tip

Point out that all of the information given in the theorem is used in the proof. Explain that this is normally the case when proving a theorem.

Error Prevention

Students may confuse the Corresponding Angles Postulate and its converse. Ask them to identify the hypotheses and conclusions of each.

Exercise

Have students work independently to complete the proof. Then have volunteers share with the class what they were thinking as they wrote each step. Elicit the fact that there are often different ways to complete a proof.

Read the problem below and then follow along with what Collin thinks as he solves the problem. Check your understanding by solving the exercise at the bottom of the page.

Copy and complete the paragraph proof of Theorem 3-5 for three coplanar lines.

If two lines are parallel to the same line, then they are parallel to each other.

Given: $\ell \parallel k$ and $m \parallel k$

Prove: $\ell \parallel m$

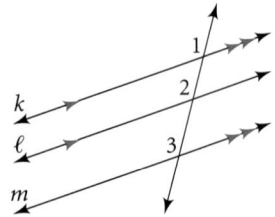

Proof: $\ell \parallel k$ means that $\angle 2 \cong \angle 1$ by the **a.** _?_ Postulate. $m \parallel k$ means that **b.** _?_ $\cong$ **c.** _?_ for the same reason. By the Transitive Property of Congruence, $\angle 2 \cong \angle 3$. By the **d.** _?_ Postulate, $\ell \parallel m$.

What Collin Thinks

Let's see. $\angle 1$ and $\angle 2$ are corresponding angles. If $\ell \parallel k$, then $\angle 1 \cong \angle 2$ by Postulate 3-1 on page 116.

Now I will use the fact that $m \parallel k$. So I'll ignore line ℓ. That leaves me with $\angle 1$ and $\angle 3$ to consider. These also are corresponding angles.

Now, $\angle 2 \cong \angle 3$ and they are corresponding angles. This fits the postulate in which the hypothesis is "corresponding angles are congruent." By Postulate 3-2 on page 122, I can conclude "the lines are parallel."

What Collin Writes

$\ell \parallel k$ means that $\angle 2 \cong \angle 1$ by the **a.** <u>Corresponding Angles</u> Postulate.

$m \parallel k$ means that **b.** <u>$\angle 1$</u> $\cong$ **c.** <u>$\angle 3$</u> for the same reason.

By the Transitive Property of Congruence, $\angle 2 \cong \angle 3$. By the **d.** <u>Converse of the Corresponding Angles</u> Postulate, $\ell \parallel m$.

EXERCISE

Copy and complete this paragraph proof of Theorem 3-5 for three coplanar lines.

If two lines are parallel to the same line, then they are parallel to each other.

Given: $q \parallel p$ and $p \parallel r$

Prove: $q \parallel r$

Proof: $q \parallel p$ means that $\angle 1 \cong \angle 2$ by the **a.** _?_ Theorem. **a. Alt. Int.** $\angle$
$p \parallel r$ means that **b.** _?_ $\cong$ **c.** _?_ by the Corresponding Angles Postulate. **b.** $\angle 2$ **c.** $\angle 3$
By the Transitive Property of Congruence, $\angle 1 \cong \angle 3$. By the **d.** _?_ Theorem, $q \parallel r$.
d. Conv. of the Alt. Int. $\angle$

3-3

Parallel Lines and the Triangle Angle-Sum Theorem

 North Carolina Objectives

2.03 Apply properties, definitions, and theorems of two-dimensional figures to solve problems and write proofs: a) Triangles.

Lesson Preview

What You'll Learn

 OBJECTIVE 1 To classify triangles and find the measures of their angles

OBJECTIVE 2 To use exterior angles of triangles

. . . And Why

To find the reclining angle of a lounge chair, as in Example 5

✓ Check Skills You'll Need

(For help, go to Lesson 1-4.)

Classify each angle as *acute*, *right*, **or** *obtuse*.

1.   right   2.   acute   3.   acute

 Algebra Solve each equation.

4. $30 + 90 + x = 180$ **60**   **5.** $55 + x + 105 = 180$ **20**

6. $x + 58 = 90$ **32**   **7.** $32 + x = 90$ **58**

New Vocabulary

- acute triangle   • right triangle   • obtuse triangle
- equiangular triangle   • equilateral triangle
- isosceles triangle   • scalene triangle
- exterior angle of a polygon   • remote interior angles

 Interactive lesson includes instant self-check, tutorials, and activities.

Lesson Preview

✓ Check Skills You'll Need

Finding Angle Measures
Lesson 1-4: Example 5
Exercises 23–25
Extra Practice, p. 690

Solving Linear Equations
Algebra Review, page 24
Examples 1, 2
Exercises 1–22

Lesson Resources

📁 **Teaching Resources**
Practice, Reteaching, Enrichment
Checkpoint Quiz 1

👥 **Reaching All Students**
Practice Workbook 3-3
Spanish Practice Workbook 3-3
Reading and Math Literacy 3B
Spanish Reading & Literacy 3B
Spanish Checkpoint Quiz 1
Technology Activities 48
Hands-On Activities 8
Informal Geometry Planning
  Guide 3-3

⏰ **Presentation Assistant Plus!**
Transparencies
- Check Skills You'll Need 3-3
- Additional Examples 3-3
- Student Edition Answers 3-3
- Lesson Quiz 3-3
PH Presentation Pro CD 3-3

ASSESSMENT SYSTEM

Checkpoint Quiz 1
Computer Test Generator CD

💰 **Technology**
Resource Pro® CD-ROM
Computer Test Generator CD
Prentice Hall Presentation Pro CD

💻 **www.PHSchool.com**
Student Site
- Teacher Web Code: afk-5500
- Self-grading Lesson Quiz
Teacher Center
- Lesson Planner
- Resources

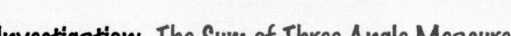

Investigation: The Sum of Three Angle Measures

- Draw and cut out a large triangle.

- Number the angles and tear them off.

- Place the three angles adjacent to each other to form one angle as shown in the figure at the right.

1. Compare your results with others. Write your observations. **The angle formed by the three angles is a straight angle.**

2. Make a conjecture about the sum of the measures of the angles of a triangle. **The sum of the measures of the angles of a triangle is 180.**

The diagrams in the Investigation suggest the Triangle Angle-Sum Theorem.

 Key Concepts

Theorem 3-7	**Triangle Angle-Sum Theorem**

The sum of the measures of the angles of a triangle is 180.

$$m\angle A + m\angle B + m\angle C = 180$$

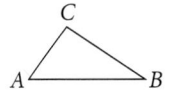

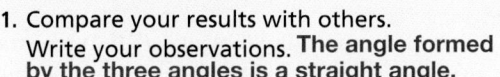 ## Ongoing Assessment and Intervention

Before the Lesson
Diagnose prerequisite skills using:
- Check Skills You'll Need

During the Lesson
Monitor progress using:
- Check Understanding
- Additional Examples
- Standardized Test Prep

After the Lesson
Assess knowledge using:
- Lesson Quiz
- Computer Test Generator CD
- Chapter Checkpoint 1 (p. 139)

Plus

2. Teach

Math Background

When alterations of Euclid's Parallel Postulate lead to different geometries, the Triangle Angle-Sum Theorem appears strikingly different. In a hyperbolic geometry, the sum of a triangle's angle measures is less than 180; in an elliptic geometry, the sum is greater than 180.

OBJECTIVE

⓵ Teaching Notes

Investigation (Optional)
Have students use geometry software to draw triangles and display the sum of their angles. Then have students manipulate the triangles and see that the sum remains 180.

English Learners
Tell students that acute, right, and obtuse *angles* can help them identify acute, right, and obtuse *triangles.* Have students prepare a chart that shows each new term with a definition and diagram to display in the classroom.

Teaching Tip
Each new lesson requires students to keep track of the names of more and more theorems, so shorthand ways to write their names can help students remember them. Point out that the symbol Σ is used in mathematics to indicate a sum. So, they could abbreviate the Triangle Angle-Sum Theorem as:

$$\triangle \angle \Sigma$$

⓵ EXAMPLE Error Prevention

Students may confuse angle measures with angle labels, thinking, for example, that ∠1 actually indicates 1°. Point out that the measure of an angle never immediately follows an angle symbol.

132

The following proof of Theorem 3-7 relies on the idea that through a point not on a given line you can draw a line parallel to the given line.

Proof

Proof of Theorem 3-7

Given: $\triangle ABC$

Prove: $m\angle A + m\angle B + m\angle 3 = 180$

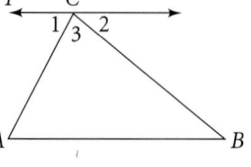

Proof: By the Protractor Postulate, you can draw $\overrightarrow{CP}$ so that $m\angle 1 = m\angle A$. Then, $\angle 1$ and $\angle A$ are congruent alternate interior angles, so $\overleftrightarrow{CP} \parallel \overline{AB}$. $\angle 2$ and $\angle B$ are also alternate interior angles, so by the Alternate Interior Angles Theorem, $m\angle 2 = m\angle B$. By substitution, $m\angle A + m\angle B + m\angle 3 = m\angle 1 + m\angle 2 + m\angle 3$, which is equal to 180 by the Angle Addition Postulate.

❓ Need Help?
Apply the Angle Addition Postulate twice to get $m\angle 1 + m\angle 2 + m\angle 3 = 180.$

1b. The sum of the measures of the ⦞ of a △ is 180. If you subtract the measure of the right ∠ from 180, you get 90. The sum of the other two ⦞ is 90, so they are comp.

① EXAMPLE Applying the Triangle Angle-Sum Theorem

Find $m\angle 1$.

$m\angle 1 + 35 + 65 = 180$	Triangle Angle-Sum Theorem
$m\angle 1 + 100 = 180$	Simplify.
$m\angle 1 = 80$	Subtract 100 from each side.

✓ **Check Understanding** ① **a.** $\triangle MNP$ is a right triangle. $\angle M$ is a right angle and $m\angle N$ is 58. Find $m\angle P$. **32**
b. Reasoning Explain why this statement must be true:
If a triangle is a right triangle, its acute angles are complementary. **See left.**

② EXAMPLE Using Algebra

Algebra Find the values of x, y, and z.

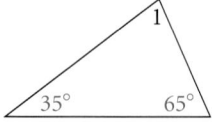

To find the value of x, use $\triangle GFJ$.

$39 + 65 + x = 180$	Triangle Angle-Sum Theorem
$104 + x = 180$	Simplify.
$x = 76$	Subtract 104 from each side.

To find the value of y, look at $\angle FJH$. It is a straight angle.

$m\angle GJF + m\angle GJH = 180$	Angle Addition Postulate
$x + y = 180$	Substitute.
$76 + y = 180$	Substitute 76 for x.
$y = 104$	Subtract 76 from each side.

To find the value of z, use $\triangle GJH$.

$21 + 104 + z = 180$	Triangle Angle-Sum Theorem
$125 + z = 180$	Simplify.
$z = 55$	Subtract 125 from each side.

✓ **Check Understanding** ② **Critical Thinking** Describe how you could use $\triangle GFH$ instead of $\triangle GJH$ to find the value of z. **For $\triangle GFH$, $65 + (39 + 21) + z = 180$. Then $125 + z = 180$ and $z = 55$.**

132   Chapter 3   Parallel and Perpendicular Lines

 **Reaching All Students**

Below Level Using geometry software to draw, measure, and manipulate the seven triangles at the top of page 133 will help students discover results such as the Isosceles Triangle Theorem.	**Advanced Learners** After Example 2, help students discover the Triangle Exterior Angle Theorem by finding x and y as sums of angles in the triangles. $x = 21° + 55°$, $y = 65° + 39°$	**English Learners** See note on page 132. **Auditory Learners** See note on page 133.

Real-World Connection

Four isosceles triangles cap the Smith Tower in Seattle.

In Chapter 1, you classified an angle by its measure. You can classify a triangle by its angles and sides.

 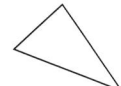 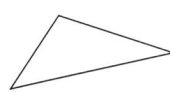

Equiangular
all angles congruent

Acute
all angles acute

Right
one right angle

Obtuse
one obtuse angle

 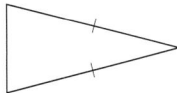 

Equilateral
all sides congruent

Isosceles
at least two sides congruent

Scalene
no sides congruent

3 EXAMPLE Classifying a Triangle

Classify the triangle by its sides and its angles.

At least two sides are congruent, so the triangle is isosceles. All the angles are acute, so the triangle is acute.

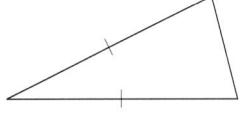

● The triangle is an acute isosceles triangle.

✔ Check Understanding

3 Draw and mark a triangle to fit each description. If no triangle can be drawn, write *not possible* and explain why. **a–c. See margin.**

a. acute scalene   **b.** isosceles right   **c.** obtuse equiangular

OBJECTIVE

2 Using Exterior Angles of Triangles

Reading Math

"Interior angle of a triangle" means the same as "angle of a triangle."

An **exterior angle of a polygon** is an angle formed by a side and an extension of an adjacent side. For each exterior angle of a triangle, the two nonadjacent interior angles are its **remote interior angles.**

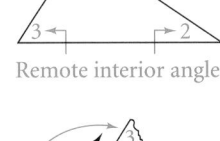

The diagram at the right suggests a relationship between an exterior angle and its two remote interior angles. Theorem 3-8 states this relationship. You will prove this theorem in Exercise 49.

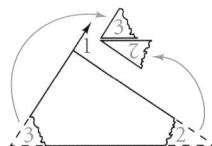

Key Concepts

Theorem 3-8	**Triangle Exterior Angle Theorem**

The measure of each exterior angle of a triangle equals the sum of the measures of its two remote interior angles.

$$m\angle 1 = m\angle 2 + m\angle 3$$

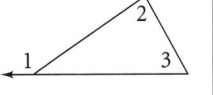

page 133 Check Understanding

3. **a.** 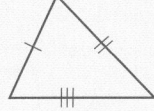   **b.**   **c.** Not possible; an equilateral △ has all acute ∠s.

---

2 EXAMPLE Alternative Method

Before finding any values, ask: *How many triangles are in the diagram?* **3** Use the question to highlight the alternate method of first finding the value of *z* using △*GFH*.

3 EXAMPLE Auditory Learners

Copy the triangles above Example 3 on the board for students to identify orally. Point out that *equi-* sounds like and means *equal*.

Math Tip

Students have not yet learned that a triangle is equilateral if and only if it is equiangular. As students see more triangles, encourage them to develop hypotheses about triangles, including what is impossible, such as an equilateral obtuse triangle.

Additional Examples

1 Find $m\angle Z$.

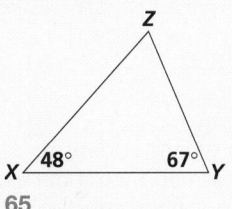

65

2 In triangle *ABC*, $\angle ACB$ is a right angle, and $\overline{CD} \perp \overline{AB}$. Find the values of *a*, *b*, and *c*.

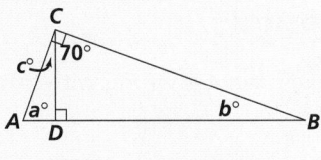

$a = 70, b = 20, c = 20$

3 Classify the triangle by its sides and its angles.

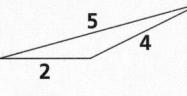

obtuse scalene

133

Tactile Learners

Encourage students to copy the triangle diagram shown immediately above the Triangle Exterior Angle Theorem. Have them cut out the exterior angle and two remote interior angles and then superimpose the interior angles over the exterior angle to demonstrate the Triangle Exterior Angle Theorem.

 EXAMPLE **Connection to Algebra**

Suggest that students let *x* represent the measure of the angle to help them associate the equations with more familiar algebraic equations.

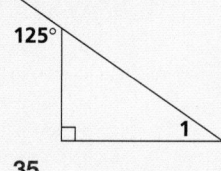 **Additional Examples**

④ Find $m\angle 1$.

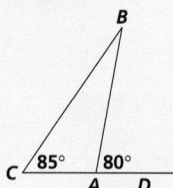
125°
35
1

⑤ Explain what happens to the angle formed by the back of the chair and the armrest as you make a lounge chair recline more. **The angle increases in measure.**

Closure

Explain what is wrong with this diagram.

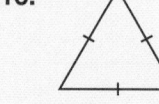
B
C 85° 80°
A D

$m\angle BAD$ **must be greater than** $m\angle BCA$.

pages 134–139 Exercises

16.

---

④ **EXAMPLE** Using the Exterior Angle Theorem

Algebra Find each missing angle measure.

a.
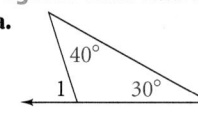
40°
1 30°

$m\angle 1 = 40 + 30$
$m\angle 1 = 70$

b.
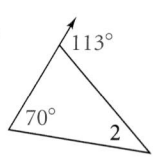
113°
70°
2

$113 = 70 + m\angle 2$
$43 = m\angle 2$

✔ **Check Understanding**

4b. If two acute ∠s of a △ are comp., then the △ is a right △. **True because the two comp. ∠s add to 90, leaving 90 for the third ∠.**

④ a. Find $m\angle 3$. **90**
b. **Critical Thinking** Give the converse of the statement in Check Understanding 1(b). State whether the converse is true. Explain.

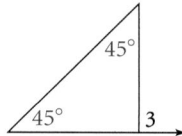
45°
45°
3

⑤ **EXAMPLE** Real-World  Connection

Furniture Design The lounge chair has different settings that change the angles formed by its parts. Suppose $m\angle 2$ is 32 and $m\angle 3$ is 81. Find $m\angle 1$, the angle formed by the back of the chair and the arm rest.

$m\angle 1 = m\angle 2 + m\angle 3$ **Exterior Angle Theorem**
$m\angle 1 = 32 + 81$ **Substitute.**
$m\angle 1 = 113$ **Simplify.**

The angle formed is a 113° angle.

✔ **Check Understanding**

⑤ a. Change the setting on the lounge chair so that $m\angle 2 = 33$ and $m\angle 3 = 97$. Find the new measure of $\angle 1$. **130**
b. Explain how you can find $m\angle 1$ *without* using the Exterior Angle Theorem.

Answers may vary. Sample: Find the measure of the third ∠ of the triangle. Subtract this from 180.

EXERCISES

For more practice, see *Extra Practice*.

Practice and Problem Solving

Ⓐ **Practice by Example**

Example 1
(page 132)

Find $m\angle 1$.

1.
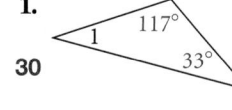
117°
1 33°
30

2.

52.2°
44.7° 1
83.1

3.
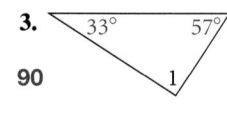
33° 57°
1
90

4. $\triangle RGT$ is a right triangle. $\angle G$ is a right angle and $m\angle R = 19$. Find $m\angle T$. **71**
5. $\triangle TNL$ is a right triangle. $\angle N$ is a right angle. Find $m\angle T + m\angle L$. **90**

17. **Not possible; a right △ will always have one longest side opp. the right ∠.**

18.
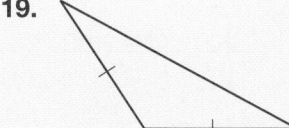

19.

Example 2 x^2 **Algebra Find the value of each variable.**
(page 132)

6.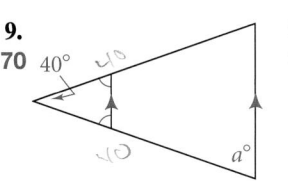
$x = 70;$
$y = 110;$
$z = 30$

7.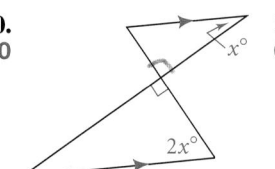
$t = 60;$
$w = 60$

8.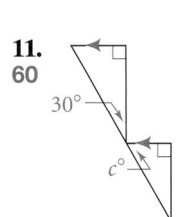
$x = 80; y = 80$

9.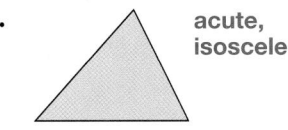
70

10.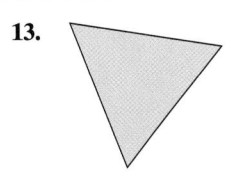
30

11.
60

Example 3 **Use a protractor and a centimeter ruler to measure the angles and the sides of each**
(page 133) **triangle. Classify each triangle by its angles and sides.**

12. 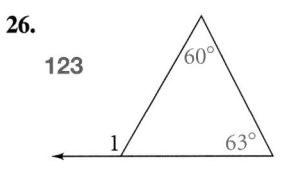 acute, isosceles

13. 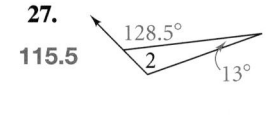 acute, equiangular, equilateral

14.  right, scalene

15. 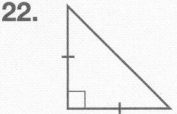 obtuse, isosceles

If possible, draw a triangle to fit each description. Mark the triangle to show known information. If no triangle can be drawn, write *not possible* and explain why.

16. acute equilateral   16–23. See margin

17. equilateral right
pp.134–135.

18. obtuse scalene

19. obtuse isosceles

20. scalene right

21. acute isosceles

22. isosceles right

23. scalene acute

Example 4 **24. a.** Which of the numbered angles at the
(page 134)   right are exterior angles? ∠5, ∠6, ∠8
b. ∠1 and ∠3 for ∠5   **b.** Name the remote interior angles for each.
∠1 and ∠2 for ∠6   **c.** How are exterior angles 6 and 8 related?
∠1 and ∠2 for ∠8   **They are ≅ vert. ∠s.**

25. a. How many exterior angles at the right
       are at each vertex of the triangle? **2**
    b. How many exterior angles does a triangle
       have in all? **6**

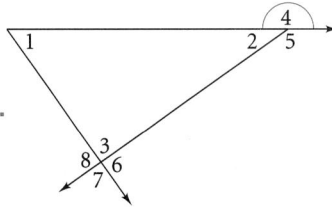

x^2 **Algebra Find each missing angle measure.**

26.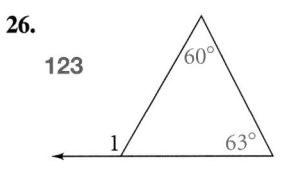
123

27.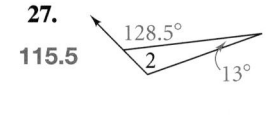
115.5

28.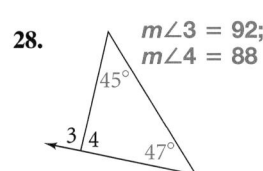
$m\angle 3 = 92;$
$m\angle 4 = 88$

20.    **21.** 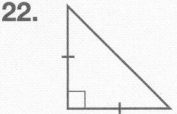   **22.**    **23.**

Assignment Guide

1 Objective
Ⓐ Ⓑ **Core** 1–23, 31–33, 37–40
Ⓒ **Extension** 56–61

2 Objective
Ⓐ Ⓑ **Core** 24–30, 34–36, 41–55
Ⓒ **Extension** 62, 63

Standardized Test Prep 64–69

Mixed Review 70–74

Exercise 7 Before students begin, ask: *What theorem relates angles t and w?* **Vert. Angles Th.**

Exercise 17 Discuss why this figure is impossible to draw. When students say that the side opposite the right angle is always longer than either of the other sides, point out that their observation is a theorem that the longest side of a triangle is always opposite the angle with the greatest measure.

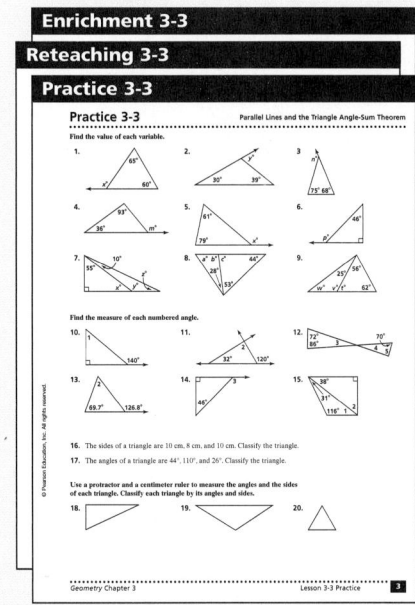

135

Connection to Music

Exercise 29 Ask students what other instruments can modify volume by blocking the escape of sound waves. For example, trumpets and trombones have "mutes" that block sound when inserted into the bells, and French horn players place their fists in the bells of their instruments to reduce the volume.

Exercises 31–36 Done together as a class, these exercises provide a good opportunity to review the cumulative knowledge of students. Ask students to justify their solutions step by step for the rest of the class, giving the names or descriptions of the theorems and postulates they use to find the angle measures.

Exercises 34, 35 Remind students to begin each problem by asking: *How many triangles are in the diagram?*

Example 5
(page 134)

29. **Music** The lid of a grand piano is held open by a prop stick whose length can vary, depending upon the effect desired. The longest prop stick makes angles as shown. What are the values of x and y? **$x = 147, y = 33$**

30. A short prop stick makes the angles shown below. What are the values of a and b? **$a = 162, b = 18$**

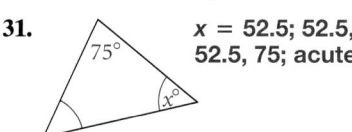

B **Apply Your Skills** x^2 **Algebra Find the values of the variables and then the measures of the angles. Classify each triangle by its angles. Note that some figures have more than one triangle.**

31. 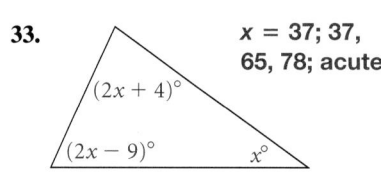 **$x = 52.5$; 52.5, 52.5, 75; acute**

32. 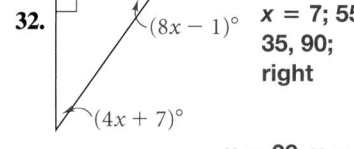 **$x = 7$; 55, 35, 90; right**

33. 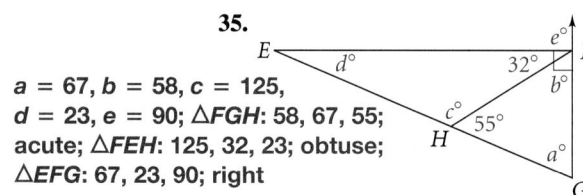 **$x = 37$; 37, 65, 78; acute**

34. 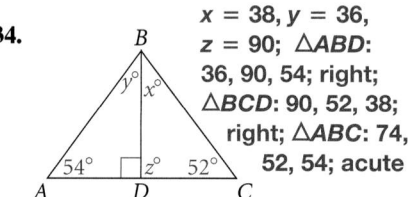 **$x = 38, y = 36, z = 90$; △ABD: 36, 90, 54; right; △BCD: 90, 52, 38; right; △ABC: 74, 52, 54; acute**

35.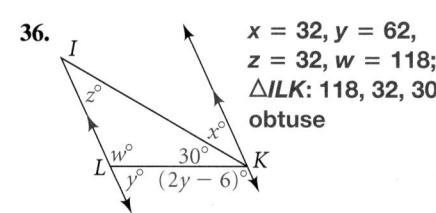

$a = 67, b = 58, c = 125, d = 23, e = 90$; △FGH: 58, 67, 55; acute; △FEH: 125, 32, 23; obtuse; △EFG: 67, 23, 90; right

36. 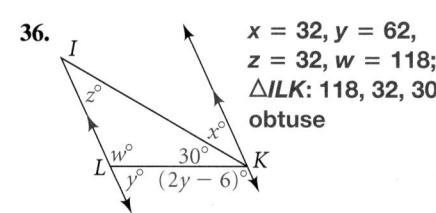 **$x = 32, y = 62, z = 32, w = 118$; △ILK: 118, 32, 30; obtuse**

37. **Reasoning** What is the measure of each angle of an equiangular triangle? Explain. **60; 180 ÷ 3 = 60**

38. **Writing** Is every equilateral triangle isosceles? Is every isosceles triangle equilateral? Explain. **See margin.**

Reading Math

In Exercise 39, two triangles are the same if you can move one onto the other.

39. **Visualization** The diagram shows a triangle on a 3-by-3 geoboard. How many different triangles can be made on this geoboard? Classify each triangle by its sides and angles. **See margin.**

40. The measure of one angle of a triangle is 115. The other two angles are congruent. Find their measures. **32.5**

41. Draw any triangle. Label it △ABC. Extend both sides of the triangle to form two exterior angles at vertex A. Use the two exterior angles to explain why it does not matter which side of a triangle is extended to form an exterior angle.

41. Check students' work. Answers may vary. Sample: The two exterior ∠ formed at vertex A are vertical ∠ and thus have the same measure.

pages 134–139 Exercises

38. Yes, an equilateral △ is isosc. because if three sides of a △ are ≅, then two sides are ≅. No, the third side of an isosc. △ does not need to be ≅ to the other two.

39. **eight**
Right isosceles

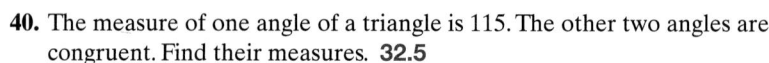

Acute isosceles

Obtuse scalene

Right scalene

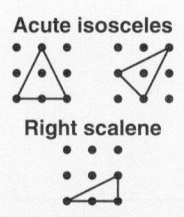

Need Help?

In Exercise 42, use x and $2x$ for the angle measures. In Exercise 43, use $2x$, $3x$, and $4x$.

$\boxed{x^2}$ **42. Algebra** A right triangle has acute angles whose measures are in the ratio 1 : 2. Find the measures of these angles. **30 and 60**

$\boxed{x^2}$ **43. a. Algebra** The ratio of the angle measures in $\triangle BCR$ is 2 : 3 : 4. Find the angle measures. **40, 60, 80**

   b. What type of triangle is $\triangle BCR$? **acute**

Use the figure at the right for Exercises 44–47.

44. Find $m\angle 5$ if $m\angle 3 = 130$ and $m\angle 4 = 30$. **160**

45. Find $m\angle 3$ if $m\angle 5 = 130$ and $m\angle 4 = 30$. **100**

46. Find $m\angle 1$ if $m\angle 5 = 142$ and $m\angle 4 = 65$. **103**

47. Find $m\angle 2$ if $m\angle 3 = 125$ and $m\angle 4 = 23$. **32**

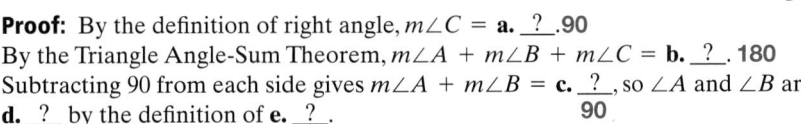

Proof 48. Developing Proof Complete the paragraph proof of the following statement.

The acute angles of a right triangle are complementary.

Given: $\triangle ABC$ with right angle C

Prove: $\angle A$ and $\angle B$ are complementary.

Proof: By the definition of right angle, $m\angle C = $ **a.** ? .**90**
By the Triangle Angle-Sum Theorem, $m\angle A + m\angle B + m\angle C = $ **b.** ? .**180**
Subtracting 90 from each side gives $m\angle A + m\angle B = $ **c.** ? , so $\angle A$ and $\angle B$ are
d. ? by the definition of **e.** ? . **90**
complementary   **comp. angles**

49. Developing Proof Complete this proof of the Triangle Exterior Angle Theorem by filling in the blanks.

Given: $\angle 1$ is an exterior angle of the triangle.

Prove: $m\angle 1 = m\angle 2 + m\angle 3$
   ∠ Add.
a. $m\angle 1 + m\angle 4 = 180$ by the ? Postulate.

b. $m\angle 2 + m\angle 3 + m\angle 4 = 180$ by the ? Theorem. **△ ∠-Sum**

c. $m\angle 1 + m\angle 4 = m\angle 2 + m\angle 3 + m\angle 4$ by the ? Property of Equality. **c. Trans.**

d. $m\angle 1 = m\angle 2 + m\angle 3$ by the ? Property of Equality.
   Subtr.

50. Reasoning Two angles of a triangle measure 64 and 48. Find the measure of the largest exterior angle. Explain. **See left.**

50. 132; since the missing ∠ is 68, the largest ext. ∠ is $180 - 48 = 132$.

Real-World Connection

Patricia Watson Tsinnie often uses isosceles triangles in her rug designs.

51. Open-Ended Study the design in the Navajo weaving below. Make a design of your own that makes repeated use of isosceles triangles. **Check students' work.**

Exercise 38 Relate the two questions to what students learned about conditionals and their converses in Chapter 2.

Alternative Method

Exercise 42 Point out that $\frac{1}{2}x$ and x also could represent the two angle measures. Although some students prefer not to use fractions, other students may find this representation more intuitive.

Exercise 43 To help students understand why $2x$, $3x$, and $4x$ are good representations of the angle measures, have students choose values for x and calculate the ratio of the angle measures.

Exercises 48, 49 Do these exercises on the board with the class to review proofs.

Diversity

Exercise 51 The textile art of some countries features patterns of triangles. Students may be able to describe, show photographs of, or bring in examples of such textiles.

Exercise 52 You may need to review for the class how to solve equations involving radicals.

Exercises 53–55 Suggest that students sketch the figures before attempting to find the measures.

Connection to Non-Euclidean Geometry

Exercise 56 In Euclidean geometry, the sum of the measures of the angles of a triangle is 180. Tell students that other courses in geometry study surfaces where the sum of the measures of the angles of a "triangle" is greater than or less than 180.

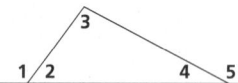
Lesson Quiz 3-3

1. A triangle with a 90° angle has sides that are 3 cm, 4 cm, and 5 cm long. Classify the triangle by its sides and angles. **scalene right triangle**

Use the diagram for Exercises 2–6.

2. Find $m\angle 3$ if $m\angle 2 = 70$ and $m\angle 4 = 42$. **68**

3. Find $m\angle 5$ if $m\angle 2 = 76$ and $m\angle 3 = 90$. **166**

4. Find x if $m\angle 1 = 4x$, $m\angle 3 = 2x + 28$, and $m\angle 4 = 32$. **30**

5. Find x if $m\angle 2 = 10x$, $m\angle 3 = 5x + 40$, and $m\angle 4 = 3x - 4$. **8**

6. Find $m\angle 3$ if $m\angle 1 = 125$ and $m\angle 5 = 160$. **105**

Alternative Assessment

Have students draw and label a triangle with an exterior angle at each vertex. They should measure and label each angle, classify the triangle, and then explain how the measurements illustrate the Triangle Angle-Sum Theorem and the Triangle Exterior Angle Theorem.

Standardized Test Prep

Resources

For additional practice with a variety of test item formats:
- Standardized Test Prep, p. 177
- Test-Taking Strategies, p. 172
- Test-Taking Strategies with Transparencies

Need Help?

In Exercise 52(a), the solution of $\sqrt{x} = 9$ is not $x = 3$.

 Challenge

56. **Greater than, because there are two ∠s with measure 90 where the meridians ⊥ the equator.**

52. The measures of the angles of $\triangle RST$ are $5\sqrt{x}$, $7\sqrt{x}$, and $8\sqrt{x}$.
    a. Find the value of x. **81**
    b. Give the measure of each angle. **45, 63, 72**
    c. What type of triangle is $\triangle RST$? **acute**

Find the measure of an angle formed by the bisectors of the indicated angles.

53. two angles of an equiangular triangle **120 or 60**

54. the acute angles of a right triangle **135 or 45**

55. two same-side interior angles formed by two parallel lines and a tranversal **90**

56. **Geometry on a Sphere** Suppose you are measuring the angles of a "triangle" on a globe. The meridians of longitude pass through both poles and are perpendicular to the equator. Will the sum of the measures of the angles of this triangle be equal to, greater than, or less than 180? Explain. **See left.**

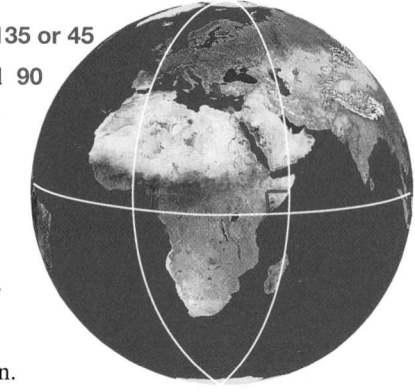

Probability **In Exercises 57–61, you know only what is given about the measures of the angles of a triangle. Find the probability that the triangle is equiangular.**

57. Each is a multiple of 30. $\frac{1}{3}$

58. Each is a multiple of 20. $\frac{1}{7}$

59. Each is a multiple of 60. **1**

60. Each is a multiple of 12. $\frac{1}{19}$

61. One is an obtuse angle of measure x. **0**

62. In the figure at the right, $\overline{CD} \perp \overline{AB}$ and $\overline{CD}$ bisects $\angle ACB$. Find $m\angle DBF$. **115**

63. What can you conclude about the bisector of an exterior angle of a triangle if the remote interior angles are congruent? Justify your response. **See margin.**

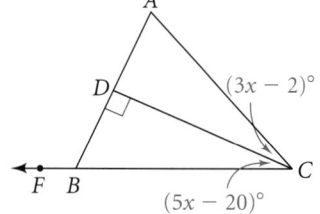

Standardized Test Prep

Multiple Choice

64. The measures of the angles of four triangles are shown. Which angle measures are *not* whole numbers? **B**
    A. a, $3a$, $2a$
    B. b, $3b$, $4b$
    C. c, $3c$, $5c$
    D. d, $3d$, $6d$

Use the diagram at the right for Exercises 65–67.

65. $m\angle M = 25$ and $m\angle L = 43$. What is $m\angle JKM$? **G**
    F. 18   G. 68   H. 117   I. 162

66. $m\angle M = 4x$, $m\angle L = 5x$, and $m\angle MKL = 6x$. What is $m\angle JKM$? **B**
    A. 72   B. 108   C. 120   D. 132

67. $m\angle JKM = 15x - 48$, $m\angle L = 5x + 12$, and $m\angle M = 40$. What is $m\angle MKL$? **H**
    F. 9   G. 57   H. 78   I. 97

pages 134–139
Exercises

63. Answers may vary. Sample: The measure of the ext. ∠ is = to the sum of the measures of the two remote int. ∠s. Since these ∠s are ≅, the ∠s formed by the bisector of the ext. ∠ are ≅ to each of them. Therefore, the bisector is ∥ to the included side of the remote ∠s by the Conv. of the Alt. Int. ∠s Thm.

68. A residential block is in the shape of a triangle. First Avenue, a side of the triangle, forms an exterior angle of measure $2x$ with one of the other sides. The remote interior angles measure $2x - 40$ and $x - 15$.
   a. Sketch and label the figure with the information in the problem.
   b. Write and solve an equation to determine the value of x. Then find the measures of the three interior angles. **a–b. See margin.**

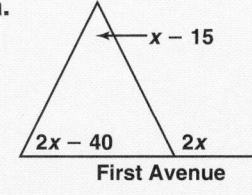

Take It to the NET
Online lesson quiz at **www.PHSchool.com**
Web Code: afa-0303

69. △*FYM* is an obtuse triangle. $m\angle F = 21$ and $\angle M$ is acute.
   a. What is the sum of $m\angle Y$ and $m\angle M$? Explain. **a–b. See margin.**
   b. What is the range of whole numbers for $m\angle M$? Justify your answer.

Mixed Review

Lesson 3-2 $\boxed{x^2}$ **Algebra Determine the value of x for which $a \parallel b$.**

70.
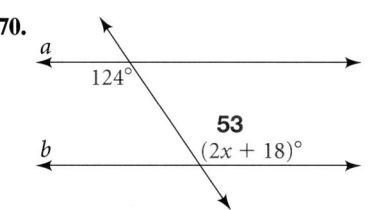
a
$124°$
53
b
$(2x + 18)°$

71.
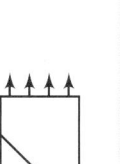
a b
$(3x - 2)°$ $44°$
46

Lesson 1-4 $\boxed{x^2}$ **72. Algebra** In the figure at the right, $m\angle AOB = 3x + 20, m\angle BOC = x + 32$, and $m\angle AOC = 80$. Find the value of x. **7**

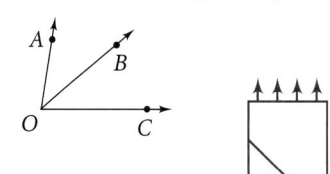

Lesson 1-1 **Draw the next figure in each sequence.**

73.
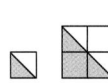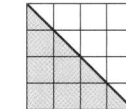

74.
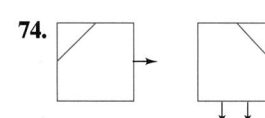

Checkpoint Quiz 1   Lessons 3-1 through 3-3

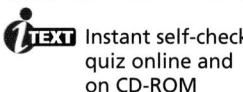 Instant self-check quiz online and on CD-ROM

Use the diagram at the right for Exercises 1–9. State the theorem or postulate that justifies each statement.

Corr. ∠ Postulate
1. $\angle 1 \cong \angle 3$

Conv. of Corr. ∠ Post.
2. If $\angle 5 \cong \angle 9$, then $d \parallel e$.

3. Same-Side Int. ∠ Thm.
3. $m\angle 1 + m\angle 2 = 180$

4. If $\angle 4 \cong \angle 7$, then $d \parallel e$.
4. Conv. of the Alt. Int. ∠ Thm.

5. $\angle 1 \cong \angle 4$
Vertical ∠ Theorem

6. $\angle 7 \cong \angle 9$
Alt. Int. ∠ Thm.

7. If $\angle 3 \cong \angle 8$, then $d \parallel e$.

8. $\angle 4 \cong \angle 5$
Corr. ∠ Postulate

9. If $m\angle 8 + m\angle 6 = 180$, then $d \parallel e$.
Conv. of Same-Side Int. ∠ Thm.

7. Converse of Corr. ∠ Postulate

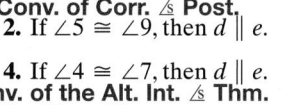

10. Find the measures of the angles of each triangle. Classify each triangle by its angles.
38, 55, 87; acute
55, 26, 99; obtuse

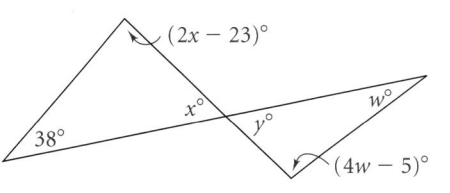
$(2x - 23)°$
$x°$ $y°$ $w°$
$38°$
$(4w - 5)°$

Lesson 3-3 Parallel Lines and the Triangle Angle-Sum Theorem **139**

---

68. **[2] a.**
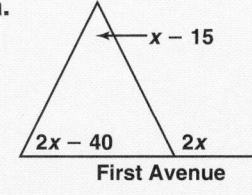
$x - 15$
$2x - 40$ $2x$
First Avenue

b. The correct equation is $2x = (2x - 40) + (x - 15)$ with the sol. $x = 55$. The three int. ∠ measure 70, 40, and 70.

[1] incorrect sketch, equation, OR solution

Exercise 64 This exercise requires knowledge of geometry, algebra, and arithmetic. Encourage students to write the sum of the angle measures of each triangle as an algebraic expression and then examine the coefficient of each expression.

Exercise 69 Have students draw and label a diagram before answering the questions.

✓ Chapter Checkpoint 1

To check understanding of Lessons 3-1 to 3-3:

Checkpoint Quiz 1 (p. 139)

📁 **Teaching Resources**
Checkpoint Quiz 1 (also in Prentice Hall Assessment System)

👥 **Reaching All Students**
Reading and Math Literacy 3B

Spanish versions available

---

69. **[2] a.** 159; the sum of the three ∠ of the △ is 180, so $m\angle Y + m\angle M + m\angle F = 180$. Since $m\angle F = 21$, $m\angle Y + m\angle M + 21 = 180$. Subtr. 21 from both sides results in $m\angle Y + m\angle M = 159$.

   b. 1 to 68; since $\angle Y$ is obtuse, its whole number range is from 91 to 158, allowing the measure of 1 for $m\angle M$ when $m\angle Y = 158$. When $m\angle Y = 91$, then $m\angle M = 68$.

[1] incorrect answer to part (a) or (b) OR incorrect computation in either part

139

 **Extension**

Exploring Spherical Geometry

Students may think that Euclidean geometry is the only geometry possible to study. This Extension shows how the basic ideas of point, line, and plane are defined on a sphere. Euclidean geometry is actually the first of many geometries students may encounter.

Resources

 Technology

Computer Test Generator CD-ROM: Chapter 0, Extension Topics

Teaching Notes

Tactile Learners

Have students slice an orange to model the intersection of a sphere and a plane.

1 EXAMPLE **Math Tip**

The order of postulates and theorems in this textbook is different from the order in which Euclid presented them.

2 EXAMPLE **Connection to History**

Sailors, explorers, and mapmakers rely on accurate measurements of longitude and latitude. Have students research the history of longitude measurement and how accurate methods were developed.

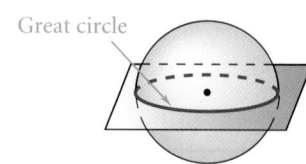

Extension # Exploring Spherical Geometry

FOR USE WITH LESSON 3-3

Euclidean geometry is the basis for high school geometry courses. Euclidean geometry is the geometry of flat planes, straight lines, and points. In spherical geometry a "plane" is the curved surface of a sphere and a "line" is a great circle. (A *great circle* is the intersection of a sphere and a plane that contains the center of the sphere.)

Great circle

1 EXAMPLE

Lines of latitude and longitude are used to identify positions on Earth. Which of these lines are great circles?

All lines of longitude are great circles. The equator is the only line of latitude that is a great circle. All other lines of latitude are circles smaller than a great circle.

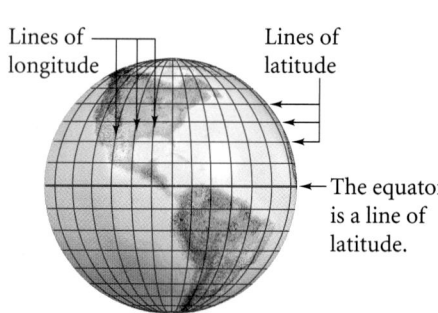

Lines of longitude — Lines of latitude

The equator is a line of latitude.

The lines of longitude all pass through the North and South Poles.

In Euclidean geometry,

Through a point not on a line, there is one and only one line parallel to the given line.

This statement is sometimes called Euclid's Parallel Postulate. Since only great circles are lines in spherical geometry, two lines always intersect. In spherical geometry, the Parallel Postulate is quite different:

Through a point not on a line, there is no line parallel to the given line.

2 EXAMPLE

The diagram at the right shows that any two lines on a sphere intersect at *two* points. What are the points of intersection of lines of longitude on Earth? What is special about these points?

Lines of longitude intersect at the North and South Poles. The poles are on a line that passes through the center of Earth. Thus, the poles lie on Earth's axis and are the endpoints of a diameter of Earth.

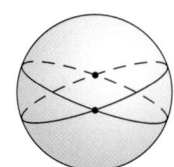

One result of Euclid's Parallel Postulate is the Triangle Angle-Sum Theorem of Lesson 3-3. Something quite different happens in spherical geometry as a result of the spherical-geometry Parallel Postulate.

3 EXAMPLE

If you hold a string taut between any two points on a sphere, you obtain an arc that is part of a great circle. Three such arcs form a triangle on the sphere. Determine the sum of the measures of the angles of each of the three triangles shown below.

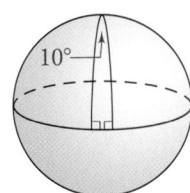 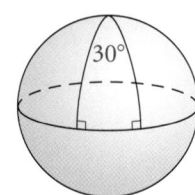 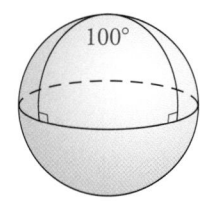

In the first triangle, the sum of the angle measures is 190. In the second triangle, it is 210, and in the third triangle the sum is 280.

EXERCISES

Draw a sketch to illustrate each property of spherical geometry. How does each property compare to what is true in Euclidean geometry?

1. There are pairs of points on a sphere through which more than one line can be drawn. **1–3. See right.**

2. A triangle can have more than one right angle.

3. You can draw two equiangular triangles such that they have different angle measures.

In Exercises 4 and 5, draw a counterexample to show that each of these properties of Euclidean geometry is *not* true in spherical geometry. **4–7. See margin.**

4. Two lines that are perpendicular to the same line do not intersect.

5. If two angles of one triangle are congruent to two angles of another triangle, then the third angles are congruent.

6. The figure at the right appears to show parallel lines on a sphere. Explain why this is not so.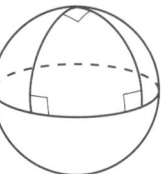

7. Explain why a piece of the top circle in the figure is *not* a line segment. (*Hint:* What must be true of line segments in spherical geometry?)

Each of the following statements is true in Euclidean geometry. Does it seem to be true in spherical geometry? Make figures on a globe, ball, or balloon to support your answer. **8–9. See margin.**

8. Vertical angles are congruent.

9. Through a point on a line ℓ there exists one and only one line perpendicular to ℓ.

1. Answers may vary. Sample:

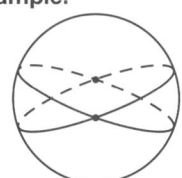

In Euclidean geometry, there is only one line through two points.

2. Answers may vary. Sample:

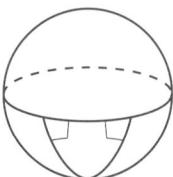

In Euclidean geometry, a triangle can have at most one right ∠.

3. Answers may vary. Sample:

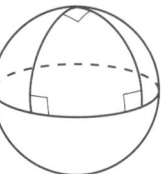

In Euclidean geometry, the only possible equiangular triangle has 60° ⦟.

---

pages 140–141   Extension

4–5. Answers may vary. Samples are given:

4.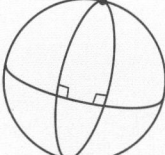

5.

∠ADB ≇ ∠ADC

3 EXAMPLE   Teaching Tip

By slicing an orange in half through the center and then slicing each half again through the center into four equal parts, students can form eight pieces of orange whose skins model spherical triangles. Ask: *How many degrees are there in each triangle?* 270

Visual Learners

If there is a globe in the classroom, suggest that students use it to help them answer the exercises.

Inclusion

Exercises 1–3 Allow visually-impaired students to trace their fingers over a globe to illustrate the properties.

6. At least one of the 2 curves is not a great circle, so it is not a line.

7. The top circle is not a line, so a piece of the top circle cannot be a line segment.

8. true

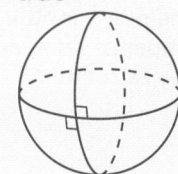

9. true

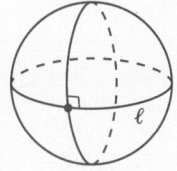

Technology Exterior Angles of Polygons

Technology

Exterior Angles of Polygons

Students will use geometry software to investigate the exterior angles of polygons. They are encouraged to make a conjecture that will be presented in Lesson 3-4 as the Polygon Exterior Angle-Sum Theorem, as well as a conjecture about which regular polygons will tessellate that will be discussed in Chapter 12.

Resources

Students may use any geometry software program to explore the exterior angles of polygons.

Teaching Notes

Geometry software enables students to manipulate the sides and angles of a polygon while calculating the sum of its exterior angles. They can observe that the sum remains constant for all sizes and shapes of polygons.

Error Prevention

The diagrams show only one exterior angle at each vertex. Make sure that students realize that they should measure only one of the two exterior angles at each vertex of a polygon.

Teaching Tip

Emphasize to students that their findings apply to all polygons. After students complete Exercise 2, survey the class to find the polygons they chose, the number of sides, and what sums they calculated.

Construct

Use geometry software. Construct a polygon similar to the one at the right. Extend each side as shown. To measure the exterior angles you will need to mark a point on each ray.

Investigate

- Measure each exterior angle.
- Calculate the sum of the measures of the exterior angles.
- Manipulate the polygon. Observe the sum of the measures of the exterior angles.

EXERCISES

1. Write a conjecture about the sum of the measures of the exterior angles (one at each vertex) of a convex polygon. **The sum of the measures of the exterior ∠s of a convex polygon is always 360.**
2. Test your conjecture with another polygon. **Check students' work.**

Extend

3. The figures below show a polygon that is decreasing in size until finally it becomes a point. Describe how you could use this to justify your conjecture in Exercise 2. **The sum of the measures of the five ∠s meeting at one point is 360.**

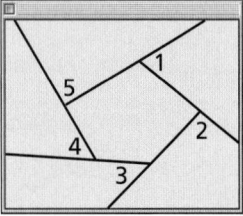 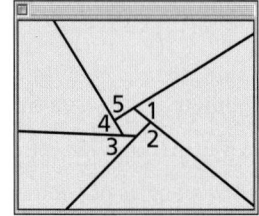 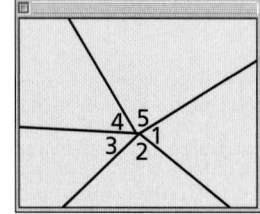

4. The figure at the right shows a square that has been copied several times. Notice that you can use the square to completely cover, or tile, a plane, without gaps or overlaps.

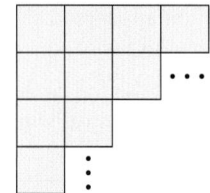

   a. Using geometry software, create several copies of other regular polygons with 3, 5, 6, and 8 sides. Regular polygons have sides of equal length and angles of equal measure. **Check students' work.**
   b. Which of the polygons you created can tile a plane? **Polygons with 3 and 6 sides can tile a plane.**
   c. Measure *one* exterior angle of each polygon (including the square). **120, 90, 72, 60, 45**
   d. Write a conjecture about the relationship between the measure of an exterior angle and your ability to tile a plane with a regular polygon. **d. To tile a plane, the exterior ∠ measure must be divisible by 30.**
   e. Test your conjecture with another regular polygon. **Check students' work.**

3-4

The Polygon Angle-Sum Theorems

North Carolina Objectives

2.03 Apply properties, definitions, and theorems of two-dimensional figures to solve problems and write proofs: c) Other polygons.

Lesson Preview

What You'll Learn

OBJECTIVE 1 To classify polygons

OBJECTIVE 2 To find the sums of the measures of the interior and exterior angles of polygons

. . . And Why

To find the measure of an angle of a triangle used in packaging, as in Example 5

✓ Check Skills You'll Need

(For help, go to Lessons 1-4 and 3-3.)

Find the measure of each angle of quadrilateral *ABCD*.

1. See below.

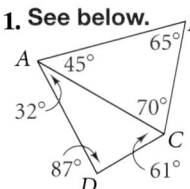

2.

$m\angle D = m\angle B = 60;$
$m\angle DAB = m\angle DCB = 120$

3. See below.

New Vocabulary • polygon • convex polygon • concave polygon
• equilateral polygon • equiangular polygon
• regular polygon

1. $m\angle DAB = 77; m\angle B = 65;$
$m\angle BCD = 131; m\angle D = 87$

3. $m\angle A = 70; m\angle ABC = 85;$
$m\angle C = 125; m\angle ADC = 80$

iTEXT Interactive lesson includes instant self-check, tutorials, and activities.

OBJECTIVE

1 Classifying Polygons

Real-World ● Connection

Polygons create striking designs on a soccer ball.

A **polygon** is a closed plane figure with at least three sides that are segments. The sides intersect only at their endpoints, and no adjacent sides are collinear.

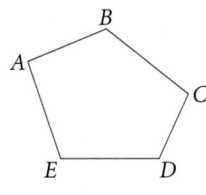

A polygon

Not a polygon; not a closed figure

Not a polygon; two sides intersect between endpoints.

To name a polygon, start at any vertex and list the vertices consecutively in a clockwise or counterclockwise direction.

1 EXAMPLE Naming Polygons

Name the polygon. Then identify its vertices, sides, and angles.

Two names for this polygon are *DHKMGB* and *MKHDBG*.
vertices: D, H, K, M, G, B
sides: $\overline{DH}, \overline{HK}, \overline{KM}, \overline{MG}, \overline{GB}, \overline{BD}$
angles: $\angle D, \angle H, \angle K, \angle M, \angle G, \angle B$

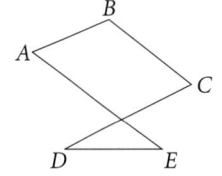

✓ Check Understanding **1** Three polygons are pictured at the right. Name each polygon, its sides, and its angles. **See margin, p.145.**

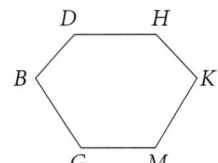

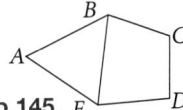

Ongoing Assessment and Intervention

Before the Lesson
Diagnose prerequisite skills using:
• Check Skills You'll Need

During the Lesson
Monitor progress using:
• Check Understanding
• Additional Examples
• Standardized Test Prep

After the Lesson
Assess knowledge using:
• Lesson Quiz
• Computer Test Generator CD

---

1. Plan

Lesson Preview

✓ Check Skills You'll Need

Using the Angle Addition Postulate
Lesson 1-4: Example 6
Exercises 27, 28
Extra Practice, p. 690

Finding Angle Measures in Triangles
Lesson 3-3: Example 1
Exercises 1–3
Extra Practice, p. 692

Lesson Resources

Teaching Resources
Practice, Reteaching, Enrichment

Reaching All Students
Practice Workbook 3-4
Spanish Practice Workbook 3-4
Hands-On Activities 9
Informal Geometry Planning
  Guide 3-4

Presentation Assistant Plus!
Transparencies
• Check Skills You'll Need 3-4
• Additional Examples 3-4
• Student Edition Answers 3-4
• Lesson Quiz 3-4
PH Presentation Pro CD 3-4

ASSESSMENT SYSTEM

Computer Test Generator CD

Technology
Resource Pro® CD-ROM
Computer Test Generator CD
Prentice Hall Presentation Pro CD

www.PHSchool.com
Student Site
• Teacher Web Code: afk-5500
• Self-grading Lesson Quiz
Teacher Center
• Lesson Planner
• Resources

Plus **iTEXT**

143

Math Background

Because each interior angle of a regular *n*-gon measures $\frac{180(n-2)}{n}$, one can readily find the set of all regular *n*-gons that tessellate a plane. Combinations of regular polygons that tessellate a plane can likewise be found with a bit more work and application of some straightforward number theory.

 **Teaching Notes**

English Learners

Some students may not know the meaning of *adjacent sides* in the definition of a polygon. Point out that adjacent sides share a vertex just as adjacent angles share a side.

① EXAMPLE Math Tip

Remind students that there are also different ways to name sides and angles in this example. Ask: *What is another name for* $\overline{HK}$? $\overline{KH}$ *What is another name for* ∠*M*? ∠*KMG* *or* ∠*GMK*

Connection to Science

The study of optics teaches that a convex lens causes rays of light to come together and that a concave lens causes rays of light to spread apart. Convex lenses are used in microscopes and telescopes. Eyeglasses may be either convex or concave.

Teaching Tip

Students may want to know that a seven-sided polygon is called a *heptagon*.

Visual Learners

To help students learn the names of polygons, have small groups make charts to be displayed in the classroom with the name of each polygon, its number of sides, and an appropriate figure.

You can classify a polygon by the number of sides it has. The table at the right shows the names of some common polygons.

Polygons are classified as convex or concave.

Sides	Name
3	triangle
4	quadrilateral
5	pentagon
6	hexagon
8	octagon
9	nonagon
10	decagon
12	dodecagon
n	*n*-gon

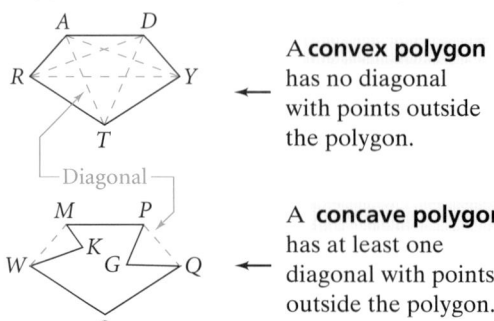

? Need Help?

A diagonal of a polygon is a segment that connects two nonconsecutive vertices.

A **convex polygon** has no diagonal with points outside the polygon.

A **concave polygon** has at least one diagonal with points outside the polygon.

In this textbook, a polygon is convex unless stated otherwise.

② EXAMPLE Real-World Connection

Tilework The tilework in the photo is a combination of different polygons that form a pleasing pattern. Classify the polygon outlined in red by using the table above. Then classify the polygon as convex or concave.

The polygon outlined in red has 6 sides. Therefore, it is a hexagon.

No diagonal of the hexagon contains points outside the hexagon. The hexagon is convex.

✓ **Check Understanding** ② Classify each polygon by its sides. Identify each as convex or concave.

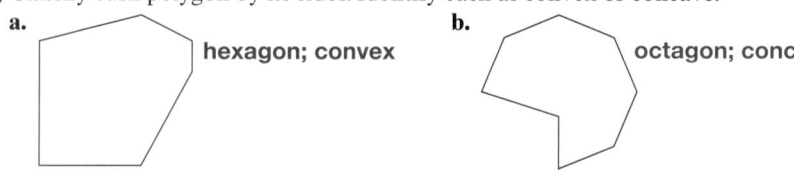

a. **hexagon; convex**

b. **octagon; concave**

c. the 12-pointed star at the center of the tilework pictured above **24-gon; concave**

👥 Reaching All Students

Below Level Have students draw a polygon on paper and cut out the exterior angles. By placing the angles so that they are adjacent, students can verify Theorem 3-10.	**Advanced Learners** Have students do the Investigation, discuss whether Theorem 3-9 applies to *concave* *n*-gons, and justify their reasoning.	**English Learners** See note at left. **Visual Learners** See note at left.

Investigation: The Sum of Polygon Angle Measures

You can use triangles and the Triangle Angle-Sum Theorem to find the sum of the measures of the angles of a polygon. Record your data in a table like the one begun below.

Polygon	Number of Sides	Number of Triangles Formed	Sum of the Interior Angle Measures
	4	■	■ • 180 = ■

- Sketch polygons with 4, 5, 6, 7, and 8 sides.

- Divide each polygon into triangles by drawing all diagonals that are possible from one vertex.

- Multiply the number of triangles by 180 to find the sum of the measures of the angles of each polygon.

See back of book.

1. Look for patterns in the table. Describe any that you find.

2. **Inductive Reasoning** Write a rule for the sum of the measures of the angles of an *n*-gon. **The sum of the measures of the angles of an *n*-gon is $(n - 2) \cdot 180$.**

Reading Math

An *n*-gon is a polygon with *n* sides, where *n* can be 3, 4, 5, 6, . . .

By dividing a polygon with *n* sides into *n* − 2 triangles, you can show that the sum of the measures of the angles of any polygon is a multiple of 180.

Key Concepts

Theorem 3-9	Polygon Angle-Sum Theorem
The sum of the measures of the angles of an *n*-gon is $(n - 2)180$.	

3 EXAMPLE Finding a Polygon Angle Sum

Find the sum of the measures of the angles of a 15-gon.

For a 15-gon, $n = 15$.

$\text{Sum} = (n - 2)180$	Polygon Angle-Sum Theorem
$= (15 - 2)180$	Substitute.
$= 13 \cdot 180$	Simplify.
$= 2340$	

The sum of the measures of the angles of a 15-gon is 2340.

✓ Check Understanding **3 a.** Find the sum of the measures of the angles of a 13-gon. **1980**
b. Critical Thinking The sum of the measures of the angles of a given polygon is 720. How can you use Sum = $(n - 2)180$ to find the number of sides in the polygon? **You can solve the equation $(n - 2)180 = 720$.**

You will sometimes use algebra with the Polygon Angle-Sum Theorem to find measures of polygon angles.

Lesson 3-4   The Polygon Angle-Sum Theorems   **145**

page 143   Check Understanding

1. *ABE*; sides: $\overline{AB}$, $\overline{BE}$, $\overline{EA}$; angles: ∠*A*, ∠*ABE*, ∠*BEA*

BCDE; sides: $\overline{BC}$, $\overline{CD}$, $\overline{DE}$, $\overline{EB}$; ⚠: ∠*EBC*, ∠*C*, ∠*D*, ∠*DEB*

ABCDE; sides: $\overline{AB}$, $\overline{BC}$, $\overline{CD}$, $\overline{DE}$, $\overline{EA}$; ⚠: ∠*A*, ∠*ABC*, ∠*C*, ∠*D*, ∠*AED*

Additional Examples

1 Name the polygon. Then identify its vertices, sides, and angles.

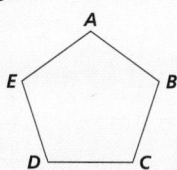

ABCDE; vertices: *A, B, C, D, E*; sides: $\overline{AB}$, $\overline{BC}$, $\overline{CD}$, $\overline{DE}$, $\overline{EA}$; angles: ∠*A*, ∠*B*, ∠*C*, ∠*D*, ∠*E*

2 Classify the polygon below by its sides. Identify it as convex or concave. **dodecagon; concave**

OBJECTIVE
2 Teaching Notes

Investigation (Optional)
Have students work in pairs to draw polygons and display the sum of their angles using geometry software. Have students manipulate the polygons to see that the sum remains constant.

Alternative Method
Students can use inductive reasoning to write the sum of the measures of the angles of an *n*-gon as $180n - 360$. Have them draw a hexagon and segments from an interior point to each vertex. Ask: *How many triangles are there?* **6** *What is the sum of the angle measures of all the triangles?* **$180 \cdot 6$, or 1080** *What is the sum of the angle measures of the triangles drawn from an interior point to the vertices of a polygon with* n *sides?* **$180n$** Point out that the sum of the angle measures around the interior point is 360. Discuss why 360 must then be subtracted from $180n$.

3 EXAMPLE Error Prevention

Some students may think the answer should be $15 \cdot 180$. Review the investigation to correct them.

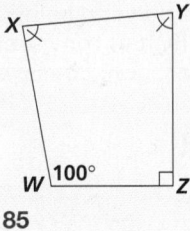
Point out that the angles of a polygon can be called *interior* angles. Also point out that the exterior angles of a regular polygon are congruent.

Additional Examples

3 Find the sum of the measures of the angles of a decagon. **1440**

4 Find $m\angle X$ in quadrilateral *XYZW*.

85

5 Explain how you know that all the angles labeled $\angle 1$ in Example 5 have equal measures. **Sample: Because the hexagon is regular, all its angles are congruent. An exterior angle is the supplement of a polygon's angles, and supplements of congruent angles all have the same measure.**

Closure

If the sum of the interior angles of a polygon equals the sum of the exterior angles, what is the name of the polygon? **quadrilateral** If each exterior angle of a regular polygon measures 30, how many sides does the polygon have? **12**

---

4 EXAMPLE **Using the Polygon Angle-Sum Theorem**

Algebra Find $m\angle Y$ in pentagon *TVYMR* at the right. Use the Polygon Angle-Sum Theorem for $n = 5$.

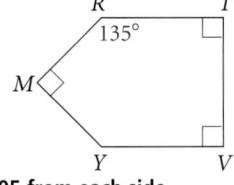

$$m\angle T + m\angle V + m\angle Y + m\angle M + m\angle R = (5 - 2)180$$

$90 + 90 + m\angle Y + 90 + 135 = 540$ **Substitute.**

$m\angle Y + 405 = 540$ **Simplify.**

$m\angle Y = 135$ **Subtract 405 from each side.**

✔ **Check Understanding** **4** Pentagon *ABCDE* has 5 congruent angles. Find the measure of each angle. **108**

You can draw exterior angles at any vertex of a polygon. The figures below show that the sum of the measures of the exterior angles, one at each vertex, is 360. This can be proved as a theorem in a way suggested in Exercise 46.

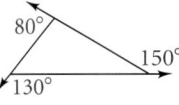 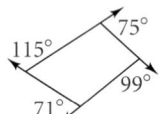 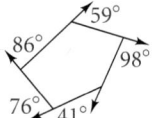

$80 + 150 + 130 = 360$ $115 + 75 + 99 + 71 = 360$ $86 + 59 + 98 + 41 + 76 = 360$

Key Concepts

Theorem 3-10	Polygon Exterior Angle-Sum Theorem

The sum of the measures of the exterior angles of a polygon, one at each vertex, is 360.

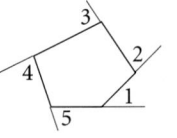

For the pentagon,
$$m\angle 1 + m\angle 2 + m\angle 3 + m\angle 4 + m\angle 5 = 360.$$

An **equilateral polygon** has all sides congruent. An **equiangular polygon** has all angles congruent. A **regular polygon** is both equilateral and equiangular.

5 EXAMPLE **Real-World** 🌐 **Connection**

Packaging The game board at the left has the shape of a regular hexagon. It is packaged in a rectangular box outlined beneath it. The box uses four right triangles made of foam in its four corners. Find $m\angle 1$ in each foam triangle.

Method 1 Find the measure of an angle of the hexagon first.

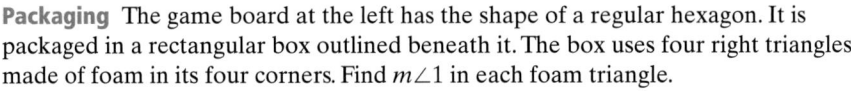

• A regular hexagon has 6 sides and 6 congruent angles.
  The sum of the measures of the interior angles $= (6 - 2)180$, or 720.

• The measure of one interior angle is $\frac{720}{6}$, or 120.

• The measure of its adjacent exterior angle, $\angle 1$, is $180 - 120$, or 60.

Method 2 Find the measure of an exterior angle directly.

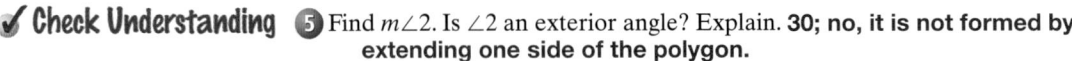

• The sum of the measures of the exterior angles is 360.

• The measure of one exterior angle, $\angle 1$, is $\frac{360}{6}$, or 60.

✔ **Check Understanding** **5** Find $m\angle 2$. Is $\angle 2$ an exterior angle? Explain. **30; no, it is not formed by extending one side of the polygon.**

EXERCISES

Practice and Problem Solving

For more practice, see *Extra Practice*.

Ⓐ **Practice by Example**

Example 1
(page 143)

Is the figure a polygon? If not, tell why.

4. No; two sides intersect between endpoints.

1.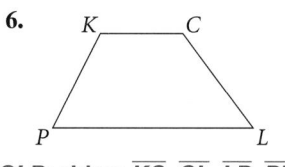
yes

2.
No; it has no sides.

3.
No; it is not a plane figure.

4.

5. *MWBFX*; sides: $\overline{MW}$, $\overline{WB}$, $\overline{BF}$, $\overline{FX}$, $\overline{XM}$; ⦟: ∠M, ∠W, ∠B, ∠F, ∠X

7. *HEPTAGN*; sides: $\overline{HE}$, $\overline{EP}$, $\overline{PT}$, $\overline{TA}$, $\overline{AG}$, $\overline{GN}$, $\overline{NH}$; ⦟: ∠H, ∠E, ∠P, ∠T, ∠A, ∠G, ∠N

Name each polygon by its vertices. Then identify its sides and angles.

5.

6.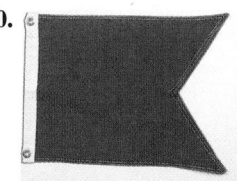
KCLP; sides: $\overline{KC}$, $\overline{CL}$, $\overline{LP}$, $\overline{PK}$; ⦟: ∠K, ∠C, ∠L, ∠P

7.

Example 2
(page 144)

Find a polygon in each photograph. Classify the polygon by its number of sides. Tell whether the polygon is convex or concave.

8.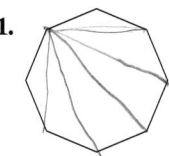
pentagon; convex

9.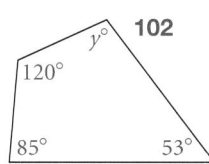
decagon; concave

10.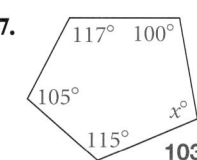
pentagon; concave

Example 3
(page 145)

Find the sum of the measures of the angles of each polygon.

11. 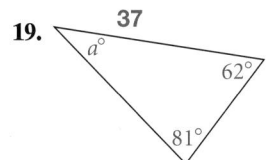 1080

12. dodecagon **1800**

13. decagon **1440**

14. 20-gon **3240**

15. 1002-gon **180,000**

Example 4 x^2 **Algebra** **Find the missing angle measures.**
(page 146)

16. 102

17. 103

18. 145

19. 37

20. 60, 60, 120, 120

21. 113, 119

Example 5
(page 146)

Find the measures of an interior angle and an exterior angle of each regular polygon.

22. pentagon
108; 72

23. dodecagon
150; 30

24. 18-gon
160; 20

25. 100-gon
176.4; 3.6

Lesson 3-4   The Polygon Angle-Sum Theorems   **147**

Assignment Guide

▼**1** Objective
  Ⓐ Ⓑ Core 1–10, 36, 50–53
  Ⓒ Extension 60–63

▼**2** Objective
  Ⓐ Ⓑ Core 11–35, 37–49, 54–56
  Ⓒ Extension 57–59

Standardized Test Prep 64–70

Mixed Review 71–86

Exercises 8–10 Point out that it is usually easier to count vertices than sides of a polygon. Because the number of vertices and sides are equal, either method is acceptable.

Connection to Language Arts
Exercises 12, 13 Point out that the two polygons differ only in the prefix *do-*, which means "two." By adding it and the prefix *deca-*, which means "ten," you get 2 + 10 = 12.

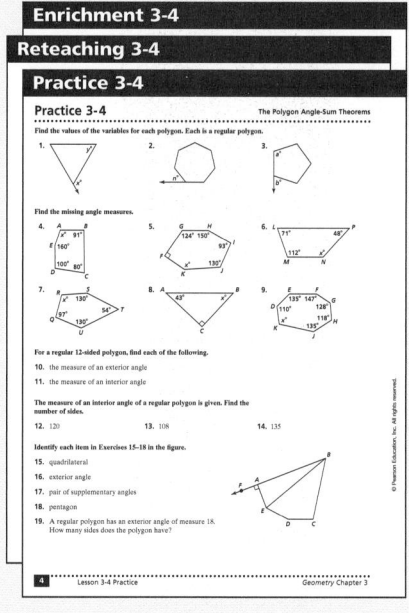

Exercise 37 Have students investigate the shapes of sports stadiums and report how polygons are used in designing them.

Exercise 38 If necessary, review how to solve equations with a variable in the denominator. Remind students that this is a *regular* polygon.

Exercise 44 After students solve this exercise, ask: *What must be true about* x? x is a factor of 360; because n ≥ 3, x ≤ 120.

Exercise 48 This is a good exercise to do together as a class.

Exercise 57 This would be a nice classroom exercise using the table feature of a graphing calculator with overhead display.

Exercise 58 Part b introduces the idea of the asymptote of a function, which students will encounter in their next algebra course.

Packaging The nut container at the right has the shape of a regular octagon. It fits in a square box. A cheese wedge fills each corner of the box.

26. Find the measure of each angle of a cheese wedge. 45, 45, 90

27. 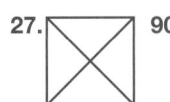 90

27. Critical Thinking Show how to rearrange the four pieces of cheese to make a regular polygon. What is the measure of each angle of the polygon? **See left.**

 **B** **Apply Your Skills**

Use a protractor. Sketch each type of regular polygon.

Sample: dodecagon

Use the protractor to equally space 12 points around a circle. (360° ÷ 12 = 30°, so mark a point every 30°.) Connect these points to form a regular dodecagon. **28–31. See margin.**

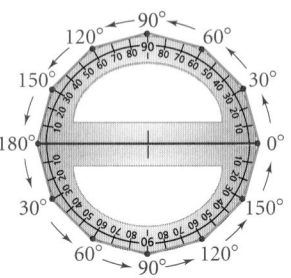

28. triangle   **29.** quadrilateral

30. hexagon   **31.** octagon

The sum of the measures of the angles of a polygon with *n* sides is given. Find *n*.

32. 180 3   **33.** 1080 8   **34.** 1980 13   **35.** 2880 18

36. To name each figure below, use as many of the letters $A, B, C, \ldots$, as you need, in order, starting with A. For each figure, how many letters do you need? With this labeling, how many different ways can you name the figure?
  a. a triangle 3; 6   **b.** a quadrilateral 4; 8   **c.** a pentagon 5; 10

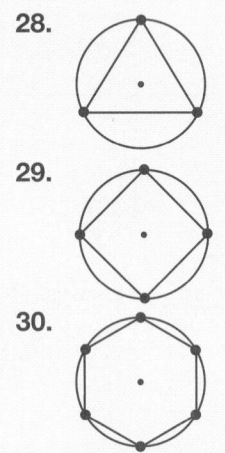

Real-World Connection

At a theater-in-the-round, seats are arranged so the audience surrounds the stage.

37. Stage Design The diagram at the right shows platforms constructed for a theater-in-the-round stage. Describe the largest platform by the type of regular polygon it suggests. Find the measure of each numbered angle.
octagon; $m\angle 1 = 135$; $m\angle 2 = 45$

38. Error Analysis Miles said that he measured an angle of a regular polygon to be 130°. Explain why this result is impossible. If you solve $\frac{(n-2)180}{n} = 130$, you get $n = 7.2$. This number is not an integer.

39. Critical Thinking A triangle has two congruent angles and an exterior angle with measure 100. Find two possible sets of measures for the angles of the triangle. 20-80-80; 50-50-80

The measure of an exterior angle of a regular polygon is given. Find the measure of an interior angle, and find the number of sides.

40. 72 108; 5   **41.** 36 144; 10   **42.** 18 162; 20   **43.** 30 150; 12   **44.** x $180 - x$; $\frac{360}{x}$

45. Probability Find the probability that the measure of an angle of a regular *n*-gon is a positive integer if *n* is an integer and $3 \le n \le 12$. $\frac{4}{5}$

x^2 **46. Algebra** A polygon has *n* sides. An interior angle of the polygon and an adjacent exterior angle form a straight angle.
  a. What is the sum of the measures of the *n* straight angles? $n \cdot 180$
  b. What is the sum of the measures of the *n* interior angles? $(n-2)180$
  c. Using your answers above, what is the sum of the measures of the *n* exterior angles? $180n - 180(n-2) = 360$
  d. What theorem do the steps above lead to? **Polygon Ext. ∠-Sum Thm.**

148   Chapter 3   Parallel and Perpendicular Lines

pages 147–150 Exercises

28.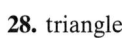

29.

30.

31.

57. a. (20, 162), (40, 171), (60, 174), (80, 175.5), (100, 176.4), (120, 177), (140, 177.4), (160, 177.8), (180, 178), (200, 178.2)

c. It is very close to 180.

d. No, two sides cannot be collinear.

58. b. As *n* gets larger, the size of the angles get closer to 180. The more sides it has, the closer the polygon is to a circle.

48. $w = 72$, $x = 59$, $y = 49$, $z = 121$; △

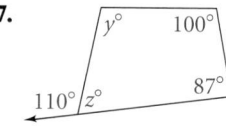 **Algebra** Find each missing angle measure. Then name the polygon.

47.

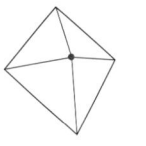

$y = 103$; $z = 70$; quad.

48.

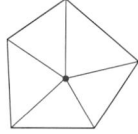

49.

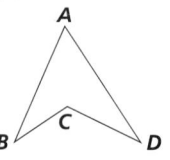

$x = 36$, $2x = 72$, $3x = 108$, $4x = 144$; quad.

For Exercises 1 and 2, if the figure is a polygon, name it by its vertices and identify its sides. If the figure is not a polygon, explain why not.

1.

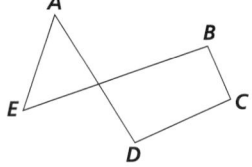

quadrilateral *ABCD*; $\overline{AB}$, $\overline{BC}$, $\overline{CD}$, $\overline{DA}$

? ...... **Need Help?**

In Exercises 51–53, sketch a figure to meet the first condition. Then adjust it to meet the second condition.

Open-Ended Sketch each figure described in Exercises 50–53.

50. a quadrilateral that is not equiangular **50–53. See back of book.**

51. an equiangular quadrilateral that is not regular

52. an equilateral polygon that is not equiangular

53. an equiangular polygon that is not equilateral

55. Answers may vary. Sample: The figure is a convex equilateral quadrilateral. The sum of its angles is $2 \cdot 180$ or 360.

2.

not a polygon because two sides intersect at a point other than endpoints

3. Find the sum of the measures of the angles in an octagon. **1080**

54. Yes; the sum of the measures of ⧍ at the int. point is 360. The sum of the measures of all the ⧍ is $180n$.
$180n - 360 = (n - 2)180$

54. Critical Thinking Ellen says she has another way to find the sum of the measures of the angles of a polygon. She picks a point inside the polygon, draws a segment to each vertex, counts the number of triangles, multiplies by 180, and then subtracts 360. Does her method work? Explain. **See left.**

55. Writing Tell what you know about the figure at the right. **See above right.**

56. The measure of an interior angle of a regular polygon is three times the measure of an exterior angle of the same polygon. What is the name of the polygon? **octagon**

4. A pentagon has two right angles, a 100° angle and a 120° angle. What is the measure of its fifth angle? **140**

ABCDEFGHIJ is a regular decagon.

5. Find $m\angle ABC$. **144**

6. $\angle XBC$ is an exterior angle at vertex B. Find $m\angle XBC$. **36**

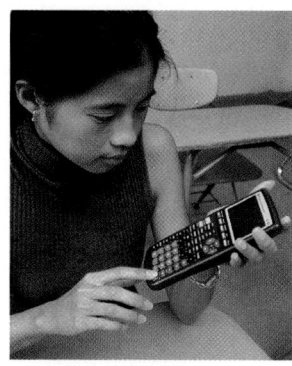

To graph the ordered pairs, use STAT and **STAT PLOT** on your graphing calculator.

 ...... **Take It to the NET**
Graphing Calculator procedures online at **www.PHSchool.com**
Web Code: afe-2120

C **Challenge** **57. a. Graphing Calculator** Find the measure of an angle of a regular *n*-gon for $n = 20, 40, 60, 80, \ldots, 200$. Record your results to the nearest tenth as ordered pairs in the form (*n*, measure of each angle). **See margin p. 148.**

b. Plot the ordered pairs using a window like the one shown at the right. **See back of book.**

c. Data Analysis Based on the graph from part (b), make a statement about the measure of an angle of a regular 1000-gon. **c–d. See margin p. 148.**

d. Is there a regular *n*-gon with an angle of 180°? Explain.

Xmin = 0   Ymin = 160
Xmax = 200 Ymax = 184
Xscl = 20   Yscl = 4

58. a. Explain why the measure of an angle of a regular *n*-gon is given by the formulas $\frac{180(n - 2)}{n}$ and $180 - \frac{360}{n}$. $[180(n - 2)] \div n = \frac{180n - 360}{n} = 180 - \frac{360}{n}$.

b. Use the second formula to explain what happens to the measures in the angles of regular *n*-gons as *n* becomes a large number. Explain also what happens to the polygons. **See margin p. 148.**

59. Two rays bisect two consecutive angles of a regular decagon and intersect in the decagon's interior. Find the measure of the acute angles formed by the intersecting rays. **36**

Draw, if possible, the concave quadrilateral described. If not possible, explain.
60–63. See margin.
60. with two pairs of congruent adjacent sides

61. with two pairs of congruent opposite sides

62. with three congruent sides

63. with four congruent sides

60–63. Answers may vary. Samples are given.

60.

61. Not possible; opp. sides would overlap.

62.

63. Not possible; opp. and adj. sides would overlap.

Standardized Test Prep

A sheet of blank grids is available in the Test-Taking Strategies with Transparencies booklet. Give this sheet to students for practice with filling in the grids.

 **Resources**
For additional practice with a variety of test item formats:
• Standardized Test Prep, p. 177
• Test-Taking Strategies, p. 172
• Test-Taking Strategies with Transparencies

Connection to Algebra

Exercise 65 If students need help, tell them to use the expression $(n - 2)180$ to write an equation. Ask: *If each angle measures 162 in a polygon with* n *sides, what must be the sum of the angle measures?* **3240**

page 151   Algebra 1 Review

10. The line is not as steep as line ℓ, but has the same tilt.

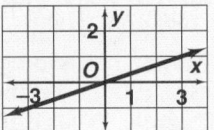

11. The line is steeper than line r, but has the same tilt.

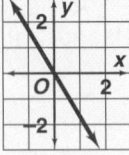

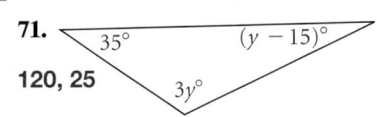
Standardized Test Prep

Gridded Response

For Exercises 64–70, you may need the formula $(n - 2)180$ for the sum of the angle measures in a polygon with n sides.

64. What is the sum of the measures of the angles of a 25-gon? **4140**

65. A company is manufacturing a gear that has the shape of a regular polygon. The measure of each angle of the gear is 162. How many sides does the gear have? **20**

66. The car at each vertex of a Ferris wheel holds a maximum of 5 people. The sum of the measures of the angles of the Ferris wheel is 7740. What is the maximum number of people that the Ferris wheel can hold? **225**

67. What is the sum of the measures of the exterior angles, one at each vertex, of an octagon? **360**

68. Exactly four angles of a hexagon are congruent. The other two angles are complementary. What is the measure of one of the four congruent angles?
157.5

69. The sum of the measures of the angles of a regular polygon is 4500. How many sides does the polygon have? **27**

70. What is the measure of an exterior angle of a regular polygon with 36 sides?
10

Take It to the NET
Online lesson quiz at
www.PHSchool.com
Web Code: afa-0304

Mixed Review

Lesson 3-3 $\boxed{x^2}$ **Find each missing angle measure.**

71.
120, 25
$35°$ $(y - 15)°$
$3y°$

104, 76, 35, 69

72.
50, 40
$(x + 23)°$ $(x + 13)°$

73.
$(2y - 1)°$
$x°$ $(x - 28)°$ $y°$

Lesson 2-4   **Name the property that justifies each statement.**

Distr. Prop.   **Subst. Prop.**
74. $4(2a - 3) = 8a - 12$ 75. If $b + c = 7$ and $b = 2$, then $2 + c = 7$.

76. $\overline{RS} \cong \overline{RS}$ 77. If $\angle 1 \cong \angle 4$, then $\angle 4 \cong \angle 1$.
Reflexive Prop. of ≅   **Symm. Prop. of ≅**
78. If $2r = 18$, then $r = 9$.   79. If $AB = BC$ and $BC = 1$, then $AB = 1$.
Div. Prop.   **Trans. Prop.**

Lessons 1-3, 1-4   **Identify the following in the diagram.**

80. a pair of opposite rays $\overrightarrow{RT}, \overrightarrow{RK}$

81. two right angles $\angle BRT, \angle BRK$

82. Answers may vary.
Sample: $\overline{BR}$ **and** $\overline{TK}$

82. two segments

83. Answers may vary.
Sample: $\angle BRM$

83. an acute angle

84. an obtuse angle $\angle TRM$

85. a straight angle $\angle TRK$

86. a midpoint R

Slope

The *slope* of a line is the ratio of the vertical change (rise) to the horizontal change (run) between any two points (x_1, y_1) and (x_2, y_2) of the line.

$$\text{slope} = \frac{\text{vertical change}}{\text{horizontal change}} = \frac{\text{rise}}{\text{run}} = \frac{y_2 - y_1}{x_2 - x_1}$$

The slope of a line indicates the line's steepness and whether it rises or falls from left to right. Line ℓ has slope 1 and rises from left to right. Line r has slope -1 and falls from left to right. Both form a 45° angle with the x-axis.

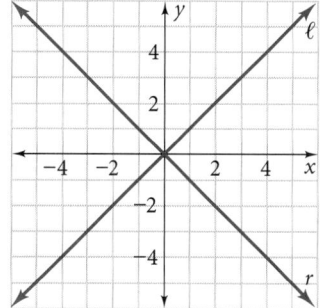

1 EXAMPLE

Find the slope of $\overleftrightarrow{AB}$, which passes through $A(-2, 4)$ and $B(1, -3)$.

Method 1 Use the formula.

$$\text{slope} = \frac{y_2 - y_1}{x_2 - x_1} = \frac{-3 - 4}{1 - (-2)} = \frac{-7}{3}, \text{ or } -\frac{7}{3}$$

Method 2 Use the graph.

$$\text{slope} = \frac{\text{vertical change (rise)}}{\text{horizontal change (run)}} = \frac{-7}{3}, \text{ or } -\frac{7}{3}$$

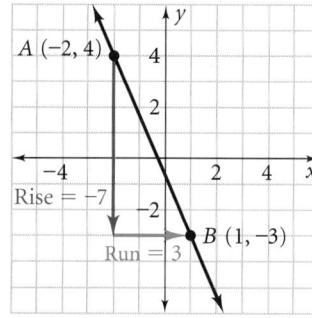

1. $\frac{8}{3}$; it is steeper than line ℓ but has the same tilt.

2. $\frac{1}{6}$; it is not as steep as line ℓ, but has the same tilt.

3. $-\frac{3}{2}$; it is steeper than line r, but has the same tilt.

2 EXAMPLE

Compare the rise or fall and the steepness of $\overleftrightarrow{AB}$ in Example 1 with that of line ℓ or r at the top of the page.

The slope of $\overleftrightarrow{AB}$ is negative, so $\overleftrightarrow{AB}$ falls from left to right, the same as line r with slope -1. The slope of $\overleftrightarrow{AB}$ has absolute value $\frac{7}{3}$, which is greater than 1, so $\overleftrightarrow{AB}$ is steeper than line r whose slope has absolute value 1.

4. $-\frac{2}{3}$; it is not as steep as line r, but has the same tilt.

5. -1; it is the same steepness and tilt as line r.

6. $\frac{1}{7}$; it is not as steep as line ℓ, but has the same tilt.

7. -5; it is steeper than line r, but has the same tilt.

8. 0; the line is horizontal.

9. Undefined; the line is vertical.

EXERCISES

Find the slope of $\overleftrightarrow{AB}$. Compare its rise or fall and its steepness with that of line ℓ or r at the top of the page.   1–9. See above.

1. $A(4, -6), B(7, 2)$

2. $A(7, -6), B(-5, -8)$

3. $A(-3, 7), B(-1, 4)$

4. $A(-2, -5), B(1, -7)$

5. $A(0, 4), B(4, 0)$

6. $A\left(-3\frac{1}{2}, 3\right), B\left(-7, 2\frac{1}{2}\right)$

7. $A(-1.4, -3.7), B(-2.4, 1.3)$

8. $A(3, -2), B(-6, -2)$

9. $A(5, 9), B(5, -6)$

Open-Ended Predict how a line with the given slope m will compare with line ℓ or r at the top of the page. Graph such a line.   10–13. See margin pp. 150-151.

10. $m = \frac{1}{3}$

11. $m = -1.7$

12. $m = 37$

13. $m = 0$

12. The line is much steeper than line ℓ, and has the same tilt. The graph of ℓ passes through (0, 0) and (1, 37).

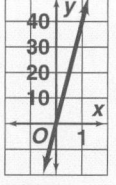

13. The line is horizontal.

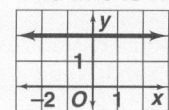

Students will review the meaning of slope and how to calculate it because they will work extensively with slope in Lessons 3-5 and 3-6.

Resources

Technology

Geometry Resource Pro® CD-ROM: Algebra 1 Review Resources
Computer Test Generator CD-ROM, Chapter 0, Integer, Decimal, and Fraction Operations

Teaching Notes

1 EXAMPLE   Error Prevention

Point out to students that the slope formula must be applied precisely.

- Both y-coordinates appear in the numerator, and both x-coordinates appear in the denominator.
- The order of coordinates must be the same in both the numerator and the denominator.

Have students explore what happens when the coordinates are substituted into the slope formula incorrectly.

2 EXAMPLE

Discuss as a class how the steepness of a line is not affected by whether it rises or falls from left to right. If necessary, review how to find the absolute value of a number.

Careers

Highway engineers are responsible for the steepness of the roads they construct. Have students investigate how they use percent to describe the grade of a road.

1. Plan

Lesson Preview

✓ Check Skills You'll Need

Slope
Algebra Review, page 151
Example 1, Exercises 1–9

Lesson Resources

📁 **Teaching Resources**
Practice, Reteaching, Enrichment

👥 **Reaching All Students**
Practice Workbook 3-5
Spanish Practice Workbook 3-5
Informal Geometry Planning
  Guide 3-5

⏱ **Presentation Assistant Plus!**
Transparencies
• Check Skills You'll Need 3-5
• Additional Examples 3-5
• Student Edition Answers 3-5
• Lesson Quiz 3-5
PH Presentation Pro CD 3-5

PRENTICE HALL
ASSESSMENT SYSTEM

Computer Test Generator CD

🪙 **Technology**
Resource Pro® CD-ROM
Computer Test Generator CD
Prentice Hall Presentation Pro CD

💻 **www.PHSchool.com**
Student Site
• Teacher Web Code: afk-5500
• Self-grading Lesson Quiz
Teacher Center
• Lesson Planner
• Resources

Plus 🅸**TEXT**

Lines in the Coordinate Plane

North Carolina Objectives 2.02 Apply properties, definitions, and theorems of angles and lines to solve problems and write proofs.

Lesson Preview

What You'll Learn

OBJECTIVE 1 To graph lines given their equations

OBJECTIVE 2 To write equations of lines

. . . And Why

To determine whether a wheelchair ramp complies with the law, as in Exercise 52

✓ Check Skills You'll Need

(For help, go to page 151.)

Find the slope of the line that contains each pair of points.

1. $A(-2, 2), B(4, -2)$ $-\frac{2}{3}$

2. $P(3, 0), X(0, -5)$ $\frac{5}{3}$ undefined or no slope

3. $R(-3, -4), S(5, -4)$ 0

4. $K(-3, 3), T(-3, 1)$ undefined or no slope

5. $C(0, 1), D(3, 3)$ $\frac{2}{3}$

6. $E(-1, 4), F(3, -2)$ $-\frac{3}{2}$

7. $G(-8, -9), H(-3, -5)$ $\frac{4}{5}$

8. $L(7, -10), M(1, -4)$ -1

New Vocabulary
• slope-intercept form
• standard form of a linear equation • point-slope form

🅸**TEXT** Interactive lesson includes instant self-check, tutorials, and activities.

OBJECTIVE

1 Graphing Lines

❓ **Need Help?**

The *y*-intercept is the *y*-coordinate of the point where a line crosses the *y*-axis. The *x*-intercept is the *x*-coordinate of the point where a line crosses the *x*-axis.

In algebra, you learned that the graph of a linear equation is a line. The **slope-intercept form** of a linear equation is $y = mx + b$, where m is the slope of the line and b is the *y*-intercept. Each line at the right has slope 2, but the lines have *y*-intercepts of 3, −1, and −4.

By Postulate 1-1 (two points determine a line), you need only two points to graph a line. The *y*-intercept gives you one point. You can use the slope to plot another.

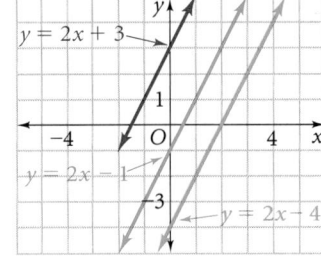

1 EXAMPLE Graphing Lines in Slope-Intercept Form

Graph the line $y = \frac{3}{4}x + 2$.

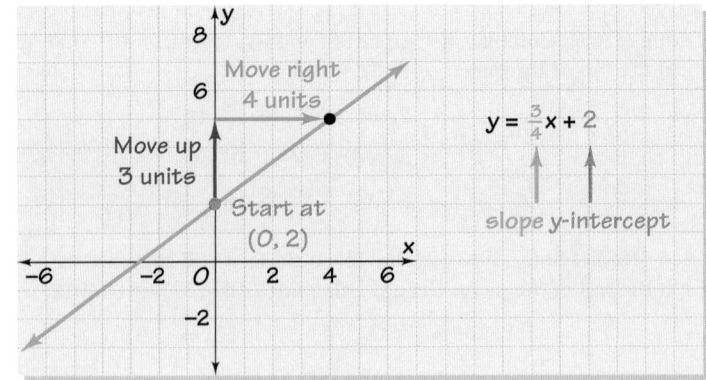

1.
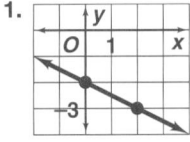

✓ **Check Understanding** ① Graph the line $y = -\frac{1}{2}x - 2$. **See left.**

🄲 Ongoing Assessment and Intervention

Before the Lesson
Diagnose prerequisite skills using:
• Check Skills You'll Need

During the Lesson
Monitor progress using:
• Check Understanding
• Additional Examples
• Standardized Test Prep

After the Lesson
Assess knowledge using:
• Lesson Quiz
• Computer Test Generator CD

Reading Math

In the "standard form," A, B, and C are constants. In Example 2, $6x + 3y = 12$ is in standard form with $A = 6$, $B = 3$, and $C = 12$.

The **standard form of a linear equation** is $Ax + By = C$, where A, B, and C are real numbers and A and B are not both zero. To graph an equation written in standard form, you can readily find two points for the graph by finding the x- and y-intercepts.

2 EXAMPLE Graphing Lines Using Intercepts

Algebra Graph $6x + 3y = 12$.

Step 1 To find the y-intercept, substitute 0 for x; solve for y.

$$6x + 3y = 12$$
$$6(0) + 3y = 12$$
$$3y = 12$$
$$y = 4$$

The y-intercept is 4.
A point on the line is $(0, 4)$.

Step 2 To find the x-intercept, substitute 0 for y; solve for x.

$$6x + 3y = 12$$
$$6x + 3(0) = 12$$
$$6x = 12$$
$$x = 2$$

The x-intercept is 2.
A point on the line is $(2, 0)$.

Step 3 Plot $(0, 4)$ and $(2, 0)$. Draw the line containing the two points.

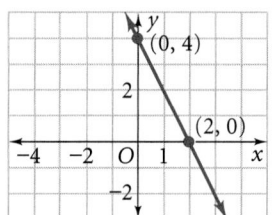

✓ **Check Understanding** **2** Graph $-2x + 4y = -8$.

2.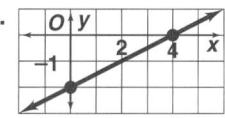

As an alternative, you can graph an equation in standard form by transforming it into slope-intercept form. Knowing the slope and y-intercept beforehand can give you a good mental image of what the graph should look like.

3 EXAMPLE Transforming to Slope-Intercept Form

Algebra Graph $4x - 2y = 9$.

Step 1 Transform the equation to slope-intercept form.

$$4x - 2y = 9$$
$$-2y = -4x + 9$$
$$\frac{-2y}{-2} = \frac{-4x}{-2} + \frac{9}{-2}$$
$$y = 2x - \frac{9}{2}$$

The y-intercept is $-4\frac{1}{2}$ and the slope is 2.

Step 2 Use the y-intercept and the slope to plot two points and draw the line containing them.

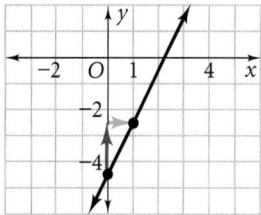

3.

✓ **Check Understanding** **3** Graph $-5x + y = -3$. **See left.**

👥 Reaching All Students

Below Level Encourage students to plot three points when graphing a linear equation. Because algebra errors produce noncollinear points, students can check their work.	**Advanced Learners** Have students find the slope and intercept of the line in standard form $ax + by = c$.	**Inclusion** See note on page 153. **English Learners** See note on page 155.

---

2. Teach

^{Professional Development}

Math Background

René Descartes published his philosophical treatise *Discours de la méthode* in 1637. Its appendix *Géométrie* contained the first published record of methods of analytic geometry, permanently sealing the partnership between geometry and algebra. Within 30 years, the methods of analytic geometry would lead to the invention of calculus.

OBJECTIVE

1 Teaching Notes

1 EXAMPLE Inclusion

Pair visually-challenged or physically-challenged students with partners to complete graphing activities.

Math Tip
For the standard form of a linear equation, review the meaning of real numbers, and consider the case $A = B = 0$, where there is no line.

3 EXAMPLE

Students are accustomed to solving for x and adding to each side of the equation. Remind them that the slope-intercept form isolates y.

Additional Examples

1 Use the slope and y-intercept to graph the line $y = -2x + 9$. Check that points $(0, 9)$ and $(1, 7)$ are on students' graphs.

2 Use the x-intercept and y-intercept to graph $5x - 6y = 30$. Check that points $(6, 0)$ and $(0, -5)$ are on students' graphs.

3 Transform the equation $-6x + 3y = 12$ to slope-intercept form, and then graph the resulting equation. $y = 2x + 4$; check that points $(1, 6)$ and $(0, 4)$ are on students' graphs.

153

Teaching Tip

Discuss with students when point-slope form is easier to use than slope-intercept form. **when you know the coordinates of one or two points other than the y-intercept**

5 EXAMPLE **Visual Learners**

Have students use coordinate graphs to see that slopes of $-\frac{4}{3}$, $\frac{-4}{3}$, and $-\frac{4}{3}$ are the same.

6 EXAMPLE **Error Prevention**

Students may think the equation of a horizontal line begins with "x =" because the x-axis is horizontal. Point out that when the value of x is constant, the value of y changes to form a vertical line like the y-axis, and when the value of y is constant, the value of x changes to form a horizontal line like the x-axis.

Additional Examples

4 Write an equation in point-slope form of the line with slope −8 that contains P(3, –6).
$y + 6 = -8(x - 3)$

5 Write an equation in point-slope form of the line that contains the points G(4, −9) and H(−1, 1).
$y + 9 = -2(x - 4)$ or
$y - 1 = -2(x + 1)$

6 Write equations for the horizontal line and the vertical line that contain A(−7, −5).
horizontal line: $y = -5$; vertical line: $x = -7$

Closure

Write the equation of the line containing the points (−3, 2) and (3, 14) in point-slope form, slope-intercept form, and standard form. $y - 2 = 2(x + 3)$ or $y - 14 = 2(x - 3)$; $y = 2x + 8$; $2x - y = -8$

A third form for an equation of a line is **point-slope form.** The point-slope form for a nonvertical line through point (x_1, y_1) with slope m is $y - y_1 = m(x - x_1)$.

4 EXAMPLE **Using Point-Slope Form**

Algebra Write an equation of the line through point $P(-1, 4)$ with slope 3.

$y - y_1 = m(x - x_1)$ Use point-slope form.

$y - 4 = 3[x - (-1)]$ Substitute 3 for *m* and (−1, 4) for (*x₁, y₁*).

$y - 4 = 3(x + 1)$ Simplify.

✓ **Check Understanding** 4 Write an equation of the line with slope −1 that contains point $P(2, -4)$.
$y + 4 = -1(x - 2)$

By Postulate 1-1, you need only two points to write an equation of a line.

5 EXAMPLE **Writing an Equation of a Line Given Two Points**

Algebra Write an equation of the line through $A(-2, 3)$ and $B(1, -1)$.

Step 1 Find the slope.

$m = \frac{y_2 - y_1}{x_2 - x_1}$

$m = \frac{-1 - 3}{1 - (-2)}$ Substitute (−2, 3) for (*x₁, y₁*) and (1, −1) for (*x₂, y₂*).

$m = -\frac{4}{3}$ Simplify.

Step 2 Select one of the points. Write an equation in point-slope form.

$y - y_1 = m(x - x_1)$

$y - 3 = -\frac{4}{3}[x - (-2)]$ Substitute (−2, 3) for (*x₁, y₁*) and $-\frac{4}{3}$ for the slope.

$y - 3 = -\frac{4}{3}(x + 2)$ Simplify.

✓ **Check Understanding** 5 Write an equation of the line that contains the points $P(5, 0)$ and $Q(7, -3)$.
$y - 0 = -\frac{3}{2}(x - 5)$ or $y + 3 = -\frac{3}{2}(x - 7)$

Recall that the slope of a horizontal line is 0 and the slope of a vertical line is undefined. Thus, horizontal and vertical lines have easily recognized equations.

6 EXAMPLE **Equations of Horizontal and Vertical Lines**

Write equations for the horizontal line and the vertical line that contain $P(3, 2)$.

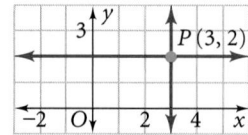

Every point on the horizontal line through $P(3, 2)$ has a y-coordinate of 2. The equation of the line is $y = 2$. It crosses the y-axis at $(0, 2)$.

Every point on the vertical line through $P(3, 2)$ has an x-coordinate of 3. The equation of the line is $x = 3$. It crosses the x-axis at $(3, 0)$.

✓ **Check Understanding** 6 Write equations of the horizontal and vertical lines that contain the point $P(5, -1)$.
$y = -1; x = 5$

pages 155–157   **Exercises**

23–28. **Equations may vary from the pt. chosen. Samples are given.**

23. $y - 5 = \frac{3}{5}(x - 0)$

24. $y - 2 = -\frac{1}{2}(x - 6)$

25. $y - 6 = 1(x - 2)$

26. $y - 4 = 1(x + 4)$

27. $y - 0 = \frac{1}{2}(x + 1)$

28. $y - 10 = \frac{2}{3}(x - 8)$

EXERCISES

For more practice, see *Extra Practice*.

Practice and Problem Solving

A Practice by Example  **Algebra** Graph each line. 1–4. See back of book.

Examples 1, 2
(pages 152, 153)

1. $y = x + 2$ **2.** $y = 3x + 4$ **3.** $y = \frac{1}{2}x - 1$ **4.** $y = -\frac{5}{3}x + 2$

x^2 **Algebra** Graph each line using intercepts. 5–10. See back of book.

5. $2x + 6y = 12$ **6.** $3x + y = 15$ **7.** $5x - 2y = 20$

8. $6x - y = 3$ **9.** $10x + 5y = 40$ **10.** $1.2x + 2.4y = 2.4$

Example 3 x^2 **Algebra** Write each equation in slope-intercept form and graph the line.
(page 153)

11–16. See back of book.

11. $y = 2x + 1$ **12.** $y - 1 = x$ **13.** $y + 2x = 4$

14. $8x + 4y = 16$ **15.** $2x + 6y = 6$ **16.** $\frac{3}{4}x - \frac{1}{2}y = \frac{1}{8}$

Example 4 x^2 **Algebra** Write an equation in point-slope form of the line that contains the given
(page 154) points and has the given slope.

$y - 3 = 2(x - 2)$ $y + 1 = 3(x - 4)$ $y - 5 = -1(x + 3)$

17. $P(2, 3)$, slope 2 **18.** $X(4, -1)$, slope 3 **19.** $R(-3, 5)$, slope -1

22. $y - 4 = 1(x - 0)$ or
$y - 4 = x$

20. $A(-2, -6)$, slope -4 **21.** $V(6, 1)$, slope $\frac{1}{2}$ **22.** $C(0, 4)$, slope 1
$y + 6 = -4(x + 2)$ $y - 1 = \frac{1}{2}(x - 6)$ See left.

Example 5 Write an equation in point-slope form of the line that contains the given points.
(page 154) 23–28. See margin p. 154.

23. $D(0, 5), E(5, 8)$ **24.** $F(6, 2), G(2, 4)$ **25.** $H(2, 6), K(-1, 3)$

26. $A(-4, 4), B(2, 10)$ **27.** $L(-1, 0), M(-3, -1)$ **28.** $P(8, 10), Q(-4, 2)$

Example 6 Write equations for (a) the horizontal line and (b) the vertical line that contain the
(page 154) given point.

a. $y = 7$ a. $y = -2$ a. $y = -1$ a. $y = 4$
29. $A(4, 7)$ **30.** $Y(3, -2)$ **31.** $N(0, -1)$ **32.** $E(6, 4)$
b. $x = 4$ b. $x = 3$ b. $x = 0$ b. $x = 6$

B Apply Your Skills Graph each line. 33–37. See back of book.

33. $x = 3$ **34.** $y = -2$ **35.** $x = 9$ **36.** $y = 4$ **37.** $y = 6$

Real-World Connection

NASA's Advanced
Communications Technology
Satellite has a capacity for
250,000 phone calls.

38. Telephone Rates The equation $C = \$.05m + \$4.95$ represents the cost (C) of
a long distance telephone call of m minutes.
  a. What is the slope of the line? **0.05**
  b. What does the slope represent in this situation? **the cost per minute**
  c. What is the y-intercept (C-intercept)? **4.95**
  d. What does the y-intercept represent in this situation? **the initial charge for a call**

39. Error Analysis A classmate claims that having no slope and having a slope of 0
are the same. Is your classmate correct? Explain. **No; a line with no slope is a vertical line. 0 slope is a horizontal line.**

40. a. What is the slope of the x-axis? Explain. **$m = 0$; it is a horizontal line.**
  b. Write an equation for the x-axis. **$y = 0$**

41. a. What is the slope of the y-axis? Explain. **Undefined; it is a vertical line.**
  b. Write an equation for the y-axis. **$x = 0$**

Identify the form of each equation. To graph the line, would you use the given form
or change to another form? Explain.
42–44. See margin.

42. $-5x - y = 2$ **43.** $y = \frac{1}{4}x - \frac{2}{7}$ **44.** $y + 2 = -(x - 4)$

Lesson 3-5 Lines in the Coordinate Plane **155**

42–44. Answers may vary.
Samples are given.

42. The eq. is in standard
form; change to slope-
intercept form, because

it is easy to graph the
eq. from that form.

43. The eq. is in slope-int.
form; use slope-int.
form, because the eq. is
already in that form.

44. The eq. is in point-slope
form; use point-slope
form, because the eq. is
already in that form.

3. Practice

Assignment Guide

1 Objective
  A B Core 1–16, 33–38,
    45, 46,
    48–51, 53
  C Extension 57–60

2 Objective
  A B Core 17–32, 39–44,
    47, 52, 54–56
  C Extension 61–63

Standardized Test Prep 64–69

Mixed Review 70–80

Exercise 38 Ask: *In which
quadrant of the coordinate plane
is the graph of this equation
relevant?* **Quadrant 1**

English Learners

Exercise 39 In some contexts, *no*
and *zero* indicate the same idea.
Use this exercise to highlight that
no slope means *undefined slope*
in mathematics.

Exercises 57–60 Suggest that
students calculate and compare
slopes.

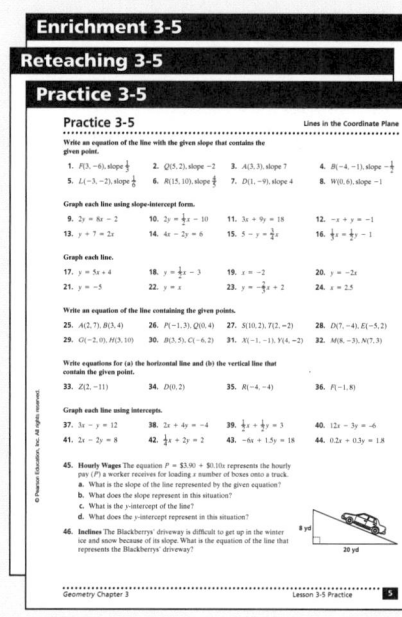

155

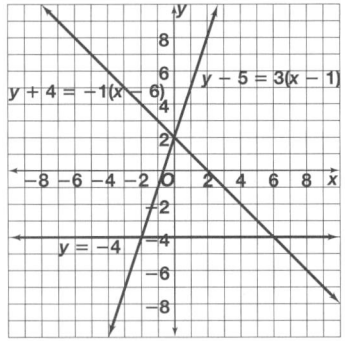

Lesson Quiz 3-5

1. Find the *x*-intercept and the *y*-intercept of the line $5x + 4y = -80$.
   x-intercept: −16,
   y-intercept: −20

Three points are on a coordinate plane: $A(1, 5)$, $B(-2, -4)$, and $C(6, -4)$.

2. Write an equation in point-slope form of the line with slope −1 that contains point *C*.
   $y + 4 = -1(x - 6)$

3. Write an equation in point-slope form of the line that contains points *A* and *B*.
   $y - 5 = 3(x - 1)$ or
   $y + 4 = 3(x + 2)$

4. Write an equation of the line that contains *B* and *C*.
   $y = -4$

5. Graph and label the equations of the lines in Exercises 2–4 above.

Alternative Assessment

Have students work in pairs to explain in writing how to write the equation of a line in three different forms. For each form, they should give an example of a question where that form would be used.

Need Help?

When you give examples as in Exercises 45 and 46, choose ones that are easy to work with.

52. $\frac{3}{10} = 0.3$, $\frac{1}{12} = 0.08\overline{3}$; $\frac{3}{10} > \frac{1}{12}$; it is possible only if the ramp zigzags.

Real-World 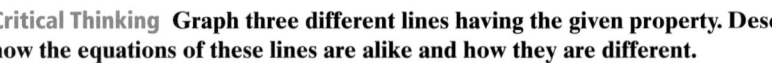 **Connection**

To visualize a slope of $\frac{1}{12}$, think "one foot over, one inch up."

56c. The abs. value of the slopes is the same, but one slope is pos. and the other is neg. One *y*-int. is at (0, 0) and the other is at (0, 10).

C **Challenge**

57. Yes; the slope of $\overline{AB}$ equals the slope of $\overline{BC}$.

58. No; the slope of $\overline{DE}$ does not equal the slope of $\overline{EF}$.

60. Yes; the slope of $\overline{JK}$ equals the slope of $\overline{KL}$.

Critical Thinking Graph three different lines having the given property. Describe how the equations of these lines are alike and how they are different.

45. The lines have slope 2.
    See back of book.

46. The lines have *y*-intercept 2.
    See margin.

47. **Graphing Calculator** Graphing calculators use slope-intercept form (rather than standard form or point-slope form) to graph lines. Choose either Exercise 45 or Exercise 46 and write three equations for the lines you graphed. Use the **Y=** window of your graphing calculator to enter your equations. Press **GRAPH**. Do the graphs on the screen confirm the description you wrote previously?
    Check students' work.

Graph each pair of lines. Then find their point of intersection.
48–51. See margin pp. 156–157.

48. $y = -4, x = 6$ 49. $x = 0, y = 0$ 50. $x = -1, y = 3$ 51. $y = 5, x = 4$

52. **Building Access** By law, the maximum slope of a ramp in new construction is $\frac{1}{12}$. The plan for the new library shows a 3-ft height from the ground to the main entrance. The distance from the sidewalk to the building is 10 ft. Can you design a ramp for the library that complies with the law? Explain. **See left.**

53. **Writing** Describe the similarities of and the differences between the graphs of the equations $y = 5x - 2$ and $y = -5x - 2$. **See margin p. 157.**

54. **Open-Ended** Write equations for three different lines that contain the point $(5, 6)$. **Answers may vary. Sample:** $x = 5$, $y - 6 = 2(x - 5)$, $y = x + 1$

55. **Critical Thinking** The *x*-intercept of a line is 2 and the *y*-intercept is 4. Use this information to write an equation for the line. **See margin p. 157.**

56. The vertices of a triangle are $A(0, 0)$, $B(2, 5)$, and $C(4, 0)$. **a.** $y - 0 = \frac{5}{2}(x - 0)$
    a. Write an equation for the line through *A* and *B*. or $y = \frac{5}{2}x$
    b. Write an equation for the line through *B* and *C*. **b.** $y - 5 = -\frac{5}{2}(x - 2)$ or
    c. Compare the slopes and *y*-intercepts of the two lines. $y = -\frac{5}{2}x + 10$

Do the three points lie on one line? Justify your answer. 57–58. See left.

57. $A(5, 6), B(3, 2), C(6, 8)$ 58. $D(-2, -2), E(4, -4), F(0, 0)$

59. $G(5, -4), H(2, 3), I(-1, 10)$ 60. $J(-2, 9), K(1, -1), L(4, -11)$
Yes; the slope of $\overline{GH}$ equals the slope of $\overline{HI}$.   See left.
A line passes through the given points. Write an equation for the line in point-slope form. Then, rewrite the equation in standard form with integer coefficients.

61. $R(-2, 2), S(0, 8)$ 62. $T(5, 5), W(7, 6)$ 63. $X(2, 6), Y(5, 8)$
    $y - 2 = 3(x + 2)$; $y - 5 = \frac{1}{2}(x - 5)$; $y - 6 = \frac{2}{3}(x - 2)$;
    $3x - y = -8$ $x - 2y = -5$ $2x - 3y = -14$

156   Chapter 3   Parallel and Perpendicular Lines

pages 155–157
Exercises

46. 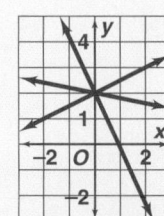   The slopes are all different, and the *y*-intercepts are the same.

48.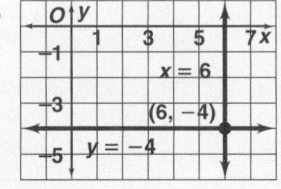

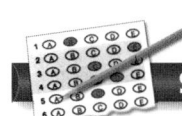
Multiple Choice

64. Which equation is equivalent to $15x + 3y = 10$? **D**

    A. $y = 5x + \frac{10}{3}$ **B.** $y = -5x - \frac{10}{3}$ **C.** $y = 5x - \frac{10}{3}$ **D.** $y = -5x + \frac{10}{3}$

65. Which pair of points $A(-2, 5)$, $B(-1, -2)$, $C(4, -5)$, and $D(7, 0)$, lie on the line with y-intercept closest to the origin? **G**

    F. A and B **G.** A and C **H.** B and C **I.** B and D

Quantitative Comparison

Compare the boxed quantity in Column A with the boxed quantity in Column B. Choose the best answer.

  A. The quantity in Column A is greater.
  B. The quantity in Column B is greater.
  C. The two quantities are equal.
  D. The relationship cannot be determined from the information given.

Column A	Column B
B 66. the y-intercept of $3x - 8y = 60$	the y-intercept of $3x + 60 = 8y$
C 67. the slope of $4y = -10$	the slope of $y = 5$
C 68. the slope of the line that passes through $(0, -9)$ and $(-4, -11)$	the slope of the line that passes through $(18, 0)$ and $(4, -7)$

Short Response

Take It to the NET
Online lesson quiz at
www.PHSchool.com
Web Code: afa-0305

69. The slope of line a is $\frac{3}{2}$ and its y-intercept is 12. Line b passes through $(4, 1)$ and $(7, -3)$.

  a. Write an equation for each line.   **a–b. See margin.**
  b. Graph both lines on the same coordinate plane. From the graph, what is their point of intersection?

Mixed Review

Lesson 3-4   **Find the sum of the measures of the angles of each polygon.**

  70. a nonagon   **71.** a pentagon   **72.** an 11-gon   **73.** a 14-gon
     1260   540   1620   2160

Lesson 2-2   **Is each statement a good definition? If not, find a counterexample.**

  74. A quadrilateral is a polygon with four sides. **yes**

  75. Skew lines are lines that don't intersect. **No; parallel lines never intersect, but they are not skew.**

  76. An acute triangle is a triangle with an acute angle.
    No; all obtuse △ have two acute ∡.

Lesson 1-5 x^2 **Algebra For Exercises 77–80, $\overrightarrow{PQ}$ is the bisector of $\angle MPR$. Solve for a and find the missing angle measure.**

  77. $m\angle MPQ = 3a, m\angle QPR = 2a + 5, m\angle MPR = \blacksquare$ $a = 5; m\angle MPR = 30$

  78. $m\angle MPQ = 7a, m\angle QPR = 4a + 12, m\angle MPR = \blacksquare$ $a = 4; m\angle MPR = 56$

  79. $m\angle MPQ = 8a - 8, m\angle QPR = 5a - 2, m\angle QPR = \blacksquare$ $a = 2; m\angle QPR = 8$

  80. $m\angle MPQ = 2a + 9, m\angle QPR = 4a - 3, m\angle MPQ = \blacksquare a = 6; m\angle MPQ = 21$

Lesson 3-5   Lines in the Coordinate Plane   **157**

49.

50.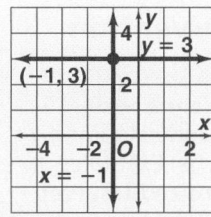

51.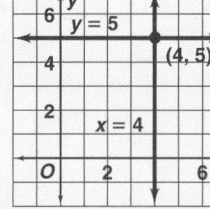

📁 **Resources**

For additional practice with a variety of test item formats:
- Standardized Test Prep, p. 177
- Test-Taking Strategies, p. 172
- Test-Taking Strategies with Transparencies

Exercise 64 Because each answer choice is in slope-intercept form, students can eliminate the two choices with negative y-intercepts and concentrate on the correct sign of the slope.

Exercises 66–68 Often it is useful to write the appropriate formulas before starting to answer quantitative comparison questions. Encourage students to write the formulas for slope and the slope-intercept form of a line before they start this set of exercises.

53. The y-intercepts are the same, and the lines have the same steepness. One line rises from left to right while the other falls from left to right.

55. $(2, 0)$, $(0, 4)$; $m = \frac{0 - 4}{2 - 0} = \frac{-4}{2} = -2$
$y - 0 = -2(x - 2)$,
$2x + y = 4$ or
$y = -2x + 4$

69. **[2] a.** Line a: $y = \frac{3}{2}x + 12$
OR equivalent equation; Line b: $3y + 4x = 19$ OR equivalent equation

  b.

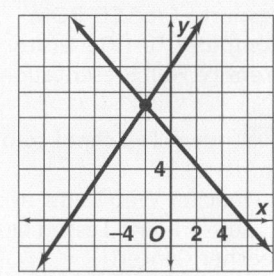

point of intersection: $(-2, 9)$

[1] at least one correct eq. or graph

157

1. Plan

Lesson Preview

✓ **Check Skills You'll Need**

Slope
Algebra Review, page 151
Example 1, Exercises 1–9

Graphing Lines
Lesson 3-5: Example 3
Exercises 11–16
Extra Practice, p. 692

Lesson Resources

📁 **Teaching Resources**
Practice, Reteaching, Enrichment
Checkpoint Quiz 2

👥 **Reaching All Students**
Practice Workbook 3-6
Spanish Practice Workbook 3-6
Reading and Math Literacy 3C
Spanish Reading & Literacy 3C
Spanish Checkpoint Quiz 2
Informal Geometry Planning
   Guide 3-6

⏰ **Presentation Assistant Plus!**
Transparencies
• Check Skills You'll Need 3-6
• Additional Examples 3-6
• Student Edition Answers 3-6
• Lesson Quiz 3-6
PH Presentation Pro CD 3-6

PRENTICE HALL
ASSESSMENT SYSTEM

Computer Test Generator CD

💿 **Technology**
Resource Pro® CD-ROM
Computer Test Generator CD
Prentice Hall Presentation Pro CD

🖥 **www.PHSchool.com**
Student Site
• Teacher Web Code: afk-5500
• Self-grading Lesson Quiz
Teacher Center
• Lesson Planner
• Resources

Plus 📱 **iTEXT**

North Carolina Objectives   2.02   Apply properties, definitions, and theorems of angles and lines to solve problems and write proofs.

Lesson Preview

What You'll Learn

OBJECTIVE **1** To relate slope and parallel lines

OBJECTIVE **2** To relate slope and perpendicular lines

. . . And Why

To write an equation that models part of a leaded glass window, as in Example 6

✓ **Check Skills You'll Need**   (For help, go to page 151 and Lesson 3-5.)

Find the slope of the line through each pair of points.

1. $F(2, 5), B(-2, 3)$ **2.** $H(0, -5), D(2, 0)$ **3.** $E(1, 1), F(2, -4)$ -5

Find the slope of each line.

4. $y = 2x - 5$ **5.** $x + y = 20$ **6.** $2x - 3y = 6 \frac{2}{3}$

7. $x = y$ **8.** $y = 7$ 0 **9.** $y = \frac{2}{3}x + 7 \frac{2}{3}$

📱 **iTEXT**   Interactive lesson includes instant self-check, tutorials, and activities.

OBJECTIVE **1**   **Slope and Parallel Lines**

The relationship between slope and parallel lines is summarized below and proved in Lesson 8-3.

🔑 **Key Concepts**

Summary	**Slopes of Parallel Lines**

If two nonvertical lines are parallel, their slopes are equal.

If the slopes of two distinct nonvertical lines are equal, the lines are parallel.

Any two vertical lines are parallel.

Real-World 🌐 **Connection**

The ramp and rails are parallel because they have the same slope.

You can test whether nonvertical lines are parallel by comparing their slopes.

1 **EXAMPLE**   **Checking for Parallel Lines**

Are lines ℓ_1 and ℓ_2 parallel? Explain.

Find and compare the slopes of the lines.

$$\text{slope of } \ell_1 = \frac{5 - (-4)}{1 - (-2)} = \frac{9}{3} = 3$$

$$\text{slope of } \ell_2 = \frac{3 - (-4)}{3 - 1} = \frac{7}{2}$$

Lines ℓ_1 and ℓ_2 are not parallel because their slopes are not equal.

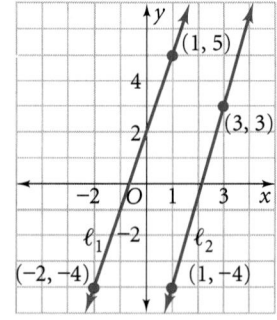

✓ **Check Understanding**   **1** Line ℓ_3 contains $A(-4, 2)$ and $B(3, 1)$. Line ℓ_4 contains $C(-4, 0)$ and $D(8, -2)$. Are ℓ_3 and ℓ_4 parallel? Explain.   **No; the slope of $\ell_3 = -\frac{1}{7}$, and the slope of $\ell_4 = -\frac{1}{6}$.**

⚡ **Ongoing Assessment and Intervention**

Before the Lesson
Diagnose prerequisite skills using:
• Check Skills You'll Need

During the Lesson
Monitor progress using:
• Check Understanding
• Additional Examples
• Standardized Test Prep

After the Lesson
Assess knowledge using:
• Lesson Quiz
• Computer Test Generator CD
• Chapter Checkpoint 2 (p. 164)

Slope-intercept form allows you to compare slopes easily in order to decide whether lines are parallel.

2 EXAMPLE Determining Whether Lines are Parallel

Algebra Are the lines $4y - 12x = 20$ and $y = 3x - 1$ parallel? Explain.

Write $4y - 12x = 20$ in slope-intercept form.

$$4y - 12x = 20$$
$$4y = 12x + 20 \qquad \text{Add 12x to each side.}$$
$$y = 3x + 5 \qquad \text{Divide each side by 4.}$$

Each line has slope 3. The y-intercepts are -1 and 5. The lines have the same slope and different y-intercepts. They are distinct lines, so they are parallel.

✓ **Check Understanding** 2 Are the lines parallel? Explain.

    a. $y = -\frac{1}{2}x + 5$ and $2x + 4y = 9$

    b. $y = -\frac{1}{2}x + 5$ and $2x + 4y = 20$

You can write an equation for a line parallel to a given line.

3 EXAMPLE Writing Equations of Parallel Lines

Write an equation for the line parallel to $y = -4x + 3$ that contains $(1, -2)$.

Step 1 Identify the slope of the given line.

$$y = \underset{\underset{\text{slope}}{\uparrow}}{-4}x + 3$$

Step 2 Use point-slope form to write an equation for the new line.

$$y - y_1 = m(x - x_1)$$
$$y - (-2) = -4(x - 1) \qquad \text{Substitute } -4 \text{ for } m \text{ and } (1, -2) \text{ for } (x_1, y_1).$$
$$y + 2 = -4(x - 1) \qquad \text{Simplify.}$$

✓ **Check Understanding** 3 Write an equation for the line parallel to $y = -x + 4$ that contains $(-2, 5)$.

OBJECTIVE
2 Slope and Perpendicular Lines

The relationship between perpendicular lines and their slopes is summarized below. These statements will be proved in Lessons 6-6 and 6-7.

 Key Concepts

Summary	Slopes of Perpendicular Lines
	If two nonvertical lines are perpendicular, the product of their slopes is -1.
	If the slopes of two lines have a product of -1, the lines are perpendicular.
	Any horizontal line and vertical line are perpendicular.

👥 Reaching All Students

Below Level Review the rules for multiplying and dividing signed numbers before students work with the slopes of perpendicular lines.	**Advanced Learners** After students complete Example 5, have them work on this problem: Line $y + ax = b$ is perpendicular to line $y - ax = b$. What are the possible values of a?	**Visual Learners** See note on page 161. **Error Prevention** See note on page 159.

Math Background

Slope is a fixed ratio that characterizes any nonvertical line. It is another example of a pure geometric concept, a line, described by algebraic methods. The product of the slopes of perpendicular lines being -1, although initially surprising, is merely the Pythagorean Theorem in an analytic geometry setting.

OBJECTIVE
1 Teaching Notes

Careers

Most buildings have walls that are perpendicular to floors, to ceilings, and to each other. Have students investigate how builders construct these.

Math Tip

After students read the Key Concepts about parallel lines, ask: *How can you state the two conditionals as a biconditional?* Two distinct nonvertical lines are parallel if and only if their slopes are equal.

2 EXAMPLE Error Prevention

Remind students that they must compare both the slopes and the y-intercepts. Ask: *If the slopes are equal and the y-intercepts are equal, are the lines parallel? Explain.* No; there is only one line.

🔖 Additional Examples

1 Line ℓ_1 contains $P(0, 3)$ and $Q(-2, 5)$. Line ℓ_2 contains $R(0, -7)$ and $S(3, -10)$. Are lines ℓ_1 and ℓ_2 parallel? Explain. Yes; each has slope -1 and different y-intercepts.

2 Are the lines $y = -5x + 4$ and $x = -5y + 4$ parallel? Explain. No; one line has slope -5 and the other line has slope $-\frac{1}{5}$.

159

You can test whether lines are perpendicular by first noting whether either line is vertical or horizontal. If not, check their slopes. If the product of the slopes is -1, the lines are perpendicular.

4 EXAMPLE **Checking for Perpendicular Lines**

Algebra Lines ℓ_1 and ℓ_2 are neither vertical nor horizontal. Are they perpendicular? Explain.

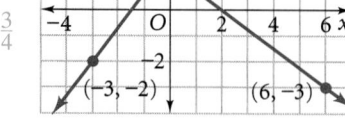

Step 1 Find the slope of each line.

$$m_1 = \text{slope of } \ell_1 = \frac{-2 - 2}{-3 - 0} = \frac{-4}{-3} = \frac{4}{3}$$

$$m_2 = \text{slope of } \ell_2 = \frac{3 - (-3)}{-2 - 6} = \frac{6}{-8} = -\frac{3}{4}$$

Step 2 Find the product of the slopes.

$$m_1 \cdot m_2 = \frac{4}{3} \cdot -\frac{3}{4} = -1$$

● Lines ℓ_1 and ℓ_2 are perpendicular because the product of their slopes is -1.

✓ **Check Understanding** ④ Are ℓ_3 and ℓ_4 perpendicular? Explain.
No; the slope of $\ell_3 = \frac{4}{9}$, and the slope of $\ell_4 = -\frac{7}{3}$, and $\frac{4}{9} \cdot -\frac{7}{3} \neq -1$.

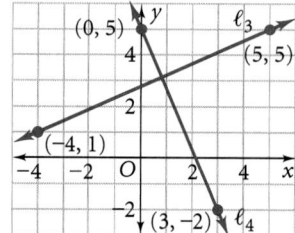

You can write an equation for a line perpendicular to a given line. If the given line is horizontal, write an equation for a vertical line. If the given line is vertical, write an equation for a horizontal line.

5 EXAMPLE **Writing Equations for Perpendicular Lines**

Write an equation for the line perpendicular to $y = -3x - 5$ that contains $(-3, 7)$.

Step 1 Identify the slope of the given line.

$$y = -3x - 5$$
$$\uparrow$$
$$\text{slope}$$

Step 2 Find the slope of the line perpendicular to the given line.

Let m be the slope of the perpendicular line.

$-3m = -1$ **The product of the slopes of perpendicular lines is -1.**

$m = \frac{1}{3}$ **Divide each side by -3.**

Step 3 Use point-slope form to write an equation for the new line.

$$y - y_1 = m(x - x_1)$$
$$y - 7 = \frac{1}{3}[x - (-3)]$$ **Substitute $\frac{1}{3}$ for m and $(-3, 7)$ for (x_1, y_1).**
$$y - 7 = \frac{1}{3}(x + 3)$$ **Simplify.**

? .... **Need Help?**

Numbers with product -1 are opposite reciprocals. In Example 5, the opposite reciprocal of -3 is $\frac{1}{3}$.

✓ **Check Understanding** ⑤ Write an equation for the line perpendicular to $5y - x = 10$ that contains $(15, -4)$.
$y + 4 = -5(x - 15)$

6 EXAMPLE Real-World  Connection

The window at the left includes some perpendicular lead strips. The line that contains $\overline{BC}$ has equation $y = -x + 10$. $\overline{AB}$ is perpendicular to $\overline{BC}$. Write an equation for $\overleftrightarrow{AB}$, the line that contains $\overline{AB}$ and point $(-1, 5)$.

The line that contains $\overline{BC}$ has slope -1. Let m be the slope of $\overleftrightarrow{AB}$.

$-1m = -1$ **The product of the slopes is -1.**

$m = 1$

$\overleftrightarrow{AB}$ has slope 1 and can be written in the form $y = 1x + b$, or $y = x + b$.

$y = x + b$ $\overleftrightarrow{AB}$ **has slope 1.**

$5 = -1 + b$ **Substitute 5 for y and -1 for x.**

$6 = b$ **Add 1 to each side.**

The equation for $\overleftrightarrow{AB}$ is $y = x + 6$.

✔ **Check Understanding** 6 If the equation for a line containing a lead strip on a different window is $y = -\frac{2}{3}x + 15$, write an equation for the line perpendicular to it that contains $(2, 8)$.

$y - 8 = \frac{3}{2}(x - 2)$ or $y = \frac{3}{2}x + 5$

EXERCISES

For more practice, see *Extra Practice*.

Practice and Problem Solving

A **Practice by Example**

Example 1
(page 158)

2. No; the slope of $\ell_1 = \frac{1}{3}$ and the slope of $\ell_2 = \frac{1}{2}$.

3. No; the slope of $\ell_1 = \frac{3}{2}$, and the slope of $\ell_2 = 2$.

In Exercises 1–5, are lines ℓ_1 and ℓ_2 parallel? Explain, using slope. 2–3. See left.

Yes; both slopes $= -\frac{1}{2}$.

1.
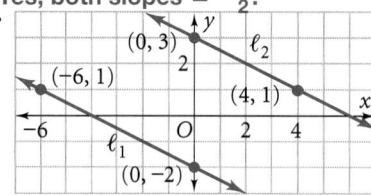

2.
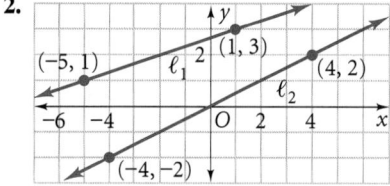

3.
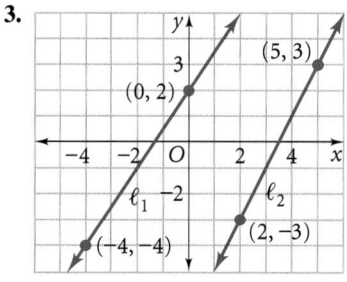

4. Yes; both slopes $= 4$.
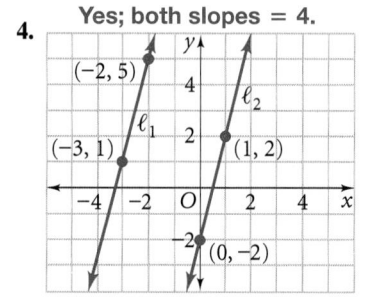

5. Line ℓ_1 contains $A(-3, 6)$ and $B(2, 6)$, and line ℓ_2 contains $C(0, 0)$ and $D(7, 0)$. Yes; both slopes $= 0$.

Example 2
(page 159)

x^2 Algebra **Are the lines parallel? Explain.** 6–11. See margin.

6. $y = 2x + 5$
$y = 2x$

7. $y = \frac{3}{4}x - 10$
$y = \frac{3}{4}x + 2$

8. $y = -x + 6$
$x + y = 20$

9. $y - 7x = 6$
$y + 7x = 8$

10. $3x + 4y = 12$
$6x + 2y = 6$

11. $2x + 5y = -1$
$10y = -4x - 20$

Lesson 3-6 Slopes of Parallel and Perpendicular Lines **161**

pages 161–164 Exercises

6. Yes; the lines both have a slope of 2 but different y-intercepts.

7. Yes; the lines both have a slope of $\frac{3}{4}$ but different y-intercepts.

8. Yes; the lines both have a slope of -1 but different y-intercepts.

9. No; one slope = 7 and the other slope = -7.

10. No; one slope = $-\frac{3}{4}$ and the other slope = -3.

11. Yes; the lines both have a slope of $-\frac{2}{5}$ but different y-intercepts.

3. Practice

Assignment Guide

▼1 Objective
Ⓐ Ⓑ Core 1–15, 31–34, 36, 37, 39
Ⓒ Extension 49

▼2 Objective
Ⓐ Ⓑ Core 16–30, 35, 38, 40–46
Ⓒ Extension 47, 48, 50

Standardized Test Prep 51–54

Mixed Review 55–63

Visual Learners

Exercises 1–4 Lines that do not intersect on the portion of the coordinate plane shown or that appear parallel may not actually be parallel. The only way to be certain that lines are parallel is to compare their slopes.

Exercises 8–11 Remind students to rewrite equations in slope-intercept form.

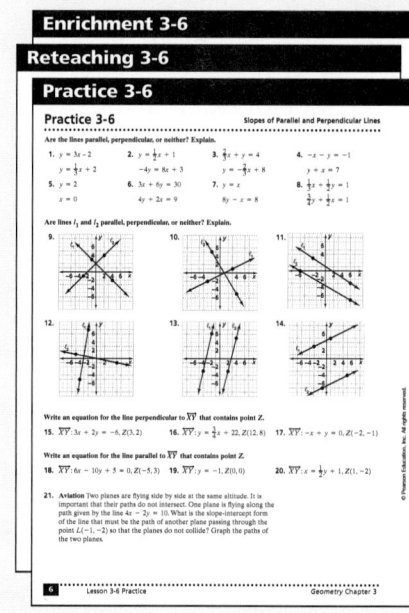

Exercises 31–34 Advise students to begin each problem by plotting the points on a sketch of the coordinate plane.

Exercise 40 Discuss as a class how the truth value of this theorem changes if the phrase *in a plane* is removed. Have students explain why the resulting statement is false.

Exercise 41 In Chapter 5 students will learn that the shortest distance from a point to a line is along the perpendicular path to that line. Discuss informally why Joe would choose the perpendicular route to the ball.

Exercises 47, 48 These exercises anticipate the study of quadrilaterals in Chapter 6. If necessary, review the distance and midpoint formulas.

pages 161–164 Exercises

12. $y - 3 = -2(x - 0)$ or
$y - 3 = -2x$

13. $y - 0 = \frac{1}{3}(x - 6)$ or
$y = \frac{1}{3}(x - 6)$

31. slope of $\overline{AB}$ = slope of $\overline{CD} = \frac{2}{3}$; $\overline{AB} \parallel \overline{CD}$
slope of $\overline{BC}$ = slope of $\overline{AD} = -3$; $\overline{BC} \parallel \overline{AD}$

32. slope of $\overline{AB}$ = slope of $\overline{CD} = -\frac{3}{4}$; $\overline{AB} \parallel \overline{CD}$
slope of $\overline{BC}$ = slope of $\overline{AD} = 1$; $\overline{BC} \parallel \overline{AD}$

33. slope of $\overline{AB} = \frac{1}{2}$; slope of $\overline{CD} = \frac{1}{4}$; $\overline{AB} \nparallel \overline{CD}$
slope of $\overline{BC} = -1$; slope of $\overline{AD} = -\frac{1}{2}$; $\overline{BC} \nparallel \overline{AD}$

34. slope of $\overline{AB}$ = slope of $\overline{CD} = 0$; $\overline{AB} \parallel \overline{CD}$
slope of $\overline{BC} = 3$ and slope of $\overline{AD} = \frac{3}{2}$; $\overline{BC} \nparallel \overline{AD}$

47. $\overline{AC}: d$
$= \sqrt{(7 - 9)^2 + (11 - 1)^2}$
$= \sqrt{104}$

$\overline{BD}: d$
$= \sqrt{(13 - 3)^2 + (7 - 5)^2}$
$= \sqrt{104}$
$\overline{AC} \cong \overline{BD}$

162

Example 3
(page 159)

Write an equation for the line parallel to $\overleftrightarrow{AB}$ that contains point C.

12. $\overleftrightarrow{AB}: y = -2x + 1, C(0, 3)$ See margin.

13. $\overleftrightarrow{AB}: y = \frac{1}{3}x, C(6, 0)$ See margin.

14. $\overleftrightarrow{AB}: -x + 2y = 4, C(-2, 4)$
$y - 4 = \frac{1}{2}(x + 2)$

15. $\overleftrightarrow{AB}: 3x + 2y = 12, C(6, -2)$
$y + 2 = -\frac{3}{2}(x - 6)$

Example 4 x^2 **Algebra** Are lines ℓ_1 and ℓ_2 perpendicular? Explain using slope.
(page 160)

16. Yes; the slope of $\ell_1 = -\frac{1}{2}$, and the slope of $\ell_2 = 2$; $-\frac{1}{2} \cdot 2 = -1$.

17. Yes; the slope of $\ell_1 = -\frac{3}{2}$, and the slope of $\ell_2 = \frac{2}{3}$; $-\frac{3}{2} \cdot \frac{2}{3} = -1$.

18. No; the slope of $\ell_1 = -1$, and the slope of $\ell_2 = \frac{4}{5}$; $-1 \cdot \frac{4}{5} \neq -1$.

19. Yes; the slope of $\ell_1 = -1$, and the slope of $\ell_2 = 1$; $-1 \cdot 1 = -1$.

16.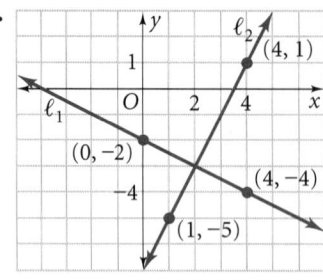

17.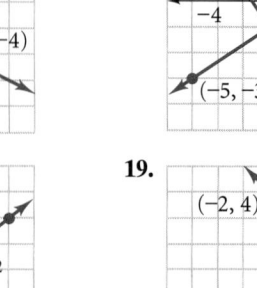

18.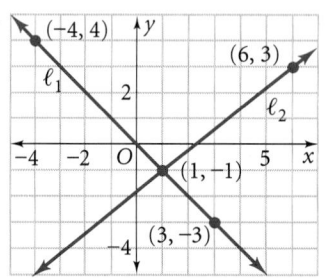

19.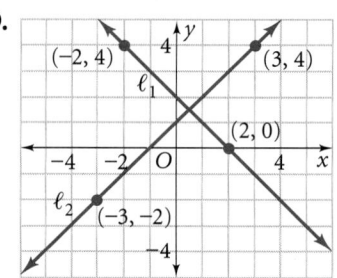

Example 5
(page 160)

Write an equation for the line perpendicular to $\overleftrightarrow{MN}$ that contains point P.

20. $\overleftrightarrow{MN}: y = \frac{2}{3}x, P(6, 6)$ $y - 6 = -\frac{3}{2}(x - 6)$

21. $\overleftrightarrow{MN}: y = \frac{1}{2}x - 5, P(4, 0)$ $y = -2(x - 4)$

22. $\overleftrightarrow{MN}: y + 2x = -8, P(4, 4)$
$y - 4 = \frac{1}{2}(x - 4)$

23. $\overleftrightarrow{MN}: 4y + 5x = 20, P(0, 0)$ $y = \frac{4}{5}x$

Example 6
(page 161)

24. **Highway Construction** Highway planners want to construct a road perpendicular to Route 3 at point O. An equation for the Route 3 line is $y = \frac{2}{3}x$. Find an equation for the line for the new road. $y = -\frac{3}{2}x$

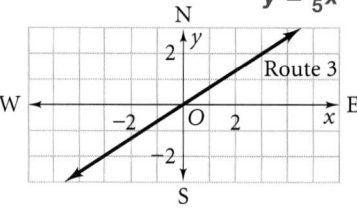

B **Apply Your Skills** x^2 **Algebra** Are the lines perpendicular? Explain.

25. $y - \frac{1}{2}x = 0$
$y - 2x = -1$
No; $\frac{1}{2} \cdot 2 \neq -1$.

26. $y = -x - 7$
$y - x = 20$
Yes; $1 \cdot (-1) = -1$.

27. $y = 3$
$x = -2$
Yes; one is vertical and the other is horizontal.

28. $3y + 2x = 12$
$y + 3x = -2$
No; $-\frac{2}{3} \cdot (-3) \neq -1$.

29. $2x + 3y = 6$
$6x - 4y = 24$
Yes; $-\frac{2}{3} \cdot \frac{3}{2} = -1$.

30. $2x - 7y = -42$
$4y = -7x - 2$
No; $\frac{2}{7} \cdot (-\frac{7}{4}) \neq -1$.

Use slopes to find whether the opposite sides of quadrilateral $ABCD$ are parallel.
31–34. See margin.

31. $A(0, 2), B(3, 4), C(2, 7), D(-1, 5)$

32. $A(-3, 1), B(1, -2), C(0, -3), D(-4, 0)$

35. Answers may vary.
Sample: $y = \frac{4}{5}x + 5$, $y = -\frac{5}{4}x + 5$

33. $A(1, 1), B(5, 3), C(7, 1), D(3, 0)$

34. $A(1, 0), B(4, 0), C(3, -3), D(-1, -3)$

35. **Open-Ended** Write equations for two perpendicular lines that have the same y-intercept and do not pass through the origin. **See left.**

36. **Writing** Can the y-intercepts of two parallel lines be the same? Explain.
No; two parallel lines with the same y-intercept are actually only one line.

162   Chapter 3   Parallel and Perpendicular Lines

48. slope of $\overline{AC} = -5$;
slope of $\overline{BD} = \frac{1}{5}$;
since $-5 \cdot \frac{1}{5} = -1$,
$\overline{AC} \perp \overline{BD}$;

midpoint $\overline{AC} = (8, 6)$;
midpoint $\overline{BD} = (8, 6)$;
since the midpoints are the same, the diagonals bisect each other.

37. $\overline{RS}$ and $\overline{VU}$ are horizontal with slope $= 0$; $\overline{RS} \parallel \overline{VU}$; slope of $\overline{RW} =$ slope of $\overline{UT}$ $= 1$; $\overline{RW} \parallel \overline{UT}$; slope of $\overline{WV} =$ slope of $\overline{ST}$ $= -1$; $\overline{WV} \parallel \overline{ST}$

37. Use slope to show that the opposite sides of hexagon *RSTUVW* at the right are parallel.

38. Use slope to determine whether a triangle with vertices $G(3, 2)$, $H(8, 5)$, and $K(0, 10)$ is a right triangle. Explain. **No; no pairs of slopes have a product of -1.**

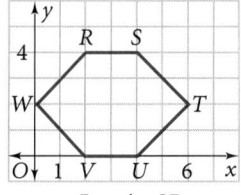
Exercise 37

Proof Developing Proof Use slope to explain why each theorem is true for three lines in the coordinate plane.

39. Theorem 3-5: If two lines are parallel to the same line, then they are parallel to each other. **The lines will have the same slope.**

40. Theorem 3-6: In a plane, if two lines are perpendicular to the same line, then they are parallel to each other. **When lines are $\perp$, the product of their slopes is -1. So, two lines $\perp$ to the same line must have the same slope.**

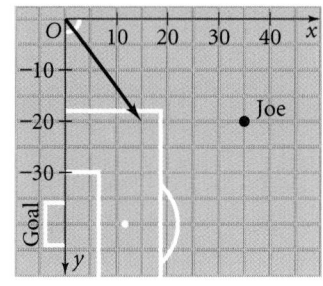

41. Soccer The coordinate system at the right is designed for a soccer field. Each unit represents one yard. Joe is at point $P(35, -20)$. The path of the ball from a corner kick is represented by the equation $y = -\frac{4}{3}x$. To have the best chance for a shot on goal, Joe wants to run toward the ball so that his path meets the path of the ball at a right angle.
a. Find an equation for the line on which Joe should run. $y + 20 = \frac{3}{4}(x - 35)$
b. Critical Thinking Why is point-slope form the best choice for the equation? **because you are given a point and can quickly find the slope**

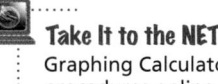
Real-World ⊕ Connection

For a corner kick, the ball is placed within a quarter circle of radius 1 yd.

Determine whether $\overleftrightarrow{AB}$ and $\overleftrightarrow{CD}$ are *parallel*, *perpendicular*, or *neither*.

42. $A\left(-1, \frac{1}{2}\right), B(-1, 2), C(3, 7), D(3, -1)$ ∥ **43.** $A(-2, 3), B(-2, 5), C(1, 4), D(2, 4)$ ⊥

44. $A(2, 4), B(5, 4), C(3, 2), D(0, 8)$ **neither**   **45.** $A(-3, 2), B(5, 1), C(2, 7), D(1, -1)$ ⊥

46. Graphing Calculator Use your graphing calculator to find the slope of $\overleftrightarrow{AB}$ in Exercise 45. Enter the x-coordinates of A and B into the L_1 list of your list editor. Enter the y-coordinates into the L_2 list. In your ⟨STAT⟩ CALC menu select LinReg $(ax + b)$. ⟨ENTER⟩ to find the slope a. Repeat to find the slope of $\overleftrightarrow{CD}$. Are $\overleftrightarrow{AB}$ and $\overleftrightarrow{CD}$ parallel, perpendicular, or neither? ⊥

Take It to the NET
Graphing Calculator procedures online at www.PHSchool.com

C **Challenge**

47. Show that the diagonals of the figure at the right are congruent. **See margin.**
48. Show that the diagonals of the figure at the right are perpendicular bisectors of each other. **See margin, p.162.**
49. a. Graph the points $P(2, 2)$, $Q(7, 4)$, and $R(3, 5)$. **a–c. See margin.**
b. Find the coordinates of a point S that, along with points P, Q, and R, will form the vertices of a quadrilateral whose opposite sides are parallel. Graph the quadrilateral.
c. Repeat part (b), finding a different point S and graphing the new quadrilateral.

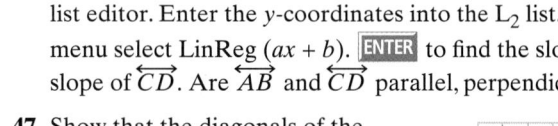
Exercises 47 and 48

50. A triangle has vertices $L(-5, 6)$, $M(-2, -3)$, and $N(4, 5)$. Write an equation for the line perpendicular to $\overline{LM}$ that contains point N. $y - 5 = \frac{1}{3}(x - 4)$

Lesson 3-6 Slopes of Parallel and Perpendicular Lines **163**

49.   a–b. Answers may vary. Sample:

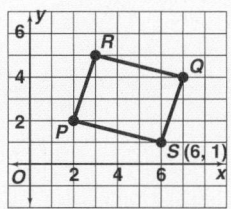

c. The other possible locations for S are $(-2, 3)$ and $(8, 7)$.

Lesson Quiz 3-6

1. Are lines ℓ_1 and ℓ_2 parallel? Explain.

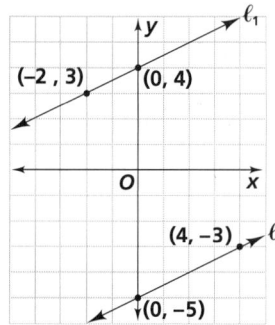

Yes; the lines have the same slope and different y-intercepts.

2. Are the lines $x + 4y = 8$ and $2x + 6y = 16$ parallel? Explain. **No; their slopes are not equal.**

3. Write an equation in point-slope form for the line parallel to $-18x + 2y = 7$ that contains $(3, 1)$. $y - 1 = 9(x - 3)$

4. Are the lines $y = \frac{2}{3}x + 5$ and $3x + 2y = 10$ perpendicular? Explain. **Yes; the product of their slopes is -1.**

5. Write an equation in point-slope form for the line perpendicular to $y = -\frac{1}{6}x - 2$ that contains $(-5, -8)$. $y + 8 = 6(x + 5)$

Alternative Assessment

Have students draw a pair of parallel lines and a pair of perpendicular lines on a coordinate plane and then use slopes to prove that the lines are parallel and perpendicular.

Standardized Test Prep

Resources
For additional practice with a variety of test item formats:
• Standardized Test Prep, p. 177
• Test-Taking Strategies, p. 172
• Test-Taking Strategies with Transparencies

163

Exercise 51 Students may need to write the equation in slope-intercept form before choosing the correct answer choice.

Chapter Checkpoint 2

To check understanding of Lessons 3-4 to 3-6:

Checkpoint Quiz 2 (p. 164)

📁 **Teaching Resources**
Checkpoint Quiz 2 (also in Prentice Hall Assessment System)

👥 **Reaching All Students**
Reading and Math Literacy 3C

Spanish versions available

---

pages 161–164 Exercises

54. [2] a. slope of line c:
$$\frac{1-(-2)}{-4-2} =$$
$$\frac{3}{-6} = -\frac{1}{2};\text{ slope of}$$
line $\perp$ to c: 2

b. 0

[1] at least one correct slope

page 164 Checkpoint Quiz 2

4.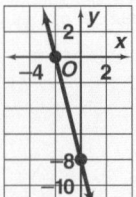

5.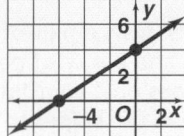

6.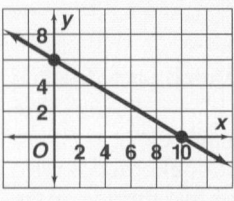

Standardized Test Prep

Multiple Choice

51. What is the slope of a line parallel to the line $6x - 4y = 12$? **B**
A. $-\frac{3}{2}$ B. $\frac{3}{2}$ C. $\frac{4}{3}$ D. $-\frac{4}{3}$

💻 **Take It to the NET**
Online lesson quiz at
www.PHSchool.com
Web Code: afa-0306

52. The slope of a line is 6. What is the slope of a line perpendicular to it? **I**
F. 6   G. -6 H. $\frac{1}{6}$ I. $-\frac{1}{6}$

53. Line f contains the points $(5, -4)$ and $(4, -6)$. What is the slope of a line perpendicular to it? **C**
A. 2   B. $\frac{1}{2}$ C. $-\frac{1}{2}$ D. -2

Short Response

54. Line c contains the points $(2, -2)$ and $(-4, 1)$.   **a–b. See margin.**
a. What is the slope of a line perpendicular to line c?
b. What is the y-intercept of the line perpendicular to line c that contains $(1, 2)$?

Mixed Review

Lesson 3-5 $\boxed{x^2}$ **Algebra** Write an equation for the line containing the given points.

55. $A(0, 3), B(6, 0)$ 56. $C(-4, 2), D(-1, 7)$ 57. $E(3, -2), F(-5, -8)$
$y - 3 = -\frac{1}{2}(x - 0)$ or $y - 3 = -\frac{1}{2}x$ $y - 2 = \frac{5}{3}(x + 4)$ $y + 2 = \frac{3}{4}(x - 3)$

Lesson 2-4   Name the property that justifies each statement.

Mult. Prop. of =
58. $\angle 4 \cong \angle 4$ **Refl. Prop. of $\cong$**   59. If $m\angle B = 8$, then $2m\angle B = 16$.

60. $-3x + 6 = 3(-x + 2)$ **Dist. Prop.**   61. If $\overline{RS} \cong \overline{MN}$, then $\overline{MN} \cong \overline{RS}$.
Symm. Prop. of $\cong$

Lesson 2-3   Use the Law of Syllogism to draw a conclusion.

62. If you are in geometry class, then you are in math class. If you are in math class, then you are at school. If you are in geometry class, then you are at school.

63. If you travel to Switzerland, then you travel to Europe. If you travel to Europe, then you have a passport. If you travel to Switzerland, then you have a passport.

✓ Checkpoint Quiz 2   Lessons 3-4 through 3-6

📱 **Instant self-check quiz online and on CD-ROM**

Use the number of sides to name the polygon. Then find the value of each variable.

1.
octagon; $n = 125$

7. slope of $\overleftrightarrow{RS} = -\frac{2}{5}$;
slope of $\overleftrightarrow{TV} = \frac{3}{5}$; neither

8. slope of $\overleftrightarrow{RS} = 1$;
slope of $\overleftrightarrow{TV} = -1$; $\perp$

9. slope of $\overleftrightarrow{RS} = -\frac{5}{4}$;
slope of $\overleftrightarrow{TV} = \frac{4}{5}$; $\perp$

2.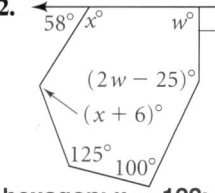
hexagon; $x = 122$; $w = 90$

3.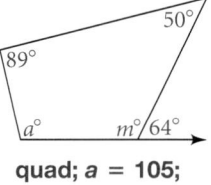
quad; $a = 105$; $m = 116$

$\boxed{x^2}$ **Algebra** Graph each line using intercepts. **4–6. See margin.**

4. $4x + y = -8$ 5. $-2x + 3y = 12$ 6. $3x + 5y = 30$

Find the slopes of $\overleftrightarrow{RS}$ and $\overleftrightarrow{TV}$. Then determine whether $\overleftrightarrow{RS}$ and $\overleftrightarrow{TV}$ are parallel, perpendicular, or neither. Explain.

7. $R(-2, 6), S(3, 4), T(3, 5), V(0, 0)$ 8. $R(6, -1), S(7, 0), T(3, -4), V(0, -1)$

9. $R(9, 1), S(5, 6), T(3, 8), V(-2, 4)$ 10. $R(5, -7), S(-4, -9), T(6, 2), V(-3, 0)$

slope of $\overleftrightarrow{RS} = \frac{2}{9}$; slope of $\overleftrightarrow{TV} = \frac{2}{9}$; $\parallel$

Constructing Parallel and Perpendicular Lines

 North Carolina Objectives

2.02 Apply properties, definitions, and theorems of angles and lines to solve problems and write proofs.

Lesson Preview

What You'll Learn

 OBJECTIVE 1 To construct parallel lines

 OBJECTIVE 2 To construct perpendicular lines

. . . And Why

To construct the shortest segment from a point to a line, as in Example 4

✓ Check Skills You'll Need

(For help, go to Lesson 1-5.)

Use a straightedge to draw each figure. Then use a straightedge and compass to construct a figure congruent to it. **1–3. See back of book.**

1. a segment   2. an obtuse angle   3. an acute angle

Use a straightedge to draw each figure. Then use a straightedge and compass to bisect it. **4–6. See back of book.**

4. a segment   5. an acute angle   6. an obtuse angle

 Interactive lesson includes instant self-check, tutorials, and activities.

OBJECTIVE 1 — Constructing Parallel Lines

You can use what you know about parallel lines, transversals, and corresponding angles to construct parallel lines.

1 EXAMPLE   Constructing $\ell \parallel m$

Construct the line parallel to a given line and through a given point that is not on the line.

Given: line ℓ and point N not on ℓ

Construct: line m through N with $m \parallel \ell$

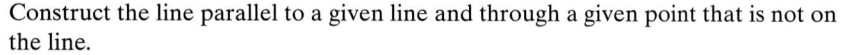

Step 1
Label two points H and J on ℓ.
Draw $\overleftrightarrow{HN}$.

Step 2
Construct $\angle 1$ with vertex at N so that $\angle 1 \cong \angle NHJ$ and the two angles are corresponding angles. Label the line you just constructed m.

$m \parallel \ell$

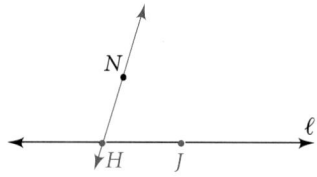
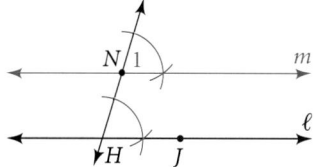

Real-World Connection

Careers Architects construct parallel and perpendicular lines when they build models of the buildings they design.

✓ **Check Understanding**   ① **Critical Thinking** Explain why lines ℓ and m must be parallel.
If corr. $\angle$s are $\cong$, the lines are $\parallel$ by the Converse of Corr. $\angle$s Postulate.

For many constructions, you will find it helpful to first visualize or sketch what the final figure should look like. This will often suggest the construction steps. In Example 2, a sketch is shown at the left of the example.

Ongoing Assessment and Intervention

Before the Lesson
Diagnose prerequisite skills using:
• Check Skills You'll Need

During the Lesson
Monitor progress using:
• Check Understanding
• Additional Examples
• Standardized Test Prep

After the Lesson
Assess knowledge using:
• Lesson Quiz
• Computer Test Generator CD

3-7

1. Plan

Lesson Preview

✓ Check Skills You'll Need

Constructing Segments and Angles
Lesson 1-5: Examples 1 and 2
Exercises 1–6
Extra Practice, p. 690

Constructing Bisectors
Lesson 1-5: Examples 3 and 5
Exercises 7, 8, 13, 14
Extra Practice, p. 690

Lesson Resources

📁 **Teaching Resources**
Practice, Reteaching, Enrichment

👥 **Reaching All Students**
Practice Workbook 3-7
Spanish Practice Workbook 3-7
Informal Geometry Planning
  Guide 3-7

⏰ **Presentation Assistant Plus!**
Transparencies
• Check Skills You'll Need 3-7
• Additional Examples 3-7
• Student Edition Answers 3-7
• Lesson Quiz 3-7
PH Presentation Pro CD 3-7

PRENTICE HALL ASSESSMENT SYSTEM

Computer Test Generator CD

💿 **Technology**
Resource Pro® CD-ROM
Computer Test Generator CD
Prentice Hall Presentation Pro CD

🌐 **www.PHSchool.com**
Student Site
• Teacher Web Code: afk-5500
• Self-grading Lesson Quiz
Teacher Center
• Lesson Planner
• Resources

Plus

165

2. Teach

Math Background

The method in this lesson for constructing parallel lines is based on the Converse of the Corresponding Angles Postulate in Lesson 3-2. An alternative method might base a construction on the Converse of the Alternate Interior Angles Theorem or on the theorem *In a plane, if two lines are perpendicular to the same line, then they are parallel to each other.* The method for constructing perpendicular lines is based on the method for constructing the perpendicular bisector of a segment in Lesson 1-5.

OBJECTIVE 1 Teaching Notes

Visual Learners

Do the constructions in this lesson on the board.

1 EXAMPLE Error Prevention

In Step 2, make sure that students realize that the angle constructed at vertex *N* must be a corresponding angle. If the congruent angle were constructed on the opposite side of $\overleftrightarrow{HN}$, the lines would not be parallel.

2 EXAMPLE Math Tip

The constructed quadrilateral is a trapezoid.

Additional Examples

❶ Draw a vertical line and a point not on the line. Demonstrate the construction of Example 1. **Check students' constructions.**

❷ Construct a quadrilateral with both pairs of sides parallel.

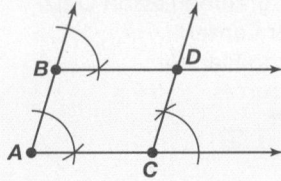

Need Help?

First, draw a sketch of the figure.

2.

✔ **Check Understanding**

---

2 EXAMPLE Constructing a Special Quadrilateral

Construct a quadrilateral with one pair of parallel sides of lengths *a* and *b*.

Given: segments of lengths *a* and *b*

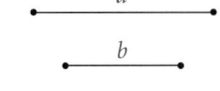

Construct: quadrilateral *ABYZ* with $AZ = a$, $BY = b$, and $\overline{AZ} \parallel \overline{BY}$

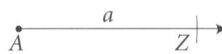

Step 1
Construct $\overline{AZ}$ with length *a*.

Step 2
Draw a point *B* not on $\overleftrightarrow{AZ}$. Then draw $\overrightarrow{AB}$.

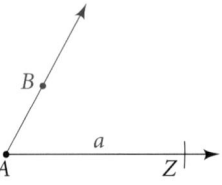

Step 3
Construct a ray parallel to $\overleftrightarrow{AZ}$ through *B*.

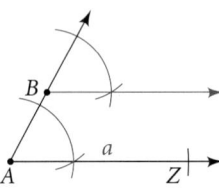

Step 4
Construct *Y* so that $BY = b$. Then draw $\overline{YZ}$.

Quadrilateral *ABYZ* has $AZ = a$, $BY = b$, and $\overline{AZ} \parallel \overline{BY}$.

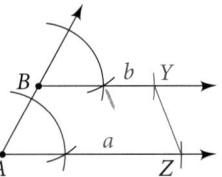

❷ Draw two segments. Label their lengths *c* and *d*. Construct a quadrilateral with one pair of parallel sides of lengths *c* and 2*d*. **See above left.**

OBJECTIVE 2 Constructing Perpendicular Lines

You can construct perpendicular lines using a compass and a straightedge.

3 EXAMPLE Perpendicular at a Point on a Line

Construct the perpendicular to a given line at a given point on the line.

Given: point *P* on line ℓ

Construct: $\overleftrightarrow{CP}$ with $\overleftrightarrow{CP} \perp \ell$

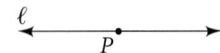

Step 1
Put the compass point on point *P*. Draw arcs intersecting ℓ in two points. Label the points *A* and *B*.

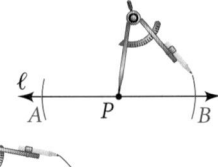

Step 2
Open the compass wider. With the compass tip on *A*, draw an arc above point *P*.

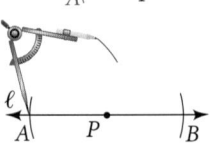

👥 Reaching All Students

| **Below Level** Ask volunteers to demonstrate and explain how to copy an angle and a segment and how to construct the perpendicular bisector of a line segment. | **Advanced Learners** Have students use the methods in Example 3 to construct a square as simply as possible. | **English Learners** See note on page 167. **Auditory Learners** See note on page 167. |

Step 3
Without changing the compass setting, place the compass point on point *B*. Draw an arc that intersects the arc from Step 2. Label the point of intersection *C*.

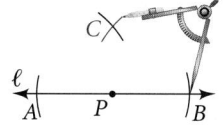

Step 4
Draw $\overleftrightarrow{CP}$.

$\overleftrightarrow{CP} \perp \ell$

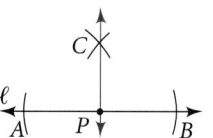

✓ **Check Understanding** ❸ Use a straightedge to draw $\overleftrightarrow{EF}$. Construct $\overleftrightarrow{FG}$ so that $\overleftrightarrow{FG} \perp \overleftrightarrow{EF}$ at point *F*.
See margin.

You will prove in Chapter 5 that the perpendicular segment is the shortest segment from a point to a line. Here is its construction.

4 EXAMPLE Perpendicular From a Point to a Line

Construct the perpendicular to a given line through a given point not on the line.

Given: line ℓ and point *R* not on ℓ
Construct: $\overleftrightarrow{RG}$ with $\overleftrightarrow{RG} \perp \ell$

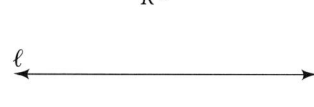

Step 1
Open your compass to a size greater than the distance from *R* to ℓ. With the compass point on point *R*, draw an arc that intersects ℓ at two points. Label the points *E* and *F*.

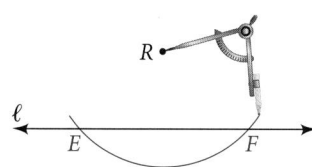

Step 2
Place the compass point on *E* and make an arc.

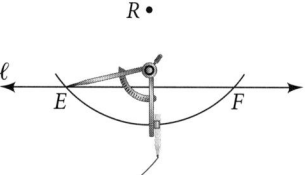

Step 3
Keep the same compass setting. With the compass tip on *F*, draw an arc that intersects the arc from Step 2. Label the point of intersection *G*.

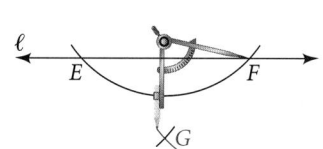

Step 4
Draw $\overleftrightarrow{RG}$.

$\overleftrightarrow{RG} \perp \ell$

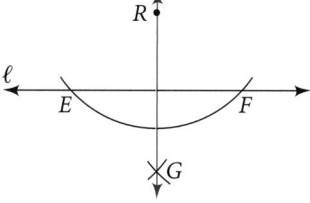

Real-World Connection

You can draw large circles using a simple, large compass.

✓ **Check Understanding** ❹ Draw a line $\overleftrightarrow{CX}$ and a point *Z* not on $\overleftrightarrow{CX}$. Construct $\overleftrightarrow{ZB}$ so that $\overleftrightarrow{ZB} \perp \overleftrightarrow{CX}$.
See back of book.

Lesson 3-7 Constructing Parallel and Perpendicular Lines **167**

page 167
Check
Understanding

3.

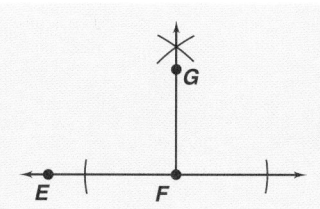

Auditory Learners

Have students work with partners to do the constructions in Examples 3 and 4, taking turns explaining the steps in each construction.

3 EXAMPLE English Learners

The word *perpendicular* is a noun in this example. Point out that *perpendicular* may mean a perpendicular line or segment. Similarly, *parallel* may mean a parallel line or segment.

4 EXAMPLE Teaching Tip

The compass setting in step 2 does not have to be the same as that in step 1. However, the compass settings must be the same in steps 2 and 3 and must be large enough that the arcs constructed in these two steps intersect.

Additional Examples

❸ Why does step 2 instruct you to open the compass wider? With the compass tip on *A* and then on *B*, the same compass setting would make arcs that intersect at point *P* on line ℓ.

❹ Examine the construction. At what special point does $\overleftrightarrow{RG}$ meet line ℓ? **the midpoint of $\overline{EF}$**

Closure

Explain how to construct a line parallel to a given line. Tell which theorem or postulate you use. **Construct congruent corresponding angles; the Converse of the Corresponding Angles Post.**

3. Practice

Assignment Guide

▼**1 Objective**

Ⓐ Ⓑ **Core** 1–7, 14–16, 21, 24, 25

Ⓒ **Extension** 27, 33–36

▼**2 Objective**

Ⓐ Ⓑ **Core** 8–13, 17–20, 22, 23, 26

Ⓒ **Extension** 28–32

Standardized Test Prep 37–40

Mixed Review 41–47

Alternative Method

Exercise 14 This exercise presents another way to construct a line parallel to a given line.

Exercise 19 Discuss as a class a plan for construction. Let students suggest, evaluate, and try different methods of constructing a square.

Exercises 21, 24, 25 These exercises encourage students to make conjectures that are actually theorems and postulates that they will study in Chapters 6, 4, and 5, respectively.

Enrichment 3-7
Reteaching 3-7
Practice 3-7

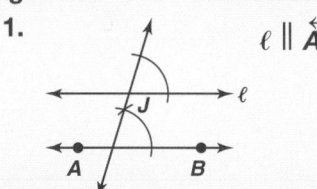

EXERCISES

For more practice, see *Extra Practice*.

Practice and Problem Solving

Ⓐ **Practice by Example**

Example 1
(page 165)

In Exercises 1–4, draw a figure like the given one. Then construct the line through point *J* and parallel to $\overleftrightarrow{AB}$. 1–4. See margin pp. 168–169.

1.
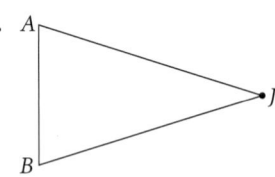

2.

3.

4.

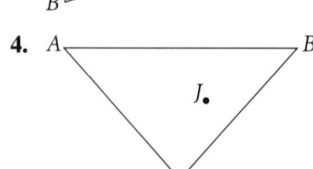

Example 2
(page 166)

For Exercises 5–7, draw two segments. Label their lengths *a* and *b*. Construct a quadrilateral with one pair of parallel sides as described. 5–7. See back of book.

5. The sides have lengths *a* and *b*.

6. The sides have lengths 2*a* and *b*.

7. The sides have lengths *a* and $\frac{1}{2}b$.

Example 3
(pages 166, 167)

In Exercises 8–9, draw a figure like the given one. Then construct the line perpendicular to $\overleftrightarrow{AB}$ at point *P*. 8–9. See back of book.

8.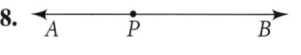

9.
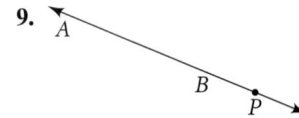

Example 4
(page 167)

In Exercises 10–13, draw a figure like the given one. Then construct the line through point *P* and perpendicular to $\overleftrightarrow{RS}$. 10–13. See back of book.

10. P•
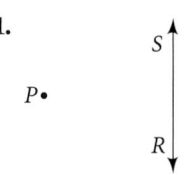

11.
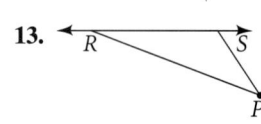

12.
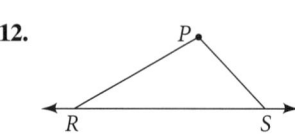

13.

Ⓑ **Apply Your Skills**

14. Draw an acute angle. Construct an angle congruent to your angle so that the two angles are alternate interior angles. (*Hint:* Think of the letter **Z**.)
See margin, p.169.

🖊 15. **Writing** Explain how to use the Converse of the Alternate Interior Angles Theorem to construct a line parallel to a given line through a point not on the line. (*Hint:* See Exercise 14.)
Construct a ≅ alt. int. ∠; then draw the ∥ line.

168 Chapter 3 Parallel and Perpendicular Lines

pages 168–170 **Exercises**

1. $\ell \parallel \overleftrightarrow{AB}$
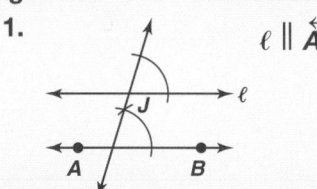

2. $\ell \parallel \overleftrightarrow{AB}$
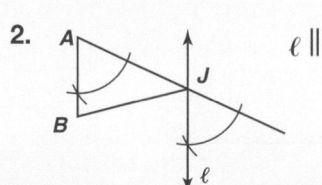

3. $\ell \parallel \overleftrightarrow{AB}$
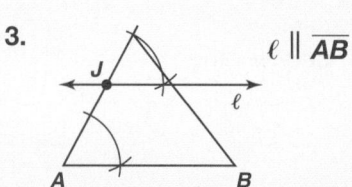

168

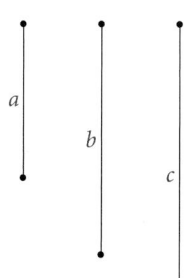

a

b

c

Exercises 17–25

16. Draw obtuse $\triangle ABC$ with obtuse $\angle B$.
  a. Construct line ℓ through point A so that $\ell \parallel \overline{BC}$. **a–b. See back**
  b. Construct line m through point C so that $m \parallel \overline{AB}$. **of book.**

For Exercises 17–25, use the segments at the left. **17–25. See back of book.**

17. Draw a line m. Construct a segment of length b that is perpendicular to line m.

18. Construct a rectangle with base b and height c.

19. Construct a square with sides of length a.

20. Construct a rectangle with one side length a and a diagonal length b.

21. a. Construct a quadrilateral with a pair of parallel sides of length c.
  b. Make a Conjecture What appears to be true about the other pair of sides in the quadrilateral you constructed?
  c. Use a protractor, a ruler, or both to check the conjecture you made in part (b).

22. Construct a right triangle with legs of lengths a and b.

23. Construct a right triangle with legs of lengths b and $\frac{1}{2}b$.

24. a. Construct a triangle with sides of lengths $a, b,$ and c.
  b. Construct a quadrilateral with sides of lengths $a, b,$ and c.
  c. Writing How many different triangles could you construct in (a)? Explain. How many different quadrilaterals could you construct in (b)? Explain.

25. a. Construct a triangle with sides of lengths $a, b,$ and c.
  b. Construct the midpoint of each side of the triangle.
  c. Form a new triangle by connecting the midpoints.
  d. Make a Conjecture How do the sides of the smaller triangle and the sides of the larger triangle appear to be related?
  e. Use a protractor, a ruler, or both to check the conjecture you made in part (d).

26. Paper Folding You can use paper folding to create a perpendicular to a given line through a given point. Fold the paper so that the line folds onto itself and the fold line contains the given point.

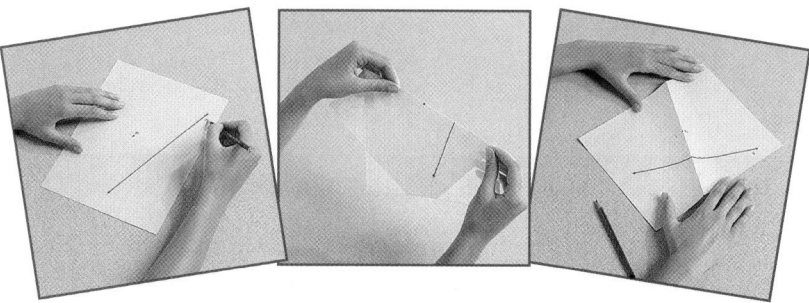

  a. Draw a line m and a point W not on the line. Use paper folding to create the perpendicular to m through W. Label this fold line k. **a–b. Check students'**
  b. Next, fold the line perpendicular to k through W. Label this fold line p. **work.**
  c. What is true of p and m? Justify your answer. **$p \parallel m$; in a plane, two lines $\perp$ to a third are $\parallel$.**

Ⓒ Challenge Draw a segment, $\overline{DG}$. Construct a quadrilateral whose diagonals are both congruent to $\overline{DG}$, bisect each other, and meet the additional condition given below. Describe the quadrilateral that you get. **27–28. See back of book.**

27. The diagonals are not perpendicular. **28.** The diagonals are perpendicular.

⎍ Lesson Quiz 3-7

Draw a figure similar to the one given. Then complete the construction. Check students' constructions.

1. Construct a line through D that is parallel to $\overleftrightarrow{XY}$.

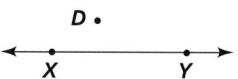

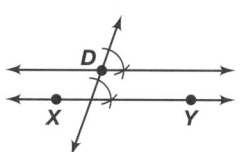

2. Construct a quadrilateral with one pair of parallel sides of lengths p and q.

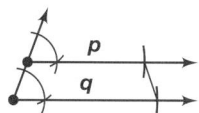

Quadrilaterals may vary. Sample:

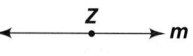

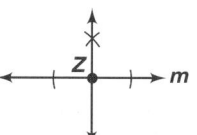

3. Construct the line perpendicular to line m at point Z.

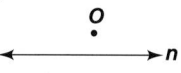

4. Construct the perpendicular to line n through point O.

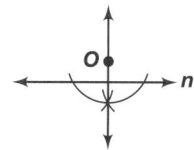

4.

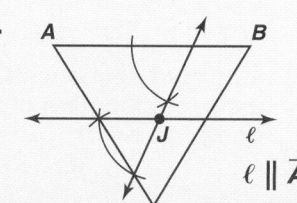

$\ell \parallel \overline{AB}$

14.

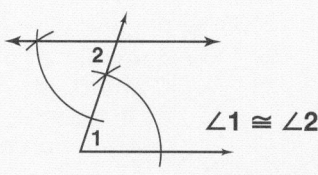

$\angle 1 \cong \angle 2$

Alternative Assessment

Have students work in pairs to construct a rectangle. Their work should include a construction diagram and a written explanation of the steps they used.

Standardized Test Prep

 **Resources**

For additional practice with a variety of test item formats:
• Standardized Test Prep, p. 177
• Test-Taking Strategies, p. 172
• Test-Taking Strategies with Transparencies

pages 168–170 Exercises

29.

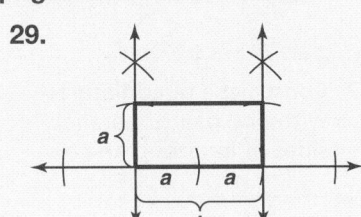

30.

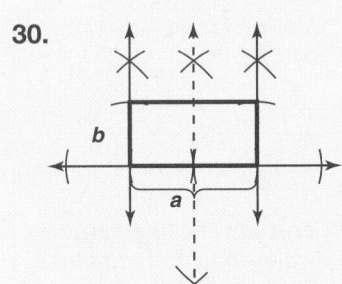

31.

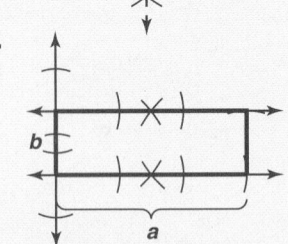

32.

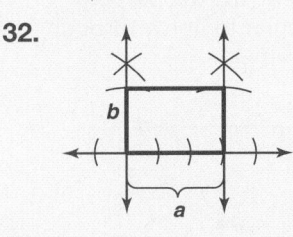

33.

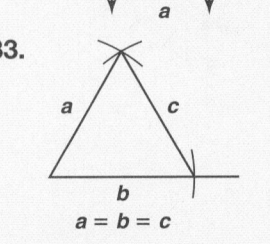

$a = b = c$

29–32.
See margin.

Construct a rectangle whose side lengths a and b meet the given condition.

29. $b = 2a$ **30.** $b = \frac{1}{2}a$ **31.** $b = \frac{1}{3}a$ **32.** $b = \frac{2}{3}a$

Construct a triangle whose side lengths a, b, and c meet the given conditions. If such a triangle is not possible, explain. 33, 35. See margin. 34. See back of book.

33. $a = b = c$ **34.** $a = b = 2c$ **35.** $a = 2b = 2c$ **36.** $a = b + c$
Not possible; The shorter sides would meet at a point on the longer side, forming a segment.

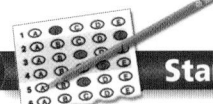

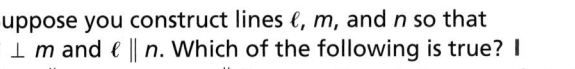
Standardized Test Prep

Multiple Choice

37. In the construction shown at the right, the two arcs with centers A and B have the same radius. What must be true of $\overline{PQ}$? **A**
   A. $\overline{PQ}$ bisects $\overline{AB}$.   **B.** $\overline{PQ} \parallel \overline{AB}$
   C. $\overline{PQ} \cong \overline{AB}$ **D.** $\overline{PQ} \cong \overline{AQ}$

38. Suppose you construct lines ℓ, m, and n so that $\ell \perp m$ and $\ell \parallel n$. Which of the following is true? **I**
   F. $m \parallel n$ **G.** $m \parallel \ell$ **H.** $n \perp \ell$ **I.** $n \perp m$

Short Response

39. Use a compass and straightedge to construct the following figure.
   a. Draw a line ℓ and a point G not on ℓ. Construct an arc centered at point G to intersect ℓ in two points. Label the points R and T. Draw $\overline{GR}$ and $\overline{GT}$.
   b. Classify $\triangle RGT$. Justify your response. **a–b. See back of book.**

40. These pictures show steps for constructing a line parallel to a given line, but they are not necessarily in order.

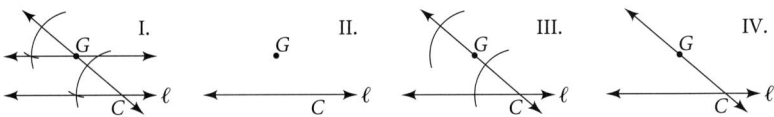

   a. List the construction steps in the correct order. **a–b. See margin.**
   b. For any step that uses a compass, describe the location(s) of the compass point.

 **Take It to the NET**
Online lesson quiz at
www.PHSchool.com
Web Code: afa-0307

Mixed Review

Lesson 3-6
Are the lines parallel? Explain.
No; the slopes are different.   Yes; the slopes are both $-\frac{1}{3}$.

41. $y = -4x - 3$ **42.** $y = \frac{1}{2}x + 1$ **43.** $x + 3y = -6$
     $y = 4x + 3$ $y = -2x - 1$ $4x + 12y = -6$
                               No; the slopes are different.

Lesson 1-6
Find the distance between the points to the nearest tenth.

44. $W(8, -2)$ and $Z(2, 6)$ **10**

45. $W(-4.5, 1.2)$ and $Z(3.5, -2.8)$ **8.9**

Lesson 1-2
Name the intersection of the planes.

46. plane ABE and plane $EBCD$ $\overleftrightarrow{EB}$

47. plane $AFDE$ and plane FCD $\overleftrightarrow{DF}$

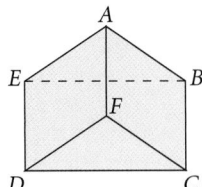

35. Not possible; if $a = 2b = 2c$, then $2a = 2b + 2c$ or $a = b + c$. The shorter sides would meet at the midpoint of the longer side, forming a segment.

40. [2] a. **II, IV, III, I**
   b. **(III): location of compass at points C and G; (I): same as III _and_ the intersection points**
of $\overleftrightarrow{CG}$ with arcs drawn in (III)

[1] incorrect sequence OR incorrect location of compass point

Using Tables and Lists

FOR USE WITH CHAPTER 3

Tables and lists on your graphing calculator allow you to study relationships both numerically and graphically. The first example reminds you how to build a table.

Take It to the NET
Graphing Calculator procedures online at **www.PHSchool.com**
Web Code: afe-2104

① EXAMPLE

Display a table showing the sums of the measures of the angles of a polygon.

Use the **Y=** screen and write the polygon angle-sum formula in the form $Y_1 = 180(X - 2)$. Use the **TBLSET** feature so that X starts at 3 and changes by 1.

● Use the **TABLE** feature to see the table of n-gon angle sums.

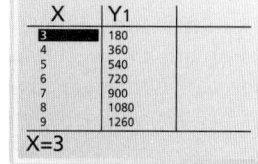

X	Y1
3	180
4	360
5	540
6	720
7	900
8	1080
9	1260

X=3

The second example suggests a powerful way to use lists. First, press **Y=** **CLEAR**.

② EXAMPLE

List and plot four ordered pairs for the line $y = 2x - 1$.

On your home screen generate four values for x in list **L₁** as follows.

$\text{seq}(X, X, -2, 4, 2)$ **STO▶** **L₁** **ENTER**.

Enter the corresponding values for y in list **L₂** as follows.

$2 \mathbf{L_1} - 1$ **STO▶** **L₂** **ENTER**.

Access **STAT PLOT**, press 1, and turn "On" Plot 1. Check that your **Xlist** is **L₁** and your **Ylist** is **L₂**. Then **GRAPH** in a standard viewing window as shown at the right.

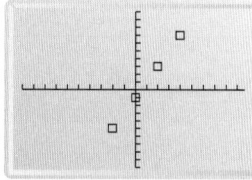

EXERCISES

1. Use lists to plot ordered pairs (x, y) for the relationship $y = 180(x - 2)$. Use the command $\text{seq}(X, X, 3, 12)$ to generate L_1 values. Store $180(L_1 - 2)$ into an L_2 list of Y values. Graph the points in an appropriate viewing window. **Check students' work.**

2. The relationship $y = 180(n - 2)/n$ or $Y_1 = 180(X - 2)/X$ gives the measure of one angle of a regular polygon for each value of n or X. **a–d. See margin.**
   a. Display a table of regular-polygon angle measures. Use TblStart = 3.
   b. Scroll down your table. What happens to the angle measures as X gets large?
   c. Create L_1, L_2 lists of (n, y) pairs for $n = 3$ to 20.
   d. Plot the (n, y) points. What happens to the angle measures as n gets large?

3. The formula $y = 360/n$ gives an exterior-angle measure for a regular n-gon. Create L_1, L_2 lists of (n, y) values and plot points. What happens to exterior-angle measures as n gets large? **They get smaller and approach 0.**

page 171   Technology
2. a. **Check students' work.**
   b. **They get larger by smaller and smaller increments.**
   c. **See back of book.**
   d. **They get larger by smaller and smaller increments.**

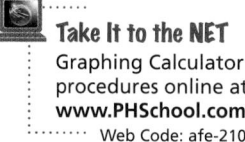
Using Tables and Lists

Students will use graphing calculators to build tables and lists of ordered pairs for functions and relationships described by Polygon Angle-Sum Theorems and to plot ordered pairs on a line.

Resources

Students may use any graphing calculator to explore tables and lists.

Teaching Notes

Graphing calculators enable students to generate tables of ordered pairs and to use lists to graph relations quickly without excess calculation. By building a table, list, and graph for the same relation, students explore algebraic, numerical, and geometric interrelationships.

Visual Learners

Seeing graphs built from lists of ordered pairs helps students understand and interpret algebraic and table-based relationships.

Teaching Tip

Different calculator brands and models may use different keys or sequences to create tables and lists. If necessary, have students with the same kind of calculator work together.

Careers

Statisticians and researchers sometimes use graphs to represent data that they have collected in order to uncover relationships. Algebraic techniques such as linear regression are used to explain relationships between variables studied.

Writing Extended Responses

This feature helps students understand how questions are scored and that a full explanation of the mathematical process used to arrive at an answer is at least as important as obtaining the correct answer.

Resources

PRENTICE HALL
ASSESSMENT SYSTEM

Test-Taking Strategies with Transparencies
• Transparency 3
• Practice sheet p. 15

Teaching Notes

Poor training can condition students to think that mathematics simply requires a correct answer. Use this feature to emphasize the importance of clear, logical reasoning.

Teaching Tip

Always encourage students to justify their reasoning; on examinations, require students to show all their work and/or justify their reasoning.

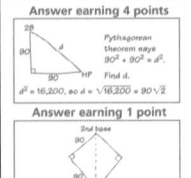

Test-Taking Strategies with Transparencies

Test-Taking Strategy: Writing Extended Responses
A major league baseball diamond is a square that is 90 ft on each side. Draw a diagram and show how to use the Pythagorean Theorem to find the distance from home plate to 2nd base (the diagonal of the square).

Scoring Guide
4 Provides a correct diagram AND applies the Pythagorean Theorem to find the correct solution showing all steps and procedures.
3 Applies the Pythagorean Theorem to find the correct solution showing the complete procedure, but there is no diagram.
2 Provides a correct diagram, but incorrectly applies the Pythagorean Theorem and solution is incorrect.
1 Provides a correct diagram, but there is no procedure shown AND no solution OR an incorrect solution given.
0 There is no response OR it is completely incorrect.

Answer earning 4 points | Answer earning 2 points
Answer earning 1 point | Answer earning 0 points

Transparency 3

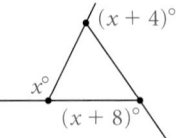
An extended-response question is usually worth a maximum of 4 points and has multiple parts. To get full credit, you need to answer each part and show all your work or justify your reasoning.

EXAMPLE

Algebra Use the triangle at the right.
a. Write an equation that you can use to find the value of x.
b. Show how to solve the equation for x.
c. Find the measure of the smallest interior angle of the triangle.

$(x + 4)°$
$x°$
$(x + 8)°$

Below are two responses and the amount of credit each received.

4 points	3 points
$x + (x + 4) + (x + 8) = 360$ $3x + 12 = 360$ $3x = 348$ $x = 116$ Exterior angles are 116°, 120°, and 124°. Interior angles are 64°, 60°, 56°. The smallest interior angle has measure 56.	$180 = 180 - x + 180 - (x + 4) + 180 - (x + 8)$ $180 = 540 - 3x + 12$ $-372 = -3x$ $x = 124$ Ext. angles: 124°, 128°, 132° Int. angles: 56°, 52°, 48° The smallest int. angle is 48°.

The 4-point response shows a correct equation and solution. The student examined all the interior angles to find the one with the smallest measure.

There is an error in the 3-point response, but the student completed the problem and answered each part.

If you make an error, you can still get some credit. It is important that you complete each part of the problem or explain how you could do the problem.

EXERCISES

Use the Example above to do each exercise.

Second line:

1. Where did the student make an error in the 3-point response? **12 should be** -12.

2. When answering an extended-response question, you can describe how you are going to do the problem and then carry out the steps. For the Example exercise, begin with the following observation and write a 4-point response.

The largest exterior angle has measure $x + 8$, and the smallest interior angle is a supplement of that angle. **See margin.**

page 172 Test-Taking Strategies

2. Answers may vary. Sample:

[4] a. $x + (x + 4) + (x + 8) = 360$

b. $3x = 348$ $x = 116$

c. Since $x + 8$ is the measure of the largest ext. $\angle$, its suppl. will be the smallest int. $\angle$. $116 + 8 = 124$ and $180 - 124 = 56$. The smallest int. $\angle$ has measure 56.

Chapter Review

Vocabulary

acute triangle (p. 133)
alternate interior angles (p. 115)
concave polygon (p. 144)
convex polygon (p. 144)
corresponding angles (p. 115)
equiangular triangle (p. 133)
equiangular polygon (p. 146)
equilateral triangle (p. 133)
equilateral polygon (p. 146)

exterior angle of a polygon (p. 133)
flow proof (p. 123)
isosceles triangle (p. 133)
obtuse triangle (p. 133)
point-slope form (p. 154)
polygon (p. 143)
regular polygon (p. 146)
remote interior angles (p. 133)
right triangle (p. 133)

same-side interior angles (p. 115)
scalene triangle (p. 133)
slope-intercept form (p. 152)
standard form of a
    linear equation (p. 153)
transversal (p. 115)
two-column proof (p. 117)

 **Reading Math**
Understanding Vocabulary

Choose the correct vocabulary term to complete each sentence.

1. In a triangle, an angle is right, obtuse, or ? . **acute**

2. A(n) ? angle has a measure between 90 and 180. **obtuse**

3. When two coplanar lines are cut by a transversal, two angles that are in similar positions on the same side of the transversal are called ? . **corresponding angles**

4. The measure of a(n) ? angle of a triangle is equal to the sum of the measures of its two remote interior angles. **exterior**

5. A polygon is ? if no diagonal contains points outside the polygon. **convex**

6. A(n) ? polygon has all angles congruent. **equiangular**

7. A(n) ? polygon is both equiangular and equilateral. **regular**

8. The linear equation $y - 3 = 4(x + 5)$ is written in ? form. **point-slope**

9. From the ? form of a linear equation, you can easily read the value of the slope and the value of the y-intercept. **slope-intercept**

10. When two coplanar lines are cut by a transversal, the angles between the two lines and on opposite sides of the transversal are called ? .
    alternate interior angles

Take It to the NET
Online vocabulary quiz
at www.PHSchool.com
Web Code: afj-0351

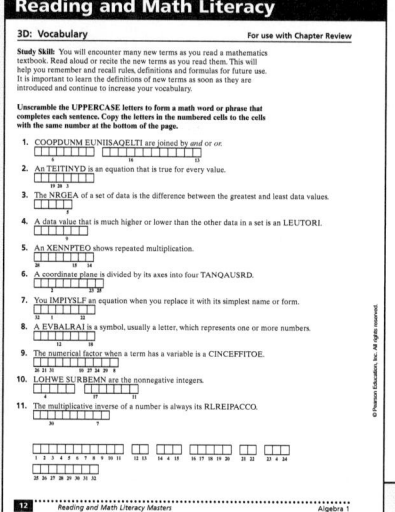

Skills and Concepts

3-1 Objectives

▼ To identify angles formed by two lines and a transversal

▼ To prove and use properties of parallel lines

A **transversal** is a line that intersects two coplanar lines at two distinct points.
∠1 and ∠4 are **corresponding angles.**
∠3 and ∠4 are **alternate interior angles.**
∠2 and ∠4 are **same-side interior angles.**

If two parallel lines are cut by a transversal, then

• corresponding angles are congruent.

• alternate interior angles are congruent.

• same-side interior angles are supplementary.

11. Suppose ℓ and k in the diagram above are parallel. If $m\angle 1 = 59$, what are the measures of ∠2, ∠3, and ∠4? **$m\angle 2 = 121$, $m\angle 3 = 59$, $m\angle 4 = 59$**

13. $m\angle1 = 75$; same side int. $\angle$s are suppl. $m\angle2 = 105$; alt. int. $\angle$s are ≅ or two $\angle$s that form a straight $\angle$ are suppl.

14. $m\angle1 = 55$; same side int. $\angle$s are suppl. $m\angle2 = 90$; alt. int. $\angle$s are ≅.

12. $m\angle1 = 120$; corr. $\angle$s are ≅. $m\angle2 = 120$; vert. $\angle$s are ≅ or alt. ext. $\angle$s are ≅.

Find $m\angle1$ and then $m\angle2$. Justify each answer. 13–14. See margin.

12.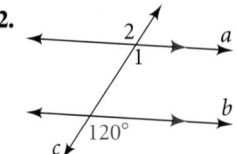

13.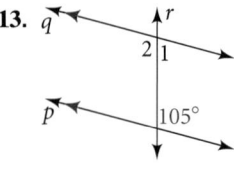

14.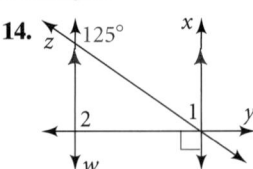

15. Writing Suppose both pairs of opposite sides of a quadrilateral are parallel. Which angles of the quadrilateral must be supplementary? Explain.

Pairs of consec. $\angle$s are supp. because the sides of the quad. are transversals and the int. $\angle$s are on the same side of the transversal.

3-2 and 3-7 Objectives

▼ To recognize conditions that result in parallel lines

▼ To construct parallel lines

▼ To construct perpendicular lines

Two lines cut by a transversal are parallel if

- corresponding angles are congruent.
- alternate interior angles are congruent.
- same-side interior angles are supplementary.

You can construct the line parallel to a given line through a given point not on the line. You can also construct the perpendicular to a given line at a given point on the line or through a given point not on the line.

A **flow proof** uses arrows to show the logical connections between the statements. Reasons are written below the statements.

19.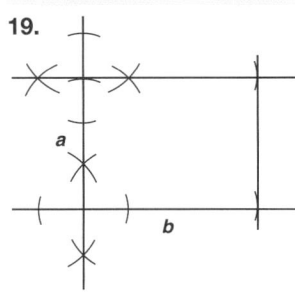

x^2 **Algebra** Find the value of x for which $\ell \parallel m$.

16.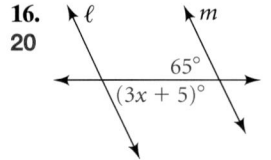
20

17.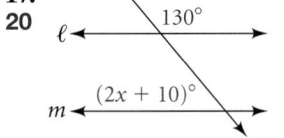
20

18.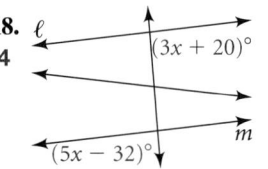
24

20.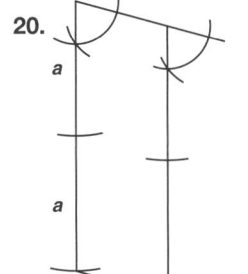

Use the segments at the right for Exercises 19 and 20.

19. Construct a rectangle with side lengths a and b.
   See above left.

20. Construct a quadrilateral with one pair of parallel opposite sides, each side of length $2a$. **See left.**

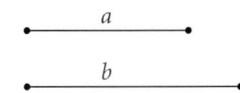

21. To construct a line parallel to a given line m through a point not on m, you need to know how to construct ___?___ angles. ≅

3-3 Objectives

▼ To classify triangles and find the measures of their angles

▼ To relate exterior angles to the angles of a triangle

The sum of the measures of the angles of a triangle is 180. The measure of each **exterior angle** of a triangle equals the sum of the measures of its two **remote interior angles**.

You can classify triangles according to their sides and angles.

Find the values of the variables. Then classify each triangle by its sides and angles.

22.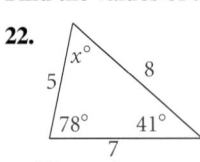
61; scalene, acute

23. $x = 60$; $y = 60$; equilateral, acute

24. $x = 45$; $y = 45$; isosc., right
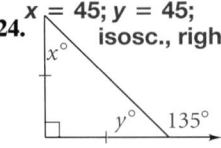

In each of Exercises 25–28, the measures of the three angles of a triangle are given. Find the value of x and then classify the triangle by its angles.

25. $x + 10, x - 20, x + 25$ **55; acute**   **26.** $x, 2x, 3x$ **30; right**

27. $20x + 10, 30x - 2, 7x + 1$ **3; acute**   **28.** $10x - 3, 14x - 20, x + 3$
  8; obtuse

29. In a right triangle, what is always true about the angles?
  One $\angle$ is 90; the remaining 2 $\triangle$s are comp.

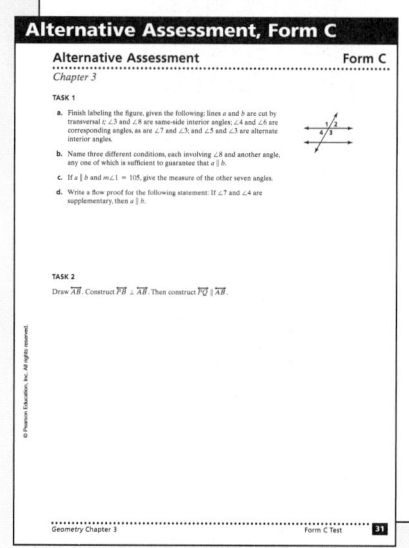
3-4 Objectives

▼ To classify polygons

▼ To find the sums of the measures of the interior and exterior angles of polygons

A **polygon** is a closed plane figure with at least three sides. To name a polygon, start at any vertex and list the vertices consecutively in a clockwise or counterclockwise direction. A polygon is **convex** if no diagonal contains points outside the polygon. Otherwise, it is **concave**.

An **equilateral polygon** has all sides congruent. An **equiangular polygon** has all angles congruent. A **regular polygon** is equilateral and equiangular.

The sum of the measures of the angles of an n-gon is $(n - 2)180$. The sum of the measures of the exterior angles of an n-gon, one at each vertex, is 360.

Find the measure of an interior angle and an exterior angle of each regular polygon.

30. a hexagon **31.** an octagon **32.** a decagon **33.** a 24-gon
  120; 60   **135; 45**   **144; 36**   **165; 15**

34. What is the sum of the measures of the exterior angles for each polygon in Exercises 30–33? **360**

3-5 Objectives

▼ To graph lines given their equations

▼ To write equations of lines

When a linear equation is in **slope-intercept form**, $y = mx + b$, the slope m and the y-intercept b are easily identified. When a linear equation is in **point-slope form**, $(y - y_1) = m(x - x_1)$, point (x_1, y_1) and slope m can easily be identified. The equation $Ax + By = C$, where A and B are not both zero, is in **standard form.** When a linear equation is in standard form, the x- and y-intercepts are readily found.

35–38.
See margin.

35. Name the slope and y-intercept of $y = 2x - 1$. Graph the line.

36. Name a point on and the slope of $y - 3 = -2(x + 5)$. Graph the line.

37. Graph $y = -\frac{1}{2}$.   **38.** Graph $3x - 4y = 12$.

39. Write an equation for the vertical line that contains $A(6, -9)$. $x = 6$

3-6 Objectives

▼ To relate slope and parallel lines

▼ To relate slope and perpendicular lines

The slopes of two nonvertical parallel lines are equal. All vertical lines are parallel.

The product of the slopes of two nonvertical perpendicular lines is -1. In a plane, every vertical line is perpendicular to every horizontal line.

Determine whether $\overleftrightarrow{AB}$ and $\overleftrightarrow{CD}$ are *parallel, perpendicular,* or *neither.*
  neither
40. $A(-1, -4), B(2, 11), C(1, 1), D(4, 10)$ **41.** $A(2, 8), B(-1, -2), C(3, 7), D(0, -3)$ $\parallel$

42. $A(-3, 3), B(0, 2), C(1, 3), D(-2, -6)$ $\perp$ **43.** $A(-1, 3), B(4, 8), C(-6, 0), D(2, 8)$ $\parallel$

✏️ **44.** Writing For $B(4, 8)$ and $D(2, 8)$, find the slope of $\overleftrightarrow{BD}$. Explain why the slope of any horizontal line is zero. **0; the difference of y-coordinates is always zero.**

Chapter 3   Chapter Review   **175**

35. $m = 2$; y-int. $= -1$

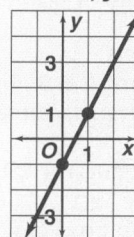

36. $m = -2$; point $= (-5, 3)$

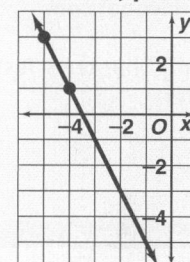

37.

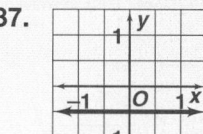

38.

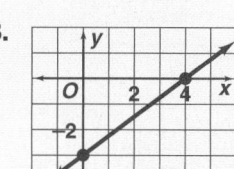

Take It to the NET
Online chapter test at
www.PHSchool.com
Web Code: afa-0352

Resources

Teaching Resources
Ch. 3 Test, Forms A & B
Ch. 3 Alternative Assessment,
Form C

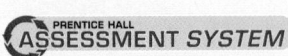

Reaching All Students
Spanish Ch. 3 Test, Forms A & B
Spanish Ch. 3 Alternative
  Assessment, Form C
Informal Geometry Ch. 3 Test,
  Forms D & E

PRENTICE HALL
ASSESSMENT SYSTEM

Assessment Masters
• Ch. 3 Test, Forms A & B
• Ch. 3 Alternative Assessment,
  Form C
Computer Test Generator CD
• Ch. 3 pre-made Test
• Make your own Ch. 3 test

www.PHSchool.com
Student Site
• Self-grading Chapter 3 Test
Teacher Center
• Resources

Plus *i* TEXT

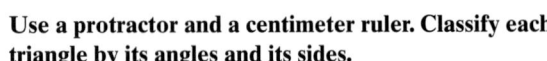

Use a protractor and a centimeter ruler. Classify each triangle by its angles and its sides.

1.

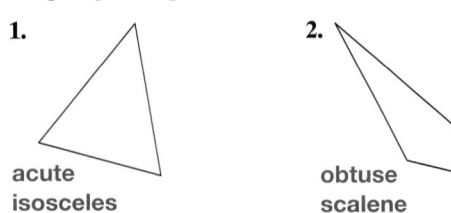

acute
isosceles

2.

obtuse
scalene

Find $m\angle 1$, then $m\angle 2$. Justify each answer.

3.

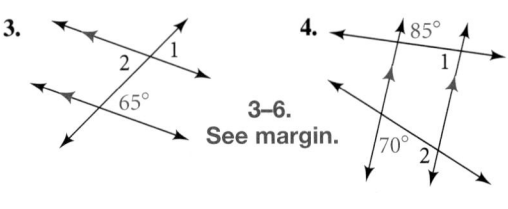

2 1
65°

4.

85°
1
70° 2

3–6.
See margin.

5.

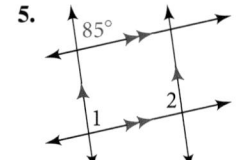

85°
1 2

6.

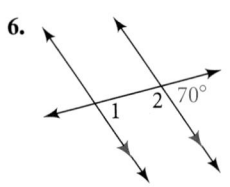

1 2 70°

Two lines are parallel and cut by a transversal. Write *yes* or *no* to indicate whether the numbers given could be the measures of a pair of same-side interior angles.

7. 40 and 140 **yes**

8. 90 and 90 **yes**

9. 60 and 60 **no**

10. 27 and 27 **no**

x^2 **Algebra Find the value of *x* for which $\ell \parallel m$.**

11.
5

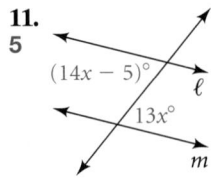

$(14x - 5)°$
ℓ
$13x°$
m

12.
25

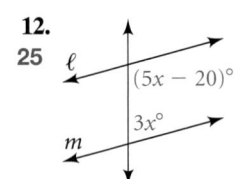

ℓ
$(5x - 20)°$
$3x°$
m

13.
6

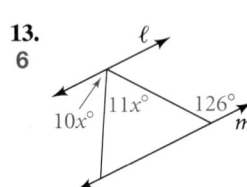

ℓ
$10x°$ $11x°$ $126°$
m

14.
75

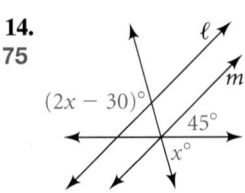

ℓ
m
$(2x - 30)°$
45°
$x°$

15. Draw a line *m* and a point *T* not on the line. Construct the line through *T* perpendicular to *m*. **See margin.**

16. Draw an angle, $\angle ABC$. Then construct line *m* through *A* so that $m \parallel \overleftrightarrow{BC}$. **See margin p. 177.**

17. Open-Ended The letter **F** illustrates a pair of same-side interior angles and a pair of corresponding angles. Find a letter that illustrates alternate interior angles. **Answers may vary. Sample: Z**

18. Open-Ended Describe two corresponding angles formed by lines in your classroom.
Check students' work.

19. Supply the reason for each step in the proof.

Given: $\ell \parallel m$ and $\angle 4 \cong \angle 2$
Prove: $n \parallel p$

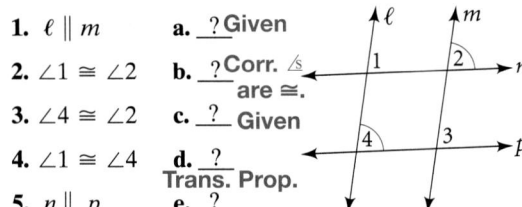

1. $\ell \parallel m$ a. ? **Given**
2. $\angle 1 \cong \angle 2$ b. ? **Corr. ∠s are ≅.**
3. $\angle 4 \cong \angle 2$ c. ? **Given**
4. $\angle 1 \cong \angle 4$ d. ? **Trans. Prop.**
5. $n \parallel p$ e. ? **If corr. ∠s are ≅, then the lines are ∥.**

20. Write an equation of the line with slope -5 and containing $A(3, -1)$. $y + 1 = -5(x - 3)$ or $y = -5x + 14$

21. Writing Explain how you can determine whether a polygon is concave or convex. **See margin p. 177.**

Find the value of each variable.

22.

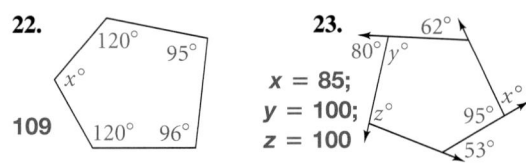

120° 95°
$x°$
109 120° 96°

23.
62°
80° $y°$
$z°$
95° $x°$
53°

$x = 85$;
$y = 100$;
$z = 100$

Sketch each pair of lines. Tell whether they are *parallel, perpendicular,* or *neither.*

24. $y = 4x + 7$ ⊥
$y = -\frac{1}{4}x - 3$

25. $y = 3x - 4$ ∥
$y = 3x + 1$

26. $y = x + 5$ **neither**
$y = -5x - 1$

27. $y = -3$ ⊥
$x = 10$

28. What is the measure of an exterior angle of a regular 12-gon? **30**

page 176 Chapter Test

3. $m\angle 1 = 65$ because corr. ∠s are ≅; $m\angle 2 = 65$ because vert. ∠s are ≅.

4. $m\angle 1 = 85$ because alt. int. ∠s are ≅; $m\angle 2 = 110$ because same-side int. ∠s are suppl.

5. $m\angle 1 = 85$ because corr. ∠s are ≅; $m\angle 2 = 95$

because same-side int. ∠s are suppl.

6. $m\angle 1 = 70$ because corr. ∠s are ≅; $m\angle 2 = 110$ because same-side int. ∠s are suppl.

15.

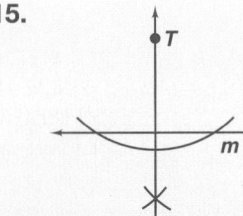

• T
m

Standardized Test Prep

Reading Comprehension Read the passage below. Then answer the questions on the basis of what is *stated* or *implied* in the passage.

Airport Plans Civic leaders in Chicago are discussing a plan to expand O'Hare Airport and build new runways. The airport's present runways, labeled A through G in the diagram, include three pairs that are parallel. Runways B and D intersect to form right angles.

The crisscrossing layout and takeoff/landing patterns prevent the runways from being used to their full capacity. This can cause travel delays. If the planned new runways are built, then four landings and two takeoffs can happen simultaneously. The plan, however, requires an additional 292 acres of land to the south and 141 acres to the north. Taking this land would lead to the demolition of 240 apartment units and more than 300 houses and 70 businesses.

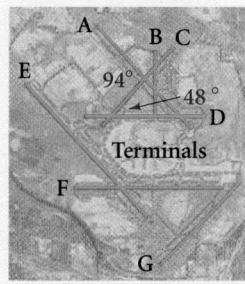

To answer the questions, students apply skills and concepts from this chapter and previous chapters.
Multiple Choice: Items 1–10, 12–14
Extended Response: Item 11

Resources

Teaching Resources
Cumulative Review
Quarter 2 Test, Forms A & B

Reaching All Students
Spanish Cumulative Review
Spanish Quarter 2 Tests

 PRENTICE HALL
ASSESSMENT SYSTEM

Standardized Test Prep Workbook
● Ch. 3 Standardized Test Practice
Assessment Masters
● Cumulative Review
● Quarter 2 Test, Forms A & B
Computer Test Generator CD
● Standardized Test Practice

 **www.PHSchool.com**
● Standardized Test Practice
● Resources

Plus **iTEXT**

1. At present, how many runways are there? **D**
   A. 3   **B.** 4   **C.** 6   **D.** 7

2. Which list best describes the parallel runways? **G**
   F. A ∥ C and B ∥ D   **G.** A ∥ E, C ∥ G, and D ∥ F
   H. A ∥ E and D ∥ F   **I.** A ∥ C, B ∥ D, and E ∥ G

3. Which runways are perpendicular? **B**
   A. A ⊥ E   **B.** B ⊥ D   **C.** C ⊥ D   **D.** E ⊥ F

4. Why can runways E and G not be used to their full capacity? **I**
   I. crisscrossing layout
   II. crisscrossing takeoff pattern
   III. crisscrossing landing pattern
   F. I only   **G.** I and II only
   H. II and III only   **I.** I, II, and III

5. What is the measure of the obtuse angle formed where runways B and C intersect? **D**
   A. 42   **B.** 90   **C.** 132   **D.** 138

6. What is the measure of the acute angle formed where runways A and D intersect? **F**
   F. 46   **G.** 48   **H.** 86   **I.** 94

7. If you extend runway C to meet runway E, what is the measure of the acute angle formed? **C**
   A. 42   **B.** 48   **C.** 86   **D.** 90

8. If you extend runway E to meet runway G, what is the measure of the obtuse angle formed? **H**
   F. 86   **G.** 90   **H.** 94   **I.** 104

9. At most, how many landings and takeoffs would be possible in one hour on the new runways? **D**
   A. 4 and 2   **B.** 40 and 20
   C. 240 and 120   **D.** cannot be determined

10. How many acres larger than the current airport will the new airport be? **I**
    F. 141   **G.** 161   **H.** 292   **I.** 433

11. Each apartment unit, house, or business is one "real estate unit." What is the average number of real estate units per acre that will be demolished in the plan? Explain your answer.
    See margin.

Suppose runways D and B are the *x*- and *y*-axes of a coordinate plane.

12. Which runway has a positive slope? **C**
    A. A   **B.** B   **C.** C   **D.** D

13. Which runway has a negative slope? **I**
    F. F   **G.** G   **H.** D   **I.** E

14. Which two runways have slopes whose product is approximately −1? **A**
    A. A, G   **B.** G, F   **C.** F, D   **D.** D, B

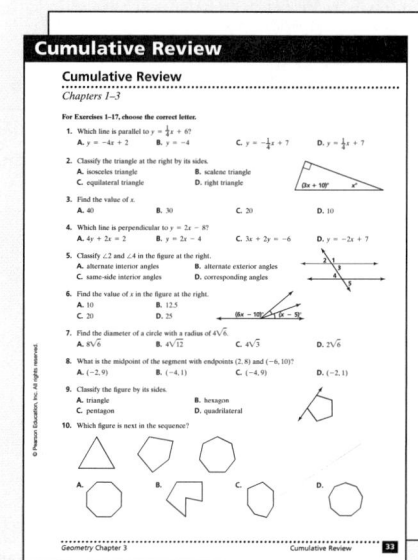

Cumulative Review
Cumulative Review
Chapters 1–3
For Exercises 1–17, choose the correct letter.

16.

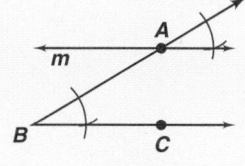

21. **Draw segments connecting nonconsecutive vertices. If no points of the segments are outside the polygon, then it is convex. Otherwise, the polygon is concave.**

page 177 **Standardized Test Prep**

11. **More than 1.4 units per acre; the average is the number of real estate units divided by the number of new acres.**

Chapter 4

Congruent Triangles

Chapter at a Glance

North Carolina Objectives

4-1 Congruent Figures 2.03c
NCTM 3, 6, 7, 8, 9, 10
  ▽ Congruent Figures

4-2 Triangle Congruence by SSS and SAS 2.03a
NCTM 3, 6, 7, 8, 9, 10
  ▽ Using the SSS and SAS Postulates

4-3 Triangle Congruence by ASA and AAS 2.03a
NCTM 3, 6, 7, 8, 9, 10
  ▽ Using the ASA Postulate and the AAS Theorem

4-4 Using Congruent Triangles: CPCTC 2.03a
NCTM 3, 6, 7, 8, 9, 10
  ▽ Proving Parts of Triangles Congruent

4-5 Isosceles and Equilateral Triangles 2.03a
NCTM 2, 3, 6, 7, 8, 9, 10
  ▽ The Isosceles Triangle Theorems

4-6 Congruence in Right Triangles 2.03a
NCTM 3, 6, 7, 8, 9, 10
  ▽ The Hypotenuse-Leg Theorem

4-7 Using Corresponding Parts of Congruent Triangles 2.03a
NCTM 3, 6, 7, 8, 9, 10
  ▽ Using Overlapping Triangles in Proofs
  ▽ Using Two Pairs of Congruent Triangles

NCTM STANDARDS 2000

1	Number and Operations	6	Problem Solving
2	Algebra	7	Reasoning and Proof
3	Geometry	8	Communication
4	Measurement	9	Connections
5	Data Analysis and Probability	10	Representation

Pacing Options

This chart suggests pacing only for the lessons and their parts. It is provided as a possible guide. It will help you determine how much time you have in your schedule to cover other components, such as the features, Chapter Review and Chapter Test.

Day	Traditional 45 min.	Two-Year 45 min.	Block 90 min.
1	4-1 ▽	4-1 ▽	4-1 ▽
2	4-2 ▽	4-1 ▽	4-2 ▽
3	4-3 ▽	4-2 ▽	4-3 ▽
4	4-4 ▽	4-2 ▽	4-4 ▽
5	4-5 ▽	4-3 ▽	4-5 ▽
6	4-6 ▽	4-3 ▽	4-6 ▽
7	4-7 ▽	4-4 ▽	4-7 ▽ ▽
8	4-7 ▽	4-4 ▽	
9		4-5 ▽	
10		4-5 ▽	
11		4-6 ▽	
12		4-6 ▽	
13		4-7 ▽	
14		4-7 ▽	
15		4-7 ▽	
16		4-7 ▽	
17			
18			
19			
20			
21			
22			

NAEP Correlation (National Assessment of Educational Progress 2000 Mathematics Objectives)

4-1	4-2	4-3	4-4	4-5	4-6	4-7
G5	M1, G7b, G8	G7a, b, G8	G7b, c, G8	G5, G7b, c	G7b, c, G8	G7b, c, G8

N = Number Sense, Properties, and Operations; **M** = Measurement; **G** = Geometry and Spatial Sense; **D** = Data Analysis, Statistics, and Probability; **A** = Algebra and Functions

Math Background

Chapter Overview

The investigations that introduce several of the lessons in this chapter are particularly helpful in promoting an intuitive understanding of ways to prove triangles congruent, especially when completed prior to discussing the material in the lesson. Students are asked to write proofs in paragraph, two-column, and flow formats to help them develop a broad understanding of the concept of proof that is not tied to a specific model or technique. Although it is possible to choose postulates for a geometry in which SSS, SAS, ASA, AAS, and HL are all proved as theorems, this text treats SSS, SAS, and ASA as postulates and proves AAS and HL. A study of congruent triangles that focuses solely on proofs and does not include examining triangles to determine whether and why they are congruent can frustrate many students. The exercise sets contain many nonproof exercises to help students gain some measure of expertise with congruent triangles while still developing their ability to write proofs.

Congruent Figures   4-1

The synonyms *identical, alike,* and *the same,* which students have used from an early age to identify objects, provide an intuitive background for understanding congruence. Make sure that students can identify congruent polygons by naming their vertices in the appropriate order. Students with weak spatial visualization skills may find it difficult to name congruent figures that have been rotated or reflected. Naming congruent figures correctly is critical to success in the lessons that follow. You may need to review the distinction between equality (numbers having the same value) and congruence (sets of points having the same size and shape).

Triangle Congruence by SSS and SAS   4-2

If you urge students to say "side-side-side" for SSS and "side-angle-side" for SAS, they are more likely to think about the three sides or the side, angle, and side that the postulates utilize. For the SAS Postulate, it is important that students recognize the importance of an *included* angle. The concept of an included part also will be employed in ASA in the next lesson. Nonmathematical uses of *included* do not usually imply the same sort of "successive betweenness" or "consecutive order" as its geometric use. Some students may need to spend time naming the consecutive parts of $\triangle ABC$ as "angle A, side AB, angle B, side BC," and so on. One way they can check their work is to review their proofs or diagrams and identify the three specific pieces of data that prove the triangles congruent.

Triangle Congruence by ASA and AAS   4-3

The order of the letters in ASA and AAS also must match the order of successive parts of a triangle. Instead of using AAS, some students may find it easier to prove the third angles in two triangles congruent and then use ASA to prove the two triangles congruent.

Using Congruent Triangles: CPCTC   4-4

Although the CPCTC abbreviation will be used in written work, it may help students if you require them in oral work to use the clause that the abbreviation represents. If students simply memorize the abbreviation CPCTC, they may mindlessly plug it into a proof after several steps, whether or not it makes sense to do so.

Isosceles and Equilateral Triangles   4-5

Point out that while an isosceles triangle has three vertices, "the" vertex of an isosceles triangle is unique if the isosceles triangle is not also equilateral. The line symmetry of equilateral and isosceles triangles can serve as a way to help students understand that equilateral triangles are also isosceles. Symmetry will be addressed in Chapter 12, but you can informally use line symmetry to help students visualize the isosceles triangle theorems. The lack of symmetry in scalene triangles demonstrates that a scalene triangle cannot have congruent sides or congruent angles. Students may enjoy finding photos that involve triangles and discussing whether they might be isosceles, equiangular, and/or congruent.

Congruence in Right Triangles   4-6

The exercises in this lesson offer students the opportunity to complete proofs using each of the three formats studied so far, furthering the impression that the format is not critical but the completeness of a proof is. After Lesson 4-3, students considered whether AAA and SSA could be used to prove triangles congruent and discovered that, in general, they cannot be so used. You may want to consider SsA as a theorem, where SsA are consecutive parts of triangles with the longer side opposite the angle and the shorter side adjacent to the angle. Interested students should have little difficulty using the altitude from the included angle to prove this restricted theorem.

Note the uses of the word *legs.* Help students discover that the intersection of the *legs* is the distinguishing vertex in both right and isosceles triangles. The third side (the base of an isosceles triangle or the hypotenuse of a right triangle) is then opposite this vertex.

Using Corresponding Parts of Congruent Triangles   4-7

Throughout this chapter students have developed their visualization skills to specify corresponding parts of congruent triangles that are in different orientations. Because the congruent triangles in this lesson overlap, the task is more difficult, particularly for students with weak orientation skills.

When students begin to solve exercises with overlapping triangles, they may benefit by copying the original diagram in addition to the separated triangles and then marking congruent parts in both sets of diagrams. However, students who draw only the separated triangles may miss sides or angles that are shared by the two triangles. Shared angles in particular are clearly visible in the original diagrams but may be missed in separated triangles.

178B

 # Ongoing Assessment and Intervention

Tools for Monitoring Student Progress

The Prentice Hall *Geometry* program provides you with many options for assessment in the Student Edition, the Teacher's Edition and the teaching resources. From these options, you may choose instructional materials and techniques that are appropriate for your students and support your district's curriculum requirements.

Instant Check System™ in Chapter 4

Allows students to check their own learning before, during, and after each lesson.

Diagnosing Readiness before the chapter (p. 178)

Check Skills You'll Need exercises in each lesson (pp. 180, 186, 194, 203, 210, 217, 224)

Check Understanding questions with each Example (pp. 180, 181, 182, 187, 188, 193, 195, 196, 203, 204, 211, 212, 218, 219, 224, 225, 226)

Checkpoint Quiz (pp. 201 and 223)

 Test Prep in Chapter 4

Teaches students strategies and gives them practice with all the test item formats they will encounter on state tests and standardized national exams.

Standardized Test Prep exercises in each lesson (pp. 185, 192, 200, 208, 216, 222, 230)

Test-Taking Strategies (p. 232: Making Quantitative Comparisons)

Standardized Test Prep (p. 237: Cumulative Review)

 PRENTICE HALL ASSESSMENT *SYSTEM*

All your assessment needs in one place!

Program Assessment

Assess student progress throughout the *Geometry* text with blackline masters and CD-ROM.

Assessment Resources

- Checkpoint Quizzes 1 & 2
- Chapter Test, Forms A & B
- Chapter Alternative Assessment

Spanish versions available. Tests for Informal Geometry also available.

 Computer Test Generator

- Unlimited questions of varying difficulty for every lesson objective.
- Create your own practice sheets, quizzes, and tests, or use the pre-made Chapter Tests.
- Diagnose readiness with questions on prerequisite skills.
- Prepare students by making tests based on standardized test objectives.
- Access Algebra 1, Geometry, and Algebra 2 content—all on one CD-ROM.

Test Preparation

A three-step approach to preparing students for high stakes, national, and state exams.

❶ Diagnose & Prescribe

Content Diagnostic Tests
- Diagnose strengths and weaknesses in content for national and state tests.
- Prescribe individualized reteaching opportunities.

❷ Review & Reteach

Skills and Concepts Review
- Provides reteaching worksheets with instruction and practice for each skill.
- Includes course prerequisite skills.

❸ Practice & Assess

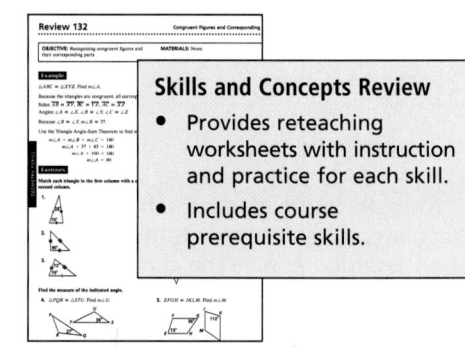

Test Preparation
- Features practice tests for End-of-Course and SAT/ACT exams.
- Includes standardized test practice by chapter for ongoing review.

Teacher's Guide with answers and correlations.

Test-Taking Strategies with Transparencies
- Support the Test-Taking Strategies pages in the Student Edition.
- Provide a teaching transparency and a practice worksheet for each strategy.

 # Reaching All Students

Support in the Student Text and Additional Resources

The textbook, the iText, and other technology components provide numerous opportunities to reach students of various ability levels and learning styles. Each Teacher's Edition lesson suggests how you can help *all* your students be successful and understand the mathematics in Chapter 4.

Below Level

Student Edition
- Diagnosing Readiness*: p. 178
- Check Skills You'll Need*: pp. 180, 186, 194, 203, 210, 217, 224

Reteaching
Chapter 4 Support File: pp. 8–14

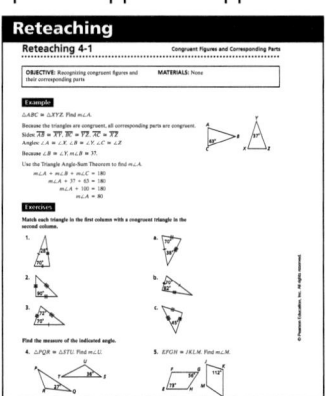

Informal Geometry Planning Guide
Chapter 4 Lesson Plans: pp. 20–26
Chapter 4 Tests: pp. 91–94

* Can be used with all ability levels to ensure mastery of prerequisite skills.

Advanced Learners

Student Edition
- Challenge exercises: pp. 184, 191, 200, 207, 215, 222, 229
- Extension: p. 231

Enrichment
Chapter 4 Support File: pp. 15–21

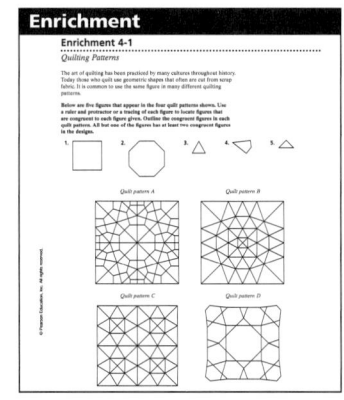

Reading and Math Literacy

Student Edition
- Vocabulary: pp. 179, 233, *plus* in every Lesson Preview
- Reading Math: pp. 188, 191, 193, 204, 207, 210, 224, 233
- Illustrated Glossary: pp. 741–777

Reading and Math Literacy Masters
Chapter 4: pp. 13–16

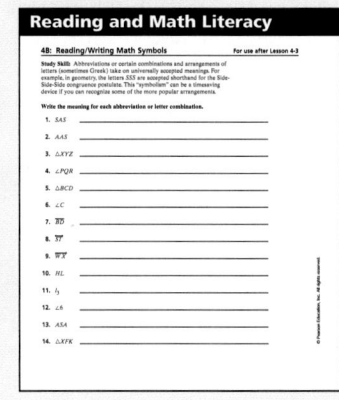

English Learners

Student Edition
- English/Spanish Illustrated Glossary: pp. 741–777

Workbook and Masters
Spanish Practice Workbook: pp. 20–26
Spanish Reading and Math Literacy Masters: pp. 13–16

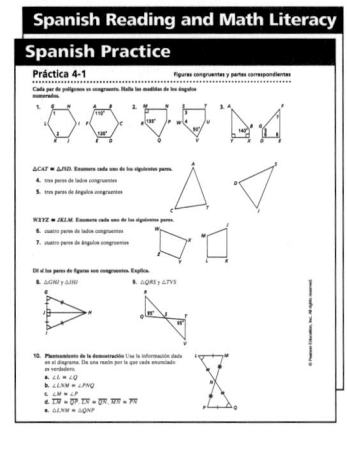

Learning Styles

Student Edition
- Investigation: pp. 186, 194, 210
- Technology: p. 202
- Writing: pp. 184, 191, 198, 215, 221, 229, 236
- DK Activities: pp. 238–239

Activity Masters
Hands-On Activities: 10, 11, 12
Technology Activities: 41, 42

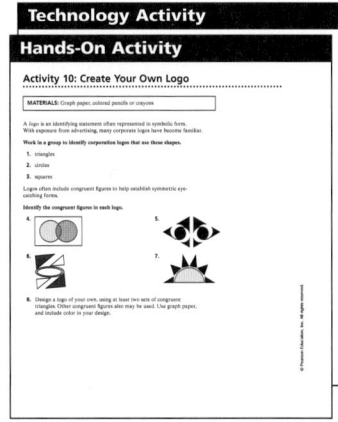

Program Resources

	Teaching Resources in Grab & Go™ Files				Resources for Reaching All Students				Spanish Resources			Transparencies				Presentation Assistant Plus!
	Practice	Reteach	Enrich	Checkpoint Quiz	Reading & Math Literacy	Technology Activities	Hands-On Activities	Informal Geometry Lesson Plans	Practice	Reading & Math Literacy	Checkpoint Quiz	Skills Check	Additional Examples	Answers to Exercises	Lesson Quiz	Prentice Hall Presentation Pro CD-ROM
4-1	■	■	■		■		■	■	■	■		■	■	■	■	■
4-2	■	■	■				■		■	■		■	■	■	■	■
4-3	■	■	■	■	■	■		■	■	■	■	■	■	■	■	■
4-4	■	■	■					■	■			■	■	■	■	■
4-5	■	■	■			■	■	■	■			■	■	■	■	■
4-6	■	■	■	■	■			■	■			■	■	■	■	■
4-7	■	■						■	■			■	■	■	■	■
For the chapter	Chapter Tests, Alternative Assessment, Cumulative Review, Cumulative Assessment				Informal Geometry Chapter Tests				Spanish Chapter Tests, Alternative Assessment, Cumulative Review, Cumulative Assessment			Classroom Aid Transparencies				

Also available for use with the chapter:

 PRENTICE HALL ASSESSMENT SYSTEM   *see page 178C.*

- Practice Workbook
- Solution Key

- For teacher support and access to student Web site materials, use Web Code afk-5500.
- For additional online and technology resources, see below.

Technology

 **Online and on CD-ROM**

Complete Interactive Student Text online and on CD-ROM—with instant feedback assessment, tutorial help, dynamic activities, instructional and real-world videos, audio, and additional practice.

 www.PHSchool.com For Students

Use **Web Codes** for easy access to online activities, chapter projects, self-grading lesson quizzes and chapter tests, vocabulary quizzes, updated data sources, graphing calculator procedures, and more.

PH SuccessNet For Teachers

Online lesson planning with built-in state correlations, all the teaching resources, complete reference library, your own calendar and Teacher Web page, professional development, and more.

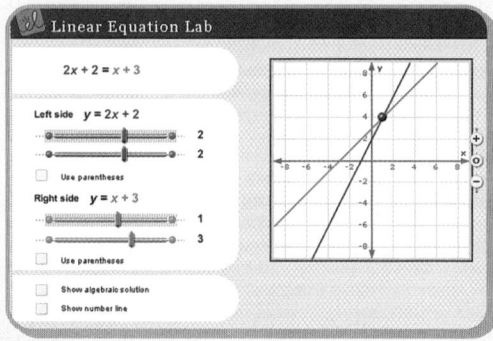

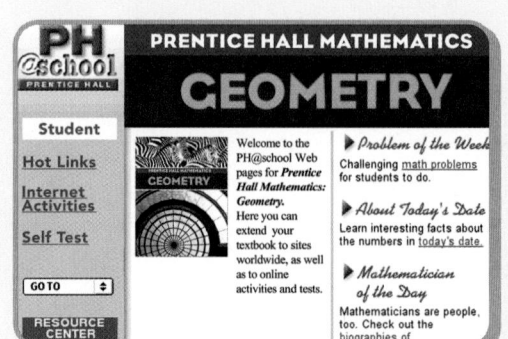

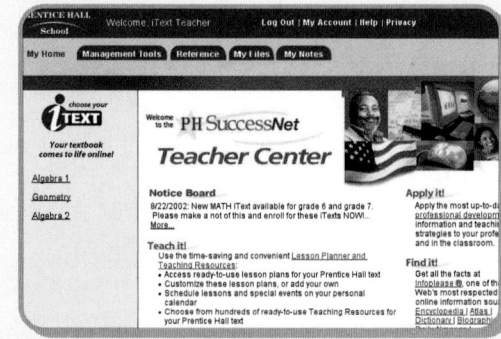

Presentation Assistant Plus!

The Prentice Hall *Presentation Assistant Plus!* provides you with the material you need to teach a lesson from beginning to end. Two easy-to-use formats—Transparencies and CD-ROM—allow you to present a lesson the way you are most comfortable.

Transparencies

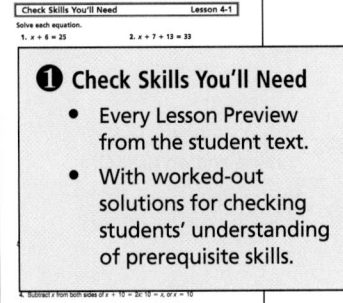

❶ Check Skills You'll Need
- Every Lesson Preview from the student text.
- With worked-out solutions for checking students' understanding of prerequisite skills.

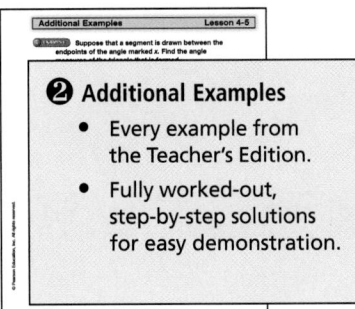

❷ Additional Examples
- Every example from the Teacher's Edition.
- Fully worked-out, step-by-step solutions for easy demonstration.

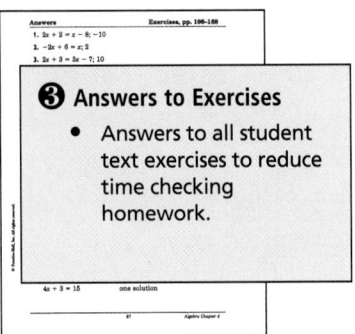

❸ Answers to Exercises
- Answers to all student text exercises to reduce time checking homework.

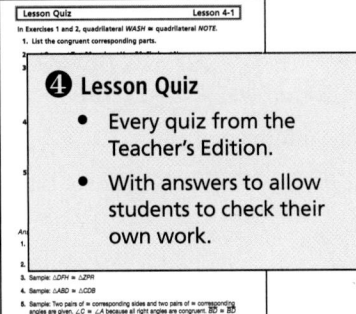

❹ Lesson Quiz
- Every quiz from the Teacher's Edition.
- With answers to allow students to check their own work.

 Throughout the Teacher's Edition, this symbol indicates material that is available on transparency in the Presentation Assistant Plus!

Prentice Hall Presentation Pro CD-ROM

- Includes all Transparencies.
- Conveniently organized by lesson so you can easily ❶ Introduce, ❷ Teach, ❸ Check Homework, and ❹ Assess each lesson.
- Animated examples allow step-by-step instruction at your own pace.
- Easy to edit so you can create custom presentations.

Teaching Chapter 4 Using Presentation Assistant Plus!

	❶ Introduce	❷ Teach	❸ Check Homework	❹ Assess
	Check Skills You'll Need	Additional Examples	Student Edition Answers	Lesson Quiz
4-1	p. 20	pp. 53–55	✔	p. 95
4-2	p. 21	pp. 56–57	✔	p. 96
4-3	p. 22	pp. 58–59	✔	p. 97
4-4	p. 23	pp. 60–61	✔	p. 98
4-5	p. 24	pp. 61–64	✔	p. 99
4-6	p. 25	pp. 65–67	✔	p. 100
4-7	p. 26	pp. 68–70	✔	p. 101

Prentice Hall Presentation Pro

CD-ROM with dynamic PowerPoint® presentations for every lesson. Helps you introduce and develop concepts, check homework, and assess progress. Part of Presentation Assistant Plus! *(See above.)*

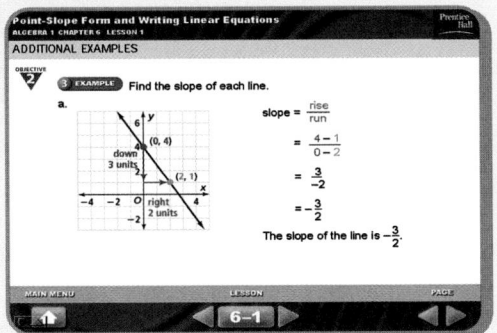

Computer Test Generator

CD-ROM to create practice sheets and tests for course objectives and standardized tests. Includes Instant Chapter Tests™, online testing, and student reports. Part of the PH Assessment System. *(See page 178C.)*

Resource Pro® with Planning Express®

CD-ROM with a lesson planning tool that allows you to import state and local objectives. Includes electronic versions of all the teaching resources.

Congruent Triangles

 Diagnosing Readiness

Students will find answers to these exercises in the back of their textbooks.

For intervention, direct students to:

The Distance Formula
Lesson 1-6: Example 1
Exercises 1–9
Extra Practice, p. 690

Proving Angles Congruent
Lesson 2-5: Example 2
Exercises 10–18
Extra Practice, p. 693

Parallel Lines and the Triangle Angle-Sum Theorem
Lesson 2-5: Example 2
Exercises 10–18
Extra Practice, p. 692
Lesson 3-3: Example 2
Exercises 6–11
Extra Practice, p. 693

Where You've Been

● In Chapter 1, you learned the meanings of congruent segments and congruent angles.

● In Chapter 2, you used deductive reasoning to prove angles congruent.

● In Chapter 3, you developed relationships involving congruent angles, parallel lines, perpendicular lines, and polygons.

 Instant self-check
online and on CD-ROM

Diagnosing Readiness   (For help, go to the Lesson in green.)

The Distance Formula (Lesson 1-6)

Find the lengths of the sides of △ABC.

1. $A(3, 1), B(-1, 1), C(-1, -2)$
$AB = 4, BC = 3, AC = 5$

2. $A(-3, 2), B(-3, -6), C(8, 6)$
$AB = 8, BC = \sqrt{265}, AC = \sqrt{137}$

3. $A(-1, -2), B(6, 1), C(2, 5)$
$AB = \sqrt{58}, BC = 4\sqrt{2}, AC = \sqrt{58}$

Proving Angles Congruent (Lesson 2-5)

Draw a conclusion based on the information given.

4. ∠A is supplementary to ∠B;
∠C is supplementary to ∠B ∠A ≅ ∠C

5. ∠A is supplementary to ∠B;
∠A ≅ ∠B $m\angle A = 90 = m\angle B$ or ∠A and ∠B are rt. ∠

6. ∠1 is complementary to ∠2

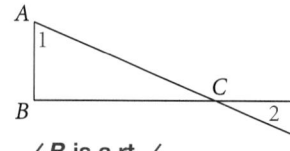

∠B is a rt. ∠.

7. $\overrightarrow{FA} \perp \overrightarrow{FC}; \overrightarrow{FB} \perp \overrightarrow{FD}$

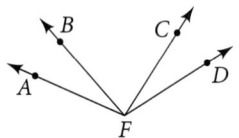

∠AFB ≅ ∠DFC

Parallel Lines and the Triangle Angle-Sum Theorem (Lesson 3-3)

What can you conclude from each diagram?

8.

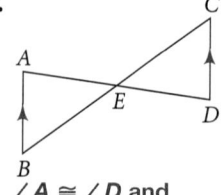

∠A ≅ ∠D and ∠B ≅ ∠C

9.

∠ACD ≅ ∠CAB and ∠DAC ≅ ∠BCA

10.

$(x + 9)°$ $(7x + 4)°$
$(6x - 1)°$

x = 12

Congruent Triangles

Key Vocabulary

- base of an isosceles triangle (p. 211)
- base angle of an isosceles triangle (p. 211)
- congruent polygons (p. 180)
- corollary (p. 212)
- CPCTC (corresponding parts of congruent triangles are congruent) (p. 203)
- hypotenuse (p. 217)
- legs of a right triangle (p. 217)
- legs of an isosceles triangle (p. 211)
- vertex angle of an isosceles triangle (p. 211)

Where You're Going

- In this chapter, you will learn the meaning of congruent polygons.

- You will learn how to prove two triangles congruent by five different methods.

- By learning how to prove triangles congruent, you will discover properties of an isosceles triangle.

- You will also learn how to draw other conclusions, once two triangles have been proved congruent.

Real-World Snapshots You will do activities involving reflected light and congruence on pages 238 and 239.

Chapter 4 Overview

Students will use their knowledge of corresponding parts of congruent polygons to study and apply postulates and theorems related to triangle congruence. These include SSS, SAS, ASA, AAS, HL, and the Isosceles Triangle Theorem. Throughout this chapter, students complete progressively more complex proofs. Their work in Chapter 4 will apply to all subsequent proofs in this course.

Reading Math
Reading Diagrams and Words, p. 193

Vocabulary
A complete list of terms, plus vocabulary exercises, appears in the Chapter Review, p. 233.

Illustrated Glossary
Examples for each vocabulary term, plus definitions in both English and Spanish, appear starting on p. 741.

Test-Taking Strategies
Making Quantitative Comparisons, p. 232

Real-World Snapshots
See pages 238–239 for a real-world application of reflections that utilizes Dorling Kindersley's (DK) unique graphic presentation.

Real-World Connections
Some of the applications you will find in this chapter are spacecraft (4-1), bridge design (4-2), lacrosse (4-3), landscaping (4-5), tent design (4-6), and engineering (4-7).

www.PHSchool.com
Internet support for this chapter includes:
- Self-grading Vocabulary and Chapter 4 Tests
- Chapter Project
- Chapter Planner
- Ch. 4 Resources

Plus 🅘TEXT

4-1

North Carolina Objectives 2.03c

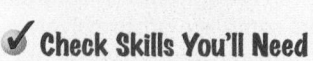

1. Plan

Lesson Preview

✓ **Check Skills You'll Need**

Solving Linear Equations
Algebra Review, page 24

Lesson Resources

📁 **Teaching Resources**
Practice, Reteaching, Enrichment

👥 **Reaching All Students**
Practice Workbook 4-1
Spanish Practice Workbook 4-1
Reading and Math Literacy 4A
Spanish Reading & Literacy 4A
Hands-On Activities 10
Informal Geometry Planning
  Guide 4-1

🕐 **Presentation Assistant Plus!**
Transparencies
• Check Skills You'll Need 4-1
• Additional Examples 4-1
• Student Edition Answers 4-1
• Lesson Quiz 4-1
PH Presentation Pro CD 4-1

ASSESSMENT SYSTEM

Computer Test Generator CD

💿 **Technology**
Resource Pro® CD-ROM
Computer Test Generator CD
Prentice Hall Presentation Pro CD

💻 **www.PHSchool.com**
Student Site
• Teacher Web Code: afk-5500
• Self-grading Lesson Quiz
Teacher Center
• Lesson Planner
• Resources

Plus 📘**TEXT**

4-1

Congruent Figures

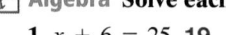 North Carolina Objectives

2.03 Apply properties, definitions, and theorems of two-dimensional figures to solve problems and write proofs: a) Triangles. c) Other polygons.

Lesson Preview

What You'll Learn

OBJECTIVE 1
To recognize congruent figures and their corresponding parts

. . . And Why

To use corresponding parts of congruent shapes in the Space Shuttle, as in Example 2

✓ Check Skills You'll Need

(For help, go to page 24.)

x^2 **Algebra** Solve each equation.

1. $x + 6 = 25$ **19**
2. $x + 7 + 13 = 33$ **13**
3. $5x = 540$ **108**
4. $x + 10 = 2x$ **10**

5. For the triangle at the right, use the Triangle Angle-Sum Theorem to find the value of y. **50**

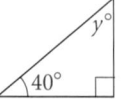

New Vocabulary
• congruent polygons

OBJECTIVE
1 **Congruent Figures**

 Interactive lesson includes instant self-check, tutorials, and activities.

Congruent figures have the same size and shape. When two figures are congruent, you can move one so that it fits exactly on the other one. Three ways to make such a move—a slide, a flip, and a turn—are shown below. You will learn much more about slides, flips, and turns in Chapter 12.

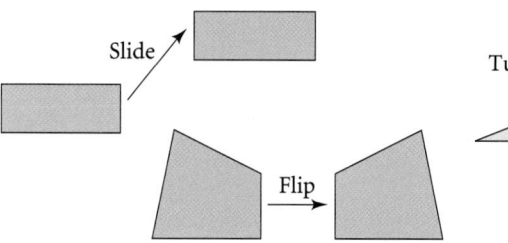

Congruent polygons have congruent corresponding parts—their matching sides and angles. Matching vertices are corresponding vertices. When you name congruent polygons, always list corresponding vertices in the same order.

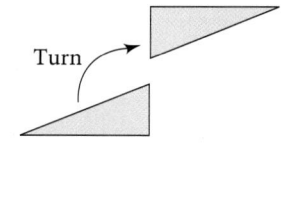

C corresponds to R.
$\angle B$ corresponds to $\angle Q$.
$\overline{AX}$ corresponds to $\overline{PY}$.
$ACBX \cong PRQY$

1 EXAMPLE **Naming Congruent Parts**

$\triangle TJD \cong \triangle RCF$. List the congruent corresponding parts.

Sides: $\overline{TJ} \cong \overline{RC}$ $\overline{JD} \cong \overline{CF}$ $\overline{DT} \cong \overline{FR}$
• Angles: $\angle T \cong \angle R$ $\angle J \cong \angle C$ $\angle D \cong \angle F$

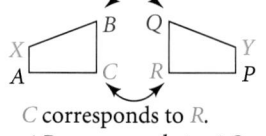

✓ **Check Understanding** **1** $\triangle WYS \cong \triangle MKV$. List the congruent corresponding parts. Use three letters to name each angle. $\angle WSY \cong \angle MVK; \angle SWY \cong \angle VMK;$ $\angle WYS \cong \angle MKV; \overline{WY} \cong \overline{MK}; \overline{WS} \cong \overline{MV}; \overline{YS} \cong \overline{KV}$

⭕ **Ongoing Assessment and Intervention**

Before the Lesson
Diagnose prerequisite skills using:
• Check Skills You'll Need

During the Lesson
Monitor progress using:
• Check Understanding
• Additional Examples
• Standardized Test Prep

After the Lesson
Assess knowledge using:
• Lesson Quiz
• Computer Test Generator CD

2 EXAMPLE Real-World Connection

Spacecraft The fins of the Space Shuttle suggest congruent pentagons. Find $m\angle B$.

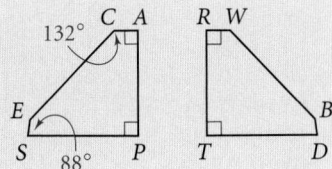

In the congruent pentagons, B corresponds to E, so you know that $\angle B \cong \angle E$. You can find $m\angle B$ by first finding $m\angle E$.

Use the Polygon Angle-Sum Theorem. It tells you that the sum of the measures of the angles of pentagon $SPACE$ is $(5-2)180$, or 540.

$m\angle S + m\angle P + m\angle A + m\angle C + m\angle E = 540$	**Polygon Angle-Sum Theorem**
$88 + 90 + 90 + 132 + m\angle E = 540$	**Substitute.**
$400 + m\angle E = 540$	**Simplify.**
$m\angle E = 140$	**Subtract 400 from each side.**

$m\angle B = m\angle E$, so $m\angle B = 140$.

 **Check Understanding** ② It is given that $\triangle WYS \cong \triangle MKV$. If $m\angle Y = 35$, what is $m\angle K$? Explain.
$m\angle K = 35$; corr. $\angle$s are $\cong$.

Two triangles are congruent when they have three pairs of congruent corresponding sides and three pairs of congruent corresponding angles.

Proof ⟶ 3 EXAMPLE Finding Congruent Triangles

Developing Proof Decide whether the triangles are congruent. Justify your answer.

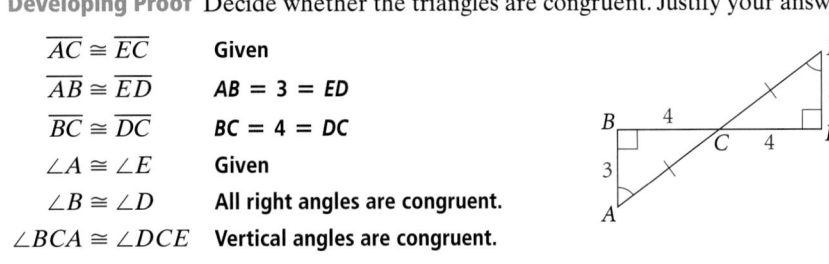

$\overline{AC} \cong \overline{EC}$	**Given**
$\overline{AB} \cong \overline{ED}$	**AB = 3 = ED**
$\overline{BC} \cong \overline{DC}$	**BC = 4 = DC**
$\angle A \cong \angle E$	**Given**
$\angle B \cong \angle D$	**All right angles are congruent.**
$\angle BCA \cong \angle DCE$	**Vertical angles are congruent.**

$\triangle ABC \cong \triangle EDC$ by the definition of congruent triangles.

 **Check Understanding** ③ Can you conclude $\triangle JKL \cong \triangle MNL$? Justify your answer.
No; corr. sides are not necessarily $\cong$.

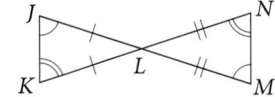

The next theorem follows from the Triangle Angle-Sum Theorem. In Exercise 45, you will explain why this theorem is true.

 Key Concepts

Theorem 4-1

If two angles of one triangle are congruent to two angles of another triangle, then the third angles are congruent.

$\angle C \cong \angle F$

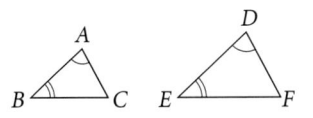

🖐 Reaching All Students

Below Level Have students name $\triangle EDC$ in six different ways, and explain why $\triangle EDC$ is correct, in the last congruence statement of Example 3, and the other five ways are incorrect.	**Advanced Learners** Have students write a two-column or flow proof of Theorem 4-1.	**Tactile Learners** See note on page 183. **Auditory Learners** See note on page 181.

2. Teach

Professional Development

Math Background

Congruent polygons have a one-to-one correspondence of equality between all of their corresponding parts. Many proofs concerning polygons and circles rely on proving triangles congruent.

OBJECTIVE
1 Teaching Notes

1 EXAMPLE Teaching Tip

Discuss how the statement $\triangle TJD \cong \triangle RCF$ allows you to list corresponding parts correctly without referring to the diagram.

Math Tip
Remind students that $\angle TJD$ can be named $\angle DJT$ and that $\overline{TJ}$ is the same segment as $\overline{JT}$.

3 EXAMPLE

As students examine the steps, ask: *Why are some angles named with one letter and other angles with three letters?* One letter is used when it is the vertex of only one angle.

Auditory Learners
When you present Theorem 4-1, ask students to suggest ideas for a Plan for Proof. Lead a discussion of students' ideas.

4 EXAMPLE

Point out that step b of the proof uses the Reflexive Property, which is used extensively in geometry. Ask: *When you look at the diagram, why would you use the Reflexive Property?* to show that the third sides of the triangles are congruent

181

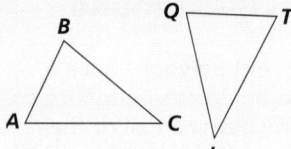

Additional Examples

1 △*ABC* ≅ △*QTJ*. List the congruent corresponding parts.

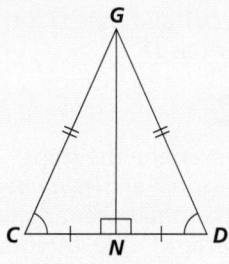

∠*A* ≅ ∠*Q*, ∠*B* ≅ ∠*T*,
∠*C* ≅ ∠*J*, $\overline{AB}$ ≅ $\overline{QT}$,
$\overline{BC}$ ≅ $\overline{TJ}$, $\overline{AC}$ ≅ $\overline{QJ}$

2 △*XYZ* ≅ △*KLM*, *m*∠*Y* = 67, and *m*∠*M* = 48. Find *m*∠*X*. **65**

3 Explain why △*ABC* is not congruent to △*CDE* in Example 3. **Corresponding sides are not congruent.**

4 Show how you can conclude that △*CNG* ≅ △*DNG*. List statements and reasons as in Example 4.

G

a. $\overline{CG}$ ≅ $\overline{DG}$ (Given)
b. $\overline{CN}$ ≅ $\overline{DN}$ (Given)
c. $\overline{GN}$ ≅ $\overline{GN}$ (Reflexive Prop. of ≅)
d. ∠*C* ≅ ∠*D* (Given)
e. ∠*CNG* ≅ ∠*DNG* (Right angles are ≅.)
f. ∠*CGN* ≅ ∠*DGN* (Th. 4-1)
g. △*CNG* ≅ △*DNG* (Def. of ≅ triangles)

Closure

Suppose that two pentagons are congruent. How many pairs of congruent corresponding parts are there? Explain. **at least 10 pairs; 5 pairs of congruent angles and 5 pairs of congruent sides**

182

Example 4 shows typical statements that appear in a proof that two triangles are congruent. Note how you can use Theorem 4-1.

4a. ∠*A* ≅ ∠*D*; ∠*E* ≅ ∠*C* (Given)
  b. ∠*ABE* ≅ ∠*DBC* (Vert. ⊿ are ≅.)
  c. $\overline{AE}$ ≅ $\overline{CD}$; $\overline{AB}$ ≅ $\overline{BD}$; $\overline{EB}$ ≅ $\overline{BC}$ (Given)
  d. △*ABE* ≅ △*DBC* (Def. of ≅ ⊿)

✓ **Check Understanding**

4 EXAMPLE Proving Triangles Congruent

Developing Proof Use the information given in the diagram. Give a reason why each statement is true.

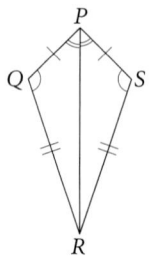

a. $\overline{PQ}$ ≅ $\overline{PS}$, $\overline{QR}$ ≅ $\overline{SR}$ Given
b. $\overline{PR}$ ≅ $\overline{PR}$ Reflexive Property of ≅
c. ∠*Q* ≅ ∠*S*, ∠*QPR* ≅ ∠*SPR* Given
d. ∠*QRP* ≅ ∠*SRP* Theorem 4-1
e. △*PQR* ≅ △*PSR* Definition of ≅ triangles

4 Show how you can conclude that the triangles are congruent. List statements and reasons as in Example 4. **See left.**

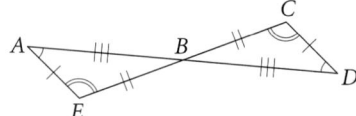

EXERCISES

For more practice, see *Extra Practice*.

Practice and Problem Solving

A Practice by Example

Example 1 (page 180)

Real-World 🌐 **Connection**

Exposed beams show the congruent triangles used in Tudor architecture.

1. Building Builders use the King Post truss, below left, for the top of a simple structure. In this truss, △*ABC* ≅ △*ABD*. List the congruent corresponding parts.
∠*CAB* ≅ ∠*DAB*; ∠*C* ≅ ∠*D*; ∠*ABC* ≅ ∠*ABD*; $\overline{AC}$ ≅ $\overline{AD}$; $\overline{AB}$ ≅ $\overline{AB}$; $\overline{CB}$ ≅ $\overline{DB}$

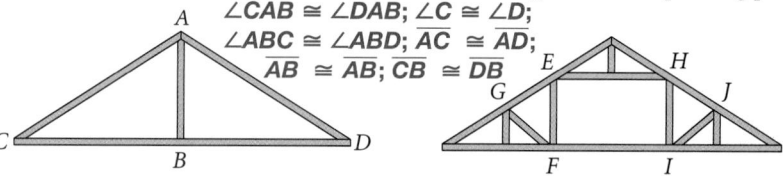

2. The Attic Frame truss, above right, provides open space in the center for storage. In this truss, △*EFG* ≅ △*HIJ*. List the congruent corresponding parts.
∠*GEF* ≅ ∠*JHI*; ∠*GFE* ≅ ∠*JIH*; ∠*EGF* ≅ ∠*HJI*; $\overline{GE}$ ≅ $\overline{JH}$; $\overline{EF}$ ≅ $\overline{HI}$; $\overline{FG}$ ≅ $\overline{IJ}$

△*LMC* ≅ △*BJK*. **Complete the congruence statements.**

3. $\overline{LC}$ ≅ _?_ $\overline{BK}$
4. $\overline{KJ}$ ≅ _?_ $\overline{CM}$
5. $\overline{JB}$ ≅ _?_ $\overline{ML}$
6. ∠*L* ≅ _?_ ∠*B*
7. ∠*K* ≅ _?_ ∠*C*
8. ∠*M* ≅ _?_ ∠*J*

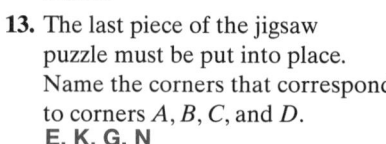

△*KJB* **9.** △*CML* ≅ _?_
10. △*KBJ* ≅ _?_ △*CLM*
11. △*MLC* ≅ _?_ △*JBK*
12. △*JKB* ≅ _?_ △*MCL*

13. The last piece of the jigsaw puzzle must be put into place. Name the corners that correspond to corners *A*, *B*, *C*, and *D*.
E, K, G, N

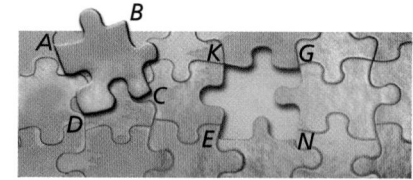

POLY ≅ *SIDE*. **List each of the following.**

14. four pairs of congruent sides
$\overline{PO}$ ≅ $\overline{SI}$; $\overline{OL}$ ≅ $\overline{ID}$; $\overline{LY}$ ≅ $\overline{DE}$; $\overline{PY}$ ≅ $\overline{SE}$

15. four pairs of congruent angles
∠*P* ≅ ∠*S*; ∠*O* ≅ ∠*I*; ∠*L* ≅ ∠*D*; ∠*Y* ≅ ∠*E*

Example 2
(page 181)

In the two lifeguard chairs, $ABCD \cong FGHI$. Find the measure of the angle or the length of the side.

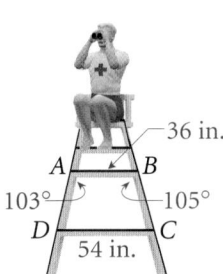

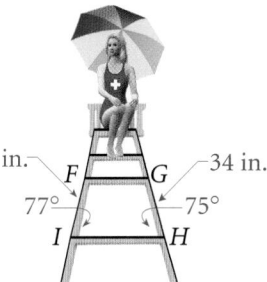

16. $\overline{AD}$ 33 in.   **17.** $\overline{HI}$ 54 in.
18. $\angle FGH$ 105 **19.** $\angle ADC$ 77
20. $\overline{FG}$ 36 in.   **21.** $\overline{BC}$ 34 in.
22. $\angle DCB$ 75   **23.** $\angle IFG$ 103

Example 3
(page 181)

24. yes; $\angle RTK \cong \angle UTK$, $\angle R \cong \angle U$ (Given) $\angle RKT \cong \angle UKT$ (If two $\angle$s of a $\triangle$ are $\cong$ to two $\angle$s of another $\triangle$, the third $\angle$s are are $\cong$.) $\overline{TR} \cong \overline{TU}, \overline{RK} \cong \overline{UK}$ (Given) $\overline{TK} \cong \overline{TK}$ (Reflexive Prop. of $\cong$) So $\triangle TRK \cong \triangle TUK$ by the def. of $\cong \triangle$s.

Developing Proof In Exercises 24–27, can you conclude the figures are congruent? Justify each answer.

24. $\triangle TRK$ and $\triangle TUK$ See left.

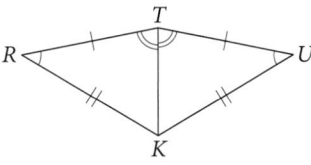

26. $\triangle XYZ$ and $\triangle XYP$ No; the corr. sides are not necessarily $\cong$.

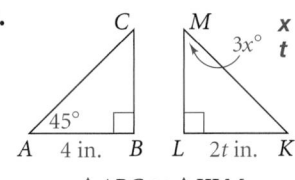

25. $\triangle SPQ$ and $\triangle TUV$

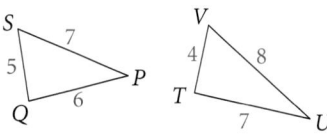

No; the corr. sides are not $\cong$.

27. $HEJK$ and $GFJK$

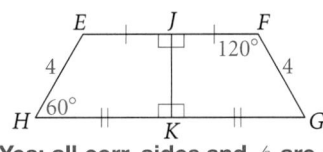

Yes; all corr. sides and $\angle$s are $\cong$.

Example 4
(page 182)

28. Developing Proof Use the information given in the diagram. Tell why each statement is true. **See margin.**
   a. $\overline{AB} \parallel \overline{DC}$ **b.** $\angle CAB \cong \angle ACD$
   c. $\angle B \cong \angle D$ **d.** $\angle BCA \cong \angle DAC$
   e. $\overline{AC} \cong \overline{AC}$ **f.** $\overline{AB} \cong \overline{DC}, \overline{BC} \cong \overline{AD}$
   g. $\triangle ABC \cong \triangle CDA$

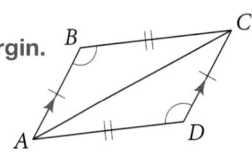

B Apply Your Skills

29. Identify the pairs of triangles that appear to be congruent.

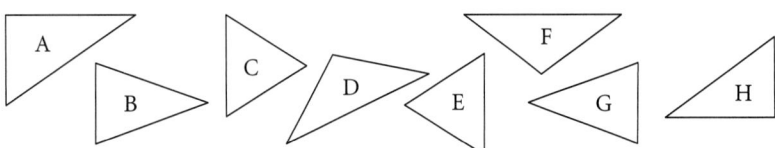

A and *H*; *B* and *G*; *C* and *E*; *D* and *F*

x^2 Algebra Find the values of the variables.

30.

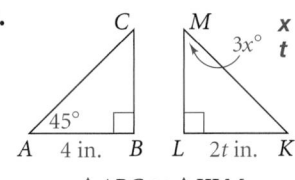

$x = 15;$
$t = 2$

$\triangle ABC \cong \triangle KLM$

31. 5

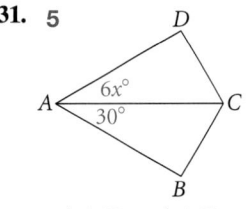

$\triangle ACD \cong \triangle ACB$

Need Help?

To review the Triangle Angle-Sum Theorem, go to Lesson 3-3.

Lesson 4-1 Congruent Figures **183**

pages 182–185 Exercises

28. a. Given

   b. If $\parallel$ **lines, then alt. int.** $\angle$**s are** $\cong$**.**

c. Given

d. If 2 $\angle$**s of one** $\triangle$ **are** $\cong$ **to two** $\angle$**s of another** $\triangle$**, then 3rd** $\angle$**s are** $\cong$**.**

e. Reflexive Prop. of $\cong$

f. Given

g. Def. of $\cong \triangle$

Assignment Guide

▼ **Objective**
   Ⓐ Ⓑ **Core** 1–45
   Ⓒ **Extension** 46–48

Standardized Test Prep 49–52

Mixed Review 53–59

Error Prevention

Exercises 3–12 Students may think that $\angle L$ corresponds to $\angle K$ because they are in the same relative positions. Encourage them to use the congruence statement to mark congruent angles and sides on copies of the triangles.

Tactile Learners

Exercises 38, 39 Have students trace and cut out the figures and then place them on top of each other to see how the corresponding parts match.

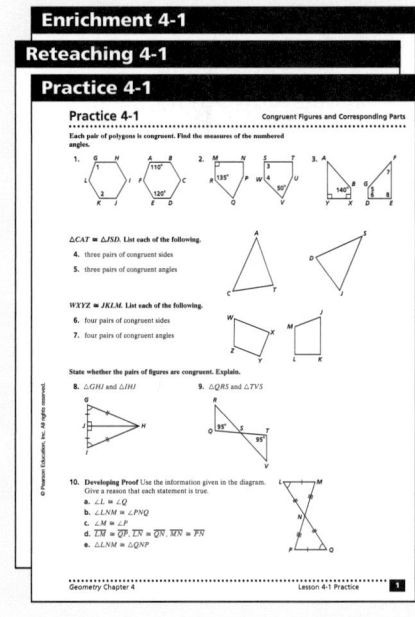

183

📖 **Lesson Quiz 4-1**

📖 **Lesson Quiz 4-1**

In Exercises 1 and 2, quadrilateral *WASH* ≅ quadrilateral *NOTE*.

1. List the congruent corresponding parts.
   $\overline{WA} \cong \overline{NO}$, $\overline{AS} \cong \overline{OT}$, $\overline{SH} \cong \overline{TE}$, $\overline{WH} \cong \overline{NE}$;
   $\angle W \cong \angle N$, $\angle A \cong \angle O$, $\angle S \cong \angle T$, $\angle H \cong \angle E$

2. $m\angle O = m\angle T = 90$ and $m\angle H = 36$. Find $m\angle N$. **144**

3. Write a statement of triangle congruence.

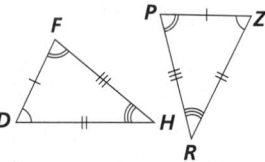

   Sample: $\triangle DFH \cong \triangle ZPR$

4. Write a statement of triangle congruence.

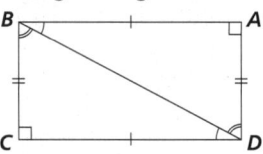

   Sample: $\triangle ABD \cong \triangle CDB$

5. Explain your reasoning in Exercise 4 above.
   Sample: Two pairs of ≅ corresponding sides and two pairs of ≅ corresponding angles are given. $\angle C \cong \angle A$ because all right angles are congruent. $\overline{BD} \cong \overline{BD}$ by the Reflexive Property of ≅. $\triangle ABD \cong \triangle CDB$ by the definition of ≅ triangles.

---

36. **Answers may vary.**
    Sample: It is important that $PACH \cong OLDE$ for the patch to completely fill the hole.

43. **Answers may vary.**
    Sample:
    $\triangle TKR \cong \triangle MJL$:
    $\overline{TK} \cong \overline{MJ}$; $\overline{TR} \cong \overline{ML}$;
    $\overline{KR} \cong \overline{JL}$;
    $\angle TKR \cong \angle MJL$;
    $\angle TRK \cong \angle MLJ$;
    $\angle KTR \cong \angle JML$

Exercise 42

🔶 **Challenge**

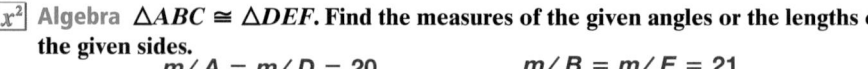 **Algebra** $\triangle ABC \cong \triangle DEF$. Find the measures of the given angles or the lengths of the given sides.

$$m\angle A = m\angle D = 20 \qquad m\angle B = m\angle E = 21$$

32. $m\angle A = x + 10$, $m\angle D = 2x$
33. $m\angle B = 3y$, $m\angle E = 21$

34. $BC = 3z + 2$, $EF = z + 6$
    $BC = EF = 8$
35. $AC = 7a + 5$, $DF = 5a + 9$
    $AC = DF = 19$

🌐 36. **Parquet Floor** Explain why it is important that $PACH \cong OLDE$.

🌐 37. **Sports Cards** The 225 cards in Tracy's sports card collection are rectangles of three different sizes. Describe how Tracy could quickly sort the cards. **Answers may vary.**

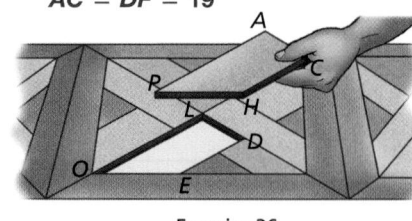

Exercise 36

Sample: Tracy should arrange them in a pile and pull out the ones of like sizes.

Write a congruence statement for each pair of triangles.

38.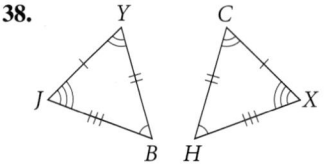
    $\triangle JYB \cong \triangle XCH$

39.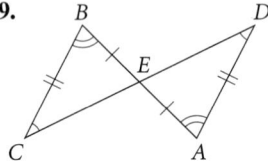
    E is the midpoint of $\overline{CD}$.
    $\triangle BCE \cong \triangle ADE$

40.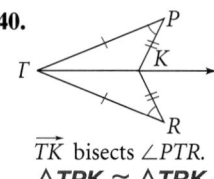
    $\overrightarrow{TK}$ bisects $\angle PTR$.
    $\triangle TPK \cong \triangle TRK$

41. Complete in two different ways:
    $\triangle JLM \cong \triangle NRZ$;
    $\triangle JLM \cong \underline{\ ?\ }$ $\triangle JLM \cong \triangle ZRN$

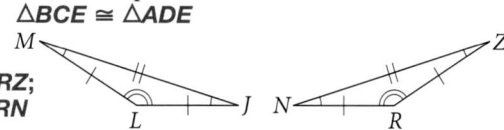

✏️ 42. **Writing** Die-cast toys are a popular collector's item. Explain why the two die-cast toys that Pearl is studying at the left have congruent shapes. **See margin.**

43. **Open-Ended** Write a congruence statement for two triangles. List the congruent sides and angles. **See above left.**

44. **Developing Proof** Use the information given in the diagram. Tell why each statement is true. **See margin.**
    a. $\overline{PR} \parallel \overline{TQ}$
    b. $\angle PRS \cong \angle QTS$
    c. $\angle RPS \cong \angle TQS$
    d. $\angle PSR \cong \angle QST$
    e. $\overline{PR} \cong \overline{QT}$, $\overline{PS} \cong \overline{QS}$
    f. $\overline{PQ}$ bisects $\overline{RT}$.
    g. $\overline{RS} \cong \overline{TS}$
    h. $\triangle PRS \cong \triangle QTS$

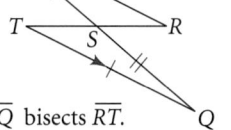

$\overline{PQ}$ bisects $\overline{RT}$.

45. **Developing Proof** If two angles of one triangle are congruent to two angles of another triangle, then the third angles are congruent (Theorem 4-1). Use algebra and the Triangle Angle-Sum Theorem to explain why this must be so. **See margin.**

Coordinate Geometry Vertices of $\triangle GHJ$ are $G(-2, -1)$, $H(-2, 3)$, and $J(1, 3)$.

46. $\triangle KLM \cong \triangle GHJ$. Find KL, LM, and KM. **$KL = 4$; $LM = 3$; $KM = 5$**

47. If L and M have coordinates $L(3, -3)$ and $M(6, -3)$, how many pairs of coordinates are possible for K? Find one such pair. **2; either (3, 1) or (3, −7)**

48. a. How many quadrilaterals (convex and concave) with different shapes or sizes can you make on a three-by-three geoboard? One is shown at the right. **15**
    b. How many quadrilaterals of each type are there? **See margin p. 185.**

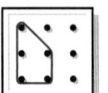

---

42. **Answers may vary.**
    Sample: The die is a mold that is used to make items that are all the same size.

44. a. Given
    b. If ∥ lines, then alt. int. ⦞ are ≅.
    c. If ∥ lines, then alt. int. ⦞ are ≅.
    d. Vertical ⦞ are ≅.
    e. Given
    f. Given
    g. Def. of segment bisector
    h. Def. of ≅ ⧍

45. **Answers may vary.**
    Sample: Since the sum of the ⦞ of a ⧍ is 180, and if 2 ⦞ of one ⧍ are the same as 2 ⦞ of a second ⧍, then their sum subtracted from 180 has to be the same.

Gridded Response

Use the diagrams at the right for Exercises 49–51.
ABCDE ≅ *PFKYM*.

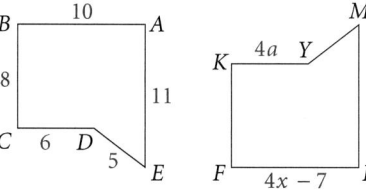

49. What is the value of *a*? **1.5**

50. What is the value of *x*? **4.25**

51. What is the perimeter of *PFKYM*? **40**

52. △*HLN* ≅ △*GST*, *m*∠*H* = 66, and *m*∠*S* = 42. What is *m*∠*T*? **72**

Take It to the NET
Online lesson quiz at
www.PHSchool.com
Web Code: afa-0401

Mixed Review

Lesson 3-7

Constructions For Exercises 53 and 54, construct the geometric figure.
53–54. See margin.

53. a square

54. a rectangle whose length is twice its width

Lesson 3-3

55. Find *m*∠*A* in the figure at the right. **100**

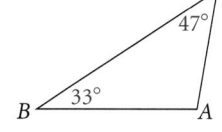

Exercise 55

Lesson 2-4

Use the given property to complete each statement.

56. Symmetric Property of Equality

If *PQ* = *RS*, then __?__. **RS = PQ**

57. Reflexive Property of Congruence

∠1 ≅ __?__ ∠1

58. Addition Property of Equality

If *m*∠*A* − 4 = 8, then *m*∠*A* = __?__.
12

59. Transitive Property of Congruence

If $\overline{AB} \cong \overline{DE}$ and $\overline{DE} \cong \overline{GH}$, then __?__.
$\overline{AB} \cong \overline{GH}$

Geometry at Work

Die Casting

Two centuries ago, people manufactured articles by hand. Each article produced was slightly different from every other. In 1800, inventor Eli Whitney recognized that he could speed up manufacturing by using congruent parts. Whitney made a die, or mold, for each part of a musket he was producing for the U.S. Army. This allowed workers to rapidly cast the parts and assemble them into standard-sized muskets. It ushered in the era of mass production.

Today, die makers are highly skilled industrial workers who shape dies out of metal, plastic, rubber, and other materials. Machines create and assemble the congruent die-cast parts into standard-sized objects, like the die-cast toy cars at the left. Other workers supply a final inspection and skilled hand finishing.

Take It to the NET For more information about die casting, go to **www.PHSchool.com**.
Web Code: afb-2031

Lesson 4-1 Congruent Figures **185**

48. b.

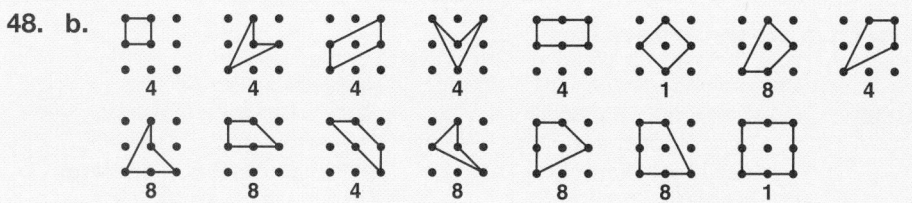

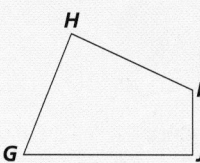
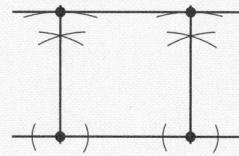
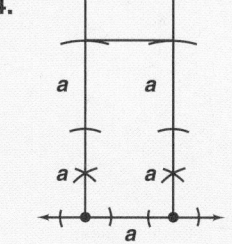

Lesson Preview

✓ **Check Skills You'll Need**

Identifying Angle Pairs
Lesson 2-5: Example 2
Exercises 10–18
Extra Practice, p. 692

Lesson Resources

📁 **Teaching Resources**
Practice, Reteaching, Enrichment

👥 **Reaching All Students**
Practice Workbook 4-2
Spanish Practice Workbook 4-2
Hands-On Activities 11
Informal Geometry Planning
   Guide 4-2

⏱ **Presentation Assistant Plus!**
Transparencies
• Check Skills You'll Need 4-2
• Additional Examples 4-2
• Student Edition Answers 4-2
• Lesson Quiz 4-2
PH Presentation Pro CD 4-2

ASSESSMENT SYSTEM
PRENTICE HALL

Computer Test Generator CD

💿 **Technology**
Resource Pro® CD-ROM
Computer Test Generator CD
Prentice Hall Presentation Pro CD

💻 **www.PHSchool.com**
Student Site
• Teacher Web Code: afk-5500
• Self-grading Lesson Quiz
Teacher Center
• Lesson Planner
• Resources

Plus 🄸TEXT

186

Triangle Congruence by SSS and SAS

2.03 Apply properties, definitions, and theorems of two-dimensional figures to solve problems and write proofs: a) Triangles.

Lesson Preview

What You'll Learn

OBJECTIVE
▼
To prove two triangles congruent using the SSS and SAS Postulates

. . . And Why

To prove that two triangles in the framework of a bridge are congruent, as in Example 1

✓ Check Skills You'll Need

(For help, go to Lesson 2-5.)

What can you conclude from each diagram?   See below.

1. $\overline{AB} \cong \overline{DE}$; $\angle C \cong \angle F$

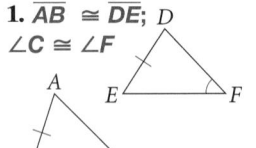

2.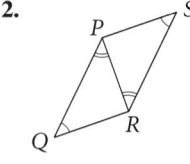

3.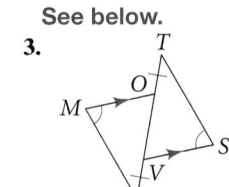

2. $\angle Q \cong \angle S$; $\angle QPR \cong \angle SRP$; $\overline{PR} \cong \overline{PR}$

3. $\angle M \cong \angle S$; $\angle MON \cong \angle SVT$; $\overline{TO} \cong \overline{NV}$; $\overline{MO} \parallel \overline{VS}$

🄸TEXT Interactive lesson includes instant self-check, tutorials, and activities.

OBJECTIVE
1 **Using the SSS and SAS Postulates**

> **Investigation:** Are the Triangles Congruent?
>
> Use straws to make a triangle with sides of 2 in., 3 in., and 4 in. Compare your triangle to the triangles made by others.
>
> 1. Make a conjecture about two triangles in which three sides of one triangle are congruent to three sides of the other triangle. **The △ are ≅.**
>
> 2. Support your conjecture by using three other lengths to make a different triangle. Compare your new triangle to the triangles made by others using different lengths. **Check students' work.**

In Lesson 4-1 you learned that if two triangles have three pairs of congruent corresponding angles and three pairs of congruent corresponding sides, then the triangles are congruent.

If you know this,   then you know this.

$\angle A \cong \angle X$ $\triangle ABC \cong \triangle XYZ$
$\angle B \cong \angle Y$
$\angle C \cong \angle Z$

$\overline{AB} \cong \overline{XY}$
$\overline{AC} \cong \overline{XZ}$
$\overline{BC} \cong \overline{YZ}$

However, you do not need to know that all six corresponding parts are congruent in order to conclude that two triangles are congruent. It is enough to know only that corresponding sides are congruent.

🄸 **Ongoing Assessment and Intervention**

Before the Lesson	**During the Lesson**	**After the Lesson**
Diagnose prerequisite skills using:	Monitor progress using:	Assess knowledge using:
• Check Skills You'll Need	• Check Understanding	• Lesson Quiz
	• Additional Examples	• Computer Test Generator CD
	• Standardized Test Prep	

Key Concepts

| Postulate 4-1 | Side-Side-Side (SSS) Postulate |

If the three sides of one triangle are congruent to the three sides of another triangle, then the two triangles are congruent.

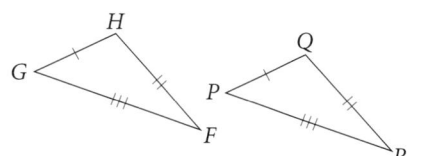

$$\triangle GHF \cong \triangle PQR$$

Proof 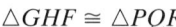 **EXAMPLE** **Real-World Connection**

Bridge Design The bridge girders are the same size, as marked.

Given: $\overline{AB} \cong \overline{CB}, \overline{AD} \cong \overline{CD}$

Is this enough information to prove the two triangles are congruent? If so, write a flow proof.

Prove: $\triangle ABD \cong \triangle CBD$

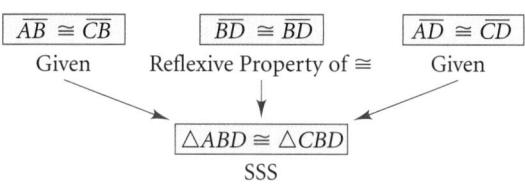

 Need Help?

The Reflexive Property of Congruence tells you that a figure, such as $\overline{BD}$ in this Example, is congruent to itself.

Plan: To prove the triangles congruent by the SSS Postulate, the three pairs of sides need to be congruent. Two pairs are given to be congruent. The third sides, $\overline{BD}$ in $\triangle ABD$ and $\overline{BD}$ in $\triangle CBD$, are congruent by the Reflexive Property of Congruence.

Proof:

| $\overline{AB} \cong \overline{CB}$ | $\overline{BD} \cong \overline{BD}$ | $\overline{AD} \cong \overline{CD}$ |
| Given | Reflexive Property of $\cong$ | Given |

$$\triangle ABD \cong \triangle CBD$$
SSS

✓ Check Understanding **1** Rewrite the proof as a paragraph proof or as a two-column proof.

You are given that $\overline{AB} \cong \overline{CB}$ and $\overline{AD} \cong \overline{CD}$. $\overline{BD} \cong \overline{BD}$ by the Refl. Prop. of $\cong$, so $\triangle ABD \cong \triangle CBD$ by the SSS post.

The word *included* is used frequently when referring to the angles and the sides of a triangle.

$\overline{BX}$ is included between $\angle B$ and $\angle X$.

$\angle N$ is included between $\overline{NB}$ and $\overline{NX}$.

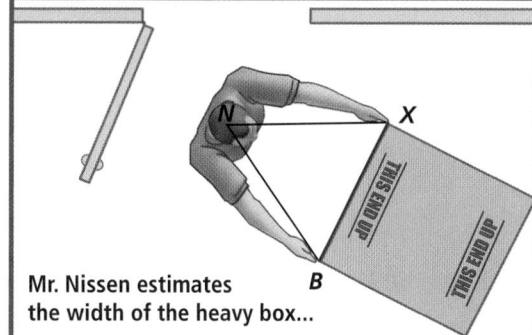

Mr. Nissen estimates the width of the heavy box...

Math Background

Six distinct congruence statements about the sides and angles of triangles necessarily follow when the triangles are congruent. However, to prove triangles congruent, it is sufficient to find any of these combinations of sides and angles congruent: SSS, SAS, ASA, or AAS.

OBJECTIVE
1 **Teaching Notes**

Investigation (Optional)
Have students also use lengths of straws that cannot form a triangle, such as 2 in., 2 in., and 4 in. Then have them make a conjecture about how the sum of the lengths of two sides of a triangle compares with the length of the third side. The conjectures should informally state the Triangle Inequality Theorem.

1 EXAMPLE **Math Tip**

Remind students that congruent figures may be reflections of each other, as $\triangle ABD$ and $\triangle CBD$ are in this example.

English Learners

The word *included* here means "contained between" and implies location. Students are familiar with using *include* and *including* to mean any part of a whole, as in "Eat your salad, including the carrots" and "The job includes writing."

2 EXAMPLE

Encourage students to find real-life applications of the SAS Postulate, such as where on an adjacent surface to hit a squash ball or billiards ball so that it rebounds on the surface exactly opposite you.

👥 Reaching All Students

| **Below Level** Students can confirm the SAS Postulate by examining triangles, such as ones with 3-in. and 5-in. sides and included 75° angles. They can easily see that all are congruent. | **Advanced Learners** Have students try to find two nonright triangles that are congruent yet have corresponding congruent sides and congruent nonincluded corresponding angles. | **English Learners** See note on page 187. **Inclusion** See note on page 190. |

 **Additional Examples**

1

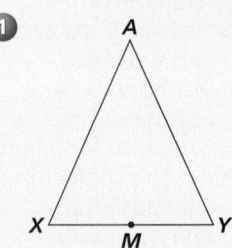

Given: *M* is the midpoint of $\overline{XY}$, $\overline{AX} \cong \overline{AY}$.

Prove: $\triangle AMX \cong \triangle AMY$
Write a paragraph proof.
$\overline{AX} \cong \overline{AY}$, midpoint *M* implies $\overline{MX} \cong \overline{MY}$, Reflexive Prop. implies $\overline{AM} \cong \overline{AM}$, SSS Post. implies $\triangle AMX \cong \triangle AMY$.

2

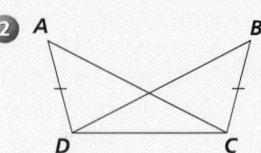

$\overline{AD} \cong \overline{BC}$. What other information do you need to prove $\triangle ADC \cong \triangle BCD$? $\overline{AC} \cong \overline{BD}$ (SSS) or $\angle ADC \cong \angle BCD$ (SAS)

3

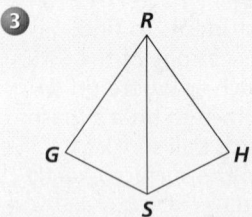

Given: $\angle RSG \cong \angle RSH$, $\overline{SG} \cong \overline{SH}$. From the information given, can you prove $\triangle RSG \cong \triangle RSH$? Explain. yes; by SAS

188

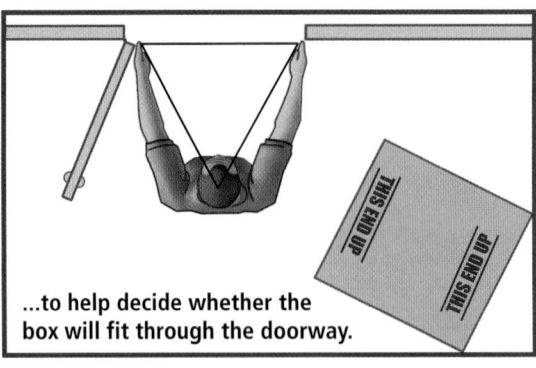

...to help decide whether the box will fit through the doorway.

Mr. Nissen kept his arms at a fixed angle as he moved from the box to the doorway. The triangle he used beside the box is congruent to the triangle he used beside the doorway He knows the two triangles are congruent because two sides and the included angle of one are congruent to two sides and the included angle of the other.

 Key Concepts

Postulate 4-2	**Side-Angle-Side (SAS) Postulate**

If two sides and the included angle of one triangle are congruent to two sides and the included angle of another triangle, then the two triangles are congruent.

$$\triangle BCA \cong \triangle FDE$$

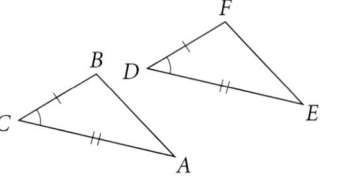

 Reading Math
The abbreviations SSS and SAS give you an easy way to remember Postulates 4-1 and 4-2.

2 **EXAMPLE** **Using SSS and SAS**

Developing Proof $\overline{RS} \cong \overline{TK}$. What other information do you need to prove $\triangle RSK \cong \triangle TKS$?

You are given $\overline{RS} \cong \overline{TK}$. Also, $\overline{KS} \cong \overline{KS}$ by the Reflexive Property of Congruence. Therefore:

Solution 1 If you know $\overline{RK} \cong \overline{TS}$, you can prove $\triangle RSK \cong \triangle TKS$ by SSS.

Solution 2 If you know $\angle RSK \cong \angle TKS$, you can prove $\triangle RSK \cong \triangle TKS$ by SAS.

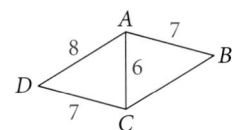

✓ **Check Understanding** **2** What other information do you need to prove $\triangle ABC \cong \triangle CDA$?
$\angle DCA \cong \angle BAC$ or $CB = 8$

3 **EXAMPLE** **Are the Triangles Congruent?**

Developing Proof From the information given, can you prove $\triangle RED \cong \triangle CAT$? Explain.

Given: $\overline{RE} \cong \overline{CA}, \overline{RD} \cong \overline{CT}, \angle R \cong \angle T$

No, there is not enough information to prove $\triangle RED \cong \triangle CAT$. $\angle T$ is not included between $\overline{CA}$ and $\overline{CT}$. $\triangle RED$ may or may not be congruent to $\triangle CAT$.

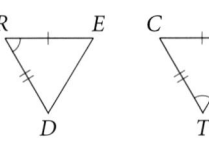

✓ **Check Understanding** **3** From the information given, can you prove $\triangle AEB \cong \triangle DBC$? Explain.

Given: $\overline{EB} \cong \overline{CB}, \overline{AE} \cong \overline{DB}$

No; you don't know that $\angle E \cong \angle DBC$ or that $\overline{AB} \cong \overline{DC}$.

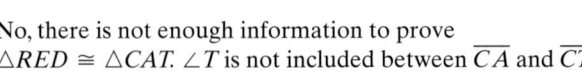

188 Chapter 4 Congruent Triangles

EXERCISES

Practice and Problem Solving

For more practice, see *Extra Practice*.

A Practice by Example
Examples 1, 3
(pages 187–188)

Developing Proof Which postulate, if any, could you use to prove that the two triangles are congruent?

1. SSS
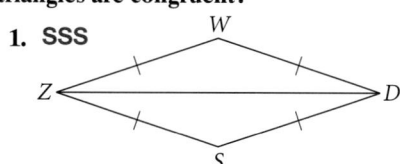

2. cannot be proved ≅
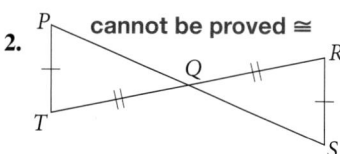

3. SAS
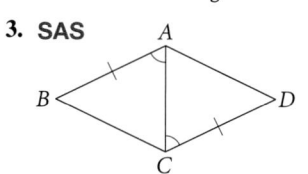

4. SSS
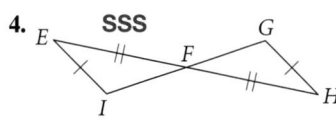

F is the midpoint of $\overline{GI}$.

5. Yes; $\overline{OB} \cong \overline{OB}$ by Refl. Prop.; ∠*BOP* ≅ ∠*BOR* since rt. ⦞ are ≅; $\overline{OP} \cong \overline{OR}$ (Given); the ⧍ are ≅ by SAS.

6. Yes; the legs have equal lengths and are joined at midpts. So $\overline{AE} \cong \overline{CE}$ and $\overline{BE} \cong \overline{DE}$; ∠*AEB* ≅ ∠*CED* by vert. ⦞ are ≅; △*AEB* ≅ △*CED* by SAS.

Developing Proof Is the information you are given below each photograph enough for you to prove that the two triangles are congruent? Explain.

5.

6.
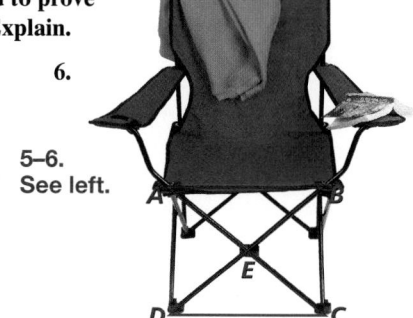

5–6. See left.

The vertical beam $\overline{OB}$ is perpendicular to the porch roof. *P*, *O*, and *R* are equally spaced.

The diagonal legs have equal lengths and are joined at their midpoints.

7. Developing Proof Copy and complete the flow proof.

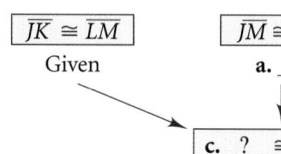

Given: $\overline{JK} \cong \overline{LM}, \overline{JM} \cong \overline{LK}$

Prove: △*JKM* ≅ △*LMK*

$\boxed{\overline{JK} \cong \overline{LM}}$
Given

$\boxed{\overline{JM} \cong \overline{LK}}$
a. ? Given

$\boxed{\overline{KM} \cong \overline{KM}}$
b. ? Reflexive

$\boxed{\text{c. } ? \cong \text{d. } ?}$
△*JKM* SSS △*LMK*

Example 2
(page 188)

Copy the triangle. Start at any vertex and label the triangle as △*WVU*.

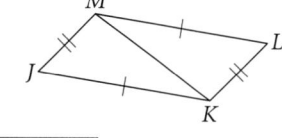

8. What sides include ∠*V*? $\overline{WV}$, $\overline{VU}$

9. What angle is included between $\overline{WV}$ and $\overline{WU}$? ∠*W*

10. What angles include $\overline{UV}$? ∠*U*, ∠*V*

11. What side is included between ∠*W* and ∠*U*? $\overline{WU}$

Lesson 4-2 Triangle Congruence by SSS and SAS **189**

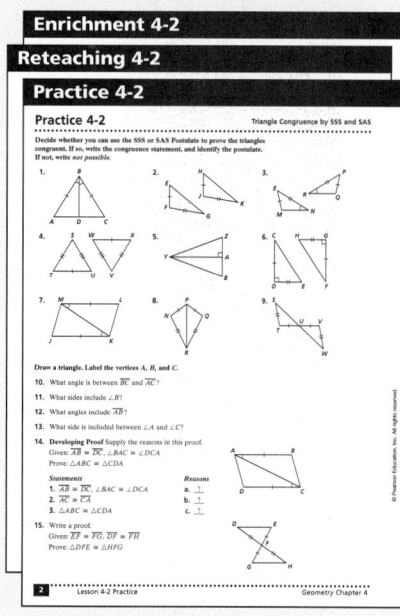

pages 189–192   Exercises

31.

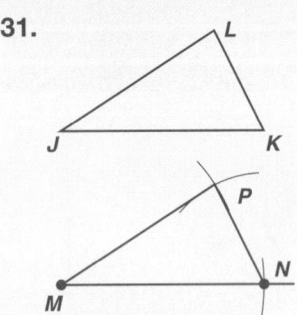

32.

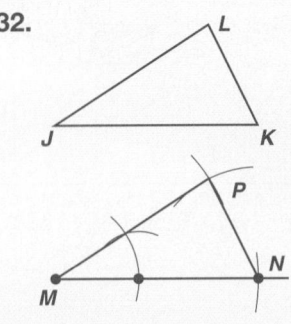

190

Name the indicated part(s) of △XYZ without drawing △XYZ.

12. the angle included between $\overline{XY}$ and $\overline{XZ}$
∠X

13. the sides that include ∠Z
$\overline{XZ}$, $\overline{YZ}$

Developing Proof What other information, if any, do you need to prove the two triangles congruent by SSS or SAS?

∠T ≅ ∠V or $\overline{RS}$ ≅ $\overline{WU}$

14. $\overline{LG}$ ≅ $\overline{MN}$
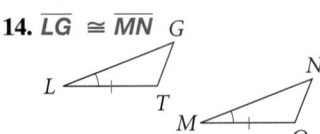

15.
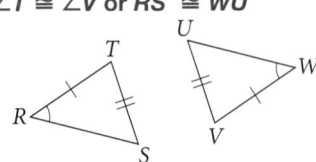

16. A $\overline{DC}$ ≅ $\overline{CB}$
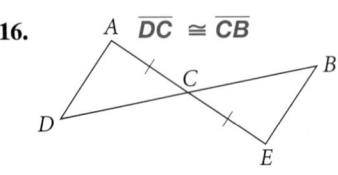

17.
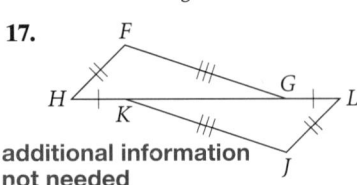
additional information not needed

Example 3
(page 188)

Developing Proof From the information given in the diagram, can you prove that the two triangles are congruent? Explain.

Yes; △ACB ≅ △EFD by SAS.

Yes; △PVQ ≅ △STR by SSS.

18.

19.

20.
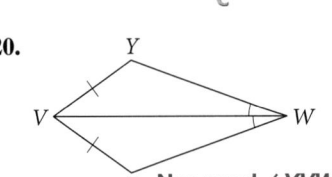
No; need ∠YVW ≅ ∠ZVW or $\overline{YW}$ ≅ $\overline{ZW}$.

21.
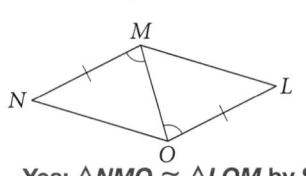
Yes; △NMO ≅ △LOM by SAS.

B Apply Your Skills

Developing Proof Is there enough information to prove the two triangles congruent? If so, write the congruence statement and name the postulate you would use. If not, write *not possible* and tell what other information you would need.

22.
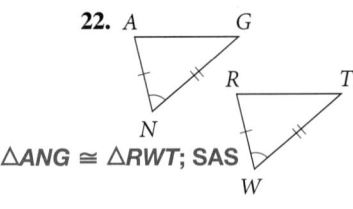
△ANG ≅ △RWT; SAS

23.
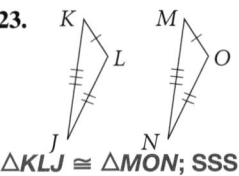
△KLJ ≅ △MON; SSS

24.
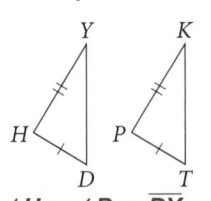
24. Not possible; need ∠H ≅ ∠P or $\overline{DY}$ ≅ $\overline{TK}$.

25.
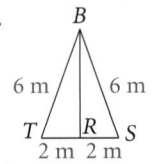
△JEF ≅ △SVF or △JEF ≅ △SFV; SSS

26.
6 m   6 m
2 m 2 m
△BRT ≅ △BRS; SSS

27.
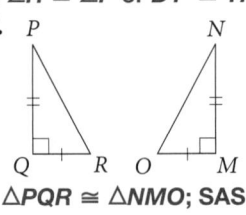
△PQR ≅ △NMO; SAS

190   Chapter 4   Congruent Triangles

35. b. ≅ △ produce a well-balanced, symmetric appearance. In construction, ≅ △ enhance designs. Highway warning signs are more easily identified if they are ≅.

38. Yes; △ADB ≅ △CBD by SAS; ∠ADB ≅ ∠DBC because if ‖ lines, then alt. int. △ are ≅.

39. Yes; △ABC ≅ △CDA by SAS; ∠DAC ≅ ∠ACB because if ‖ lines, then alt. int. △ are ≅.

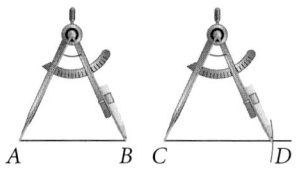

A   *B*   *C*   *D*

When you construct $\overline{AB} \cong \overline{CD}$, SAS tells you that the triangles outlined here are congruent.

Developing Proof From the information given, can you prove the two triangles congruent? Explain.

            No; even though the ⓢ are ≅, the sides may not be.

28. $\triangle ABC$ and $\triangle DEF$ with $\angle A \cong \angle D, \angle B \cong \angle E, \angle C \cong \angle F$

29. $\triangle GHI$ and $\triangle JKL$ with $\overline{GH} \cong \overline{JK}, \overline{HI} \cong \overline{KL}, \angle I \cong \angle L$

            No; you would need $\angle H \cong \angle K$ or $\overline{GI} \cong \overline{JL}$.

30. $\triangle MNP$ and $\triangle QRS$ with $\overline{MN} \cong \overline{QR}, \angle N \cong \angle R, \overline{NP} \cong \overline{RS}$ **yes; SAS**

Constructions Use a straightedge to draw $\triangle JKL$. Construct $\triangle MNP \cong \triangle JKL$ using the given postulate.   **31–32. See margin p. 190.**

31. SSS   **32.** SAS

33. Developing Proof Supply the reasons in this proof.

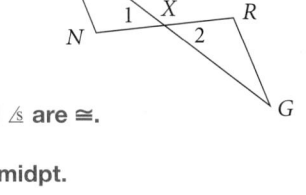

Given: X is the midpoint of $\overline{AG}$ and of $\overline{NR}$.

Prove: $\triangle ANX \cong \triangle GRX$

Statements	Reasons
1. $\angle 1 \cong \angle 2$	**a.** $\underline{\ ?\ }$ Vertical ⓢ are ≅.
2. X is the midpoint of $\overline{AG}$.	**b.** $\underline{\ ?\ }$ Given
3. $\overline{AX} \cong \overline{GX}$	**c.** $\underline{\ ?\ }$ Def. of midpt.
4. X is the midpoint of $\overline{NR}$.	**d.** $\underline{\ ?\ }$ Given
5. $\overline{NX} \cong \overline{RX}$	**e.** $\underline{\ ?\ }$ Def. of midpt.
6. $\triangle ANX \cong \triangle GRX$	**f.** $\underline{\ ?\ }$ SAS

34. Error Analysis A friend conjectures that there should be an AAA Congruence Postulate since there is a SSS Congruence Postulate. Give a counterexample to disprove your friend's conjecture. **See left.**

34. Answers may vary. Sample:

35. a. Open-Ended List three real-life uses of congruent triangles. **See left.**

35a. Answers may vary. Sample: wallpaper designs; ironwork on a bridge; highway warning signs

     b. Writing For each, tell whether you think congruence is necessary and why. **See margin p. 190.**

Developing Proof What can you prove about $\triangle ISP$ and $\triangle OSP$ given the information in the diagram and the information below?

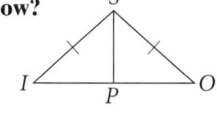

For help with reading and solving Exercise 36, see p. 193.

Reading Math

                       $\angle ISP \cong \angle PSO;$

36. $\overline{SP}$ is the bisector of $\angle ISO$. $\triangle ISP \cong \triangle OSP$ by SAS

37. $\overline{SP}$ is a bisector of $\overline{IO}$.

     $\overline{IP} \cong \overline{PO}; \triangle ISP \cong \triangle OSP$ by SSS

Developing Proof In $ABCD$, $\overline{AD} \parallel \overline{BC}$ and $\overline{AD} \cong \overline{BC}$. Can you prove the two triangles congruent? Explain.

38. $\triangle ADB$ and $\triangle CBD$ **39.** $\triangle ABC$ and $\triangle CDA$

     38–39. See margin p. 190.

40. Critical Thinking Four sides of polygon $ABCD$ are congruent to four sides of polygon $EFGH$. Must the two quadrilaterals also be congruent? Explain.

       No; $ABCD$ could be a square with side 5 and $EFGH$ could be a polygon with side 5 but no rt. ⓢ.

C Challenge *Proof* Write a proof.

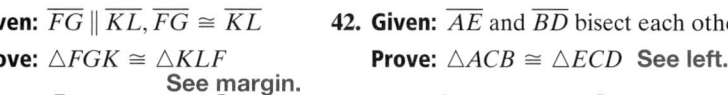

41. Given: $\overline{FG} \parallel \overline{KL}, \overline{FG} \cong \overline{KL}$

     Prove: $\triangle FGK \cong \triangle KLF$

            See margin.

42. Given: $\overline{AE}$ and $\overline{BD}$ bisect each other.

     Prove: $\triangle ACB \cong \triangle ECD$ **See left.**

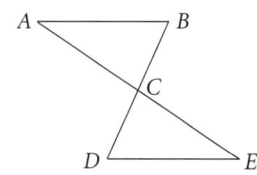

42. $\overline{AE}$ and $\overline{BD}$ bisect each other so $\overline{AC} \cong \overline{CE}$ and $\overline{BC} \cong \overline{CD}$. $\angle ACB \cong \angle DCE$ because vert. ⓢ are ≅. $\triangle ACB \cong \triangle ECD$ by SAS.

41. 1. $\overline{FG} \parallel \overline{KL}$ (Given)

     2. $\angle GFK \cong \angle FKL$ (If $\parallel$ lines, then alt. int. ⓢ are ≅).

     3. $\overline{FG} \cong \overline{KL}$ (Given)

     4. $\overline{FK} \cong \overline{FK}$ (Reflexive Prop. of ≅)

     5. $\triangle FGK \cong \triangle KLF$ (SAS)

---

4. Assess

Lesson Quiz 4-2

1. In $\triangle VGB$, which sides include $\angle B$? $\overline{BG}$ and $\overline{BV}$

2. In $\triangle STN$, which angle is included between $\overline{NS}$ and $\overline{TN}$? $\angle N$

3. Which triangles can you prove congruent? Tell whether you would use the SSS or SAS Postulate.

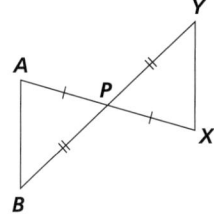

$\triangle APB \cong \triangle XPY$; SAS

4. What other information do you need to prove $\triangle DWO \cong \triangle DWG$?

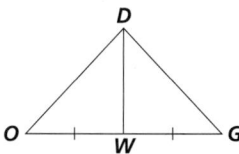

If you know $\overline{DO} \cong \overline{DG}$, the triangles are ≅ by SSS; if you know $\angle DWO \cong \angle DWG$, they are ≅ by SAS.

5. Can you prove $\triangle SED \cong \triangle BUT$ from the information given? Explain.

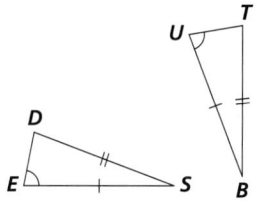

No; corresponding ≅ angles are not between corresponding ≅ sides.

191

44. $\overline{AM} \cong \overline{MB}$ because M is the midpt. of $\overline{AB}$. $\angle B \cong \angle AMC$ because all right $\angle$s are $\cong$. $\overline{CM} \cong \overline{DB}$ is given. $\triangle AMC \cong \triangle MBD$ by SAS.

43. Given: $\overline{GK}$ bisects $\angle JGM$, $\overline{GJ} \cong \overline{GM}$.

Prove: $\triangle GJK \cong \triangle GMK$
See back of book.

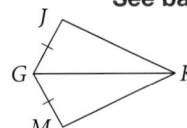

44. Given: $\overline{AB} \perp \overline{CM}, \overline{AB} \perp \overline{DB}$, M is the midpoint of $\overline{AB}$, $\overline{CM} \cong \overline{DB}$.

Prove: $\triangle AMC \cong \triangle MBD$ See left.

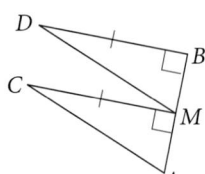

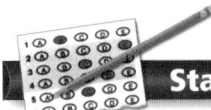

Standardized Test Prep

Multiple Choice

Use the figures at the right for Exercises 45–47.

45. Suppose $\overline{TM} \cong \overline{GL}$ and $\angle M \cong \angle G$. What additional information is needed to prove $\triangle MTD \cong \triangle GLS$ by SAS? **D**

  A. $\angle T \cong \angle L$ **B.** $\angle T \cong \angle S$ **C.** $\overline{TD} \cong \overline{SL}$ **D.** $\overline{MD} \cong \overline{SG}$

46. Suppose $\overline{TD} \cong \overline{SG}$ and $\overline{MD} \cong \overline{SL}$. What additional information is needed to prove the two triangles congruent by SAS? **G**

  F. $\angle T \cong \angle S$ **G.** $\angle D \cong \angle S$ **H.** $\angle S \cong \angle L$ **I.** $\angle D \cong \angle G$

47. Suppose $TD = 10$ cm, $DM = 9$ cm, $TM = 11$ cm, $SL = 11$ cm, and $SG = 9$ cm. What else do you need to know in order to prove that the two triangles are congruent by SSS? **C**

  A. $LG = 9$ cm   **B.** $TD = SL$ **C.** $GL = 10$ cm   **D.** $TM = SG$

Short Response

Take It to the NET
Online lesson quiz at
www.PHSchool.com
········· Web Code: afa-0402

48. In the diagram, $\overline{WB} \cong \overline{BZ}$ and $\angle W \cong \angle ABZ$. **a–b.**
 a. State another conclusion you can make. **See margin.** Name the property that justifies your conclusion.
 b. Based on the information given in the diagram, can you prove the two triangles congruent? Justify your answer.

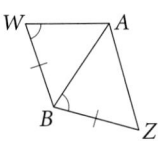

Mixed Review

Lesson 4-1

$ABCD \cong EFGH$. **Name the angle or side that corresponds to the given part.**

49. $\angle A$ $\angle E$ **50.** $\overline{EF}$ $\overline{AB}$ **51.** $\overline{BC}$ $\overline{FG}$ **52.** $\angle G$ $\angle C$

Lesson 2-2

53. The product of the slopes of two lines is -1 if and only if the lines are $\perp$.

53. The following two statements are about lines with defined slopes. Combine them into a single biconditional. **See left.**

If the product of the slopes of two lines is -1, then the lines are perpendicular. If two lines are perpendicular, then the product of their slopes is -1.

54. Write the two conditional statements that form this biconditional:

$x = 2$ if and only if $2x = 4$.
If $x = 2$, then $2x = 4$. If $2x = 4$, then $x = 2$.

Lesson 2-1

Write the converse of the statement. Decide whether the statement and its converse are true or false. 55–56. See margin.

55. If $x = 3$ then $2x = 6$.   **56.** If $x = 3$ then $x^2 = 9$.

Reading Diagrams and Words

Read the problem below and follow the discussion. Check your understanding by solving the exercise at the bottom of the page.

What can you prove about △ISP and △OSP given the information in the diagram and the information below?

   $\overline{SP}$ is the bisector of ∠ISO.

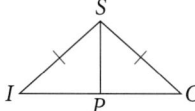

To complete this problem, you must get information from both the statement and the diagram.

The Statement

$\overline{SP}$ is the bisector of ∠ISO.

To "bisect" means to divide into two congruent parts.
Therefore ∠ISP ≅ ∠OSP by definition of an angle bisector.

The Diagram

Analyze the diagram carefully.
It may be helpful to write out in words what you see.

For example:
• There is a large triangle, △ISO, which consists of two smaller triangles, △ISP and △OSP.
• Two segments, $\overline{IS}$ and $\overline{OS}$, are marked.
  The marks show that $\overline{IS}$ and $\overline{OS}$ are congruent, or $\overline{IS} ≅ \overline{OS}$.

Putting all this information together, you have ∠ISP ≅ ∠OSP and $\overline{IS} ≅ \overline{OS}$.
Look carefully at △ISP and △OSP. Can you find another pair of corresponding congruent parts? Yes! They share a side, $\overline{SP}$. Clearly $\overline{SP} ≅ \overline{SP}$.

Sketch your own version of the diagram to show all this information. You can use double tick marks on the segment that you cite as being congruent to itself.

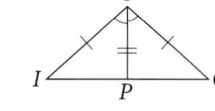

Now you see that you can use SAS to prove that △ISP ≅ △OSP.

EXERCISE

What can you prove about △ABC and △ADC given the information in the diagram, and given that $\overline{AC}$ bisects $\overline{BD}$. **△ABC ≅ △ADC by SSS.**

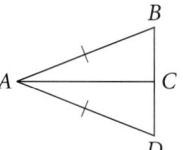

Reading Diagrams and Words

Geometry exercises often involve information from a combination of diagrams, words, and symbols. For students to solve such problems successfully, they must process and integrate the different forms of information.

Teaching Notes

As students examine the statement and diagram, point out that the given two pieces of information by themselves do not lead to any new conclusions. State: *You often must find another piece of information when solving a geometry problem or completing a proof.* In this example, the information needed is the fact that $\overline{SP} ≅ \overline{SP}$.

Error Prevention

After students finish reading the example, ask: *Is it correct to conclude that △ISP ≅ △POS? Explain.* **No; the congruent corresponding parts of the two triangles are not listed in the same order.**

Teaching Tip

You can use an X instead of tick marks to indicate a reflexive congruence. Show students how this can be done to show $\overline{SP} ≅ \overline{SP}$.

Exercise

Have students work independently to solve the problem, showing the steps they used. Then have volunteers share with the class what they were thinking as they reasoned through the problem. Elicit the fact that there are often different ways to arrive at the solution of a problem.

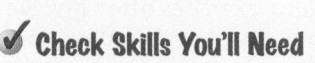
1. Plan

4-3

Triangle Congruence
by ASA and AAS

North Carolina Objectives

2.03 Apply properties, definitions, and theorems of two-dimensional figures to solve problems and write proofs: a) Triangles.

Lesson Preview

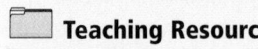
✓ Check Skills You'll Need

Using the SAS and SSS Postulates
Lesson 4-2: Example 2
Exercises 8–13
Extra Practice, p. 693

Proving Triangles Congruent
Lesson 4-1: Example 4, Exercise 28
Extra Practice, p. 693

Lesson Resources

📁 Teaching Resources
Practice, Reteaching, Enrichment
Checkpoint Quiz 1

👥 Reaching All Students
Practice Workbook 4-3
Spanish Practice Workbook 4-3
Reading and Math Literacy 4B
Spanish Reading & Literacy 4B
Technology Activities 41
Informal Geometry Planning
   Guide 4-3

🕐 Presentation Assistant Plus!
Transparencies
• Check Skills You'll Need 4-3
• Additional Examples 4-3
• Student Edition Answers 4-3
• Lesson Quiz 4-3
PH Presentation Pro CD 4-3

PRENTICE HALL ASSESSMENT *SYSTEM*

Checkpoint Quiz 1
Computer Test Generator CD

💿 Technology
Resource Pro® CD-ROM
Computer Test Generator CD
Prentice Hall Presentation Pro CD

💻 www.PHSchool.com
Student Site
• Teacher Web Code: afk-5500
• Self-grading Lesson Quiz
Teacher Center
• Lesson Planner
• Resources

Plus

194

Lesson Preview

What You'll Learn

OBJECTIVE 1
To prove two triangles congruent using the ASA Postulate and the AAS Theorem

. . . And Why
To prove that the two sides of a lacrosse goal are congruent triangles, as in Example 2

✓ Check Skills You'll Need

(For help, go to Lesson 4-2.)

In $\triangle JHK$, which side is included between the given pair of angles?
1. $\angle J$ and $\angle H$ $\overline{JH}$ **2.** $\angle H$ and $\angle K$ $\overline{HK}$

In $\triangle NLM$, which angle is included between the given pair of sides?
3. $\overline{LN}$ and $\overline{LM}$ $\angle L$ **4.** $\overline{NM}$ and $\overline{LN}$ $\angle N$

Give a reason to justify each statement. If 2 ∠ of a △ are ≅ to 2 ∠ of another
5. $\overline{PR} \cong \overline{PR}$ Reflexive Prop. of ≅   **6.** $\angle A \cong \angle D$ △, the third ∠ are ≅.

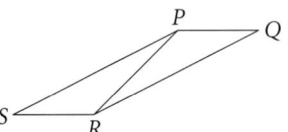

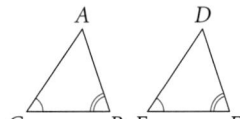

OBJECTIVE 1
Using the ASA Postulate and the AAS Theorem

iTEXT Interactive lesson includes instant self-check, tutorials, and activities.

Investigation: Are the Triangles Congruent?

Draw a triangle. Label your triangle
$\triangle ABC$.

• Construct $\overline{XY}$ so that $\overline{XY} \cong \overline{AB}$.

• At X, construct $\angle X$ so that $\angle X \cong \angle A$.
At Y, construct $\angle Y$ so that $\angle Y \cong \angle B$.
Label point Z as shown.

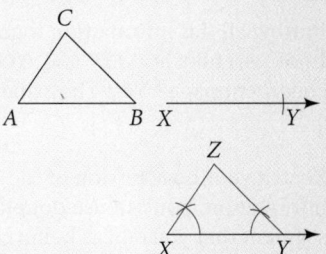

1. Cut out $\triangle ABC$ and $\triangle XYZ$. Place $\triangle ABC$ over $\triangle XYZ$ so that corresponding angles match. Are the triangles congruent? Compare your results with others. **Check students' work.**

2. Make a conjecture. What seems to be true when two angles and the included side of one triangle are congruent to two angles and the included side of another triangle? **The △ are ≅.**

In Lesson 4-2 you learned that two triangles are congruent if
   two pairs of sides are congruent and the included angles are congruent (SAS).
The construction shown above suggests that two triangles are also congruent if
   two pairs of angles are congruent and the included sides are congruent (ASA).

194 Chapter 4 Congruent Triangles

🔄 Ongoing Assessment and Intervention

Before the Lesson Diagnose prerequisite skills using:	**During the Lesson** Monitor progress using:	**After the Lesson** Assess knowledge using:
• Check Skills You'll Need	• Check Understanding • Additional Examples • Standardized Test Prep	• Lesson Quiz • Computer Test Generator CD • Chapter Checkpoint 1 (p. 201)

Key Concepts

Postulate 4-3	Angle-Side-Angle (ASA) Postulate

If two angles and the included side of one triangle are congruent to two angles and the included side of another triangle, then the two triangles are congruent.

$\triangle HGB \cong \triangle NKP$

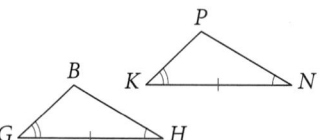

Proof  **1 EXAMPLE** Using ASA

Developing Proof Name two triangles that are congruent by the ASA Postulate.

$\triangle CAT \cong \triangle GDO$ because

$\angle C \cong \angle G$,

$\overline{CA} \cong \overline{GD}$,

$\angle A \cong \angle D$.

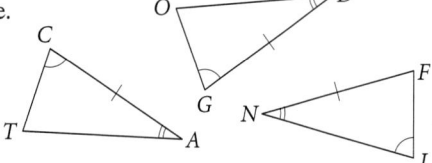

✔ **Check Understanding** ① Can you conclude that $\triangle INF$ is congruent to either of the other two triangles? Explain. **No; the ≅ side is not the included side.**

Real-World 🌐 **Connection**

The Iroquois Nationals compete for the World Lacrosse Championship every four years.

Here is how you can use the ASA Postulate in a proof.

2 EXAMPLE Real-World 🌐 Connection

Lacrosse Study what you are given and what you are to prove about the lacrosse goal. Then write a paragraph proof that uses ASA.

Given: $\angle CAB \cong \angle DAE$, $\overline{AB} \cong \overline{AE}$, $\angle ABC$ and $\angle AED$ are right angles.

Prove: $\triangle ABC \cong \triangle AED$

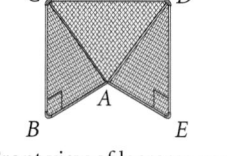

Front view of lacrosse goal

Proof: $\angle ABC \cong \angle AED$ because all right angles are congruent. You are given that $\overline{AB} \cong \overline{AE}$ and $\angle CAB \cong \angle DAE$. Thus, $\triangle ABC \cong \triangle AED$ by ASA.

✔ **Check Understanding** ② Write a two-column proof that $\triangle ABC \cong \triangle AED$. **See back of book.**

You can use the ASA Postulate to prove the Angle-Angle-Side Congruence Theorem. A flow proof is shown on the next page.

 Key Concepts

Theorem 4-2	Angle-Angle-Side (AAS) Theorem

If two angles and a nonincluded side of one triangle are congruent to two angles and the corresponding nonincluded side of another triangle, then the triangles are congruent.

$\triangle CDM \cong \triangle XGT$

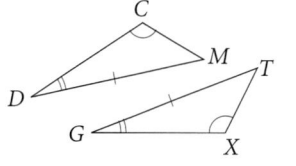

👥 **Reaching All Students**

Below Level Students may substitute specific measures for the congruent angles in the flow proof of the AAS Theorem to see the dependence on the ASA Postulate before proceeding to the general proof.	**Advanced Learners** After students read the ASA Postulate and the AAS Theorem, ask: *If you could use only one in the remainder of this course, which would you choose and why?*	**Visual Learners** See note on page 199. **Error Prevention** See note on page 199.

Math Background

ASA is presented in this lesson as a postulate, but it could be established as a theorem (whose proof requires constructing congruent segments) that follows from the SAS postulate, much as SSS also could be established as a theorem that follows from the SAS Postulate. The proof of the AAS Theorem follows from the ASA Postulate and the Triangle Angle-Sum Theorem.

OBJECTIVE

 Teaching Notes

Investigation (Optional)

Have a student suggest a segment length and two angle measures whose sum is less than 180 for a triangle. Then have each student use a ruler and a protractor to draw the segment with an angle at each endpoint. When the rays drawn for the sides of the two angles intersect, students can compare the triangles formed to see why the ASA Postulate is reasonable.

2 EXAMPLE Diversity

Lacrosse originated as "baggataway," a Native American game with up to 200 players on each side. Its modern name comes from French Canadians.

Teaching Tip

Examine the flow proof of the AAS Theorem as a class. Point out the three arrows leading to the conclusion. Ask: *Why are there three arrows?* Each arrow is from one of the congruence statements needed to prove the AAS Theorem.

3 EXAMPLE

Point out that an effective Plan for Proof may involve the strategy *working backward.* In this Plan for Proof, the conclusion of the conditional statement is what must be proved. The second sentence of the Plan for Proof tells why the hypothesis is true.

195

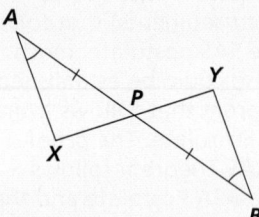
1 Use the triangles in Example 1. Suppose that $\angle F$ is congruent to $\angle C$ and $\angle I$ is *not* congruent to $\angle C$. Name the triangles that are congruent by the ASA Postulate.
$\triangle FNI \cong \triangle CAT \cong \triangle GDO$

2 Write a paragraph proof.

Given: $\angle A \cong \angle B$, $\overline{AP} \cong \overline{BP}$

Prove: $\triangle APX \cong \triangle BPY$
$\angle APX \cong \angle BPY$ by the Vertical Angles Theorem, so $\triangle APX \cong \triangle BPY$ by ASA.

3 Write a Plan for Proof that uses AAS.

Given: $\angle B \cong \angle D$, $\overline{AB} \parallel \overline{CD}$

Prove: $\triangle ABC \cong \triangle CDA$ Because $\overline{AB} \parallel \overline{CD}$, $\angle BAC \cong \angle DCA$ (alt. int. angles). $\triangle ABC \cong \triangle CDA$ by AAS if $\overline{AB} \cong \overline{CD}$, $\overline{BC} \cong \overline{DA}$, or $\overline{AC} \cong \overline{AC}$. By Reflexive Prop., $\overline{AC} \cong \overline{AC}$.

4 Write a two-column proof of Additional Example 3.
1. $\angle B \cong \angle D$, $\overline{AB} \parallel \overline{CD}$ (Given)
2. $\angle BAC \cong \angle DCA$ (If lines are $\parallel$, then alt. int. angles are $\cong$.)
3. $\overline{AC} \cong \overline{AC}$ (Reflexive Prop. of $\cong$)
4. $\triangle ABC \cong \triangle CDA$ (AAS)

Closure

Explain why the letters of ASA and AAS are written in a different order. ASA compares triangles in which $\cong$ sides are between the two pairs of $\cong$ angles, and AAS compares triangles in which $\cong$ sides are not between pairs of $\cong$ angles.

Proof **Flow Proof of the Angle-Angle-Side Theorem**

Given: $\angle A \cong \angle X$, $\angle B \cong \angle Y$, $\overline{BC} \cong \overline{YZ}$

Prove: $\triangle ABC \cong \triangle XYZ$

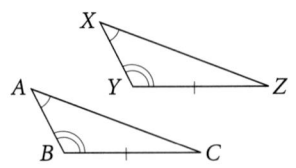

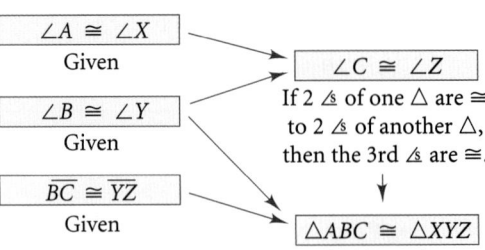

Need Help?
A statement in a flow proof can be deduced from the facts that point to it.

Here are two examples of how to use the AAS Theorem.

3 EXAMPLE Planning a Proof

Developing Proof Study what you are given and what you are to prove. Then plan a proof that uses AAS.

Given: $\angle S \cong \angle Q$, $\overline{RP}$ bisects $\angle SRQ$.

Prove: $\triangle SRP \cong \triangle QRP$

Plan: $\triangle SRP \cong \triangle QRP$ by AAS if $\overline{SP} \cong \overline{QP}$ or $\overline{RP} \cong \overline{RP}$.

The second statement is true by the Reflexive Property of Congruence.

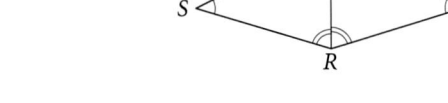

✓ **Check Understanding** **3** Use the plan from Example 3 and write a flow proof. **See back of book.**

Proof **4 EXAMPLE Writing a Proof**

Study what you are given and what you are to prove. Then write a two-column proof that uses AAS.

Given: $\overline{XQ} \parallel \overline{TR}$, $\overline{XR}$ bisects $\overline{QT}$.

Prove: $\triangle XMQ \cong \triangle RMT$

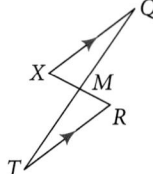

Statements	Reasons
1. $\overline{XQ} \parallel \overline{TR}$	1. Given
2. $\angle Q \cong \angle T$, $\angle X \cong \angle R$	2. _?_
3. $\overline{XR}$ bisects $\overline{QT}$.	3. Given
4. $\overline{QM} \cong \overline{TM}$	4. Definition of segment bisector
5. $\triangle XMQ \cong \triangle RMT$	5. AAS

✓ **Check Understanding** **4 a.** Supply the reason that justifies Step 2. **If $\parallel$ lines, then alt. int. $\angle$s are $\cong$.**
b. Critical Thinking Explain how you could prove $\triangle XMQ \cong \triangle RMT$ by ASA. **$\triangle XMQ \cong \triangle RMT$ because vert. $\angle$s are $\cong$.**

EXERCISES

Practice and Problem Solving

Ⓐ Practice by Example

Example 1
(page 195)

Developing Proof **Name two triangles that are congruent by the ASA Postulate.**

1.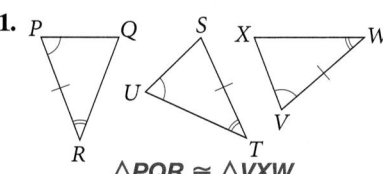

$\triangle PQR \cong \triangle VXW$

2.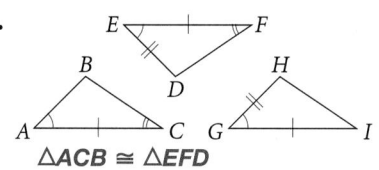

$\triangle ACB \cong \triangle EFD$

Answer each question without drawing the triangle.

3. Which side is included between $\angle R$ and $\angle S$ in $\triangle RST$? $\overline{RS}$

4. Which angles include $\overline{NO}$ in $\triangle NOM$? $\angle N$ and $\angle O$

Example 2
(page 195)

Developing Proof **Tell whether the ASA Postulate can be used to prove the triangles congruent. If not, write *not possible*.**

5. yes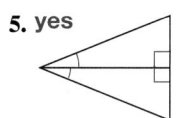

6. not possible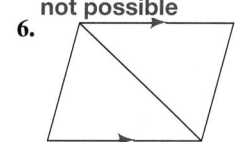

7. yes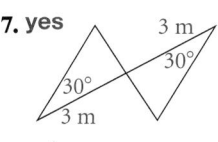

8. Developing Proof Complete the paragraph proof by filling in the blanks.

Given: $\angle LKM \cong \angle JKM$,
$\angle LMK \cong \angle JMK$

Prove: $\triangle LKM \cong \triangle JKM$

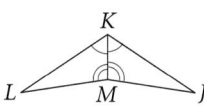

Proof: $\angle LKM \cong \angle JKM$ and $\angle LMK \cong \angle JMK$ are given. $\overline{KM} \cong \overline{KM}$ by the **a.** ___?___ Property of Congruence. **Reflexive**
$\triangle LKM \cong \triangle JKM$ by the **b.** ___?___ Postulate. **ASA**

Example 3
(page 196)

Developing Proof **Tell whether the AAS Theorem or the ASA Postulate can be applied directly to prove the triangles congruent. If not, write *not possible*.**

9.

AAS

10. ASA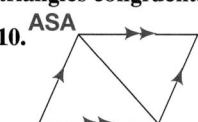

11.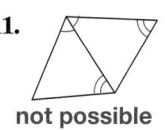

not possible

12. $\angle E \cong \angle I$ and $\overline{FE} \cong \overline{GI}$. What else must you know to prove $\triangle FDE \cong \triangle GHI$ by AAS? by ASA? $\angle FDE \cong \angle GHI$; $\angle DFE \cong \angle HGI$

13. Developing Proof Complete the proof plan by filling in the blanks.

Given: $\angle UWT$ and $\angle UWV$ are right angles,
$\angle T \cong \angle V$.

Prove: $\triangle UWT \cong \triangle UWV$

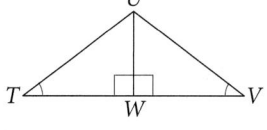

Plan: $\triangle UWT \cong \triangle UWV$ by AAS if $\angle T \cong \angle V$,
$\angle UWT \cong$ **a.** ___?___, and $\overline{UW} \cong$ **b.** ___?___. $\angle UWV$; $\overline{UW}$
$\angle UWT \cong \angle UWV$ because all **c.** ___?___ angles are congruent. **right**
$\overline{UW} \cong \overline{UW}$ by the **d.** ___?___ Property of Congruence. **Reflexive**

Assignment Guide

▼ **1 Objective**
  Ⓐ Ⓑ **Core** 1–35
  Ⓒ **Extension** 36–41

Standardized Test Prep 42–45

Mixed Review 46–52

Teaching Tip
Students practice several different methods of writing and planning proofs in this lesson. Point out that a good plan uses only the necessary information and clearly states the reasons. The goal is to plan and write clear and correct proofs. Learning multiple techniques will help students reach that goal.

Enrichment 4-3
Reteaching 4-3
Practice 4-3

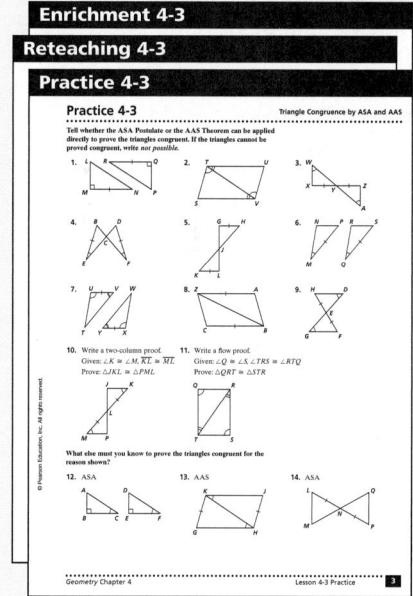

Error Prevention

Exercise 11 By labeling the third pair of congruent angles, students should be able to see why these triangles cannot be proven congruent.

Exercise 15 After students complete the exercise, ask: *Suppose* $\overline{MO} \cong \overline{NO}$. *Can you use SAS to prove the triangles congruent? Explain.* Yes; you must first explain why $\angle MOU \cong \angle NOU$, and use $\overline{OU} \cong \overline{OU}$.

Alternative Method

Exercise 18 Challenge students to find a second way to complete the proof. Ask: *Suppose that you did not know the Vertical Angles Theorem. How could you find another pair of congruent angles?* Because $\angle N \cong \angle S$, $\overline{NT} \parallel \overline{RS}$ by the Converse of the Alt. Int. Angles Thm., so $\angle T \cong \angle R$ because they are alt. int. angles. $\overline{QT} \cong \overline{QR}$ by definition of a bisector, and $\triangle NQT \cong \triangle SQR$ by AAS.

Exercise 27 Discuss how the first sentence in the Plan for Proof is an example of working backward from what needs to be proved to what will prove it, using the Given. The second and third sentences justify the statements of the proof. Point out that this is only one way to write a Plan for Proof.

pages 197–201   Exercises

22. $\triangle TUX \cong \triangle DEO$; AAS

23. The ⧍ are not ≅ because no sides are ≅.

24. $\triangle TXU \cong \triangle ODE$; ASA

25. The ⧍ are not ≅ because the ≅ ⧍ are not included ⧍.

26. Yes; if 2 ⧍ of a △ are ≅ to 2 ⧍ of another △, then the 3rd ⧍ are ≅. So, an AAS proof can be rewritten as an ASA proof.

Example 4
(page 196)

Developing Proof What else must you know to prove the triangles congruent for the reason shown?

14. AAS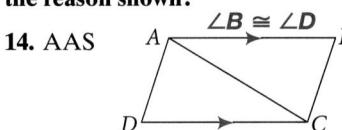

15. SAS $\overline{MU} \cong \overline{UN}$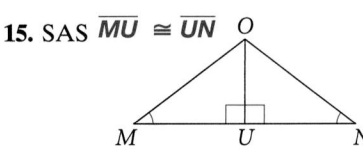

16. ASA $\overline{PQ} \cong \overline{QS}$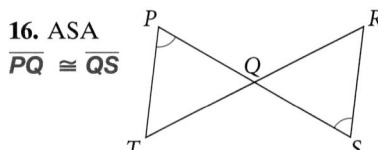

17. AAS $\angle WZV \cong \angle WZY$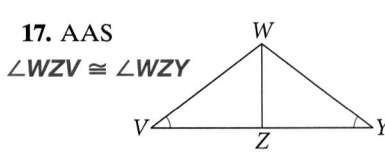

18. **Developing Proof** Complete the two-column proof by filling in the blanks.

Given: $\angle N \cong \angle S$, line ℓ bisects $\overline{TR}$ at Q.

Prove: $\triangle NQT \cong \triangle SQR$

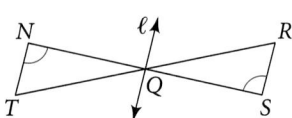

Statements	Reasons
1. $\angle N \cong \angle S$	1. Given
2. $\angle NQT \cong \angle SQR$	a. _?_ Vert. ⧍ are ≅.
3. ℓ bisects $\overline{TR}$ at Q.	b. _?_ Given
c. _?_ $\overline{TQ} \cong \overline{QR}$	4. Definition of bisect
5. $\triangle NQT \cong \triangle SQR$	d. _?_ AAS

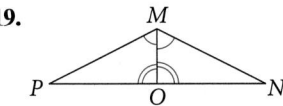 **Apply Your Skills**

Developing Proof Write a congruence statement for each pair of triangles. Name the postulate or theorem that justifies your statement.

$\triangle ZVY \cong \triangle WVY$; AAS

19.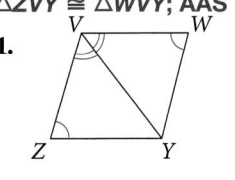

$\triangle PMO \cong \triangle NMO$; ASA

20.

$\triangle UTS \cong \triangle RST$; AAS

21.

Developing Proof If the two triangles are congruent for the given conditions, write a congruence statement. Justify your conclusion. 22–25. See margin.

22. $\angle D \cong \angle T, \angle E \cong \angle U, \overline{EO} \cong \overline{UX}$

23. $\angle D \cong \angle T, \angle E \cong \angle U, \angle O \cong \angle X$

24. $\overline{DO} \cong \overline{TX}, \angle D \cong \angle X, \angle O \cong \angle T$

25. $\overline{EO} \cong \overline{UX}, \angle E \cong \angle U, \overline{DO} \cong \overline{TX}$

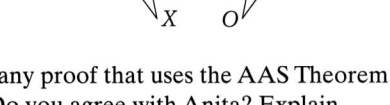

Real-World 🌐 **Connection**

Congruent lapel and collar triangles help you look sharp.

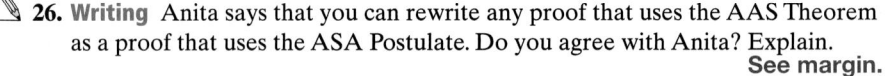

26. **Writing** Anita says that you can rewrite any proof that uses the AAS Theorem as a proof that uses the ASA Postulate. Do you agree with Anita? Explain.
See margin.

Developing Proof In Exercises 27–29, complete each proof or proof plan.

27. **Given:** $\overline{PQ} \parallel \overline{SR}, \angle Q \cong \angle S$

Prove: $\triangle QPR \cong \triangle SRP$

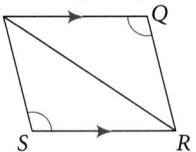

Plan: $\triangle QPR \cong \triangle SRP$ by AAS if $\angle SRP$; $\overline{PR}$ $\angle Q \cong \angle S, \angle QPR \cong$ **a.** _?_, and $\overline{PR} \cong$ **b.** _?_.

27c. alt. int. $\angle QPR \cong \angle SRP$ because they are **c.** _?_ angles for the given parallel lines and the transversal **d.** _?_. $\overline{PR} \cong \overline{PR}$ by the **e.** _?_ Property of Congruence.
$\overline{PR}$ — Reflexive

198   Chapter 4   Congruent Triangles

28. Given: $\overline{SQ}$ bisects $\angle PSR$, $\angle P \cong \angle R$.
Prove: $\triangle PSQ \cong \triangle RSQ$

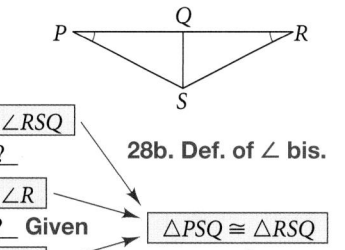

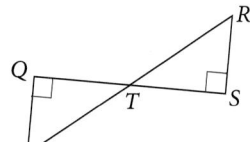

$\overline{SQ}$ bisects $\angle PSR.$ $\longrightarrow$ $\angle PSQ \cong \angle RSQ$

a. _?_ Given

b. _?_

28b. Def. of $\angle$ bis.

$\angle P \cong \angle R$

c. _?_ Given

$\overline{SQ} \cong \overline{SQ}$

$\triangle PSQ \cong \triangle RSQ$

e. _?_ AAS

d. _?_
Reflexive Prop. of $\cong$

29. Given: $\overline{PQ} \perp \overline{QS}, \overline{RS} \perp \overline{QS},$
T is the midpoint of $\overline{PR}$.
Prove: $\triangle PQT \cong \triangle RST$

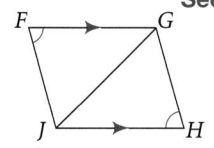

Statements	Reasons
1. $\overline{PQ} \perp \overline{QS}, \overline{RS} \perp \overline{QS}$	**1.** Given
2. $\angle Q$ and $\angle S$ are right angles.	**a.** _?_ Def. of $\perp$
3. $\angle Q \cong \angle S$	**b.** _?_ All right $\angle$ are $\cong$.
c. _?_ $\angle QTP \cong \angle STR$	**4.** Vertical angles are congruent.
5. T is the midpoint of $\overline{PR}$.	**5.** Given
6. $\overline{PT} \cong \overline{RT}$	**d.** _?_ Def. of midpt.
7. $\triangle PQT \cong \triangle RST$	**e.** _?_ AAS

30. Constructions Using a straightedge, draw a triangle. Label it $\triangle JKL$. Construct $\triangle MNP \cong \triangle JKL$ so you know that the triangles are congruent by ASA.
See left.

Developing Proof Can you deduce the "Conclusion" from the "Given" information? Explain. **31.** Yes; by AAS since $\angle MON \cong \angle QOP$.

31. Given: $\angle N \cong \angle P, \overline{MO} \cong \overline{QO}$
Conclusion: $\triangle MON \cong \triangle QOP$

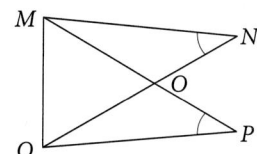

32. Given: $\angle F \cong \angle H, \overline{FG} \parallel \overline{JH}$
Conclusion: $\triangle FGJ \cong \triangle HJG$
See left.

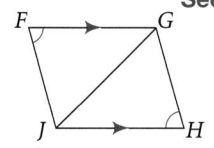

33. Given: $\overline{AE} \parallel \overline{BD}, \overline{AE} \cong \overline{BD},$
$\angle E \cong \angle D$
Conclusion: $\triangle AEB \cong \triangle BDC$
See left.

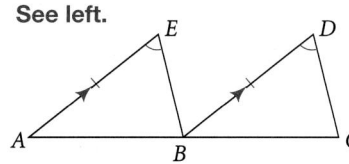

34. Given: $\overline{DH}$ bisects $\angle BDF,$
$\angle 1 \cong \angle 2.$
Conclusion: $\triangle BDH \cong \triangle FDH$
See left.

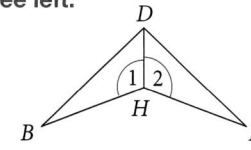

35. Reasoning If possible, draw two noncongruent triangles that have two pairs of congruent angles and one pair of congruent sides. If this is not possible, explain why. **See left.**

30.

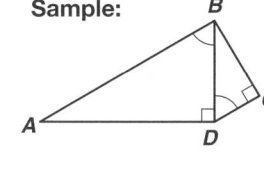

---

30 figure labels: L, J, K, P, M, N

Need Help?
In Exercise 30, copy one angle, a side, and then another angle so that the copied angles include the copied side.

32. Yes; by AAS since $\angle FGJ \cong \angle HJG$ because when lines are $\parallel$, then alt. int. $\angle$ are $\cong$ and $\overline{GJ} \cong \overline{GJ}$ by the Reflexive Prop. of $\cong$.

33. Yes; by ASA, since $\angle EAB \cong \angle DBC$ because $\parallel$ lines have $\cong$ corr. $\angle$.

34. Yes; by ASA since $\angle BDH \cong \angle FDH$ by def. of $\angle$ bis. and $\overline{DH} \cong \overline{DH}$ by the Reflexive Prop. of $\cong$.

35. Answers may vary. Sample:

Error Prevention

Exercise 28 Students sometimes think an angle bisector also bisects the opposite side or is a perpendicular bisector. Ask: *From the Given, can you conclude* $\angle PQS \cong \angle RQS$ *or* $\overline{PQ} \cong \overline{RQ}$? no Review how angle bisectors, segment bisectors, and perpendicular bisectors are different.

Exercises 28, 29 Have students write Plans for Proof before completing the proofs. They then can compare their plans with the actual proofs to improve their proof-writing technique.

Visual Learners

Exercise 33 Because the parallel segments terminate at the transversal $\overline{AC}$, students may have difficulty spotting corresponding angles. Have them copy just the parallel segments $\overline{AE}$ and $\overline{BD}$ and the transversal $\overline{AC}$ to help them find the corresponding angles more easily.

Exercise 39 Remind students that they can make at least six congruence statements about two congruent triangles.

Connection to Discrete Math

Exercise 40 There are 20 ways because $_6C_3 = \frac{6 \cdot 5 \cdot 4}{3 \cdot 2 \cdot 1} = 20$. To list the sets of three efficiently, suggest that students rename the congruence statements 1, 2, 3, 4, 5, and 6.

1. Which side is included between ∠R and ∠F in △FTR? **RF**

2. Which angles in △STU include $\overline{US}$? **∠S and ∠U**

Tell whether you can prove the triangles congruent by ASA or AAS. If you can, state a triangle congruence and the postulate or theorem you used. If not, write *not possible*.

3.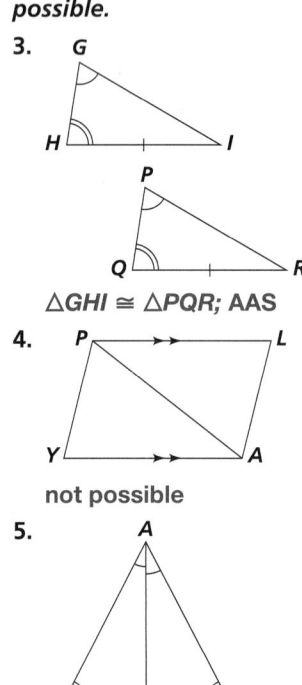

△GHI ≅ △PQR; AAS

4.

not possible

5.

△ABX ≅ △ACX; AAS

Alternative Assessment

Have students explain the four ways they have learned to prove triangles congruent—SSS, SAS, ASA, and AAS—and include a diagram with each method.

Challenge

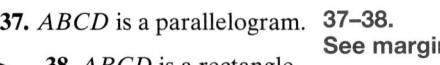

Real-World Connection

The two triangles above are congruent if just one additional condition is met.

41.

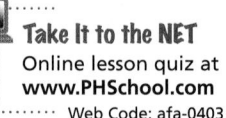

36. a. Open-Ended Draw a triangle. Draw a second triangle that shares a common side with the first one and is congruent to it. **Check students' work.**
   b. Think about how you drew your second triangle. What postulate or theorem did you use to make the second triangle congruent to the first one? **most likely ASA**

Use the figure at the right. Name as many pairs of congruent triangles as you can for the information given.

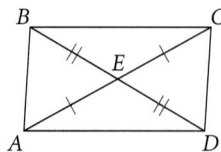

37. *ABCD* is a parallelogram. **37–38. See margin.**

38. *ABCD* is a rectangle.

39. Reasoning △JKL ≅ △MNP. What additional information about $\overline{KQ}$ and $\overline{NR}$ will allow you to conclude that △JKQ ≅ △MNR? Explain. **They are ∠ bisectors; ASA.**

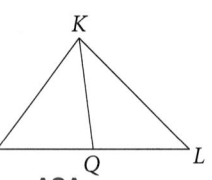

40. Probability Here are six congruence statements about the triangles at the right. $\frac{13}{20}$

$$\angle A \cong \angle X \qquad \angle B \cong \angle Y \qquad \angle C \cong \angle Z$$
$$\overline{AB} \cong \overline{XY} \qquad \overline{AC} \cong \overline{XZ} \qquad \overline{BC} \cong \overline{YZ}$$

There are 20 ways to choose a group of three statements from these six. What is the probability that three statements chosen at random from the six will guarantee that the triangles are congruent?

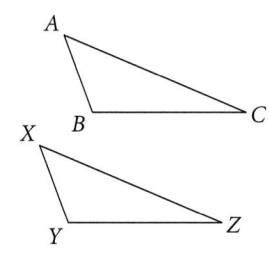

41. △RST at the right is with RS = 5, RT = 9, and m∠T = 30. Show that there is no SSA congruence rule by constructing △UVW with UV = 5, UW = 9, and m∠W = 30, but with △UVW ≇ △RST. **See left.**

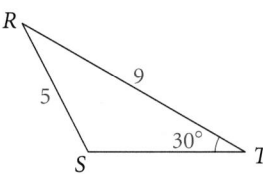

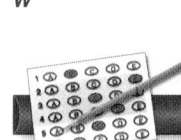

Standardized Test Prep

Multiple Choice

42. Which of the following is NOT a method used to prove triangles congruent? **D**
   A. AAS   B. ASA   C. SAS   D. SSA

43. Suppose $\overline{RT} \cong \overline{ND}$ and ∠R ≅ ∠N. What additional information is needed to prove △RTJ ≅ △NDF by ASA? **F**
   F. ∠T ≅ ∠D   G. ∠R ≅ ∠N   H. ∠J ≅ ∠D   I. ∠T ≅ ∠F

Short Response

44. $\overline{PQ}$ bisects ∠RPS and ∠RQS. Justify each answer.
   a. Which pairs of angles, if any, are congruent?
   b. By what theorem or postulate can you prove that △PRQ ≅ △PSQ? **See margin.**

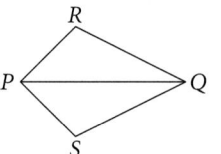

Extended Response

Take It to the NET
Online lesson quiz at
www.PHSchool.com
Web Code: afa-0403

45. $\overline{LJ} \parallel \overline{KG}$ and M is the midpoint of $\overline{LG}$.
   a. Why is $\overline{LM} \cong \overline{GM}$? **a–c. See margin, p. 201.**
   b. Can the two triangles be proved congruent by ASA? Explain.
   c. Can the two triangles be proved congruent by AAS? Explain.

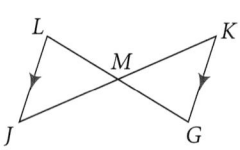

pages 197–201   **Exercises**

37. △AEB ≅ △CED,
   △BEC ≅ △DEA,
   △ABC ≅ △CDA,
   △BAD ≅ △DCB

38. △AEB ≅ △CED,
   △BEC ≅ △DEA,
   △ABC ≅ △CDA,
   △ABD ≅ △DCA,
   △BAD ≅ △DCB,
   △ABD ≅ △DCB,
   △CBA ≅ △DAB,
   △BCD ≅ △ADC

44. [2] a. ∠RPQ ≅ ∠SPQ,
   ∠RQP ≅ ∠SQP
   (Def. of ∠ bisector)

   b. ASA

   [1] one part correct

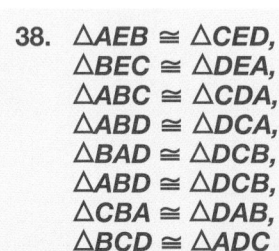

Lesson 4-2

In Exercises 46 and 47, decide whether you can use the SSS Postulate or the SAS Postulate to prove the triangles congruent. If so, write the congruence statement and name the postulate. If not, write *not possible*.

46.
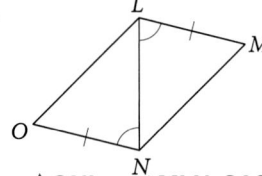
△*ONL* ≅ △*MLN*; SAS

47.
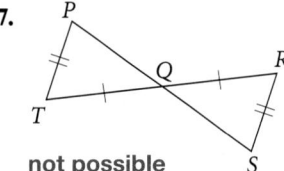
not possible

48. For any △*ABC*, which sides are *not* included between ∠*A* and ∠*B*? $\overline{AC}$ and $\overline{CB}$

Lesson 3-2

49. State the theorem or postulate that justifies the statement:
If ∠1 ≅ ∠3, then *a* ∥ *b*.
If corr. ∡ are ≅, then the lines are ∥.
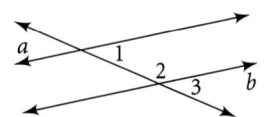

Lesson 1-7

Photography You want to arrange class-trip photos without overlap to make a 2 ft-by-3 ft poster. You collect 3 in.-by-5 in. and 4 in.-by-6 in. photos. What is the greatest number of each type of photo that you can fit on your poster?

50. 3 in.-by-5 in. 56

51. 4 in.-by-6 in. 36

52. What percent more paper is used for a large photo than a regular photo?
60% more paper

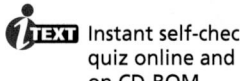

Checkpoint Quiz 1   **Lessons 4-1 through 4-3**

ETEXT Instant self-check quiz online and on CD-ROM

1. △*RST* ≅ △*JKL*. List the three pairs of congruent corresponding sides and the three pairs of congruent corresponding angles.
$\overline{RS}$ ≅ $\overline{JK}$; $\overline{ST}$ ≅ $\overline{KL}$; $\overline{RT}$ ≅ $\overline{JL}$; ∠*R* ≅ ∠*J*; ∠*S* ≅ ∠*K*; ∠*T* ≅ ∠*L*

State the postulate or theorem you can use to prove the triangles congruent. If the triangles cannot be proven congruent, write *not possible*.

2. ASA
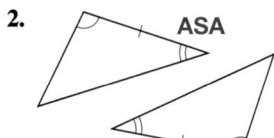

3. SSS
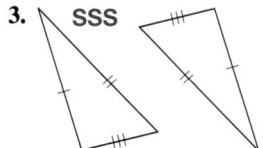

4. SAS
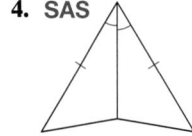

5.

not possible

6.
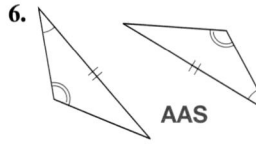
AAS

7.
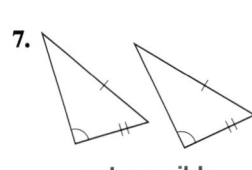
not possible

Use the information given in the diagram. Tell why each statement is true.

8. ∠*H* ≅ ∠*K*   If ∥ lines, then alt. int. ∡ ≅.

9. ∠*HNL* ≅ ∠*KNJ* Vert. ∡ are ≅.

10. △*HNL* ≅ △*KNJ* ASA or AAS

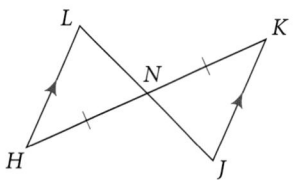

Standardized Test Prep

Resources
For additional practice with a variety of test item formats:
• Standardized Test Prep, p. 237
• Test-Taking Strategies, p. 232
• Test-Taking Strategies with Transparencies

Exercise 43 Remind students to read each question carefully before answering. When students realize that they must use ASA to prove the triangles congruent, they will readily see that the angle on the other endpoint of $\overline{RT}$ must be congruent to the angle on the other endpoint of $\overline{ND}$.

Chapter Checkpoint 1

To check understanding of Lessons 4-1 to 4-3:

Checkpoint Quiz 1 (p. 201)

Teaching Resources
Checkpoint Quiz 1 (also in Prentice Hall Assessment System)

Reaching All Students
Reading and Math Literacy 4B

Spanish versions available

45. [4] a. Def. of midpt.

b. Yes; ∠*JLM* ≅ ∠*KGM* because they are alt. int. ∡ of ∥ lines, and ∠*LMJ* ≅ ∠*GMK* because vertical ∡ are ≅. So the △ are ≅ by ASA.

c. Yes; if two ∡ of one △ are ≅ to 2 ∡ of another △, the third ∡ are ≅.

[3] incorrect ∡ for part b or c, but otherwise correct

[2] correct conclusions but incomplete explanations for parts b and c

[1] at least one part correct

Exploring AAA and SSA

Students will use geometry software to investigate AAA and SSA relationships for triangles.

Resources

Students may use any geometry software program to explore AAA and SSA relationships.

Teaching Notes

Using software enables students to manipulate segments and measure lengths and angles. They then see that AAA and SSA relationships do not necessarily mean congruent triangles.

Tactile Learners

Students can model the exploration using rulers and protractors or compasses and straightedges.

Alternative Method

To see why SSA does not prove triangle congruence, use geometry software to follow these steps.

1. Draw a segment of any length. Label its endpoints A and B.
2. Construct congruent angles whose measures add up to less than 180 at points A and B. Label point C where the sides of ∠A and ∠B intersect. Software measurement tools will show that $\overline{CA} \cong \overline{CB}$.
3. Draw a segment from point C to a point X on $\overline{AB}$ closer to A than to B.

Students can readily see that △CAX and △CBX fit the SSA conditions but are not congruent.

After students complete Lesson 4-5, they will be able to demonstrate this method without using geometry software by using the properties of isosceles triangles.

So far, four statements allow you to conclude that two triangles are congruent. You can refer to them as SSS, SAS, ASA, and AAS. It is good mathematics to wonder about the other two possibilities, AAA and SSA.

Construct

Use geometry software to construct $\overrightarrow{AB}$ and $\overrightarrow{AC}$.
Construct $\overline{BC}$ to create △ABC.
Construct a line parallel to $\overline{BC}$ that intersects $\overrightarrow{AB}$ and $\overrightarrow{AC}$ at points D and E to form △ADE.

Investigate

Are the three angles of △ABC congruent to the three angles of △ADE? Manipulate the figure to change the positions of $\overline{DE}$ and $\overline{BC}$. Do the corresponding angles of the triangles remain congruent? Are the two triangles congruent? Can the two triangles be congruent?

In Exercise 1, you will be asked to make a conjecture about this investigation.

Construct

Construct $\overrightarrow{AB}$. Draw a circle with center C that intersects $\overrightarrow{AB}$ in two points. Construct $\overline{AC}$.
Construct a point E on the circle and construct $\overline{CE}$.

Investigate

Move point E around the circle until E is on $\overrightarrow{AB}$ and forms △ACE. Then move E on the circle to the other point on $\overrightarrow{AB}$ to form another △ACE.

Compare the measures of $\overline{AC}, \overline{CE}$, and ∠A in one triangle with the measures of $\overline{AC}, \overline{CE}$, and ∠A in the other triangle. Are two sides and a nonincluded angle of one triangle congruent to two sides and a nonincluded angle of the other triangle? Are the two triangles congruent? Do you get the same results if you change the size of ∠A and the size of the circle?

EXERCISES

1. **Make a Conjecture** Based on your first investigation above, is there an AAA congruence theorem? Explain. **No; there are many noncongruent △ with all 3 pairs of ∠ ≅.**

For Exercises 2–4, use what you learned in your second investigation above.

2. **Make a Conjecture** Do you think there is an SSA congruence theorem? Why? **No; explanations may vary.**
3. Manipulate the figure so that ∠A is obtuse. Decide whether the circle can intersect $\overrightarrow{AB}$ twice to form two triangles. Could there be an SSA congruence theorem if the congruent angles are obtuse? Explain. **See above right.**
4. Suppose you are given $\overline{CE}, \overline{AC}$, and ∠A. What must be true about CE, AC, and m∠A so that you can construct exactly one △ACE? (*Hint:* Consider cases.) **If ∠A is obtuse or right there will be only one △. If ∠A is acute there may be exactly one △, provided CE and AC are large enough to form △ACE.**

3. No; the circle intersects $\overrightarrow{AB}$ just once, so only one △ is formed. If the ≅ △ are obtuse, then there could be an SSA congruency since a △ can have only one obtuse ∠.

4-4

Using Congruent Triangles: CPCTC

 North Carolina Objectives

2.03 Apply properties, definitions, and theorems of two-dimensional figures to solve problems and write proofs: a) Triangles.

Lesson Preview

What You'll Learn

OBJECTIVE 1
To use triangle congruence and CPCTC to prove that parts of two triangles are congruent

. . . And Why

To measure distance indirectly, as in Example 2

✓ Check Skills You'll Need

(For help, go to Lesson 4-1.)

In the diagram, $\triangle JRC \cong \triangle HVG$. **1–4. See back of book.**

1. List the congruent corresponding angles.
2. List the congruent corresponding sides.

You are given that $\triangle TIC \cong \triangle LOK$.

3. List the congruent corresponding angles.
4. List the congruent corresponding sides.

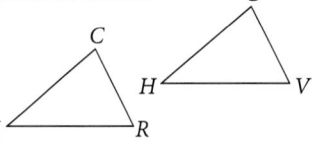

New Vocabulary • CPCTC

---

1. Plan

Lesson Preview

✓ **Check Skills You'll Need**

Listing Congruent Parts
Lesson 4-1: Example 1
Exercises 1–15
Extra Practice, p. 693

Lesson Resources

📁 **Teaching Resources**
Practice, Reteaching, Enrichment

👥 **Reaching All Students**
Practice Workbook 4-4
Spanish Practice Workbook 4-4
Informal Geometry Planning Guide 4-4

⏰ **Presentation Assistant Plus!**
Transparencies
• Check Skills You'll Need 4-4
• Additional Examples 4-4
• Student Edition Answers 4-4
• Lesson Quiz 4-4
PH Presentation Pro CD 4-4

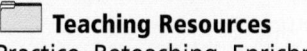 **ASSESSMENT SYSTEM**

Computer Test Generator CD

💿 **Technology**
Resource Pro® CD-ROM
Computer Test Generator CD
Prentice Hall Presentation Pro CD

💻 **www.PHSchool.com**
Student Site
• Teacher Web Code: afk-5500
• Self-grading Lesson Quiz
Teacher Center
• Lesson Planner
• Resources

Plus

OBJECTIVE

1 **Proving Parts of Triangles Congruent**

With SSS, SAS, ASA, and AAS, you know how to use three parts of triangles to show that the triangles are congruent. Once you have triangles congruent, you can make conclusions about their other parts because, by definition, corresponding parts of congruent triangles are congruent. You can abbreviate this as **CPCTC**.

Real-World 🌐 Connection

Shapes formed by the ribs, stretchers, and shaft are congruent whether an umbrella is open or closed.

Proof **1 EXAMPLE** **Real-World 🌐 Connection**

Umbrella Frames In an umbrella frame, the stretchers are congruent and they open to angles of equal measure.

Given: $\overline{SL} \cong \overline{SR}$,
$\quad\angle 1 \cong \angle 2$

Prove that the angles formed by the shaft and the ribs are congruent.

Prove: $\angle 3 \cong \angle 4$

Proof: It is given that $\overline{SL} \cong \overline{SR}$ and $\angle 1 \cong \angle 2$. $\overline{SC} \cong \overline{SC}$ by the Reflexive Property of Congruence. $\triangle LSC \cong \triangle RSC$ by SAS, so $\angle 3 \cong \angle 4$ by CPCTC.

1a. They are ≅ because suppl. of ≅ ⦞ are ≅.

✓ **Check Understanding** **1** **a.** In Example 1, what can you say about $\angle 5$ and $\angle 6$? Explain.
b. *Critical Thinking* When fabric is stretched by the umbrella frame, do $\triangle LSC$ and $\triangle RSC$ remain congruent? Explain.
As point S is moved toward point C, $\angle LSC$ and $\angle RSC$ change shape, but they are always ≅ to each other.

You can use congruent triangles and CPCTC to measure distances, such as the distance across a river, indirectly.

⏱ Ongoing Assessment and Intervention

Before the Lesson	During the Lesson	After the Lesson
Diagnose prerequisite skills using:	**Monitor progress using:**	**Assess knowledge using:**
• Check Skills You'll Need	• Check Understanding • Additional Examples • Standardized Test Prep	• Lesson Quiz • Computer Test Generator CD

Math Background

Proving triangles congruent is usually not an end in itself. When polygons are divided into triangles, applying CPCTC to congruent triangles can lead to congruence statements that otherwise would have been difficult or impossible to prove.

OBJECTIVE

1 Teaching Notes

1 EXAMPLE English Learners

Have students write the abbreviation CPCTC and expand each word beneath its first letter.

2 EXAMPLE Tactile Learners

Students can reenact the officer's measurement technique by measuring the distance across a playing field.

Error Prevention

Remind students that corresponding parts of congruent triangles are clearly indicated by the order of vertices in the triangle congruence statement. Have students practice identifying corresponding parts without referring to diagrams.

Additional Examples

1 What other congruence statements can you prove from the diagram and paragraph proof in Example 1? $\angle CLS \cong \angle CRS$, $\overline{CL} \cong \overline{CR}$

2 The Example 2 Given states that $\angle DEG$ and $\angle DEF$ are right angles. What conditions must hold for that to be true? **The officer must stand perpendicular to the ground.**

Closure

Explain why CPCTC is useful. Sample: It allows you to make conclusions about the other parts of congruent triangles.

204

Proof **2 EXAMPLE** Real-World Connection

History According to legend, one of Napoleon's officers used congruent triangles to estimate the width of a river. On the riverbank, the officer stood up straight and lowered the visor of his cap until the farthest thing he could see was the edge of the opposite bank. He then turned and noted the spot on his side of the river that was in line with his eye and the tip of his visor.

not to scale

Given: $\angle DEG$ and $\angle DEF$ are right angles; $\angle EDG \cong \angle EDF$.

The officer then paced off the distance to this spot and declared that distance to be the width of the river! Use congruent triangles to prove that he was correct.

Prove: $\overline{EF} \cong \overline{EG}$

Statements	Reasons
1. $\angle EDG \cong \angle EDF$	1. Given
2. $\overline{DE} \cong \overline{DE}$	2. Reflexive Property of Congruence
3. $\angle DEG$ and $\angle DEF$ are right angles.	3. Given
4. $\angle DEG \cong \angle DEF$	4. All right angles are congruent.
5. $\triangle DEF \cong \triangle DEG$	5. ASA Postulate
● 6. $\overline{EF} \cong \overline{EG}$	6. CPCTC

 Check Understanding **2** About how wide was the river if the officer stepped off 20 paces and each pace was about $2\frac{1}{2}$ ft long? **50 ft**

EXERCISES

For more practice, see *Extra Practice*.

Practice and Problem Solving

A Practice by Example

Example 1
(page 203)

1. The diagram provides enough information for you to conclude that $\triangle QPS \cong \triangle RSP$ by AAS. What other pairs of sides and angles can you conclude are congruent by CPCTC? $\angle PSQ \cong \angle SPR$; $\overline{SQ} \cong \overline{RP}$; $\overline{PQ} \cong \overline{SR}$

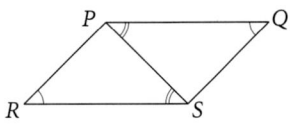

Developing Proof **State why the two triangles are congruent. Give the congruence statement. Then tell what other parts are congruent by CPCTC.**

2–4. See margin, p. 205.

2. **3.** **4.**

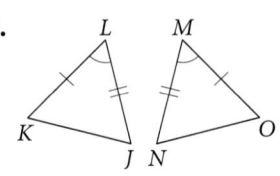

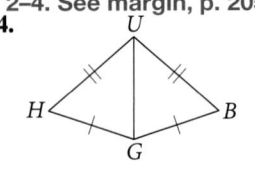

5. For $\triangle RST$ and $\triangle XYZ$, $\angle R \cong \angle X$, $\angle S \cong \angle Y$, and $\overline{ST} \cong \overline{YZ}$. What can you say about the exterior angles at T and Z? Explain.
They are $\cong$; the $\triangle$ are $\cong$ by AAS, so all corr. ext. $\angle$ are also $\cong$.

Reaching All Students

| **Below Level** Use a real umbrella to demonstrate that the corresponding angles in Example 1 are congruent for all openings of the umbrella. | **Advanced Learners** Have students discuss why $\angle DEG$ and $\angle DEF$ are both right angles in Example 2, and then suggest places on a riverbank where the angles would not be right angles. | **English Learners** See note on page 204. **Tactile Learners** See note on page 204. |

6. Developing Proof Two cars of the same model have hood braces that are identical, connect to the body of the car in the same place, and fit into the same slot in the hood.

Given: $\overline{CA} \cong \overline{VE}, \overline{AR} \cong \overline{EH}, \overline{RC} \cong \overline{HV}$

Complete the proof that the hood braces hold the hoods open at the same angle.

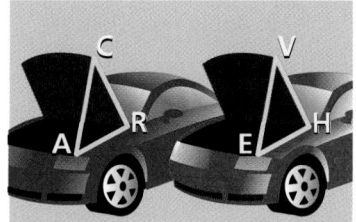

Prove: $\angle ARC \cong \angle EHV$

Proof: It is given that the three sides of the triangles are congruent, so $\triangle ARC \cong \triangle EHV$ by **a.** ___?___ . Thus, $\angle ARC \cong \angle EHV$ by **b.** ___?___ .
SSS   CPCTC

Example 2
(page 204)

Developing Proof **Explain how you can use SSS, SAS, ASA, or AAS with CPCTC to prove the statement true. 7–10. See left.**

7. $\triangle ABD \cong \triangle CBD$ by ASA because $\overline{BD} \cong \overline{BD}$ by Reflexive Prop. of $\cong$; $\overline{AB} \cong \overline{CB}$ by CPCTC

8. $\triangle MOE \cong \triangle REO$ by SSS because $\overline{OE} \cong \overline{OE}$ by Reflexive Prop. of $\cong$; $\angle M \cong \angle R$ by CPCTC

9. $\triangle SPT \cong \triangle OPT$ by SAS because $\overline{TP} \cong \overline{TP}$ by Reflexive Prop. of $\cong$; $\angle S \cong \angle O$ by CPCTC

10. $\triangle PNK \cong \triangle MNL$ by SAS because $\angle KNP \cong \angle LNM$ by vert. $\angle$s are $\cong$; $\overline{KP} \cong \overline{LM}$ by CPCTC

11. $\triangle CYT \cong \triangle RYP$ by AAS; $\overline{CT} \cong \overline{RP}$ by CPCTC

12. $\triangle ATM \cong \triangle RMT$ by SAS because $\angle ATM \cong \angle RMT$ by alt. int. $\angle$s; $\angle AMT \cong \angle RTM$ by CPCTC

13. Yes; $\triangle ABD \cong \triangle CBD$ by SSS so $\angle A \cong \angle C$ by CPCTC.

7. $\overline{AB} \cong \overline{CB}$
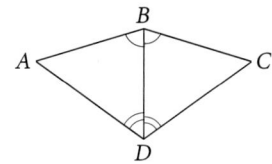

8. $\angle M \cong \angle R$
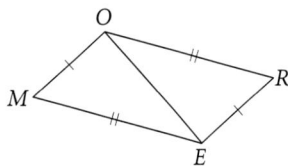

9. $\angle S \cong \angle O$
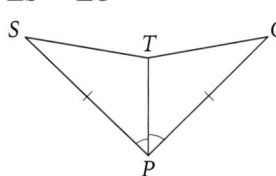

10. $\overline{KP} \cong \overline{LM}$
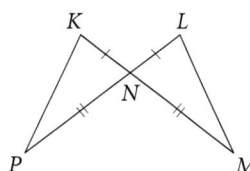

11. $\overline{CT} \cong \overline{RP}$
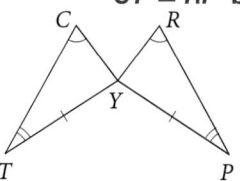

12. $\angle AMT \cong \angle RTM$ See left.
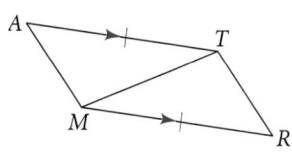

13. Karen cut this pattern for the stained glass shown here so that $AB = CB$ and $AD = CD$. Must $\angle A$ be congruent to $\angle C$? Explain. **See left.**
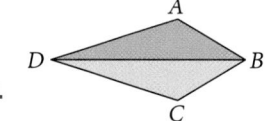

14. **Developing Proof** Complete the two-column proof by filling in the blanks.

Given: $\angle QPS \cong \angle RSP, \angle Q \cong \angle R$
Prove: $\overline{PQ} \cong \overline{SR}$
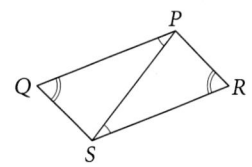

Statements	Reasons	
1. $\angle QPS \cong \angle RSP$	a. ___?___	Given
2. $\angle Q \cong \angle R$	b. ___?___	Given
3. $\overline{PS} \cong \overline{PS}$	c. ___?___	Reflexive Prop. of $\cong$
4. $\triangle PQS \cong \triangle SRP$	d. ___?___	AAS
5. $\overline{PQ} \cong \overline{SR}$	5. CPCTC	

Need Help?
For Reason 4, look at Statements 1–3.

Lesson 4-4   Using Congruent Triangles: CPCTC   **205**

3. Practice

Assignment Guide

1 **Objective**
 Ⓐ Ⓑ **Core** 1–25
 Ⓒ **Extension** 26, 27

Standardized Test Prep 28–33

Mixed Review 34–39

Exercise 1 Have students copy the diagram and mark all the other pairs of congruent parts using tick marks and arcs.

Exercise 14 To provide additional practice with proofs, ask students to rewrite this exercise as a flow proof or paragraph proof.

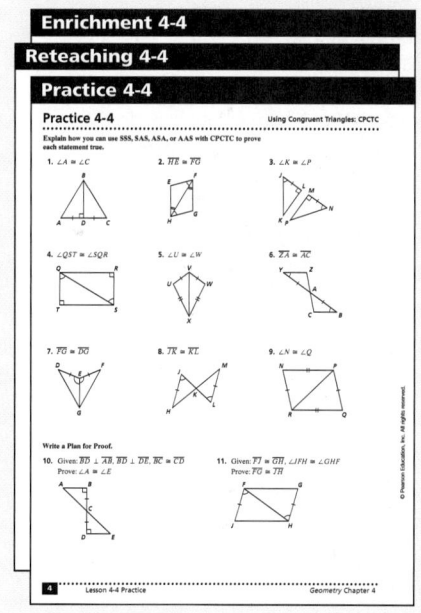

pages 204–208 **Exercises**

2. AAS; $\triangle ABC \cong \triangle EBD$; $\angle A \cong \angle E$; $\overline{CB} \cong \overline{DB}$; $\overline{DE} \cong \overline{CA}$ by CPCTC

3. SAS; $\triangle KLJ \cong \triangle OMN$; $\angle K \cong \angle O$; $\angle J \cong \angle N$; $\overline{KJ} \cong \overline{ON}$ by CPCTC

4. SSS; $\triangle HUG \cong \triangle BUG$; $\angle H \cong \angle B$; $\angle HUG \cong \angle BUG$; $\angle UGH \cong \angle UGB$ by CPCTC

Exercises 15–17 These exercises preview the study of isosceles triangles in Lesson 4-5.

Connection to History

Exercise 18 The city of Ubar, believed to have existed in southwestern Oman from 2800 B.C. to about A.D. 100, fell into a sinkhole created by the collapse of an underground limestone cavern. Called "Atlantis of the Sands" by Lawrence of Arabia, the fabled city was located in 1992 using images from satellites and spacecraft.

Exercises 20, 25 The constructions in Lesson 1-5 were presented without justification. Discuss as a class how these exercises provide rationales for those constructions. Reflect with the class on the value of geometry in explaining why constructions "work."

Exercise 21 Students will need to use the Segment Addition Postulate to complete the proof.

Exercises 26, 27 These exercises anticipate the study of quadrilaterals in Chapter 6. Ask: *What special name does quadrilateral* PRGM *have?* parallelogram *How can you state the results of the two proofs as theorems?* A diagonal divides a parallelogram into ≅ triangles. Opposite sides of a parallelogram are ≅.

B **Apply Your Skills**

15. ∠PKL ≅ ∠QKL by def. of ∠ bisect, and $\overline{KL} \cong \overline{KL}$ by Reflexive Prop. of ≅, so the ⧍ are ≅ by SAS.

16. $\overline{KL} \cong \overline{KL}$ by Reflexive Prop. of ≅; $\overline{PL} \cong \overline{LQ}$ by Def. of ⊥ bis.; ∠KLP ≅ ∠KLQ by Def. of ⊥; the ⧍ are ≅ by SAS.

17. ∠KLP ≅ ∠KLQ because all rt ⧍ are ≅; $\overline{KL} \cong \overline{KL}$ by Reflexive Prop. of ≅; and ∠PKL ≅ ∠QKL by def. of bisect; the ⧍ are ≅ by ASA.

Developing Proof Copy and mark the figure to show the given information. Explain how you would use SSS, SAS, ASA, or AAS with CPCTC to prove ∠P ≅ ∠Q. **15–17. See left.**

15. Given: $\overline{PK} \cong \overline{QK}$, $\overline{KL}$ bisects ∠PKQ.

16. Given: $\overline{KL}$ is the perpendicular bisector of $\overline{PQ}$.

17. Given: $\overline{KL} \perp \overline{PQ}$, $\overline{KL}$ bisects ∠PKQ.

18. Earth Science Some distances are best measured indirectly.

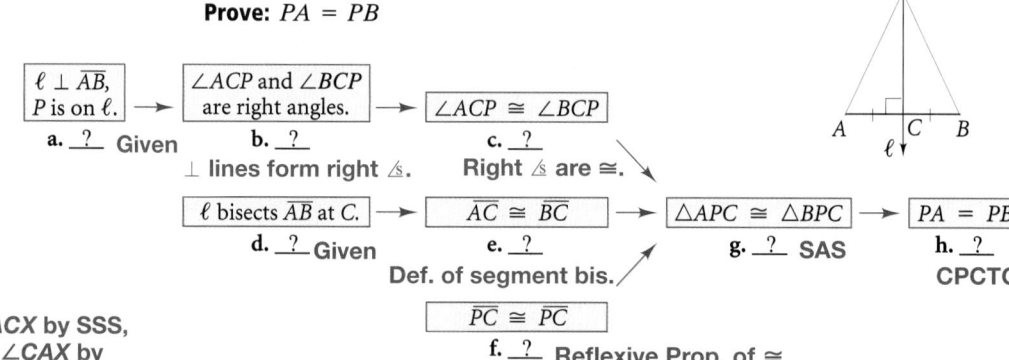

Sinkhole Swallows House

The large sinkhole in this photo occurred suddenly in 1981 in Winter Park, Florida, following a severe drought. Increased water consumption lowers the water table. Sinkholes form when caverns in the underlying limestone dry up and collapse.

A geometry class indirectly measured the distance across a sinkhole. The distances they measured are shown in the diagram. Explain how to use their measurements to find the distance across the sinkhole. **See margin.**

19. Developing Proof Complete this flow proof by filling in the blanks.

Given: $\ell \perp \overline{AB}$, ℓ bisects $\overline{AB}$ at C, P is on ℓ.

Prove: $PA = PB$

$\boxed{\ell \perp \overline{AB}, \; P \text{ is on } \ell.} \rightarrow \boxed{\angle ACP \text{ and } \angle BCP \text{ are right angles.}} \rightarrow \boxed{\angle ACP \cong \angle BCP}$

a. ? Given **b.** ? ⊥ lines form right ⧍. **c.** ? Right ⧍ are ≅.

$\boxed{\ell \text{ bisects } \overline{AB} \text{ at } C.} \rightarrow \boxed{\overline{AC} \cong \overline{BC}} \rightarrow \boxed{\triangle APC \cong \triangle BPC} \rightarrow \boxed{PA = PB}$

d. ? Given **e.** ? Def. of segment bis. **g.** ? SAS **h.** ? CPCTC

$\boxed{\overline{PC} \cong \overline{PC}}$

f. ? Reflexive Prop. of ≅

20. △ABX ≅ △ACX by SSS, so ∠BAX ≅ ∠CAX by CPCTC. Thus $\overrightarrow{AX}$ bisects ∠BAC by the Def. of ∠ bisector.

?
...
Need Help?
In the third diagram, what two triangles must be congruent, and why?

20. Constructions In the construction of the bisector of ∠A below, $\overline{AB} \cong \overline{AC}$ because they are radii of the same circle. $\overline{BX} \cong \overline{CX}$ because both arcs had the same compass setting. Tell why you can conclude that $\overrightarrow{AX}$ bisects ∠BAC. **See left.**

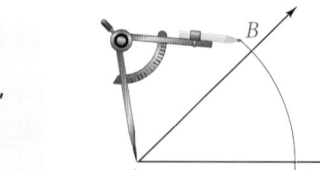 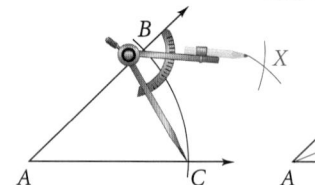 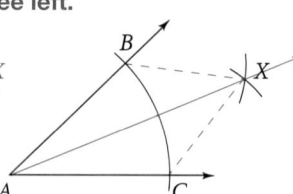

206   Chapter 4   Congruent Triangles

pages 204–208   Exercises

18. The ⧍ are ≅ by SAS so the distance across the sinkhole is 26.5 yd by CPCTC.

25. b. The diagram is constructed in such a way that the ⧍ are ≅ by SSS. ∠CPA ≅ ∠CPB by CPCTC.

Since these ⧍ are ≅ and suppl., they are right ⧍. Thus, $\overleftrightarrow{CP}$ is ⊥ to ℓ.

21. Prove $\triangle ABE \cong \triangle CDF$ by SAS since $\overline{AE} \cong \overline{FC}$ by subtr.

22. Prove $\triangle KJM \cong \triangle QPM$ by ASA since $\angle P \cong \angle J$ and $\angle K \cong \angle Q$ by alt. int. $\angle$s.

Reading Math

It is good strategy to read an exercise through to the end before trying to do it.

24. $\overline{BA} \cong \overline{BC}$ is given; $\overline{BD} \cong \overline{BD}$ by the Reflexive Prop. of $\cong$ and since $\overline{BD}$ bisects $\angle ABC$, $\angle ABD \cong \angle CBD$ by Def. of an $\angle$ bisector; thus, $\triangle ABD \cong \triangle CBD$ by SAS; $\overline{AD} \cong \overline{DC}$ by CPCTC so $\overline{BD}$ bisects $\overline{AC}$ by Def. of a bis.; $\angle ADB \cong \angle CDB$ by CPCTC and $\angle ADB$ and $\angle CDB$ are supp.; thus, $\angle ADB$ and $\angle CDB$ are right $\angle$s and $\overline{BD} \perp \overline{AC}$ by Def. of $\perp$.

Developing Proof In Exercises 21 and 22, name two triangles you would prove congruent in order to use CPCTC. Tell how you would show them congruent.

21. Given: $\overline{BE} \perp \overline{AC}, \overline{DF} \perp \overline{AC}, \overline{BE} \cong \overline{DF}, \overline{AF} \cong \overline{EC}$
Prove: $\overline{AB} \cong \overline{DC}$

21–22. See left.

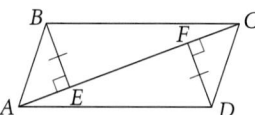

22. Given: $\overline{JK} \parallel \overline{QP}, \overline{JK} \cong \overline{QP}$
Prove: $\overline{KQ}$ bisects $\overline{JP}$.

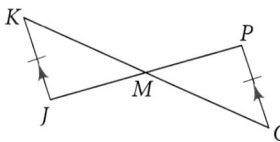

23. Developing Proof The reasons given in this proof are correct, but they are listed incorrectly. List them in the correct order.

Given: $\angle A \cong \angle C, \overline{BD}$ bisects $\angle ABC$.
Prove: $\overline{AB} \cong \overline{CB}$ b or e, e or b, d, c, f, a

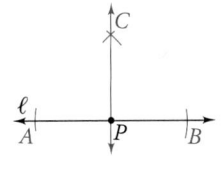

Statements	Reasons
1. $\angle A \cong \angle C$	a. CPCTC
2. $\overline{BD}$ bisects $\angle ABC$.	b. Given
3. $\angle 1 \cong \angle 2$	c. Reflexive Property of Congruence
4. $\overline{BD} \cong \overline{BD}$	d. Definition of angle bisector
5. $\triangle ABD \cong \triangle CBD$	e. Given
6. $\overline{AB} \cong \overline{CB}$	f. AAS Theorem

Proof **24.** Use the plan to write a paragraph proof. **See left.**

Given: $\overline{BA} \cong \overline{BC}, \overline{BD}$ bisects $\angle ABC$.
Prove: $\overline{BD} \perp \overline{AC}, \overline{BD}$ bisects $\overline{AC}$.

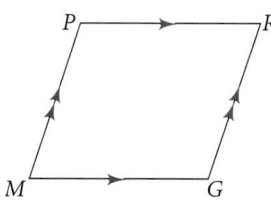

Plan: To show $\overline{BD} \perp \overline{AC}$, you can show that $\angle BDA \cong \angle BDC$ and use the fact that congruent supplementary angles are right angles. To show that $\overline{BD}$ bisects $\overline{AC}$, you can show that $\overline{AD} \cong \overline{CD}$. The desired congruent angles and segments are corresponding parts of $\triangle ABD$ and $\triangle CBD$. So, first show that $\triangle ABD \cong \triangle CBD$.

25. Constructions The construction of a line perpendicular to line ℓ through point P on ℓ is shown here.
  a. Which lengths or distances are equal by construction? $\overline{AP} \cong \overline{PB}; \overline{AC} \cong \overline{BC}$
  b. Explain why you can conclude that $\overleftrightarrow{CP}$ is perpendicular to ℓ. (*Hint:* Do the construction. Then draw $\overline{CA}$ and $\overline{CB}$.) See margin, p. 206.

 **Challenge** **For Exercises 26 and 27, write a proof.**

Proof **26. Given:** $\overline{PR} \parallel \overline{MG}, \overline{MP} \parallel \overline{GR}$ See margin.
  Prove: Each diagonal of $PRGM$ divides $PRGM$ into two congruent triangles.

Proof **27. Given:** $\overline{PR} \parallel \overline{MG}, \overline{MP} \parallel \overline{GR}$
  Prove: $\overline{PR} \cong \overline{MG}, \overline{MP} \cong \overline{GR}$
  (*Hint:* See Exercise 26.)
  Since $\triangle PGM \cong \triangle GPR$ (or $\triangle PMR \cong \triangle GRM$), then $\overline{PR} \cong \overline{MG}$ and $\overline{MP} \cong \overline{GR}$ by CPCTC.

Lesson 4-4 Using Congruent Triangles: CPCTC **207**

26. 1. $\overline{PR} \parallel \overline{MG}; \overline{MP} \parallel \overline{GR}$ (Given)

2. Draw $\overline{PG}$. (2 pts. determine a line.)

3. $\angle RPG \cong \angle PGM$ and $\angle RGP \cong \angle GPM$ (If $\parallel$ lines, then alt. int. $\angle$s are $\cong$.)

4. $\triangle PGM \cong \triangle GPR$ (ASA) A similar proof can be written if diagonal $\overline{RM}$ is drawn.

Lesson Quiz 4-4

1. What does "CPCTC" stand for? Corresponding parts of $\cong$ triangles are $\cong$.

Use the diagram for Exercises 2 and 3.

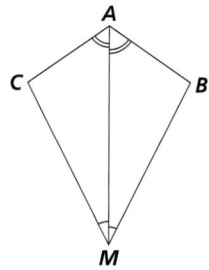

2. Tell how you would show $\triangle ABM \cong \triangle ACM$. You are given two pairs of $\cong \angle$s, $\overline{AM} \cong \overline{AM}$ by the Reflexive Prop., so $\triangle ABM \cong \triangle ACM$ by ASA.

3. Tell what other parts are congruent by CPCTC. $\overline{AB} \cong \overline{AC}, \overline{BM} \cong \overline{CM}, \angle B \cong \angle C$

Use the diagram for Exercises 4 and 5.

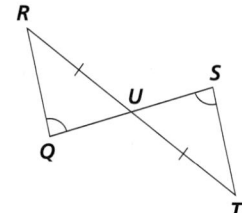

4. Tell how you would show $\triangle RUQ \cong \triangle TUS$. You are given a pair of $\cong \angle$s and a pair of $\cong$ sides, $\angle RUQ \cong \angle TUS$ because vert. angles are $\cong$, so $\triangle RUQ \cong \triangle TUS$ by AAS.

5. Tell what other parts are congruent by CPCTC. $\overline{RQ} \cong \overline{TS}, \overline{UQ} \cong \overline{US}, \angle R \cong \angle T$

Have students work in pairs. Instruct each student to draw and label two congruent triangles, mark two of the corresponding parts congruent, and tell which parts must be proven congruent. Students then should exchange diagrams and take turns explaining how they can prove the triangles congruent.

Standardized Test Prep

📁 **Resources**

For additional practice with a variety of test item formats:
- Standardized Test Prep, p. 237
- Test-Taking Strategies, p. 232
- Test-Taking Strategies with Transparencies

Visual Learners

Exercise 28 Have students copy the diagram and use the given statement △RXW ≅ △JXT to label the six pairs of congruent parts.

Error Prevention

Exercise 32 The relationship between *BE* and *DE* does not follow immediately from the statement △ABC ≅ △ADC. However, that does not mean that choice D is the correct answer. Instead, students can prove △ABE ≅ △ADE and then *BE* = *DE* by CPCTC. Discuss how showing a relationship between two quantities in quantitative comparison questions may take more than one step.

pages 204–208 Exercises

33. [2] a. △KBV ≅ △KBT; yes; SAS

b. CPCTC

[1] one part correct

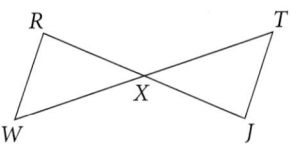

Standardized Test Prep

Multiple Choice

28. In the diagram, △RXW ≅ △JXT. Which statement is NOT necessarily true? **C**

A. ∠J ≅ ∠R   B. ∠W ≅ ∠T
C. $\overline{WX} \cong \overline{JX}$ D. $\overline{RW} \cong \overline{JT}$

Quantitative Comparison

Compare the boxed quantity in Column A with the boxed quantity in Column B. Choose the best answer.

A. The quantity in Column A is greater.
B. The quantity in Column B is greater.
C. The two quantities are equal.
D. The relationship cannot be determined from the information given.

△ABC ≅ △ADC

Exercises 29–32

	Column A	Column B
C 29.	BC	DC
D 30.	m∠ABC	m∠DAB
B 31.	AE	AC
C 32.	BE	DE

Short Response

📷 **Take It to the NET**
Online lesson quiz at
www.PHSchool.com
Web Code: afa-0404

33. In the diagram, $\overline{KB}$ bisects ∠VKT and $\overline{KV} \cong \overline{KT}$.

a. What do you need to show in order to conclude ∠KBV ≅ ∠KBT? State whether it is possible to show this and justify your answer.

b. Show that $\overline{VB} \cong \overline{TB}$. **a–b. See margin.**

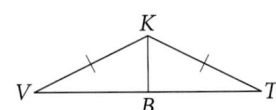

Mixed Review

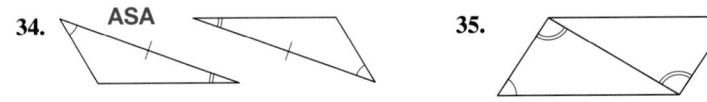

Lesson 4-3

What postulate or theorem can you use to prove the triangles congruent?

34. **ASA**   35. **AAS**

Lesson 2-5

36. The measure of an angle is 10 more than the measure of its supplement. Find the measures of both angles. **95; 85**

Lesson 2-3

If possible, use the Law of Detachment to draw a conclusion. If it is not possible to draw a conclusion, write *not possible*.

37. If two nonvertical lines are parallel, then their slopes are equal. Line *m* is nonvertical and parallel to line *n*. **The slope of line *m* is the same as the slope of line *n*.**

38. If a convex polygon is a quadrilateral, then the sum of its angle measures is 360. Convex polygon *ABCDE* has five sides. **not possible**

39. If a quadrilateral is a square, then it has four congruent sides. Quadrilateral *ABCD* has four congruent sides. **not possible**

Systems of Linear Equations

FOR USE WITH LESSON 4-5

You can solve a system of equations in two variables by using substitution to create a one-variable equation.

1 EXAMPLE

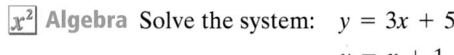 **Algebra** Solve the system: $y = 3x + 5$
$$y = x + 1$$

$y = x + 1$	**Start with one equation.**
$3x + 5 = x + 1$	**Substitute $3x + 5$ for y.**
$2x = -4$	**Solve for x.**
$x = -2$	

Substitute -2 for x in either equation and solve for y.

$$y = x + 1$$
$$= (-2) + 1 = -1$$

Since $x = -2$ and $y = -1$, the solution is $(-2, -1)$. This is the point of intersection of the two lines.

The graph of a linear system with *infinitely many solutions* is one line, and the graph of a linear system with *no solution* is two parallel lines.

2 EXAMPLE

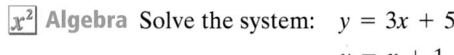 **Algebra** Solve the system: $x + y = 3$
$$4x + 4y = 8$$

$x + y = 3$	
$x = 3 - y$	**Solve the first equation for x.**
$4(3 - y) + 4y = 8$	**Substitute $3 - y$ for x in the second equation.**
$12 - 4y + 4y = 8$	**Solve for y.**
$12 = 8$	**False!**

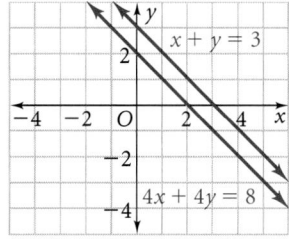

Since $12 = 8$ is a false statement, the system has no solution.

EXERCISES

Solve each system of equations.

1. $y = x - 4$ **(-3, -7)**
   $y = 3x + 2$

2. $2x - y = 8$ **(5, 2)**
   $x + 2y = 9$

3. $3x + y = 4$ **no sol.**
   $-6x - 2y = 12$

4. $2x - 3 = y + 3$ **(0, -3)**
   $2x + y = -3$

5. $y = x + 1$ **inf. many sol.**
   $x = y - 1$

6. $x - y = 4$ **no sol.**
   $3x - 3y = 6$

7. $y = -x + 2$ **inf. many sol.**
   $2y = 4 - 2x$

8. $y = 2x + 1$ **(8, 17)**
   $y = 3x - 7$

9. $x - y = 2$ $\left(\frac{3}{2}, -\frac{1}{2}\right)$
   $x + y = 1$

Systems of Linear Equations

Students will review how to solve systems of two linear equations in two variables. They will solve systems of equations to find unknown angle measures of isosceles and equilateral triangles in Lesson 4-5.

Resources

Technology
Geometry Resource Pro®:
   Algebra Review Resources
Computer Test Generator CD-ROM, Chapter 4, Review Topics

Teaching Notes

1 EXAMPLE Math Tip

Point out that students can check their solutions by substituting the values of both x and y into each equation. If the substitutions lead to two true statements, the solution is correct.

Visual Learners

Exercises 5, 7 Solving these systems also can result in the true statement $0 = 0$. To see why this means that the equations describe the same line, students can graph each equation.

Careers

Medical researchers study how different variables affect health. For example, a study might consider how cholesterol level is related to weight, exercise, meat consumption, and stress and how the factors relate to one another. Much medical research involves systems of equations.

1. Plan

Lesson Preview

✓ **Check Skills You'll Need** 🔖

Using Exterior Angles of Triangles
Lesson 3-3: Example 4
Exercises 24–28
Extra Practice, pages 692 and 693

Lesson Resources

📁 **Teaching Resources**
Practice, Reteaching, Enrichment

👥 **Reaching All Students**
Practice Workbook 4-5
Spanish Practice Workbook 4-5
Technology Activities 42
Hands-On Activities 12
Informal Geometry Planning
   Guide 4-5

⏱ **Presentation Assistant Plus!**
Transparencies
• Check Skills You'll Need 4-5
• Additional Examples 4-5
• Student Edition Answers 4-5
• Lesson Quiz 4-5
PH Presentation Pro CD 4-5

PRENTICE HALL
ASSESSMENT SYSTEM

Computer Test Generator CD

💿 **Technology**
Resource Pro® CD-ROM
Computer Test Generator CD
Prentice Hall Presentation Pro CD

🖥 **www.PHSchool.com**
Student Site
• Teacher Web Code: afk-5500
• Self-grading Lesson Quiz
Teacher Center
• Lesson Planner
• Resources

Plus 🅸 **TEXT**

210

4-5   Isosceles and Equilateral Triangles

North Carolina Objectives   2.03   Apply properties, definitions, and theorems of two-dimensional figures to solve problems and write proofs: a) Triangles.

Lesson Preview

What You'll Learn

OBJECTIVE
1   To use and apply properties of isosceles triangles

. . . And Why

To find the angles of a garden path, as in Example 4

✓ Check Skills You'll Need

(For help, go to Lesson 3-3.)

1. Name the angle opposite $\overline{AB}$. ∠C
2. Name the angle opposite $\overline{BC}$. ∠A
3. Name the side opposite ∠A. $\overline{BC}$
4. Name the side opposite ∠C. $\overline{BA}$
x^2 5. **Algebra**   Find the value of x. 105

New Vocabulary

• legs of an isosceles triangle
• base of an isosceles triangle
• vertex angle of an isosceles triangle
• base angles of an isosceles triangle   • corollary

 Interactive lesson includes instant self-check, tutorials, and activities.

OBJECTIVE
1   **The Isosceles Triangle Theorems**

📖 **Reading Math**

Isosceles is derived from the Greek *isos* for equal and *skelos* for leg.

1. ∠A ≅ ∠B; isosc. △ have ≅ base △.

Investigation: Isosceles Triangles

Construct an isosceles triangle and then cut it out.

• Name your triangle △ABC, with A and B opposite the congruent sides.

• Bisect ∠C by folding the triangle so that the congruent sides overlap. Label the intersection of the fold line and $\overline{AB}$ as point D.

• Repeat the above steps with a different triangle. If your first triangle was acute, make your second triangle obtuse, and vice versa.

1. What do you notice about ∠A and ∠B in both of your triangles? Compare results with others. Make a conjecture. **See left.**

2. a. What type of angle does each of ∠CDA and ∠CDB appear to be? **right △**
    b. What do you notice about $\overline{AD}$ and $\overline{BD}$? **They are ≅.**
    c. Use your answers to parts (a) and (b) to complete the conjecture: $\overline{CD}$ is the ___?___ of $\overline{AB}$. **⊥ bis.**

✅ **Ongoing Assessment and Intervention**

Before the Lesson	During the Lesson	After the Lesson
Diagnose prerequisite skills using:	**Monitor progress using:**	**Assess knowledge using:**
• Check Skills You'll Need	• Check Understanding	• Lesson Quiz
	• Additional Examples	• Computer Test Generator CD
	• Standardized Test Prep	

Isosceles triangles are common in the real world. You can find them in structures such as bridges and buildings. The congruent sides of an isosceles triangle are its **legs.** The third side is the **base.** The two congruent sides form the **vertex angle.** The other two angles are the **base angles.**

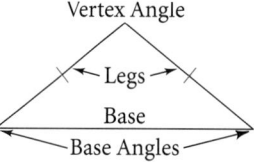

An isosceles triangle has a certain type of *symmetry* about a line through its vertex angle. This line is represented by the fold line $\overline{CD}$ in the last diagram on page 210. You can see this symmetry in the theorems below. You will learn more about this line symmetry in Lesson 12-5.

 Key Concepts

Theorem 4-3   **Isosceles Triangle Theorem**

If two sides of a triangle are congruent, then the angles opposite those sides are congruent.

$$\angle A \cong \angle B$$

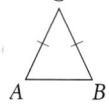

Theorem 4-4   **Converse of Isosceles Triangle Theorem**

If two angles of a triangle are congruent, then the sides opposite the angles are congruent.

$$\overline{AC} \cong \overline{BC}$$

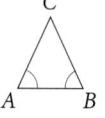

Theorem 4-5

The bisector of the vertex angle of an isosceles triangle is the perpendicular bisector of the base.

$$\overline{CD} \perp \overline{AB} \text{ and } \overline{CD} \text{ bisects } \overline{AB}.$$

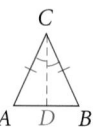

In one proof of the Isosceles Triangle Theorem, you use a special segment, the bisector of the vertex angle. Theorems 4-4 and 4-5 are proven in the Exercises.

1 EXAMPLE   **Proving the Isosceles Triangle Theorem**

Developing Proof To prove the Isosceles Triangle Theorem, begin with isosceles $\triangle XYZ$ with $\overline{XY} \cong \overline{XZ}$. Draw $\overline{XB}$, the bisector of the vertex angle $\angle YXZ$.

Given: $\overline{XY} \cong \overline{XZ}, \overline{XB}$ bisects $\angle YXZ$.

Show the base angles are congruent using a paragraph proof.

Prove: $\angle Y \cong \angle Z$

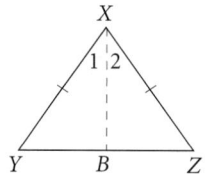

Proof: You are given that $\overline{XY} \cong \overline{XZ}$. By the definition of angle bisector, $\angle 1 \cong \angle 2$. By the Reflexive Property of Congruence, $\overline{XB} \cong \overline{XB}$. Therefore, by the SAS Postulate, $\triangle XYB \cong \triangle XZB$, and $\angle Y \cong \angle Z$ by CPCTC.

Real-World Connection

This A-shaped roof has congruent legs and congruent base angles.

 **Check Understanding**   ① Plan a proof, then prove the Converse of the Isosceles Triangle Theorem. (*Hint:* You can carefully parallel the proof above, but you cannot use SAS.)
Draw $\overline{XB}$, the bisector of $\angle YXZ$. Then, since $\angle Z \cong \angle Y$ and $\overline{XB} \cong \overline{XB}$ by the Reflexive Prop. of $\cong$, $\triangle ZXB \cong \triangle YXB$ by AAS. Then $\overline{XZ} \cong \overline{XY}$ by CPCTC.

Lesson 4-5 Isosceles and Equilateral Triangles   **211**

 Reaching All Students

| **Below Level** Discuss whether the equilateral-equiangular relationship holds for polygons with more than 3 sides. Ask students to support their reasoning with examples. | **Advanced Learners** Have students explain why Theorems 4-3, 4-4, and 4-5 do or do not apply to equilateral triangles. | **Visual Learners** See note on page 211. **Auditory Learners** See note on page 213. |

 Professional Development

Math Background

Understanding the vocabulary, including legs, vertex angle, and base angles, is necessary for solving many exercises in this section. Help students remember the meanings of terms by having them describe everyday objects with the same words. Mention that *isosceles* derives from the Greek *iso* (same) and *skelos* (leg). Trapezoids, which will be studied in Chapter 4, can also be isosceles, and have two bases.

OBJECTIVE
① Teaching Notes

Investigation (Optional)
Students can use protractors and rulers to confirm their conjectures. Point out that each conjecture in the investigation will be proved in this lesson.

Connection to Chemistry
Ask: *What are different forms of a chemical element with the same atomic number called?* isotopes Point out that the prefix *iso-*, meaning "equal," is a variation of the prefix *isos-* in *isosceles*.

Visual Learners
Students may think that the base of an isosceles triangle is always at the bottom. Illustrate by rotating a physical model that the base can be in any orientation, as in Exercise 30.

① EXAMPLE Alternative Method

Draw identical copies of $\triangle XYZ$ side by side. Then label congruent parts, asking the class to justify each step.
- Use a single tick mark to show $\overline{XY}$ on the first copy $\cong \overline{XZ}$ on the second copy.
- Use an arc to show $\angle X$ on the first copy $\cong \angle X$ on the second copy.
- Use double tick marks to show $\overline{XZ}$ on the first copy $\cong \overline{XY}$ on the second copy.

Ask: *Which triangles are congruent? By what postulate?* $\triangle XYZ \cong \triangle XZY$; SAS *Which angles are congruent by CPCTC?* $\angle Y$ and $\angle Z$

211

EXAMPLE

2 EXAMPLE **Math Tip**

Point out that every corollary is a theorem that can be proved.

4 EXAMPLE **Teaching Tip**

Have students calculate the total measure of the four angles formed by the *x*-axis and the *y*-axis at the origin. Discuss the fact that there are 360° about any point. Ask students to suggest other ways to show that there are 360° about any point, such as drawing a straight angle and adding the measures on each side.

Additional Examples

1 Examine the diagram for Example 1 again. Suppose that you draw $\overline{XB} \perp \overline{YZ}$. Can you use SAS to prove $\triangle XYB \cong \triangle XZB$? Explain. **No; the ≅ angles are not included between ≅ sides.**

2 Explain why $\triangle ABC$ is isosceles.

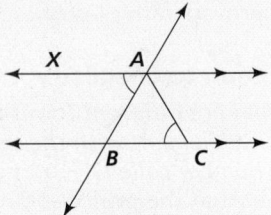

Because $\overleftrightarrow{XA} \parallel \overleftrightarrow{BC}$, $\angle ABC \cong \angle XAB$. By the angles marked ≅ and the Transitive Prop., $\angle ABC \cong \angle ACB$. $\triangle ABC$ is isosceles by Converse of the Isosceles Triangle Thm.

3 Use the diagram for Example 3. Suppose that $m\angle L \neq 63$ and $m\angle L = y$. Find the values of *x* and *y*. **x = 90, y = 45**

4 In the drawing for Example 4, suppose that a segment is drawn between the endpoints of the segments that determine the angle marked *x*°. Find the angle measures of the triangle that is formed. **120, 30, 30**

Closure

An angle exterior to the vertex of an isosceles triangle measures 80. Find the angle measures of the triangle. **100, 40, 40**

212

Proof → **2** EXAMPLE **Using the Isosceles Triangle Theorems**

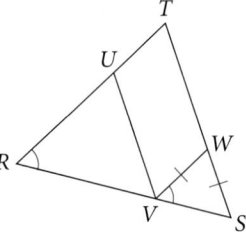

Developing Proof Explain why $\triangle RST$ is isosceles.

$\angle WVS \cong \angle S$ by the Isosceles Triangle Theorem. The diagram shows that $\angle R \cong \angle WVS$, so $\angle R \cong \angle S$ by the Transitive Property of Congruence. $\overline{TS} \cong \overline{TR}$ by the Converse of the Isosceles Triangle Theorem, and $\triangle RST$ is isosceles by the definition of isosceles triangle.

✓ **Check Understanding** **2** In Example 2, can you deduce that $\triangle RUV$ is isosceles? Explain. **No; neither ∠RVU nor ∠RUV can be shown ≅ to ∠R.**

3 EXAMPLE **Using Algebra**

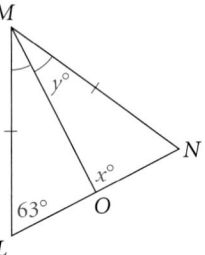

Algebra Find the values of *x* and *y*.

By Theorem 4-5, you know that $\overline{MO} \perp \overline{LN}$, so $x = 90$. $\triangle MLN$ is isosceles, so $\angle L \cong \angle N$ and $m\angle N = 63$.

$m\angle N + x + y = 180$	**Triangle Angle-Sum Theorem**
$63 + 90 + y = 180$	**Substitute for $m\angle N$ and x.**
$y = 27$	**Subtract 153 from each side.**

✓ **Check Understanding** **3** Suppose $m\angle L = 43$. Find the values of *x* and *y*. **x = 90; y = 47**

A **corollary** is a statement that follows immediately from a theorem. Here are corollaries to the Isosceles Triangle Theorem and its converse (proven in Exercise 32).

Key Concepts

? Need Help?

Equilateral:
Congruent sides
Equiangular:
Congruent angles

Corollary	**Corollary to Theorem 4-3**

If a triangle is equilateral, then the triangle is equiangular.

$$\angle X \cong \angle Y \cong \angle Z$$

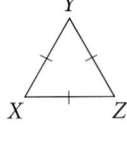

Corollary	**Corollary to Theorem 4-4**

If a triangle is equiangular, then the triangle is equilateral.

$$\overline{XY} \cong \overline{YZ} \cong \overline{ZX}$$

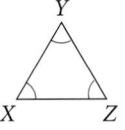

4 EXAMPLE **Real-World** **Connection**

Landscaping A landscaper uses rectangles and equilateral triangles for the path around the hexagonal garden. Find the value of *x*.

In a rectangle, an angle measure is 90; in an equilateral triangle, it is 60.

$$x + 90 + 60 + 90 = 360$$
$$x = 120$$

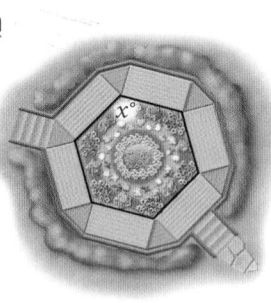

✓ **Check Understanding** **4** What is the measure of the angle at each outside corner of the path? **150**

EXERCISES

Practice and Problem Solving

For more practice, see *Extra Practice*.

A Practice by Example

Example 1
(page 211)

1. Developing Proof Supply the missing parts in this proof of the Converse of the Isosceles Triangle Theorem.

Begin with △*PRQ* with ∠*P* ≅ ∠*Q*.
Draw **a.** _?_ , the bisector of ∠*PRQ*. $\overline{RS}$

Given: ∠*P* ≅ ∠*Q*, **b.** _?_ bisects ∠*PRQ*. $\overline{RS}$
Prove: $\overline{PR} \cong \overline{QR}$

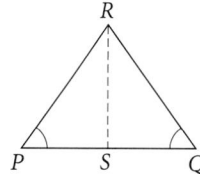

Statements	Reasons
1. $\overline{RS}$ bisects ∠*PRQ*.	**c.** _?_ Given
2. ∠*PRS* ≅ ∠*QRS*	**d.** _?_ Def. of ∠ bisector
3. ∠*P* ≅ ∠*Q*	3. Given
4. $\overline{RS} \cong \overline{RS}$	**e.** _?_ Reflexive Prop. of ≅
5. △*PRS* ≅ △*QRS*	**f.** _?_ AAS
6. $\overline{PR} \cong \overline{QR}$	6. CPCTC

2. Developing Proof Here is another way to prove the Isosceles Triangle Theorem. Supply the missing parts.

Begin with isosceles △*HKJ* with $\overline{KH} \cong \overline{KJ}$.
Draw **a.** _?_ , a bisector of the base $\overline{HJ}$. $\overline{KM}$

Given: $\overline{KH} \cong \overline{KJ}$, **b.** _?_ bisects $\overline{HJ}$. $\overline{KM}$
Prove: ∠*H* ≅ ∠*J*

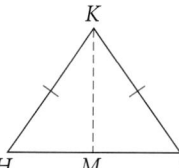

3. $\overline{VX}$; Converse of the Isosc. △ Thm.

4. $\overline{UW}$; Converse of the Isosc. △ Thm.

5. $\overline{VY}$; *VT* = *VX* (Ex. 3) and *UT* = *YX* (Ex. 4), so *VU* = *VY* by the Subtr. Prop. of =.

6. Answers may vary. Sample: ∠*VUY*; ⚞ opposite ≅ sides are ≅.

Statements	Reasons
1. $\overline{KM}$ bisects $\overline{HJ}$.	**c.** _?_ By construction
2. $\overline{HM} \cong \overline{JM}$	**d.** _?_ Def. of segment bisector
3. $\overline{KH} \cong \overline{KJ}$	3. Given
4. $\overline{KM} \cong \overline{KM}$	**e.** _?_ Reflexive Prop. of ≅
5. △*KHM* ≅ △*KJM*	**f.** _?_ SSS
6. ∠*H* ≅ ∠*J*	**g.** _?_ CPCTC

Example 2
(page 212)

Developing Proof Complete each statement. Explain why it is true.

3. $\overline{VT} \cong$ _?_   3–6. See above left.

4. $\overline{UT} \cong$ _?_ ≅ $\overline{YX}$

5. $\overline{VU} \cong$ _?_

6. ∠*VYU* ≅ _?_

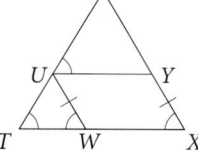

Example 3
(page 212)

x^2 **Algebra Find the values of *x* and *y*.**

7.

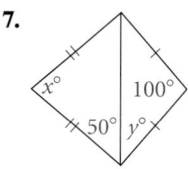

x = 80; *y* = 40

8.

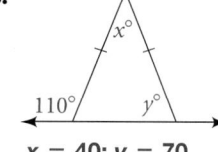

x = 40; *y* = 70

9.

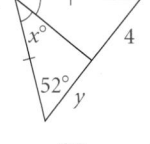

x = 38; *y* = 4

Lesson 4-5 Isosceles and Equilateral Triangles   **213**

Assignment Guide

1 Objective
- **A B** Core 1–36
- **C** Extension 37–45

Standardized Test Prep 46–49

Mixed Review 50–53

Exercise 2 Have students compare this proof with the proof in Example 1. Point out that proofs often can be completed in a number of different ways.

Auditory Learners

Exercises 3–6 Students will be tempted to complete the exercises visually rather than by applying the theorems in Lesson 4-5. Complete the problems as a class, and have students justify their conclusions orally.

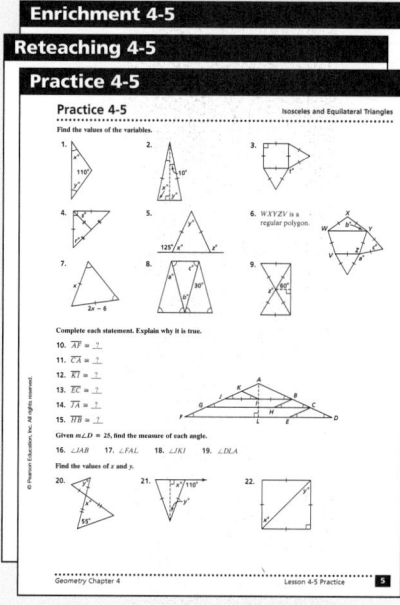

Enrichment 4-5

Reteaching 4-5

Practice 4-5

pages 213–216   Exercises

214

x^2 **Algebra Find the values of x and y.**

10.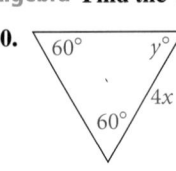

Perimeter is 54.
$x = 4\frac{1}{2}$; $y = 60$

11.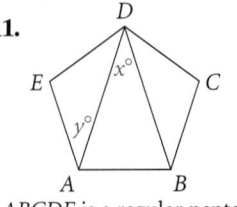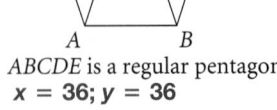

ABCDE is a regular pentagon.
$x = 36$; $y = 36$

12. $x = 92$; $y = 7$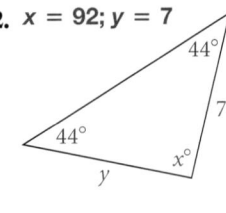

Find each value.

13. If $m\angle L = 58$, then $m\angle LKJ = $ ■. **64**

14. If $JL = 5$, then $ML = $ ■. **$2\frac{1}{2}$**

15. If $m\angle JKM = 48$, then $m\angle J = $ ■. **42**

16. If $m\angle J = 55$, then $m\angle JKM = $ ■. **35**

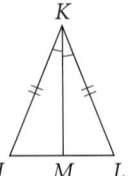

Example 4 (page 212)

17. A square and a regular hexagon are placed so that they have a common side. Find $m\angle SHA$ and $m\angle HAS$. **150; 15**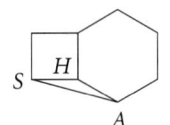

18. Five fences meet at a point to form angles with measures $x, 2x, 3x, 4x$, and $5x$ around the point. Find the measure of each angle.
24, 48, 72, 96, 120

B Apply Your Skills

19a.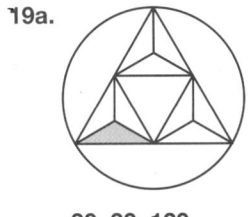

30, 30, 120

19. **Graphic Arts** The former logo for the National Council of Teachers of Mathematics is shown at the right. Trace the logo onto paper.
    a. Highlight an obtuse isosceles triangle in the design. Then find its angle measures. **See left.**
    b. How many different sizes of angles can you find in the logo? What are their measures? **5; 30, 60, 90, 120, 150**
    c. **Open-Ended** Design a logo using isosceles triangles. Give the measures of the angles in your logo. **Check students' work.**

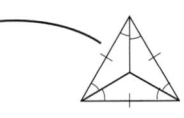

The triangles in the logo have these congruent sides and angles.

20. **Architecture** Seventeen spires, pictured at the left, grace the majestic Cadet Chapel at the Air Force Academy in Colorado Springs, Colorado. Each spire is an isosceles triangle with a 40° vertex angle. Find the measure of each base angle.
70

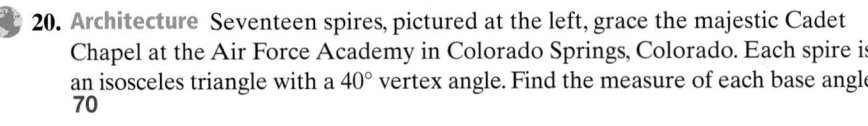

Exercise 20

Mental Math Find the value of x.

21. 50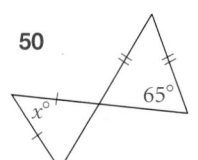

22. 140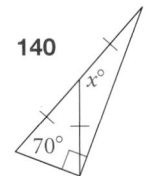

23.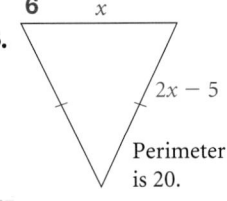
Perimeter is 20.

x^2 **Algebra Find the values of x and y.**

24.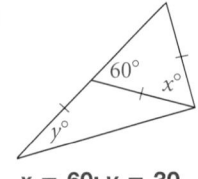
$x = 60$; $y = 30$

25.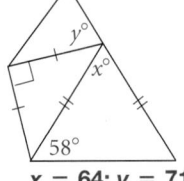
$x = 64$; $y = 71$

26.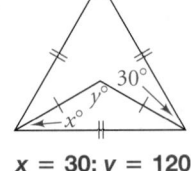
$x = 30$; $y = 120$

214   Chapter 4   Congruent Triangles

Real-World Connection

Careers Radio broadcasters must respond to opinions given by "call-in" listeners.

27. Two sides of a △ are ≅ if and only if the ∠s opp. those sides are ≅.

---

27. Write the Isosceles Triangle Theorem and its converse as a biconditional.
See left.

28. **Critical Thinking** An exterior angle of an isosceles triangle has measure 100. Find two possible sets of measures for the angles of the triangle.
80, 80, 20; 80, 50, 50

29. a. **Communications** In the diagram at the right, what type of triangles are formed by the cables of the same height and the ground? **isosc. △**
   b. What are the two different base lengths of the triangles? **900 ft; 1100 ft**
   c. How is the tower related to each of the triangles? **The tower is the ⊥ bis. of the base of each △.**

30. **Critical Thinking** Curtis defines the base of an isosceles triangle as its "bottom side." Is his definition a good one? Explain. **See margin, p. 214.**

31. **Reasoning** What are the measures of the base angles of an isosceles right triangle? Explain. **45; they are = and have sum 90.**

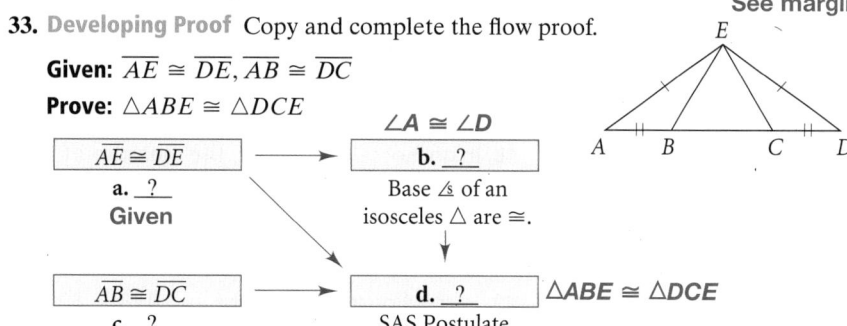

Radio Tower 1009 ft tall

Cables

|← 450 ft →|← 550 ft →|
Tower cables extend to both widths.

32. **Writing** Explain how each corollary on page 212 follows from its theorem. First, write one explanation and then write the second similar to the first.
See margin.

33. **Developing Proof** Copy and complete the flow proof.

Given: $\overline{AE} \cong \overline{DE}, \overline{AB} \cong \overline{DC}$

Prove: $\triangle ABE \cong \triangle DCE$

```
┌─────────────┐      ┌──────────┐
│ AE ≅ DE     │ ───→ │ ∠A ≅ ∠D  │
└─────────────┘      │  b. ?    │
   a. ?              └──────────┘
   Given            Base ∠s of an
                    isosceles △ are ≅.

┌─────────────┐      ┌──────────┐
│ AB ≅ DC     │ ───→ │  d. ?    │  △ABE ≅ △DCE
└─────────────┘      └──────────┘
   c. ?              SAS Postulate
   Given
```

x^2 **Algebra** Find the values of *m* and *n*.

34. 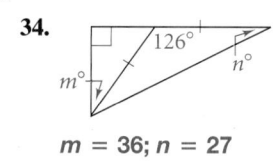 $m = 36; n = 27$

35. 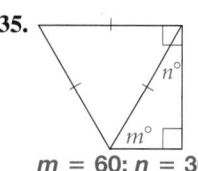 $m = 60; n = 30$

36. 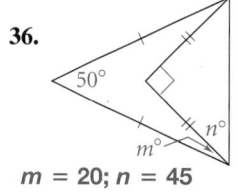 $m = 20; n = 45$

© **Challenge**

Coordinate Geometry For each pair of points, there are six points that could be the third vertex of an isosceles right triangle. Find the coordinates of each point.

37. (0, 0), (4, 4), (−4, 0), (0, −4), (8, 4), (4, 8)

38. (5, 0); (0, 5); (−5, 5); (5, −5); (0, 10); (10, 0)

39. (5, 3); (2, 6); (2, 9); (8, 3); (−1, 6); (5, 0))

37. (4, 0) and (0, 4)   38. (0, 0) and (5, 5)   39. (2, 3) and (5, 6)
   37–39. See left.

x^2 40. **Algebra** A triangle has angle measures $x + 15, 3x − 35,$ and $4x$.
   a. Find the value of *x*. **25**   b. Find the measure of each angle. **40; 40; 100**
   c. What type of triangle is it? Why? **Obtuse isosc. △; 2 of the ∠s are ≅ and one ∠ is obtuse.**

Proof 41. Write a paragraph proof of Theorem 4-5 using the diagram next to it on page 211. **See margin, p. 214.**

42. State the converse of Theorem 4-5. If the converse is true, write a paragraph proof. If the converse is false, give a counterexample. **See margin.**

Since $\overline{CD} \cong \overline{CD}$ by Refl. Prop., $\triangle ACD \cong \triangle BCD$ by SAS. So $\angle ACD \cong \angle BCD$ by CPCTC, and $\overline{CD}$ bisects $\angle ACB$.

Lesson Quiz 4-5

Use the diagram for Exercises 1–3.

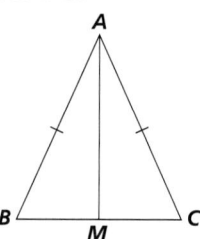

1. If $m\angle BAC = 38$, find $m\angle C$. **71**

2. If $m\angle BAM = m\angle CAM = 23$, find $m\angle BMA$. **90**

3. If $m\angle B = 3x$ and $m\angle BAC = 2x − 20$, find *x*. **25**

4.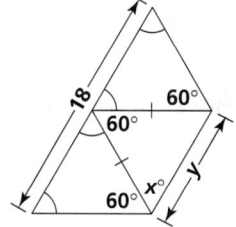

Find the values of *x* and *y*.
$x = 60; y = 9$

5. *ABCDEF* is a regular hexagon. Find $m\angle BAC$.

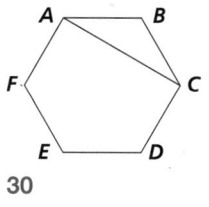

30

Alternative Assessment

Draw the diagram below on the board.

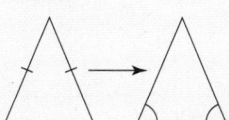

The diagram illustrates the Isosceles Triangle Theorem. Have the class draw similar diagrams to illustrate the Converse of the Isosceles Triangle Theorem and the two corollaries from this lesson.

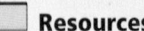

Resources

For additional practice with a variety of test item formats:
- Standardized Test Prep, p. 237
- Test-Taking Strategies, p. 232
- Test-Taking Strategies with Transparencies

Exercise 46 Have students draw △*ABC* so that they can see the relationship between the sides and angles in this isosceles triangle.

pages 213–216   Exercises

49. [2] a. 60; since
    $m\angle PAB =$
    $m\angle PBA$ and
    $m\angle PAB +$
    $m\angle PBA = 120,$
    $m\angle PAB = 60.$

    b. 120; $m\angle APB = 60$
    so $m\angle PAB = 60.$
    Since $\angle PAB$ and
    $\angle QAB$ are compl.,
    $m\angle QAB = 30.$
    △*QAB* is isosc. so
    $m\angle AQB = 120.$

[1] one part correct

Real-World 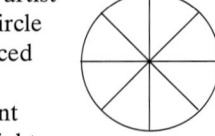 **Connection**

The circle is a basic shape for many tile designs.

43. Crafts The design in Step 3 is used in Hmong crafts and in Islamic and Mexican tiles. To create it, the artist starts by drawing a circle and four equally spaced diameters.

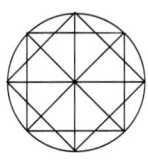 

a. How many different sizes of isosceles right triangles can you find in Step 2? Trace an example of each onto your paper. **5**

Step 1   **Step 2**   **Step 3**

b. How many times does a triangle of each size in part (a) appear in the Step 2 diagram? **See back of book.**

Reasoning What measures are possible for the base angles of each type of triangle? **Explain.**

44. an isosceles obtuse triangle
    0 < measure of base ∠ < 45

45. an isosceles acute triangle
    45 < measure of base ∠ < 90

Standardized Test Prep

Multiple Choice

46. In isosceles △*ABC*, the vertex angle is ∠*A*. What can be proved? **C**
   A. $AB = CB$ **B.** $\angle A \cong \angle B$
   C. $m\angle B = m\angle C$ **D.** $\overline{BC} \cong \overline{AC}$

47. In the diagram at the right, $m\angle 1 = 40$. What is $m\angle 2$? **G**
   F. 40   **G.** 50   **H.** 80   **I.** 100

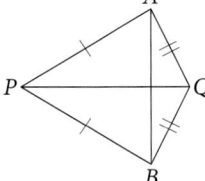

48. In an isosceles triangle, the measure of the vertex angle is 4*x*. The measure of each base angle is $2x + 10$. What is the measure of the vertex angle? **D**
   A. 10   **B.** 20   **C.** 50   **D.** 80

Short Response

Take It to the NET
Online lesson quiz at
www.PHSchool.com
····· Web Code: afa-0405

49. In the figure at the right, $m\angle APB = 60$.
   a. What is $m\angle PAB$? Explain.
   b. ∠*PAB* and ∠*QAB* are complementary. What is $m\angle AQB$? Show your work.
   a–b. See margin.

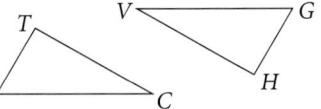

Mixed Review

Lesson 4-4

50. $m\angle R = 59$, $m\angle T = 93 = m\angle H$, $m\angle V = 28$, and $RT = GH$. What, if anything, can you conclude about RC and GV? Explain.

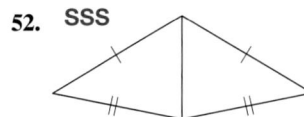

$RC = GV$; $\overline{RC} \cong \overline{GV}$ by CPCTC since △*RTC* ≅ △*GHV* by ASA.

Lessons 4-2, 4-3

Which congruence statement, SSS, SAS, ASA, or AAS, would you use to conclude that the two triangles are congruent?

51. 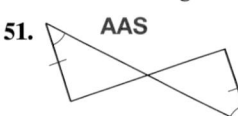 **AAS**   **52.** **SSS**

Lesson 3-4

53. How many sides are in a regular polygon whose exterior angles measure 15°?
    24 sides

Congruence in Right Triangles

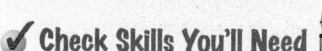
North Carolina Objectives   2.03 Apply properties, definitions, and theorems of two-dimensional figures to solve problems and write proofs: a) Triangles.

Lesson Preview

What You'll Learn

OBJECTIVE 1
To prove triangles congruent using the HL Theorem

. . . And Why

To show that one pattern can be used to cut the fabric for the two entrance flaps of a tent, as in Example 1

✔ **Check Skills You'll Need**   (For help, go to Lessons 4-2 and 4-3.)

Tell whether the abbreviation identifies a congruence statement.

1. SSS yes
2. SAS yes
3. SSA no
4. ASA yes
5. AAS yes
6. AAA no

Can you conclude that the two triangles are congruent? Explain.

7.   yes; SAS

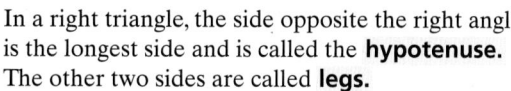

8.

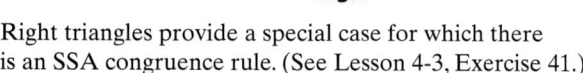

yes; SAS

New Vocabulary • hypotenuse • legs of a right triangle

1. Plan

Lesson Preview

✔ **Check Skills You'll Need**

Using the SSS and SAS Postulates
Lesson 4-2: Examples 1 and 2
Exercises 1–6, 14–17
Extra Practice, p. 693

Using the ASA Postulate
Lesson 4-3: Examples 1 and 2
Exercises 1, 2, 5–7
Extra Practice, p. 693

Lesson Resources

📁 **Teaching Resources**
Practice, Reteaching, Enrichment
Checkpoint Quiz 2

👥 **Reaching All Students**
Practice Workbook 4-6
Spanish Practice Workbook 4-6
Reading and Math Literacy 4C
Spanish Reading & Literacy 4C
Informal Geometry Planning
   Guide 4-6

🕐 **Presentation Assistant Plus!**
Transparencies
• Check Skills You'll Need 4-6
• Additional Examples 4-6
• Student Edition Answers 4-6
• Lesson Quiz 4-6
PH Presentation Pro CD 4-6

ASSESSMENT SYSTEM
Checkpoint Quiz 2
Computer Test Generator CD

💿 **Technology**
Resource Pro® CD-ROM
Computer Test Generator CD
Prentice Hall Presentation Pro CD

💻 **www.PHSchool.com**
Student Site
• Teacher Web Code: afk-5500
• Self-grading Lesson Quiz
Teacher Center
• Lesson Planner
• Resources

Plus

OBJECTIVE

1   **The Hypotenuse-Leg Theorem**

 Interactive lesson includes instant self-check, tutorials, and activities.

In a right triangle, the side opposite the right angle is the longest side and is called the **hypotenuse**. The other two sides are called **legs**.

Right triangles provide a special case for which there is an SSA congruence rule. (See Lesson 4-3, Exercise 41.) It occurs when hypotenuses are congruent and one pair of legs are congruent.

🔑 **Key Concepts**

Theorem 4-6	Hypotenuse-Leg (HL) Theorem

If the hypotenuse and a leg of one right triangle are congruent to the hypotenuse and a leg of another right triangle, then the triangles are congruent.

Proof **Paragraph Proof of the HL Theorem**

Given: $\triangle PQR$ and $\triangle XYZ$ are right triangles, with right angles Q and Y respectively. $\overline{PR} \cong \overline{XZ}$, and $\overline{PQ} \cong \overline{XY}$.

Prove: $\triangle PQR \cong \triangle XYZ$

Proof: On $\triangle XYZ$ at the right, draw $\overrightarrow{ZY}$. Mark point S as shown so that $YS = QR$. Then, $\triangle PQR \cong \triangle XYS$ by SAS. By CPCTC, $\overline{PR} \cong \overline{XS}$. It is given that $\overline{PR} \cong \overline{XZ}$, so $\overline{XS} \cong \overline{XZ}$ by the Transitive Property of Congruence.

By the Isosceles Triangle Theorem, $\angle S \cong \angle Z$, so $\triangle XYS \cong \triangle XYZ$ by AAS. Therefore, $\triangle PQR \cong \triangle XYZ$ by the Transitive Property of Congruence.

Lesson 4-6   Congruence in Right Triangles   **217**

Before the Lesson
Diagnose prerequisite skills using:
• Check Skills You'll Need

During the Lesson
Monitor progress using:
• Check Understanding
• Additional Examples
• Standardized Test Prep

After the Lesson
Assess knowledge using:
• Lesson Quiz
• Computer Test Generator CD
• Chapter Checkpoint 2 (p.223)

Math Background

The HL Theorem is an example of using a SSA relationship to prove triangles congruent. This is not generally possible. The HL Theorem also can be proved by first proving the Pythagorean Theorem and then applying it to establish SSS congruence.

OBJECTIVE

① **Teaching Notes**

Teaching Tip
Before reading the proof of the HL Theorem, discuss a Plan for Proof with the class. Draw △*XYZ*, and discuss why you might want to extend $\overline{ZY}$ to form another right angle. Make sure that the class understands that point *S* can be located on $\overrightarrow{ZY}$ so that *YS* = *QR*. This may seem like an arbitrary construction, but careful consideration of the subsequent triangle congruence statements will help students appreciate its usefulness.

① **EXAMPLE**

Point out that applying the Transitive Property of Congruence to triangles is an extension of the same property for segments and angles.

② **EXAMPLE**

Highlight how three statements come together in the conclusion of the flow proof. Discuss how this is similar to the way triangles are proved congruent using SSS, SAS, ASA, or AAS. Point out that the flow proof uses the three bulleted statements just before Example 2.

page 218 **Check Understanding**

2. $\overline{CB} \cong \overline{EB}$ and $m\angle CBD = m\angle EBA$ because $\overline{AD}$ is the ⊥ bis. of $\overline{CE}$. It is given that $\overline{CD} \cong \overline{EA}$. △*CBD* ≅ △*EBA* by HL.

218

---

① **EXAMPLE** **Real-World** **Connection**

Tent Design On the tent, ∠*CPA* and ∠*MPA* are right angles and $\overline{CA} \cong \overline{MA}$. Write a paragraph to explain why △*CPA* and △*MPA* are congruent. Give an application of this congruence.

You are given that ∠*CPA* and ∠*MPA* are right angles. Therefore, △*CPA* and △*MPA* are right triangles. $\overline{PA}$ is a leg of both △*CPA* and △*MPA*. $\overline{PA} \cong \overline{PA}$ by the Reflexive Property of Congruence. You are given that $\overline{CA} \cong \overline{MA}$. Thus, △*CPA* ≅ △*MPA* by the HL Theorem.

Application: Since the triangles are the same shape and size, you would need just one pattern to cut fabric for both flaps of the tent.

✓ Check Understanding **①** Which two triangles are congruent by the HL Theorem? Write a correct congruence statement. △*LMN* ≅ △*OQP*

To use the HL Theorem, you must show that three conditions are met.
- There are two right triangles.
- The triangles have congruent hypotenuses.
- There is one pair of congruent legs.

Proof → **②** **EXAMPLE** **Flow Proof—Using the HL Theorem**

Given: $\overline{CD} \cong \overline{EA}$, $\overline{AD}$ is the perpendicular bisector of $\overline{CE}$.

Use a flow proof to show that two triangles are congruent.

Prove: △*CBD* ≅ △*EBA*.

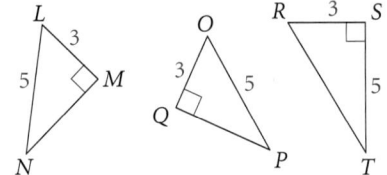

✓ Check Understanding **②** Write a paragraph proof for Example 2. **See margin.**

218 Chapter 4 Congruent Triangles

👥 Reaching All Students

Below Level Have students use the diagram in the paragraph proof of the HL Theorem to explain why the HL Theorem is *not* a special case of the SAS Postulate.	**Advanced Learners** After completing Example 3, have students prove that *WZKJ* must contain four right angles.	**English Learners** See note on page 220. **Visual Learners** See note on page 221.

Proof ③ EXAMPLE Two-Column Proof—Using the HL Theorem

Given: $\overline{WJ} \cong \overline{KZ}$, $\angle W$ and $\angle K$ are right angles.

Use a two-column proof to show that two triangles are congruent.

Prove: $\triangle JWZ \cong \triangle ZKJ$

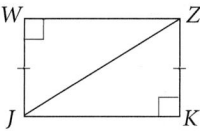

Statements	Reasons
1. $\angle W$ and $\angle K$ are right angles.	1. Given
2. $\triangle JWZ$ and $\triangle ZKJ$ are right triangles.	2. Definition of right triangle
3. $\overline{JZ} \cong \overline{JZ}$	3. Reflexive Property of Congruence
4. $\overline{WJ} \cong \overline{KZ}$	4. Given
5. $\triangle JWZ \cong \triangle ZKJ$	5. HL Theorem

✓ **Check Understanding** ③ **Critical Thinking** You know that two legs of one right triangle are congruent to two legs of another right triangle. Explain how to prove the triangles are congruent. The △ are ≅ by SAS.

EXERCISES

For more practice, see *Extra Practice*.

Practice and Problem Solving

Ⓐ **Practice by Example**

Example 1
(page 218)

1. $\triangle ABC \cong \triangle DEF$ by HL. Both △ are rt. △, $\overline{AC} \cong \overline{DF}$, and $\overline{CB} \cong \overline{FE}$.

2. $\triangle SPR \cong \triangle QRP$ by HL. Both △ are rt. △, $\overline{SP} \cong \overline{QR}$ (Given) and $\overline{PR} \cong \overline{PR}$ by the Reflexive Prop. of ≅.

3. $\triangle LMP \cong \triangle OMN$ by HL. Both △ are rt. △ because vert. △ are ≅; $\overline{LP} \cong \overline{NO}$, and $\overline{LM} \cong \overline{OM}$.

4. $\triangle AEB \cong \triangle DCB$ by HL. Both △ are rt. △. $\overline{AB} \cong \overline{BD}$ and $\overline{EB} \cong \overline{CB}$ by the Def. of midpt.

8. Right △ are needed, either $\angle A$ and $\angle G$ or $\angle AQC$ and $\angle GJC$.

Developing Proof Write a short paragraph to explain why the two triangles are congruent. 1–4. See left.

1.
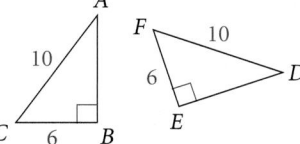

2.
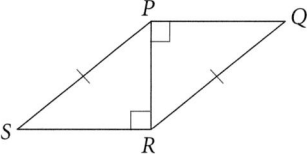

3.
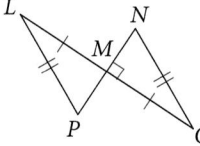

4.
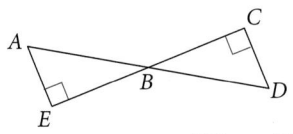

B is the midpoint of $\overline{AD}$ and $\overline{EC}$.

Developing Proof What additional information do you need to prove the triangles congruent by the HL Theorem?

5. $\triangle BLT$ and $\triangle RKQ$
$\angle T$ and $\angle Q$ are rt. △.
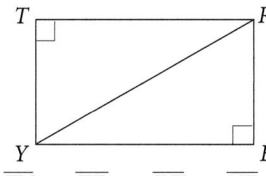

6. $\triangle XRV$ and $\triangle TRV$
$\overline{RX} \cong \overline{RT}$ or $\overline{XV} \cong \overline{TV}$
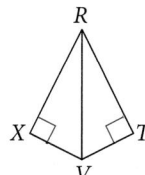

7. $\triangle TRY$ and $\triangle EYR$
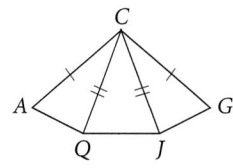
$\overline{TY} \cong \overline{ER}$ or $\overline{RT} \cong \overline{YE}$

8. $\triangle ACQ$ and $\triangle GCJ$ See left.

Lesson 4-6 Congruence in Right Triangles **219**

③ EXAMPLE

As students read the proof, ask: *Why is step 2 included in the proof?* It establishes a needed condition for the HL Thm. to apply.

⬛ **Additional Examples**

① In Example 1, one student wrote "$\triangle CPA \cong \triangle MPA$ by SAS." Is the student correct? Explain. No; the congruent angles are not included angles.

② $\triangle XYZ$ is isosceles. From vertex X, a perpendicular is drawn to $\overline{YZ}$, intersecting $\overline{YZ}$ at point M. Explain why $\triangle XMY \cong \triangle XMZ$. $\triangle XMY$ and $\triangle XMZ$ are right triangles, $\overline{XY} = \overline{XZ}$ by def. of isosceles, and $\overline{XM} \cong \overline{XM}$ by Reflexive Prop., so $\triangle XMY \cong \triangle XMZ$ by HL Thm.

③ Write a two-column proof.
Given: $\angle ABC$ and $\angle DCB$ are right angles, $\overline{AC} \cong \overline{DB}$.
Prove: $\triangle ABC \cong \triangle DCB$

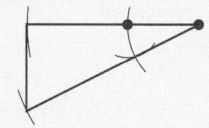

1. $\angle ABC$ and $\angle DCB$ are rt. angles. (Given)
2. $\triangle ABC$ and $\triangle DCB$ are rt. triangles. (Def. of rt. triangle)
3. $\overline{AC} \cong \overline{DB}$ (Given)
4. $\overline{BC} \cong \overline{CB}$ (Reflexive Prop. of ≅)
5. $\triangle ABC \cong \triangle DCB$ (HL Thm.)

Closure

How are SAS and HL alike, and how are they different? Both prove triangles congruent using two pairs of sides and one pair of angles. SAS is a postulate, and the angle is an included angle. HL is a theorem, the triangle must be right, and the angle is not an included angle.

219

Assignment Guide

1 Objective
A B Core 1–32
C Extension 33, 34

Standardized Test Prep 35–38

Mixed Review 39–47

English Learners
Exercises 1–4 Have students work in pairs to help each other write clear and concise explanations.

Exercises 6, 7 More than one answer is possible.

Error Prevention
Exercise 9 Students may forget that the triangles under consideration are △BDC and △FEA and write $\overline{AB} \cong \overline{CF}$ as their answer. Point out that they should always begin a problem by focusing on the given information.

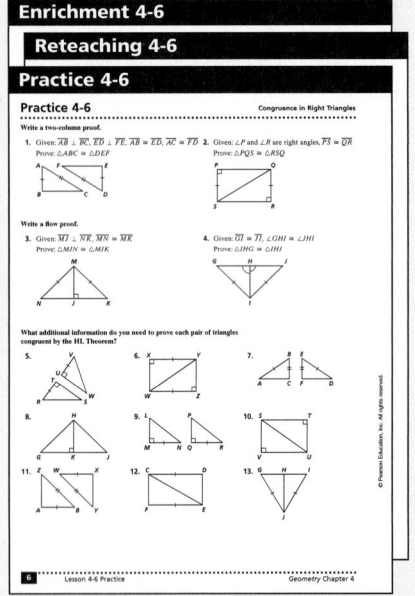

Developing Proof What additional information do you need to prove the triangles congruent by the HL Theorem?

9. △BDC and △FEA $\overline{BC} \cong \overline{FA}$

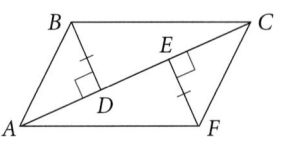

10. △STR and △PQN $\overline{RT} \cong \overline{NQ}$

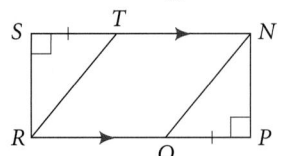

Example 2
(page 218)

Developing Proof Complete each flow proof.

11. Given: $\overline{AD} \cong \overline{CB}$, ∠D and ∠B are right angles.
Prove: △ADC ≅ △CBA

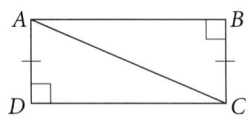

11c. Reflexive Prop. of ≅

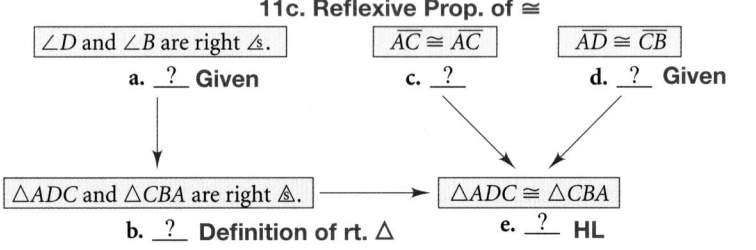

12. Given: $\overline{PS} \cong \overline{PT}$, ∠PRS ≅ ∠PRT
Prove: △PRS ≅ △PRT

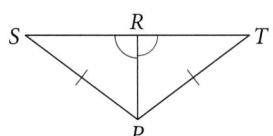

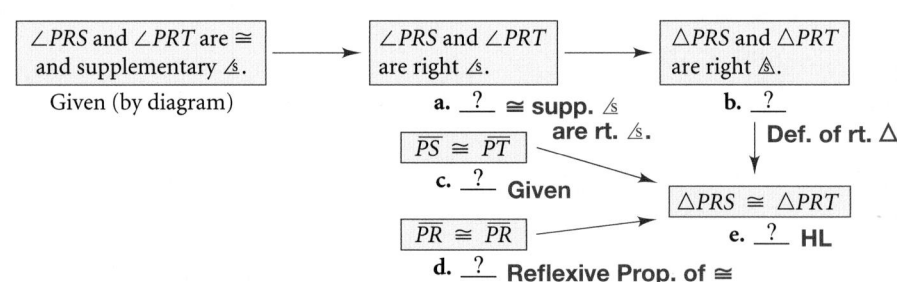

Need Help?

For Exercise 13, recall how to classify △SPT. Then recall what is true about this type of triangle.

13. $\overline{PS} \cong \overline{PT}$ so ∠S ≅ ∠T by the isosc. △ thm. ∠PRS ≅ ∠PRT. △PRS ≅ △PRT by AAS.

13. Developing Proof There is a different set of steps that will prove △PRS ≅ △PRT in Exercise 12. Decide what they are. Then write a short paragraph to explain the steps. **See left.**

Developing Proof Tell whether the HL Theorem can be used to prove the two triangles congruent. If so, explain. If not, write *not possible*.

14. 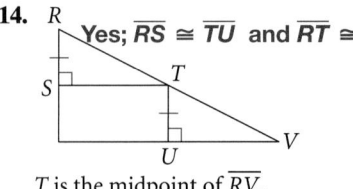 Yes; $\overline{RS} \cong \overline{TU}$ and $\overline{RT} \cong \overline{TV}$.

T is the midpoint of $\overline{RV}$.

15.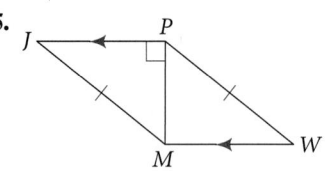

Yes; $\overline{PM} \cong \overline{PM}$ and ∠PMW is a rt. ∠ since $\overline{JP} \parallel \overline{MW}$.

Example 3
(page 219)

Developing Proof Complete each two-column proof.

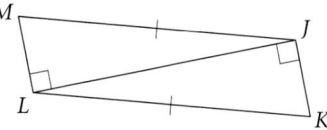

16. Given: $\overline{JL} \perp \overline{LM}$, $\overline{LJ} \perp \overline{JK}$, $\overline{MJ} \cong \overline{KL}$

Prove: $\triangle JLM \cong \triangle LJK$

Statements	Reasons
1. $\overline{JL} \perp \overline{LM}$ and $\overline{LJ} \perp \overline{JK}$	a. __?__ Given
2. $\angle JLM$ and $\angle LJK$ are right angles.	b. __?__ Def. of $\perp$
c. __?__ $\triangle MLJ$ and $\triangle KJL$ are rt. $\triangle$s.	3. Definition of a right triangle
4. $\overline{MJ} \cong \overline{KL}$	d. __?__ Given
e. __?__ $\overline{LJ} \cong \overline{LJ}$	5. Reflexive Property of Congruence
6. $\triangle JLM \cong \triangle LJK$	f. __?__ HL

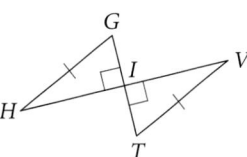

17. Given: $\overline{HV} \perp \overline{GT}$, $\overline{GH} \cong \overline{TV}$, I is the midpoint of $\overline{HV}$.

Prove: $\triangle IGH \cong \triangle ITV$

Statements	Reasons
1. $\overline{HV} \perp \overline{GT}$, $\overline{GH} \cong \overline{TV}$	a. __?__ Given
$\triangle IGH$ b. __?__ and $\triangle ITV$ are right triangles.	c. __?__ Def. of rt. $\triangle$
d. __?__ I is the midpt. of $\overline{HV}$.	3. Given
4. $\overline{HI} \cong \overline{VI}$	e. __?__ Def. of midpt.
f. __?__ $\triangle IGH \cong \triangle ITV$	5. HL Theorem

B **Apply Your Skills**

18. Antiques To repair an antique clock, a 12-toothed wheel has to be made by cutting right triangles out of a regular polygon that has twelve 4-cm sides. The hypotenuse of each triangle is a side of the regular polygon, and the shorter leg is 1 cm long. Explain why the 12 triangles must be congruent.
HL; each rt. $\triangle$ has a $\cong$ hyp. and side.

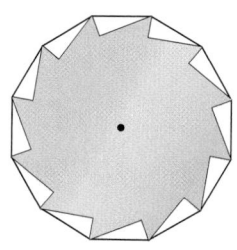

x^2 **Algebra** In Exercises 19 and 20, for what values of x and y are the triangles congruent by HL?

19.

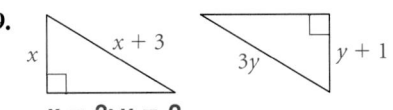

$x = 3; y = 2$

20.

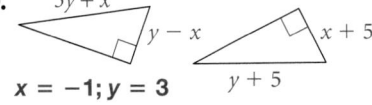

$x = -1; y = 3$

21. Critical Thinking While working for a landscape architect, you are told to lay out a flower bed in the shape of a right triangle with sides of 3 yd and 7 yd. Explain what else you need to know in order to make the flower bed.
whether the 7-yd side is the hyp. or a leg

22. Reasoning Polygon $ABCD$ has $AB = AD$, $BC = DC$, and right angles as marked. Name all the pairs of congruent right triangles in the figure. Explain why each pair is congruent. **See left.**

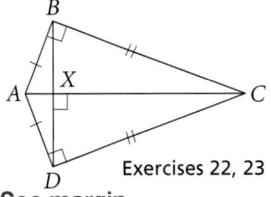

Exercises 22, 23

Real-World Connection

Interest in antiques and shifts in fashion have stabilized the need for dial-clock repair skills.

22. $\triangle ABX \cong \triangle ADX$; HL
$\triangle ABC \cong \triangle ADC$; SSS or SAS $\triangle BXC \cong \triangle DXC$; HL

23. Developing Proof You are given what is shown in the figure, except for the right angle at X, and you are asked to prove that $\angle AXD$ is a right angle. **a–b. See margin.**
a. Writing Explain how you could complete the proof without using HL.
b. Write a paragraph proof that $\angle AXD$ must be a right angle.

Lesson 4-6 Congruence in Right Triangles **221**

Exercise 14 This exercise provides a good opportunity to assess how well students read diagrams. Discuss what students think they can and cannot conclude from the diagram. For example, $\overline{RS}$ and $\overline{TU}$ appear parallel but cannot be proven so.

Visual Learners

Exercise 15 Students may need to copy the diagram and extend $\overline{PM}$ to see that it is a transversal for the parallel lines in the diagram.

Connection to Physics

Exercise 18 Modern mechanical clocks can be traced to the seventeenth century. A mechanical clock has an energy source such as a falling weight (as in a grandfather clock) or a tightly wound spring (as in a pocket watch). The energy source turns a wheel that engages gears, which then move the hands of the clock.

Connection to Algebra

Exercises 19, 20 Students must solve a system of two equations. If necessary, have them reread the Algebra Review on page 209.

Exercises 24–27 Students will need compasses and straightedges. Have students demonstrate and explain their constructions to partners.

Exercises 28, 29 Encourage students to begin by writing a Plan for Proof.

Connection to Coordinate Geometry

Exercise 31 Students need to remember that lines whose slopes have product -1 are perpendicular.

pages 219–223 Exercises

23. a. Answers may vary.
Sample: You could show that suppl. $\angle$s AXB and AXD are $\cong$.

b. $\triangle ABC \cong \triangle ADC$ by SSS so $\angle BAC \cong \angle DAC$ by CPCTC. $\triangle ABX \cong \triangle ADX$ by SAS so $\angle AXB \cong \angle AXD$. $\angle AXB$ is suppl. and $\cong$ to $\angle AXD$ so they are both rt. $\angle$s.

221

Lesson Quiz 4-6

For Exercises 1 and 2, tell whether the HL Theorem can be used to prove the triangles congruent. If so, explain. If not, write *not possible*.

1.

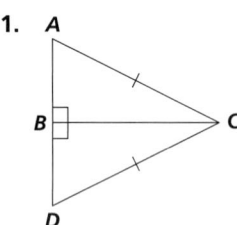

Yes; use congruent hypotenuses and leg $\overline{BC}$ to prove $\triangle ABC \cong \triangle DBC$.

2.

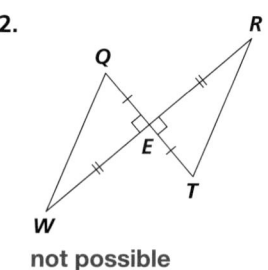

not possible

For Exercises 3 and 4, what additional information do you need to prove the triangles congruent by the HL Theorem?

3. $\triangle LMX \cong \triangle LOX$

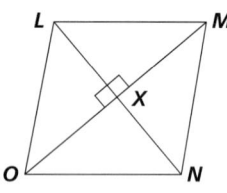

$\overline{LM} \cong \overline{LO}$

4. $\triangle AMD \cong \triangle CNB$

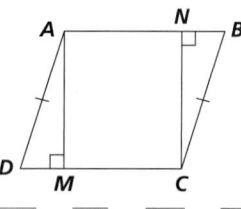

$\overline{AM} \cong \overline{CN}$ or $\overline{MD} \cong \overline{NB}$

Constructions Copy the triangle and construct a triangle congruent to it using the method stated.

24. by SAS
25. by HL
26. by ASA
27. by SSS

24–27. See back of book.

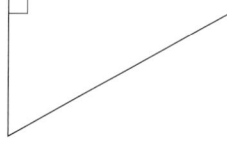

Proof **Write a flow proof or a two-column proof.**

28. 1. $\overline{EB} \cong \overline{DB}$; $\angle A$ and $\angle C$ are rt. $\angle$s. (Given)
2. $\triangle BEA$ and $\triangle BDC$ are rt. $\angle$s. (Def. of rt. $\triangle$)
3. B is the midpt. of $\overline{AC}$. (Given)
4. $\overline{AB} \cong \overline{BC}$ (Def. of midpt.)
5. $\triangle BEA \cong \triangle BDC$ (HL)

28. **Given:** $\overline{EB} \cong \overline{DB}$, $\angle A$ and $\angle C$ are right angles, and B is the midpoint of $\overline{AC}$.
Prove: $\triangle BEA \cong \triangle BDC$
See left.

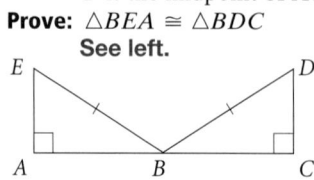

29. **Given:** $\overline{LO}$ bisects $\angle MLN$, $\overline{OM} \perp \overline{LM}$, and $\overline{ON} \perp \overline{LN}$.
Prove: $\triangle LMO \cong \triangle LNO$
See margin.

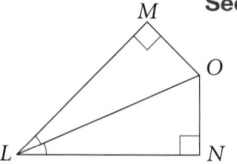

30. **Open-Ended** You are the DJ for the school dance. To set up, you have placed one speaker in the corner of the platform. What measurement(s) could you make with a tape measure to make sure that a matching speaker is in the other corner at exactly the same angle? Explain why your method works. **See margin.**

31. a. **Coordinate Geometry** Use grid paper. Graph the points $E(-1, -1)$, $F(-2, -6)$, $G(-4, -4)$, and $D(-6, -2)$. Connect the points with segments.
b. Find the slope for each of $\overline{DG}$, $\overline{GF}$, and $\overline{GE}$. **a–c. See back of book.**
c. Use your answer to part (b) to describe $\angle EGD$ and $\angle EGF$.
d. Use the Distance Formula to find DE and FE. **$DE = \sqrt{26}$; $FE = \sqrt{26}$**
e. Write a paragraph to prove that $\triangle EGD \cong \triangle EGF$. **See back of book.**

Exercise 30

32. **Critical Thinking** "A HA!" exclaims Francis. "There is an HA Theorem . . . , something like the HL Theorem!" Explain what Francis is saying and why he is correct or incorrect. **An HA Thm. is the same as AAS with AAS corr. to the rt. $\angle$, an acute $\angle$, and the hyp.**

C **Challenge** **Geometry in 3 Dimensions** Use the figure at the right for Exercises 33 and 34.

Proof 33. Write a paragraph proof.
Given: $\overline{BE} \perp \overline{EA}$, $\overline{BE} \perp \overline{EC}$, $\triangle ABC$ is equilateral.
Prove: $\triangle AEB \cong \triangle CEB$ **See margin, p. 223.**

34. **Given:** $\triangle AEB \cong \triangle CEB$, $\overline{BE} \perp \overline{EA}$, and $\overline{BE} \perp \overline{EC}$. Can you prove that $\triangle ABC$ is equilateral? Explain.
No; $\overline{AB} \cong \overline{CB}$ because $\triangle AEB \cong \triangle CEB$, but $\overline{AC}$ doesn't have to be $\cong$ to $\overline{AB}$ or to $\overline{CB}$.

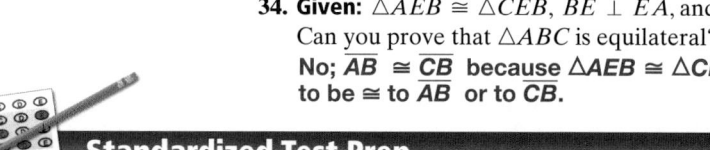

Standardized Test Prep

Multiple Choice In Exercises 35 and 36, which additional congruence statement could you use to prove that $\triangle BJK \cong \triangle CFH$ by HL?

35. **Given:** $\overline{BJ} \cong \overline{CF}$ **A**
A. $\overline{JK} \cong \overline{FH}$ B. $\angle B \cong \angle C$
C. $\overline{AJ} \cong \overline{AF}$ D. $\angle BJK \cong \angle CFH$

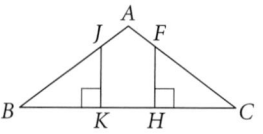

36. **Given:** $\overline{BK} \cong \overline{CH}$ **H**
F. $\overline{JK} \cong \overline{FH}$ G. $\angle B \cong \angle C$ H. $\overline{JB} \cong \overline{FC}$ I. $\angle BJK \cong \angle CFH$

pages 219–223 Exercises

29. 1. $\overline{LO}$ bisects $\angle MLN$, $\overline{OM} \perp \overline{LM}$, $\overline{ON} \perp \overline{LN}$ (Given)
2. $\angle M$ and $\angle N$ are rt. $\angle$s (Def. of $\perp$)
3. $\angle MLO \cong \angle NLO$ (Def. of $\angle$ bis.)
4. $\angle M \cong \angle N$ (All rt. $\angle$s are $\cong$.)
5. $\overline{LO} \cong \overline{LO}$ (Reflexive Prop. of $\cong$)
6. $\triangle LMO \cong \triangle LNO$ (AAS)

30. Answers may vary. Sample: Measure 2 sides of the $\triangle$ formed by the amp. and the platform's corner. Since the $\angle$s will be $\cong$ by HL or SAS, the $\angle$s are the same.

37. Which congruence statement can be used to prove that the two triangles are congruent? **D**
A. SAS   B. SSS
C. ASA   D. HL

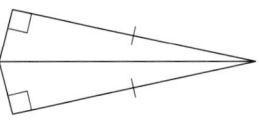

Short Response

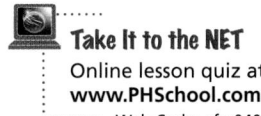
Take It to the NET
Online lesson quiz at
www.PHSchool.com
Web Code: afa-0406

38. a. Use the diagram at the right to name all the pairs of triangles you could prove congruent by using the HL Theorem. **a–b. See margin.**
b. Suppose you need to prove △*RFW* ≅ △*RGW*. What specifically do you need to prove before you can use the HL Theorem?

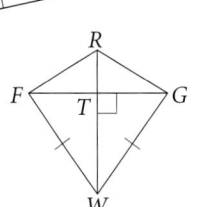

Mixed Review

Lesson 4-5   For Exercises 39 and 40, what type of triangle must △*XYZ* be?

39. △*XYZ* ≅ △*ZYX* **isosceles**   **40.** △*XYZ* ≅ △*ZXY* **equilateral**

Lesson 3-6   **41.** Connect $A(3,3)$, $B(5,5)$, $C(9,1)$, and $D(9,-3)$ in order. Are any sides of the figure parallel? Are any sides perpendicular? Explain. **See back of book.**

Lesson 3-1   State the postulate or theorem that justifies each statement.

42. ∠5 ≅ ∠8   **43.** $m∠4 + m∠8 = 180$ **42–47.**
44. ∠6 ≅ ∠9   **45.** ∠4 ≅ ∠10 **See back of book.**
46. ∠1 ≅ ∠6   **47.** ∠6 and ∠3 are supplementary.

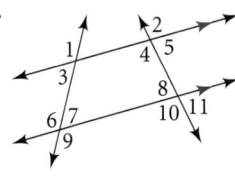

✓ Checkpoint Quiz 2   Lessons 4-4 Through 4-6

📱 TEXT Instant self-check quiz online and on CD-ROM

1. In the diagram at the right, △*PQR* ≅ △*SRQ* by SAS. What other pairs of sides and angles can you conclude are congruent by CPCTC? $\overline{PR} ≅ \overline{SQ}$; ∠P ≅ ∠S; ∠*PRQ* ≅ ∠*SQR*

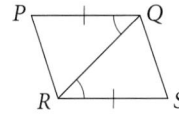

2. Complete the plan for a proof.

Given: Isosceles △*JKL* with $\overline{JK} ≅ \overline{JL}$; $\overline{KM}$ and $\overline{LM}$ are bisectors of the base angles.

Prove: △*KML* is isosceles.

Plan: Since △*JKL* is isosceles, ∠*JKL* ≅ ∠*JLK* by the **a.** _?_ Theorem. Since $\overline{KM}$ and $\overline{LM}$ are angle **Isosc. △** bisectors, ∠*MKL* **b.** _?_ ∠*MLK*. Therefore, △*KML* ≅ is isosceles by the **c.** _?_ Theorem. **Converse of the Isosc. △ Thm.**

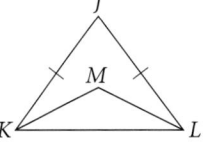

3. Six triangles are pictured in the diagram at the left. Which of the triangles are isosceles? Explain. **See margin.**

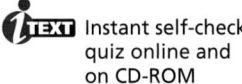
Exercise 3

4. Why are these triangles congruent?   **HL**

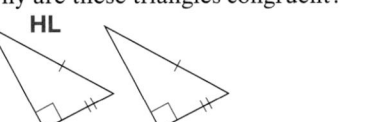

5. Explain why $\overline{GW} ≅ \overline{ST}$. **See margin.**

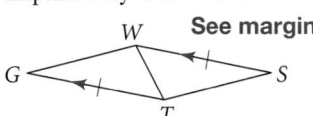

33. Since $\overline{BE} ⊥ \overline{EA}$ and $\overline{BE} ⊥ \overline{EC}$, △*AEB* and △*CEB* are both rt. △. $\overline{AB} ≅ \overline{BC}$ because △*ABC* is equilateral, and $\overline{BE} ≅ \overline{BE}$. △*AEB* ≅ △*CEB* by HL.

38. **[2] a.** △*TFW* ≅ △*TGW*
b. ∠*RFW* and ∠*RGW* are rt. △.
[1] one part correct

page 223 Checkpoint Quiz 2

3. △*AED*; ∠*EAB* ≅ ∠*EDC* (Given)
△*EBC*; ∠*EBC* ≅ ∠*ECB* (Suppl. of ≅ △ are ≅.)

5. △*GTW* ≅ △*SWT* by SAS since $\overline{WT} ≅ \overline{WT}$, ∠*WTG* ≅ ∠*TWS*, and $\overline{GT} ≅ \overline{SW}$. So $\overline{GW} ≅ \overline{ST}$ by CPCTC.

1. Plan

Lesson Preview

✓ Check Skills You'll Need

Planning a Proof
Lesson 4-3: Example 3
Exercises 9–13
Extra Practice, p. 693

Using the HL Theorem
Lesson 4-6: Examples 2 and 3
Exercises 11–17
Extra Practice, p. 693

Lesson Resources

📁 **Teaching Resources**
Practice, Reteaching, Enrichment

👥 **Reaching All Students**
Practice Workbook 4-7
Spanish Practice Workbook 4-7
Informal Geometry Planning
   Guide 4-7

⏰ **Presentation Assistant Plus!**
Transparencies
• Check Skills You'll Need 4-7
• Additional Examples 4-7
• Student Edition Answers 4-7
• Lesson Quiz 4-7
PH Presentation Pro CD 4-7

PRENTICE HALL
ASSESSMENT SYSTEM

Computer Test Generator CD

💿 **Technology**
Resource Pro® CD-ROM
Computer Test Generator CD
Prentice Hall Presentation Pro CD

🖥 **www.PHSchool.com**
Student Site
• Teacher Web Code: afk-5500
• Self-grading Lesson Quiz
Teacher Center
• Lesson Planner
• Resources

Plus 🄸TEXT

224

4-7 Using Corresponding Parts of Congruent Triangles

North Carolina Objectives **2.03** Apply properties, definitions, and theorems of two-dimensional figures to solve problems and write proofs: a) Triangles.

Lesson Preview

What You'll Learn

OBJECTIVE **1** To identify congruent overlapping triangles

OBJECTIVE **2** To prove two triangles congruent by first proving two other triangles congruent

. . . And Why

To identify overlapping triangles in scaffolding, as in Example 1

✓ Check Skills You'll Need

(For help, go to Lessons 1-1 and 4-3.)

1. How many triangles will the next two figures in this pattern have? **15; 31**

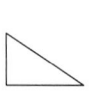

2. Can you conclude that the triangles are congruent? Explain.

a. △AZK and △DRS
yes; SAS

b. △SDR and △JTN
yes; AAS

c. △ZKA and △NJT
yes; Trans. Prop. of ≅

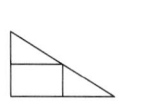

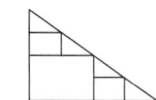

OBJECTIVE
1 Using Overlapping Triangles in Proofs

🄸TEXT **Interactive lesson includes instant self-check, tutorials, and activities.**

📖 **Reading Math**

Overlapping triangles share part or all of one or more sides.

Some triangle relationships are difficult to see because the triangles overlap. Overlapping triangles may have a common side or angle. You can simplify your work with overlapping triangles by separating and redrawing the triangles.

1 EXAMPLE Identifying Common Parts

Separate and redraw △DFG and △EHG. Identify the common angle.

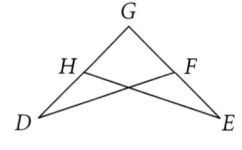

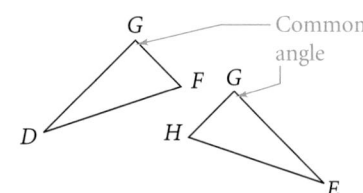

Common angle

✓ Check Understanding

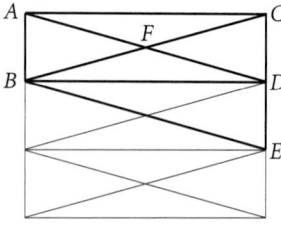

1 Engineering The diagram at the left shows triangles from the scaffolding that workers used when they repaired and cleaned the Statue of Liberty.
a. Name the common side in △ADC and △BCD. **CD**
b. Name another pair of triangles that share a common side. Name the common side. **Answers may vary.**
Sample: △ABD and △CBD; BD

In overlapping triangles, a common side or angle is congruent to itself by the Reflexive Property of Congruence.

Ongoing Assessment and Intervention

Before the Lesson	**During the Lesson**	**After the Lesson**
Diagnose prerequisite skills using:	Monitor progress using:	Assess knowledge using:
• Check Skills You'll Need	• Check Understanding • Additional Examples • Standardized Test Prep	• Lesson Quiz • Computer Test Generator CD

Proof ② EXAMPLE Proving Two Segments Congruent

Given: $\angle ZXW \cong \angle YWX$, $\angle ZWX \cong \angle YXW$

Write a plan and then a flow proof to show that the two "outside" segments are congruent.

Prove: $\overline{ZW} \cong \overline{YX}$

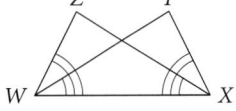

Plan: First, separate the overlapping triangles. $\overline{ZW} \cong \overline{YX}$ by CPCTC if $\triangle ZXW \cong \triangle YWX$. Show this congruence by ASA.

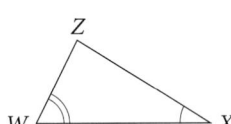 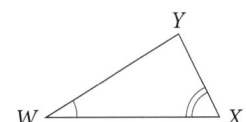

Proof:

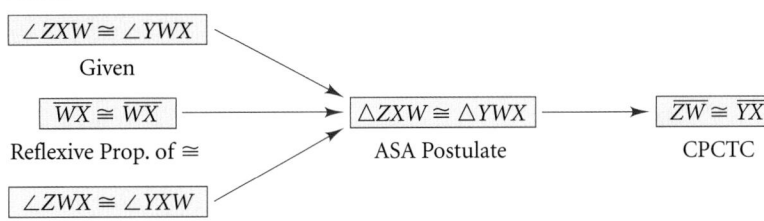

| $\boxed{\angle ZXW \cong \angle YWX}$ |
| Given |

| $\boxed{\overline{WX} \cong \overline{WX}}$ |
| Reflexive Prop. of $\cong$ |

| $\boxed{\angle ZWX \cong \angle YXW}$ |
| Given |

$\to \boxed{\triangle ZXW \cong \triangle YWX} \to \boxed{\overline{ZW} \cong \overline{YX}}$
ASA Postulate   CPCTC

2. 1. $\triangle ACD \cong \triangle BDC$ (Given)

2. $\angle ADC \cong \angle BCD$ (CPCTC)

3. $\overline{CE} \cong \overline{DE}$ (If base $\angle$s are $\cong$, the opp. sides are $\cong$.)

✓ **Check Understanding** ② Plan a proof. Then follow your plan and write a proof in paragraph, flow, or two-column form. **See left.**

Given: $\triangle ACD \cong \triangle BDC$
Prove: $\overline{CE} \cong \overline{DE}$

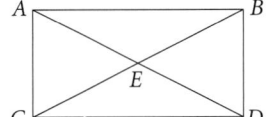

OBJECTIVE
2 Using Two Pairs of Congruent Triangles

Sometimes you can prove one pair of triangles congruent and then use their congruent corresponding parts to prove another pair congruent.

Proof ③ EXAMPLE Using SAS and Then ASA

Given: In the quilt, E is the midpoint of $\overline{AC}$ and $\overline{DB}$.
Prove: $\triangle GED \cong \triangle JEB$

Write a plan and then a paragraph proof.

Plan: $\triangle GED \cong \triangle JEB$ by ASA if $\angle D \cong \angle B$. These angles are congruent by CPCTC if $\triangle AED \cong \triangle CEB$. These triangles are congruent by SAS.

Proof: E is the midpoint of $\overline{AC}$ and $\overline{DB}$, so $\overline{AE} \cong \overline{CE}$ and $\overline{DE} \cong \overline{BE}$. $\angle AED \cong \angle CEB$ because vertical angles are congruent. Therefore, $\triangle AED \cong \triangle CEB$ by SAS. $\angle D \cong \angle B$ by CPCTC, and $\angle GED \cong \angle JEB$ because they are vertical angles. Therefore, $\triangle GED \cong \triangle JEB$ by ASA.

✓ **Check Understanding** ③ Plan a proof. Then follow your plan and write a proof in paragraph, flow, or two-column form.

Given: $\overline{PS} \cong \overline{RS}$, $\angle PSQ \cong \angle RSQ$ **See back of book.**
Prove: $\triangle QPT \cong \triangle QRT$

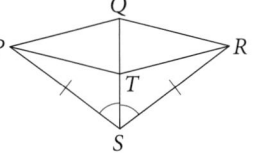

Lesson 4-7 Using Corresponding Parts of Congruent Triangles **225**

🫶 Reaching All Students

| **Below Level** Use separable transparencies on an overhead projector and different-colored pens to help students distinguish overlapping triangles and congruent corresponding parts. | **Advanced Learners** Have students copy the diagram in Example 2, drawing $\overline{ZY}$. Then have them prove that $\overline{ZY}$ and $\overline{WX}$ are parallel. | **Visual Learners** See note on page 227. **Error Prevention** See note on page 226. |

Students may think they can prove △*GED* ≅ △*JEB* directly from the information given. After reading the Plan for Proof with the class, discuss how proving △*AED* ≅ △*CEB* acts as a bridge from the Given to proving △*GED* ≅ △*JEB*. Point out that a proof often involves finding such a bridge between ideas.

Additional Examples

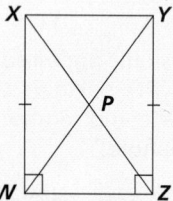

3 Write a paragraph proof.

Given: $\overline{XW} \cong \overline{YZ}$, ∠*XWZ* and ∠*YZW* are right angles.

Prove: △*XPW* ≅ △*YPZ* $\overline{XW} \cong \overline{YZ}$ (Given), ∠*XWZ* ≅ ∠*YZW* (right angles) and $\overline{WZ} \cong \overline{ZW}$ (Reflexive Prop.), so △*XWZ* ≅ △*YZW* by SAS. ∠*WXZ* ≅ ∠*ZYW* by CPCTC, ∠*XPW* ≅ ∠*YPZ* (vert. angles are ≅), and $\overline{XW} \cong \overline{YZ}$ (Given), so △*XPW* ≅ △*YPZ* by AAS.

4 Use the Given from Example 4 to write a two-column proof to show that ∠*CBE* ≅ ∠*CDA*.
1. ∠*BCE* ≅ ∠*DCA* (Reflexive)
2. $\overline{CA} \cong \overline{CE}$, $\overline{BA} \cong \overline{DE}$ (Given)
3. *CA* − *BA* = *CE* − *DE* (Subtraction Prop. of Equality)
4. *CA* − *BA* = *CB*, *CE* − *DE* = *CD* (Seg. Add. Post.)
5. *CB* = *CD* (Substitution)
6. $\overline{CB} \cong \overline{CD}$ (Def. of ≅)
7. △*CBE* ≅ △*CDA* (SAS)
8. ∠*CBE* ≅ ∠*CDA* (CPCTC)

Closure

Explain how CPCTC can be used in the middle of a proof. Sometimes you can prove a pair of triangles congruent and then use CPCTC to prove another pair congruent.

When triangles overlap, you can keep track of information by drawing other diagrams that separate the overlapping triangles.

Proof→ 4 EXAMPLE   Separating Overlapping Triangles

Given: $\overline{CA} \cong \overline{CE}$, $\overline{BA} \cong \overline{DE}$

Write a plan and then a two-column proof to show that two small segments inside the triangle are congruent.

Prove: $\overline{BX} \cong \overline{DX}$

Plan: $\overline{BX} \cong \overline{DX}$ by CPCTC if △*BXA* ≅ △*DXE*. This congruence holds by AAS if ∠*ABX* ≅ ∠*EDX*. These are congruent by CPCTC in △*BAE* and △*DEA*, which are congruent by SAS.

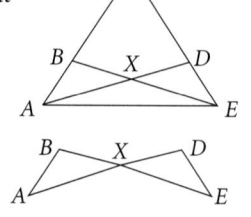

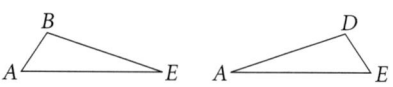

Proof:

Statements	Reasons
1. $\overline{BA} \cong \overline{DE}$	1. Given
2. $\overline{CA} \cong \overline{CE}$	2. Given
3. ∠*CAE* ≅ ∠*CEA*	3. Isosceles Triangle Theorem
4. $\overline{AE} \cong \overline{AE}$	4. Reflexive Property of Congruence
5. △*BAE* ≅ △*DEA*	5. SAS
6. ∠*ABE* ≅ ∠*EDA*	6. CPCTC
7. ∠*BXA* ≅ ∠*DXE*	7. Vertical angles are congruent.
8. △*BXA* ≅ △*DXE*	8. AAS
9. $\overline{BX} \cong \overline{DX}$	9. CPCTC

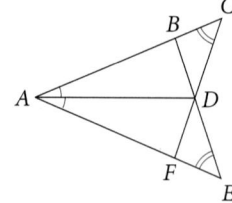

Real-World Connection

The Japanese paper-folding art of origami involves many overlapping triangles.

✓ **Check Understanding**

4 Plan a proof. Separate the overlapping triangles in your plan. Then follow your plan and write a proof. **See margin.**

Given: ∠*CAD* ≅ ∠*EAD*, ∠*C* ≅ ∠*E*

Prove: $\overline{BD} \cong \overline{FD}$

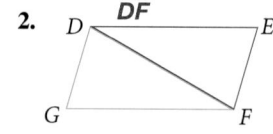

EXERCISES

For more practice, see *Extra Practice*.

Practice and Problem Solving

A Practice by Example

Example 1
(page 224)

In each diagram, the red and blue triangles are congruent. Identify their common side or angle.

1. ∠*M*

2. $\overline{DF}$

3. $\overline{XY}$

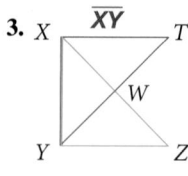

226   Chapter 4   Congruent Triangles

---

page 226   **Check Understanding**

4.   1. ∠*CAD* ≅ ∠*EAD*; ∠*C* ≅ ∠*E* (Given)

2. $\overline{AD} \cong \overline{AD}$ (Reflexive Prop. of ≅)

3. △*ACD* ≅ △*AED* (AAS)

4. $\overline{CD} \cong \overline{ED}$ (CPCTC)

5. ∠*BDC* ≅ ∠*FDE* (Vert. ∠ are ≅.)

6. △*BDC* ≅ △*FDE* (ASA)

7. $\overline{BD} \cong \overline{FD}$ (CPCTC)

Separate and redraw the indicated triangles. Identify any common angles or sides.

4. △PQS and △QPR

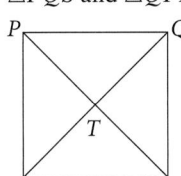

4–9.
See back
of book.

5. △ACB and △PRB

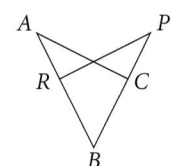

6. △TRQ and △PQR

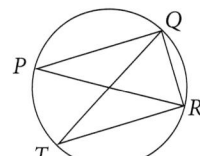

7. △ABE and △BAC

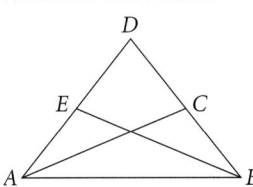

8. △JKL and △MLK

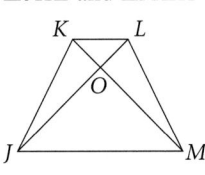

9. △PSU and △QVT

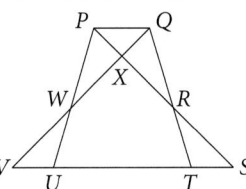

Example 2
(page 225)

10. Developing Proof Complete the flow proof.

Given: ∠T ≅ ∠R, $\overline{PQ}$ ≅ $\overline{PV}$

Prove: ∠PQT ≅ ∠PVR

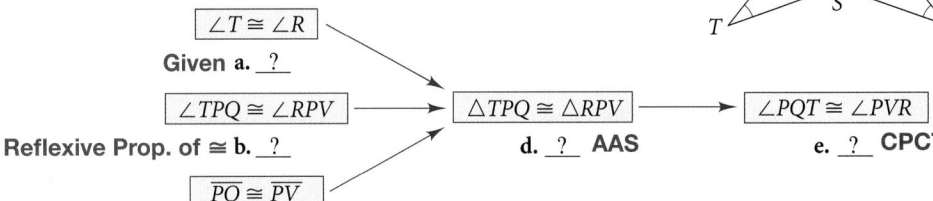

| ∠T ≅ ∠R |
Given a. ?

| ∠TPQ ≅ ∠RPV |
Reflexive Prop. of ≅ b. ?

| $\overline{PQ}$ ≅ $\overline{PV}$ |
c. ? Given

→ | △TPQ ≅ △RPV |
d. ? AAS

→ | ∠PQT ≅ ∠PVR |
e. ? CPCTC

Developing Proof Name a pair of overlapping congruent triangles in each diagram. State whether the triangles are congruent by SSS, SAS, ASA, AAS, or HL.

△LQP ≅ △PML; HL
11. Given: $\overline{MP}$ ≅ $\overline{QL}$, $\overline{LP}$ ⊥ $\overline{LM}$,
$\overline{LP}$ ⊥ $\overline{PQ}$

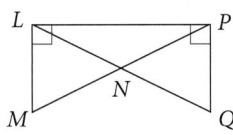

△RST ≅ △UTS; SSS
12. Given: $\overline{RS}$ ≅ $\overline{UT}$, $\overline{RT}$ ≅ $\overline{US}$

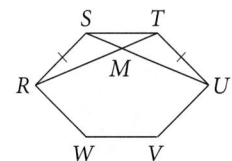

△QDA ≅ △UAD; SAS
13. Given: $\overline{QD}$ ≅ $\overline{UA}$,
∠QDA ≅ ∠UAD

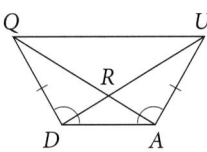

△QPT ≅ △RUS; AAS
14. Given: $\overline{PQ}$ ∥ $\overline{UR}$, $\overline{TQ}$ ∥ $\overline{SR}$,
$\overline{TQ}$ ≅ $\overline{SR}$

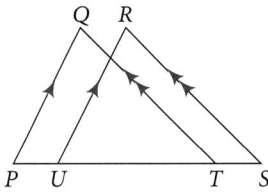

Assignment Guide

 **Objective**
 Ⓐ Ⓑ **Core** 1–14, 19–22
 Ⓒ **Extension** 31

 **Objective**
 Ⓐ Ⓑ **Core** 15–18, 23–30
 Ⓒ **Extension** 32, 33

Standardized Test Prep 34–38

Mixed Review 39–48

Visual Learners

Exercises 4–9 Students may trace and copy these exercises using two different colors to distinguish the triangles from each other.

Error Prevention

Exercise 10 In step b, identifying ∠P using two different names may confuse students and prevent them from realizing that the Reflexive Property of Congruence applies. Ask: *Why is ∠P named in two ways?* to show the order of the corresponding vertices in △TPQ and △RPV

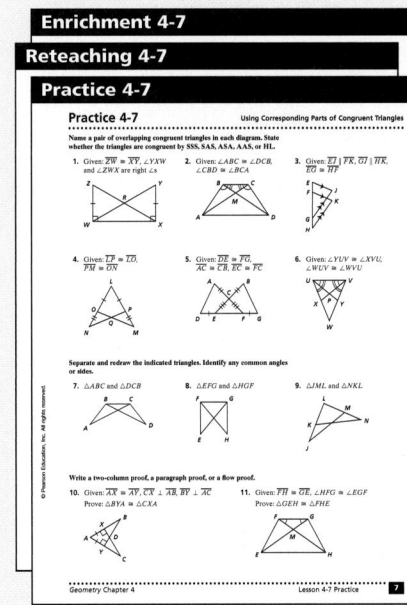

pages 227–230 Exercises

21. a.

b.

22. a.

b.

Examples 3, 4
(pages 225 and 226)

15. $\overline{TD} \cong \overline{RO}$ if △*TDI* ≅ △*ROE* by AAS. ∠*TID* ≅ ∠*REO* if △*TEI* ≅ △*RIE*. △*TEI* ≅ △*RIE* by SSS.

16. $\overline{AE} \cong \overline{DE}$ if △*AEB* ≅ △*DEC* by AAS. $\overline{AB} \cong \overline{DC}$ and ∠*A* ≅ ∠*D* since they are corr. parts of △*ABC* and △*DCB*, which are ≅ by HL.

17. △*QET* ≅ △*QEU* by SAS if $\overline{QT} \cong \overline{QU}$. $\overline{QT}$ and $\overline{QU}$ are corr. parts of △*QTB* and △*QUB* which are ≅ by ASA.

18. △*ADC* ≅ △*EDG* by ASA if ∠*A* ≅ ∠*E*. ∠*A* and ∠*E* are corr. parts in △*ADB* and △*EDF*, which are ≅ by SAS.

B **Apply Your Skills**

19.

20.

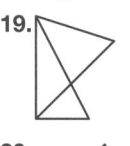

Developing Proof **Plan a proof. As part of your plan, separate the overlapping triangles you use.   15–18. See left.**

15. Given: $\overline{TE} \cong \overline{RI}, \overline{TI} \cong \overline{RE}$, ∠*TDI* and ∠*ROE* are right ∆.

Prove: $\overline{TD} \cong \overline{RO}$

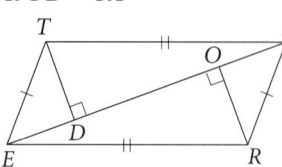

16. Given: $\overline{AB} \perp \overline{BC}, \overline{DC} \perp \overline{BC}$, $\overline{AC} \cong \overline{DB}$

Prove: $\overline{AE} \cong \overline{DE}$

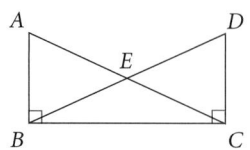

17. Given: ∠1 ≅ ∠2, ∠3 ≅ ∠4

Prove: △*QET* ≅ △*QEU*

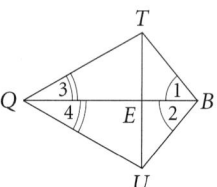

18. Given: $\overline{AD} \cong \overline{ED}$, *D* is the midpoint of $\overline{BF}$.

Prove: △*ADC* ≅ △*EDG*

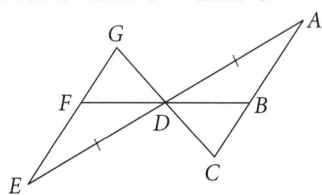

Open-Ended Draw the diagram described.   **19–22. Answers may vary. Samples are given.**

19. Draw a vertical segment on your paper. On the right side of the segment draw two triangles that share the given segment as a common side. **See left.**

20. Draw an angle. On your angle draw two triangles that have the given angle as a common angle. **See left.**

21. Draw two regular pentagons, each with its five diagonals. **a–b. See margin.**
  a. In one, shade two triangles that share a common angle.
  b. In the other, shade two triangles that share a common side.

22. Draw two regular hexagons and their diagonals. For these diagrams, do parts (a) and (b) of the preceding exercise. **See margin.**

Real-World Connection

Careers A clothing designer must carefully measure angles and segments to create a sewing pattern.

Proof **Name a pair of overlapping congruent triangles in each diagram. State whether the triangles are congruent by SSS, SAS, ASA, AAS, or HL. Plan and write a proof.**

23. Given: $\overline{AC} \cong \overline{BC}$, ∠*A* ≅ ∠*B*

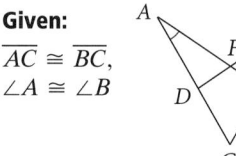

23–24. See margin.

24. Given: $\overline{WY} \perp \overline{YX}$, $\overline{ZX} \perp \overline{YX}$, $\overline{WX} \cong \overline{ZY}$

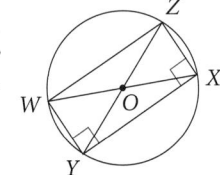

Clothes Design **The figure at the right is part of a clothing design pattern. In the figure, $\overline{AB} \parallel \overline{DE} \parallel \overline{FG}, \overline{AB} \perp \overline{BC}$, and $\overline{GC} \perp \overline{AC}$. △*DEC* is isosceles with base $\overline{DC}$, and m∠*A* = 56.**

25. Find the measures of all the numbered angles in the figure. **See margin.**

26. $\overline{AB} \cong \overline{FC}$. Name two congruent triangles and tell how you can prove them congruent.
  △*ABC* ≅ △*FCG*; ASA

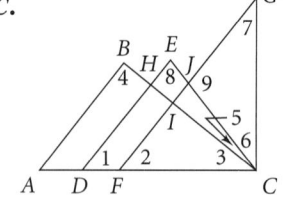

23. △*ACE* ≅ △*BCD* by ASA; $\overline{AC} \cong \overline{BC}$, ∠*A* ≅ ∠*B* (Given); ∠*C* ≅ ∠*C* (Reflexive Prop. of ≅); △*ACE* ≅ △*BCD* (ASA)

24. △*WYX* ≅ △*ZXY* by HL; $\overline{WY} \perp \overline{YX}$, $\overline{ZX} \perp \overline{YX}$, $\overline{WX} \cong \overline{ZY}$ (Given); ∠*WYX* and ∠*ZXY* are rt. ∆ (Def. of ⊥); $\overline{XY} \cong \overline{XY}$ (Reflexive Prop. of ≅.) △*WYX* ≅ △*ZXY* (HL)

25. m∠1 = 56; m∠2 = 56; m∠3 = 34; m∠4 = 90; m∠5 = 22; m∠6 = 34; m∠7 = 34; m∠8 = 68; m∠9 = 112

Developing Proof Exercises 27 and 28 are proofs for
Exercises 15 and 16. Copy and complete each proof.
Does the proof match your plan?

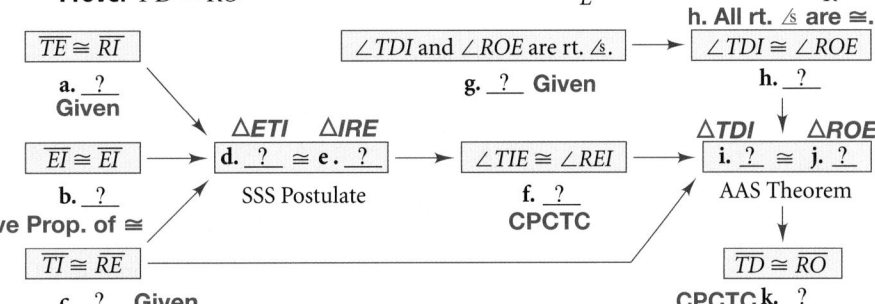

27. Given: $\overline{TE} \cong \overline{RI}, \overline{TI} \cong \overline{RE}$,
  $\angle TDI$ and $\angle ROE$ are right angles.

Prove: $\overline{TD} \cong \overline{RO}$

Need Help?
In each of Exercises 27
and 28, use CPCTC
twice.

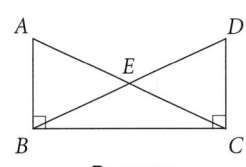

$\overline{TE} \cong \overline{RI}$	$\angle TDI$ and $\angle ROE$ are rt. $\angle$s. → $\angle TDI \cong \angle ROE$ **h. All rt. $\angle$s are $\cong$.**
a. ? **Given**	**g.** ? **Given** **h.** ?

$\overline{EI} \cong \overline{EI}$ → $\triangle ETI$ $\triangle IRE$ **d.** ? $\cong$ **e.** ? → $\angle TIE \cong \angle REI$ → $\triangle TDI$ ↓ $\triangle ROE$ **i.** ? $\cong$ **j.** ?

b. ?   **SSS Postulate**   **f.** ?   **CPCTC**   **AAS Theorem**

Reflexive Prop. of $\cong$

$\overline{TI} \cong \overline{RE}$ $\overline{TD} \cong \overline{RO}$

c. ? **Given**   **CPCTC k.** ?

29. It is given that $\angle 1 \cong \angle 2$
and $\angle 3 \cong \angle 4$. Since
$\overline{QB} \cong \overline{QB}$ by the
Reflexive Prop. of $\cong$,
$\triangle QTB \cong \triangle QUB$ by ASA.
So $\overline{QT} \cong \overline{QU}$ by CPCTC.
Since $\overline{QE} \cong \overline{QE}$ by the
Reflexive Prop. of $\cong$,
then $\triangle QET \cong \triangle QEU$
by SAS.

31b. Use $\overline{DB} \cong \overline{DB}$ (Refl.
Prop.) and alt. int. $\angle$s to
show $\triangle ADB \cong \triangle CBD$
(ASA). $\overline{AB} \cong \overline{DC}$ and
$\overline{AD} \cong \overline{BC}$ (CPCTC).
$\triangle AEB \cong \triangle CED$ (ASA)
and $\triangle AED \cong \triangle CEB$
(ASA). Then $\overline{AE} \cong \overline{EC}$
and $\overline{DE} \cong \overline{EB}$ (CPCTC).

28. Given: $\overline{AB} \perp \overline{BC}, \overline{DC} \perp \overline{BC}, \overline{AC} \cong \overline{DB}$
Prove: $\overline{AE} \cong \overline{DE}$

Statements	Reasons
1. $\overline{AB} \perp \overline{BC}, \overline{DC} \perp \overline{BC}$	**a.** ? Given
2. $\angle ABC$ and $\angle DCB$ are right angles.	**b.** ? Def. of $\perp$
3. $\triangle ABC$ and $\triangle DCB$ are right triangles.	**c.** ? Def. of rt. $\triangle$
4. $\overline{AC} \cong \overline{DB}$	**d.** ? Given
5. ? $\cong$? $\overline{BC} \cong \overline{BC}$ 28f. Reflexive	**e.** ? $\cong$? Property of Congruence
6. $\triangle ABC \cong \triangle DCB$	**g.** ? HL
7. $\angle A \cong \angle D, \overline{AB} \cong \overline{DC}$	**h.** ? CPCTC
i. $\angle AEB \cong \angle$? DEC	**j.** ? Vert. $\angle$s are $\cong$.
9. $\triangle ABE \cong \triangle DCE$	**k.** ? AAS
l. ? $\cong$? $\overline{AE} \cong \overline{DE}$	**m.** ? CPCTC

Proof Follow your plan for the given Exercise and write a proof.

29. Exercise 17   **See above left.**   **30.** Exercise 18   **See margin.**

C Challenge

31. Reasoning Draw a quadrilateral $ABCD$ with $\overline{AB} \parallel \overline{DC}$ and $\overline{AD} \parallel \overline{BC}$, and
its diagonals $\overline{AC}$ and $\overline{DB}$ intersecting at E. Label your diagram to indicate the
parallel sides. $\overline{AD} \cong \overline{BC}$; $\overline{AB} \cong \overline{DC}$; $\overline{AE} \cong \overline{EC}$; $\overline{DE} \cong \overline{EB}$
  a. List all the pairs of congruent segments that you can find in your diagram.
  b. Writing Explain how you know that the segments you listed are congruent.
    See above left.

Proof Write a proof.

32.1. $\overline{AC} \cong \overline{EC}; \overline{CB} \cong \overline{CD}$
(Given)

2. $\angle C \cong \angle C$ (Reflexive
Prop. of $\cong$)

3. $\triangle ACD \cong \triangle ECB$ (SAS)

4. $\angle A \cong \angle E$ (CPCTC)

32. Given: $\overline{AC} \cong \overline{EC}, \overline{CB} \cong \overline{CD}$
Prove: $\angle A \cong \angle E$ See left.

33. Given: $\overline{QT} \perp \overline{PR}, \overline{QT}$ bisects $\overline{PR}$,
  $\overline{QT}$ bisects $\angle VQS$.
Prove: $\overline{VQ} \cong \overline{SQ}$
  See margin.

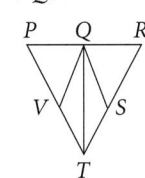

30. 1. $\overline{AD} \cong \overline{ED}$ (Given)
  2. D is the midpt. of $\overline{BF}$.
    (Given)
  3. $\overline{FD} \cong \overline{DB}$ (Def. of
    midpt.)
  4. $\angle FDE \cong \angle ADB$ (Vert.
    $\angle$s are $\cong$.)

5. $\triangle FDE \cong \triangle BDA$ (SAS)
6. $\angle E \cong \angle A$ (CPCTC)
7. $\angle GDE \cong \angle CDA$ (Vert.
  $\angle$s are $\cong$.)
8. $\triangle ADC \cong \triangle EDG$ (ASA)

33. $\overline{PQ} \cong \overline{RQ}$ and $\angle PQT \cong$
$\angle RQT$ by Def. of $\perp$
bisector. $\overline{QT} \cong \overline{QT}$ so
$\triangle PQT \cong \triangle RQT$ by SAS.
$\angle P \cong \angle R$ by CPCTC.
$\overline{QT}$ bisects $\angle VQS$ so
$\angle VQT \cong \angle SQT$ and

$\angle PQT$ and $\angle RQT$ are
both rt. $\angle$s. So $\angle VQP \cong$
$\angle SQR$ since they are
compl. of $\cong \angle$s. $\triangle PQV \cong$
$\triangle RQS$ by ASA so $\overline{QV} \cong$
$\overline{QS}$ by CPCTC.

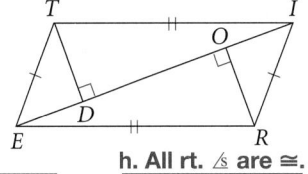
Lesson Quiz 4-7

1. Identify any common sides
and angles in $\triangle AXY$ and
$\triangle BYX$.

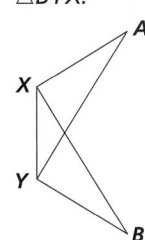

$\overline{XY}$

For Exercises 2 and 3, name a
pair of congruent overlapping
triangles. State the theorem
or postulate that proves them
congruent.

2.
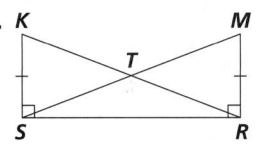

$\triangle KSR \cong \triangle MRS$; SAS

3.
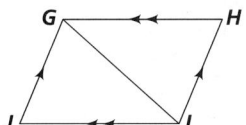

$\triangle GHI \cong \triangle IJG$; ASA

4. Plan a proof.

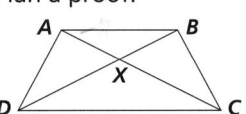

Given: $\overline{AC} \cong \overline{BD}, \overline{AD} \cong \overline{BC}$

Prove: $\overline{XD} \cong \overline{XC}$
$\overline{XD} \cong \overline{XC}$ by CPCTC if
$\triangle DXA \cong \triangle CXB$. This
congruence holds by AAS
if $\triangle BAD \cong \triangle ABC$. Show
$\triangle BAD \cong \triangle ABC$ by SSS.

229

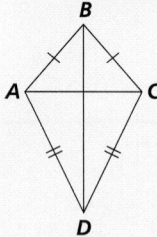
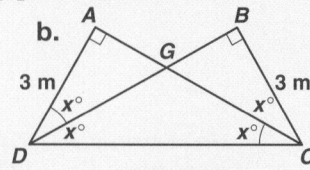
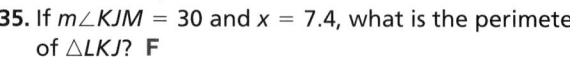
Multiple Choice   Use the diagram at the right for Exercises 34–36.

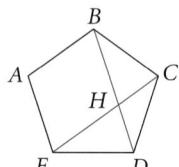

34. If $m\angle KJM = 25$, what is $m\angle LKJ$? **C**
    A. 25   **B.** 30   **C.** 65   **D.** 85

35. If $m\angle KJM = 30$ and $x = 7.4$, what is the perimeter of $\triangle LKJ$? **F**
    F. 44.4   **G.** 22.2   **H.** 14.8   **I.** 7.4

36. If $m\angle LJK = 47$, what is $m\angle LJM$? **A**
    A. 23.5   **B.** 25   **C.** 43   **D.** 47

Short Response

37. The pentagon at the right is equilateral and equiangular.
   a. What two triangles must be congruent to prove $\overline{HB} \cong \overline{HE}$?
   b. Plan a proof to show $\overline{HB} \cong \overline{HE}$.
   a–b. See margin.

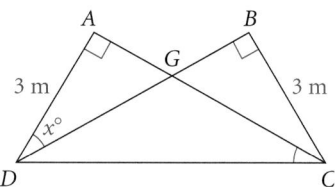

Extended Response

38. a. In the figure at the right, why is $\triangle ACD \cong \triangle BDC$? **a–e. See margin.**
   b. Copy the figure. Mark each angle that has measure x.
   c. What is the value of x? Explain how you found your answer.
   d. What is $m\angle AGB$?
   e. What is CD? Explain your answer.

Mixed Review

Lesson 4-6

39. Complete the plan for a proof.

   Given: $\angle A$ and $\angle D$ are right angles, $\overline{AB} \cong \overline{DB}$.
   Prove: $\triangle ABC \cong \triangle DBC$
   Plan: $\triangle ABC$ and $\triangle DBC$ are **a.** $\underline{\ ?\ }$ triangles with legs that are given to be **b.** $\underline{\ ?\ }$. The hypotenuse is ≅ congruent to itself by the **c.** $\underline{\ ?\ }$ Property of Congruence. **Reflexive** $\triangle ABC \cong \triangle DBC$ by the **d.** $\underline{\ ?\ }$ Theorem. **HL**

right (above a.)

40.
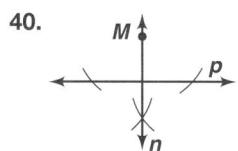

Lesson 3-7

Constructions Draw a line p and a point M not on p. Construct the described line.

40. line n through M so that $n \perp p$
   See left.

41. line r through M so that $r \parallel p$
   See margin.

Lesson 3-5

Write an equation in point-slope form of the line that contains the given point and has the given slope.

42. $P(2, -6)$; slope $\frac{1}{2}$ $y + 6 = \frac{1}{2}(x - 2)$ **43.** $Q(0, 5)$; slope 1 $y - 5 = 1(x - 0)$

44. $R(-3, 6)$; slope -2 **45.** $S(0, 0)$; slope $-\frac{1}{3}$ $y - 0 = -\frac{1}{3}(x - 0)$
   $y - 6 = -2(x + 3)$

Write an equation in point-slope form of the line that contains the given points.

46–48. Eqs. may vary, depending on pt. chosen.

46. $A(1, 4)$, $B(0, 2)$ **47.** $E(3, -5)$, $F(6, 0)$ **48.** $X(-4, -3)$, $Y(2, -8)$
   $y - 4 = 2(x - 1)$ $y + 5 = \frac{5}{3}(x - 3)$ $y + 3 = -\frac{5}{6}(x + 4)$

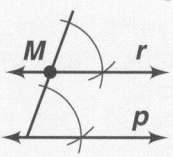

Writing Flow Proofs

Proofs can get long and complex. While a two-column proof may appear more organized, a flow proof can show the logic flow better and thus be easier to follow.

To write a flow proof, sketch the logic "paths" of a proof on scratch paper. Then organize your work into a neat, easy-to-follow flow diagram, as in this Example.

EXAMPLE

Given: $\overline{KJ} \cong \overline{LM}, \angle KJN \cong \angle LMN, \overline{JN} \cong \overline{MN}$

Prove: $\overline{JL} \cong \overline{MK}$

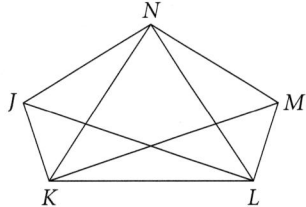

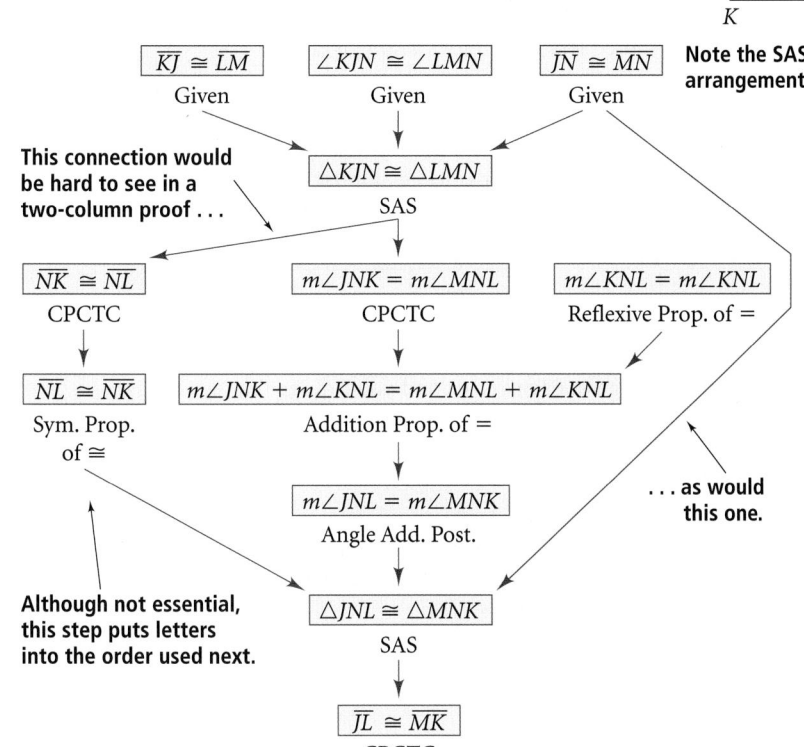

Note the SAS arrangement.

$\overline{KJ} \cong \overline{LM}$ — Given

$\angle KJN \cong \angle LMN$ — Given

$\overline{JN} \cong \overline{MN}$ — Given

$\triangle KJN \cong \triangle LMN$ — SAS

This connection would be hard to see in a two-column proof . . .

$\overline{NK} \cong \overline{NL}$ — CPCTC

$m\angle JNK = m\angle MNL$ — CPCTC

$m\angle KNL = m\angle KNL$ — Reflexive Prop. of =

$\overline{NL} \cong \overline{NK}$ — Sym. Prop. of $\cong$

$m\angle JNK + m\angle KNL = m\angle MNL + m\angle KNL$ — Addition Prop. of =

$m\angle JNL = m\angle MNK$ — Angle Add. Post.

. . . as would this one.

Although not essential, this step puts letters into the order used next.

$\triangle JNL \cong \triangle MNK$ — SAS

$\overline{JL} \cong \overline{MK}$ — CPCTC

EXERCISES

Write a flow proof. Make the flow of logic as easy to follow as you can. 1–2. See back of book.

1. Given: $\overline{AB} \cong \overline{DC}$, E is the midpoint of $\overline{AD}$, and $\overline{CE} \cong \overline{BE}$.

Prove: $\overline{AC} \cong \overline{DB}$

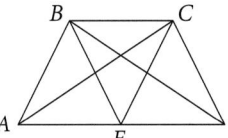

2. Given: $\overline{RQ} \cong \overline{RS}$, $\overline{RP} \cong \overline{RT}$, $\overline{QP} \cong \overline{ST}$

Prove: $\overline{QT} \cong \overline{SP}$

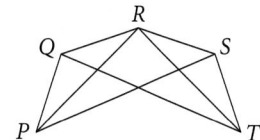

Extension

Writing Flow Proofs

Because this extension focuses on a proof that involves many steps and the use of overlapping triangles, it provides an opportunity for students to see the power of a flow diagram in constructing and illustrating the sequence of logic in a good proof.

Resources

Technology
Computer Test Generator CD-ROM, Chapter 0, Extension Topics

Teaching Notes

The flow diagram presented here is neat and complete. Discuss as a class how a flow diagram may be the result of several unsuccessful attempts at proof, with dead ends and extraneous steps occurring along the way. Emphasize this again as students work on Exercises 1 and 2.

Alternative Method

Have students complete the proof by proving $\triangle JKL \cong \triangle MLK$ instead of $\triangle JNL \cong \triangle MNK$. As a class, discuss which parts of the flow proof change and which remain the same.

Teaching Tip

Exercises 1, 2 Have students compare the flow proofs for these two exercises side-by-side. Ask them to state how the two proofs are alike and how they are different.

Making Quantitative Comparisons

This feature helps students understand the basic answer choices for quantitative-comparison questions and provides insight into how to avoid common errors in answering them.

Resources

Test-Taking Strategies with Transparencies
- Transparency 4
- Practice sheet p. 16

Teaching Notes

Students must recognize what is necessary and/or sufficient information to form conclusions and logical deductions from limited information.

Error Prevention

Students should avoid the temptation of substituting a simpler problem, such as substituting an equilateral triangle for the equilateral pentagon. They also should not assume that answer choice D is usually correct.

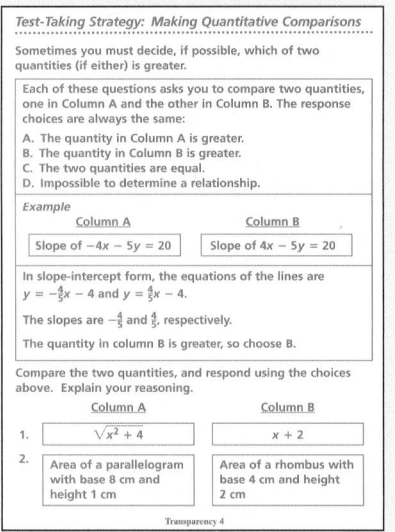

232

For a Quantitative Comparison test item, you must compare two given quantities. You have to decide which quantity is greater, that the two quantities are equal, or that there is not enough information to make a comparison. You must read the directions carefully and understand the two uses of each capital letter A and B.

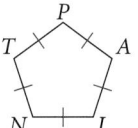 **EXAMPLE**   **Comparing Quantities That Look Equal**

Compare the boxed quantity in Column A with the boxed quantity in Column B. Choose the best answer.

- **A.** The quantity in Column A is greater.
- **B.** The quantity in Column B is greater.
- **C.** The two quantities are equal.
- **D.** The relationship cannot be determined from the information given.

Remember: A diagram can show what *may* be true. You decide what *must* be true.

Column A	Column B
$m\angle N$	$m\angle T$

The given pentagon has congruent sides. It may have congruent angles (as the diagram suggests). However, imagine a hinge at each vertex and you can see that a pentagon can be equilateral without being equiangular. The best answer is D.

EXERCISES

x^2 **Algebra** **Compare the quantity in Column A with the quantity in Column B. Choose the best answer from those listed in the Example. Justify your answer.**

1. 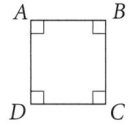 D; quadrilateral may not be regular.

Column A	Column B
AB	BC

2. 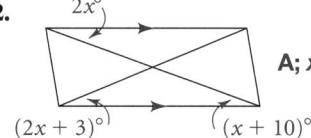 A; $x = 10$

Column A	Column B
x	5

3. 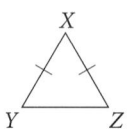 D; triangles may not be equilateral.

Column A	Column B
XZ	QR

4. 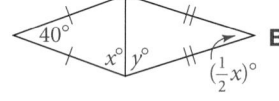 B; $x = 70$, $y = 72.5$

Column A	Column B
x	y

Chapter Review

Vocabulary

base of an isosceles triangle (p. 211)
base angles of an isosceles triangle
    (p. 211)
congruent polygons (p. 180)
corollary (p. 212)

CPCTC (corresponding parts of
    congruent triangles are congruent)
    (p. 203)
hypotenuse (p. 217)
legs of a right triangle (p. 217)

legs of an isosceles triangle (p. 211)
vertex angle of an isosceles triangle
    (p. 211)

 **Reading Math**
**Understanding
Vocabulary**

Choose the correct term to complete each sentence.

1. The two congruent sides of an isosceles triangle are the ___?___. **legs**

2. The two congruent sides of an isosceles triangle form the ___?___. **vertex angle**

3. If you know that two triangles are congruent, then the corresponding
    sides and angles of the triangles are congruent because ___?___. **CPCTC**

4. The side opposite the right angle of a right triangle is the ___?___. **hypotenuse**

5. The angles of an isosceles triangle that are not the vertex angle are
    called the ___?___. **base angles**

6. A ___?___ to a theorem is a statement that follows immediately from
    the theorem. **corollary**

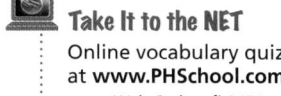 **Take It to the NET**
Online vocabulary quiz
at **www.PHSchool.com**
Web Code: afj-0451

7. The ___?___ are the two sides of a right triangle that are not the hypotenuse. **legs**

8. ___?___ have congruent corresponding parts. **Congruent polygons**

9. The side of an isosceles triangle that is not a leg is called the ___?___. **base**

Skills and Concepts

4-1 Objectives

▼ To recognize congruent
  figures and their
  corresponding parts

Congruent polygons have congruent corresponding parts. When you name
congruent polygons, always list corresponding vertices in the same order.

Two triangles are congruent when they have three pairs of congruent
corresponding sides and three pairs of congruent corresponding angles.

***RSTUV ≅ KLMNO*. Complete the congruence statements.**

10. $\overline{TS} \cong$ ___?___ **ML**

11. $\angle N \cong$ ___?___ **∠U**

12. $\overline{LM} \cong$ ___?___ **ST**

13. *VUTSR ≅* ___?___ **ONMLK**

***WXYZ ≅ PQRS*. Find the measure of the angle or the length of the side.**

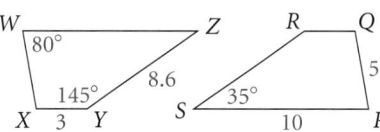

14. $\angle P$ **80**   **15.** $\overline{QR}$ **3**   **16.** $\overline{WX}$ **5**   **17.** $\angle Z$ **35**   **18.** $\angle X$ **100**

Resources

Student Edition
Extra Practice Ch. 4, p. 693
English/Spanish Glossary, p. 741
Postulates and Theorems, p. 732
Table of Symbols, p. 725

 Reaching All Students
Reading and Math Literacy 4D
Spanish Reading and Literacy 4D

(ASSESSMENT SYSTEM PRENTICE HALL

Standardized Test Prep
● Ch. 4 practice in standardized
test formats

 **www.PHSchool.com**
Student Site
● Self-grading Vocabulary Test
Teacher Center
● Resources

Plus **iTEXT**

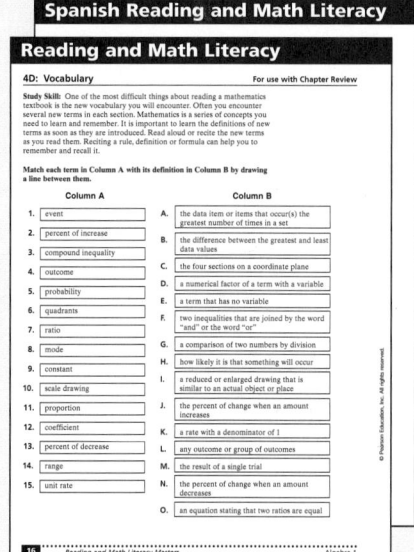

4-2 and 4-3 Objectives

▼ To prove two triangles congruent using the SSS and SAS Postulates

▼ To prove two triangles congruent using the ASA Postulate and the AAS Theorem

If three sides of one triangle are congruent to three sides of another triangle, then the two triangles are congruent by the **Side-Side-Side (SSS) Postulate.**

If two sides and the included angle of one triangle are congruent to two sides and the included angle of another triangle, then the two triangles are congruent by the **Side-Angle-Side (SAS) Postulate.**

If two angles and the included side of one triangle are congruent to two angles and the included side of another triangle, then the two triangles are congruent by the **Angle-Side-Angle (ASA) Postulate.**

If two angles and a nonincluded side of one triangle are congruent to two angles and the corresponding nonincluded side of another triangle, then the two triangles are congruent by the **Angle-Angle-Side (AAS) Theorem.**

Which postulate or theorem, if any, could you use to prove the two triangles congruent? If the triangles *cannot* be proven congruent, write *not possible*.

19. SSS

20.  not possible

21. SAS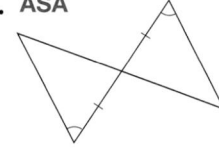

22. not possible

23. 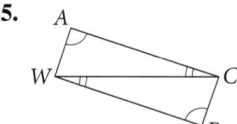 AAS

24. ASA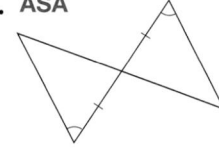

Write a congruence statement for each pair of triangles. Name the postulate or theorem that justifies your statement. If the triangles *cannot* be proven congruent, write *not possible*.

25.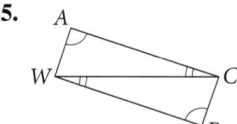
△AWC ≅ △RCW; AAS

26.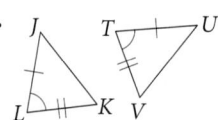
△JKL ≅ △UVT; SAS

27.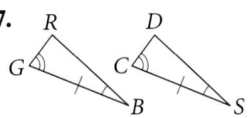
△RGB ≅ △DCS; ASA

4-4 Objectives

▼ To use triangle congruence and CPCTC to prove that parts of two triangles are congruent

Once you know that triangles are congruent, you can make conclusions about corresponding segments and angles because, by definition, **corresponding parts of congruent triangles are congruent (CPCTC).** You can use congruent triangles in the proofs of many theorems.

Explain how you can use SSS, SAS, ASA, or AAS with CPCTC to prove the statement true.

28. △VTY ≅ △WYX by AAS so $\overline{TV} ≅ \overline{YW}$ by CPCTC.

28. $\overline{TV} ≅ \overline{YW}$
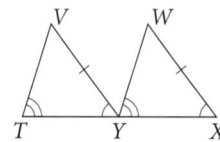

29. $\overline{BE} ≅ \overline{DE}$
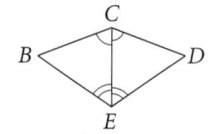
△BCE ≅ △DCE by ASA so $\overline{BE} ≅ \overline{DE}$ by CPCTC.

30. $\overline{KN} ≅ \overline{ML}$
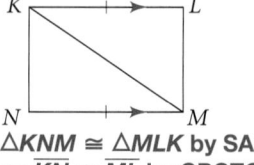
△KNM ≅ △MLK by SAS so $\overline{KN} ≅ \overline{ML}$ by CPCTC.

4-5 and 4-6 Objectives

▼ To use and apply properties of isosceles triangles

▼ To prove triangles congruent using the HL Theorem

If two sides of a triangle are congruent, then the angles opposite those sides are also congruent by the **Isosceles Triangle Theorem.** If two angles of a triangle are congruent, then the sides opposite the angles are congruent by the **Converse of the Isosceles Triangle Theorem.**

The bisector of the vertex angle of an isosceles triangle is the perpendicular bisector of the base.

If the hypotenuse and a leg of one right triangle are congruent to the hypotenuse and a leg of another right triangle, then the triangles are congruent by the **Hypotenuse-Leg (HL) Theorem.**

x^2 **Algebra** Find the values of x and y.

31. $x = 4, y = 65$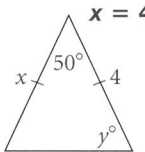

32. $x = 55, y = 62.5$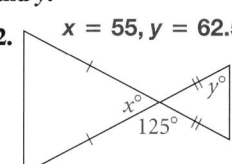

33. $x = 65, y = 90$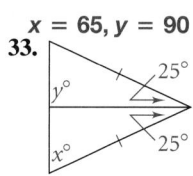

Write a paragraph explaining how to deduce what you want to prove from the given information.

34. **Given:** $\overline{PS} \perp \overline{SQ}, \overline{RQ} \perp \overline{QS}, \overline{PQ} \cong \overline{RS}$

    Prove: $\triangle PSQ \cong \triangle RQS$
    Since $\overline{PS} \perp \overline{SQ}$ and $\overline{RQ} \perp \overline{QS}$, $\triangle PSQ$ and $\triangle RQS$ are rt. △.
    $\overline{PQ} \cong \overline{RS}$ and $\overline{QS} \cong \overline{SQ}$ so $\triangle PSQ \cong \triangle RQS$ by HL.

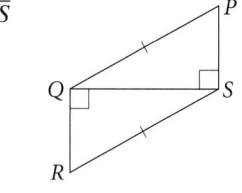

35. **Given:** $\overline{LN} \perp \overline{KM}, \overline{KL} \cong \overline{ML}$

    Prove: $\triangle KLN \cong \triangle MLN$
    Since $\overline{LN} \perp \overline{KM}, m\angle LNK = m\angle LNM = 90$. $\overline{KL} \cong \overline{ML}$ and $\overline{LN} \cong \overline{LN}$ so $\triangle KLN \cong \triangle MLN$ by HL.

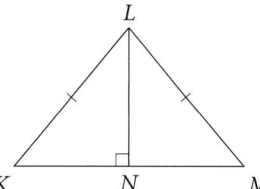

4-7 Objectives

▼ To identify congruent overlapping triangles

▼ To prove two triangles congruent by first proving two other triangles congruent

You can prove overlapping triangles congruent. You can also use the common or shared sides and angles of triangles in congruence proofs.

Name a pair of overlapping congruent triangles in each diagram. State whether the triangles are congruent by SSS, SAS, ASA, AAS, or HL.

36. $\triangle AEC \cong \triangle ABD$ by SAS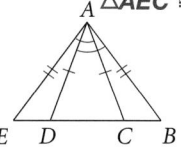

37. $\triangle FIH \cong \triangle GHI$ by SAS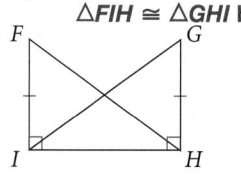

38. $\triangle PTS \cong \triangle RTA$ by ASA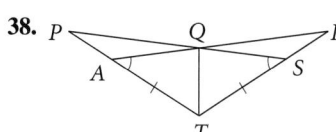

39. $\triangle CFE \cong \triangle DEF$ by ASA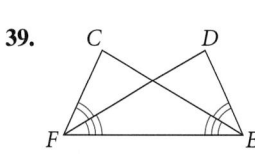

Chapter 4   Chapter Review   **235**

Resources

Teaching Resources
Ch. 4 Test, Forms A & B
Ch. 4 Alternative Assessment

Reaching All Students
Spanish Ch. 4 Test, Forms A & B
Spanish Ch. 4 Alternative
  Assessment, Form C
Informal Geometry Ch. 4 Test,
  Forms D & E

PRENTICE HALL
ASSESSMENT SYSTEM

Assessment Masters
• Ch. 4 Test, Forms A & B
• Ch. 4 Alternative Assessment,
  Form C
Computer Test Generator CD
• Ch. 4 pre-made Test
• Make your own Ch. 4 test

 **www.PHSchool.com**
Student Site
• Self-grading Chapter 4 Test
Teacher Center
• Resources

Plus **iTEXT**

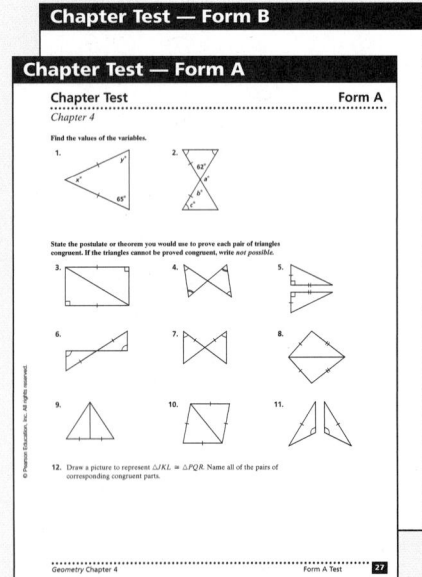

Chapter Test

Chapter 4

Take It to the NET
Online chapter test at
www.PHSchool.com
Web Code: afa-0452

Write a congruence statement for each pair of triangles.

1.
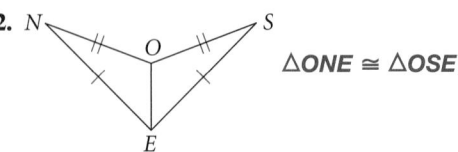
$\triangle PAY \cong \triangle APL$

2.
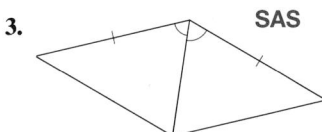
$\triangle ONE \cong \triangle OSE$

Which postulate, if any, could you use to prove the two triangles congruent? If not enough information is given, write *not possible*.

3. 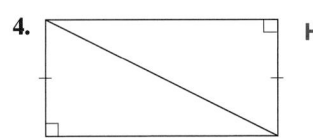 SAS

4. 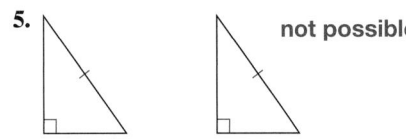 HL

5. 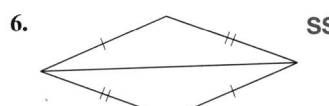 not possible

6. 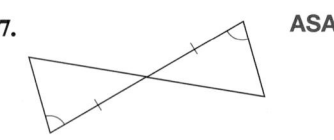 SSS

7. ASA

8. AAS

9. Writing Explain why you cannot use AAA to prove two triangles congruent.   **Answers may vary. Sample: The corr. sides of the two △ may not be ≅.**

236   Chapter 4   Chapter Test

10. Open-Ended Draw a picture to represent $\triangle CEO \cong \triangle HDF$. Name all of the pairs of corresponding congruent parts. **See back of book.**

11. If two game boards have the same area, are the game boards congruent? Explain your answer. **No; the lengths may be different.**

x^2 **12. Algebra** Find the value of the variable.
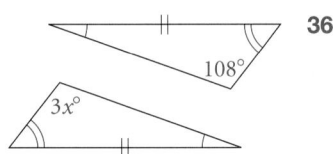
36
108°
$3x°$

Write a paragraph explaining how to deduce what you want to prove from the given information.

13. Given: $\overline{AT} \cong \overline{GS}$,
$\overline{AT} \parallel \overline{GS}$
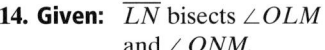
Prove: $\triangle GAT \cong \triangle TSG$
See margin.

14. Given: $\overline{LN}$ bisects $\angle OLM$ and $\angle ONM$.
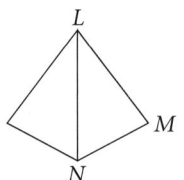
Prove: $\triangle OLN \cong \triangle MLN$
See margin.

Name a pair of overlapping congruent triangles in each diagram. State whether the triangles are congruent by SSS, SAS, ASA, AAS, or HL.

15. Given: $\overline{CE} \cong \overline{DF}$,
$\overline{CF} \cong \overline{DE}$
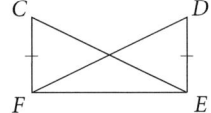
$\triangle CFE \cong \triangle DEF$; SSS

16. Given: $\overline{RT} \cong \overline{QT}$,
$\overline{AT} \cong \overline{ST}$
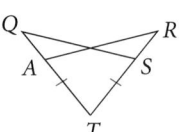
$\triangle TQS \cong \triangle TRA$; SAS

17. Open-Ended Draw two parallel lines and draw two parallel transversals through your parallel lines. Then draw a third transversal to create two congruent triangles. Label your triangles and write the congruence statement. **See back of book.**

page 236   Chapter Test

13. $\overline{AT} \parallel \overline{GS}$, so $\angle ATG \cong \angle SGT$ because they are alt. int. △s. It is given that $\overline{AT} \cong \overline{GS}$, and $\overline{GT} \cong \overline{GT}$ by the Reflexive Prop. of ≅, so $\triangle GAT \cong \triangle TSG$ by SAS.

14. Since $\overline{LN}$ bisects $\angle OLM$ and $\angle ONM$, $\angle OLN \cong \angle MLN$ and $\angle ONL \cong \angle MNL$. $\overline{LN} \cong \overline{LN}$ by the Reflexive Prop. of ≅, so $\triangle OLN \cong \triangle MLN$ by ASA.

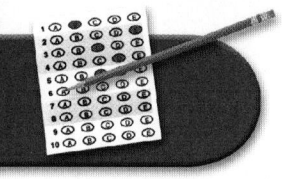

Standardized Test Prep

Multiple Choice

For Exercises 1–6, choose the correct letter.

1. What is $m\angle CDF$? **B**

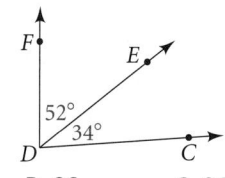

   A. 18   **B.** 86   **C.** 94   **D.** 274

2. Which angles could an obtuse triangle have? **G**

   I. a right angle
   II. two acute angles
   III. an obtuse angle
   IV. two vertical angles

   F. I and II   **G.** II and III
   H. III and IV   **I.** I and IV

3. What is the area in square units of a rectangle with vertices $(-2, 5)$, $(3, 5)$, $(3, -1)$, and $(-2, -1)$? **B**
   A. 56   **B.** 30   **C.** 25   **D.** 24

4. Quadrilateral $ABCD \cong QRST$. Which segment is congruent to $\overline{TS}$? **I**
   F. $\overline{AB}$ **G.** $\overline{BC}$ **H.** $\overline{CB}$ **I.** $\overline{DC}$

5. By which postulate or theorem are the triangles congruent? **A**

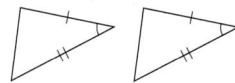

   A. SAS   **B.** SSS   **C.** ASA   **D.** AAS

6. Which condition(s) will allow you to prove that $\ell \parallel m$? **I**

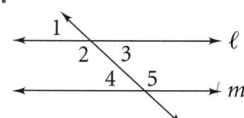

   I. $\angle 1 \cong \angle 4$
   II. $\angle 2 \cong \angle 5$
   III. $m\angle 2 + m\angle 4 = 180$
   IV. $\angle 3 \cong \angle 4$

   F. III only   **G.** I and III only
   H. II and IV only   **I.** I, II, III, and IV

Quantitative Comparison

Compare the boxed quantity in Column A with the boxed quantity in Column B. Choose the best answer.

   A. The quantity in Column A is greater.
   B. The quantity in Column B is greater.
   C. The two quantities are equal.
   D. The relationship cannot be determined from the information given.

Column A	Column B

Lines ℓ and t are nonvertical and perpendicular.

D 7.

the slope of ℓ	the slope of t

B 8.

the product of the slopes of ℓ and t	the slope of a horizontal line

Gridded Response

9. An isosceles triangle has two angles measuring 54.5 and 71. What is the measure of the third angle? **54.5**

10. What is the number of feet in the circumference of a circle with a diameter of 10 ft? Use 3.14 for π. **31.4**

11. What is the measure of the complement of a 56° angle? **34**

12. What is the measure of the supplement of a 35° angle? **145**

Short Response

Explain your work. 13–14. See back of book.

13. Draw an angle. Then construct another angle congruent to the first.

14. Construct the perpendicular bisector of a segment $\overline{MN}$.

Extended Response

15. Find CD and the coordinates of the midpoint of $\overline{CD}$ if the endpoints are $C(5, 7)$ and $D(10, -5)$. Explain your work.
    See back of book.

Resources

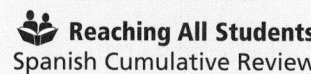

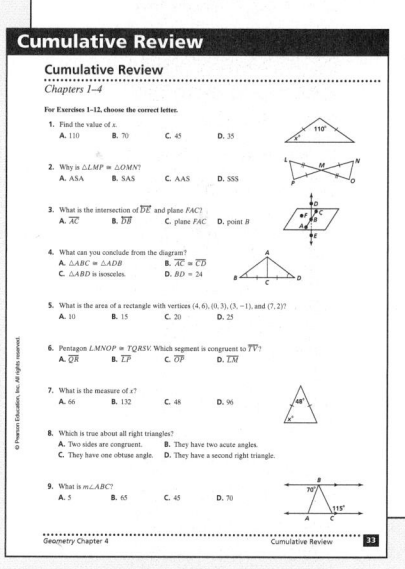

Item	Lesson	Item	Lesson
1	1-4	9	3-3
2	3-3	10	1-7
3	1-6	11	2-5
4	4-1	12	2-5
5	4-2	13	1-5
6	3-2	14	1-5
7	3-6	15	1-6
8	3-6		

The Science of Reflection

In these activities students apply their knowledge of the relationships between angles that are formed when a transversal cuts parallel lines.

Connecting to Prior Knowledge

Have students discuss their own experiences with reflections. For example, they may have used a kaleidoscope as a toy, a microscope for scientific investigation, or a camera for art or pleasure.

Teaching Notes

Have students read the introductory paragraph. Then ask: *What does it mean to say that a mirror's image is reversed?* **Sample: Left becomes right and right becomes left.** This idea is a key to understanding Activity 2.

Science Connection

When Galileo visited Venice in 1609, he learned of the invention of the telescope and immediately made one for himself. This enabled him to study astronomy in ways not possible for earlier scientists.

Connection to Calculus

Point out that Sir Isaac Newton is one of two men (Gottfried Leibniz is the other) credited with inventing the calculus. The work of both Newton and Leibniz contributed to the discipline of optics, the branch of physics that studies light.

 **Real-World Snapshots**

The Science of Reflection

Applying Parallel Lines When you look at the surface of a still pool of water, your reflection looks back at you. This is because the water acts like a mirror, reflecting a clear, although reversed, image. The type of reflection you see in a mirror depends on the surface of the mirror. Two flat mirrors placed at right angles to each other will seem to magnify the light hitting them by reflecting it directly back to its source.

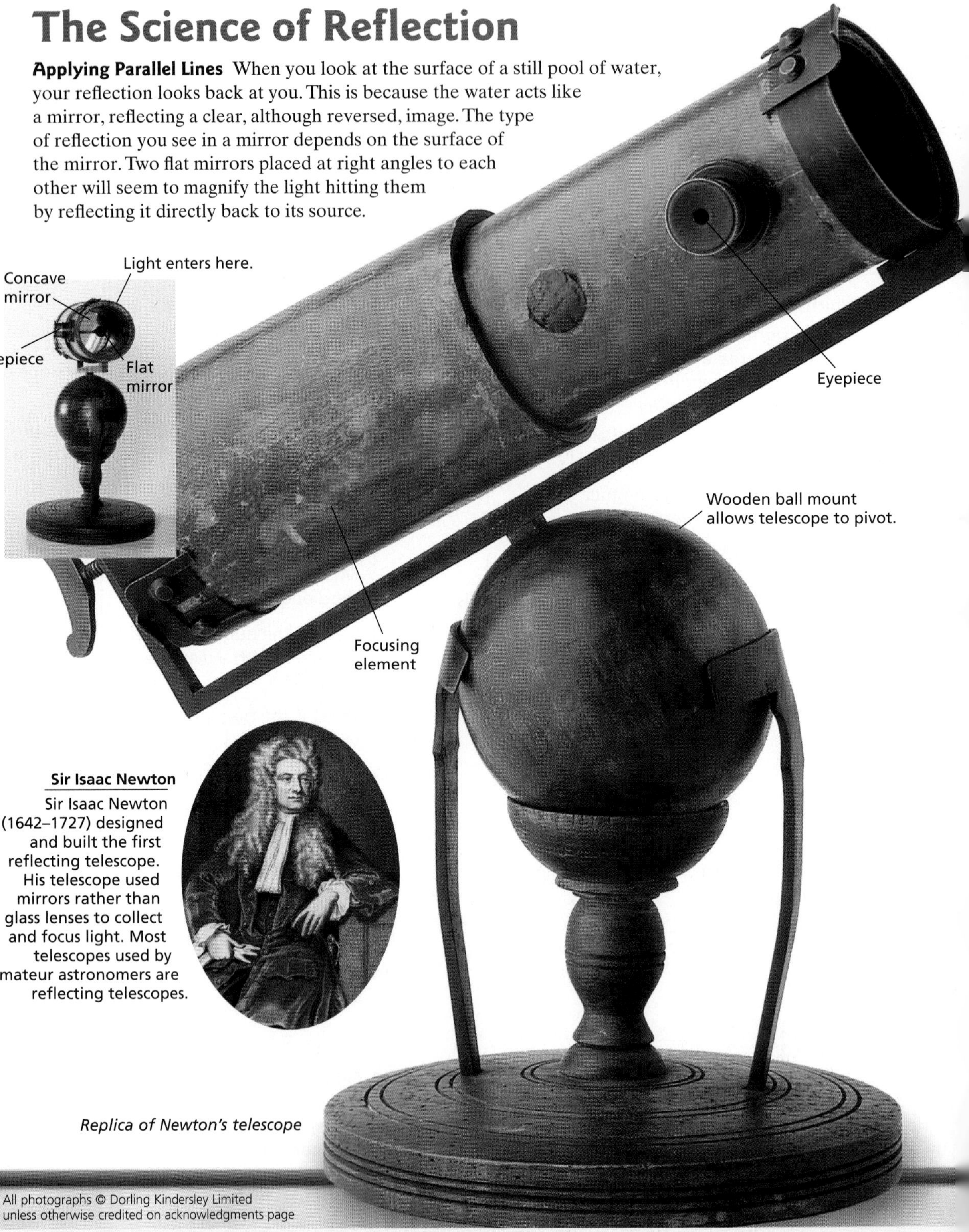

Light enters here.

Concave mirror

Eyepiece

Flat mirror

Eyepiece

Wooden ball mount allows telescope to pivot.

Focusing element

Sir Isaac Newton

Sir Isaac Newton (1642–1727) designed and built the first reflecting telescope. His telescope used mirrors rather than glass lenses to collect and focus light. Most telescopes used by amateur astronomers are reflecting telescopes.

Replica of Newton's telescope

Measuring Distances

Astronauts have placed a cube-corner reflector on the surface of the moon. Each corner provides three perpendicular reflecting planes. By measuring the time it takes a laser beam to bounce back from the reflector, scientists are able to measure the distance from Earth to the moon.

Activity 1

Examine the diagram below. Notice that the mirrors are perpendicular and that each angle of reflection is congruent to the corresponding angle of incidence. Given these two facts, explain why incident and reflected rays must be parallel.

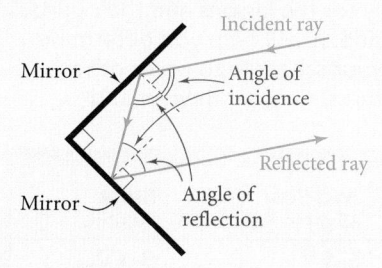

Incident ray

Mirror

Angle of incidence

Reflected ray

Mirror

Angle of reflection

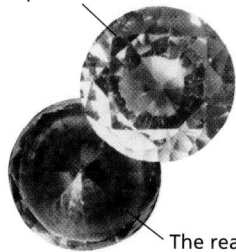

The front view sparkles.

Cut Diamonds
A cut diamond reflects most of the light that falls on its front.

The rear view is dark.

Safety
A bicycle doesn't have the electric taillights that a car does, so it comes equipped with reflectors. Some helmets also have reflectors.

Activity 2

Materials: two flat mirrors

Arrange two flat mirrors so that they form a right angle. Look at your face in one of the mirrors and wink. Then look into the seam where the two mirrors meet, find your face, and wink. How does the reflection in the perpendicular mirrors differ from the reflection in the single mirror?

Hall of Mirrors
The Hall of Mirrors at France's Palace of Versailles is brightly lit even on a cloudy day, because each of its windows is placed opposite a mirror of the same size and shape.

 Take It to the NET For more information about mirrors and reflections, go to **www.PHSchool.com**.
Web Code: afe-0453

239

239

Chapter 5

Relationships Within Triangles

Chapter at a Glance

North Carolina Objectives

5-1	**Midsegments of Triangles**	2.03a
NCTM 1, 2, 3, 4, 6, 7, 8, 9, 10	▼ Using Properties of Midsegments	

5-2	**Bisectors in Triangles**	2.03a
NCTM 3, 6, 7, 8, 9, 10	▼ Perpendicular Bisectors and Angle Bisectors	

5-3	**Concurrent Lines, Medians, and Altitudes**	2.03a
NCTM 3, 4, 6, 8, 9, 10	▼ Properties of Bisectors ▼ Medians and Altitudes	

5-4	**Inverses, Contrapositives, and Indirect Reasoning**	2.01
NCTM 1, 3, 6, 7, 8, 9, 10	▼ Writing the Negation, Inverse, and Contrapositive ▼ Using Indirect Reasoning	

5-5	**Inequalities in Triangles**	2.03a
NCTM 2, 3, 6, 7, 8, 9, 10	▼ Inequalities Involving Angles of Triangles ▼ Inequalities Involving Sides of Triangles	

NCTM STANDARDS 2000

1	Number and Operations	6	Problem Solving
2	Algebra	7	Reasoning and Proof
3	Geometry	8	Communication
4	Measurement	9	Connections
5	Data Analysis and Probability	10	Representation

Pacing Options

This chart suggests pacing only for the lessons and their parts. It is provided as a possible guide. It will help you determine how much time you have in your schedule to cover other components, such as the features, Chapter Review and Chapter Test.

Day	Traditional 45 min.	Two-Year 45 min.	Block 90 min.
1	5-1 ▼	5-1 ▼	5-1 ▼
2	5-2 ▼	5-1 ▼	5-2 ▼
3	5-3 ▼	5-2 ▼	5-3 ▼ ▼
4	5-3 ▼	5-2 ▼	5-4 ▼ ▼
5	5-4 ▼	5-3 ▼	5-5 ▼ ▼
6	5-4 ▼	5-3 ▼	
7	5-5 ▼	5-3 ▼	
8	5-5 ▼	5-4 ▼	
9		5-4 ▼	
10		5-4 ▼	
11		5-4 ▼	
12		5-5 ▼	
13		5-5 ▼	
14		5-5 ▼	
15			
16			
17			
18			
19			
20			
21			
22			

NAEP Correlation (National Assessment of Educational Progress 2000 Mathematics Objectives)

5-1	5-2	5-3	5-4	5-5
M9, G5, G9a	G5, G9a	G5, G9a	G7b, c, DGa	N2e, G7b, A4A

N = Number Sense, Properties, and Operations; **M** = Measurement; **G** = Geometry and Spatial Sense; **D** = Data Analysis, Statistics, and Probability; **A** = Algebra and Functions

Math Background

Chapter Overview

This chapter opens with a fairly straightforward study of segments in a triangle. The role of proof in geometry is expanded with the introduction of coordinate proof and indirect proof. Coordinate proofs will be studied in more detail in Chapter 6. The exercise sets in this chapter also contain exercises with proof formats from earlier sections. Students who complete these exercises will improve their ability to write proofs.

There is extensive practice in forming negations and contrapositives to extend logical reasoning. Both are needed to support indirect proof.

Midsegments of Triangles   5-1

The Midsegment Theorem is visually self-evident, but its proof is more difficult than might be expected. A coordinate proof employs the distance and midpoint formulas from Chapter 1. Coordinate proofs show again the power of integrating algebra and geometry. Students are not asked to write entire coordinate proofs in this lesson.

Bisectors in Triangles   5-2

The proofs of the Perpendicular Bisector and Angle Bisector Theorems and their converses, along with isosceles triangle theorems, justify the construction procedures given earlier for angle bisectors and perpendicular bisectors. Make sure that students understand the definition of the distance from a point to a line, as it lays the groundwork for studying the apothems of various polygons. Another way to think about the distance from a point to a line is to visualize the length of the *shortest* segment from the point to the line. The shortest segment is perpendicular to the line. Students can experience this by securing a string to a point on a wall and noting that the shortest length of string needed to reach a horizontal mark is measured along the perpendicular.

Concurrent Lines, Medians, and Altitudes   5-3

Students can use inductive reasoning to hypothesize that particular segments in a triangle such as altitudes, medians, angle bisectors, or perpendicular bisectors are always concurrent. Clarify for students that the point of concurrency of the angle bisectors (the incenter) is not equidistant from the angles but from the sides of the triangle. In a similar fashion, clarify that the point of concurrency of the perpendicular bisectors of the sides (the circumcenter) is not equidistant from the three sides but from the three vertices.

Students can easily draw or construct altitudes to the sides of an acute triangle, but it is important that they also draw or construct altitudes for right and obtuse triangles. Some students may enjoy constructing coordinate proofs of Theorems 5-6 through 5-9. For example, to prove Theorem 5-6, place one side of a triangle along the positive x-axis with a vertex at the origin. (There is no loss of generality in selecting convenient coordinates for all the vertices, though it may be necessary for some students to consider an obtuse as well as an acute triangle.) Find the equations of the perpendicular bisectors of the sides using the point-slope form of a line. Show first that all three have a common point of intersection and then that the distances from that point to the vertices are equal.

Inverses, Contrapositives, and Indirect Reasoning   5-4

Indirect proofs can be very challenging for students who find it confusing to argue validly by beginning with a negation. Very few exercises in this lesson ask students to write their own indirect proofs. Instead, the emphasis is on writing portions of indirect proofs, such as the first sentence of the proof (the negation of the Prove statement). Generally, negations are easier for students to write than contrapositives because a contrapositive requires students to negate both phrases of a conditional and then to form converses of the resulting negations. However, some negations are more difficult than others. Students who write the negation of $x < 20$ as $x > 20$, disregarding the fact that $x = 20$ is also a negation of the original statement, need to be reminded of the Trichotomy Law (*If a and b are real numbers, either* $a < b$, *or* $a = b$, *or* $a > b$). In similar fashion, students may write the negation of "All rabbits are mild-tempered" as "No rabbits are mild-tempered," for which a better negation might be "All rabbits are not mild-tempered" or, best of all, "At least one rabbit is not mild-tempered."

Venn diagrams can help students find contrapositives. They provide visual cues to students who might otherwise have difficulty with the relationships between various conditional statements and their truth values.

Inequalities in Triangles   5-5

It may help students to think of Theorems 5-10 and 5-11 as *hinge* theorems. Let them imagine or make two pieces of wood of unequal length hinged together and propped on a flat surface to form a triangle. As the angle of the hinge changes, so do the measures of the other two angles and the length of the side on the surface, as described by Theorems 5-10 and 5-11.

The Triangle Inequality Theorem appears in various guises in many places in mathematics. Using the Triangle Inequality Theorem, groups of students should be able to determine a reasonable method for finding the range of the third side of a triangle, given the lengths of the other two sides. (Add the lengths of the two known sides; their sum is the upper bound for the range of the third side. The absolute value of the difference between these two lengths is the lower bound.) Students who develop this strategy themselves (they could use the hinge model above) understand the underlying mathematical relationships.

 # Ongoing Assessment and Intervention

Tools for Monitoring Student Progress

The Prentice Hall *Geometry* program provides you with many options for assessment in the Student Edition, the Teacher's Edition and the teaching resources. From these options, you may choose instructional materials and techniques that are appropriate for your students and support your district's curriculum requirements.

Instant Check System™ in Chapter 5

Allows students to check their own learning before, during, and after each lesson.

Diagnosing Readiness before the chapter (p. 240)

Check Skills You'll Need exercises in each lesson (pp. 243, 249, 256, 264, 273)

Check Understanding questions with each Example (pp. 244, 245, 250, 251, 257, 258, 259, 264, 265, 266, 267, 271, 274, 275, 276)

Checkpoint Quiz (p. 263)

 Test Prep in Chapter 5

Teaches students strategies and gives them practice with all the test item formats they will encounter on state tests and standardized national exams.

Standardized Test Prep exercises in each lesson (pp. 248, 254, 262, 269, 279)

Test-Taking Strategies (p. 280: Using a Variable)

Standardized Test Prep (p. 285: Reading Comprehension)

 PRENTICE HALL ASSESSMENT *SYSTEM*

All your assessment needs in one place!

Program Assessment

Assess student progress throughout the *Geometry* text with blackline masters and CD-ROM.

Assessment Resources
- Checkpoint Quiz 1
- Chapter Test, Forms A & B
- Chapter Alternative Assessment

Spanish versions available. Tests for Informal Geometry also available.

 Computer Test Generator

- Unlimited questions of varying difficulty for every lesson objective.
- Create your own practice sheets, quizzes, and tests, or use the pre-made Chapter Tests.
- Diagnose readiness with questions on prerequisite skills.
- Prepare students by making tests based on standardized test objectives.
- Access Algebra 1, Geometry, and Algebra 2 content—all on one CD-ROM.

Test Preparation

A three-step approach to preparing students for high stakes, national, and state exams.

❶ **Diagnose & Prescribe**

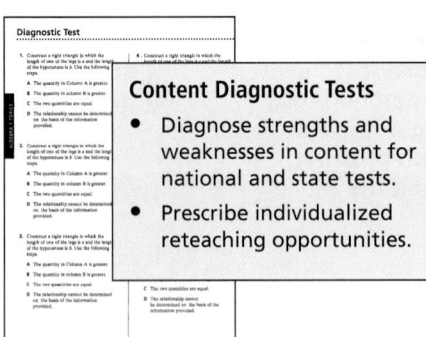

Content Diagnostic Tests
- Diagnose strengths and weaknesses in content for national and state tests.
- Prescribe individualized reteaching opportunities.

❷ **Review & Reteach**

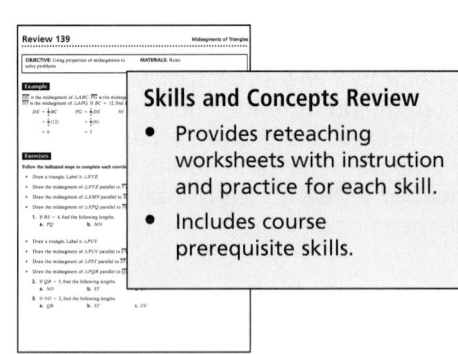

Skills and Concepts Review
- Provides reteaching worksheets with instruction and practice for each skill.
- Includes course prerequisite skills.

❸ **Practice & Assess**

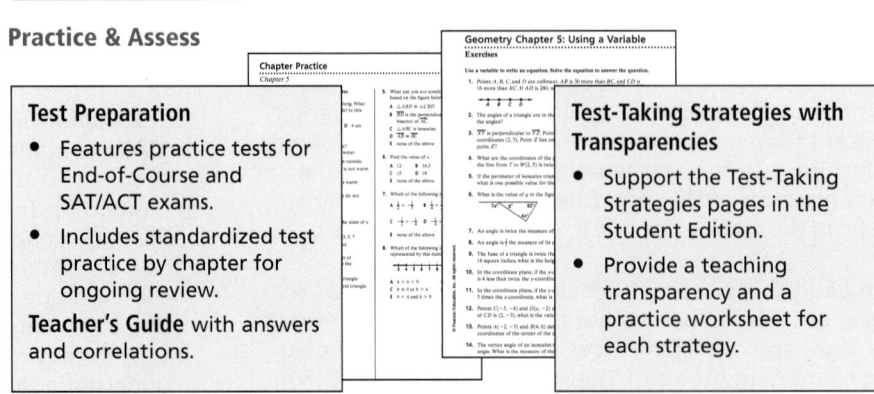

Test Preparation
- Features practice tests for End-of-Course and SAT/ACT exams.
- Includes standardized test practice by chapter for ongoing review.

Teacher's Guide with answers and correlations.

Test-Taking Strategies with Transparencies
- Support the Test-Taking Strategies pages in the Student Edition.
- Provide a teaching transparency and a practice worksheet for each strategy.

Reaching All Students

Support in the Student Text and Additional Resources

The textbook, the iText, and other technology components provide numerous opportunities to reach students of various ability levels and learning styles. Each Teacher's Edition lesson suggests how you can help *all* your students be successful and understand the mathematics in Chapter 5.

Below Level

Student Edition
- Diagnosing Readiness*: p. 240
- Check Skills You'll Need*: pp. 243, 249, 256, 264, 273

Reteaching
Chapter 5 Support File: pp. 6–10

Informal Geometry Planning Guide
Chapter 5 Lesson Plans: pp. 27–31
Chapter 5 Tests: pp. 95–98

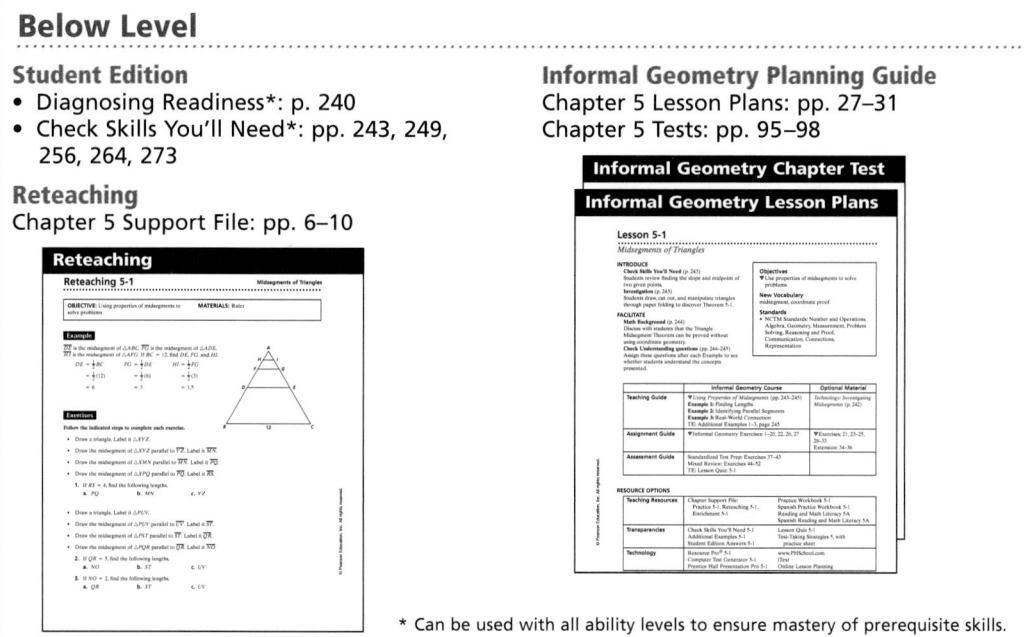

* Can be used with all ability levels to ensure mastery of prerequisite skills.

Advanced Learners

Student Edition
- Challenge exercises: pp. 248, 253, 262, 269, 278

Enrichment
Chapter 5 Support File: pp. 11–15

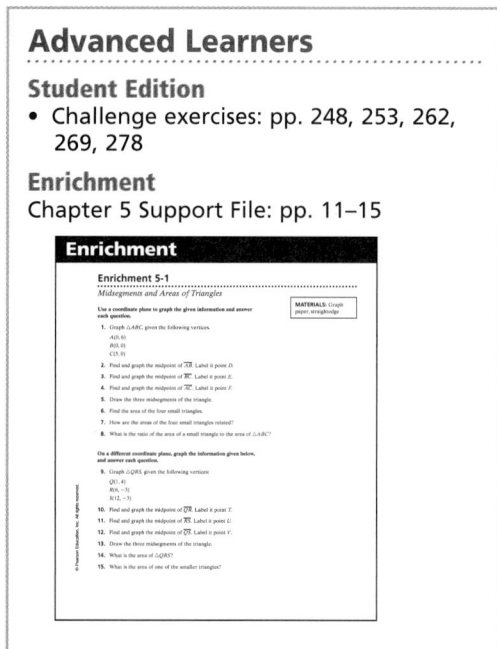

Reading and Math Literacy

Student Edition
- Vocabulary: pp. 241, 281, *plus* in every Lesson Preview
- Reading Math: pp. 257, 262, 264, 268, 271, 281
- Illustrated Glossary: pp. 741–777

Reading and Math Literacy Masters
Chapter 5: pp. 17–20

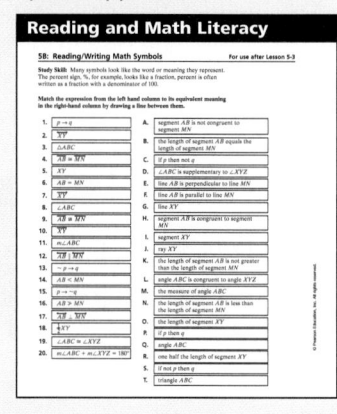

English Learners

Student Edition
- English/Spanish Illustrated Glossary: pp. 741–777

Workbook and Masters
Spanish Practice Workbook: pp. 27–31
Spanish Reading and Math Literacy Masters: pp. 17–20

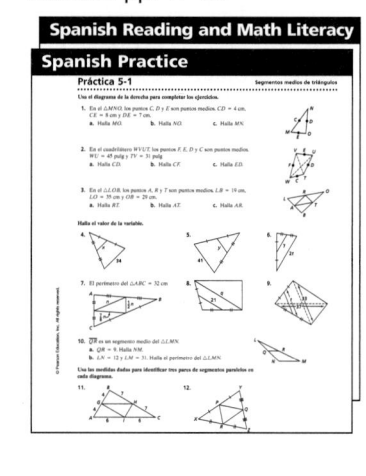

Learning Styles

Student Edition
- Investigation: pp. 243, 256
- Technology: pp. 242, 255
- Writing: pp. 247, 252, 260, 263, 268, 277, 284

Activity Masters
Hands-On Activities: 13, 14, 15
Technology Activities: 43

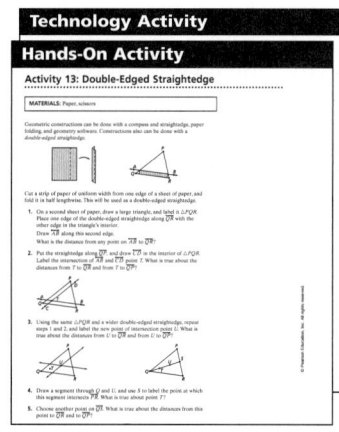

Program Resources

	Teaching Resources in Grab & Go™ Files				Resources for Reaching All Students				Spanish Resources			Transparencies				Presentation Assistant Plus!
	Practice	Reteach	Enrich	Checkpoint Quiz	Reading & Math Literacy	Technology Activities	Hands-On Activities	Informal Geometry Lesson Plans	Practice	Reading & Math Literacy	Checkpoint Quiz	Skills Check	Additional Examples	Answers to Exercises	Lesson Quiz	Prentice Hall Presentation Pro CD-ROM
5-1	■	■	■		■			■	■	■		■	■	■	■	■
5-2	■	■	■				■	■	■	■		■	■	■	■	■
5-3	■	■	■	■	■	■	■	■	■	■	■	■	■	■	■	■
5-4	■	■						■	■	■		■	■	■	■	■
5-5	■	■			■		■	■	■			■	■	■	■	■
For the chapter	Chapter Tests, Alternative Assessment, Cumulative Review, Cumulative Assessment				Informal Geometry Chapter Tests				Spanish Chapter Tests, Alternative Assessment, Cumulative Review, Cumulative Assessment			Classroom Aid Transparencies				

Also available for use with the chapter:

 *see page 240C.*

- Practice Workbook
- Solution Key

- For teacher support and access to student Web site materials, use Web Code afk-5500.
- For additional online and technology resources, see below.

Technology

iTEXT Online and on CD-ROM

Complete Interactive Student Text online and on CD-ROM—with instant feedback assessment, tutorial help, dynamic activities, instructional and real-world videos, audio, and additional practice.

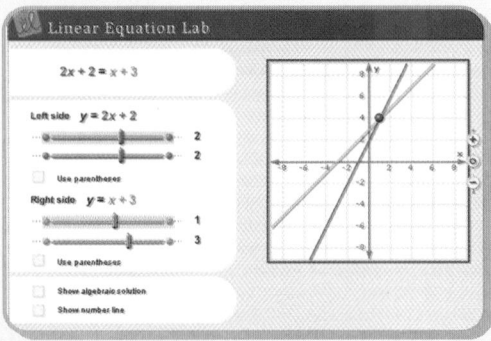

www.PHSchool.com For Students

Use **Web Codes** for easy access to online activities, chapter projects, self-grading lesson quizzes and chapter tests, vocabulary quizzes, updated data sources, graphing calculator procedures, and more.

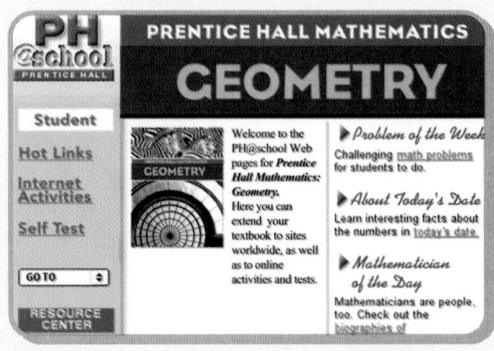

PH SuccessNet For Teachers

Online lesson planning with built-in state correlations, all the teaching resources, complete reference library, your own calendar and Teacher Web page, professional development, and more.

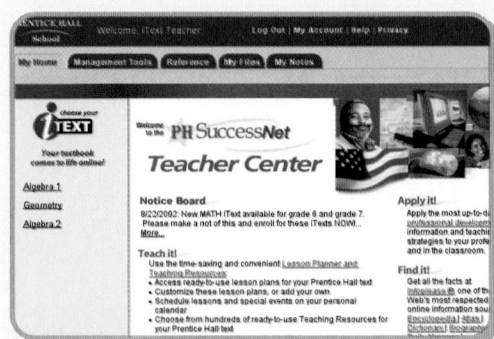

Presentation Assistant Plus!

The Prentice Hall *Presentation Assistant Plus!* provides you with the material you need to teach a lesson from beginning to end. Two easy-to-use formats—Transparencies and CD-ROM—allow you to present a lesson the way you are most comfortable.

 ## Transparencies

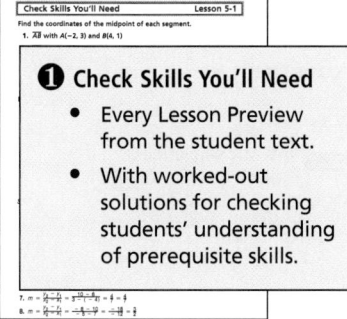

❶ **Check Skills You'll Need**
- Every Lesson Preview from the student text.
- With worked-out solutions for checking students' understanding of prerequisite skills.

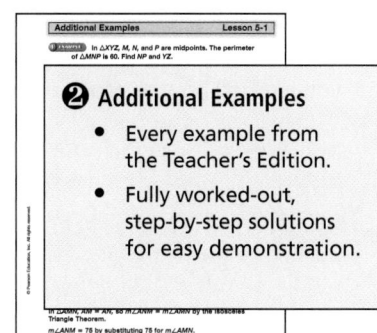

❷ **Additional Examples**
- Every example from the Teacher's Edition.
- Fully worked-out, step-by-step solutions for easy demonstration.

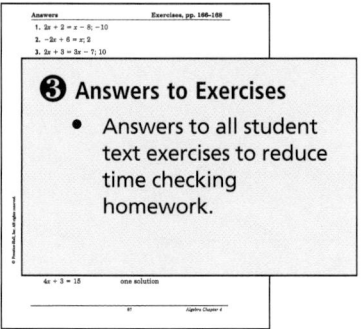

❸ **Answers to Exercises**
- Answers to all student text exercises to reduce time checking homework.

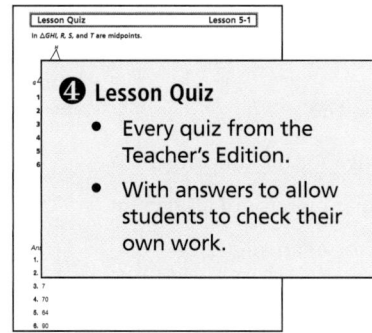

❹ **Lesson Quiz**
- Every quiz from the Teacher's Edition.
- With answers to allow students to check their own work.

 Throughout the Teacher's Edition, this symbol indicates material that is available on transparency in the Presentation Assistant Plus!

 ## Prentice Hall Presentation Pro CD-ROM

- Includes all Transparencies.
- Conveniently organized by lesson so you can easily ❶ Introduce, ❷ Teach, ❸ Check Homework, and ❹ Assess each lesson.
- Animated examples allow step-by-step instruction at your own pace.
- Easy to edit so you can create custom presentations.

Teaching Chapter 5 Using Presentation Assistant Plus!

	❶ Introduce	❷ Teach	❸ Check Homework	❹ Assess
	Check Skills You'll Need	Additional Examples	Student Edition Answers	Lesson Quiz
5-1	p. 27	pp. 71–72	✔	p. 102
5-2	p. 28	pp. 73–74	✔	p. 103
5-3	p. 29	pp. 75–77	✔	p. 104
5-4	p. 30	pp. 77–80	✔	p. 105
5-5	p. 31	pp. 80–83	✔	p. 106

 ### Prentice Hall Presentation Pro

CD-ROM with dynamic PowerPoint® presentations for every lesson. Helps you introduce and develop concepts, check homework, and assess progress. Part of Presentation Assistant Plus! *(See above.)*

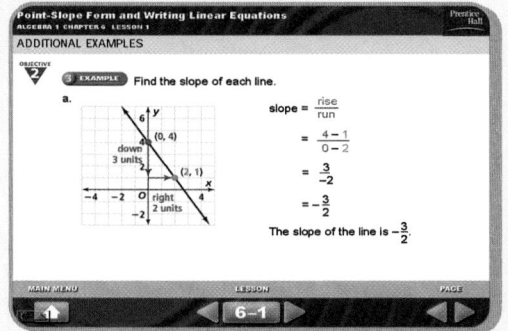

 ### Computer Test Generator

CD-ROM to create practice sheets and tests for course objectives and standardized tests. Includes Instant Chapter Tests™, online testing, and student reports. Part of the PH Assessment System. *(See page 240C.)*

 ### Resource Pro® with Planning Express®

CD-ROM with a lesson planning tool that allows you to import state and local objectives. Includes electronic versions of all the teaching resources.

Chapter

5

Relationships Within Triangles

 Diagnosing Readiness

Students will find answers to these exercises in the back of their textbooks.

For intervention, direct students to:

Slope
Algebra 1 Review, p. 151

Midpoint Formula
Lesson 1-6: Example 3
Exercises 18–23
Extra Practice, p. 690

Distance Formula
Lesson 1-6: Example 1
Exercises 1–9
Extra Practice, p. 690.

Basic Constructions
Lesson 1-5: Examples 3, 5
Exercises 7, 8, 13, 14
Extra Practice, p. 690

Inequalities
Previous Course

Where You've Been

- In Chapter 1, you learned how to identify segments, lines, and angles. You also learned the meaning of some important terms such as bisector, congruence, midpoint, perpendicular, and parallel.

- In Chapters 2 and 3, you made conjectures about angles, parallel lines, and perpendicular lines, and learned how to use deductive reasoning to prove the conjectures true.

- In Chapter 4, you learned how to prove triangles congruent.

TEXT Instant self-check online and on CD-ROM

Diagnosing Readiness   (For help, go to the Lesson in green.)

Inequalities (Previous Course)

x^2 **Algebra** Solve each inequality.

1. $3x + 10 \le 22$
$x \le 4$

2. $4x - 1 > 2x + 14$
$x > \frac{15}{2}$

3. $30 - 5x \ge x + 24$
$x \le 1$

Basic Constructions (Lesson 1-5)

Use a compass and straightedge for the following.

4. Construct the perpendicular bisector of a segment.

5. Construct the angle bisector of an angle.
See back of book.

4.

Distance Formula (Lesson 1-6)

Find the distance between each pair of points.

6. $(1, 4), (4, 8)$ **5**

7. $(-6, 2), (-1, 14)$ **13**

8. $(-3, -2), (5, -6)$ **4$\sqrt{5}$**

Midpoint Formula (Lesson 1-6)

Find the midpoint of the segments whose endpoints are given.

9. $(4, 11), (6, 3)$ **(5, 7)**

10. $(-8, -3), (2, -4)$ $\left(-3, -\frac{7}{2}\right)$

11. $(-7, 15), (-2, -10)$
$\left(-\frac{9}{2}, \frac{5}{2}\right)$

Slope (Algebra 1 Review, page 151)

Find the slope of the line containing each pair of points.

12. $(8, 3), (7, 12)$ **−9**

13. $(3, -2), (0, 6)$ **−$\frac{8}{3}$**

14. $(-5, 4), (-2, 4)$ **0**

240   Chapter 5

Relationships Within Triangles

Chapter 5

Where You're Going

- In this chapter, you will learn about geometric relationships within triangles.

- You will learn about three lines that pass through one point and find the four sets of such lines that exist for every triangle.

- You will learn about two other types of statements that are related to a conditional, as well as another type of reasoning—indirect reasoning.

- You will apply indirect reasoning to deduce information about inequalities in triangles.

Real-World Connection Applying what you learn, you will prove a basic theorem about shortcuts on page 278.

Key Vocabulary

- altitude of a triangle (p. 259)
- centroid (p. 258)
- circumcenter of a triangle (p. 257)
- circumscribed about (p. 257)
- concurrent (p. 257)
- contrapositive (p. 264)
- coordinate proof (p. 244)
- distance from a point to a line (p. 250)
- equivalent statements (p. 265)
- incenter of a triangle (p. 257)
- indirect proof (p. 265)
- indirect reasoning (p. 265)
- inscribed in (p. 257)
- inverse (p. 264)
- median of a triangle (p. 258)
- midsegment (p. 243)
- negation (p. 264)
- orthocenter of a triangle (p. 259)
- point of concurrency (p. 257)

Chapter 5 Overview

This chapter will focus on presenting and proving relationships within a triangle that students can, in turn, use to prove relationships within other figures. Some of the relationships involve midsegments, angle bisectors, perpendicular bisectors, altitudes, medians, and inequalities. Students will learn how to form inverses and contrapositives, which prepares them to prove several theorems indirectly and provides another invaluable technique of proof.

Reading Math
Reading Indirect Proof, p. 271

Vocabulary
A complete list of terms, plus vocabulary exercises, appears in the Chapter Review, p. 281.

Illustrated Glossary
Examples for each vocabulary term, plus definitions in both English and Spanish, appear starting on p. 741.

Test-Taking Strategies
Using a Variable, p. 280

Real-World Connections
Some of the applications you will find in this chapter are national landmarks (5-2), city planning (5-3), literature (5-4), and deck design (5-5).

www.PHSchool.com
Internet support for this chapter includes:
- Self-grading Vocabulary and Chapter 5 Tests
- Chapter Project
- Chapter Planner
- Ch. 5 Resources

Plus **i TEXT**

241

Technology

Investigating Midsegments

Students will use geometry software to investigate the shapes of figures whose sides are the midsegments of triangles and quadrilaterals.

Resources

Students may use any geometry software program to investigate midsegments.

Teaching Notes

Students will prove in Lesson 5-1 that the segment joining the midpoints of two sides of a triangle is parallel to and half the length of the third side. By using the measurement tools and slope calculations of geometry software, students can discover these relationships for themselves.

Exercise 3 Discuss as a class why this is a conjecture and not a theorem.

Visual Learners

As students work on Exercise 7, encourage them to manipulate quadrilateral *RSTU* while observing that *YXWV* remains a parallelogram for all shapes of quadrilateral *RSTU*.

page 242 Technology

1. Midsegments have slopes that are the same as the slopes of the third side, and lengths that are $\frac{1}{2}$ the length of the third side.

2. Yes; the slopes are the same and the lengths are $\frac{1}{2}$ the lengths of the ∥ sides.

3. a. $\overline{AD} \cong \overline{DB} \cong \overline{EF}$; $\overline{AE} \cong \overline{EC} \cong \overline{DF}$; $\overline{DE} \cong \overline{BF} \cong \overline{FC}$

   b. The 4 ▲ are ≅ by Post. 4-1: If 3 sides of one △ are ≅ to 3 sides of

242

Construct

Use geometry software to draw a triangle. Label it △*ABC*. Construct the midpoints *D* and *E* of $\overline{AB}$ and $\overline{AC}$, respectively. Connect the midpoints with a *midsegment*.

Investigate

- Measure the lengths of $\overline{DE}$ and $\overline{BC}$. Calculate $\frac{DE}{BC}$.
- Measure the slopes of $\overline{DE}$ and $\overline{BC}$.
- Manipulate the triangle and observe the lengths and slopes of $\overline{DE}$ and $\overline{BC}$.

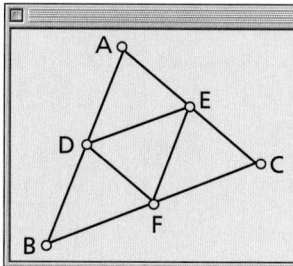

EXERCISES

1. Make conjectures about the lengths and slopes of midsegments. **See margin.**

2. Construct the midpoint *F* of $\overline{BC}$. Then construct the other two midsegments of △*ABC*. Test whether these midsegments support your conjectures in Exercise 1. **See margin.**

3. △*ABC* and the three midsegments form four small triangles.
   a. Measure the sides of the four small triangles and list those that you find are congruent.
   b. Use a postulate from Chapter 4 to make a conjecture about the four small triangles. **See margin.**

For the remaining exercises, assume your conjectures in Exercises 1 and 3 are true.

4. What can you say about the areas of the four small triangles in the window above? **They are =.**

5. How does △*ABC* compare to each small triangle
   a. in area? **See margin.**
   b. in perimeter? **The perimeter of △*ABC* is twice the perimeter of each small △.**

6. Construct the three midsegments of △*DEF*. Label this triangle △*GHI*. How does △*ABC* compare to △*GHI*
   a. in area?   **a–b. See margin.**
   b. in perimeter?
   c. Suppose you construct the midsegment triangle inside △*GHI*. Predict how △*ABC* would compare to this third midsegment triangle in area and perimeter. **See margin.**

7. • Draw quadrilateral *RSTU*.
   • Construct the midpoints of each side of the quadrilateral.
   • Join consecutive midpoints to form quadrilateral *YXWV*.
   • Manipulate the figure and observe the shape of quadrilateral *YXWV*.

   Make a conjecture about the sides of quadrilateral *YXWV*. **See back of book.**

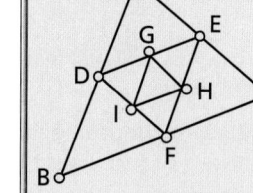

Exercise 6

another △, the ▲ are ≅.

5. a. The area of △*ABC* is 4 times the area of each small △.

6. a. The area of △*GHI* is $\frac{1}{16}$ the area of △*ABC*.

   b. The perimeter of △*GHI* is $\frac{1}{4}$ the perimeter of △*ABC*.

c. For the next midsegment △, the area would be $\frac{1}{64}$ the area of △*ABC* and the perimeter would be $\frac{1}{8}$ the perimeter of △*ABC*.

Midsegments of Triangles

 North Carolina Objectives

2.03 Apply properties, definitions, and theorems of two-dimensional figures to solve problems and write proofs: a) Triangles.

Lesson Preview

What You'll Learn

OBJECTIVE
1 To use properties of midsegments to solve problems

. . . And Why

To use indirect measurement to find the length of a lake, as in Example 3

 Check Skills You'll Need   (For help, go to Lesson 1-6 and page 151.)

Find the coordinates of the midpoint of each segment.

1. $\overline{AB}$ with $A(-2, 3)$ and $B(4, 1)$ **(1, 2)**

2. $\overline{CD}$ with $C(0, 5)$ and $D(3, 6)$ $\left(\frac{3}{2}, \frac{11}{2}\right)$

3. $\overline{EF}$ with $E(-4, 6)$ and $F(3, 10)$ $\left(-\frac{1}{2}, 8\right)$

4. $\overline{GH}$ with $G(7, 10)$ and $H(-5, -8)$ **(1, 1)**

Find the slope of the line containing each pair of points.

5. $A(-2, 3)$ and $B(3, 1)$ $-\frac{2}{5}$ **6.** $C(0, 5)$ and $D(3, 6)$ $\frac{1}{3}$

7. $E(-4, 6)$ and $F(3, 10)$ $\frac{4}{7}$ **8.** $G(7, 10)$ and $H(-5, -8)$ $\frac{3}{2}$

New Vocabulary • midsegment • coordinate proof

OBJECTIVE
1 **Using Properties of Midsegments**

 Interactive lesson includes instant self-check, tutorials, and activities.

Investigation: Midsegments of Triangles

Draw, label, and cut out a large scalene triangle. Do the same with other right, acute, and obtuse triangles. Label the vertices *A*, *B*, and *C*.

• For each triangle fold *A* onto *C* to find the midpoint of $\overline{AC}$. Do the same for $\overline{BC}$. Label the midpoints *L* and *N*, then draw $\overline{LN}$.

• Fold each triangle on $\overline{LN}$.

1. $LN = \frac{1}{2}AB$; Explanations may vary.

• Fold *A* to *C*. Fold *B* to *C*.

1. How does *LN* compare to *AB*? Explain.

2. Make a conjecture about how the segment joining the midpoints of two sides of a triangle is related to the third side of the triangle. See left.

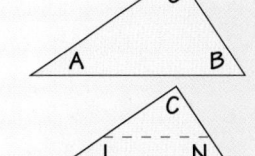

2. Answers may vary.
Sample: The midsegment is ‖ to the 3rd side of the △ and is half its length.

In △*ABC* above, $\overline{LN}$ is a triangle midsegment. A **midsegment** of a triangle is a segment connecting the midpoints of two sides.

 **Ongoing Assessment and Intervention**

Before the Lesson
Diagnose prerequisite skills using:
• Check Skills You'll Need

During the Lesson
Monitor progress using:
• Check Understanding
• Additional Examples
• Standardized Test Prep

After the Lesson
Assess knowledge using:
• Lesson Quiz
• Computer Test Generator CD

---

1. Plan

Lesson Preview

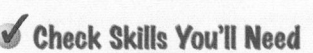 **Check Skills You'll Need**

Finding the Midpoint of a Segment
Lesson 1-6: Example 3
Exercises 14–19
Extra Practice, p. 690

Slope
Algebra Review, page 151

Lesson Resources

Teaching Resources
Practice, Reteaching, Enrichment

Reaching All Students
Practice Workbook 5-1
Spanish Practice Workbook 5-1
Reading and Math Literacy 5A
Spanish Reading & Literacy 5A
Informal Geometry Planning
  Guide 5-1

Presentation Assistant Plus!
Transparencies
• Check Skills You'll Need 5-1
• Additional Examples 5-1
• Student Edition Answers 5-1
• Lesson Quiz 5-1
PH Presentation Pro CD 5-1

ASSESSMENT SYSTEM
Computer Test Generator CD

Technology
Resource Pro® CD-ROM
Computer Test Generator CD
Prentice Hall Presentation Pro CD

www.PHSchool.com
Student Site
• Teacher Web Code: afk-5500
• Self-grading Lesson Quiz
Teacher Center
• Lesson Planner
• Resources

Plus iTEXT

Math Background

Euclid did not use coordinate geometry to prove any theorems. The Triangle Midsegment Theorem can be proved without coordinate geometry, but the proof requires theorems concerning parallelograms that are not presented in this text until Chapter 6.

OBJECTIVE
1 Teaching Notes

Investigation (Optional)
Have students place labels for the vertices inside the triangle on both sides of the paper so they will appear on the cut-out figures. Instruct students to label the obtuse or right angle vertex C to ensure that the first folded triangle lies inside $\triangle ABC$.

Connection to Algebra
The proof of the Triangle Midsegment Theorem uses the Midpoint and Distance Formulas from Chapter 1 and the calculation of slope from Chapter 3. Ask: *Why are variables used in the proof instead of numbers?* Using numbers proves the theorem for one set of points. Because any number can be substituted for a variable, using variables proves the theorem for all sets of points.

Math Tip
Discuss as a class why the vertices in the proof of the Triangle Midsegment Theorem are labeled $O(0, 0)$, $Q(a, 0)$, and $P(b, c)$. Explain that translating, rotating, or reflecting a triangle so that two of its vertices are at $(0, 0)$ and $(a, 0)$ simplifies using the Midpoint and Distance Formulas.

1 EXAMPLE Auditory Learners

Have students read through Example 1 in small groups. Then ask volunteers to explain how the example applies the Triangle Midsegment Theorem.

 **Key Concepts**

Theorem 5-1	Triangle Midsegment Theorem

If a segment joins the midpoints of two sides of a triangle, then the segment is parallel to the third side, and is half its length.

One way to prove the Triangle Midsegment Theorem is to use coordinate geometry and algebra. This style of proof is called a **coordinate proof.** You begin the proof by placing a triangle in a convenient spot on the coordinate plane. You then choose variables for the coordinates of the vertices.

Proof

Coordinate Proof of Theorem 5-1

Given: R is the midpoint of $\overline{OP}$.
　　　S is the midpoint of $\overline{QP}$.

Prove: $\overline{RS} \parallel \overline{OQ}$ and $RS = \frac{1}{2}OQ$

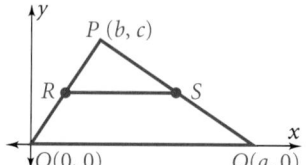

? Need Help?

The Midpoint Formula:
$\left(\frac{x_1 + x_2}{2}, \frac{y_1 + y_2}{2}\right)$

The Distance Formula:
$\sqrt{(x_2 - x_1)^2 + (y_2 - y_1)^2}$

• Use the Midpoint Formula to find the coordinates of R and S.

$R: \left(\frac{0 + b}{2}, \frac{0 + c}{2}\right) = \left(\frac{b}{2}, \frac{c}{2}\right)$

$S: \left(\frac{a + b}{2}, \frac{0 + c}{2}\right) = \left(\frac{a + b}{2}, \frac{c}{2}\right)$

• To prove that $\overline{RS}$ and $\overline{OQ}$ are parallel, show that their slopes are equal. Because the y-coordinates of R and S are the same, the slope of $\overline{RS}$ is zero. The same is true for $\overline{OQ}$. Therefore, $\overline{RS} \parallel \overline{OQ}$.

• Use the Distance Formula to find RS and OQ.

$$RS = \sqrt{\left(\frac{a + b}{2} - \frac{b}{2}\right)^2 + \left(\frac{c}{2} - \frac{c}{2}\right)^2}$$

$$= \sqrt{\left(\frac{a}{2} + \frac{b}{2} - \frac{b}{2}\right)^2 + 0^2} = \sqrt{\left(\frac{a}{2}\right)^2} = \frac{a}{2} = \frac{1}{2}a$$

$$OQ = \sqrt{(a - 0)^2 + (0 - 0)^2}$$

$$= \sqrt{a^2 + 0^2} = a$$

Therefore, $RS = \frac{1}{2}OQ$.

1 EXAMPLE Finding Lengths

In $\triangle EFG$, H, J, and K are midpoints. Find HJ, JK, and FG.

$HJ = \frac{1}{2}EG$ or $\frac{1}{2}(100)$; $HJ = 50$

$JK = \frac{1}{2}EF$ or $\frac{1}{2}(60)$; $JK = 30$

HK or $40 = \frac{1}{2}FG$; $FG = 80$

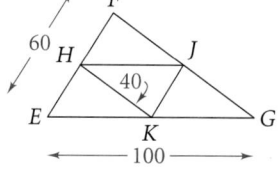

✓ **Check Understanding** ❶ $AB = 10$ and $CD = 18$. Find EB, BC, and AC.
$EB = 9$; $BC = 10$; $AC = 20$

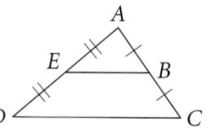

👥 Reaching All Students

Below Level To eliminate the fractions in proving Theorem 5-1, let the respective coordinates of points Q and P be $(2a, 0)$ and $(2b, 2c)$.	**Advanced Learners** Have students use Theorem 5-1 to prove that the midpoints of three sides of a triangle can be used to form four congruent triangles.	**English Learners** See note on page 245. **Auditory Learners** See note on page 244.

2 EXAMPLE Identifying Parallel Segments

In △DEF, A, B, and C are midpoints. Name pairs of parallel segments.

The midsegments are $\overline{AB}$, $\overline{BC}$, and $\overline{CA}$.

By the Triangle Midsegment Theorem,
$\overline{AB} \parallel \overline{DF}$, $\overline{BC} \parallel \overline{ED}$, and $\overline{AC} \parallel \overline{EF}$

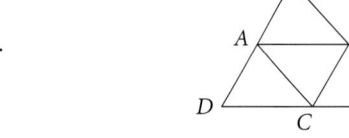

✓ **Check Understanding** ② **Critical Thinking** Find $m\angle VUZ$. Justify your answer.
65; $\overline{UV} \parallel \overline{XY}$ so $\angle VUZ$ and $\angle YXZ$ are corr. and ≅.

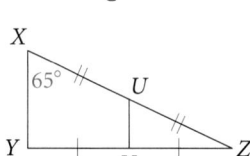

You can use the Triangle Midsegment Theorem to find lengths of segments that might be difficult to measure directly.

3 EXAMPLE Real-World 🌐 Connection

Indirect Measurement Dean plans to swim the length of the lake, as shown in the photo. How far would Dean swim?

Here is what Dean does to find the distance he would swim across the lake.

Step 1: He measures his stride and adjusts it so that it averages about 3 ft.

Step 2: Then he begins at the left edge of the lake (first diagram). He paces 35 strides along the edge of the lake and sets a stake.

Step 3: He paces 35 more strides in the same direction and sets another stake.

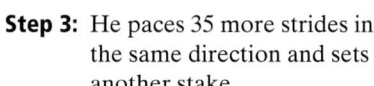

Step 4: He paces to where his swim will end at the other side of the lake, counting 236 strides.

Step 5: Then (second diagram) he paces 118 strides, or half the distance, back towards the second stake.

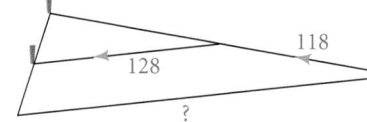

Step 6: He paces to the first stake, counting 128 strides.

Step 7: He converts strides to feet.

$$128 \text{ strides} \times \frac{3 \text{ ft}}{1 \text{ stride}} = 384 \text{ ft}$$

Step 8: He uses Theorem 5-1. The distance across the lake is twice the length of the midsegment.

$$2(384 \text{ ft}) = 768 \text{ ft}$$

Dean would swim approximately 768 ft.

✓ **Check Understanding** ③ **a.** $\overline{CD}$ is a new bridge being built over a lake as shown. Find the length of the bridge. **1320 ft**
b. How long is the bridge in miles? $\frac{1}{4}$ **mi**

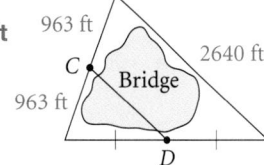

Connection to Astronomy

Astronomers use indirect measurement to measure great distances. Have students research how astronomers measure distances in the universe.

Additional Examples

❶ In △XYZ, M, N, and P are midpoints. The perimeter of △MNP is 60. Find NP and YZ.

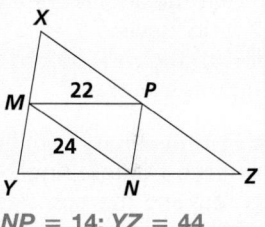

NP = 14; *YZ* = 44

❷ Find $m\angle AMN$ and $m\angle ANM$.

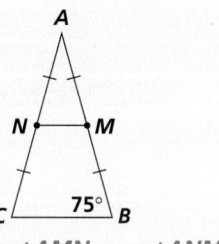

$m\angle AMN = m\angle ANM = 75$

❸ Explain why Dean could use the Triangle Midsegment Theorem to measure the length of the lake. He paced between the midpoints of two sides of a triangle.

Closure

The perimeter of a triangle is 78 ft. Find the perimeter of the triangle formed by its midsegments. **39 ft**

EXERCISES   For more practice, see *Extra Practice.*

Practice and Problem Solving

Assignment Guide

1 Objective

Ⓐ Ⓑ Core 1–36

Ⓒ Extension 37–39

Standardized Test Prep 40–46

Mixed Review 47–55

Error Prevention

Exercise 13 Students may misapply the Triangle Midsegment Theorem, thinking that the angles are also in a 1 : 2 ratio. Review the theorem with the class before beginning this exercise.

Exercise 31 If necessary, remind students of the Triangle Angle-Sum Theorem and the Isosceles Triangle Theorem.

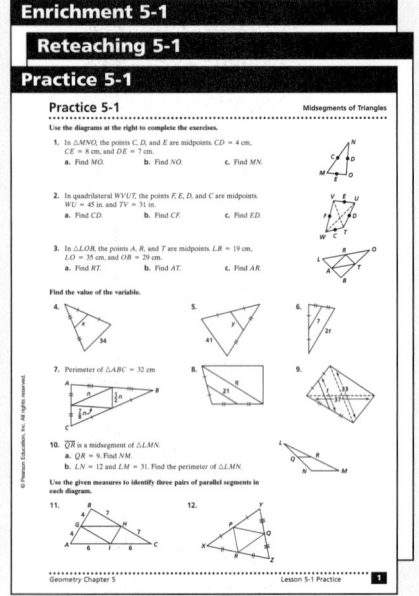

Ⓐ **Practice by Example**

Example 1
(page 244)

Mental Math Find the value of *x*.

1. 9

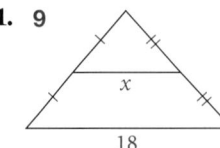

2.

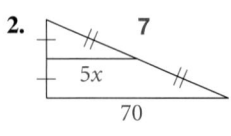

3. 14

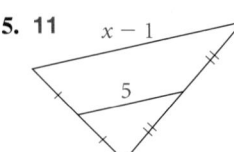

4.

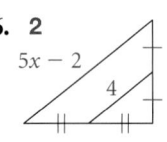

5. 11

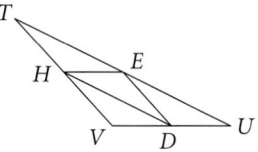

6. 2

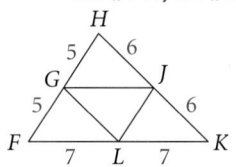

Points *E*, *D*, and *H* are midpoints of △*TUV*. *UV* = 80, *TV* = 100, and *HD* = 80.

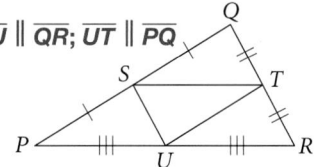

7. Find *HE*. **40**   **8.** Find *ED*. **50**

9. Find *TU*. **160**   **10.** Find *TE*. **80**

Example 2
(page 245)

Identify pairs of parallel segments in each diagram. $\overline{GJ} \parallel \overline{FK}; \overline{JL} \parallel \overline{HF}; \overline{GL} \parallel \overline{HK}$

11. $\overline{UW} \parallel \overline{TX}; \overline{UY} \parallel \overline{VX};$ **12.**
$\overline{YW} \parallel \overline{TV}$

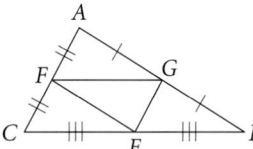

13. a. In the figure at the right, identify pairs of parallel segments. $\overline{ST} \parallel \overline{PR}; \overline{SU} \parallel \overline{QR}; \overline{UT} \parallel \overline{PQ}$
b. If $m\angle QST = 40$, find $m\angle QPR$.
$m\angle QPR = 40$

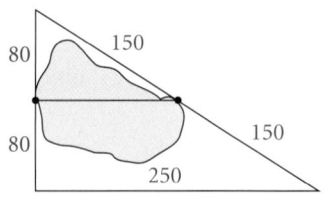

Name the segment that is parallel to the given segment.

14. $\overline{AB}$ **FE**   **15.** $\overline{BC}$ **FG**

16. $\overline{EF}$ **AB**   **17.** $\overline{CA}$ **EG**

18. $\overline{GE}$ **AC**   **19.** $\overline{FG}$ **CB**

Example 3
(page 245)

20a. 1050 ft

20. Indirect Measurement Kate wants to paddle her canoe across the lake. To determine how far she must paddle, she paced out a triangle, counting the number of strides, as shown.
a. If Kate's strides average 3.5 ft, what is the length of the longest side of the triangle?
b. What distance must Kate paddle across the lake? **437.5 ft**

B Apply Your Skills

21. a. Architecture The triangular face of the Rock and Roll Hall of Fame in Cleveland, Ohio, is isosceles. The length of the base is 229 ft 6 in. What is the length of the highlighted segment? **114 ft 9 in.**

b. Writing Explain your reasoning. **See left.**

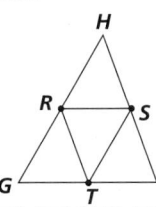

21b. Answers may vary. Sample: The highlighted segment is a midsegment of the triangular face of the building.

X is the midpoint of $\overline{UV}$. Y is the midpoint of $\overline{UW}$.

22. If $m\angle UXY = 60$, find $m\angle V$. **60**

23. If $m\angle W = 45$ find $m\angle UYX$. **45**

24. If $XY = 50$, find VW. **100**

25. If $VW = 110$, find XY. **55**

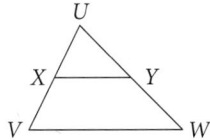

26b. Slope of $\overline{HJ} = \frac{2}{2} = 1$; slope of $\overline{EF} = \frac{4}{4} = 1$; therefore $\overline{HJ} \parallel \overline{EF}$.

c. $HJ = \sqrt{2^2 + 2^2} = \sqrt{8} = 2\sqrt{2}$; $EF = \sqrt{4^2 + 4^2} = \sqrt{32} = 4\sqrt{2}$; therefore $HJ = \frac{1}{2}EF$.

26. Coordinate Geometry The coordinates of the vertices of a triangle are $E(1, 2)$, $F(5, 6)$, and $G(3, -2)$.   **a. $H(2, 0); J(4, 2)$**

a. Find the coordinates of H, the midpoint of $\overline{EG}$, and J, the midpoint of $\overline{FG}$.

b. Verify that $\overline{HJ} \parallel \overline{EF}$. **b–c. See left.**

c. Verify that $HJ = \frac{1}{2}EF$.

$\overline{IJ}$ is a midsegment of $\triangle FGH$. $IJ = 7$, $FH = 10$, and $GH = 13$. Find the perimeter of each triangle.

27. $\triangle IJH$ **$18\frac{1}{2}$**

28. $\triangle FGH$ **37**

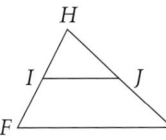

 Algebra Find the value of each variable.

29.

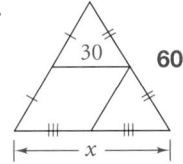

30.

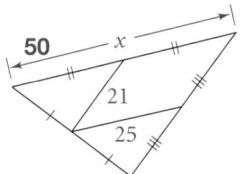

31.

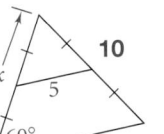

32.

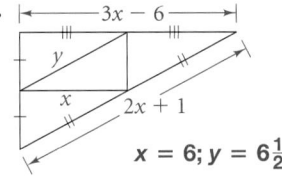

$x = 6; y = 6\frac{1}{2}$

Exercise 33

33. Kite Design Marita is designing a kite to look like the one on the left. Its diagonals are to measure 64 cm and 90 cm. She will use ribbon to connect the midpoints of its sides. How much ribbon will Marita need? **154 cm**

Use the figure at the right for Exercises 34–36.

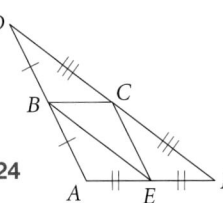

34. If $DF = 24$, $BC = 6$, and $DB = 8$, find the perimeter of $\triangle ADF$. **52**

35. Algebra If $BE = 2x + 6$ and $DF = 5x + 9$, find the value of x, then find DF. **$x = 3$; $DF = 24$**

36. Algebra If $EC = 3x - 1$ and $AD = 5x + 7$, find the value of x, then find EC. **$x = 9$; $EC = 26$**

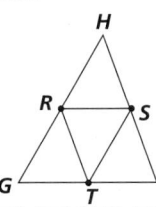
Alternative Assessment

Draw the figure below on the board. Label the vertices of the large triangle and the midpoints of the sides. Name the triangles and the midsegments.

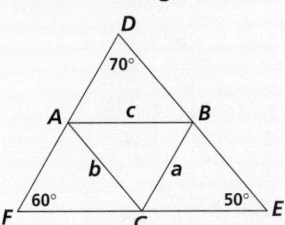

Have students use the given information to find the lengths of the sides of $\triangle DEF$ and the measures of the angles of $\triangle ABC$. Then have students explain in writing how they found the measures of the sides and angles.

pages 246–248 Exercises

37. Answers may vary. Sample: Draw $\overline{CA}$ and extend $\overrightarrow{CA}$ to P so that $CA = AP$. Find B, the midpt. of $\overline{PD}$. Then, by the △ Midsegment Thm., $\overline{AB} \parallel \overline{CD}$ and $AB = \frac{1}{2}CD$.

39. △*UTS*; Proofs may vary. Sample: $\overline{VS} \cong \overline{SY}$, $\overline{YT} \cong \overline{TZ}$, and $\overline{VU} \cong \overline{UZ}$ because S, T, and U are midpts. of the respective sides; $ST = \frac{1}{2}VZ$ so $\overline{ST} \cong \overline{VU} \cong \overline{UZ}$; $SU = \frac{1}{2}YZ$ so $\overline{SU} \cong \overline{YT} \cong \overline{TZ}$; and $TU = \frac{1}{2}VY$ so $\overline{TU} \cong \overline{SY} \cong \overline{SV}$; therefore △*YST* ≅ △*TUZ* ≅ △*SVU* ≅ △*UTS* by SSS.

50.

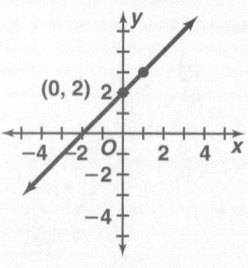

$y = x + 2$

51.

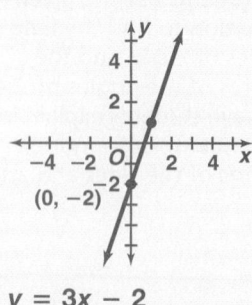

$y = 3x - 2$

C Challenge

37. Open-Ended Explain how you could use the Triangle Midsegment Theorem as the basis for this construction. Draw $\overline{CD}$. Draw point A not on $\overline{CD}$. Construct $\overline{AB}$ so that $\overline{AB} \parallel \overline{CD}$ and $AB = \frac{1}{2}CD$. **See margin.**

38. Coordinate Geometry In △*GHJ*, $K(2, 3)$ is the midpoint of $\overline{GH}$, $L(4, 1)$ is the midpoint of $\overline{HJ}$, and $M(6, 2)$ is the midpoint of $\overline{GJ}$. Find the coordinates of G, H, and J. **G(4, 4); H(0, 2); J(8, 0)**

Proof 39. Write a paragraph proof.

   Given: S, T, and U are midpoints.
   Prove: △*YST* ≅ △*TUZ* ≅ △*SVU* ≅ ___?___ .
   See margin.

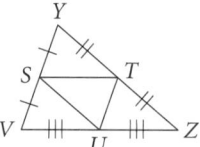

Standardized Test Prep

Gridded Response

Q and P are midpoints of the sides of △*RST*.

40. What is RS? **248**

41. What is TQ? **174**

42. What is TS? **418**

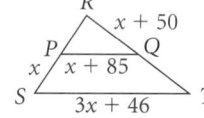

43. What is $m\angle ABC$? **70**

44. What is $m\angle D$? **40**

45. What is $m\angle A$? **70**

46. What is $m\angle CBE$? **40**

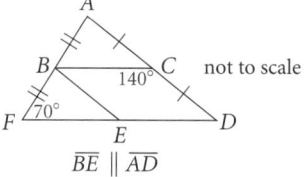

$\overline{BE} \parallel \overline{AD}$

Mixed Review

Lesson 4-7 Name a pair of overlapping congruent triangles in each diagram. State whether the triangles are congruent by SSS, SAS, ASA, AAS, or HL.

47.

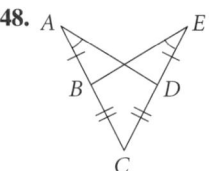

△*SXT* ≅ △*TYS*; SAS

48.

△*ADC* ≅ △*EBC*; ASA

49.

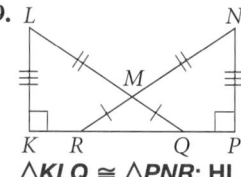

△*KLQ* ≅ △*PNR*; HL

Lesson 3-5 x^2 **Algebra Graph each line. 50–52. See margin.**

50. $y = x + 2$ **51.** $y = 3x - 2$ **52.** $y = -x - 5$

Lesson 3-2 x^2 **Algebra Determine the value of x for which $\ell \parallel m$.**

53.

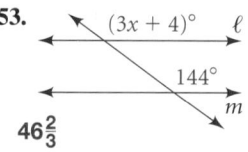

$46\frac{2}{3}$

54.

35

55.

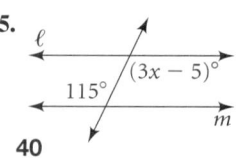

40

52.

$y = -x - 5$

5-2

Bisectors in Triangles

2.03 Apply properties, definitions, and theorems of two-dimensional figures to solve problems and write proofs: a) Triangles.

Lesson Preview

What You'll Learn

OBJECTIVE 1
To use properties of perpendicular bisectors and angle bisectors

. . . And Why

To locate places equidistant from two given points on a map, as in Example 1

✓ **Check Skills You'll Need** (For help, go to Lesson 1-5.)

Use a compass and a straightedge for the following. 1–4. See back of book.

1. Draw a triangle, $\triangle XYZ$. Construct $\triangle STV$ so that $\triangle STV \cong \triangle XYZ$.

2. Draw acute $\angle P$. Construct $\angle Q$ so that $\angle Q \cong \angle P$.

3. Draw $\overline{AB}$. Construct a line $\overleftrightarrow{CD}$ so that $\overleftrightarrow{CD} \perp \overline{AB}$ and $\overleftrightarrow{CD}$ bisects $\overline{AB}$.

4. Draw acute angle $\angle E$. Construct the bisector of $\angle E$.

$\overrightarrow{TM}$ bisects $\angle STU$ so that $m\angle STM = 5x + 4$ and $m\angle MTU = 6x - 2$.

 5. Algebra Find the value of x. 6   **6.** Find $m\angle STU$. 68

New Vocabulary • distance from a point to a line

OBJECTIVE 1

Perpendicular Bisectors and Angle Bisectors

Triangles play a key role in relationships involving perpendicular bisectors and angle bisectors.

In the diagram below on the left, $\overleftrightarrow{CD}$ is the perpendicular bisector of $\overline{AB}$. $\overleftrightarrow{CD}$ is perpendicular to $\overline{AB}$ at its midpoint. In the diagram on the right, $\overline{CA}$ and $\overline{CB}$ are drawn to complete the triangles, $\triangle CAD$ and $\triangle CBD$.

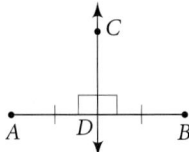 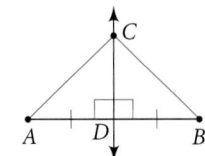

Need Help?

$\overline{CD} \cong \overline{CD}$ by the Reflexive Property and $\triangle CAD \cong \triangle CBD$ by SAS.

You should recognize from your work in Chapter 4 that $\triangle CAD \cong \triangle CBD$. Thus, you can conclude that $\overline{CA} \cong \overline{CB}$, that $CA = CB$, or simply that C is equidistant from points A and B.

This suggests a proof of Theorem 5-2 below. Its converse is also true and is stated as Theorem 5-3. You will prove these theorems in the exercises.

 Key Concepts

Theorem 5-2	**Perpendicular Bisector Theorem**

If a point is on the perpendicular bisector of a segment, then it is equidistant from the endpoints of the segment.

Theorem 5-3	**Converse of the Perpendicular Bisector Theorem**

If a point is equidistant from the endpoints of a segment, then it is on the perpendicular bisector of the segment.

5-2

1. Plan

Lesson Preview

✓ **Check Skills You'll Need**

Constructing Congruent Segments and Angles
Lesson 1-5: Examples 1, 2
Exercises 1–6
Extra Practice, p. 690

Constructing Bisectors
Lesson 1-5: Examples 3, 5
Exercises 7, 8, 13, 14
Extra Practice, p. 690

Lesson Resources

📁 **Teaching Resources**
Practice, Reteaching, Enrichment

👥 **Reaching All Students**
Practice Workbook 5-2
Spanish Practice Workbook 5-2
Hands-On Activities 13
Informal Geometry Planning
  Guide 5-2

⏱ **Presentation Assistant Plus!**
Transparencies
• Check Skills You'll Need 5-2
• Additional Examples 5-2
• Student Edition Answers 5-2
• Lesson Quiz 5-2
PH Presentation Pro CD 5-2

PRENTICE HALL ASSESSMENT SYSTEM

Computer Test Generator CD

💿 **Technology**
Resource Pro® CD-ROM
Computer Test Generator CD
Prentice Hall Presentation Pro CD

💻 **www.PHSchool.com**
Student Site
• Teacher Web Code: afk-5500
• Self-grading Lesson Quiz
Teacher Center
• Lesson Planner
• Resources

 Plus **iTEXT**

Ongoing Assessment and Intervention

Before the Lesson
Diagnose prerequisite skills using:
• Check Skills You'll Need

During the Lesson
Monitor progress using:
• Check Understanding
• Additional Examples
• Standardized Test Prep

After the Lesson
Assess knowledge using:
• Lesson Quiz
• Computer Test Generator CD

Math Background

The Perpendicular Bisector and Angle Bisector Theorems are examples of *characterization* or *locus* theorems. Each characterizes the set of points that satisfy a given condition: A *perpendicular bisector* is the set of all points equidistant from the endpoints of a segment; an *angle bisector* is the set of all points equidistant from an angle's sides.

OBJECTIVE

▼ **Teaching Notes**

1 EXAMPLE

Remind students of the steps in constructing a perpendicular bisector. Ask: *Which construction step guarantees that the points on the perpendicular bisector are equidistant from the endpoints of the segment?* **drawing equal arcs from the endpoints**

2 EXAMPLE   Teaching Tip

Ask: *Does this example apply the Angle Bisector Theorem or its converse?* **Angle Bisector Theorem**

Additional Examples

1 Describe the set of points that are equidistant from the Lincoln Memorial and the Capitol. **all points on the perpendicular bisector of the segment whose endpoints are at the Lincoln Memorial and the Capitol**

2 Suppose $FB = 2x + 5$ and $FD = 7x - 37$ in the diagram for Example 2. Find x, FB, and FD. **8.4; 21.8; 21.8**

Closure

State the Perpendicular Bisector Theorem and its converse as a biconditional. **A point is on the perpendicular bisector of a segment if and only if it is equidistant from the endpoints of the segment.**

250

---

1 EXAMPLE   Real-World 🌐 Connection

National Landmarks Find the set of points on the map of Washington, D.C. that are equidistant from the Jefferson Memorial and the White House.

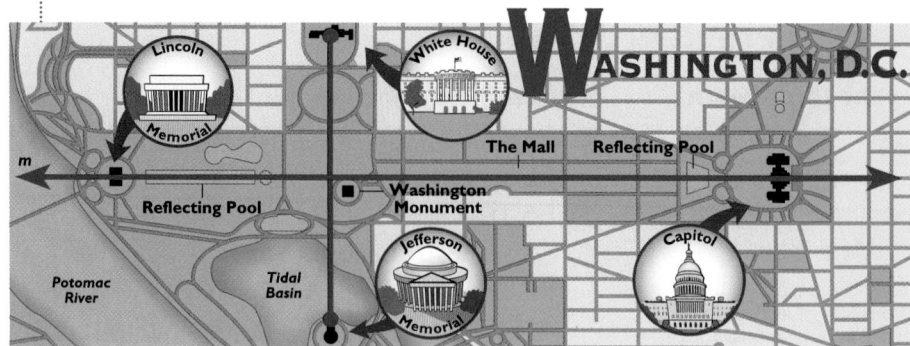

The red segment connects the Jefferson Memorial and the White House. All points on the perpendicular bisector m of this segment are equidistant from the Jefferson Memorial and the White House.

✔ **Check Understanding** **1** Use the information given in the diagram. $\overleftrightarrow{CD}$ is the perpendicular bisector of $\overline{AB}$. Find CA and DB. Explain your reasoning.
$CA = 5$; $DB = 6$; $\overleftrightarrow{CD}$ is the ⊥ bis. of $\overline{AB}$; therefore $CA = CB$ and $DA = DB$.

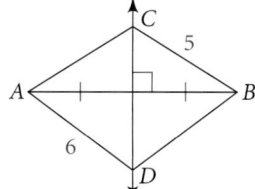

The **distance from a point to a line** is the length of the perpendicular segment from the point to the line. In the diagram, $\overrightarrow{AD}$ is the bisector of $\angle CAB$. If you measure the lengths of the perpendicular segments from D to the two sides of the angle, you will find that the lengths are equal so D is equidistant from the sides.

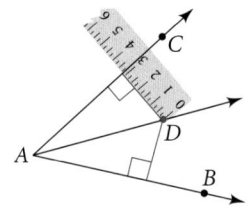

🔑 **Key Concepts**

Theorem 5-4	**Angle Bisector Theorem**
If a point is on the bisector of an angle, then the point is equidistant from the sides of the angle.	

Theorem 5-5	**Converse of the Angle Bisector Theorem**
If a point in the interior of an angle is equidistant from the sides of the angle, then the point is on the angle bisector.	

You will use congruent triangles to prove these theorems in the exercises.

You can combine Theorems 5-4 and 5-5 into a biconditional: A point in the interior of an angle is equidistant from the sides of the angle if and only if it is on the angle bisector.

👥 **Reaching All Students**

Below Level Have students use a compass and straightedge to model the theorems in this lesson and to verify their claims.	**Advanced Learners** After students understand Theorems 5-2 and 5-3, have them describe the set of points in space that are equidistant from the endpoints of a segment. **plane**	**Error Prevention** See note on page 251. **Error Prevention** See note on page 252.

2 EXAMPLE **Using the Angle Bisector Theorem**

Algebra Find the value of x, then find FD and FB.

From the diagram you can see that F is on the bisector of $\angle ACE$. Therefore, $FB = FD$.

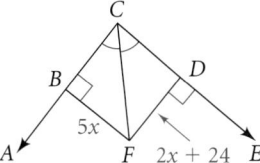

$$FB = FD$$
$5x = 2x + 24$	**Substitute.**
$3x = 24$	**Subtract 2x.**
$x = 8$	**Divide by 3.**
$FB = 5x = 5(8) = 40$	**Substitute.**
$FD = 40$	**Substitute.**

✔ **Check Understanding**
2 a. According to the diagram, how far is K from $\overrightarrow{EH}$? From $\overrightarrow{ED}$? **10; 10**
b. What can you conclude about $\overrightarrow{EK}$? **See below.**
c. Find the value of x. **20**
d. Find $m\angle DEH$. **80**

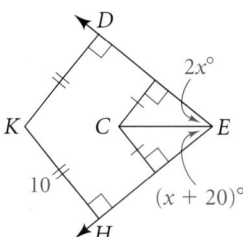

2b. $\overrightarrow{EK}$ is the $\angle$ bis. of $\angle DEH$.

EXERCISES

For more practice, see *Extra Practice*.

Practice and Problem Solving

A **Practice by Example**

Example 1
(page 250)

Use the figure at the right for Exercises 1–4.

1. From the information given in the figure, how is $\overline{AC}$ related to $\overline{BD}$? $\overline{AC}$ is the $\perp$ bis. of $\overline{BD}$.

2. Find AB. **15**   **3.** Find BC. **18**   **4.** Find ED. **8**

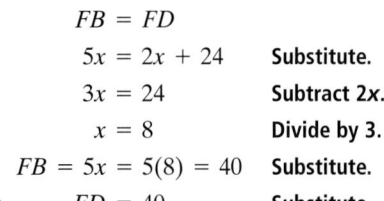

5. The set of points equidistant from H and S is the $\perp$ bis. of $\overline{HS}$.

5. On a piece of paper, mark a point H for home and a point S for school. Describe the set of points equidistant from H and S **See left.**

Example 2
(page 251)

 6. Algebra Find x, JK, and JM.

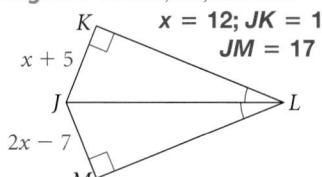

$x = 12$; $JK = 17$; $JM = 17$

7. Algebra Find y, ST, and TU.

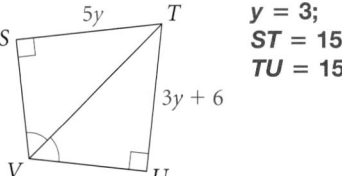

$y = 3$; $ST = 15$; $TU = 15$

8. $\overrightarrow{HL}$ is the $\angle$ bis. of $\angle JHG$ because a point on $\overrightarrow{HL}$ is equidistant from J and G.

Use the figure at the right for Exercises 8–11.

8. From the information given in the figure, how is $\overrightarrow{HL}$ related to $\angle JHG$? Explain. **See left.**

9. Find the value of y, then find $m\angle FHL$ and $m\angle KHL$.
$y = 9$; $m\angle FHL = 54$; $m\angle KHL = 54$

10. Find EF. **27**

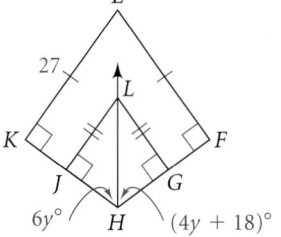

11. What can you conclude about point E?
Point E is on the bisector of $\angle KHF$.

Assignment Guide

1 Objective
A B Core 1–46
C Extension 47–49

Standardized Test Prep 50–54

Mixed Review 55–66

Error Prevention

Exercises 1–4 Students may think that $\overline{BD}$ is the perpendicular bisector of $\overline{AC}$. To show why this is not necessarily so, draw the figure on the board with point C farther from point A.

Exercises 12–14 Point out that although these exercises use the Perpendicular Bisector Theorem and Example 2 uses the Angle Bisector Theorem, the method of solution is the same as in Example 2.

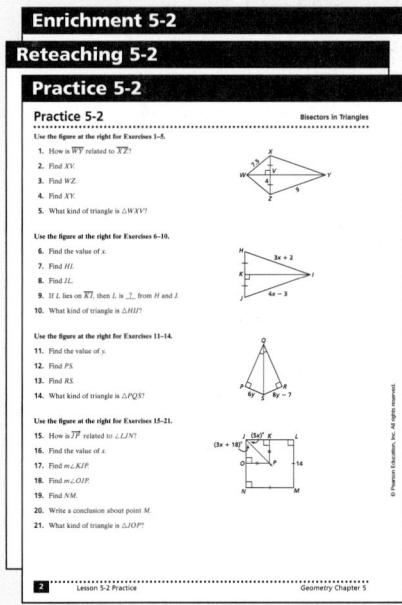

pages 251–254 **Exercises**

28. **No; A is not equidistant from the sides of ∠X.**

29. **Yes; AX bis. ∠TXR.**

30. **Yes; A is equidistant from the sides of ∠X.**

32. a.

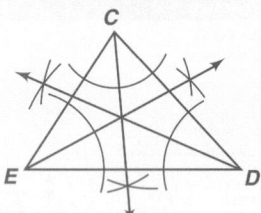

b. **The ∠ bisectors intersect at the same point.**

33. a.

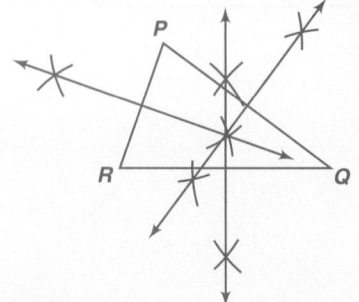

B **Apply Your Skills** **Algebra** Use the figure, below right, for Exercises 12–16.

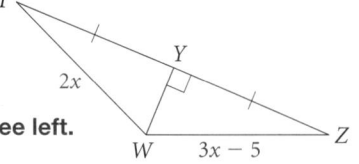

12. Find the value of x. **5**

13. Find TW. **10**

14. Find WZ. **10**

15. **Isosceles; it has 2 ≅ sides.**

15. What kind of triangle is △TWZ? Explain. **See left.**

16. If R is on the perpendicular bisector of $\overline{TZ}$, then R is ? from T and Z, or ? = ? .
equidistant; RT = RZ

17. **A point is on the ⊥ bis. of a segment if and only if it is equidistant from the endpts. of the segment.**

17. Write Theorems 5-2 and 5-3 as a single biconditional statement. **See left.**

$\overleftrightarrow{CD}$ is the perpendicular bisector of both $\overline{XY}$ and $\overline{ST}$, and CY = 16. Find each length.

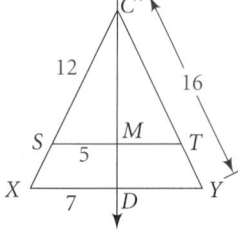

18. CT **12**   19. TY **4**

20. SX **4**   21. CX **16**

22. MT **5**   23. ST **10**

24. DY **7**   25. XY **14**

26. What kind of triangles are △SCT and △XCY? Explain. **Isosceles; CS = CT and CX = CY by the ⊥ Bis. Thm.**

27. **Answers may vary. Sample: The student needs to know that $\overline{QS}$ bisects $\overline{PR}$.**

27. **Error Analysis** To prove that △PQR is isosceles, a student began by stating that since Q is on the segment perpendicular to $\overline{PR}$, Q is equidistant from the endpoints of $\overline{PR}$. What additional information does the student need in order to make that statement? **See left.**

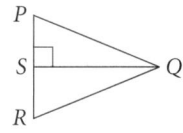

✏ **Writing** Determine whether point A must be on the bisector of ∠TXR. Explain.
28–30. See margin.

28.   29.   30.

 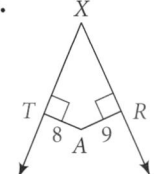 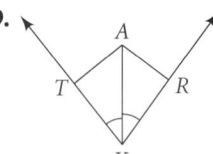 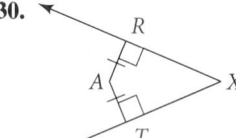

Real-World 🌐 **Connection**

On a baseball field, second base is equidistant from the foul lines and 127 feet from home plate.

31. 🌐 **Baseball** What is the common name for the part of a baseball field that is equidistant from the foul lines and 60 ft 6 in. from home plate? **the pitcher's plate**

32. a. **Constructions** Draw a large triangle, △CDE. Construct the angle bisectors of each angle.

   b. **Make a Conjecture** What appears to be true about the angle bisectors? **a–b. See margin.**

   c. Test your conjecture with another triangle. **Check students' work.**

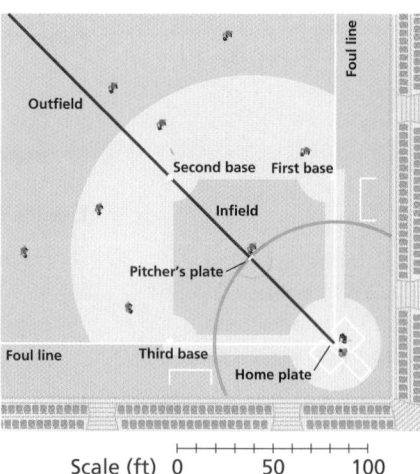

Scale (ft) 0 — 50 — 100

252 Chapter 5 Relationships Within Triangles

34–39. **Answers may vary. Samples are given.**

34. C(0, 2), D(1, 2); AC = BC = 2, AD = BD = √5

35. C(3, 2), D(3, 0); AC = BC = 3, AD = BD = √13

36. C(3, 0), D(0, 0); AC = BC = 3, AD = BD = 3√2

37. C(0, 0), D(1, 1); AC = BC = 3, AD = BD = √5

38. C(2, 2), D(4, 3); AC = BC = √5, AD = BD = √10

39. C($\frac{5}{2}$, $\frac{5}{2}$), D(5, 3); AC = BC = $\frac{\sqrt{26}}{2}$, AD = BD = √13

33. a. Constructions Draw a large acute scalene triangle, △PQR. Construct the perpendicular bisectors of each side. **See margin.**
   b. Make a Conjecture What appears to be true about the perpendicular bisectors? **The ⊥ bisectors intersect at the same point.**
   c. Test your conjecture with another triangle. **Check students' work.**

Coordinate Geometry Find two points on the perpendicular bisector of $\overline{AB}$. Verify your results by showing each point is equidistant from *A* and *B*.
34–39. See margin.

34. $A(0,0), B(0,4)$ **35.** $A(0,2), B(6,2)$ **36.** $A(3,3), B(3,-3)$

37. $A(3,0), B(0,3)$ **38.** $A(3,0), B(1,4)$ **39.** $A(3,0), B(2,5)$

40a. $\ell : y = -\frac{3}{4}x + \frac{25}{2}$
$m : x = 10$

40. Coordinate Geometry You are given points $A(6,8), O(0,0)$, and $B(10,0)$.
   a. Write equations of lines ℓ and m such that $\ell \perp \overrightarrow{OA}$ at *A* and $m \perp \overrightarrow{OB}$ at *B*. **See left.**
   b. Find the intersection *C* of lines ℓ and *m*. **(10, 5)**
   c. Show that $CA = CB$. **$CA = CB = 5$**
   d. Explain why *C* is on the bisector of $\angle AOB$. **C is equidist. from $\overrightarrow{OA}$ and $\overrightarrow{OB}$.**

Real-World Connection

The picture hangs straight when the hook is on the perpendicular bisector of the picture's top edge.

Proof 41. Developing Proof Complete this paragraph proof of the Perpendicular Bisector Theorem.

     Given: $\overleftrightarrow{CD} \perp \overline{AB}, \overleftrightarrow{CD}$ bisects $\overline{AB}$.

     Prove: $DA = DB$

     Proof: $\overline{AC} \cong \overline{BC}$ by definition of _?_. **bisector**
     $\overleftrightarrow{CD} \perp \overline{AB}$, so $\angle DCA$ and $\angle DCB$ are _?_ angles. **right**
     Therefore, $\angle DCA \cong \angle DCB$.
     $\overline{DC} \cong \overline{DC}$ by the _?_ Property of Congruence. **Reflexive**
     Therefore, $\triangle CDA \cong \triangle CDB$ by _?_. $\overline{DA} \cong \overline{DB}$ because _?_, so $DA = DB$.
     SAS   **CPCTC**

42. Developing Proof Complete the paragraph proof of the Converse of the Perpendicular Bisector Theorem.

     Given: $AP = AQ$ with $\overline{AB} \perp \overline{PQ}$ at *B*.

     Prove: $\overline{AB}$ is the perpendicular bisector of _?_. **$\overline{PQ}$**

     Proof: $\triangle ABP$ and $\triangle ABQ$ are right triangles with a common leg and congruent hypotenuses. **$\triangle BAQ$;**
     Thus $\triangle BAP \cong$ _?_ by the HL Theorem. $\overline{PB} \cong \overline{BQ}$ using _?_, so $\overline{AB}$ bisects $\overline{PQ}$ by the definition of _?_. Hence, $\overline{AB}$ is the perpendicular bisector of $\overline{PQ}$.
     CPCTC; bisector

43. Developing Proof Use the paragraph proof from Exercise 41 or 42 to help you write a flow proof of either the Perpendicular Bisector Theorem or the Converse of the Perpendicular Bisector Theorem. **See back of book.**

Coordinate Geometry Write an equation of the perpendicular bisector of $\overline{AB}$.

44. $A(0,0), B(6,0)$ **x = 3**   **45.** $A(1,-1), B(3,1)$ **46.** $A(-2,0), B(2,8)$
                              $y = -(x - 2)$ **$y = -\frac{1}{2}x + 4$**

 **Challenge**

47. Reasoning Sketch a line equidistant from three noncollinear points. Explain your procedure. **See margin.**

Proof 48. Write a paragraph proof of the Angle Bisector Theorem.
     See back of book.

     Given: $\overrightarrow{PB} \perp \overrightarrow{AB}, \overrightarrow{PC} \perp \overrightarrow{AC}$,
     $\overrightarrow{AP}$ bisects $\angle BAC$.

     Prove: $PB = PC$

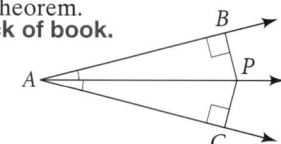

Lesson 5-2 Bisectors in Triangles   **253**

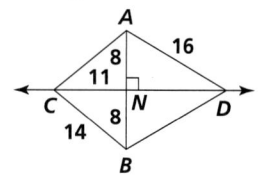
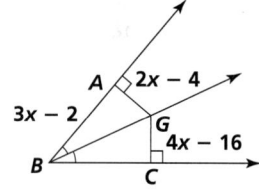
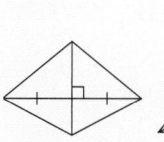 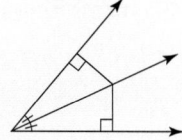
47.

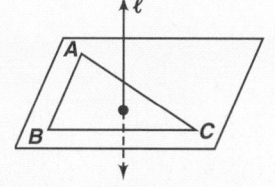

Line ℓ is equidistant from points *A*, *B*, and *C* if it is ⊥ to the plane determined by *A*, *B*, and *C* and if it goes through the point that is the intersection of the ⊥ bisectors of the sides of △*ABC*.

Standardized Test Prep

Resources

For additional practice with a variety of test item formats:
- Standardized Test Prep, p. 285
- Test-Taking Strategies, p. 280
- Test-Taking Strategies with Transparencies

Exercises 50–52 Use the Converse of the Angle Bisector Theorem to prove that point *R* lies on the bisector of ∠*PTK*.

Exercise 54 Recall Postulate 1-1: *Through any two points there is exactly one line.*

pages 251–254   Exercises

54. **[4]** $\overline{MK} \cong \overline{MR}$. By the Reflexive Prop. of ≅, $\overline{MV} \cong \overline{MV}$. It is given that ∠*MKV* and ∠*MRV* are rt. ∠s. By HL, △*MKV* ≅ △*MRV*. By CPCTC, $\overline{KV} \cong \overline{RV}$. By the Converse of the ⊥ Bisector Thm., points *M* and *V* lie on the ⊥ bisector, so $\overline{MV}$ is the ⊥ bisector of $\overline{KR}$.

[3] appropriate steps with one logical error OR one incorrect reason statement

[2] two logical errors OR two incorrect reasons statements

[1] proved ≅ ∠s but failed to reach desired conclusion

64. $C\left(3, \frac{13}{2}\right); AB = 3\sqrt{5}$, $AC = CB = \frac{3\sqrt{5}}{2}$

65. $C\left(0, \frac{7}{2}\right); AB = \sqrt{97}$, $AC = BC = \frac{\sqrt{97}}{2}$

66. $C\left(\frac{11}{2}, 5\right); AB = \sqrt{17}$, $AC = BC = \frac{\sqrt{17}}{2}$

Proof 49. Write a proof of the Converse of the Angle Bisector Theorem. **See back of book.**

Given: $\overrightarrow{SP} \perp \overrightarrow{QP}, \overrightarrow{SR} \perp \overrightarrow{QR}, SP = SR$
Prove: $\overrightarrow{QS}$ bisects ∠*PQR*.

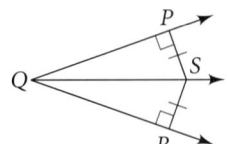

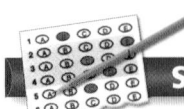

Standardized Test Prep

Multiple Choice   Use the figure at the right for Exercises 50–52.

50. What is *TK*? **D**
   A. 4   **B.** 5   **C.** 15   **D.** 25

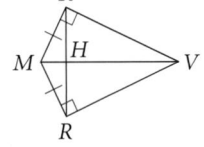

51. If *m*∠*CTR* = 27, what is *m*∠*K*? **H**
   F. 27   **G.** 54   **H.** 63   **I.** 76

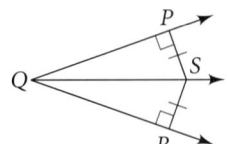
Take It to the NET
Online lesson quiz at
www.PHSchool.com
Web Code: afa-0502

52. Suppose *RK* = 8. What is the perimeter of △*TPK*? **D**
   A. 25   **B.** 33   **C.** 50   **D.** 66

Short Response

53. In the figure at the right, explain why $\overline{MV}$ is the angle bisector of ∠*KVR*. **See below.**

Extended Response

54. In the figure at the right, explain why $\overline{MV}$ is the perpendicular bisector of $\overline{KR}$. **See margin.**

53. **[2]** Since $\overline{MK} \cong \overline{MR}$, $\overline{MK} \perp \overline{KV}$, and $\overline{MR} \perp \overline{RV}$, the ∠ Bisector Thm. states that $\overline{MV}$ is the ∠ bisector of ∠*KVR*.
   [1] partially correct logical argument

Mixed Review

Lesson 5-1 $\boxed{x^2}$ **Algebra** Find the value of *x*.

55. 8

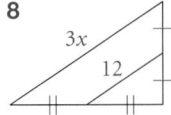

56. 4

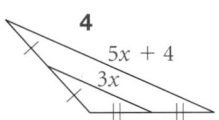

57. 6

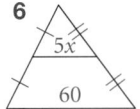

Lesson 2-4   **Name the property that justifies each statement.**

58. $AB = AB$ **Reflexive Prop. of =**

59. If $2x = 30$, then $x = 15$. **Div. Prop. of =**

60. If $x = 30 - x$, then $2x = 30$. **Add. Prop. of =**

61. $3(4x - 1) = 12x - 3$ **Distr. Prop.**   62. **Subst. or Transitive Prop. of =**

62. If $m∠3 = m∠4$ and $m∠4 = m∠5$, then $m∠3 = m∠5$.

63. If $∠3 \cong ∠4$ and $∠4 \cong ∠5$, then $∠3 \cong ∠5$. **Trans. Prop. of ≅**

Lesson 1-6   **Coordinate Geometry** Find *C* the midpoint of $\overline{AB}$. Then show that $AC = CB = \frac{1}{2}AB$. **64–66. See margin.**

64. $A(0, 5), B(6, 8)$ 65. $A(-2, 8), B(2, -1)$ 66. $A(5, 3), B(6, 7)$

Special Segments in Triangles

FOR USE WITH LESSON 5-3

Construct

Use geometry software.

- Construct a triangle and the three perpendicular bisectors of its sides.
- Construct a triangle and its three angle bisectors.
- An *altitude* of a triangle is the perpendicular segment from a vertex to the line containing the opposite side. Construct a triangle. Through a vertex of the triangle construct a line that is perpendicular to the line containing the side opposite that vertex. Next construct the altitudes from the other two vertices.
- A *median* of a triangle is the segment joining the midpoint of a side and the opposite vertex. Construct a triangle. Construct the midpoint of one side. Draw the median. Then construct the other two medians.

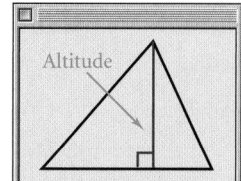

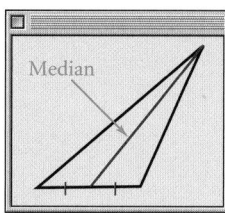

EXERCISES

1. In the constructions above, what property do the perpendicular bisectors, angle bisectors, lines containing altitudes, and medians seem to have? **Each set of 3 lines intersect in one point.**

2. Manipulate the triangles. Does the property still hold as you manipulate the triangles? **yes**

3. List your conjectures about the perpendicular bisectors, angle bisectors, lines containing altitudes, and medians of a triangle.
   Each set of 3 lines, ∠ bisectors, ⊥ bisectors, lines containing altitudes, and the medians of a △ meet in one point.

Extend

4. Copy the table. Think about acute triangles, right triangles, and obtuse triangles. Use *inside*, *on*, or *outside* to describe the location of the intersection of the segments or lines for each type of triangle.

	Perpendicular Bisectors	Angle Bisectors	Lines Containing the Altitudes	Medians
Acute Triangle	inside	inside	inside	inside
Right Triangle	on	inside	on	inside
Obtuse Triangle	outside	inside	outside	inside

5. What observations, if any, can you make about these special segments for isosceles triangles? Equilateral triangles? **See margin.**

6. Your Exercise 3 conjecture should identify some special points. One of these points is equidistant from the three vertices of its triangle, no matter what shape the triangle has. Use your software. Find which special segments locate this extra-special point. **The point is the intersection of the ⊥ bis. of the sides of the △.**

---

page 242   Technology

5. **For isosc. and equilateral △, all the special segments will lie inside the △.**

5-3

Concurrent Lines, Medians, and Altitudes

 North Carolina Objectives   2.03 Apply properties, definitions, and theorems of two-dimensional figures to solve problems and write proofs: a) Triangles.

1. Plan

Lesson Preview

✓ **Check Skills You'll Need**

Constructing Perpendicular Bisectors
Lesson 1-5: Example 3
Exercises 7, 8
Extra Practice, p. 690

Constructing Angle Bisectors
Lesson 1-5: Example 5
Exercises 13, 14
Extra Practice, p. 690

Lesson Resources

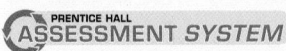 **Teaching Resources**
Practice, Reteaching, Enrichment
Checkpoint Quiz 1

Reaching All Students
Practice Workbook 5-3
Spanish Practice Workbook 5-3
Reading and Math Literacy 5B
Spanish Reading & Literacy 5B
Spanish Checkpoint Quiz 1
Technology Activities 43
Hands-On Activities 14
Informal Geometry Planning
  Guide 5-3

Presentation Assistant Plus!
Transparencies
• Check Skills You'll Need 5-3
• Additional Examples 5-3
• Student Edition Answers 5-3
• Lesson Quiz 5-3
PH Presentation Pro CD 5-3

PRENTICE HALL ASSESSMENT SYSTEM

Computer Test Generator CD

Technology
Resource Pro® CD-ROM
Computer Test Generator CD
Prentice Hall Presentation Pro CD

 **www.PHSchool.com**
Student Site
• Teacher Web Code: afk-5500
• Self-grading Lesson Quiz
Teacher Center
• Lesson Planner
• Resources

Plus **iTEXT**

256

Lesson Preview

What You'll Learn

OBJECTIVE 1 To identify properties of perpendicular bisectors and angle bisectors

OBJECTIVE 2 To identify properties of medians and altitudes of a triangle

. . . And Why

To find a location in a backyard for the largest possible swimming pool, as in Example 2

✓ Check Skills You'll Need   (For help, go to Lesson 1-5.)

For Exercises 1–2, draw a large triangle. Construct each figure. 1–4. See back of book.

1. an angle bisector

2. a perpendicular bisector of a side

3. Draw $\overline{GH}$. Construct $\overleftrightarrow{CD} \perp \overline{GH}$ at the midpoint of $\overline{GH}$.

4. Draw $\overleftrightarrow{AB}$ with a point E not on $\overleftrightarrow{AB}$. Construct $\overleftrightarrow{EF} \perp \overleftrightarrow{AB}$.

New Vocabulary
• concurrent • point of concurrency
• circumcenter of a triangle • circumscribed about
• incenter of a triangle • inscribed in
• median of a triangle • centroid • altitude of a triangle
• orthocenter of a triangle

iTEXT Interactive lesson includes instant self-check, tutorials, and activities.

OBJECTIVE 1 Properties of Bisectors

Investigation: Paper Folding Bisectors

• Draw and cut out five different triangles: two acute, two right, and one obtuse.

• Step 1: Use paper folding to create the angle bisectors of each angle of an acute triangle. What do you notice about the angle bisectors?

• Step 2: Repeat Step 1 with a right triangle and an obtuse triangle. Does your discovery from Step 1 still hold true?

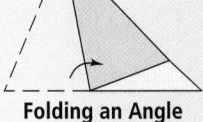
Folding an Angle Bisector

1. Make a conjecture about the bisectors of the angles of a triangle.

1. The bisectors of the ∠s of a △ meet at a point inside the △.

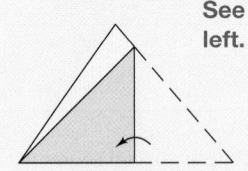
Folding a Perpendicular Bisector

See left.

• Step 3: Use paper folding to create the perpendicular bisector of each side of an acute triangle. What do you notice about the perpendicular bisectors?

• Step 4: Repeat Step 3 with a right triangle. What do you notice?

2. The ⊥ bis. of the sides of a △ intersect at a point that might fall inside, outside, or on the △.

2. Make a conjecture about the perpendicular bisectors of the sides of a triangle. See left.

Ongoing Assessment and Intervention

Before the Lesson	During the Lesson	After the Lesson
Diagnose prerequisite skills using:	**Monitor progress using:**	**Assess knowledge using:**
• Check Skills You'll Need	• Check Understanding	• Lesson Quiz
	• Additional Examples	• Computer Test Generator CD
	• Standardized Test Prep	• Chapter Checkpoint 1 (p. 263)

When three or more lines intersect in one point, they are **concurrent**. The point at which they intersect is the **point of concurrency.** For any triangle, four different sets of lines are concurrent. Theorems 5-6 and 5-7 tell you about two of them.

 Key Concepts

Theorem 5-6

The perpendicular bisectors of the sides of a triangle are concurrent at a point equidistant from the vertices.

Theorem 5-7

The bisectors of the angles of a triangle are concurrent at a point equidistant from the sides.

You will prove these theorems in the exercises.

Reading Math

The prefix *circum* is Latin for "around" or "about."

This figure shows $\triangle QRS$ with the perpendicular bisectors of its sides concurrent at C. The point of concurrency of the perpendicular bisectors of a triangle is called the **circumcenter of the triangle.**

Points Q, R, and S are equidistant from C, the circumcenter. The circle is **circumscribed about** the triangle.

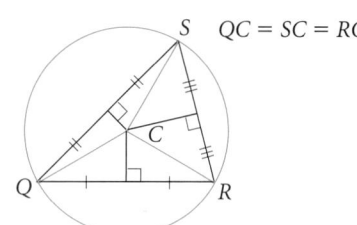
$QC = SC = RC$

1 EXAMPLE **Finding the Circumcenter**

Coordinate Geometry Find the center of the circle that you can circumscribe about $\triangle OPS$.

Two perpendicular bisectors of sides of $\triangle OPS$ are $x = 2$ and $y = 3$. These lines intersect at $(2, 3)$. This point is the center of the circle.

✓ Check Understanding
1 **a.** Find the center of the circle that you can circumscribe about the triangle with vertices $(0, 0)$, $(-8, 0)$, and $(0, 6)$. **(−4, 3)**
b. **Critical Thinking** In Example 1, explain why it is not necessary to find the third perpendicular bisector.
Thm. 5-6: All of the ⊥ bis. of the sides of a △ are concurrent.

This figure shows $\triangle UTV$ with the bisectors of its angles concurrent at I. The point of concurrency of the angle bisectors of a triangle is called the **incenter of the triangle.**

Points X, Y, and Z are equidistant from I, the incenter. The circle is **inscribed in** the triangle.

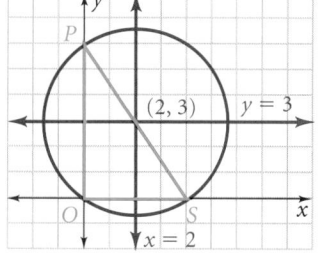
$XI = YI = ZI$

Reaching All Students

Below Level	Advanced Learners	Tactile Learners
Have students use a compass or algebra to confirm that point (2, 3) is the center of the circle that contains points O, P, and S in Example 1.	Have students investigate Ceva's Theorem and how it can be used to prove Theorem 5-8.	See note on page 258. **Error Prevention** See note on page 259.

Professional Development

Math Background

The theorems in this lesson can be related to Ceva's Theorem, which Giovanni Ceva published in 1678: Let sides $\overline{AB}$, $\overline{AC}$, and $\overline{BC}$ of $\triangle ABC$ be divided at X, Y, and Z respectively. Then $\overline{AZ}$, $\overline{BY}$, and $\overline{CX}$ are concurrent if and only if $\frac{AX}{XB} \cdot \frac{BZ}{ZC} \cdot \frac{CY}{YA} = 1$. Concurrency theorems will be applied later to inscribed and circumscribed circles and to the study of centroids in physics.

OBJECTIVE
1 **Teaching Notes**

Investigation (Optional)
Students may construct the angle bisectors and perpendicular bisectors using techniques they learned in Lesson 1-5.

Teaching Tip
When discussing Theorems 5-6 and 5-7, emphasize that the point of concurrency is equidistant from *vertices* for *perpendicular bisectors* and equidistant from *sides* for *angle bisectors.*

1 EXAMPLE **Connection to Algebra**

Remind students that the equation of a horizontal line is $y = a$ and the equation of a vertical line is $x = a$.

2 EXAMPLE **Diversity**

Remember that some students have little or no experience with houses that have yards big enough to hold a swimming pool.

Additional Examples

1 Find the center of the circle that circumscribes $\triangle XYZ$. **(3, 4)**

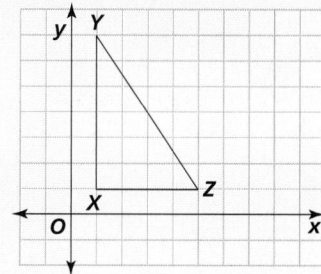

② City planners want to locate a fountain equidistant from three straight roads that enclose a park. Explain how they can find the location.

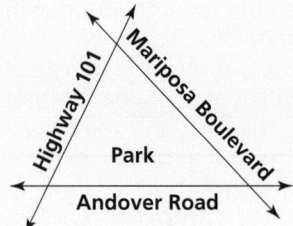

Highway 101
Mariposa Boulevard
Park
Andover Road

Locate the fountain at the point of concurrency of the angle bisectors of the triangle formed by the three roads.

Tactile Learners

Students can use paper-folding techniques to find altitudes and medians of triangles here and in Exercise 25.

Connection to Physical Science

Have students read the Dorling Kindersly (DK) feature on pages 344–345, and do the Activity involving the centroid as a point of balance.

Teaching Tip

The proofs of Theorems 5-8 and 5-9 are postponed until students have the tools necessary to complete them.

③ EXAMPLE **Math Tip**

Point out that another way to state Theorem 5-8 is that each median is broken into segments that have a ratio of 2 : 1. This can help students use mental math to find lengths. Ask: *If BD = 22, what does DE equal?* **11**

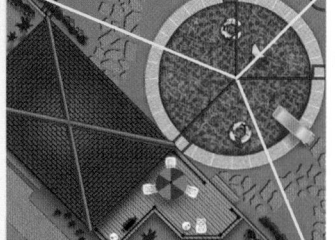

2 EXAMPLE Real-World **Connection**

Pools The Jacksons want to install the largest possible circular pool in their triangular backyard. Where would the largest possible pool be located?

Locate the center of the pool at the point of concurrency of the angle bisectors. This point is equidistant from the sides of the yard. If you choose any other point as the center of the pool, it will be closer to at least one of the sides of the yard, and the pool will be smaller.

✓ **Check Understanding**

2a. Draw segments connecting the towns. Build the library at the inters. pt. of the ⊥ bisectors of the segments.

2 a. The towns of Adamsville, Brooksville, and Cartersville want to build a library that is equidistant from the three towns. Trace the diagram and show where they should build the library. **See left.**

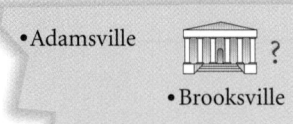
• Adamsville ?
• Brooksville
• Cartersville

b. What theorem did you use to find the location? **The ⊥ bisectors of the sides of a △ are concurrent at a point equidistant from the vertices.**

A **median of a triangle** is a segment whose endpoints are a vertex and the midpoint of the opposite side.

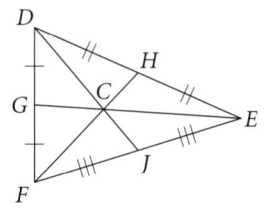
Median

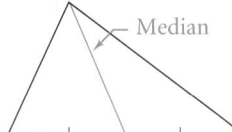 **Key Concepts**

Theorem 5-8

The medians of a triangle are concurrent at a point that is two thirds the distance from each vertex to the midpoint of the opposite side.

$$DC = \tfrac{2}{3}DJ \qquad EC = \tfrac{2}{3}EG \qquad FC = \tfrac{2}{3}FH$$

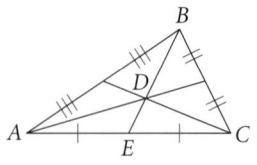

In a triangle, the point of concurrency of the medians is the **centroid.** The point is also called the center of gravity of a triangle because it is the point where a triangular shape will balance. (See Real-World Snapshots, page 345.) You will prove Theorem 5-8 in Chapter 6.

3 EXAMPLE **Finding Lengths of Medians**

D is the centroid of $\triangle ABC$ and $DE = 6$. Find BE.

Since D is a centroid, $BD = \tfrac{2}{3}BE$ and $DE = \tfrac{1}{3}BE$.

$\tfrac{1}{3}BE = DE$

$\tfrac{1}{3}BE = 6$ **Substitute 6 for DE.**

$BE = 18$

✓ **Check Understanding** **3** Find BD. Check that $BD + DE = BE$. **12**

An **altitude of a triangle** is the perpendicular segment from a vertex to the line containing the opposite side. Unlike angle bisectors and medians, an altitude of a triangle can be a side of a triangle or it may lie outside the triangle.

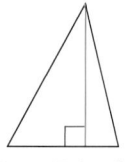

Acute Triangle:
Altitude is inside.

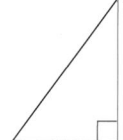

Right Triangle:
Altitude is a side.

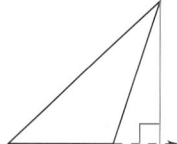

Obtuse Triangle:
Altitude is outside.

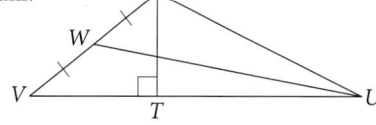

Identifying Medians and Altitudes

Is $\overline{ST}$ a median, an altitude, or neither? Explain.

$\overline{ST}$ is a segment extending from vertex S to the side opposite S. Also, $\overline{ST} \perp \overline{VU}$.
$\overline{ST}$ is an altitude of $\triangle VSU$.

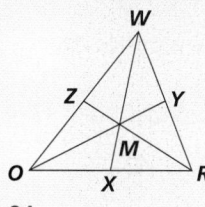

 Check Understanding ④ Is $\overline{UW}$ a median, an altitude, or neither? Explain.
Median; $\overline{UW}$ is a segment drawn from vertex U to the midpt. of the opp. side.

The lines containing the altitudes of a triangle are concurrent at the **orthocenter of the triangle.** A proof of this theorem appears in Chapter 6.

 **Key Concepts**

Theorem 5-9
The lines that contain the altitudes of a triangle are concurrent.

EXERCISES

For more practice, see *Extra Practice.*

Practice and Problem Solving

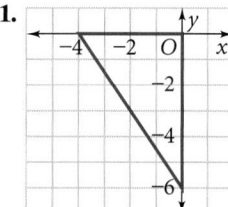 **Practice by Example**

Example 1
(page 257)

Coordinate Geometry Find the center of the circle that you can circumscribe about each triangle.

1.

(−2, −3)

2.

(0, 0)

Coordinate Geometry Find the center of the circle that you can circumscribe about $\triangle ABC$.

3. $A(0,0)$	4. $A(0,0)$	5. $A(-4,5)$	6. $A(-1,-2)$	7. $A(1,4)$
$B(3,0)$	$B(4,0)$	$B(-2,5)$	$B(-5,-2)$	$B(1,2)$
$C(3,2)$	$C(4,-3)$	$C(-2,-2)$	$C(-1,-7)$	$C(6,2)$
$\left(1\frac{1}{2}, 1\right)$	$\left(2, -1\frac{1}{2}\right)$	$\left(-3, 1\frac{1}{2}\right)$	$\left(-3, -4\frac{1}{2}\right)$	$\left(3\frac{1}{2}, 3\right)$

Students may think that $\overline{ST}$ and $\overline{UW}$ meet at the centroid or orthocenter of $\triangle VSU$. Point out that since $\overline{ST}$ is an altitude and $\overline{UW}$ is a median, their point of intersection cannot be categorized.

Additional Examples

③ M is the centroid of $\triangle WOR$, and $WM = 16$. Find WX.

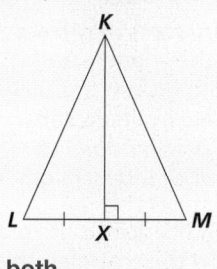

24

④ Is $\overline{KX}$ a median, an altitude, neither, or both?

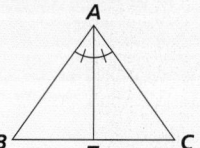

both

Closure

Use the diagram above to explain why the following must be true: The bisector of the vertex angle of an isosceles triangle is both an altitude and a median. **The bisector of the vertex angle of an isosceles triangle is the perpendicular bisector of the base by Theorem 4-5. Because the bisector is perpendicular, it is an altitude. Because it bisects the opposite side, it is a median.**

Assignment Guide

1 Objective

Ⓐ Ⓑ **Core** 1–10, 17–19, 30, 31

2 Objective

Ⓐ Ⓑ **Core** 11–16, 20–29, 32

Ⓒ **Extension** 33–36

Standardized Test Prep 37–41

Mixed Review 42–51

Alternative Method

Exercise 2 Students may trace and cut out the triangle and use paper folding, or carefully construct the perpendicular bisectors on graph paper, to find the point of intersection.

Exercises 3–7 If students use graph paper to draw the triangles, they will easily find the horizontal and vertical perpendicular bisectors.

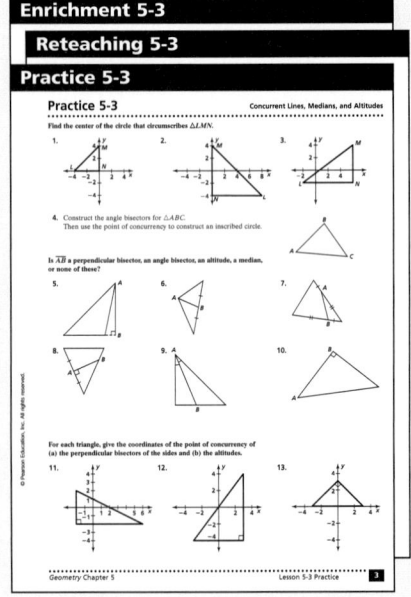

Example 2
(page 258)

Name the point of concurrency of the angle bisectors.

8.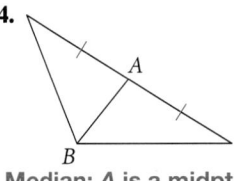

9.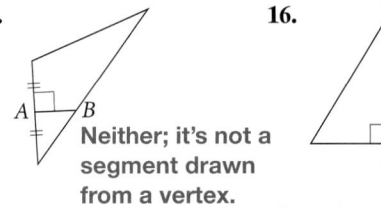

10. **City Planning** Copy the diagram of Altgeld Park. Show where park officials should place a drinking fountain so that it is equidistant from the tennis court, the playground, and the volleyball court.

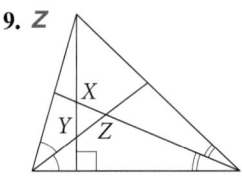 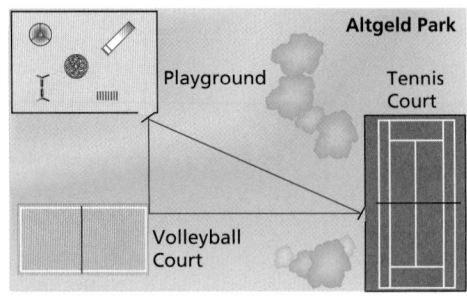 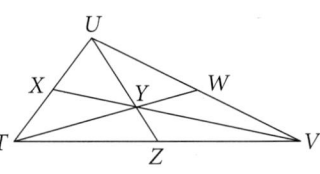

Find the ⊥ bisectors of the sides of the △ formed by the tennis court, the playground, and the volleyball court. That point will be equidistant from the vertices of the △.

Example 3
(page 258)

In △TUV, Y is the centroid.

11. If $YW = 9$, find TY and TW. $TY = 18; TW = 27$

12. If $YU = 9$, find ZY and ZU. $ZY = 4\frac{1}{2};$ $ZU = 13\frac{1}{2}$

13. If $VX = 9$, find VY and YX. $VY = 6; YX = 3$

Example 4
(page 259)

Is $\overline{AB}$ a median, an altitude, or neither? Explain.

16. Altitude; $\overline{AB}$ is a segment drawn from a vertex of a △ perp. to the opp. side.

14. **Median; *A* is a midpt.**

15. **Neither; it's not a segment drawn from a vertex.**

16. **See left.**

Ⓑ **Apply Your Skills**

Constructions **Draw the triangle. Then construct the inscribed circle and the circumscribed circle.** 17–18. See margin.

17. right triangle, △DEF

18. obtuse triangle, △STU

In Exercises 19–22, name each figure in △BDF.

19. an angle bisector $\overline{BE}$

20. a median $\overline{FC}$

21. a perpendicular bisector $\overrightarrow{CA}$

22. an altitude $\overline{DG}$

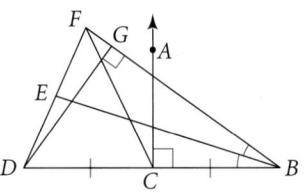

23. **Critical Thinking** A centroid separates a median into two segments. What is the ratio of the lengths of those segments? **1 : 2 or 2 : 1**

24. **Writing** Ivars found a yellowed parchment inside an antique book. It read:
From the spot I buried Olaf's treasure, equal sets of paces did I measure; each of three directions in a line, there to plant a seedling Norway pine. I could not return for failing health; now the hounds of Haiti guard my wealth.—Karl
After searching Caribbean islands for five years, Ivars found one with three tall Norway pines. How might Ivars find where Karl buried Olaf's treasure?

24. Find the circumcenter of the triangle formed by the three pines.

The figures below show how to construct medians and altitudes by paper folding.

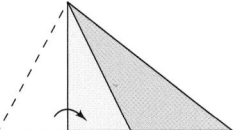 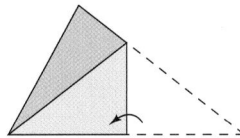 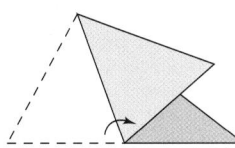

To find an altitude, fold the triangle so that a side overlaps itself and the fold contains the opposite vertex.

To find a median, fold one vertex to another vertex. This locates the midpoint of a side.

Then fold so that the fold contains the midpoint and the opposite vertex.

25–26. Check students' work.

25. Cut out a large triangle. Paper-fold very carefully to construct the three medians of the triangle and demonstrate Theorem 5-8.

26. Cut out a large acute triangle. Paper-fold very carefully to construct the three altitudes of the triangle and demonstrate Theorem 5-9.

Is $\overline{AB}$ a perpendicular bisector, an angle bisector, a median, an altitude, or none of these? Explain.

28. None of these; it is a midsegment.

27.
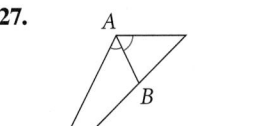
∠ bisector; it bisects an ∠.

28.

29.
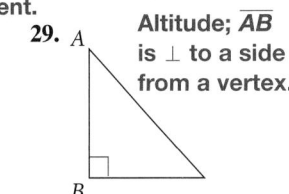
Altitude; $\overline{AB}$ is ⊥ to a side from a vertex.

Proof **30. Developing Proof** Complete this proof of Theorem 5-6 by filling in the blanks.

Given: Lines $\ell, m,$ and n are perpendicular bisectors of the sides of △ABC. X is the intersection of lines ℓ and m.

Prove: Line n contains point X, and $XA = XB = XC$.

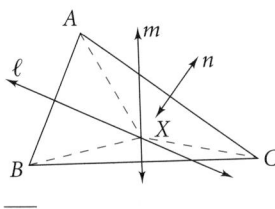

$\overline{AB}$

Proof: Since ℓ is the perpendicular bisector of **a.** ? , $XA = XB$. Since m is the perpendicular bisector of **b.** ? , $XB =$ **c.** ? . Thus $XA = XB = XC$. Since $XA = XC,$ X is on line n by the Converse of the **d.** ? Theorem.

30b. $\overline{BC}$ 30c. $\overline{XC}$ 30d. ⊥ bis.

31. Developing Proof Complete the flow proof of Theorem 5-7.

Given: Rays $\ell, m,$ and n are bisectors of the angles of △ABC. X is the intersection of rays ℓ and m and $\overline{XD} \perp \overline{AC}, \overline{XE} \perp \overline{AB}, \overline{XF} \perp \overline{BC}.$

Prove: Ray n contains point X, and $XD = XE = XF.$

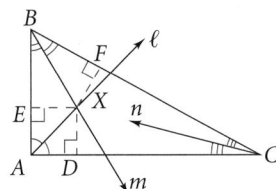

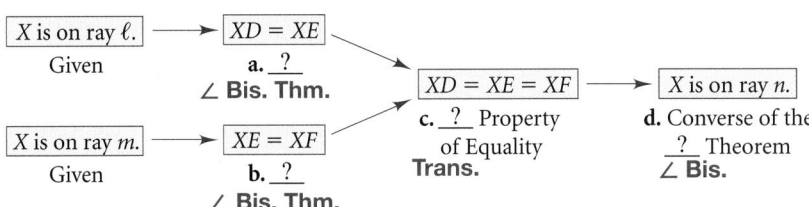

$\boxed{X \text{ is on ray } \ell.}$ ⟶ $\boxed{XD = XE}$
Given   **a.** ?
              ∠ Bis. Thm.

$\boxed{XD = XE = XF}$ ⟶ $\boxed{X \text{ is on ray } n.}$
c. ? Property   **d.** Converse of the
of Equality   ? Theorem
Trans.   ∠ Bis.

$\boxed{X \text{ is on ray } m.}$ ⟶ $\boxed{XE = XF}$
Given   **b.** ?
              ∠ Bis. Thm.

Lesson 5-3 Concurrent Lines, Medians, and Altitudes **261**

Error Prevention

Exercise 10 Students may not realize that the playground and courts locate points. Discuss as a class why these particular points on the playground and courts might have been chosen.

Exercise 15 Point out that $\overline{AB}$ meets only half the conditions to be an altitude and only half the conditions to be a median, which means that it is neither.

Exercises 17, 18 If necessary, have students review how to construct angle bisectors and perpendicular bisectors in Lesson 1-5.

Exercises 30, 31 Because using properties from two segments to prove concurrence is a new and sophisticated idea, discuss these proofs as a class after students complete them. Encourage students to ask questions about the strategy chosen for each proof.

Connection to Discrete Math

Exercise 36 Euler (pronounced "oiler") is also responsible for the Seven Bridges of Königsberg problem, the proof of which was fundamental to the development of graph theory. Have students research Euler's contributions to mathematics.

pages 259–263 Exercises

17.

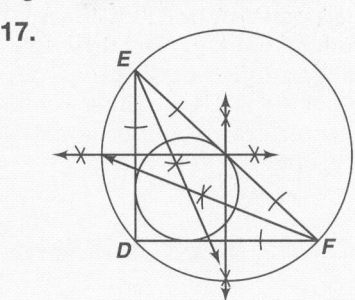

18.

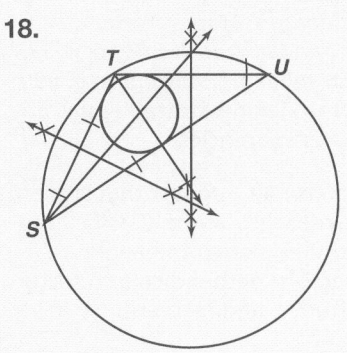

Lesson Quiz 5-3

1. Complete the sentence: To find the centroid of a triangle, you need to draw at least __?__ median(s). **two**

2. △FGH has vertices F(–1, 2), G(9, 2), and H(9, 0). Find the center of the circle that circumscribes △FGH. **(4, 1)**

Use the diagram for Exercises 3–5.

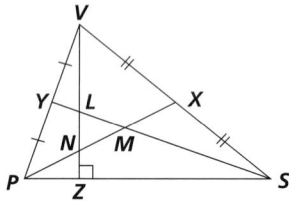

3. Identify all medians and altitudes drawn in △PSV. **PX and SY are medians; VZ is an altitude.**

4. If SY = 15, find SM and MY. **SM = 10 and MY = 5**

5. If MX = 14, find PM and PX. **PM = 28 and PX = 42**

Alternative Assessment

P is a point inside △ABC. Have students work in pairs to write a full description of the properties of point P if it is the circumcenter, incenter, centroid, or orthocenter of △ABC.

Standardized Test Prep

Resources

For additional practice with a variety of test item formats:
• Standardized Test Prep, p. 285
• Test-Taking Strategies, p. 280
• Test-Taking Strategies with Transparencies

Exercise 40 Suggest that students draw each triangle classification and then sketch the angle bisectors, perpendicular bisectors, altitudes, and medians.

262

Reading Math

You can prove Theorem 5-8 for a general △ABC with coordinates A(0, 0), B(2b, 2d), and C(2c, 0) by following the steps for the particular △ABC in Exercise 32.

Challenge

32b. $\overleftrightarrow{AM}$: $y = \frac{3}{5}x$;
$\overleftrightarrow{BN}$: $y = -3x + 12$;
$\overleftrightarrow{CL}$: $y = -\frac{3}{7}x + \frac{24}{7}$

32d. $-\frac{3}{7}\left(\frac{10}{3}\right) + \frac{24}{7} = -\frac{10}{7} + \frac{24}{7} = \frac{14}{7} = 2$

35. Answers may vary. Sample: Let △ABC be isosc. with base ∡ B and C. If AD bisects ∠A, then it is ⊥ to $\overline{BC}$, and therefore the altitude from ∠A. So, $\overleftrightarrow{AD}$ contains the circumcenter, incenter, centroid, and orthocenter.

---

32. **Coordinate Geometry** Complete the following steps to locate the centroid.
   a. Find the coordinates of midpoints L, M, and N. **L(1, 3); M(5, 3); N(4, 0)**
   b. **See below left.** Find equations of $\overleftrightarrow{AM}$, $\overleftrightarrow{BN}$, and $\overleftrightarrow{CL}$.
   c. Find the coordinates of P, the intersection of $\overleftrightarrow{AM}$ and $\overleftrightarrow{BN}$. This is the centroid. $\left(\frac{10}{3}, 2\right)$
   d. Show that point P is on $\overleftrightarrow{CL}$. **See left.**
   e. Use the Distance Formula to show that point P is $\frac{2}{3}$ of the distance from each vertex to the midpoint of the opposite side. **See margin.**

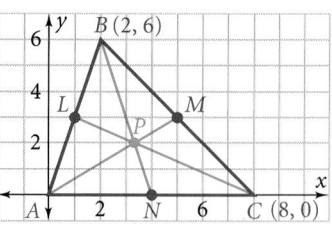

For Exercises 33 and 34, points of concurrency have been drawn for two triangles. Match the points with the lines and segments listed in I–IV.

33. **I-D; II-B; III-C; IV-A**

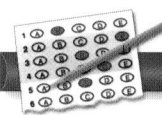

34. **I-A; II-C; III-B; IV-D**

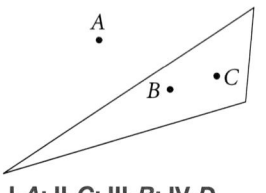

I. perpendicular bisectors of sides   II. angle bisectors
III. medians   IV. lines containing altitudes

35. In an isosceles triangle, show that the circumcenter, incenter, centroid, and orthocenter can be four different points but all four must be collinear. **See left.**

36. **History** In 1765 Leonhard Euler proved that for any triangle, three of the four points of concurrency are collinear. The line that contains these three points is known as Euler's Line. Use Exercises 33 and 34 to determine which point of concurrency does not necessarily lie on Euler's Line. **∠ bisectors**

Standardized Test Prep

Multiple Choice   Use the figure at the right for Exercises 37–39.

37. What is RD if RL = 54 cm? **C**
   A. 81 cm   B. 108 cm
   C. 162 cm   D. 216 cm

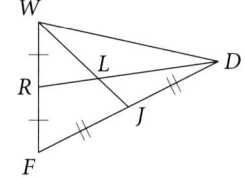

Take It to the NET
Online lesson quiz at **www.PHSchool.com**
Web Code: afa-0503

38. What is WL if WJ = 210 mm? **H**
   F. 70 mm   G. 105 mm
   H. 140 mm   I. 157.5 mm

39. What is x if WL = 15x and LJ = 5x + 3? **D**
   A. 0.3   B. 0.4   C. 0.6   D. 1.2

Short Response

40. Name all types of triangles for which the centroid, circumcenter, incenter, and orthocenter are all inside the triangle. Classify the triangles according to the sides as well as the angles. **See margin.**

Extended Response

41. The point of concurrency of the three altitudes of a triangle lies outside the triangle. Where are its circumcenter, incenter, and centroid located in relation to the triangle? Draw and label a diagram to support each of your answers. **See back of book.**

Lesson 5-2 | **Determine whether point *B* must be on the bisector of ∠*T*. Explain.**

44. No; point *B* is not necessarily equidistant from the sides.

42.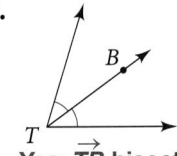
Yes; $\overrightarrow{TB}$ bisects the ∠.

43.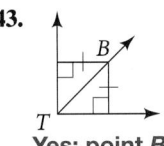
Yes; point *B* is equidistant from the sides.

44. 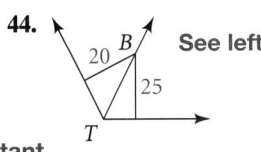 See left.

Lesson 3-3 | **Classify each △*JKL* by its angles.**

45. $m\angle J = 37, m\angle K = 53, m\angle L = 90$
right

46. $m\angle J = 47, m\angle K = 98, m\angle L = 35$
obtuse

Lesson 1-3 | **In the figure at the right, *ABCD* is a square. Identify each of the following.** 47–51. Answers may vary.

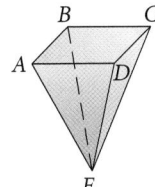

47. a line skew to $\overleftrightarrow{ED}$ $\overleftrightarrow{AB}$

48. a line skew to $\overleftrightarrow{EB}$ $\overleftrightarrow{AD}$

49. *ABC* and *ADE*
50. $\overline{AB}$ and $\overline{CD}$

49. two intersecting planes

50. two parallel segments

51. the intersection of plane *ABC* and plane *BCE* $\overleftrightarrow{BC}$

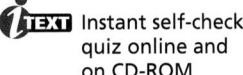 **Checkpoint Quiz 1**   **Lessons 5-1 through 5-3**

iTEXT Instant self-check quiz online and on CD-ROM

$\boxed{x^2}$ **Algebra** Find the value of *x*.

1.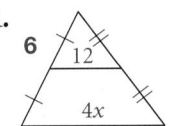

2.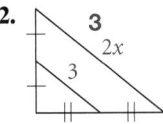

3. a. $\overline{AB}$ is a midsegment of △*XYZ*. $AB = 52$. Find *YZ*. **104**
   b. $AX = 26$ and $BZ = 36$. Find the perimeter of △*XYZ*. **228**

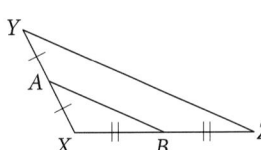

Use the diagram. What can you conclude about each of the following? Explain.

4. ∠*CDB* right ∠; supp. to ∠*ADB*

5. △*ABD* and △*CBD*

5. △*ABD* ≅ △*CBD*; HL

6. $\overline{AD}$ and $\overline{DC}$
   $\overline{AD}$ ≅ $\overline{DC}$; CPCTC

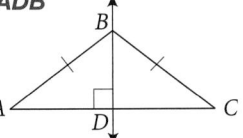

7. $\overrightarrow{XY}$ bisects ∠*ZXW*; *Y* is equidist. from $\overrightarrow{XZ}$ and $\overrightarrow{XW}$.

Use the figure at the right. 7–8. See left.

7. What can you conclude about $\overrightarrow{XY}$? Explain.

8. Find *XZ*. Justify your response.

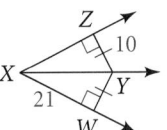

8. 21; △*XYZ* ≅ △*XYW* by HL, so *XZ* = 21 by CPCTC.

 Writing **For a given triangle, describe how you can construct the following.**

9. a median 9–10. See margin.

10. an altitude

To check understanding of Lessons 5-1 to 5-3:

Checkpoint Quiz 1 (p. 263)

📁 **Teaching Resources**
Checkpoint Quiz 1 (also in Prentice Hall Assessment System)

👥 **Reaching All Students**
Reading and Math Literacy 5B

Spanish versions available

---

pages 259–263   Exercises

32. e. $AM = \sqrt{34}$; $AP = \sqrt{\frac{136}{9}} = \frac{2}{3}\sqrt{34}$;

$BN = \sqrt{40} = 2\sqrt{10}$;

$BP = \sqrt{\frac{160}{9}} = \frac{4}{3}\sqrt{10}$;

$CL = \sqrt{58}$; $CP = \sqrt{\frac{232}{9}} = \frac{2}{3}\sqrt{58}$

40. [2] any acute △; or a list that contains all of the following: equiangular △, equilateral △, acute isosceles △, acute scalene △

[1] a list that does not contain equiangular △, equilateral △, acute isosceles △, or scalene △

page 263   Checkpoint Quiz 1

9. Answers may vary. Sample: Bisect a side of a △. Connect the opp. vertex with the midpt.

10. Use the procedure for constructing a ⊥ to a line from a point not on the line.

1. Plan

Lesson Preview

Check Skills You'll Need

Converses
Lesson 2-1: Example 5
Exercises 23–26
Extra Practice, p. 691

Separating Biconditionals into Parts
Lesson 2-2: Example 2
Exercises 7–12
Extra Practice, p. 691

Lesson Resources

Teaching Resources
Practice, Reteaching, Enrichment

Reaching All Students
Practice Workbook 5-4
Spanish Practice Workbook 5-4
Informal Geometry Planning
 Guide 5-4

Presentation Assistant Plus!
Transparencies
• Check Skills You'll Need 5-4
• Additional Examples 5-4
• Student Edition Answers 5-4
• Lesson Quiz 5-4
PH Presentation Pro CD 5-4

PRENTICE HALL
ASSESSMENT SYSTEM

Computer Test Generator CD

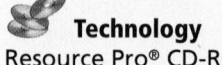
Technology
Resource Pro® CD-ROM
Computer Test Generator CD
Prentice Hall Presentation Pro CD

www.PHSchool.com
Student Site
• Teacher Web Code: afk-5500
• Self-grading Lesson Quiz
Teacher Center
• Lesson Planner
• Resources

Plus *i***TEXT**

264

5-4 Inverses, Contrapositives, and Indirect Reasoning

North Carolina Objectives   2.01   Use logic and deductive reasoning to draw conclusions and solve problems.

Lesson Preview

What You'll Learn

OBJECTIVE **1** To write the negation of a statement and the inverse and contrapositive of a conditional statement

OBJECTIVE **2** To use indirect reasoning

...And Why

To describe how an advertisement can be misunderstood, as in Exercise 28

✓ Check Skills You'll Need   (For help, go to Lessons 2-1 and 2-2.)

Write the converse of each statement.
1. If it snows tomorrow, then we will go skiing.   If we go skiing, then it snows tomorrow.
2. If two lines are parallel, then they do not intersect.   If 2 lines do not intersect, then they are parallel.
3. If $x = -1$, then $x^2 = 1$. If $x^2 = 1$, then $x = -1$.

Write two conditional statements that make up each biconditional.
4. A point is on the bisector of an angle if and only if it is equidistant from the sides of the angle. 4–6. See margin p. 266.
5. A point is on the perpendicular bisector of a segment if and only if it is equidistant from the endpoints of the segment.
6. You will pass a geometry course if and only if you are successful with your homework.

New Vocabulary • negation • inverse • contrapositive
• equivalent statements • indirect reasoning
• indirect proof

  Interactive lesson includes instant self-check, tutorials, and activities.

OBJECTIVE
1 Writing the Negation, Inverse, and Contrapositive

The statement, "Knoxville is the capital of Tennessee," is false. The **negation** of a statement has the opposite truth value. The negation, "Knoxville is not the capital of Tennessee," is true.

1 EXAMPLE Writing the Negation of a Statement

Write the negation of each statement.
a. Statement: $\angle ABC$ is obtuse.
   Negation: $\angle ABC$ is not obtuse.
b. Statement: Lines m and n are not perpendicular.
   Negation: Lines m and n are perpendicular.

✓ **Check Understanding** **1** Write the negation of each statement.
a. $m\angle XYZ > 70$. The measure of $\angle XYZ$ is not more than 70.
b. Today is not Tuesday. Today is Tuesday.

Reading Math
The prefix *contra* is Latin for "against."

The **inverse** of a conditional statement negates both the hypothesis and the conclusion. The **contrapositive** of a conditional switches the hypothesis and the conclusion and negates both.

Ongoing Assessment and Intervention

Before the Lesson	**During the Lesson**	**After the Lesson**
Diagnose prerequisite skills using:	**Monitor progress using:**	**Assess knowledge using:**
• Check Skills You'll Need	• Check Understanding • Additional Examples • Standardized Test Prep	• Lesson Quiz • Computer Test Generator CD

"If you don't stand for something, you'll fall for anything."
—Maya Angelou, poet and author

2 EXAMPLE Writing the Inverse and Contrapositive

Write the inverse and the contrapositive of the conditional statement.

Conditional: If a figure is a square, then it is a rectangle.

                    ↓   **Negate both.**   ↓

Inverse: If a figure is not a square, then it is not a rectangle.

Conditional: If a figure is a square, then it is a rectangle.

                    Switch and negate both.

● Contrapositive: If a figure is not a rectangle, then it is not a square.

✓ Check Understanding

2 Write (a) the inverse and (b) the contrapositive of Maya Angelou's statement under the photo at the left. **See left.**

2a. If you stand for something, you won't fall for anything.

b. If you won't fall for anything, then you stand for something.

You know that a conditional statement and its converse can have different truth values. A conditional statement and its inverse can also have different truth values. The contrapositive of a conditional statement, however, always has the same truth value as the conditional. A conditional statement and its contrapositive are equivalent. **Equivalent statements** have the same truth value.

🖐 Key Concepts

Summary	Negation, Inverse, and Contrapositive Statements		
Statement	**Example**	**Symbolic Form**	**You Read It**
Conditional	If an angle is a straight angle, then its measure is 180.	$p \rightarrow q$	If p, then q.
Negation (of p)	An angle is not a straight angle.	$\sim p$	Not p.
Inverse	If an angle is not a straight angle, then its measure is not 180.	$\sim p \rightarrow \sim q$	If not p, then not q.
Contrapositive	If an angle's measure is not 180, then it is not a straight angle.	$\sim q \rightarrow \sim p$	If not q, then not p.

OBJECTIVE 2 Using Indirect Reasoning

Suppose your brother tells you, "Susan called a few minutes ago." You think through these three steps.

Step 1 You have two friends named Susan.

Step 2 You know that one of them is at band practice.

Step 3 You conclude that the other Susan must have been the caller.

This type of reasoning is called indirect reasoning. In **indirect reasoning,** all possibilities are considered and then all but one are proved false. The remaining possibility must be true.

A proof involving indirect reasoning is an **indirect proof.** In an indirect proof, a statement and its negation often are the only possibilities.

Lesson 5-4 Inverses, Contrapositives, and Indirect Reasoning   **265**

👥 Reaching All Students

Below Level Have students give examples illustrating that conditionals and their contrapositives are equivalent statements to help reinforce the legitimacy of indirect proof.	**Advanced Learners** As an alternative method, students can try proving indirectly theorems that they have already proved directly.	**English Learners** See note on page 268. **Visual Learners** See note on page 268.

Math Background

An indirect or *non-constructive* proof shows that something exists or is true by showing that its non-existence leads to a contradiction. Some mathematicians have tried to disallow non-constructive proofs, and in many cases a direct or *constructive* proof can replace an indirect proof. However, there are theorems whose very nature precludes a direct proof.

OBJECTIVE 1 Teaching Notes

1 EXAMPLE Error Prevention

Some students may think that the truth value of a conditional determines the truth value of its inverse or converse. Have them examine the conditional *If x = 2, then x² = 4* to see that this is not so.

2 EXAMPLE Math Tip

Point out to the class two other ways to find the contrapositive of a conditional:
• Find the converse of the inverse.
• Find the inverse of the converse.

Teaching Tip
Students may have difficulty understanding why a conditional and its contrapositive are equivalent. This concept is fundamental to indirect reasoning. To help students, have them examine several conditionals and their contrapositives and compare their truth values.

 Additional Examples

1 Write the negation of "*ABCD* is not a convex polygon." *ABCD* **is a convex polygon.**

2 Write the inverse and contrapositive of the conditional statement "If △*ABC* is equilateral, then it is isosceles." **Inverse: If △*ABC* is not equilateral, then it is not isosceles. Contrapositive: If △*ABC* is not isosceles, then it is not equilateral.**

265

Teaching Tip

Expect some students to find indirect proof more difficult at first than direct proof. Provide real-life examples of how people use indirect reasoning in daily life.

4 EXAMPLE Auditory Learners

Discuss why each possible pair of statements is consistent or contradictory, making sure that students remember the meanings of *acute*, *scalene*, and *equiangular*.

5 EXAMPLE

Have students write step 2 as a flow proof for the class to examine.

Additional Examples

3 Write the first step of an indirect proof.

Prove: A triangle cannot contain two right angles. Assume that a triangle contains two right angles.

4 Identify the two statements that contradict each other.

I. *P*, *Q*, and *R* are coplanar.
II. *P*, *Q*, and *R* are collinear.
III. *M*∠*PQR* = 60 II and III

5 Write an indirect proof.
Prove: △*ABC* cannot contain two obtuse angles. Assume that ∠*A* and ∠*B* are obtuse. Then *m*∠*A* + *m*∠*B* > 180. Because *m*∠*A* + *m*∠*B* + *m*∠*C* = 180, the assumption is false.

Closure

Determine which are true: the conditional below, its converse, its inverse, its contrapositive.

If lines are perpendicular, then they are not skew. conditional and contrapositive

page 264   Check Skills You'll Need

4. If a point is on the bisector of an angle, then it is equidistant from the sides of the angle. If a point is equidistant from the sides of an angle, then it is on the bisector of the angle.

266

🔑 **Key Concepts**

Summary	Writing an Indirect Proof

Step 1 State as an assumption the opposite (negation) of what you want to prove.

Step 2 Show that this assumption leads to a contradiction.

Step 3 Conclude that the assumption must be false and that what you want to prove must be true.

In the first step of an indirect proof you assume as true the opposite of what you want to prove.

Proof → **3 EXAMPLE**   The First Step of an Indirect Proof

Developing Proof Write the first step of an indirect proof.

a. Prove: Quadrilateral *QRWX* does not have four acute angles.

  Assume that quadrilateral *QRWX* has four acute angles.

b. Prove: An integer *n* is divisible by 5.

  Assume that the integer *n* is not divisible by 5.

✓ **Check Understanding** **3** You want to prove each statement true. Write the first step of an indirect proof.

a. The shoes cost no more than $20.   **b.** $m\angle A > m\angle B$
  The shoes cost more than $20. $m\angle A \leq m\angle B$

To do an indirect proof, you have to be able to identify a contradiction.

4 EXAMPLE   Identifying Contradictions

Developing Proof Identify the two statements that contradict each other.

  I. △*ABC* is acute.   II. △*ABC* is scalene.   III. △*ABC* is equiangular.

A triangle can be acute and scalene. I and II do not contradict each other.

An equiangular triangle is an acute triangle. I and III do not contradict each other.

An equiangular triangle must be equilateral, so it cannot be scalene. II and III contradict each other.

✓ **Check Understanding** **4** Identify the two statements that contradict each other. **I and II**
  I. $\overline{FG} \parallel \overline{KL}$ II. $\overline{FG} \perp \overline{KL}$ III. $\overline{FG} \cong \overline{KL}$

5 EXAMPLE   Indirect Proof

Developing Proof Read the conditional statement. Think about what is given and what you are to prove. Then give the steps of an indirect proof.

If Jaeleen spends more than $50 to buy two items at a bicycle shop, then at least one of the items costs more than $25.

Given: The cost of two items is more than $50.

Prove: At least one of the items costs more than $25.

Jack, 18, is a good driver. Jack concludes he will get a good insurance rate. His insurance bill is a contradiction.

5. If a point is on the ⊥ bis. of a segment, then it is equidistant from the endpoints of the segment. If a point is equidistant from the endpoints of a

segment, then it is on the ⊥ bis. of the segment.

6. If you will pass a geometry course, then you are successful with

your homework. If you are successful with your homework, then you will pass a geometry course.

Step 1 Assume as true the opposite of what you want to prove. That is, assume that neither item costs more than $25.

Step 2 This means that each item costs $25 or less. This, in turn, means that the two items together cost $50 or less. This contradicts the given information that the amount spent is more than $50.

Step 3 Conclude that the assumption is false. One item must cost more than $25.

✔ **Check Understanding** ⑤ **Critical Thinking** You plan to write an indirect proof showing that $\angle X$ is an obtuse angle. In the first step you assume that $\angle X$ is an acute angle. What have you overlooked? *$\angle X$ could be a right $\angle$.*

EXERCISES

Practice and Problem Solving

For more practice, see *Extra Practice*.

 A **Practice by Example**

Example 1
(page 264)

1. Two angles are not congruent.

Example 2
(page 265)

Example 3
(page 266)

Example 4
(page 266)

Write the negation of each statement.

1. Two angles are congruent.

2. You are not sixteen years old.
   You are sixteen years old.

3. The angle is not obtuse.
   The angle is obtuse.

4. The soccer game is on Friday.
   The soccer game is not on Friday.

5. The figure is a triangle.
   The figure is not a triangle.

6. $m\angle A < 90$
   $m\angle A \geq 90$

Write (a) the inverse and (b) the contrapositive of each conditional statement.
7–9. See margin.

7. If you eat all of your vegetables, then you will grow.

8. If a figure is a square, then all of its angles are right angles.

9. If a figure is a rectangle, then it has four sides.

Developing Proof **Write the first step of an indirect proof.**

10. It is raining outside. **10–13. See margin.**

11. $\angle J$ is not a right angle.

12. $\triangle PEN$ is isosceles.

13. At least one angle is obtuse.

14. $\overline{XY} \cong \overline{AB}$
    Assume that $\overline{XY} \not\cong \overline{AB}$.

15. $m\angle 2 > 90$
    Assume that $m\angle 2 \leq 90$.

Developing Proof **Identify the two statements that contradict each other.**

16. I. $\triangle PQR$ is equilateral. **I and II**
    II. $\triangle PQR$ is a right triangle.
    III. $\triangle PQR$ is isosceles.

17. I. In right $\triangle ABC$, $m\angle A = 60$. **I and II**
    II. In right $\triangle ABC$, $\angle A \cong \angle C$.
    III. In right $\triangle ABC$, $m\angle B = 90$.

18. I. ℓ and m are skew. **I and III**
    II. ℓ and m do not intersect.
    III. $\ell \parallel m$

19. I. Each of the two items that Val bought costs more than $10.
    II. Val spent $34 for the two items. **II and III**
    III. Neither of the two items that Val bought costs more than $15.

---

pages 267–270 Exercises

7. a. If you don't eat all of your vegetables, then you won't grow.
   b. If you won't grow, then you don't eat all of your vegetables.

8. a. If a figure is not a square, then at least one of its angles is not a right angle.
   b. If at least one of the angles is not a right angle, then the figure is not a square.

9. a. If a figure isn't a rectangle, then it doesn't have four sides.
   b. If a figure doesn't have four sides, then it isn't a rectangle.

 **Assignment Guide**

 **1 Objective**
Ⓐ Ⓑ **Core** 1–9, 22–28, 33–35

2 Objective
Ⓐ Ⓑ **Core** 10–21, 29–32, 36–38
Ⓒ **Extension** 39–41

Standardized Test Prep 42–46

Mixed Review 47–55

Exercises 16–19 Have students work with partners to search for contradictions in each possible pair of statements.

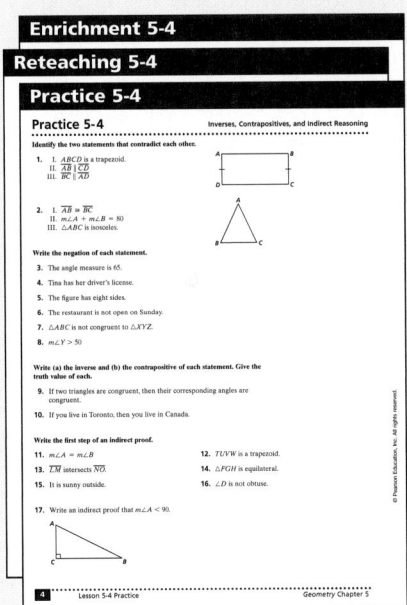

10. Assume that it is not raining outside.

11. Assume that $\angle J$ is a right angle.

12. Assume that $\triangle PEN$ is not isosceles.

13. Assume that none of the angles is obtuse.

267

Example 5
(page 266)

20a. 20 or more

b. the Debate Club and the Chess Club have fewer than 20 members

c. the Debate Club has fewer than 10 members

Reading Math

For help with reading and solving Exercise 21, see p. 271.

B **Apply Your Skills**

22a. If you don't live in Sarasota, then you don't live in Florida; false.

b. If you don't live in Florida, then you don't live in Sarasota; true.

Real-World 🌐 **Connection**

Water freezes at 32°F. Sidewalk "salt" lowers the freezing point of water.

268   Chapter 5   Relationships Within Triangles

---

20. **Developing Proof** Fill in the blanks to prove the following statement. If the Debate and Chess Clubs together have fewer than 20 members and the Chess Club has 10 members, then the Debate Club has fewer than 10 members.

    Given: The total membership of the Debate Club and the Chess Club is fewer than 20. The Chess Club has 10 members.

    Prove: The Debate Club has fewer than 10 members.

    Proof: Assume that the Debate Club has 10 or more members. This means that together the two clubs have **a.** _?_ members. This contradicts the given information that **b.** _?_. The assumption is false. Therefore it is true that **c.** _?_.

21. **Developing Proof** Fill in the blanks to prove the following statement. In a given triangle, $\triangle LMN$, there is at most one right angle.

    Given: $\triangle LMN$

    Prove: $\triangle LMN$ has at most one right angle.

    21a. right angle
    b. right angles
    21c–i. See below.

    Proof: Assume that $\triangle LMN$ has more than one **a.** _?_. That is, assume that both $\angle M$ and $\angle N$ are **b.** _?_. If $\angle M$ and $\angle N$ are both right angles, then $m\angle M = m\angle N =$ **c.** _?_. By the Triangle Angle-Sum Theorem, $m\angle L + m\angle M + m\angle N =$ **d.** _?_. Use substitution to find $m\angle L +$ **e.** _?_ $+$ **f.** _?_ $= 180$. When you solve for $m\angle L$, you find that $m\angle L =$ **g.** _?_. This means that there is no $\triangle LMN$, which contradicts the given statement. So the assumption that $\triangle LMN$ has **h.** _?_ must be false. Therefore, $\triangle LMN$ has **i.** _?_.   **h. more than one right angle**
    c. 90   d. 180   e. 90   f. 90   g. 0   **i. at most one right angle**

    Write (a) the inverse and (b) the contrapositive of each statement. Give the truth value of each.   23a. If four points aren't collinear, then they aren't coplanar; false.

22. If you live in Sarasota, then you live in Florida.   **See left.**

23. If four points are collinear, then they are coplanar.   23a. See above.
    23b. If four points aren't coplanar, then they aren't collinear; true.

    Open-Ended **Write a true conditional statement for each given condition. If such a statement is not possible, tell why.**   24–27. See margin.

24. The inverse is false.   25. The inverse is true.

26. The contrapositive is false.   27. The contrapositive is true.

28. **Error Analysis** Angie saw an ad that stated "If you don't drink Muscle Rex, then you won't build muscles." Angie bought Muscle Rex and drank it, and nothing happened. She sent an e-mail to the company asking for her money back. The company would not refund her money. They claimed that her reasoning was faulty. Using one or more of the terms *converse*, *inverse*, or *contrapositive*, explain why Angie's reasoning was faulty.   **See back of book.**

✏️ **Writing** **For Exercises 29–32, write a convincing argument that uses indirect reasoning.** 29–32. See back of book.

29. Fresh skid marks appear behind a green car at the scene of an accident. Show that the driver of the green car applied the brakes.

30. Ice is forming on the sidewalk in front of Toni's house. Show that the temperature of the sidewalk surface must be 32°F or lower.

31. An obtuse triangle cannot contain a right angle.

32. In a plane, a line has no more than one perpendicular at any of its points.

33. If the animal is a kitten, then it is a cat. If the animal isn't a cat, then it's not a kitten.

34. If the angle measures 120, then it is obtuse. If the angle isn't obtuse, then it doesn't measure 120.

35. If a number is a whole number, then it is an integer. If a number isn't an integer, then it isn't a whole number.

Need Help?

To review Venn diagrams, see page 69.

Write the conditional statement illustrated by each Venn diagram. Then write its contrapositive. 33–35. See margin.

33.

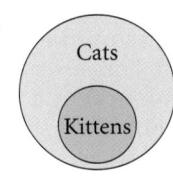

34.

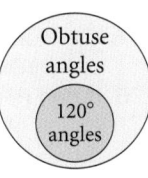

35.

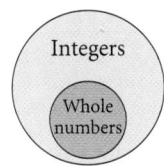

CHARLES FROHMAN PRESENTS
William Gillette
IN HIS NEW FOUR ACT DRAMA
"SHERLOCK HOLMES"

Real-World Connection

The key to Sherlock Holmes's success is his use of deductive reasoning.

36. Open-Ended Describe a real-life situation in which you used an indirect argument to convince someone of your point of view. Outline your argument. **Check students' work.**

37. Earl lives near a noisy construction site at which work ends promptly at 5:00 each workday. Earl thinks, "Today is Tuesday. If it were before 5:00, I would hear construction noise, but I don't hear any. So it must be later than 5:00."
a. What does Earl prove? **b.** What assumption does he make?
c. What fact would contradict the assumption? **a–c. See margin.**

 38. Literature In Arthur Conan Doyle's story "The Sign of the Four," Sherlock Holmes talks to his friend Watson about how a culprit enters a room that has only four entrances: a door, a window, a chimney, and a hole in the roof.
   "You will not apply my precept," he said, shaking his head. "How often have I said to you that when you have eliminated the impossible, whatever remains, however improbable, must be the truth? We know that he did not come through the door, the window, or the chimney. We also know that he could not have been concealed in the room, as there is no concealment possible. Whence, then, did he come?"
How did the culprit enter the room? Explain. **See margin.**

C **Challenge** *Proof* **39.** Use indirect reasoning to prove the following.

39. Assume ∠A ≅ ∠B. Then $\overline{BC} \cong \overline{AC}$ since if the base ⓢ are ≅, the sides opp. them are ≅. But this contradicts the given BC > AC. Thus ∠A ≇ ∠B.

Given: △ABC with BC > AC **See left.**
Prove: ∠A ≇ ∠B

Proof **40.** Write an indirect proof. **See margin.**

Given: △XYZ is isosceles.
Prove: Neither base angle is a right angle.

Proof **41.** Write an indirect proof. **See margin.**

Given: △ABC is scalene, $m\angle ABX = 36$, and $m\angle CBX = 36$.
Prove: $\overline{XB}$ is not perpendicular to $\overline{AC}$.

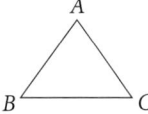

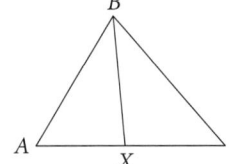

Standardized Test Prep

Multiple Choice

42. What is the negation of $x \le 10$? **D**
   A. $x \le -10$ **B.** $-x \le 10$ **C.** $-x > 10$ **D.** $x > 10$

43. What is the negation of $y > 8$? **G**
   F. $y \le -8$ **G.** $y \le 8$ **H.** $-y > 8$ **I.** $y > 8$

44. What is the inverse of $p \to q$? **D**
   A. $q \to p$ **B.** $\sim q \to \sim p$ **C.** $p \to q$ **D.** $\sim p \to \sim q$

Lesson 5-4 Inverses, Contrapositives, and Indirect Reasoning **269**

37. a. Earl proves that it's later than 5:00.
   b. He starts with the assumption that it is before 5:00.
   c. It is not noisy.

38. The culprit entered the room through a hole in the roof; the other possibilities were eliminated.

40. Assume one base ∠ is a right ∠. Then the other

base ∠ is also a right ∠ since the base ⓢ of an isosceles △ are congruent. But a △ can have at most one right ∠. So neither base ∠ is a right ∠.

269

4. Assess

 Lesson Quiz 5-4

1. Write the negation of the statement "∠D is a straight angle." ∠D is not a straight angle.

2. Identify two statements that contradict each other.
   I. x and y are perfect squares.
   II. x and y are odd.
   III. x and y are prime.
   I and III

For Exercises 3–6, use the following statement:
If ℓ is parallel to m, then ∠1 and ∠2 are supplementary.

3. Write the converse. **If ∠1 and ∠2 are supplementary, then ℓ is parallel to m.**

4. Write the inverse. **If ℓ is not parallel to m, then ∠1 and ∠2 are not supplementary.**

5. Write the contrapositive. **If ∠1 and ∠2 are not supplementary, then ℓ is not parallel to m.**

6. Write the first step of an indirect proof. **Assume that ∠1 and ∠2 are not supplementary.**

Alternative Assessment

Conditional: If △XYZ is acute, then △XYZ is right.
Have students work in pairs to
• write the converse, inverse, and contrapositive.
• explain why each of the four statements is true or false.

41. Assume $\overline{XB} \perp \overline{AC}$. Then ∠AXB and ∠CXB are right ⓢ. Since $m\angle ABX = m\angle CBX = 36$, then ∠A ≅ ∠C because if two ⓢ of a △ are ≅, the third ⓢ are ≅. Then AB = BC since sides opp. ≅ ⓢ are ≅ and △ABC is an isosceles △. But this contradicts the given statement that △ABC is scalene. Thus, $\overline{XB}$ is not ⊥ to $\overline{AC}$.

Take It to the NET
Online lesson quiz at
www.PHSchool.com
Web Code: afa-0504

Short Response

45. What is the contrapositive of the following statement? **H**
If two parallel lines are cut by a transversal, then the corresponding angles are congruent.
  F. If two lines are cut by a transversal and the corresponding angles are congruent, then the two lines are parallel.
  G. If two nonparallel lines are cut by a transversal, then the corresponding angles are not congruent.
  H. If two lines are cut by a transversal and the corresponding angles are not congruent, then the two lines are not parallel.
  I. If two parallel lines are cut by a transversal, then the corresponding angles are not congruent.

46. Use indirect reasoning to give a convincing argument that an obtuse triangle has at most one obtuse angle.

46. [2] Assume that a △ can have more than one obtuse ∠. Then the sum of the measures of the two obtuse ⩘ is greater than 180. But this contradicts the △-∠-Sum Thm. So a △ can have at most one obtuse ∠.
[1] partially incorrect logical argument

Mixed Review

Lesson 5-3

Is $\overline{XY}$ a perpendicular bisector, an angle bisector, an altitude, a median, or none of these? Explain.   47–49. See margin.

47.

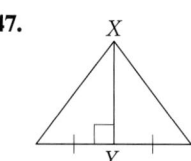

48.

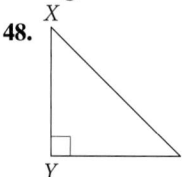

49.

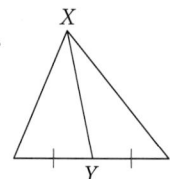

Lesson 3-1

Classify each pair of angles as *alternate interior angles*, *same-side interior angles*, or *corresponding angles*.

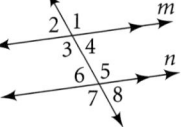

same-side int. ⩘

50. ∠1 and ∠5 **corr.** ⩘   **51.** ∠4 and ∠5

52. ∠3 and ∠5 **alt. int.** ⩘   **53.** ∠3 and ∠7 **corr.** ⩘

Lesson 2-4

Use the given property to complete each statement.

54. Addition Property of Equality
If $5x - 10 = 25$, then $5x = \underline{\ ?\ }$.
35

55. Symmetric Property of Equality
If $m\angle ABC = 45$, then $\underline{\ ?\ }$.
$45 = m\angle ABC$

Geometry at Work

······· **Industrial Designer**

Industrial designers work on two-dimensional surfaces to develop products that have three-dimensional appeal to consumers. They use computer-aided design (CAD) software to create two-dimensional screen images and manipulate them for three-dimensional effects. Fashion designers use CAD to study their creations on electronic human forms from various angles and distances.

Take It to the NET For more information about industrial design go to **www.PHSchool.com**.
Web Code: afb-2031

270   Chapter 5   Relationships Within Triangles

pages 267–270   **Exercises**

47. $\overline{XY}$ is an altitude because of the right ∠ and a median because Y is the midpoint of the opp. side. $\overline{XY}$ is also a ⊥ bis. and an ∠ bis.

48. $\overline{XY}$ is an altitude since it goes through a vertex and is ⊥ to the opp. side.

49. $\overline{XY}$ is a median since it has endpoints at a vertex and the midpoint of the opp. side.

Reading Indirect Proof

FOR USE WITH PAGE 268, EXERCISE 21

Read the problem below and then follow what Resa thinks as she solves the problem. Check your understanding by solving the exercise at the bottom of the page.

Fill in the blanks to prove the following statement.
  In a given triangle, $\triangle LMN$, there is at most one right angle.

Given: $\triangle LMN$

Prove: $\triangle LMN$ has at most one right angle.

Proof: Assume that $\triangle LMN$ has more than one **a.** __?__. That is, assume that both $\angle M$ and $\angle N$ are **b.** __?__. If $\angle M$ and $\angle N$ are both right angles, then $m\angle M = m\angle N =$ **c.** __?__. By the Triangle Angle-Sum Theorem, $m\angle L + m\angle M + m\angle N =$ **d.** __?__. Use substitution to find $m\angle L +$ **e.** __?__ $+$ **f.** __?__ $= 180$. When you solve for $m\angle L$, you find that $m\angle L =$ **g.** __?__. This means that there is no $\triangle LMN$, which contradicts the information you are given. So the assumption that $\triangle LMN$ has **h.** __?__ must be false. Therefore, $\triangle LMN$ has **i.** __?__.

What Resa Thinks

To prove $\triangle LMN$ has at most one right angle, I will assume that it does not have *at most* one. This means that it has more than one.

Now I'll copy the next line in the proof. Huh? Where did $\angle M$ and $\angle N$ come from? Oh, I see. "more than one" means "at least two," so I have to choose at least two angles and assume they are right angles.
The measure of a right angle is 90.

The Triangle Angle-Sum Theorem says that the sum of the measures of the angles in a triangle is 180. "Use substitution." I can substitute 90 for $m\angle M$ and for $m\angle N$. Solving for $m\angle L$ is easy.

But wait! How can $m\angle L = 0$?
Oh! I remember. In an indirect proof, I'm looking for a contradiction. Well, I've got one! The rest is easy.

What Resa Writes

Assume that $\triangle LMN$ has more than one **a.** right angle.

That is, assume that both $\angle M$ and $\angle N$ are **b.** right angles.

If $\angle M$ and $\angle N$ are both right angles, then $m\angle M = m\angle N =$ **c.** 90.

$m\angle L + m\angle M + m\angle N =$ **d.** 180.
Substitute to find
$m\angle L +$ **e.** 90 $+$ **f.** 90 $= 180$.
$m\angle L =$ **g.** 0.

So the assumption that $\triangle LMN$ has **h.** more than one right angle must be false. Therefore $\triangle LMN$ has **i.** at most one right angle.

EXERCISE

Complete Exercise 20, page 268.

a. 20 or more

b. the Debate Club and the Chess Club have fewer than 20 members

c. the Debate Club has fewer than 10 members

Reading Indirect Proof

The technique of indirect proof is an invaluable tool in many mathematics situations, both in geometry and in more advanced mathematics studies. This feature helps students understand how indirect proofs are developed, reinforces the negation of "at most one," and helps students begin generating their own indirect proofs.

Teaching Notes

The essence of indirect proof is assuming that the negation of a statement's conclusion leads to the negation of its hypothesis. This is equivalent to proving the contrapositive of the original statement. Because a statement and its contrapositive are logically equivalent, proving one true is equivalent to proving both true.

Visual Learners

Have a student provide a diagram for the class to follow as the proof unfolds.

Teaching Tip

Ask the class for examples of conditional statements and their contrapositives. Ask: *How could you write the contrapositive of "If figure* LMN *is a triangle, then it contains at most one right angle"?* **Sample: If figure *LMN* contains more than one right angle, then it is not a triangle.**

Exercise

Have students work independently to solve the problem, showing the steps they used. Then have volunteers share with the class what they were thinking as they wrote each step. Elicit the fact that there are often different ways to arrive at the solution of a problem.

Solving Inequalities

Solving Inequalities

Students will review solving algebraic inequalities before solving inequalities involving the side lengths and angle measures of triangles in Lesson 5-5.

Resources

 Technology
Geometry Resource Pro®:
   Algebra Review Resources
Computer Test Generator CD-ROM,
   Chapter 0, Extension Topics

Teaching Notes

The techniques used to solve inequalities mirror those for solving equations, with one important exception for division and multiplication by a negative number. Have students justify each step in several exercises to reinforce the similarities and differences between solving equations and inequalities.

Error Prevention

Students commonly do not reverse the inequality symbol when multiplying each side by a negative number. Ask them to multiply several inequalities by −1 and compare the products using a number line.

EXAMPLE Alternative Method

Students may find reversing the order of an inequality mysterious. Have them add the variable term with a negative coefficient to each side, as in the example below.

$$-6x + 7 > 25$$
$$7 > 25 + 6x$$
$$-18 > 6x$$
$$-3 > x$$

Point out that the last step is equivalent to $x < -3$.

The solutions of an inequality are all the numbers that make the inequality true. The following chart reviews the Properties of Inequality.

Property	Properties of Inequality
	For all real numbers $a, b, c,$ and d:
Addition Property	If $a > b$ and $c \geq d$, then $a + c > b + d$.
Multiplication Property	If $a > b$ and $c > 0$, then $ac > bc$.
	If $a > b$ and $c < 0$, then $ac < bc$.
Transitive Property	If $a > b$ and $b > c$, then $a > c$.
Comparison Property	If $a = b + c$ and $c > 0$, then $a > b$.

You use the Addition and Multiplication Properties of Inequality to solve inequalities.

EXAMPLE

Algebra Solve $-6x + 7 > 25$.

$-6x + 7 - 7 > 25 - 7$ Add −7 to each side (or subtract 7 from each side).

$\dfrac{-6x}{-6} < \dfrac{18}{-6}$ Multiply each side by $-\frac{1}{6}$ (or divide each side by −6). Remember to reverse the order of the inequality.

$x < -3$ Simplify.

EXERCISES

 **Algebra** Solve each inequality.

1. $7x - 13 \leq -20$ $x \leq -1$ **2.** $3x + 8 > 16$ $x > \frac{8}{3}$ **3.** $-2x - 5 < 16$ $x > -\frac{21}{2}$

4. $8y + 2 \geq 14$ $y \geq \frac{3}{2}$ **5.** $5a + 1 \leq 91$ $a \leq 18$ **6.** $-x - 2 > 17$ $x < -19$

7. $-4z - 10 < -12$ $z > \frac{1}{2}$ **8.** $9x - 8 \geq 82$ $x \geq 10$ **9.** $6n + 3 \leq -18$ $n \leq -\frac{7}{2}$

10. $c + 13 > 34$ $c > 21$ **11.** $3x - 5x + 2 < 12$ $x > -5$ **12.** $x - 19 < -78$ $x < -59$

13. $-n - 27 \leq 92$ $n \geq -119$ **14.** $-9t + 47 < 101$ $t > -6$ **15.** $8x - 4 + x > -76$ $x > -8$

16. $2(y - 5) > -24$ $y > -7$ **17.** $8b + 3 \geq 67$ $b \geq 8$ **18.** $-3(4x - 1) \geq 15$ $x \leq -1$

19. $r - 9 \leq -67$ $r \leq -58$ **20.** $\frac{1}{2}(4x - 7) \geq 19$ $x \geq \frac{45}{4}$ **21.** $5x - 3x + 2x < -20$ $x < -5$

22. $9x - 10x + 4 < 12$ $x > -8$ **23.** $-3x - 7x \leq 97$ $x \geq -9.7$ **24.** $8y - 33 > -1$ $y > 4$

25. $4a + 17 \geq 13$ $a \geq -1$ **26.** $-4(5z + 2) > 20$ $z < -\frac{7}{5}$ **27.** $x + 78 \geq -284$ $x \geq -362$

28. $6c \geq -12 - 24$ $c \geq -6$ **29.** $27 - 12 < 3x$ $x > 5$ **30.** $8y - 4y + 11 \leq -33$ $y \leq -11$

31. $5x - 2x + 13 > -8$ $x > -7$ **32.** $4(5a + 3) \leq -8$ $a \leq -1$ **33.** $8c + 2c + 7 < -10 - 3c$ $c < -2$

Inequalities in Triangles

2.03 Apply properties, definitions, and theorems of two-dimensional figures to solve problems and write proofs: a) Triangles.

Lesson Preview

What You'll Learn

OBJECTIVE 1 To use inequalities involving angles of triangles

OBJECTIVE 2 To use inequalities involving sides of triangles

. . . And Why

To locate the largest corners on a triangular backyard deck, as in Example 2

✔ **Check Skills You'll Need** (For help, go to Lessons 1-6 and 5-4.)

Graph the triangles with the given vertices. List the sides in order from shortest to longest. 1–4. See back of book.

1. $A(5, 0), B(0, 8), C(0, 0)$

2. $P(2, 4), Q(-5, 1), R(0, 0)$

3. $G(3, 0), H(4, 3), J(8, 0)$

4. $X(-4, 3), Y(-1, 1), Z(-1, 4)$

Recall the steps for indirect proof.

5. You want to prove $m\angle A > m\angle B$. Assume that $m\angle A \leq m\angle B$. Write the first step of an indirect proof.

6. In an indirect proof, you deduce that $AB \geq AC$ is false. What conclusion can you make? **$AB < AC$**

 Interactive lesson includes instant self-check, tutorials, and activities.

OBJECTIVE
1 Inequalities Involving Angles of Triangles

When you empty a container of juice into two glasses, it is difficult to be sure that the glasses get equal amounts. You can be sure, however, that each glass holds less than the original amount in the container. This is a simple application of the Comparison Property of Inequality.

🔑 **Key Concepts**

Property	Comparison Property of Inequality
	If $a = b + c$ and $c > 0$, then $a > b$.

Proof **Proof of the Comparison Property**

Given: $a = b + c, c > 0$

Prove: $a > b$

Statements	Reasons
1. $c > 0$	1. Given
2. $b + c > b + 0$	2. Addition Property of Inequality
3. $b + c > b$	3. Simplify.
4. $a = b + c$	4. Given
5. $a > b$	5. Substitute a for $b + c$ in Statement 3.

The Comparison Property of Inequality allows you to prove the following corollary to the Exterior Angle Theorem for triangles (Theorem 3-8).

Ongoing Assessment and Intervention

Before the Lesson	During the Lesson	After the Lesson
Diagnose prerequisite skills using:	**Monitor progress using:**	**Assess knowledge using:**
• Check Skills You'll Need	• Check Understanding	• Lesson Quiz
	• Additional Examples	• Computer Test Generator CD
	• Standardized Test Prep	

1. Plan

Lesson Preview

✔ **Check Skills You'll Need** 🖳

Finding Distance
Lesson 1-6: Example 1
Exercises 1–9
Extra Practice, p. 690

Indirect Proof
Lesson 5-4: Examples 3, 5
Exercises 10–15, 20, 21
Extra Practice, p. 694

Lesson Resources

📁 **Teaching Resources**
Practice, Reteaching, Enrichment

📖 **Reaching All Students**
Practice Workbook 5-5
Spanish Practice Workbook 5-5
Reading and Math Literacy 5C
Spanish Reading & Literacy 5C
Hands-On Activities 15
Informal Geometry Planning Guide 5-5

⏰ **Presentation Assistant Plus!**
Transparencies
• Check Skills You'll Need 5-5
• Additional Examples 5-5
• Student Edition Answers 5-5
• Lesson Quiz 5-5
PH Presentation Pro CD 5-5

 **PRENTICE HALL ASSESSMENT SYSTEM**

Computer Test Generator CD

💿 **Technology**
Resource Pro® CD-ROM
Computer Test Generator CD
Prentice Hall Presentation Pro CD

 www.PHSchool.com
Student Site
• Teacher Web Code: afk-5500
• Self-grading Lesson Quiz
Teacher Center
• Lesson Planner
• Resources

Plus

Math Background

Theorems 5-10 and 5-11 can be treated as extending the Isosceles Triangle Theorem and its converse to the case of inequality. These theorems enable students to prove in Exercise 41 that the shortest segment from a point to a line is perpendicular to the line.

OBJECTIVE

1 **Teaching Notes**

1 EXAMPLE

Remind students that a corollary is both a statement that follows directly from a theorem and a theorem itself.

2 EXAMPLE **Tactile Learners**

Have students construct a triangle to model the problem, using sides 18 cm, 21 cm, and 27 cm long to see that the larger angles are opposite the longer sides.

Additional Examples

1 Explain why $m\angle 4 > m\angle 5$.

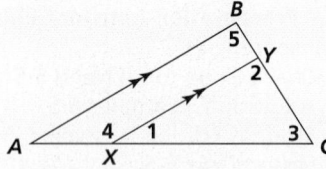

$m\angle 4 > m\angle 2$ by the Corollary to the Exterior Angle Theorem, $m\angle 2 = m\angle 5$ because $\angle 2$ and $\angle 5$ are congruent corresponding angles, and $m\angle 4 > m\angle 5$ by substitution.

2 In $\triangle RGY$, $RG = 14$, $GY = 12$, and $RY = 20$. List the angles from largest to smallest. $\angle G, \angle Y, \angle R$

 Key Concepts

Corollary	Corollary to the Triangle Exterior Angle Theorem

The measure of an exterior angle of a triangle is greater than the measure of each of its remote interior angles.

$$m\angle 1 > m\angle 2 \text{ and } m\angle 1 > m\angle 3$$

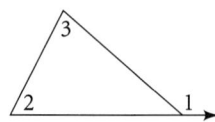

Proof **Proof of the Corollary**

Given: $\angle 1$ is an exterior angle of the triangle.

Prove: $m\angle 1 > m\angle 2$ and $m\angle 1 > m\angle 3$.

Proof: By the Exterior Angle Theorem, $m\angle 1 = m\angle 2 + m\angle 3$. Since $m\angle 2 > 0$ and $m\angle 3 > 0$, you can apply the Comparison Property of Inequality and conclude that $m\angle 1 > m\angle 2$ and $m\angle 1 > m\angle 3$.

1 EXAMPLE **Applying the Corollary**

In the diagram, $m\angle 2 = m\angle 1$ by the Isosceles Triangle Theorem. Explain why $m\angle 2 > m\angle 3$.

By the corollary to the Exterior Angle Theorem, $m\angle 1 > m\angle 3$. So, $m\angle 2 > m\angle 3$ by substitution.

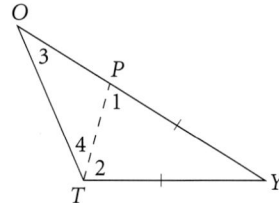

✓ Check Understanding **1** Explain why $m\angle OTY > m\angle 3$. **$m\angle OTY > m\angle 2$** **by the Comparison Prop. of Ineq. Since it was proven that $m\angle 2 > m\angle 3$, then by the Trans. Prop. $m\angle OTY > m\angle 3$.** You will prove the following inequality theorem in the exercises.

 Key Concepts

Theorem 5-10

If two sides of a triangle are not congruent, then the larger angle lies opposite the longer side.

If $XZ > XY$, then $m\angle Y > m\angle Z$.

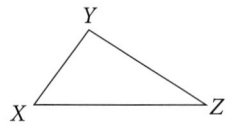

Real-World Connection

Careers Landscape architects blend structures with decorative plantings.

2 EXAMPLE **Real-World 🌐 Connection**

Deck Design A landscape architect is designing a triangular deck. She wants to place benches in the two larger corners. Which corners have the larger angles?

Corners B and C have the larger angles. They are opposite the two longer sides of 27 ft and 21 ft.

✓ Check Understanding **2** List the angles of $\triangle ABC$ in order from smallest to largest. $\angle A, \angle C, \angle B$

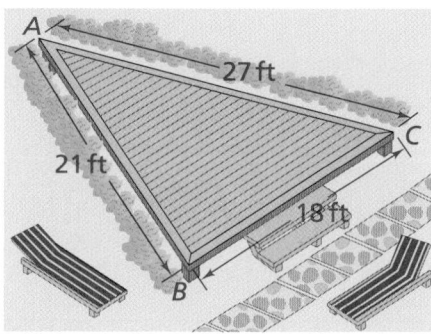

👥 Reaching All Students

Below Level Using geometry software to alter the sides and angles of triangles (beginning with an isosceles triangle) may help students understand Theorems 5-10 and 5-11.	**Advanced Learners** Have students find the range of possible values for the length of the third side of a triangle whose other side lengths are a and b. If $b \geq a$, $b - a < c < a + b$.	**English Learners** See note on page 277. **Visual Learners** See note on page 276.

Theorem 5-10 on the preceding page states that the larger angle is opposite the longer side. The converse is also true.

 Key Concepts

Theorem 5-11

If two angles of a triangle are not congruent,
then the longer side lies opposite the larger angle.

If $m\angle A > m\angle B$, then $BC > AC$.

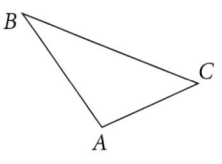

Proof

Need Help?

Indirect proof steps:
1. Assume the opposite.
2. Find a contradiction.
3. State a conclusion.

Indirect Proof of Theorem 5-11

Given: $m\angle A > m\angle B$

Prove: $BC > AC$

Step 1 Assume $BC \not> AC$. That is, assume $BC < AC$ or $BC = AC$.

Step 2 If $BC < AC$, then $m\angle A < m\angle B$ (Theorem 5-10). This contradicts the given fact that $m\angle A > m\angle B$. Therefore, $BC < AC$ must be false.

If $BC = AC$, then $m\angle A = m\angle B$ (Isosceles Triangle Theorem). This also contradicts $m\angle A > m\angle B$. Therefore, $BC = AC$ must be false.

Step 3 The assumption $BC \not> AC$ is false, so $BC > AC$.

3 **EXAMPLE** **Using Theorem 5-11**

In $\triangle TUV$, which side is shortest?

By the Triangle Angle-Sum Theorem, $m\angle T = 60$.
The smallest angle in $\triangle TUV$ is $\angle U$. It follows, by
Theorem 5-11, that the shortest side is $\overline{TV}$.

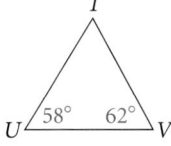

✓ Check Understanding

3 List the sides of the $\triangle XYZ$ in order from
shortest to longest. Explain your listing.
$\overline{YZ} < \overline{XY} < \overline{XZ}$ since $m\angle Y = 80$.

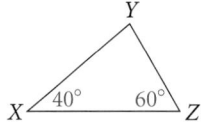

Not every set of three segments can form a triangle. The lengths of the segments must be related in a certain way.

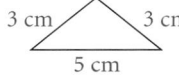

3 cm, 3 cm, 5 cm   2 cm, 2 cm, 6 cm

Notice that only one of the sets of three segments above can form a triangle. The sum of the smallest two lengths must be greater than the greatest length. This is Theorem 5-12 (see next page). You will prove it in the exercises.

Teaching Tip
The proof of Theorem 5-11 uses Theorem 5-10, which students have not yet proved. You may wish to prove it as a class in Exercise 33 before using it in step 2 of the proof of Theorem 5-11.

3 **EXAMPLE** **Error Prevention**

Emphasize that Theorems 5-10 and 5-11 apply only within triangles, not between triangles.

4 **EXAMPLE** **Math Tip**

Ask: *Why does comparing only the sum of the two shorter sides and the longest side tell whether a triangle can have the given lengths?* If the least sum is greater than the greatest length, the other inequalities must be true also.

5 **EXAMPLE**

Discuss why "$x > 2$ and $x > -2$" can be written as $x > 2$. Point out that the possible lengths are written as a compound inequality.

Additional Examples

3 In $\triangle ABC$, $\angle C$ is a right angle. Which is the longest side? $\overline{AB}$

4 Can a triangle have sides with the given lengths? Explain.
a. 2 cm, 2 cm, 4 cm no; $2 + 2 \not> 4$
b. 8 in., 15 in., 12 in. yes; $8 + 12 > 15$

5 In $\triangle FGH$, $FG = 9$ m and $GH = 17$ m. Describe the possible lengths of $\overline{FH}$. $8 < FH < 26$

Closure

Explain why each triangle below is impossible.

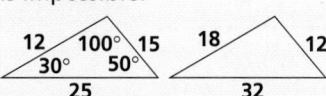

In the first triangle, the side opposite the smallest angle is not the shortest side; the second triangle violates the Triangle Inequality Theorem.

3. Practice

Assignment Guide

 **Objective**
- **A** **B** Core 1–9, 30, 33

2 Objective
- **A** **B** Core 10–29, 31, 32, 34–36
- **C** Extension 37–41

Standardized Test Prep 42–47

Mixed Review 48–59

Exercise 1 If necessary, remind students of the Vertical Angles Theorem.

Exercise 5 Ask: *How do you know x > 0?* Side lengths must be positive numbers.

Exercise 6 Make sure that students can explain why ∠*I* is the largest angle in △*GHI*.

Visual Learners

Exercises 7–9 Have students draw and label each triangle to make sure that they identify opposite angles correctly.

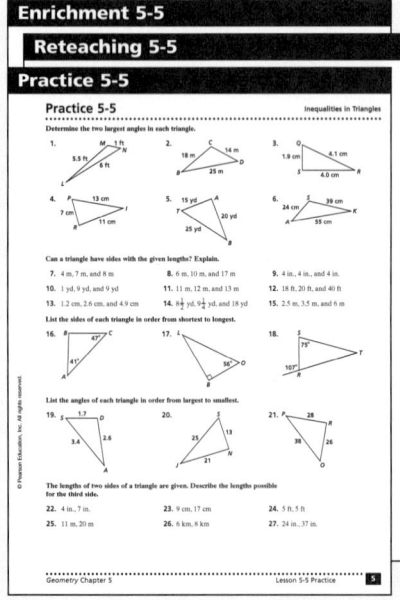

 **Key Concepts**

 Need Help?
You may find it easier to recall this theorem as "The shortest path between two points is the straight path."

Theorem 5-12 | **Triangle Inequality Theorem**

The sum of the lengths of any two sides of a triangle is greater than the length of the third side.

$$XY + YZ > XZ$$
$$YZ + ZX > YX$$
$$ZX + XY > ZY$$

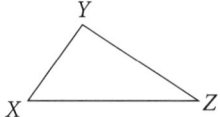

---

4 EXAMPLE Using the Triangle Inequality Theorem

Can a triangle have sides with the given lengths? Explain.

a. 3 ft, 7 ft, 8 ft

$3 + 7 > 8$
$8 + 7 > 3$
$3 + 8 > 7$ Yes

The sum of any two lengths is greater than the third length.

b. 3 cm, 6 cm, 10 cm

$3 + 6 \not> 10$ No

The sum of 3 and 6 is not greater than 10, contradicting Theorem 5-12.

✓ **Check Understanding** **4** Can a triangle have sides with the given lengths? Explain.
a. 2 m, 7 m, and 9 m
no; $2 + 7 \not> 9$
b. 4 yd, 6 yd, and 9 yd
yes; $4 + 6 > 9$; $6 + 9 > 4$; and $4 + 9 > 6$

5 EXAMPLE Finding Possible Side Lengths

Algebra A triangle has sides of lengths 8 cm and 10 cm. Describe the lengths possible for the third side.

Let x represent the length of the third side. By the Triangle Inequality Theorem,

$x + 8 > 10$ $x + 10 > 8$ $8 + 10 > x$
$x > 2$ $x > -2$ $x < 18$

The third side must be longer than 2 cm and shorter than 18 cm.

✓ **Check Understanding** **5** A triangle has sides of lengths 3 in. and 12 in. Describe the lengths possible for the third side. **9 < x < 15**

EXERCISES

For more practice, see *Extra Practice*.

Practice and Problem Solving

A **Practice by Example**

Example 1 (page 274)

Explain why $m\angle 1 > m\angle 2$. 1–3. See margin.

1.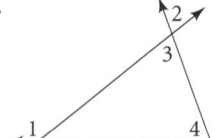

2.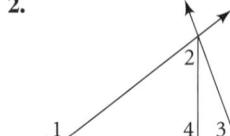

3.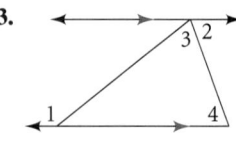

---

pages 276–279 Exercises

1. ∠3 ≅ ∠2 because they are vertical ⧌ and m∠1 > m∠3 by Corollary to the Ext. ∠ Thm. So, m∠1 > m∠2 by subst.

2. An ext. ∠ of a △ is larger than either remote int. ∠.

3. m∠1 > m∠4 by Corollary to the Ext. ∠ Thm. and ∠4

≅ ∠2 because if ‖ lines, then alt. int. ⧌ are ≅.

16. No; $2 + 3 \not> 6$.

17. Yes; $11 + 12 > 15$; $12 + 15 > 11$; $11 + 15 > 12$.

Visual Learners

Exercises 13–15 Have students draw and label each triangle to make sure that they identify opposite sides correctly.

Example 2
(page 274)

List the angles of each triangle in order from smallest to largest.

4.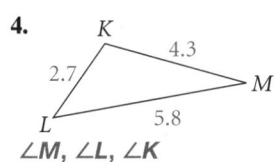
∠*M*, ∠*L*, ∠*K*

5. ∠*D*, ∠*C*, ∠*E*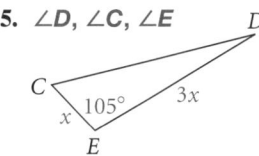

6.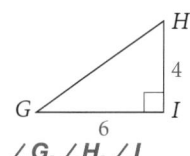
∠*G*, ∠*H*, ∠*I*

7. △*ABC*, where *AB* = 8, *BC* = 5, and *CA* = 7
∠*A*, ∠*B*, ∠*C*

8. △*DEF*, where *DE* = 15, *EF* = 18, and *DF* = 5
∠*E*, ∠*F*, ∠*D*

9. △*XYZ*, where *XY* = 12, *YZ* = 24, and *ZX* = 30
∠*Z*, ∠*X*, ∠*Y*

Example 3
(page 275)

List the sides of each triangle in order from shortest to longest.

10.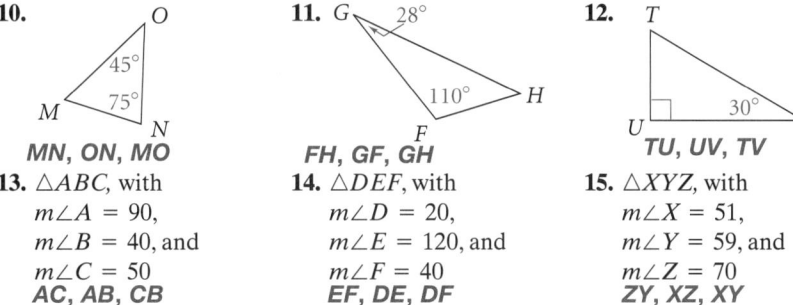
MN, *ON*, *MO*

11. *FH*, *GF*, *GH*

12. *TU*, *UV*, *TV*

13. △*ABC*, with
    m∠*A* = 90,
    m∠*B* = 40, and
    m∠*C* = 50
    AC, *AB*, *CB*

14. △*DEF*, with
    m∠*D* = 20,
    m∠*E* = 120, and
    m∠*F* = 40
    EF, *DE*, *DF*

15. △*XYZ*, with
    m∠*X* = 51,
    m∠*Y* = 59, and
    m∠*Z* = 70
    ZY, *XZ*, *XY*

English Learners

Exercise 22–27 Have students practice writing the solutions both as compound inequalities and in words.

Careers

Exercise 28 Traveling sales representatives make a great effort to plan their routes efficiently. When traveling to multiple destinations over the course of a day, week, or month, a sales representative makes a schedule of routes that minimizes travel time and maximizes time with customers.

Exercise 29 Check that students use the Triangle Inequality Theorem in their explanation.

Example 4
(page 276)

Can a triangle have sides with the given lengths? Explain. **16–21. See margin.**

16. 2 in., 3 in., 6 in.

17. 11 cm, 12 cm, 15 cm

18. 8 m, 10 m, 19 m

19. 1 cm, 15 cm, 15 cm

20. 2 yd, 9 yd, 10 yd

21. 4 m, 5 m, 9 m

Example 5
(page 276)

 **Algebra** **The lengths of two sides of a triangle are given. Describe the lengths possible for the third side.**

22. 8 ft, 12 ft **4 < *s* < 20**

23. 5 in., 16 in. **11 < *s* < 21**

24. 6 cm, 6 cm **0 < *s* < 12**

25. 18 m, 23 m **5 < *s* < 41**

26. 4 yd, 7 yd **3 < *s* < 11**

27. 20 km, 35 km **15 < *s* < 55**

Technology Tip

Exercise 30 Students can use geometry software to investigate the Hinge Theorem and its converse.

Exercise 40 You may wish to use this as a class proof to assess students' understanding of the ideas in this lesson.

B **Apply Your Skills**

28. **Error Analysis** The Shau family is crossing Kansas on Highway 70. A sign reads "Wichita 90 miles, Topeka 110 miles." Avi says, "I didn't know that it was only 20 miles from Wichita to Topeka." Explain to Avi why the distance between the two cities doesn't have to be 20 miles. **See margin.**

29. **Writing** Explain why the distance between the two peaks in the photograph is greater than the difference of the distances from the hiker to each of the peaks.
    See margin.

30. **The Hinge Theorem** The hypothesis of the Hinge Theorem is stated below. The conclusion is missing. **a–d. See margin.**

    Suppose two sides of one triangle are congruent to two sides of another triangle. If the included angle of the first triangle is larger than the included angle of the second triangle, then ___?___ .

    a. Draw a diagram to illustrate the hypothesis.
    b. The conclusion of the Hinge Theorem concerns the sides opposite the two angles mentioned in the hypothesis. Write the conclusion.
    c. Draw a diagram to illustrate the converse.
    d. **Converse of the Hinge Theorem** Write the conclusion to this theorem.

    Suppose two sides of one triangle are congruent to two sides of another triangle. If the third side of the first triangle is greater than the third side of the second triangle, then ___?___ .

Exercise 29

30. a.

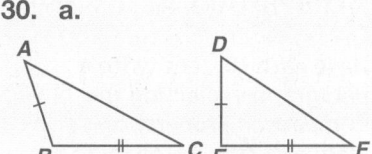

b. The third side of the 1st △ is longer than the third side of the 2nd △.

c. See diagram in part (a).

d. The included ∠ of the first △ is greater than the included ∠ of the second △.

Lesson 5-5 Inequalities in Triangles **277**

18. No; 8 + 10 ≯ 19.

19. Yes; 1 + 15 > 15; 15 + 15 > 1.

20. Yes; 2 + 9 > 10; 9 + 10 > 2; 2 + 10 > 9.

21. No; 4 + 5 ≯ 9.

28. Answers may vary. Sample: If *Y* is the distance between Wichita and Topeka, then 20 < *Y* < 200.

29. Let the distance between the peaks be *d* and the distances from the hiker to each of the peaks be *a* and *b*. Then *d* + *a* > *b* and *d* + *b* > *a*. Thus, *d* > *b* − *a* and *d* > *a* − *b*.

4. Assess

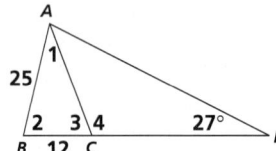

Lesson Quiz 5-5

Use the figure for
Exercises 1–3.

1. Explain why $m\angle 4 > m\angle 1$.
   $m\angle 4 > m\angle 1$ by the
   Corollary to the Exterior
   Angle Theorem.

2. Explain why $m\angle 3 > m\angle 1$.
   By Theorem 5-10, if two
   sides are not congruent,
   the larger angle lies
   opposite the longer side,
   so $m\angle 3 > m\angle 1$.

3. Use $\triangle ABC$ to describe the
   possible lengths of $\overline{AC}$.
   $13 < AC < 37$

4. Can a triangle have lengths
   of 2 mm, 3 mm, and 6 mm?
   Explain. no; $2 + 3 \not> 6$

5. In $\triangle XYZ$, $XY = 5$, $YZ = 8$,
   and $XZ = 7$. Which angle
   is largest? $\angle X$

6. In $\triangle PQT$, $m\angle P = 50$ and
   $m\angle T = 70$. Which side is
   shortest? $\overline{QT}$

Alternative Assessment

Have each student write a
paragraph explaining the
Comparison Property of
Inequality, the Corollary to the
Exterior Angle Theorem, the
two theorems that relate the
relative positions of the angles
and sides of a triangle, and the
Triangle Inequality Theorem.

pages 276–279 Exercises

31. **Answers may vary.**
    Sample: The shortcut
    across the grass is
    shorter than the sum of
    the two paths.

278

Exercise 31

 Need Help?

Exercise 33 plan: Get
$m\angle 4 + m\angle 2 > m\angle 2$,
$m\angle 2 = m\angle 1$, and
$m\angle 1 > m\angle 3$.

C Challenge

38. (2, 4), (2, 6), (3, 3),
    (3, 4), (3, 5), (3, 6),
    (3, 7), (4, 3), (4, 4),
    (4, 5), (4, 6), (4, 7),
    (4, 8)

---

31. **Shortcuts** Explain how the student in the photograph is applying the Triangle
    Inequality Theorem. **See margin.**

x^2 32. **Algebra** Find the longest side of $\triangle ABC$, if $m\angle A = 70$, $m\angle B = 2x - 10$, and
    $m\angle C = 3x + 20$. $\overline{AB}$

Proof 33. **Developing Proof** Fill in the blanks to complete a proof of Theorem 5-10:
    If two sides of a triangle are not congruent, then the larger angle lies opposite
    the longer side.

Given: $\triangle TOY$, with $YO > YT$.

Prove: a. __?__ > b. __?__ $m\angle OTY$; $m\angle 3$

Mark P on $\overline{YO}$ so that $\overline{YP} \cong \overline{YT}$. Draw $\overline{TP}$.

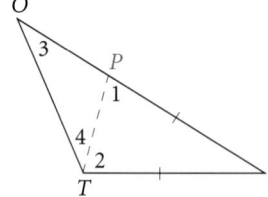

Statements	Reasons
1. $\overline{YP} \cong \overline{YT}$	1. Ruler Post.
2. $m\angle 1 = m\angle 2$	c. __?__ Base $\angle$s of an isos. $\triangle$ are $\cong$.
3. $m\angle OTY = m\angle 4 + m\angle 2$	d. __?__ $\angle$ Add. Post.
4. $m\angle OTY > m\angle 2$	e. __?__ Comparison Prop. of Ineq.
5. $m\angle OTY > m\angle 1$	f. __?__ Sub. (step 2)
6. $m\angle 1 > m\angle 3$	g. __?__ An ext. $\angle$ of a $\triangle$ is greater than
7. $m\angle OTY > m\angle 3$	either remote int. $\angle$.
	h. __?__ Trans. Prop. of Ineq.

Critical Thinking Determine which segment is shortest in each diagram.

34. $\overline{RS}$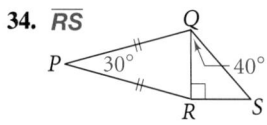

35. $\overline{CD}$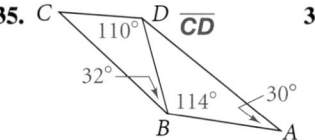

36. $\overline{XY}$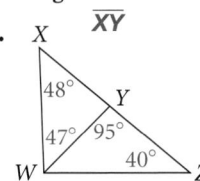

37. **Probability** A student has two straws, one 6 cm long and the other 9 cm long.
    She picks a third straw at random from a group of four straws whose lengths
    are 3 cm, 5 cm, 11 cm, and 15 cm. What is the probability that the straw she
    picks will allow her to form a triangle? $\frac{1}{2}$

For Exercises 38 and 39, x and y are whole numbers, $1 < x < 5$, and $2 < y < 9$.

38. The sides of a triangle are 5 cm, x cm, and y cm. List possible (x, y) pairs.
    See left.

39. **Probability** What is the probability that you can draw an isosceles triangle that
    has sides 5 cm, x cm, and y cm, with x and y chosen at random? $\frac{5}{18}$

Proof 40. Prove Theorem 5-12: The sum of the lengths of any two sides
    of a triangle is greater than the length of the third side.

Given: $\triangle ABC$ **See margin.**

Prove: $AC + CB > AB$

(*Hint:* On $\overrightarrow{BC}$ mark a point D not on $\overline{BC}$, so that $DC = AC$.
Draw $\overline{DA}$ and use Theorem 5-11 with $\triangle ABD$.)

41. **Reasoning** A corollary to Theorem 5-11 states:
    The perpendicular segment from a point to a line
    is the shortest segment from the point to the line.
    Given that $\overline{PT} \perp \overline{TA}$, show that $PA > PT$. **See margin**
    p. 279.

278 Chapter 5 Relationships Within Triangles

40.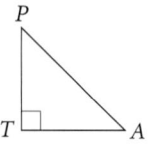

$CD = AC$ is given so
$\triangle ACD$ is isosc. by def.

of isosc. $\triangle$. This means
$m\angle D = m\angle CAD$. Then
$m\angle DAB > m\angle CAD$ by
the Comparison Prop.
of Ineq. So by subst.,
$m\angle DAB > m\angle D$ and by
Thm. 5-11 $DB > AB$.

Since $DC + CB = DB$,
by subst.
$DC + CB > AB$. Using
subst. again, $AC +$
$CB > AB$.

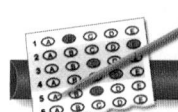

Standardized Test Prep

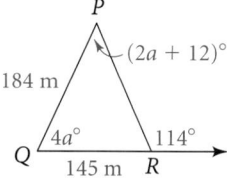

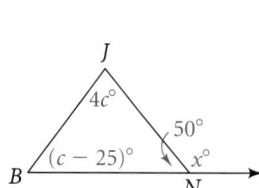

Multiple Choice

42. Which is the best estimate for *PR*? **D**
   A. 137 m   **B.** 145 m
   C. 163 m   **D.** 187 m

Quantitative Comparison

Compare the boxed quantity in Column A with the boxed quantity in Column B. Choose the best answer.
   A. The quantity in Column A is greater.
   B. The quantity in Column B is greater.
   C. The two quantities are equal.
   D. The relationship cannot be determined from the information given.

not to scale

	Column A	Column B
A 43.	x	c
B 44.	*JN*	*BN*
C 45.	$x - 4c$	$c - 25$
B 46.	*JB*	*BN*

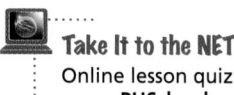

Short Response

Take It to the NET
Online lesson quiz at
www.PHSchool.com
Web Code: afa-0505

47. In △*ABC*, $m\angle A > m\angle C > m\angle B$. **a–b. See margin.**
   a. Of $\overline{AB}$ and $\overline{AC}$, one measures 5 inches and the other measures 9 inches. Which measures 9 inches? Explain.
   b. Based on your conclusion for part (a), find all possible whole-number measures for the third side. Explain.

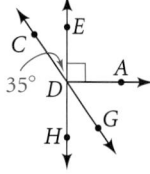

Mixed Review

Lesson 5-4   Write the negation of each statement.

48. $m\angle A \le m\angle B$ $m\angle A > m\angle B$

49. $m\angle X > m\angle B$ $m\angle X \le m\angle B$

50. The angle is a right angle.
The angle is not a right angle.

51. The triangle is not obtuse.
The triangle is obtuse.

Lesson 2-5   Use the diagram. Find the measure of each angle.

52. ∠*ADH* 90   **53.** ∠*GDH* 35

54. ∠*CDH* 145   **55.** ∠*ADG* 55

Lesson 1-7   Find to the nearest tenth of a square unit the area of each circle with the given radius *r* or diameter *d*.

56. $r = 1.6$ ft
   8.0 ft²

57. $d = 35$ mm
   962.1 mm²

58. $r = 0.5$ m
   0.8 m²

59. $d = 20$ mi
   314.2 mi²

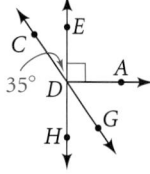

Lesson 5-5   Inequalities in Triangles   **279**

---

41. ∠*T* is the largest ∠ in △*PTA*. Thus *PA* > *PT* because the longest side of a △ is opp. the largest ∠.

47. [2] a. Since $m\angle A > m\angle C > m\angle B$, the sides opp. them are related in the same way: *BC* > *AB* > *AC*. Of $\overline{AB}$ and $\overline{AC}$, $\overline{AB}$ is longer than $\overline{AC}$. Since 9 in. > 5 in., *AB* = 9 in. and *AC* = 5 in.

b. $\overline{BC}$ is the longest side, and 9 < *BC* < 14. The possible whole number measures for $\overline{BC}$ are 10 in., 11 in., 12 in., and 13 in.

[1] part (a) OR part (b) incorrect

279

Using a Variable

Assessment tests at the high school level typically assume that a student has facility with basic algebraic ideas and techniques. This feature helps students understand how to use a variable or variables to represent and solve problems that are fundamentally geometric.

Resources

PRENTICE HALL
ASSESSMENT SYSTEM

Test-Taking Strategies with Transparencies
- Transparency 5
- Practice sheet p. 17

Teaching Notes

Help students understand that algebraic techniques can be effectively employed in problems that might not seem algebraic. The example and exercises in this feature come from geometry, but all yield to algebraic methods of solution.

Visual Learners

Have students use the information in the exercises to draw or construct diagrams that accurately represent Exercises 1, 2, 4, and 5.

Test-Taking Strategies with Transparencies

Test-Taking Strategy: Using a Variable

Sometimes you can use a variable to solve a problem.

Example A taxi ride costs a flat fee of $1.75 plus $.80 per mile. What is the fare for traveling 5 miles?

  A. $4.00   B. $1.75   C. $5.75   D. $41.75

Choose variables: Let m = miles traveled and c = cost.

Describe the situation in words:

    Cost = flat fee + cost for traveling m miles

Use variables to express the cost: $c = 1.75 + 0.80m$

Substitute $m = 5$: $c = 1.75 + 0.80(5)$

           = 1.75 + 4

           = $5.75

The answer is $5.75, or choice C.

Use a variable to find the answer. Explain your reasoning.

1. The measures of the angles of a triangle are in the ratio 2 : 4 : 6. Find the measure of the smallest angle.

    A. 15°   B. 20°   C. 30°   D. 60°

2. One side of a rectangle is 3 times the other side. The perimeter is 16 cm. How long is the long side?

    F. 8 cm   G. 2 cm   H. 3 cm   I. 16 cm

Solutions

1. C

2. I

Transparency 5

280

You can solve many problems by using a variable to represent an unknown quantity. You use the variable to write an equation or inequality. In the Example, Method 1 uses one variable and Method 2 uses two variables.

EXAMPLE

Algebra Points A, B, and C are collinear. BC is 6 less than twice AB, and $AC = 30$. What is the length of $\overline{BC}$?

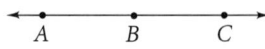

Method 1

Let $AB = x$,

then $BC = 30 - x$.   **The length of $\overline{AC}$ is 30.**

BC is 6 less than twice AB,

  $30 - x = 2x - 6$

  $36 - x = 2x$ **Solve for x.**

     $36 = 3x$

      $x = 12$

Therefore $AB = 12$ and $BC = 30 - 12 = 18$.

Method 2

Let $AB = x$ and $BC = y$.

Since $AC = AB + BC = 30, x + y = 30$.

Since BC is 6 less than twice AB, $y = 2x - 6$.

  $x + (2x - 6) = 30$ **Substitute $2x - 6$ for y.**

      $3x - 6 = 30$

         $3x = 36$

          $x = 12$

Therefore $AB = 12$ and $BC = 2(12) - 6 = 18$.

EXERCISES

x^2 **Algebra** **Write and solve an equation to answer each question.**

1. Points A, B, C, and D are collinear. AB is 15 more than BC, and CD is 8 more than BC. If AD is 5 less than twice AB, what are the lengths AB, BC, and CD? **17, 2, 10**

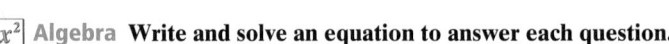

2. $\overline{AB}$ is perpendicular to $\overline{BN}$ in the diagram at the right. What are the coordinates of point N? $\left(8\frac{1}{3}, 0\right)$

3. The angles of a triangle are three consecutive even integers. What are the measures of the angles? **58, 60, 62**

4. Point P is on the x-axis, 13 units from point $C(7, 5)$. What are the possible coordinates of P? **(19, 0), (−5, 0)**

5. What are the coordinates of the point P on the x-axis such that the slope of a line from P to $A(1, 4)$ is twice the slope of a line from P to $B(9, 10)$? **(−1, 0)**

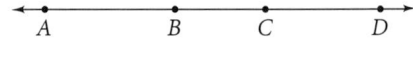

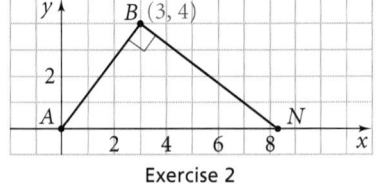

Exercise 2

Chapter Review

Vocabulary

altitude of a triangle (p. 259)
centroid (p. 258)
circumcenter of a triangle (p. 257)
circumscribed about (p. 257)
concurrent (p. 257)
contrapositive (p. 264)
coordinate proof (p. 244)

distance from a point to a line (p. 250)
equivalent statements (p. 265)
incenter of a triangle (p. 257)
indirect proof (p. 265)
indirect reasoning (p. 265)
inscribed in (p. 257)

inverse (p. 264)
median of a triangle (p. 258)
midsegment (p. 243)
negation (p. 264)
orthocenter of a triangle (p. 259)
point of concurrency (p. 257)

Reading Math
Understanding
Vocabulary

2. distance from the point
to the line

Take It to the NET
Online vocabulary quiz
at **www.PHSchool.com**
Web Code: afj-0551

Choose the correct vocabulary term to complete each sentence.

1. A *(centroid, median of a triangle)* is a segment whose endpoints are a vertex and the midpoint of the side opposite the vertex. **median of a △**

2. The length of the perpendicular segment from a point to a line is the *(midsegment, distance from the point to the line)*.

3. If T is a point on the perpendicular bisector of $\overline{FG}$, then $TF = TG$ because of the *(Perpendicular Bisector Theorem, Angle Bisector Theorem)*. **⊥ Bis. Thm.**

4. The *(altitude, median)* of a triangle is a perpendicular segment from a vertex to the line containing the side opposite the vertex. **altitude**

5. The notation $\sim q \rightarrow \sim p$ is the *(inverse, contrapositive)* of $p \rightarrow q$. **contrapositive**

6. To write a(n) *(indirect proof, negation)*, you start by assuming that the opposite of what you want to prove is true. **indirect proof**

7. In $\triangle ABC$, $AB + BC > AC$ because of the *(Comparison Property of Inequality, Triangle Inequality Theorem)*. **△ Ineq. Thm.**

8. The *(circumcenter, incenter)* of a triangle is the point of concurrency of the angle bisectors of the triangle. **incenter**

9. The *(Angle Bisector Theorem, Triangle Inequality Theorem)* says that if a point is on the bisector of an angle, then it is equidistant from the sides of the angle. **∠ Bis. Thm.**

10. A point where three lines intersect is a *(point of concurrency, incenter)*. **point of concurrency**

Skills and Concepts

5-1 and 5-2 Objectives

▼ To use properties of midsegments to solve problems

▼ To use properties of perpendicular bisectors and angle bisectors

A **midsegment** of a triangle is a segment that connects the midpoints of two sides. A midsegment is parallel to the third side, and is half its length.

In a **coordinate proof**, a figure is drawn on a coordinate plane and formulas are used to prove properties of the figure.

The **distance from a point to a line** is the length of the perpendicular segment from the point to the line. The Perpendicular Bisector Theorem together with its converse states that a point is on the perpendicular bisector of a segment if and only if it is equidistant from the endpoints of the segment. The Angle Bisector Theorem together with its converse states that a point is on the bisector of an angle if and only if it is equidistant from the sides of the angle.

Resources

Student Edition
Extra Practice Ch. 5, p. 694
English/Spanish Glossary, p. 741
Postulates and Theorems, p. 732
Table of Symbols, p. 725

Reaching All Students
Reading and Math Literacy 5D
Spanish Reading and Literacy 5D

PRENTICE HALL ASSESSMENT SYSTEM

Standardized Test Prep
● Ch. 5 practice in standardized test formats

www.PHSchool.com
Student Site
● Self-grading Vocabulary Test
Teacher Center
● Resources

Plus **iTEXT**

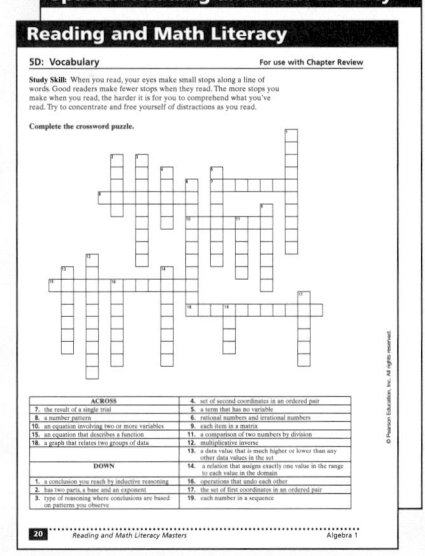

x^2 **Algebra** Find the value of x.

11.
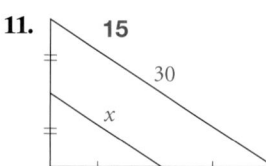

12. 11
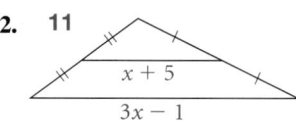

Use the figure to find each segment length or angle measure.

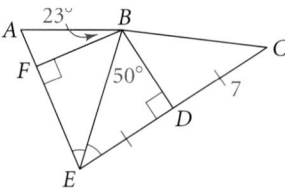

13. $m\angle BEF$ 40

14. FE 7

15. EC 14

16. $m\angle CEA$ 80

5-3 Objectives

▼ To identify properties of perpendicular bisectors and angle bisectors

▼ To identify properties of medians and altitudes of a triangle

When three or more lines intersect in one point, they are **concurrent**.

The **median of a triangle** is a segment whose endpoints are a vertex and the midpoint of the opposite side. The **altitude of a triangle** is a perpendicular segment from a vertex to the line containing the opposite side.

For any given triangle, special segments and lines are concurrent:

- the perpendicular bisectors of the sides at the circumcenter, the center of the circle that can be **circumscribed about** the triangle
- the bisectors of the angles at the incenter, the center of the circle that can be **inscribed in** the triangle
- the medians at the **centroid**
- the lines containing the altitudes at the **orthocenter of the triangle.**

Graph $\triangle ABC$ **with vertices** $A(2, 3)$, $B(-4, -3)$, **and** $C(2, -3)$. **Find the coordinates of each point of concurrency.**

17. circumcenter $(-1, 0)$　　**18.** centroid $(0, -1)$　　**19.** orthocenter $(2, -3)$

Determine whether $\overline{AB}$ **is a perpendicular bisector, an angle bisector, a median, an altitude, or none of these. Explain.**

20.
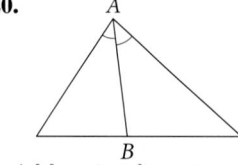
∠ bisector, because it bisects an ∠

21.
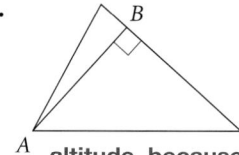
altitude, because it is ⊥ to a side

22.
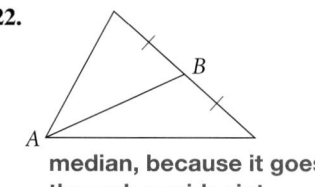
median, because it goes through a midpoint

5-4 Objectives

▼ To write the negation of a statement and the inverse and contrapositive of a conditional statement

▼ To use indirect reasoning

The **negation** of a statement has the opposite truth value. The **inverse** of a conditional statement is the negation of both the hypothesis and the conclusion. The **contrapositive** of a conditional statement switches the hypothesis and the conclusion and negates both. Statements that always have the same truth value are **equivalent statements.**

To use **indirect reasoning,** consider all possibilities and then prove all but one false. The remaining possibility must be true.

23. Inverse: If it is not snowing, then it is not cold outside. Contrapositive: If it is not cold outside, then it is not snowing.

24. Inverse: If an angle is not obtuse, then its measure is not greater than 90 and less than 180. Contrapositive: If an angle's measure is not greater than 90 and less than 180, then it is not obtuse.

25. Inverse: If a figure is not a square, then its sides are not congruent. Contrapositive: If a figure's sides are not congruent, then it is not a square.

The three steps of an **indirect proof** are:

Step 1 State as an assumption the opposite (negation) of what you want to prove.

Step 2 Show that this assumption leads to a contradiction.

Step 3 Conclude that the assumption must be false and that what you want to prove must be true.

Write the inverse and the contrapositive of each statement.

23. If it is snowing, then it is cold outside. **23–25. See left.**

24. If an angle is obtuse, then its measure is greater than 90 and less than 180.

25. If a figure is a square, then its sides are congruent.

26. If you are in Australia, then you are south of the equator. See margin.

Write a convincing argument that uses indirect reasoning. **27–30. See margin.**

27. The product of two numbers is even. Show that at least one of the two numbers must be even.

28. Show that a right angle cannot be formed by the intersection of nonperpendicular lines.

29. Show that a triangle can have at most one obtuse angle.

30. Show that an equilateral triangle cannot have an obtuse angle.

5-5 Objectives

▼ To use inequalities involving angles of triangles

▼ To use inequalities involving sides of triangles

If two sides of a triangle are not congruent, then the larger angle lies opposite the longer side. The converse is also true. If two angles are not congruent, then the longer side lies opposite the larger angle.

The measure of an exterior angle of a triangle is greater than the measure of each of its remote interior angles. The sum of the lengths of any two sides of a triangle is greater than the length of the third side.

List the angles and sides in order from smallest to largest.

31.

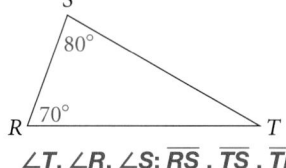

$\angle T, \angle R, \angle S; \overline{RS}, \overline{TS}, \overline{TR}$

32.

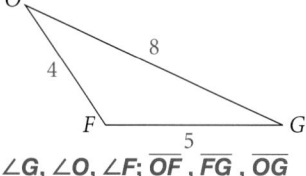

$\angle G, \angle O, \angle F; \overline{OF}, \overline{FG}, \overline{OG}$

Is it possible for a triangle to have sides with the given lengths? Explain.

34. Yes; each pair > 3rd.

35. Yes; each pair > 3rd.

33. 5 in., 8 in., 15 in. **No; 5 + 8 ≯ 15.**

34. 10 cm, 12 cm, 20 cm

35. 20 m, 22 m, 24 m

36. 3 ft, 6 ft, 8 ft **Yes; each pair > 3rd.**

37. 1 yd, 1 yd, 3 yd **No; 1 + 1 ≯ 3.**

38. 5 km, 6 km, 7 km **Yes; each pair > 3rd.**

Two side lengths of a triangle are given. Write an inequality to show the range of values, x, for the length of the third side.

39. 4 in., 7 in. **$3 < x < 11$**

40. 8 m, 15 m **$7 < x < 23$**

41. 2 cm, 8 cm **$6 < x < 10$**

42. 12 ft, 13 ft **$1 < x < 25$**

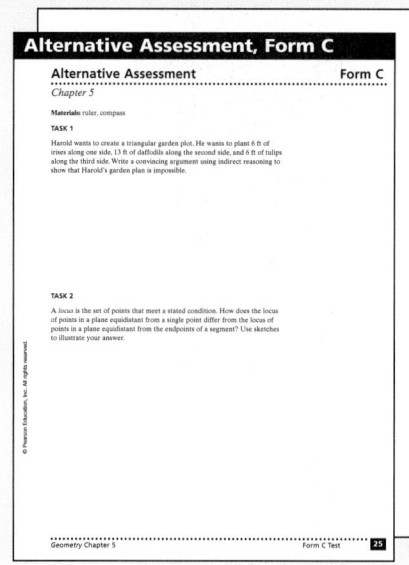

page 281   Chapter Review

26. Inverse: If you are not in Australia, then you are not south of the equator. Contrapositive: If you are not south of the equator, then you are not in Australia.

27. Assume that both numbers are odd. The product of 2 odd numbers is always odd, which contradicts that the product is even. Therefore, at least one number must be even.

28. Assume a right ∠ can be formed by non-perp. lines. Then by the def. of ⊥, the lines are ⊥. Therefore, the assumption is false.

29. Assume that a △ has 2 obtuse ⦞. Then these ⦞ by def. are greater than 90, which makes their sum greater than 180. But the sum of the measures of the ⦞ of a △ = 180, so the assumption must be false.

30. Assume an ∠ is obtuse, and therefore has measure greater than 90. Since the △ is equilateral, it is equiangular, and each ∠ measures 60.

283

Chapter Test

Take It to the NET
Online chapter test at
www.PHSchool.com
Web Code: afa-0552

Write (a) the inverse and (b) the contrapositive of
each statement.   1–3. See margin.

1. If a polygon has eight sides, then it is an octagon.

2. If it is a leap year, then it is an even-numbered year.

3. If it is snowing, then it is not summer.

4. What can you conclude
   from the diagram?
   Justify your answer.
   See back of book.

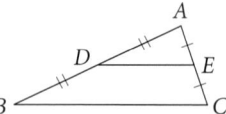

Identify the two statements that contradict each other.

5. I. $\triangle PQR$ is a right triangle. **I and II**
    II. $\triangle PQR$ is an obtuse triangle.
    III. $\triangle PQR$ is scalene.

6. I. $\angle DAS \cong \angle CAT$ **II and III**
    II. $\angle DAS$ and $\angle CAT$ are vertical.
    III. $\angle DAS$ and $\angle CAT$ are adjacent.

List the angles of $\triangle ABC$ from smallest to largest.

7. $AB = 9, BC = 4, AC = 12$ $\angle A, \angle C, \angle B$

8. $AB = 10, BC = 11, AC = 9$ $\angle B, \angle C, \angle A$

9. $AB = 3, BC = 9, AC = 7$ $\angle C, \angle B, \angle A$

10. **Open-Ended** Write three lengths that cannot
    be the lengths of the three sides of a triangle.
    Explain your answer. **Answers may vary.**
    Sample: 2, 4, 8 because 2 + 4 ≯ 8

List the sides of each triangle in order from shortest
to longest.

11.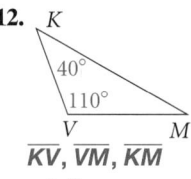
$\overline{ST}, \overline{SR}, \overline{RT}$

12.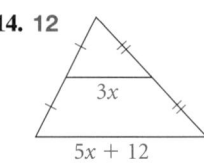
$\overline{KV}, \overline{VM}, \overline{KM}$

x^2 **Algebra** Find the value of x in each figure.

13. **6.5**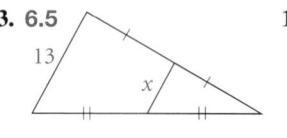

14. **12**

15. **Writing** Use indirect reasoning to explain why the
    following statement is true: If an isosceles triangle
    is obtuse, then the obtuse angle is the vertex angle.
    See back of book.

x^2 **Algebra** Find the values of x and KM in each figure.

16. **7; 27**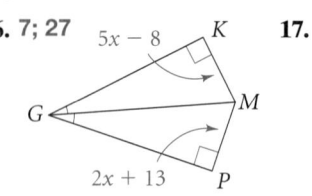

17. **G** $\frac{2}{3}; \frac{8}{3}$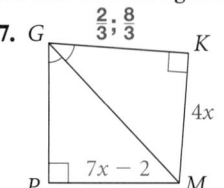

Coordinate Geometry Find the center of the circle
that circumscribes $\triangle ABC$.

18. $A(0,0), B(0,-3), C(-5,-3)$ $\left(-2\frac{1}{2}, -1\frac{1}{2}\right)$

19. $A(0,5), B(-4,5), C(-4,-3)$ $(-2, 1)$

20. $A(3,-1), B(-2,-1), C(3,-8)$ $\left(\frac{1}{2}, -4\frac{1}{2}\right)$

21. $\triangle ABC$ has vertices $A(2,5), B(2,-3), C(10,-3)$.
    What point of concurrency is at $(6,1)$?
    circumcenter

22. Complete the paragraph proof below.

   Given: $\overleftrightarrow{PQ}$ is the perpendicular bisector of $\overline{AB}$.
   $\overleftrightarrow{QT}$ is the perpendicular bisector of $\overline{AC}$.

   Prove: $QC = QB$

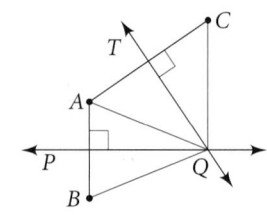

   Proof: $QC = $ **a.** ?
   and **b.** ? $= QB$. **QA**
   Therefore, $QC = QB$
   by the **c.** ? .
   Trans. Prop. of =

23. What can you
    conclude about
    point Y? Explain.
    See margin.

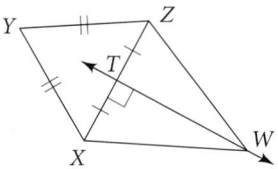

24. In the figure, $WK = KR$.
    What can you conclude
    about point A? Explain.
    A is on $\overrightarrow{CK}$, the $\angle$ bisector
    of $\angle SCD$.

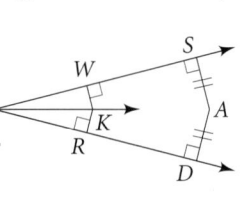

page 284   Chapter Test

1. a. If a polygon does not have 8
      sides, then it is not an octagon.
   b. If a polygon is not an octagon,
      then it does not have 8 sides.

2. a. If it is not a leap year, then it is not
      an even-numbered year.
   b. If it is not an even-numbered year,
      then it is not a leap year.

3. a. If it is not snowing, then it is
      summer.

b. If it is summer, then it is not
   snowing.

23. **Y** is on $\overleftrightarrow{TW}$, the ⊥ bis.
    of $\overline{XZ}$; **Y** is equidist. from
    X and **Z**.

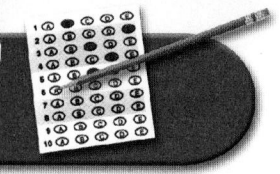

Standardized Test Prep

Reading Comprehension Read the passage below. Then answer the questions on the basis of what is *stated* or *implied* in the passage.

The Kitchen Triangle Architects, builders, and anyone who has ever prepared a full meal in a kitchen know that in most kitchen activities you go back and forth between the sink, the stove, and the refrigerator. Those three locations form what is called the "work triangle" or the "kitchen triangle."

A large apartment complex made this table of kitchen triangle dimensions for four of its units.

Kitchen Triangle Distances (cm)

Apt.	Stove to Sink	to Fridge	to Stove
A	250	280	240
B	145	320	165
C	115	220	330
D	310	152	270

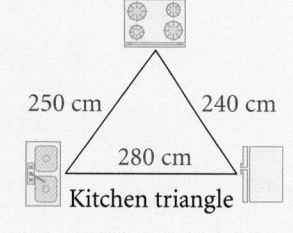

250 cm   240 cm

280 cm

Kitchen triangle

To have an efficient kitchen, it should be easy to traverse each side of the kitchen triangle.

---

1. Why are the sink, stove, and refrigerator the vertices of the kitchen triangle? **B**
   A. Architects and builders say they are.
   B. You walk between these three appliances in most kitchen activities.
   C. Most apartments have these appliances.
   D. A sink, stove, and refrigerator form an efficient kitchen.

2. In apartment A, which appliance is at the vertex of the largest angle? **G**
   F. the sink
   G. the stove
   H. the refrigerator
   I. cannot be determined

3. In apartment D, which appliance is at the vertex of the smallest angle? **B**
   A. the sink
   B. the stove
   C. the refrigerator
   D. cannot be determined

4. The description of one kitchen triangle is incorrect. Which one? Justify your answer.
   See margin.

5. In which kitchen is it least efficient for two persons to work? Justify your answer.
   See margin.

In kitchen triangle A, a microwave is halfway between the stove and sink, and an electric can opener is halfway between the fridge and sink.

6. What is the distance between the microwave and the can opener? Justify your answer.
   F. 120 cm   G. 125 cm   H. 240 cm   I. 265 cm
   See margin.

7. To go from the microwave to the can opener, you must go in the direction you would travel from the stove to the refrigerator. Why?
   A midsegment is ∥ to the 3rd side.

8. Which kitchen triangle has a midsegment triangle with smallest perimeter? **C**
   A. A
   B. D
   C. C
   D. cannot be determined

9. For which kitchen triangle do you need the fewest steps to go from one vertex to another and then to the third? Justify your answer.
   F. A   G. C
   H. D   I. cannot be determined
   See below.

10. In Apartment D, how far is it from stove to sink by way of the refrigerator? **C**
    A. 270 cm   B. 310 cm   C. 422 cm   D. 462 cm

9. G; since only two sides of the △ are needed, C has the least sum.

Students must be able to extract information from reading passages, answer multiple-choice questions, and construct responses in order to be successful on current state and national assessments.

To answer the questions, students apply skills and concepts from this chapter and previous chapters.
Multiple Choice: Items 1–3, 6, 8–10
Extended Response: Items 4, 5, 7

Resources

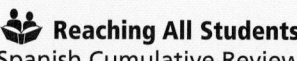 **Teaching Resources**
Cumulative Review

 **Reaching All Students**
Spanish Cumulative Review

 PRENTICE HALL
ASSESSMENT SYSTEM

Standardized Test Prep Workbook
• Ch. 5 standardized Test Practice
Assessment Masters
• Cumulative Review
Computer Test Generator CD
• Standardized Test Practice

www.PHSchool.com
• Standardized Test Practice
• Resources

Plus

Cumulative Review

Cumulative Review
Chapters 1–5

For Exercises 1–16, choose the best answer.

1. At the local bakery a small chocolate chip cookie has a diameter of 2 in. How much more cookie do you get if you buy a supercookie with a diameter of 6 in.?
   A. 8π in.²   B. 10π in.²   C. 32π in.²   D. 40π in.²

2. Find the value of x in the diagram at the right.
   A. 5.5   B. 11   C. 22   D. 44

3. Which side lengths would not make a triangle?
   A. 2, 4, 5   B. 3, 8, 6   C. 4, 5, 1, 9   D. 4, 3, 7

4. Find the value of y in the diagram at the right.
   A. ⅛   B. ½   C. 3   D. 5

5. The lengths of the sides of △ABC are AB = 8, BC = 6, and AC = 10. Put the angles in order from smallest to largest.
   A. ∠A, ∠B, ∠C   C. ∠B, ∠C, ∠A
   B. ∠B, ∠C, ∠A   D. ∠B, ∠A, ∠C

6. What can you conclude about the diagram at the right?
   A. △LNO is isosceles.   B. NP is a midsegment.
   C. ∠LMP = ∠LPM   D. ½MP = NO

7. What is the next number in the sequence?
   128, 64, 32, 16, 8, ...
   A. 5   B. 10   C. 15   D. 4

8. Which is not a point of concurrency?
   A. centroid   B. orthocenter   C. median   D. incenter

9. Which are the appropriate names for the polygon shown at the right?
   I. quadrilateral   II. rectangle   III. parallelogram   IV. rhombus
   A. I and IV   B. I and II   C. III and IV   D. I and III

10. Which line is perpendicular to y = ½x + 9?
    A. 3y = −9x + 1   B. 4y = 12x − 7
    C. 3y = −6x + 11   D. 6y = 2x − 1

11. What is the inverse of the statement "If the sky is blue, then it is not raining"?
    A. If the sky is not blue, then it is raining.
    B. If it is not raining, then the sky is blue.
    C. If it is raining, then the sky is not blue.
    D. If the sky is blue, then it is raining.

---

page 285   Standardized Test Prep

4. B; the sum of two sides of the △ (145 and 165) is not greater than the third side (320).

5. B; the △ has the least perimeter, so two people have less room.

6. F; it is a midsegment of the △ and is half the length of the third side.

Chapter 6

Quadrilaterals

Chapter at a Glance

North Carolina Objectives

6-1 Classifying Quadrilaterals	2.03b

NCTM 1, 2, 3, 4, 7, 8, 9, 10
  ▽ Classifying Special Quadrilaterals

6-2 Properties of Parallelograms	2.03b

NCTM 2, 3, 6, 7, 8, 9, 10
  ▽ Properties: Sides and Angles
  ▽ Properties: Diagonals and Transversals

6-3 Proving That a Quadrilateral Is a Parallelogram	2.03b

NCTM 2, 3, 6, 7, 8, 9, 10
  ▽ Is the Quadrilateral a Parallelogram?

6-4 Special Parallelograms	2.03b

NCTM 3, 4, 5, 6, 7, 8, 9, 10
  ▽ Diagonals of Rhombuses and Rectangles
  ▽ Is the Parallelogram a Rhombus or a Rectangle?

6-5 Trapezoids and Kites	2.03b

NCTM 3, 4, 6, 7, 8, 9, 10
  ▽ Properties of Trapezoids and Kites

6-6 Placing Figures in the Coordinate Plane	2.03b

NCTM 2, 3, 7, 8, 9, 10
  ▽ Naming Coordinates

6-7 Proofs Using Coordinate Geometry	2.03b

NCTM 2, 3, 4, 6, 7, 8, 9, 10
  ▽ Building Proofs in the Coordinate Plane

NCTM STANDARDS 2000

1	Number and Operations	6	Problem Solving
2	Algebra	7	Reasoning and Proof
3	Geometry	8	Communication
4	Measurement	9	Connections
5	Data Analysis and Probability	10	Representation

Pacing Options

This chart suggests pacing only for the lessons and their parts. It is provided as a possible guide. It will help you determine how much time you have in your schedule to cover other components, such as the features, Chapter Review and Chapter Test.

Day	Traditional 45 min.	Two-Year 45 min.	Block 90 min.
1	6-1 ▽	6-1 ▽	6-1 ▽
2	6-2 ▽	6-1 ▽	6-2 ▽ ▽
3	6-2 ▽	6-2 ▽	6-3 ▽
4	6-3 ▽	6-2 ▽	6-4 ▽ ▽
5	6-4 ▽	6-2 ▽	6-5 ▽
6	6-4 ▽	6-2 ▽	6-6 ▽
7	6-5 ▽	6-3 ▽	6-7 ▽
8	6-6 ▽	6-3 ▽	
9	6-7 ▽	6-4 ▽	
10		6-4 ▽	
11		6-4 ▽	
12		6-4 ▽	
13		6-5 ▽	
14		6-5 ▽	
15		6-6 ▽	
16		6-6 ▽	
17		6-7 ▽	
18		6-7 ▽	
19			
20			
21			
22			

NAEP Correlation (National Assessment of Educational Progress 2000 Mathematics Objectives)

6-1	6-2	6-3	6-4	6-5	6-6	6-7
G1a, b, G9a	G1a, b	G1a, b	G1a, b	G1a, b	G9a	G9a

N = Number Sense, Properties, and Operations; **M** = Measurement; **G** = Geometry and Spatial Sense;
D = Data Analysis, Statistics, and Probability; **A** = Algebra and Functions

286A

Math Background

Chapter Overview

The focus of this chapter is on the hierarchy of special quadrilaterals, their properties, and the applications of those properties. Most of the proofs in this chapter are written as paragraph, two-column, flow, and coordinate proofs.

Classifying Quadrilaterals   6-1

The hierarchy of quadrilaterals can help students who are troubled by questions such as "Is a square always a rectangle?" or "Is a rectangle always a square?" They also may gain insight by using the hierarchy to make a Venn diagram. Practice in using definitions and theorems helps students who have not thought much about classifying relationships to determine, for example, whether theorems true for squares are always true for rectangles, or vice versa.

Students who easily master and use this hierarchy, which is arranged by the number of pairs of parallel sides of a quadrilateral, may be interested in or already know alternative definitions that result in different connections among quadrilaterals.

For example, use the following definitions: A quadrilateral is a kite if it has two distinct pairs of congruent adjacent sides; a trapezoid if it has at least one pair of parallel sides; an isosceles trapezoid if it is a trapezoid and has at least one pair of congruent base angles. Using these definitions, a rhombus is a kite, a parallelogram is a trapezoid, and a rectangle is an isosceles trapezoid. Here is the revised hierarchy.

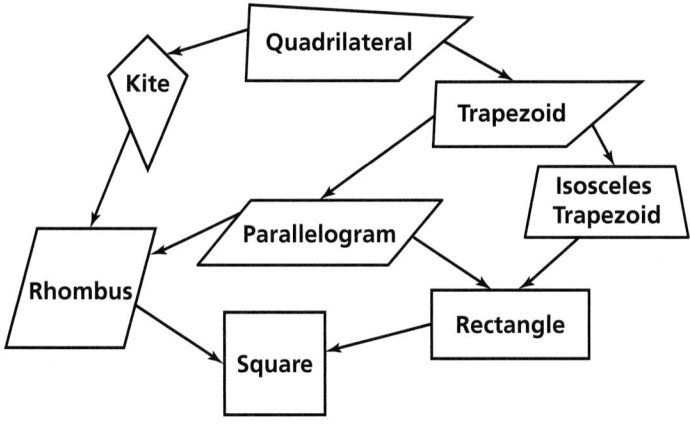

Definitions are a matter of agreement, and changing them usually changes the relationships defined by them. In the revised hierarchy, a rhombus is both a kite and a trapezoid. Theorems may apply to more types of quadrilaterals in the revised hierarchy than in the text's hierarchy. For example, proving that the diagonals of a kite are perpendicular is relatively easy with the text's hierarchy, but is not true in the revised hierarchy.

An alternative way to categorize quadrilaterals is by symmetries. For example, squares, rectangles, and isosceles trapezoids have base-bisector symmetry about a line through the midpoints of opposite bases, so they may be categorized together. Squares also have angle-bisector symmetry about a line through one diagonal, as do rhombuses and kites. Students may enjoy classifying quadrilaterals by the number of each type of symmetry (square: 2 base-bisector and 2 angle-bisector symmetries; rhombus: 2 angle-bisector symmetries; rectangle: 2 base-bisector symmetries; kite: 1 angle-bisector symmetry; isosceles trapezoid: 1 base-bisector symmetry). Exploring symmetries in either hierarchy may bring home to students that, despite all their other properties, parallelograms generally are not symmetric.

Parallelograms and Their Properties   6-2, 6-3, 6-4

It is important to treat proofs as a means to an end and not as the goal of these lessons. Remind students that, for example, because a square is a special rhombus, it has all the properties of a rhombus. Students may find it helpful to copy the hierarchy on a large sheet of paper and then list the properties proved in these lessons under the most general applicable quadrilateral. This also might help them observe that many of these theorems are converses of each other. For example, Theorems 6-7 and 6-8 are converses of Theorems 6-1 and 6-2. In addition to stating theorems and their converses in *if and only if* format, students might discuss ways of grouping the theorems. For example, there are five ways (including the definition) to determine that a quadrilateral is a parallelogram.

Trapezoids and Kites   6-5

You might point out to students that engineers often construct walls, dams, and levees with trapezoidal cross sections to strengthen them. And, the outline of a pair of chair legs is often trapezoidal rather than rectangular, for stability.

Students who worked with the alternate hierarchy should verify that the theorems in this lesson about trapezoids also hold true in the alternate hierarchy. All kite theorems apply both to convex and concave kites, although "opposite sides" is not applied to concave polygons.

Using the Coordinate Plane   6-6, 6-7

Keys to effective coordinate proofs are (1) confidence with distance, midpoint, and slope formulas, and (2) proper placement of the figure in the coordinate plane. Encourage students to develop expertise in all five proof formats (paragraph, two-column, flow, indirect, and coordinate) so that they may more easily select the best proof format for a specific exercise.

Ongoing Assessment and Intervention

Tools for Monitoring Student Progress

The Prentice Hall *Geometry* program provides you with many options for assessment in the Student Edition, the Teacher's Edition and the teaching resources. From these options, you may choose instructional materials and techniques that are appropriate for your students and support your district's curriculum requirements.

 Instant Check System™ in Chapter 6

Allows students to check their own learning before, during, and after each lesson.

Diagnosing Readiness before the chapter (p. 286)

Check Skills You'll Need exercises in each lesson (pp. 288, 294, 303, 312, 320, 326, 332)

Check Understanding questions with each Example (pp. 289, 290, 295, 296, 297, 302, 305, 306, 313, 314, 315, 321, 322, 327, 333)

Checkpoint Quiz (pp. 310 and 331)

Test Prep in Chapter 6

Teaches students strategies and gives them practice with all the test item formats they will encounter on state tests and standardized national exams.

Standardized Test Prep exercises in each lesson (pp. 293, 301, 309, 318, 325, 330, 337)

Test-Taking Strategies (p. 338: Drawing a Diagram)

Standardized Test Prep (p. 343: Cumulative Review)

 PRENTICE HALL ASSESSMENT SYSTEM

All your assessment needs in one place!

Program Assessment

Assess student progress throughout the *Geometry* text with blackline masters and CD-ROM.

Assessment Resources

- Checkpoint Quizzes 1 & 2
- Chapter Test, Forms A & B
- Chapter Alternative Assessment

Spanish versions available. Tests for Informal Geometry also available.

Computer Test Generator

- Unlimited questions of varying difficulty for every lesson objective.
- Create your own practice sheets, quizzes, and tests, or use the pre-made Chapter Tests.
- Diagnose readiness with questions on prerequisite skills.
- Prepare students by making tests based on standardized test objectives.
- Access Algebra 1, Geometry, and Algebra 2 content—all on one CD-ROM.

Test Preparation

A three-step approach to preparing students for high stakes, national, and state exams.

❶ **Diagnose & Prescribe**

Content Diagnostic Tests

- Diagnose strengths and weaknesses in content for national and state tests.
- Prescribe individualized reteaching opportunities.

❷ **Review & Reteach**

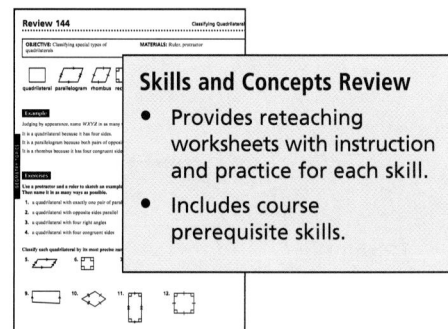

Skills and Concepts Review

- Provides reteaching worksheets with instruction and practice for each skill.
- Includes course prerequisite skills.

❸ **Practice & Assess**

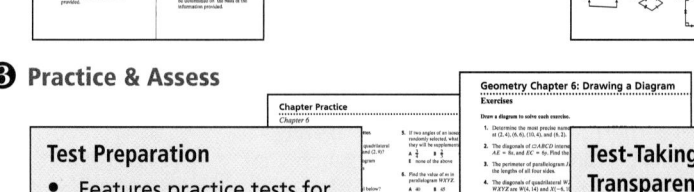

Test Preparation

- Features practice tests for End-of-Course and SAT/ACT exams.
- Includes standardized test practice by chapter for ongoing review.

Teacher's Guide with answers and correlations.

Test-Taking Strategies with Transparencies

- Support the Test-Taking Strategies pages in the Student Edition.
- Provide a teaching transparency and a practice worksheet for each strategy.

Reaching All Students

Support in the Student Text and Additional Resources

The textbook, the iText, and other technology components provide numerous opportunities to reach students of various ability levels and learning styles. Each Teacher's Edition lesson suggests how you can help *all* your students be successful and understand the mathematics in Chapter 6.

Below Level

Student Edition
- Diagnosing Readiness*: p. 286
- Check Skills You'll Need*: pp. 288, 294, 303, 312, 320, 326, 332

Reteaching
Chapter 6 Support File: pp. 8–14

Informal Geometry Planning Guide
Chapter 6 Lesson Plans: pp. 32–38
Chapter 6 Tests: pp. 99–102

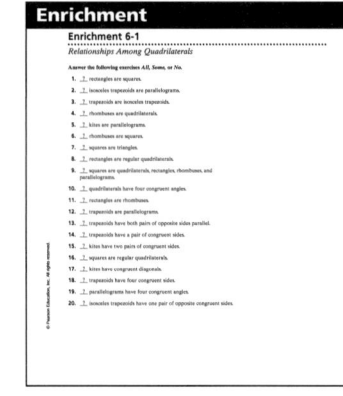

* Can be used with all ability levels to ensure mastery of prerequisite skills.

Advanced Learners

Student Edition
- Challenge exercises: pp. 293, 301, 309, 318, 324, 329, 336

Enrichment
Chapter 6 Support File: pp. 15–21

Reading and Math Literacy

Student Edition
- Vocabulary: pp. 287, 339, *plus* in every Lesson Preview
- Reading Math: pp. 289, 294, 299, 302, 316, 326, 334, 339
- Illustrated Glossary: pp. 741–777

Reading and Math Literacy Masters
Chapter 6: pp. 21–24

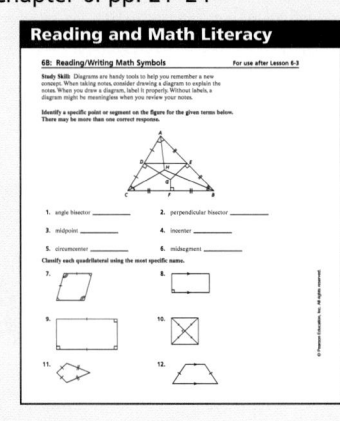

English Learners

Student Edition
- English/Spanish Illustrated Glossary: pp. 741–777

Workbook and Masters
Spanish Practice Workbook: pp. 32–38
Spanish Reading and Math Literacy Masters: pp. 21–24

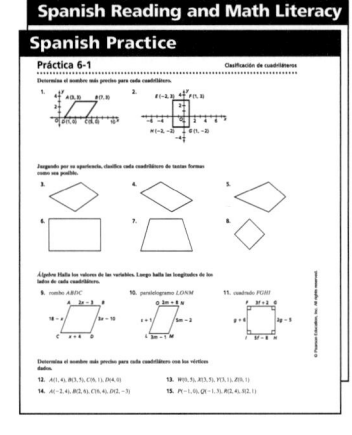

Learning Styles

Student Edition
- Investigation: pp. 303, 326
- Technology: pp. 311, 319
- Writing: pp. 291, 300, 308, 316, 319, 324, 329, 342
- DK Activities: pp. 344–345

Activity Masters
Hands-On Activities: 16, 17, 18
Technology Activities: 44, 45, 46, 47

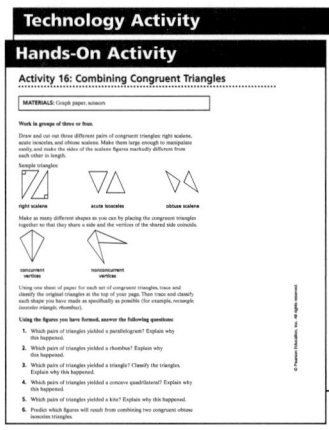

Program Resources

	Teaching Resources in Grab & Go™ Files				Resources for Reaching All Students				Spanish Resources			Presentation Assistant Plus! Transparencies				Prentice Hall Presentation Pro CD-ROM
	Practice	Reteach	Enrich	Checkpoint Quiz	Reading & Math Literacy	Technology Activities	Hands-On Activities	Informal Geometry Lesson Plans	Practice	Reading & Math Literacy	Checkpoint Quiz	Skills Check	Additional Examples	Answers to Exercises	Lesson Quiz	
6-1	■	■	■		■	■	■	■	■	■		■	■	■	■	■
6-2	■	■	■			■	■		■	■		■	■	■	■	■
6-3	■	■	■	■		■		■	■		■	■	■	■	■	■
6-4	■	■	■			■		■	■			■	■	■	■	■
6-5	■	■	■				■	■	■			■	■	■	■	■
6-6	■	■	■	■	■			■	■		■	■	■	■	■	■
6-7	■	■	■					■	■			■	■	■	■	■
For the chapter	Chapter Tests, Alternative Assessment, Cumulative Review, Cumulative Assessment				Informal Geometry Chapter Tests				Spanish Chapter Tests, Alternative Assessment, Cumulative Review, Cumulative Assessment			Classroom Aid Transparencies				

Also available for use with the chapter:

 *see page 286C.*

- Practice Workbook
- Solution Key

- For teacher support and access to student Web site materials, use Web Code afk-5500.
- For additional online and technology resources, see below.

Technology

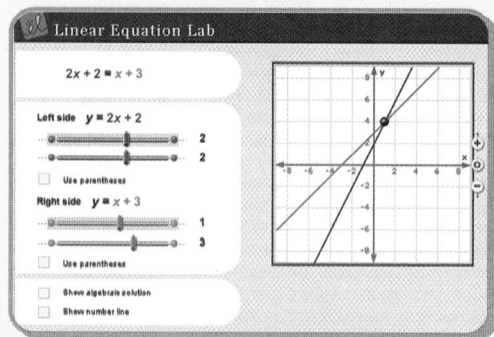

iTEXT **Online and on CD-ROM**

Complete Interactive Student Text online and on CD-ROM—with instant feedback assessment, tutorial help, dynamic activities, instructional and real-world videos, audio, and additional practice.

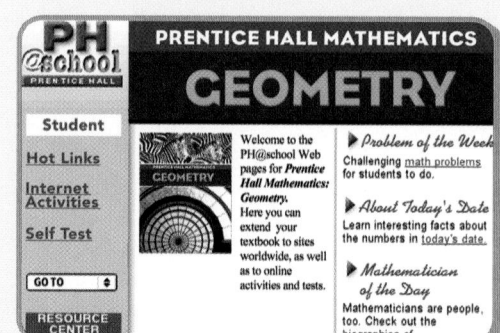

 www.PHSchool.com For Students

Use **Web Codes** for easy access to online activities, chapter projects, self-grading lesson quizzes and chapter tests, vocabulary quizzes, updated data sources, graphing calculator procedures, and more.

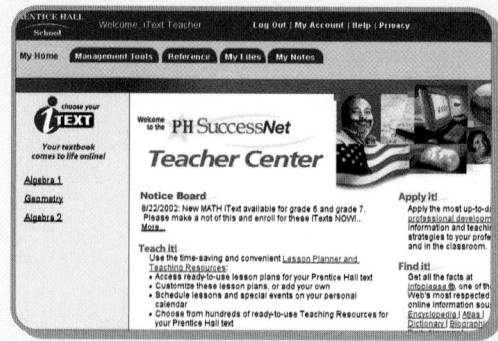

PH SuccessNet **For Teachers**

Online lesson planning with built-in state correlations, all the teaching resources, complete reference library, your own calendar and Teacher Web page, professional development, and more.

Presentation Assistant Plus!

The Prentice Hall *Presentation Assistant Plus!* provides you with the material you need to teach a lesson from beginning to end. Two easy-to-use formats—Transparencies and CD-ROM—allow you to present a lesson the way you are most comfortable.

Transparencies

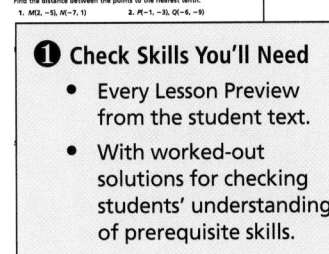

❶ **Check Skills You'll Need**
- Every Lesson Preview from the student text.
- With worked-out solutions for checking students' understanding of prerequisite skills.

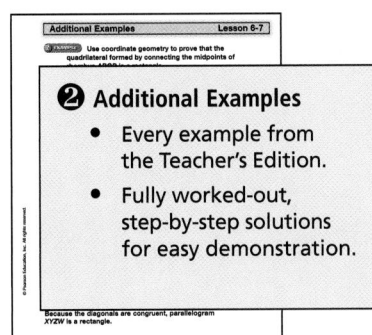

❷ **Additional Examples**
- Every example from the Teacher's Edition.
- Fully worked-out, step-by-step solutions for easy demonstration.

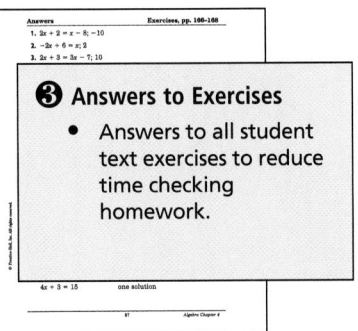

❸ **Answers to Exercises**
- Answers to all student text exercises to reduce time checking homework.

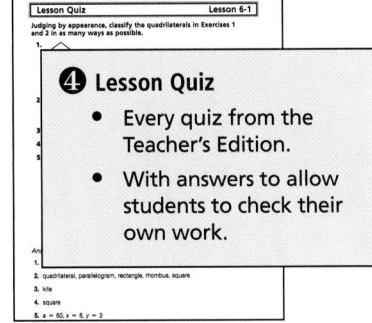

❹ **Lesson Quiz**
- Every quiz from the Teacher's Edition.
- With answers to allow students to check their own work.

 Throughout the Teacher's Edition, this symbol indicates material that is available on transparency in the Presentation Assistant Plus!

Prentice Hall Presentation Pro CD-ROM

- Includes all Transparencies.
- Conveniently organized by lesson so you can easily ❶ Introduce, ❷ Teach, ❸ Check Homework, and ❹ Assess each lesson.
- Animated examples allow step-by-step instruction at your own pace.
- Easy to edit so you can create custom presentations.

Teaching Chapter 6 Using Presentation Assistant Plus!

	❶ Introduce	❷ Teach	❸ Check Homework	❹ Assess
	Check Skills You'll Need	Additional Examples	Student Edition Answers	Lesson Quiz
6-1	p. 32	pp. 84–85	✔	p. 107
6-2	p. 33	pp. 86–88	✔	p. 108
6-3	p. 34	pp. 89–90	✔	p. 109
6-4	p. 35	pp. 91–92	✔	p. 110
6-5	p. 36	pp. 93–94	✔	p. 111
6-6	p. 37	pp. 95–96	✔	p. 112
6-7	p. 38	pp. 97–98	✔	p. 113

Prentice Hall Presentation Pro

CD-ROM with dynamic PowerPoint® presentations for every lesson. Helps you introduce and develop concepts, check homework, and assess progress. Part of Presentation Assistant Plus! *(See above.)*

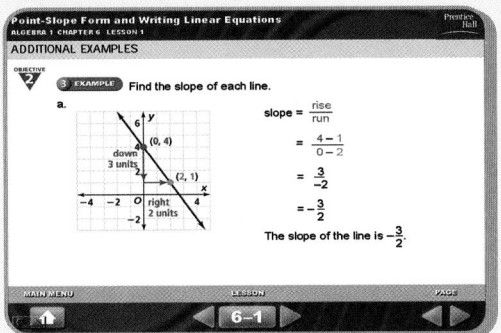

Computer Test Generator

CD-ROM to create practice sheets and tests for course objectives and standardized tests. Includes Instant Chapter Tests™, online testing, and student reports. Part of the PH Assessment System. *(See page 286C.)*

Resource Pro® with Planning Express®

CD-ROM with a lesson planning tool that allows you to import state and local objectives. Includes electronic versions of all the teaching resources.

Chapter 6

Quadrilaterals

 Diagnosing Readiness

Students will find answers to these exercises in the back of their textbooks.

For intervention, direct students to:

Properties of Parallel Lines
Lesson 3-1: Example 5
Exercises 14–16
Extra Practice, p. 692

Proving Lines Parallel
Lesson 3-2: Example 2
Exercises 1–3
Extra Practice, p. 692

Using Slope to Determine Parallel and Perpendicular Lines
Lesson 3-6: Examples 2, 4
Exercises 6–11, 16–19
Extra Practice, p. 692

Proving Triangles Congruent
Lesson 4-2: Example 2
Exercises 14–17
Lesson 4-3: Examples 1, 3
Exercises 1–4, 9–11
Extra Practice, p. 693

Where You've Been

- In Chapter 3, you learned that parallel lines produce pairs of angles that are congruent or supplementary.

- In Chapter 4, you learned how to prove triangles congruent. You also learned how to use CPCTC to draw additional conclusions.

- In Chapter 5, you learned that properties of special segments of a triangle can provide additional information about a triangle.

 **Instant self-check** online and on CD-ROM

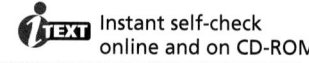 **Diagnosing Readiness**   (For help, go to the Lesson in green.)

Properties of Parallel Lines (Lesson 3-1)

x^2 **Algebra** Use properties of parallel lines to find the value of x.

1.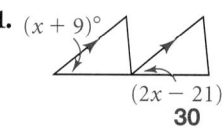

2.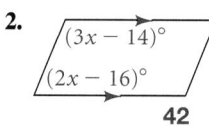

3.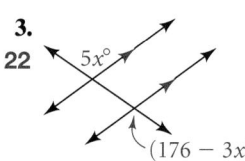

Proving Lines Parallel (Lesson 3-2)

x^2 **Algebra** Determine whether $\overleftrightarrow{AB}$ (or $\overline{AB}$) is parallel to $\overleftrightarrow{CD}$ (or $\overline{CD}$).

4.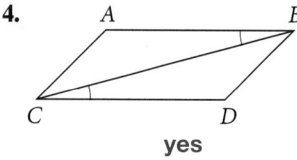
yes

5.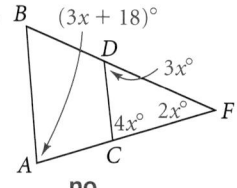
no

6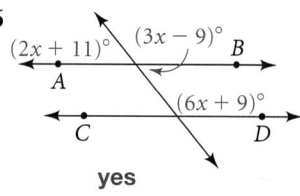
yes

Using Slope to Determine Parallel and Perpendicular Lines (Lesson 3-6)

x^2 **Algebra** Determine whether each pair of lines is parallel, perpendicular, or neither.

7. $y = -2x;\ y = -2x + 4$
parallel

8. $y = -\frac{3}{5}x + 1;\ y = \frac{5}{3}x - 3$
perpendicular

9. $2x - 3y = 1;\ 3x - 2y = 8$
neither

Proving Triangles Congruent (Lessons 4-2 and 4-3)

Determine the postulate or theorem that makes each pair of triangles congruent.

10.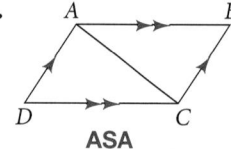
ASA

11.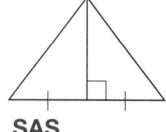
SAS

12.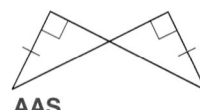
AAS

Quadrilaterals

Chapter
6

Where You're Going

- In this chapter, you will learn properties of parallelograms and other special quadrilaterals.

- You will learn properties of quadrilaterals that allow you to classify quadrilaterals.

- You will use these properties to help you place figures in the coordinate plane.

- You will verify properties of figures using coordinate techniques.

Real-World Snapshots Applying what you learn, you will do activities involving balance on pages 344 and 345.

Key Vocabulary

- base angles of a trapezoid (p. 320)
- consecutive angles (p. 294)
- isosceles trapezoid (p. 288)
- kite (p. 288)
- midsegment of a trapezoid (p. 332)
- parallelogram (p. 288)
- rectangle (p. 288)
- rhombus (p. 288)
- square (p. 288)
- trapezoid (p. 288)

Chapter 6 Overview

Students apply triangle relationships, algebraic techniques, and methods of proof to the study of quadrilaterals. A thorough study of parallelograms leads to an analysis of special parallelograms (rhombuses, rectangles, squares), trapezoids, and kites. Finally, coordinate proof is introduced and used to prove the Trapezoid Midsegment Theorem.

Reading Math
Reading a Plan for Proof p. 302

Vocabulary
A complete list of terms, plus vocabulary exercises, appears in the Chapter Review, p. 339.

Illustrated Glossary
Examples for each vocabulary term, plus definitions in both English and Spanish, appear starting on p. 741.

Test-Taking Strategies
Drawing a Diagram, p. 338

Real-World Snapshots
See pages 344–345 for a real-world application of medians and centroids of triangles that utilizes Dorling Kindersley's (DK) unique graphic presentation.

Real-World Connections
Some of the applications you will find in this chapter are art (6-1), measuring (6-2), navigation (6-3), community service (6-4), architecture (6-5), and flags (6-7).

www.PHSchool.com
Internet support for this chapter includes:
- Self-grading Vocabulary and Chapter 6 Tests
- Chapter Project
- Chapter Planner
- Ch. 6 Resources

Plus

287

1. Plan

Classifying Quadrilaterals

Lesson Preview

2.03 Apply properties, definitions, and theorems of two-dimensional figures to solve problems and write proofs: b) Quadrilaterals.

What You'll Learn

OBJECTIVE 1 To define and classify special types of quadrilaterals

. . . And Why

To use the properties of special quadrilaterals with a kite, as in Example 3

✓ **Check Skills You'll Need**   (For help, go to Lesson 1-6 and page 151.)

Find the distance between the points to the nearest tenth.

1. $M(2, -5), N(-7, 1)$ **10.8**   **2.** $P(-1, -3), Q(-6, -9)$ **7.8**   **3.** $C(-4, 6), D(5, -3)$ **12.7**

Find the slope of the line through each pair of points.

4. $X(0, 6), Y(4, 9)$ $\frac{3}{4}$ **5.** $R(3, 8), S(6, 0)$ $-\frac{8}{3}$ **6.** $A(4, 3), B(2, 1)$ **1**

New Vocabulary • **parallelogram** • **rhombus** • **rectangle** • **square**
  • **kite** • **trapezoid** • **isosceles trapezoid**

  Interactive lesson includes instant self-check, tutorials, and activities.

OBJECTIVE 1

Classifying Special Quadrilaterals

Seven important types of quadrilaterals are defined below.

🔑 **Key Concepts**

Definitions   **Special Quadrilaterals**

A **parallelogram** is a quadrilateral with both pairs of opposite sides parallel.

A **rhombus** is a parallelogram with four congruent sides.

A **rectangle** is a parallelogram with four right angles.

A **square** is a parallelogram with four congruent sides and four right angles.

A **kite** is a quadrilateral with two pairs of adjacent sides congruent and no opposite sides congruent.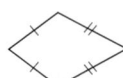

A **trapezoid** is a quadrilateral with exactly one pair of parallel sides. The **isosceles trapezoid** at the right is a trapezoid whose nonparallel opposite sides are congruent.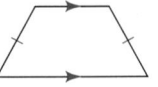

Real-World 🌐 Connection

A "kite" is not the only special quadrilateral used to make a kite!

⏱ **Ongoing Assessment and Intervention**

Before the Lesson
Diagnose prerequisite skills using:
• Check Skills You'll Need

During the Lesson
Monitor progress using:
• Check Understanding
• Additional Examples
• Standardized Test Prep

After the Lesson
Assess knowledge using:
• Lesson Quiz
• Computer Test Generator CD

1 EXAMPLE Classifying a Quadrilateral

Judging by appearance, classify *DEFG*
in as many ways as possible.

DEFG is a quadrilateral because it has four sides.

It is a parallelogram because both pairs of opposite sides are parallel.

It is a rectangle because it has four right angles.

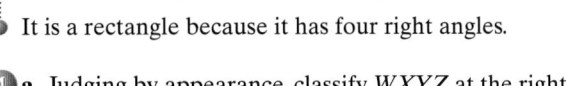

✓ Check Understanding

1a. *WXYZ* is a quad. because it has 4 sides; it is a ▱ because both pairs of opp. sides are ∥; it is a rhombus because all 4 sides are ≅.

b. rhombus, because that means it is a ▱ and quad. with 4 sides that are ≅

1 a. Judging by appearance, classify *WXYZ* at the right in as many ways as possible.
b. **Critical Thinking** Which name gives the most information about *WXYZ*? Explain.

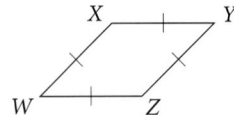

The diagram below shows the relationships among special quadrilaterals.

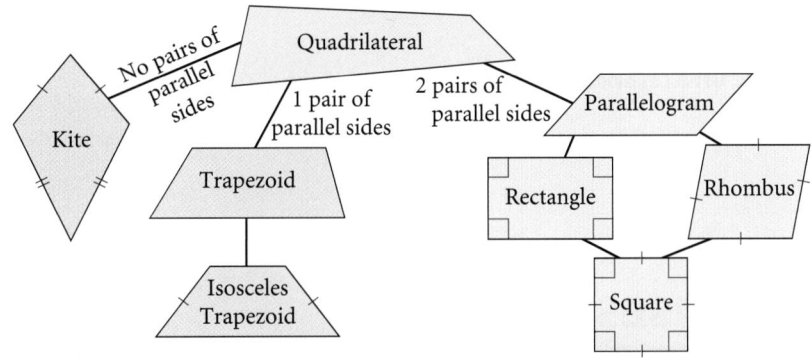

You can use what you know about slope and distance to classify a quadrilateral.

2 EXAMPLE Classifying by Coordinate Methods

Coordinate Geometry Determine the most precise name for quadrilateral *LMNP*.

Step 1 Find the slope of each side.

slope of $\overline{LM} = \frac{3-2}{3-1} = \frac{1}{2}$

slope of $\overline{NP} = \frac{2-1}{5-3} = \frac{1}{2}$

slope of $\overline{MN} = \frac{3-2}{3-5} = -\frac{1}{2}$

slope of $\overline{LP} = \frac{2-1}{1-3} = -\frac{1}{2}$

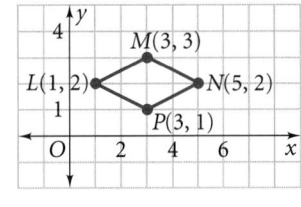

Both pairs of opposite sides are parallel, so *LMNP* is a parallelogram. No sides are perpendicular, so *LMNP* is not a rectangle.

Reading Math
Although *LMNP* is a parallelogram, rhombus is the more *precise* name because it gives more information about the quadrilateral.

Step 2 Use the Distance Formula to see if any pairs of sides are congruent.

$LM = \sqrt{(3-1)^2 + (3-2)^2} = \sqrt{5}$ $MN = \sqrt{(3-5)^2 + (3-2)^2} = \sqrt{5}$

$NP = \sqrt{(5-3)^2 + (2-1)^2} = \sqrt{5}$ $LP = \sqrt{(1-3)^2 + (2-1)^2} = \sqrt{5}$

All sides are congruent, so *LMNP* is a rhombus.

✓ Check Understanding

2 Determine the most precise name for quadrilateral *ABCD* with vertices $A(-3,3)$, $B(2,4)$, $C(3,-1)$, and $D(-2,-2)$. **square**

Lesson 6-1 Classifying Quadrilaterals **289**

👥 Reaching All Students

Below Level Students can use geoboards to model the quadrilaterals in this lesson.	**Advanced Learners** Have students explain why the word *exactly* is necessary in the definition of a trapezoid.	**English Learners** See note on page 289. **Inclusion** See note on page 291.

Math Background

The classification in this lesson categorizes quadrilaterals first by the number of pairs of parallel sides, and then shows their subsets. Other hierarchies are possible. (See Interleaf p. 286B.)

OBJECTIVE
1 ▼ Teaching Notes

English Learners
Students may need help distinguishing the new terms. Have them design a class poster that displays and defines each quadrilateral, and refer to it as needed.

1 EXAMPLE Tactile Learners

Use geoboards to model quadrilaterals.

2 EXAMPLE Connection to Coordinate Geometry

If necessary, display the formulas for slope and distance.

📓 Additional Examples

1 Judging by appearance, classify *ABCD* in as many ways as possible.

quadrilateral, trapezoid

2 Determine the most precise name for the quadrilateral with vertices $Q(-4, 4)$, $B(-2, 9)$, $H(8, 9)$, and $A(10, 4)$. **isosceles trapezoid**

3 In parallelogram *RSTU*, $m\angle R = 2x - 10$ and $m\angle S = 3x + 50$. Find x. **28**

Closure

ABCD is a square. Which classifications from this lesson also apply? Which do *not* apply?
parallelogram, rectangle, rhombus; trapezoid, isosceles trapezoid, kite

289

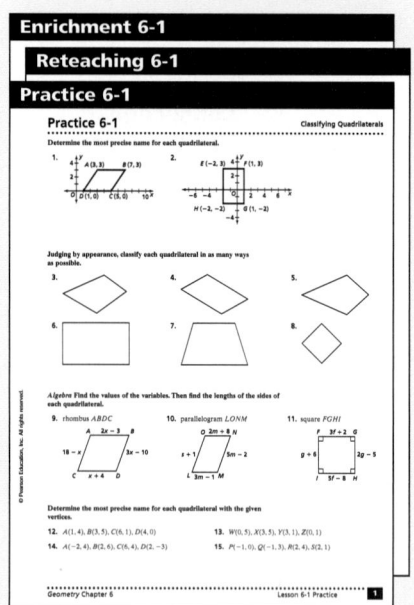
You can use the definitions of special quadrilaterals and algebra to find lengths of sides.

3 EXAMPLE Using the Properties of Special Quadrilaterals

Algebra Find the values of the variables for the kite.

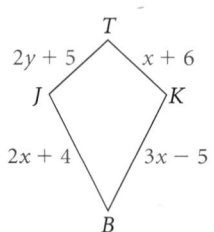

$KB = JB$	Definition of kite
$3x - 5 = 2x + 4$	Substitute.
$x - 5 = 4$	Subtract 2x from each side.
$x = 9$	Add 5 to each side.
$KT = x + 6 = 15$	Substitute 9 for x.
$KT = JT$	Definition of kite
$15 = 2y + 5$	Substitute.
$10 = 2y$	Subtract 5 from each side.
$5 = y$	Divide each side by 2.

✓ **Check Understanding** 3 Find the values of the variables for the rhombus. Then find the lengths of the sides.
$a = 2, b = 4; LN = ST = NT = SL = 14$

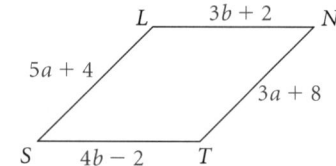

EXERCISES

For more practice, see *Extra Practice*.

Practice and Problem Solving

A **Practice by Example**

Example 1
(page 289)

These quadrilaterals are made from a toy building set. Judging by appearance, classify each quadrilateral in as many ways as possible.

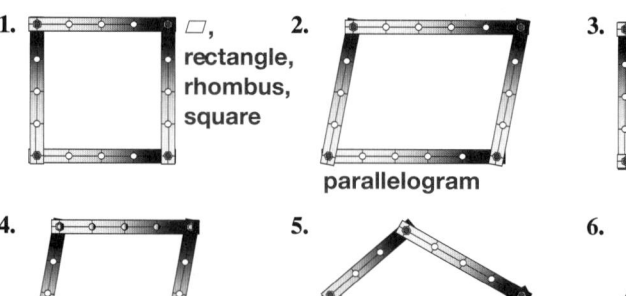

1. ▭, rectangle, rhombus, square

2. parallelogram

3. trapezoid

4. ▭, rhombus

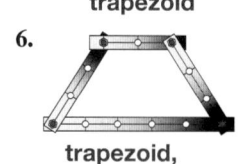

5. kite

6. trapezoid, isosc. trapezoid

Example 2
(page 289)

Determine the most precise name for each quadrilateral.

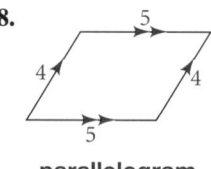

7. rhombus

8. parallelogram

9. rhombus

10.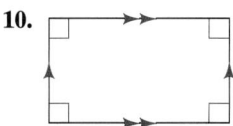
rectangle

11.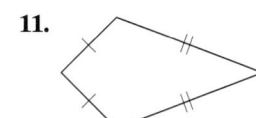
kite

12.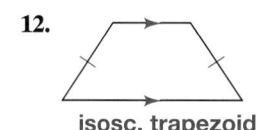
isosc. trapezoid

Coordinate Geometry Graph and label each quadrilateral with the given vertices. Then determine the most precise name for each quadrilateral. 13–18. See back of book.

13. $A(3, 5)$, $B(7, 6)$, $C(6, 2)$, $D(2, 1)$

14. $W(-1, 1)$, $X(0, 2)$, $Y(1, 1)$, $Z(0, -2)$

15. $J(2, 1)$, $K(5, 4)$, $L(7, 2)$, $M(2, -3)$

16. $R(-2, -3)$, $S(4, 0)$, $T(3, 2)$, $V(-3, -1)$

17. $N(-6, -4)$, $P(-3, 1)$, $Q(0, 2)$, $R(-3, 5)$

18. $E(-3, 1)$, $F(-7, -3)$, $G(6, -3)$, $H(2, 1)$

Example 3
(page 290)

x^2 **Algebra** Find the values of the variables. Then find the lengths of the sides.

19. $x = 11$, $y = 29$; 13, 13, 23, 23

19. kite
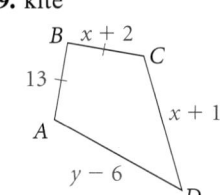

20. kite
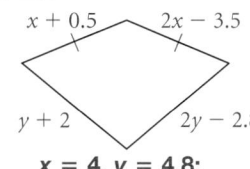
$x = 4$, $y = 4.8$; 4.5, 4.5, 6.8, 6.8

21. kite
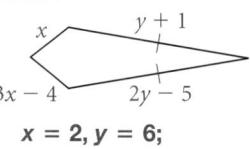
$x = 2$, $y = 6$; 2, 7, 7, 2

35. A rhombus has 4 ≅ sides, while a kite has 2 pairs of adj. sides ≅, but no opp. sides are ≅. Opp. sides of a rhombus are ∥, while opp. sides of a kite are not ∥.

22. isosceles trapezoid
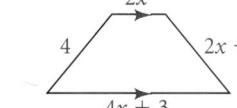
$x = 1$; 4, 2, 4, 7

23. rhombus
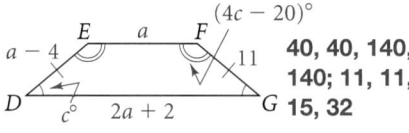
$x = 3$, $y = 5$; 15, 15, 15, 15

24. square
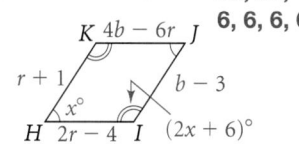
$x = 5$, $y = 4$; 3, 3, 3, 3

B Apply Your Skills x^2 **Algebra** In each figure, find the measures of the angles and the lengths of the sides.

25. isosceles trapezoid $DEFG$
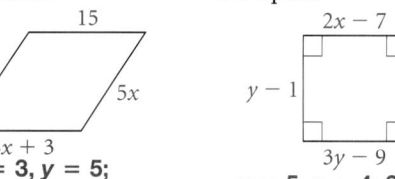
40, 40, 140, 140; 11, 11, 15, 32

26. rhombus $HKJI$
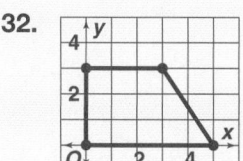
58, 58, 122, 122; 6, 6, 6, 6

Exercise 27

27. **Art** American artist Charles Demuth created *My Egypt*, the oil painting pictured at the left. It is in an art style called Cubism, in which subjects are made of cubes and other geometric forms. Identify the types of special quadrilaterals you see in the painting. **rectangle, square, trapezoid**

28. Identify a parallelogram, rhombus, rectangle, square, kite, and trapezoid in your classroom. State whether your trapezoid is isosceles. **Check students' work.**

Draw each figure on graph paper. If not possible, explain. 29–34. See margin.

29. a parallelogram that is neither a rectangle nor a rhombus

30. an isosceles trapezoid with vertical and horizontal congruent sides

31. a trapezoid with only one right angle

32. a trapezoid with two right angles

33. a rhombus that is not a square

34. a kite with two right angles

35. **Writing** Describe the difference between a rhombus and a kite. See above left.

Lesson 6-1 Classifying Quadrilaterals **291**

pages 290–293 Exercises 29–34. Answers may vary. Samples are given.

29.
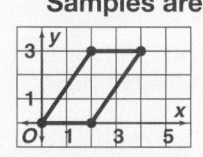

30.
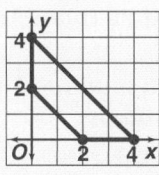

31. Impossible; a trapezoid with one rt. ∠ must have another, since two sides are ∥.

Diversity

Exercise 27 Point out that artists have used representations of geometric figures for hundreds of years. For example, Arabian tiles show geometric shapes that tessellate. Ask students to describe other art forms that use geometric figures.

Inclusion

Exercises 29–34 Have physically-challenged students describe the figure to partners who actually draw them.

Error Prevention

Exercise 35 As students describe a kite, make sure that they include the stipulation that opposite sides are not congruent. Point out that without that condition, squares and rhombuses would be considered kites.

Tactile Learners

Exercises 51–54 For each exercise, have students cut out cardboard triangles to connect in every possible way.

Exercises 55 Ask: *If N has coordinates (0, −2), will KLMN be a kite? Explain.* **No; *KLMN* will be a rhombus.**

32.
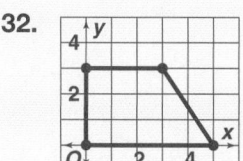

33.
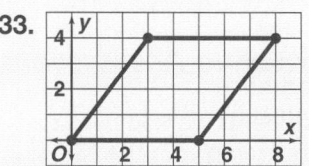

34.
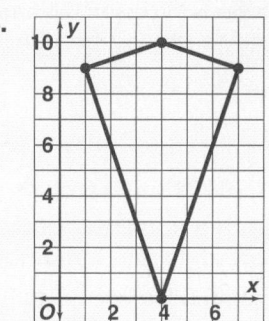

291

Lesson Quiz 6-1

Judging by appearance, classify the quadrilaterals in Exercises 1 and 2 in as many ways as possible.

1.

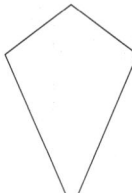

quadrilateral, kite

2.

quadrilateral, parallelogram, rectangle, rhombus, square

3. What is the most precise name for the figure in Exercise 1? **kite**

4. What is the most precise name for the figure in Exercise 2? **square**

5. Find the values of the variables in the rhombus below.

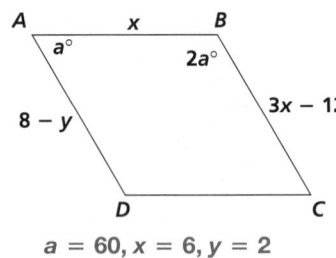

$a = 60, x = 6, y = 2$

Alternative Assessment

Have students work in pairs to identify examples in the school building of four of the special quadrilaterals in Lesson 6-1 and then justify each classification.

Real-World 🌐 Connection

To make this butterfly, an origami square was folded first on its diagonals.

36. Copy the Venn diagram. Add the labels *Rectangles, Rhombuses,* and *Trapezoids* to the diagram in the appropriate places.

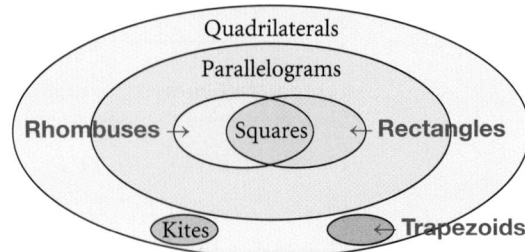

State whether each statement is *true* or *false*. Justify your response. You may find the diagram from Exercise 36 helpful. 37–42. See margin.

37. All squares are rectangles.

38. A trapezoid is a parallelogram.

39. A rhombus can be a kite.

40. Some parallelograms are squares.

41. Every quadrilateral is a parallelogram.

42. All rhombuses are squares.

🌐 **43. Paper Folding** Fold a nonsquare, rectangular piece of paper in half horizontally and then vertically, as shown at the right. Draw and then cut along the line connecting the two opposite corners containing a fold. What quadrilateral do you find when you unfold the paper? Why doesn't it matter what size rectangle you start with? **Rhombus; all 4 sides are ≅ because they come from the same cut.**

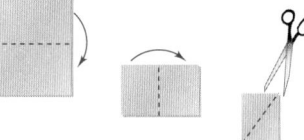

Identify a parallelogram, rhombus, rectangle, square, kite and trapezoid at each site. State whether your trapezoid is isosceles. 44–45. Check students' work.

44. home

45. somewhere other than school and home

Name each type of special quadrilateral that can meet the given condition. Make sketches to support your answers. 46–49. See margin.

46. exactly one pair of congruent sides

47. two pairs of parallel sides

48. four right angles

49. adjacent sides that are congruent

50. Error Analysis Lauren argues, "A parallelogram has two pairs of parallel sides, so it certainly has one pair of parallel sides. Therefore a parallelogram must also be a trapezoid." What is the error in Lauren's argument? **A trapezoid has only one pair of ∥ sides.**

Name the type of special quadrilateral it appears that you can form by joining the triangles in each pair. Make sketches to support your answers.

Sample two congruent scalene triangles

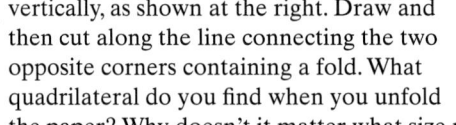

parallelogram

51–54. Check students' sketches.
51. rectangle, ▱, kite
52. rhombus, ▱
53. square, rhombus, ▱
54. rhombus, ▱, kite

51. two congruent scalene right triangles

52. two congruent equilateral triangles

53. two congruent isosceles right triangles

54. two congruent isosceles acute triangles

? Need Help?

In Exercises 51–54, if you flip one of the two triangles, you may find different quadrilaterals.

pages 290–293 Exercises

37. True; a square is both a rectangle and a rhombus.

38. False; a trapezoid only has one pair of ∥ sides.

39. False; a kite does not have ≅ opp. sides.

40. True; all squares are Ⓢ.

41. False; kites are not Ⓢ.

42. False; only rhombuses with rt. ∠ are squares.

46–49. Check students' sketches.

46. some isos. trapezoids, some trapezoids

47. ▱, rhombus, rectangle, square

48. rectangle, square

49. rhombus, square, kite, some trapezoids

55. a. Open-Ended Graph and label points $K(-3, 0)$, $L(0, 2)$, and $M(3, 0)$.
Find possible coordinates for point N so that $KLMN$ is a kite.
b. Explain why there is more than one possible fourth vertex.
a–b. See margin.

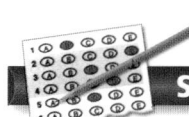 **Challenge**

Reasoning A scrap of paper covers part of each quadrilateral. Name all the special quadrilaterals that each could be. Explain each choice. **56–59. See margin.**

56. 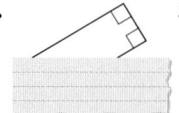   **57.**   **58.**    **59.**

Standardized Test Prep

Multiple Choice

60. Which statement is NEVER true? **C**
A. Square $ABCD$ is a rhombus.
B. Parallelogram $PQRS$ is a square.
C. Trapezoid $GHJK$ is a parallelogram.
D. Square $WXYZ$ is a parallelogram.

61. Which statement is true for some, but not all, rectangles? **I**
F. Opposite sides are parallel.
G. It is a parallelogram.
H. Adjacent sides are perpendicular.
I. All sides are congruent.

Take It to the NET
Online lesson quiz at
www.PHSchool.com
Web Code: afa-0601

62. A parallelogram has four congruent sides. Which name best describes the figure? **C**
A. trapezoid   B. parallelogram   C. rhombus   D. square

63. Which name best describes a parallelogram with four congruent angles? **H**
F. kite   G. rhombus   H. rectangle   I. square

Short Response

64. $A(-3, 1)$, $B(-1, -2)$, and $C(2, 1)$ are three points of quadrilateral $ABCD$. Could $ABCD$ be a rectangle? Explain. **See margin.**

Mixed Review

Lesson 5-5

Can a triangle have sides with the given lengths? Explain.

65. 8 mm, 6 mm, 3 mm   **66.** 5 ft, 20 ft, 7 ft   **67.** 3 m, 5 m, 8 m
     See margin.   No; $5 + 7 \not> 20$.   No; $3 + 5 \not> 8$.

Lesson 4-1

Quadrilaterals $RSTV$ and $NMQP$ are congruent. Find the length of the side or the measure of the angle.

68. $\overline{MN}$ 28 mm   **69.** $\overline{VT}$ 16 mm

70. $\overline{ST}$ 12 mm   **71.** $\angle S$ 82

72. $\angle V$ 90   **73.** $\angle R$ 58

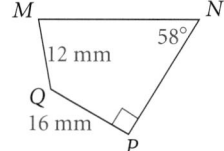

Lesson 3-6

74. Write an equation for the line parallel to $y = -3x - 5$ that contains point $(0, 4)$.
$y = -3x + 4$

Lesson 6-1 Classifying Quadrilaterals   **293**

55. Answers may vary.
Sample:

a.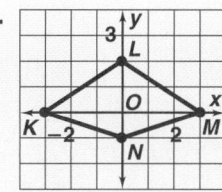

N can be anywhere on the y-axis except $(0, 0)$, $(0, 2)$, and $(0, -2)$.

b. For points N mentioned above, $KL = LM$ and $KN = NM$, but $KL \neq KN$.

Standardized Test Prep

Resources
For additional practice with a variety of test item formats:
• Standardized Test Prep, p. 343
• Test-Taking Strategies, p. 338
• Test-Taking Strategies with Transparencies

Exercise 60 Remind students to look for the words *never* and *not* when reading a multiple-choice problem.

Exercises 62, 63 For each exercise, students should ask: *What can I prove about each figure?*

56–59. Explanations may vary.

56. ▱, rectangle, trapezoid

57. ▱, kite, rhombus, trapezoid, isos. trapezoid

58. kite, ▱, rhombus, trapezoid, isos. trapezoid

59. ▱, rectangle, square, rhombus, kite, trapezoid

64. [2] Slope of $\overline{AB}$ is $-\frac{3}{2}$. The slope of $\overline{BC}$ is 1, so $\overline{AB}$ and $\overline{BC}$ are not $\perp$. Since 1 $\angle$ is not a right $\angle$ and a rectangle requires all 4 ⦞ to be right ⦞, the figure could not be a rectangle.

[1] incorrect slope OR failure to recognize the information provided by the slopes

65. Yes; the sum of the lengths of any 2 sides is greater than the third side.

293

6-2

1. Plan

Lesson Preview

✔ Check Skills You'll Need

Congruent Figures
Lesson 4-1: Example 1
Exercises 3–12
Extra Practice, p. 693

Using the ASA Postulate
Lesson 4-3: Example 1
Exercises 1–4
Extra Practice, p. 693

Lesson Resources

 **Teaching Resources**
Practice, Reteaching, Enrichment

Reaching All Students
Practice Workbook 6-2
Spanish Practice Workbook 6-2
Technology Activities 46
Hands-On Activities 17
Informal Geometry Planning
   Guide 6-2

Presentation Assistant Plus!
Transparencies
- Check Skills You'll Need 6-2
- Additional Examples 6-2
- Student Edition Answers 6-2
- Lesson Quiz 6-2
PH Presentation Pro CD 6-2

PRENTICE HALL **ASSESSMENT SYSTEM**

Computer Test Generator CD

Technology
Resource Pro® CD-ROM
Computer Test Generator CD
Prentice Hall Presentation Pro CD

 **www.PHSchool.com**
Student Site
- Teacher Web Code: afk-5500
- Self-grading Lesson Quiz
Teacher Center
- Lesson Planner
- Resources

Plus **iTEXT**

294

6-2

Properties of Parallelograms

2.03 Apply properties, definitions, and theorems of two-dimensional figures to solve problems and write proofs: b) Quadrilaterals.

Lesson Preview

What You'll Learn

 OBJECTIVE 1 To use relationships among sides and among angles of parallelograms

OBJECTIVE 2 To use relationships involving diagonals of parallelograms or transversals.

. . . And Why

To divide a blank card into three parts of equal heights without a ruler, as in Example 4

✔ Check Skills You'll Need

(For help, go to Lessons 4-1 and 4-3.)

Use the figure at the right.

1. Name the postulate or theorem that justifies the congruence △EFG ≅ △GHE. **ASA**

2. Complete each statement.
   a. ∠FEG ≅ ? b. ∠EFG ≅ ?
   c. ∠FGE ≅ ? d. $\overline{EF}$ ≅ ?
   e. $\overline{FG}$ ≅ ? f. $\overline{GE}$ ≅ ?
   a. ∠HGE b. ∠GHE c. ∠HEG
   d. $\overline{GH}$ e. $\overline{HE}$ f. $\overline{EG}$

3. What other relationship exists between $\overline{FG}$ and $\overline{EH}$?
   They are ∥.

New Vocabulary • consecutive angles

 **Interactive lesson includes instant self-check, tutorials, and activities.**

OBJECTIVE 1 Properties: Sides and Angles

You can use what you know about parallel lines and transversals to prove some theorems about parallelograms.

 Key Concepts

Theorem 6-1
Opposite sides of a parallelogram are congruent.

Proof → **Proof of Theorem 6-1**

Given: □ABCD
Prove: $\overline{AB} \cong \overline{CD}, \overline{BC} \cong \overline{DA}$

 Reading Math
Read "□" as "parallelogram." The plural is "▱."

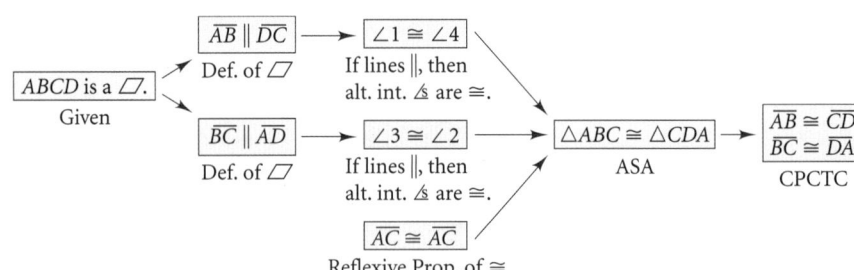

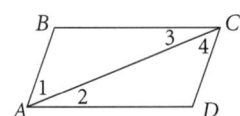

Angles of a polygon that share a side are **consecutive angles.** A parallelogram has opposite sides parallel. Its consecutive angles are same-side interior angles so they are supplementary. In □ABCD, consecutive angles B and C are supplementary, as are consecutive angles C and D.

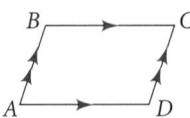

294 Chapter 6 Quadrilaterals

Ongoing Assessment and Intervention

Before the Lesson
Diagnose prerequisite skills using:
- Check Skills You'll Need

During the Lesson
Monitor progress using:
- Check Understanding
- Additional Examples
- Standardized Test Prep

After the Lesson
Assess knowledge using:
- Lesson Quiz
- Computer Test Generator CD

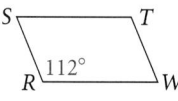 **1 EXAMPLE** **Using Consecutive Angles**

Find $m\angle S$ in $\square RSTW$.

$\angle R$ and $\angle S$ are consecutive angles of a parallelogram. They are supplementary.

$m\angle R + m\angle S = 180$ **Definition of supplementary angles**

$112 + m\angle S = 180$ **Substitute.**

$m\angle S = 68$ **Subtract 112 from each side.**

 Check Understanding **1** **Critical Thinking** If consecutive angles of a quadrilateral are supplementary, must the quadrilateral be a parallelogram? Explain. **Yes; by the Converse of the Same-Side Int. ∠ Thm., both pairs of opp. sides are ∥.**

A proof of Theorem 6-2 uses the consecutive angles of a parallelogram, and the fact that supplements of the same angle are congruent.

Key Concepts

Theorem 6-2

Opposite angles of a parallelogram are congruent.

Real-World Connection

Opposite angles in the "cat's cradle" parallelogram (center) are congruent.

Plan for Proof of Theorem 6-2

Given: $\square MNPQ$

Prove: $\angle M \cong \angle P$ and $\angle N \cong \angle Q$

Plan: $\angle M \cong \angle P$ if they are supplements of the same angle, $\angle N$. Each is a supplement of $\angle N$ because same side interior angles are supplementary. $\angle N \cong \angle Q$ using similar reasoning with $\angle M$.

You can complete a flow proof of Theorem 6-2 in Exercise 37. You can write another proof—also a flow proof—that follows the plan above in Exercise 38. You can use Theorems 6-1 and 6-2 along with algebra to find unknown values in parallelograms.

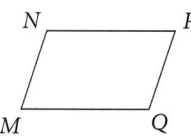 **2 EXAMPLE** **Using Algebra**

Algebra Find the value of x in $\square PQRS$. Then find QR and PS.

$3x - 15 = 2x + 3$ **Opposite sides of a $\square$ are congruent.**

$x - 15 = 3$ **Subtract 2x from each side.**

$x = 18$ **Add 15 to each side.**

$QR = 3x - 15 = 39$ **Substitute.**

$\overline{PS} \cong \overline{QR}$, so $PS = 39$.

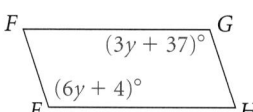

Check Understanding **2** Find the value of y in $\square EFGH$. Then find $m\angle E, m\angle G, m\angle F,$ and $m\angle H$. **11; $m\angle E = 70, m\angle G = 70,$ $m\angle F = 110, m\angle H = 110$**

Reaching All Students

Below Level Students can draw a parallelogram, cut along a diagonal, and manipulate the triangles thus formed to see the congruence relationships described in Theorems 6-1 and 6-2.	**Advanced Learners** Before reading the proof of Theorem 6-1, copy the diagram, and ask students which segments and angles can be marked congruent.	**English Learners** See note on page 295. **Inclusion** See note on page 299.

---

2. Teach

Math Background

The parallelogram has the most subsets in this text's hierarchy of quadrilaterals, so it is natural to develop its properties first. In this way, any property of a parallelogram can be applied to any rectangle, rhombus, or square.

OBJECTIVE

 **Teaching Notes**

English Learners

Check that, in a plane, students do not confuse consecutive angles with adjacent angles. Remind students that adjacent angles have a common vertex and a common side but no common interior points.

1 EXAMPLE

Have students find all four angle measures in *RSTW* to prepare them for Theorem 6-2.

Alternative Method

Another way to prove Theorem 6-2 is to draw a diagonal and compare corresponding parts of congruent triangles twice, as was done once in the proof of Theorem 6-1.

Additional Examples

1 Use $\square KMOQ$ to find $m\angle O$.

145

2 Find the value of x in $\square ABCD$. Then find $m\angle A$.

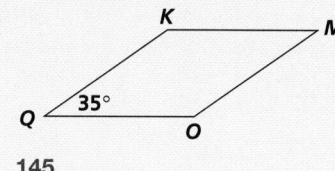

60; 105

Technology Tip
Have students use geometry software to draw three or more parallel lines that cut off congruent segments on a transversal, and then have them investigate the segment lengths on a different transversal. Ask: *Are the segments on the new transversal the same length?* yes

4 EXAMPLE Tactile Learners

Instruct students to repeat the example for themselves, tracing the edge of the blank card on the lined paper to help them see that the segments are congruent.

Additional Examples

3 Find the values of x and y in $\square KLMN$.

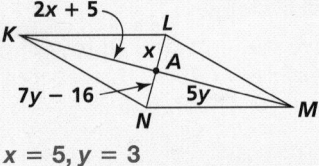

$x = 5, y = 3$

4 Explain how to divide a blank card into five equal rows using Theorem 6-4 and a piece of lined paper. Place the card on the lined paper so that one corner of the card touches the first line of the paper and a consecutive corner of the card touches the sixth line. Mark the points where the lines intersect the card. Repeat the procedure on the opposite edge of the card. Connect the marks on opposite edges of the card using a straightedge.

Closure

Lesson 6-1 defined a rectangle as a parallelogram with four right angles. Explain why you can now define a rectangle as a parallelogram with one right angle. Because opposite △s of a parallelogram are ≅, there are two rt. △s. Because consecutive △s are supplementary, there are two more rt. △s.

The diagonals of parallelograms have a special property.

🔑 **Key Concepts**

> **Theorem 6-3**
>
> The diagonals of a parallelogram bisect each other.

Proof ➡ **Proof of Theorem 6-3**

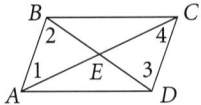

Given: $\square ABCD$
Prove: $\overline{AC}$ and $\overline{BD}$ bisect each other at E.

Statements	Reasons
1. $ABCD$ is a parallelogram.	1. Given
2. $\overline{AB} \parallel \overline{DC}$	2. Definition of parallelogram
3. $\angle 1 \cong \angle 4; \angle 2 \cong \angle 3$	3. Parallel lines form ≅ alt. int. △s.
4. $\overline{AB} \cong \overline{DC}$	4. Opposite sides of a $\square$ are ≅.
5. $\triangle ABE \cong \triangle CDE$	5. ASA
6. $\overline{AE} \cong \overline{CE}; \overline{BE} \cong \overline{DE}$	6. CPCTC
7. $\overline{AC}$ and $\overline{BD}$ bisect each other at E.	7. Definition of bisector

You can use Theorem 6-3 to find unknown lengths in parallelograms.

Real-World 🌐 Connection

The railing braces are diagonals of parallelograms so they bisect each other.

3 EXAMPLE Using Algebra

Solve a system of linear equations to find the values of x and y in $\square ABCD$. Then find $AE, EC, BE,$ and ED.

① $\quad 3y - 7 = 2x$	The diagonals of a parallelogram bisect each other.
② $\qquad y = x + 1$	
$3(x + 1) - 7 = 2x$	Substitute $x + 1$ for y in equation ①.
$3x + 3 - 7 = 2x$	Distribute.
$3x - 4 = 2x$	Simplify.
$\qquad 3x = 2x + 4$	Add 4 to each side.
$\qquad\quad x = 4$	Subtract $2x$ from each side.
$3y - 7 = 2(4) = 8$	Substitute 4 for x in equations ① and ②.
$\qquad y = 4 + 1 = 5$	

● $AE = EC = 8$ and $BE = ED = 5$.

✓ **Check Understanding** **3** Find the values of a and b.
$a = 16, b = 14$

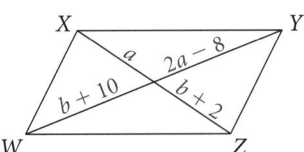

In Exercise 55, you will use Theorem 6-1, opposite sides of a parallelogram are congruent, to prove the following theorem.

Key Concepts

Theorem 6-4

If three (or more) parallel lines cut off congruent segments on one transversal, then they cut off congruent segments on every transversal.

$$\overline{BD} \cong \overline{DF}$$

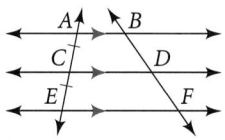

4 EXAMPLE Real-World 🌐 Connection

Measurement Show how to separate a blank card into three strips that are the same height by using lined paper, a straightedge, and Theorem 6-4.

The lines of the paper are parallel and equally spaced. Place a corner of the top edge of the card on the first line of the paper. Place the corner of the bottom edge on the fourth line. Mark the points where the second and third lines intersect the card. The marks will be equally spaced because the edge of the card is a transversal for the equally spaced parallel lines of the paper. Repeat for the other side of the card. Connect the marks using a straightedge.

✓ **Check Understanding** ④ In the figure at the right, $\overleftrightarrow{DH} \parallel \overleftrightarrow{CG} \parallel \overleftrightarrow{BF} \parallel \overleftrightarrow{AE}$, $AB = BC = CD = 2$, and $EF = 2.5$. Find EH.
7.5

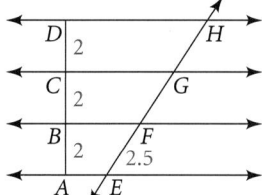

3. Practice

Assignment Guide

▼**1** Objective
Ⓐ Ⓑ Core 1–16, 34–41, 45–49
Ⓒ Extension 59, 60

▼**2** Objective
Ⓐ Ⓑ Core 17–33, 42–44, 50–58
Ⓒ Extension 61, 62

Standardized Test Prep 63–69

Mixed Review 70–76

Exercises 1–6 These exercises can be done orally using mental math. As students answer, have them explain and justify their methods of solving for x.

Exercises 7–16 Ask students to name the property described in the theorem they use.

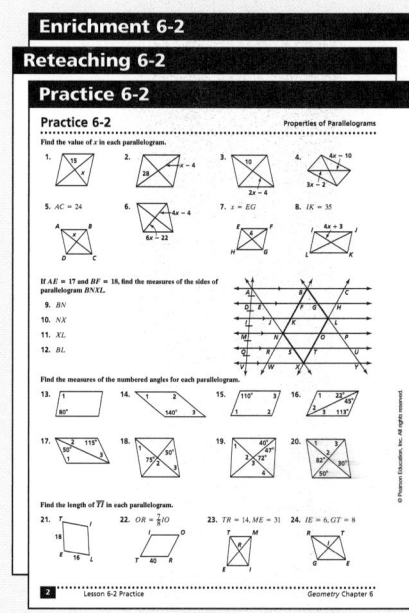

Enrichment 6-2
Reteaching 6-2
Practice 6-2

EXERCISES

For more practice, see *Extra Practice*.

Practice and Problem Solving

 A Practice by Example x^2 **Algebra** Find the value of x in each parallelogram.

Example 1
(page 295)

1. 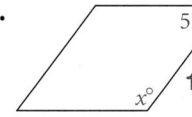 $53°$ / $x°$ / **127**

2. **76** / $113°$ $x°$ / **67**

3. $104°$ / $x°$

4. $56°$ / $x°$ / **124**

5. $x°$ / $80°$ / **100**

6. $x°$ / $62°$ / **118**

Example 2 x^2 **Algebra** Find the value of x.
(page 295)

7. $\frac{3}{4}$ / 8 / $4x + 5$

8. 4 / $3x + 2$ / 14

9. 4 / $7x - 2$ / $5x + 6$

pages 297–301 Exercises

15. 12; $m\angle Q = m\angle S = 36$, $m\angle P = m\angle R = 144$

16. 6; $m\angle H = m\angle J = 30$, $m\angle I = m\angle K = 150$

17. $x = 6, y = 8$

18. $x = 5, y = 7$

19. $x = 7, y = 10$

20. $x = 6, y = 9$

21. $x = 3, y = 4$

34. $BC = AD = 14.5$ in.; $AB = CD = 9.5$ in.

35. $BC = AD = 33$ cm; $AB = CD = 13$ cm

23. Pick 4 equally spaced lines on the paper. Place the paper so that the first button is on the first line and the last button is on the fourth line. Draw a line between the first and last buttons. The remaining buttons should be placed where the drawn line crosses the 2 ∥ lines on the paper.

Find the value of x and the length of each side.

10.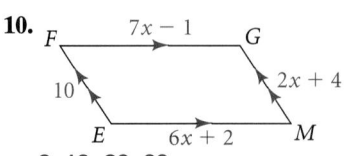

3; 10, 20, 20

11.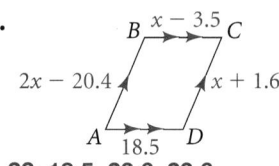

22; 18.5, 23.6, 23.6

x^2 **Algebra** **Find the value of a.**

12.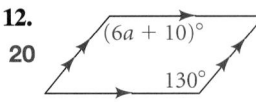
20

13.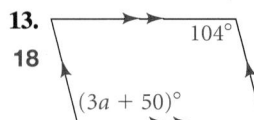
18

14.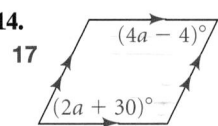
17

Find the value of a and the measure of each angle in each parallelogram.

15.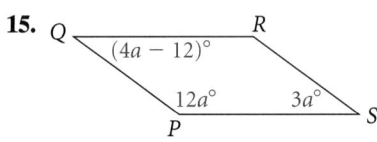

16.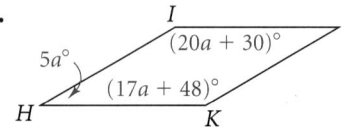

15–21. See margin.

Example 3
(page 296)

x^2 **Algebra** **Find the values of x and y in $\square PQRS$.**

17. $PT = 2x, TR = y + 4, QT = x + 2, TS = y$

18. $PT = x + 2, TR = y, QT = 2x, TS = y + 3$

19. $PT = y, TR = x + 3, QT = 2y, TS = 3x - 1$

20. $PT = 2x, TR = y + 3, QT = 3x, TS = 2y$

21. $PT = 8x, TR = 6y, QT = 2x + 2, TS = 2y$

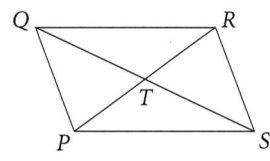

Example 4
(page 297)

Exercise 23

22. Find ED and FD in the figure at the right. **12; 24**

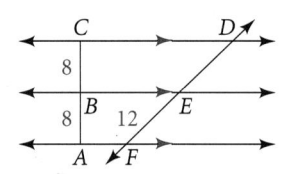

23. **Sewing** Suppose you don't have a ruler. Explain how to space four buttons equally on a shirt if you know where the first and last buttons must be placed and you have a large piece of lined paper. **See above left.**

In the figure, the horizontal lines are parallel and $PQ = QR = RS$. Find each length.

24. ZU **3**

25. XZ **3**

26. XU **6**

27. TZ **6**

28. TU **9**

29. XV **2.25**

30. YX **2.25**

31. YV **4.5**

32. WX **4.5**

33. WV **6.75**

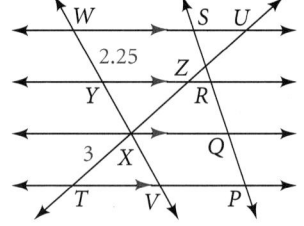

B **Apply Your Skills** x^2 **Algebra** **Use the given information to find the lengths of all four sides of $\square ABCD$.**

34. The perimeter is 48 in. AB is 5 in. less than BC.

35. The perimeter is 92 cm. AD is 7 cm more than twice AB.

34–35. See margin.

Need Help?

Use the flow proof on p. 294.

36 a. $\overline{DC}$

b. $\overline{AD}$

c. ≅

d. Reflexive

e. ASA

f. CPCTC

Proof 36. Developing Proof Complete this paragraph proof of Theorem 6-1 by filling in the blanks.

Given: ▱$ABCD$

Prove: $\overline{AB} \cong \overline{CD}$ and $\overline{BC} \cong \overline{DA}$

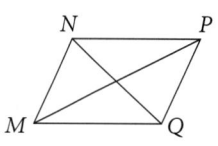

Proof: $ABCD$ is a parallelogram, therefore $\overline{AB} \parallel$ **a.** _?_ and $\overline{BC} \parallel$ **b.** _?_. ∠1 ≅ ∠4 and ∠3 ≅ ∠2, because alternate interior angles are **c.** _?_. $\overline{AC} \cong \overline{AC}$ by the **d.** _?_ Property of Congruence. Therefore △ABC ≅ △CDA by **e.** _?_. So, $\overline{AB} \cong \overline{CD}$ and $\overline{BC} \cong \overline{DA}$ because **f.** _?_.

Developing Proof Exercises 37 and 38 ask you for two different flow proofs of Theorem 6-2.

37. Complete this flow proof of Theorem 6-2 by filling in the blanks.

Given: ▱$MNPQ$

Prove: ∠NMQ ≅ ∠QPN and ∠MNP ≅ ∠PQM

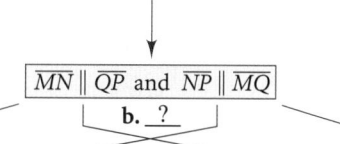

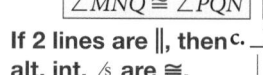

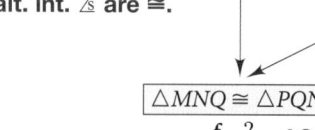

Reading Math

For help with reading and solving Exercise 38, see p. 302.

38. Write a flow proof for Theorem 6-2 that follows the plan on page 295.

See back of book.

Find the measures of the numbered angles for each parallelogram.

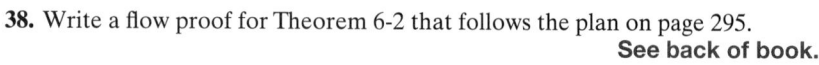

39.

38, 32, 110

40.

81, 28, 71

41.

95, 37, 37

42. Error Analysis Brian states that $QV = 10$ cm in the figure at the right. Explain why Brian's statement may not be correct. **See margin.**

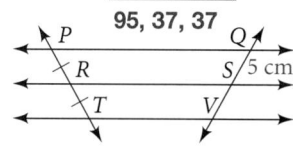

x^2 **43. Algebra** In a parallelogram one angle is 9 times the size of another. Find the measures of the angles. **18, 162**

42. The lines going across may not be ∥ since they are not marked as ∥.

Exercise 36 As an extension, have students write the proof in two-column format.

Exercise 37 Discuss the proof as a class, and point out that it actually contains two separate proofs with reasons that mirror each other.

Exercises 39–41 Remind students to use these properties to analyze angles in a parallelogram:
• Opposite angles are congruent.
• Consecutive angles are supplementary.
• Alternate interior angles formed by a diagonal are congruent.

Exercise 44 Use this exercise to remind students not to assume anything just from the appearance of a diagram.

Exercises 44–52 Pair students who are confused by the many labels on the diagrams with partners who can form the equations necessary to solve the system of equations.

Tactile Learners

Exercise 54 Part a can be demonstrated quickly by threading string through four pieces of straws (two of length a and two of length b, arranged in the order a-b-a-b) and manipulating the shape to form different parallelograms.

Visual Learners

Exercise 55 This proof is much easier to walk through as a group than it is to read. Copy the diagram on the board, and use different colors to highlight the different parallelograms in the proof. Also mark the congruent angles in step f with arc marks. If your class includes students who are color blind, you may want to label the parallelograms X and Y.

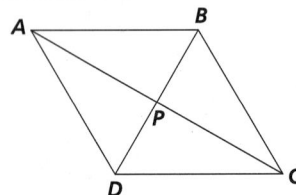

Lesson Quiz 6-2

Use parallelogram *ABCD* for Exercises 1–5.

1. If *AB* = 3*x* + 11, *BC* = 2*x* + 19, and *CD* = 7*x* − 17, find *x*. **7**

2. If *m∠BAD* = *y* and *m∠ADC* = 4*y* − 70, find *y*. **50**

3. If *m∠ABC* = 2*x* + 100 and *m∠ADC* = 6*x* + 84, find *m∠BCD*. **72**

4. If *m∠BCD* = 80 and *m∠CAD* = 34, find *m∠ACD*. **46**

5. If *AP* = 3*x*, *BP* = *y*, *CP* = *x* + *y*, and *DP* = 6*x* − 40, find *x* and *y*. **x = 10, y = 20**

Alternative Assessment

Have students draw and label a parallelogram and then name all the congruent sides, angles, and diagonals.

---

pages 297–301   Exercises

53. The opp. ∠s are ≅, so they have = measures. Consecutive ∠s are suppl., so their sum is 180.

54. a. Answers may vary. Check students' work.

   b. No; the corr. sides can be ≅ but the ∠s may not be.

56. Answers may vary. Sample:

Real-World Connection

As the box is flattened, the shape remains a parallelogram with opposite sides and angles congruent and consecutive angles supplementary.

---

x^2 **Algebra** Find the value(s) of the variable(s) in each parallelogram.

44.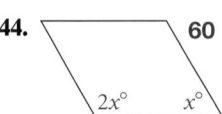

45.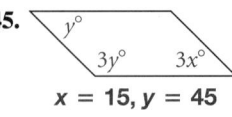
x = 15, y = 45

46.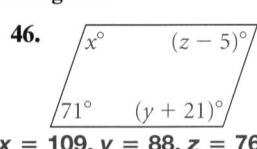
x = 109, y = 88, z = 76

47.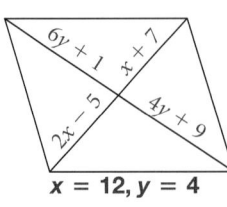
x = 25, y = 115

48.
$x + y$
x
y
$3y − 6$
x = y = 6

49.
$x − 2$
y
$8 − y$
$2x − 12$
x = 10, y = 4

50.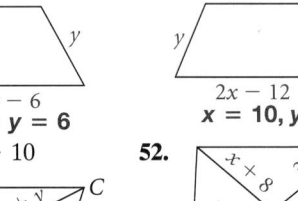
x = 12, y = 4

51. *AC* = 4*x* + 10
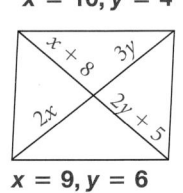
x = 0, y = 5

52.
x = 9, y = 6

53. **Writing** Explain how to find the measures of the remaining three angles of a parallelogram if you already know the measure of one of the angles. **See margin.**

54. a. **Open-Ended** Sketch two parallelograms whose corresponding sides are congruent but whose corresponding angles are not congruent.

   b. **Critical Thinking** Is there an SSSS congruence theorem for parallelograms? Explain. **a–b. See margin.**

55. **Developing Proof** A proof of Theorem 6-4 is outlined below. Supply the reasons for each step.

   Given: $\overleftrightarrow{AB} \parallel \overleftrightarrow{CD} \parallel \overleftrightarrow{EF}$ and $\overline{AC} \cong \overline{CE}$
   Prove: $\overline{BD} \cong \overline{DF}$

   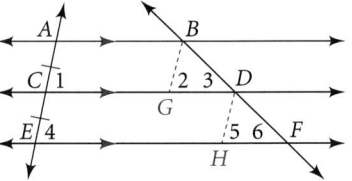

   Draw lines through *B* and *D* parallel to $\overleftrightarrow{AE}$ and intersecting $\overleftrightarrow{CD}$ at *G* and $\overleftrightarrow{EF}$ at *H*.

   a. $\overleftrightarrow{AB} \parallel \overleftrightarrow{CD} \parallel \overleftrightarrow{EF}$ and $\overline{AC} \cong \overline{CE}$ **Given**
   b. *ABGC* and *CDHE* are parallelograms. **Def. of a ▱**
   c. $\overline{BG} \cong \overline{AC}$ and $\overline{DH} \cong \overline{CE}$ **Opp. sides of a ▱ are ≅.**
   d. $\overline{BG} \cong \overline{DH}$ **Trans. Prop. of ≅**
   e. $\overline{BG} \parallel \overline{DH}$ **If 2 lines are ∥ to the same line, then they are ∥ to each other.**
   f. ∠2 ≅ ∠1, ∠1 ≅ ∠4, ∠4 ≅ ∠5, and ∠3 ≅ ∠6 **If 2 lines are ∥, then the corr. ∠s are ≅.**
   g. ∠2 ≅ ∠5 **Trans. Prop. of ≅**
   h. △*BGD* ≅ △*DHF* **AAS**
   i. $\overline{BD} \cong \overline{DF}$ **CPCTC**

Proof Write a paragraph proof, a flow proof, or a two-column proof.

56–58. See margin, pp. 300–301.

56. **Given:** ▱*LENS* and ▱*NGTH*
   Prove: ∠*L* ≅ ∠*T*

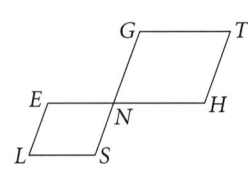

57. **Given:** ▱*LENS* and ▱*NGTH*
   Prove: $\overline{LS} \parallel \overline{GT}$

58. **Given:** ▱*LENS* and ▱*NGTH*
   Prove: ∠*E* is supplementary to ∠*T*.

? **Need Help?**

For each of Exercises 56–58, sketch the diagram and mark it as you think through a proof.

---

3. ∠*ENS* ≅ ∠*GNH* (Vertical ∠s are ≅.)

4. ∠*ELS* ≅ ∠*GTH* (Trans. Prop. of ≅)

57. Answers may vary. Sample: In ▱ *LENS*

and *NGTH*, $\overline{GT} \parallel \overline{EH}$ and $\overline{EH} \parallel \overline{LS}$ by the Def. of a ▱. Therefore $\overline{LS} \parallel \overline{GT}$ because if 2 lines are ∥ to the same line then they are ∥ to each other.

58. Answers may vary. Sample:

1. *LENS* and *NGTH* are ▱ (Given)

2. ∠*GTH* ≅ ∠*GNH* (Opp. ∠s of a ▱ are ≅.)

56. Answers may vary. Sample:

1. *LENS* and *NGTH* are ▱s. (Given)

2. ∠*ELS* ≅ ∠*ENS* and ∠*GTH* ≅ ∠*GNH* (Opp. ∠s of a ▱ are ≅.)

C **Challenge** *Proof* **Write a paragraph proof, a flow proof, or a two-column proof.**

59. Given: ▱*RSTW* and ▱*XYTZ*
    Prove: ∠*R* ≅ ∠*X*

59–61.
See margin.

60. Given: ▱*RSTW* and ▱*XYTZ*
    Prove: $\overline{XY} \parallel \overline{RS}$

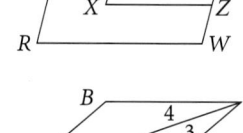

61. Given: ▱*ABCD* and $\overline{AC}$ bisects ∠*DAB*.
    Prove: $\overline{AC}$ bisects ∠*DCB*.

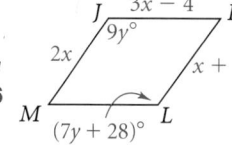

Proof **62. a.** Prove that if two sides and the included angle of one parallelogram are congruent to corresponding parts of another parallelogram, then the parallelograms are congruent. (*Hint:* Prove that all the corresponding parts of the parallelograms are congruent.) **a–b. See margin.**

    b. Is there a theorem similar to SAS for trapezoids? Explain.

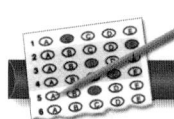

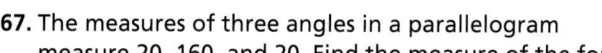

Standardized Test Prep

Gridded Response

Use the parallelogram at the right for Exercises 63–66. Find the indicated segment length or angle measure.

63. *JM* **10**   **64.** *ML* **11**   **65.** m∠*L* **126**   **66.** m∠*J* **126**

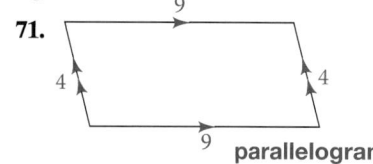

67. The measures of three angles in a parallelogram measure 20, 160, and 20. Find the measure of the fourth angle. **160**

68. The measures of two angles in a parallelogram are 32 and 32. Find the measure of one of the other two angles. **148**

Take It to the NET
Online lesson quiz at
www.PHSchool.com
Web Code: afa-0602

69. Two consecutive angles in a parallelogram have measures $x + 5$ and $4x - 10$. Find the measure of the smaller angle. **42**

Mixed Review

Lesson 6-1   **Determine the most precise name for each figure.**

70.   **71.**

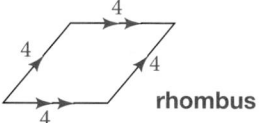

rhombus

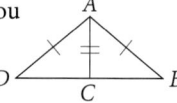

parallelogram

Lesson 4-6   **72.** What additional information do you need to prove △*ADC* ≅ △*ABC* by the HL Theorem?
    $\overline{AC} \perp \overline{DB}$

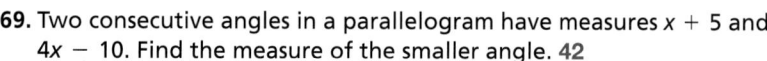

Lesson 3-1   **In the figure at the right, $\overrightarrow{PQ} \parallel \overrightarrow{RS}$. Find each measure.**

73. m∠1 **49**   **74.** m∠2 **131**   **75.** m∠3 **49**   **76.** m∠4 **131**

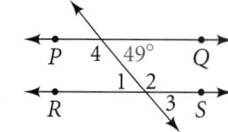

3. ∠*ENS* ≅ ∠*GNH* (Vertical ⩘ are ≅.)

4. ∠*LEN* is supp. to ∠*ENS* (Consec. ⩘ in a ▱ are suppl.)

5. ∠*ENS* ≅ ∠*GTH* (Trans. Prop. of ≅)

6. ∠*E* is suppl. to ∠*T* (Suppl. of ≅ ⩘ are suppl.)

59. Answers may vary. Sample: In ▱ *RSTW* and ▱ *XYTZ*, ∠*R* ≅ ∠*T* and ∠*X* ≅ ∠*T* because opp.

⩘ of a ▱ are ≅. Then ∠*R* ≅ ∠*X* by the Trans. Prop. of ≅.

60. In ▱ *RSTW* and ▱ *XYTZ*, $\overline{XY} \parallel \overline{TW}$ and $\overline{RS} \parallel \overline{TW}$ by the def. of a ▱. Then $\overline{XY} \parallel \overline{RS}$ because if 2

A sheet of blank grids is available in the Test-Taking Strategies with Transparencies booklet. Give this sheet to students for practice with filling in the grids.

 **Resources**

For additional practice with a variety of test item formats:
- Standardized Test Prep, p. 343
- Test-Taking Strategies, p. 338
- Test-Taking Strategies with Transparencies

lines are ∥ to the same line, then they are ∥ to each other.

61. $\overline{AB} \parallel \overline{DC}$ and $\overline{AD} \parallel \overline{BC}$ by def. of ▱. ∠2 ≅ ∠3 and ∠1 ≅ ∠4 because if 2 lines are ∥, then alt. int. ⩘ are ≅. ∠3 ≅ ∠4 because if 2 ⩘ are each ≅ to 2 ≅ ⩘, then they are ≅. By def. of bisect, $\overline{AC}$ bisects ∠*DCB*.

62. a. Given: 2 sides and the included ∠ of ▱*ABCD* are ≅ to the corr. parts of ▱*WXYZ*. Let ∠*A* ≅ ∠*W*, $\overline{AB} \cong \overline{WX}$ and $\overline{AD} \cong \overline{WZ}$. Since opp. ⩘ of a ▱ are ≅, ∠*A* ≅ ∠*C* and ∠*W* ≅ ∠*Y*. Thus ∠*C* ≅ ∠*Y* by the Trans. Prop. of ≅. Similarly, opp. sides of a ▱ are ≅, thus $\overline{AB} \cong \overline{CD}$ and $\overline{WX} \cong \overline{ZY}$. Using the Trans. Prop. of ≅, $\overline{CD} \cong \overline{ZY}$. The same can be done to prove $\overline{BC} \cong \overline{XY}$. Since consec. ⩘ of a ▱ are suppl., ∠*A* is suppl. to ∠*D*, and ∠*W* is suppl. to ∠*Z*. Suppls. of ≅ ⩘ are ≅, thus ∠*D* ≅ ∠*Z*. The same can be done to prove ∠*B* ≅ ∠*X*. Therefore, since all corr. ⩘ and sides are ≅, ▱*ABCD* ≅ ▱*WXYZ*.

b. No; opp. ⩘ and sides are not necessarily ≅ in a trapezoid.

301

Reading a Plan for Proof

Textbook proofs often appear to flow effortlessly. In fact, planning a proof is an essential first step for all proofs. Students must learn how to approach the planning process in order to become competent at proof. This feature helps students better understand how to write a plan for proof.

Teaching Notes

Before you begin reading through the plan for proof and flow proof, ask students to focus on the information that is given. Have volunteers suggest information that can be directly derived from what is given. Then have students apply their thoughts to what they are trying to prove.

Math Tip

The key idea in Ravi's plan is a property of parallel lines. Point out that the given information did not name pairs of parallel lines; they were deduced as a property of the parallelogram. Proofs often require students to justify using key concepts.

Exercise

Have students work independently to complete the proof, showing the steps in their proofs. Then have volunteers share with the class what they were thinking as they wrote each step. Elicit the fact that there are often different ways to complete a proof.

page 302   Reading Math

1. **LENS** is a □. **NGTH** is a □. (Given)

2. ∠L ≅ ∠ENS, ∠HNG ≅ ∠T

3. ∠ENS ≅ ∠HNG (Vert. ∠s are ≅.)

4. ∠L ≅ ∠T (Trans. Prop. of ≅)

302

Follow along with Ravi as he writes a flow proof for Theorem 6-2 that follows the plan on page 295. Then check your understanding by solving the exercise at the bottom of the page.

Theorem 6-2 Opposite angles of a parallelogram are congruent.

Given: □MNPQ

Prove: ∠M ≅ ∠P and ∠N ≅ ∠Q

Plan: ∠M ≅ ∠P if they are supplements of the same angle, ∠N. Each is a supplement of ∠N because same-side interior angles are supplementary. ∠N ≅ ∠Q using similar reasoning with ∠M.

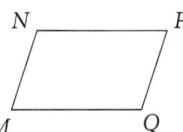

What Ravi Thinks

The second sentence of the plan is

"Each is a supplement of ∠N because same-side interior angles are supplementary."

This tells me where to begin. Opposite sides of a parallelogram are parallel while the other sides act as transversals. The opposite sides and transversals form same-side interior angles.

Same-side interior angles are supplementary and supplements of the same angle are congruent.

This gives me half the proof.

The last sentence of the plan is

"∠N ≅ ∠Q using similar reasoning with ∠M."

This tells me I can repeat the first part of the proof, but with different angles.

I have found a clever way to add this second part to my flow proof. It's in red.

What Ravi Writes

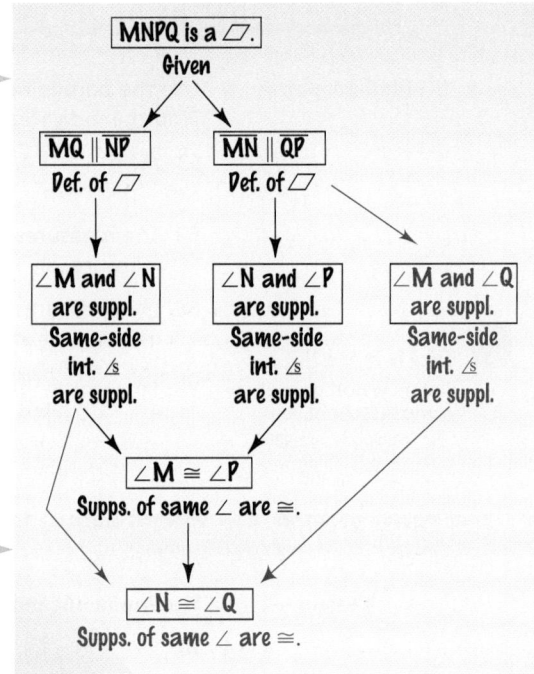

EXERCISE

For Exercise 56 on page 300, follow this plan and write a proof.

Given: □LENS and □NGTH

Prove: ∠L ≅ ∠T

Plan: ∠L ≅ ∠T if their opposite angles, ∠ENS and ∠HNG, are congruent. ∠ENS ≅ ∠HNG because they are vertical angles.
See margin.

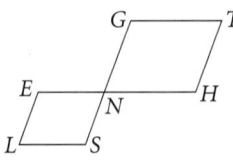

page 303   Check Skills You'll Need

1. $\left(\frac{5}{2}, \frac{3}{2}\right)$, $\left(\frac{5}{2}, \frac{3}{2}\right)$; they bisect each other.

2. Slope of $\overline{BC} = \frac{1}{3}$, slope of $\overline{AD} = \frac{1}{3}$. The slopes are =.

3. Yes; they are vertical lines.

6-3

Proving That a Quadrilateral Is a Parallelogram

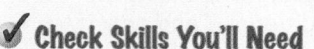
 North Carolina Objectives

2.03 Apply properties, definitions, and theorems of two-dimensional figures to solve problems and write proofs: b) Quadrilaterals.

Lesson Preview

What You'll Learn

OBJECTIVE 1 To determine whether a quadrilateral is a parallelogram

. . . And Why

To use a parallel rule to plot a ship's course, as in Example 3

✓ **Check Skills You'll Need**   (For help, go to Lessons 1-6 and 3-6.)

Use the figure at the right.

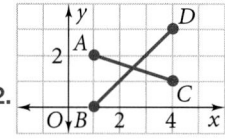

1. Find the coordinates of the midpoints of $\overline{AC}$ and $\overline{BD}$. What is the relationship between $\overline{AC}$ and $\overline{BD}$?

2. Find the slopes of $\overline{BC}$ and $\overline{AD}$. How do they compare?   **1–3. See margin, p. 302.**

3. Are $\overline{AB}$ and $\overline{DC}$ parallel? Explain.

4. What type of figure is $ABCD$?   **parallelogram**

OBJECTIVE 1

Is the Quadrilateral a Parallelogram?

 Interactive lesson includes instant self-check, tutorials, and activities.

Investigation: Is It a Parallelogram?

By definition, a quadrilateral is a parallelogram if both pairs of opposite sides are parallel. Use a geoboard to explore other ways to determine whether a quadrilateral is a parallelogram.   **1–4. See margin, p. 305.**

1. The segments on this geoboard bisect each other. Connect the endpoints to form a quadrilateral. Find the slopes of pairs of opposite sides and determine what type of quadrilateral it is.

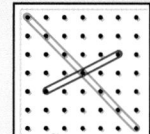

2. Make several pairs of bisecting segments on a geoboard. Join the endpoints to form quadrilaterals. Classify the quadrilaterals. Make a conjecture about quadrilaterals whose diagonals bisect each other.

3. The segments on this geoboard are congruent and parallel. Connect the endpoints to form a quadrilateral. Find the slopes of these new sides and determine what type of quadrilateral it is.

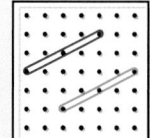

4. Make several pairs of congruent parallel segments on a geoboard. Join the endpoints to form quadrilaterals. Classify the quadrilaterals. Make a conjecture about quadrilaterals that have one pair of congruent and parallel sides.

In Lesson 6-2, you learned what you could deduce, given a parallelogram. In this lesson, you will learn how to deduce that a figure is a parallelogram.

 Ongoing Assessment and Intervention

Before the Lesson	**During the Lesson**	**After the Lesson**
Diagnose prerequisite skills using:	**Monitor progress using:**	**Assess knowledge using:**
• Check Skills You'll Need	• Check Understanding	• Lesson Quiz
	• Additional Examples	• Computer Test Generator CD
	• Standardized Test Prep	• Chapter Checkpoint 1 (p. 310)

Lesson Preview

✓ **Check Skills You'll Need**

Finding the Midpoint
Lesson 1-6: Example 3
Exercises 18–23
Extra Practice, p. 690

Slope
Algebra Review, p. 151:
Example 1 Exercises 1–9

Checking for Parallel Lines
Lesson 3-6: Example 1
Exercises 1–4
Extra Practice, p. 692

Lesson Resources

📁 **Teaching Resources**
Practice, Reteaching, Enrichment

👥 **Reaching All Students**
Practice Workbook 6-3
Spanish Practice Workbook 6-3
Reading and Math Literacy 6B
Spanish Reading & Literacy 6B
Spanish Checkpoint Quiz 1
Informal Geometry Planning Guide 6-3

⏱ **Presentation Assistant Plus!**
Transparencies
• Check Skills You'll Need 6-3
• Additional Examples 6-3
• Student Edition Answers 6-3
• Lesson Quiz 6-3
PH Presentation Pro CD 6-3

ASSESSMENT SYSTEM
Computer Test Generator CD

🖱 **Technology**
Resource Pro® CD-ROM
Computer Test Generator CD
Prentice Hall Presentation Pro CD

💻 **www.PHSchool.com**
Student Site
• Teacher Web Code: afk-5500
• Self-grading Lesson Quiz
Teacher Center
• Lesson Planner
• Resources

Plus

303

Math Background

The conditions necessary for a quadrilateral to be a parallelogram are also sufficient, as proved in this lesson. This allows using the biconditional *if and only if* to combine and catalogue the theorems and their converses in these lessons.

 OBJECTIVE 1 Teaching Notes

Investigation (Optional)
Students may use geometry software to construct segments that bisect each other and then connect the endpoints of the segments and compare the slopes of the sides to show that the quadrilateral is a parallelogram.

This lesson introduces several more theorems about parallelograms. Have students begin a class chart that displays all the theorems they learn about parallelograms, and refer to it during class discussions of proofs.

Teaching Tip
Throughout the lesson, prompt students to relate the new theorems to their converses in Lesson 6-2.

Auditory Learners
Before students actually read the flow proof for Theorem 6-5, have them focus on the diagram of *ABCD* and suggest a Plan for Proof. Students who suggest the same basic ideas found in the proof will profit from the logical sequencing of their ideas in the proof.

Math Tip
Theorem 6-6 is the only theorem in this lesson that is not the converse of a theorem from Lesson 6-2.

Theorem 6-5 is the converse of Theorem 6-3 of the previous lesson.

 **Key Concepts**

Theorem 6-5

If the diagonals of a quadrilateral bisect each other, then the quadrilateral is a parallelogram.

Proof **Proof of Theorem 6-5**

Given: $\overline{AC}$ and $\overline{BD}$ bisect each other at *E*.

Prove: *ABCD* is a parallelogram.

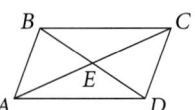

 Need Help?
Remember to mark your diagram as your proof develops.

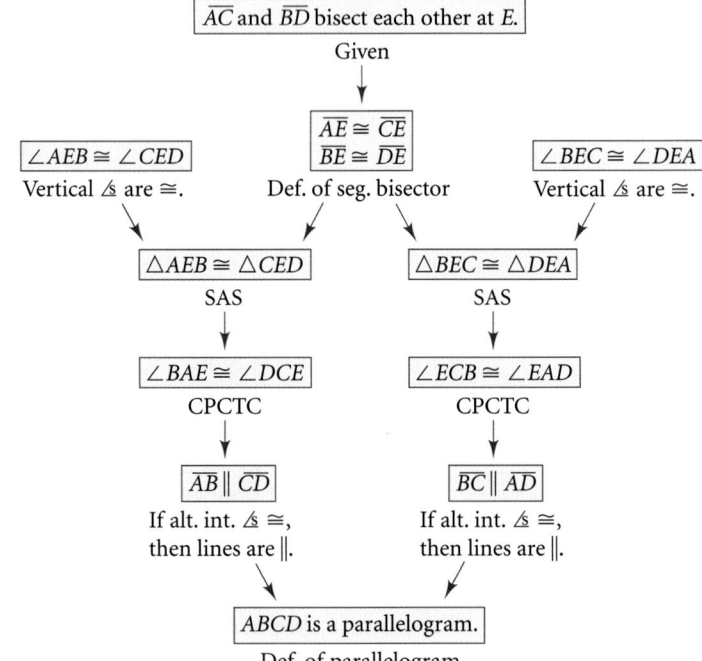

Theorem 6-6 suggests that if you keep two objects of the same length parallel, such as cross-country skis, then the quadrilateral determined by their endpoints must be a parallelogram. You will help plan a proof for Theorem 6-6 in Exercise 17.

 **Key Concepts**

Theorem 6-6

If one pair of opposite sides of a quadrilateral is both congruent and parallel, then the quadrilateral is a parallelogram.

You can use algebra and Theorems 6-5 and 6-6 to find values for which quadrilaterals are parallelograms.

👬 Reaching All Students

Below Level Students may find the proof of Theorem 6-7 easier to follow than that of Theorem 6-5, so you may want to prove Theorem 6-7 first and use it to prove Theorem 6-5.	**Advanced Learners** Have students find counterexamples if the word *both* is deleted from Theorems 6-7 and 6-8.	**English Learners** See note on page Xxx. **Inclusion** See note on page Xxx.

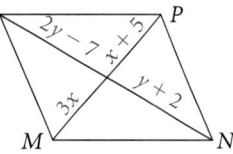

1 EXAMPLE   Finding Values for Parallelograms

Algebra Find values of x and y for which $MLPN$ must be a parallelogram.

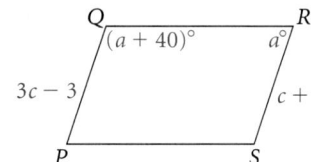

$$2y - 7 = y + 2 \quad \xleftarrow{} \quad \text{Diagonals of parallelograms} \quad \xrightarrow{} \quad 3x = x + 5$$
$$\text{bisect each other.}$$
$$y - 7 = 2 \quad \xleftarrow{} \text{Collect the variables on one side.} \xrightarrow{} \quad 2x = 5$$
$$y = 9 \quad \xleftarrow{} \text{Solve.} \xrightarrow{} \quad x = \frac{5}{2}$$

● If $y = 9$ and $x = \frac{5}{2}$, then $MLPN$ is a parallelogram.

✓ Check Understanding ① Find the values of a and c for which $PQRS$ must be a parallelogram. **70, 2**

Theorems 6-7 and 6-8 are converses of Theorems 6-1 and 6-2, respectively, from the previous lesson. They provide two more ways to conclude that a quadrilateral is a parallelogram.

🔑 Key Concepts

> **Theorem 6-7**
>
> If both pairs of opposite sides of a quadrilateral are congruent, then the quadrilateral is a parallelogram.

Proof of Theorem 6-7

Real-World 🌐 Connection

The frame remains a parallelogram as it is raised and lowered, and the backboard stays vertical.

Given: $\overline{WX} \cong \overline{ZY}$ and $\overline{XY} \cong \overline{WZ}$
Prove: $WXYZ$ is a parallelogram.

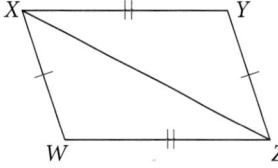

Proof: Draw diagonal $\overline{XZ}$. Since opposite sides of $WXYZ$ are congruent, $\triangle WXZ \cong \triangle YZX$ by SSS. Using CPCTC, $\angle WXZ \cong \angle YZX$, so $\overline{WX} \parallel \overline{ZY}$. Since $\overline{WX}$ and $\overline{ZY}$ are both congruent and parallel, $WXYZ$ is a parallelogram by Theorem 6-6.

You will complete a two-column proof of Theorem 6-8 in Exercise 19.

🔑 Key Concepts

> **Theorem 6-8**
>
> If both pairs of opposite angles of a quadrilateral are congruent, then the quadrilateral is a parallelogram.

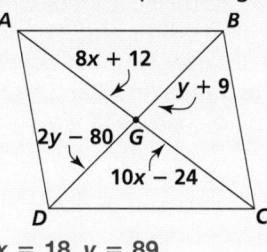
page 303 Investigation

1. -4 and $-\frac{2}{5}$; parallelogram

2. If diag. of a quad. bisect each other, then it is a ▱.

3. The slope of both new sides is -1. It is a ▱.

4. If a quad. has 1 pair of ≅ and ∥ sides, then the quad. is a ▱.

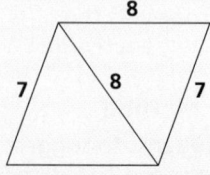
2 Determine whether the quadrilateral must be a parallelogram. Explain.

a.

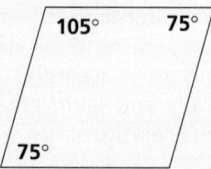

No; you do not know whether both pairs of opposite sides are congruent.

b.

105°   75°

75°

Yes; both pairs of opposite angles are congruent.

3 The captain of a fishing boat plots a course toward a school of bluefish. One side of a parallel rule connects the boat with the school of bluefish. The other side makes a 36° angle north of due east on the chart's compass. Explain how the captain knows in which direction to sail to reach the bluefish. Because the parallel rule forms a parallelogram, the captain should sail 36° north of due east.

Closure

Using the theorems you have learned in Chapter 6, write two different biconditionals about parallelograms. **Sample:** A quadrilateral is a parallelogram if and only if both pairs of opposite angles are congruent. A quadrilateral is a parallelogram if and only if its diagonals bisect each other.

page 306 **Check Understanding**

3. Once in place, both rulers show the direction and remain ∥. Keep the second ruler in place and move the first ruler to get the compass reading.

306

Proof 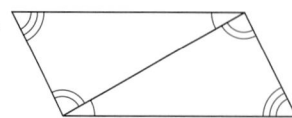 **Is the Quadrilateral a Parallelogram?**

Developing Proof Based on the information given, can you determine that the quadrilateral must be a parallelogram? Explain.

a. 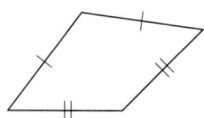   **b.**

Yes, both pairs of opposite angles are congruent.   No, the figure could be a kite.

✓ **Check Understanding** **2** Determine whether the quadrilateral must be a parallelogram. Explain.

a. 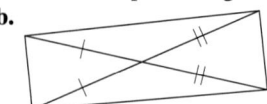   **b.**

Yes; a pair of opp. sides are ∥ and ≅.   No; the figure could be a trapezoid.

You can use the theorems of this lesson in a variety of ways.

3 **EXAMPLE** **Real-World** **Connection**

Navigation A parallel rule is a navigation tool that is used to plot ship routes on charts. It is made of two rulers connected with congruent crossbars, such that $AB = DC$ and $AD = BC$. You place one ruler on the line connecting the ship's present position to its destination. Then you move the other ruler onto the chart's compass to find the direction of the route. Explain why this instrument works.

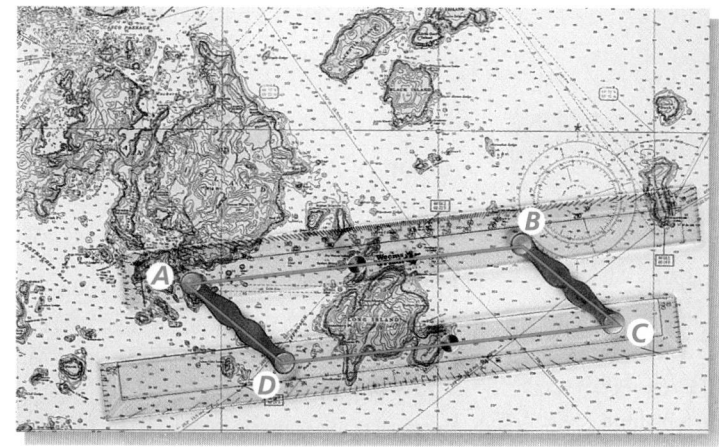

The crossbars and the sections of the rulers are congruent no matter how they are positioned. So, $ABCD$ is always a parallelogram. Since $ABCD$ is a parallelogram, the rulers are parallel. Therefore, the direction the ship should travel is the same as the direction shown on the chart's compass.

✓ **Check Understanding** **3** **Critical Thinking** Suppose the ruler connecting the ship's position to its destination point gets in the way of reading the compass. How can you manipulate the tool to get the desired reading? **See margin.**

Real-World **Connection**

Careers A marine navigator has great responsibility for the ship, its crew, its cargo, its mission, and the surrounding natural marine environment.

pages 307–310 **Exercises**

7. Yes; both pairs of opp. sides are ≅.

8. No; the quad. could be a kite.

9. Yes; both pairs of opp. ∠s are ≅.

10. No; the quad. could be a trapezoid.

11. Yes; both pairs of opp. sides are ∥ because alt. int. ∠s are ≅.

12. Yes; one pair of opp. sides are ∥ and ≅.

13. Yes; both pairs of opp. sides are ∥.

14. No; opp. sides are not ∥.

EXERCISES

For more practice, see *Extra Practice*.

Practice and Problem Solving

 **Practice by Example** x^2 **Algebra** Find the values of *x* and *y* for which *ABCD* must be a parallelogram.

Example 1
(page 305)

1.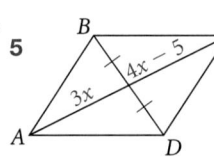

2.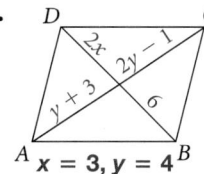
$x = 3, y = 4$

3.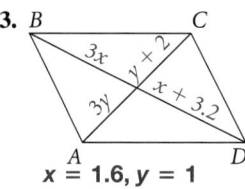
$x = 1.6, y = 1$

4.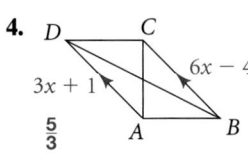

5.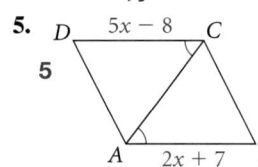

6.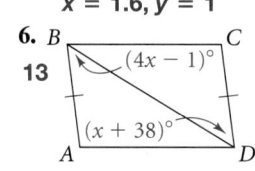

7–15. See margin, pp. 306–307.

Example 2
(page 306)

Determine whether the quadrilateral must be a parallelogram. Explain.

7.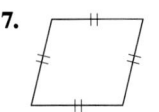

8.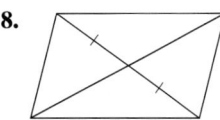

9.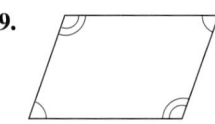

10.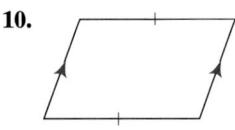

11.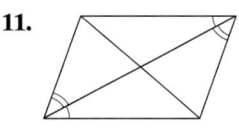

12.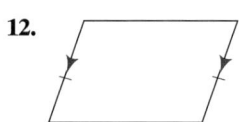

13.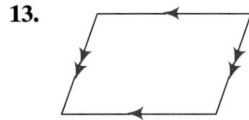

14.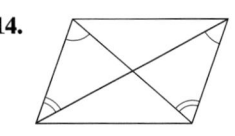

15.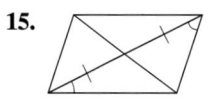

Example 3
(page 306)

16. Fishing Quadrilaterals are formed on on the side of this fishing tackle box by the adjustable shelves and connecting pieces. Explain why the quadrilaterals remain parallelograms no matter what position the shelves are in. **See margin.**

B **Apply Your Skills** *Proof* **17. Developing Proof** Complete this plan for a proof of Theorem 6-6. **See margin.**

Given: $\overline{TW} \parallel \overline{YX}$ and $\overline{TW} \cong \overline{YX}$

Prove: *TWXY* is a parallelogram.

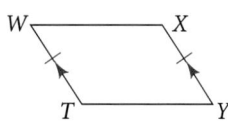

? **Need Help?**

For Exercise 18, you can review biconditionals in Lesson 2-2.

Plan: Draw diagonals $\overline{TX}$ and $\overline{WY}$ intersecting at *R*. Now, *TWXY* is a parallelogram if the diagonals **a.** ? each other. $\overline{WR} \cong \overline{YR}$ and $\overline{TR} \cong$ **b.** ? by CPCTC if $\triangle TWR \cong$ **c.** ? . These triangles are congruent by **d.** ? because $\overline{TW} \parallel \overline{YX}$ and **e.** ? angles are congruent.

18. Combine Theorems 6-1 and 6-7 into a biconditional statement. **See margin.**

Lesson 6-3 Proving That a Quadrilateral Is a Parallelogram **307**

15. No; the quad. could be a kite.

16. It remains a ▱ because the shelves and connecting pieces remain ∥.

17. a. bisect
b. $\overline{XR}$
c. $\triangle XYR$
d. ASA
e. alt. interior

18. Opp. sides of a quad. are ≅ if and only if the quad. is a ▱.

Exercises 1–6 Have students identify the theorems they use to establish that the quadrilateral is a parallelogram.

Error Prevention

Exercise 7 Remind students that parallelograms with more precise names are still parallelograms. Ask: *Are both pairs of opposite sides congruent?* yes *What figure has this description?* parallelogram

Exercise 10 Remind students not to form conclusions from the appearance of a diagram. Ask: *What quadrilateral has one pair of sides parallel and the other pair of sides congruent and is not a parallelogram?* isosceles trapezoid

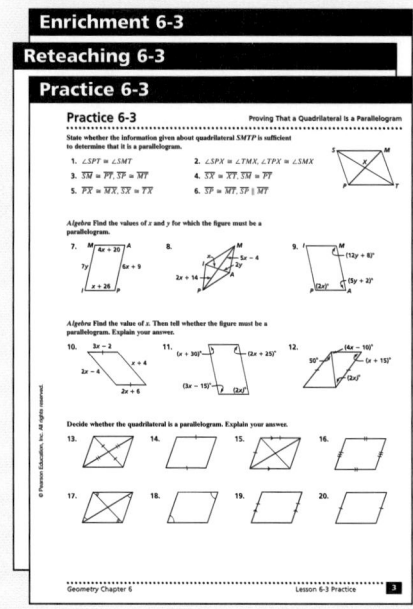

307

Exercises 20–25 Students should copy the diagram and label the information given for each exercise. This will help them form the visual associations that are helpful in planning proofs.

Exercises 26–29 If necessary, review solving systems of equations.

Tactile Learners

Exercise 30 Manipulating two pencils can illustrate the idea. Have students place a pencil on a sheet of paper, then place the midpoint of a second pencil on the midpoint of the first pencil and mark all four endpoints on the paper. Have students rotate the second pencil and repeat the markings. When they connect each set of markings, they can see that the figures are noncongruent parallelograms.

Exercises 32–34 Students should use slope and the distance formula to find the solutions.

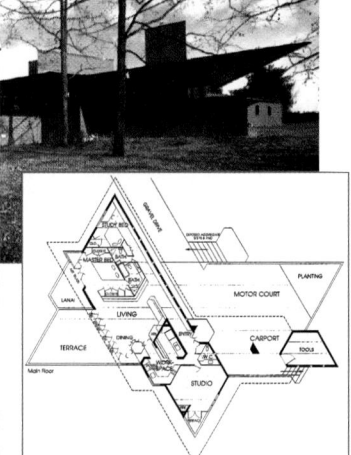

pages 307–310   Exercises

20. Yes; both pairs of opp. ∠s are ≅.

21. No; the figure could be a kite.

22. Yes; a pair of opp. sides is ∥ and ≅.

23. No; the figure could be a trapezoid.

24. Yes; both pairs of opp. sides are ≅.

25. Yes; diag. bisects each other.

30. Answers may vary. Sample:

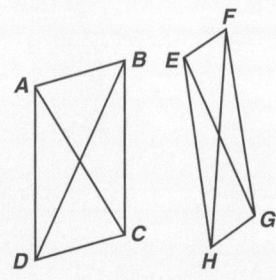

308

Need Help?

$x + y + x + y = 2x + 2y$
$= 2(x + y)$

The last step is the Distributive Property.

19. **Developing Proof** Complete the two-column proof of Theorem 6-8.

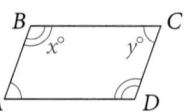

Given: $\angle A \cong \angle C$ and $\angle B \cong \angle D$

Prove: $ABCD$ is a parallelogram.

Statements	Reasons
1. $x + y + x + y = 360$	1. The sum of the measures of the angles of a quadrilateral $= 360$.
2. $2(x + y) = 360$	a. _?_ Distr. Prop.
3. $x + y = 180$	b. _?_ Div. Prop. of Eq.
4. $\angle A$ and $\angle B$ are supplementary. $\angle A$ and $\angle D$ are supplementary.	4. Definition of supplementary
c. _?_ ∥ _?_ , _?_ ∥ _?_ See below.	d. _?_ If same-side int. ∠s are supp., the lines are ∥.
6. $ABCD$ is a parallelogram.	e. _?_ Def. of ▱

c. $\overline{AD} \parallel \overline{BC}, \overline{AB} \parallel \overline{DC}$

Developing Proof State whether the given information is enough to conclude that $RSTW$ is a parallelogram. Explain.

20. $\angle SRW \cong \angle WTS, \angle RST \cong \angle TWR$

21. $\angle TSZ \cong \angle RSZ, \angle TWZ \cong \angle RWZ$

22. $\overline{RS} \parallel \overline{WT}, \overline{RS} \cong \overline{WT}$

23. $\overline{RS} \parallel \overline{WT}, \overline{ST} \cong \overline{RW}$

24. $\overline{RS} \cong \overline{WT}, \overline{ST} \cong \overline{RW}$

25. $\overline{RZ} \cong \overline{TZ}, \overline{SZ} \cong \overline{WZ}$

20–25. See margin.

x^2 **Algebra** Find the values of the variables for which $ABCD$ must be a parallelogram.

26.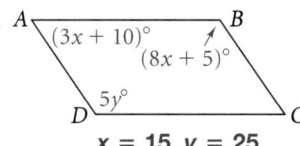

$x = 15, y = 25$

27.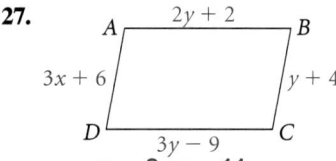

$x = 3, y = 11$

28.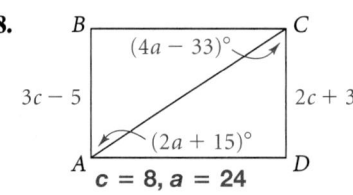

$c = 8, a = 24$

29.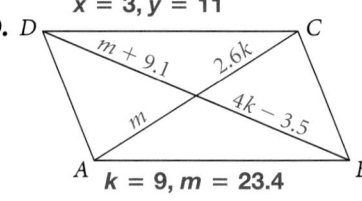

$k = 9, m = 23.4$

30. **Open-Ended** Sketch two noncongruent parallelograms $ABCD$ and $EFGH$ such that $\overline{AC} \cong \overline{EG}$ and $\overline{BD} \cong \overline{FH}$. See margin.

31. **Probability** If two opposite angles of a quadrilateral measure 120 and the measures of the other angles are multiples of 10, what is the probability that the quadrilateral is a parallelogram? $\frac{1}{6}$

Real-World Connection

Frank Lloyd Wright, a famous architect, used parallelograms in designs of many houses, such as the Kraus House in Kirkwood, Missouri.

Coordinate Geometry Given points A, B, and C in the coordinate plane as shown, find the fourth point described below.

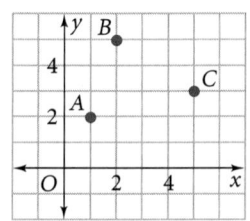

32. point D so that $ABCD$ is a parallelogram (4, 0)

33. point E so that $ABEC$ is a parallelogram (6, 6)

34. point F so that $AFBC$ is a parallelogram (−2, 4)

35. **Writing** Summarize the ways to show that a quadrilateral is a parallelogram. See margin.

---

35. You can show a quad. is a ▱ if both pairs of opp. sides are ∥ or ≅, if both pairs of opp. ∠s are ≅, if diagonals bisect each other, if all consecutive ∠s are suppl., or if one pair of opp. sides are both ∥ and ≅.

36. Answers may vary. Sample:

1. $\triangle TRS \cong \triangle RTW$ (Given)

2. $\overline{RS} \cong \overline{TW}, \angle SRT \cong \angle WTR$ (CPCTC)

3. $\overline{SR} \parallel \overline{WT}$ (If alt. int. ∠s are ≅, then lines are ∥.)

4. $RSTW$ is a ▱. (If one pair of opp. sides are ∥ and ≅, then it is a ▱.)

C Challenge *Proof* **36.** Write a paragraph proof, a flow proof, or a two-column proof. **See margin, p. 308.**

Given: $\triangle TRS \cong \triangle RTW$

Prove: $RSTW$ is a parallelogram.

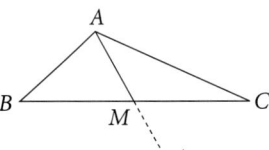

Proof **37.** In the figure at the right, point D is constructed by drawing two arcs. One has center C and radius AB. The other has center B and radius AC. Prove that $\overline{AM}$ is a median of $\triangle ABC$. **See margin.**

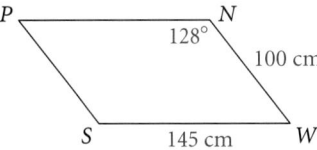

38. Coordinate Geometry The diagonals of quadrilateral $EFGH$ intersect at $D(-1, 4)$. Two vertices of $EFGH$ are $E(2, 7)$ and $F(-3, 5)$. What must be the coordinates of G and H to ensure that $EFGH$ is a parallelogram?
G(−4, 1), H(1, 3)

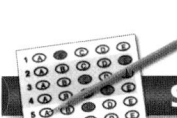

Standardized Test Prep

Multiple Choice

39. In $\square PNWS$, what is $m\angle W$? **C**
 A. 128   **B.** 90   **C.** 52   **D.** 26

40. In $\square PNWS$, what is $m\angle S$? **F**
 F. 128   **G.** 90   **H.** 52   **I.** 26

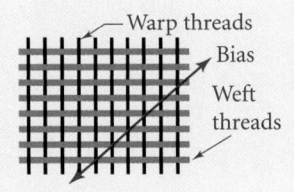

Reading Comprehension

Read the passage below, then answer the questions on the basis of what is *stated* or *implied* in the passage.

> Fabric is made by weaving threads vertically (the warp) and horizontally (the weft), forming small rectangles. Pull the fabric vertically or horizontally and it will not distort. The rectangles will remain as rectangles. Pull the fabric along its diagonals and parallel threads remain parallel but form small nonrectangular parallelograms.

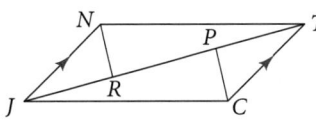

41. What is formed by the warp and the weft? **C**
 A. threads woven vertically   **B.** threads woven horizontally
 C. small rectangles   **D.** nonrectangular parallelograms

42. How does pulling fabric along its diagonal affect the shape of the fabric? **H**
 F. It becomes a longer rectangle.   **G.** It becomes a shorter rectangle.
 H. It is no longer a rectangle.   **I.** The shape is unchanged.

Short Response

43. Given: $\triangle NRJ \cong \triangle CPT$, $\overline{JN} \parallel \overline{CT}$
 Prove: $JNTC$ is a parallelogram.
        See margin, p. 310.

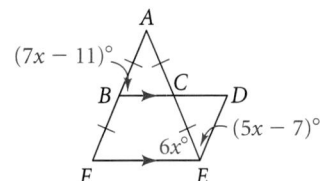

Extended Response

44. a. Write an equation and solve for x.
 b. Is $\overline{AF} \parallel \overline{DE}$? Explain.
 c. Is $BDEF$ a parallelogram? Explain.
        See back of book.

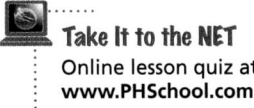

Take It to the NET
Online lesson quiz at
www.PHSchool.com
Web Code: afa-0603

Lesson 6-3 Proving That a Quadrilateral Is a Parallelogram **309**

37. Answers may vary. Sample:
1. $\overline{AB} \cong \overline{CD}$, $\overline{AC} \cong \overline{BD}$ (Given)
2. $ACDB$ is a $\square$. (If opp. sides are $\cong$, then it is a $\square$.)
3. M is the midpoint of $\overline{BC}$. (The diagonals of a $\square$ bisect each other.)
4. $\overline{AM}$ is a median. (Def. of a median)

Lesson Quiz 6-3

Find the values of the variables for which *GHIJ* must be a parallelogram.

1.

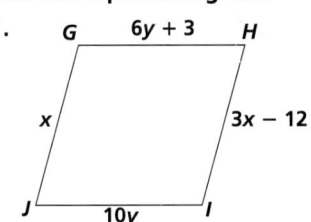

$x = 6, y = 0.75$

2.

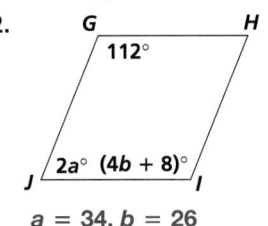

$a = 34, b = 26$

Determine whether the quadrilateral must be a parallelogram. Explain.

3.

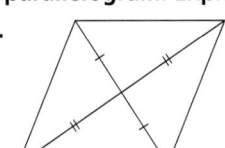

Yes; the diagonals bisect each other.

4.

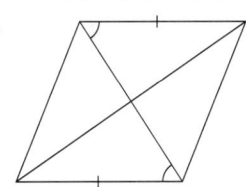

Yes; one pair of opposite sides is both congruent and parallel.

5.

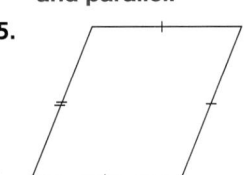

No; both pairs of opposite sides are not congruent.

309

Mixed Review

Lesson 6-2 x^2 **Algebra** Find the value of each variable in each parallelogram. **45–47. See margin.**

45.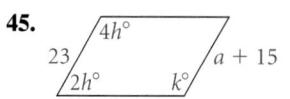
46.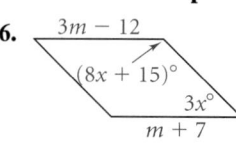
47.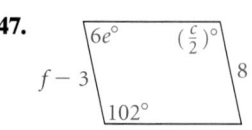

Lesson 4-7
48. Explain how you can use overlapping congruent triangles to prove $\overline{AC} \cong \overline{BD}$. **See margin.**

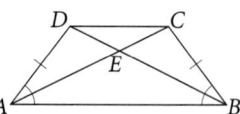

Lesson 2-2 Write the two conditional statements that make up each biconditional.

49. The diagonals of a quadrilateral bisect each other if and only if the quadrilateral is a parallelogram. **See margin.**

50. Two lines are parallel if and only if the two lines and a transversal form corresponding angles that are congruent. **See margin, p. 311.**

51. Two nonvertical lines are perpendicular if and only if the product of their slopes is −1. **See margin, p. 311.**

Checkpoint Quiz 1   Lessons 6-1 through 6-3

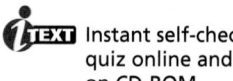 **Instant self-check quiz online and on CD-ROM**

Find the measures of the numbered angles for each parallelogram. **1–3. See left.**

1. $m\angle 1 = 59, m\angle 2 = 121, m\angle 3 = 59$

2. $m\angle 1 = 43, m\angle 2 = 62, m\angle 3 = 62$

3. $m\angle 1 = 106, m\angle 2 = 74, m\angle 3 = 26$

1.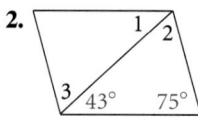
2.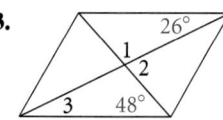
3.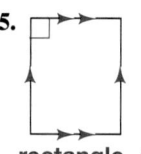

Classify each quadrilateral in as many ways as possible.

4.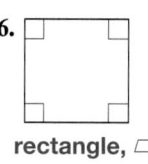
trapezoid, isosc. trapezoid

5. rectangle, ▱

6. rectangle, ▱

x^2 **Algebra** Find the values of the variables for which *ABCD* is a parallelogram.

7.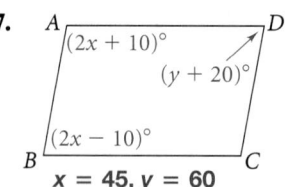
x = 45, y = 60

8.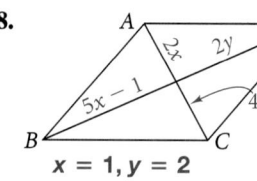
x = 1, y = 2

9. In the figure at the right, $\overleftrightarrow{AB} \parallel \overleftrightarrow{CD} \parallel \overleftrightarrow{EF}$. Find *AE*. **20.6**

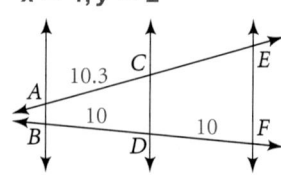

10. What is the most precise name for a quadrilateral with vertices (3, 5), (−1, 4), (3, −5), and (7, 4)? **kite**

Diagonals of Parallelograms

FOR USE WITH LESSON 6-4

Construct

Use geometry software to construct a parallelogram.

- Construct segments $\overline{AB}$ and $\overline{BC}$.
- Construct a line through C parallel to $\overline{AB}$ and a line through A parallel to $\overline{BC}$. Label the point where the two lines intersect as D.
- Hide the lines and construct $\overline{AD}$ and $\overline{CD}$.
- Construct the diagonals of $\square ABCD$ and label their point of intersection E.

Set up the following measurements. Use them where indicated.

M1: $m\angle DAB$, or some other angle of the parallelogram, so that you can tell when the parallelogram is a rectangle

M2: AB and AD, or some other adjacent sides of the parallelogram, so you can tell when it is a rhombus

M3: $m\angle AED$, or some other angle at the intersection of the diagonals, so you can tell when the diagonals are perpendicular

M4: AC and DB, the diagonal lengths, so you can tell when they are equal

M5: the angles at each vertex of the parallelogram, so you can tell when the diagonals bisect the angles of the parallelogram

Investigate

- Manipulate the parallelogram to get a rectangle (M1). Make note of what appear to be any special properties of the diagonals of a rectangle. Manipulate the rectangle to check whether the properties hold (M3–5).

- Manipulate the parallelogram to get a rhombus (M2). Make note of what appear to be any special properties of the diagonals of a rhombus. Manipulate the rhombus to check whether the properties hold (M3–5).

EXERCISES

Make as many conjectures as you can about each of the following. 1–7. See margin.

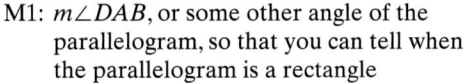 **1.** the diagonals of rectangles   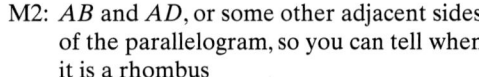 **2.** the diagonals of rhombuses   **3.** the diagonals of squares

Extend

4. Manipulate the diagonals so they are perpendicular (M3). Make a conjecture about the type of parallelogram that is determined by perpendicular diagonals.

5. Manipulate the diagonals so they are congruent (M4). Make a conjecture about the type of parallelogram that is determined by congruent diagonals.

6. Manipulate the diagonals so they bisect the angles of the parallelogram (M5). Make a conjecture about the type of parallelogram that is determined by diagonals that bisect the angles.

7. Construct a trapezoid and then its two diagonals. Manipulate the trapezoid until the diagonals are the same length. Make a conjecture about the type of trapezoid that is determined by congruent diagonals.

 **Technology**

Diagonals of Parallelograms

Students will use geometry software to investigate the diagonals of a parallelogram.

Resources

Students may use any geometry software program to explore the diagonals of a parallelogram.

Teaching Notes

By manipulating parallelograms and measuring segment lengths and angle measures, students will find special relationships between diagonals in rhombuses, rectangles, and squares.

Math Tip
Ask: *If a parallelogram has one right angle, what can you conclude about its other angles?* **They are right angles.** Students can conclude that a parallelogram is a rectangle when they know that the measure of one angle is 90°.

Teaching Tip
When students complete the investigation, have the class make a list of all the conjectures for students to refer to in Lesson 6-4.

3. Diagonals of a square are both ≅ and ⊥, and bisect the ⦞.

4. In a □ ⊥ diagonals determine a rhombus.

5. Diagonals that are ≅ yield a rectangle.

6. Diagonals that bisect the ⦞ of the □ determine a rhombus.

7. In a trapezoid, ≅ diagonals yield an isosc. trapezoid.

---

50. If two lines and a transversal form ≅ corr. ⦞, then the two lines are ∥; if two lines are ∥, then a transversal forms ≅ corr. ⦞.

51. If the prod. of the slopes of two nonvertical lines is −1, then they are ⊥; if two nonvertical lines are ⊥, then the prod. of their slopes is −1.

page 311   Technology
1. Diagonals of a rectangle are ≅.
2. Diagonals of a rhombus are ⊥, and bisect the ⦞.

1. Plan

Lesson Preview

 **Check Skills You'll Need**

Properties: Sides and Angles
Lesson 6-2: Examples 1, 2
Exercises 1–16
Extra Practice, p. 695

Properties: Diagonals and Transversals
Lesson 6-2: Example 3
Exercises 17–21
Extra Practice, p. 695

Lesson Resources

📁 **Teaching Resources**
Practice, Reteaching, Enrichment

👥 **Reaching All Students**
Practice Workbook 6-4
Spanish Practice Workbook 6-4
Technology Activities 47
Informal Geometry Planning
    Guide 6-4

⏰ **Presentation Assistant Plus!**
Transparencies
• Check Skills You'll Need 6-4
• Additional Examples 6-4
• Student Edition Answers 6-4
• Lesson Quiz 6-4
Prentice Hall Presentation Pro CD

PRENTICE HALL
ASSESSMENT SYSTEM

Computer Test Generator CD

💿 **Technology**
Resource Pro® CD-ROM
Computer Test Generator CD
Prentice Hall Presentation Pro CD

🖥 **www.PHSchool.com**
Student Site
• Teacher Web Code: afk-5500
• Self-grading Lesson Quiz
Teacher Center
• Lesson Planner
• Resources

Plus 📘**iTEXT**

312

 6-4

Special Parallelograms

 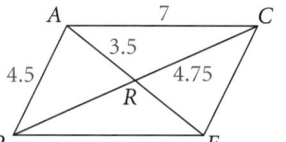
2.03   Apply properties, definitions, and theorems of two-dimensional figures to solve problems and write proofs: b) Quadrilaterals.

Lesson Preview

What You'll Learn

OBJECTIVE 1
To use properties of diagonals of rhombuses and rectangles

OBJECTIVE 2
To determine whether a parallelogram is a rhombus or a rectangle

. . . And Why

To lay out a rectangular patio, as in Example 4

✔ Check Skills You'll Need

(For help, go to Lesson 6-2.)

PACE is a parallelogram and $m\angle PAC = 109$.
Complete each of the following.

1. $EC = \blacksquare$ 4.5
2. $EP = \blacksquare$ 7
3. $m\angle CEP = \blacksquare$ 109
4. $PR = \blacksquare$ 4.75
5. $RE = \blacksquare$ 3.5
6. $CP = \blacksquare$ 9.5
7. $m\angle EPA = \blacksquare$ 71
8. $m\angle ECA = \blacksquare$ 71

9. Draw a rhombus that is not a square. Draw a rectangle that is not a square. Explain why each is not a square. **See margin, p. 314.**

📘**iTEXT** **Interactive lesson includes instant self-check, tutorials, and activities.**

OBJECTIVE 1

Diagonals of Rhombuses and Rectangles

If you draw two congruent isosceles triangles with base $\overline{PQ}$, you have drawn a rhombus. Note that $\angle RPQ$, $\angle SPQ$, $\angle RQP$, and $\angle SQP$ are all congruent. This suggests Theorem 6-9 and its proof.

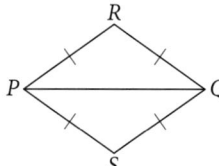

🔑 **Key Concepts**

Theorem 6-9

Each diagonal of a rhombus bisects two angles of the rhombus.

Proof **Proof of Theorem 6-9**

Given: rhombus *ABCD*
Prove: $\overline{AC}$ bisects $\angle BAD$ and $\angle BCD$.

Proof: *ABCD* is a rhombus, so its sides are all congruent. $\overline{AC} \cong \overline{AC}$ by the Reflexive Property of Congruence. Therefore, $\triangle ABC \cong \triangle ADC$ by the SSS Postulate. $\angle 1 \cong \angle 2$ and $\angle 3 \cong \angle 4$ by CPCTC. Therefore, $\overline{AC}$ bisects $\angle BAD$ and $\angle BCD$ by the definition of bisect.

You can show similarly that $\overline{BD}$ bisects $\angle ABC$ and $\angle ADC$.

 Need Help?

A segment bisects an angle if and only if it divides the angle into two congruent angles.

The diagonals of a rhombus provide an interesting application of the Converse of the Perpendicular Bisector Theorem.

⭐ **Ongoing Assessment and Intervention**

Before the Lesson
Diagnose prerequisite skills using:
• Check Skills You'll Need

During the Lesson
Monitor progress using:
• Check Understanding
• Additional Examples
• Standardized Test Prep

After the Lesson
Assess knowledge using:
• Lesson Quiz
• Computer Test Generator CD

In the rhombus at the right, points B and D are equidistant from A and C. By the Converse of the Perpendicular Bisector Theorem, they are on the perpendicular bisector of $\overline{AC}$. This proves the next theorem. In Exercise 54, you will prove it a second way.

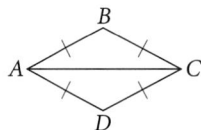

 Key Concepts

Theorem 6-10
The diagonals of a rhombus are perpendicular. $\overline{AC} \perp \overline{BD}$ 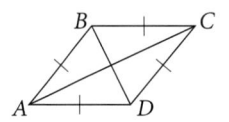

pantograph

You can use Theorems 6-9 and 6-10 to find angle measures in rhombuses.

1 EXAMPLE Finding Angle Measures

MNPQ is a rhombus and $m\angle N = 120$.
Find the measures of the numbered angles.

$m\angle 1 = m\angle 3$ **Isosceles Triangle Theorem**
$m\angle 1 + m\angle 3 + 120 = 180$ **Triangle Angle-Sum Theorem**
$2(m\angle 1) + 120 = 180$ **Substitute.**
$2(m\angle 1) = 60$ **Subtract 120 from each side.**
$m\angle 1 = 30$ **Divide each side by 2.**

Therefore, $m\angle 1 = m\angle 3 = 30$. By Theorem 6-9, $m\angle 1 = m\angle 2$ and $m\angle 3 = m\angle 4$.
Therefore, $m\angle 1 = m\angle 2 = m\angle 3 = m\angle 4 = 30$.

Real-World Connection

The diagonals of the rhombus formed by the pantograph stay perpendicular when the pantograph lifts or lowers.

 Check Understanding ① Find the measures of the numbered angles in the rhombus. $\angle 1 = 90$, $\angle 2 = 50$, $\angle 3 = 50$, $\angle 4 = 40$

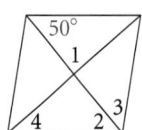

The diagonals of a rectangle, another parallelogram, also have a special property.

 Key Concepts

Theorem 6-11
The diagonals of a rectangle are congruent.

Proof → **Proof of Theorem 6-11**

Given: Rectangle *ABCD*
Prove: $\overline{AC} \cong \overline{BD}$

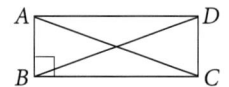

Proof: *ABCD* is a rectangle, so it is also a parallelogram.
$\overline{AB} \cong \overline{DC}$ because opposite sides of a parallelogram are congruent.
$\overline{BC} \cong \overline{BC}$ by the Reflexive Property of Congruence.
$\angle ABC$ and $\angle DCB$ are right angles by the definition of rectangle.
$\angle ABC \cong \angle DCB$ because all right angles are congruent.
$\triangle ABC \cong \triangle DCB$ by SAS. $\overline{AC} \cong \overline{BD}$ by CPCTC.

Lesson 6-4   Special Parallelograms   **313**

 Reaching All Students

Below Level Have students use paper folding to explore and explain Theorems 6-9 and 6-10.	**Advanced Learners** Have students rewrite Theorems 6-12, 6-13, and 6-14 so that the parallelogram must be a square.	**Visual Learners** See note on page 314. **Diversity** See note on page 316.

---

2. Teach

Math Background

The definitions in Lesson 6-1 of rhombus, rectangle, and square included more information than necessary. Definitions with less restrictive conditions can often be used. For example, a rectangle can be defined as a parallelogram with one right angle. The fact that it has four right angles follows from the properties of a parallelogram. Using a definition with less restrictive conditions makes establishing sufficient conditions easier.

OBJECTIVE
▼ 1 Teaching Notes

Alternate Method
Challenge students to suggest a way to prove that each diagonal of a rhombus bisects two angles of the rhombus without using congruent triangles. They could use the Isosceles Triangle Theorem and a property of parallel lines to show that $\angle 1 \cong \angle 2 \cong \angle 3 \cong \angle 4$.

1 EXAMPLE

Point out that the diagonals form eight angles at the vertices of the rhombus. When the measure of one angle is known, the other seven angle measures can be found using properties of a rhombus.

Additional Examples

① Find the measures of the numbered angles in the rhombus.

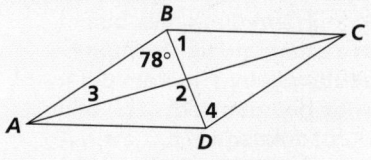

$m\angle 1 = 78$, $m\angle 2 = 90$,
$m\angle 3 = 12$, $m\angle 4 = 78$

② One diagonal of a rectangle has length $8x + 2$. The other diagonal has length $5x + 11$. Find the length of each diagonal.
26, 26

313

Teaching Tip

Theorems 6-12, 6-13, and 6-14 can be proved as class exercises when they are presented. Encourage students to suggest as many plans as they can to prove each theorem.

3 **EXAMPLE** Visual Learners

Students may wish to try drawing the figures described before answering the questions.

4 **EXAMPLE** Careers

Making sure that an angle is right or that a line is straight is necessary for a carpenter building the frame of a house or a surveyor marking off a plot of land.

Additional Examples

3 The diagonals of *ABCD* are perpendicular. *AB* = 16 cm and *BC* = 8 cm. Can *ABCD* be a parallelogram? Explain. **No; perpendicular diagonals in a parallelogram mean that the figure is a rhombus, but *ABCD* is not a rhombus because its side lengths are not equal.**

4 Explain how you could use the properties of diagonals to stake the vertices of a play area shaped like a rhombus. **Sample: Position ropes at right angles to each other at their midpoints, and stake the endpoints.**

Closure

A quadrilateral has congruent diagonals. Explain why it may or may not be a rectangle. **Sample: If congruent diagonals bisect each other, the figure must be a rectangle by Theorem 6-14. If they do not bisect each other, the quadrilateral is not even a parallelogram, so it is not a rectangle by the contrapositive of Theorem 6-3.**

314

2 **EXAMPLE** Finding Diagonal Length

Algebra Find the length of the diagonals of rectangle *GFED* if $FD = 2y + 4$ and $GE = 6y - 5$.

$2y + 4 = 6y - 5$	Diagonals of a rectangle are congruent.
$9 = 4y$	Subtract $2y$ from each side and add 5 to each side.
$\frac{9}{4} = y$	Divide each side by 4.

$FD = GE = 2\left(\frac{9}{4}\right) + 4 = \frac{17}{2}$, or $8\frac{1}{2}$.

✓ **Check Understanding** 2 Find the length of the diagonals of *GFED* if $FD = 5y - 9$ and $GE = y + 5$. **$8\frac{1}{2}$**

OBJECTIVE
2 **Is the Parallelogram a Rhombus or a Rectangle?**

The following theorems are the converses of Theorems 6-9, 6-10, and 6-11 respectively. You will prove these theorems in Exercises 61–63.

Key Concepts

> **Theorem 6-12**
>
> If one diagonal of a parallelogram bisects two angles of the parallelogram, then the parallelogram is a rhombus.
>
> **Theorem 6-13**
>
> If the diagonals of a parallelogram are perpendicular, then the parallelogram is a rhombus.
>
> **Theorem 6-14**
>
> If the diagonals of a parallelogram are congruent, then the parallelogram is a rectangle.

You can use Theorems 6-12, 6-13, and 6-14 to classify quadrilaterals.

3 **EXAMPLE** Recognizing Special Parallelograms

Determine whether the quadrilateral can be a parallelogram. If not, write *impossible*.

Need Help?
Assume the quadrilateral described can be a parallelogram. Then look for an example or a contradiction.

a. The quadrilateral has congruent diagonals and one angle of 60°.

Impossible. A parallelogram with congruent diagonals is a rectangle with four right angles.

b. The quadrilateral has perpendicular diagonals and four right angles.

The figure can be a parallelogram. Perpendicular diagonals means that it would be a rhombus, and four right angles means that it would be a rectangle. Both properties together mean that it would be a square.

✓ **Check Understanding** 3 A diagonal of a parallelogram bisects two angles of the parallelogram. Is it possible for the parallelogram to have sides of lengths 5, 6, 5, and 6? Explain.
No; if one diagonal bisects two ∡, then the figure is a rhombus and cannot have noncongruent sides.

314 Chapter 6 Quadrilaterals

page 312 **Check Skills You'll Need**

9.

The rhombus is not a square because it has no right ∡. The rectangle is not a square because all 4 sides aren't ≅.

You can use properties of diagonals to construct special parallelograms.

4 EXAMPLE Real-World  Connection

Community Service Builders use properties of diagonals to "square up" rectangular shapes like building frames and playing-field boundaries.

Suppose you are on the volunteer building team at the right. You are helping to lay out a rectangular patio. Explain how to use properties of diagonals to locate the four corners.

To locate the corners, you can use two theorems:

* Theorem 6-5: If the diagonals of a quadrilateral bisect each other, then the quadrilateral is a parallelogram.
* Theorem 6-14: If the diagonals of a parallelogram are congruent, then the parallelogram is a rectangle.

First, cut two pieces of rope that will be the diagonals of the foundation rectangle. Cut them the same length because of Theorem 6-14. Join them at their midpoints because of Theorem 6-5. Then pull the ropes straight and taut. The ends of the ropes will be the corners of a rectangle.

Real-World Connection

A well-planned volunteer effort can frame a small house in a day.

✓ **Check Understanding** ❹ Kate thinks that they can adapt this method slightly to stake off a square play area. Is she right? Explain. **Yes; if the ropes are ⊥ to each other, then the endpoints of the ropes determine a square.**

EXERCISES

For more practice, see *Extra Practice*.

Practice and Problem Solving

Ⓐ **Practice by Example**

Example 1
(page 313)

4. 33.5, 33.5, 113, 33.5

5. 32, 90, 58, 32

6. 90, 60, 60, 30

Find the measures of the numbered angles in each rhombus.

1.
38, 38, 38, 38

2.
26, 128, 128

3.
118, 31, 31

4.
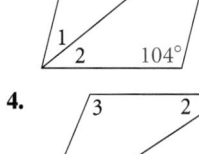

5.
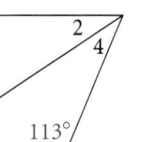

6.
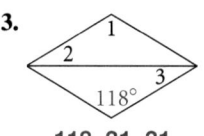

7.
55, 35, 55, 90

8.
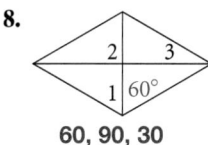
60, 90, 30

9.
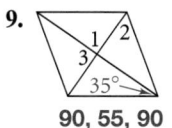
90, 55, 90

Example 2 x^2 **Algebra** *LMNP* is a rectangle. Find the value of x and the length of each diagonal.
(page 314)

10–15.
See margin.

10. $LN = x$ and $MP = 2x - 4$

11. $LN = 5x - 8$ and $MP = 2x + 1$

12. $LN = 3x + 1$ and $MP = 8x - 4$

13. $LN = 9x - 14$ and $MP = 7x + 4$

14. $LN = 7x - 2$ and $MP = 4x + 3$

15. $LN = 3x + 5$ and $MP = 9x - 10$

Lesson 6-4 Special Parallelograms **315**

10. 4; *LN* = *MP* = 4

11. 3; *LN* = *MP* = 7

12. 1; *LN* = *MP* = 4

13. 9; *LN* = *MP* = 67

14. $\frac{5}{3}$; *LN* = *MP* = $\frac{29}{3}$ = $9\frac{2}{3}$

15. $\frac{5}{2}$; *LN* = *MP* = $12\frac{1}{2}$

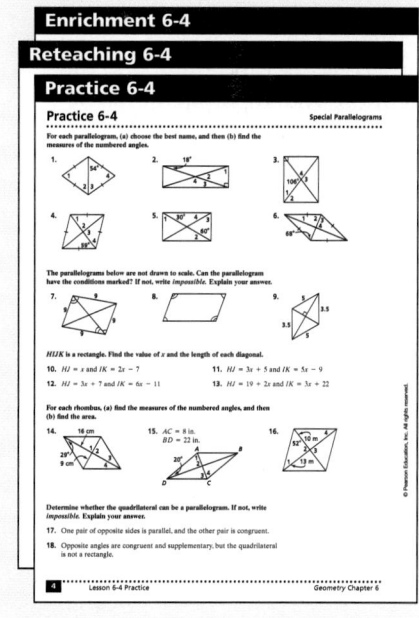

Error Prevention

Exercise 18 Some students may not think that the figure described here is possible. Consider a quadrilateral formed by 2 non-congruent right triangles whose only common points are their common hypotenuse.

Diversity

Exercise 22 Depending on where students live, older screen doors may not be familiar sights.

Exercise 24 Ask: *What is a name for a rectangle that is also a rhombus?* **square**

Exercises 35, 36 Suggest that students add symbols for trapezoids and kites after the appropriate properties in Exercises 25–34 to summarize all their work in Chapter 6.

Exercise 50 If necessary, review the methods for solving a system of equations.

Alternate Method

Exercise 61 After students have filled in steps 4–7, let them suggest as many ways as they can to prove that *ABCD* is a rhombus, even if they alter the other steps in the exercise. For example, students may omit the reflexive statement and congruent triangles and use properties of a parallelogram and the Converse of the Isosceles Triangle Theorem.

pages 315–318   Exercises

16. **Impossible; if the diagonals of a ▱ are ≅, then it would have to be a rectangle and have right ∠.**

17. **Yes; ≅ diagonals in a ▱ mean it can be a rectangle with two opposite sides 2 cm long.**

18. **Impossible; in a ▱, consecutive ∠ must be supp., so all ∠ must be right. This would make it a rectangle.**

19. **Impossible; if the figure is a ▱, then the ∠ opp.**

316

Example 3
(page 314)

Determine whether the quadrilateral can be a parallelogram. (The diagrams in Exercises 19–21 may not be to scale.) If not, write *impossible*. Explain.
16–21. See margin.

16. The diagonals are congruent, but the quadrilateral has no right angles.

17. Each diagonal is 3 cm long and two opposite sides are 2 cm long.

18. Two opposite angles are right angles, but the quadrilateral is not a rectangle.

19. 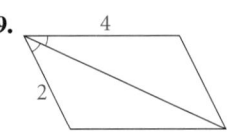   **20.** 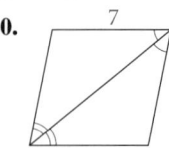   **21.**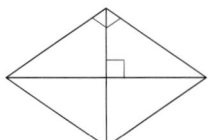

Example 4
(page 315)

B **Apply Your Skills**

22. Hardware You can use a simple device called a turnbuckle to "square up" structures that are parallelograms. For the gate pictured at the right, you tighten or loosen the turnbuckle on the diagonal cable so that the cable stays congruent to the other diagonal. Explain why a frame that normally is rectangular will, when it sags, keep the shape of a parallelogram.
See margin.

23. Carpentry A carpenter is building a bookcase. How can she use a tape measure to check that the bookshelf is rectangular? Justify your answer and name any theorems used.
See margin.

24. Reasoning Suppose the diagonals of a parallelogram are both perpendicular and congruent. What type of special quadrilateral is it? Explain your reasoning. **See back of book.**

Turnbuckle

Using Symbols **Create your own distinctive symbols for parallelogram, rhombus, rectangle, and square. Then copy the properties in Exercises 25–34. After each property, use your symbols to list the quadrilaterals having that property.**

25. All sides are ≅.

26. Opposite sides are ≅.

27. Opposite sides are ∥.

28. Opposite ∠ are ≅.

29. All ∠ are right ∠.

30. Consecutive ∠ are supplementary.

31. Diagonals bisect each other.

32. Diagonals are ≅.

33. Diagonals are ⊥.

34. Each diagonal bisects opposite ∠.

25–34. See back of book.

Which, if any, of the properties in Exercises 25–34 can the following type of quadrilateral have? Draw diagrams to illustrate. 35–37. See back of book.

35. a trapezoid

36. a kite

37. a quadrilateral that is not a special quadrilateral

Reading Math

In Exercises 39–44, the "given diagonals" are two segments you draw. The constructed figures must have diagonals that match.

38. Writing Summarize the properties of squares that follow from a square being **(a)** a parallelogram, **(b)** a rhombus, and **(c)** a rectangle. **See back of book.**

Constructions **Explain how to construct each figure, given its diagonals.**
39–44. See back of book.

39. parallelogram   **40.** rectangle   **41.** rhombus

42. square   **43.** kite   **44.** trapezoid

---

the bisected ∠ is also bisected, and the figure is a rhombus. But the sides are not ≅.

20. **Yes; the ∠ are bisected so it could be a rhombus, which is a ▱.**

21. **Yes; the diagonals are ⊥ so it could be a square, which is a ▱.**

22. **The pairs of opp. sides of the frame remain ≅, so the frame remains a ▱.**

23. **After measuring the sides, she can measure the diagonals.**

Need Help?

To review what makes a good definition, see Lesson 2-2.

Reasoning Decide whether each of these is a good definition. Justify your answer.

45. A rectangle is a quadrilateral with four right angles. 45–47. See margin.

46. A rhombus is a quadrilateral with four congruent sides.

47. A square is a quadrilateral with four right angles and four congruent sides.

x^2 **Algebra** Find the value(s) of the variable(s) for each parallelogram.

48. $RZ = 2x + 5$, $SW = 5x - 20$

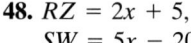
30

49. $m\angle 1 = 3y - 6$

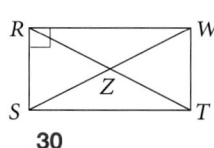

$x = 5, y = 32, z = 7.5$

50. $BD = 4x - y + 1$

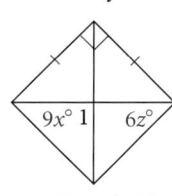

$x = 7.5, y = 3$

Open-Ended Given two segments with lengths a and b ($a \neq b$), what special quadrilaterals can you sketch that meet these conditions? Show each sketch.

51–53. See back of book.

51. Both diagonals have length a.   **52.** The two diagonals have lengths a and b.

53. One diagonal has length a, one side of the quadrilateral has length b.

54a. Def. of a rhombus

b. Diagonals of a $\square$ bisect each other.

c. $\overline{AE} \cong \overline{AE}$

d. Reflexive Prop. of $\cong$

e. $\triangle ABE \cong \triangle ADE$

f. CPCTC

g. $\angle$ Add. Post.

h. $\angle AEB$ and $\angle AED$ are rt. $\angle$s.

i. $\cong$ suppl. $\angle$s are rt. $\angle$s Thm.

j. Def. of $\perp$

Proof **54. Developing Proof** Complete the flow proof of Theorem 6-10.

Given: $ABCD$ is a rhombus.

Prove: $\overline{AC} \perp \overline{BD}$

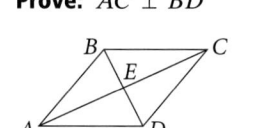

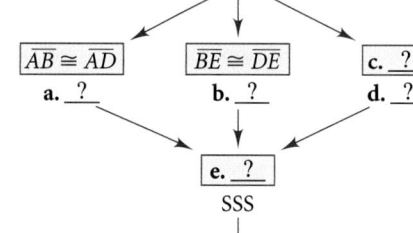

$ABCD$ is a rhombus.
Given

$\overline{AB} \cong \overline{AD}$ $\overline{BE} \cong \overline{DE}$ **c.** _?_
a. _?_   **b.** _?_   **d.** _?_

e. _?_
SSS

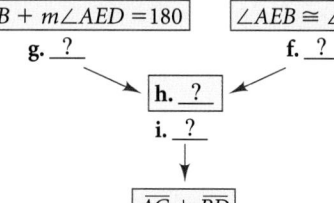

$m\angle AEB + m\angle AED = 180$ $\angle AEB \cong \angle AED$
g. _?_   **f.** _?_

h. _?_

i. _?_

$\overline{AC} \perp \overline{BD}$
j. _?_

55. Critical Thinking The hypothesis of Theorem 6-12 mentions one diagonal of a parallelogram. Why doesn't it include both diagonals? **Answers may vary. Sample: only one diagonal is needed.**

Proof **56.** In Theorem 6-12, replace "two angles" with "one angle." Write a paragraph that proves this new statement true or show a counterexample to prove it false. **See margin.**

x^2 **Algebra** $ABCD$ is a rectangle. Find the length of each diagonal.

16, 16   2, 2
57. $AC = 2(x - 3)$ and $BD = x + 5$ **58.** $AC = 2(5a + 1)$ and $BD = 2(a + 1)$

59. $AC = \frac{3y}{5}$ and $BD = 3y - 4$ **1, 1**   **60.** $AC = \frac{3c}{9}$ and $BD = 4 - c$ **1, 1**

Lesson 6-4 Special Parallelograms **317**

Lesson Quiz 6-4

1. The diagonals of a rectangle have lengths $4 + 2x$ and $6x - 20$. Find x and the length of each diagonal. **6; each diagonal has length 16.**

Find the measures of the numbered angles in each rhombus.

2.

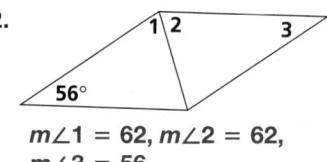
56°

$m\angle 1 = 62, m\angle 2 = 62$, $m\angle 3 = 56$

3.

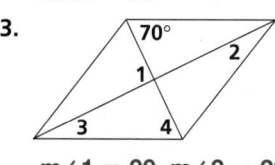
70°

$m\angle 1 = 90, m\angle 2 = 20$, $m\angle 3 = 20, m\angle 4 = 70$

Determine whether the quadrilateral can be a parallelogram. If not, write _impossible._ Explain.

4. Each diagonal is 15 cm long, and one angle of the quadrilateral has measure 45. **Impossible; if diagonals of a parallelogram are congruent, the quadrilateral is a rectangle, but a rectangle has four right angles.**

5. The diagonals are congruent, perpendicular and bisect each other. **Yes; if diagonals of a parallelogram are congruent, the quadrilateral is a rectangle, and if diagonals of a parallelogram are perpendicular, the quadrilateral is a rhombus, and a rectangle that is a rhombus is a square.**

Have students draw *theorems without words* to illustrate each of the theorems in Lesson 6-4. For example, the figure below illustrates Theorem 6-9: *Each diagonal of a rhombus bisects two angles of the rhombus.*

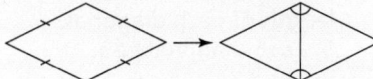

Standardized Test Prep

 **Resources**

For additional practice with a variety of test item formats:
• Standardized Test Prep, p. 343
• Test-Taking Strategies, p. 338
• Test-Taking Strategies with Transparencies

Exercise 66 When a problem does not include a figure, students need to spend a few moments incorporating the information that is given into an accurate representation. The time spent drawing should pay off in time saved solving the problem.

pages 315–318 Exercises

61. 4. △*ABC* ≅ △*ADC* (ASA)
    5. $\overline{AB} \cong \overline{AD}$ (CPCTC)
    6. $\overline{AB} \cong \overline{DC}$, $\overline{AD} \cong \overline{BC}$
       (Opp. sides of a ▱ are ≅.)
    7. $\overline{AB} \cong \overline{BC} \cong \overline{CD} \cong \overline{AD}$
       (Trans. Prop. of ≅)

62. Answers may vary.
    Sample: The diagonals of a ▱ bisect each other so $\overline{AE} \cong \overline{CE}$. Both ∠*AED* and ∠*CED* are right ∡ because $\overline{AC} \perp \overline{BD}$, and since $\overline{DE} \cong \overline{DE}$ by the Reflexive Prop., △*AED* ≅ △*CED* by SAS. By CPCTC $\overline{AD} \cong \overline{CD}$, and since opp. sides of a ▱ are ≅, $\overline{AB} \cong \overline{BC} \cong \overline{CD} \cong \overline{AD}$. So *ABCD* is a rhombus because it has 4 ≅ sides.

66. [2] Since diagonals of a rhombus bisect each other, *QS* = 9 cm. Also, since all sides are ≅, *RS* = 9 cm. So △*QRS* is an

318 equilateral △ and

---

61. **Developing Proof** Fill in Steps 4–7 that are missing from this proof of Theorem 6-12. (Using more than four steps is acceptable.)
    See margin.

    Given: *ABCD* is a parallelogram; $\overline{AC}$ bisects ∠*BAD* and ∠*BCD*.

    Prove: *ABCD* is a rhombus.

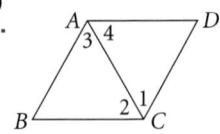

Statements	Reasons
1. *ABCD* is a parallelogram. $\overline{AC}$ bisects ∠*BAD* and ∠*BCD*.	1. Given
2. ∠1 ≅ ∠2, ∠3 ≅ ∠4	2. Definition of bisect
3. $\overline{AC} \cong \overline{AC}$ ⋮	3. Reflexive Property of Congruence ⋮
8. *ABCD* is a rhombus.	8. Definition of rhombus

ⓒ Challenge *Proof* **62.** Write a paragraph proof (Thm. 6-13). **63.** Write a flow proof (Thm. 6-14).

Given: ▱*ABCD*; $\overline{AC} \perp \overline{BD}$ at *E*.
Prove: *ABCD* is a rhombus.
See margin.

Given: ▱*ABCD*; $\overline{AC} \cong \overline{BD}$
Prove: *ABCD* is a rectangle.
See back of book.

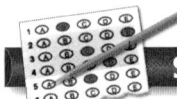

Standardized Test Prep

Multiple Choice

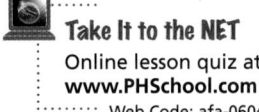
Take It to the NET
Online lesson quiz at
www.PHSchool.com
Web Code: afa-0604

64. The diagonals of a quadrilateral are perpendicular bisectors of each other. What name best describes the quadrilateral? **D**
    A. rectangle   B. parallelogram   C. quadrilateral   D. rhombus

65. The diagonals of a quadrilateral bisect both pairs of opposite angles. What name best describes the quadrilateral? **I**
    F. parallelogram   G. quadrilateral   H. rectangle   I. rhombus

Short Response

66. **Given:** *QRST* is a rhombus, $\overline{QS}$ intersects $\overline{RT}$ at *P*, *QR* = 9 cm, and *QP* = 4.5 cm. Find *m*∠*RST*. Explain your work. **See margin.**

Mixed Review

Lesson 6-3 Can you conclude that the quadrilateral is a parallelogram? Explain.

67. 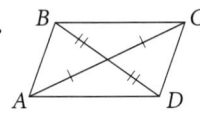   68.   69.

67–69. See margin.

Lesson 5-1 In △*PQR*, points *S*, *T*, and *U* are midpoints. Complete each statement.

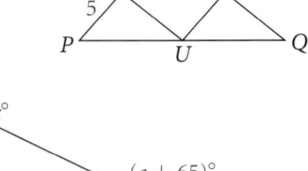

70. *TQ* = __?__ **6**   71. *PQ* = __?__ **16**   72. *TU* = __?__ **5**

73. $\overline{SU} \parallel$ __?__ $\overline{RQ}$ 74. $\overline{TU} \parallel$ __?__ $\overline{RP}$ 75. $\overline{PQ} \parallel$ __?__ $\overline{ST}$

Lesson 3-3 $\boxed{x^2}$ **76. Algebra** Find the value of *c*. **89**

each interior ∠ is $\frac{180}{3}$ or 60°. △*QTS* is also an equilateral △, so its ∡ are 60°. By ∠ add. (*m*∠*PST* + *m*∠*PSR* = *m*∠*RST*), *m*∠*RST* = 60 + 60 or 120.

[1] no work shown OR a response that is only partially correct

67. Yes; both pairs of opp. sides are ≅.

68. No; there are not necess. 2 opp. sides that are both ∥ and ≅.

69. Yes; the diag. bisect each other.

Quadrilaterals in Quadrilaterals

Construct

- Use geometry software to construct a quadrilateral *ABCD*.
- Construct the midpoint of each side of *ABCD*.
- Construct segments joining the midpoints, in order, to form quadrilateral *EFGH*.

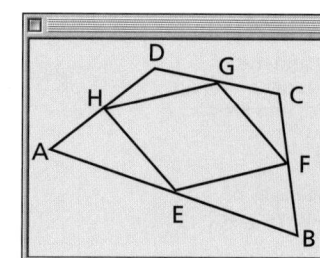

Investigate

- Measure the lengths of the sides of *EFGH* and their slopes.
- Measure the angles of *EFGH*.

What kind of quadrilateral does *EFGH* appear to be?

EXERCISES

1. Manipulate quadrilateral *ABCD*. **a–c. Answers may vary.**
   a. Make a conjecture about the quadrilateral whose vertices are the midpoints of the sides of a quadrilateral.
   b. Does your conjecture hold when *ABCD* is concave? **yes**
   c. Can you manipulate *ABCD* so that your conjecture doesn't hold? **no**

   a. The figure formed by connecting the midpoints of the sides of a quad. is a ▱.

Extend

2. Draw the diagonals of *ABCD*.
   a. Describe *EFGH* when the diagonals are perpendicular. **rectangle**
   b. Describe *EFGH* when the diagonals are congruent. **rhombus**
   c. Describe *EFGH* when the diagonals are both perpendicular and congruent. **square**

3. Construct the midpoints of *EFGH* and use them to construct quadrilateral *IJKL*. Construct the midpoints of *IJKL* and use them to construct quadrilateral *MNOP*. For *MNOP* and *EFGH*, compare the ratios of the lengths of the sides, perimeters, and areas. How are the sides of *MNOP* and *EFGH* related? **See margin.**

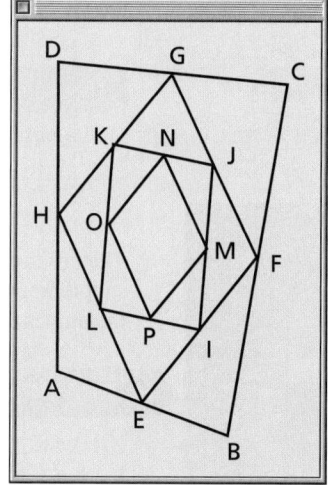

 4. **Writing** During the investigation, you made a conjecture as to the type of quadrilateral *EFGH* appears to be. Write a paragraph proof that justifies your conclusion. Include in your proof the Midsegment Theorem, "If a segment joins the midpoint of two sides of a triangle, then the segment is parallel to the third side and half its length." **See margin.**

Quadrilaterals in Quadrilaterals

Students will use geometry software to investigate the new quadrilateral that is formed when the midpoints of a given quadrilateral are joined.

Resources

Students may use any geometry software program to explore quadrilaterals within quadrilaterals.

Teaching Notes

When the midpoints of the four sides of a quadrilateral are joined, the resultant quadrilateral is always a parallelogram. This result holds whether or not the original quadrilateral is convex.

Visual Learners
In general, students are amazed that the quadrilateral formed by joining the midpoints of any quadrilateral is always a parallelogram. Encourage them to manipulate the shape of *ABCD* as much as possible while watching the shape of *EFGH*.

Exercise 4 Students will need to draw the diagonals of *ABCD* before they can use the Triangle Midsegment Theorem. After students draw the diagonals, they will see that the proof becomes almost transparent. Following the surprise of the result, the straightforwardness of the proof illustrates an elegance that students do not often see at this level of mathematics.

page 319   Technology

3. For *MNOP* and *EFGH*, the ratio of the sides and perimeters is 1:2 and the ratios of the areas is 1:4.

The sides of *MNOP* and *EFGH* are ∥.

4. Answers may vary. Sample: By the Midsegment Thm.

both $\overline{EF}$ and $\overline{HG}$ are ∥ to $\overline{AC}$ and each is half the length of $\overline{AC}$. Thus $\overline{EF}$ ∥ $\overline{HG}$ and $\overline{EF} \cong \overline{HG}$, so *EFGH* is a ▱ by Thm. 6-6.

1. Plan

Lesson Preview

 **Check Skills You'll Need**

**Using Properties of
Special Quadrilaterals**
Lesson 6-1: Example 3
Exercises 19–24
Extra Practice, p. 695

Lesson Resources

📁 **Teaching Resources**
Practice, Reteaching, Enrichment

👥 **Reaching All Students**
Practice Workbook 6-5
Spanish Practice Workbook 6-5
Hands-On Activities 18
Informal Geometry Planning
   Guide 6-5

🕐 **Presentation Assistant Plus!**
Transparencies
• Check Skills You'll Need 6-5
• Additional Examples 6-5
• Student Edition Answers 6-5
• Lesson Quiz 6-5
Presentation Pro CD-ROM 6-5

**PRENTICE HALL
ASSESSMENT SYSTEM**

Computer Test Generator CD

✏️ **Technology**
Resource Pro® CD-ROM
Computer Test Generator CD
Prentice Hall Presentation Pro CD

💻 **www.PHSchool.com**
Student Site
• Teacher Web Code: afk-5500
• Self-grading Lesson Quiz
Teacher Center
• Lesson Planner
• Resources

Plus 📘**TEXT**

6-5

Trapezoids and Kites

North Carolina Objectives

2.03 Apply properties, definitions, and theorems of two-dimensional figures to solve
problems and write proofs: b) Quadrilaterals.

Lesson Preview

What You'll Learn

OBJECTIVE 1
To verify and use properties of trapezoids and kites

. . . And Why

To find angle measures of trapezoidal windows, as in Example 2

 **Check Skills You'll Need**   (For help, go to Lesson 6-1.)

2. 3; 4.8, 16.4, 18, 18

x^2 **Algebra Find the values of the variables. Then find the lengths of the sides.**

1.
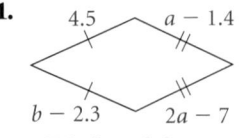
$a = 5.6, b = 6.8;$
$4.5, 4.2, 4.5, 4.2$

2.
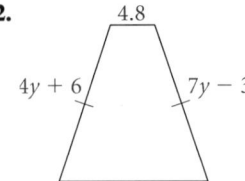

3.
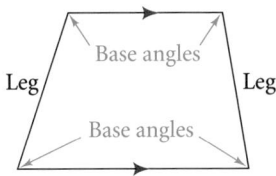
$m = 5, n = 15;$
$15, 15, 21, 21$

New Vocabulary • base angles of a trapezoid

📘**TEXT** Interactive lesson includes instant
self-check, tutorials, and activities.

OBJECTIVE

1   **Properties of Trapezoids and Kites**

The parallel sides of a trapezoid are its bases.
The nonparallel sides are its legs. Two angles
that share a base of a trapezoid are **base angles**
of the trapezoid.

The following theorem is about each pair of base
angles. You will be asked to prove it in Exercise 26.

🔑 **Key Concepts**

Theorem 6-15

The base angles of an isosceles trapezoid are congruent.

Real-World 🌐 Connection

In the isosceles trapezoids at
the top of this electric tea
kettle, each pair of base
angles are congruent.

The bases of a trapezoid are parallel. Therefore the two angles that share a leg are
supplementary. This fact and Theorem 6-15 allow you to solve problems involving
the angles of a trapezoid.

1 EXAMPLE   **Finding Angle Measures in Trapezoids**

$ABCD$ is an isosceles trapezoid and $m\angle B = 102$.
Find $m\angle A, m\angle C,$ and $m\angle D$.

$m\angle A + m\angle B = 180$ **Two angles that share a
leg are supplementary.**

$m\angle A + 102 = 180$ **Substitute.**

$m\angle A = 78$ **Subtract 102 from each side.**

● By Theorem 6-15, $m\angle C = m\angle B = 102$ and $m\angle D = m\angle A = 78$.

320   Chapter 6 Quadrilaterals

🔄 **Ongoing Assessment and Intervention**

**Before the Lesson
Diagnose prerequisite skills using:**
• Check Skills You'll Need

**During the Lesson
Monitor progress using:**
• Check Understanding
• Additional Examples
• Standardized Test Prep

**After the Lesson
Assess knowledge using:**
• Lesson Quiz
• Computer Test Generator CD

✓ **Check Understanding** ① In the isosceles trapezoid, $m\angle S = 70$. Find $m\angle P, m\angle Q,$ and $m\angle R$.
110, 110, 70

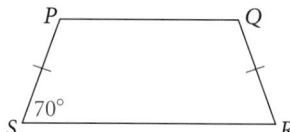

② **EXAMPLE** Real-World Connection

Architecture The second ring of the ceiling shown at the left is made from congruent isosceles trapezoids that create the illusion of circles. What are the measures of the base angles of these trapezoids?

Each trapezoid is part of an isosceles triangle whose base angles are the acute base angles of the trapezoid. The isosceles triangle has a vertex angle that is half as large as an angle at the center of the ceiling.

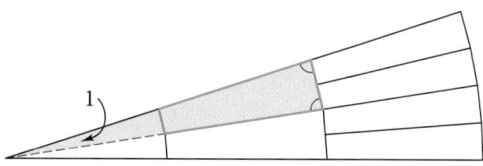

The measure of each angle at the center of the ceiling is $\frac{360}{20}$ or 18.

The measure of $\angle 1$ is $\frac{18}{2}$, or 9.

The measure of each acute base angle is $\frac{180 - 9}{2}$, or 85.5.

● The measure of each obtuse base angle is $180 - 85.5$, or 94.5.

You are looking up at Harbour Centre Tower in Vancouver, Canada.

✓ **Check Understanding** ② A glass ceiling like the one above has 18 angles meeting at the center instead of 20. What are the measures of the base angles of the trapezoids in its second ring? **85, 95**

Like the diagonals of parallelograms, the diagonals of an isosceles trapezoid have a special property.

Key Concepts

> **Theorem 6-16**
>
> The diagonals of an isosceles trapezoid are congruent.

Proof **Proof of Theorem 6-16**

Given: Isosceles trapezoid $ABCD$ with $\overline{AB} \cong \overline{DC}$
Prove: $\overline{AC} \cong \overline{DB}$

It is given that $\overline{AB} \cong \overline{DC}$. Because the base angles of an isosceles trapezoid are congruent, $\angle ABC \cong \angle DCB$. By the Reflexive Property of Congruence, $\overline{BC} \cong \overline{BC}$. Then, by the SAS Postulate, $\triangle ABC \cong \triangle DCB$. Therefore, $\overline{AC} \cong \overline{DB}$ by CPCTC.

Another special quadrilateral that is not a parallelogram is a kite. The diagonals of a kite, like the diagonals of a rhombus, are perpendicular. A proof of this for a kite (next page) is quite like its proof for a rhombus (at the top of page 313).

Lesson 6-5 Trapezoids and Kites **321**

Reaching All Students

| Below Level Help students associate Theorem 6-15 with the Isosceles Triangle Theorem by extending the nonparallel sides of an isosceles trapezoid to form an isosceles triangle. | Advanced Learners After students read the proof of Theorem 6-16, have them write a paragraph explaining whether the diagonals of an isosceles trapezoid bisect each other. | English Learners See note on page 321. Visual Learners See note on page 321. |

Math Background

A kite can be described as the union of two isosceles triangles without their common base or the figure formed by the radii from the centers of two intersecting circles to the points of intersection. Many construction methods depend on this relationship to circles and on the perpendicularity of the diagonals of a kite.

OBJECTIVE
① **Teaching Notes**

English Learners

Have students compare and contrast isosceles trapezoids with isosceles triangles.

① EXAMPLE Error Prevention

Some students may think the base angles of an isosceles trapezoid have vertices only on the "bottom" side. This misconception stems from the common use of the word *base* to mean "the side of a figure on which it rests." Point out that each isosceles trapezoid has two bases, which may lie in any orientation, and two pairs of base angles.

② EXAMPLE Careers

Architects design modern office buildings with striking results using not only trapezoids and squares but also triangles, circles, and ellipses.

Connection to Engineering

Have students find how a keystone is used and how its shape relates to this lesson.

Visual Learners

When proving that the diagonals of an isosceles trapezoid are congruent, have students separately draw and label the overlapping triangles *ABC* and *DCB* to help them see how the parts correspond and why the triangles are congruent.

Additional Examples

1 *XYZW* is an isosceles trapezoid, and $m\angle X = 156$. Find $m\angle Y$, $m\angle Z$, and $m\angle W$.

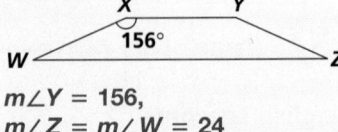

$m\angle Y = 156$,
$m\angle Z = m\angle W = 24$

2 Half of a spider's web is shown below, formed by layers of congruent isosceles trapezoids. Find the measures of the angles in *ABDC*.

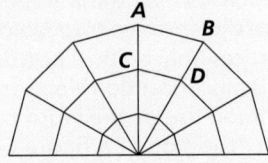

$m\angle A = m\angle B = 75$,
$m\angle C = m\angle D = 105$

3 Find $m\angle 1$, $m\angle 2$, and $m\angle 3$ in the kite.

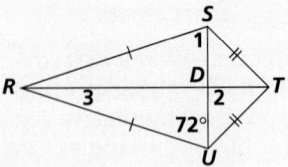

$m\angle 1 = 72$, $m\angle 2 = 90$,
$m\angle 3 = 18$

Closure

Draw and label an isosceles trapezoid, a (convex) kite, and their diagonals. Then write congruence statements for all pairs of triangles that you can prove congruent. Students should find three pairs of congruent triangles for each figure.

 **Key Concepts**

Theorem 6-17
The diagonals of a kite are perpendicular.

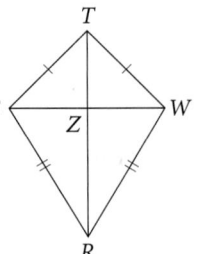

Proof **Proof of Theorem 6-17**

Given: Kite *RSTW* with $\overline{TS} \cong \overline{TW}$ and $\overline{RS} \cong \overline{RW}$
Prove: $\overline{TR} \perp \overline{SW}$

Both *T* and *R* are equidistant from *S* and *W*. By the Converse of the Perpendicular Bisector Theorem, *T* and *R* lie on the perpendicular bisector of $\overline{SW}$. Since there is exactly one line through any two points (Postulate 1-1), $\overline{TR}$ must be the perpendicular bisector of $\overline{SW}$. Therefore, $\overline{TR} \perp \overline{SW}$.

You can use Theorem 6-17 to find angle measures in kites.

3 EXAMPLE **Finding Angle Measures in Kites**

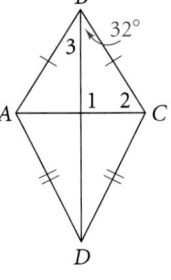

Find $m\angle 1$, $m\angle 2$, and $m\angle 3$ in the kite.

$m\angle 1 = 90$	**Diagonals of a kite are perpendicular.**
$90 + m\angle 2 + 32 = 180$	**Triangle Angle-Sum Theorem**
$122 + m\angle 2 = 180$	**Simplify.**
$m\angle 2 = 58$	**Subtract 122 from each side.**

$\triangle ABD \cong \triangle CBD$ by SSS.

• By CPCTC, $m\angle 3 = m\angle DBC = 32$.

✓ **Check Understanding** **3** Find $m\angle 1$, $m\angle 2$, and $m\angle 3$ in the kite.
90, 46, 44

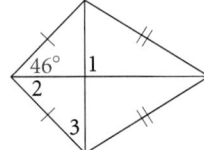

EXERCISES

For more practice, see *Extra Practice*.

Practice and Problem Solving

A Practice by Example

Example 1
(page 320)

Each trapezoid is isosceles. Find the measure of each angle.

1.

77, 103, 103

2. 69, 69, 111

3.

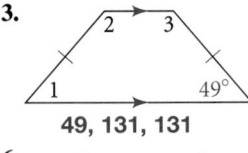

49, 131, 131

4. 105, 75, 75

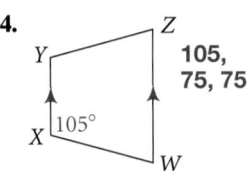

5.

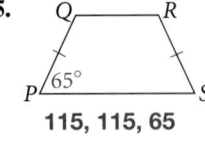

115, 115, 65

6.

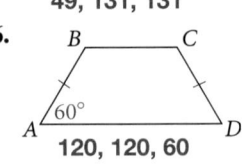

120, 120, 60

pages 322–325 Exercises

17. **Answers may vary.
Sample:**

Example 2
(page 321)

7. Design Each patio umbrella is made of eight panels that are congruent isosceles triangles with parallel stripes. A sample panel is shown at the right. The vertex angle of the panel measures 42.

7a. isosc. trapezoids

a. Classify the quadrilaterals shown as blue stripes on the panel.

b. Find the measures of the quadrilaterals' interior angles.
69, 69, 111, 111

Assignment Guide

1 Objective
Ⓐ Ⓑ **Core** 1–38
Ⓒ **Extension** 39–44

Standardized Test Prep 45–50

Mixed Review 51–56

Example 3
(page 322)

Find the measures of the numbered angles in each kite.

8. 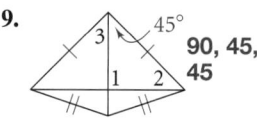 **90, 68**

9. 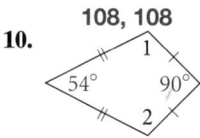 **90, 45, 45**

10. **108, 108**

11. 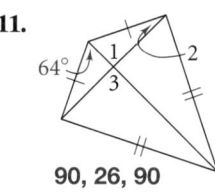 **90, 26, 90**

12. 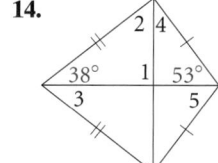 **90, 40, 90**

13.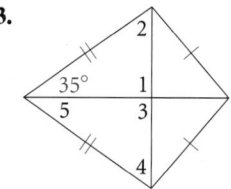

13. 90, 55, 90, 55, 35

14. 90, 52, 38, 37, 53

15. 90, 90, 90, 90, 46, 34, 56, 44, 56, 44

16. 112, 112

14.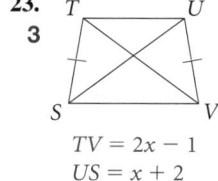

15.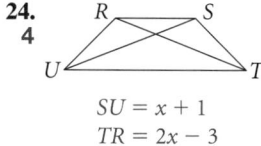

16.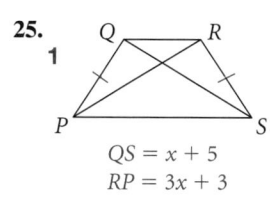

17. Open-Ended Sketch two kites that are not congruent, but with the diagonals of one congruent to the diagonals of the other. **See margin.**

18. The perimeter of a kite is 66 cm. The length of one of its sides is 3 cm less than twice the length of another. Find the length of each side of the kite.
12, 12, 21, 21

19. Critical Thinking If $KLMN$ is an isosceles trapezoid, is it possible for $\overline{KM}$ to bisect $\angle LMN$ and $\angle LKN$? Explain. **See margin.**

Ⓑ **Apply Your Skills** x^2 **Algebra** Find the value of the variable in each isosceles trapezoid.

20.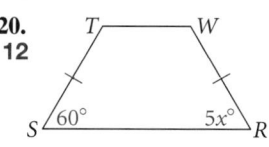
12

21.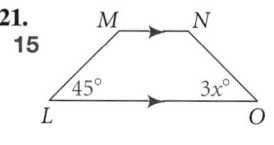
15

22.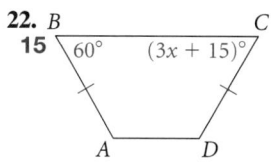
15

23.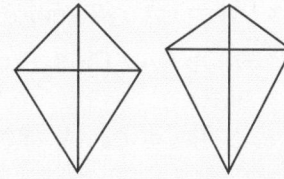
3
$TV = 2x - 1$
$US = x + 2$

24.
4
$SU = x + 1$
$TR = 2x - 3$

25.
1
$QS = x + 5$
$RP = 3x + 3$

19. No; explanations may vary. Sample: If both ⩘ are bisected, then this combined with $\overline{KM} \cong \overline{KM}$ by the Reflexive Prop. means $\triangle KLM \cong \triangle KNM$ by SAS. So by

CPCTC, opp. ⩘ L and N are $\cong$, so it is not an isos. trapezoid.

Enrichment 6-5
Reteaching 6-5
Practice 6-5

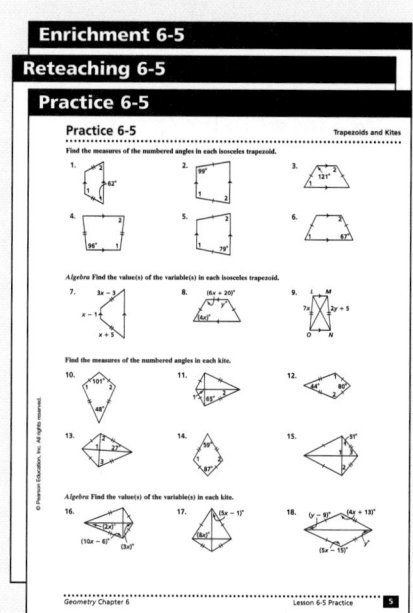

Diversity

Exercise 7 The word *umbrella* comes from a Latin word meaning "shaded area or shadow," suggesting protection against the rain or sun. Ask whether students know the word for umbrella in other languages. For example, the Spanish word *paraguas* literally means "for water," and a *sombrilla* is a parasol.

Exercise 10 Discuss ways to prove $m\angle 1 = m\angle 2$.

Exercise 26 Have students work together to write this proof. Even with the Plan, the proof is complex and worthy of class discussion.

323

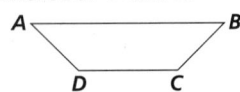

Lesson Quiz 6-5

Use isosceles trapezoid *ABCD* for Exercises 1 and 2.

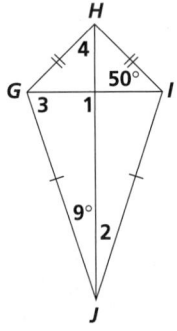

1. If $m\angle A = 45$, find $m\angle B$, $m\angle C$, and $m\angle D$.
   $m\angle B = 45$,
   $m\angle C = m\angle D = 135$

2. If $AC = 3x - 16$ and $BD = 10x - 86$, find x. **10**

Use kite *GHIJ* for Exercises 3–6.

3. Find $m\angle 1$. **90**
4. Find $m\angle 2$. **9**
5. Find $m\angle 3$. **81**
6. Find $m\angle 4$. **40**

Alternative Assessment

Have students work in pairs to write answers to the following questions:

- How are a kite and a rhombus similar? How are they different?
- How are an isosceles trapezoid and a rectangle similar? How are they different?

pages 322–325 Exercises

35. No; if two consecutive ⦞ are suppl., then another pair must be also because one pair of opp. ⦞ is ≅. Therefore, the opp. ⦞ would be ≅, which means the figure would be a ▱ and not a kite.

324

---

32. Yes, the ≅ ⦞ can be obtuse.

33. Yes, the ≅ ⦞ can be obtuse, as well as one other ∠.

34. Yes; if 2 ≅ ⦞ are rt. ⦞, they are suppl. The other 2 ⦞ are also suppl.

39. *D* is any point on $\overleftrightarrow{BN}$ such that $ND \neq BN$ and *D* is below *N*.

Exercises 30–31

Challenge

43. It is one half the sum of the lengths of the bases; draw a diag. of the trap. to form 2 ⧍. The bases *B* and *b* of the trap. are each a base of a ⧍. Then the segment joining the midpts. of the non-∥ sides is the sum of the midsegments of the ⧍. This sum is $\frac{1}{2}B + \frac{1}{2}b = \frac{1}{2}(B + b)$.

324 Chapter 6 Quadrilaterals

36. Yes; the ≅ ⦞ must be 45° or 135° each.
37. No; if two consecutive ⦞ were compl., then the kite would be concave.
38. Rhombuses and squares would be kites since opp. sides can be ≅ also.

Proof 26. **Developing Proof** The plan suggests a proof of Theorem 6-15. Follow the plan and write a paragraph, two-column, or flow proof. **See back of book.**

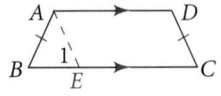

Given: Isosceles trapezoid *ABCD* with $\overline{AB} \cong \overline{DC}$

Prove: $\angle B \cong \angle C$ and $\angle BAD \cong \angle D$

Plan: Begin by drawing $\overline{AE} \parallel \overline{DC}$ to form parallelogram *AECD* so that $\overline{AE} \cong \overline{DC} \cong \overline{AB}$. $\angle B \cong \angle C$ because $\angle B \cong \angle 1$ and $\angle 1 \cong \angle C$. Also, $\angle BAD \cong \angle D$ because they are supplements of the congruent angles, $\angle B$ and $\angle C$.

$\boxed{x^2}$ **Algebra Find the value(s) of the variable(s) in each kite.**

27.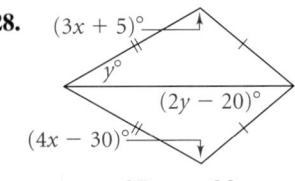

28.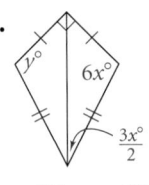
    $x = 35$, $y = 30$

29. $x = 18$, $y = 108$

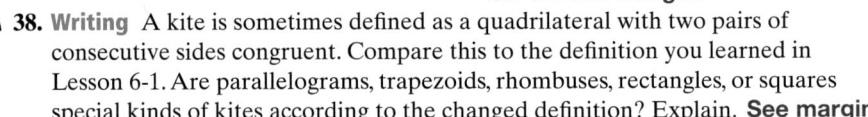

Bridge Design A quadrilateral is formed by the beams of the bridge at the left.

30. Classify the quadrilateral. Explain your reasoning. Isosc. trapezoid; all the large rt. ⧍ appear to be ≅.

31. Find the measures of the other interior angles of the quadrilateral. **112, 68, 68**

Critical Thinking Can two angles of a kite be as follows? Explain.
  32–34. See above left.

32. opposite and acute   33. consecutive and obtuse

34. opposite and supplementary   35. consecutive and supplementary

36. opposite and complementary   37. consecutive and complementary
  35–37. See margin.

38. **Writing** A kite is sometimes defined as a quadrilateral with two pairs of consecutive sides congruent. Compare this to the definition you learned in Lesson 6-1. Are parallelograms, trapezoids, rhombuses, rectangles, or squares special kinds of kites according to the changed definition? Explain. **See margin.**

Challenge

39. $\overleftrightarrow{BN}$ is the perpendicular bisector of $\overline{AC}$ at *N*. Describe the set of points, *D*, for which *ABCD* is a kite. **See above left.**

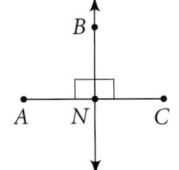

Proof 40. Prove that the angles formed by the noncongruent sides of a kite are congruent. (*Hint:* Draw a diagonal of the kite.) **See back of book.**

Proof **Write a proof. Use the given figure with additional lines as needed.**

41. **Given:** Isosceles trapezoid *TRAP* with $\overline{TR} \cong \overline{PA}$

    Prove: $\angle RTA \cong \angle APR$ **See margin.**

42. **Given:** Isosceles trapezoid *TRAP* with $\overline{TR} \cong \overline{PA}$; $\overline{BI}$ is the perpendicular bisector of $\overline{RA}$ intersecting $\overline{RA}$ at *B* and $\overline{TP}$ at *I*. **See margin.**

    Prove: $\overline{BI}$ is the perpendicular bisector of $\overline{TP}$.

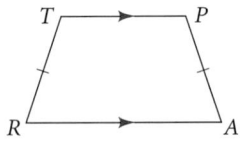

For a trapezoid, consider the segment joining the midpoints of the two given segments. How are its length and the lengths of the two parallel sides of the trapezoid related? Justify your answer.

43. the two nonparallel sides See left.

44. the diagonals See margin.

---

41. Answers may vary. Sample: Draw $\overline{TA}$ and $\overline{RP}$.

   1. isosc. trapezoid *TRAP* (Given)

   2. $\overline{TA} \cong \overline{PR}$ (Diagonals of an isosc. trap. are ≅.)

   3. $\overline{TR} \cong \overline{PA}$ (Given)

   4. $\overline{RA} \cong \overline{RA}$ (Refl. Prop. of ≅)

   5. $\triangle TRA \cong \triangle PAR$ (SSS)

   6. $\angle RTA \cong \angle APR$ (CPCTC)

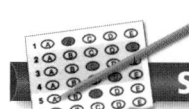
Multiple Choice

45. Which statement is true for every trapezoid? **B**
  A. Exactly two sides are congruent.   **B.** Exactly two sides are parallel.
  C. Opposite angles are supplementary.   **D.** The diagonals bisect each other.

46. Which statement is true for every kite? **I**
  F. Opposite sides are congruent.   **G.** At least two sides are parallel.
  H. Opposite angles are supplementary.   **I.** The diagonals are perpendicular.

Quantitative Comparison

Compare the boxed quantity in Column A with the boxed quantity in Column B. Choose the best answer.
  A. The quantity in Column A is greater.
  B. The quantity in Column B is greater.
  C. The two quantities are equal.
  D. The relationship cannot be determined from the information given.

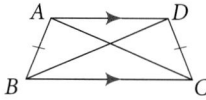

Trapezoid

Column A	Column B
C 47. $m\angle ABC$	$m\angle BCD$
C 48. AC	BD
D 49. AD	BC

Short Response

50. Diagonal $\overline{RB}$ of kite $RHBW$ forms an equilateral triangle with two of the sides. $m\angle BWR = 40$. Draw and label a diagram showing the diagonal and the measures of all the angles. Which angles of the kite are largest? **See margin.**

Mixed Review

Lesson 6-4   **Find the indicated angle measures for the rhombus.**

51. $m\angle 1$ **126**   **52.** $m\angle 2$ **27**   **53.** $m\angle 3$ **27**

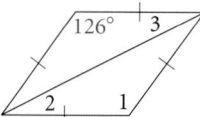

Lesson 5-2 x^2 **Algebra Find the values indicated.**

54. a. a
  b. FG
  c. GH
  a. 4
  b. 5
  c. 5

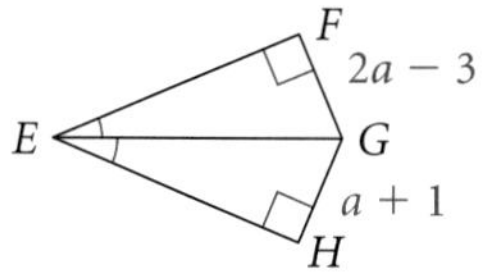

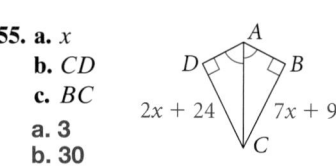

55. a. x
  b. CD
  c. BC
  a. 3
  b. 30
  c. 30

Lesson 4-2   **56.** State the postulate that justifies the statement $\triangle ABC \cong \triangle DEF$. **SAS**

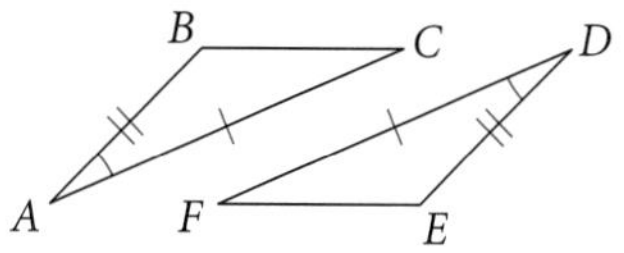

Side notes (right column)

Standardized Test Prep

📁 **Resources**
For additional practice with a variety of test item formats:
• Standardized Test Prep, p. 343
• Test-Taking Strategies, p. 338
• Test-Taking Strategies with Transparencies

Exercise 50 Students need to remember that an equilateral triangle is equiangular.

44. It is one half the difference of the lengths of the bases; from Ex. 43, the length of the segment joining the midpts. of the non- ∥ sides is $\frac{1}{2}(B + b)$. The middle part of this segment joins the midpts. of the diags. Each outer segment measures $\frac{1}{2}B$. So the length of the segment connecting the midpts. of the diags. is $\frac{1}{2}(B - b)$.

50. [2]

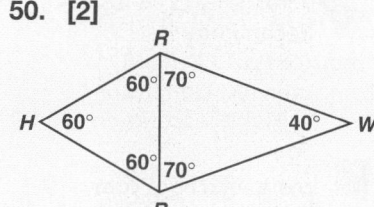

∠HRW and ∠HBW

[1] incorrect diagram OR no work shown

Bottom answer block

42. Draw $\overline{BI}$ as described, then draw $\overline{BT}$ and $\overline{BP}$.

1. $\overline{TR} \cong \overline{PA}$ (Given)
2. $\angle R \cong \angle A$ (Base ▵ of isosc. trap. are ≅.)
3. $\overline{RB} \cong \overline{AB}$ (Def. of bisector)

4. $\triangle TRB \cong \triangle PAB$ (SAS)
5. $\overline{BT} \cong \overline{BP}$ (CPCTC)
6. $\angle RBT \cong \angle ABP$ (CPCTC)
7. $\angle TBI \cong \triangle PBI$ (Compl. of ≅ ▵ are ≅.)
8. $\overline{BI} \cong \overline{BI}$ (Refl. Prop. of ≅)

9. $\triangle TBI \cong \triangle PBI$ (SAS)
10. $\angle BIT \cong \angle BIP$ (CPCTC)
11. $\angle BIT$ and $\angle BIP$ are rt. ▵. (≅ supp. ▵ are rt. ▵.)
12. $\overline{TI} \cong \overline{PI}$ (CPCTC)
13. $\overline{BI}$ is ⊥ bis. of $\overline{TP}$. (Def. of ⊥ bis.)

1. Plan

Lesson Preview

✓ **Check Skills You'll Need**

Classifying Special Quadrilaterals
Lesson 6-1: Example 2
Exercises 13–18
Extra Practice, p. 695

Lesson Resources

📁 **Teaching Resources**
Practice, Reteaching, Enrichment
Checkpoint Quiz 2

👥 **Reaching All Students**
Practice Workbook 6-6
Spanish Practice Workbook 6-6
Reading and Math Literacy 6C
Spanish Reading & Math Literacy 6C
Spanish Checkpoint Quiz 2
Informal Geometry Planning
   Guide 6-6

⏱ **Presentation Assistant Plus!**
Transparencies
• Check Skills You'll Need 6-6
• Additional Examples 6-6
• Student Edition Answers 6-6
• Lesson Quiz 6-6
PH Presentation Pro CD 6-6

PRENTICE HALL ASSESSMENT SYSTEM

Computer Test Generator CD

💿 **Technology**
Resource Pro® CD-ROM
Computer Test Generator CD
Prentice Hall Presentation Pro CD

🖥 **www.PHSchool.com**
Student Site
• Teacher Web Code: afk-5500
• Self-grading Lesson Quiz
Teacher Center
• Lesson Planner
• Resources

Plus 📘 **TEXT**

326

Placing Figures in the Coordinate Plane

ALGEBRA

North Carolina Objectives

2.03   Apply properties, definitions, and theorems of two-dimensional figures to solve problems and write proofs: b) Quadrilaterals.

Lesson Preview

What You'll Learn

OBJECTIVE
▼ To name coordinates of special figures by using their properties

. . . And Why

To examine a T-shirt design, as in Example 2

✓ **Check Skills You'll Need**   (For help, go to Lesson 6-1.)

Draw a quadrilateral with the given vertices. Then determine the most precise name for each quadrilateral. 1–4. See back of book.

1. $H(-5, 0), E(-3, 2), A(3, 2), T(5, 0)$

2. $S(0, 0), A(4, 0), N(3, 2), D(-1, 2)$

3. $R(0, 0), A(5, 5), I(8, 4), N(7, 1)$

4. $W(-3, 0), I(0, 3), N(3, 0), D(0, -3)$

📲 **TEXT**   **Interactive lesson includes instant self-check, tutorials, and activities.**

OBJECTIVE
1   **Naming Coordinates**

1. Answers may vary. Sample: Squares with sides on the axes; it's easiest to find horiz. and vertical slopes.

2. Answers may vary. Sample:
   a. Place one side on the x-axis and another on the y-axis.
   b. Place one side on the x-axis with one endpt. at the origin. Determine the height. Place the opposite side parallel to the x-axis at the required height, so that one vertex is on the y-axis.

📖 **Reading Math**

A rectangle centered at the origin has opposite sides equidistant from the origin.

Investigation: Figures in the Coordinate Plane

• Use graph paper to draw a number of coordinate planes with x- and y-coordinates from −12 to 12. On each, draw one or more squares with sides 10 units long. Draw the squares in different positions, with sides on one or both axes, parallel to the axes, or not parallel to either axis. Use more than one quadrant. Label each square *ABCD*.

• On each square, record the slope of each side, the slope of each diagonal, and the coordinates of the midpoints of the diagonals.
                                          See left.
1. Which positions for your squares made your calculations easiest? Generalize your conclusions and explain your reasons.

2. For ease of calculations in the coordinate plane, explain how you would position (a) a rectangle and (b) a parallelogram.

In the coordinate plane, the position of a figure affects the ease with which you can work with its coordinates. In coordinate proofs, it generally is good practice to center the figure on the origin, or place a vertex at the origin and one side of the figure on an axis.

1 **EXAMPLE**   **Naming Coordinates**

Algebra In the diagram, rectangle *KLMN* is centered at the origin with sides parallel to the axes. Find the missing coordinates.

L has coordinates (a, b), so the coordinates of the other vertices are $K(-a, b), M(a, -b)$, and $N(-a, -b)$.

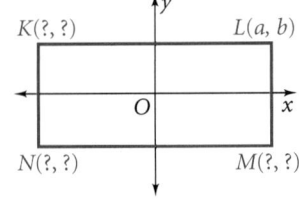

326   Chapter 6   Quadrilaterals

🔵 **Ongoing Assessment and Intervention**

Before the Lesson	**During the Lesson**	**After the Lesson**
Diagnose prerequisite skills using:	**Monitor progress using:**	**Assess knowledge using:**
• Check Skills You'll Need	• Check Understanding	• Lesson Quiz
	• Additional Examples	• Computer Test Generator CD
	• Standardized Test Prep	• Chapter Checkpoint 2 (p. 331)

✓ **Check Understanding** ① Use the properties of parallelogram $OPQR$ to find the missing coordinates. Do not use any new variables. $Q(s + b, c)$

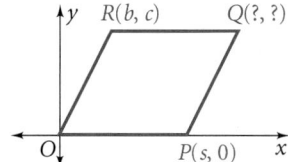

It is often convenient to use coordinates that are multiples of 2. The next example uses multiples of 2 to avoid fractions when finding midpoints.

② **EXAMPLE**   **Real-World** **Connection**

T-Shirt Design An art class creates T-shirt designs by drawing quadrilaterals, connecting their midpoints to form other quadrilaterals, and then coloring the regions. Tiana claims that everyone's inner quadrilateral will be a parallelogram. Is she correct? Explain.

Step 1

Draw quadrilateral $OACE$ with one vertex at the origin and one side on the x-axis. Since you are finding midpoints, use coordinates that are multiples of 2. Find the coordinates of the midpoints T, W, V, and U.

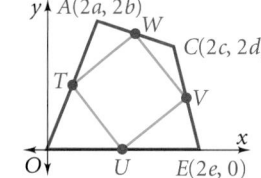

$$T = \text{midpoint of } \overline{OA} = \left(\frac{2a + 0}{2}, \frac{2b + 0}{2}\right) = (a, b)$$

$$W = \text{midpoint of } \overline{AC} = \left(\frac{2a + 2c}{2}, \frac{2b + 2d}{2}\right) = (a + c, b + d)$$

$$V = \text{midpoint of } \overline{CE} = \left(\frac{2c + 2e}{2}, \frac{2d + 0}{2}\right) = (c + e, d)$$

$$U = \text{midpoint of } \overline{OE} = \left(\frac{0 + 2e}{2}, \frac{0 + 0}{2}\right) = (e, 0)$$

Need Help?

Use the Distributive Property.

$$\frac{2a + 2c}{2} = \frac{2(a + c)}{2}$$
$$= a + c$$

Step 2

Find the slopes of the sides of $TWVU$.

$$\text{slope of } \overline{TW} = \frac{b - (b + d)}{a - (a + c)} = \frac{d}{c}$$

$$\text{slope of } \overline{VU} = \frac{d - 0}{(c + e) - e} = \frac{d}{c}$$

The slopes are equal, so $\overline{TW} \parallel \overline{VU}$.

$$\text{slope of } \overline{WV} = \frac{(b + d) - d}{(a + c) - (c + e)} = \frac{b}{a - e}$$

$$\text{slope of } \overline{TU} = \frac{b - 0}{a - e} = \frac{b}{a - e}$$

The slopes are equal, so $\overline{WV} \parallel \overline{TU}$.

2. Midpoint of $\overline{TV} =$ $\left(\frac{a + c + e}{2}, \frac{b + d}{2}\right) =$ midpoint of $\overline{UW}$. So, the diagonals bisect each other and $TWVU$ is a ▱.

Since both pairs of opposite sides of $TWVU$ are parallel, $TWVU$ is a parallelogram, and Tiana is correct.

✓ **Check Understanding** ② Use a different method to show that $TWVU$ is a parallelogram by finding the midpoints of the diagonals. **See left.**

👥 **Reaching All Students**

| **Below Level** Work through Examples 1 and 2 using numerical coordinates before introducing variables. Generalize with variables only after students understand the arithmetic. | **Advanced Learners** Have students rework Example 2 without using coordinate geometry. | **Visual Learners** See note on page 327. **Auditory Learners** See note on page 328. |

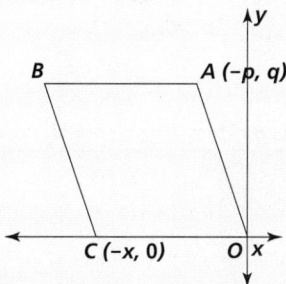

For more practice, see *Extra Practice.*

EXERCISES

Practice and Problem Solving

Assignment Guide

1 Objective

Ⓐ Ⓑ **Core** 1–32
Ⓒ **Extension** 33, 34

Standardized Test Prep 35–41

Mixed Review 42–45

Auditory Learners

Exercises 1–6 If you do these as class exercises, ask students to explain their choices of coordinates. Encourage other students to challenge any misapplications of properties of quadrilaterals.

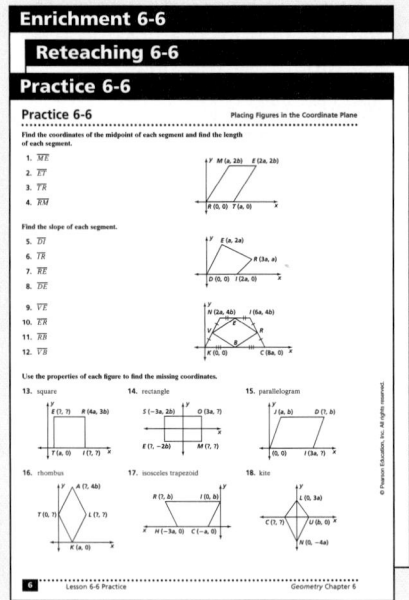

Ⓐ **Practice by Example** x^2 **Algebra** **Give coordinates for points W and Z without using any new variables.**

Example 1
(page 326)

1. rectangle
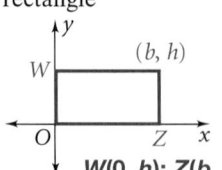
$W(0, h)$; $Z(b, 0)$

2. square
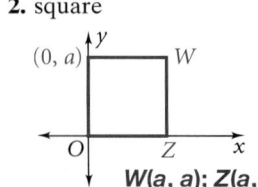
$W(a, a)$; $Z(a, 0)$

3. square
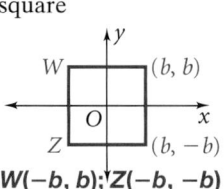
$W(-b, b)$; $Z(-b, -b)$

4. parallelogram
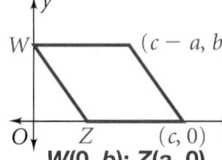
$W(0, b)$; $Z(a, 0)$

5. rhombus
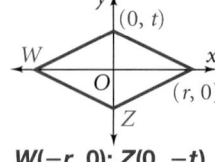
$W(-r, 0)$; $Z(0, -t)$

6. isosceles trapezoid
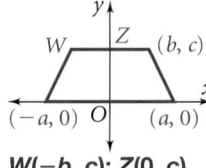
$W(-b, c)$; $Z(0, c)$

Example 2
(page 327)

In each exercise, find the coordinates of the midpoint of $\overline{WZ}$ and the slope of $\overline{WZ}$.

7. Exercise 1   **8.** Exercise 2   **9.** Exercise 3

10. Exercise 4   **11.** Exercise 5   **12.** Exercise 6
7–13. See margin.

13. Developing Proof Complete the steps to show that the midpoint of the hypotenuse of a right triangle is equidistant from the vertices of the triangle.

Given: Right $\triangle ABC$ with M the midpoint of hypotenuse $\overline{AB}$

Prove: $MA = MB = MC$

Step 1: Draw right $\triangle ABC$ on a coordinate plane. Locate the right angle, $\angle C$, at the origin and leg $\overline{CA}$ on the positive x-axis.

Step 2: You seek a midpoint, so label coordinates using multiples of 2. The coordinates of point A are **a.** __?__ . The coordinates of point B are **b.** __?__ .

Step 3: By the Midpoint Formula, the coordinates of midpoint M are **c.** __?__ .

Step 4: By the Distance Formula, $MA = $ **d.** __?__ , $MB = $ **e.** __?__ , and $MC = $ **f.** __?__ .

Step 5: Conclusion: **g.** __?__

Ⓑ **Apply Your Skills**

14–19. Answers may vary. Samples are given.

Here are coordinates for eight points in the coordinate plane ($q > p > 0$).
$A(0, 0)$, $B(p, 0)$, $C(q, 0)$, $D(p + q, 0)$, $E(0, q)$, $F(p, q)$, $G(q, q)$, $H(p + q, q)$
Which four points, if any, are the vertices for each type of figure?

14. parallelogram A, C, H, F **15.** rhombus B, D, H, F **16.** rectangle A, B, F, E

17. square A, C, G, E **18.** trapezoid A, C, F, E **19.** isosceles trapezoid A, D, G, F

Refer to the diagrams in Exercises 1–6. Use the coordinates given below in place of the ones shown. Then give the coordinates for points W and Z without using any new variables. The new diagram for Exercise 20 is shown here.

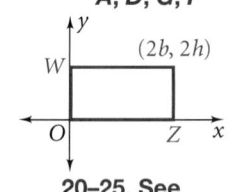

20. Ex. 1, $(2b, 2h)$ **21.** Ex. 2, $(0, 2a)$

22. Ex. 3, $(2b, 2b)$, $(2b, -2b)$ **23.** Ex. 4, $(2c, 0)$, $(2c - 2a, b)$

24. Ex. 5, $(2r, 0)$, $(0, 2t)$ **25.** Ex. 6, $(-2a, 0)$, $(2a, 0)$, $(2b, 2c)$

20–25. See back of book.

328 Chapter 6 Quadrilaterals

pages 328–331 **Exercises**

7. $\left(\frac{b}{2}, \frac{h}{2}\right)$; $-\frac{h}{b}$

8. $\left(a, \frac{a}{2}\right)$; undefined

9. $(-b, 0)$; undefined

10. $\left(\frac{a}{2}, \frac{b}{2}\right)$; $-\frac{b}{a}$

11. $\left(-\frac{r}{2}, -\frac{t}{2}\right)$; $-\frac{t}{r}$

12. $\left(-\frac{b}{2}, c\right)$; 0

13. **a.** $(2a, 0)$
b. $(0, 2b)$
c. (a, b)

d. $\sqrt{b^2 + a^2}$

e. $\sqrt{b^2 + a^2}$

f. $\sqrt{b^2 + a^2}$

g. $MA = MB = MC$

26. a. What property of a rhombus makes it convenient to place its diagonals on the *x*- and *y*-axes? **a–b. See back of book.**

🖊 **b. Writing** Suppose a parallelogram is not a rhombus. Explain why it may not be convenient to place opposite vertices on the *y*-axis.

27. Open-Ended Choose values for *r* and *t* in Exercise 5. Find the slope and length of each side. State why the figure satisfies the definition of a rhombus.
See back of book.

Give the coordinates for point *P* without using any new variables.

28. isosceles trapezoid   **29.** trapezoid with a right ∠   **30.** kite

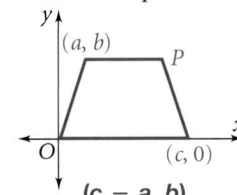 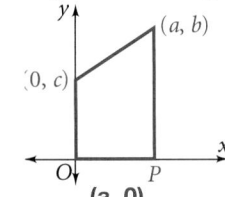 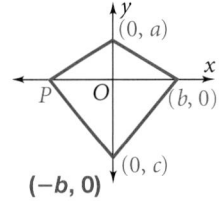

31. a. Draw a square whose diagonals of length 2*b* lie on the *x*- and *y*-axes.
b. Give the coordinates of the vertices of the square. **a–b, e. See back of book.**
c. Compute the length of a side of the square. $b\sqrt{2}$
d. Find the slopes of two adjacent sides of the square. **1, −1**
e. Do the slopes show that the sides are perpendicular? Explain.

32. Make two drawings of an isosceles triangle with base length 2*b* and height 2*c*.
a. In one drawing, place the base on the *x*-axis with a vertex at the origin.
b. In the second, place the base on the *x*-axis with its midpoint at the origin.
c. Find the lengths of the legs of the triangle as placed in part (a).
d. Find the lengths of the legs of the triangle as placed in part (b).
e. How do the results of parts (c) and (d) compare? **a–e. See margin.**

C Challenge 🌐 **33. Marine Archaeology** Marine archaeologists sometimes use a coordinate system on the ocean floor. They record the coordinates of points where artifacts are found. Assume that each diver searches a square area and can go no farther than *b* units from the starting points. Draw a model for the region one diver can search. Assign coordinates to the vertices without using any new variables. **See margin.**

 **34. Coordinate Proof** Follow the steps below to prove:
If two nonvertical lines are perpendicular, the product of their slopes is −1.

Step 1: Two nonvertical lines, ℓ_1 and ℓ_2, intersect. Which coordinate point might be the easiest to work with as the point of intersection? **(0, 0)**

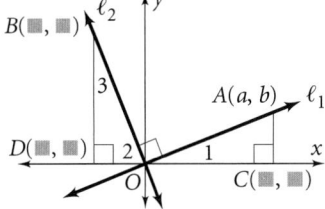

Step 2: To work with the slope of a line, you need two points on the line. Choose one point $A(a, b)$ on ℓ_1. What are the coordinates of *C*? **(a, 0)**

Step 3: Notice that ∠1 and ∠3 are both complements of ∠2. Why? **See margin.**

Step 4: This means that the two triangles pictured have congruent angles. Thus, if any pair of sides are congruent, the two triangles are congruent. Congruent triangles are desirable, so what would be a good choice for the coordinates of point *D*? **(−b, 0)**

Step 5: If you made a choice for *D* so that △*ACO* ≅ △*ODB* what must be the coordinates of point *B*? **(−b, a)**

Step 6: Now, complete the proof that the product of slopes is −1. **See margin.**

32. a.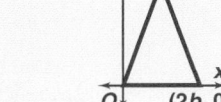
b.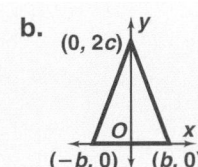
c. $\sqrt{b^2 + 4c^2}$
d. $\sqrt{b^2 + 4c^2}$
e. The lengths are =.

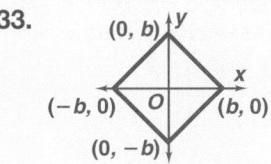

329

4. Assess

Lesson Quiz 6-6

Find the missing coordinates of each figure.

1. parallelogram

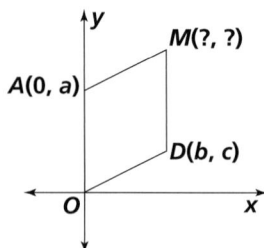

$M(b, c + a)$

2. rhombus

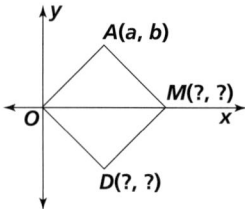

$M(2a, 0), D(a, -b)$

3. rectangle

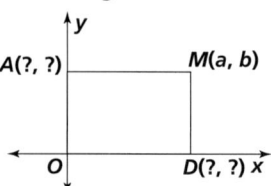

$A(0, b), D(a, 0)$

Find the coordinates of the midpoint and the slope.

4. $\overline{OM}$ in Exercise 1 midpoint: $\left(\frac{b}{2}, \frac{c + a}{2}\right)$; slope: $\frac{c + a}{b}$

5. $\overline{AD}$ in Exercise 2 midpoint: $(a, 0)$; slope: undefined

6. $\overline{AD}$ in Exercise 3 midpoint: $\left(\frac{a}{2}, \frac{b}{2}\right)$; slope: $-\frac{b}{a}$

Alternative Assessment

Have students draw two of these figures in a coordinate plane, label the vertices, and explain how they chose the coordinates: *parallelogram, square, isosceles trapezoid, kite.*

330

Standardized Test Prep

Multiple Choice

35. The vertices of a rhombus are located at $(a, 0)$, $(0, b)$, $(-a, 0)$, and $(0, -b)$, where $a, b > 0$. What is the midpoint of the side that is in Quadrant II? **B**

A. $\left(\frac{a}{2}, \frac{b}{2}\right)$ B. $\left(-\frac{a}{2}, \frac{b}{2}\right)$ C. $\left(-\frac{a}{2}, -\frac{b}{2}\right)$ D. $\left(\frac{a}{2}, -\frac{b}{2}\right)$

36. The vertices of a kite are located at $(0, a)$, $(b, 0)$, $(0, -c)$, and $(-b, 0)$, where $a, b, c, d > 0$. What is the slope of the side in Quadrant IV? **F**

F. $\frac{c}{b}$ G. $\frac{b}{c}$ H. $-\frac{b}{c}$ I. $-\frac{c}{b}$

37. The vertices of a square are located at $(a, 0)$, (a, a), $(0, a)$, and $(0, 0)$. What is the length of a diagonal? **C**

A. a B. $2a$ C. $a\sqrt{2}$ D. $2\sqrt{a}$

Quantitative Comparison

Compare the boxed quantity in Column A with the boxed quantity in Column B. Choose the best answer.

A. The quantity in Column A is greater.
B. The quantity in Column B is greater.
C. The two quantities are equal.
D. The relationship cannot be determined from the information given.

The points $A(p, p + 2)$, $B(r, s)$, and $C(3p, 3p)$ are collinear, and $p \neq 0$. B is the midpoint of $\overline{AC}$.

	Column A	Column B
C **38.**	r	$2p$
A **39.**	s	$2p$
C **40.**	the slope of $\overline{AC}$	$1 - \frac{1}{p}$

Take It to the NET

Online lesson quiz at
www.PHSchool.com
Web Code: afa-0606

Short Response

41. The vertices of a rectangle are $(2b, 0)$, $(2b, 2a)$, $(0, 2a)$, and $(0, 0)$. What are the coordinates of the midpoint of each diagonal? What can you conclude from your answers? **See margin.**

Mixed Review

Lesson 6-5 x^2 **42. Algebra** Find the measure of each angle and the value of x in the isosceles trapezoid. **62, 118, 118; 2.5**

Lesson 5-3 **Find the center of the circle that circumscribes $\triangle ABC$.**

43. $A(1, 1), B(5, 3), C(5, 1)$ **(3, 2)**   **44.** $A(-5, 0), B(-1, -8), C(-1, 0)$ **(-3, -4)**

Lesson 4-3 **45.** Supply the words that complete the paragraph proof.

Given: $\angle ACD \cong \angle ACB$ and $\angle D \cong \angle B$

Prove: $\triangle ADC \cong \triangle ABC$

$\angle ACD \cong \angle ACB$ and $\angle D \cong \angle B$. $\overline{AC} \cong \overline{AC}$ by the
a. _?_ Property of Congruence. So, $\triangle ADC \cong \triangle ABC$ by the **b.** _?_ Theorem.
Reflexive   **AAS**

330 Chapter 6 Quadrilaterals

pages 328–331 **Exercises**

41. **[2]** (b, a); the diagonals of a rectangle bisect each other.

[1] no conclusion given

 **Checkpoint Quiz 2** **Lessons 6-4 through 6-6**

 Instant self-check quiz online and on CD-ROM

x^2 **Algebra Find the value(s) of the variable(s).**

1. $x = 51, y = 51$

2. $x = 58, y = 32$

3. $x = 2, y = 4$

1.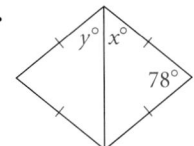

2.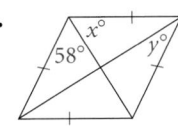

3.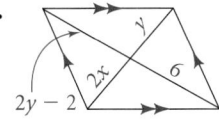

4.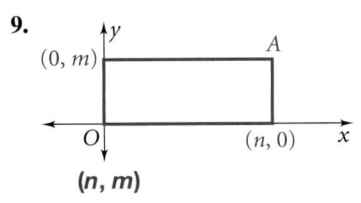

$x = 3$

5.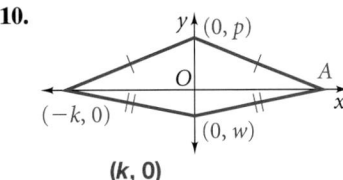

$x = \frac{5}{3}, y = \frac{9}{2}, b = 90$

In Exercises 6–8, decide whether the statement is *true* or *false*. If true, explain why. If false, show a counterexample. 6–8. See margin.

6. A quadrilateral with congruent diagonals is an isosceles trapezoid or rectangle.

7. A quadrilateral with congruent and perpendicular diagonals is a square.

8. Each diagonal of a kite bisects two angles of the kite.

Give the coordinates for point *A* without using any new variables.

9.

(n, m)

10.

(k, 0)

 **A P•int in Time**

400   200 B.C.   0   A.D. 200   2000

Many walls in ancient Egypt were decorated with reliefs. The relief in the photo was created in the year 255 B.C. First, the artist sketched the scene on papyrus overlaid with a grid. Next, the wall was marked with a grid the size of the intended sculpture. To draw each line, a tightly stretched string that had been dipped in red ochre was plucked, like a guitar string.

Using the grid squares as guides, the artist transferred the drawing to the wall. Then, a sculptor cut the background away, leaving the scene slightly raised. Finally, an artist painted the scene.

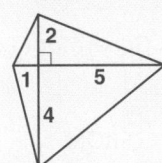 **Take It to the NET** For more information about Egyptian reliefs, go to **www.PHSchool.com**.
Web Code: afe-2032

Lesson 6-6 Placing Figures in the Coordinate Plane **331**

---

page 331   Checkpoint Quiz 2

6–8. Counterexamples may vary.

6. false;

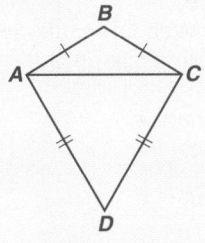

7. False; a kite can have ≅ ⊥ diags.

8. false

∠BAC ≇ ∠CAD

331

1. Plan

Lesson Preview

✓ **Check Skills You'll Need**

Finding Midpoints
Lesson 1-6: Example 3
Exercises 14–19
Extra Practice, p. 690

Finding Missing Coordinates
Lesson 6-6: Examples 1, 2
Exercises 1–12
Extra Practice, p. 695

Lesson Resources

📁 **Teaching Resources**
Practice, Reteaching, Enrichment

👥 **Reaching All Students**
Practice Workbook 6-7
Spanish Practice Workbook 6-7
Informal Geometry Planning
   Guide 6-7

⏱ **Presentation Assistant Plus!**
Transparencies
• Check Skills You'll Need 6-7
• Additional Examples 6-7
• Student Edition Answers 6-7
• Lesson Quiz 6-7
PH Presentation Pro CD 6-7

ⓅRENTICE HALL ASSESSMENT SYSTEM

Computer Test Generator CD

💿 **Technology**
Resource Pro® CD-ROM
Computer Test Generator CD
Prentice Hall Presentation Pro CD

🖥 **www.PHSchool.com**
Student Site
• Teacher Web Code: afk-5500
• Self-grading Lesson Quiz
Teacher Center
• Lesson Planner
• Resources

Plus **ⓘTEXT**

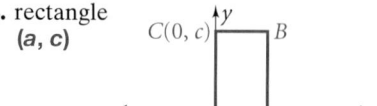 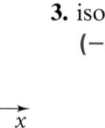

6-7 Proofs Using Coordinate Geometry

 North Carolina Objectives

2.03 Apply properties, definitions, and theorems of two-dimensional figures to solve problems and write proofs: b) Quadrilaterals.

Lesson Preview

What You'll Learn

OBJECTIVE 1
To prove theorems using figures in the coordinate plane

. . . And Why

To use coordinate geometry to prove that a flag design includes a rhombus, as in Example 2

✓ **Check Skills You'll Need** (For help, go to Lesson 6-6.)

1. Graph the rhombus with vertices $A(2, 2)$, $B(7, 2)$, $C(4, -2)$, and $D(-1, -2)$. Then, connect the midpoints of consecutive sides to form a quadrilateral. What do you notice about the quadrilateral? **The quad. is a rectangle.**

x^2 **Algebra** **Give the coordinates of B without using any new variables.**

2. rectangle **(a, c)**

3. isosceles triangle **(−a, 0)**

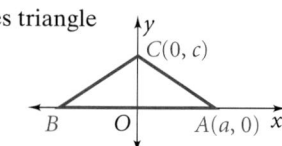

New Vocabulary
• midsegment of a trapezoid

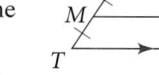 **Interactive lesson includes instant self-check, tutorials, and activities.**

OBJECTIVE

1 Building Proofs in the Coordinate Plane

In Lesson 5-1, you learned about midsegments of triangles. A trapezoid also has a midsegment. The **midsegment of a trapezoid** is the segment that joins the midpoints of the nonparallel opposite sides. It has two unique properties.

🔑 **Key Concepts**

Theorem 6-18	**Trapezoid Midsegment Theorem**

(1) The midsegment of a trapezoid is parallel to the bases.
(2) The length of the midsegment of a trapezoid is half the sum of the lengths of the bases.

$$\overline{MN} \parallel \overline{TP}, \overline{MN} \parallel \overline{RA}, \text{ and } MN = \tfrac{1}{2}(TP + RA).$$

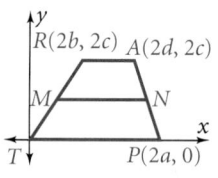

Formulas for slope, midpoint, and distance are used in a proof of Theorem 6-18.

Proof **1 EXAMPLE** **Planning a Coordinate Geometry Proof**

Developing Proof Plan a coordinate proof of Theorem 6-18.

Given: $\overline{MN}$ is the midsegment of trapezoid *TRAP*.
Prove: $\overline{MN} \parallel \overline{TP}, \overline{MN} \parallel \overline{RA}$, and $MN = \tfrac{1}{2}(TP + RA)$.

Plan: Place the trapezoid in the coordinate plane with a vertex at the origin and a base along the *x*-axis. Since midpoints will be involved, use multiples of 2 to name coordinates. To show lines are parallel, check for equal slopes. To compare lengths, use the Distance Formula.

INSTANT CHECK SYSTEM **Ongoing Assessment and Intervention**

Before the Lesson	**During the Lesson**	**After the Lesson**
Diagnose prerequisite skills using:	**Monitor progress using:**	**Assess knowledge using:**
• Check Skills You'll Need	• Check Understanding	• Lesson Quiz
	• Additional Examples	• Computer Test Generator CD
	• Standardized Test Prep	

✓ Check Understanding ① Complete the coordinate proof of Theorem 6-18. **See margin, p 334.**
 a. Find the coordinates of midpoints M and N. How do the multiples of 2 help?
 b. Find and compare the slopes of $\overline{MN}$, $\overline{TP}$, and $\overline{RA}$.
 c. Find and compare the lengths MN, TP, and RA.
 d. In parts (b) and (c), how does placing a base along the x-axis help?

② EXAMPLE **Real-World Connection**

Algebra The rectangular flag at the left is constructed by connecting the midpoints of its sides. Use coordinate geometry to prove that the quadrilateral formed by connecting the midpoints of the sides of a rectangle is a rhombus.

Given: $MNPO$ is a rectangle.
 T, W, V, U are midpoints of its sides.

Prove: $TWVU$ is a rhombus.

Plan: Place the rectangle in the coordinate plane with two sides along the axes. Use multiples of 2 to name coordinates.
A rhombus is a parallelogram with four congruent sides. From Lesson 6-6, Example 2, you know that $TWVU$ is a parallelogram. To show $\overline{TW} \cong \overline{WV} \cong \overline{VU} \cong \overline{UT}$, use the Distance Formula.

Coordinate Proof: By the Midpoint Formula, the coordinates of the midpoints are $T(0, b)$, $W(a, 2b)$, $V(2a, b)$, and $U(a, 0)$. By the Distance Formula,

$$TW = \sqrt{(a-0)^2 + (2b-b)^2} = \sqrt{a^2 + b^2}$$

$$WV = \sqrt{(2a-a)^2 + (b-2b)^2} = \sqrt{a^2 + b^2}$$

$$VU = \sqrt{(a-2a)^2 + (0-b)^2} = \sqrt{a^2 + b^2}$$

$$UT = \sqrt{(0-a)^2 + (b-0)^2} = \sqrt{a^2 + b^2}$$

● $\overline{TW} \cong \overline{WV} \cong \overline{VU} \cong \overline{UT}$, so parallelogram $TWVU$ is a rhombus.

✓ Check Understanding ② **Critical Thinking** Explain why the proof using $M(0, 2b)$, $N(2a, 2b)$, $P(2a, 0)$, and $O(0, 0)$ is easier than a proof using $M(0, b)$, $N(a, b)$, $P(a, 0)$, and $O(0, 0)$. **See back of book.**

Real-World Connection
A flag's length, called the *fly*, usually is greater than its width, called the *hoist*.

EXERCISES
For more practice, see *Extra Practice*.

Practice and Problem Solving

A **Practice by Example**
 Example 1
 (page 332)

1.a. $W\left(\frac{a}{2}, \frac{b}{2}\right); Z\left(\frac{c+e}{2}, \frac{d}{2}\right)$
 b. $W(a, b); Z(c+e, d)$
 c. $W(2a, 2b);$
  $Z(2c+2e, 2d)$
 d. c; it uses multiples of 2 to name the coordinates of W and Z.

1. W and Z are the midpoints of $\overline{OR}$ and $\overline{ST}$, respectively. In parts (a)–(c), find the coordinates of W and Z. **a–d. See left.**

a.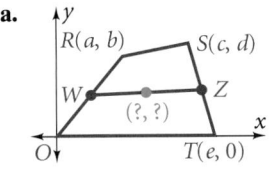
b.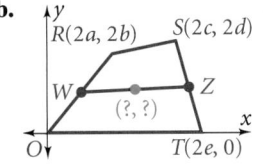
c.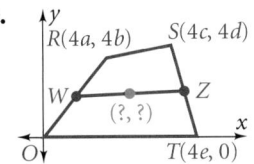

 d. You are to plan a coordinate proof involving the midpoint of $\overline{WZ}$. Which of the figures (a)–(c) would you prefer to use? Explain.

Lesson 6-7 Proofs Using Coordinate Geometry **333**

👥 Reaching All Students

Below Level Before discussing the proofs, review the formulas for distance, midpoint, and slope.	**Advanced Learners** After reading Example 2, students should be able to prove that the quadrilateral formed by connecting the midpoints of a square is also a square.	**Tactile Learners** See note on page 335. **Error Prevention** See note on page 334.

Math Background

The Trapezoid Midsegment Theorem is an extension of the Triangle Midsegment Theorem. This becomes clear by successively decreasing the shorter base of a trapezoid until it measures 0.

OBJECTIVE
▽ 1 **Teaching Notes**

① EXAMPLE **Connection to Algebra**

Help students understand that $2a$ is a valid coordinate by encouraging them to try the proof using other coordinates. They will see that the choice of variable is arbitrary.

Additional Examples

① Examine trapezoid *TRAP*. Explain why you can assign the same y-coordinate to points R and A. Since $\overline{TP} \parallel \overline{RA}$ and $\overline{TP}$ is horizontal, $\overline{RA}$ is horizontal.

② Use coordinate geometry to prove that the quadrilateral formed by connecting the midpoints of rhombus *ABCD* is a rectangle.

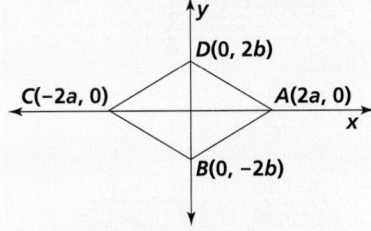

Sample method: Show that diagonals are congruent.

Closure

How are the midsegments of trapezoids and triangles alike? How are they different? **Both are parallel to bases; triangle midsegments are half the length of the third side, but trapezoid midsegments are the average length of both bases.**

333

3. Practice

Assignment Guide

1 Objective

Ⓐ Ⓑ **Core** 1–34

Ⓒ **Extension** 35–41

Standardized Test Prep 42–45

Mixed Review 46–54

Error Prevention

Exercise 1 Help students observe that only (a) requires the use of fractions.

Exercises 2, 3 These exercises plan coordinate proofs for theorems already proved by geometric methods. As a class, discuss the similarities and differences between the methods. Point out that each new theorem and method of proof provides more resources to use in proving new theorems.

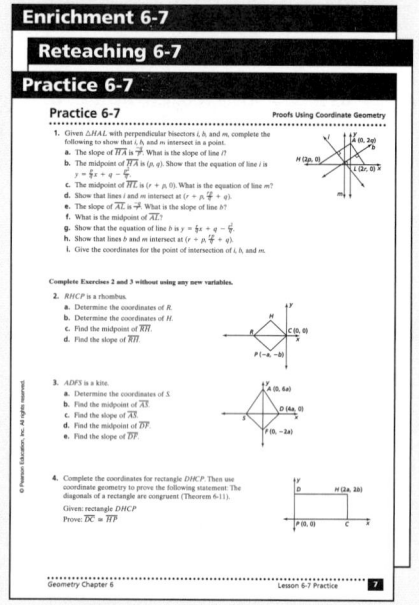

page 333 Check Understanding

1. a. *M* (*b*, *c*), *N* (*a* + *d*, *c*); by starting with multiples of 2 you eliminate fractions when using the midpoint formula.

 b. 0, 0, 0; they are =.

 c. *MN* = *d* + *a* − *b*, *TP* = 2*a*, *RA* = 2*d* − 2*b*; so *RA* + *TP* =

334

Reading Math

When you read large blocks of math text, cover all but a few lines to help you focus.

2a. origin
 b. *x*-axis
 c. 2
 d. coordinates

3a. *y*-axis
 b. Distance

4a. rt. ∠
 b. legs
 c. multiples of 2
 d. *M*
 e. *N*
 f. Midpoint
 g. Distance

Example 2
(page 333)

Developing Proof **Complete the plan for each coordinate proof.**

2. The diagonals of a parallelogram bisect each other (Theorem 6-3).

 Given: Parallelogram *ABCD*

 Prove: $\overline{AC}$ bisects $\overline{BD}$, and $\overline{BD}$ bisects $\overline{AC}$.

 Plan: Place the parallelogram in the coordinate plane with a vertex at the **a.** ? and a base along the **b.** ? . Since midpoints will be involved, use multiples of **c.** ? to name coordinates. To show segments bisect each other, show the midpoints have the same **d.** ? .

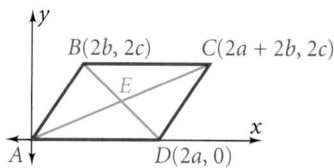

3. The diagonals of an isosceles trapezoid are congruent (Theorem 6-16).

 Given: Trapezoid *EFGH* with $\overline{FE} \cong \overline{GH}$

 Prove: $\overline{EG} \cong \overline{HF}$

 Plan: The trapezoid is isosceles, so place one base on the *x*-axis so that the **a.** ? bisects its bases. To show the diagonals are congruent, use the **b.** ? Formula.

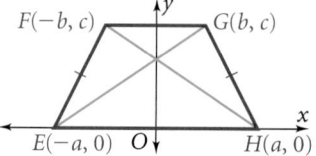

4. The median to the hypotenuse of a right triangle is half the hypotenuse.

 Given: △*MNO* is a right triangle with right ∠*MON*. *P* is the midpoint of $\overline{MN}$.

 Prove: $OP = \frac{1}{2}MN$

 Plan: Place the right triangle in the coordinate plane with the vertex of the **a.** ? at the origin and the **b.** ? along each axis. Since midpoints will be involved, use **c.** ? to name coordinates for points **d.** ? and **e.** ? . Use the **f.** ? Formula to find the coordinates of *P*. To compare lengths, use the **g.** ? Formula.

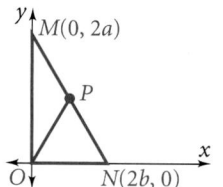

5. The segments joining the midpoints of consecutive sides of an isosceles trapezoid form a rhombus. **a–g. See margin.**

 Given: Trapezoid *TRAP* with $\overline{TR} \cong \overline{PA}$; *D*, *E*, *F*, and *G* are midpoints of the indicated sides.

 Prove: *DEFG* is a rhombus.

 Plan: The trapezoid is **a.** ? , so place one base on the **b.** ? so that the **c.** ? bisects its bases. Use multiples of 2 to name coordinates since **d.** ? will be involved. A rhombus is a parallelogram with four **e.** ? . To show opposite sides are parallel, show that their **f.** ? are the same. To show sides are congruent, use **g.** ? .

Developing Proof **Follow the plans above to complete the coordinate proofs.**

6. (Exercise 3) The diagonals of an isosceles trapezoid are congruent.

 Proof: By the Distance Formula, *EG* = **a.** ? and *HF* = **b.** ? . Therefore, $\overline{EG} \cong \overline{HF}$ by the definition of congruence. **a–b. See margin.**

7. (Exercise 4) The median from the vertex of the right angle of a right triangle is half as long as the hypotenuse.

 Proof: By the Distance Formula, *OP* = **a.** ? and *MN* = **b.** ? . Therefore, $OP = \frac{1}{2}MN$. **a–b. See margin.**

334 Chapter 6 Quadrilaterals

2*d* + 2*a* − 2*b* which is twice *MN*. So the midsegment is half the sum of the lengths of the bases.

 d. The base along the *x*-axis allows us to

calculate length by subtracting *x*–values.

pages 333–337 Exercises
5. a. isos.
 b. *x*-axis
 c. *y*-axis
 d. midpoints

 e. ≅ sides
 f. slopes
 g. the Distance Formula

6. a. $\sqrt{(b + a)^2 + c^2}$
 b. $\sqrt{(a + b)^2 + c^2}$

8. (Exercise 5) The segments joining the midpoints of consecutive sides of an isosceles trapezoid form a rhombus. **a–k. See margin.**

   Proof: The midpoints have coordinates **a.** $D(\underline{\;?\;},\underline{\;?\;})$, $E(\underline{\;?\;},\underline{\;?\;})$, $F(\underline{\;?\;},\underline{\;?\;})$, and $G(\underline{\;?\;},\underline{\;?\;})$. By the Distance Formula, $DE =$ **b.** $\underline{\;?\;}$, $EF =$ **c.** $\underline{\;?\;}$, $FG =$ **d.** $\underline{\;?\;}$, and $GD =$ **e.** $\underline{\;?\;}$. The slope of $DE =$ **f.** $\underline{\;?\;}$ and the slope of $FG =$ **g.** $\underline{\;?\;}$. The slope of $EF =$ **h.** $\underline{\;?\;}$ and that of $GD =$ **i.** $\underline{\;?\;}$. Thus, $DEFG$ is a parallelogram with congruent **j.** $\underline{\;?\;}$, so **k.** $\underline{\;?\;}$ is a rhombus by the definition of rhombus.

9a. (a, b)
b. (a, b)
c. the same point

9. Use coordinate geometry to prove that the diagonals in the rectangular flag bisect each other (Theorem 6-3).

   Proof: The midpoint of $\overline{AC}$ is **a.** $\underline{\;?\;}$. The midpoint of $\overline{BD}$ is **b.** $\underline{\;?\;}$. The midpoints are **c.** $\underline{\;?\;}$, so the diagonals bisect each other.

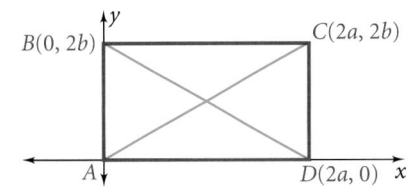

B Apply Your Skills

10. **Open-Ended** Give an example of a statement that you think is easier to prove with a coordinate geometry proof than with a paragraph, flow, or two-column proof. Explain your choice. **See back of book.**

11. **Developing Proof** Complete the coordinate proof. **a–h. See back of book.**

   The midpoints of the sides of a kite determine a rectangle.

   Given: Kite $DEFG$ with $DE = EF$ and $DG = GF$; K, L, M, and N are midpoints of the sides.

   Prove: $KLMN$ is a rectangle.

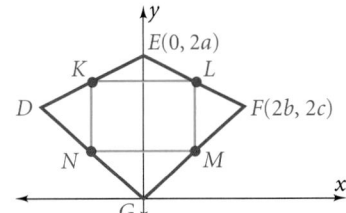

   Proof: The kite has two pairs of **a.** $\underline{\;?\;}$ sides, so place congruent sides opposite each other across the y-axis. Use multiples of 2 to name coordinates since **b.** $\underline{\;?\;}$ are involved. Name E as $(0, 2a)$. Name F as $(2b, 2c)$. Then, in terms of b and c, D must be **c.** $\underline{\;?\;}$. By the Midpoint Formula, the midpoints are **d.** $L(\underline{\;?\;},\underline{\;?\;})$, $M(\underline{\;?\;},\underline{\;?\;})$, $N(\underline{\;?\;},\underline{\;?\;})$, and $K(\underline{\;?\;},\underline{\;?\;})$. Slopes for $\overline{KL}$ and $\overline{NM}$ are **e.** $\underline{\;?\;}$, so $\overline{KL}$ and $\overline{NM}$ are parallel. Slopes for $\overline{KN}$ and $\overline{LM}$ are undefined, so $\overline{KN}$ and $\overline{LM}$ are **f.** $\underline{\;?\;}$. Thus, opposite sides are **g.** $\underline{\;?\;}$ and consecutive sides are **h.** $\underline{\;?\;}$, so $KLMN$ is a rectangle.

? Need Help?

Lines with undefined slope are vertical lines. All vertical lines are parallel.

State whether each type of conclusion shown here could be reached using coordinate methods. Give a reason for each answer. 12–24. See back of book.

12. $\overline{AB} \cong \overline{CD}$ 13. $\overline{AB} \parallel \overline{CD}$ 14. $\overline{AB} \perp \overline{CD}$

15. $\overline{AB}$ bisects $\overline{CD}$.   16. $\overline{AB}$ bisects $\angle CAD$.   17. $\angle A \cong \angle B$

18. $\angle A$ is a right angle.   19. $AB + BC = AC$ 20. $\triangle ABC$ is isosceles.

21. $\angle A$ and $\angle B$ are supplementary.   22. $\overline{AB}, \overline{CD}$, and $\overline{EF}$ are concurrent.

23. A, B, and C are collinear.   24. Quadrilateral $ABCD$ is a rhombus.

A and B have coordinates -2 and 10 on a number line. Find the coordinates of the points that separate $\overline{AB}$ into the given number of congruent segments.

25. 4   26. 6   27. 10   28. 50   29. n

25–29. See margin.

7. **a.** $\sqrt{a^2 + b^2}$
   b. $2\sqrt{a^2 + b^2}$

8. **a.** $D(-a - b, c), E(0, 2c),$ $F(a + b, c), G(0, 0)$
   b. $\sqrt{(a + b)^2 + c^2}$

   c. $\sqrt{(a + b)^2 + c^2}$
   d. $\sqrt{(a + b)^2 + c^2}$
   e. $\sqrt{(a + b)^2 + c^2}$
   f. $\dfrac{c}{a + b}$
   g. $\dfrac{c}{a + b}$

   h. $-\dfrac{c}{a + b}$
   i. $-\dfrac{c}{a + b}$
   j. sides
   k. $DEFG$

25. 1, 4, 7

Exercise 11 Discuss with students why point D must have coordinates $(-2b, 2c)$. Use this discussion to help assess students' understanding of coordinate geometry and how it illustrates what they learned about kites in Lesson 6-5.

Exercise 38 Have students experiment with classroom objects, such as pens, pencils, and books, using trial and error to identify the centroids.

Exercise 39 Review, if necessary, how to find the equation of a line.

Exercise 40 Before students begin, ask: *When two nonvertical lines are perpendicular, what is the product of their slopes?* −1

26. 0, 2, 4, 6, 8

27. −0.8, 0.4, 1.6, 2.8, 4, 5.2, 6.4, 7.6, 8.8

28. −1.76, −1.52, −1.28, . . . , 9.52, 9.76

29. $-2 + \dfrac{12}{n}, -2 + 2\left(\dfrac{12}{n}\right),$ $-2 + 3\left(\dfrac{12}{n}\right), \ldots,$ $-2 + (n - 1)\left(\dfrac{12}{n}\right)$

335

4. Assess

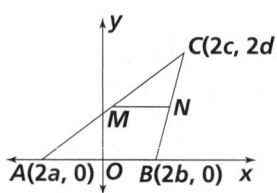
33. $(-2.76, 5.2)$, $(-2.52, 5.4)$,
$(-2.28, 5.6)$, . . . ,
$(8.52, 14.6)$, $(8.76, 14.8)$

34. $\left(-3 + \frac{12}{n}, 5 + \frac{10}{n}\right)$,
$\left(-3 + 2\left(\frac{12}{n}\right), 5 + 2\left(\frac{10}{n}\right)\right)$,
. . . , $\left(-3 + (n-1)\left(\frac{12}{n}\right)\right)$,
$5 + (n-1)\left(\frac{10}{n}\right)\right)$

336

 **Challenge**

30. $(0, 7.5)$, $(3, 10)$, $(6, 12.5)$

31. $\left(-1, 6\frac{2}{3}\right)$, $\left(1, 8\frac{1}{3}\right)$, $(3, 10)$,
$\left(5, 11\frac{2}{3}\right)$, $\left(7, 13\frac{1}{3}\right)$

32. $(-1.8, 6)$, $(-0.6, 7)$,
$(0.6, 8)$, $(1.8, 9)$, $(3, 10)$,
$(4.2, 11)$, $(5.4, 12)$,
$(6.6, 13)$, $(7.8, 14)$

Real-World Connection

Carefully balanced metal
shapes hang from wires in the
mobiles of Alexander Calder
(1898–1976).

The endpoints of $\overline{AB}$ are $A(-3, 5)$ and $B(9, 15)$. Find the coordinates of the points
that separate $\overline{AB}$ into the given number of congruent segments.

30. 4   **31.** 6   **32.** 10   **33.** 50   **34.** n
30–32. See left.   33–34. See margin.

The endpoints of $\overline{AB}$ are as given. Find the coordinates of the points that separate
$\overline{AB}$ into n congruent segments. 35–36. See back of book.

35. A has coordinate a and B has coordinate b on a number line.

36. A has coordinates (a, c) and B has coordinates (b, d) in the coordinate plane.

37. Use the diagram at the right.
   a. Explain using area why $\frac{1}{2}ad = \frac{1}{2}bc$ and hence
      $ad = bc$. (*Hint*: Area of triangle $= \frac{1}{2} \cdot$ base $\cdot$ height)
   b. Use slope and part (a) to show:
      If $\frac{a}{b} = \frac{c}{d}$, then $ad = bc$. **a–b. See back of book.**

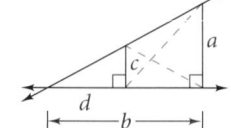

38. Physics For a mobile to be in balance, you suspend each part of the mobile at
its center of mass. The center of mass, or centroid, is the point around which the
weight of an object appears to be evenly distributed. You learned a method for
finding the centroid of a triangle in Lesson 5-3. Now use it to help you find the
centroid of a quadrilateral. (*Hint:* Where is the centroid of a segment?)
See margin.

Proof **39.** You learned in Lesson 5-3 (Theorem 5-8) that the centroid of a triangle,
the point where the medians meet, is $\frac{2}{3}$ of the distance from each vertex
to the midpoint of the opposite side. Complete the following steps
to prove this theorem. **a–e. See margin.**

   a. Find the coordinates of points L, M, and
      N, the midpoints of the sides of $\triangle ABC$.
   b. Find equations of $\overleftrightarrow{AM}, \overleftrightarrow{BN}$, and $\overleftrightarrow{CL}$.
   c. Find the coordinates of point P, the
      intersection of $\overleftrightarrow{AM}$ and $\overleftrightarrow{BN}$.
   d. Show that point P is on $\overleftrightarrow{CL}$.
   e. Use the Distance Formula to show that
      point P is $\frac{2}{3}$ of the distance from each
      vertex to the midpoint of the opposite side.

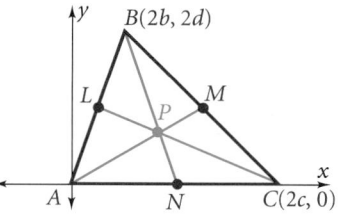

Proof **40.** Complete the following steps to prove
Theorem 5-9. You are given $\triangle ABC$ with
altitudes p, q, and r. Show that p, q, and r
intersect in a point (called the orthocenter
of the triangle). **a–h. See back of book.**

   a. The slope of $\overline{BC}$ is $\frac{c}{-b}$.
      What is the slope of line p?
   b. Show that the equation of line p is $y = \frac{b}{c}(x - a)$.
   c. What is the equation of line q?
   d. Show that lines p and q intersect at $\left(0, \frac{-ab}{c}\right)$.
   e. The slope of $\overline{AC}$ is $\frac{c}{-a}$. What is the slope of line r?
   f. Show that the equation of line r is $y = \frac{a}{c}(x - b)$.
   g. Show that lines r and q intersect at $\left(0, \frac{-ab}{c}\right)$.
   h. Give the coordinates of the orthocenter of $\triangle ABC$.

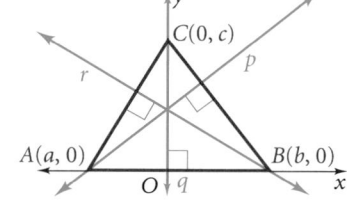

38. Divide the quad. into 2 ⧍.
Find the centroid for

each △ and connect them. Now
divide the quad. into
2 other ⧍ and follow the same
steps. Where the two lines
meet connecting the centroids

of the 4 ⧍ is the centroid of the
quad.

39. a. $L(b, d)$, $M(b + c, d)$, $N(c, 0)$

   b. $\overleftrightarrow{AM}: y = \frac{d}{b + c} x$;
      $\overleftrightarrow{BN}: y = \frac{2d}{2b - c}(x - c)$;

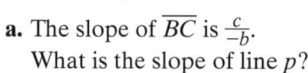

$\overleftrightarrow{CL}: y = \frac{d}{b - 2c}(x - 2c)$;

   c. $P\left(\frac{2(b + c)}{3}, \frac{2d}{3}\right)$

   d. Pt. P satisfies the eqs. fo_
      $\overleftrightarrow{AM}$ and $\overleftrightarrow{CL}$.

   e. $AM = \sqrt{(b + c)^2 + d^2}$;

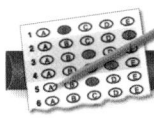

Proof 41. Write a coordinate proof of the theorem:
If the slopes of two lines have product -1, the lines are perpendicular.

    a. First, argue that neither line can be horizontal or vertical.
    b. Then, tell why the lines must intersect. (*Hint:* Use indirect reasoning.)
    c. Knowing that they do intersect, place the lines in the coordinate plane, choose a point on ℓ_1, find a related point on ℓ_2, and complete the proof.
    a–c. See back of book.

Standardized Test Prep

Resources
For additional practice with a variety of test item formats:
• Standardized Test Prep, p. 343
• Test-Taking Strategies, p. 338
• Test-Taking Strategies with Transparencies

Exercises 42, 43 Drawing a diagram often helps students understand geometry problems more quickly. In this case, using the slope formula provides the fastest solution.

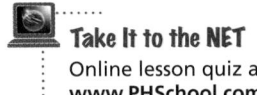

Standardized Test Prep

Multiple Choice

42. Two points on a line are $(-7, 10)$ and $(9, 2)$. Two points on a line parallel to that line are $(1, -3)$ and $(x, 4)$. What is the value of x? **A**
    A. -13 **B.** 13   **C.** 15   **D.** -15

43. Two points on a line are $(-4, 0)$ and $(8, 8)$. Two points on a line perpendicular to that line are $(8, -1)$ and $(6, y)$. What is the value of y? **G**
    F. 3   **G.** 2   **H.** $-\frac{7}{3}$ **I.** -4

Short Response

44. The endpoints of a segment are $(7, -3)$ and (a, b). The midpoint is $(3, 4)$.
    a. What are the coordinates of the other endpoint? Show your work.
    b. What is the length of the segment? Show your work. **See back of book.**

Extended Response

Take It to the NET
Online lesson quiz at
www.PHSchool.com
Web Code: afa-0607

45. Given: $\triangle ABC$; P, Q, and R are the midpoints of $\overline{AB}$, $\overline{AC}$, and $\overline{BC}$, respectively.
    a. Place $\triangle ABC$ in the coordinate plane by writing coordinates for A, B, and C. **a–c. See margin.**
    b. What are the coordinates of P, Q, and R?
    c. Use coordinate geometry to prove $\triangle APQ \cong \triangle RQP$ by SSS.

Mixed Review

Lesson 6-6

46. Rectangle $LMNP$ at the right is centered at the origin. Give coordinates for point P without using any new variables. **$(-a, b)$**

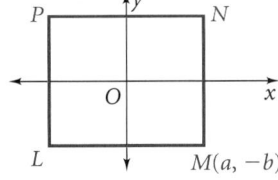

Lesson 5-4

Write (a) the inverse and (b) the contrapositive of each statement. 47–51. See margin.

47. If the sum of the angles of a polygon is not $360°$, then the polygon is not a quadrilateral.

48. If $x = 51$, then $2x = 102$.   **49.** If $a = 5$, then $a^2 = 25$.

50. If $b < -4$, then b is negative.   **51.** If $c > 0$, then c is positive.

Lesson 4-4

Explain how you can use SSS, SAS, ASA, or AAS with CPCTC to prove each statement true. 52–54. See margin.

52. $\overline{AB} \cong \overline{CB}$ **53.** $\angle 1 \cong \angle 2$ **54.** $\angle K \cong \angle M$

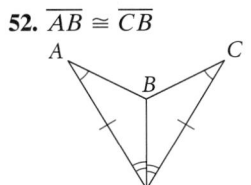 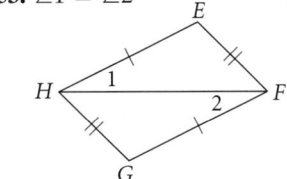 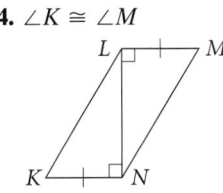

47. a. If the sum of the $\angle$s of a polygon is $360°$, then the polygon is a quad.
    b. If a polygon is a quad., then the sum of its $\angle$s is $360°$.

48. a. If $x \neq 51$, then $2x \neq 102$.
    b. If $2x \neq 102$, then $x \neq 51$.

49. a. If $a \neq 5$, then $a^2 \neq 25$.
    b. If $a^2 \neq 25$, then $a \neq 5$.

50. a. If $b \geq -4$, then b is not neg.
    b. If b is not neg., then $b \geq -4$.

51. a. If $c \leq 0$, then c is not pos.
    b. If c is not pos., then $c \leq 0$.

52. $\angle A \cong \angle C$, $\overline{AD} \cong \overline{CD}$ and $\angle ADB \cong \angle CDB$ so by ASA $\triangle ADB \cong \triangle CDB$ and by CPCTC $\overline{AB} \cong \overline{CB}$.

53. $\overline{HE} \cong \overline{FG}$, $\overline{EF} \cong \overline{GH}$, and $\overline{HF} \cong \overline{HF}$ by the Reflexive Prop. of $\cong$, so $\triangle HEF \cong \triangle FGH$ by SSS. Then by CPCTC $\angle 1 \cong \angle 2$.

54. $\overline{LM} \cong \overline{NK}$ is given, $\overline{NL} \cong \overline{LN}$ by the Reflexive Prop., and $\angle LNK \cong \angle NLM$ by all rt. $\angle$s are $\cong$. So $\triangle LNK \cong \triangle NLM$ by SAS, and $\angle K \cong \angle M$ by CPCTC.

$AP = \sqrt{\left(\frac{2(b+c)}{2}\right)^2 + \left(\frac{2d}{3}\right)^2} =$

$\sqrt{\left(\frac{2}{3}\right)^2\left((b+c)^2 + d^2\right)} =$

$\frac{2}{3}\sqrt{(b+c)^2 + d^2} = \frac{2}{3}\,AM$

The other 2 distances are found similarly.

45. [4] a–b. Sample:

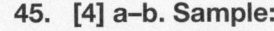
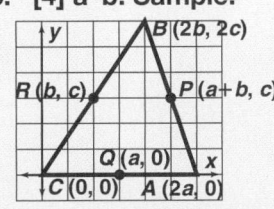

c. $AP = \sqrt{(b-a)^2 + c^2} = RQ$
$PQ = PQ$
$AQ = a = RP$
$\triangle APQ \cong \triangle RQP$ by SSS.
[3] minor computational error
[2] parts a and b correct
[1] one part correct

337

Drawing a Diagram

Assessment tests often include problems without accompanying diagrams. This feature helps students recognize when a problem can be solved more easily by drawing a diagram and gives them practice in drawing appropriate diagrams.

Resources

Test-Taking Strategies with Transparencies
- Transparency 6
- Practice sheet p. 18

Teaching Notes

Help students understand that drawing a diagram can assist them in deciding which data are important and which are extraneous in a given problem. A diagram also can inspire ideas about methods of solution. Have students discuss ways that drawing a diagram helps them.

Inclusion

Students who are physically challenged may have difficulty drawing neat diagrams. Point out that any diagrams they draw do not need to be neat, just useful.

338

Sometimes, if a problem does not have a diagram, you should draw one. A diagram helps you to see the given information so that you can use the information to make inferences.

1 EXAMPLE

Side $\overline{AB}$ of square $ABCD$ has endpoints $A(0,0)$ and $B(5,2)$. What are the possible locations of point C?

You need to draw a diagram to do this problem. Point C can be in two different locations.

First draw the segment $\overline{AB}$, and then begin the two possible squares that have $\overline{AB}$ as a side. To locate C from B you can either go up 5 units and left 2 units, or you can go down 5 units and right 2 units. The coordinates of point C can be either $(3, 7)$ or $(7, -3)$.

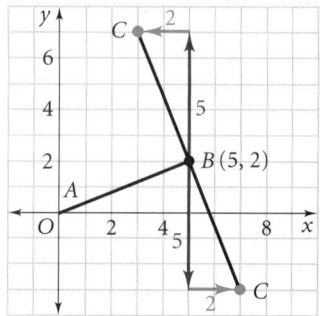

2 EXAMPLE

The midpoints of the sides of a rhombus are joined to form a quadrilateral. What special quadrilateral is formed? Explain.

Draw a rhombus and join the midpoints of the sides. The midpoint quadrilateral is a parallelogram since both pairs of sides are parallel to a diagonal of the rhombus. The diagonals of the rhombus are perpendicular, so adjacent sides of the parallelogram are perpendicular to each other.

The quadrilateral formed is a rectangle.

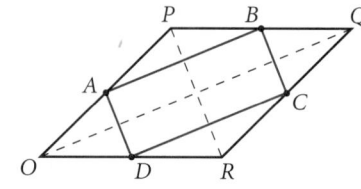

EXERCISES

Draw a diagram to help you answer each question.

1. Angie says that if the diagonals of a quadrilateral are perpendicular, then the quadrilateral is a kite or a rhombus. Provide a counterexample to Angie's claim by sketching a quadrilateral with perpendicular diagonals that is neither a rhombus nor a kite.

   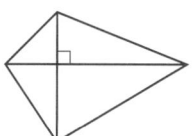

2. Three vertices of parallelogram $ABCD$ are $A(0,0)$, $B(5,2)$, and $C(8,5)$. What are the possible locations of point D? **(3, 3)**

3. Three vertices of a parallelogram are $(0,0)$, $(5,2)$ and $(8,5)$. What are the possible locations of the fourth vertex? **(3, 3), (13, 7), (−3, −3)**

4. The diagonal $\overline{AC}$ of square $ABCD$ has endpoints $A(0,0)$ and $C(6,4)$. What are the coordinates of the other two vertices of the square? **(1, 5), (5, −1)**

5. The midpoints of the sides of an isosceles trapezoid are joined to form a quadrilateral. What special quadrilateral is formed? Explain. **rhombus; ▱ with ≅ sides**

Chapter Review

Vocabulary

base angles of a trapezoid (p. 320)
consecutive angles (p. 294)
isosceles trapezoid (p. 288)
kite (p. 288)

midsegment of a trapezoid (p. 332)
parallelogram (p. 288)
rectangle (p. 288)

rhombus (p. 288)
square (p. 288)
trapezoid (p. 288)

 Reading Math
Understanding
Vocabulary

To complete each definition, find the appropriate word in the second column.

1. A(n) __?__ is a parallelogram with four right angles. **F**

2. A(n) __?__ is a quadrilateral with two pairs of adjacent sides congruent and no opposite sides congruent. **H**

3. Angles of a polygon that share a common side are __?__. **G**

4. A(n) __?__ is a quadrilateral with exactly one pair of parallel sides. **B**

5. A(n) __?__ is a parallelogram with four congruent sides. **I**

6. The __?__ of a trapezoid is the segment that joins the midpoints of the nonparallel opposite sides. **J**

7. A(n) __?__ is a quadrilateral with both pairs of opposite sides parallel. **A**

8. A(n) __?__ is a parallelogram with four congruent sides and four right angles. **C**

9. A(n) __?__ is a trapezoid whose nonparallel opposite sides are congruent. **E**

10. Two angles that share a base of a trapezoid are its __?__. **D**

A. parallelogram

B. trapezoid

C. square

D. base angles

E. isosceles trapezoid

F. rectangle

G. consecutive angles

H. kite

I. rhombus

J. midsegment

Take It to the NET
Online vocabulary quiz
at **www.PHSchool.com**
Web Code: afj-0651

Skills and Concepts

6-1 Objective

▼ To define and classify special types of quadrilaterals

Special quadrilaterals are defined by their characteristics.

A **parallelogram** is a quadrilateral with both pairs of opposite sides parallel.
A **rhombus** is a parallelogram with four congruent sides.
A **rectangle** is a parallelogram with four right angles.
A **square** is a parallelogram with four congruent sides and four right angles.
A **kite** is a quadrilateral with two pairs of adjacent sides congruent and no opposite sides congruent.
A **trapezoid** is a quadrilateral with exactly one pair of parallel sides.
An **isosceles trapezoid** is a trapezoid whose nonparallel opposite sides are congruent.

Draw and label each quadrilateral with the given vertices. Then determine the most precise name for each quadrilateral. 11–12. See back of book.

11. $N(-1, 2), M(3, 4), L(1, -2), K(5, 0)$ 12. $P(-4, 2), Q(-1, 3), R(7, 0), S(4, -1)$

Resources

Student Edition
Extra Practice Ch. 6, p. 695
English/Spanish Glossary, p. 741
Postulates and Theorems, p. 732
Table of Symbols, p. 726

 **Reaching All Students**
Reading and Math Literacy 6D
Spanish Reading and Literacy 6D

PRENTICE HALL
ASSESSMENT *SYSTEM*

Standardized Test Prep
● Ch. 6 practice in standardized test formats

www.PHSchool.com
Student Site
● Self-grading Vocabulary Test
Teacher Center
● Resources

Plus **i TEXT**

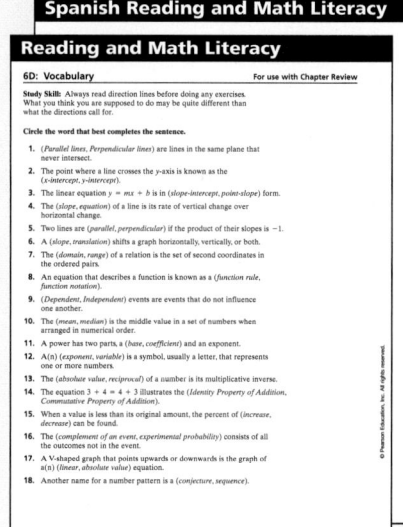

$\boxed{x^2}$ **Algebra** Find the values of the variables and the lengths of the sides.

13. isosceles trapezoid $ABCD$

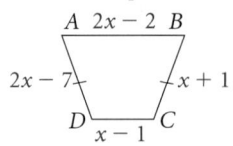

$x = 8;\ 9,\ 14,\ 9,\ 7$

14. kite $KLMN$

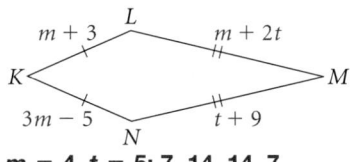

$m = 4,\ t = 5;\ 7,\ 14,\ 14,\ 7$

6-2 and 6-3 Objectives

▼ To use relationships among sides and among angles of parallelograms

▼ To use relationships involving diagonals of parallelograms or transversals

▼ To determine whether a quadrilateral is a parallelogram

Opposite sides and opposite angles of a parallelogram are congruent. The diagonals of a parallelogram bisect each other.

If three (or more) parallel lines cut off congruent segments on one transversal, then they cut off congruent segments on every transversal.

A quadrilateral is a parallelogram if any one of the following is true.
 The diagonals bisect each other.
 One pair of opposite sides is both congruent and parallel.
 Both pairs of opposite sides are congruent.
 Both pairs of opposite angles are congruent.

Find the measures of the numbered angles for each parallelogram.

15.

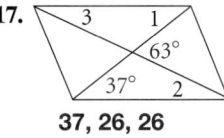

101, 79, 101

16.

38, 43, 99

17.

37, 26, 26

Determine whether the quadrilateral must be a parallelogram.

18.

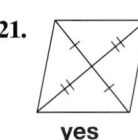

yes

19.

yes

20.

no

21.

yes

$\boxed{x^2}$ **Algebra** Find the values of the variables for which $ABCD$ must be a parallelogram.

22.

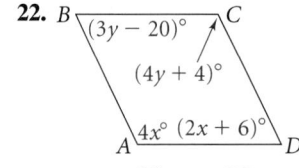

$x = 29,\ y = 28$

23.

$x = 4,\ y = 5$

6-4 and 6-5 Objectives

▼ To use properties of diagonals of rhombuses and rectangles

▼ To determine whether a parallelogram is a rhombus or a rectangle

▼ To verify and use properties of trapezoids and kites

Each diagonal of a rhombus bisects two angles of the rhombus. The diagonals of a rhombus are perpendicular.

The diagonals of a rectangle are congruent.

If one diagonal of a parallelogram bisects two angles of the parallelogram, then the parallelogram is a rhombus. If the diagonals of a parallelogram are perpendicular, then the parallelogram is a rhombus. If the diagonals of a parallelogram are congruent, then the parallelogram is a rectangle.

The parallel sides of a trapezoid are its bases and the nonparallel sides are its legs. Two angles that share a base of a trapezoid are **base angles** of the trapezoid.

The base angles of an isosceles trapezoid are congruent. The diagonals of an isosceles trapezoid are congruent.

The diagonals of a kite are perpendicular.

Find the measures of the numbered angles in each quadrilateral.

24.
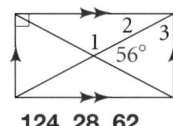
124, 28, 62

25.
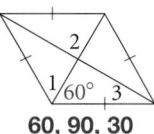
60, 90, 30

26.
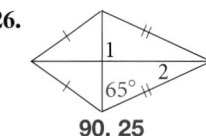
90, 25

Find *AC* for each quadrilateral.

27.
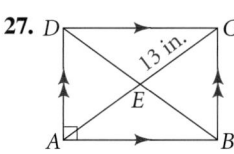
26 in.

28.
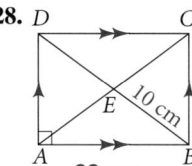
20 cm

29.
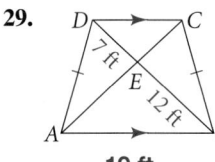
19 ft

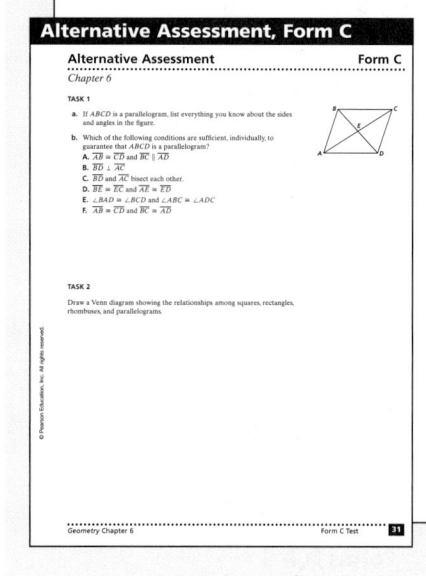

6-6 and 6-7 Objectives

▼ To name coordinates of special figures by using their properties

▼ To prove theorems using figures in the coordinate plane

In coordinate proofs, it generally is good practice to center the figure on the origin or place a vertex at the origin and one side of the figure on an axis.

The segment that joins the midpoints of the nonparallel sides of a trapezoid is the **midsegment** of the trapezoid. It is parallel to the bases and half as long as the sum of the lengths of the bases.

The formulas for slope, midpoint, and distance are used in coordinate proofs.

Give the coordinates of point *P* without using any new variable.

30. rectangle
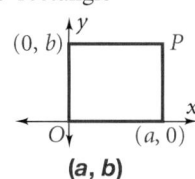
(a, b)

31. square
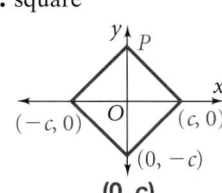
(0, c)

32. parallelogram
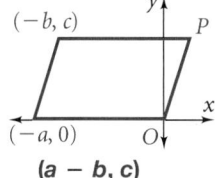
(a − b, c)

Complete each coordinate proof.

33a. −1

  b. 1

  c. The prod. of the slopes is −1.

33. The diagonals of a square are perpendicular.

  Given: Square *FGHI* with vertices $I(0, 0)$, $H(a, 0)$, $G(a, a)$, and $F(0, a)$

  Prove: $\overline{FH} \perp \overline{GI}$

  The slope of $\overline{FH}$ is **a.** <u>?</u> . The slope of $\overline{GI}$ is **b.** <u>?</u> . $\overline{FH} \perp \overline{GI}$ because **c.** <u>?</u> .

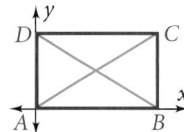

34a. *a*

  b. (0, *b*)

  c. $\sqrt{a^2 + b^2}$

  d. $\sqrt{a^2 + b^2}$

  e. *BD*

34. The diagonals of a rectangle are congruent.

  Given: Rectangle *ABCD*

  Prove: $\overline{AC} \cong \overline{BD}$

  Vertex *A* is at the origin with coordinates $(0, 0)$. Name *B* as $(a, 0)$, *C* as $(\mathbf{a.}\ \underline{?}\ , b)$, and *D* as **b.** <u>?</u> . $AC = \mathbf{c.}\ \underline{?}$ and $BD = \mathbf{d.}\ \underline{?}$. So, $AC = \mathbf{e.}\ \underline{?}$, and $\overline{AC} \cong \overline{BD}$.

Chapter 6   Chapter Review   **341**

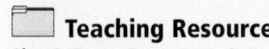
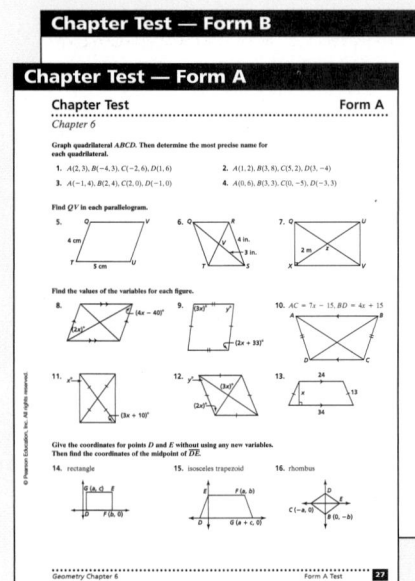

Chapter Test

Take It to the NET
Online chapter test at
www.PHSchool.com
Web Code: afa-0652

Graph each quadrilateral *ABCD*. Then determine the most precise name for it. 1–4. See back of book.

1. $A(1, 2), B(11, 2), C(7, 5), D(4, 5)$

2. $A(3, -2), B(5, 4), C(3, 6), D(1, 4)$

3. $A(1, -4), B(1, 1), C(-2, 2), D(-2, -3)$

4. **Open-Ended** Write the coordinates of four points that determine each figure with the given conditions. One vertex is at the origin and one side is 3 units long.
   a. square   b. parallelogram
   c. rectangle   d. trapezoid

Find *AN* for each parallelogram.

5.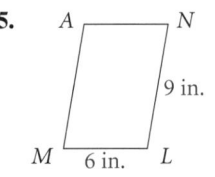

6.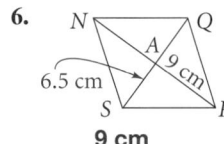
9 cm

7. Sketch two noncongruent parallelograms *ABCD* and *EFGH* such that $\overline{AC} \cong \overline{BD} \cong \overline{EG} \cong \overline{FH}$. **Check students' work.**

x^2 **Algebra** Find the values of the variables for each parallelogram.

8. 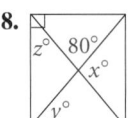 8–11. **See margin.**

9.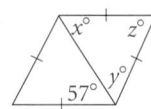

10.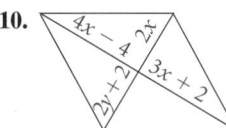

11.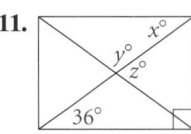

Does the information allow you to prove that *ABCD* is a parallelogram? Explain.

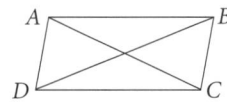

12. $\overline{AC}$ bisects $\overline{BD}$. 12–15. **See margin.**

13. $\overline{AB} \cong \overline{DC}; \overline{AB} \parallel \overline{DC}$ 14. $\overline{AB} \cong \overline{DC}; \overline{BC} \cong \overline{AD}$

15. $\angle DAB \cong \angle BCD$ and $\angle ABC \cong \angle CDA$

✏️ 16. **Writing** Explain why a square cannot be a kite. **See back of book.**

x^2 17. **Algebra** Determine the values of the variables for which *ABCD* is a parallelogram.
x = 2, y = 1

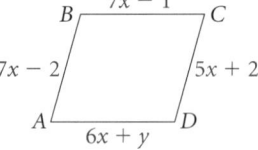

Find the measures of ∠1 and ∠2.

18.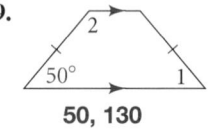
90, 30

19.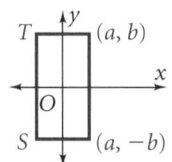
50, 130

Give the coordinates for points *S* and *T* without using any new variables. Then find the midpoint and the slope of $\overline{ST}$.

20. rectangle
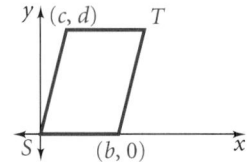

21. parallelogram
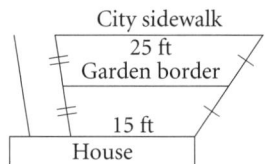

20–21. See back of book.

22. You want a garden border halfway between the front of your house and the city sidewalk, which are parallel to each other. You've measured those two edges. Find the length of the garden border. **20 ft**

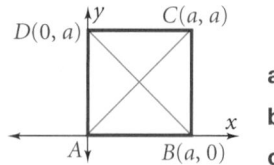

City sidewalk
25 ft
Garden border
15 ft
House

23. Complete this coordinate proof that the diagonals of a square are congruent.

   Given: Square *ABCD* with vertices $A(0, 0), B(a, 0), C(a, a),$ and $D(0, a)$
   Prove: $\overline{AC} \cong \overline{BD}$

   $D(0, a)$ $C(a, a)$
   A $B(a, 0)$

   a. $a\sqrt{2}$
   b. $a\sqrt{2}$
   c. *AC*

   $AC =$ **a.** ? , and $BD =$ **b.** ? . So, **c.** ? $= BD$ and $\overline{AC} \cong \overline{BD}$.

page 342 Chapter Test

8. $x = 100, y = 50, z = 40$

9. $x = 57, y = 57, z = 66$

10. $x = 6, y = 5$

11. $x = 36, y = 108, z = 72$

12. No; both diag. must bisect each other.

13. Yes; if one pair of opp. sides of a quad. is ∥ and ≅, then the quad. is a ▱.

14. Yes; if both pairs of opp. sides of a quad. are ≅, then the quad. is a ▱.

15. Yes; if both pairs of opp. ∆ in a quad. are ≅, the quad is a ▱.

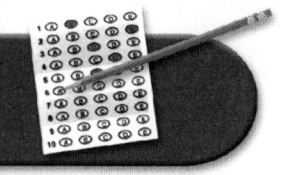

Standardized Test Prep

Multiple Choice

For Exercises 1–6, choose the correct letter.

1. What is a name for the quadrilateral below? **C**

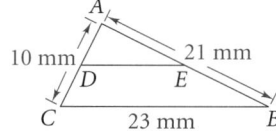

    I. square
    II. rectangle
    III. rhombus
    IV. parallelogram

A. I only   **B.** IV only
C. II and IV   **D.** I, II, and IV

2. An isosceles triangle has two angles measuring 48 and 84. What is the measure of the third angle? **I**

F. 84   **G.** 51   **H.** 49   **I.** 48

3. $\overline{DE}$ is a midsegment of $\triangle ABC$. What is DE? **A**

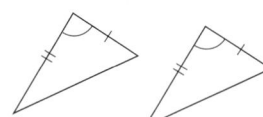

A. 11.5 mm   **B.** 11 mm
C. 10.5 mm   **D.** 10 mm

4. Which can you use to prove that two lines are parallel? **G**
  F. supplementary corresponding angles
  G. congruent alternate interior angles
  H. congruent vertical angles
  I. congruent same-side interior angles

5. How can you prove that the two triangles are congruent? **C**

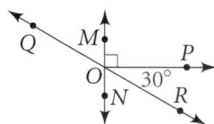

A. ASA   **B.** SSS   **C.** SAS   **D.** CPCTC

6. What is the measure of $\angle MOQ$? **I**

F. 15   **G.** 30   **H.** 45   **I.** 60

Quantitative Comparison

Compare the boxed quantity in Column A with the boxed quantity in Column B. Choose the best answer.

  A. The quantity in Column A is greater.
  B. The quantity in Column B is greater.
  C. The two quantities are equal.
  D. The relationship cannot be determined from the information given.

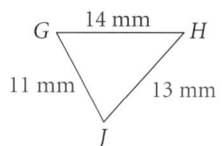

Column A	Column B
A 7. $m\angle G$	$m\angle H$
B 8. $m\angle G$	$m\angle J$
B 9. $m\angle H$	$m\angle J$

Gridded Response

10. In the parallelogram, DB is 15. What is DE? **7.5**

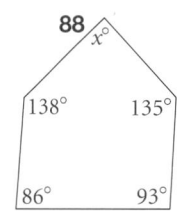

x^2 **11. Algebra** What is the value of x?

12–13. See back of book.

Short Response

12. In rectangle $ABCD$, $AC = 5(x - 2)$ and $BD = 3(x + 2)$. What is the value of x?

Extended Response

13. A parallelogram has vertices $L(-2, 5)$, $M(3, 3)$, $N(1, 0)$. What are possible coordinates for its

Resources

Teaching Resources
Cumulative Review
Quarter 2 Test, Forms A & B
Mid-Course Test, Forms A & B

Reaching All Students
Spanish Cumulative Review
Spanish Quarter 2 Tests
Spanish Mid-Course Tests
Informal Geometry
    Mid-Course Tests

PRENTICE HALL
ASSESSMENT SYSTEM

Standardized Test Prep
• Ch. 6 standardized Test Practice
Assessment Masters
• Cumulative Review
• Quarter 2 Test, Forms A & B
• Mid-Course Test, Forms A & B
Computer Test Generator CD
• Standardized Test Practice

www.PHSchool.com
• Standardized Test Practice
• Resources

Plus TEXT

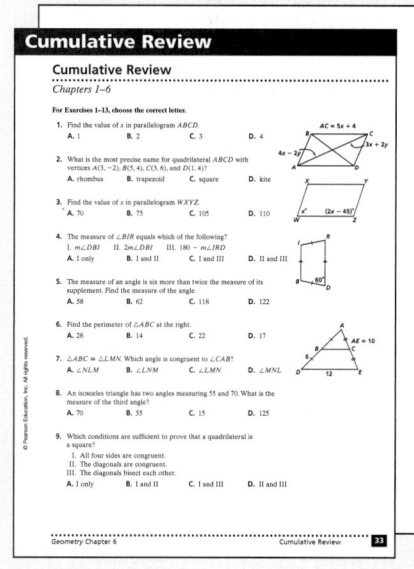

Item	1	2	3	4	5	6	7	8	9	10	11	12	13
Lesson	6-1	4-5	5-1	3-2	4-2	1-4	5-5	5-5	5-5	6-2	3-4	5-4	3-7

Mathematically Inclined

In this activity students apply their knowledge of triangles, medians, and centroids.

Connecting to Prior Knowledge

Have students brainstorm why many spinning objects have circular designs. Have them make a list of the objects they discuss, such as rotors and tornadoes.

Teaching Notes

Have a volunteer read aloud the introductory paragraph. Ask: *Do you remember how hard it was to balance when you were learning to ride a bicycle?* Have students share their recollections with the class.

To find the centroid of a quadrilateral, draw a diagonal to form two triangles, then find the centroid of each triangle and draw the line through them. Then draw a different diagonal to form two triangles, find the centroid of each and draw the line through them. The centroid of the quadrilateral is the point of intersection of the two lines.

Tactile Learners

If possible, provide a gyroscope for students to examine and test.

Sports Connection

Have students research how a figure skater can speed up or slow down a spin.

Science Connection

Point out that Earth is not a perfect sphere but is actually flattened out at the poles, making it appear to have an *equatorial bulge.* Also, the Southern Hemisphere is slightly larger—Earth has a 'pear' shape.

Point of Balance

Applying Theorems About Polygons For an object to spin smoothly, its weight must be evenly distributed around its central axis. A toy

top, an ice skater, and a carousel all spin around a central axis. If the spin goes slightly out of alignment, the spinning object begins to wobble and may eventually tip over.

Gyroscopes

A gyroscope is a wheel mounted in a set of rings so that the axis of the wheel can turn in any direction. When the wheel spins rapidly, a small gyroscope becomes so stable that it can balance on the tip of a pencil.

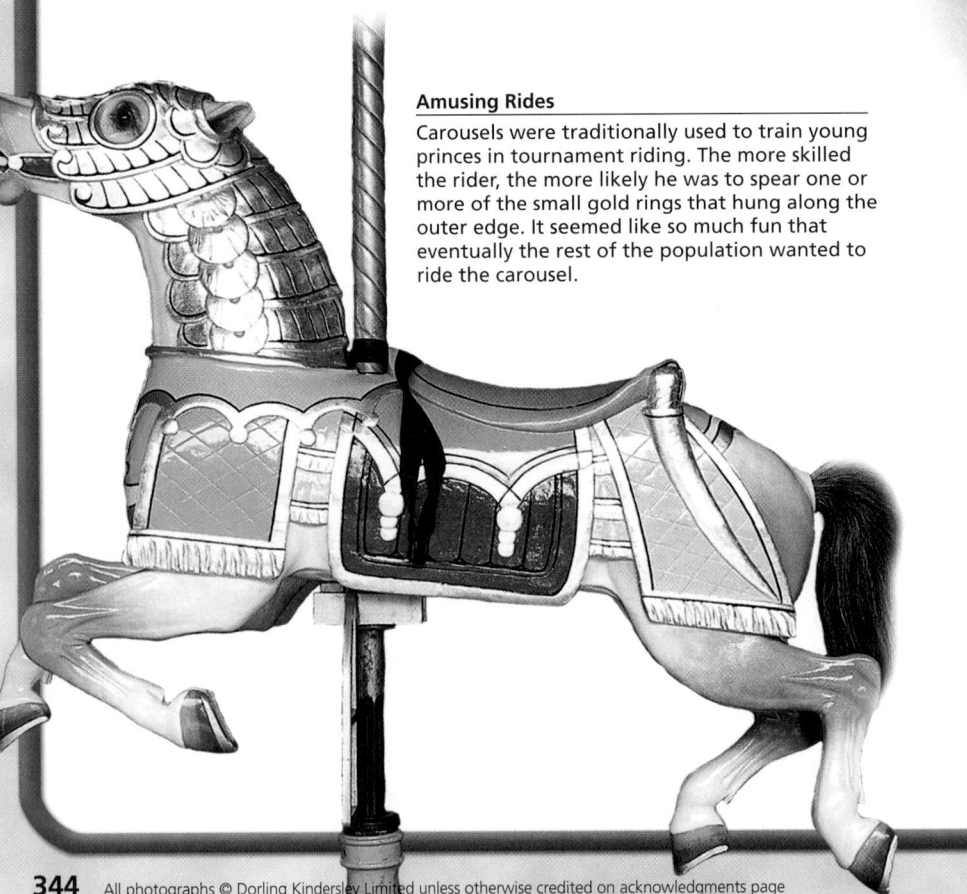

Amusing Rides

Carousels were traditionally used to train young princes in tournament riding. The more skilled the rider, the more likely he was to spear one or more of the small gold rings that hung along the outer edge. It seemed like so much fun that eventually the rest of the population wanted to ride the carousel.

The Spin

Figure skaters at the Olympic Games compete in a short program (33.3% of the total score) and a long program (66.7%). A short program can last a maximum of 2 min 40 s and must include three spins.

344

The Bicycle as a Gyroscope

The spinning wheels of a bicycle act as gyroscopes and help to keep the bike upright. Like all gyroscopes, the wheels tend to remain spinning in the same plane, giving the bicycle stability.

Earth as a Gyroscope

The axis of Earth is remarkably stable, but our planet does wobble slightly. It takes 25,800 years for each circular wobble. This wobble is largely caused by the gravitational pull of the sun and moon on Earth's equatorial bulge.

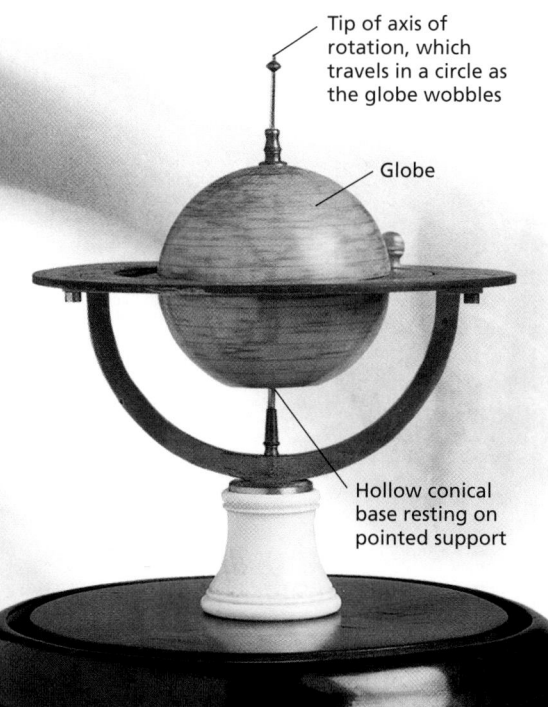

Tip of axis of rotation, which travels in a circle as the globe wobbles

Globe

Hollow conical base resting on pointed support

Activity

Materials: cardboard, straightedge, scissors, compass, graph paper, pencil

Draw a large triangle on the cardboard. Construct its medians. Locate the centroid, the point at which the medians meet. Cut out the triangle.

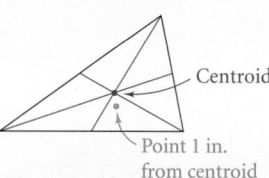

Centroid

Point 1 in. from centroid

a. Balance your triangle by placing the centroid on the point of your pencil and pushing down slightly to dent the cardboard. Give your triangle a gentle spin and watch it as it moves. Describe the movement.

b. Locate a point 1 in. from the centroid. Support your triangle on your pencil at this point. Give your triangle a gentle spin and watch it as it moves. Describe any differences from its movement in part (a).

c. Suppose the coordinates of the vertices of a triangle are $(0, 0)$, $(16, 0)$, and $(20, 18)$. Find the coordinates of the centroid. Test your work by making a graph of the triangle. Glue the graph to a piece of cardboard and then cut out the triangle. Try to balance the triangle at the coordinates you calculated.

d. Draw a large convex quadrilateral on the cardboard. Locate its centroid. (See page 336, Exercise 38.) Cut out the quadrilateral and test its balance with spins as described in parts (a) and (b). Describe what you find.

 Take It to the NET For more information about objects that spin, go to **www.PHSchool.com**.
Web Code: afe-0653

pages 344–345   **Real-World Snapshots**

Activity
a–b. Answers may vary.

Sample:
a. The triangle wobbles slightly.
b. The triangle does not balance on the pencil.
c. (12, 6)

d. Answers may vary.
Sample: The quadrilateral spins smoothly with the pencil point at the centroid. The quadrilateral wobbles with the pencil tip 1 in. from the centroid.

Chapter at a Glance

North Carolina Objectives

7-1	Areas of Parallelograms and Triangles	1.02
NCTM 2, 3, 4, 6, 8, 9, 10	V Area of a Parallelogram V Area of a Triangle	

7-2	The Pythagorean Theorem and Its Converse	2.03a
NCTM 2, 3, 4, 6, 7, 8, 9, 10	V The Pythagorean Theorem V The Converse of the Pythagorean Theorem	

7-3	Special Right Triangles	2.03a
NCTM 2, 3, 4, 6, 8, 9, 10	V Using 45°-45°-90° Triangles V Using 30°-60°-90° Triangles	

7-4	Areas of Trapezoids, Rhombuses, and Kites	1.02
NCTM 1, 2, 3, 4, 6, 8, 9, 10	V Area of a Trapezoid V Finding Areas of Rhombuses and Kites	

7-5	Areas of Regular Polygons	1.02
NCTM 2, 3, 4, 6, 7, 8, 9, 10	V Areas of Regular Polygons	

7-6	Circles and Arcs	1.02
NCTM 2, 3, 4, 5, 6, 7, 8, 9, 10	V Central Angles and Arcs V Circumference and Arc Length	

7-7	Areas of Circles and Sectors	1.02
NCTM 2, 3, 4, 6, 7, 8, 9, 10	V Finding Areas of Circles and Parts of Circles	

7-8	Geometric Probability	1.03
NCTM 3, 5, 6, 7, 8, 9, 10	V Using Segment and Area Models	

NCTM STANDARDS 2000

1	Number and Operations	6	Problem Solving
2	Algebra	7	Reasoning and Proof
3	Geometry	8	Communication
4	Measurement	9	Connections
5	Data Analysis and Probability	10	Representation

Pacing Options

This chart suggests pacing only for the lessons and their parts. It is provided as a possible guide. It will help you determine how much time you have in your schedule to cover other components, such as the features, Chapter Review and Chapter Test.

Day	Traditional 45 min.	Two-Year 45 min.	Block 90 min.
1	7-1 V	7-1 V	7-1 V V
2	7-1 V	7-1 V	7-2 V V
3	7-2 V	7-1 V	7-3 V V
4	7-2 V	7-2 V	7-4 V V
5	7-3 V	7-2 V	7-5 V
6	7-3 V	7-2 V	7-6 V V
7	7-4 V	7-2 V	7-7 V
8	7-4 V	7-3 V	7-8 V
9	7-5 V	7-3 V	
10	7-6 V	7-3 V	
11	7-6 V	7-3 V	
12	7-7 V	7-4 V	
13	7-8 V	7-4 V	
14	7-8 V	7-4 V	
15		7-5 V	
16		7-5 V	
17		7-6 V	
18		7-6 V	
19		7-6 V	
20		7-6 V	
21		7-7 V	
22		7-7 V	
23		7-8 V	
24		7-8 V	

NAEP Correlation (National Assessment of Educational Progress 2000 Mathematics Objectives)

7-1	7-2	7-3	7-4	7-5	7-6	7-7	7-8
M4a, M5, G2	M1, G6b	G6b	N4a, M5, G6b	M4a	M4a, D2b	N3d, M4a, G2	M5, D11a

N = Number Sense, Properties, and Operations; M = Measurement; G = Geometry and Spatial Sense; D = Data Analysis, Statistics, and Probability; A = Algebra and Functions

Math Background

Chapter Overview

This chapter develops a number of area formulas, principally for triangles, quadrilaterals, and circles, but also for regular polygons and sectors. Several derivations are presented that students should be encouraged to understand because recalling the derivations will help them write the formulas. Lengths and areas are used to evaluate geometric models of probabilities.

Areas of Parallelograms and Triangles   7-1

Common formulas may have different variable names. Rectangle dimensions may be named "width and height," "length and width," or as in this lesson, "base and height." The name of a variable does not affect its use in a formula. The area of a rectangle in square units is the product of its two dimensions, no matter how they are named.

Most students already will be familiar with the formula $A = \frac{1}{2}bh$ for the area of a triangle, but they may not have realized that any triangle can be represented as half of a parallelogram. Students who have difficulty determining appropriate units of measurement should be encouraged to write units in equations; for example, 7 m + 2 m = $(7 + 2)$ m = 9 m and 7 m $\times$ 2 m = $(7 \times 2)(m \times m) = 14 \text{ m}^2$.

The Pythagorean Theorem and Its Converse   7-2

The Pythagorean Theorem, known in Babylonia before the sixteenth century B.C. and in India before 800 B.C., is among the oldest and most famous theorems in mathematics. It relates to Fermat's Last Theorem *(The equation $x^n + y^n = z^n$ is not solvable in integers* x, y, *and* z, *for any integer n > 2),* which remained unproved for over a century until Andrew Wiles (and others) finally proved it in 1993–1994, winning the Royal Academy at Göttingen's monetary prize for the first solution. There are hundreds of proofs for the Pythagorean Theorem, dating from various periods and many countries; for example, Plato, Socrates, Sir Isaac Newton, Galileo, Copernicus, James A. Garfield (the twentieth president of the United States), and numerous high school students have published proofs.

Students may need careful drawings and practical illustrations to help them distinguish which are leg measures and which are hypotenuse measures in real-world applications. Remind them that simplest radical form expresses irrational numbers exactly, but a calculator computation of simplest radical form is approximate.

Beginning with a construction (to prove the Converse of the Pythagorean Theorem) is probably a new technique for all students. Suggest that any students who made a hinge tool, as described in the Math Background for Lesson 5-5, use it to illustrate Theorems 7-6 and 7-7.

Special Right Triangles   7-3

Encourage students to draw a diagonal of a square to derive the Pythagorean triple 1, 1, $\sqrt{2}$ and to draw an altitude of an equilateral triangle to derive the Pythagorean triple 1, $\sqrt{3}$, 2. Point out that Pythagorean triples for 45°-45°-90° and 30°-60°-90° triangles *always* involve at least one irrational number.

Areas of Trapezoids, Rhombuses, and Kites   7-4

Because a diagonal of a trapezoid separates it into two triangles of the same height, students may build on their knowledge of the formula for the area of a triangle and write the area of the trapezoid as $\frac{1}{2}b_1h + \frac{1}{2}b_2h$. Students who explored the alternative hierarchy in the Math Background for Lesson 6-1 should observe that the formula for the area of a trapezoid also holds for the area of a parallelogram: $b = b_1 = b_2$, so $\frac{1}{2}b_1h + \frac{1}{2}b_2h = bh$.

Encourage students to practice visualizing the rectangle circumscribing a kite or rhombus. It clearly illustrates the relationship between the area of the kite or rhombus and the area of the rectangle.

Areas of Regular Polygons   7-5

Students who easily master Example 4 might enjoy applying Heron's formula (found above Exercises 47–51 in Lesson 7-1) to Example 4 and then comparing the results.

Circles, Arcs, and Areas of Circles and Sectors   7-6, 7-7

In 1999 Japanese mathematicians used a supercomputer to calculate the value of π to more than 206 billion decimal places, but the record for pencil-and-paper calculation (707 decimal places) was set by William Shanks in 1874; in 1945 computers showed that he had made a mistake in place 527! Most students have used $\frac{22}{7}$, 3.14, or even 3 as estimates for π. In 240 B.C. Archimedes used $\frac{223}{71}$ to estimate π, and in A.D. 480 Wang Fan used $\frac{355}{113}$, which is still the best fractional estimate of π.

Circumference and area formulas may be distinguished by using diameter to compute circumference ($C = \pi d$) and radius to compute area ($A = \pi r^2$). As a further help, the length of $\overset{\frown}{EF}$ may be written as $\frac{m\overset{\frown}{EF}}{360} \cdot C$ and the area of sector *EOF* as $\frac{m\overset{\frown}{EF}}{360} \cdot A$. Students may find it useful to repeat "segment area equals sector area minus triangle area."

Geometric Probability   7-8

Interpreting real-world events in terms of game theory and geometric models intuitively appeals to many students. Designing such models is much more difficult than computing their associated probabilities.

Ongoing Assessment and Intervention

Tools for Monitoring Student Progress

The Prentice Hall *Geometry* program provides you with many options for assessment in the Student Edition, the Teacher's Edition and the teaching resources. From these options, you may choose instructional materials and techniques that are appropriate for your students and support your district's curriculum requirements.

Instant Check System™ in Chapter 7

Allows students to check their own learning before, during, and after each lesson.

Diagnosing Readiness before the chapter (p. 346)

Check Skills You'll Need exercises in each lesson (pp. 348, 357, 366, 373, 380, 386, 395, 402)

Check Understanding questions with each Example (pp. 349, 350, 351, 358, 359, 360, 365, 366, 367, 368, 369, 374, 375, 380, 381, 382, 387, 388, 389, 396, 397, 402, 403, 404)

Checkpoint Quiz (pp. 372 and 400)

 Test Prep in Chapter 7

Teaches students strategies and gives them practice with all the test item formats they will encounter on state tests and standardized national exams.

Standardized Test Prep exercises in each lesson (pp. 354, 364, 371, 378, 385, 393, 400, 407)

Test-Taking Strategies (p. 408: Finding Multiple Correct Answers)

Standardized Test Prep (p. 413: Reading Comprehension)

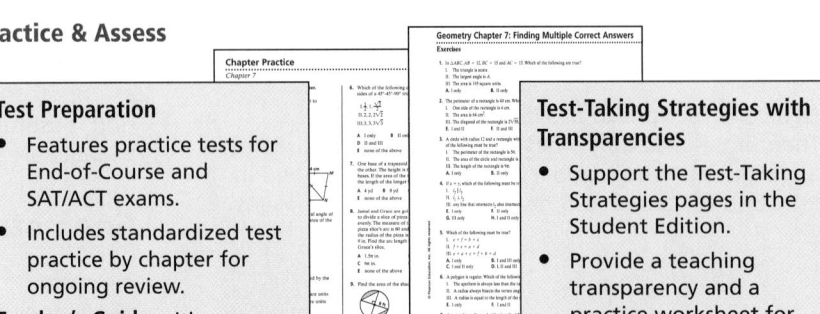
All your assessment needs in one place!

Program Assessment

Assess student progress throughout the *Geometry* text with blackline masters and CD-ROM.

Assessment Resources

- Checkpoint Quizzes 1 & 2
- Chapter Test, Forms A & B
- Chapter Alternative Assessment

Spanish versions available. Tests for Informal Geometry also available.

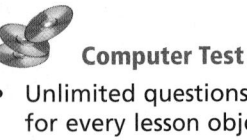

Computer Test Generator

- Unlimited questions of varying difficulty for every lesson objective.
- Create your own practice sheets, quizzes, and tests, or use the pre-made Chapter Tests.
- Diagnose readiness with questions on prerequisite skills.
- Prepare students by making tests based on standardized test objectives.
- Access Algebra 1, Geometry, and Algebra 2 content—all on one CD-ROM.

Test Preparation

A three-step approach to preparing students for high stakes, national, and state exams.

❶ Diagnose & Prescribe

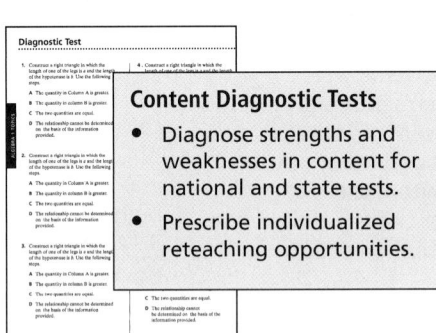

Content Diagnostic Tests
- Diagnose strengths and weaknesses in content for national and state tests.
- Prescribe individualized reteaching opportunities.

❷ Review & Reteach

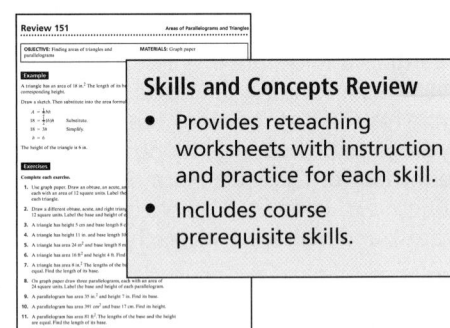

Skills and Concepts Review
- Provides reteaching worksheets with instruction and practice for each skill.
- Includes course prerequisite skills.

❸ Practice & Assess

Test Preparation
- Features practice tests for End-of-Course and SAT/ACT exams.
- Includes standardized test practice by chapter for ongoing review.

Teacher's Guide with answers and correlations.

Test-Taking Strategies with Transparencies
- Support the Test-Taking Strategies pages in the Student Edition.
- Provide a teaching transparency and a practice worksheet for each strategy.

Reaching All Students

Support in the Student Text and Additional Resources

The textbook, the iText, and other technology components provide numerous opportunities to reach students of various ability levels and learning styles. Each Teacher's Edition lesson suggests how you can help *all* your students be successful and understand the mathematics in Chapter 7.

Below Level

Student Edition
- Diagnosing Readiness*: p. 346
- Check Skills You'll Need*: pp. 348, 357, 366, 373, 380, 386, 395, 402

Reteaching
Chapter 7 Support File: pp. 10–17

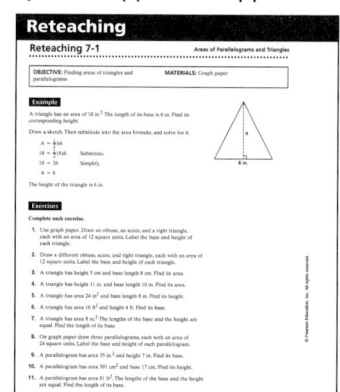

Informal Geometry Planning Guide
Chapter 7 Lesson Plans: pp. 39–46
Chapter 7 Tests: pp. 103–106

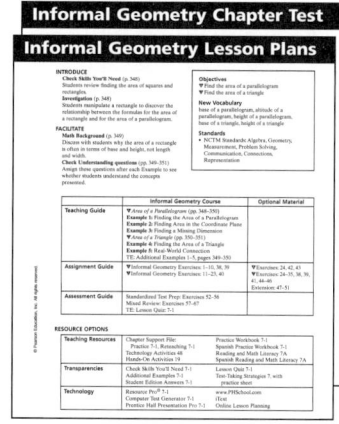

* Can be used with all ability levels to ensure mastery of prerequisite skills.

Advanced Learners

Student Edition
- Challenge exercises: pp. 353, 363, 371, 378, 384, 392, 399, 406

Enrichment
Chapter 7 Support File: pp. 18–25

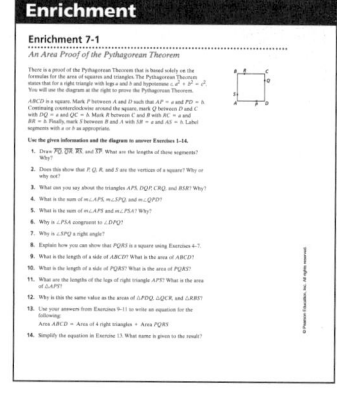

Reading and Math Literacy

Student Edition
- Vocabulary: pp. 347, 409, *plus* in every Lesson Preview
- Reading Math: pp. 349, 362, 365, 374, 380, 386, 402, 409
- Illustrated Glossary: pp. 741–777

Reading and Math Literacy Masters
Chapter 7: pp. 25–28

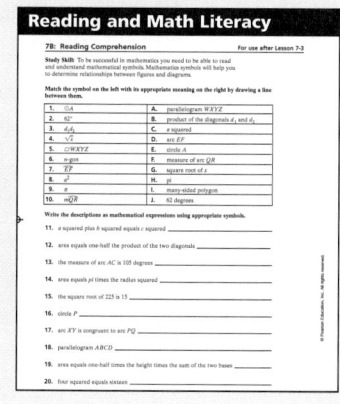

English Learners

Student Edition
- English/Spanish Illustrated Glossary: pp. 741–777

Workbook and Masters
Spanish Practice Workbook: pp. 39–46
Spanish Reading and Math Literacy Masters: pp. 25–28

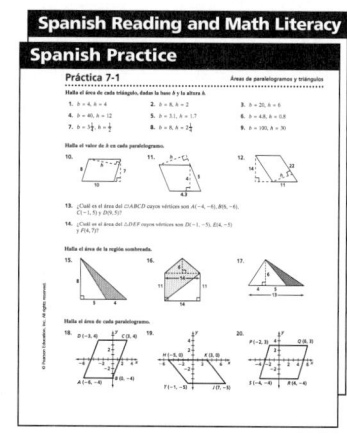

Learning Styles

Student Edition
- Investigation: pp. 348, 356, 373, 395
- Technology: pp. 352, 355, 358, 365, 367, 369, 381, 382, 388, 396, 397, 401, 406
- Writing: pp. 353, 362, 378, 383, 392, 399, 406, 412

Activity Masters
Hands-On Activities: 19, 20, 21
Technology Activities: 48, 49

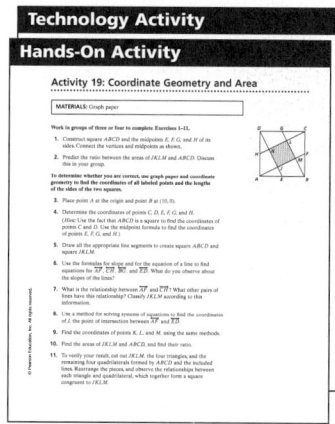

Program Resources

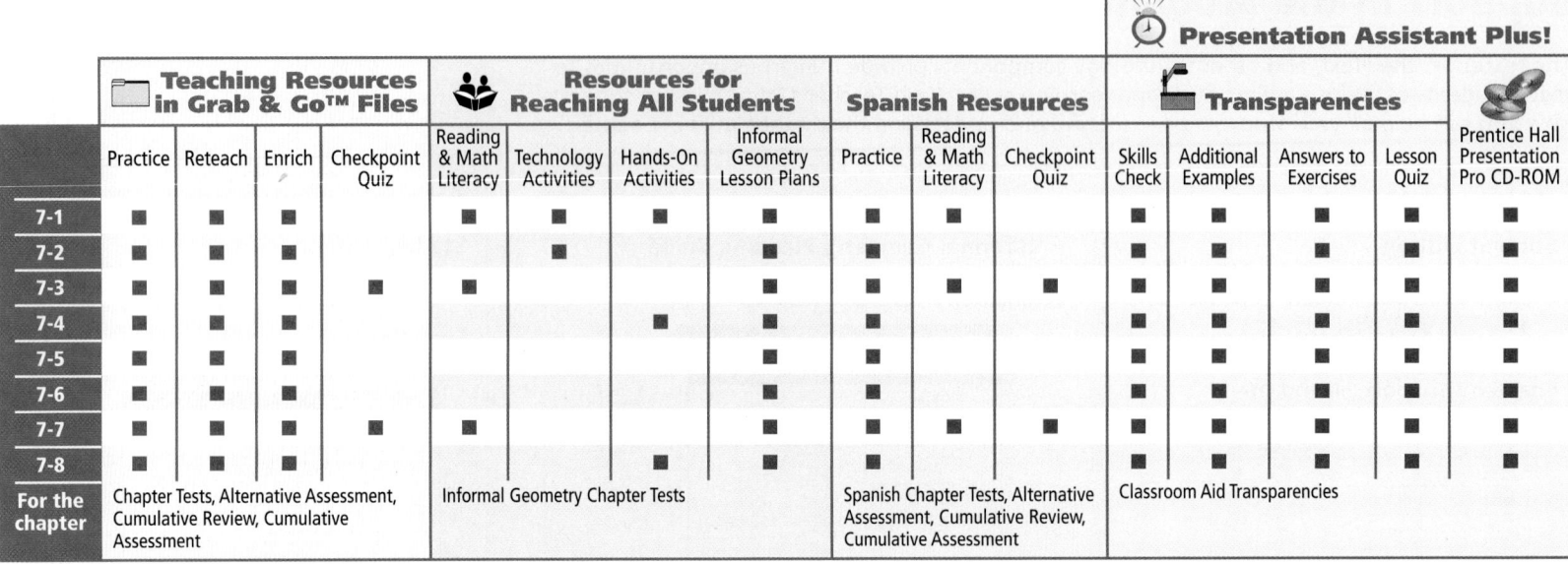

	Teaching Resources in Grab & Go™ Files				Resources for Reaching All Students				Spanish Resources			Transparencies				Prentice Hall Presentation Pro CD-ROM
	Practice	Reteach	Enrich	Checkpoint Quiz	Reading & Math Literacy	Technology Activities	Hands-On Activities	Informal Geometry Lesson Plans	Practice	Reading & Math Literacy	Checkpoint Quiz	Skills Check	Additional Examples	Answers to Exercises	Lesson Quiz	
7-1	■	■	■		■	■	■	■	■			■	■	■	■	■
7-2	■	■	■			■		■	■			■	■	■	■	■
7-3	■	■	■	■	■			■	■		■	■	■	■	■	■
7-4	■	■	■				■	■	■			■	■	■	■	■
7-5	■	■	■					■	■			■	■	■	■	■
7-6	■	■	■					■	■			■	■	■	■	■
7-7	■	■	■		■			■	■			■	■	■	■	■
7-8	■	■	■				■	■	■			■	■	■	■	■
For the chapter	Chapter Tests, Alternative Assessment, Cumulative Review, Cumulative Assessment				Informal Geometry Chapter Tests				Spanish Chapter Tests, Alternative Assessment, Cumulative Review, Cumulative Assessment			Classroom Aid Transparencies				

Also available for use with the chapter:

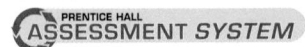 *see page 346C.*

- Practice Workbook
- Solution Key

- For teacher support and access to student Web site materials, use Web Code afk-5500.
- For additional online and technology resources, see below.

 Technology

 Online and on CD-ROM

Complete Interactive Student Text online and on CD-ROM—with instant feedback assessment, tutorial help, dynamic activities, instructional and real-world videos, audio, and additional practice.

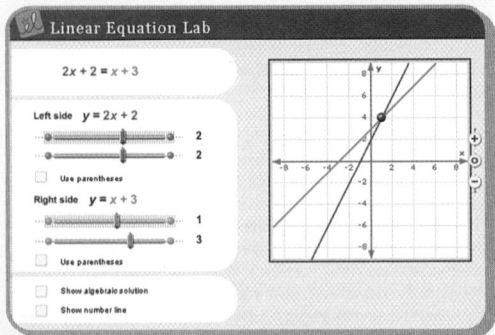

www.PHSchool.com
For Students

Use **Web Codes** for easy access to online activities, chapter projects, self-grading lesson quizzes and chapter tests, vocabulary quizzes, updated data sources, graphing calculator procedures, and more.

PH SuccessNet **For Teachers**

Online lesson planning with built-in state correlations, all the teaching resources, complete reference library, your own calendar and Teacher Web page, professional development, and more.

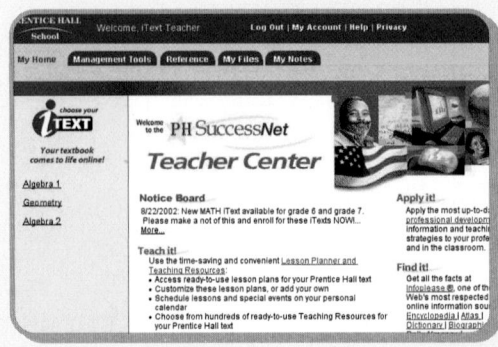

Presentation Assistant Plus!

The Prentice Hall *Presentation Assistant Plus!* provides you with the material you need to teach a lesson from beginning to end. Two easy-to-use formats—Transparencies and CD-ROM—allow you to present a lesson the way you are most comfortable.

Transparencies

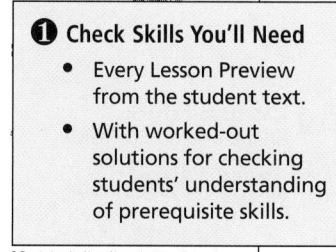

❶ Check Skills You'll Need
- Every Lesson Preview from the student text.
- With worked-out solutions for checking students' understanding of prerequisite skills.

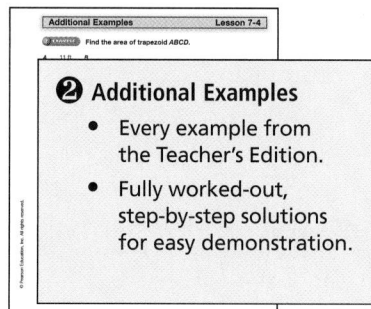

❷ Additional Examples
- Every example from the Teacher's Edition.
- Fully worked-out, step-by-step solutions for easy demonstration.

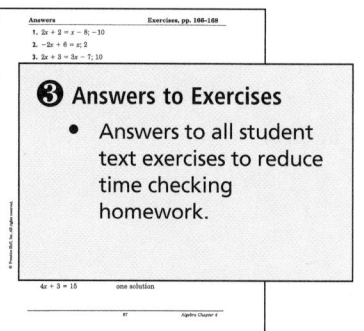

❸ Answers to Exercises
- Answers to all student text exercises to reduce time checking homework.

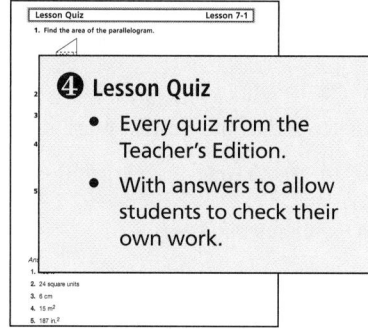

❹ Lesson Quiz
- Every quiz from the Teacher's Edition.
- With answers to allow students to check their own work.

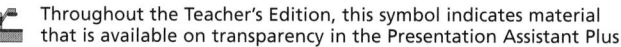

Throughout the Teacher's Edition, this symbol indicates material that is available on transparency in the Presentation Assistant Plus!

Prentice Hall Presentation Pro CD-ROM

- Includes all Transparencies.
- Conveniently organized by lesson so you can easily ❶ Introduce, ❷ Teach, ❸ Check Homework, and ❹ Assess each lesson.
- Animated examples allow step-by-step instruction at your own pace.
- Easy to edit so you can create custom presentations.

Teaching Chapter 7 Using Presentation Assistant Plus!

	❶ Introduce	❷ Teach	❸ Check Homework	❹ Assess
	Check Skills You'll Need	Additional Examples	Student Edition Answers	Lesson Quiz
7-1	p. 39	pp. 99–102	✔	p. 114
7-2	p. 40	pp. 103–106	✔	p. 115
7-3	p. 41	pp. 107–110	✔	p. 116
7-4	p. 42	pp. 111–114	✔	p. 117
7-5	p. 43	pp. 115–117	✔	p. 118
7-6	p. 44	pp. 118–121	✔	p. 119
7-7	p. 45	pp. 122–123	✔	p. 120
7-8	p. 46	pp. 124–126	✔	p. 121

Prentice Hall Presentation Pro

CD-ROM with dynamic PowerPoint® presentations for every lesson. Helps you introduce and develop concepts, check homework, and assess progress. Part of Presentation Assistant Plus! *(See above.)*

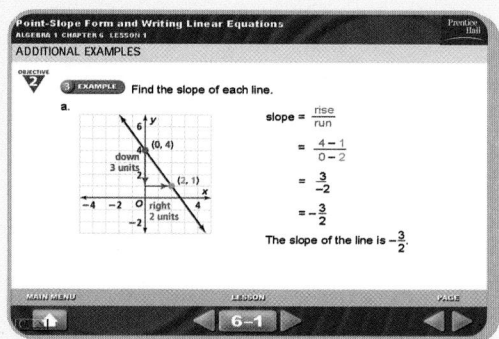

Computer Test Generator

CD-ROM to create practice sheets and tests for course objectives and standardized tests. Includes Instant Chapter Tests™, online testing, and student reports. Part of the PH Assessment System. *(See page 346C.)*

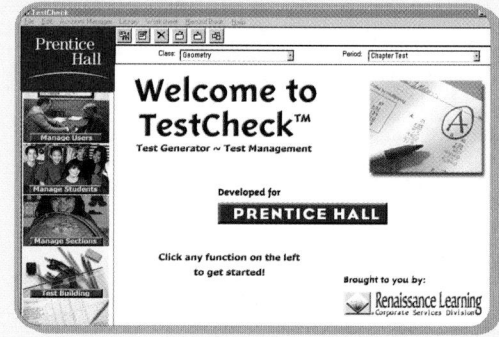

Resource Pro® with Planning Express®

CD-ROM with a lesson planning tool that allows you to import state and local objectives. Includes electronic versions of all the teaching resources.

Area

Chapter 7

 Diagnosing Readiness

Students will find answers to these exercises in the back of their textbooks.

For intervention, direct students to:

Squaring Numbers and Finding Square Roots
Skills Handbook, p. 715

Simplifying Radicals
Skills Handbook, p. 717

Classifying Quadrilaterals
Lesson 6-1: Example 1
Exercises 1–6
Extra Practice, p. 695

Probability
Skills Handbook, p. 724.

Where You've Been

- In Chapter 1, you learned two postulates about area and how to find the areas of rectangles and circles.

- In Chapters 3 and 6, you learned how to classify polygons, including special quadrilaterals.

- In Chapter 4, you learned conditions necessary for two polygons, particularly triangles, to be congruent.

 Instant self-check
online and on CD-ROM

Diagnosing Readiness   (For help, go to the Lesson in green.)

Squaring Numbers and Finding Square Roots (Skills Handbook page 715)

Simplify.

1. 3^2 **9**   **2.** 8^2 **64**   **3.** 12^2 **144**   **4.** 15^2 **225**

5. $\sqrt{16}$ **4**   **6.** $\sqrt{64}$ **8**   **7.** $\sqrt{100}$ **10**   **8.** $\sqrt{169}$ **13**

Solve each quadratic equation. Round to the nearest tenth or whole number.

9. $x^2 = 36$ **±6**   **10.** $a^2 = 104$ **±10.2**   **11.** $x^2 - 48 = 0$ **±6.9**   **12.** $b^2 - 65 = 0$ **±8.1**

Simplifying Radicals (Skills Handbook page 717)

Simplify. Leave your answer in simplest radical form.

13. $\sqrt{8}$ $2\sqrt{2}$ **14.** $\sqrt{27}$ $3\sqrt{3}$ **15.** $\sqrt{48}$ $4\sqrt{3}$ **16.** $6\sqrt{72}$ $36\sqrt{2}$

Probability (Skills Handbook page 724)

A jar contains 3 red balls and 2 green balls. You draw one ball at random.
Determine the probability of selecting a ball of the given color.

17. red $\frac{3}{5}$ **18.** green $\frac{2}{5}$ **19.** blue **0**   **20.** red or green **1**

Classifying Quadrilaterals (Lesson 6-1)

Classify each quadrilateral as specifically as possible.

21.  rhombus   **22.** 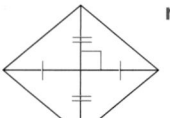 parallelogram   **23.** rhombus

Area

Key Vocabulary

- adjacent arcs (p. 387)
- apothem of a regular polygon (p. 380)
- arc length (p. 389)
- central angle (p. 386)
- circumference (p. 388)
- concentric circles (p. 388)
- congruent arcs (p. 389)
- diameter (p. 386)
- geometric probability (p. 402)
- major arc (p. 387)
- minor arc (p. 387)
- Pythagorean triple (p. 357)
- radius (p. 386)
- radius of a regular polygon (p. 380)
- sector of a circle (p. 396)
- segment of a circle (p. 397)
- semicircle (p. 387)

347

Where You're Going

- In this chapter, you will learn how finding the area of a rectangle can help you find the areas of parallelograms and triangles.
- You will learn the Pythagorean Theorem and its converse.
- You will use the Pythagorean Theorem to find relationships in special right triangles.
- You will also learn how to find the areas of special quadrilaterals and regular polygons.

Real-World Connection Applying what you learned, you will find the distance to Earth's horizon from the Hubble Space Telescope on page 363.

Chapter 7 Overview

In this chapter, students will use concepts from their study of triangles and quadrilaterals to develop area formulas, first for quadrilaterals and then for circles. The special relationships in 30°-60°-90° and 45°-45°-90° triangles will be derived, and students will have an opportunity to prove the Pythagorean Theorem using areas. Special area formulas will be derived for parallelograms, rhombuses, trapezoids, and kites. Finally, students will consider arcs and sectors of circles and apply their areas to geometric probability.

Reading Math
Reading for Problem Solving, p. 365

Vocabulary
A complete list of terms, plus vocabulary exercises, appears in the Chapter Review, p. 409.

Illustrated Glossary
Examples for each vocabulary term, plus definitions in both English and Spanish, appear starting on p. 741.

Test-Taking Strategies
Finding Multiple Correct Answers, p. 408

Real-World Connections
Some of the applications you will find in this chapter are design (7-3), geography (7-4), racing (7-5), food (7-7), and carnival games (7-8).

www.PHSchool.com
Internet support for this chapter includes:
- Self-grading Vocabulary and Chapter 7 Tests
- Chapter Project
- Chapter Planner
- Ch. 7 Resources

Plus

Lesson Preview

Check Skills You'll Need

Finding the Area of a Rectangle
Lesson 1-7: Example 4
Exercises 20–26
Extra Practice, p. 690

Lesson Resources

📁 **Teaching Resources**
Practice, Reteaching, Enrichment

👥 **Reaching All Students**
Practice Workbook 7-1
Spanish Practice Workbook 7-1
Reading and Math Literacy 7A
Spanish Reading & Literacy 7A
Technology Activities 49
Hands-On Activities 19
Informal Geometry Planning
   Guide 7-1

⏰ **Presentation Assistant Plus!**
Transparencies
• Check Skills You'll Need 7-1
• Additional Examples 7-1
• Student Edition Answers 7-1
• Lesson Quiz 7-1
PH Presentation Pro CD 7-1

PRENTICE HALL
ASSESSMENT *SYSTEM*

Computer Test Generator CD

💿 **Technology**
Resource Pro® CD-ROM
Computer Test Generator CD
Prentice Hall Presentation Pro CD

🖥️ **www.PHSchool.com**
Student Site
• Teacher Web Code: afk-5500
• Self-grading Lesson Quiz
Teacher Center
• Lesson Planner
• Resources

Plus

Areas of Parallelograms and Triangles

North Carolina Objectives

1.02   Use length, area, and volume of geometric figures to solve problems. Include perimeter, area, and volume of composite figures.

Lesson Preview

What You'll Learn

OBJECTIVE 1 To find the area of a parallelogram

OBJECTIVE 2 To find the area of a triangle

. . . And Why

To find the force of wind against the side of a building, as in Example 5

✓ **Check Skills You'll Need**   (For help, go to Lesson 1-7.)

Find the area of each figure.   1. 25 cm^2 2. 28 in.^{2} 4. $\frac{3}{2}$ ft^2

1. a square with 5-cm sides   2. a rectangle with base 4 in. and height 7 in.

3. a 4.6 m-by-2.5 m rectangle   4. a rectangle with length 3 ft and width $\frac{1}{2}$ ft
   11.5 m^2

Each rectangle is divided into two congruent triangles. Find the area of each triangle.

5.   6 units^2 6. 2 units^2 7. 8 units^2

New Vocabulary   • base of a parallelogram   • altitude of a parallelogram
                   • height of a parallelogram   • base of a triangle
                   • height of a triangle

OBJECTIVE 1
Area of a Parallelogram

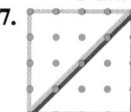 **Interactive lesson includes instant self-check, tutorials, and activities.**

The rectangle and ▱ have the same base length, height, and area. Their shapes are different.

Investigation: Area of a Parallelogram

• Cut a rectangle out of centimeter grid paper by cutting along grid lines.

• Record the base, height, and area of the rectangle.

• Cut a right triangle from one end of the rectangle. Tape the triangle to the opposite end to form a parallelogram as shown below.

• Compare the original rectangle with the parallelogram formed. List the ways the rectangle and the parallelogram are the same and the ways they are different. **See left.**

348   Chapter 7 Area

Ongoing Assessment and Intervention

Before the Lesson
Diagnose prerequisite skills using:
• Check Skills You'll Need

During the Lesson
Monitor progress using:
• Check Understanding
• Additional Examples
• Standardized Test Prep

After the Lesson
Assess knowledge using:
• Lesson Quiz
• Computer Test Generator CD

The picture on page 348 shows that a parallelogram with the same base and height as a rectangle has the same area as the rectangle.

 Key Concepts

| Theorem 7-1 | Area of a Rectangle |

The area of a rectangle is the product of its base and height.

$$A = bh$$

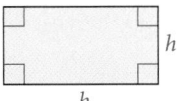

| Theorem 7-2 | Area of a Parallelogram |

The area of a parallelogram is the product of a base and the corresponding height.

$$A = bh$$

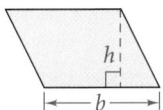

 Reading Math

The term *base* is used to represent both a segment and its length.

A **base of a parallelogram** is any of its sides. The corresponding **altitude** is a segment perpendicular to the line containing that base drawn from the side opposite the base. The **height** is the length of an altitude.

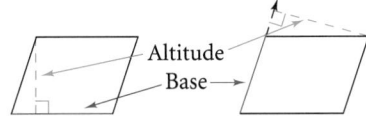

1 EXAMPLE Finding the Area of a Parallelogram

Find the area of each parallelogram.

a.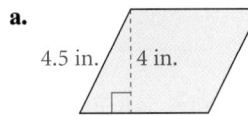

b.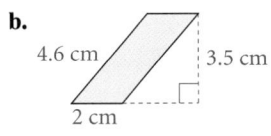

You are given each height. Choose the corresponding side to use as the base.

$A = bh$ $A = bh$
$= 5(4) = 20$ ←Substitute.→ $= 2(3.5) = 7$
The area is 20 in.^{2}.   The area is 7 cm^2.

✔ **Check Understanding** ① Find the area of a parallelogram with base 12 m and height 9 m. **108 m^2**

2 EXAMPLE Finding Area in the Coordinate Plane

Find the area of ▱*PQRS* with vertices $P(1, 2)$, $Q(6, 2)$, $R(8, 5)$, and $S(3, 5)$.

Graph ▱*PQRS*. If you choose $\overline{PQ}$ as the base, then the height is 3.

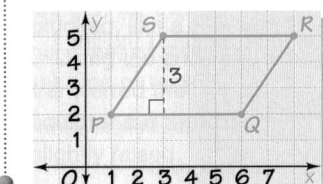

$b = PQ = 5$
$h = 3$
$A = bh = 5(3)$
$= 15$

The area of ▱*PQRS* is 15 square units.

✔ **Check Understanding** ② Find the area of ▱*EFGH* with vertices $E(-4, 3)$, $F(0, 3)$, $G(1, -2)$, and $H(-3, -2)$. **20 units^2**

Lesson 7-1   Areas of Parallelograms and Triangles   **349**

👥 **Reaching All Students**

| **Below Level** After students find the area in Example 2 algebraically, have them count the number of squares and parts of squares and compare their answers with 15 square units. | **Advanced Learners** After Examples 1–3, have students explore possible areas for a parallelogram with side lengths 12 cm and 10 cm. They should justify their conclusions. | **Tactile Learners** See note on page 350. **Auditory Learners** See note on page 352. |

Math Background

The area of, or number of square units covered by, a quadrilateral, can be described algebraically as the product of its base and height. You can demonstrate this by transforming, cutting, and pasting sections of the quadrilateral to form a rectangle. Base and height also appear in the formulas for the area of a triangle (half of a parallelogram) and the lateral surface areas of prisms and pyramids. Because of this, the area of a rectangle is often given in terms of base and height, not length and width.

OBJECTIVE
▼1 Teaching Notes

Investigation (Optional)
Ask: *Why must the rectangle and the parallelogram have the same area?* The parallelogram and the rectangle are formed from the same pieces.

1 EXAMPLE

Make sure that students understand that 5 in. is the measure of the entire base in part a.

2 EXAMPLE Math Tip

Ask: *Why does choosing a horizontal side as a base make finding the area easier?* You can count squares to find both base and height.

3 EXAMPLE Error Prevention

If students think the base that corresponds to height *CF* is *AF* rather than *AD*, remind them that the base is always a side of the parallelogram.

 Additional Examples

① Find the area of the parallelogram.

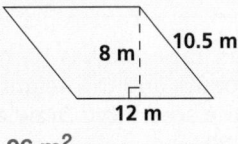

96 m^2

349

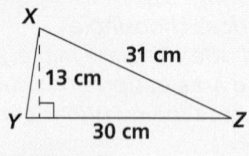
3 EXAMPLE **Finding a Missing Dimension**

For ▱*ABCD*, find *CF* to the nearest tenth.

First, find the area of ▱*ABCD*. Then use the area formula a second time to find *CF*.

$A = bh$

$\quad = 10(12) = 120$ **Use base AB and height DE.**

The area of ▱*ABCD* is 120 in.².

$A = bh$

$120 = 13(CF)$ **Use base AD and height CF.**

$CF = \frac{120}{13} \approx 9.2$

● *CF* is about 9.2 in.

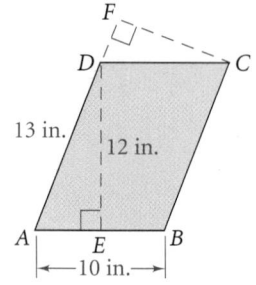

✓ **Check Understanding** **3** A parallelogram has sides 15 cm and 18 cm. The height corresponding to a 15-cm base is 9 cm. Find the height corresponding to an 18-cm base. **7.5 cm**

OBJECTIVE
 **Area of a Triangle**

A diagonal divides any parallelogram into two congruent triangles.

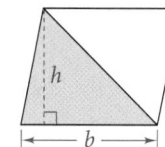 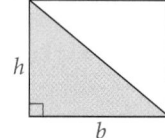 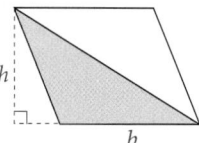

Therefore, the area of each triangle is half the area of the parallelogram.

 Key Concepts

Theorem 7-3 **Area of a Triangle**
The area of a triangle is half the product of a base and the corresponding height. 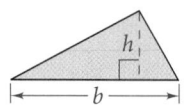 $A = \frac{1}{2}bh$

A **base of a triangle** is any of its sides. The corresponding **height** is the length of the altitude to the line containing that base.

4 EXAMPLE **Finding the Area of a Triangle**

Find the area of the shaded triangle at the left.

$A = \frac{1}{2}bh$

$\quad = \frac{1}{2}(10)(6.4) = 32$ **Substitute and simplify.**

● The area of the shaded triangle is 32 ft².

✓ **Check Understanding** **4** Find the area of the triangle at the right. **30 cm²**

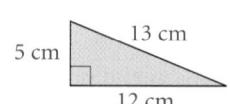

5 EXAMPLE Real-World  Connection

Structural Design When designing a building, you must be sure that the building can withstand hurricane-force winds, which have a velocity of 73 mi/h or more. The formula $F = 0.004Av^2$ gives the force F in pounds exerted by a wind blowing against a flat surface. A is the area of the surface in square feet, and v is the wind velocity in miles per hour.

How much force is exerted by a 73 mi/h wind blowing directly against the side of the building shown here?

Find the area of the side of the building.

triangle area $= \frac{1}{2}bh = \frac{1}{2}(20)6 = 60$ ft^2

rectangle area $= bh = 20(12) = 240$ ft^2

area of the side $= 60 + 240 = 300$ ft^2

Use the area of the side of the building and the velocity of the wind to find the force.

$F = 0.004Av^2$ **Use the formula for force.**

$= 0.004(300)(73)^2$ **Substitute 300 for A and 73 for v.**

$= 6394.8$

● The force is about 6400 lb, or 3.2 tons.

Real-World  Connection

In 1992 this building in Homestead, Florida, succumbed to the 145 mi/h winds of Hurricane Andrew.

✓ **Check Understanding** ❺ **Critical Thinking** Suppose the bases of the rectangle and triangle in the building above are doubled to 40 ft, but the height of each figure remains the same. How is the force of the wind against the side of the building affected?
The force is doubled.

EXERCISES

For more practice, see *Extra Practice*.

Practice and Problem Solving

A Practice by Example

Example 1
(page 349)

Find the area of each parallelogram.

1.

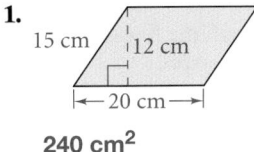
15 cm   12 cm
←— 20 cm —→

240 cm²

2.

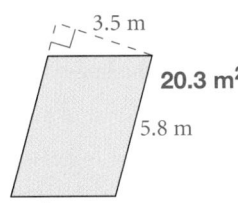
3.5 m
20.3 m²
5.8 m
4 m

3.

26.79 in.²

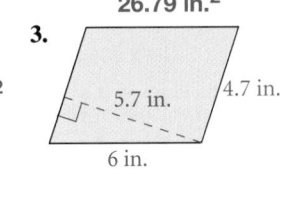
5.7 in.   4.7 in.
6 in.

Example 2
(page 349)

4. 20 units²
5. 9 units²

Coordinate Geometry **Find the area of the parallelogram with the given vertices.**

4. $A(2, 0), B(7, 0), C(8, 4), D(3, 4)$

5. $E(-4, 0), F(-1, 0), G(1, -3), H(-2, -3)$

6. $I(2, 2), J(4, 2), K(2, -3), L(0, -3)$
10 units²

7. $M(-6, -1), N(-5, 0), P(1, 0), Q(0, -1)$
6 units²

Example 3
(page 350)

Find the value of h for each parallelogram.

8. 11.2

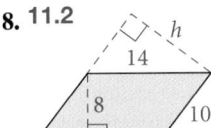
h
14
8   10

9.

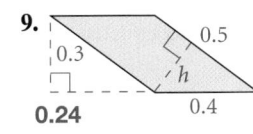
0.3   0.5
h
0.4
0.24

10.

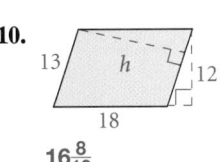
13   h 12
18
$16\frac{8}{13}$

---

3. Practice

Assignment Guide

▼**1 Objective**
Ⓐ Ⓑ Core 1–10, 22, 36, 37, 42, 43

▼**2 Objective**
Ⓐ Ⓑ Core 11–21, 23–35, 38–41, 44–46
Ⓒ Extension 47–51

Standardized Test Prep 52–56

Mixed Review 57–67

Exercises 1–3 Make sure that students also square the unit of measurement.

Exercises 8–10 To help students find corresponding heights and bases, suggest that they rotate their textbooks so that each parallelogram has a horizontal base and vertical height.

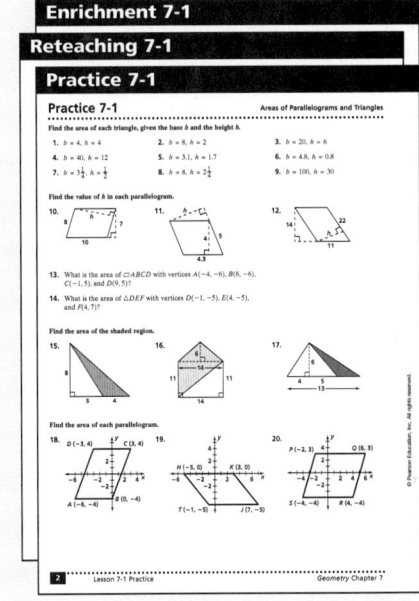

351

Exercise 14 Ask: *Why might parking spaces be arranged diagonally instead of perpendicular to the driving region?*
Sample: It is easier to drive in and out of the parking spaces.

Exercises 23, 24 Discuss as a class how to write and solve the quadratic equations in these problems.

Exercises 25–28 Students may need to work in pairs to review slope-intercept form.

Technology Tip
Exercise 29 Students can duplicate this activity using geometry software and discover for themselves that the area of △*ABD* remains constant as point *D* is moved along line *k*.

Auditory Learners
Exercises 30–32 Have students describe different ways to solve each problem.

Connection to History
Exercises 47–51 Heron, also known as Hero, invented the first turbine, called an aeolipile, about 200 B.C. After he filled a flask with water and heated it, steam released from two spouts at the side of the flask caused the flask to spin.

pages 351–354 Exercises

25. **a.**
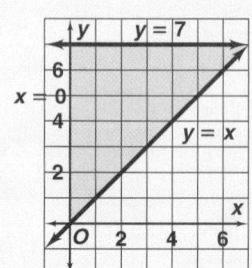

b. 24.5 units²

26. **a.**
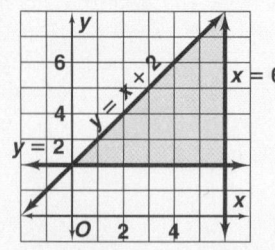

b. 18 units²

352

Example 4
(page 350)

Example 5
(page 351)

14b. Find the entire area of the lot and subtract the area for the flowers.

14c. 1550 − 160 = 1390 ft²

15. 15 units²

16. 6 units²

17. 6 units²

18. 12 units²

19. 27 units²

20. 3 units²

B Apply Your Skills

? Need Help?
The line *x* = *a* is vertical and crosses the *x*-axis at *x* = *a*.

29. The area does not change; the height and base *AB* do not change.

Find the area of each shaded triangle.

11. 14 m²
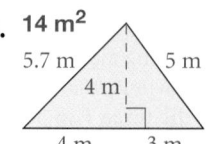

12.
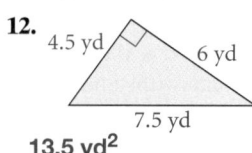
13.5 yd²

13. 3 ft²
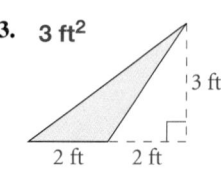

14. **Landscaping** Taisha's Bakery has a plan for a 50 ft-by-31 ft parking lot. The four parking spaces are congruent parallelograms, the driving region is a rectangle, and the two unpaved areas for flowers are congruent triangles.
   a. Find the area of the surface to be paved by adding the areas of the driving region and the four parking spaces. 1390 ft²
   b. Describe another method for finding the area of the surface to be paved.
   c. Use your method from part (b) to find the area. Then compare answers from parts (a) and (b) to check your work.

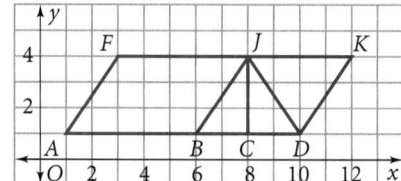

Find the area of each figure.

15. □*ABJF*   16. △*BDJ*

17. △*DKJ*   18. □*BDKJ*

19. □*ADKF*   20. △*BCJ*

21. *ADJF* 21 units²

22. The area of a parallelogram is 24 in.² and the height is 6 in. Find the corresponding base. 4 in.

23. An isosceles right triangle has area of 98 cm². Find the length of each leg. 14 cm

x^2 24. **Algebra** In a triangle, a base and a corresponding height are in the ratio 3 : 2. The area is 108 in.². Find the base and the corresponding height. 18 in.; 12 in.

In Exercises 25–28, (a) graph the lines and (b) find the area of the triangle enclosed by the lines. 25–28. See margin.

25. $y = x, x = 0, y = 7$

26. $y = x + 2, y = 2, x = 6$

27. $y = -\frac{1}{2}x + 3, y = 0, x = -2$

28. $y = \frac{3}{4}x - 2, y = -2, x = 4$

29. **Technology** Ki used geometry software to create the figure at the right. She constructed $\overleftrightarrow{AB}$ and a point *C* not on $\overleftrightarrow{AB}$. Then she constructed line *k* parallel to $\overleftrightarrow{AB}$ through point *C*. Next, Ki constructed point *D* on line *k* as well as $\overline{AD}$ and $\overline{BD}$. She dragged point *D* along line *k* to manipulate △*ABD*. How does the area of △*ABD* change? Explain. **See left.**

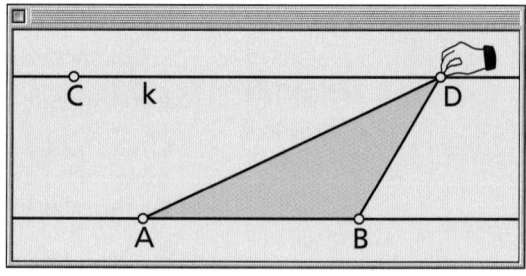

352 Chapter 7 Area

27. **a.**

b. 16 units²

28. **a.**
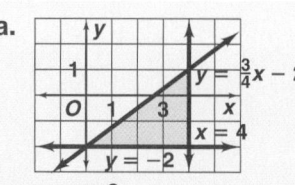

b. 6 units²

Find the area of each figure.

30.  8 units^2 31. 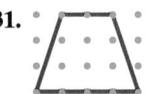 9 units^2 32.  8 units^2

33. Find the area of the yellow triangular patch in the large field in the photo at the left. It has a base of 60 yd and a height of 140 yd. **4200 yd^2**

34. **Open-Ended** Using graph paper, draw an acute triangle, an obtuse triangle, and a right triangle, each with area 12 units^2. **See margin.**

35. **Probability** Ann drew these three figures on a grid. A fly lands at random at a point on the grid.

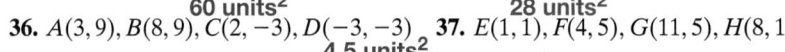

 a. **Writing** Is the fly more likely to land on one of the figures or on the blank grid? Explain. **Blank grid; area is 84 units^2 while figures are 36 units^2.**
   b. Suppose you know the fly lands on one of the figures. Is the fly more likely to land on one figure than on another? Explain.
   No; the figures have the same area.

Coordinate Geometry Find the area of a polygon with the given vertices.

60 units^2   **28 units^2**
36. $A(3, 9), B(8, 9), C(2, -3), D(-3, -3)$ 37. $E(1, 1), F(4, 5), G(11, 5), H(8, 1)$
                          4.5 units^2
38. $M(-2, -5), L(1, -5), N(2, -2)$ 39. $R(-7, 2), S(-3, -1), T(3, -1)$ **9 units^2**

40. $W(1, 2), X(1, 6), Y(4, 1)$ **6 units^2**   41. $A(-8, 0), B(-7, 4), C(-3, 3)$ **8.5 units^2**

42. $D(0, 0), E(2, 4), F(6, 4), G(6, 0)$ 43. $K(-7, -2), L(-7, 6), M(1, 6), N(7, -2)$
20 units^2   **88 units^2**

Find the area of each figure.

44. 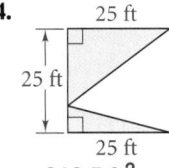   45. 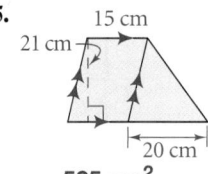   46.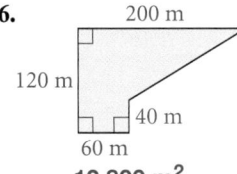
312.5 ft^2   **525 cm^2**   **12,800 m^2**

C Challenge 🌐 **History** The ancient Greek mathematician Heron is most famous for this formula for the area of a triangle in terms of the lengths of its sides *a*, *b*, and *c*.

$$A = \sqrt{s(s - a)(s - b)(s - c)}, \text{ where } s = \tfrac{1}{2}(a + b + c)$$

Use Heron's Formula and a calculator to find the area of each triangle. Round your answer to the nearest whole number.

47. $a = 8$ in., $b = 9$ in., $c = 10$ in. **34 in.^{2}** 48. $a = 15$ m, $b = 17$ m, $c = 21$ m **126 m^2**

49. $a = 6$ cm, $b = 7$ cm, $c = 11$ cm   50. $a = 10$ ft, $b = 10.2$ ft, $c = 11$ ft
                          19 cm^2   **47 ft^2**
51. a. Use Heron's Formula to find the area of the triangle at the right. **54 in.^{2}**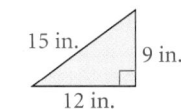
    b. Verify your answer to part (a) by using the formula $A = \tfrac{1}{2}bh$. **54 in.^{2}**

Lesson 7-1 Areas of Parallelograms and Triangles   **353**

34. **Answers may vary.**
    Sample:

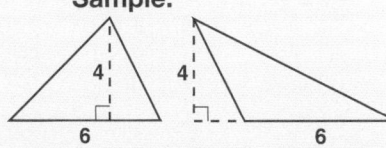   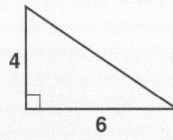

📘 **Lesson Quiz 7-1**

1. Find the area of the parallelogram.

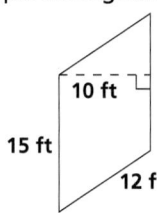

10 ft
15 ft
12 ft

150 ft^2

2. Find the area of $\square XYZW$ with vertices $X(-5, -3)$, $Y(-2, 3)$, $Z(2, 3)$ and $W(-1, -3)$. **24 square units**

3. A parallelogram has 6-cm and 8-cm sides. The height corresponding to the 8-cm base is 4.5 cm. Find the height corresponding to the 6-cm base. **6 cm**

4. Find the area of $\triangle RST$.

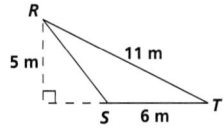

5 m   11 m   6 m

15 m^2

5. A rectangular flag is divided into four regions by its diagonals. Two of the regions are shaded. Find the total area of the shaded regions.

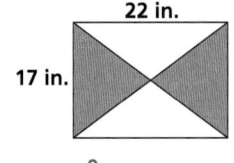

22 in.
17 in.

187 in.^{2}

Alternative Assessment

Have each student draw and label a triangle and a parallelogram, each with an area of 40 in.^{2} Have them write a paragraph explaining how they calculated the area of each figure.

Resources

For additional practice with a variety of test item formats:
- Standardized Test Prep, p. 413
- Test-Taking Strategies, p. 408
- Test-Taking Strategies with Transparencies

Exercise 52 To solve this problem, students need to know which sides are perpendicular. Although using the Pythagorean Theorem could easily determine this, it has not yet been taught. However, students can use the theorem from Lesson 5-5 that the side opposite the largest angle is longest in order to identify the side opposite the right angle.

pages 351–354   Exercises

56. [2] a. It is the distance between $y = 2$ and $y = -3$, so $2 - (-3) = 5$.

b. 25 units^2

[1] incorrect explanation OR incorrect answer

65.

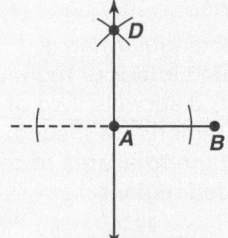

66.

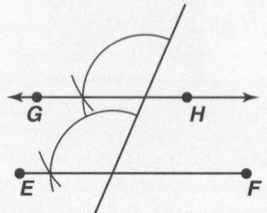

67.

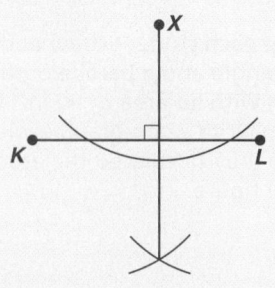

Multiple Choice

52. The lengths of the sides of a right triangle are 10 in., 24 in., and 26 in. What is the area of the triangle? **B**
    A. 116 in.^{2} **B.** 120 in.^{2} **C.** 130 in.^{2} **D.** 156 in.^{2}

53. What is the area of ▱$ABCD$ at the right? **G**
    F. 32 in.^{2} **G.** 64 in.^{2}
    H. 91.2 in.^{2} **I.** 45.6 in.^{2}

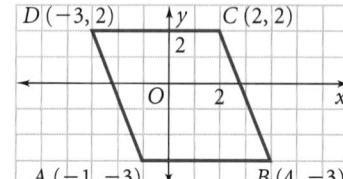

54. A parallelogram has adjacent sides of 176 ft and 312 ft. The altitude to the shorter side is 290 ft. What is the area of the parallelogram? **A**
    A. 51,040 ft^2 **B.** 51,352 ft^2 **C.** 54,912 ft^2 **D.** 55,202 ft^2

55. The perimeter of an equilateral triangle is 60 m. Its height is 17.3 m. What is its area? **F**
    F. 173 m^2 **G.** 200 m^2 **H.** 348 m^2 **I.** 1044 m^2

Short Response

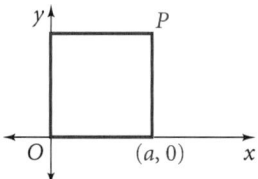

Take It to the NET
Online lesson quiz at
www.PHSchool.com
Web Code: afa-0701

56. **a.** For ▱$ABCD$, explain how to determine the length of an altitude drawn to base $\overline{AB}$.
    b. Find the area of ▱$ABCD$.
    See margin.

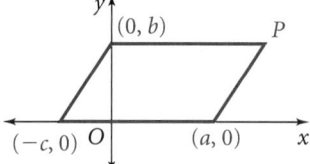

Mixed Review

Lesson 6-7

Give the coordinates for point P without using any new variables.

57. square   **(a, a)**

58. parallelogram **($a + c, b$)**

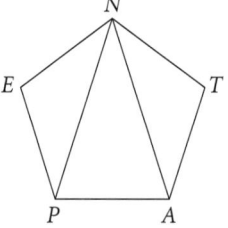

Lesson 4-5

The base of the isosceles triangle is a side of a regular pentagon $PENTA$. Find the measure of each angle.

59. $\angle APE$ **108**   60. $\angle APN$ **72**

61. $\angle PAN$ **72**   62. $\angle PNA$ **36**

63. $\angle EPN$ **36**   64. $\angle ANT$ **36**

65–67. See margin.

Lesson 3-7

Use a compass and straightedge for the following constructions.

65. Draw a segment and label it $\overline{AB}$. Construct $\overleftrightarrow{AD}$ so that $\overleftrightarrow{AD} \perp \overline{AB}$ at point A.

66. Draw a segment. Label it $\overline{EF}$. Construct a line $\overleftrightarrow{GH}$ so that $\overleftrightarrow{GH} \parallel \overline{EF}$.

67. Draw a segment and label it $\overline{KL}$. Draw a point X not on $\overleftrightarrow{KL}$. Construct a perpendicular from point X to $\overline{KL}$ (or to $\overleftrightarrow{KL}$).

Simplifying Radicals

FOR USE WITH LESSON 7-2

You can multiply and divide numbers that are under radical signs.

1 EXAMPLE

Simplify the expressions $\sqrt{2} \cdot \sqrt{8}$ and $\sqrt{294} \div \sqrt{3}$.

$$\sqrt{2} \cdot \sqrt{8} = \sqrt{2 \cdot 8} \qquad \leftarrow \textbf{Rewrite using one radical sign.} \rightarrow \qquad \sqrt{294} \div \sqrt{3} = \sqrt{\frac{294}{3}}$$
$$= \sqrt{16} \qquad \leftarrow \textbf{Simplify the expression under the radical.} \rightarrow \qquad = \sqrt{98}$$
$$= 4 \qquad \leftarrow \textbf{Factor out perfect squares and simplify.} \rightarrow \qquad = \sqrt{49 \cdot 2}$$
$$= 7\sqrt{2}$$

A radical expression is in simplest form when all the following are true.
- The number under the radical sign has no perfect square factors other than 1.
- The number under the radical sign does not contain a fraction.
- A denominator does not contain a radical expression.

2 EXAMPLE

Write $\sqrt{\frac{4}{3}}$ in simplest form.

$\sqrt{\frac{4}{3}} = \frac{\sqrt{4}}{\sqrt{3}}$ **Rewrite the single radical as a quotient.**

$= \frac{2}{\sqrt{3}}$ **Simplify the numerator.**

$= \frac{2}{\sqrt{3}} \cdot \frac{\sqrt{3}}{\sqrt{3}}$ **Multiply by a form of 1 to rationalize the denominator.**

$= \frac{2\sqrt{3}}{3}$ **Simplify.**

Check using a calculator: $\sqrt{\frac{4}{3}} \approx 1.1547005$ and $\frac{2\sqrt{3}}{3} \approx 1.1547005$.

EXERCISES

Simplify each expression.

1. $\sqrt{5} \cdot \sqrt{10}$ $5\sqrt{2}$ 2. $\sqrt{243}$ $9\sqrt{3}$ 3. $\sqrt{128} \div \sqrt{2}$ 8   4. $\sqrt{\frac{125}{4}}$ $\frac{5\sqrt{5}}{2}$

5. $\sqrt{6} \cdot \sqrt{8}$ $4\sqrt{3}$ 6. $\frac{\sqrt{36}}{\sqrt{3}}$ $2\sqrt{3}$ 7. $\frac{\sqrt{144}}{\sqrt{2}}$ $6\sqrt{2}$ 8. $\sqrt{3} \cdot \sqrt{12}$ 6

9. $\sqrt{72} \div \sqrt{2}$ 6   10. $\sqrt{169}$ 13   11. $28 \div \sqrt{8}$ $7\sqrt{2}$ 12. $\sqrt{300} \div \sqrt{5}$ $2\sqrt{15}$

13. $\sqrt{12} \cdot \sqrt{2}$ $2\sqrt{6}$ 14. $\frac{\sqrt{24}}{\sqrt{3}}$ $2\sqrt{2}$ 15. $\sqrt{\frac{75}{3}}$ 5   16. $\sqrt{18} \cdot \sqrt{2}$ 6

17. $\sqrt{68}$ $2\sqrt{17}$ 18. $\sqrt{3} \cdot \sqrt{15}$ $3\sqrt{5}$ 19. $\frac{\sqrt{20}}{\sqrt{5}}$ 2   20. $45 \div \sqrt{3}$ $15\sqrt{3}$

21. $\sqrt{\frac{25}{20}}$ $\frac{\sqrt{5}}{2}$ 22. $\sqrt{\frac{8}{28}}$ $\frac{\sqrt{14}}{7}$ 23. $\frac{\sqrt{6} \cdot \sqrt{3}}{\sqrt{9}}$ $\sqrt{2}$ 24. $\frac{\sqrt{3} \cdot \sqrt{15}}{\sqrt{2}}$ $\frac{3\sqrt{10}}{2}$

Algebra 1 Review

Simplifying Radicals

Students will use the skill of simplifying radicals in Lessons 7-2 and 7-3 when they apply the Pythagorean Theorem.

Resources

 Technology

Geometry Resource Pro® CD-ROM:
    Algebra 1 Review Resources
Computer Test Generator CD-ROM,
    Chapter 7, Review Topics

Teaching Notes

1 EXAMPLE Alternative Method

Point out that $\sqrt{2} \cdot \sqrt{8}$ also can be simplified as follows:
$\sqrt{2} \cdot \sqrt{8} = \sqrt{2}(\sqrt{2} \cdot \sqrt{4}) = (\sqrt{2} \cdot \sqrt{2})2 = 2 \cdot 2 = 4$. Have students explain the steps shown.

2 EXAMPLE Teaching Tip

To simplify $\frac{2}{\sqrt{3}}$, the irrational number in the denominator must be replaced with a rational number without changing the fraction's value. Discuss as a class when the form $\frac{2\sqrt{3}}{3}$ is easier to use than $\frac{2}{\sqrt{3}}$.

The Pythagorean Theorem

The Pythagorean Theorem

Students will use rectangles, triangles, and squares cut from graph paper to develop the Pythagorean Theorem. Using eight right triangles with side lengths a, b, and c and squares with side lengths a, b, and c, students will form two squares that have the same area, leading them algebraically to the relationship $a^2 + b^2 = c^2$.

Teaching Notes

This hands-on approach enables students to relate the Pythagorean Theorem to area, which is how the Greek mathematician Pythagoras proved the theorem over 2500 years ago.

Visual Learners

There are different ways to form a Group 1 square. Point out that each Group 1 square has area $a^2 + b^2 + 2ab$ because the same six pieces form the square.

Alternative Method

Students also can develop the Pythagorean Theorem using only the square formed in Group 2.
- Express the area as the sum of the areas of the five pieces: $c^2 + 2ab$.
- Express the area using the formula for the area of a square with sides $a + b$: $(a + b)^2 = a^2 + 2ab + b^2$.
- Equate the two area expressions, and simplify to get $a^2 + b^2 = c^2$.

The Pythagorean Theorem is introduced in Lesson 7-2. The investigation and exercises below will help you understand why the theorem works.

Using graph paper, draw any rectangle. Label the sides a and b. Cut four rectangles with length a and width b from the graph paper. Then cut each rectangle on its diagonal, c, forming eight congruent triangles.

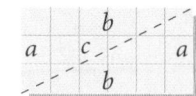

Cut three squares from colored paper, one with sides of length a, one with sides of length b, and one with sides of length c.

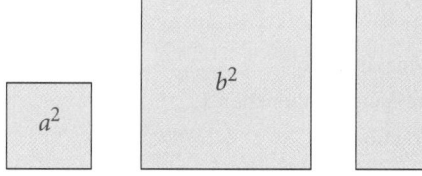

Separate the eleven pieces into groups.

    Group 1: four triangles and the two smaller squares

    Group 2: four triangles and the largest square

Arrange the pieces of each group to form a square.

EXERCISES

1. **a.** How do the areas of the two squares you formed in the last step above compare? **The areas are =.**
   b. Write an algebraic expression for the area of each of these squares. $a^2 + b^2 + 2ab$, $c^2 + 2ab$
   c. What can you conclude about the areas of the three squares you cut from colored paper? **The area of the two smaller squares = the area of the larger square.**

2. Repeat this investigation using a new rectangle with different a and b values. What do you notice? **The same relationship occurs.**

3. Express your conclusion as an algebraic equation. $a^2 + b^2 = c^2$

4. Use your ruler with any rectangle to find actual measures for a, b, and c. Do these measures confirm that $a^2 + b^2 = c^2$? **yes**

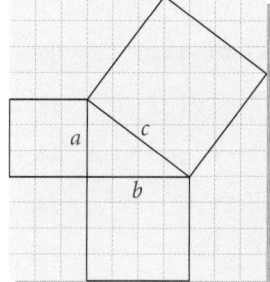

Extend

5. Explain how the diagram at the right represents your conclusion in Exercise 3. **The sum of the squares of the lengths of the two legs = the square of the length of the hyp.**

6. Does the equation from Exercise 4 work for triangles other than right triangles? Explore and explain.
   No; for an obtuse $\triangle$, $c^2 > a^2 + b^2$; for an acute $\triangle$, $c^2 < a^2 + b^2$.

356 Investigation The Pythagorean Theorem

7-2

The Pythagorean Theorem and Its Converse

North Carolina Objectives

2.03 Apply properties, definitions, and theorems of two-dimensional figures to solve problems and write proofs: a) Triangles.

Lesson Preview

What You'll Learn

 OBJECTIVE 1 To use the Pythagorean Theorem

 OBJECTIVE 2 To use the Converse of the Pythagorean Theorem

. . . And Why

To find the distance between two docks on a lake, as in Example 3

✓ **Check Skills You'll Need** (For help, go to the Skills Handbook, p. 715)

Square the lengths of the sides of each triangle. What do you notice?

1.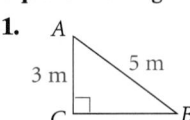
   A, 3 m, 5 m, C, 4 m, B

   1. $3^2 + 4^2 = 5^2$
   2. $5^2 + 12^2 = 13^2$

2.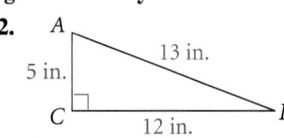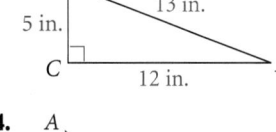
   A, 13 in., 5 in., C, 12 in., B

3.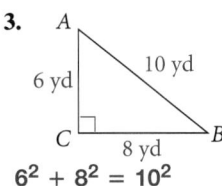
   A, 6 yd, 10 yd, C, 8 yd, B

   $6^2 + 8^2 = 10^2$

4.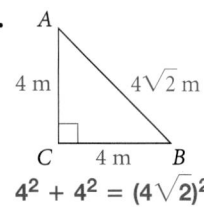
   A, 4 m, $4\sqrt{2}$ m, C, 4 m, B

   $4^2 + 4^2 = (4\sqrt{2})^2$

New Vocabulary • Pythagorean triple

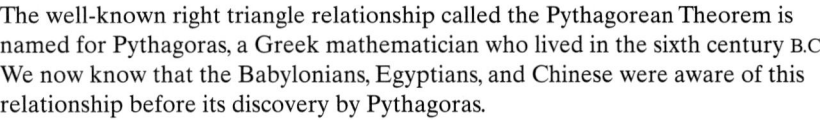

OBJECTIVE

1 The Pythagorean Theorem

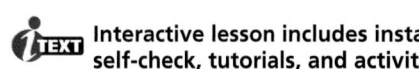 **iTEXT** Interactive lesson includes instant self-check, tutorials, and activities.

The well-known right triangle relationship called the Pythagorean Theorem is named for Pythagoras, a Greek mathematician who lived in the sixth century B.C. We now know that the Babylonians, Egyptians, and Chinese were aware of this relationship before its discovery by Pythagoras.

There are many proofs of the Pythagorean Theorem. You will see an area proof in Exercise 60.

 Key Concepts

Theorem 7-4	Pythagorean Theorem

In a right triangle, the sum of the squares of the lengths of the legs is equal to the square of the length of the hypotenuse.

$$a^2 + b^2 = c^2$$

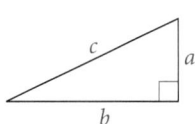

Need Help?

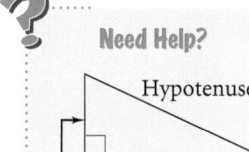

Hypotenuse

Legs

A **Pythagorean triple** is a set of nonzero whole numbers a, b, and c that satisfy the equation $a^2 + b^2 = c^2$. Here are some common Pythagorean triples.

3, 4, 5   5, 12, 13   8, 15, 17   7, 24, 25

If you multiply each number in a Pythagorean triple by the same whole number, the three numbers that result also form a Pythagorean triple.

Lesson 7-2 The Pythagorean Theorem and Its Converse **357**

1. Plan

Lesson Preview

✓ **Check Skills You'll Need** 🔖

For help use
Skills Handbook, p. 715

Lesson Resources

📁 **Teaching Resources**
Practice, Reteaching, Enrichment

👥 **Reaching All Students**
Practice Workbook 7-2
Spanish Practice Workbook 7-2
Technology Activities 50
Informal Geometry Planning Guide 7-2

🕐 **Presentation Assistant Plus!**
Transparencies
• Check Skills You'll Need 7-2
• Additional Examples 7-2
• Student Edition Answers 7-2
• Lesson Quiz 7-2
PH Presentation Pro CD 7-2

PRENTICE HALL ASSESSMENT SYSTEM

Computer Test Generator CD

💿 **Technology**
Resource Pro® CD-ROM
Computer Test Generator CD
Prentice Hall Presentation Pro CD

💻 **www.PHSchool.com**
Student Site
• Teacher Web Code: afk-5500
• Self-grading Lesson Quiz
Teacher Center
• Lesson Planner
• Resources

Plus **iTEXT**

Ongoing Assessment and Intervention

Before the Lesson
Diagnose prerequisite skills using:
• Check Skills You'll Need

During the Lesson
Monitor progress using:
• Check Understanding
• Additional Examples
• Standardized Test Prep

After the Lesson
Assess knowledge using:
• Lesson Quiz
• Computer Test Generator CD

357

Math Background

Some mathematical ideas assumed to be true have yet to be proved, such as Goldbach's conjecture: *Every even number greater than 2 can be expressed as the sum of two prime numbers.* Although several ancient cultures postulated the Pythagorean Theorem and used it to measure distances, the first proof of it was attributed by Euclid to Pythagoras. The distance formula is a coordinate form of the Pythagorean Theorem, which is the foundation of all trigonometric functions.

OBJECTIVE

▼ Teaching Notes

Connection to Algebra

As you read the Pythagorean Theorem with the class, point out how much simpler the theorem is when stated algebraically than it is in words. Emphasize this power of algebra to express difficult ideas simply.

1 EXAMPLE

Let students know that they will use Pythagorean triples in most math courses. Students should memorize the more common ones at the bottom of page 357 and be aware of their multiples because these often appear on standardized tests.

2 EXAMPLE Error Prevention

Some students may assume that the legs are always the known quantities. Point out that c is always the hypotenuse when applying the formula $a^2 + b^2 = c^2$ to a right triangle.

---

1 EXAMPLE Pythagorean Triples

Find the length of the hypotenuse of $\triangle ABC$. Do the lengths of the sides of $\triangle ABC$ form a Pythagorean triple?

$a^2 + b^2 = c^2$	Use the Pythagorean Theorem.
$21^2 + 20^2 = c^2$	Substitute 21 for a and 20 for b.
$441 + 400 = c^2$	Simplify.
$841 = c^2$	
$c = 29$	Take the square root.

The length of the hypotenuse is 29. The lengths of the sides, 20, 21, and 29, form a Pythagorean triple because they are whole numbers that satisfy $a^2 + b^2 = c^2$.

✓ **Check Understanding** ❶ A right triangle has a hypotenuse of length 25 and a leg of length 10. Find the length of the other leg. Do the lengths of the sides form a Pythagorean triple?
$5\sqrt{21}$; no

In some cases, you will write the length of a side in simplest radical form.

Need Help?

To review simplest radical form, see page 355.

2 EXAMPLE Using Simplest Radical Form

Algebra Find the value of x. Leave your answer in simplest radical form.

$a^2 + b^2 = c^2$	Pythagorean Theorem
$8^2 + x^2 = 20^2$	Substitute.
$64 + x^2 = 400$	Simplify.
$x^2 = 336$	Subtract 64 from each side.
$x = \sqrt{336}$	Take the square root.
$x = \sqrt{16(21)}$	Simplify.
$x = 4\sqrt{21}$	

✓ **Check Understanding** ❷ The hypotenuse of a right triangle has length 12. One leg has length 6. Find the length of the other leg. Leave your answer in simplest radical form.
$6\sqrt{3}$

3 EXAMPLE Real-World  Connection

Recreation The Parks Department rents paddle boats at docks near each entrance to the park. About how far is it to paddle from one dock to the other?

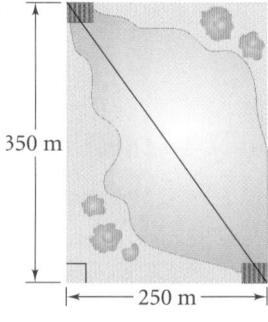

$a^2 + b^2 = c^2$	Pythagorean Theorem
$250^2 + 350^2 = c^2$	Substitute.
$185{,}000 = c^2$	Simplify.
$c = \sqrt{185{,}000}$	Take the square root.
$c = 430.11626$	Use a calculator.

It is about 430 m from one dock to the other.

✓ **Check Understanding** ❸ **Critical Thinking** When you want to know how far you have to paddle a boat, why is an approximate answer more useful than an answer in simplest radical form?
You want to know the nearest whole number value, which may not be apparent in a radical expression.

358 Chapter 7 Area

👥 Reaching All Students

Below Level Before the lesson, list the squares of whole numbers less than 20. Also review how to simplify a radical expression.	**Advanced Learners** After Example 4, have students find a formula for the area of an isosceles triangle with side lengths a, a, and b, in terms of a and b.	**Inclusion** See note on page 362. **English Learners** See note on page 362.

You can use the Pythagorean Theorem to help you find area.

4 EXAMPLE Finding Area

Find the area of the triangle.

The large triangle is an isosceles triangle. The altitude to the base bisects the base and forms two right triangles. You can use the Pythagorean Theorem with the triangle at the right to find the height of the large triangle.

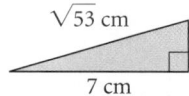
12 m   h   12 m
20 m

12 m   h
10 m

$$10^2 + h^2 = 12^2$$

$100 + h^2 = 144$ **Simplify.**

$h^2 = 44$ **Subtract 100 from each side.**

$h = \sqrt{44}$ **Take the square root of each side.**

$h = 2\sqrt{11}$ **Write in simplest radical form.**

The large triangle has base 20 m and height $2\sqrt{11}$ m.

$A = \frac{1}{2}bh$ **Use the triangle area formula from Theorem 7-3.**

$A = \frac{1}{2}(20)(2\sqrt{11})$ **Substitute 20 for b and $2\sqrt{11}$ for h.**

$A = 20\sqrt{11}$ **Simplify.**

The area of the triangle is $20\sqrt{11}$ m^2.

✓ **Check Understanding** **4** Find the area of the triangle at the right.
7 cm^2

$\sqrt{53}$ cm
7 cm

The diagram above illustrates an ancient Greek proof of the Pythagorean Theorem for an isosceles right triangle.

OBJECTIVE

2 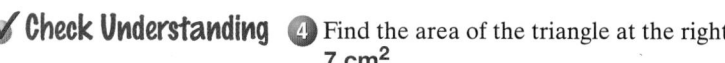 **The Converse of the Pythagorean Theorem**

You can use the Converse of the Pythagorean Theorem to determine whether a triangle is a right triangle. You will prove Theorem 7-5 in Exercise 70.

 Key Concepts

Theorem 7-5	Converse of the Pythagorean Theorem

If the square of the length of one side of a triangle is equal to the sum of the squares of the lengths of the other two sides, then the triangle is a right triangle.

5 EXAMPLE Is It a Right Triangle?

Is this triangle a right triangle?

85
84
13

$c^2 \stackrel{?}{=} a^2 + b^2$

$85^2 \stackrel{?}{=} 13^2 + 84^2$ **Substitute the greatest length for c.**

$7225 \stackrel{?}{=} 169 + 7056$ **Simplify.**

$7225 = 7225$ ✓

$c^2 = a^2 + b^2$, so the triangle is a right triangle.

✓ **Check Understanding** **5** A triangle has sides of lengths 16, 48, and 50. Is the triangle a right triangle?
no

Lesson 7-2   The Pythagorean Theorem and Its Converse   **359**

Students may wonder why they are asked to use a calculator in some exercises but not in other similar exercises. Tell them that real-world applications typically require decimal answers. Point out that radicals are exact, so they are preferred when exercises are of a purely mathematical nature or to avoid rounding errors in continuing computations.

4 EXAMPLE

This is a good opportunity to review proofs. As a class, prove *The altitude to the base of an isosceles triangle bisects the base.*

Additional Examples

1 A right triangle has legs of length 16 and 30. Find the length of the hypotenuse. Do the lengths of the sides form a Pythagorean triple? **34; yes**

2 Find the value of *x*. Leave your answer in simplest radical form.

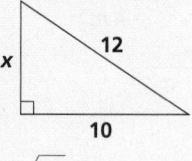
x   12
10

$2\sqrt{11}$

3 A baseball diamond is a square with 90-ft sides. Home plate and second base are at opposite vertices of the square. About how far is home plate from second base? **about 127 ft**

4 The hypotenuse of an isosceles right triangle has length 20 cm. Find the area. **100 cm^2**

OBJECTIVE

2 Teaching Notes

Technology Tip

Have students use geometry software to explore and demonstrate the theorems *If $c^2 > a^2 + b^2$, the triangle is obtuse* and *If $c^2 < a^2 + b^2$, the triangle is acute.* Direct students to keep *a* and *b* constant while manipulating *c* by altering the angle opposite *c*.

6 EXAMPLE Error Prevention

Remind students that *c* must be the longest side of the triangle for the comparison of c^2 and $a^2 + b^2$ to give a valid triangle classification. Also, students should use the Triangle Inequality Theorem to check that $a + b > c$ so that the side lengths form a triangle.

Additional Examples

5 Is this triangle a right triangle?

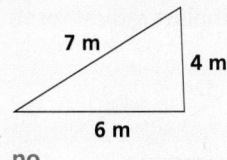

no

6 The numbers represent the lengths of the sides of a triangle. Classify each triangle as acute, obtuse, or right.

a. 15, 20, 25 **right**
b. 10, 15, 20 **obtuse**

Closure

The area of △*ABC* is 20 ft². Find *AC* and *BC*. Leave your answer in simplest radical form.

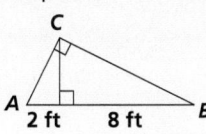

$AC = 2\sqrt{5}$ ft; $BC = 4\sqrt{5}$ ft

Suppose a triangle has sides of lengths *a*, *b*, and *c*, where *c* is the length of the longest side. If $c^2 > a^2 + b^2$, the Converse of the Pythagorean Theorem leads to the conclusion that the angle opposite side *c* must have measure greater than 90. Thus, the triangle is obtuse. Similarly, if $c^2 < a^2 + b^2$, the triangle is acute.

These observations are summarized in the theorems below.

 Key Concepts

Theorem 7-6

If the square of the length of the longest side of a triangle is greater than the sum of the squares of the lengths of the other two sides, the triangle is obtuse.

If $c^2 > a^2 + b^2$, the triangle is obtuse.

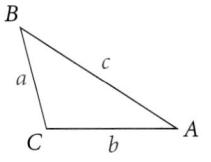

Theorem 7-7

If the square of the length of the longest side of a triangle is less than the sum of the squares of the lengths of the other two sides, the triangle is acute.

If $c^2 < a^2 + b^2$, the triangle is acute.

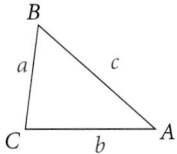

Real-World Connection

The length to the brace along each leg is 36 in. The brace is 26 in. long to guarantee that the triangle is acute.

6 EXAMPLE Classifying Triangles as Acute, Obtuse, or Right

The lengths of the sides of a triangle are given. Classify each triangle as acute, obtuse, or right.

a. 6, 11, 14

$14^2 \overset{?}{=} 6^2 + 11^2$ **Compare c^2 to $a^2 + b^2$. Substitute the greatest length for c.**

$196 \overset{?}{=} 36 + 121$

$196 > 157$

Since $c^2 > a^2 + b^2$, the triangle is obtuse.

b. 12, 13, 15

$15^2 \overset{?}{=} 12^2 + 13^2$ **Compare c^2 to $a^2 + b^2$. Substitute the greatest length for c.**

$225 \overset{?}{=} 144 + 169$

$225 < 313$

Since $c^2 < a^2 + b^2$, the triangle is acute.

✓ Check Understanding **6** A triangle has sides of lengths 7, 8, and 9. Classify the triangle by its angles.
acute

EXERCISES

For more practice, see *Extra Practice*.

 **Practice and Problem Solving**

A Practice by Example $\boxed{x^2}$ **Algebra** **Find the value of x.**

Example 1
(page 358)

1.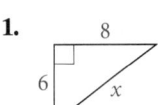

2.

3.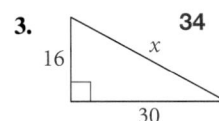

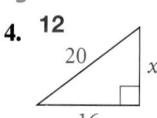 **Algebra** Find the value of x.

4.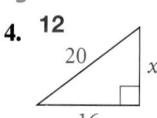

5.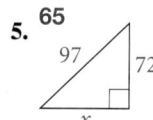

6.

Does each set of numbers form a Pythagorean triple? Explain.

7. $4, 5, 6$
no; $4^2 + 5^2 \neq 6^2$

8. $10, 24, 26$
yes; $10^2 + 24^2 = 26^2$

9. $15, 20, 25$
yes; $15^2 + 20^2 = 25^2$

Example 2
(page 358)

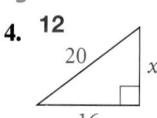 **Algebra** Find the value of x. Leave your answer in simplest radical form.

10.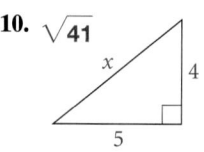

11.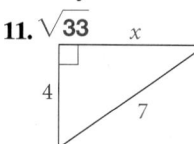

12.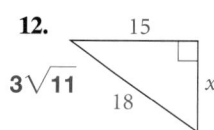

13.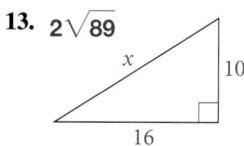

14.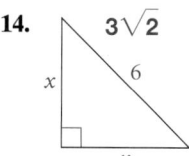

15.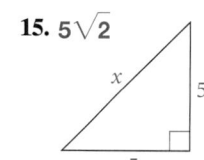

Example 3
(page 358)

16. Home Maintenance A painter leans a 15-ft ladder against a house. The base of the ladder is 5 ft from the house. To the nearest foot, how high on the house does the ladder reach? **14 ft**

17. A walkway forms the diagonal of a square playground. The walkway is 24 m long. To the nearest tenth of a meter, how long is a side of the playground? **17.0 m**

Example 4
(page 359)

Find the area of each triangle. Leave your answer in simplest radical form.

18.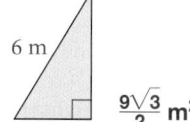
$\frac{9\sqrt{3}}{2}$ m²

19.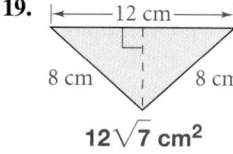
$12\sqrt{7}$ cm²

20.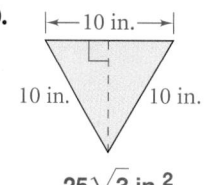
$25\sqrt{3}$ in.²

Example 5
(page 359)

Is each triangle a right triangle? Explain.

21.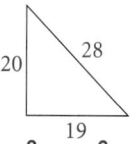
no; $19^2 + 20^2 \neq 28^2$

22.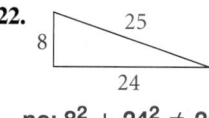
no; $8^2 + 24^2 \neq 25^2$

23.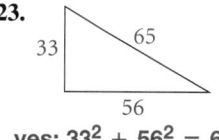
yes; $33^2 + 56^2 = 65^2$

Example 6
(page 360)

The lengths of the sides of a triangle are given. Classify each triangle as acute, right, or obtuse.

24. $15, 8, 21$ **obtuse**

25. $12, 16, 20$ **right**

26. $4, 5, 6$ **acute**

27. $30, 34, 16$ **right**

28. $0.3, 0.4, 0.6$ **obtuse**

29. $11, 12, 15$ **acute**

30. $\sqrt{3}, 2, 3$ **obtuse**

31. $18, 80, 82$ **right**

32. $20, 21, 28$ **acute**

33. $31, 23, 12$ **obtuse**

34. $30, 40, 50$ **right**

35. $\sqrt{11}, \sqrt{7}, 4$ **acute**

Assignment Guide

1 Objective
A B **Core** 1–20, 36–47
C **Extension** 65–69

2 Objective
A B **Core** 21–35, 48–64
C **Extension** 70

Standardized Test Prep 71–75

Mixed Review 76–83

Exercises 14, 15 These exercises anticipate the special right triangle relationships in Lesson 7-3. Ask: *What is the ratio* a : b : c *in each triangle?* $1 : 1 : \sqrt{2}$

Exercises 24–35 In only some of the exercises do the first two lengths represent *a* and *b*. Remind students to compare the sum of the squares of the two smaller lengths with the square of the greatest length.

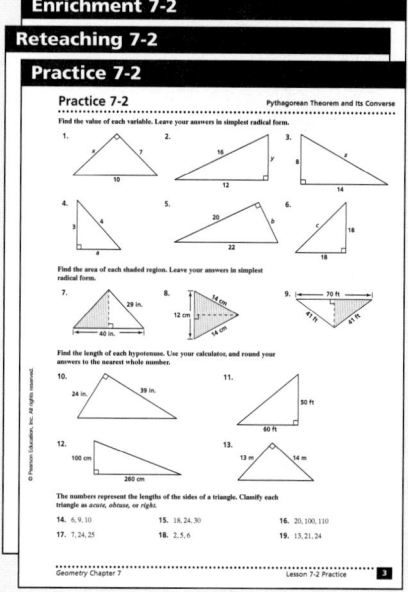

 **Apply Your Skills** **Algebra** Find the value of x. Leave your answer in simplest radical form.

36.
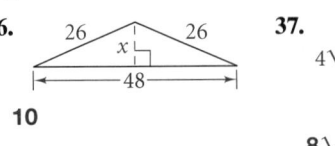
10

37.
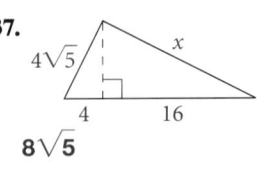
$8\sqrt{5}$

38.
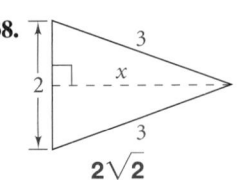
$2\sqrt{2}$

39. Answers may vary.
Sample: Have three people hold the rope 3 units, 4 units, and 5 units apart in the shape of a triangle.

39. Writing Each year in an ancient land, a large river overflowed its banks, often destroying boundary markers. The royal surveyors used a rope with knots at 12 equal intervals to help reconstruct boundaries. Explain how a surveyor could use this rope to form a right angle. (*Hint:* Use the Pythagorean triple 3, 4, 5.)

Find the area of each figure.

40.
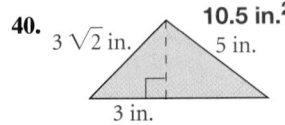
10.5 in.^{2}

41.
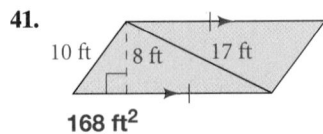
168 ft^2

42.
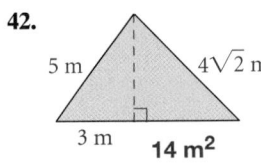
14 m^2

43.
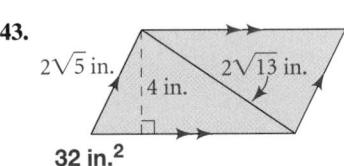
32 in.^{2}

Reading Math
For help with reading and solving Exercise 44, see p. 365.

44. Embroidery You want to embroider a square design. You have an embroidery hoop with a 6 in. diameter. Find the largest value of x so that the entire square will fit in the hoop. Round to the nearest tenth. **4.2 in.**
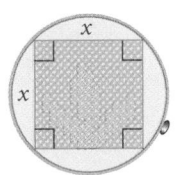

45. In parallelogram $RSTW$, $RS = 7$, $ST = 24$, and $RT = 25$. Is $RSTW$ a rectangle? Explain.
Yes; $7^2 + 24^2 = 25^2$, so $\angle RST$ is a rt. $\angle$.

Proof **46. Coordinate Geometry** You can use the Pythagorean Theorem to prove the Distance Formula. Let points $P(x_1, y_1)$ and $Q(x_2, y_2)$ be the endpoints of the hypotenuse of a right triangle.
   a. Write an algebraic expression to complete each of the following:
   $PR = $ ■ and $QR = $ ■. $|x_2 - x_1|$; $|y_2 - y_1|$

46b. $PQ^2 = (x_2 - x_1)^2 + (y_2 - y_1)^2$

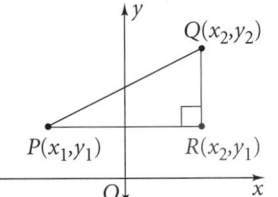

   b. By the Pythagorean Theorem, $PQ^2 = PR^2 + QR^2$. Rewrite this statement substituting the algebraic expressions you found for PR and QR in part (a).
   c. Complete the proof by taking the square root of each side of the equation that you wrote in part (b). $PQ = \sqrt{(x_2 - x_1)^2 + (y_2 - y_1)^2}$

47. Constructions Explain how to construct a segment of length $\sqrt{n}$, where n is any positive integer, and you are given a segment of length 1. (*Hint:* See the diagram.) **See margin.**
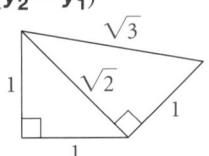

Find a third whole number so that the three numbers form a Pythagorean triple.

48. 20, 21 **29**   49. 14, 48 **50**   50. 13, 85 **84**   51. 12, 37 **35**

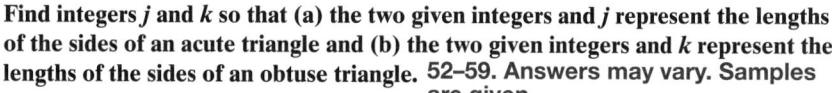

Need Help?

Remember that the sum of the lengths of any two sides of a triangle must be greater than the length of the third side.

Find integers j and k so that (a) the two given integers and j represent the lengths of the sides of an acute triangle and (b) the two given integers and k represent the lengths of the sides of an obtuse triangle. **52–59. Answers may vary. Samples are given.**

52. 4, 5 **6; 7**   **53.** 2, 4 **4; 5**   **54.** 6, 9 **8; 11**   **55.** 5, 10 **11; 12**

56. 6, 7 **8; 10**   **57.** 9, 12 **14; 16**   **58.** 8, 17 **18; 19**   **59.** 9, 40 **39; 42**

Proof **60. Reasoning** You can use the diagram at the right to prove the Pythagorean Theorem.
  a. Find the area of the large square in terms of c. c^2
  b. Find the area of the large square in terms of a and b by adding the areas of the four triangles and the small square. $2ab + (b - a)^2$
  c. Write an equation setting your answers to part (a) and part (b) equal to each other. Simplify the equation to complete the proof.
  $$c^2 = a^2 + b^2$$

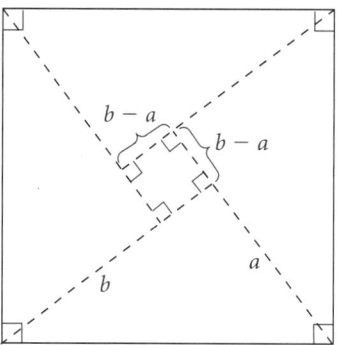

61. Astronomy The Hubble Space Telescope is orbiting Earth 600 km above Earth's surface. Earth's radius is about 6370 km. Use the Pythagorean Theorem to find the distance x from the telescope to Earth's horizon. Round your answer to the nearest ten kilometers. **2830 km**

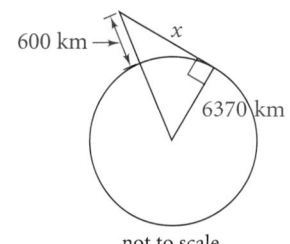

not to scale

The figures below are drawn on centimeter grid paper. Find the perimeter of each shaded figure to the nearest tenth.

62. **12 cm**   **63.** **12.5 cm**   **64.** **17.9 cm**

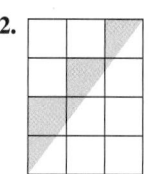 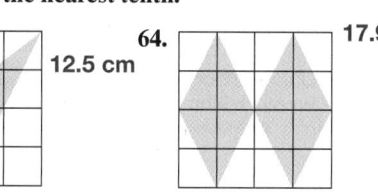

Real-World 🌐 **Connection**

Research by Edwin Hubble (1889–1953), here guiding a telescope in 1923, led to the Big Bang Theory of the formation of the universe.

C **Challenge**

65a. Answers may vary.
Sample: $n = 6$; 12, 35, 37

65. a. The ancient Greek philosopher Plato used the expressions $2n$, $n^2 - 1$, and $n^2 + 1$ to produce Pythagorean triples. Choose any integer greater than 1. Substitute for n and evaluate the three expressions.
  b. Verify that your answers to part (a) form a Pythagorean triple. $12^2 + 35^2 = 37^2$

66. Geometry in 3 Dimensions The box at the right is a rectangular solid.
  a. Use $\triangle ABC$ to find the length d_1 of the diagonal of the base. **5 in.**
  b. Use $\triangle ABD$ to find the length d_2 of the diagonal of the box. $\sqrt{29}$
  c. You can generalize the steps in parts (a) and (b). Use the facts that $AC^2 + BC^2 = d_1{}^2$ and $d_1{}^2 + BD^2 = d_2{}^2$ to write a one-step formula to find d_2. $d_2 = \sqrt{BD^2 + AC^2 + BC^2}$
  d. Use the formula you wrote to find the length of the longest fishing pole you can pack in a box with dimensions 18 in., 24 in., and 16 in. **34 in.**

1. Find the value of x.

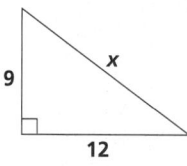

15

2. Find the value of x. Leave your answer in simplest radical form.

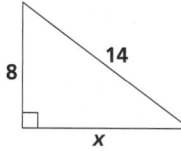

$2\sqrt{33}$

3. The town of Elena is 24 mi north and 8 mi west of Holberg. A train runs on a straight track between the two towns. How many miles does it cover? Round your answer to the nearest whole number. **25 mi**

4. Find the area of the shaded region. Leave your answer in simplest radical form.

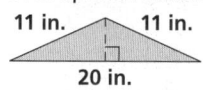

11 in.   11 in.
20 in.

$10\sqrt{21}$

5. The lengths of the sides of a triangle are 5 cm, 8 cm, and 10 cm. Is it acute, right, or obtuse? **obtuse**

Alternative Assessment

Have students use the Pythagorean Theorem to find the length of the diagonal of their notebook paper and explain in writing how the Pythagorean Theorem was used. Then have them measure the diagonal to confirm the length found using the Pythagorean Theorem.

A sheet of blank grids is available in the Test-Taking Strategies with Transparencies booklet. Give this sheet to students for practice with filling in the grids.

Resources

For additional practice with a variety of test item formats:
- Standardized Test Prep, p. 413
- Test-Taking Strategies, p. 408
- Test-Taking Strategies with Transparencies

Exercises 71–75 Remind students to begin by sketching each figure and labeling it carefully.

pages 360–364 Exercises

70. Draw right $\triangle FDE$ with legs $\overline{DE}$ of length a and $\overline{EF}$ of length b, and hyp. of length x. Then $a^2 + b^2 = x^2$ by the Pythagorean Thm. We are given $\triangle ABC$ with sides of length a, b, c and $a^2 + b^2 = c^2$. By subst., $c^2 = x^2$, so $c = x$. Since all side lengths of $\triangle ABC$ and $\triangle FDE$ are the same, $\triangle ABC \cong \triangle FDE$ by SSS. $\angle C \cong \angle E$ by CPCTC, so $m\angle C = 90$. Therefore, $\triangle ABC$ is a right $\triangle$.

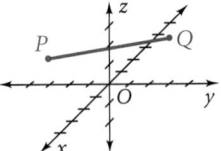

Geometry in 3 Dimensions Points $P(x_1, y_1, z_1)$ and $Q(x_2, y_2, z_2)$ at the left are points in a three-dimensional coordinate system. Use the following formula to find PQ. Leave your answer in simplest radical form.

$$d = \sqrt{(x_2 - x_1)^2 + (y_2 - y_1)^2 + (z_2 - z_1)^2}$$

67. $P(0,0,0), Q(1,2,3)$ 68. $P(0,0,0), Q(-3,4,-6)$ 69. $P(-1,3,5), Q(2,1,7)$
$\sqrt{14}$ $\sqrt{61}$ $\sqrt{17}$

Proof 70. Use the plan and write a paragraph proof of Theorem 7-5, the Converse of the Pythagorean Theorem.

Given: $\triangle ABC$ with sides of length a, b, and c where $a^2 + b^2 = c^2$

Prove: $\triangle ABC$ is a right triangle.

Plan: Draw a right triangle (not $\triangle ABC$) with legs of lengths a and b. Label the hypotenuse x. By the Pythagorean Theorem, $a^2 + b^2 = x^2$. Use substitution to compare the lengths of the sides of your triangle and $\triangle ABC$. Then prove the triangles congruent. **See margin.**

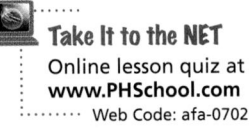

Standardized Test Prep

Gridded Response

71. The lengths of the legs of a right triangle are 17 m and 20 m. To the nearest tenth of a meter, what is the length of the hypotenuse? **26.2**

72. The hypotenuse of a right triangle is 34 ft. One leg is 16 ft. Find the length of the other leg in feet. **30**

73. What whole number forms a Pythagorean triple with 40 and 41? **9**

74. The two shorter sides of an obtuse triangle are 20 and 30. What is the least whole number length possible for the third side? **37**

Take It to the NET
Online lesson quiz at
www.PHSchool.com
Web Code: afa-0702

75. Each leg of an isosceles right triangle has measure 10 cm. To the nearest tenth of a centimeter, what is the length of the hypotenuse? **14.1**

Mixed Review

Lesson 7-1

76. Find the area of an isosceles right triangle that has one leg of length 12 cm. **72 cm²**

77. An isosceles right triangle has area of 112.5 ft². Find the length of each leg. **15 ft**

Lesson 5-2

In the figure, $\overrightarrow{PS}$ bisects $\angle RPT$. Solve for each variable. Then find RS.

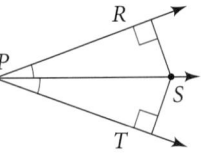

78. $RS = 2x + 19, ST = 7x - 16$; $x = \blacksquare, RS = \blacksquare$ **7; 33**

79. $RS = 2(7y - 11), ST = 5y + 5$; $y = \blacksquare, RS = \blacksquare$ **3; 20**

Lesson 4-1

$\triangle PQR \cong \triangle STV$. Solve for each variable.

80. $m\angle P = 4w + 5, m\angle S = 6w - 15$ **10**   81. $RQ = 10y - 6, VT = 5y + 9$ **3**

82. $m\angle T = 2x - 40, m\angle Q = x + 10$ **50**   83. $PR = 2z + 3, SV = 4z - 11$ **7**

Reading for Problem Solving

FOR USE WITH PAGE 362, EXERCISE 44

Read through the problem below and then follow along with what Sharleen thinks as she solves the problem. Check your understanding with the exercise at the bottom of the page.

You want to embroider a square design. You have an embroidery hoop with a 6 in. diameter. Find the largest value of x so that the entire square will fit in the hoop. Round to the nearest tenth.

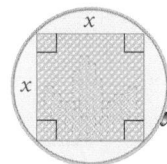

Reading Math

Reading for Problem Solving

Students must be able to identify the word sentences necessary to solve real-world problems and be able to write them as math sentences. This feature helps students analyze written material and extract relevant information.

Teaching Notes

As you read through the solution of the problem with the class, point out the importance of drawing a diagram as a first step. The diagram makes using the Pythagorean Theorem obvious, and each subsequent step in the solution hinges on that diagram.

Diversity

Provide an example of embroidery and embroidery hoops to students who are unfamiliar with them.

Exercise

Have students work independently to solve the problem, showing the steps they used. Then have volunteers share with the class what they were thinking as they wrote each step. Elicit the fact that there are often different ways to arrive at the solution of a problem.

What Sharleen Thinks

I'll draw the diagram without the embroidery and mark in it the information I know. In particular, I'll show a 6-in. diameter that *also* happens to be a diagonal of the square.

Now I have two right triangles. Each right triangle has two legs of length x in. and a hypotenuse of 6 in. I can apply the Pythagorean Theorem to find x.

Combine like terms.

Divide each side by 2.

Take the square root of each side.

Use a calculator. Then round to the nearest tenth.

The largest square that you can embroider with this hoop has sides of 4.2 in. (Don't forget to include the unit of measure.)

What Sharleen Writes

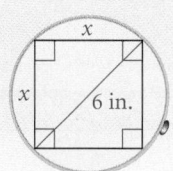

Diameter = 6, so length of diagonal = 6

$$a^2 + b^2 = c^2$$

$a = x, b = x,$ and $c = 6$

$$x^2 + x^2 = 6^2$$

$$2x^2 = 36$$

$$x^2 = 18$$

$$x = \sqrt{18}$$

$$x \approx 4.2426$$

$$x \approx 4.2 \text{ in.}$$

EXERCISE

Find each measurement for $\triangle ABC$. Round to the nearest tenth.

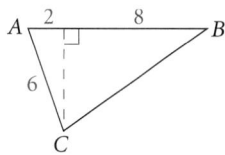

a. the perimeter   **25.8 units**
b. the area   **28.3 units²**

Lesson Preview

 **Check Skills You'll Need**

Measuring Angles
Lesson 1-4: Example 5
Exercises 23–25
Extra Practice, p. 690

Lesson Resources

 **Teaching Resources**
Practice, Reteaching, Enrichment
Checkpoint Quiz 1

Reaching All Students
Practice Workbook 7-3
Spanish Practice Workbook 7-3
Reading and Math Literacy 7B
Spanish Reading & Literacy 7B
Spanish Checkpoint Quiz 1
Informal Geometry Planning
   Guide 7-3

Presentation Assistant Plus!
Transparencies
• Check Skills You'll Need 7-3
• Additional Examples 7-3
• Student Edition Answers 7-3
• Lesson Quiz 7-3
PH Presentation Pro CD 7-3

PRENTICE HALL
ASSESSMENT SYSTEM

Checkpoint Quiz 1
Computer Test Generator CD

 **Technology**
Resource Pro® CD-ROM
Computer Test Generator CD
Prentice Hall Presentation Pro CD

www.PHSchool.com
Student Site
• Teacher Web Code: afk-5500
• Self-grading Lesson Quiz
Teacher Center
• Lesson Planner
• Resources

Plus **iTEXT**

366

7-3

Special Right Triangles

2.03 Apply properties, definitions, and theorems of two-dimensional figures to solve problems and write proofs: a) Triangles.

Lesson Preview

What You'll Learn

OBJECTIVE 1 To use the properties of 45°-45°-90° triangles

OBJECTIVE 2 To use the properties of 30°-60°-90° triangles

...And Why

To find the distance from home plate to second base on a softball diamond, as in Example 3

✔ Check Skills You'll Need

(For help, go to Lesson 1-4.)

Use a protractor to find the measures of the angles of each triangle.

1.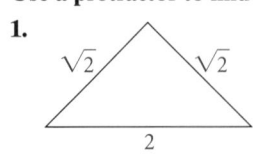
45, 45, 90

2.
30, 60, 90

3.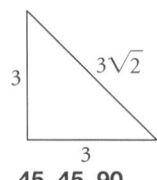
45, 45, 90

OBJECTIVE 1 Using 45°-45°-90° Triangles

 iTEXT Interactive lesson includes instant self-check, tutorials, and activities.

The acute angles of an isosceles right triangle are both 45° angles. Another name for an isosceles right triangle is a 45°-45°-90° triangle. If each leg has length x and the hypotenuse has length y, you can solve for y in terms of x.

$x^2 + x^2 = y^2$ **Use the Pythagorean Theorem.**

$2x^2 = y^2$ **Simplify.**

$x\sqrt{2} = y$ **Take the square root of each side.**

You have just proved the following theorem.

🔑 **Key Concepts**

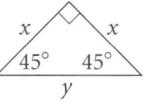

| Theorem 7-8 | 45°-45°-90° Triangle Theorem |

In a 45°-45°-90° triangle, both legs are congruent and the length of the hypotenuse is $\sqrt{2}$ times the length of a leg.

hypotenuse = $\sqrt{2}$ · leg

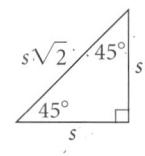

1 EXAMPLE Finding the Length of the Hypotenuse

Find the value of each variable.

a.

b.

$h = \sqrt{2} \cdot 9$ ⟵hypotenuse = $\sqrt{2}$ · leg⟶ $x = \sqrt{2} \cdot 2\sqrt{2}$

$h = 9\sqrt{2}$ ⟵ Simplify. ⟶ $x = 4$

✔ **Check Understanding** 1 Find the length of the hypotenuse of a 45°-45°-90° triangle with legs of length $5\sqrt{3}$.
$5\sqrt{6}$

366 Chapter 7 Area

 Ongoing Assessment and Intervention

Before the Lesson
Diagnose prerequisite skills using:
• Check Skills You'll Need

During the Lesson
Monitor progress using:
• Check Understanding
• Additional Examples
• Standardized Test Prep

After the Lesson
Assess knowledge using:
• Lesson Quiz
• Computer Test Generator CD
• Chapter Checkpoint 1 (p. 372)

You can use the 45°-45°-90° Triangle Theorem to find the length of a leg.

2 EXAMPLE **Finding the Length of a Leg**

Algebra Find the value of x.

$6 = \sqrt{2} \cdot x$ hypotenuse $= \sqrt{2} \cdot$ leg

$x = \dfrac{6}{\sqrt{2}}$ Divide each side by $\sqrt{2}$.

$x = \dfrac{6}{\sqrt{2}} \cdot \dfrac{\sqrt{2}}{\sqrt{2}} = \dfrac{6\sqrt{2}}{2}$ Multiply by a form of 1.

$x = 3\sqrt{2}$ Simplify.

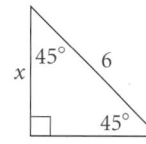

✓ **Check Understanding** ❷ Find the length of a leg of a 45°-45°-90° triangle with a hypotenuse of length 10.
$5\sqrt{2}$

When you apply the 45°-45°-90° Triangle Theorem to a real-life example, you can use a calculator to evaluate square roots.

3 EXAMPLE **Real-World Connection**

Softball A high school softball diamond is a square. The distance from base to base is 60 ft. To the nearest foot, how far does a catcher throw the ball from home plate to second base?

The distance d from home plate to second base is the length of the hypotenuse of a 45°-45°-90° triangle.

$d = 60\sqrt{2}$ hypotenuse $= \sqrt{2} \cdot$ leg

$d = 84.852814$ Use a calculator.

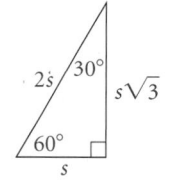

On a high school softball diamond, the catcher throws the ball about 85 ft from home plate to second base.

Real-World 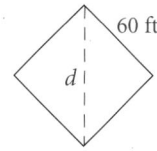 Connection

Careers Opportunities for coaching in women's sports have soared since the passage of Title IX in 1972.

✓ **Check Understanding** ❸ A square garden has sides 100 ft long. You want to build a brick path along a diagonal of the square. How long will the path be? Round your answer to the nearest foot. **141 ft**

OBJECTIVE

2 **Using 30°-60°-90° Triangles**

Another type of special right triangle is a 30°-60°-90° triangle.

 Key Concepts

Theorem 7-9	30°-60°-90° Triangle Theorem

In a 30°-60°-90° triangle, the length of the hypotenuse is twice the length of the shorter leg. The length of the longer leg is $\sqrt{3}$ times the length of the shorter leg.

hypotenuse $= 2 \cdot$ shorter leg

longer leg $= \sqrt{3} \cdot$ shorter leg

Professional Development

Math Background

The ratio of the lengths of any two sides of a right triangle is a function of either acute angle. This can be proved using similarity theorems and is the basis for the six trigonometric functions. The fixed side-length ratios of 45°-45°-90° and 30°-60°-90° triangles, easily found by applying the Pythagorean Theorem, provide benchmark values for the trigonometric functions sine, cosine, and tangent of 30°, 45°, and 60° angles.

OBJECTIVE

1 **Teaching Notes**

1 EXAMPLE **Technology Tip**

Point out that using mental math is much faster than using a calculator for part b. The calculator answer also would be inexact, whereas squaring the square root of a number is always exact.

2 EXAMPLE **Auditory Learners**

Have several students explain aloud to the class how to rationalize a denominator.

Additional Examples

❶ Find the length of the hypotenuse of a 45°-45°-90° triangle with legs of length $5\sqrt{6}$.
$10\sqrt{3}$

❷ Find the length of a leg of a 45°-45°-90° triangle with a hypotenuse of length 22. $11\sqrt{2}$

❸ The distance from one corner to the opposite corner of a square playground is 96 ft. To the nearest foot, how long is each side of the playground? **68 ft**

👥 **Reaching All Students**

Below Level In the diagram for Theorem 7-9, construct a 30° angle adjacent to the 30° angle, using a leg as one side. Extend the base so that it intersects the new side. Discuss why this forms an equilateral triangle.	**Advanced Learners** After students learn and apply Theorem 7-8, have them write a formula for the area of an isosceles right triangle whose hypotenuse has length s.	**Auditory Learners** See note on page 367. **Visual Learners** See note on page 368.

Visual Learners

Suggest that students distinguish between the 45°-45°-90° and the 30°-60°-90° Triangle Theorems by using the "ratio" diagrams below.

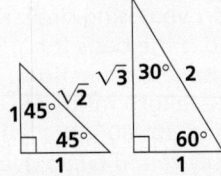

4 EXAMPLE Error Prevention

Whenever the length of a hypotenuse or longer leg of a 30°-60°-90° triangle is given, encourage students to find the length of the shorter leg first.

5 EXAMPLE Math Tip

Students can use the Pythagorean Theorem to check their work.

Additional Examples

4 Find the lengths of the legs of a 30°-60°-90° triangle with hypotenuse of length $4\sqrt{3}$.
shorter leg: $2\sqrt{3}$; longer leg: 6

5 The longer leg of a 30°-60°-90° triangle has length 18. Find the lengths of the shorter leg and the hypotenuse. shorter leg: $6\sqrt{3}$; hypotenuse: $12\sqrt{3}$

6 A garden shaped like a rhombus has a perimeter of 100 ft and a 60° angle. Find the area of the garden to the nearest square foot. 541 ft^2

Closure

In quadrilateral ABCD, AD = DC and AC = 20. Find the area of ABCD. Leave your answer in simplest radical form.

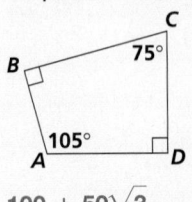

$100 + 50\sqrt{3}$

To prove Theorem 7-9, draw the a 30°-60°-90° triangle using an equilateral triangle.

Proof

Proof of Theorem 7-9

For 30°-60°-90° $\triangle WXY$ in equilateral $\triangle WXZ$, $\overline{WY}$ is the perpendicular bisector of $\overline{XZ}$.
Thus, $XY = \frac{1}{2}XZ = \frac{1}{2}XW$, or $XW = 2XY = 2s$.
Also,

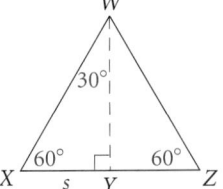

$XY^2 + YW^2 = XW^2$	Use the Pythagorean Theorem.
$s^2 + YW^2 = (2s)^2$	Substitute s for XY and 2s for XW.
$YW^2 = 4s^2 - s^2$	Subtract s^2 from each side.
$YW^2 = 3s^2$	Simplify.
$YW = s\sqrt{3}$	Find the square root of each side.

? Need Help?

In equilateral $\triangle WXZ$, $\overline{WY}$ is the bisector of $\angle XWZ$, the altitude and median to $\overline{XZ}$, and the perpendicular bisector of $\overline{XZ}$.

4 EXAMPLE Finding the Lengths of the Legs

Algebra Find the value of each variable.

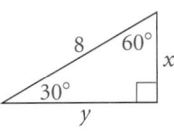

$8 = 2x$	hypotenuse = 2 · shorter leg
$x = 4$	Solve for x.
$y = x\sqrt{3}$	longer leg = $\sqrt{3}$ · shorter leg
$y = 4\sqrt{3}$	Substitute 4 for x.

✓ **Check Understanding** **4** Find the lengths of the legs of a 30°-60°-90° triangle with hypotenuse of length 12.
6; $6\sqrt{3}$

5 EXAMPLE Using the Length of a Leg

Algebra Find the value of each variable.

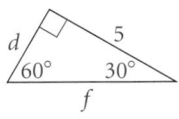

$5 = d\sqrt{3}$	longer leg = $\sqrt{3}$ · shorter leg
$d = \frac{5}{\sqrt{3}} \cdot \frac{\sqrt{3}}{\sqrt{3}} = \frac{5\sqrt{3}}{3}$	Solve for d.
$f = 2d$	hypotenuse = 2 · shorter leg
$f = 2 \cdot \frac{5\sqrt{3}}{3} = \frac{10\sqrt{3}}{3}$	Substitute $\frac{5\sqrt{3}}{3}$ for d.

✓ **Check Understanding** **5** The shorter leg of a 30°-60°-90° triangle has length $\sqrt{6}$. What are the lengths of the other two sides? Leave your answers in simplest radical form.
$3\sqrt{2}$; $2\sqrt{6}$

You can use the properties of 30°-60°-90° triangles to find the dimensions you need to calculate area.

6 EXAMPLE Real-World Connection

Road Signs The moose warning sign at the left is an equilateral triangle. Each side is 1 m long. Find the area of the sign.

To find the area, copy the triangle, draw an altitude h and find its length. The altitude bisects the base and divides the triangle into two 30°-60°-90° triangles.

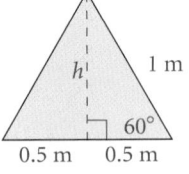

$h = 0.5\sqrt{3}$ longer leg = $\sqrt{3}$ · shorter leg

Use the value of h to find the area of the triangle.

$A = \frac{1}{2}bh$ **Use the formula for area of a triangle.**

$A = \frac{1}{2}(1)(0.5\sqrt{3})$ **Substitute 1 for b and $0.5\sqrt{3}$ for h.**

$A = 0.4330127$ **Use a calculator.**

● The area of the sign is about 0.4 m².

✓ **Check Understanding** ⑥ A rhombus has 10-in. sides, two of which meet to form the indicated angle. Find the area of the rhombus. (*Hint:* Use a special right triangle to find height.)
a. a 30° angle **50 in.²**   **b.** a 60° angle **50√3 in.²**

EXERCISES

For more practice, see *Extra Practice*.

Practice and Problem Solving

Ⓐ **Practice by Example**

Find the value of each variable. If your answer is not an integer, leave it in simplest radical form.

Example 1
(page 366)

1.  $x = 8; y = 8\sqrt{2}$ **2.** 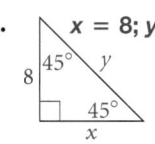 $x = \sqrt{2}; y = 2$ **3.** 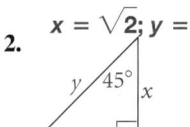 $y = 60\sqrt{2}$

Examples 2, 3
(page 367)

4. 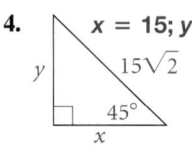 $x = 15; y = 15$ **5.** 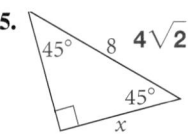   **6.** 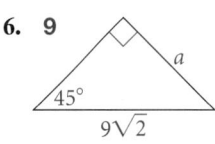 **9**

7. 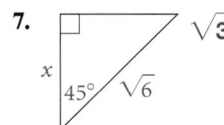   **8.** 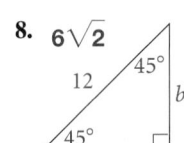   **9.**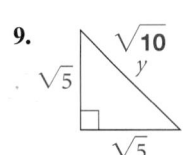

Exercise 10

10. Dinnerware Design You are designing dinnerware. What is the length of a side of the smallest square plate on which a 20-cm chopstick can fit along a diagonal without any overhang? Round your answer to the nearest tenth of a centimeter. **14.1 cm**

11. Helicopters The four blades of a helicopter meet at right angles and are all the same length. The distance between the tips of two adjacent blades is 36 ft. How long is each blade? Round your answer to the nearest tenth. **25.5 ft**

Example 4 [x²] **Algebra Find the value of each variable. If your answer is not an integer, leave it in simplest radical form.**
(page 368)

12. 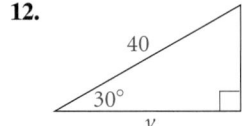 $x = 20; y = 20\sqrt{3}$ **13.** 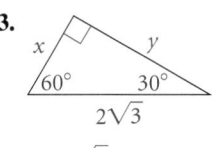 $x = \sqrt{3}; y = 3$ **14.** 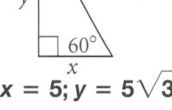 $x = 5; y = 5\sqrt{3}$

Lesson 7-3   Special Right Triangles   **369**

3. Practice

Assignment Guide

1 Objective
  Ⓐ Ⓑ Core 1–11, 23, 28, 29, 34, 36, 37
  Ⓒ Extension 40

2 Objective
  Ⓐ Ⓑ Core 12–22, 24–27, 30–33, 35, 38, 39
  Ⓒ Extension 41

Standardized Test Prep 42–46

Mixed Review 47–55

Diversity
Exercise 10 Some of your students may eat with chopsticks every day, and others may never have seen chopsticks. Ask a volunteer to bring chopsticks to class and demonstrate how to use them.

Exercise 11 Point out that it is not necessary to rationalize the denominator before using a calculator to find the approximate length of the blade.

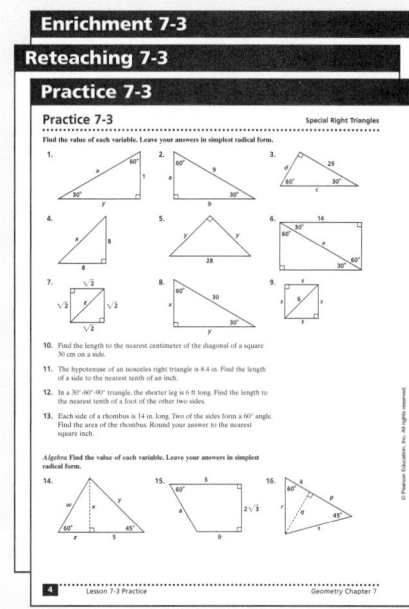

Exercise 22 If students use the area formula for a parallelogram, ask: *What figures are formed if you draw the diagonals of the rhombus instead of an altitude?* **four congruent 30°-60°-90° triangles** Discuss as a class how to find the area of the rhombus using this approach. Students should check that the area of the rhombus is the same using both methods.

Exercises 24–26 Point out that knowing the side-lengths ratios of 45°-45°-90° and 30°-60°-90° triangles helps students recognize patterns. Students should first find any side length that can be derived using a given side. After the first length is found, the other lengths often fall into place.

Exercises 27–29 Each of these exercises requires constructing an altitude to form a rectangle. Students may work with partners to discuss a plan of solution before actually finding the values.

Exercise 30 Ask: *How can you tell that Rika is correct without using the theorems in this lesson?* **The longer leg must be opposite the greater angle.**

Exercise 33 This is a good exercise to discuss as a class to assess how well students understand and apply both theorems in this lesson.

Example 5   **Algebra Find the value of each variable. Leave your answer in simplest radical form.**
(page 368)

15.
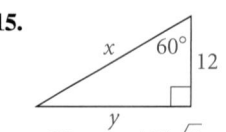
$x = 24; y = 12\sqrt{3}$

16.
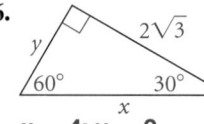
$x = 4; y = 2$

17.
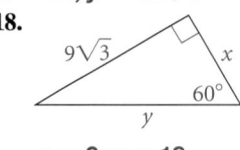
$x = 4\sqrt{3}; y = 6$

18.
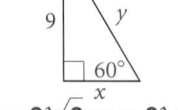
$x = 9; y = 18$

19.

$x = 3\sqrt{3}; y = 6\sqrt{3}$

20.

$x = 5\sqrt{3}; y = 10\sqrt{3}$

Example 6
(page 368)

Find the area of each figure. Round your answer to the nearest tenth.

21. an equilateral triangle with sides 10 cm **43.3 cm²**

22. a rhombus with a 60° angle and sides 5 cm long **21.7 cm²**

23. a rhombus with a 45° angle and sides 12 m long **101.8 m²**

B Apply Your Skills **Algebra Find the value of each variable. Leave your answer in simplest radical form.**

24. $a = 7; b = 14; c = 7;$
$d = 7\sqrt{3}$

25. $a = 6; b = 6\sqrt{2};$
$c = 2\sqrt{3}; d = 6$

26. $a = 10\sqrt{3}; b = 5\sqrt{3};$
$c = 15; d = 5$

24.
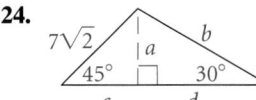

25.
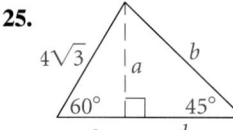

26.
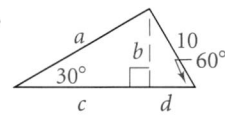

27.
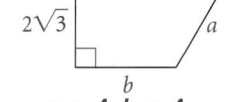
$a = 4; b = 4$

28.
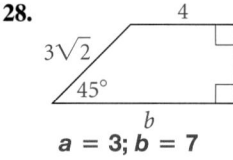
$a = 3; b = 7$

29.
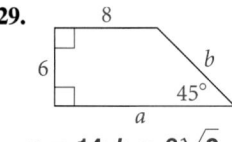
$a = 14; b = 6\sqrt{2}$

30. Rika; Sandra marked the shorter leg as opposite the 60° angle.

30. Error Analysis Sandra drew the triangle at the right. Rika said that the lengths couldn't be correct. With which student do you agree? Explain your answer.

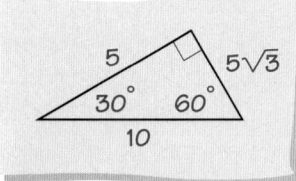

31. Open-Ended Write a real-life problem that you can solve using a 30°-60°-90° triangle with a 12 ft hypotenuse. Show your solution. **See margin.**

Exercise 32

32. Farming A conveyor belt carries bales of hay from the ground to the barn loft 24 ft above the ground. The belt makes a 60° angle with the ground.
a. How far does a bale of hay travel from one end of the conveyor belt to the other? Round your answer to the nearest foot. **28 ft**
b. The conveyor belt moves at 100 ft/min. How long does it take for a bale of hay to go from the ground to the barn loft? **0.28 min**

33. House Repair After heavy winds damaged a farmhouse, workers placed a 6-m brace against its side at a 45° angle. Then, at the same spot on the ground, they placed a second, longer brace to make a 30° angle with the side of the house.
a. How long is the longer brace? Round your answer to the nearest tenth of a meter. **8.5 m**
b. How much higher on the house does the longer brace reach than the shorter brace? **3.1 m**

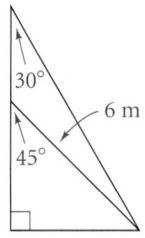

pages 369–372 Exercises

31. Answers may vary. Sample: A ramp up to a door is 12 ft long. It has an incline of 30°. How high off the ground is the door? sol.: 6 ft

Find the area of each figure. When an answer is not a whole number, round to the nearest tenth.

34. 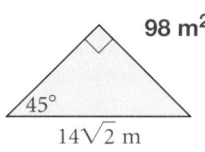 98 m²

35. 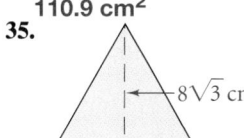 110.9 cm²

36. 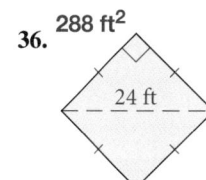 288 ft²

37. 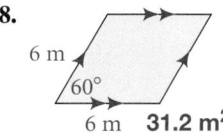 11.3 yd²

38. 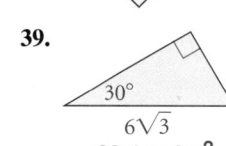 31.2 m²

39. 23.4 units²

 **Challenge**

40a. √3 units
 b. 2√3 units
 c. s√3 units

40. Geometry in 3 Dimensions Find the length d, in simplest radical form, of the diagonal of a cube with sides of the given length. **See left.**
 a. 1 unit **b.** 2 units **c.** s units

41. a. Find the area of an equilateral triangle with altitude 1 unit. Leave your answer in simplest radical form. $\frac{\sqrt{3}}{3}$ units²
 b. Use the relationships among the lengths of the sides in a 30°-60°-90° triangle to find a formula for the area of an equilateral triangle in terms of the length h of an altitude. $A = \frac{h^2\sqrt{3}}{3}$
 c. Use your formula from part (b) to find the area of an equilateral triangle with altitude of length 6 units. $12\sqrt{3}$ units²

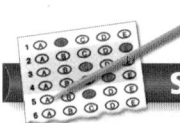
Standardized Test Prep

Quantitative Comparison

Compare the boxed quantity in Column A with the boxed quantity in Column B. Choose the best answer.
 A. The quantity in Column A is greater.
 B. The quantity in Column B is greater.
 C. The two quantities are equal.
 D. The relationship cannot be determined from the information given.

Column A	Column B
A 42. the length of the diagonal of a square with sides of length 3	the length of a leg of a 45°-45°-90° triangle with hypotenuse of length 3
C 43. the length of the shorter leg of a 30°-60°-90° triangle with hypotenuse of length 4	the length of the hypotenuse of a 30°-60°-90° triangle with longer leg of length √3
D 44. the length of an altitude of an equilateral triangle	the length of the shorter leg of a 30°-60°-90° triangle

Take It to the NET
Online lesson quiz at
www.PHSchool.com
Web Code: afa-0703

Multiple Choice

45. What is the length of a diagonal of a square with sides of length 4? **D**
 A. 2 **B.** √2 **C.** 2√2 **D.** 4√2

Lesson 7-3 Special Right Triangles **371**

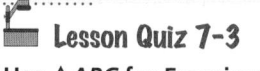
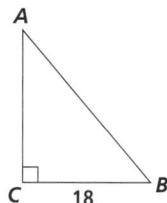
371

To check understanding of
Lessons 7-1 to 7-3:

Checkpoint Quiz 1 (p. 372)

📁 **Teaching Resources**
Checkpoint Quiz 1 (also in
   Prentice Hall Assessment
   System)

👥 **Reaching All Students**
Reading and Math Literacy 7B

Spanish versions available

---

pages 369–372 Exercises

46. **[2] a.** Let a leg measure
       x. Then $\frac{1}{2}x^2 = 16$
       and $x = 4\sqrt{2}$ m.

    b. The hypotenuse is
       $\sqrt{2}$ · leg, so
       $4\sqrt{2} \cdot \sqrt{2} = 8$ m.

    [1] incorrect calculation
       OR no explanation

49. **no**
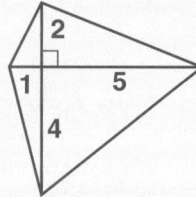

Short Response

46. An isosceles right triangle has area 16 m². **See margin.**
    a. Find the length of each leg. Leave your answer in simplest radical form.
       Justify your answer.
    b. Find the length of the hypotenuse. Justify your answer.

Mixed Review

Lesson 7-2

An isosceles triangle has 20-cm legs and a 16-cm base. Find each of the following.
Leave your answers in simplest radical form.

47. the length of the altitude to the base $4\sqrt{21}$ **cm**

48. the area of the triangle $32\sqrt{21}$ **cm²**

Lesson 6-4

Determine whether each quadrilateral must be a parallelogram. If not, provide
a counterexample.

49. The diagonals are congruent and perpendicular to each other. **See margin.**

50. Two opposite angles are right angles and two opposite sides are 5 cm long. **yes**

51. One pair of sides is congruent and the other pair of sides is parallel.
    no; an isosceles trapezoid

Lesson 4-3

Can you conclude that $\triangle TRY \cong \triangle ANG$ from the given conditions? If so, name
the postulate or theorem that justifies your conclusion.

52. **yes; AAS Thm.** 52. $\angle A \cong \angle T, \angle Y \cong \angle G, \overline{TR} \cong \overline{AN}$ 53. $\angle T \cong \angle A, \angle R \cong \angle N, \angle Y \cong \angle G$ **no**

54. $\angle R \cong \angle N, \overline{TR} \cong \overline{AN}, \overline{TY} \cong \overline{AG}$ **no** 55. $\angle G \cong \angle Y, \angle N \cong \angle R, \overline{RY} \cong \overline{NG}$
     yes; ASA Post.

✓ Checkpoint Quiz 1   Lessons 7-1 through 7-3

📱 **iTEXT** Instant self-check
quiz online and
on CD-ROM

Find the area of each figure.

1.

8 in.
21 in.
84 in.²

2.
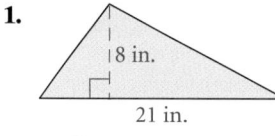
16 cm
14 cm
8 cm
112 cm²

3.
10 m
6 m   6 m
48 m²

📦 **Algebra Find the value of each variable. Leave your answer in simplest radical form.**

4.
x
15
9
12

5.
x
y
10
x = 10; y = 10√2

6.
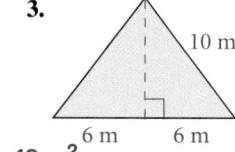
12
y
30°
x
x = 12√3; y = 24

**The lengths of the sides of a triangle are given. Classify each triangle as *acute*,
obtuse, or *right*.**

7. 7, 8, 9 **acute**   8. 15, 36, 39 **right**   9. 10, 12, 16 **obtuse**

10. A square has a 40-cm diagonal. How long is each side of the square? Round
    your answer to the nearest tenth of a centimeter. **28.3 cm**

Areas of Trapezoids, Rhombuses, and Kites

 North Carolina Objectives

1.02   Use length, area, and volume of geometric figures to solve problems. Include perimeter, area, and volume of composite figures.

Lesson Preview

What You'll Learn

 OBJECTIVE 1
To find the area of a trapezoid

 OBJECTIVE 2
To find the area of a rhombus or a kite

. . . And Why

To use a map and the trapezoid area formula to approximate the area of Arkansas, as in Example 1

✓ Check Skills You'll Need

(For help, go to Lesson 7-1.)

Write the formula for the area of each type of figure.

1. a rectangle $A = bh$ or $A = \ell w$ **2.** a triangle $A = \frac{1}{2}bh$

Find the area of each trapezoid by using the formulas for area of a rectangle and area of a triangle.

3.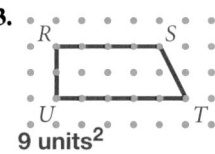
9 units^2

4.
7 units^2

5.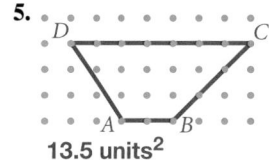
13.5 units^2

New Vocabulary   • height of a trapezoid

 iTEXT   Interactive lesson includes instant self-check, tutorials, and activities.

OBJECTIVE

1   **Area of a Trapezoid**

Investigation: Finding the Area of a Trapezoid

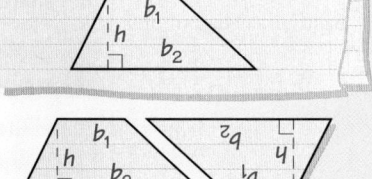

• Fold a piece of lined paper in half along one of the lines. On two lines of the folded paper, draw parallel segments of different lengths. Connect the endpoints of the segments to form a trapezoid.

• Cut through both layers of the folded paper, so that you will have two congruent trapezoids. Label b_1, b_2, and h for each trapezoid.

• Arrange the congruent trapezoids to form a parallelogram as shown at the right above.

1a. $b_1 + b_2$

1. a. Write an expression for the length of the base of the parallelogram.
   b. Write an expression for the area of the parallelogram using b_1, b_2, and h. $h(b_1 + b_2)$

2. How does the area of each trapezoid compare to the area of the parallelogram?   The area of each trapezoid is half the area of the parallelogram.

3. Use your answers to Exercises 1 and 2 to write a formula for the area of each trapezoid. $A = \frac{1}{2}h(b_1 + b_2)$

---

1. Plan

Lesson Preview

✓ **Check Skills You'll Need**

Finding the Area of a Parallelogram
Lesson 7-1: Example 1
Exercises 1–3
Extra Practice, p. 696

Finding the Area of a Triangle
Lesson 7-1: Example 4
Exercises 11–13
Extra Practice, p. 696

Lesson Resources

📁 **Teaching Resources**
Practice, Reteaching, Enrichment

👥 **Reaching All Students**
Practice Workbook 7-4
Spanish Practice Workbook 7-4
Hands-On Activities 20
Informal Geometry Planning
   Guide 7-4

⏱ **Presentation Assistant Plus!**
Transparencies
• Check Skills You'll Need 7-4
• Additional Examples 7-4
• Student Edition Answers 7-4
• Lesson Quiz 7-4
PH Presentation Pro CD 7-4

PRENTICE HALL ASSESSMENT SYSTEM

Computer Test Generator CD

💿 **Technology**
Resource Pro® CD-ROM
Computer Test Generator CD
Prentice Hall Presentation Pro CD

💻 **www.PHSchool.com**
Student Site
• Teacher Web Code: afk-5500
• Self-grading Lesson Quiz
Teacher Center
• Lesson Planner
• Resources

Plus  **iTEXT**

 **Ongoing Assessment and Intervention**

Before the Lesson	During the Lesson	After the Lesson
Diagnose prerequisite skills using:	**Monitor progress using:**	**Assess knowledge using:**
• Check Skills You'll Need	• Check Understanding • Additional Examples • Standardized Test Prep	• Lesson Quiz • Computer Test Generator CD

2. Teach

Math Background

Area formulas for trapezoids, rhombuses, and kites are derived from area formulas for triangles and parallelograms, and depend on properties of quadrilaterals such as *opposite sides of a parallelogram are parallel* and *diagonals of a rhombus and of a kite are perpendicular.*

OBJECTIVE
1 Teaching Notes

Investigation (Optional)
As students arrange the trapezoids, they should note that the horizontal sides of the figure are both congruent and parallel. This allows them to conclude that the figure is a parallelogram.

Alternative Method
The formula for the area of a trapezoid also can be written $A = \frac{1}{2}b_1h + \frac{1}{2}b_2h$. Have students partition a trapezoid into two triangles to illustrate the formula above, as is done in Exercise 38.

2 EXAMPLE Teaching Tip

Ask: *Why do you need to divide the longer base into 2-m and 5-m segments?* You need to know the length of the shorter leg to find *h*.

Additional Examples

1 A car window is shaped like the trapezoid shown. Find the area of the window.

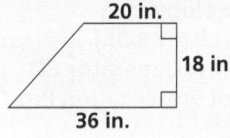

504 in.²

2 Find the area of trapezoid *ABCD*.

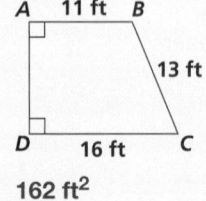

162 ft²

374

Reading Math

The term *base* can refer to either a line segment or its length.

In Lesson 6-5, you learned that the bases of a trapezoid are the parallel sides and the legs are the nonparallel sides. The **height of a trapezoid** is the perpendicular distance *h* between the bases.

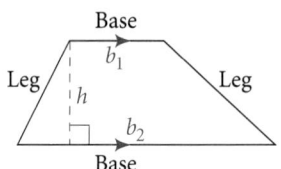

The pictures on the previous page suggest the following theorem.

Key Concepts

Theorem 7-10	Area of a Trapezoid

The area of a trapezoid is half the product of the height and the sum of the bases.

$$A = \frac{1}{2}h(b_1 + b_2)$$

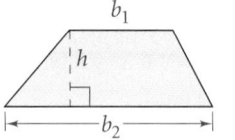

1 EXAMPLE Real-World Connection

Geography Approximate the area of Arkansas by finding the area of the trapezoid shown.

$$A = \frac{1}{2}h(b_1 + b_2) \quad \text{Use the formula for area of a trapezoid.}$$
$$= \frac{1}{2}(242)(190 + 250) \quad \text{Substitute 242 for } h, 190 \text{ for } b_1, \text{ and } 250 \text{ for } b_2.$$
$$= 53{,}240 \quad \text{Simplify.}$$

● The area of Arkansas is about 53,240 mi².

✓ Check Understanding **1** Find the area of a trapezoid with height 7 cm and bases 12 cm and 15 cm. **94.5 cm²**

Properties of special right triangles can help you find the area of a trapezoid.

2 EXAMPLE Finding Area Using a Right Triangle

Find the area of trapezoid *PQRS*. Leave your answer in simplest radical form.

You can draw an altitude that divides the trapezoid into a rectangle and a 30°-60°-90° triangle. Since the opposite sides of a rectangle are congruent, the longer base of the trapezoid is divided into segments of lengths 2 m and 5 m.

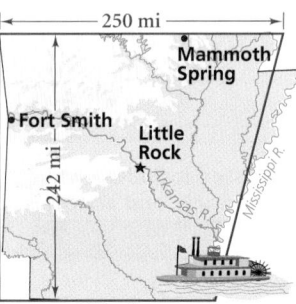

Find *h*.

$$h = 2\sqrt{3} \quad \text{longer leg = shorter leg} \cdot \sqrt{3}$$
$$A = \frac{1}{2}h(b_1 + b_2) \quad \text{Use the trapezoid area formula.}$$
$$= \frac{1}{2}(2\sqrt{3})(7 + 5) \quad \text{Substitute.}$$
$$= 12\sqrt{3} \quad \text{Simplify.}$$

7 m – 5 m = 2 m

● The area of trapezoid *PQRS* is $12\sqrt{3}$ m².

✓ Check Understanding **2** In Example 2, suppose *h* is made smaller so that $m\angle P = 45$ while bases and angles *R* and *Q* are unchanged. Find the area of trapezoid *PQRS*. **12 m²**

374   Chapter 7   Area

👥 Reaching All Students

Below Level After the visual proof of Theorem 7-11, have students draw and color a kite or a rhombus within a rectangle and then use paper cutting to match pairs of congruent triangles.	**Advanced Learners** Have students explore whether a quadrilateral that is not a rhombus or a kite can satisfy the formula in Theorem 7-11.	**Tactile Learners** See note on page 375. **Auditory Learners** See note on page 376.

2 Finding Areas of Rhombuses and Kites

Rhombuses and kites have perpendicular diagonals. This property allows you to find areas using the following theorem.

 Key Concepts

> **Theorem 7-11**   **Area of a Rhombus or a Kite**
>
> The area of a rhombus or a kite is half the product of the lengths of its diagonals.
>
> $$A = \frac{1}{2}d_1 d_2$$
>
>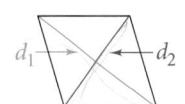

Proof →   **Visual Proof:** The rectangle has sides d_1 and d_2 congruent to the diagonals of the kite or rhombus. Each triangle shaded blue in the diagram is congruent to the triangle shaded green that shares its hypotenuse. Thus, the area of the kite or rhombus is half the area of the rectangle.

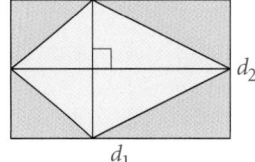

3 EXAMPLE   Finding the Area of a Kite

Find the area of kite *KLMN*.

For the two diagonals, $KM = 2 + 5 = 7$ m and $LN = 3 + 3 = 6$ m.

$A = \frac{1}{2}d_1 d_2$ **Use the formula for area of a kite.**

$A = \frac{1}{2}(7)(6)$ **Substitute 7 for d_1 and 6 for d_2.**

$A = 21$ **Simplify.**

● The area of kite *KLMN* is 21 m^2.

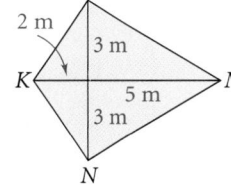

54 in.^{2}

✓ **Check Understanding**   **3** Find the area of a kite with diagonals that are 12 in. and 9 in. long.

The fact that the diagonals of a rhombus bisect each other can help you find the area.

4 EXAMPLE   Finding the Area of a Rhombus

Find the area of rhombus *ABCD*.

△*BEC* is a right triangle. Using a Pythagorean triple, $BE = 9$. Since the diagonals of a rhombus bisect each other, $AC = 24$ and $BD = 18$.

$A = \frac{1}{2}d_1 d_2$ **Use the formula for area of a rhombus.**

$A = \frac{1}{2}(24)(18)$ **Substitute 24 for d_1 and 18 for d_2.**

$A = 216$ **Simplify.**

● The area is 216 m^2.

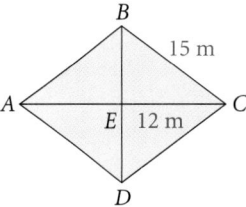

✓ **Check Understanding**   **4** **Critical Thinking** In Example 4, explain how you can use a Pythagorean triple to conclude that $BE = 9$. $9^2 + 12^2 = 15^2$

Tactile Learners

For the Visual Proof of the Area of a Rhombus or a Kite Theorem, have students draw a kite or rhombus and use paper folding to identify the diagonals. Have students carefully cut along the diagonals and then fold back the right triangles along the sides of the rhombus or kite. The right angles will be vertices of a rectangle with area twice that of the original figure.

3 EXAMPLE **Alternative Method**

Students also can find the area by adding the areas of the four right triangles.

Additional Examples

3 Find the area of kite *XYZW*.

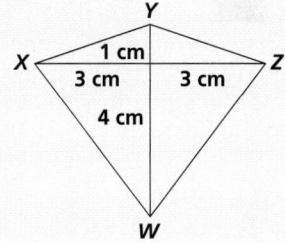

15 cm^2

4 Find the area of rhombus *RSTU*.

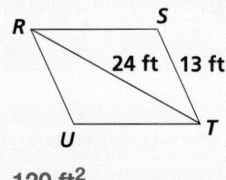

120 ft^2

Closure

Use the formula for the area of a rhombus to show that the area of a square with 30-in. sides is 900 in.^{2}

$A = \frac{1}{2}(30\sqrt{2})(30\sqrt{2}) = \frac{1}{2}(30)(30)(2) = 900$ in.^{2}

375

Assignment Guide

1 Objective
Ⓐ Ⓑ **Core** 1–13, 21, 22, 24–27
Ⓒ **Extension** 39–40

2 Objective
Ⓐ Ⓑ **Core** 14–20, 23, 28–38
Ⓒ **Extension** 41

Standardized Test Prep 42–47

Mixed Review 48–54

Auditory Learners
Exercise 6 Discuss as a class how to write and solve the appropriate formula. Have one student give each step verbally while another student writes the steps on the board.

Error Prevention
Exercise 13 Students may conclude that the nonparallel sides of the trapezoid are congruent because of the theorem *Base angles of an isosceles trapezoid are congruent.* Discuss as a class how this conclusion actually uses the converse of the theorem.

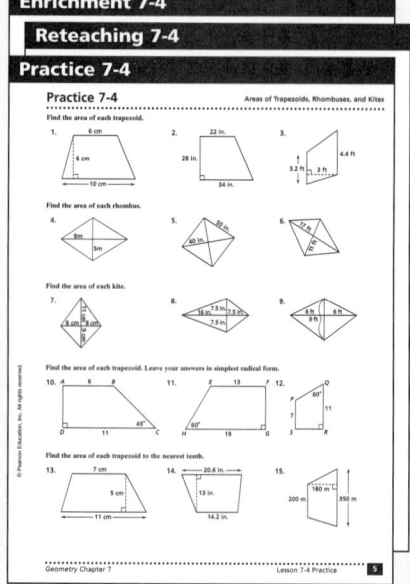

Ⓐ **Practice by Example**

Example 1
(page 374)

Find the area of each trapezoid.

1.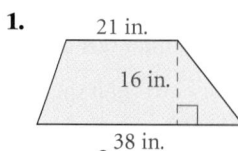
21 in. / 16 in. / 38 in.
472 in.²

2.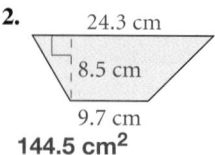
24.3 cm / 8.5 cm / 9.7 cm
144.5 cm²

3.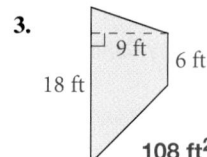
9 ft / 6 ft / 18 ft
108 ft²

4. Geography Approximate the area of Nevada by finding the area of the trapezoid shown. **110,622 mi²**

5. Find the area of a trapezoid with bases 12 cm and 18 cm and height 10 cm. **150 cm²**

6. Find the area of a trapezoid with bases 2 ft and 3 ft and height $\frac{1}{3}$ ft. $\frac{5}{6}$ **ft²**

7. Geography The border of Tennessee resembles a trapezoid with bases 342 mi and 438 mi, and height 111 mi. Approximate the area of Tennessee by finding the area of this trapezoid. **about 43,290 mi²**

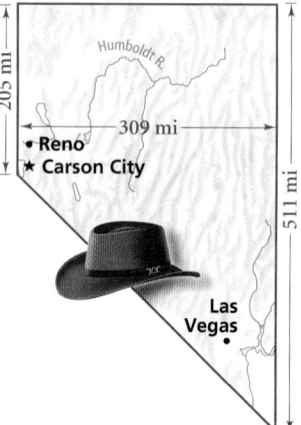
Humboldt R. / 205 mi / 309 mi / Reno / Carson City / 511 mi / Las Vegas

Example 2
(page 374)

Find the area of each trapezoid. If your answer is not an integer, leave it in simplest radical form.

8. 5 ft / 3 ft / 6 ft
30 ft²

9.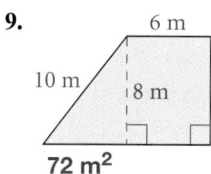
6 m / 10 m / 8 m
72 m²

10.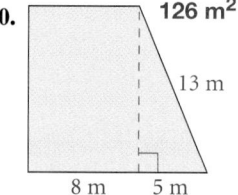
126 m² / 13 m / 8 m / 5 m

11. 8 ft / 60°
52√3 ft² 15 ft

12.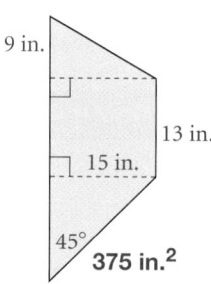
9 in. / 13 in. / 15 in. / 45°
375 in.²

13.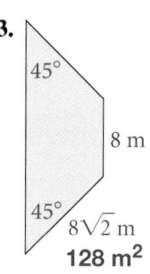
45° / 8 m / 45° / 8√2 m
128 m²

Example 3
(page 375)

Find the area of each kite.

14.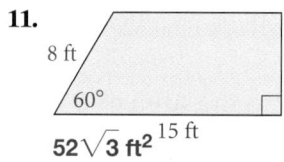
2 in. / 8 in. / 8 in. / 8 in.
80 in.²

15.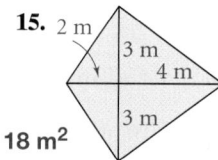
2 m / 3 m / 4 m / 3 m
18 m²

16.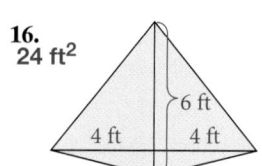
24 ft² / 6 ft / 4 ft / 4 ft

17. A kite has diagonals 7 ft and 16 ft. What is the area of the kite? **56 ft²**

Example 4
(page 375)

Find the area of each rhombus.

18.
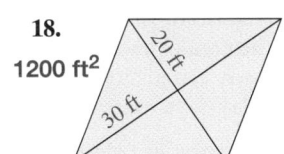
1200 ft²

19.
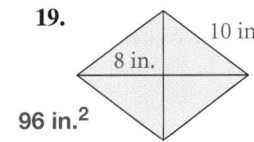
96 in.²

20.
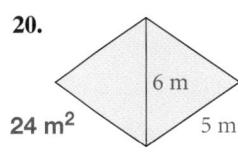
24 m²

 **Apply Your Skills**

21. The end of the rain gutter has the shape of a trapezoid with the measurements shown. Find the area of this end. **20 in.²**
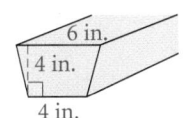

22. A trapezoid has two right angles, 12-m and 18-m bases, and 8-m height. **a–c. See margin.**
   a. Sketch the trapezoid.   **b.** Find the perimeter.   **c.** Find the area.

23. **Open-Ended** Draw a kite. Measure the lengths of its diagonals. Find its area.
   Check students' work.

Gold Bars Find the area of each trapezoidal face of the gold bars.

24. End face: bases 4 cm and 2 cm, height 3 cm. **9 cm²**

25. Side face: bases 8 cm and 5 cm, height 3 cm. **19.5 cm²**

Find the area of each trapezoid to the nearest tenth.

26. **11.3 cm²**
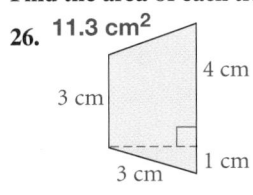

27.
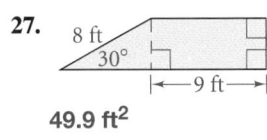
49.9 ft²

28. **1.8 m²**
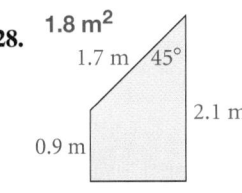

Coordinate Geometry In Exercises 29–32, find the area of quadrilateral *QRST*.

29. **18 units²**
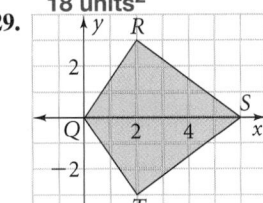

30. **15 units²**
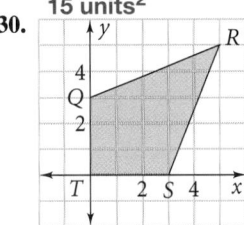

31. **15 units²**
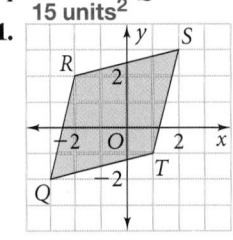

32. *QRST* has vertices *Q*(0, 0), *R*(0, 5), *S*(5, 5), and *T*(7, 0). **30 units²**

33. Find the area of the kite at the right. **135 m²**
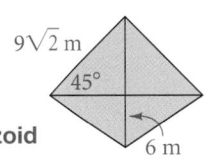

34. **a. Coordinate Geometry** Graph the lines
   $x = 0, x = 6, y = 0$, and $y = x + 4$. **See left.**
   b. What type of quadrilateral do the lines form? **trapezoid**
   c. Find the area of the quadrilateral. **42 units²**

34a.
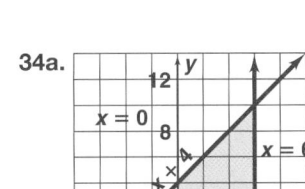

Find the area of each rhombus. Leave your answer in simplest radical form.

35. **18 cm²**
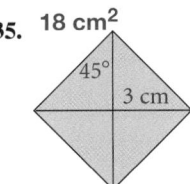

36. **32√3 m²**
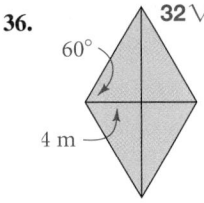

37.
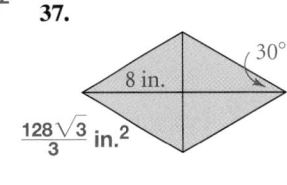
$\frac{128\sqrt{3}}{3}$ **in.²**

Real-World Connection

On each gold bar the four trapezoidal faces tip inwards. This simplifies the molding process.

 **Need Help?**

In Exercises 35–37, recall what is true about the diagonals of a rhombus.

---

pages 376–379 **Exercises**

22. **a.**
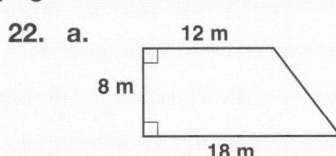
   b. **48 m**
   c. **120 m²**

Margin notes:

Diversity

Exercise 21 Because some houses do not have rain gutters, discuss the function of rain gutters. Suggest that students look for rain gutters on their way home from school and report their findings to the class.

Exercises 29–31 Have students suggest different methods for calculating the areas of the quadrilaterals, and compare their answers to check for arithmetic or reasoning errors.

Alternative Method

Exercise 35 Challenge students to prove that the rhombus is a square, find the length of a side, and then use the formula for the area of a square.

Connection to Algebra

Exercise 39 Students must solve a quadratic equation in *x*.

Connection to Calculus

Exercise 40 Approximating the area between a curve and the *x*-axis by using trapezoids is taught in integral calculus. Using calculus, the exact area of shapes with curved sides can be found. Ask: *For what curved figure do you already know an area formula?* **circle**

Exercise 41 To solve, students must draw perpendicular segments to $\overline{DC}$ from point *A* and point *B*.

Lesson Quiz 7-4

1. Find the area of a trapezoid with bases 3 cm and 19 cm and height 9 cm. **99 cm²**

2. Find the area of a trapezoid in a coordinate plane with vertices at (1, 1), (1, 6), (5, 9), and (5, 1). **26 square units**

Find the area of each figure in Exercises 3–5. Leave your answers in simplest radical form.

3. trapezoid *ABCD*

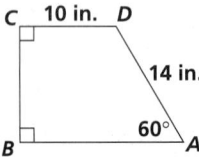

94.5√3 in.²

4. kite with diagonals 20 m and 10√2 m long **100√2 m²**

5. rhombus *MNOP*

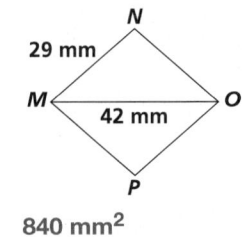

840 mm²

Alternative Assessment

Have students work with partners to draw and label a trapezoid, a rhombus, and a kite, each with an area of 100 cm², and write a paragraph explaining how they calculated the area of each figure.

---

38. Draw a trapezoid. Label its bases and height b_1, b_2, and h, respectively. Then draw a diagonal of the trapezoid. $A = \frac{1}{2}b_1h$; $A = \frac{1}{2}b_2h$
    ✏️ a. Write equations for the area of each of the two triangles formed.
    ✏️ b. **Writing** Explain how you can justify the trapezoid area formula using the areas of the two triangles. **See margin.**

C Challenge x^2 39. **Algebra** One base of a trapezoid is twice the other. The height is the average of the two bases. The area is 324 cm². Find the height and the bases. (*Hint:* Let the smaller base be $2x$.) $b_1 = 12$ cm, $b_2 = 24$ cm, $h = 18$ cm

🌐 40. **Gravity Sports** Ty wants to paint one end of his homemade skateboarding ramp. The ramp is 4 m wide. Its surface is modeled by the equation $y = 0.25x^2$. Use the trapezoids and triangles shown to estimate the area to be painted. **1.5 m²**

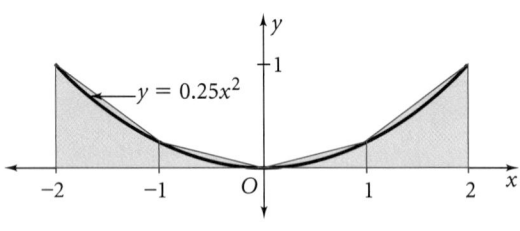

41. In trapezoid $ABCD$, $\overline{AB} \parallel \overline{DC}$. Find the area of $ABCD$.
    $100 + 50\sqrt{3}$ or about 186.6 in.²

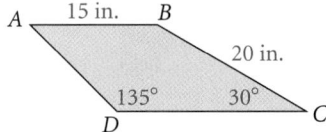

Real-World 🌐 Connection

The curve of a half pipe is two quarter circles joined by a horizontal segment.

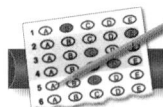

Standardized Test Prep

Multiple Choice

42. The area of a kite is 120 cm². The length of one diagonal is 20 cm. What is the length of the other diagonal? **A**
    A. 12 cm   B. 20 cm
    C. 24 cm   D. 48 cm

43. What is the area of the trapezoid at the right? **H**
    F. 39 m²   G. 60 m²
    H. 78 m²   I. 96 m²

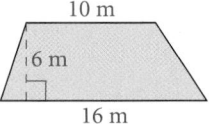

Quantitative Comparison

Compare the boxed quantity in Column A with the boxed quantity in Column B. Choose the best answer.
    A. The quantity in Column A is greater.
    B. The quantity in Column B is greater.
    C. The two quantities are equal.
    D. The relationship cannot be determined from the information given.

Column A	Column B
C 44. the area of a kite with 10-in. and 12-in. diagonals	the area of a rhombus with 10-in. and 12-in. diagonals
D 45. the area of a rhombus with sides of length 5 cm	the area of a kite with 5-cm and 6-cm diagonals
B 46. the area of a triangle with an 8-m base and a 10-m height	the area of a rhombus with congruent 9-m diagonals

💻 **Take It to the NET**
Online lesson quiz at
www.PHSchool.com
Web Code: afa-0704

378 Chapter 7 Area

---

pages 376–379 **Exercises**

38. b. **The area of the trapezoid is the sum of the areas of the triangles, so**

$A = \frac{1}{2}b_1h + \frac{1}{2}b_2h = \frac{1}{2}h(b_1 + b_2)$.

Short Response

47. The area of an isosceles trapezoid is 160 cm². Its height is 8 cm and the length of one leg is 10 cm. **See margin.**
    a. Draw and label a diagram representing the given information.
    b. Find the length of each base. Show your work.

Mixed Review

Lesson 7-3

48. The hypotenuse of an isosceles right triangle has length $50\sqrt{2}$ in. Find the area of the triangle. **1250 in.²**

49. A diagonal of a square is 10 units. Find the length of a side of the square. Leave your answer in simplest radical form. **$5\sqrt{2}$ units**

50. The area of a square is 20 cm². Find the length of its diagonal to the nearest tenth. **6.3 cm**

Lesson 5-3

Fill in the blank with *always*, *sometimes*, or *never* to form a true statement.

51. The incenter of a triangle __?__ lies inside the triangle. **always**

52. The orthocenter of a triangle __?__ lies outside the triangle. **sometimes**

53. The centroid of a triangle __?__ lies on the triangle. **never**

Lesson 3-4

54. Find the measure of an interior angle of a regular 9-gon. **140**

Resources
For additional practice with a variety of test item formats:
• Standardized Test Prep, p. 413
• Test-Taking Strategies, p. 408
• Test-Taking Strategies with Transparencies

Tactile Learners

Exercise 45 By connecting the ends of a plastic straw and bending it into four equal lengths, students can model a rhombus with sides of length 5 cm. As they squeeze and release opposite vertices, they can see that the area can be almost 0 or as great as 25 cm² (when the rhombus is a square).

47. [2] a.

10 cm / 8 cm

b. In the rt. △ shown, the other leg is 6 cm. Since there are $2 \cong$ △, the longer base is $x + 12$ and the shorter base is x. $160 = \frac{1}{2}(8)(x + x + 12)$ and $x = 14$. Bases are 14 cm and 26 cm.

[1] correct answer without explanation OR correct explanation and calculation error

---

A P•int in Time

1500   1600   1700   1800   1900   2000

Presidents are known more often for their foreign policy than for their mathematical creativity. James Garfield, the 20th President of the United States, is an exception. In 1876, Garfield demonstrated this proof of the Pythagorean Theorem.

In the diagram, $\triangle NRM$ and $\triangle RPQ$ are congruent right triangles with sides of lengths a, b, and c. The legs of isosceles right triangle NRP have length c. The three triangles form trapezoid $MNPQ$. The sum of the areas of the three triangles equals the area of trapezoid $MNPQ$.

Areas of Triangles = Area of Trapezoid

$$\frac{1}{2}ab + \frac{1}{2}ab + \frac{1}{2}c^2 = \frac{1}{2}(a+b)(a+b)$$

$$ab + \frac{1}{2}c^2 = \frac{1}{2}a^2 + ab + \frac{1}{2}b^2$$

$$\frac{1}{2}c^2 = \frac{1}{2}a^2 + \frac{1}{2}b^2$$

$$c^2 = a^2 + b^2$$

Take It to the NET For more information about Pythagorean Theorem proofs, go to **www.PHSchool.com**.
Web Code: afe-2032

1. Plan

Lesson Preview

✓ Check Skills You'll Need

Using 45°-45°-90° Triangles
Lesson 7-3: Example 2
Exercises 4–9
Extra Practice, p. 696

Using 30°-60°-90° Triangles
Lesson 7-3: Examples 5 and 6
Exercises 15–23
Extra Practice, p. 696

Lesson Resources

📁 Teaching Resources
Practice, Reteaching, Enrichment

👥 Reaching All Students
Practice Workbook 7-5
Spanish Practice Workbook 7-5
Informal Geometry Planning
   Guide 7-5

⏱ Presentation Assistant Plus!
Transparencies
• Check Skills You'll Need 7-5
• Additional Examples 7-5
• Student Edition Answers 7-5
• Lesson Quiz 7-5
PH Presentation Pro CD 7-5

PRENTICE HALL ASSESSMENT SYSTEM

Computer Test Generator CD

💰 Technology
Resource Pro® CD-ROM
Computer Test Generator CD
Prentice Hall Presentation Pro CD

🖥 www.PHSchool.com
Student Site
• Teacher Web Code: afk-5500
• Self-grading Lesson Quiz
Teacher Center
• Lesson Planner
• Resources

Plus 🄸TEXT

380

7-5

Areas of Regular Polygons

North Carolina Objectives

1.02 Use length, area, and volume of geometric figures to solve problems. Include
perimeter, area, and volume of composite figures.

Lesson Preview

What You'll Learn

OBJECTIVE 1
To find the area of a regular polygon

...And Why

To find the area of pieces of honeycomb material used to build boats, as in Example 3

✓ Check Skills You'll Need

(For help, go to Lesson 7-3.)

Find the area of each regular polygon. If your answer involves a radical, leave it in simplest radical form.

1. 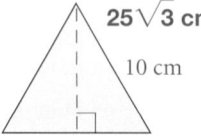 $25\sqrt{3}$ cm²   10 cm

2. 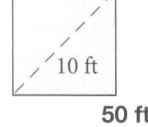   10 ft   50 ft²

3. 10 m $\frac{100\sqrt{3}}{3}$ m²

Find the perimeter of the regular polygon.

4. a hexagon with sides of 4 in. **24 in.**

5. an octagon with sides of $2\sqrt{3}$ cm
   16√3 cm

New Vocabulary • center of a regular polygon • radius of a regular polygon
• apothem of a regular polygon

OBJECTIVE 1   Areas of Regular Polygons

🄸TEXT Interactive lesson includes instant self-check, tutorials, and activities.

📖 Reading Math

The terms *radius* and *apothem* (AP uh them) can each refer to either a segment or its length.

You can circumscribe a circle about any regular polygon. The **center of a regular polygon** is the center of the circumscribed circle. The **radius** is the distance from the center to a vertex. The **apothem** is the perpendicular distance from the center to a side.

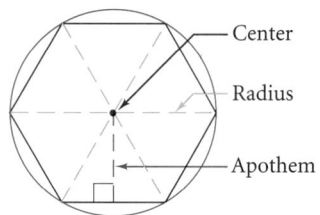

Center
Radius
Apothem

1 EXAMPLE   Finding Angle Measures

The figure at the right is a regular pentagon with radii and an apothem drawn. Find the measure of each numbered angle.

$m\angle 1 = \frac{360}{5} = 72$ Divide 360 by the number of sides.

$m\angle 2 = \frac{1}{2}m\angle 1$ The apothem bisects the vertex angle of the isosceles triangle formed by the radii.

$= \frac{1}{2}(72) = 36$

$90 + 36 + m\angle 3 = 180$ The sum of the measures of the angles of a triangle is 180.

$m\angle 3 = 54$

● $m\angle 1 = 72, m\angle 2 = 36$, and $m\angle 3 = 54$

✓ Check Understanding

1 At the right, a portion of a regular octagon has radii and an apothem drawn. Find the measure of each numbered angle.
$m\angle 1 = 45; m\angle 2 = 22.5; m\angle 3 = 67.5$

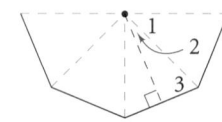

🔄 Ongoing Assessment and Intervention

Before the Lesson
Diagnose prerequisite skills using:
• Check Skills You'll Need

During the Lesson
Monitor progress using:
• Check Understanding
• Additional Examples
• Standardized Test Prep

After the Lesson
Assess knowledge using:
• Lesson Quiz
• Computer Test Generator CD

Suppose you have a regular n-gon with side s. The radii divide the figure into n congruent isosceles triangles. Each isosceles triangle has area equal to $\frac{1}{2}as$.

Since there are n congruent triangles, the area of the n-gon is $A = n \cdot \frac{1}{2}as$. The perimeter p of the n-gon is ns. Substituting p for ns results in a formula for the area in terms of a and p: $A = \frac{1}{2}ap$.

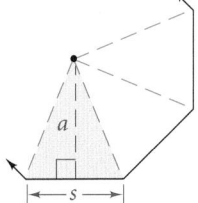

 Key Concepts

Theorem 7-12	Area of a Regular Polygon

The area of a regular polygon is half the product of the apothem and the perimeter.

$$A = \tfrac{1}{2}ap$$

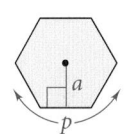

2 EXAMPLE Finding the Area of a Regular Polygon

Find the area of a regular decagon with a 12.3-in. apothem and 8-in. sides.

$p = ns$ **Find the perimeter.**

$= 10(8) = 80$ in.   **A decagon has 10 sides, so $n = 10$.**

$A = \frac{1}{2}ap$ **Use the formula for the area of a regular polygon.**

$= \frac{1}{2}(12.3)(80) = 492$

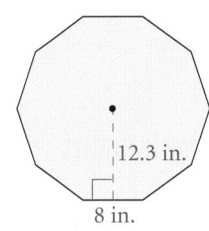

12.3 in.

8 in.

● The regular decagon has area 492 in.^{2}.

✓ **Check Understanding** ❷ Find the area of a regular pentagon with 11.6-cm sides and an 8-cm apothem.
232 cm²

3 EXAMPLE Real-World  Connection

Boat Racing Some boats used for racing have bodies made of a honeycomb of regular hexagonal prisms sandwiched between two layers of outer material. At the right is an end of one hexagonal cell. Find its area.

The radii form six 60° angles at the center. You can use a 30°-60°-90° triangle to find the apothem a.

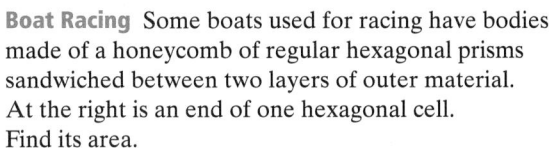

30°   60°

a 10 mm

5 mm

$a = 5\sqrt{3}$ **longer leg $= \sqrt{3} \cdot$ shorter leg**

$p = ns$ **Find the perimeter of the hexagon.**

$= 6(10) = 60$ **Substitute 6 for n and 10 for s.**

$A = \frac{1}{2}ap$ **Find the area.**

$= \frac{1}{2}(5\sqrt{3})(60)$ **Substitute $5\sqrt{3}$ for a and 60 for p.**

≈ 259.80762 **Use a calculator.**

● The area is about 260 mm^2.

✓ **Check Understanding** ❸ The side of a regular hexagon is 16 ft. Find the area of the hexagon.
384$\sqrt{3}$ ft²

 **Reaching All Students**

Below Level While working through Example 1, have students discuss why the five triangles formed by the radii must be congruent.	**Advanced Learners** After Example 3, have students write formulas for the areas of regular hexagons, one with sides of length s and the other with apothem of length a.	**Alternative Method** See note on page 381. **Error Prevention** See note on page 383.

2. Teach

Math Background

A regular n-gon can be constructed by using n adjacent congruent angles with measure $\frac{360}{n}$. The intersection of the angle sides and any circle centered at the common vertex are the vertices of the regular n-gon. Thus a regular inscribed n-gon shares a center and radius with the circumscribing circle. As n increases, the n-gon approaches a circle.

OBJECTIVE

1 Teaching Notes

Teaching Tip
The perpendicular bisectors of the sides of a triangle are concurrent at the circumcenter, which is also the center of the circle that circumscribes the triangle.

1 EXAMPLE Alternative Method

Ask: *What is the sum of the measures of the angles of a pentagon?* 540 *What is the measure of each angle of a regular pentagon?* 108 *What is the measure of $\angle 3$?* 54 Have students first find $m\angle 2$ using the Triangle-Angle Sum Theorem and then find $m\angle 1$.

2 EXAMPLE Math Tip

The side s and apothem a of a regular n-gon are related by the formula $s = 2a \tan(\frac{180}{n})$. The tangent ratio will be discussed in Chapter 9.

Connection to Natural Science
Regular hexagons appear often in nature, for example in bees' honeycombs. Students will learn in Chapter 12 which regular polygons tessellate.

4 EXAMPLE

To make the relationships more easily seen, copy and label the small triangle on the board before going through the example.

Additional Examples

1 A portion of a regular hexagon has apothem and radii drawn. Find the measure of each numbered angle.

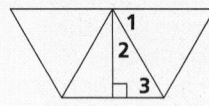

$m\angle 1 = 60$; $m\angle 2 = 30$; $m\angle 3 = 60$

2 Find the area of a regular polygon with twenty 12-in. sides and a 37.9-in. apothem. **4548 in.²**

3 A library is a regular octagon. Each side is 18.0 ft. The radius of the octagon is 23.5 ft. Find the area of the library to the nearest 10 ft.

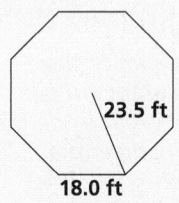

23.5 ft

18.0 ft

about 1560 ft²

4 Find the area of an equilateral triangle with apothem 8 cm. Leave your answer in simplest radical form. **192√3 cm²**

Closure

Find the area of a regular pentagon with 7.2-ft sides and a 6.1-ft radius.

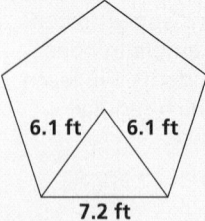

6.1 ft   6.1 ft

7.2 ft

about 88 ft² or 89 ft²

4 EXAMPLE **Real-World Connection**

Art The smaller triangles in the Minneapolis sculpture at the left are equilateral. Each has a 12.7-in. radius. What is the area of each to the nearest square inch?

You can use a 30°-60°-90° triangle to find the apothem a and the length s of a side.

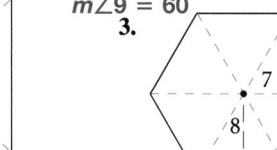

$12.7 = 2 \cdot a$	hypotenuse $= 2 \cdot$ shorter leg
$a = 6.35$	
$\frac{s}{2} = 6.35\sqrt{3}$	longer leg $= \sqrt{3} \cdot$ shorter leg
$s = 12.7\sqrt{3}$	
$p = ns$	Find the perimeter.
$= 3(12.7\sqrt{3})$	Substitute 3 for n and $12.7\sqrt{3}$ for s.
$= 38.1\sqrt{3}$	
$A = \frac{1}{2}ap$	Use the formula for area of a regular polygon.
$= \frac{1}{2}(6.35)(38.1\sqrt{3})$	Substitute 6.35 for a and $38.1\sqrt{3}$ for p.
≈ 209.52186	Use a calculator.

● The area of each smaller triangle is about 210 in.².

✓ Check Understanding **4** **Critical Thinking** In the Minneapolis sculpture, the 10 smaller triangles form a large triangle. What is the area of the large triangle? **about 3352 in.²**

EXERCISES

For more practice, see *Extra Practice*.

Practice and Problem Solving

A **Practice by Example**

Example 1
(page 380)

Each regular polygon has radii and apothem as shown. Find the measure of each numbered angle.

$m\angle 7 = 60$; $m\angle 8 = 30$; $m\angle 9 = 60$

1.

2.

3.

$m\angle 1 = 120$; $m\angle 2 = 60$; $m\angle 3 = 30$

$m\angle 4 = 90$; $m\angle 5 = 45$; $m\angle 6 = 45$

Example 2
(page 381)

Find the area of each regular polygon with the given apothem a and side length s.

4. pentagon, $a = 24.3$ cm, $s = 35.3$ cm
2144.475 cm²
5. 7-gon, $a = 29.1$ ft, $s = 28$ ft
2851.8 ft²
6. octagon, $a = 60.4$ in., $s = 50$ in.
12,080 in.²
7. nonagon, $a = 27.5$ in., $s = 20$ in.
2475 in.²
8. decagon, $a = 19$ m, $s = 12.3$ m
1168.5 m²
9. dodecagon, $a = 26.1$ cm, $s = 14$ cm
2192.4 cm²

Example 3
(page 381)

Find the area of each regular polygon. Round your answer to the nearest tenth.

10.

18 ft

841.8 ft²

11.

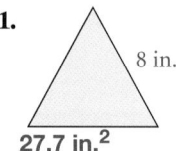

8 in.

27.7 in.²

12.

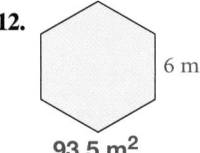

6 m

93.5 m²

Example 4
(page 382)

13. 72 cm²

14. 384 $\sqrt{3}$ in.²

15. 300 $\sqrt{3}$ ft²

16. 162 $\sqrt{3}$ m²

17. 75 $\sqrt{3}$ m²

18. 12 $\sqrt{3}$ in.²

Find the area of each regular polygon with the given radius or apothem. If your answer is not an integer, leave it in simplest radical form.

13.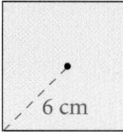
6 cm

14.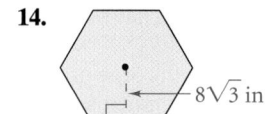
8$\sqrt{3}$ in.

15.
20 ft

16.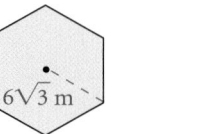
6$\sqrt{3}$ m

17.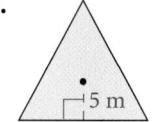
5 m

18.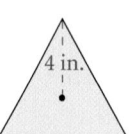
4 in.

 Apply Your Skills

Find the measures of the angles formed by (a) two consecutive radii and (b) a radius and a side of the given regular polygon.

19. pentagon
a. 72 b. 54

20. octagon
a. 45 b. 67.5

21. nonagon
a. 40 b. 70

22. dodecagon
a. 30 b. 75

23. 310.4 ft²

23. **Architecture** The gazebo in the photo is built in the shape of a regular octagon. Each side is 8 ft long, and its apothem is 9.7 ft. To the nearest tenth, find the area enclosed by the gazebo.

24d. **Answers may vary.**
Sample: About 4 in.; the length of a side of a pentagon should be between 3.7 in. and 6 in.

24. The area of a regular polygon is 36 in.². Find the length of a side if the polygon has the given number of sides. Round your answer to the nearest tenth.
a. 3 9.1 in. b. 4 6 in. c. 6 3.7 in.
d. **Estimation** Suppose the polygon is a pentagon. What would you expect the length of its side to be? Explain. **See left.**

Need Help?

In Exercise 25, $m\angle 1$ is what part of 360?

25. A portion of a regular decagon has radii and an apothem drawn. Find the measure of each numbered angle. $m\angle 1 = 36$; $m\angle 2 = 18$; $m\angle 3 = 72$

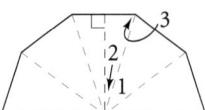

26. The apothem is one leg of a rt. △ and the radius is the hypotenuse.

26. **Writing** Explain why the radius of a regular polygon is greater than the apothem. **See left.**

27. **Satellites** One of the smallest space satellites ever developed has the shape of a pyramid. Each of the four faces of the pyramid is an equilateral triangle with sides about 13 cm long. What is the area of one equilateral triangular face of the satellite? Round your answer to the nearest whole number. **73 cm²**

Find the area of each equilateral triangle with the given radius. Round your answers to the nearest whole number.

28. $r = 10$ in.
130 in.²

29. $r = 4.6$ m
27 m²

30. $r = 8.9$ ft
103 ft²

31. $r = 13$ cm
220 cm²

32. **Constructions** Use a compass to construct a circle. **32a–c. See margin.**
a. Construct four perpendicular radii of the circle.
b. Construct radii that bisect each of the four right angles.
c. Connect the consecutive points where the radii intersect the circle. What regular polygon have you constructed? **regular octagon**
d. **Critical Thinking** How can a circle help you construct a regular hexagon? **Construct a 60° angle with the vertex at circle's center.**

Lesson 7-5 Areas of Regular Polygons **383**

pages 382–385 **Exercises**

32. a–c.

Assignment Guide

▼ **Objective**
Ⓐ Ⓑ **Core** 1–42
Ⓒ **Extension** 43–45

Standardized Test Prep 46–50

Mixed Review 51–57

Error Prevention
Exercises 13–18 Have students state whether segments are radii or apothems to help them apply the area formula correctly.

Exercise 23 Have students suggest ways to construct a regular octagon.

Exercise 26 Recommend that students write out the theorems they use.

Exercise 34 You may want to have students color their designs and display them in the classroom. Briefly discuss tessellations. Point out that tessellations will be studied in Lesson 12-6.

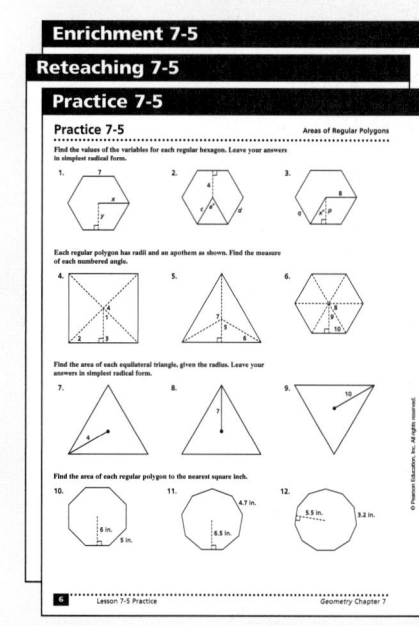

383

Lesson Quiz 7-5

Use the portion of the regular decagon for Exercises 1–3.

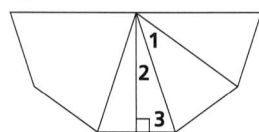

1. Find $m\angle 1$. 36

2. Find $m\angle 2$. 18

3. Find $m\angle 3$. 72

4. Find the area of a regular 9-sided figure with a 9.6-cm apothem and 7-cm side. 302.4 cm²

For Exercises 5 and 6, find the area of each regular polygon. Leave your answer in simplest radical form.

5.

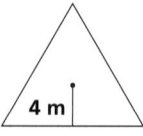

4 m

48√3 m²

6.

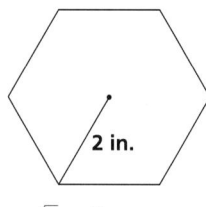

2 in.

6√3 in.²

Alternative Assessment

Provide each student with a copy of a regular polygon. Have students explain in detail what the formula $A = \frac{1}{2}ap$ means for their polygons and justify the formula in writing, using constructions where appropriate.

---

35. 128 cm²

36. 24√3 cm², 41.6 cm²

37. 900√3 m², 1558.8 m²

38. 100 ft²

39. 16√3 in.², 27.7 in.²

40. $\frac{81\sqrt{3}}{2}$ m², 70.1 m²

41a. $b = s; h = \frac{\sqrt{3}}{2}s$
$A = \frac{1}{2}bh$
$A = \frac{1}{2}s \cdot \frac{\sqrt{3}}{2}s$
$A = \frac{1}{4}s^2\sqrt{3}$

41b. apothem = $\frac{s\sqrt{3}}{6}$;
$A = \frac{1}{2}ap = \frac{1}{2}(\frac{s\sqrt{3}}{6})(3s)$
$= \frac{1}{4}s^2\sqrt{3}$

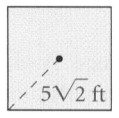
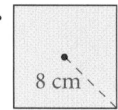

---

33. A regular hexagon has perimeter 120 m. Find its area. 600√3 m²

34. **Open-Ended** Create a design using equilateral triangles and regular hexagons that have sides of the same length. Find the area of the completed design. **Check students' work.**

Find the area of each regular polygon. Show your answers in simplest radical form and rounded to the nearest tenth.

35.

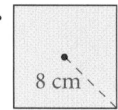

8 cm

36.

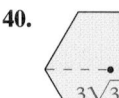

4 cm

37.

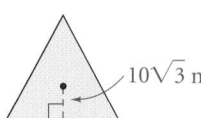

10√3 m

38.

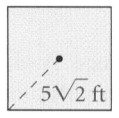

5√2 ft

39.

8 in.

40.

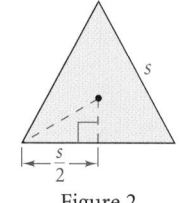

3√3 m

41. To find the area of an equilateral triangle, you can use the formula $A = \frac{1}{2}bh$ or $A = \frac{1}{2}ap$. A third way to find the area of an equilateral triangle is to use the formula $A = \frac{1}{4}s^2\sqrt{3}$. Verify the formula $A = \frac{1}{4}s^2\sqrt{3}$ in two ways as follows:

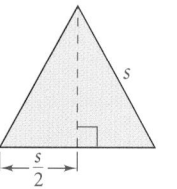

s
$\frac{s}{2}$
Figure 1

s
$\frac{s}{2}$
Figure 2

  a. Find the area of Figure 1 using the formula $A = \frac{1}{2}bh$. **41a–b. See left.**
  b. Find the area of Figure 2 using the formula $A = \frac{1}{2}ap$.

Proof 42. For Example 1 on page 380, write a proof that the apothem bisects the vertex angle of the isosceles triangle formed by the radii. **See margin.**

C **Challenge** *Proof* 43. Prove that the bisectors of the angles of a regular polygon (given congruent sides and angles) are concurrent and that they are, in fact, radii of the polygon. (*Hint:* For regular n-gon $ABCDE \ldots$, let P be the intersection of the bisectors of $\angle ABC$ and $\angle BCD$. Show that $\overrightarrow{DP}$ must be the bisector of $\angle CDE$.) **See margin, p. 385.**

44. **Coordinate Geometry** A regular octagon with center at the origin and radius 4 is graphed in the coordinate plane.
  a. Since V_2 lies on the line $y = x$, its x- and y-coordinates are equal. Use the Distance Formula to find the **(2.8, 2.8)** coordinates of V_2 to the nearest tenth.
  b. Use the coordinates of V_2 and the formula $A = \frac{1}{2}bh$ to find the area of $\triangle V_1OV_2$ to the nearest tenth. **5.6 units²**
  c. Use your answer to part (b) to find the area of the octagon to the nearest whole number. **45 units²**

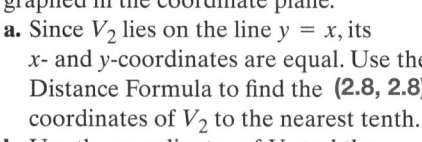

45. a. Find the area of the triangle if the area of each square is 10 cm². $\frac{5\sqrt{3}}{2}$ **cm²**
  b. When a square and an equilateral triangle share a common side, what is the ratio of the area of the triangle to the area of the square? Leave your answer in simplest radical form. $\frac{\sqrt{3}}{4}$

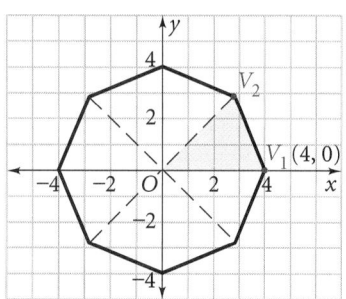

Real-World Connection

Horizontal cross sections of the Wenfeng Pagoda in Yangzhou, China, are regular octagons.

---

384 Chapter 7 Area

---

pages 382–385 **Exercises**

42. The apothem is ⊥ to a side of the pentagon. Two right ⧍ are formed with the radii of the pentagon. So the ⧍ are

≅ by HL. Therefore the ⧍ formed by the apothem and radii are ≅ by CPCTC, and the apothem bisects the vertex ∠.

43. For reg. n-gon $ABCDE \ldots$, let P be the intersection of the bisectors of $\angle ABC$ and $\angle BCD$. $\overline{BC} \cong \overline{DC}$, $\angle BCP \cong \angle DCP$, and $\overline{CP} \cong \overline{CP}$, so $\triangle BCP \cong$

$\triangle DCP$, and $\angle CBP \cong \angle CDP$ by CPCTC. Since $\angle BCP$ is half the size of $\angle ABC$ and $\angle ABC \cong \angle CDE$, $\angle CDP$ is half the size of $\angle CDE$. By a similar argument, P is on

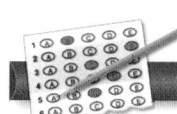

Multiple Choice

46. What is the area of a regular pentagon whose apothem is 25.1 mm and perimeter is 182 mm? **B**

A. 913.6 mm²   B. 2284.1 mm²   C. 3654.6 mm²   D. 4568.2 mm²

47. The area of a regular octagonal garden is 1235.2 yd². The apothem is 19.3 yd. What is the perimeter of the garden? **F**

F. 128 yd   G. 154.4 yd   H. 186.6 yd   I. 192 yd

48. The radius of a regular hexagonal sandbox is 5 ft. What is the area to the nearest square foot? **B**

A. 30 ft²   B. 65 ft²   C. 75 ft²   D. 130 ft²

Short Response

49. The perimeter of a regular decagon is 220 in. Its radius is 35.6 in.
a. Explain how to use the given information to find its area.
b. Find the area. **49a–b. See margin.**

Extended Response

Take It to the NET
Online lesson quiz at
www.PHSchool.com
Web Code: afa-0705

50. In regular hexagon *ABCDEF*, *BC* = $8\sqrt{3}$ ft.
a. Find the area of △*BCG*.
b. Find the area of hexagon *ABCDEF*.
c. Describe two different methods for finding the area of hexagon *ABCDEF*.
50a–c. See margin.

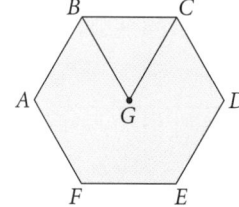

Mixed Review

Lesson 7-4

51. Find the area of a kite with diagonals 8 m and 11.5 m. **46 m²**

52. The area of a kite is 150 in.². The length of one diagonal is 10 in. Find the length of the other diagonal. **30 in.**

53. The area of a trapezoid is 42 m². The trapezoid has a height of 7 m and one base of 4 m. Find the length of the other base. **8 m**

Lesson 4-4

Name the pairs of triangles you would have to prove congruent so that the indicated congruences are true by CPCTC.

Given: ∠*DAB* ≅ ∠*CBA*,
$\overline{AD}$ ≅ $\overline{BC}$,
$\overline{DF}$ bisects ∠*ADB*,
$\overline{CG}$ bisects ∠*BCA*.

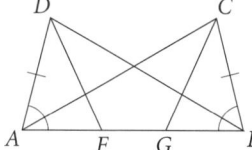

54. $\overline{AC}$ ≅ $\overline{BD}$

55. $\overline{AG}$ ≅ $\overline{BF}$ **54.** △*DAB* and △*CBA*   **55.** △*ACG* and △*BDF*

56. ∠*DFA* ≅ ∠*CGB*   △*DFA* and △*CGB*

Lesson 1-7  **57. a. Biology** The size of a jaguar's territory depends on how much food is available. Where there is a lot of food, such as in a forest, jaguars have circular territories about 3 mi in diameter. Use 3.14 for π to estimate the area of such a region to the nearest tenth. **7.1 mi²**
b. Where food is less available, a jaguar may need up to 200 mi². Estimate the radius of this circular territory. **about 8 mi**

the bisector of each ∠
around the polygon. The
smaller ⅍ formed by
each of the ∠ bisectors
are all ≅. By the Conv. of
the Isosc. △ Thm., each
of ⅍*APB, BPC, CPD*,

etc., are isosc. with
$\overline{AP}$ ≅ $\overline{BP}$ ≅ $\overline{CP}$, etc.
Thus, *P* is equidistant
from the polygon's
vertices, so *P* is the
center of the polygon
and the ∠ bis. are radii.

Resources
For additional practice with a
variety of test item formats:
• Standardized Test Prep, p. 413
• Test-Taking Strategies, p. 408
• Test-Taking Strategies with
 Transparencies

Exercise 47 Explain to students how to use mental math to double the rounded value of the area and then divide by the rounded value of the apothem.

Exercise 49 Students may find it helpful to draw the triangle formed by the radius, apothem, and half a side before using the Pythagorean Theorem to find the apothem.

49. [2] a. Divide the decagon into 10 ≅ ⚠. Consider one △ with hyp. of 35.6 and leg 11. The apothem can be found using the Pyth. Thm., so $(35.6)^2 - 11^2 = 1146.36$ and leg ≈ 33.9 in.

b. $A ≈ \frac{1}{2}(33.9)(220) = 3729$ in.²

[1] incorrect calculation and correct explanation OR correct calculation and no explanation

50. [4] a. Area of △*BCG* = $\frac{1}{2}bh = \frac{1}{2}(8\sqrt{3})(12) = 48\sqrt{3}$.

b. Area of *ABCDEF* = $6 \cdot 48\sqrt{3} = 288\sqrt{3}$.

c. Find the area of one △ and mult. by 6 or use the formula for the area of a reg. polygon.

[3] appropriate methods, but with one computational error

[2] incorrect formulas OR no explanation

[1] incorrect calculations, correct explanation

385

1. Plan

Lesson Preview

✓ **Check Skills You'll Need**

Finding Circumference
Lesson 1-7: Example 2
Exercises 8–10
Extra Practice, p. 690

Finding Percentages of a Number
Skills Handbook, p. 723

Lesson Resources

📁 **Teaching Resources**
Practice, Reteaching, Enrichment

👥 **Reaching All Students**
Practice Workbook 7-6
Spanish Practice Workbook 7-6
Informal Geometry Planning
  Guide 7-6

🕐 **Presentation Assistant Plus!**
Transparencies
- Check Skills You'll Need 7-6
- Additional Examples 7-6
- Student Edition Answers 7-6
- Lesson Quiz 7-6
PH Presentation Pro CD 7-6

ASSESSMENT SYSTEM

Computer Test Generator CD

💰 **Technology**
Resource Pro® CD-ROM
Computer Test Generator CD
Prentice Hall Presentation Pro CD

🖥️ **www.PHSchool.com**
Student Site
- Teacher Web Code: afk-5500
- Updated Data
- Self-grading Lesson Quiz
Teacher Center
- Lesson Planner
- Resources

Plus

7-6

Circles and Arcs

North Carolina Objectives

1.02   Use length, area, and volume of geometric figures to solve problems. Include arc length and area of sectors of circles.

Lesson Preview

What You'll Learn

OBJECTIVE 1 To find the measures of central angles and arcs

OBJECTIVE 2 To find circumference and arc length

. . . And Why

To use the turning radius of a car to compare the distances that its tires travel, as in Example 4

✓ **Check Skills You'll Need**   (For help, go to Lesson 1-7 and Skills Handbook, p. 723.)

Find the diameter or radius of each circle.

1. $r = 7$ cm, $d = $ ■   **14 cm**   **2.** $r = 1.6$ m, $d = $ ■   **3.2 m**

3. $d = 10$ ft, $r = $ ■   **5 ft**   **4.** $d = 5$ in., $r = $ ■   **2.5 in.**

Round to the nearest whole number.

5. 9% of 360   **32**   **6.** 38% of 360   **137**   **7.** 50% of 360   **180**   **8.** 21% of 360 **76**

New Vocabulary   • circle   • center   • radius   • congruent circles
                    • diameter   • central angle   • semicircle   • minor arc
                    • major arc   • adjacent arcs   • circumference   • pi
                    • concentric circles   • arc length   • congruent arcs

📱 **iTEXT** Interactive lesson includes instant self-check, tutorials, and activities.

OBJECTIVE 1   **Central Angles and Arcs**

In a plane, a **circle** is the set of all points equidistant from a given point called the **center.** You name a circle by its center. Circle P (⊙P) is shown at the right.

A **radius** is a segment that has one endpoint at the center and the other endpoint on the circle. $\overline{PC}$ is a radius. $\overline{PA}$ and $\overline{PB}$ are also radii. **Congruent circles** have congruent radii.

A **diameter** is a segment that contains the center of a circle and has both endpoints on the circle. $\overline{AB}$ is a diameter.

A **central angle** is an angle whose vertex is the center of the circle. $\angle CPA$ is a central angle.

📖 **Reading Math**

Diameter comes from the classical Greek words *dia*, meaning through, and *meter*, meaning measure.

1 EXAMPLE   Real-World 🌐 Connection

Data Analysis To learn how people really spend their time, a research firm studied the hour-by-hour activities of 3600 people. The participants were between 18 and 90 years old. Each participant was sent a 24-hour recording sheet every March for three years from 2000 to 2002.

The study found that people spend most of their time sleeping, working, and watching television. Some information from the study is shown in this circle graph. Find the measure of each central angle in the circle graph.

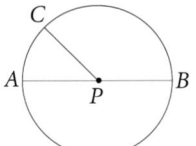

Sleep 31%   Other 15%   Entertainment 18%   Must Do 7%   Work 20%   Food 9%

Ongoing Assessment and Intervention

Before the Lesson	During the Lesson	After the Lesson
Diagnose prerequisite skills using:	**Monitor progress using:**	**Assess knowledge using:**
• Check Skills You'll Need	• Check Understanding • Additional Examples • Standardized Test Prep	• Lesson Quiz • Computer Test Generator CD

There are 360 degrees in a circle. To find the measure of each central angle in the circle graph, find the corresponding percent of 360.

Sleep: 31% of 360 = 111.6   Other: 15% of 360 = 54

Food: 9% of 360 = 32.4   Entertainment: 18% of 360 = 64.8

Work: 20% of 360 = 72   Must Do: 7% of 360 = 25.2

✓ **Check Understanding** ❶ **a. Critical Thinking** Each section of the circle graph represents a measurable quantity. What is that quantity? **number of hours spent doing an activity**
b. Each section of the circle graph represents an average. Explain.
Each section represents the average of the 3000+ participants' answers.

An arc is a part of a circle. One type of arc, a **semicircle,** is half of a circle. A **minor arc** is smaller than a semicircle. A **major arc** is greater than a semicircle.

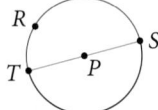 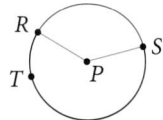 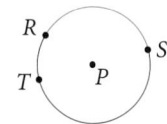

$\overset{\frown}{TRS}$ is a semicircle. $\overset{\frown}{RS}$ is a minor arc. $\overset{\frown}{RTS}$ is a major arc.
$m\overset{\frown}{TRS} = 180$ $m\overset{\frown}{RS} = m\angle RPS$ $m\overset{\frown}{RTS} = 360 - m\overset{\frown}{RS}$

The water line separates a circle into a major arc and a minor arc.

The measure of a semicircle is 180. The measure of a minor arc is the measure of its corresponding central angle. The measure of a major arc is 360 minus the measure of its related minor arc.

② EXAMPLE   Identifying Arcs

Identify the following in $\odot O$.

a. the minor arcs

$\overset{\frown}{AD}, \overset{\frown}{CE}, \overset{\frown}{AC},$ and $\overset{\frown}{DE}$ are minor arcs.

b. the semicircles

$\overset{\frown}{ACE}, \overset{\frown}{CED}, \overset{\frown}{EDA},$ and $\overset{\frown}{DAC}$ are semicircles.

c. the major arcs that contain point A

$\overset{\frown}{ACD}, \overset{\frown}{CEA}, \overset{\frown}{EDC},$ and $\overset{\frown}{DAE}$ are major arcs that contain point A.

✓ **Check Understanding** ❷ Identify the four major arcs of $\odot O$ that contain point E.
$\overset{\frown}{CEA}$, $\overset{\frown}{DAE}$, $\overset{\frown}{ACD}$, $\overset{\frown}{EDC}$

Adjacent arcs are arcs of the same circle that have exactly one point in common. You can add the measures of adjacent arcs just as you can add the measures of adjacent angles.

 Key Concepts

Postulate 7-1	Arc Addition Postulate

The measure of the arc formed by two adjacent arcs is the sum of the measures of the two arcs.

$$m\overset{\frown}{ABC} = m\overset{\frown}{AB} + m\overset{\frown}{BC}$$

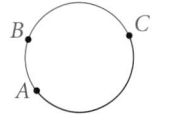

Lesson 7-6 Circles and Arcs   **387**

Reaching All Students

Below Level Students may use objects such as aluminum cans and pieces of string to help them understand the formula for the circumference of a circle.	**Advanced Learners** After Example 4, ask students to calculate which is greater, the height or the circumference of a can of three tennis balls.	**English Learners** See note on page 387. **Error Prevention** See note on page 389.

2. Teach

Math Background

The ratio π of a circle's circumference to its diameter is independent of the size of the circle ($C = \pi d$). Ancient calculations of π range from the rather crude 3 to a remarkably accurate $\frac{355}{113}$. In 1999, a computer calculated the constant π to 206,158,430,000 decimal places. Results such as this are used to check the accuracy of other computer programs.

OBJECTIVE
❶ Teaching Notes

English Learners
Have students work together to make a poster that defines new vocabulary with words and diagrams. Display the poster until English learners are familiar with the new vocabulary.

❶ EXAMPLE   Careers

Statisticians are *applied mathematicians.* Most public and private companies hire statisticians to gather and analyze data using mathematical techniques. Colleges offer programs to prepare students for careers as statisticians.

❷ EXAMPLE

Because two points name two arcs on a circle, naming an arc using just two points can cause confusion. Point out that this book uses two points to name minor arcs and three points to name semicircles and major arcs.

Teaching Tip
When you introduce adjacent arcs, ask: *If two arcs are adjacent, are their corresponding central angles adjacent?* yes *What do adjacent angles have in common?* one side

387

Relate the Arc Addition Postulate to the Angle Addition Postulate in Lesson 1-4.

Additional Examples

1 A researcher surveyed 2000 members of a club to find their ages. The graph shows the survey results. Find the measure of each central angle in the circle graph.

Members' Ages

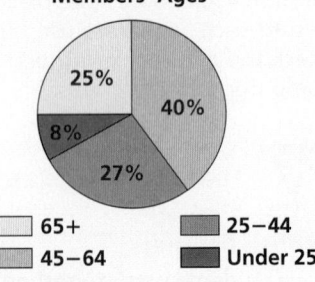

| | 65+ | | 25–44 |
| | 45–64 | | Under 25 |

65+: 90; 45–64: 144; 25–44: 97.2; Under 25: 28.8

2 Identify the minor arcs, major arcs, and semicircles in ⊙P with point A as an endpoint.

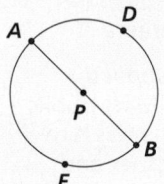

minor arcs: $\overset{\frown}{AD}$, $\overset{\frown}{AE}$;
major arcs: $\overset{\frown}{ADE}$, $\overset{\frown}{AED}$;
semicircles: $\overset{\frown}{ADB}$, $\overset{\frown}{AEB}$

3 Find $m\overset{\frown}{XY}$ and $m\overset{\frown}{DXM}$ in ⊙C.

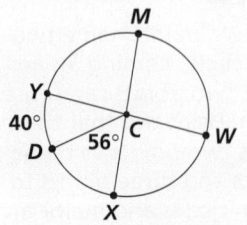

$m\overset{\frown}{XY} = 96$; $m\overset{\frown}{DXM} = 236$

---

3 EXAMPLE **Finding the Measures of Arcs**

Find the measure of each arc.

a. $\overset{\frown}{BC}$ $m\overset{\frown}{BC} = m\angle BOC = 32$

b. $\overset{\frown}{BD}$ $m\overset{\frown}{BD} = m\overset{\frown}{BC} + m\overset{\frown}{CD}$
  $m\overset{\frown}{BD} = 32 + 58 = 90$

c. $\overset{\frown}{ABC}$ $\overset{\frown}{ABC}$ is a semicircle.
  $m\overset{\frown}{ABC} = 180$

d. $\overset{\frown}{AB}$ $m\overset{\frown}{AB} = 180 - 32 = 148$

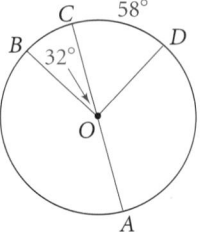

✓ **Check Understanding** **3** Find $m\angle COD$, $m\overset{\frown}{CDA}$, $m\overset{\frown}{AD}$ and $m\overset{\frown}{BAD}$. 58; 180; 122; 270

OBJECTIVE

2 Circumference and Arc Length

The **circumference** of a circle is the distance around the circle. The number **pi** (π) is the ratio of the circumference of a circle to its diameter.

Key Concepts

Theorem 7-13	**Circumference of a Circle**

The circumference of a circle is π times the diameter.

$$C = \pi d \text{ or } C = 2\pi r$$

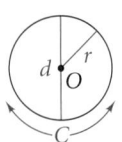

Since the number π is irrational, you cannot write it as a terminating or repeating decimal. To approximate π, you can use 3.14, $\frac{22}{7}$, or the $\boxed{\pi}$ key on your calculator.

Circles that lie in the same plane and have the same center are **concentric circles**.

4 EXAMPLE **Real-World** 🌐 **Connection**

Automobiles A car has a turning radius of 16.1 ft. The distance between the two front tires is 4.7 ft. In completing the (outer) turning circle, how much farther does a tire travel than a tire on the concentric inner circle?

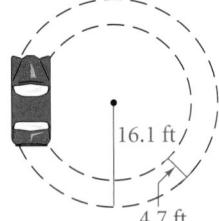

16.1 ft

4.7 ft

To find the radius of the inner circle, subtract 4.7 ft from the turning radius.

circumference of outer circle = $C = 2\pi r = 2\pi(16.1) = 32.2\pi$

radius of the inner circle = $16.1 - 4.7 = 11.4$

circumference of inner circle = $C = 2\pi r = 2\pi(11.4) = 22.8\pi$

The difference in the two distances is $32.2\pi - 22.8\pi$, or 9.4π.

$9.4\pi \approx 29.530971$ **Use a calculator.**

A tire on the turning circle travels about 29.5 ft farther than a tire on the inner circle.

✓ **Check Understanding** **4** The diameter of a bicycle wheel is 22 in. To the nearest whole number, how many revolutions does the wheel make when the bicycle travels 100 ft?
17 revolutions

The measure of an arc is in degrees while the **arc length** is a fraction of a circle's circumference. An arc of 60° represents $\frac{60}{360}$ or $\frac{1}{6}$ of the circle. Its arc length is $\frac{1}{6}$ the circumference of the circle. This observation suggests the following theorem.

 Key Concepts

Theorem 7-14	Arc Length

The length of an arc of a circle is the product of the ratio $\frac{\text{measure of the arc}}{360}$ and the circumference of the circle.

$$\text{length of } \overset{\frown}{AB} = \frac{m\overset{\frown}{AB}}{360} \cdot 2\pi r$$

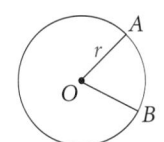

5 EXAMPLE Finding Arc Length

Find the length of each arc shown in red. Leave your answer in terms of π.

a.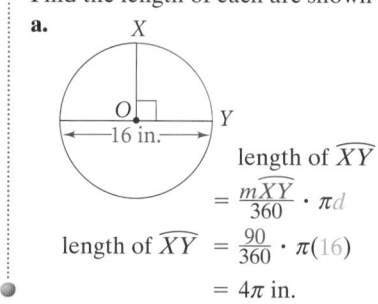

$$\text{length of } \overset{\frown}{XY}$$
$$= \frac{m\overset{\frown}{XY}}{360} \cdot \pi d$$
$$\text{length of } \overset{\frown}{XY} = \frac{90}{360} \cdot \pi(16)$$
$$= 4\pi \text{ in.}$$

b.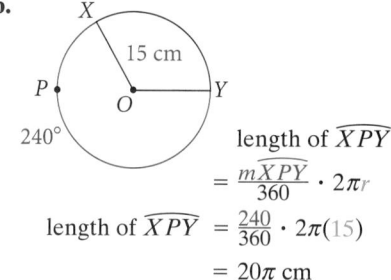

$$\text{length of } \overset{\frown}{XPY}$$
$$= \frac{m\overset{\frown}{XPY}}{360} \cdot 2\pi r$$
$$\text{length of } \overset{\frown}{XPY} = \frac{240}{360} \cdot 2\pi(15)$$
$$= 20\pi \text{ cm}$$

✓ **Check Understanding** **5** Find the length of a semicircle with radius 1.3 m. Leave your answer in terms of π.
1.3π m

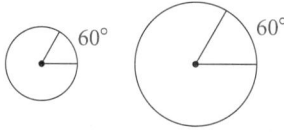

It is possible for two arcs of different circles to have the same measure but different lengths, as shown at the left. It is also possible for two arcs of different circles to have the same length but different measures. **Congruent arcs** are arcs that have the same measure *and* are in the same circle or in congruent circles.

EXERCISES

For more practice, see *Extra Practice*.

Practice and Problem Solving

 Practice by Example
Example 1
(page 386)

Trash The graph shows types of trash in a typical American city. Find the measure of each central angle to the nearest whole number.

1. Glass **25**   2. Metals **29**

3. Plastics **32**   4. Wood **22**

25 5. Food Waste   6. Yard Waste **58**

7. Other **32**   8. Paper and Paperboard **137**

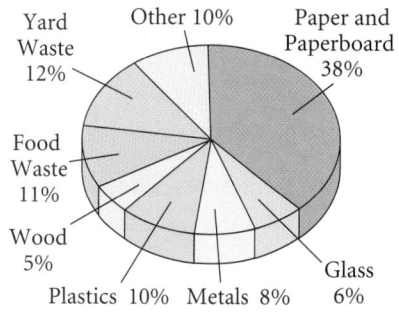

SOURCE: Environmental Protection Agency, 2001.
Go to **www.PHSchool.com** for a data update.
Web Code: afg-2041

4 EXAMPLE **Connection to Engineering**

Ask: *If the left wheels travel a different distance from the right wheels in the same amount of time, what can you conclude about their speeds?* **The left wheels spin faster than the right wheels.** The car's *differential* enables the wheels to do this.

Connection to Algebra

Point out that, although π is a symbol, it is a constant, not a variable.

Error Prevention

Some students may confuse arc length with the measure of an arc. Point out that arc length is often given in terms of π, unlike the measure of an arc.

5 EXAMPLE

Have students explain why 4π and 20π are exact answers, but $4(\frac{22}{7})$ and $20(3.14)$ are estimates.

 **Additional Examples**

4 A circular swimming pool with a 16-ft diameter will be enclosed in a circular fence 4 ft from the pool. What length of fencing material is needed? Round to the nearest whole number. **75 ft**

5 Find the length of $\overset{\frown}{ADB}$ in $\odot M$ in terms of π.

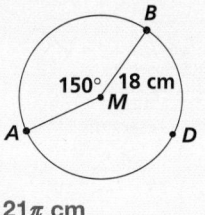

21π cm

Closure

One section of a circle graph with a radius of 15 in. is labeled "Radio: 20%." Find the measure and length of the arc corresponding to this section of the circle graph. **measure: 72; length: 6π in.**

Assignment Guide

1 Objective
  Ⓐ Ⓑ Core 1–26, 40–54
  Ⓒ Extension 70

2 Objective
  Ⓐ Ⓑ Core 27–39, 55–69
  Ⓒ Extension 71, 72

Standardized Test Prep 73–75

Mixed Review 76–83

Exercise 14 Have students explain why the two angles are congruent.

Error Prevention

Exercises 15–26 Remind students that this textbook names minor arcs with two points and semicircles and major arcs with three points.

Exercise 40 Challenge students to construct a central angle on ⊙*A* and construct a congruent central angle on ⊙*B*.

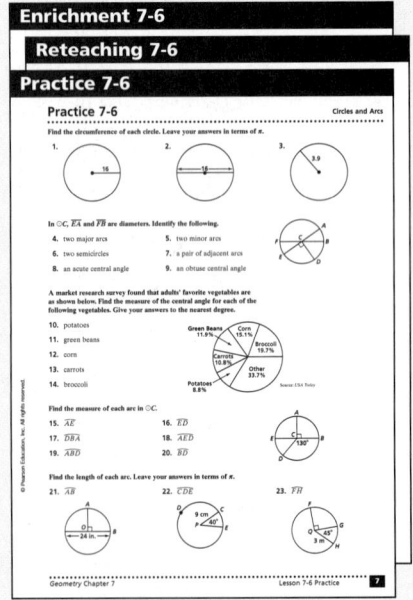

9–14. Answers may vary.
Samples are given.

Example 2
(page 387)

Identify the following in ⊙*O*.

9. a minor arc $\overset{\frown}{ED}$
10. a major arc $\overset{\frown}{FEB}$
11. a semicircle $\overset{\frown}{BFE}$
12. a pair of adjacent arcs $\overset{\frown}{FE}$ and $\overset{\frown}{ED}$
13. an acute central angle ∠*FOE*
14. a pair of congruent angles ∠*FOE* and ∠*BOC*

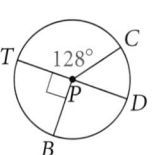

Example 3
(page 388)

Find the measure of each arc in ⊙*P*.

15. $\overset{\frown}{TC}$ 128
16. $\overset{\frown}{TBD}$ 180
17. $\overset{\frown}{BTC}$ 218
18. $\overset{\frown}{TCB}$ 270
19. $\overset{\frown}{CD}$ 52
20. $\overset{\frown}{CBD}$ 308
21. $\overset{\frown}{TCD}$ 180
22. $\overset{\frown}{DB}$ 90
23. $\overset{\frown}{TDC}$ 232
24. $\overset{\frown}{TB}$ 90
25. $\overset{\frown}{BC}$ 142
26. $\overset{\frown}{BCD}$ 270

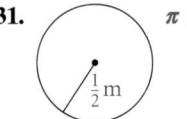

Example 4
(page 388)

Find the circumference of each circle. Leave your answer in terms of π.

27. 20π cm
28. 6π ft
29. 8.4π m
30. 14π in.
31. π m
32. 58π cm

33. The wheel of an adult's bicycle has diameter 26 in. The wheel of a child's bicycle has diameter 18 in. To the nearest inch, how much farther does the larger bicycle wheel travel in one revolution than the smaller bicycle wheel? **25 in.**

Example 5
(page 389)

Find the length of each arc shown in red. Leave your answer in terms of π.

34. $\frac{7\pi}{2}$ cm
35. 8π ft
36. 27π m
37. 33π in.
38. $\frac{23\pi}{2}$ m
39. $\frac{5\pi}{4}$ m

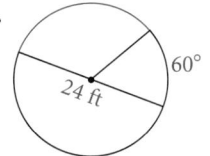
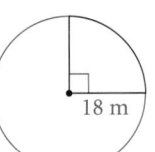
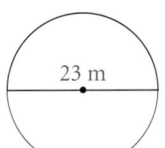
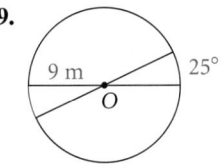

Ⓑ **Apply Your Skills**

40. Use a compass to draw ⊙*A* and ⊙*B* with different radii. Then use a protractor to draw $\overset{\frown}{XY}$ on ⊙*A* and $\overset{\frown}{ZW}$ on ⊙*B* so that $m\overset{\frown}{XY} = m\overset{\frown}{ZW}$. Is $\overset{\frown}{XY} \cong \overset{\frown}{ZW}$? **See margin, p. 391.**

41. **Environment** Use the data in the table to construct a circle graph. **See margin, p. 391.**

World Carbon Dioxide Emissions from Burning Fossil Fuels 2005 Projections

United States	24%
Eastern Europe and the former Soviet Union	13%
China	13%
Other Industrialized Countries	25%
Other Developing Countries	26%

SOURCE: Energy Information Admin., 2001.

Go to **www.PHSchool.com** for a data update.
Web Code: afg-2041

Find each indicated measure for ⊙O.

42. $m\angle EOF$ **70**   **43.** $m\widehat{EJH}$ **180**   **44.** $m\widehat{FH}$ **110**

45. $m\angle FOG$ **55**   **46.** $m\widehat{JEG}$ **235**   **47.** $m\widehat{HFJ}$ **290**

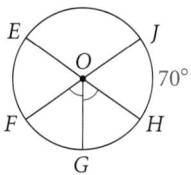

48. Open-Ended Make a circle graph showing how you spend a 24-hour weekday. **Check students' work.**

🌐 **Time** **Hands of a clock suggest an angle whose measure is continually changing.**

49. Through how many degrees does a minute hand move in each time interval?
 a. 1 minute **6**   **b.** 5 minutes **30**   **c.** 20 minutes **120**

50. Through how many degrees does an hour hand move in each time interval?
 a. 1 minute **0.5**   **b.** 5 minutes **2.5**   **c.** 20 minutes **10**

51. What is the measure of the angle formed by the hands of a clock at 7:20? **100**

$\boxed{x^2}$ **Algebra** **Find the value of each variable.**

52. 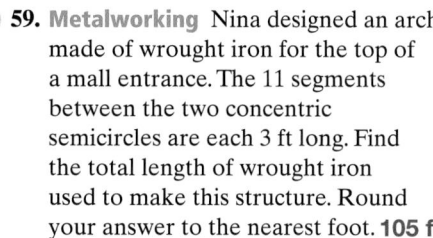 **38**

53. 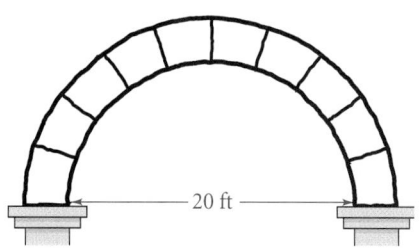 **40**

Real-World 🌐 Connection

In 5 minutes, the tip of the minute hand of Boston's Custom House Tower travels 6 ft 10 in.

🌐 **54. Traffic** Five streets come together at a traffic circle. Vehicles travel counterclockwise around the circle. Use arc measure to give directions to someone who wants to get to East Street from Neponset Street. **Travel 220° from Neponset to East St.**

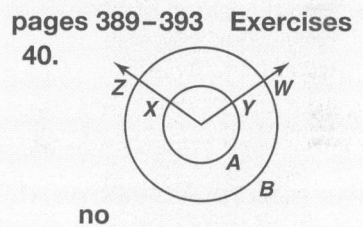

The circumference of a circle is 100π in. Find each of the following.

55. the diameter **100 in.**   **56.** the radius **50 in.**

57. the length of an arc of 120° $\frac{100\pi}{3}$ **in.**

58. A 60° arc of ⊙A has the same length as a 45° arc of ⊙B. Find the ratio of the radius of ⊙A to the radius of ⊙B. **3:4**

🌐 **59. Metalworking** Nina designed an arch made of wrought iron for the top of a mall entrance. The 11 segments between the two concentric semicircles are each 3 ft long. Find the total length of wrought iron used to make this structure. Round your answer to the nearest foot. **105 ft**

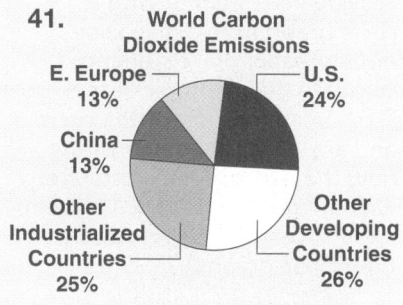

20 ft

60. History In Exercise 24 on page 120, you learned that in 220 B.C., Eratosthenes estimated the circumference of Earth. He did so by finding that on a great circle of Earth, an arc of approximately 500 mi has a central angle of 7.2°.
 25,000 mi a. Use Eratosthenes's measurements to estimate the circumference of Earth.
 b. Compare your answer in part (a) to the actual circumference of Earth (at the equator) of 24,902 mi. **The estimate seems quite accurate.**

? ....
Need Help?

For Exercise 58, draw ⊙A and ⊙B concentric. Draw 60° and 45° angles that share a side. To have equal arc lengths, which circle must be larger?

Connection to Environmental Science

Exercise 41 Have students investigate why carbon dioxide emissions are considered dangerous to the environment.

Math Tip

Exercise 58 Suggest that students pick a whole-number value for the radius of one circle and then find r for the other circle. Point out that the strategy *stepping back* from abstract to concrete is often a good way to begin solving.

Exercise 61 Remind students to use the Midpoint Formula.

Exercise 69 Point out that length means *arc length* here.

Exercise 70 Ask: *Do the arcs in part a have the same length? Explain.* No; the circles have different radii.

Connection to Sports

Exercise 72 Ask: *Why might a runner prefer to run on the inner part of the track rather than the outer?* Sample: The distance is less.

pages 389–393   Exercises

40.

[figure: concentric circles with points Z, X, Y, W, A, B]

no

41.   **World Carbon Dioxide Emissions**

[pie chart]
E. Europe 13%
U.S. 24%
China 13%
Other Developing Countries 26%
Other Industrialized Countries 25%

392

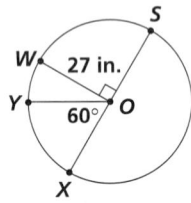
Lesson Quiz 7-6

1. A circle graph has a section marked "Potatoes: 28%." What is the measure of the central angle of this section? **100.8**

2. Explain how a major arc differs from a minor arc. **A major arc is greater than a semicircle. A minor arc is smaller than a semicircle.**

Use ⊙O for Exercises 3–6.

3. Find m$\widehat{YW}$. **30**
4. Find m$\widehat{WXS}$. **270**
5. Suppose that ⊙P has a diameter 2 in. greater than the diameter of ⊙O. How much greater is its circumference? Leave your answer in terms of π. **2π in.²**
6. Find the length of $\widehat{XY}$. Leave your answer in terms of π. **9π in.²**

Alternative Assessment

Provide each student with a circle graph from a magazine or newspaper. Have students calculate the measures of the arcs, circumferences of the circles, and arc lengths to demonstrate how the Arc Addition Postulate, Circumference of a Circle Theorem, and Arc Length Theorem apply to their circle graphs.

Need Help?

The Distance and Midpoint Formulas are on pages 43 and 45.

Coordinate Geometry A diameter of a circle has endpoints A(1, 3) and B(4, 7). Find each of the following.

61. the coordinates of the center **(2.5, 5)**   62. the circumference **5π units**

Find the length of each arc shown in red. Leave your answer in terms of π.

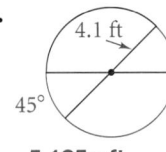
63.
5.125π ft

64.
2.6π in.

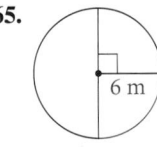
65.
3π m

Use what you learn from Calvin's father to answer Exercises 66 and 67.

Calvin and Hobbes   by Bill Watterson

66. In one revolution, how much farther does a point 10 cm from the center of the record travel than a point 3 cm from the center? Round your answer to the nearest tenth. **44.0 cm**

67. Outside; a point on the outside travels farther in the same time, so it goes faster.

67. **Writing** Kendra and her mother plan to ride the carousel. Two horses on the carousel are side by side. For a more exciting ride, should Kendra sit on the inside or the outside? Explain your reasoning. **See left.**

68. In ⊙O, the length of $\widehat{AB}$ is 6π cm and m$\widehat{AB}$ is 120. What is the diameter of ⊙O? **18 cm**

69. **Coordinate Geometry** Find the length of a semicircle with endpoints (3, 7) and (3, −1). Round your answer to the nearest tenth. **12.6 units**

 **Challenge**

70a. Answers may vary. Sample: $\widehat{BD}$ and $\widehat{FE}$

70. The two circles shown below are concentric.
   a. Name two arcs that have the same measure.
   b. Find the value of x. **35**

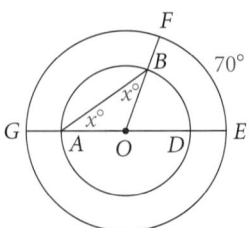

71. Find the perimeter of the shaded portion of the figure below. Leave your answer in terms of π. Explain your reasoning and state what assumptions you make.
2π in.; assumptions may vary.

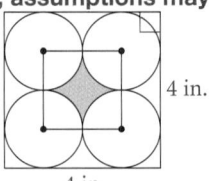

392   Chapter 7   Area

72. Sports An athletic field is a rectangle, 100 yd by 40 yd, with a semicircle at each of the short sides. A running track 10 yd wide surrounds the field. Find the perimeter of the outside of the running track to the nearest tenth of a yard. **388.5 yd**

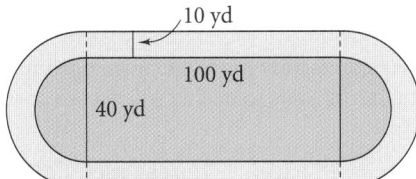

10 yd

100 yd

40 yd

Standardized Test Prep

Multiple Choice

73. The radius of a circle is 12 cm. What is the length of a 60° arc? **B**

  A. 3π cm   **B.** 4π cm   **C.** 5π cm   **D.** 6π cm

74. A 240° arc has length 16π ft. What is the radius of the circle? **G**

  F. 6 ft   **G.** 12 ft   **H.** 15 ft   **I.** 24 ft

Short Response

75. Amy is constructing a curved path through a rectangular yard. She will edge the two sides of the curved path with plastic edging. Find the total length, in meters, of plastic edging she will need. Show your work or explain how you found the total. **See margin.**

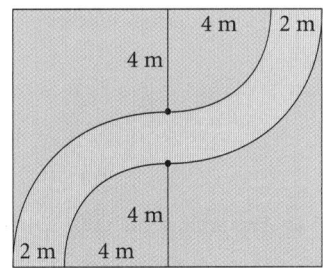

4 m   2 m

4 m

4 m

2 m   4 m

Mixed Review

Lesson 7-5

76. $m\angle 1 = 30$; $m\angle 2 = 15$; $m\angle 3 = 75$; $m\angle 4 = 30$

Part of a regular 12-gon is shown at the right.

76. Find the measure of each numbered angle.

77. The radius is about 19.3 mm. Each side is 10 mm. Find the apothem. **18.6 mm**

78. Find the area of the 12-gon to the nearest square millimeter. **1116 mm²**

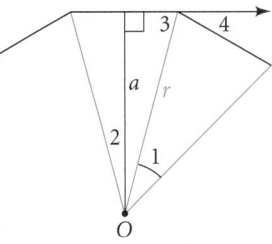

3   4

a   r

2   1

O

Lesson 6-3

Can you conclude that the figure is a parallelogram? Explain. 79–81. See margin.

79.

80.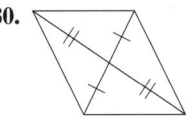

81.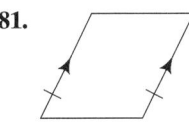

Lesson 3-6

Indicate whether each statement is *always*, *sometimes*, or *never* true.

82. Two nonvertical parallel lines have the same slope. **always**

83. Two perpendicular lines have slopes that are reciprocals. **never**

pages 389–393 Exercises

75. [2] $\frac{1}{2}(2\pi \cdot 6) + \frac{1}{2}(2\pi \cdot 4) =$
$6\pi + 4\pi = 10\pi$;
10π m or about
31.4 m

[1] no work shown

79. No; it could be an isosc. trap.

80. Yes; if the diagonals bisect each other, it is a ▱.

81. Yes; if one pair of sides is both ≅ and ∥, it is a ▱.

Dimensional Analysis

Algebra 1 Review

Dimensional Analysis

Students will use the skill of dimensional analysis when converting between units of area.

Resources

Technology

Geometry Resource Pro® CD-ROM: Algebra 1 Review Resources
Computer Test Generator CD-ROM, Chapter 7, Integer, Decimal, and Fraction Operations

Teaching Notes

1 EXAMPLE

Writing ft^2 as ft · ft helps students understand why the conversion to square inches requires multiplication by $\frac{12 \text{ in.}}{1 \text{ ft}} \cdot \frac{12 \text{ in.}}{1 \text{ ft}}$.

Teaching Tip

Emphasize that dimensional analysis always requires multiplying by a form of 1, where the numerator and the denominator must be equivalent.

Connection to Chemistry

Dimensional analysis often is needed in chemistry courses. If any of your students are currently studying or have completed a chemistry course, ask them to give an example in which dimensional analysis is used in chemistry.

You can use conversion factors to change from one unit of measure to another. The process of analyzing units to decide which conversion factors to use is called *dimensional analysis*.

Since 60 min = 1 h, $\frac{60 \text{ min}}{1 \text{ h}}$ equals 1. You can use $\frac{60 \text{ min}}{1 \text{ h}}$ to convert hours to minutes.

$7 \text{ h} \cdot \frac{60 \text{ min}}{1 \text{ h}} = 420 \text{ min}$ **The hour units cancel, and the result is minutes.**

Sometimes you need to use a conversion factor more than once.

EXAMPLE

The area of the top of a circular table is 8 ft^2. Convert the area to square inches.

You need to convert feet to inches.

feet to inches   feet to inches
↓   ↓

$8 \text{ ft} \cdot \text{ft} \cdot \frac{12 \text{ in.}}{1 \text{ ft}} \cdot \frac{12 \text{ in.}}{1 \text{ ft}} = 8 \text{ ft} \cdot \text{ft} \cdot \frac{12 \text{ in.}}{1 \text{ ft}} \cdot \frac{12 \text{ in.}}{1 \text{ ft}}$ **The feet units cancel. The result is square inches.**

$= 8 \cdot 12 \cdot 12 \text{ in.}^2$ **Simplify.**

$= 1152 \text{ in.}^2$

The area of the table top is 1152 in.^2.

EXERCISES

Choose the correct conversion factor for changing the units.

1. centimeters to meters **B**
  A. $\frac{100 \text{ cm}}{1 \text{ m}}$ B. $\frac{1 \text{ m}}{100 \text{ cm}}$

2. yards to feet **A**
  A. $\frac{3 \text{ ft}}{1 \text{ yd}}$ B. $\frac{1 \text{ yd}}{3 \text{ ft}}$

3. inches to yards **B**
  A. $\frac{36 \text{ in.}}{1 \text{ yd}}$ B. $\frac{1 \text{ yd}}{36 \text{ in.}}$

4. square feet to square inches **A**
  A. $\frac{12 \text{ in.}}{1 \text{ ft}}$ B. $\frac{1 \text{ ft}}{12 \text{ in.}}$

5. cubic meters to cubic kilometers **B**
  A. $\frac{1000 \text{ m}}{1 \text{ km}}$ B. $\frac{1 \text{ km}}{1000 \text{ m}}$

Write each quantity in the given unit.

6. $4 \text{ m} = \blacksquare \text{ cm}$ **400**

7. $360 \text{ in.} = \blacksquare \text{ yd}$ **10**

8. $9 \text{ mm} = \blacksquare \text{ cm}$ **0.9**

9. $17 \text{ yd} = \blacksquare \text{ ft}$ **51**

10. $2.5 \text{ ft} = \blacksquare \text{ in.}$ **30**

11. $35 \text{ m} = \blacksquare \text{ km}$ **0.035**

12. $2 \text{ yd} = \blacksquare \text{ in.}$ **72**

13. $23 \text{ cm} = \blacksquare \text{ mm}$ **230**

14. $2 \text{ ft}^2 = \blacksquare \text{ in.}^2$ **288**

15. $500 \text{ mm}^2 = \blacksquare \text{ cm}^2$ **5**

16. $840 \text{ in.}^2 = \blacksquare \text{ ft}^2$ **$5\frac{5}{6}$**

17. $3 \text{ km}^2 = \blacksquare \text{ cm}^2$ **30,000,000,000**

18. $7 \text{ m}^2 = \blacksquare \text{ km}^2$ **0.000007**

19. $360 \text{ in.}^2 = \blacksquare \text{ yd}^2$ **$\frac{5}{18}$**

20. $900 \text{ cm}^3 = \blacksquare \text{ m}^3$ **0.0009**

21. $4 \text{ yd}^3 = \blacksquare \text{ ft}^3$ **108**

22. $75 \text{ m}^2 = \blacksquare \text{ km}^2$ **0.000075**

23. $250 \text{ in.}^2 = \blacksquare \text{ yd}^2$ **$\frac{125}{648}$**

24. $3 \text{ km}^3 = \blacksquare \text{ m}^3$ **3,000,000,000**

25. $2 \text{ km}^2 = \blacksquare \text{ mm}^2$ **2,000,000,000,000**

26. $60 \text{ in.}^2 = \blacksquare \text{ yd}^2$ **$\frac{5}{108}$**

Areas of Circles and Sectors

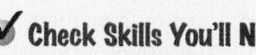

  1.02 Use length, area, and volume of geometric figures to solve problems. Include arc length and area of sectors of circles.

Lesson Preview

What You'll Learn

 OBJECTIVE 1
To find the areas of circles, sectors, and segments of circles

. . . And Why

To compare the area of different-size pizzas, as in Example 1

✓ Check Skills You'll Need   (For help, go to Lesson 7-6.)

1. What is the radius of a circle with diameter 9 cm? **4.5 cm**
2. What is the diameter of a circle with radius 8 ft? **16 ft**
3. Find the circumference of a circle with diameter 12 in. **12π or about 37.7 in.**
4. Find the circumference of a circle with radius 3 m. **6π or about 18.8 m**

New Vocabulary   • sector of a circle   • segment of a circle

---

OBJECTIVE

1 Finding Areas of Circles and Parts of Circles

 Interactive lesson includes instant self-check, tutorials, and activities.

Investigation: Exploring the Area of a Circle

• Use a compass to draw a large circle. Fold the circle horizontally and vertically. Cut the circle into four wedges on the fold lines.

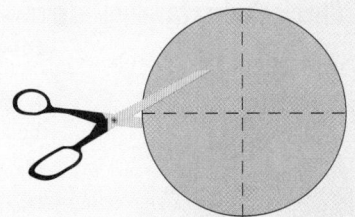

• Fold each wedge into quarters. Cut each wedge on the fold lines. You will have 16 wedges.

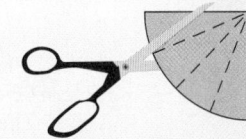

• Tape the wedges to a piece of paper to form the figure shown here.

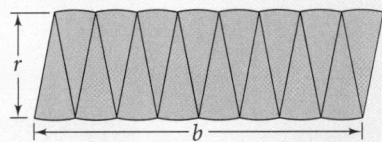

1. How does the area of the figure compare with area of the circle? **They are equal.**
2. The base of the figure is formed by arcs of the circle. Explain how the length b relates to the circumference C of the circle. **$b \approx \frac{1}{2}C$**
3. Explain how the length b relates to the radius r of the circle. **$b \approx \pi r$**
4. If you increase the number of wedges, the figure you create becomes more and more like a rectangle with base b and height r. Write an expression for the area of the rectangle in terms of r. **πr^2**

---

1. Plan

Lesson Preview

✓ Check Skills You'll Need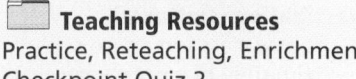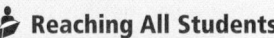

Finding Circumference
Lesson 7-6: Example 4
Exercises 27–33
Extra Practice, p. 696

Lesson Resources

📁 **Teaching Resources**
Practice, Reteaching, Enrichment
Checkpoint Quiz 2

👥 **Reaching All Students**
Practice Workbook 7-7
Spanish Practice Workbook 7-7
Reading and Math Literacy 7C
Spanish Reading & Literacy 7C
Spanish Checkpoint Quiz 2
Informal Geometry Planning Guide 7-7

⏱ **Presentation Assistant Plus!**
Transparencies
• Check Skills You'll Need 7-7
• Additional Examples 7-7
• Student Edition Answers 7-7
• Lesson Quiz 7-7
PH Presentation Pro CD 7-7

PRENTICE HALL ASSESSMENT SYSTEM

Checkpoint Quiz 2
Computer Test Generator CD

💿 **Technology**
Resource Pro® CD-ROM
Computer Test Generator CD
Prentice Hall Presentation Pro CD

💻 **www.PHSchool.com**
Student Site
• Teacher Web Code: afk-5500
• Self-grading Lesson Quiz
Teacher Center
• Lesson Planner
• Resources

Plus

Ongoing Assessment and Intervention

Before the Lesson
Diagnose prerequisite skills using:
• Check Skills You'll Need

During the Lesson
Monitor progress using:
• Check Understanding
• Additional Examples
• Standardized Test Prep

After the Lesson
Assess knowledge using:
• Lesson Quiz
• Computer Test Generator CD
• Chapter Checkpoint 2 (p. 400)

Math Background

Math Background

Areas of circles and sectors can be estimated without using the constant π. One estimation technique measures the areas of inscribed and circumscribed polygons much as lower and upper sums estimate Riemann integrals. Calculating geometric probability may require calculating the areas of sectors and circles.

OBJECTIVE

Teaching Notes

Investigation (Optional)
Discuss as a class why base b is approximately but not exactly equal to πr. Students should mention that a segment is shorter than a curved path between the same two points.

Connection to Calculus
The Investigation's method of finding the area of a curved region is further developed in the study of calculus.

1 EXAMPLE Math Tip

Discuss the fact that the medium pizza has a 20 percent greater radius but a 44 percent greater area than the small pizza. Have students verify these figures and explain the difference in the percents of increase.

2 EXAMPLE

Ask: *How is finding the area of a sector like finding arc length?* **Both have the ratio $\frac{\text{measure of the arc}}{360}$ as a factor.**

English Learners
Students may need help distinguishing the phrase *segment of a circle* from the term *segment* for a line segment.

In the diagrams on the preceding page,
    area of a circle = area of a "parallelogram" $\approx b \cdot r \approx \frac{1}{2} C \cdot r = \pi r^2$,
and the approximations improve as the circle is cut into more pieces.

 Key Concepts

Theorem 7-15	Area of a Circle

The area of a circle is the product of π and the square of the radius.
$$A = \pi r^2$$

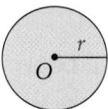

1 EXAMPLE Real-World Connection

Food How much more pizza is in a 12-in.-diameter pizza than in a 10-in. pizza?

$$\text{radius of small pizza} = \frac{10}{2} = 5$$

$$\text{radius of medium pizza} = \frac{12}{2} = 6 \qquad \textbf{Find the radii.}$$

$$\text{area of small pizza} = \pi(5)^2 = 25\pi$$

$$\text{area of medium pizza} = \pi(6)^2 = 36\pi \qquad \textbf{Use the formula for area of a circle.}$$

$$\text{difference in area} = 36\pi - 25\pi = 11\pi$$

$$\approx 34.557519 \qquad \textbf{Use a calculator.}$$

● There is about 35 in.^{2} more pizza in the medium pizza.

✓**Check Understanding** ① How much more pizza is in a 14-in.-diameter pizza than in a 12-in. pizza?
about 41 in.^{2}

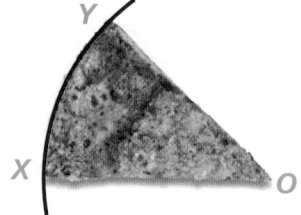

A **sector of a circle** is a region bounded by an arc of the circle and the two radii to the arc's endpoints. You name a sector using one arc endpoint, the center of the circle, and the other arc endpoint. The slice of pizza at the left is sector *XOY* of a circle *O*.

The area of a sector is a fractional part of the area of a circle. The ratio of a sector's area to a circle's area is $\frac{\text{measure of the arc}}{360}$.

Key Concepts

Theorem 7-16	Area of a Sector of a Circle

The area of a sector of a circle is the product of the ratio $\frac{\text{measure of the arc}}{360}$ and the area of the circle.
$$\text{Area of sector } AOB = \frac{m\widehat{AB}}{360} \cdot \pi r^2$$

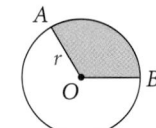

2 EXAMPLE Finding the Area of a Sector of a Circle

Find the area of sector *ZOM*. Leave your answer in terms of π.

$$\text{area of sector } ZOM = \frac{m\widehat{ZM}}{360} \cdot \pi r^2$$
$$= \frac{72}{360} \cdot \pi(20)^2$$
$$= 80\pi$$

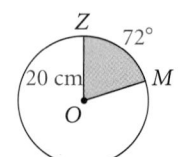

● The area of sector *ZOM* is 80π cm^2.

✓**Check Understanding** ② **Critical Thinking** A circle has a diameter of 20 cm. What is the area of a sector bounded by a 208° major arc? Round your answer to the nearest tenth.
181.5 cm^2

👥 Reaching All Students

Below Level Encourage students to label parts when finding areas within circles. For example, label the segment "I" and the triangle "II" in Example 3.	**Advanced Learners** Following Example 1, have students investigate how to make a pizza with twice the area of another pizza.	**English Learners** See note on page 396. **Visual Learners** See note on page 398.

This pizza is cut into two segments.

A part of a circle bounded by an arc and the segment joining its endpoints is a **segment of a circle.** To find the area of a segment for a minor arc, draw radii to form a sector. The area of the segment equals the area of the sector minus the area of the triangle formed.

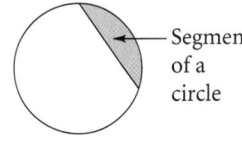

Segment of a circle

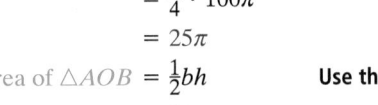
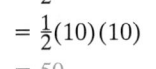

Area of sector — Area of triangle = Area of segment

3 EXAMPLE Finding the Area of a Segment of a Circle

Find the area of the shaded segment. Round your answer to the nearest tenth.

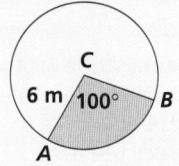

area of sector $AOB = \dfrac{m\widehat{AB}}{360} \cdot \pi r^2$ **Use the formula for area of a sector.**

$= \dfrac{90}{360} \cdot \pi(10)^2$ **Substitute.**

$= \dfrac{1}{4} \cdot 100\pi$

$= 25\pi$

area of $\triangle AOB = \dfrac{1}{2}bh$ **Use the formula for area of a triangle.**

$= \dfrac{1}{2}(10)(10)$ **Substitute.**

$= 50$

area of segment $= 25\pi - 50$

≈ 28.539816 **Use a calculator.**

The area of the segment is about 28.5 in.^{2}

✔ **Check Understanding** ❸ A circle has a radius of 12 cm. Find the area of the smaller segment of the circle determined by a 60° arc. Round your answer to the nearest tenth. **13.0 cm²**

EXERCISES

For more practice, see *Extra Practice*.

Practice and Problem Solving

Ⓐ **Practice by Example**

Example 1 (page 396)

Find the area of each circle. Leave your answer in terms of π.

1.
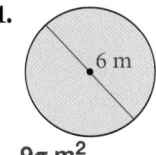
6 m

9π m²

2.
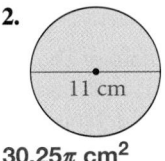
11 cm

30.25π cm²

3.
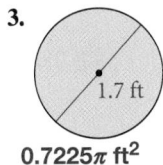
1.7 ft

0.7225π ft²

4.
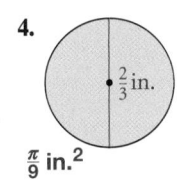
$\frac{2}{3}$ in.

$\frac{\pi}{9}$ in.²

5. **Agriculture** Some farmers use a circular irrigation method. An irrigation arm acts as the radius of an irrigation circle. How much more land is covered with an irrigation arm of 300 ft than by an irrigation arm of 250 ft? **about 86,394 ft²**

6. What is the difference in the areas of a circular table with diameter 6 ft and a circular table with diameter 8 ft? **about 22 ft²**

---

3 EXAMPLE

Students may cut apart segments of a circle and relate the areas to the area of the circle.

Additional Examples

❶ A circular archery target has a 2-ft diameter. It is yellow except for a red bull's-eye at the center with a 6-in. diameter. Find the area of the yellow region. Round to the nearest whole number. **424 in.²**

❷ Find the area of sector *ACB*. Leave your answer in terms of π.

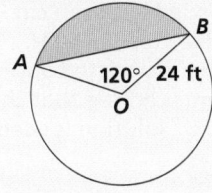

C
6 m 100°
B
A

10π m²

❸ Find the area of the shaded segment. Round your answer to the nearest tenth.

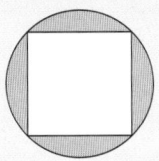

B
A 120° 24 ft
O

353.8 ft²

Closure

A circle with a diameter of 10 in. contains an inscribed square as shown below. Find the area of the shaded segments. Leave your answer in terms of π.

(25π − 50) in.²

3. Practice

Assignment Guide

▼ **Objective**
  Ⓐ Ⓑ Core 1–34
  Ⓒ Extension 35–40

Standardized Test Prep 41–43

Mixed Review 44–48

Error Prevention
Exercises 1–4 Some students may substitute d for r in the formula $A = \pi r^2$. Use these exercises to identify and correct the error.

Visual Learners
Exercises 25–27 Have students draw a circle inscribed in a square, fold the square along its diagonals, cut out the circle, and then cut the circle along the fold lines. By using all the sectors to copy the art, students can see that the same method of solution is used.

Diversity
Exercise 40 Point out that the bow of a canoe is its front end.

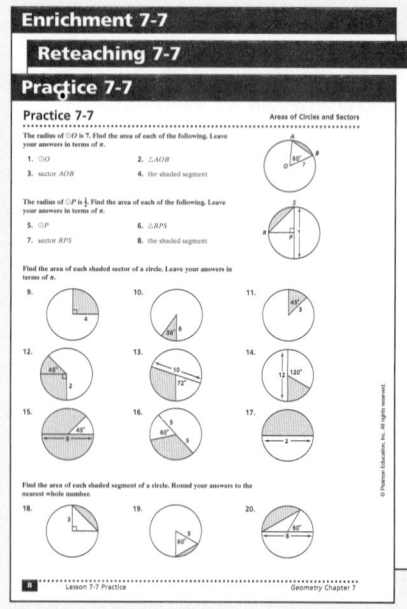

Example 2
(page 396)

Find the area of each shaded sector of a circle. Leave your answer in terms of π.

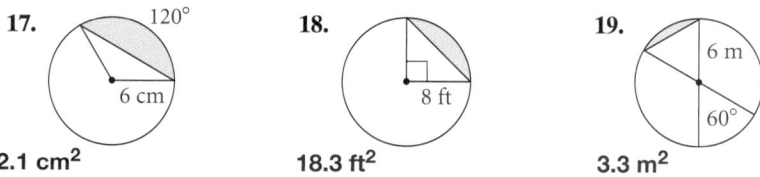

7. 45° 18 yd **40.5π yd²**
8. 16 cm **64π cm²**
9. 26 m 120° **$\frac{169\pi}{6}$ m²**
10. 30° 12 in. **12π in.²**
11. 4 ft **12π ft²**
12. 16 cm 45° **56π cm²**

Find the area of sector TOP in $\odot O$ using the given information. Leave your answer in terms of π.

13. $r = 5$ m, $m\widehat{TP} = 90°$ **$\frac{25\pi}{4}$ m²**
14. $r = 6$ ft, $m\widehat{TP} = 15°$ **$\frac{3\pi}{2}$ ft²**
15. $d = 16$ in., $m\widehat{PT} = 135°$ **24π in.²**
16. $d = 15$ cm, $m\widehat{PT} = 180°$ **28.125π cm²**

Example 3
(page 397)

Find the area of each shaded segment. Round your answer to the nearest tenth.

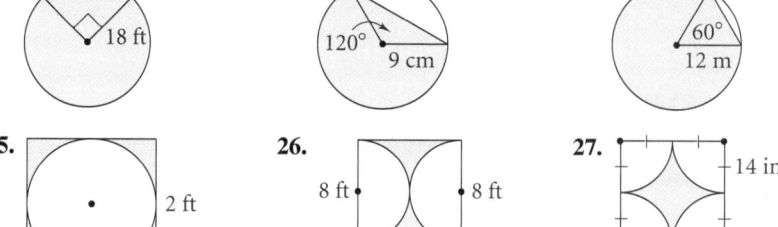

17. 120° 6 cm **22.1 cm²**
18. 8 ft **18.3 ft²**
19. 6 m 60° **3.3 m²**

A circle has the given radius. Find the area of the smaller segment of the circle determined by an arc with the given measure. Round to the nearest tenth.

20. radius 15 m, arc 60° **20.4 m²**
21. radius 14 cm, arc 120° **120.4 cm²**

Ⓑ **Apply Your Skills**

Find the area of the shaded region. Leave your answer in terms of π and in simplest radical form. 22–27. See left.

22. $(243\pi + 162)$ ft²
23. $(54\pi + 20.25\sqrt{3})$ cm²
24. $(120\pi + 36\sqrt{3})$ m²
25. $(4 - \pi)$ ft²
26. $(64 - 16\pi)$ ft²
27. $(784 - 196\pi)$ in.²

22. 18 ft
23. 120° 9 cm
24. 60° 12 m
25. 2 ft
26. 8 ft · 8 ft
27. 14 in.

28. **Marine Biology** The diver at the right is working to bring up samples of organisms from the ocean floor. The line to the diver is 100 ft long, and the diver is working at a depth of 80 ft. What is the area of the circle that the diver can cover? Round your answer to the nearest square foot. **11,310 ft²**

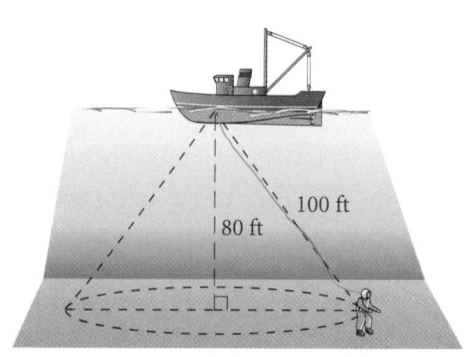

100 ft
80 ft

pages 397–400   Exercises

29. Lower outside; the lower inside and top pieces have base areas 8π in.², but the lower outside pieces have base areas 8.75π in.².

Real-World  **Connection**

Careers Training as a pastry chef is part of the background of many executive chefs.

29. Writing The American Institute of Baking suggests a technique for cutting and serving a tiered cake. The tiers of a cake have the same height and have radii 8 in. and 13 in. The top tier and the cake directly under it are each cut into 8 wedges as shown. The outer ring of the 13-inch tier is cut into 12 pieces. Which would be larger, a piece from the top or a piece from the outer ring? Explain. **See margin, p. 398.**

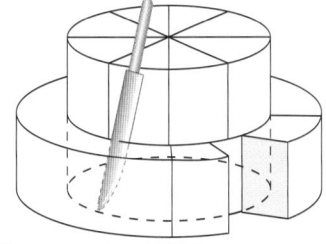

30. How many circles with radius 4 in. will have the same total area as a circle with radius 12 in.? **9 circles**

31. Games A dart board has diameter 20 in. and is divided into 20 congruent sectors. Find the area of one sector. Round your answer to the nearest tenth.
15.7 in.²

32. In a circle, a 90° sector has area 36π in.². What is the circle's radius? **12 in.**

33. Open-Ended Draw a circle and a sector so that the area of the sector is 16π cm². Give the radius of the circle and the measure of the arc of the sector. **See margin.**

34. A method for finding the area of a segment determined by a minor arc is described on page 397. **34a. See margin.**
   a. Describe two ways to find the area of a segment determined by a major arc.
   b. If $m\widehat{AB} = 90$ in a circle of radius 10, find the areas of the two segments determined by $\widehat{AB}$. **$25\pi - 50$; $75\pi + 50$**

🅒 **Challenge**

38. Blue region; let $AB = 2x$. Area of blue = $4x^2 - \pi x^2$; area of yellow = $\pi x^2 - 2x^2$.

39. $\frac{200\pi}{3} - 50\sqrt{3}$ units²

Find the area of the shaded region. Leave your answer in terms of π.

35.
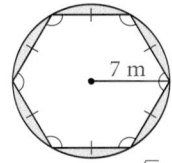
7 m
$(49\pi - 73.5\sqrt{3})$ m²

36.
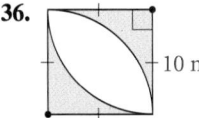
10 m
$(200 - 50\pi)$ m²

37.
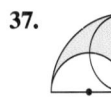
4 m
4π m²

38. Circle O at the right is inscribed in square $ABCD$ and circumscribed about square $PQRS$. Which is smaller, the blue region or the yellow region? Explain.

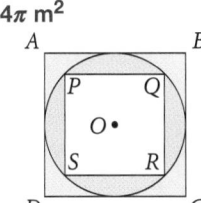

39. Circles T and U each have a radius 10 and $TU = 10$. Find the area of the region that is contained inside both circles.

Need Help?

For Exercise 39, where must T and U lie in a diagram of $\odot T$ and $\odot U$?

40a.
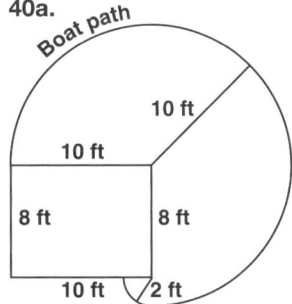

40b. Find the area of $\frac{3}{4}$ of a circle of radius 10 and add $\frac{1}{4}$ of a circle of radius 2.

🌐 **40. Recreation** An 8 ft-by-10 ft floating dock is anchored in the middle of a pond. The bow of a canoe is tied to a corner of the dock with a 10-ft rope as shown in the picture below.
   a. Sketch a diagram of the region in which the bow of the canoe can travel.
   b. Write a plan for finding the area. **40a–b. See left.**
   c. Find the area. Round your answer to the nearest square foot. **239 ft²**

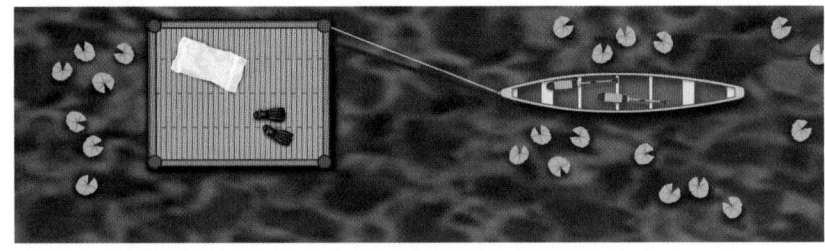

4. Assess

Lesson Quiz 7-7

Solve.

1. A park contains two circular playgrounds. One has a diameter of 60 m, and the other has a diameter of 40 m. How much greater is the area of the larger playground? Round to the nearest whole number.
1571 m²

2. A circle has an 8-in. radius. Find the area of a sector whose arc measures 135. Leave your answer in terms of π. **24π in.²**

For Exercises 3 and 4, find the area of the shaded segment. Round to the nearest whole unit.

3.
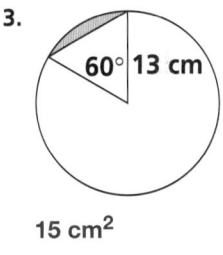
60° 13 cm
15 cm²

4.
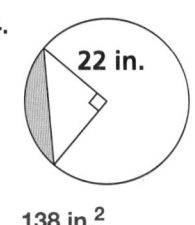
22 in.
138 in.²

Alternative Assessment

Have student partners plan how to sell pizzas. Using the area formulas from this lesson, they should select two different sizes and price them proportionately. Have students write a paragraph explaining how the size of each pizza justifies its price.

Lesson 7-7   Areas of Circles and Sectors   **399**

33. Answers may vary. Sample: 8 cm radius;
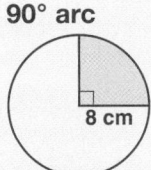
90° arc
8 cm

34. a. Answers may vary. Sample: Subtract the minor arc segment area from the area of the circle, or add the areas of the major sector and △ formed.

399

Standardized Test Prep

 Resources

For additional practice with a variety of test item formats:
- Standardized Test Prep, p. 413
- Test-Taking Strategies, p. 408
- Test-Taking Strategies with Transparencies

Exercises 41, 42 Sometimes an exercise is not as complicated as it originally looks. Each of these exercises can be solved using the ratio $\frac{\text{measure of the arc}}{360}$ without knowing either the formula $A = \pi r^2$ or the radius.

 Chapter Checkpoint 2

To check understanding of Lessons 7-4 to 7-7:

Checkpoint Quiz 2 (p. 400)

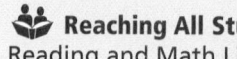 **Teaching Resources**
Checkpoint Quiz 2 (also in Prentice Hall Assessment System)

Reaching All Students
Reading and Math Literacy 7C

Spanish versions available

---

pages 398–400   Exercises

43. [2] area of rectangle = $2 \cdot 12 = 24$
   area of semicircles = $3 \cdot \left(\frac{1}{2}\pi \cdot 2^2\right) = 6\pi$
   $24 - 6\pi \approx 5.2$ m^2

   [1] no work shown

48. Show that $\triangle BCE \cong \triangle ACD$ by ASA. Then use $\overline{CE} \cong \overline{CD}$ and segment subtraction to show that $\overline{BD} \cong \overline{AE}$. Now with vertical $\angle s$ $\angle BFD \cong \angle AFE$, $\triangle BDF \cong \triangle AEF$ by ASA.

 **Standardized Test Prep**

Multiple Choice

41. A circle has area 72π yd^2. What is the area of a 10° sector of the circle? **A**
   A. 2π yd^2 B. 3π yd^2 C. 4π yd^2 D. 6π yd^2

42. A sector of 90° has area π mm. What is the area of the circle? **G**
   F. 2π mm^2 G. 4π mm^2 H. 8π mm^2 I. 4 mm^2

Short Response

Take It to the NET
Online lesson quiz at
www.PHSchool.com
Web Code: afa-0707

43. Each of three water sprinklers covers a semicircle of radius 2 m. The shaded region remains dry. Find the area of the shaded region to the nearest square meter. Show your work or explain how you found the area. **See margin.**

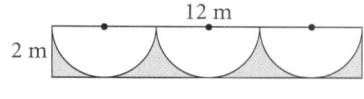

Mixed Review

Lesson 7-6   Find the length of $\widehat{AB}$ in each circle. Leave your answers in terms of π.

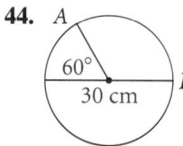
44.
10π cm

45.
2π m

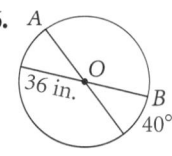
46.
28π in.

Lesson 6-5

47. Three sides of a trapezoid are congruent. The fourth side is 4 in. longer than each of the other three. The perimeter is 49 in. Find the length of each side.
   $11\frac{1}{4}$ in., $11\frac{1}{4}$ in., $11\frac{1}{4}$ in., $15\frac{1}{4}$ in.

Lesson 4-7

48. Write a plan for a proof. (*Hint:* First prove overlapping triangles are congruent.)

   Given: $\overline{AC} \cong \overline{BC}$, $\angle A \cong \angle B$ **See margin.**
   Prove: $\triangle BDF \cong \triangle AEF$

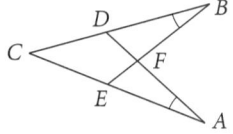

 Checkpoint Quiz 2   **Lessons 7-4 through 7-7**

Instant self-check quiz online and on CD-ROM

1. 135 in.^{2}
2. 58.5 m^2
3. $72\sqrt{3}$ in.^{2}
4. $27\sqrt{3}$ ft^2
5. 32 yd^2
6. 100π in.^{2}
7. 27π m^2
8. $(16\pi - 32)$ cm^2

Find the area of each trapezoid, rhombus, regular polygon, circle, sector or segment. When necessary, leave answers in terms of π and in simplest radical form.

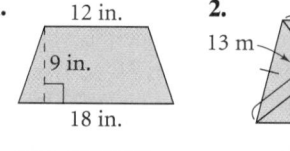
1.

2.

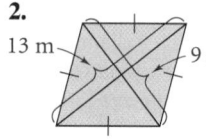
3.

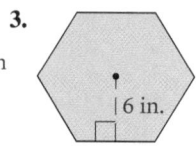
4.

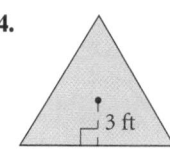

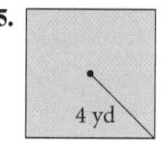
5.

6.

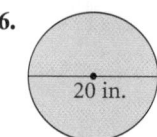
7.

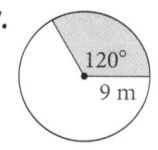
8.

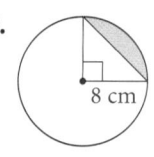

9. Find the circumference of a circle with radius 5 m. Round to the nearest tenth. **31.4 m**

10. In a circle of radius 18 mm, $m\widehat{AB} = 45$. Find the length of $\widehat{AB}$ in terms of π. $\frac{9\pi}{2}$ mm

Exploring Area and Circumference

A polygon that is *inscribed* in a circle has all its vertices on the circle. Work in pairs or small groups. Investigate the ratios of the perimeters and areas of inscribed regular polygons to the circumference and area of the circle in which they are inscribed.

Begin by making a table like this.

Regular Polygon			Circle		Ratios	
Sides	Perimeter	Area	Circumference	Area	Perimeter / Circumference	Polygon Area / Circle Area
3						

Construct

Use geometry software to construct a circle. Find its circumference and area and record them in your table. Inscribe an equilateral triangle in the circle. Your software may be able to do this for you automatically, or you can construct three points on the circle and move them so they are approximately evenly spaced on the circle. Then draw a triangle.

Investigate

Use your geometry software to measure the perimeter and area of the triangle and to calculate the ratios $\frac{\text{triangle perimeter}}{\text{circle circumference}}$ and $\frac{\text{triangle area}}{\text{circle area}}$. Record the results.

Manipulate the circle to change its size. Do the ratios you calculate stay the same or change?

Now inscribe a square in a circle and fill in your table for a polygon of four sides. Do the same for a regular pentagon.

EXERCISES

1. **Make a Conjecture** What will happen to the ratios
   $\frac{\text{perimeter}}{\text{circumference}}$ and $\frac{\text{polygon area}}{\text{circle area}}$
   as you increase the number of sides of the polygon?
   Each ratio will approach 1.

Extend

2. Extend your table to include polygons of 12 sides.
   a. Does your conjecture still hold? **yes**
   b. Compare the two columns of ratios in your table.
      How do they differ? **The ratio of perimeter to circumference approaches 1 faster than the area ratios.**
3. Estimate the perimeter and area of a polygon of 100 sides that is inscribed in a circle with a radius of 10 cm. **about 63 cm; about 314 cm^2**

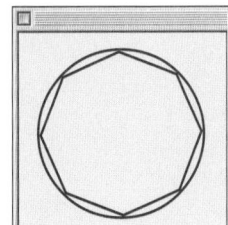

regular octagon

Exploring Area and Circumference

Students will use geometry software to investigate how the perimeter and area of regular polygons are related to the circumference and area of the circles in which they are inscribed.

Resources

Students may use any geometry software program to explore area and circumference and to calculate the ratios $\frac{\text{perimeter}}{\text{circumference}}$ and $\frac{\text{polygon area}}{\text{circle area}}$.

Teaching Notes

By inscribing regular n-gons where $n = 3, 4, 5,$ and 12 in circles, students find that the perimeter and area of an n-gon become closer to the circumference and area of the circles as n increases.

Alternative Method

A regular n-gon can be constructed by dividing a circle into n congruent arcs. The following method works well for polygons where the number of sides is a factor of 360. Measure a central angle of $\frac{360°}{n}$. Use a compass to measure the chord connecting the ends of the intercepted arc. Mark another point on the circumference this same distance apart. Repeat this process until there are n points on the circle, then connect consecutive points to form a regular n-gon.

Visual Learners

Students should observe that regular n-gons fit more and more tightly inside a circle as n increases, so the ratio of the areas of the n-gons and the circle nears 1.

1. Plan

Lesson Preview

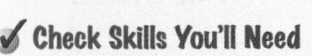 **Check Skills You'll Need**

For help use
Skills Handbook, pp. 718, 721

Lesson Resources

📁 **Teaching Resources**
Practice, Reteaching, Enrichment

👥 **Reaching All Students**
Practice Workbook 7-8
Spanish Practice Workbook 7-8
Hands-On Activities 21
Informal Geometry Planning
   Guide 7-8

⏱ **Presentation Assistant Plus!**
Transparencies
• Check Skills You'll Need 7-8
• Additional Examples 7-8
• Student Edition Answers 7-8
• Lesson Quiz 7-8
PH Presentation Pro CD 7-8

(ASSESSMENT *SYSTEM*)

Computer Test Generator CD

💿 **Technology**
Resource Pro® CD-ROM
Computer Test Generator CD
Prentice Hall Presentation Pro CD

💻 **www.PHSchool.com**
Student Site
• Teacher Web Code: afk-5500
• Self-grading Lesson Quiz
Teacher Center
• Lesson Planner
• Resources

Plus

7-8

Geometric Probability

1.03 Use length, area, and volume to model and solve problems involving probability.

(North Carolina Objectives)
Lesson Preview

What You'll Learn

OBJECTIVE 1
To use segment and area models to find the probabilities of events

. . . And Why

To find the probability of winning a carnival game, as in Example 4

✔ Check Skills You'll Need

(For help, go to Skills Handbook pages 718 and 724.)

Find and simplify each ratio.

1. $\frac{BD}{AE}$ $\frac{1}{3}$ 2. $\frac{CE}{AF}$ $\frac{1}{2}$ 3. $\frac{AB}{BC}$ 1

A   B   C D   E F
0 1 2 3 4 5 6 7 8 9 10

4. Two circles have radii 1 m and 2 m, respectively. What is the simplest form of the fraction with numerator equal to the area of the smaller circle and denominator equal to the area of the larger circle? $\frac{1}{4}$

You roll a number cube. Find the probability of rolling each of the following.

5. 4 $\frac{1}{6}$
6. an odd number $\frac{1}{2}$
7. 2 or 5 $\frac{1}{3}$
8. a prime number $\frac{1}{2}$

New Vocabulary • geometric probability

OBJECTIVE
1 Using Segment and Area Models

🅣🅔🅧🅣 **Interactive lesson includes instant self-check, tutorials, and activities.**

📖 **Reading Math**
P(event) is read "the probability of an event."

You may recall that the probability of an event is the ratio of the number of favorable outcomes to the number of possible outcomes.

$$P(\text{event}) = \frac{\text{favorable outcomes}}{\text{possible outcomes}}$$

Sometimes you can use a **geometric probability** model in which you let points represent outcomes. You find probabilities by comparing measurements of sets of points. For example, if points of segments represent outcomes, then

$$P(\text{event}) = \frac{\text{length of favorable segment}}{\text{length of entire segment}}.$$

1 EXAMPLE **Finding Probability Using Segments**

A gnat lands at a random point on the ruler's edge. Find the probability that the point is between 3 and 7.

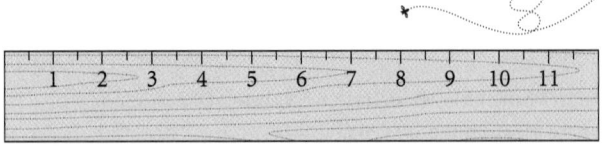

$P(\text{landing between 3 and 7}) = \dfrac{\text{length of favorable segment}}{\text{length of entire segment}} = \dfrac{4}{12}, \text{ or } \dfrac{1}{3}$

✔ **Check Understanding** ① A point on $\overline{AB}$ is selected at random. What is the probability that it is a point on $\overline{CD}$? $\frac{2}{5}$

A   C   D   B
0 1 2 3 4 5 6 7 8 9 10

🔵 Ongoing Assessment and Intervention

Before the Lesson Diagnose prerequisite skills using:	**During the Lesson** Monitor progress using:	**After the Lesson** Assess knowledge using:
• Check Skills You'll Need	• Check Understanding • Additional Examples • Standardized Test Prep	• Lesson Quiz • Computer Test Generator CD

Real-World Connection

If the bus runs on schedule, Elena's average wait (Example 2) will be 12.5 min.

You can use a segment model to find the probability of how long you will wait for a bus.

2 EXAMPLE Real-World Connection

Commuting Elena's bus runs every 25 minutes. If she arrives at her bus stop at a random time, what is the probability that she will have to wait at least 10 minutes for the bus?

Assume that a stop takes very little time, and let $\overline{AB}$ represent the 25 minutes between buses.

A _____ B
0 5 10 15 20 25

If Elena arrives at any time between A and C, she has to wait at least 10 minutes until B.

A _____ C ____ B
0 5 10 15 20 25

$$P(\text{waiting at least 10 min}) = \frac{\text{length of } \overline{AC}}{\text{length of } \overline{AB}} = \frac{15}{25}, \text{ or } \frac{3}{5}$$

The probability that Elena will have to wait at least 10 minutes for the bus is $\frac{3}{5}$ or 60%.

✓ **Check Understanding** **2** What is the probability that Elena will have to wait no more than 10 minutes for the bus? $\frac{2}{5}$

If the points of a region represent equally-likely outcomes, then you can find probabilities by comparing areas.

$$P(\text{event}) = \frac{\text{area of favorable region}}{\text{area of entire region}}$$

3 EXAMPLE Finding Probability Using Area

Target Game Assume that a dart you throw will land on the 1-ft square dartboard and is equally likely to land at any point on the board. Find the probability of hitting each of the blue, yellow, and red regions. The radii of the concentric circles are 1, 2, and 3 inches, respectively.

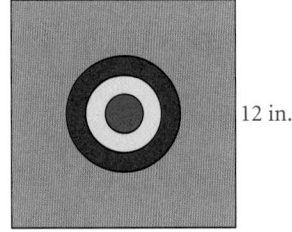

12 in.

12 in.

? Need Help?

You can think of a probability like 0.022 as "22 times out of a thousand."

$$P(\text{blue}) = \frac{\text{area of blue region}}{\text{area of square}} = \frac{\pi(1)^2}{12^2} = \frac{\pi}{144} \approx 0.022, \text{ or } 2.2\% \quad \textbf{Use a calculator.}$$

$$P(\text{yellow}) = \frac{\text{area of yellow region}}{\text{area of square}} = \frac{\pi(2)^2 - \pi(1)^2}{12^2} = \frac{3\pi}{144} \approx 0.065, \text{ or } 6.5\%$$

$$P(\text{red}) = \frac{\text{area of red region}}{\text{area of square}} = \frac{\pi(3^2) - \pi(2)^2}{12^2} = \frac{5\pi}{144} \approx 0.109, \text{ or } 10.9\%$$

The probabilities of hitting the blue, yellow, and red regions are about 2.2%, 6.5%, and 10.9%, respectively.

✓ **Check Understanding** **3** If you change the blue circle as indicated, how does the probability of hitting the blue circle change? Explain.

a. Double the radius.
It becomes about 8.7%, or about 4 times greater.

b. Triple the radius.
It becomes about 19.6%, or about 9 times greater.

---

2. Teach

Professional Development

Math Background

The definition of probability is numerical in nature, but it allows for geometric consideration. Geometric probability is defined to be the ratio of favorable length, area, or volume to the entire length, area, or volume.

OBJECTIVE
1 Teaching Notes

1 EXAMPLE Connection to Probability

Discuss with students the probability of the gnat landing exactly on 6. By the text's definition, the probability is 0, since the length of a point is 0.

2 EXAMPLE

Remind students that probabilities can be written as fractions, decimals, or percents.

3 EXAMPLE Teaching Tip

Have students explain how to calculate the numerator of each of the three probabilities shown. Ask: *Why are terms subtracted in two of the numerators?* You are finding the difference between two areas.

4 EXAMPLE Tactile Learners

Suggest that students model the example by constructing the game board and measuring quarters on it. Ask: *Where does the fraction $\frac{17}{32}$ come from?* Because the circle has radius 1 in. and a quarter has radius $\frac{15}{32}$ in., the quarter will land within the circle if it lies within $1 - \frac{15}{32} = \frac{17}{32}$ in. of the center of the circle.

👥 Reaching All Students

| **Below Level** Have students design "probability boards" in which regions of different colors are labeled with the probability that a dart or coin that lands on the board lands in that region. | **Advanced Learners** Suppose Elena's bus brings her to another stop, where an express van runs every 15 minutes. What is the probability that her total waiting time is more than 20 minutes? | **Visual Learners** See note on page 405. **Tactile Learners** See note on page 403. |

1 A gnat lands at random on the edge of the ruler in Example 1. Find the probability that the gnat lands on a point between 2 and 10. $\frac{2}{3}$

2 A museum offers a tour every hour. If Benny arrives at the tour site at a random time, what is the probability that he will have to wait at least 15 min? $\frac{3}{4}$

3 A circle is inscribed in a square target with 20-cm sides. Find the probability that a dart landing randomly within the square does not land within the circle.

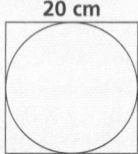

20 cm

about 21.5%

4 To win a prize, you must toss a quarter so that it lands entirely between the two circles below. Find the probability that this happens with a quarter of radius $\frac{15}{32}$ in. Assume that the quarter is equally likely to land anywhere completely inside the large circle.

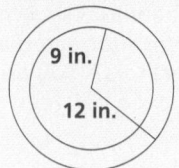

9 in.

12 in.

about 32.6%

Closure

A target with diameter 16 in. is formed by two concentric circles. Assume that a dart is equally likely to land at any point on the target, and the probability of landing in either region is 50 percent. Find the radius of the smaller circle. Round to the nearest tenth. **5.7 in.**

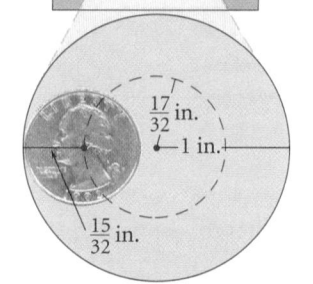

8 in.

8 in.

1 in.

$\frac{17}{32}$ in.

1 in.

$\frac{15}{32}$ in.

As Example 3 suggests, you can apply geometric probability to some games. This can help you decide how easy or difficult it may be to win such games.

4 **EXAMPLE** **Real-World Connection**

Coin Toss To win a prize in a carnival game, you must toss a quarter so that it lands entirely within the circle as shown at the left. Find the probability of this happening on one toss. Assume that the center of a tossed quarter is equally likely to land at any point within the 8-in. square.

The radius of the circle is 1 in. The radius of a quarter is $\frac{15}{32}$ in. The favorable points are those that are less than $\frac{17}{32}$ in. from the center of the circle. They are the points within the dashed circle.

$$P(\text{quarter landing in circle}) = \frac{\text{area of dashed circle}}{\text{area of square}}$$

$$= \frac{\pi\left(\frac{17}{32}\right)^2}{8^2} \approx 0.014, \text{ or } 1.4\%$$

● The probability of a quarter landing in the circle is about 1.4%.

✓ **Check Understanding** **4** **Critical Thinking** Suppose you toss 100 quarters. Would you expect to win a prize? Explain. **Yes; theoretically you should win 1.4 times out of 100.**

EXERCISES

For more practice, see *Extra Practice*.

Practice and Problem Solving

A **Practice by Example**

Example 1 (page 402)

Find the probability that a point chosen at random from $\overline{AK}$ is on the given segment.

A B C D E F G H I J K

0 1 2 3 4 5 6 7 8 9 10

1. $\overline{CH}$ $\frac{1}{2}$ **2.** $\overline{FG}$ $\frac{1}{10}$ **3.** $\overline{DJ}$ $\frac{3}{5}$ **4.** $\overline{EI}$ $\frac{2}{5}$ **5.** $\overline{AK}$ 1

6. Points M and N are on $\overline{ZB}$ with $ZM = 5$, $NB = 9$, and $ZB = 20$. A point is chosen at random from $\overline{ZB}$. What is the probability that the point is on $\overline{MN}$? $\frac{3}{10}$

Example 2 (page 403)

7. **Transportation** A rapid transit line runs trains every 10 minutes. Draw a geometric model and find the probability that randomly arriving passengers will not have to wait more than 4 minutes. **See margin.**

Traffic Patterns Main Street intersects each street below. The traffic lights on Main follow the cycles shown. As you travel along Main and approach the intersection, what is the probability that the first color you see is green?

8. Durham Avenue: green 30 s, yellow 5 s, red 25 s $\frac{1}{2}$ or 50%

9. Martin Luther King Boulevard: green 20 s, yellow 5 s, red 50 s $\frac{4}{15}$ or about 27%

10. Yonge Street: green 40 s, yellow 5 s, red 25 s $\frac{4}{7}$ or about 57%

11. International Drive: green 25 s, yellow 5 s, red 45 s $\frac{1}{3}$ or about 33%

12. Tamiami Trail: green 35 s, yellow 8 s, red 32 s $\frac{7}{15}$ or about 47%

13. Flutie Pass: green 50 s, yellow 4 s, red 26 s $\frac{5}{8}$ or 62.5%

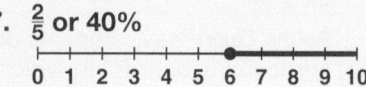

pages 404–407 Exercises

7. $\frac{2}{5}$ or 40%

0 1 2 3 4 5 6 7 8 9 10

14. During May, a certain drawbridge over the Intracoastal Waterway is raised every half hour to allow boats to pass. It remains open for 5 min. What is the probability that a motorist arriving at the bridge in May will find it raised? $\frac{1}{6}$

Examples 3, 4
(pages 403 and 404)

Target Games Darts are thrown at each of the boards shown below. A dart hits the board at a random point. Judging by appearances, find the probability that it will land in the shaded region.

15. 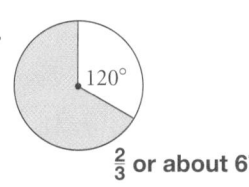 $\frac{1}{4}$ or 25%

16. 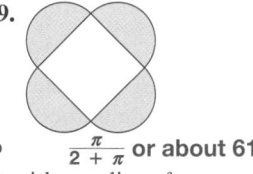 25%

17. 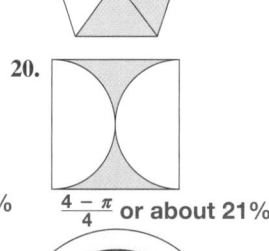 $\frac{2}{5}$ or 40%

18. 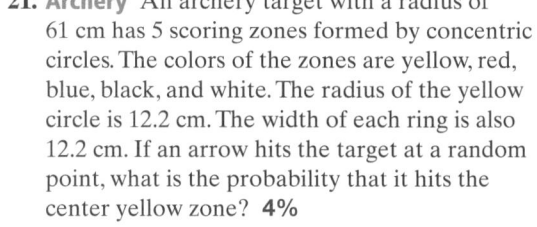 $120°$ $\frac{2}{3}$ or about 67%

19. $\frac{\pi}{2+\pi}$ or about 61%

20. 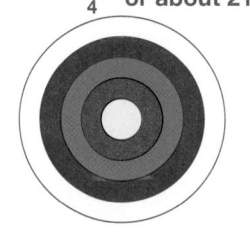 $\frac{4-\pi}{4}$ or about 21%

B Apply Your Skills

21. Archery An archery target with a radius of 61 cm has 5 scoring zones formed by concentric circles. The colors of the zones are yellow, red, blue, black, and white. The radius of the yellow circle is 12.2 cm. The width of each ring is also 12.2 cm. If an arrow hits the target at a random point, what is the probability that it hits the center yellow zone? **4%**

22. $\overline{BZ}$ contains $\overline{MN}$ and $BZ = 20$. A point is chosen at random from $\overline{BZ}$. The probability that the point is also on $\overline{MN}$ is 0.3, or 30%. Find MN. **6**

🌐 **Target Games** A dart hits each square dartboard at a random point. Find the probability that the dart lands inside a circle. Leave your answer in terms of π.

23. 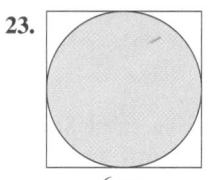 $\frac{\pi}{4}$
6 cm

24. 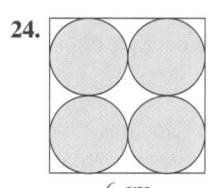 $\frac{\pi}{4}$
6 cm

25. 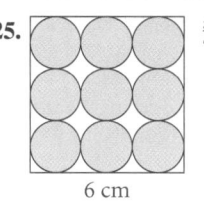 $\frac{\pi}{4}$
6 cm

26. A dartboard is a square of radius 10 in. You throw a dart and hit the target. Find the probability that the dart lies within $\sqrt{10}$ in. of the center of the square. $\frac{10\pi}{200}$ or about 16%

27. Critical Thinking Use the information given in Example 4.
   a. For each 1000 quarters tossed, about how many prizes would be won? **14 prizes**
   b. Suppose the game prize costs the carnival $10. About how much profit would the carnival expect for every 1000 quarters tossed? **$110**

🌐 **28. Commuting** Suppose a bus arrives at a bus stop every 25 min and waits 5 min before leaving. Sketch a geometric model. Use it to find the probability that a person has to wait more than 10 min for a bus to leave. **See margin.**

🌐 **29. Traffic Patterns** The traffic lights at Fourth and Commercial Streets repeat themselves in 60-second cycles. Ms. Li regularly has students drive on Fourth Street through the Commercial Street intersection. By experience, she knows that they will face a red light 60% of the time. Use this information to estimate how long the Fourth Street light is red during each 1-min cycle. **36 s**

28. $\frac{3}{5}$ or 60%

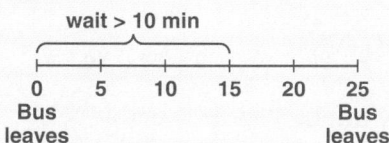
wait > 10 min
0 5 10 15 20 25
Bus   Bus
leaves   leaves

---

3. Practice

Assignment Guide

1 Objective
   A B Core 1–45
   C Extension 46, 47

Standardized Test Prep 48–51

Mixed Review 52–57

Error Prevention

Exercise 7 For students confused by the phrase *not . . . more than 4 minutes,* ask: *What is another way to state the waiting time?* **4 min or less**

Visual Learners

Exercises 15–17, 19, 20 Discuss as a class how to solve these exercises, which have no measurements given.

Diversity

Exercise 21 Men's and women's archery are Olympic sports. Ask students who are familiar with archery to explain the sport.

Exercise 26 Remind students that the radius of a square is the distance from the center to a vertex.

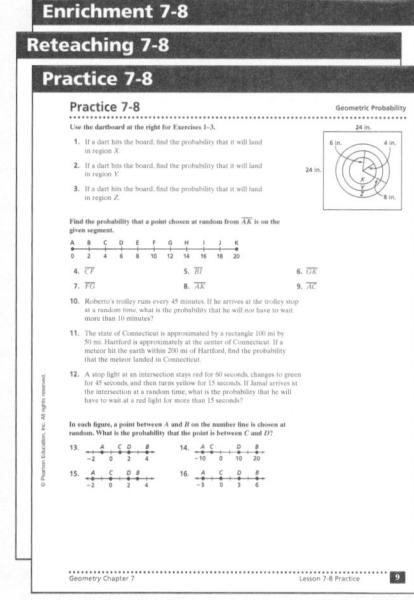

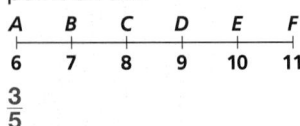

4. Assess

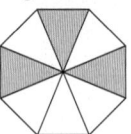
1. A point on $\overline{AF}$ is chosen at random. What is the probability that it is a point on $\overline{BE}$?

A	B	C	D	E	F
6	7	8	9	10	11

$\frac{3}{5}$

2. Express elevators to the top of a tall building leave the ground floor every 40 seconds. What is the probability that a person would have to wait more than 30 seconds for an express elevator? $\frac{1}{4}$

A dart you throw is equally likely to land at any point on each board shown. For Exercises 3–5, find the probability of its landing in the shaded area.

3. regular octagon

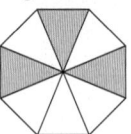

$\frac{3}{8}$, or 37.5%

4. square

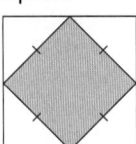

$\frac{1}{2}$, or 50%

5. circle

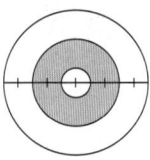

$\frac{8}{25}$, or 32%

Alternative Assessment

Have teams of four students work together to design a game that uses geometric probability. They should produce a working model of the game, a set of rules, and the calculations for all the probabilities involved.

406

$39. \ \frac{\sqrt{10} - \sqrt{2}}{10\pi} \approx 0.06$

Need Help?

$0 \le P(\text{event}) \le 1$

$P(\text{event}) = 0$ means the event will not occur.

$P(\text{event}) = 1$ means the event will occur.

Real-World Connection

A mere touch of the target by the ball triggers the dunk.

For Exercises 30 and 31, sketch a geometric model and solve.

30. **Astronomy** Meteoroids (mostly dust-particle size) are continually bombarding Earth. The surface area of Earth is about 65.7 million square miles. The area of the United States is about 3.7 million square miles. What is the probability that a meteoroid landing on Earth will land in the United States? **See back of book.**

31. **Tape Recording** Amy made a tape recording of a chorus rehearsal. The recording began 21 min into the 60-min tape and lasted 8 min. Later she accidentally erased a 15-min segment somewhere on the tape. **a–b. See margin.**
   a. In your model show the possible starting times of the erasure. Explain how you know that the erasure did not start after the 45-min mark.
   b. In your model show the starting times of the erasures that would erase the entire rehearsal. Find the probability that the entire rehearsal was erased.

x^2 **Algebra** Find the probability that coordinate x of a point chosen at random from $\overline{AK}$ satisfies the inequality.

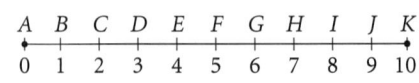

A	B	C	D	E	F	G	H	I	J	K
0	1	2	3	4	5	6	7	8	9	10

32. $2 \le x \le 8\frac{3}{5}$ 33. $x \ge 7\frac{3}{10}$ 34. $2x \le 9\frac{9}{20}$ 35. $\frac{1}{2}x - 5 \ge 0$ **0**

36. $2 \le 4x \le 3\frac{1}{40}$ 37. $0 \le \frac{1}{3}x + 1 \le 5$ **1**   38. $|x - 6| \le 1.5\frac{3}{10}$ 39. $\sqrt{2} \le \pi x \le \sqrt{10}$ **See left.**

Dunk Tank At a fund-raiser, a volunteer sits on a platform above a tank of water. She gets dunked when you throw a ball and hit the red target. The radius of the ball is 3.6 cm. What is the probability that a ball heading randomly for the given background shape would hit the given target shape?

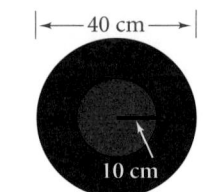

|← 40 cm →|

10 cm

40. Background (at right): a circle 40 cm across
    Target: a circle with 10-cm radius **about 46%**

41. Background: a square with 40-cm sides
    Target: a circle with 10-cm radius **about 36%**

42. Background: a circle 40-cm across   43. Background: a square with 40-cm sides
    Target: a square with 20-cm sides   Target: a square with 20-cm sides
                        about 58%   **about 46%**

44. Kimi has a 4-in. straw and a 6-in. straw. She wants to cut the 6-in. straw into two pieces so that the three pieces form a triangle.
   a. If she cuts the straw to get two 3-in. pieces, can she form a triangle? **yes**
   b. If the two pieces are 1 in. and 5 in., can she form a triangle? **no**
   c. If Kimi cuts the straw at a random point, what is the probability that she can form a triangle? $\frac{2}{3}$

45. a. **Open-Ended** Design a dartboard game to be used at a charity fair. Specify the size and shape of the regions of the board. **Check students' work.**
   b. **Writing** Describe the rules for using your dartboard and the prizes that winners receive. Explain how much money you would expect to raise if the game were played 100 times. **Check students' work.**

C Challenge 46. **Graphing Calculator** A circular dartboard has radius 1 m and a yellow circle in the center. Assume you hit the target at a random point. For what radius of the yellow center region would P(hitting yellow) equal each of the following? Use the table feature of a calculator to generate all six answers. Round to the nearest centimeter.
   a. 0.2 **45 cm**   b. 0.4 **63 cm**   c. 0.5 **71 cm**
   d. 0.6 **77 cm**   e. 0.8 **89 cm**   f. 1.0 **100 cm**

pages 404–407   **Exercises**

31. a.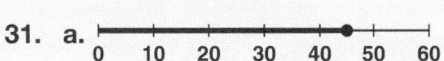

| 0 | 10 | 20 | 30 | 40 | 50 | 60 |

If it starts after 45 min, you cannot erase 15 min of a 60 min tape.

b.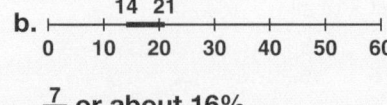

14 21

| 0 | 10 | 20 | 30 | 40 | 50 | 60 |

$\frac{7}{45}$ or about 16%

47. Target Game A target has a central circle and three concentric rings. The diameters of the circles are 2 cm, 6 cm, 10 cm, and 14 cm. Find the probability of landing in the gray region. Compare it with the probability of landing in *either* the blue or red region. $\frac{24}{49} \approx 49\%$; the probability is the same.

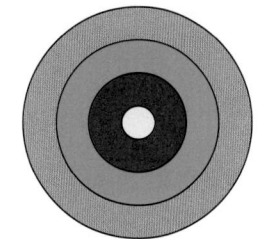

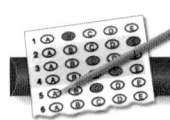

Standardized Test Prep

Multiple Choice

48. A dart hits the dartboard shown. Find the probability that it lands in the shaded region. **A**
   A. 21%   **B.** 25%   **C.** 50%   **D.** 79%

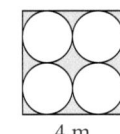
4 m

49. A dart hits the dartboard shown. Find the probability that it lands in a circle. **I**
   F. 21%   **G.** 25%   **H.** 50%   **I.** 79%

Short Response

50. On this dartboard, the circle with 1-m radius is inscribed in an equilateral triangle. Find the probability that a dart that hits the board lands in the circular region. Justify your answer. **See margin.**

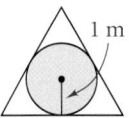
1 m

Extended Response

51. The radius of a circle is 28 m. The measure of the central angle is 120. **51a–b. See margin.**
   a. Find the area of the sector in terms of π. Justify your answer.
   b. Find the area of the shaded segment to the nearest tenth. Justify your answer.

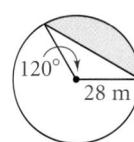
120°
28 m

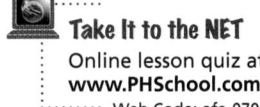
Take It to the NET
Online lesson quiz at
www.PHSchool.com
Web Code: afa-0708

Mixed Review

Lesson 7-7

52. A circle has circumference 20π ft. What is its area? **100π ft^2**

53. A circle has radius 12 cm. What is the area of a sector of the circle with a 30° central angle? **12π cm^2**

54. What is the area of a semicircle with diameter 20 ft? **50π ft^2**

Lesson 6-2

x^2 **Algebra** **Find the values of the variables in each parallelogram.**

55.
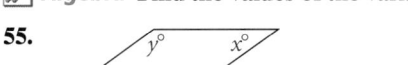
$x = 36; y = 144$

56.
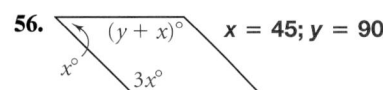
$x = 45; y = 90$

Lesson 5-1

57. The coordinates of the vertices of a triangle are $A(1, -4)$, $B(5, 6)$, and $C(-3, 2)$.
   a. Find the coordinates of D, the midpoint of $\overline{AB}$, and E, the midpoint of $\overline{BC}$.
57a. $D(3, 1); E(1, 4)$
   b. Find the slope of $\overline{DE}$ and the slope of $\overline{AC}$. slope $\overline{DE} = -\frac{3}{2}$; slope $\overline{AC} = -\frac{3}{2}$
   c. Verify that $\overline{DE} \parallel \overline{AC}$. $\overline{DE}$ and $\overline{AC}$ have the same slope.
   d. Find DE and AC. $DE = \sqrt{13}$; $AC = 2\sqrt{13}$
   e. Verify that $DE = \frac{1}{2}AC$. $\sqrt{13} = \frac{1}{2} \cdot 2\sqrt{13}$

Lesson 7-8 Geometric Probability   **407**

Standardized Test Prep

📁 **Resources**
For additional practice with a variety of test item formats:
• Standardized Test Prep, p. 413
• Test-Taking Strategies, p. 408
• Test-Taking Strategies with Transparencies

Exercise 50 The center of a regular polygon is both the center of the circle that circumscribes it and the center of an inscribed circle. Students can find the side length of the triangle using a 30°-60°-90° triangle and apply the formula $A = \frac{1}{2}ap$ to find the area using the radius 1 m as an apothem.

50. **[2]** $\frac{\text{area of circle}}{\text{area of triangle}} = \frac{\pi(1)^2}{3\sqrt{3}}$
$\approx 0.6 = 60\%$

[1] no work shown OR correct explanation and a computational error

51. **[4] a.** $\frac{1}{3}$ (area of circle) = $\frac{1}{3}(\pi \cdot 28^2) = \frac{784\pi}{3}$ m^2

   b. Area of $\triangle$ = $\frac{1}{2}bh = \frac{1}{2}(28\sqrt{3})(14)$ = $196\sqrt{3}$, so area of segment = $\frac{784\pi}{3} - 196\sqrt{3} \approx$ 481.5 m^2; the shaded area is the area of the 120° sector minus the area of the $\triangle$.

[3] one computational error OR incorrect explanation

[2] one computational error and incorrect explanation

[1] one correct answer OR a correct explanation

407

Finding Multiple Correct Answers

This feature helps students understand the nature of multiple-choice questions, and teaches how to use a *process-of-elimination* strategy to find the correct answer choice.

Resources

Test-Taking Strategies with Transparencies
- Transparency 7
- Practice sheet p. 19

Teaching Notes

Students may sometimes be able to determine that two of the statements are true or false but then cannot decide about a third statement. Point out that such a situation still helps the student reduce the possible answer choices.

English Learners

Point out that the example and exercises include the phrases *could be true* and *always true*. Ask students to suggest other phrases that modify truth value; for example, *sometimes true* and *never true*. Discuss ways to distinguish the modifiers *could be, always, sometimes,* and *never.*

Test-Taking Strategies with Transparencies

Test-Taking Strategy: Finding Multiple Correct Answers

Examine each choice to see which one(s) are true.

Example Which of the following are true about the graph of the line $y = -4x - 5$?

I. The slope is 4.
II. The y-intercept is −5.
III. The point (1, −9) is on the line.

A. None   B. II only   C. III only   D. II and III only

The line is in slope-intercept form: $y = mx + b$, so its slope is −4 and its y-intercept is −5.

So, choice I is false, and choice II is true.

Notice, −9 = −4(1) − 5, so choice III is true.

The answer is II and III only are true, or choice D.

Find the answer. Explain your reasoning.

1. If 3x + 4 < 5, which of the following are true?
   I. 6x + 8 < 10   II. −6x − 8 < −10   III. −3x > −1
   A. None   B. I only   C. III only   D. I and III only
2. Use the data: 3, 5, 7, 10, 15. Which of the following are true?
   I. The mean is 8.   II. The median is 7.   III. The range is 12.
   F. None   G. I and II only   H. II only   I. All

Solutions
1. D
2. I

Transparency 7

408

In Multiple-Correct-Answer questions, you have to determine whether a number of statements are true or false. As you test each statement, mark it as true or false. You then choose those that are true.

EXAMPLE

The perimeter of a rectangle is 20 cm.
Which of the following could be true?
   I. One side of the rectangle is 2 cm.
   II. The area of the rectangle is 24 cm².
   III. The diagonal of the rectangle is 5 cm.

A. I and II only   **B.** II and III only   **C.** I and III only   **D.** I, II, and III

Test each statement to see if it could be true in a rectangle with perimeter 20 cm.

Statement I is possible in a rectangle with dimensions 2-cm by 8-cm.

Statement II is possible in a rectangle with dimensions 4-cm by 6-cm.

Statement III is not possible. A diagonal is longer than each side. In any rectangle with perimeter 20 cm, at least one side has to be 5 cm or more.

Only statements I and II could be true. The correct choice is A.

EXERCISES

1. Explain why it is possible for the rectangle in the Example to have a side of length 0.1 cm. What would its area be? **Sides are 0.1 cm and 9.9 cm; 0.99 cm²**

2. In $\triangle ABC$, $AB = \sqrt{1}$, $BC = \sqrt{2}$, and $AC = \sqrt{3}$.
   Which of the following are true? **C**
      I. The largest angle is $\angle B$.
      II. The triangle is a right triangle.
      III. One angle of the triangle has measure 30.

   A. I only   **B.** II only   **C.** I and II only   **D.** I, II, and III

3. A square and an equilateral triangle each have apothem of length 1 cm.
   Which of the following are always true? **H**
      I. The perimeter of the square is greater than the perimeter of the triangle.
      II. The area of the square is less than the area of the triangle.
      III. The radius of the square is less than the radius of the triangle.

   F. I only   **G.** I and II only   **H.** II and III only   **I.** I, II, and III

4. A polygon is equilateral.
   Which of the following are always true? **B**
      I. The sum of the measures of its exterior angles, one at each vertex, is 360.
      II. The sum of the measures of its interior angles is divisible by 180.
      III. The polygon is equiangular.

   A. I only   **B.** I and II only   **C.** II and III only   **D.** I, II, and III

Chapter Review

Vocabulary

adjacent arcs (p. 387)
altitude of a parallelogram (p. 349)
apothem of a regular polygon (p. 380)
arc length (p. 389)
base of a parallelogram (p. 349)
base of a triangle (p. 350)
center of a circle (p. 386)
center of a regular polygon (p. 380)
central angle (p. 386)
circle (p. 386)

circumference (p. 388)
concentric circles (p. 388)
congruent arcs (p. 389)
congruent circles (p. 386)
diameter (p. 386)
geometric probability (p. 402)
height of a parallelogram (p. 349)
height of a trapezoid (p. 374)
height of a triangle (p. 350)

major arc (p. 387)
minor arc (p. 387)
pi (p. 388)
Pythagorean triple (p. 357)
radius (p. 386)
radius of a regular polygon (p. 380)
sector of a circle (p. 396)
segment of a circle (p. 397)
semicircle (p. 387)

 Reading Math
Understanding
Vocabulary

Take It to the NET
Online vocabulary quiz
at **www.PHSchool.com**
Web Code: afj-0751

Choose the correct term to complete each sentence.

1. You can use any side as the (*altitude, base*) of a triangle. **base**

2. A (*sector, segment*) of a circle is a region bounded by two radii and the intercepted arc. **sector**

3. A segment that contains the center of a circle and has both endpoints on the circle is the (*diameter, circumference*) of a circle. **diameter**

4. In a regular polygon, the perpendicular distance from the center to a side is the (*apothem, radius*) of the parallelogram. **apothem**

5. Two arcs of a circle with exactly one point in common are (*congruent arcs, adjacent arcs*). **adjacent arcs**

Skills and Concepts

**7-1, 7-4, and 7-5
Objectives**

▼ To find the area of a parallelogram

▼ To find the area of a triangle

▼ To find the area of a trapezoid

▼ To find the area of a rhombus or a kite

▼ To find the area of a regular polygon

You can find the area of a rectangle, a parallelogram, or a triangle if you know the **base**, b, and **height**, h. The area of a rectangle or a parallelogram is $A = bh$.

The area of a triangle is $A = \frac{1}{2}bh$.

The **height of a trapezoid**, h, is the perpendicular distance between the bases, b_1 and b_2. The area of a trapezoid is $A = \frac{1}{2}h(b_1 + b_2)$.

The **center of a regular polygon**, C, is the center of its circumscribed circle. The **radius**, r, is the distance from the center to a vertex. The **apothem**, a, is the perpendicular distance from the center to a side. The area of a regular polygon with apothem a and perimeter p is $A = \frac{1}{2}ap$.

The area of a rhombus or kite is $A = \frac{1}{2}d_1d_2$.

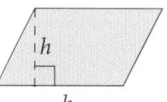

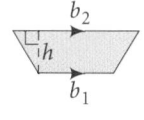

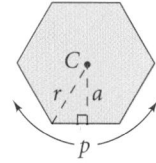

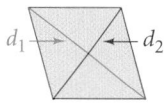

Resources

Student Edition
Extra Practice Ch. 7, p. 696
English/Spanish Glossary, p. 741
Postulates and Theorems, p. 732
Table of Symbols, p. 725

 **Reaching All Students**
Reading and Math Literacy 7D
Spanish Reading and Literacy 7D

ASSESSMENT SYSTEM

Standardized Test Prep Workbook
• Ch. 7 practice in standardized test formats

www.PHSchool.com
Student Site
• Self-grading Vocabulary Test
Teacher Center
• Resources

Plus **TEXT**

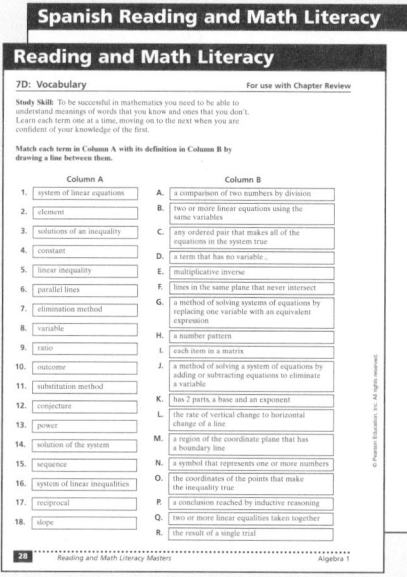

12.

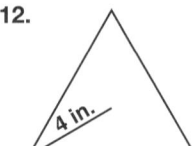

4 in.

13.

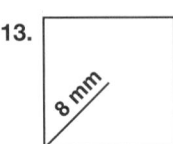

8 mm

14.

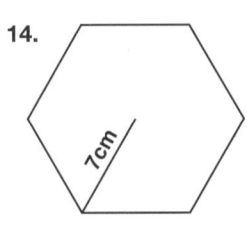

7cm

Find the area of each figure. If your answer is not an integer, leave it in simplest radical form.

6. 10 m²

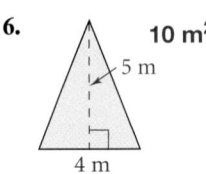

5 m

4 m

7. 90 in.²

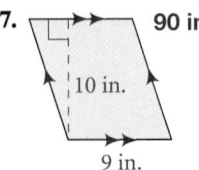

10 in.

9 in.

8. 33 ft²

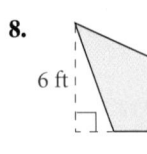

6 ft

11 ft

9. 11 mm

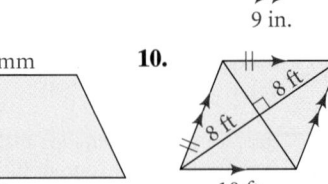

60°

6 mm   15 mm

96√3 mm²

10.

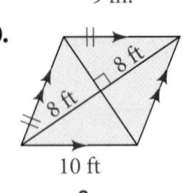

8 ft   8 ft

10 ft

96 ft²

11. 6.5 cm

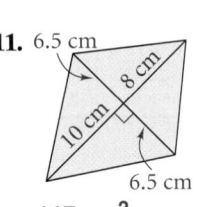

8 cm

10 cm

6.5 cm

117 cm²

Sketch each regular polygon with the given radius. Then find its area. Round your answers to the nearest tenth. 12–14. For sketches, see left.

12. triangle; radius 4 in.

20.8 in.²

13. square; radius 8 mm

128 mm²

14. hexagon; radius 7 cm

127.3 cm²

7-2 and 7-3 Objectives

▼ To use the Pythagorean Theorem

▼ To use the Converse of the Pythagorean Theorem

▼ To use properties of 45°-45°-90° triangles

▼ To use properties of 30°-60°-90° triangles

The **Pythagorean Theorem** states that in a right triangle, the sum of the squares of the lengths of the legs equals the square of the length of the hypotenuse, or $a^2 + b^2 = c^2$.

Positive integers a, b, and c form a **Pythagorean triple** if $a^2 + b^2 = c^2$.

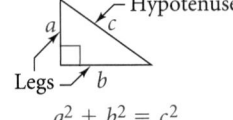

Hypotenuse

Legs

$a^2 + b^2 = c^2$

The **Converse of the Pythagorean Theorem** states that if the square of the length of one side of a triangle is equal to the sum of the squares of the lengths of the other two sides, then the triangle is a right triangle.

In a triangle with longest side c, if $c^2 > a^2 + b^2$, the triangle is obtuse; if $c^2 < a^2 + b^2$, the triangle is acute.

In a 45°-45°-90° triangle, the legs are congruent and the length of the hypotenuse is $\sqrt{2}$ times the length of a leg.

In a 30°-60°-90° triangle, the length of the hypotenuse is twice the length of the shorter leg. The length of the longer leg is $\sqrt{3}$ times the length of the shorter leg.

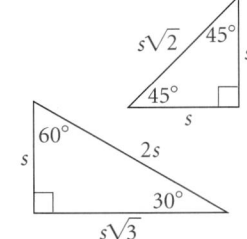

$s\sqrt{2}$ 45° s

45° s

60°   2s

s 30°

$s\sqrt{3}$

Find the value of each variable. If your answer is not an integer, leave it in simplest radical form.

15.

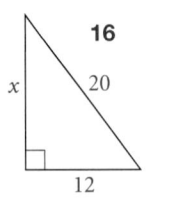

16

x 20

12

16. 14 $2\sqrt{113}$

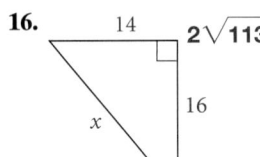

x 16

17.   17

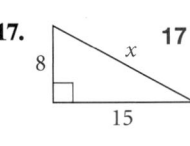

8   x

15

18.

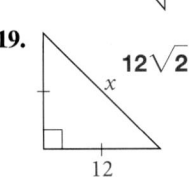

x 9

30°

y

$x = 9\sqrt{3}; y = 18$

19.

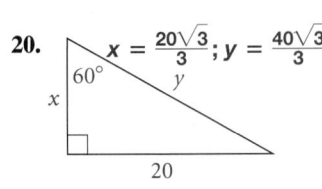

$12\sqrt{2}$

x

12

20.

$x = \dfrac{20\sqrt{3}}{3}; y = \dfrac{40\sqrt{3}}{3}$

60°

x

y

20

7-6 and 7-7 Objectives

▼ To find the measures of central angles and arcs

▼ To find circumference and arc length

▼ To find the areas of circles, sectors, and segments of circles

A **circle** is the set of all points in a plane equidistant from one point called the **center.** The measure of a **minor arc** is the measure of its corresponding central angle. The measure of a **major arc** is 360 minus the measure of its related minor arc. **Adjacent arcs** have exactly one point in common.

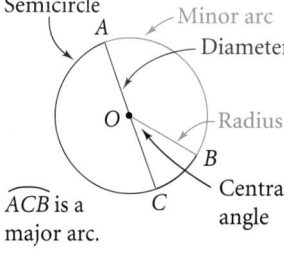

Semicircle
A
Minor arc
Diameter
O
Radius
B
$\widehat{ACB}$ is a major arc.
Central angle
C

The **circumference** of a circle is $C = \pi d$ or $C = 2\pi r$. The area of a circle is $A = \pi r^2$.

Arc length is a fraction of a circle's circumference. The length of $\widehat{AB} = \frac{m\widehat{AB}}{360} \cdot 2\pi r$.

A **sector of a circle** is a region bounded by two radii and their intercepted arc.
The area of sector $APB = \frac{m\widehat{AB}}{360} \cdot \pi r^2$.

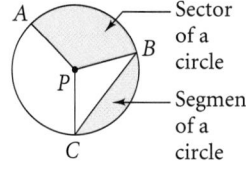

A
B
P
C
Sector of a circle
Segment of a circle

A **segment of a circle** is the part of a circle bounded by an arc and the segment joining its endpoints. The area of a segment of a circle is the difference between the areas of the related sector and the related triangle.

Find each measure.

D
A
60°
B
P
C

21. $m\angle APD$ **30**   **22.** $m\widehat{AC}$ **120**

23. $m\widehat{ABD}$ **330**   **24.** $m\angle CPA$ **120**

Find the length of each arc shown in red. Leave your answer in terms of π.

25. 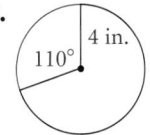 $\frac{22}{9}\pi$ **in.**

110°
4 in.

26. 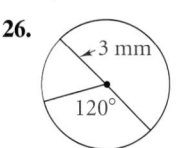 π **mm**

3 mm
120°

Find the area of each shaded region. Round your answer to the nearest tenth.

27. 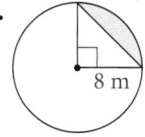 **18.3 m²**

8 m

28. 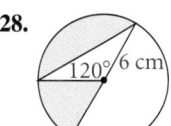 **41.0 cm²**

120° 6 cm

7-8 Objectives

▼ To use segment and area models to find the probabilities of events

Geometric probability uses geometric figures to represent occurrences of events. You can use a segment model or an area model. Compare the part that represents favorable outcomes to the whole, which represents all outcomes.

A dart hits each dartboard at a random point. Find the probability that it lands in the shaded area.

29.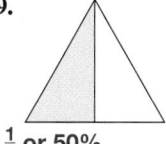
$\frac{1}{2}$ or 50%

30.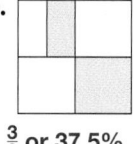
$\frac{3}{8}$ or 37.5%

31.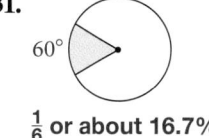
60°
$\frac{1}{6}$ or about 16.7%

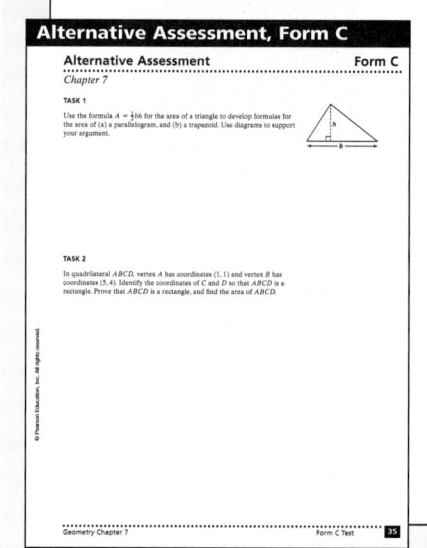

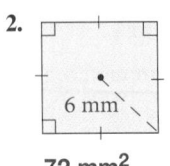

Chapter **7**

Chapter Test

Take It to the NET
Online chapter test at
www.PHSchool.com
····· Web Code: afa-0752

Resources

Teaching Resources
Ch. 7 Test, Forms A & B
Ch. 7 Alternative Assessment

Reaching All Students
Spanish Ch. 7 Test, Forms A & B
Spanish Ch. 7 Alternative
   Assessment, Form C
Informal Geometry Ch. 7 Test,
   Forms D & E

PRENTICE HALL
ASSESSMENT SYSTEM

Assessment Masters
• Ch. 7 Test, Forms A & B
• Ch. 7 Alternative Assessment,
   Form C
Computer Test Generator CD
• Ch. 7 pre-made Test
• Make your own Ch. 7 test

www.PHSchool.com
Student Site
• Self-grading Chapter 7 Test
Teacher Center
• Resources

Plus **iTEXT**

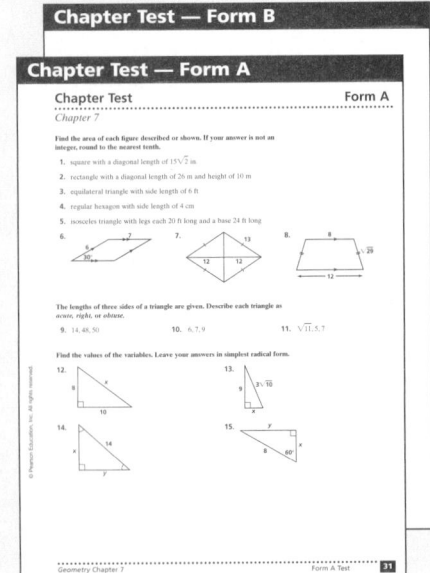

Find the area of each figure. If your answer is not an integer, round to the nearest tenth.

1. **78 ft²**

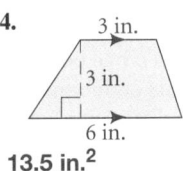
12 ft
13 ft

2. **72 mm²**

6 mm

3. 8 m
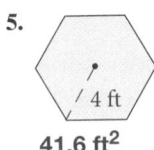
9 m
60°
62.4 m²

4. 3 in.
3 in.
6 in.
13.5 in.²

Find the area of each regular polygon. Round to the nearest tenth.

5. **41.6 ft²**
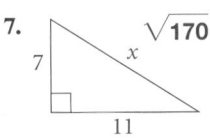
4 ft

6. **172.8 cm²**
6 cm
7.2 cm

x^2 **Algebra Find the value of each variable. Leave your answer in simplest radical form.**

7. $\sqrt{170}$
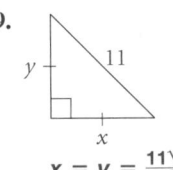
7
x
11

8. $2\sqrt{14}$
15
x
13

9. y
11
x

10. y
x
30°
12

$x = y = \dfrac{11\sqrt{2}}{2}$ $x = 4\sqrt{3}; y = 8\sqrt{3}$

The lengths of three sides of a triangle are given. Describe each triangle as *acute*, *right*, or *obtuse*.

11. 9 cm, 10 cm, 12 cm   **acute**

12. 8 m, 15 m, 17 m   **right**

13. 5 in., 6 in., 10 in.   **obtuse**

---

14. **Writing** Explain how you can use the length of the shorter leg of a 30°-60°-90° triangle to find the lengths of the other two sides. **See margin.**

Find each measure for ⊙P.

15. $m\angle BPC$ **40**   16. $m\widehat{AB}$ **50**

17. $m\widehat{ADC}$ **270**   18. $m\widehat{ADB}$ **310**

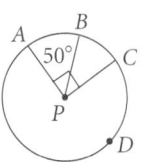
A B
50° C
P
D

Find the length of each arc shown in red. Leave your answer in terms of π.

19. $\dfrac{10}{3}\pi$ in.
5 in.
120°

20. **1.5π cm**
3 cm

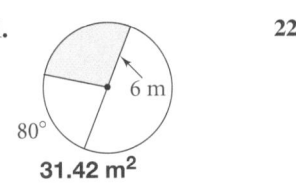

Find the area of each shaded region to the nearest hundredth.

21. **31.42 m²**
6 m
80°

22. **30.10 ft²**
120°
7 ft

23. **Open-Ended** Use a compass to draw a circle. Shade a sector of the circle and find its area. **Check students' work.**

Find the area of each shaded region. Leave your answers in terms of π.

24. 12 cm
12 cm
(72 + 18π) cm²

25. 6 m
6 m   3 m
(54 − 9π) m²

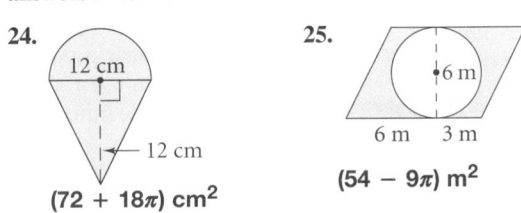

26. **Probability** Every 20 minutes from 4:00 P.M. to 7:00 P.M., a commuter train crosses Main Street. For three minutes a gate stops cars from passing as the train goes by. What is the probability that a motorist approaching the train crossing during this time interval will have to stop for the train? $\dfrac{3}{20}$

---

page 412   Chapter Test

14. The ratio of the length of the longer leg to the length of the shorter leg is $\sqrt{3}$:1. The ratio of the length of the hypotenuse to the length of the shorter leg is 2:1. Find the length of the shorter leg first, then use it to find the remaining lengths.

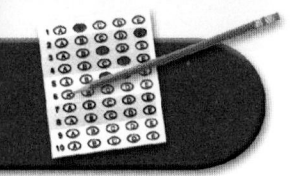

Standardized Test Prep

Standardized Test Prep

Reading Comprehension Read the passage below. Then answer the questions on the basis of what is *stated* or *implied* in the passage.

Hanging a Picture A picture has a wire from side to side across its back. Hang the picture from one hook and it can easily swing, or slide into a tilt. Use two hooks and the picture will hang level. Here is how to place two hooks on the wall to hang the picture level and precisely where you want it.

On your wall, mark two level points *A* and *B* where you want the top corners of the picture. For example, assume the back of a 21-in. wide picture is rigged as shown at the left and you want the two hooks 12 in. apart.

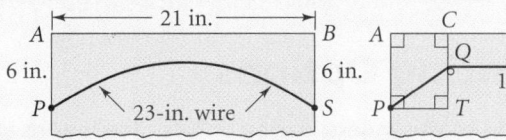

At the right, the matching diagrams in the upper corners locate points *Q* and *R* where hooks would hold the wire. Determine measurements as follows:

    Calculate to find that $QP = 5.5$ in. $= RS$.
    Calculate to find that $TP = 4.5$ in. $= VS$.
    Then $QT = \sqrt{5.5^2 - 4.5^2} \approx 3.2$ in. $= RV$, so $CQ = 2.8$ in. $= DR$.

From points *A* and *B* on the wall, measure 4.5 in. towards each other and 2.8 in. down to find points *Q* and *R*, respectively. Attach picture hangers to support the wire at *Q* and *R*, and hang your picture perfectly!

---

1. From the passage, what should you learn about hanging a picture? **B**
   A. How to use one hook so that you can easily slide the picture to hang straight.
   B. How to use two hooks so that the picture hangs straight and where you want it.
   C. How to use one hook so that the picture can easily swing, or slide into a tilt.
   D. How to use two hooks at the top corners.

2. How do you calculate *QP*? **F**
   F. $\dfrac{\text{wire length} - 12}{2}$ G. $\dfrac{PQ + RS}{2}$
   H. $\dfrac{AB - 10}{2}$ I. $\dfrac{PT + SV + 2}{2}$

3. How do you calculate *TP*? **C**
   A. $\dfrac{\text{wire length} - 14}{2}$ B. $\dfrac{PQ + RS - 2}{2}$
   C. $\dfrac{AB - 12}{2}$ D. $\dfrac{PT + SV}{2}$

4. Which theorem do you use to calculate *QT*? **H**
   F. 30°-60°-90° Triangle   G. 45°-45°-90° Triangle
   H. Pythagorean   I. Triangle Midsegment

5. How do you calculate *CQ*? **D**
   A. $CQ = DR$ B. $CQ + QP = 8.3$
   C. $CQ = 6 - CQ$ D. $CQ + QT = CT$

6. What kind of quadrilateral is *DBSV*? Justify your answer. **Rectangle; it has 4 right angles.**

Describe how to locate the hooks for hanging.

7. A picture is 30 in. wide. The hanging wire is 34 in. long, attached at the sides of the picture, 9 in. from the top. The hooks are 14 in. apart. **See margin.**

8. A circular mirror has diameter 22 in. The hanging wire is 28 in. long, attached at the endpoints of a diameter. The hooks are 10 in. apart. **See margin.**

Students must be able to extract information from reading passages, answer multiple-choice questions, and construct responses in order to be successful on current state and national assessments.

To answer the questions, students apply skills and concepts from this chapter and previous chapters.
Multiple Choice: Items 1–5
Extended Response: Items 6–8

Resources

 **Teaching Resources**
Cumulative Review

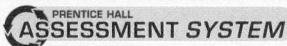 **Reaching All Students**
Spanish Cumulative Review

 PRENTICE HALL **ASSESSMENT SYSTEM**

Standardized Test Prep Workbook
• Ch. 7 standardized test practice
Assessment Masters
• Cumulative Review
Computer Test Generator CD
• Standardized Test Practice

 **www.PHSchool.com**
• Standardized Test Practice
• Resources

Plus **i TEXT**

Cumulative Review

Cumulative Review
Chapters 1–7

---

page 413   **Standardized Test Prep**

7. Mark two level points on the wall where you want the top corners of the picture. From these points, measure 8 in. towards each other and 3 in. down.

8. Mark two level points on the wall where you want widest part of the mirror. From these points, measure 6 in. towards each other and 6.7 in. up.

Similarity

Chapter at a Glance

North Carolina Objectives

8-1	Ratios and Proportions	1.02

NCTM
1, 2, 6,
8, 9, 10

▽ Using Ratios and Proportions

8-2	Similar Polygons	2.03a, b, c, d

NCTM
2, 3, 6,
8, 9, 10

▽ Similar Polygons
▽ Applying Similar Polygons

8-3	Proving Triangles Similar	2.03a

NCTM
2, 3, 4,
6, 7, 8,
9, 10

▽ The AA Postulate and the SAS and SSS Theorems
▽ Applying AA, SAS, and SSS Similarity

8-4	Similarity in Right Triangles	2.03a

NCTM
2, 3, 6,
7, 8, 9,
10

▽ Using Similarity in Right Triangles

8-5	Proportions in Triangles	2.03a

NCTM
2, 3, 4,
6, 7, 8,
9, 10

▽ Using the Side-Splitter Theorem
▽ Using the Triangle-Angle-Bisector Theorem

8-6	Perimeters and Areas of Similar Figures	2.03a, b, c

NCTM
1, 2, 3,
4, 6, 7,
8, 9, 10

▽ Finding Perimeters and Areas of Similar Figures

NCTM STANDARDS 2000

1	Number and Operations	6	Problem Solving
2	Algebra	7	Reasoning and Proof
3	Geometry	8	Communication
4	Measurement	9	Connections
5	Data Analysis and Probability	10	Representation

Pacing Options

This chart suggests pacing only for the lessons and their parts. It is provided as a possible guide. It will help you determine how much time you have in your schedule to cover other components, such as the features, Chapter Review and Chapter Test.

Day	Traditional 45 min.	Two-Year 45 min.	Block 90 min.
1	8-1 ▽	8-1 ▽	8-1 ▽
2	8-2 ▽	8-1 ▽	8-2 ▽ ▽
3	8-2 ▽	8-2 ▽	8-3 ▽ ▽
4	8-3 ▽	8-2 ▽	8-4 ▽
5	8-3 ▽	8-2 ▽	8-5 ▽ ▽
6	8-4 ▽	8-2 ▽	8-6 ▽
7	8-5 ▽	8-3 ▽	
8	8-5 ▽	8-3 ▽	
9	8-6 ▽	8-3 ▽	
10		8-3 ▽	
11		8-4 ▽	
12		8-4 ▽	
13		8-5 ▽	
14		8-5 ▽	
15		8-5 ▽	
16		8-5 ▽	
17		8-6 ▽	
18		8-6 ▽	
19			
20			
21			
22			

NAEP Correlation (National Assessment of Educational Progress 2000 Mathematics Objectives)

8-1	8-2	8-3	8-4	8-5	8-6
N5a, b, M8	N5c, N6b, G6c	N5c, M1, G6c	N5c, M1, G6c	N5c, M1, G6c	N5b, N5c, M4a

N = Number Sense, Properties, and Operations; **M** = Measurement; **G** = Geometry and Spatial Sense;
D = Data Analysis, Statistics, and Probability; **A** = Algebra and Functions

Math Background

Chapter Overview

The critical topics of algebraic ratio and proportional reasoning are extended to geometry by way of the concept of scale. Similar polygons are defined, after which ways to prove triangles similar and properties of similar triangles are explored. Proportions involving parts of specific triangles and their subdivisions are presented. Finally, the perimeters and areas of proportional figures are compared.

Ratios and Proportion   8-1

The text gives the justification for the Cross-Product Property. The second and third properties are obtained by dividing both sides of this first property equation by ac and dc, respectively. The fourth property can be justified by adding 1 $\left(\frac{b}{b} = \frac{d}{d} = 1\right)$ to both sides of the proportion $\frac{a}{b} = \frac{c}{d}$ so that $\frac{a}{b} + \frac{b}{b} = \frac{c}{d} + \frac{d}{d}$, which simplifies to $\frac{a + b}{b} = \frac{c + d}{d}$. This fourth property will be needed for the Side-Splitter Theorem in Lesson 8-5.

Similar Polygons   8-2

Similarity in triangles ABC and XYZ can be determined by checking that the ratios of the lengths of corresponding sides are equal $\left(\frac{AB}{XY} = \frac{BC}{YZ} = \frac{AC}{XZ}\right)$ or that each ratio of the lengths of sides within a triangle equals the ratio of the lengths of the corresponding sides $\left(\frac{AB}{AC} = \frac{XY}{XZ}, \frac{AB}{BC} = \frac{XY}{YZ}, \text{ and } \frac{BC}{CA} = \frac{YZ}{ZX}\right)$.

A *golden rectangle* has dimensions ℓ and w that satisfy the equation $\frac{\ell}{w} = \frac{\ell + w}{\ell}$. The numerical value of $\frac{\ell}{w}$ is $\frac{1 + \sqrt{5}}{2}$, which the astronomer Johannes Kepler called the *golden ratio*. It is the limit of a sequence based on the Fibonacci sequence. (The first two terms of a Fibonacci sequence are 1 and 1; adding consecutive terms generates the next term. Fibonacci's work, published in A.D. 1202, was the first book written in Europe to use Hindu-Arabic numbers.) To construct a *golden section*, take a right triangle with one leg half the length of the other, and mark a segment on the hypotenuse equal to and adjacent to the shorter leg. The arc from the other endpoint of the hypotenuse through this point cuts the longer leg into segments, the ratio of whose lengths is the golden ratio. Constructions of golden rectangles and logarithmic spirals associated with them are equally direct, and students enjoy exploring them. The golden ratio appears in golden rectangles and triangles in art and architecture and in pentagram stars.

Proving Triangles Similar   8-3

The Greek philosopher Thales (c. 624–c. 547 B.C.) is credited with using similar triangles created by shadows to measure the heights of Egyptian pyramids and the distances of ships from shore.

The similarity postulates and theorems parallel the congruence postulates and theorems, except that AA ensures ASA similarity. Students who explored the golden rectangle may enjoy researching the golden triangle, an isosceles triangle with a 36° vertex angle. Bisecting a base angle divides the opposite side into segments whose lengths are in the golden ratio and creates a similar isosceles triangle. Continuing the process generates another golden logarithmic spiral.

Similarity in Right Triangles   8-4

An algebraic proof may help students better understand and remember the second corollary. The legs with lengths a and b, and the altitude h, are the geometric means, or *mean segments,* in the corollary. Have students orient a right triangle so that the hypotenuse is the horizontal base and draw an altitude from the right angle.

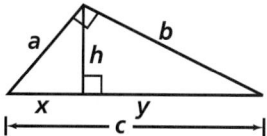

$c = x + y$	Segment Addition Postulate
$c^2 = a^2 + b^2$	Pythagorean Theorem
$a^2 = x^2 + h^2$	
$b^2 = y^2 + h^2$	
$x^2 + 2xy + y^2 = (x^2 + h^2) + (y^2 + h^2)$	Substitute in $c^2 = a^2 + b^2$.
$xy = h^2$	Simplify.
$\frac{x}{h} = \frac{h}{y}$	Divide both sides by hy.
$x^2 + xy = x(x + y) = a^2$	Substitute xy for h^2 in $a^2 = x^2 + h^2$.
$xc = a^2$	Substitute c for $x + y$.
$\frac{c}{a} = \frac{a}{x}$	Divide each side by ax.
$xy + y^2 = y(x + y) = b^2$	Substitute xy for h^2 in $b^2 = y^2 + h^2$.
$yc = b^2$	Substitute c for $x + y$.
$\frac{c}{b} = \frac{b}{y}$	Divide each side by by.

The geometric means a, b, and h, are often stated equivalently as $a = \sqrt{xc}$, $b = \sqrt{yc}$, and $h = \sqrt{xy}$. Each is the square root of the product of the two hypotenuse segments to which it is adjacent.

Proportions in Triangles   8-5

Students may confuse the proportional relationships within a triangle with the proportional relationships of similar triangles. For example, from the diagram below they may form the incorrect proportion $\frac{AB}{BD} = \frac{BC}{DE}$. Emphasize that BD and CE are not sides of a triangle and so can appear only in a proportion that involves collinear segments in both ratios. This can be made clearer by having students separate and redraw the similar triangles ABC and ADE.

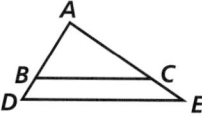

Perimeters and Areas of Similar Figures   8-6

It is not too difficult for students to prove Theorem 8-6 for similar rectangles $ABCD$ and $EFGH$ with lengths x and r and widths y and s, respectively, and similarity ratio k. By substitution they can show that $2x + 2y = (2kr + 2ks)$, or $\frac{2x + 2y}{2r + 2s} = k$, and $xy = (kr)(ks)$, or $\frac{xy}{rs} = k^2$.

 # Ongoing Assessment and Intervention

Tools for Monitoring Student Progress

The Prentice Hall *Geometry* program provides you with many options for assessment in the Student Edition, the Teacher's Edition and the teaching resources. From these options, you may choose instructional materials and techniques that are appropriate for your students and support your district's curriculum requirements.

Instant Check System™ in Chapter 8

Allows students to check their own learning before, during, and after each lesson.

Diagnosing Readiness before the chapter (p. 414)

Check Skills You'll Need exercises in each lesson (pp. 416, 423, 432, 439, 446, 454)

Check Understanding questions with each Example (pp. 416, 417, 418, 423, 424, 425, 433, 434, 435, 440, 441, 447, 448, 453, 455, 456)

Checkpoint Quiz (pp. 429 and 452)

Test Prep in Chapter 8

Teaches students strategies and gives them practice with all the test item formats they will encounter on state tests and standardized national exams.

Standardized Test Prep exercises in each lesson (pp. 420, 428, 438, 444, 451, 459)

Test-Taking Strategies (p. 460: Testing Multiple Choices)

Standardized Test Prep (p. 465: Cumulative Review)

 PRENTICE HALL ASSESSMENT *SYSTEM*

All your assessment needs in one place!

Program Assessment

Assess student progress throughout the *Geometry* text with blackline masters and CD-ROM.

Assessment Resources

- Checkpoint Quizzes 1 & 2
- Chapter Test, Forms A & B
- Chapter Alternative Assessment

Spanish versions available. Tests for Informal Geometry also available.

 Computer Test Generator

- Unlimited questions of varying difficulty for every lesson objective.
- Create your own practice sheets, quizzes, and tests, or use the pre-made Chapter Tests.
- Diagnose readiness with questions on prerequisite skills.
- Prepare students by making tests based on standardized test objectives.
- Access Algebra 1, Geometry, and Algebra 2 content—all on one CD-ROM.

Test Preparation

A three-step approach to preparing students for high stakes, national, and state exams.

❶ Diagnose & Prescribe

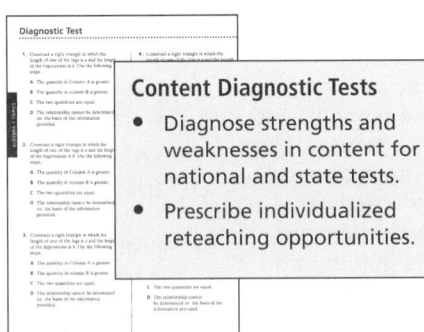

Content Diagnostic Tests

- Diagnose strengths and weaknesses in content for national and state tests.
- Prescribe individualized reteaching opportunities.

❷ Review & Reteach

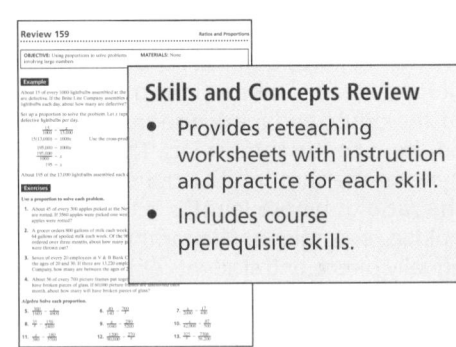

Skills and Concepts Review

- Provides reteaching worksheets with instruction and practice for each skill.
- Includes course prerequisite skills.

❸ Practice & Assess

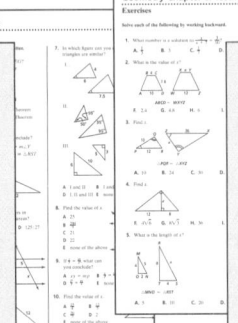

Test Preparation

- Features practice tests for End-of-Course and SAT/ACT exams.
- Includes standardized test practice by chapter for ongoing review.

Teacher's Guide with answers and correlations.

Test-Taking Strategies with Transparencies

- Support the Test-Taking Strategies pages in the Student Edition.
- Provide a teaching transparency and a practice worksheet for each strategy.

👥 Reaching All Students

Support in the Student Text and Additional Resources

The textbook, the iText, and other technology components provide numerous opportunities to reach students of various ability levels and learning styles. Each Teacher's Edition lesson suggests how you can help *all* your students be successful and understand the mathematics in Chapter 8.

Below Level

Student Edition
- Diagnosing Readiness*: p. 414
- Check Skills You'll Need*: pp. 416, 423, 432, 439, 446, 454

Reteaching
Chapter 8 Support File: pp. 8–13

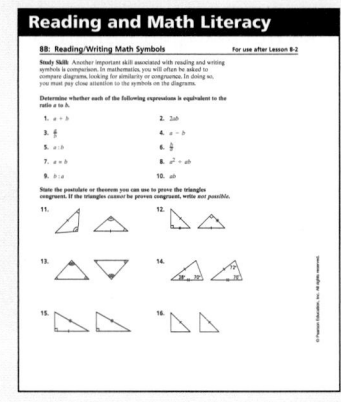

Informal Geometry Planning Guide
Chapter 8 Lesson Plans: pp. 47–52
Chapter 8 Tests: pp. 107–110

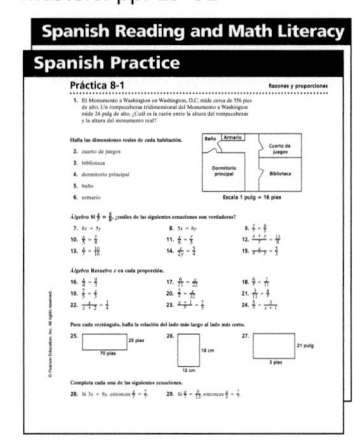

* Can be used with all ability levels to ensure mastery of prerequisite skills.

Advanced Learners

Student Edition
- Challenge exercises: pp. 420, 428, 437, 443, 451, 459
- Extension: pp. 430–431

Enrichment
Chapter 8 Support File: pp. 14–19

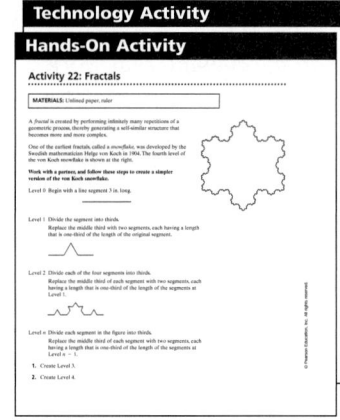

📖 Reading and Math Literacy

Student Edition
- Vocabulary: pp. 415, 461, *plus* in every Lesson Preview
- Reading Math: pp. 416, 417, 427, 442, 446, 453, 461
- Illustrated Glossary: pp. 741–777

Reading and Math Literacy Masters
Chapter 8: pp. 29–32

English Learners

Student Edition
- English/Spanish Illustrated Glossary: pp. 741–777

Workbook and Masters
Spanish Practice Workbook: pp. 47–52
Spanish Reading and Math Literacy Masters: pp. 29–32

Learning Styles

Student Edition
- Investigation: pp. 432, 439, 454
- Technology: pp. 422, 424, 425, 445
- Writing: pp. 419, 426, 437, 442, 450, 458, 464
- DK Activities: pp. 466–467

Activity Masters
Hands-On Activities: 22, 23, 24
Technology Activities: 50

Program Resources

	Teaching Resources in Grab & Go™ Files				Resources for Reaching All Students				Spanish Resources			Transparencies				Presentation Assistant Plus!
	Practice	Reteach	Enrich	Checkpoint Quiz	Reading & Math Literacy	Technology Activities	Hands-On Activities	Informal Geometry Lesson Plans	Practice	Reading & Math Literacy	Checkpoint Quiz	Skills Check	Additional Examples	Answers to Exercises	Lesson Quiz	Prentice Hall Presentation Pro CD-ROM
8-1	■	■	■		■			■	■	■		■	■	■	■	■
8-2	■	■	■	■	■	■	■	■	■	■	■	■	■	■	■	■
8-3	■	■	■					■	■			■	■	■	■	■
8-4	■	■	■				■	■	■			■	■	■	■	■
8-5	■	■	■	■	■		■	■	■			■	■	■	■	■
8-6	■	■	■					■	■			■	■	■	■	■
For the chapter	Chapter Tests, Alternative Assessment, Cumulative Review, Cumulative Assessment				Informal Geometry Chapter Tests				Spanish Chapter Tests, Alternative Assessment, Cumulative Review, Cumulative Assessment			Classroom Aid Transparencies				

Also available for use with the chapter:

 **PRENTICE HALL ASSESSMENT SYSTEM** *see page 414C.*

- Practice Workbook
- Solution Key

- For teacher support and access to student Web site materials, use Web Code afk-5500.
- For additional online and technology resources, see below.

 ## Technology

TEXT Online and on CD-ROM

Complete Interactive Student Text online and on CD-ROM—with instant feedback assessment, tutorial help, dynamic activities, instructional and real-world videos, audio, and additional practice.

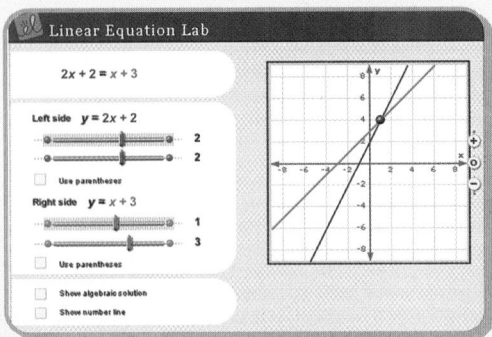

www.PHSchool.com For Students

Use **Web Codes** for easy access to online activities, chapter projects, self-grading lesson quizzes and chapter tests, vocabulary quizzes, updated data sources, graphing calculator procedures, and more.

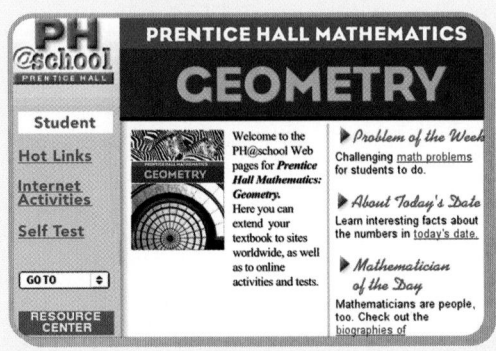

PH SuccessNet For Teachers

Online lesson planning with built-in state correlations, all the teaching resources, complete reference library, your own calendar and Teacher Web page, professional development, and more.

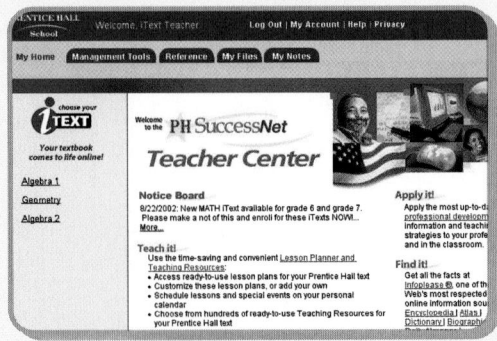

Presentation Assistant Plus!

The Prentice Hall *Presentation Assistant Plus!* provides you with the material you need to teach a lesson from beginning to end. Two easy-to-use formats—Transparencies and CD-ROM—allow you to present a lesson the way you are most comfortable.

 ## Transparencies

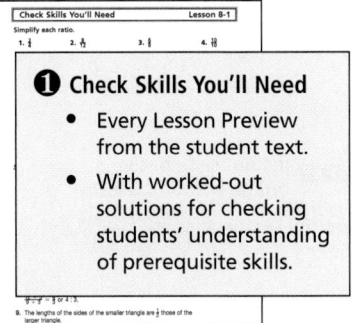

❶ Check Skills You'll Need
- Every Lesson Preview from the student text.
- With worked-out solutions for checking students' understanding of prerequisite skills.

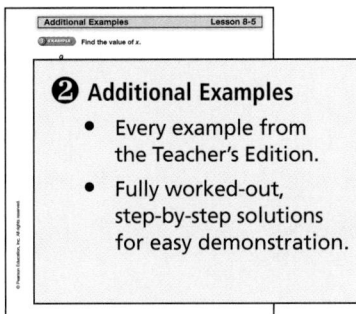

❷ Additional Examples
- Every example from the Teacher's Edition.
- Fully worked-out, step-by-step solutions for easy demonstration.

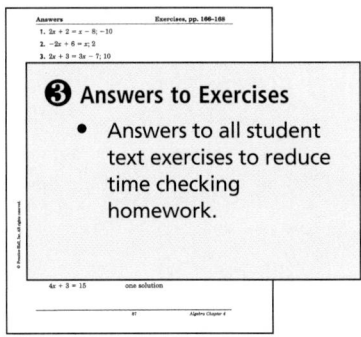

❸ Answers to Exercises
- Answers to all student text exercises to reduce time checking homework.

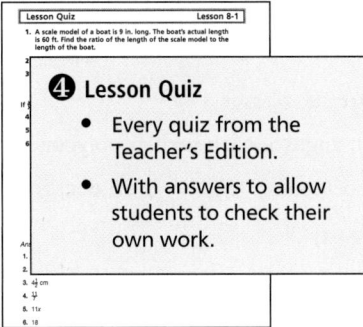

❹ Lesson Quiz
- Every quiz from the Teacher's Edition.
- With answers to allow students to check their own work.

 Throughout the Teacher's Edition, this symbol indicates material that is available on transparency in the Presentation Assistant Plus!

Prentice Hall Presentation Pro CD-ROM

- Includes all Transparencies.
- Conveniently organized by lesson so you can easily ❶ Introduce, ❷ Teach, ❸ Check Homework, and ❹ Assess each lesson.
- Animated examples allow step-by-step instruction at your own pace.
- Easy to edit so you can create custom presentations.

Teaching Chapter 8 Using Presentation Assistant Plus!

	❶ Introduce	❷ Teach	❸ Check Homework	❹ Assess
	Check Skills You'll Need	Additional Examples	Student Edition Answers	Lesson Quiz
8-1	p. 47	pp. 127–128	✔	p. 122
8-2	p. 48	pp. 128–130	✔	p. 123
8-3	p. 49	pp. 131–133	✔	p. 124
8-4	p. 50	pp. 134–135	✔	p. 125
8-5	p. 51	pp. 136–137	✔	p. 126
8-6	p. 52	pp. 137–139	✔	p. 127

 ### Prentice Hall Presentation Pro

CD-ROM with dynamic PowerPoint® presentations for every lesson. Helps you introduce and develop concepts, check homework, and assess progress. Part of Presentation Assistant Plus! *(See above.)*

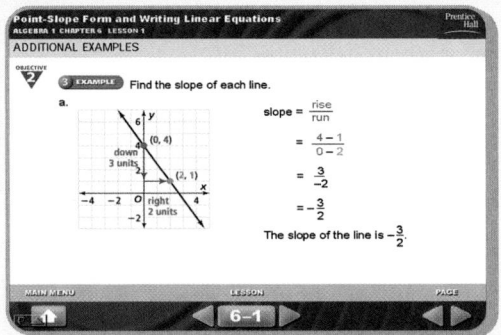

 ### Computer Test Generator

CD-ROM to create practice sheets and tests for course objectives and standardized tests. Includes Instant Chapter Tests™, online testing, and student reports. Part of the PH Assessment System. *(See page 414C.)*

 ### Resource Pro® with Planning Express®

CD-ROM with a lesson planning tool that allows you to import state and local objectives. Includes electronic versions of all the teaching resources.

Similarity

 Diagnosing Readiness

Students will find answers to these exercises in the back of their textbooks.

For intervention, direct students to:

Simplifying Ratios
Skills Handbook, p. 718

Congruent Figures
Lesson 4-1: Example 1
Exercises 1–15
Extra Practice, p. 693

Polygon Angle-Sum Theorems
Lesson 3-4: Example 5
Exercises 22–25
Extra Practice, p. 692

Special Right Triangles
Lesson 7-3: Examples 1, 2, 4
Exercises 1–14
Extra Practice, p. 696

Areas of Regular Polygons
Lesson 7-5: Example 2
Exercises 4–9
Extra Practice, p. 696

Where You've Been

- In Chapter 4, you learned several different methods for proving triangles congruent. You learned how to use CPCTC to find additional information about congruent triangles.

- In Chapter 5, you learned that a midsegment of a triangle is parallel to a side of the triangle and half its length.

- In Chapter 7, you learned the Pythagorean Theorem, and how to find area for triangles, quadrilaterals, and regular polygons.

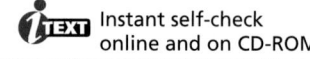 **i TEXT** Instant self-check online and on CD-ROM

 **Diagnosing Readiness**   (For help, go to the Lesson in green.)

Simplifying Ratios (Skills Handbook page 718)

Simplify each ratio.

1. $12 : 18$ $\frac{2}{3}$

2. $\frac{55}{11}$ 5

3. $\frac{20a^2}{15a^5}$ $\frac{4}{3a^3}$

4. $\frac{3x^2 - 12x}{x^3 - x^2}$ $\frac{3x - 12}{x^2 - x}$

Polygon Angle-Sum Theorems (Lesson 3-4)

Determine the measure of an angle of each regular polygon.

5. pentagon 108

6. octagon 135

7. decagon 144

8. 27-gon $166\frac{2}{3}$

Congruent Figures (Lesson 4-1)

$\triangle PAC \cong \triangle DHL$. Complete the congruence statements.

9. $\overline{PC} \cong$? $\overline{DL}$

10. $\angle H \cong$? $\angle A$

11. $\angle PCA \cong$? $\angle DLH$

12. $\triangle HDL \cong$? $\triangle APC$

Special Right Triangles (Lesson 7-3)

$\boxed{x^2}$ **Algebra** Find the value of x. Leave your answer in simplest radical form.

13. $10\sqrt{3}$

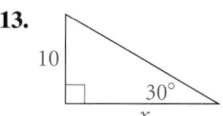

14. $3\sqrt{2}$

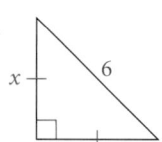

15. $2\sqrt{3}$

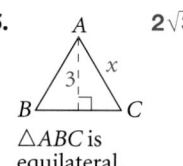

$\triangle ABC$ is equilateral.

Areas of Regular Polygons (Lesson 7-5)

Find the area of each regular polygon.

16. regular hexagon with perimeter 24 units **$24\sqrt{3}$ units^2**

17. regular octagon with sides 9 units and apothem 10.9 units **392.4 units^2**

Similarity

Where You're Going

- In this chapter, you will learn that similar polygons are polygons that have the same shape but not necessarily the same size.

- You will learn how to prove triangles similar.

- Through proving triangles similar, you will find additional relationships within triangles.

- You will also learn how the perimeters and areas of similar figures are related.

 **Real-World Snapshots** Applying what you have learned, you will do activities on pages 466 and 467 involving views from the tops of tall structures.

Key Vocabulary

- Cross-Product Property (p. 417)
- extended proportion (p. 417)
- geometric mean (p. 440)
- golden ratio (p. 425)
- golden rectangle (p. 425)
- indirect measurement (p. 434)
- proportion (p. 417)
- ratio (p. 416)
- scale (p. 418)
- scale drawing (p. 418)
- similar (p. 423)
- similarity ratio (p. 423)

Chapter 8 Overview

In this chapter, students will learn properties of ratios and proportions that are needed to study similarity. They will learn ways to prove triangles similar using the definition of similar polygons. Students will find proportional relationships formed by parallel segments, and by angle bisectors within triangles as well as by altitudes to the hypotenuse in right triangles. Finally, students will examine the ratios of the perimeters and of the areas of similar figures.

Reading Math
Reading a Two-Column Proof, p. 453

Vocabulary
A complete list of terms, plus vocabulary exercises, appears in the Chapter Review, p. 461.

Illustrated Glossary
Examples for each vocabulary term, plus definitions in both English and Spanish, appear starting on p. 741.

Test-Taking Strategies
Testing Multiple Choices, p. 460

Real-World Snapshots
See pages 466–467 for a real-world application of the Pythagorean Theorem that utilizes Dorling Kindersley's (DK) unique graphic presentation.

Real-World Connections
Some of the applications you will find in this chapter are photography (8-1), geology (8-3), sail making (8-5), and community service (8-6).

www.PHSchool.com
Internet support for this chapter includes:
- Self-grading Vocabulary and Chapter 8 Tests
- Chapter Project
- Chapter Planner
- Ch. 8 Resources

Plus

1. Plan

Lesson Preview

✓ **Check Skills You'll Need**

Simplifying Expressions
Skills Handbook, p. 718

Midsegments of Triangles
Lesson 5-1: Example 1
Exercises 1–10
Extra Practice, p. 694

Lesson Resources

📁 **Teaching Resources**
Practice, Reteaching, Enrichment

👥 **Reaching All Students**
Practice Workbook 8-1
Spanish Practice Workbook 8-1
Reading and Math Literacy 8A
Spanish Reading & Literacy 8A
Informal Geometry Planning
    Guide 7-1

⏱ **Presentation Assistant Plus!**
Transparencies
• Check Skills You'll Need 8-1
• Additional Examples 8-1
• Student Edition Answers 8-1
• Lesson Quiz 8-1
PH Presentation Pro CD 8-1

ASSESSMENT SYSTEM

Computer Test Generator CD

💿 **Technology**
Resource Pro® CD-ROM
Computer Test Generator CD
Prentice Hall Presentation Pro CD

🖥 **www.PHSchool.com**
Student Site
• Teacher Web Code: afk-5500
• Self-grading Lesson Quiz
Teacher Center
• Lesson Planner
• Resources

Plus

416

Ratios and Proportions

North Carolina Objectives

1.02 Use length, area, and volume of geometric figures to solve problems.

Lesson Preview

What You'll Learn

OBJECTIVE 1
To write ratios and solve proportions

. . . And Why

To find dimensions from a scale drawing, as in Example 4

✓ **Check Skills You'll Need** (For help, go to Skills Handbook p. 718 and Lesson 5-1.)

Simplify each ratio.

1. $\frac{2}{4}$ $\frac{1}{2}$
2. $\frac{8}{12}$ $\frac{2}{3}$
3. $\frac{6}{8}$ $\frac{3}{4}$
4. $\frac{10}{10}$ 1

5. $20:30$ $\frac{2}{3}$
6. 8 to 2 4
7. 2 to 8 $\frac{1}{4}$
8. $12:9$ $\frac{4}{3}$

9. Draw a triangle. Then draw its three midsegments to form a smaller triangle. How do the lengths of the sides of the smaller triangle compare to the lengths of the sides of the larger triangle?
Each side of the smaller $\triangle$ is $\frac{1}{2}$ the length of a side of the larger $\triangle$.

New Vocabulary • proportion • extended proportion • Cross-Product Property • scale drawing • scale

---

OBJECTIVE

1 ▶ **Using Ratios and Proportions**

📖 **Reading Math**

You can read $a : b$ as "the ratio a to b."

Interactive lesson includes instant self-check, tutorials, and activities.

A ratio is a comparison of two quantities. You can write the ratio of a to b or $a : b$ as the quotient $\frac{a}{b}$ when $b \neq 0$. Unless otherwise stated, the terms and expressions appearing in ratios in this book are assumed to be nonzero.

1 **EXAMPLE** **Real-World** 🌐 **Connection**

Photography A photo that is 8 in. wide and $5\frac{1}{3}$ in. high is enlarged to a poster that is 2 ft wide and $1\frac{1}{3}$ ft high. What is the ratio of the width of the photo to the width of the poster?

$$\frac{\text{width of photo}}{\text{width of poster}} = \frac{8 \text{ in.}}{2 \text{ ft}} = \frac{8 \text{ in.}}{24 \text{ in.}} = \frac{8}{24} = \frac{1}{3}$$

● The ratio of the width of the photo to the width of the poster is $1 : 3$ or $\frac{1}{3}$.

✓ **Check Understanding** ① What is the ratio of the height of the photo to the height of the poster? **1:3**

416 Chapter 8 Similarity

Ongoing Assessment and Intervention

Before the Lesson	During the Lesson	After the Lesson
Diagnose prerequisite skills using:	**Monitor progress using:**	**Assess knowledge using:**
• Check Skills You'll Need	• Check Understanding	• Lesson Quiz
	• Additional Examples	• Computer Test Generator CD
	• Standardized Test Prep	

Reading Math

You can read both $\frac{a}{b} = \frac{c}{d}$ and $a : b = c : d$ as "a is to b as c is to d."

A **proportion** is a statement that two ratios are equal. You can write a proportion in these forms:

$$\frac{a}{b} = \frac{c}{d} \quad \text{and} \quad a : b = c : d$$

When three or more ratios are equal, you can write an **extended proportion.** For example, you could write the following:

$$\frac{6}{24} = \frac{4}{16} = \frac{1}{4}$$

Two equations are equivalent when either can be deduced from the other using the Properties of Equality. Several equations are equivalent to a proportion. Some of them are important enough to be called Properties of Proportions.

 Key Concepts

Property	Properties of Proportions
$\frac{a}{b} = \frac{c}{d}$ is equivalent to	(1) $ad = bc$ (2) $\frac{b}{a} = \frac{d}{c}$ (3) $\frac{a}{c} = \frac{b}{d}$ (4) $\frac{a+b}{b} = \frac{c+d}{d}$

Multiplying both sides of $\frac{a}{b} = \frac{c}{d}$ by bd results in the first property, called the **Cross-Product Property.** You may state this property as "The product of the extremes is equal to the product of the means."

$$\begin{array}{c} \text{means} \\ \downarrow \quad \downarrow \\ a : b = c : d \\ \uparrow \text{extremes} \uparrow \\ \frac{a}{b} = \frac{c}{d} \\ ad = bc \end{array}$$

2 EXAMPLE **Properties of Proportions**

Algebra If $\frac{x}{y} = \frac{5}{6}$, complete each statement.

a. $6x = \blacksquare$

    $6x = 5y$

b. $\frac{y}{x} = \frac{\blacksquare}{\blacksquare}$

    $\frac{y}{x} = \frac{6}{5}$

c. $\frac{x}{5} = \frac{\blacksquare}{\blacksquare}$

    $\frac{x}{5} = \frac{y}{6}$

d. $\frac{x+y}{y} = \frac{\blacksquare}{\blacksquare}$

    $\frac{x+y}{y} = \frac{11}{6}$

✓ **Check Understanding** **2** **Critical Thinking** Write two proportions that are equivalent to $\frac{m}{4} = \frac{n}{11}$.
Answers may vary. Sample: $\frac{4}{m} = \frac{11}{n}, \frac{m+4}{4} = \frac{n+11}{11}$

You solve a proportion by finding the value of the variable.

3 EXAMPLE **Solving for a Variable**

Algebra Solve each proportion.

a. $\frac{x}{5} = \frac{12}{7}$

    $7x = 5(12)$ ← **Cross-Product Property** →

    $7x = 60$

    $x = \frac{60}{7}$

b. $\frac{y+3}{8} = \frac{y}{4}$

    $4(y+3) = 8y$

    $4y + 12 = 8y$

    $12 = 4y$

    $y = 3$

✓ **Check Understanding** **3** Solve each proportion.

a. $\frac{5}{z} = \frac{20}{3}$ **0.75**

b. $\frac{18}{n+6} = \frac{6}{n}$ **3**

Reaching All Students

Below Level Have students make a list of equivalent fractions and test them for equivalence by applying the properties of proportions.	**Advanced Learners** *Ask: If* $\frac{a}{b} = \frac{c}{d}$, *does* $\frac{a^2}{b^2}$ *equal* $\frac{c^2}{d^2}$? *Does* $\frac{a}{b}$ *equal* $\frac{a^2}{b^2}$? **Yes; yes, only if** $a = b$ **or** $a = 0$	**Auditory Learners** See note on page 418. **Error Prevention** See note on page 418.

Math Background

The properties of proportions are variations of applying the Multiplication and Addition Properties of Equality. Thus the same units must be within each ratio or in comparable positions in a proportion.

OBJECTIVE

1 **Teaching Notes**

1 EXAMPLE **Math Tip**

Students should understand that units of measurement must be the same.

2 EXAMPLE **Teaching Tip**

Replace the variables with numbers to verify that the proportions are equivalent.

4 EXAMPLE

Point out that the scale compares inches to feet, so each ratio has inches in the numerator and feet in the denominator.

Additional Examples

1 A scale model of a car is 4 in. long. The actual car is 15 ft long. What is the ratio of the length of the model to the length of the car? **1 : 45**

2 Complete: If $\frac{a}{4} = \frac{12}{b}$, then $\frac{b}{12} = \frac{?}{?} \cdot \frac{4}{a}$

3 Solve each proportion.

a. $\frac{2}{5} = \frac{n}{35}$ **14**

b. $\frac{x+1}{3} = \frac{x}{2}$ **2**

4 Two cities are $3\frac{1}{2}$ in. apart on a map with the scale 1 in. = 50 mi. Find the actual distance. **175 mi**

Closure

A baseball batting average is the ratio of hits to at-bats, expressed as a decimal. If a player with 540 at-bats has a batting average of 0.350, how many hits did the player make? **189 hits**

3. Practice

Assignment Guide

1 **Objective**
  A B Core 1–55
  C Extension 56–61

Standardized Test Prep 62–66

Mixed Review 67–77

Error Prevention

Exercise 2 Ask: *Why is writing the ratio as $\frac{6}{185}$ incorrect?* 185 ft first must be converted to inches, or 6 in. to feet.

Auditory Learners

Exercises 3–11 Have students explain their reasoning aloud to the class, citing the Property of Proportions.

In a **scale drawing,** the **scale** compares each length in the drawing to the actual length. The lengths used in a scale can be in different units. A scale might be written as 1 in. to 100 mi, 1 in. = 12 ft, or 1 mm : 1 m. You can use proportions to find the actual dimensions represented in a scale drawing.

4 EXAMPLE **Real-World Connection**

Drafting Measure the dimensions of the bedroom in the scale drawing. Use those dimensions to find the dimensions of the actual bedroom.

Use a ruler to find that the bedroom in the scale drawing is $\frac{7}{8}$ in. by $\frac{5}{8}$ in.

$$\frac{1}{16} = \frac{\frac{7}{8}}{x} \quad \longleftarrow \frac{\text{drawing length (in.)}}{\text{actual length (ft)}} \longrightarrow \quad \frac{1}{16} = \frac{\frac{5}{8}}{y}$$

$$x = 16\left(\frac{7}{8}\right) \quad \longleftarrow \text{Cross-Product Property} \longrightarrow \quad y = 16\left(\frac{5}{8}\right)$$

$$x = 14 \qquad\qquad\qquad\qquad\qquad\qquad y = 10$$

● The actual bedroom is 14 ft by 10 ft.

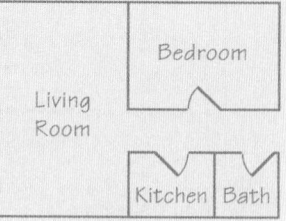

Scale: 1 in. = 16 ft

✓ Check Understanding **4** You want to make a new scale drawing with a scale of 1 in. = 4 ft. What would be the dimensions of your 14 ft-by-10 ft bedroom in this scale drawing? $3\frac{1}{2}$ in. by $2\frac{1}{2}$ in.

EXERCISES

For more practice, see *Extra Practice*.

Practice and Problem Solving

A **Practice by Example**
  Example 1
  (page 416)

1. The base of the pyramid at the right is a square whose sides measure 0.675 m. The intent was for the sides to measure 675 m. What is the ratio of the length of a base side in the small pyramid to the length of a base side in the intended pyramid? **1:1000**

2. Models The Leaning Tower of Pisa in Italy is about 185 ft tall. A model of the Leaning Tower is 6 in. tall. What is the ratio of the height of the model to the height of the real tower? **1:370**

"We had a little problem with the decimal point."

Example 2
(page 417)

$\boxed{x^2}$ **Algebra** If $\frac{a}{b} = \frac{3}{4}$, complete each statement.

3. $4a = \blacksquare \ 3b$

4. $\frac{b}{a} = \frac{\blacksquare}{} \ \frac{4}{3}$

5. $\frac{a}{3} = \frac{\blacksquare}{} \ \frac{b}{4}$

6. $\frac{4}{3} = \frac{\blacksquare}{} \ \frac{b}{a}$

7. $\frac{4}{b} = \frac{\blacksquare}{} \ \frac{3}{a}$

8. $3b = \blacksquare \ 4a$

9. $\frac{a+b}{b} = \frac{\blacksquare}{} \ \frac{7}{4}$

10. $\frac{a}{a+b} = \frac{\blacksquare}{} \ \frac{3}{7}$

11. $\frac{a+3}{3} = \frac{\blacksquare}{} \ \frac{b+4}{4}$

418 Chapter 8 Similarity

Example 3
(page 417)

x^2 **Algebra** Solve each proportion.

12. $\frac{x}{2} = \frac{8}{4}$ 4

13. $\frac{9}{5} = \frac{3}{x}$ $1\frac{2}{3}$

14. $\frac{1}{3} = \frac{x}{12}$ 4

15. $\frac{5}{x} = \frac{8}{11}$ 6.875

16. $\frac{4}{x} = \frac{5}{9}$ 7.2

17. $\frac{5}{6} = \frac{6}{x}$ 7.2

18. $\frac{x+3}{3} = \frac{10+4}{4}$ 7.5

19. $\frac{x+7}{7} = \frac{15}{5}$ 14

20. $\frac{3}{5} = \frac{6}{x+3}$ 7

Example 4
(page 418)

21. **Geography** The scale for this map of Louisiana is 1 in. = 40 mi. On the map, the distance from Lake Charles **125 mi** to Baton Rouge is about $3\frac{1}{8}$ in. About how far apart are the two cities?

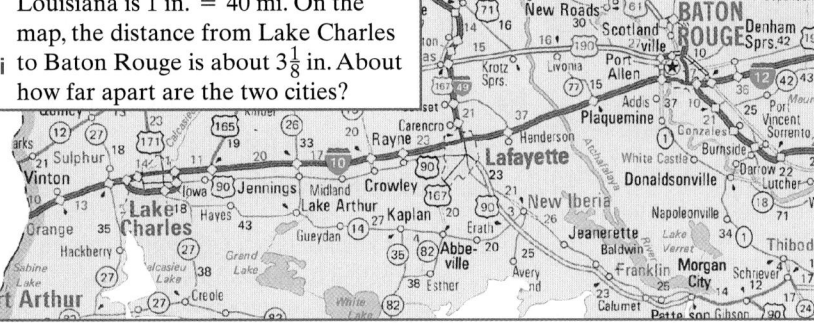

Need Help?

In Exercise 21 and other scale problems, use mental math to estimate the answer first.

Map Reading Measure the map distance. Then find the actual distance.

22. Morgan City to Rayne
    about 75 mi

23. Vinton to New Roads
    about 135 mi

24. Kaplan to Plaquemine
    about 67.5 mi

25. **Design** You want to make a scale drawing of your bedroom to help you arrange your furniture. You decide on a scale of 3 in. = 2 ft. Your bedroom is a 12 ft-by-15 ft rectangle. What should be its dimensions in your scale drawing? **18 in. by 22.5 in.**

B **Apply Your Skills** For each rectangle, find the ratio of the longer side to the shorter side.

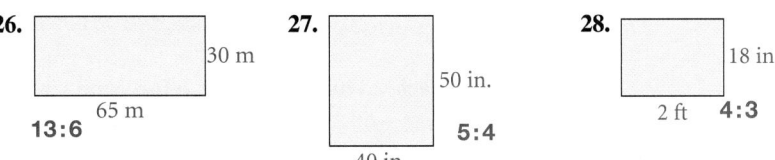

26. 30 m, 65 m **13:6**

27. 50 in., 40 in. **5:4**

28. 18 in., 2 ft **4:3**

29. **Miniatures** The diameter of a dinner plate is 1 ft. In a dollhouse set, the diameter of a dinner plate is $1\frac{1}{4}$ in. What is the ratio, using whole numbers, of the diameter of the dollhouse plate to the diameter of the full-size plate? $\frac{5}{48}$

Complete each statement.

30. If $\frac{x}{7} = \frac{y}{3}$, then $\frac{x}{y} = \blacksquare$. $\frac{7}{3}$

31. If $4m = 9n$, then $\frac{m}{n} = \blacksquare$. $\frac{9}{4}$

32. If $\frac{30}{t} = \frac{18}{r}$, then $\frac{t}{r} = \blacksquare$. $\frac{30}{18}$

33. If $\frac{a+5}{5} = \frac{b+2}{2}$, then $\frac{a}{5} = \blacksquare$. $\frac{b}{2}$

34. **Writing** Use a map in your classroom or a map from a textbook. Give the scale of the map. Explain how to use a ruler and the scale of the map to approximate an actual distance. Give an example. (If you do not have access to another map, use the map above.) **Check students' work.**

x^2 **Algebra** Solve each proportion.

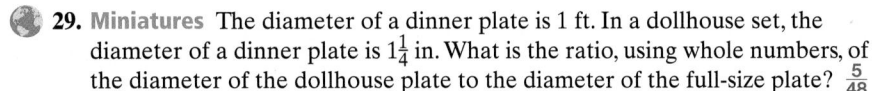

35. $\frac{y}{10} = \frac{15}{25}$ 6

36. $\frac{9}{24} = \frac{12}{n}$ 32

37. $\frac{11}{14} = \frac{b}{21}$ 16.5

38. $\frac{5}{x-3} = \frac{10}{x}$ 6

39. $\frac{8}{n+4} = \frac{4}{n}$ 4

40. $\frac{2b-1}{5} = \frac{b}{12}$ $\frac{12}{19}$

41. $\frac{2}{7} = \frac{x-5}{x}$ 7

42. $\frac{3y-5}{y} = \frac{12}{5}$ $\frac{25}{3}$

Exercises 12–20 Remind students to check their answers by substituting the solution for x in the original proportion. Ask: *How can you tell whether your answer is correct?* The proportion with the substituted value is true.

Exercise 21 Provide students with copies of a map of your own state. Have them write and solve problems similar to the one in Exercise 21 and then exchange and solve one another's problems.

Exercise 50 The baskets on each end of a basketball court are 10 ft above the floor. Have students explain how they would represent baskets on their scale drawings.

Connection to Algebra

Exercises 56–58 You can do these as class exercises by having students provide steps and reasons in prooflike fashion. For each exercise, a possible first step is using the Cross-Product Property.

Exercises 59–61 If students need help getting started, suggest that they break each extended proportion into two proportions.

Lesson Quiz 8-1

1. A scale model of a boat is 9 in. long. The boat's actual length is 60 ft. Find the ratio of the length of the scale model to the length of the boat. **1 : 80**

2. Solve the proportion $\frac{10}{8} = \frac{15}{x}$. **12**

3. A map uses the scale 1 cm = 20 mi. A county is 90 mi wide. How wide is the county on the map? **$4\frac{1}{2}$ cm**

If $\frac{x}{y} = \frac{7}{11}$, complete each of the following.

4. $\frac{y}{x} = \frac{?}{?}$ **$\frac{11}{7}$**

5. $7y = ?$ **$11x$**

6. $\frac{x + y}{y} = \frac{?}{11}$ **18**

Alternative Assessment

Show the class a wall map of the continental United States, making sure that you cover the scale. Ask students to measure the width of the United States on the map from San Francisco, California, to Washington, D.C. Point out that the actual width of the United States is about 3000 mi. Have students use this information to estimate the scale on the map. When they finish their work, uncover the scale so that students can compare it with their answers.

pages 418–421   Exercises

48–51. Answers may vary.
       Samples are given.

48.
┌─────────────┐
│   │
└─────────────┘
Scale 1 in. = 5 ft

420

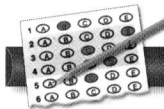

Real-World 🌐 Connection

This sandwich shop is on Museum Wharf in Boston, Massachusetts.

43. **Models** The sandwich shop at the left is 40 ft tall. The shop is an enlargement of an actual milk bottle. The scale used in construction is 5 ft = 2 cm. Find the height of the actual milk bottle. **16 cm**

44. **Geography** Students at the University of Minnesota in Minneapolis built a model globe 42 ft in diameter using a scale of 1 : 1,000,000. About how tall is Mount Everest on the model? (Mount Everest is about 29,000 ft tall.) **0.348 in.**

Complete each extended proportion.

45. $\frac{8}{12} = \frac{6}{\blacksquare} = \frac{12}{\blacksquare}$ **9; 18**   46. $\frac{\blacksquare}{15} = \frac{15}{25} = \frac{\blacksquare}{20}$ **9; 12**   47. $\frac{14}{\blacksquare} = \frac{\blacksquare}{12} = \frac{35}{20}$ **8; 21**

🌐 **Games** Choose a scale and make a scale drawing of the playing region.

48–51. See margin.

48. A pool table is 5 ft by 10 ft.   49. A bowling lane is 3.5 ft by 60 ft.

50. A basketball court is 92 ft by 50 ft.   51. A football field is 160 ft by 120 yd.

52. **Error Analysis** One rectangle has length 3 in. and width 4 ft. Another rectangle has length 3 ft and width 4 yd. Elaine claims that the two rectangles are similar because their corresponding angles are congruent and their corresponding sides are in proportion. Explain why Elaine's reasoning is incorrect. **Elaine did not convert units, and thought the ratios equaled 1.**

If $\frac{a}{b} = \frac{c}{d}$, complete each statement.

53. $\frac{a + b}{c + d} = \frac{\blacksquare}{\blacksquare}$ **$\frac{b}{d}$ or $\frac{a}{c}$**   54. $\frac{a + c}{b + d} = \frac{\blacksquare}{\blacksquare}$ **$\frac{c}{d}$ or $\frac{a}{b}$**   55. $\frac{a + 2b}{b} = \frac{\blacksquare}{\blacksquare}$ **$\frac{c + 2d}{d}$**

C Challenge x^2 Algebra **Justify the indicated property of proportions.** 56–58. See margin p. 421.

56. Property (2): If $\frac{a}{b} = \frac{c}{d}$, then $\frac{b}{a} = \frac{d}{c}$.

57. Property (3): If $\frac{a}{b} = \frac{c}{d}$, then $\frac{a}{c} = \frac{b}{d}$.

58. Property (4): If $\frac{a}{b} = \frac{c}{d}$, then $\frac{a + b}{b} = \frac{c + d}{d}$.

Solve each extended proportion for x and y with $x > 0$ and $y > 0$.

59. $\frac{x}{6} = \frac{x + 10}{18} = \frac{4x}{y}$ 60. $\frac{x}{5} = \frac{9}{y} = \frac{y}{25}$ 61. $\frac{1}{x} = \frac{4}{x + 9} = \frac{7}{y}$

$x = 5; y = 24$ $x = 3; y = 15$ $x = 3; y = 21$

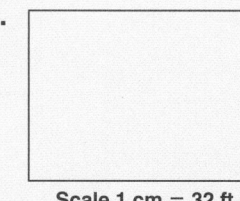

Standardized Test Prep

Multiple Choice

Take It to the NET
Online lesson quiz at
www.PHSchool.com
····· Web Code: afa-0801

Solve each proportion.

62. $\frac{21}{x} = \frac{7}{3}$ **C**   A. 3   B. 7   C. 9   D. 14

63. $\frac{4}{x - 1} = \frac{1}{x}$ **G**   F. −3   G. $-\frac{1}{3}$ H. $\frac{1}{3}$ I. 3

64. $\frac{x}{x + 6} = \frac{2}{3}$ **D**   A. 4   B. 6   C. 8   D. 12

65. $\frac{3}{8} = \frac{x + 3}{9}$ **H**   F. $3\frac{3}{8}$ G. 3   H. $\frac{3}{8}$ I. $\frac{1}{3}$

Short Response

66a. $\frac{2.75}{16} = \frac{23.2}{x}$ **(OR equivalent proportion)**

b. **135 km**

66. A map of Long Island has the scale 2.75 cm = 16 km. On the map, Target Rock is 23.2 cm from Lake Montauk.
   a. Write a proportion that you can solve to determine the actual distance from Target Rock to Lake Montauk. **a–b. See left.**
   b. Find the actual distance. Round your answer to the nearest kilometer.

49.
┌─────────────────────────┐
│   │
└─────────────────────────┘
Scale 1 cm = 10 ft

50.
┌─────────────────────┐
│   │
│   │
└─────────────────────┘
Scale 1 in. = 46 ft

51.
┌─────────────────────┐
│   │
└─────────────────────┘
Scale 1 cm = 32 ft

Lesson 7-8

67. **Probability** A shuttle bus to an airport terminal leaves every 20 min from a remote parking lot. Draw a geometric model and find the probability that a traveler who arrives at a random time will have to wait at least 8 min for the bus to leave the parking lot. **See left.**

67. ⊢─┼─┼─┼─┼─┤ 60%
    0 4 8 12 16 20

🌐 **68.** **Games** A dartboard is a circle with a 12-in. radius. You throw a dart that hits the dartboard. What is the probability that the dart lands within 6 in. of the center of the dartboard? **25%**

Lesson 6-1

Graph each quadrilateral *ABCD.* **Classify** *ABCD* **in as many ways as possible.**
69–72. See margin.

69. $A(-1, -2), B(3, -2), C(1, 4), D(-3, 4)$

70. $A(2, -1), B(6, 2), C(8, 2), D(10, -1)$

71. $A(-7, 1), B(-5, 3), C(0, -2), D(-2, -4)$

72. $A(1, 1), B(-4, 4), C(1, 7), D(6, 4)$

Lesson 5-4

In each exercise, identify two statements that contradict each other.

73. I. $\triangle PQR$ is isosceles. **I and III**
II. $\triangle PQR$ is an obtuse triangle.
III. $\triangle PQR$ is scalene.

74. I. $\angle 1 \cong \angle 2$ **II and III**
II. $\angle 1$ and $\angle 2$ are complementary.
III. $m\angle 1 + m\angle 2 = 180$

Write (a) the inverse and (b) the contrapositive of each statement. 75–77.
See margin.

75. If an angle is acute, then it has measure between 0 and 90.

76. If two lines are parallel, then they are coplanar.

77. If two angles are complementary, then both angles are acute.

A Point in Time

←─┼──┼──┼──┼──┼──┼──┼──→
1500 1600 1700 1800 1900 2000

In 1675, Danish astronomer Ole Römer used proportions to estimate the speed of light. He carefully measured the movements of Jupiter's moons. With Earth at point *B*, a moon emerged from behind Jupiter 16.6 min later than when Earth was at point *A*. He reasoned that it must have taken 16.6 min for the light to travel from point *A* to point *B*. Using proportions, Römer estimated the speed of light to be 150,000 mi/s. This estimate is about 81% of today's accepted value of 186,282 mi/s.

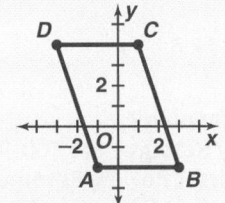

Jupiter
Sun
A ● ● B
Moon
Earth
not drawn to scale

 Take It to the NET For more information about the speed of light, go to **www.PHSchool.com.**
Web Code: afe-2032

56. $\frac{a}{b} = \frac{c}{d}$ (Given); $ad = bc$ (Cross-Product Prop.); $bc = ad$ (Symm. Prop. of =); $\frac{bc}{ac} = \frac{ad}{ac}$ (Div. Prop. of =); $\frac{b}{a} = \frac{d}{c}$ (Simplify.)

57. $\frac{a}{b} = \frac{c}{d}$ (Given); $ad = bc$ (Cross-Prod. Prop.); $\frac{ad}{cd} = \frac{bc}{cd}$ (Div. Prop. of =); $\frac{a}{c} = \frac{b}{d}$ (Simplify.)

58. $\frac{a}{b} = \frac{c}{d}$ (Given); $\frac{a}{b} + 1 = \frac{c}{d} + 1$ (Add. Prop. of =); $\frac{a}{b} + \frac{b}{b} = \frac{c}{d} + \frac{d}{d}$ (Subst.); $\frac{a+b}{b} = \frac{c+d}{d}$ (Simplify.)

Standardized Test Prep

📁 **Resources**
For additional practice with a variety of test item formats:
• Standardized Test Prep, p. 465
• Test-Taking Strategies, p. 460
• Test-Taking Strategies with Transparencies

Exercises 62–65 Each proportion can be solved algebraically or by using a guess-and-test strategy.

69.
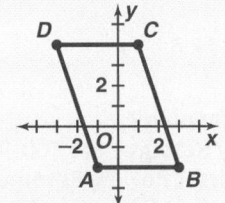
parallelogram

70.
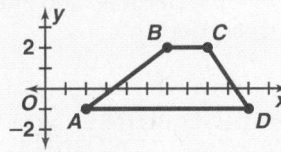
trapezoid

71.
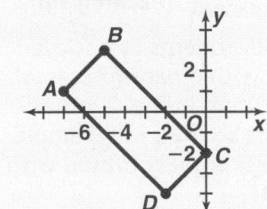
rectangle, parallelogram

72.
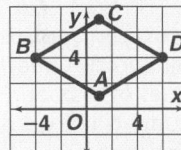
rhombus, parallelogram

75. a. If an $\angle$ is not acute, then it does not have measure between 0 and 90.
b. If an $\angle$ does not have measure between 0 and 90, then it is not acute.

76. a. If two lines are not ∥, then they are not coplanar.
b. If two lines are not coplanar, then they are not ∥.

77. a. If two ⩽ are not compl., then the ⩽ are not both acute.
b. If two ⩽ are not both acute, then they are not compl.

Solving Quadratic Equations

Solving Quadratic Equations

Students will use the skill of solving quadratic equations in Exercise 51 of Lesson 8-2.

Resources

Technology
Geometry Resource Pro® CD-ROM:
   Algebra 1 Review Resources
Computer Test Generator CD:
   Algebra 1, Chapter 0,
   Integer, Decimal, and Fraction
   Operations

Teaching Notes

1 EXAMPLE Teaching Tip

Remind students to enclose values within parentheses when substituting in the Quadratic Formula so that, for example, 4 (7)(−1) is not confused with 47 − 1.

2 EXAMPLE Technology Tip

Some calculators can approximate solutions of quadratic equations when the values of *a*, *b*, and *c* are entered. If students use graphing calculators, they can graph the parabola $y = -3x^2 - 5x + 1$ and find the value of *x* where the graph intersects the *x*-axis at $y = 0$.

Error Prevention

Exercises 5–7 Remind students that quadratic equations must be in standard form (one side of the equation equals 0) before applying the Quadratic Formula.

The *standard form* of a quadratic equation is

$$ax^2 + bx + c = 0, a \neq 0.$$

You can solve a quadratic equation by substituting the values for *a*, *b*, and *c* in the *Quadratic Formula*.

$$x = \frac{-b \pm \sqrt{b^2 - 4ac}}{2a}$$

1 EXAMPLE

Solve for *x*: $7x^2 + 6x - 1 = 0$.   **The equation is in standard form.**

$a = 7, b = 6, c = -1$

$x = \dfrac{-6 \pm \sqrt{6^2 - 4(7)(-1)}}{2(7)}$ **Substitute in the Quadratic Formula.**

$x = \dfrac{-6 \pm \sqrt{36 + 28}}{14}$ **Simplify.**

$x = \dfrac{-6 \pm \sqrt{64}}{14}$

$x = \dfrac{-6 + 8}{14}$ or $x = \dfrac{-6 - 8}{14}$

$x = \frac{1}{7}$ or $x = -1$

Sometimes you may need a calculator to approximate the solutions.

2 EXAMPLE

Solve for *x*: $-3x^2 - 5x + 1 = 0$.

$a = -3, b = -5, c = 1$

$x = \dfrac{-(-5) \pm \sqrt{(-5)^2 - 4(-3)(1)}}{2(-3)}$ **Substitute in the Quadratic Formula.**

$x = \dfrac{5 \pm \sqrt{25 + 12}}{-6}$ **Simplify.**

$x = \dfrac{5 + \sqrt{37}}{-6}$ or $x = \dfrac{5 - \sqrt{37}}{-6}$

$x \approx -1.85$ or $x \approx 0.18$ **Use a calculator and round.**

EXERCISES

Solve for *x*. Round answers that are not integers to the nearest hundredth.

1. $x^2 + 5x - 14 = 0$ **−7, 2**   **2.** $4x^2 - 13x + 3 = 0$ **0.25, 3**   **3.** $2x^2 + 7x + 3 = 0$ **−0.5, −3**

4. $5x^2 + 2x - 2 = 0$ **0.46, −0.86** **5.** $6x^2 + 10x = 5$ **0.40, −2.07**   **6.** $1 = 2x^2 - 6x$ **3.16, −0.16**

7. $x^2 - 6x = 27$ **9, −3**   **8.** $2x^2 - 10x + 11 = 0$ **3.37, 1.63** **9.** $8x^2 - 2x - 3 = 0$ **0.75, −0.5**

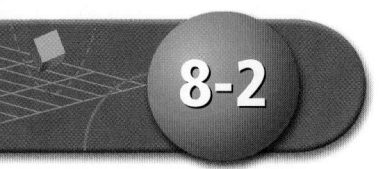

Similar Polygons

North Carolina Objectives

2.03 Apply properties, definitions, and theorems of two-dimensional figures to solve problems and write proofs: a) Triangles. b) Quadrilaterals. c) Other polygons. d) Circles.

Lesson Preview

What You'll Learn

 OBJECTIVE 1 To identify similar polygons

 OBJECTIVE 2 To apply similar polygons

. . . And Why

To find the size of a video image, as in Example 4

✓ Check Skills You'll Need

(For help, go to Lessons 4-1 and 8-1.)

1. $\triangle ABC \cong \triangle HIJ$. Name three pairs of congruent sides.
$\overline{AB} \cong \overline{HI}; \overline{BC} \cong \overline{IJ}; \overline{AC} \cong \overline{HJ}$

x^2 **Algebra** Solve each proportion.

2. $\frac{3}{4} = \frac{x}{8}$ 6   3. $\frac{2}{x} = \frac{8}{24}$ 6   4. $\frac{x}{9} = \frac{1}{3}$ 3   5. $\frac{10}{25} = \frac{2}{x}$ 5

New Vocabulary • similar • similarity ratio • golden rectangle • golden ratio

---

1. Plan

Lesson Preview

✓ **Check Skills You'll Need**

Congruent Figures
Lesson 4-1: Example 1
Exercises 1–15
Extra Practice, p. 693

Solving Proportions
Lesson 8-1: Example 3
Exercises 12–20
Extra Practice, p. 697

Lesson Resources

📁 **Teaching Resources**
Practice, Reteaching, Enrichment
Checkpoint Quiz 1

👥 **Reaching All Students**
Practice Workbook 8-2
Spanish Practice Workbook 8-2
Reading & Math Literacy 8B
Spanish Reading & Literacy 8B
Spanish Checkpoint Quiz 1
Technology Activities 50
Hands-On Activities 22
Informal Geometry Planning
  Guide 8-2

⏱ **Presentation Assistant Plus!**
Transparencies
• Check Skills You'll Need 8-2
• Additional Examples 8-2
• Student Edition Answers 8-2
• Lesson Quiz 8-2
PH Presentation Pro CD 8-2

PRENTICE HALL ASSESSMENT SYSTEM

Checkpoint Quiz 1
Computer Test Generator CD

💿 **Technology**
Resource Pro® CD-ROM
Computer Test Generator CD
Prentice Hall Presentation Pro CD

 www.PHSchool.com
Student Site
• Teacher Web Code: afk-5500
• Self-grading Lesson Quiz
Teacher Center
• Lesson Planner
• Resources

Plus **iTEXT**

OBJECTIVE

1 Similar Polygons

🔴 **iTEXT** Interactive lesson includes instant self-check, tutorials, and activities.

Two figures that have the same shape but not necessarily the same size are similar (∼). Two polygons are **similar** if (1) corresponding angles are congruent and (2) corresponding sides are proportional. The ratio of the lengths of corresponding sides is the **similarity ratio**.

1 EXAMPLE Understanding Similarity

$ABCD \sim EFGH$. Complete each statement.

a. $m\angle E = \blacksquare$
$m\angle E = m\angle A = 53$ **Corresponding angles are ≅.**

b. $\frac{AB}{EF} = \frac{AD}{\blacksquare}$
$\frac{AB}{EF} = \frac{AD}{EH}$ **Corresponding sides are proportional.**

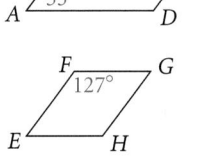

✓ **Check Understanding** ① Complete: $m\angle B = \blacksquare$ and $\frac{GH}{CD} = \frac{FG}{\blacksquare}$ $m\angle F = 127$; BC

2 EXAMPLE Determining Similarity

Determine whether the triangles are similar. If they are, write a similarity statement and give the similarity ratio.

Three pairs of angles are congruent.
Also, corresponding sides are proportional.

$\frac{AC}{FD} = \frac{18}{24} = \frac{3}{4}$ $\frac{AB}{FE} = \frac{15}{20} = \frac{3}{4}$ $\frac{BC}{ED} = \frac{12}{16} = \frac{3}{4}$

$\triangle ABC \sim \triangle FED$ with a similarity ratio of $\frac{3}{4}$ or 3 : 4.

? Need Help?
You can also say $\triangle FED \sim \triangle ABC$ with similarity ratio $\frac{4}{3}$.

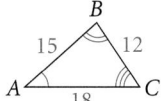
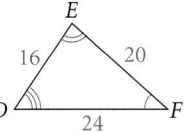

✓ **Check Understanding** ② Sketch $\triangle XYZ$ and $\triangle MNP$ with $\angle X \cong \angle M$, $\angle Y \cong \angle N$, and $\angle Z \cong \angle P$. Also, $XY = 12$, $YZ = 14$, $ZX = 16$, $MN = 18$, $NP = 21$, and $PM = 24$. Can you conclude that the two triangles are similar? Explain.
Yes; corr. ∠s are ≅ and corr. sides are prop.

Lesson 8-2 Similar Polygons **423**

 ## Ongoing Assessment and Intervention

Before the Lesson
Diagnose prerequisite skills using:
• Check Skills You'll Need

During the Lesson
Monitor progress using:
• Check Understanding
• Additional Examples
• Standardized Test Prep

After the Lesson
Assess knowledge using:
• Lesson Quiz
• Computer Test Generator CD
• Chapter Checkpoint 1 (p. 429)

2. Teach

 Professional Development

Math Background

As with congruence, the similarity relation is reflexive, symmetric, and transitive, thus qualifying as an equivalence relation. Because proportionality of sides is a consequence of similarity, ancient Greeks used similar figures to make indirect measurements.

 OBJECTIVE

1 Teaching Notes

English Learners

Compare the common use of the word *similar* with its use in geometry. Point out that its mathematical use is defined more precisely than its common use.

1 EXAMPLE Visual Learners

Copy the similar polygons, one drawn inside the other, to help students assign corresponding parts correctly.

2 EXAMPLE Math Tip

Ask: *If the similarity ratio had been 1 : 1, what could you have concluded?* triangle congruence

3 EXAMPLE Alternative Method

Point out that x can be found using the proportion $\frac{LM}{ON} = \frac{QR}{TS}$. Students may find working with ratios within figures easier. Ask: *How do you know that this is a valid proportion?* It is Property (3) of Proportions in Lesson 8-1.

 Additional Examples

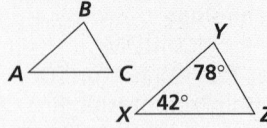

1 $\triangle ABC \sim \triangle XYZ$.

Complete each statement.
a. $m\angle B = \underline{\ ?\ }$ 78
b. $\frac{BC}{YZ} = \frac{?}{XZ}$ AC

424

You can use proportions to find unknown lengths in similar polygons.

3 EXAMPLE Using Similar Figures

Algebra $LMNO \sim QRST$
Find the value of x.

Write a proportion.

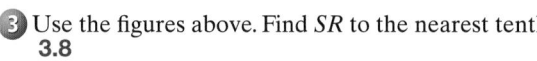

$\frac{LM}{QR} = \frac{ON}{TS}$ Corresponding sides of $\sim$ polygons are proportional.

$\frac{5}{6} = \frac{2}{x}$ Substitute.

$5x = 12$ Cross-Product Property

$x = 2.4$ Solve for x.

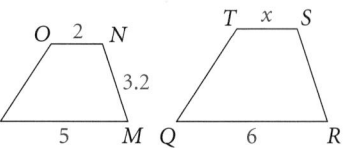

✔ **Check Understanding** ③ Use the figures above. Find SR to the nearest tenth.
3.8

OBJECTIVE

2 Applying Similar Polygons

You can use similar polygons to find measures when using enlarged or reduced images.

4 EXAMPLE Real-World Connection

Technology If you have a vision problem, a magnification system can help you read. You choose a level of magnification. Then you place an image under the viewer. A similar, magnified image appears on the video screen.

The video screen pictured is 16 in. wide by 12 in. tall. What is the largest complete video image possible for a block of text that is 6 in. wide by 4 in. tall?

The 6-in. width can be magnified at most to a rectangle with a longer side of 16 in. Let the shorter side of the video image have length x.

Need Help?
To calculate image size, estimate which screen dimension, width or height, will fill first as the image expands.

$\frac{6}{16} = \frac{4}{x}$ Corresponding sides of $\sim$ polygons are proportional.

$6x = 64$ Cross-Product Property

$x = 10\frac{2}{3}$ Solve for x.

The 4-in. height of the block of text enlarges to $10\frac{2}{3}$ in. This is less than the 12-in. height of the video screen, so the entire block of text fits on the screen.

The largest complete video image possible for the block of text is 16 in. by $10\frac{2}{3}$ in.

✔ **Check Understanding** ④ On the video screen in Example 4, what is the largest complete image possible for a photograph that is 3 in. wide by 5 in. tall? **7.2 in. by 12 in.**

424 Chapter 8 Similarity

👥 Reaching All Students

Below Level Have students fold a sheet of paper in half and then measure and reason to decide whether the folded sheet is similar to the original sheet.

Advanced Learners Use any two natural numbers to write a sequence like Fibonacci's, and then show that the sequence of ratios of 20 successive terms approaches the golden ratio.

English Learners See note on page 424.
English Learners See note on page 427.

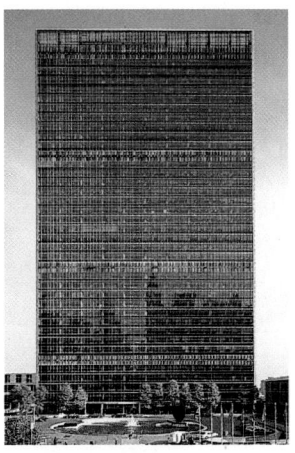

Real-World Connection

The United Nations Secretariat building in New York City suggests a golden rectangle.

A **golden rectangle** is a rectangle that can be divided into a square and a rectangle that is similar to the original rectangle. A pattern of repeated golden rectangles is shown at the right. Each golden rectangle that is formed is copied and divided again. Each golden rectangle is similar to the original rectangle.

In any golden rectangle, the length and width are in the **golden ratio** which is about 1.618 : 1. You will derive this ratio in Exercise 51.

The golden rectangle is considered pleasing to the human eye. It has appeared in architecture and art since ancient times. It has intrigued artists including Leonardo da Vinci (1452–1519). Da Vinci illustrated *The Divine Proportion*, a book about the golden rectangle.

You can apply the golden ratio to real-life design problems.

⑤ EXAMPLE Real-World Connection

Art An artist plans to paint a picture. He wants the canvas to be a golden rectangle with its longer horizontal sides 30 cm wide. How high should the canvas be?

Let h be the height of the canvas.

$\frac{30}{h} = \frac{1.618}{1}$	Write a proportion.
$1.618h = 30$	Cross-Product Property
$h = \frac{30}{1.618}$	Solve for h.
$h = 18.541409$	Use a calculator.

● The canvas should be about 18.5 cm high.

 **Check Understanding** ⑤ A golden rectangle has shorter sides of length 20 cm. Find the length of the longer sides. **about 32.4 cm**

EXERCISES

For more practice, see *Extra Practice*.

Practice and Problem Solving

Ⓐ Practice by Example

Example 1 (page 423)

JDRT ~ JHYX. Complete the congruence and proportion statements.

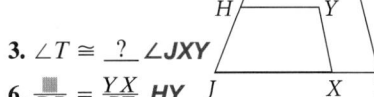

1. $\angle D \cong \underline{\ ?\ } \angle JHY$ 2. $\angle Y \cong \underline{\ ?\ } \angle R$ 3. $\angle T \cong \underline{\ ?\ } \angle JXY$

4. $\frac{JD}{JH} = \frac{DR}{\blacksquare}$ HY   5. $\frac{RT}{YX} = \frac{\blacksquare}{JX}$ JT   6. $\frac{\blacksquare}{DR} = \frac{YX}{RT}$ HY

Example 2 (page 423)

Are the polygons similar? If they are, write a similarity statement and give the similarity ratio. If they are not, explain.

7.

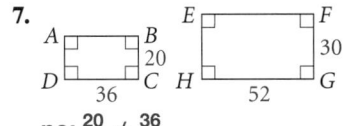

no; $\frac{20}{30} \neq \frac{36}{52}$

8.

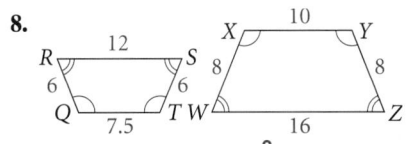

yes; *QRST ~ XWZY*; $\frac{3}{4}$

Lesson 8-2 Similar Polygons **425**

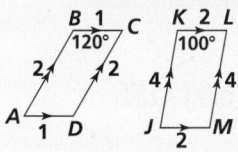
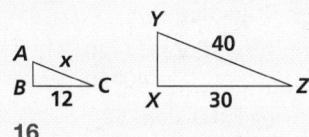

3. Practice

Assignment Guide

1 Objective

Ⓐ Ⓑ **Core** 1–16, 21–30, 32–39

Ⓒ **Extension** 51

2 Objective

Ⓐ Ⓑ **Core** 17–20, 31, 40–50

Ⓒ **Extension** 52

Standardized Test Prep 53–56

Mixed Review 57–66

Auditory Learners

Exercises 7–12 These can be done as class exercises. Ask students to use the vocabulary introduced in this lesson to explain their reasoning.

Exercises 13–16 If necessary, have students work with partners to review the techniques for writing and solving proportions.

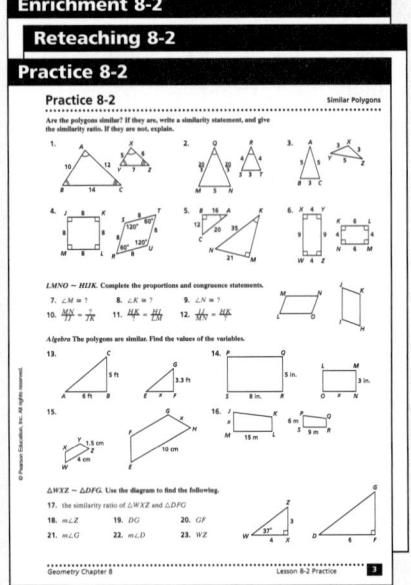

Are the polygons similar? If they are, write a similarity statement and give the similarity ratio. If they are not, explain.

9.
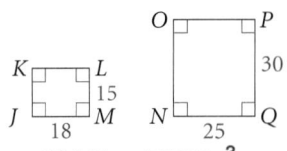
yes; _KLMJ_ ~ _PQNO_; $\frac{3}{5}$

10. **yes; _ABCD_ ~ _FGHE_; $\frac{4}{5}$**
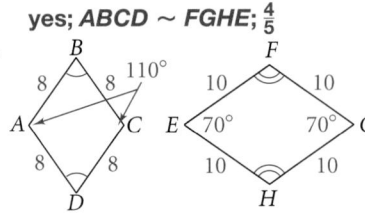

11.
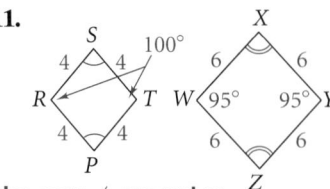
No; corr. ∡ are not ≅.

12.
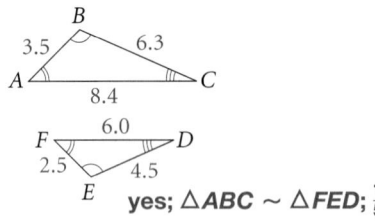
yes; △_ABC_ ~ △_FED_; $\frac{7}{5}$

Example 3 (page 424) x^2 **Algebra** The polygons are similar. Find the value of each variable.

13. **_x_ = 4; _y_ = 3**
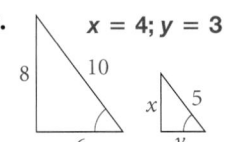

14. **_x_ = 20; _y_ = 17.5; _z_ = 7.5**
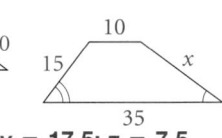

15.
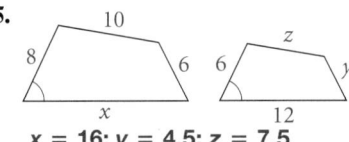
_x_ = 16; _y_ = 4.5; _z_ = 7.5

16.
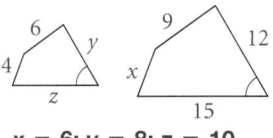
_x_ = 6; _y_ = 8; _z_ = 10

Example 4 (page 424)

17. **Drawing** You want to draw an enlargement of a design that is painted on a 3 in.-by-5 in. card. You plan to draw on an $8\frac{1}{2}$ in.-by-11 in. piece of paper. What are the dimensions of the largest complete enlargement you can draw? **6.6 in. by 11 in.**

18. A map has dimensions 9 in. by 15 in. You want to reduce the map so that it will fit on a 4 in.-by-6 in. index card. What are the dimensions of the largest possible complete map that you can fit on the index card? **3.6 in. by 6 in.**

Example 5 (page 425)

19. **Electrical Equipment** A switch plate for a standard wall switch has the shape of a golden rectangle. The longer side of the switch plate is about 114 mm. How long is the shorter side? Round your answer to the nearest millimeter. **70 mm**

20. **Design** You want the banner you are creating from one piece of cloth to be a golden rectangle. The cloth will be cut from a bolt that is 54 in. wide. What are the dimensions of the largest banner that you can make? **54 in. by 87.37 in.**

Ⓑ **Apply Your Skills**

△_DFG_ ~ △_HKM_. Use the diagram to find the following.

21. the similarity ratio of △_DFG_ to △_HKM_ **2:3**

22. the similarity ratio of △_HKM_ to △_DFG_ **3:2**

23. _m∠F_ **50**   24. _m∠K_ **50**   25. _m∠M_ **70**

26. $\frac{DF}{HK}$ **$\frac{2}{3}$**   27. _HM_ **7.5 m**   28. _GF_ **5.6 m**

 29. **Writing** Are two congruent figures similar? Explain.
Yes; corresponding ∡ and sides are ≅.

426   Chapter 8   Similarity

PEANUTS   By CHARLES SCHULZ

30a. equal sign, similarity
    symbol
  b. Answers may vary.
    Sample: ≅ figures
    are similar with =
    areas.

30. a. Reading Math What two symbols combine to form the congruence symbol?
  b. Explain why the congruence symbol makes sense.   **a-b. See left.**

31. Art An art class is painting a rectangular mural for a community festival. The students planned the mural with a diagram that is 80 in. long and 16 in. high. The mural is 4 ft high. Find its length.   **20 ft**

Real-World Connection

Murals provide a visual way to express feelings.

$\boxed{x^2}$ **Algebra** **Find the values of the variables.**

32. $x = 60, y = 25$

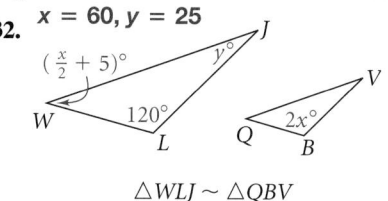

$\triangle WLJ \sim \triangle QBV$

33. 2.6 cm

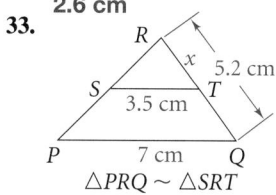

$\triangle PRQ \sim \triangle SRT$

The polygons in each exercise are similar. Find the similarity ratio of the first to the second.

34. 3:4

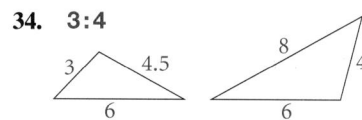

35. 3:1

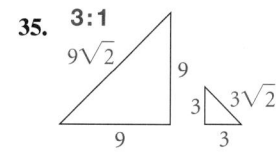

36. Exercise 13 **2:1**   **37.** Exercise 14 **1:2**   **38.** Exercise 15 **4:3**   **39.** Exercise 16 **2:3**

Reading Math

A value reduced *by n%* is reduced *to (100 − n)%*, and vice versa.

Logo Design A company logo is a rhombus with 4-cm sides and angles of 60° and 120°. Find the angle measures and side lengths if the logo is changed as follows.
40–45. See margin.
40. reduced by 50%   **41.** reduced to 50%   **42.** reduced by 20%

43. reduced to 20%   **44.** reduced by 75%   **45.** reduced to 75%

Find the other side length of the golden rectangle to the nearest tenth of an inch.

46. The shorter side is 10 in. **16.2 in.**   **47.** The longer side is 10 in. **6.2 in.**

48. No; corr. sides are
    not in proportion.

48. Money From 1861 to 1928, U. S. paper currency measured 7.42 in. by 3.13 in. The dimensions of a current bill are shown here. Are the old and new bills similar rectangles? Explain.

6.14 in.

Lesson 8-2 Similar Polygons **427**

English Learners

Exercise 20 Students may be unfamiliar with a *bolt* of fabric. Point out that some fabric is sold from large rolls that look like enormous rolls of paper towels. The width of the roll is fixed, for example, at 54 in. If a customer asks for 3 yd of fabric, the salesperson cuts a length of fabric 3 yd long and 54 in. wide.

Exercises 21, 22 Ask: *How are the two ratios related?* **They are reciprocals.**

Exercise 33 This exercise introduces similar overlapping triangles, helping prepare students for figures contained within larger similar figures in Lesson 8-5.

Exercise 35 Generalize from this exercise that all isosceles right triangles are similar. Challenge students to prove this as a theorem.

Error Prevention

Exercise 43 Check to be sure that students do not reduce the angle measures by 20%. Point out that the sum of the angle measures of the rhombus still must be 360.

Diversity

Exercise 48 Have students bring in currency from other countries to compare with U.S. currency.

Connection to Literature

Exercises 51, 52 *The Divine Proportion* by H. E. Huntley is a good resource for students who want to learn more about the golden ratio.

pages 425–429   **Exercises**

40. sides of 2 cm; ∠ of 60° and 120°

41. sides of 2 cm; ∠ of 60° and 120°

42. sides of 3.2 cm; ∠ of 60° and 120°

43. sides of 0.8 cm; ∠ of 60° and 120°

44. sides of 1 cm; ∠ of 60° and 120°

45. sides of 3 cm; ∠ of 60° and 120°

427

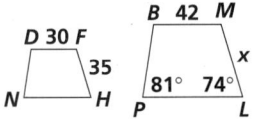

Alternative Assessment

Have students work in pairs to measure a room in your school. Then, have them plan and draw an accurate floor plan of the room. Finally, have them explain which concepts in this lesson they used.

Standardized Test Prep

Resources

For additional practice with a variety of test item formats:
• Standardized Test Prep, p. 465
• Test-Taking Strategies, p. 460
• Test-Taking Strategies with Transparencies

428

---

49. **Critical Thinking** Are all circles similar? Explain.   **See margin.**

50. **Open-Ended** Draw two polygons with sides in the ratio 2 : 1 that are not similar. **See margin.**

 **Challenge** x^2

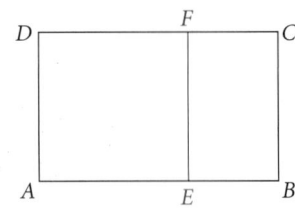

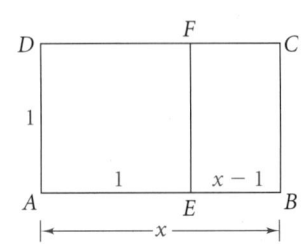

52a. 21, 34, 55, 89, 144, 233, 377

b. 1.6; 1.625; 1.6154; 1.6190; 1.6176; 1.6182; 1.6180; 1.6181; 1.6180

51. **a.** **Algebra** You know that the golden ratio is about 1.618 : 1. You can use the definition of a golden rectangle to derive this ratio. Let $ABCD$ at the left be a golden rectangle with width 1. By the definition of golden rectangle, $ABCD \sim BCFE$. Fill in the reasons in the following argument.

1. $\dfrac{AB}{BC} = \dfrac{BC}{CF}$ 1. $\underline{\ ?\ }$ **Corr. sides of ~ polygons are prop.**
2. $\dfrac{x}{1} = \dfrac{1}{x-1}$ 2. $\underline{\ ?\ }$ **Subst.**
3. $x^2 - x = 1$ 3. $\underline{\ ?\ }$ **Cross-Product Prop.**
4. $x^2 - x - 1 = 0$ 4. $\underline{\ ?\ }$ **Subtr. Prop.**   **b. The value of a length cannot be negative.**

b. Using the quadratic formula to solve the equation in part (a), you get $x = \dfrac{1 \pm \sqrt{5}}{2}$. Explain why $x = \dfrac{1 - \sqrt{5}}{2}$ does not make sense in this situation.

c. The golden ratio is the ratio $x : 1$, or $\dfrac{1 + \sqrt{5}}{2} : 1$. Use a calculator to find the value of $x = \dfrac{1 + \sqrt{5}}{2}$ to the nearest ten thousandth. **1.6180**

52. **a.** In the Fibonacci Sequence (see Lesson 1-1), each term after the first two is the sum of the two preceding terms. The first seven terms of the Fibonacci Sequence are 1, 1, 2, 3, 5, 8, and 13. Find the next seven terms.

b. Start with the second term. Here is the ratio of each term to the prior term.
$\dfrac{1}{1} = 1 \qquad \dfrac{2}{1} = 2 \qquad \dfrac{3}{2} = 1.5 \qquad \dfrac{5}{3} = 1.6667$
Find the next nine ratios. Round to the nearest ten thousandth.

c. Compare the ratios that you found in part (b) to the golden ratio. **The ratios get closer to the golden ratio.**

Standardized Test Prep

Quantitative Comparison

Compare the boxed quantity in Column A with the boxed quantity in Column B. Choose the best answer.
  A. The quantity in Column A is greater.
  B. The quantity in Column B is greater.
  C. The two quantities are equal.
  D. The relationship cannot be determined from the information given.

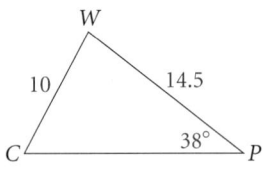 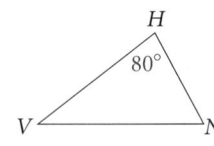

$\triangle WCP \sim \triangle HNV$

Column A	Column B
D 53. VH	WC
C 54. $m\angle N$	$m\angle C$
A 55. $m\angle N$	$m\angle P$

Take It to the NET
Online lesson quiz at
www.PHSchool.com
Web Code: afa-0802

---

pages 425–429 Exercises

49. Yes; explanations may vary. Sample: The ratios of radii, diameters, and circumferences of 2 circles are =.

50. Answers may vary. Sample:

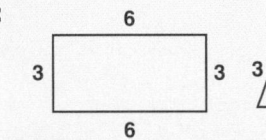

56. Quadrilateral *ABCD* ~ quadrilateral *JKLM* with a similarity ratio of 2 : 3.
   a. If *BC* = 8 cm, find *KL*.   **a-b. See margin.**
   b. If $m\angle BCD$ = 38, find $m\angle KLM$.

Exercises 53–55 Whenever similar figures are given, students should check the corresponding vertices as a first step. Because these similar triangles have different orientations, students will find it helpful to draw the figures in the same orientation and mark the congruent angles.

Mixed Review

Lesson 8-1

If $\frac{x}{7} = \frac{y}{9}$, complete each of the following using properties of proportions.

57. $9x = \blacksquare$ **7y**

58. $\frac{x}{y} = \frac{\blacksquare}{\blacksquare}$ $\frac{7}{9}$

59. $\frac{x + 7}{7} = \frac{\blacksquare}{\blacksquare}$ $\frac{y + 9}{9}$

Lesson 6-3

Can you conclude that the quadrilateral is a parallelogram? Explain.   **60–62. See margin.**

60.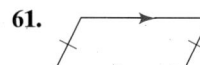

61.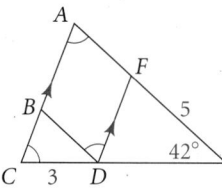

62.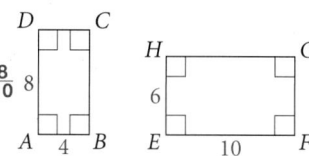

Lesson 4-5

63. △*CEA*, △*FED*, △*BCD*

Use the marked △*CEA* for Exercises 63–66.

63. Name the isosceles triangles in the figure.

64. $\overline{CD} \cong \underline{\ ?\ } \cong \underline{\ ?\ }$ **BD, FA**

Find the value of each of the following.

65. *AE*   **8**

66. $m\angle A$ **69**

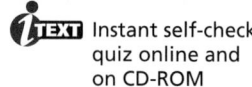

✓ Checkpoint Quiz 1   Lessons 8-1 through 8-2

TEXT Instant self-check quiz online and on CD-ROM

1. Models A table is 4 ft high. A small model of the table is 6 in. high. What is the ratio of the height of the model table to the height of the real table?   **1:8**

2. If $\frac{a}{b} = \frac{9}{10}$, complete this statement: $\frac{a}{9} = \frac{\blacksquare}{\blacksquare}$ $\frac{b}{10}$

3. Are the polygons at the right similar? If so, give the similarity ratio of the first polygon to the second. If not, explain. **no; $\frac{4}{6} \ne \frac{8}{10}$**

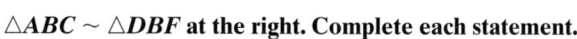

Solve each proportion.

4. $\frac{y}{6} = \frac{18}{54}$ **2**

5. $\frac{5}{7} = \frac{x - 2}{4}$ $\frac{34}{7}$

6. The scale of a scale drawing is 2 in. = 5 ft. A room is 5 in. long on the scale drawing. Find the actual length of the room.   **12.5 ft**

△*ABC* ~ △*DBF* at the right. Complete each statement.

7. $m\angle A = m\angle \underline{\ ?\ }$ **∠BDF**

8. $\frac{AB}{DB} = \frac{BC}{\blacksquare}$ **BF**

9. A postcard is 6 in. by 4 in. A printing shop will enlarge it so that the longer side is any length up to 3 ft. Find the dimensions of the biggest enlargement.   **3 ft by 2 ft**

$\boxed{x^2}$ **10. Algebra** The polygons at the right are similar. Find the value of *x*. $3\frac{1}{3}$

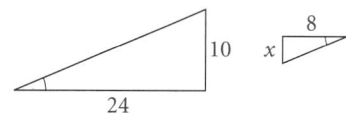

56. **[2] a. 12 cm**
     b. $m\angle KLM = 38$
   [1] incorrect length OR incorrect angle measure

60. **Yes; the diagonals bisect each other.**

61. **no; only one pair of ∥ sides**

62. **Yes; both pairs of sides are ∥.**

✓ **Chapter Checkpoint 1**

To check understanding of Lessons 8-1 to 8-2:

Checkpoint Quiz 1 (p. 429)

📁 **Teaching Resources**
Checkpoint Quiz 1 (also in Prentice Hall Assessment System)

👥 **Reaching All Students**
Reading and Math Literacy 8B

Spanish versions available

Fractals

Over the past 20 years, fractal geometry has increased in importance as a way to describe real-world phenomena. In this extension, students are not asked to find the iterations used to form fractals, but they can see how extraordinarily complex shapes can be generated from a simple set of rules and can use iterations to form new stages of fractals.

Resources

Technology

Computer Test Generator CD-ROM, Chapter 0, Extension Topics

Teaching Notes

Fractals may involve complicated geometric ideas, but they are built in stages, starting with basic geometric figures like segments and polygons. Here, students explore how concepts encountered in geometry class can lead to remarkable figures and conclusions when iteration is carried beyond a finite limit.

1 EXAMPLE

Ask: *What rule describes how the new branches are drawn at each step?* **Each new branch forms a 45° angle with the top third of the segment.**

2 EXAMPLE **Math Tip**

Point out how the Koch curve displays self-similarity. For example, discuss how Stage 2 contains four sections, all of which are similar to Stage 1. Have students find more examples of self-similarity.

Extension **Fractals**

FOR USE WITH LESSON 8-2

Fractals are objects that have three important properties:

- You can form them by repeating steps—a process called *iteration*.

- They require infinitely many iterations. In practice, you can continue until the objects become too small to draw. Even then the steps could continue in your mind.

- At each stage, a portion of the object is a reduced copy of the entire object at the previous stage. This property is called *self-similarity*.

1 EXAMPLE

The segment below of length 1 unit is Stage 0 of a fractal tree. Draw Stage 1 and Stage 2 of the tree. For each stage, draw two branches from the top third of each segment.

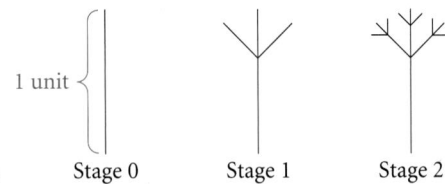

Stage 0   Stage 1   Stage 2

Amazingly, some fractals are used to describe natural formations such as mountain ranges and clouds. In 1904, Swedish mathematician Helge von Koch created the Koch Curve, a fractal that is used to model coastlines.

2 EXAMPLE

The segment at the right of length 1 unit is Stage 0 of a Koch Curve. Draw Stages 1–4 of the curve. For each stage, replace the middle third of each segment with two segments, both equal in length to the middle third.

- For Stage 1, replace the middle third with two segments, both $\frac{1}{3}$ unit long.

- For Stage 2, replace the middle third of each segment with two segments, both $\frac{1}{9}$ unit long.

- Continue with a third and fourth iteration.

Stages 0–4 are shown at the right.

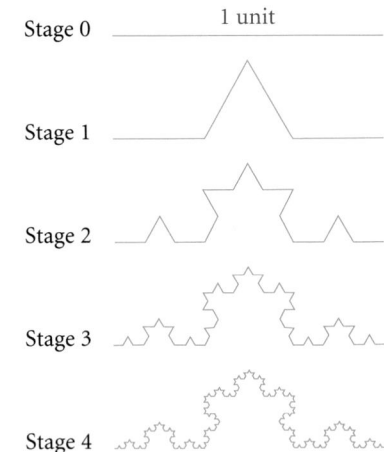

Stage 0 ——— 1 unit

Stage 1

Stage 2

Stage 3

Stage 4

You can construct a Koch Curve on each side of an equilateral triangle and get a Koch Snowflake.

3 EXAMPLE

The equilateral triangle at the right is Stage 0 of a Koch Snowflake. Draw Stage 1.

- Draw an equilateral triangle on the middle third of each side.

- Erase the middle third of each side to get Stage 1 of the snowflake. (Continued in Exercises 5–9.)

1 unit

Stage 0   Stage 1

EXERCISES

1. Draw Stage 3 of the fractal tree in Example 1.

Use the Koch Curve in Example 2 for Exercises 2–4.

2. Complete the table to find the length of the Koch Curve at each stage.

3. Examine the results of Exercise 2 and look for a pattern. Use this pattern to predict the length of the Koch Curve at Stage 3; at Stage 4. $\frac{64}{27}$; $\frac{256}{81}$

Stage	0	1	2
Length	1	■ $\frac{4}{3}$	■ $\frac{16}{9}$

4. Suppose you are able to complete a Koch Curve to Stage n.
   a. Write an expression for the length of the curve. $\frac{4^n}{3^n}$
   b. What happens to the length of the curve as n gets large?
      It increases without bound.

5. Draw Stage 2 of the Koch Snowflake in Example 3. **See margin.**

Stage 3 of the Koch Snowflake is shown at the right. Use it and the earlier stages to answer Exercises 6–8.

6. At each stage, is the snowflake equilateral? **yes**

7. a. Complete the table to find the perimeter at each stage.

Stage	Number of Sides	Length of a Side	Perimeter
0	3	1	3
1	■ 12	$\frac{1}{3}$	■ 4
2	48	■ $\frac{1}{9}$	■ $\frac{16}{3}$
3	■ 192	■ $\frac{1}{27}$	■ $\frac{64}{9}$

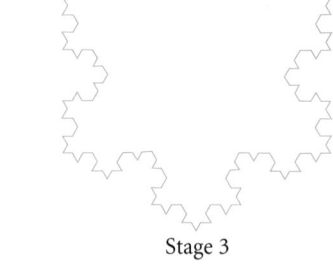

Stage 3

   b. Predict the perimeter at Stage 4. $\frac{256}{27}$
   c. Will there be a stage at which the perimeter is greater then 100 units? Explain.
      Yes; the perimeter is increasing by a factor of $\frac{4}{3}$ at each stage.

8. What can you conclude about the area of this Koch Snowflake?
   See margin.

9. To draw the Sierpinski Triangle fractal, start with an equilateral triangle. For each stage, connect the midpoints of all of the triangles "pointed upwards." Stages 0–2 are shown at the right. Draw Stage 3.
   See margin.

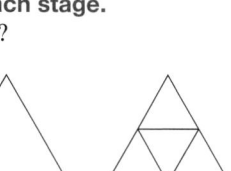 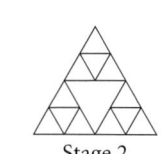

Stage 0   Stage 1   Stage 2

---

page 431 Extension

5.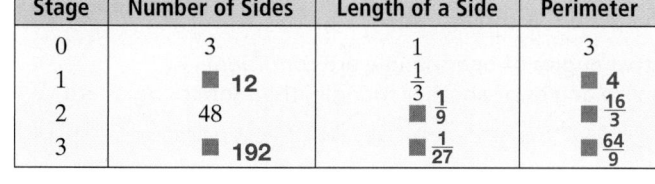

8. **Answers may vary. Sample:
   Its area is some number
   close to**

$$\frac{\sqrt{3}}{4}\left[1 + \frac{1}{3} + \frac{1}{3}\left(\frac{4}{9}\right) + \left(\frac{4}{9}\right)^2 + \dots\right]$$

$$= \frac{2\sqrt{3}}{5} \approx 0.693.$$

9.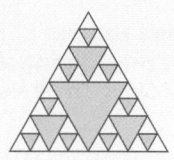

Tactile Learners

To help reinforce the iterative process, have students construct a Koch curve or a Koch snowflake through Stage 3 or Stage 4 without looking at the illustrations.

3 EXAMPLE Teaching Tip

Discuss as a class how to continue the creation of the Koch snowflake beyond Stage 1. Refer students to Example 2. **Ask:** *How is the Koch snowflake related to the Koch curve?* It is composed of three copies of the Koch curve.

Exercise 7 Discuss as a class that there is no limit to the perimeter of the Koch snowflake. Then help students see that its area, on the other hand, is finite. Students can see this by imagining a circle that bounds the Koch snowflake. In fact, an infinite series can be evaluated to show that the limit of the area of a Koch snowflake is exactly 1.6 times the area of the original triangle.

Connection to Poetry

Jonathan Swift wrote this verse of *On Poetry, A Rhapsody* in 1733 before fractals were discovered:
   So, naturalists observe, a flea
   Hath smaller fleas that on him prey;
   And these have smaller still to bite 'em,
   And so proceed ad infinitum.
   Thus every poet, in his kind,
   Is bit by him that comes behind.

✓ Check Skills You'll Need

Using SSS and SAS Postulates
Lesson 4-2: Example 1
Exercises 1–4
Extra Practice, p. 693

Using ASA Postulate
Lesson 4-3: Example 1
Exercises 1–4
Extra Practice, p. 693

Lesson Resources

📁 **Teaching Resources**
Practice, Reteaching, Enrichment

👥 **Reaching All Students**
Practice Workbook 8-3
Spanish Practice Workbook 8-3
Informal Geometry Planning
  Guide 8-3

🕐 **Presentation Assistant Plus!**
Transparencies
• Check Skills You'll Need 8-3
• Additional Examples 8-3
• Student Edition Answers 8-3
• Lesson Quiz 8-3
PH Presentation Pro CD 8-3

PRENTICE HALL ASSESSMENT SYSTEM

Computer Test Generator CD

💾 **Technology**
Resource Pro® CD-ROM
Computer Test Generator CD
Prentice Hall Presentation Pro CD

💻 **www.PHSchool.com**
Student Site
• Teacher Web Code: afk-5500
• Self-grading Lesson Quiz
Teacher Center
• Lesson Planner
• Resources

Plus **iTEXT**

8-3

Proving Triangles Similar

North Carolina Objectives → **2.03** Apply properties, definitions, and theorems of two-dimensional figures to solve problems and write proofs: a) Triangles.

Lesson Preview

What You'll Learn

OBJECTIVE 1 To use AA, SAS, and SSS similarity statements

OBJECTIVE 2 To apply AA, SAS, and SSS similarity statements

. . . And Why

To measure height indirectly, as in Example 4

✓ Check Skills You'll Need

(For help, go to Lessons 4-2 and 4-3.)

Name the postulate or theorem you can use to prove the triangles congruent.

1. SSS   **2.** SAS   **3.** ASA

New Vocabulary • indirect measurement

---

iTEXT Interactive lesson includes instant self-check, tutorials, and activities.

OBJECTIVE 1

The AA Postulate and the SAS and SSS Theorems

Real-World 🌐 **Connection**

The gables on the historic House of the Seven Gables in Salem, Massachusetts, suggest similar triangles.

Investigation: Triangles with Two Pairs of Congruent Angles

• Draw two triangles of different sizes, each with a 50° angle and a 60° angle.

• Measure the sides of each triangle to the nearest millimeter.

• Find the ratio of the lengths of each pair of corresponding sides.

1. What conclusion can you make about the two triangles? **They are similar.**

2. Complete this conjecture:

If two angles of one triangle are congruent to two angles of another triangle, then the triangles are __?__. **similar**

In this lesson, you will show triangles are similar without using the definition of similar triangles. The two triangles shown above suggest the following postulate.

🔑 **Key Concepts**

Postulate 8-1 **Angle-Angle Similarity (AA ~) Postulate**

If two angles of one triangle are congruent to two angles of another triangle, then the triangles are similar.

$\triangle TRS \sim \triangle PLM$

432 Chapter 8 Similarity

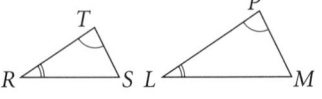

Ongoing Assessment and Intervention

Before the Lesson
Diagnose prerequisite skills using:
• Check Skills You'll Need

During the Lesson
Monitor progress using:
• Check Understanding
• Additional Examples
• Standardized Test Prep

After the Lesson
Assess knowledge using:
• Lesson Quiz
• Computer Test Generator CD

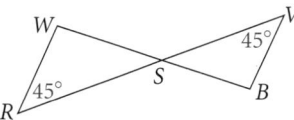

1 EXAMPLE   Using the AA ~ Postulate

Explain why the triangles are similar.
Write a similarity statement.

$\angle RSW \cong \angle VSB$ because vertical angles are
congruent. $\angle R \cong \angle V$ because their measures
are equal. $\triangle RSW \sim \triangle VSB$ by the Angle-Angle
Similarity Postulate.

 Check Understanding ① **Critical Thinking** In Example 1, you have enough information to write a similarity statement. Do you have enough information to find the similarity ratio? Explain.
No; we don't know any of the side lengths.

The next two theorems follow from the AA Similarity Postulate.

Key Concepts

Theorem 8-1	Side-Angle-Side Similarity (SAS ~) Theorem

If an angle of one triangle is congruent to an angle of a second triangle, and the sides including the two angles are proportional, then the triangles are similar.

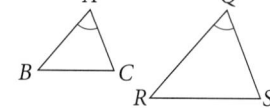

Proof **Proof of Theorem 8-1**

Given: $\angle A \cong \angle Q$, $\frac{AB}{QR} = \frac{AC}{QS}$

Prove: $\triangle ABC \sim \triangle QRS$

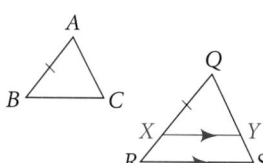

Choose X on $\overline{QR}$ so that $QX = AB$. (See figures at left.) Draw $\overline{XY} \parallel \overline{RS}$.
Then $\angle QXY \cong \angle R$. By the AA ~ Postulate, $\triangle QXY \sim \triangle QRS$. Thus $\frac{QX}{QR} = \frac{QY}{QS}$.
Combining this proportion, the given proportion, and the fact that $AB = QX$
shows that $\frac{AC}{QS} = \frac{QY}{QS}$. Hence, $AC = QY$.

Then $\triangle ABC \cong \triangle QXY$ by the SAS Congruence Postulate. $\angle B \cong \angle QXY$ by
CPCTC, and $\angle B \cong \angle R$ by the Transitive Property. Thus, $\triangle ABC \sim \triangle QRS$ by the
AA ~ Postulate.

 Key Concepts

Theorem 8-2	Side-Side-Side Similarity (SSS ~) Theorem

If the corresponding sides of two triangles are proportional, then the triangles are similar.

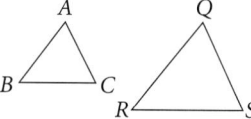

Proof **Proof of Theorem 8-2**

Given: $\frac{AB}{QR} = \frac{BC}{RS} = \frac{AC}{QS}$

Prove: $\triangle ABC \sim \triangle QRS$

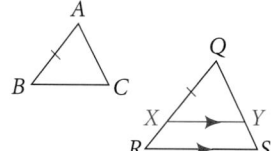

Draw $\overline{XY}$ as in the proof of Theorem 8-1. By the AA ~ Postulate,
$\triangle QXY \sim \triangle QRS$. Thus $\frac{QX}{QR} = \frac{XY}{RS} = \frac{QY}{QS}$. Combining this proportion, the given
proportion, and the fact that $AB = QX$ shows that $BC = XY$ and $AC = QY$.

Then $\triangle ABC \cong \triangle QXY$ by the SSS Congruence Postulate and, as in the proof
above, $\triangle ABC \sim \triangle QRS$ by the AA ~ Postulate.

Lesson 8-3 Proving Triangles Similar   **433**

🤝 Reaching All Students

Below Level Have students connect the midpoints of two sides of a large triangle, measure all angles and sides, and then use AA, SAS, and SSS Similarity to explain why the triangles are similar.	**Advanced Learners** Have students explain how $\triangle ABC$ and $\triangle XYZ$ can have five congruent pairs of angles and sides and not be congruent.	**Auditory Learners** See note on page 433. **Tactile Learners** See note on page 434.

Math Background

Pedagogical considerations dictate introducing the Angle-Angle Similarity in this lesson as a postulate. An alternate approach might reorder the topics by proving the Side-Splitter Theorem from Lesson 8-5 now, and then proving Angle-Angle Similarity as a theorem.

OBJECTIVE
▼1 Teaching Notes

Investigation (Optional)
Students can use measurement tools in geometry software to calculate ratios on the computer screen.

1 EXAMPLE Auditory Learners

Have students work in pairs to practice naming the corresponding parts.

Teaching Tip
In the proof of the SAS ~ Theorem, discuss why $AC = QY$. Substitute QX for AB in the given proportion so $\frac{AC}{QS} = \frac{QY}{QS}$ and then $AC = QY$. Similar reasoning is used to prove Theorem 8-2.

2 EXAMPLE

Encourage students to copy and label $\triangle QRP$ and $\triangle XYZ$ so that they do not overlap. This will make it easier for them to see the proportional relationship.

📐 Additional Examples

① $\overline{MX} \perp \overline{AB}$. Explain why the triangles are similar. Write a similarity statement.

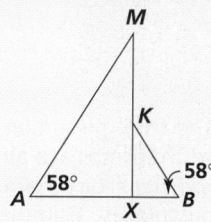

$\triangle AMX \sim \triangle BKX$ by
AA ~ Postulate

433

2 Explain why the triangles must be similar. Write a similarity statement.

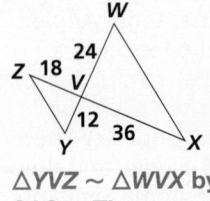

$\triangle YVZ \sim \triangle WVX$ by SAS $\sim$ Theorem

OBJECTIVE
2 **Teaching Notes**

3 EXAMPLE **Error Prevention**

If students have trouble identifying corresponding parts, have them compare the lengths of the sides: Because $12 < 16$ and $18 < 24$, $\overline{AB}$ corresponds to $\overline{EB}$.

4 EXAMPLE **Tactile Learners**

If time permits, have students use mirrors and tape measures to measure indirectly the height of the school building.

Additional Examples

3 $ABCD$ is a parallelogram. Find WY.

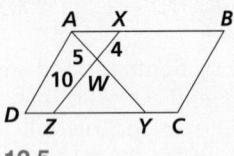

12.5

4 Joan places a mirror 24 ft from the base of a tree. When she stands 3 ft from the mirror, she can see the top of the tree reflected in it. If her eyes are 5 ft above the ground, how tall is the tree? 40 ft

Closure

Explain how the triangle similarity postulates and theorems are alike and how they differ from triangle congruence postulates. **Sample: In both cases, there are SAS and SSS theorems or postulates. For similarity, sides are proportional**

434

---

2 EXAMPLE **Using Similarity Theorems**

Explain why the triangles must be similar. Write a similarity statement.

$\angle QRP \cong \angle XYZ$ because they are right angles.

$\frac{QR}{XY} = \frac{3}{4}$ and $\frac{PR}{ZY} = \frac{6}{8} = \frac{3}{4}$.

Therefore, $\triangle QRP \sim \triangle XYZ$ by the SAS $\sim$ Theorem.

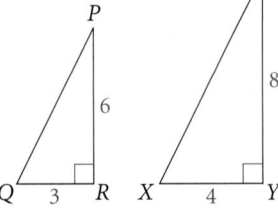

✔ Check Understanding **2** Explain why the triangles must be similar. Write a similarity statement.
$\frac{AC}{EG} = \frac{CB}{GF} = \frac{AB}{EF} = \frac{3}{4}$,
so the $\triangle$ are $\sim$ by SSS $\sim$ Thm.;
$\triangle ABC \sim \triangle EFG$

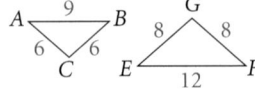

OBJECTIVE
2 **Applying AA, SAS, and SSS Similarity**

You can apply the AA Similarity Postulate and the SAS and SSS Similarity Theorems to find the lengths of sides in similar triangles.

3 EXAMPLE **Finding Lengths in Similar Triangles**

Explain why the triangles are similar. Write a similarity statement. Then find DE.

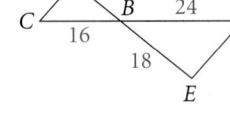

$\angle ABC \cong \angle EBD$ because vertical angles are congruent.

$\frac{AB}{EB} = \frac{12}{18} = \frac{2}{3}$ and $\frac{CB}{DB} = \frac{16}{24} = \frac{2}{3}$

Therefore, $\triangle ABC \sim \triangle EBD$ by the SAS $\sim$ Theorem.

$\frac{CA}{DE} = \frac{2}{3}$	**Corresponding sides of $\sim$ triangles are proportional.**
$\frac{10}{DE} = \frac{2}{3}$	**Substitute.**
$2DE = 30$	**Cross-Product Property**
$DE = 15$	**Solve for DE.**

✔ Check Understanding **3** Find the value of x in the figure at the right.
9

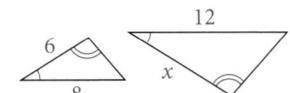

You can use similar triangles and measurements to find distances that are difficult to measure directly. This is called **indirect measurement.**

One method of indirect measurement uses the fact that light reflects off a mirror at the same angle at which it hits the mirror. A second method uses the similar triangles that are formed by certain figures and their shadows.

Both methods are illustrated in Example 4.

434 Chapter 8 Similarity

instead of congruent. Also, similarity has an AA Postulate that has no counterpart for congruence.

4 EXAMPLE Real-World ⊕ Connection

Geology Ramon places a mirror on the ground 40.5 ft from the base of a geyser. He walks backwards until he can see the top of the geyser in the middle of the mirror. At that point, Ramon's eyes are 6 ft above the ground and he is 7 ft from the image in the mirror. Use similar triangles to find the height of the geyser.

? Need Help?

$\angle HVT \cong \angle JVS$ follows from the fact that the angle of incidence equals the angle of reflection. See p. 38, Exercise 18.

$\triangle HTV \sim \triangle JSV$ **AA ~ Postulate**

$\dfrac{HT}{JS} = \dfrac{TV}{SV}$ **Corresponding sides of ~ triangles are proportional.**

$\dfrac{6}{x} = \dfrac{7}{40.5}$ **Substitute.**

$243 = 7x$ **Cross-Product Property**

$34.7 \approx x$ **Solve for x.**

● The geyser is about 35 ft high.

✓ Check Understanding

4 In sunlight, a cactus casts a 9-ft shadow. At the same time a person 6 ft tall casts a 4-ft shadow. Use similar triangles to find the height of the cactus. **13.5 ft**

EXERCISES

For more practice, see *Extra Practice*.

Practice and Problem Solving

Ⓐ Practice by Example

Examples 1 and 2
(pages 433 and 434)

Can you conclude the triangles are similar? If so, write a similarity statement and name the postulate or theorem you used. If not, explain.

1.

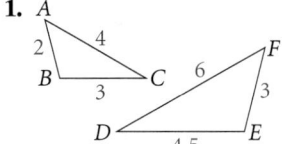

Yes; $\triangle ABC \sim \triangle FED$; SSS ~ Thm.

2. No; not enough information is given.

R
8, 10, S, T
Z, 20, X, 15, Y

3. If possible, find the similarity ratio for each pair of similar triangles in Exercises 1 and 2. If not possible, explain.   Ex. 1: $\frac{2}{3}$ (for $\triangle ABC$ to $\triangle FED$);
    Ex. 2: Not possible; the △ aren't necessarily similar.

3. Practice

Assignment Guide

1 Objective
Ⓐ Ⓑ Core   1–9, 22, 24–27, 40
Ⓒ Extension   44

2 Objective
Ⓐ Ⓑ Core   10–21, 23, 28–39, 41
Ⓒ Extension   42, 43

Standardized Test Prep   45–48

Mixed Review   49–57

Exercises 10–15 For each exercise, have students explain how they know the triangles are similar.

Exercise 18 Ask: *What must you assume about the boy and the giraffe if the triangles are similar? They are perpendicular to the ground.*

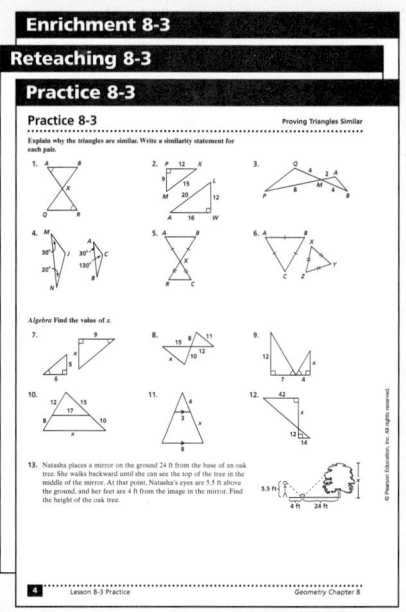

Lesson 8-3   Proving Triangles Similar   **435**

435

4. yes; △FHG ~ △KHJ; AA ~ Post.

5. No; $\frac{6}{3} \neq \frac{10}{4}$.

6. No; $\frac{20}{45} \neq \frac{25}{55}$.

7. Yes; △APJ ~ △ABC; SSS ~ Thm. or SAS ~ Thm.

8. Yes; △NMP ~ △NQR; SAS ~ Thm.

9. No; $\frac{32}{22} \neq \frac{45}{30}$.

Are the triangles similar? If so, write a similarity statement and name the postulate or theorem you used. If not, explain. 4-9. See left.

4.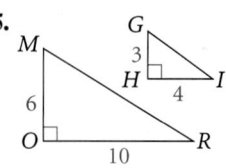
5.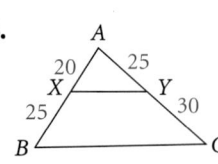
6.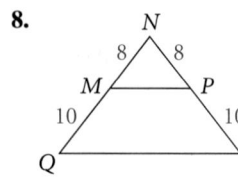

7.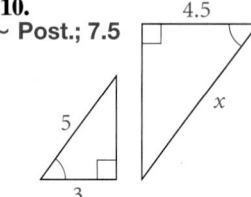
8.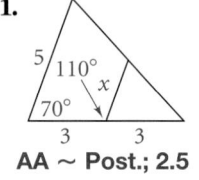
9.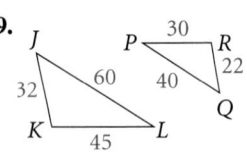

Example 3 x^2 **Algebra Explain why the triangles are similar. Then find the value of x.**
(page 434)

10.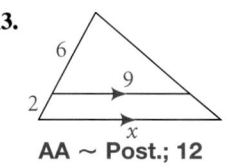
AA ~ Post.; 7.5

11.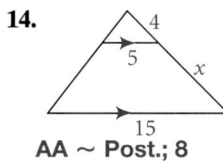
AA ~ Post.; 2.5

12.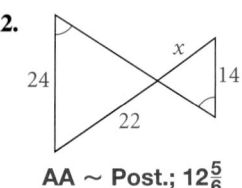
AA ~ Post.; $12\frac{5}{6}$

13.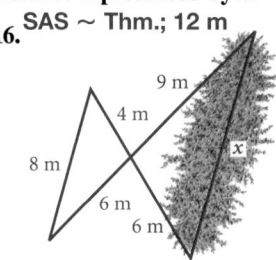
AA ~ Post.; 12

14.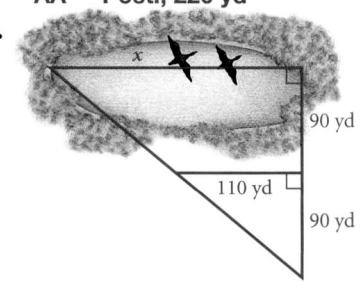
AA ~ Post.; 8

15.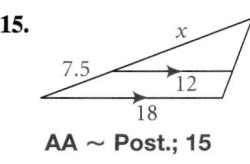
AA ~ Post.; 15

Example 4 **Indirect Measurement Explain why the triangles are similar. Then find the distance represented by x.**
(page 435)

16. SAS ~ Thm.; 12 m
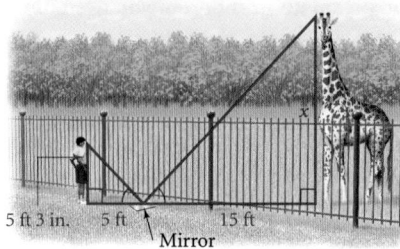

17. AA ~ Post.; 220 yd
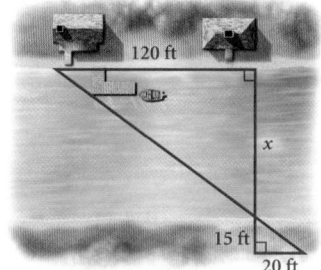

18.
AA ~ Post.; 15 ft 9 in.

19.
AA ~ Post.; 90 ft

b. Yes; every isosc. rt. △ is a 45°-45°-90° △. Therefore, by AA ~ Thm. they are all ~.

24. Yes; △GMK ~ △SMP; SAS ~ Thm.

25. Yes; △AWV ~ △AST; SAS ~ Thm.

26. Yes; △XYZ ~ △MNK; SSS ~ Thm.

27. No; there is only one ∠ of each △ ≅.

40. Check students' work. Draw △ABC. Construct ∠A ≅ ∠R. Construct $\overline{RS}$ such that RS = 3AB, and $\overline{RT}$ such that RT = 3AC. Connect points S and T.

B Apply Your Skills

Skyscraper? Nein!

Hannelore Kraus of Frankfurt, Germany, stopped the development of a skyscraper because she wanted her apartment to get its fair amount of sunlight. To halt the construction she used a German law that specifies that every homeowner is entitled to sunlight.

Kraus was offered 1.6 million dollars to drop her lawsuit, but she refused. The skyscraper was scheduled to be 265 m tall and was to be built only 60 m from Kraus's apartment.

Tall Buildings Use the news article for Exercises 20 and 21.

 20. **Writing** Explain how Hannelore Kraus could use indirect measurement to estimate the length of the shadow of the building at a particular time of day. **See margin p. 436.**

21. **Indirect Measurement** Suppose Ms. Kraus is 1.75 m tall. When her shadow is 1 m long, about how long would the shadow of the proposed building be? **151 m**

22. **a.** Classify *RSTW*. **trapezoid**
b. Must any of the triangles shown be similar? Explain.
△*RSZ* ~ △*TWZ*; **AA ~ Post.**

23. **a.** Critical Thinking Are two isosceles triangles always similar? Explain.
b. Are two isosceles right triangles always similar? Explain.
a–b. See margin p. 436.

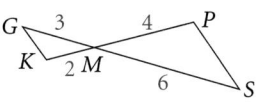

Can you conclude that the triangles are similar? If so, write a similarity statement and name the postulate or theorem you used. If not, explain. 24–27. See margin. p. 436.

24.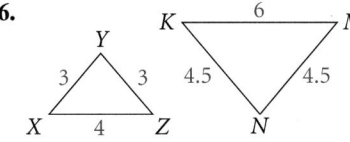

25.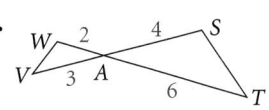

26.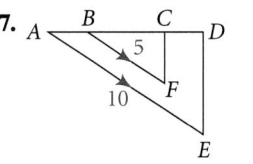

27.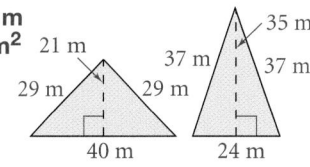

28. **Indirect Measurement** In sunlight, a vertical yardstick casts a 1-ft shadow at the same time that a nearby tree casts a 15-ft shadow. How tall is the tree? **45 ft**

29. **Open-Ended** Name something with a height that would be difficult to measure directly. Describe how you could measure it indirectly. **Check students' work.**

Find the similarity ratio of the larger to the smaller triangle in each exercise.

30. Ex. 10 **3:2** 31. Ex. 11 **2:1** 32. Ex. 12 **12:7** 33. Ex. 13 **4:3** 34. Ex. 14 **3:1**

35. Ex. 15 **3:2** 36. Ex. 16 **3:2** 37. Ex. 17 **2:1** 38. Ex. 18 **3:1** 39. Ex.19 **6:1**

40. **Constructions** Draw any △*ABC*. Use a straightedge and a compass to construct △*RST* so that △*ABC* ~ △*RST* with similarity ratio 1 : 3. **See margin p. 436.**

41c. No; the △ given are a counterexample to this conjecture, since the sides are not in proportion.

41. For each triangle at the right, find: **a. 98 m; 98 m**
a. the perimeter   **b.** the area **420 m²; 420 m²**
c. Critical Thinking Can you conclude that any two triangles with equal perimeters and equal areas are similar? Explain.

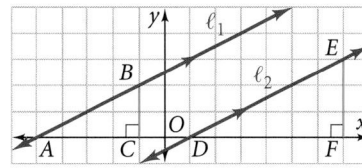

C Challenge *Proof* 42. Write a proof of the following:
Any two nonvertical parallel lines have equal slopes. **See margin.**

Given: nonvertical lines ℓ_1 and ℓ_2,
$\ell_1 \parallel \ell_2, \overline{EF}$ and $\overline{BC} \perp$ to the *x*-axis

Prove: $\frac{BC}{AC} = \frac{EF}{DF}$

Hint: Use the *x*-axis as a transversal to show that $\angle BAC \cong \angle EDF$.

Lesson 8-3 Proving Triangles Similar   **437**

42. 1. $\ell_1 \parallel \ell_2, \overline{EF} \perp \overline{AF}, \overline{BC} \perp \overline{AF}$ **(Given)**

2. $\angle EFD$ and $\angle BCA$ are right △. **(Def. of ⊥)**

3. $\angle EFD \cong \angle BCA$ **(All rt. △ are ≅.)**

4. $\angle BAC \cong \angle EDF$ **(If ∥ lines, then corr. △ are ≅.)**

5. △*ABC* ~ △*DEF* **(AA ~)**

6. $\frac{BC}{AC} = \frac{EF}{DF}$ **(Def. of similar)**

Are the triangles similar? If so, write a similarity statement and name the postulate or theorem you used. If not, explain.

1.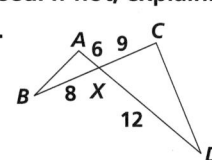

△*ABX* ~ △*CDX* by
SAS ~ Theorem

2.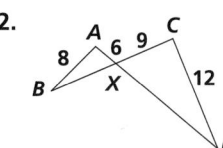

The congruent angle is not included between the proportional sides, so you cannot conclude that the triangles are similar.

3.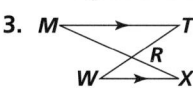

△*MRT* ~ △*XRW* by
AA ~ Postulate

4. Find the value of *x*.

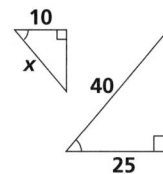

16

5. When a 6 ft tall man casts a shadow 18 ft long, a nearby tree casts a shadow 93 ft long. How tall is the tree?
31 ft

Alternative Assessment

Have students work in pairs to plan how to measure indirectly the height of your classroom. Each pair should prepare a written explanation or demonstrate their method.

437

Resources

For additional practice with a variety of test item formats:
• Standardized Test Prep, p. 465
• Test-Taking Strategies, p. 460
• Test-Taking Strategies with Transparencies

Exercise 45 It may help to redraw and label the overlapping triangles as separate triangles.

Exercises 47, 48 Drawing diagrams will not only help students relate the information given but also will help them figure out how to solve these exercises.

Proof **43.** Use the diagram in Exercise 42 on the preceding page.
Prove: Any two nonvertical lines with equal slopes are parallel. **See margin.**

Proof **44.** Write a proof of the following.

Given: $RT \cdot TQ = MT \cdot TS$

Prove: $\triangle RTM \sim \triangle STQ$
See margin.

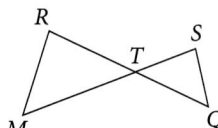

Standardized Test Prep

Multiple Choice

45. Complete the statement $\triangle ABC \sim \underline{\ ?\ }$, and identify the reason why the triangles are similar. **C**
  A. $\triangle AKN$; SSS $\sim$
  B. $\triangle AKN$; SAS $\sim$
  C. $\triangle ANK$; SAS $\sim$
  D. $\triangle ANK$; AA $\sim$

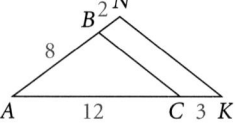

46. Complete the statement $\triangle ABC \sim \underline{\ ?\ }$, and identify the reason why the triangles are similar. **I**
  F. $\triangle LGC$; SSS $\sim$
  G. $\triangle GLC$; SSS $\sim$
  H. $\triangle LGC$; AA $\sim$
  I. $\triangle GLC$; AA $\sim$

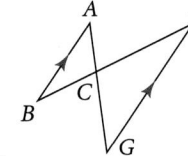

Short Response

47. Suppose $\triangle VLQ \sim \triangle PSX$. **a–b. See margin.**
  a. Explain how you would find $m\angle X$ if $m\angle V = 48$ and $m\angle L = 80$.
  b. Find $m\angle X$.

Extended Response

Take It to the NET
Online lesson quiz at
www.PHSchool.com
Web Code: afa-0803

48. Hank is 6 ft tall. Hank measured the shadow of a tree and found it to be 30 ft long. He then measured his own shadow. It was 10 ft long.
  a. Draw and label a diagram that you could use to find the height of the tree. Write a similarity statement and justify your answer.
  b. Write a proportion and solve it to find the height of the tree.
    a–b. See margin.

---

pages 437–438   **Exercises**

43. 1. $\frac{BC}{AC} = \frac{EF}{DF}$, $\overline{EF} \perp \overline{AF}$,
$\overline{BC} \perp \overline{AF}$ (Given)

2. $\angle ACB$ and $\angle DFE$ are rt. $\angle$s. (Def. of $\perp$)

3. $\angle ACB \cong \angle DFE$ (All rt. $\angle$s are $\cong$.)

4. $\triangle ABC \sim \triangle DEF$ (SAS $\sim$)

5. $\angle BAC \cong \angle EDF$ (Def. of similar)

6. $\ell_1 \parallel \ell_2$ (If corr. $\angle$s are $\cong$, then $\parallel$ lines.)

44. 1. $RT \cdot TQ = MT \cdot TS$ (Given)

2. $\frac{MT}{TQ} = \frac{RT}{TS}$ (Prop. of Proportions)

3. $\angle RTM \cong \angle STQ$ (Vert. $\angle$s are $\cong$.)

4. $\triangle RTM \sim \triangle STQ$ (SAS $\sim$ Thm.)

47. [2]a. All corr $\angle$s of similar $\angle$s are $\cong$. $\angle Q \cong \angle X$; subtract $m\angle V$ and $m\angle L$ from 180 to get $m\angle Q = m\angle X$.

b. 52

[1] incorrect explanation OR incorrect $\angle$ measure

Mixed Review

Lesson 8-2

$TRAP \sim EZYD$. **Complete each statement.**

49. $\angle T \cong \underline{\ ?\ } \angle E$
50. $\angle D \cong \underline{\ ?\ } \angle P$
51. $\angle A \cong \underline{\ ?\ } \angle Y$

52. $\frac{AP}{YD} = \frac{RA}{\blacksquare} ZY$
53. $\frac{TR}{RA} = \frac{\blacksquare}{ZY} EZ$
54. $\frac{DE}{PT} = \frac{\blacksquare}{AR} YZ$

Lesson 6-6

Give possible coordinates of points W and Z without using any new variables.
55–56. x-values may vary. Samples are given.

55.

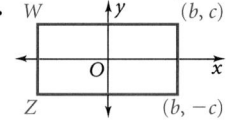

Rectangle
$W(-b, c)$; $Z(-b, -c)$

56.

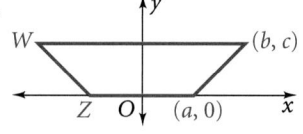

Isosceles trapezoid
$W(-b, c)$; $Z(-a, 0)$

Lesson 5-5

57. A triangle has sides with lengths 9 m and 15 m. Write an inequality that shows the range of possible lengths for the third side. $6 < x < 24$

48. [4] a.

$\triangle ABC \sim \triangle ADE$; AA $\sim$ Thm.

b. $\frac{6}{10} = \frac{h}{30}$
18 ft

[3] appropriate methods and appropriate

diagram but incorrect solution

[2] correct diagram and similarity statement OR correct proportion

[1] correct height, no work shown

Similarity in Right Triangles

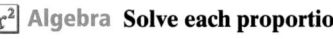

2.03 Apply properties, definitions, and theorems of two-dimensional figures to solve problems and write proofs: a) Triangles.

Lesson Preview

What You'll Learn

OBJECTIVE 1
To find and use relationships in similar right triangles

...And Why

To find a distance indirectly, as in Example 3

✓ Check Skills You'll Need

(For help, go to Lesson 8-1 and page 355.)

 Algebra Solve each proportion.

1. $\frac{x}{8} = \frac{18}{24}$ 6

2. $\frac{2}{3} = \frac{x}{7}$ $\frac{14}{3}$

3. $\frac{15}{4} = \frac{18}{x}$ $\frac{24}{5}$

4. $\frac{51}{x} = \frac{17}{13}$ 39

5. $\frac{4}{10} = \frac{x}{5}$ 2

6. $\frac{3}{m} = \frac{9}{8}$ $\frac{8}{3}$

7. $\frac{w}{2} = \frac{20}{9}$ $\frac{40}{9}$

8. $\frac{9}{6} = \frac{27}{a}$ 18

9. Draw a right triangle. Label the triangle $\triangle ABC$ with right angle $\angle C$. Draw the altitude to the hypotenuse. Label the altitude $\overline{CD}$. Name the two smaller right triangles that are formed. **See back of book.**

New Vocabulary   • geometric mean

OBJECTIVE 1
Using Similarity in Right Triangles

🖳 **iTEXT** Interactive lesson includes instant self-check, tutorials, and activities.

Investigation: Similarity in Right Triangles

• Draw one diagonal on a rectangular sheet of paper. Cut the paper on the diagonal to make two congruent right triangles.

• In one of the triangles, use paper folding to locate the altitude to the hypotenuse. Cut the triangle along the altitude to make two smaller right triangles.

• Label the angles of the three triangles as shown.

• Compare the angles of the three triangles by placing the angles on top of one another.

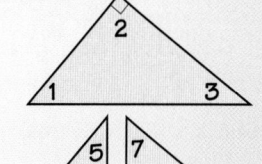

1. Which angles have the same measure as $\angle 1$? $\angle 4$ and $\angle 7$

2. Which angles have the same measure as $\angle 2$? $\angle 6$ and $\angle 8$

3. Which angles have the same measure as $\angle 3$? $\angle 5$ and $\angle 9$

4. Based on your results, what is true about the three triangles?
They are ~.

5. Use the diagram at the right to complete the similarity statement.
$\triangle RST \sim \triangle\ \underline{?}\ \sim \triangle\ \underline{?}$
RWS; SWT

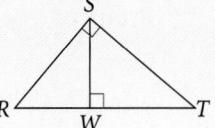

INSTANT CHECK ✓ **Ongoing Assessment and Intervention**

Before the Lesson	During the Lesson	After the Lesson
Diagnose prerequisite skills using:	**Monitor progress using:**	**Assess knowledge using:**
• Check Skills You'll Need	• Check Understanding	• Lesson Quiz
	• Additional Examples	• Computer Test Generator CD
	• Standardized Test Prep	

North Carolina Objectives 2.03a

1. Plan

Lesson Preview

✓ **Check Skills You'll Need** 🖳

Ratios and Proportions
Lesson 8-1: Example 3
Exercises 12–20
Extra Practice, p. 697

Medians and Altitudes
Lesson 5-3: Example 4
Exercises 14–16
Extra Practice, p. 694

Lesson Resources

📁 **Teaching Resources**
Practice, Reteaching, Enrichment

👥 **Reaching All Students**
Practice Workbook 8-4
Spanish Practice Workbook 8-4
Hands-On Activities 23
Informal Geometry Planning Guide 8-4

🕐 **Presentation Assistant Plus!**
Transparencies
• Check Skills You'll Need 8-4
• Additional Examples 8-4
• Student Edition Answers 8-4
• Lesson Quiz 8-4
PH Presentation Pro CD 8-4

PRENTICE HALL **ASSESSMENT SYSTEM**

Computer Test Generator CD

💿 **Technology**
Resource Pro® CD-ROM
Computer Test Generator CD
Prentice Hall Presentation Pro CD

 www.PHSchool.com
Student Site
• Teacher Web Code: afk-5500
• Self-grading Lesson Quiz
Teacher Center
• Lesson Planner
• Resources

Plus 🖳 **iTEXT**

Math Background

The geometric mean g of two positive numbers a and b has the algebraic formulation $g = \sqrt{ab}$, but the theorems in this lesson show how the mean can be viewed *geometrically*. The geometric mean of n positive numbers $a_1, a_2, a_3, \ldots, a_n$ is defined as $g = \sqrt[n]{a_1 a_2 a_3 \cdot \ldots \cdot a_n}$.

OBJECTIVE

▼ 1 Teaching Notes

Investigation (Optional)
Suggest that students use single and double arcs indicating congruent acute angles to help them order the letters of the similar triangles correctly.

In discussing the proof of Theorem 8-3, have students refer to the right triangles they formed for the Investigation on page 439. Ask: *Which property allows you to conclude that the corresponding angles of the smaller triangles are congruent?* **Transitive Property of Congruence**

English Learners
Tell students that the word *mean* has a precise mathematical definition. Remind them that b and c are the means in the proportion $\frac{a}{b} = \frac{c}{d}$, so x is the mean in the proportion $\frac{a}{x} = \frac{x}{b}$. The value of x in the proportion is $\sqrt{ab}$. This special value is the *geometric mean* of a and b.

1 EXAMPLE Error Prevention

Check that students do not calculate the *arithmetic* mean, or average, when asked for the geometric mean. To help distinguish the two terms, have students calculate examples of each.

Visual Learners
Discuss as a class visual ways to remember Corollaries 1 and 2.

In a right triangle, the altitude to the hypotenuse yields three similar triangles.

🔑 **Key Concepts**

Theorem 8-3

The altitude to the hypotenuse of a right triangle divides the triangle into two triangles that are similar to the original triangle and to each other.

Proof **Proof of Theorem 8-3**

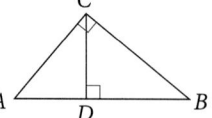

Given: Right triangle, $\triangle ABC$, with $\overline{CD}$ the altitude to the hypotenuse

Prove: $\triangle ABC \sim \triangle ACD \sim \triangle CBD$

Proof: Both smaller triangles are right triangles. Each also shares an angle with $\triangle ABC$. Thus each smaller triangle is similar to $\triangle ABC$ by the AA $\sim$ Postulate. Since both smaller triangles are similar to $\triangle ABC$, their corresponding angles are congruent. Thus they are similar to each other.

Need Help?

In the proportion
$$\frac{a}{b} = \frac{c}{d},$$
b and c are the means.

Proportions in which the means are equal occur frequently in geometry. For any two positive numbers a and b, the **geometric mean** of a and b is the positive number x such that $\frac{a}{x} = \frac{x}{b}$. Note that $x = \sqrt{ab}$.

1 EXAMPLE Finding the Geometric Mean

Algebra Find the geometric mean of 4 and 18.

$\frac{4}{x} = \frac{x}{18}$ **Write a proportion.**

$x^2 = 72$ **Cross-Product Property**

$x = \sqrt{72}$ **Take the square root.**

$x = 6\sqrt{2}$ **Write in simplest radical form.**

The geometric mean of 4 and 18 is $6\sqrt{2}$.

✓ **Check Understanding** ❶ Find the geometric mean of 15 and 20. $10\sqrt{3}$

Two important corollaries of Theorem 8-3 involve a geometric mean.

🔑 **Key Concepts**

Corollary   **Corollary 1 to Theorem 8-3**

The length of the altitude to the hypotenuse of a right triangle is the geometric mean of the lengths of the segments of the hypotenuse.

Proof **Proof of Corollary 1**

Given: Right triangle, $\triangle ABC$, with $\overline{CD}$ the altitude to the hypotenuse

Prove: $\frac{AD}{CD} = \frac{CD}{DB}$

Proof: By Theorem 8-3, $\triangle ACD \sim \triangle CBD$. Since corresponding sides of similar triangles are proportional, $\frac{AD}{CD} = \frac{CD}{DB}$.

👥 Reaching All Students

| **Below Level** Have students illustrate each theorem with a diagram and summarize each using proportions or similarity statements. | **Advanced Learners** After Example 1, challenge students to prove that the geometric mean of two numbers is always less than or equal to their arithmetic mean. | **English Learners** See note on page 440. **Visual Learners** See note on page 440. |

Key Concepts

Corollary	Corollary 2 to Theorem 8-3

The altitude to the hypotenuse of a right triangle separates the hypotenuse so that the length of each leg of the triangle is the geometric mean of the length of the adjacent hypotenuse segment and the length of the hypotenuse.

Proof

Proof of Corollary 2

Given: Right triangle, $\triangle ABC$, with $\overline{CD}$ the altitude to the hypotenuse

Prove: $\dfrac{AD}{AC} = \dfrac{AC}{AB}$, $\dfrac{DB}{CB} = \dfrac{CB}{AB}$

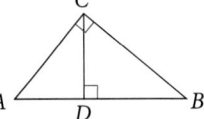

Proof: By Theorem 8-3, $\triangle ACD \sim \triangle ABC$. Their corresponding sides are proportional, so $\dfrac{AD}{AC} = \dfrac{AC}{AB}$. Similarly, $\triangle CBD \sim \triangle ABC$ and $\dfrac{DB}{CB} = \dfrac{CB}{AB}$.

2 EXAMPLE Applying Corollaries 1 and 2

Algebra Solve for x and y.

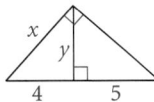

Use Corollary 2 to solve for x: Use Corollary 1 to solve for y:

$\dfrac{4}{x} = \dfrac{x}{4+5}$ ← Write a proportion. → $\dfrac{4}{y} = \dfrac{y}{5}$

$x^2 = 36$ ← Cross-Product Property → $y^2 = 20$

$x = 6$ ← Take the square root. → $y = 2\sqrt{5}$

✓ **Check Understanding** **2** Solve for x and y.
$x = 8$; $y = 4\sqrt{3}$

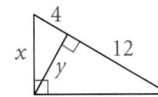

3 EXAMPLE **Real-World**  **Connection**

Recreation The 300-m path to the information center and the 400-m path to the canoe rental dock meet at a right angle at the parking lot. Marla walks straight from the parking lot to the lake as shown. How far is Marla from the information center?

$\overline{CD}$, the perpendicular segment from point C to $\overline{AB}$, is the shortest path to the lake. $\triangle ABC$ is a right triangle. Using Pythagorean triples, $AB = 500$ m. To find AD, apply Corollary 2.

$\dfrac{AD}{AC} = \dfrac{AC}{AB}$ Corollary 2

$\dfrac{AD}{300} = \dfrac{300}{500}$ Substitute.

$AD = \dfrac{300}{500} \cdot 300$ Solve for AD.

$AD = 180$

Marla is 180 m from the information center.

Real-World  **Connection**

Paddling a canoe burns about 175 calories per hour.

✓ **Check Understanding** **3** How far did Marla walk from the parking lot to the lake?
240 m

Lesson 8-4 Similarity in Right Triangles **441**

2 EXAMPLE

Students may have trouble remembering the corollaries. Remind them that they can use Theorem 8-3 to write similarity statements for three triangles and then derive the proportions from the similar triangles.

3 EXAMPLE

Have students explain why and how they can use Pythagorean triples to find AB.

Additional Examples

1 Find the geometric mean of 3 and 12. **6**

2 Solve for x and y.

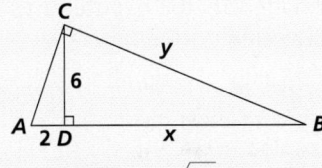

$x = 18, y = 6\sqrt{10}$

3 At a golf course, Maria drove her ball 192 yd straight toward the cup. Her brother Gabriel drove his ball straight 240 yd, but not toward the cup. The diagram shows the results. Find x and y, their remaining distances from the cup.

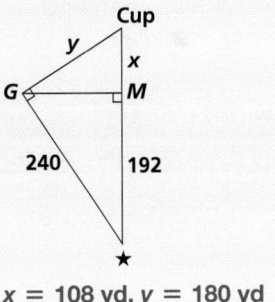

$x = 108$ yd, $y = 180$ yd

Closure

Draw a right triangle with legs 8 cm and 15 cm long. Find each length.
a. hypotenuse **17**
b. altitude to the hypotenuse $\dfrac{120}{17}$
c. segments of the hypotenuse formed by the altitude $\dfrac{64}{17}, \dfrac{225}{17}$

441

Assignment Guide

▼ **Objective**

Ⓐ Ⓑ **Core** 1–48

Ⓒ **Extension** 49–56

Standardized Test Prep 57–61

Mixed Review 62–69

Exercises 15–20 Have students copy the diagrams and use single and double arcs to indicate congruent angles. This will help them identify the hypotenuses of the similar triangles.

Exercise 24 Ask: *What special type of right triangle must this be?* **isosceles**

Connection to Algebra

Exercise 37 Suggest that students use x and $2x$ for the segments of the hypotenuse.

Alternative Method

Exercise 49 Students can use arguments based on similarity or area to explain Lauren's corollary.

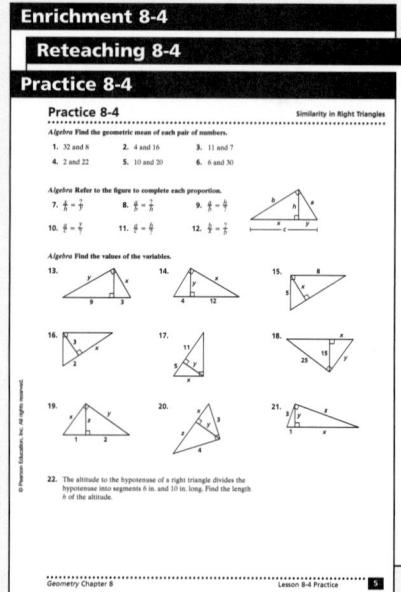

Ⓐ **Practice by Example**

x^2 **Algebra** **Find the geometric mean of each pair of numbers.**

Example 1
(page 440)

1. 4 and 9 **6**   **2.** 4 and 10 $2\sqrt{10}$ **3.** 4 and 12 $4\sqrt{3}$ **4.** 3 and 48 **12**

5. 7 and 56 $14\sqrt{2}$ **6.** 5 and 125 **25**   **7.** 9 and 24 $6\sqrt{6}$ **8.** 7 and 9 $3\sqrt{7}$

Example 2
(page 441)

x^2 **Algebra** **Refer to the figure to complete each proportion.**

9. $\frac{r}{h} = \frac{h}{\blacksquare}$ **s**   **10.** $\frac{c}{a} = \frac{a}{\blacksquare}$ **r**   **11.** $\frac{\blacksquare}{b} = \frac{b}{s}$ **c**

12. $\frac{r}{\blacksquare} = \frac{\blacksquare}{c}$ **a; a**   **13.** $\frac{r}{h} = \frac{\blacksquare}{s}$ **h**   **14.** $\frac{s}{b} = \frac{\blacksquare}{c}$ **b**

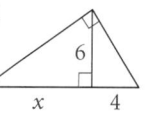

x^2 **Algebra** **Solve for x.**

15. **9**

16. **20** 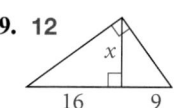 **40** **50**

17. **10** **4** **21** **x**

18. $6\sqrt{3}$ **x** **3** **9**

19. **12** **x** **16** **9**

20. **60** **x** **144** **25**

Example 3
(page 441)

21. a. Civil Engineering Study the plan at the right. A service station will be built on the highway, and a road will connect it with Cray. How far from Blare should the service station be located so that the proposed road will be perpendicular to the highway? **18 mi**

  b. How long will the new road be? **24 mi**

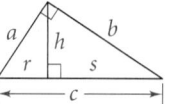
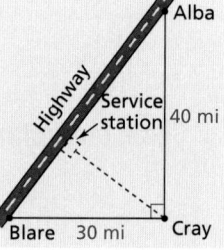

Ⓑ **Apply Your Skills**

24a.
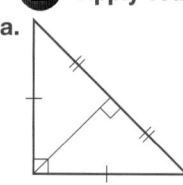

b. They are =.
Explanations may vary.
Sample: The altitude and hyp. segments are ≅ sides of two isosc. △.

Reading Math

"Respectively" in Exercise 25 means you match the lists in the order named: $A(4, 2)$, $D(4, 6)$, $B(4, 15)$.

22. Complete:
$\triangle JKL \sim \triangle \underline{\ ?\ } \sim \triangle \underline{\ ?\ }$
KNL; JNK

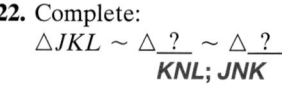

23. a. The altitude to the hypotenuse of a right triangle divides the hypotenuse into segments 2 cm and 8 cm long. Find the length h of the altitude. **4 cm**

  b. Drawing Use the value you found for h in part (a), along with the lengths 2 cm and 8 cm, to draw the right triangle accurately. **b–c. See margin.**

  c. Writing Explain how you drew the triangle in part (b).

24. a. Open-Ended Draw a right triangle so that the altitude from the right angle to the hypotenuse bisects the hypotenuse. **a–b. See left.**

  b. How does the length of the altitude compare with the lengths of the segments of the hypotenuse? Explain.

25. Coordinate Geometry $\overline{CD}$ is the altitude to the hypotenuse of right $\triangle ABC$. The coordinates of A, D, and B are $(4, 2)$, $(4, 6)$, and $(4, 15)$, respectively. Find all possible coordinates of point C. **(10, 6), (−2, 6)**

x^2 **Algebra** **Find the geometric mean of each pair of numbers.**

$\sqrt{14}$

26. 3 and 16 $4\sqrt{3}$ **27.** 4 and 49 **14**   **28.** $\sqrt{8}$ and $\sqrt{2}$ **4**   **29.** $\sqrt{28}$ and $\sqrt{7}$

30. $\frac{1}{2}$ and 2 **1**   **31.** 5 and 1.25 **2.5**   **32.** 1 and 1000
$10\sqrt{10}$ **33.** 11 and 1331 **121**

---

pages 442–444 **Exercises**

23. b.

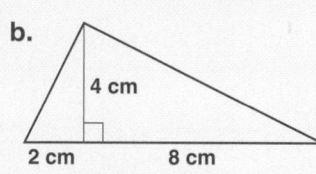

4 cm

2 cm   8 cm

c. Answers may vary.
Sample: Draw a 10-cm segment; 2 cm from one endpoint, construct a ⊥ of length 4 cm. Connect to form a △.

x^2 **Algebra** Find the values of the variables. 36. $x = 4$; $y = 2\sqrt{13}$; $z = 3\sqrt{13}$

34.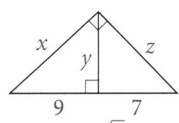
$x = 12$; $y = 3\sqrt{7}$; $z = 4\sqrt{7}$

35.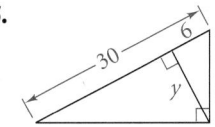
$x = 12\sqrt{5}$; $y = 12$; $z = 6\sqrt{5}$

36.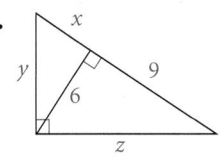

x^2 **37. Algebra** The altitude to the hypotenuse of a right triangle divides the hypotenuse into segments with lengths in the ratio $1 : 2$. The length of the altitude is 8. How long is the hypotenuse? $12\sqrt{2}$

Proof **38. Pythagorean Theorem** You can use Corollary 2 to Theorem 8-3 to prove the Pythagorean Theorem. Complete the following proof.

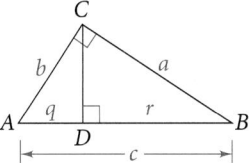

Given: Right $\triangle ABC$ with altitude $\overline{CD}$
Prove: $c^2 = a^2 + b^2$

Statements	Reasons
1. Right $\triangle ABC$ with altitude $\overline{CD}$	a. _?_ Given
2. $\frac{c}{a} = \frac{a}{r}$, $\frac{c}{b} = \frac{b}{q}$	b. _?_ Corollary 2 to Thm. 8-3
3. $cr = a^2$, $cq = b^2$	c. _?_ Cross-Product Prop.
4. $cr + cq = a^2 + b^2$	d. _?_ Addition Prop. of =
5. $c(r + q) = a^2 + b^2$	e. _?_ Dist. Prop.
6. $r + q = c$	f. _?_ Segment Add. Post.
7. $c^2 = a^2 + b^2$	g. _?_ Subst.

39. Indirect Measurement To estimate the height of a totem pole, Jorge uses a small square of plastic. He holds the square up to his eyes and walks backward from the pole. He stops when the bottom of the pole lines up with the bottom edge of the square and the top of the pole lines up with the top edge of the square. Jorge's eye level is about 2 m from the ground. He is about 3 m from the pole. Estimate the height of the totem pole. **about 6.5 m**

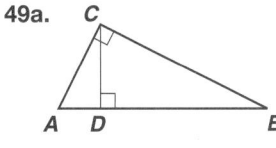
Exercise 39

40. The length of the shorter leg of a 30°-60°-90° triangle is 10 cm. Find the length of the altitude to the hypotenuse. $5\sqrt{3}$ cm

For a right triangle, denote lengths as follows: ℓ_1 and ℓ_2 the legs, h the hypotenuse, a the altitude, and h_1 and h_2 the hypotenuse segments determined by the altitude. For the two given measures, find the other four. Use simplest radical form.
41–48. See margin.

41. $\ell_1 = 3, \ell_2 = 4$ **42.** $h_1 = 4, h_2 = 9$ **43.** $a = 6, h_1 = 6$ **44.** $\ell_1 = 5, a = 4$

45. $h = 13, \ell_2 = 12$ **46.** $\ell_1 = 4, h_1 = 3$ **47.** $a = 8, h_1 = 16$ **48.** $h_1 = 3, \ell_2 = 6\sqrt{3}$

C **Challenge**

49. a. Lauren thinks she has found a new corollary: The product of the lengths of the two legs of a right triangle is equal to the product of the lengths of the hypotenuse and the altitude to the hypotenuse. Draw a figure for this corollary. Write the *Given* information and what you are to *Prove*.
 b. Critical Thinking Is Lauren's corollary true? Explain.
 Yes; $AC \cdot BC = 2 \times$ area $\triangle ABC$ and $AB \cdot CD = 2 \times$ area $\triangle ABC$.

49a.

Given: rt. $\triangle ABC$ with alt. $\overline{CD}$;
Prove: $AC \cdot BC = AB \cdot CD$

x^2 **Algebra** Find the value of x.

50. 3

51. 4

52. 4.5

Lesson 8-4 Similarity in Right Triangles **443**

---

41. $h = 5, a = \frac{12}{5}, h_1 = \frac{9}{5}$, $h_2 = \frac{16}{5}$

42. $\ell_1 = 2\sqrt{13}, \ell_2 = 3\sqrt{13}$, $h = 13, a = 6$

43. $\ell_1 = \ell_2 = 6\sqrt{2}$, $h = 12, h_2 = 6$

44. $\ell_2 = \frac{20}{3}, h = \frac{25}{3}, h_1 = 3$, $h_2 = \frac{16}{3}$

45. $\ell_1 = 5, a = \frac{60}{13}, h_1 = \frac{25}{13}$, $h_2 = \frac{144}{13}$

46. $\ell_2 = \frac{4\sqrt{7}}{3}, h = \frac{16}{3}$, $a = \sqrt{7}, h_2 = \frac{7}{3}$

47. $\ell_1 = 8\sqrt{5}, \ell_2 = 4\sqrt{5}$, $h_2 = 4, h = 20$

48. $\ell_1 = 6, h = 12$, $a = 3\sqrt{3}, h_2 = 9$

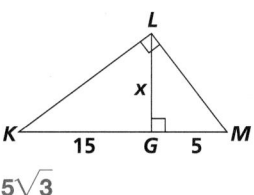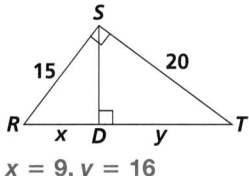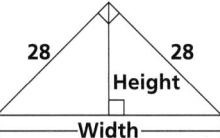
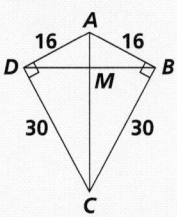

Each Pythagorean triple below represents the lengths of the sides of a right triangle. For each triangle, find the length of the altitude to the hypotenuse.

53. 3, 4, 5 $\frac{12}{5}$ **54.** 5, 12, 13 $\frac{60}{13}$ **55.** 8, 15, 17 $\frac{120}{17}$ **56.** 20, 21, 29 $\frac{420}{29}$

Standardized Test Prep

Multiple Choice

57. What is the geometric mean of 12 and 18? **D**
  A. 1.5   B. $\sqrt{6}$ C. 15   D. $6\sqrt{6}$

58. What is the geometric mean of 2 and 36? **G**
  F. 17   G. $6\sqrt{2}$ H. 38   I. $2\sqrt{6}$

59. Solve for m. **C**
  A. 7   B. 15
  C. 20   D. 25

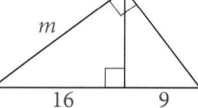

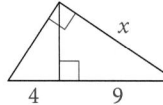 **Take It to the NET**
Online lesson quiz at
www.PHSchool.com
Web Code: afa-0804

60. The altitude to the hypotenuse of a right triangle divides the hypotenuse into segments of lengths 5 and 15. What is the length of the altitude? **H**
  F. 3   G. 10   H. $5\sqrt{3}$ I. $5\sqrt{5}$

Short Response

61. a. Explain how you could solve for x.
  b. What is the value of x?
  a–b. See margin.

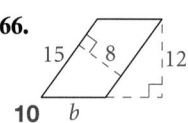

Mixed Review

Lesson 8-3

If the triangles are similar, **(a)** write a similarity statement and **(b)** name the postulate or theorem you used. If the triangles are not similar, write *not similar*.

62.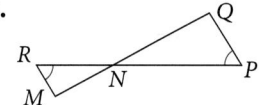

63.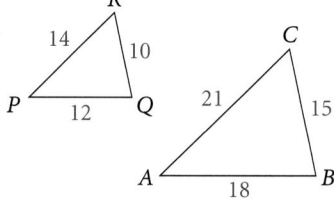

64.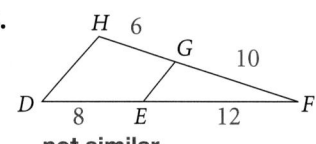
not similar

Lesson 7-1 x^2 **Algebra** Solve for the variables in each parallelogram.

65.

7.5

66.
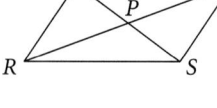

Lesson 6-2 x^2 **Algebra** Find the values of x and y in ▱RSTV.

  $x = 5; y = 8$
67. $RP = 2x, PT = y + 2, VP = y, PS = x + 3$

68. $x = 6; y = 9$

68. $RP = 4x, PT = 3y - 3, VP = 2x + 3, PS = y + 6$

69. $RV = 2x + 3, VT = 5x, TS = y + 5, SR = 4y - 1$
  $x = 3; y = 4$

Exploring Proportions in Triangles

FOR USE WITH LESSON 8-5

Construct

- Use geometry software. Draw $\triangle ABC$ and construct point D on $\overline{AB}$.
- Construct a line through D parallel to $\overline{AC}$.
- Construct the intersection E of the parallel line with $\overline{BC}$.

Investigate

- Measure $\overline{BD}, \overline{DA}, \overline{BE}$, and $\overline{EC}$.
- Calculate the ratios $\frac{BD}{DA}$ and $\frac{BE}{EC}$.
- Manipulate $\triangle ABC$ and observe the ratios $\frac{BD}{DA}$ and $\frac{BE}{EC}$.
  (Save your observations for Exercise 1.)

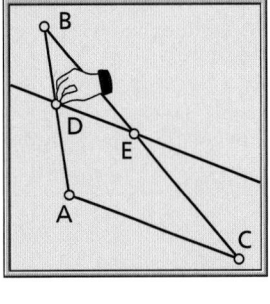

Construct

- Use geometry software. Draw $\triangle ABC$. Construct the bisector of $\angle A$. Construct point D, the intersection of the bisector and $\overline{CB}$.

Investigate

- Measure $\overline{AC}, \overline{AB}, \overline{CD}$, and $\overline{DB}$.
- Calculate the ratios $\frac{AC}{AB}$ and $\frac{CD}{DB}$.
- Manipulate $\triangle ABC$ and observe the ratios $\frac{AC}{AB}$ and $\frac{CD}{DB}$.
  (Save your observations for Exercise 2.)

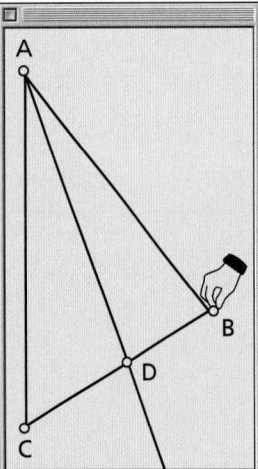

EXERCISES

1. Suppose a line parallel to one side of a triangle intersects the other two sides. Make a conjecture about the four segments formed.
   It divides the sides into prop. segments.
2. The bisector of an angle of a triangle divides the opposite side into two segments. Make a conjecture about the two segments and the other two sides of the triangle.
   The segments are prop. to the lengths of the other sides of the $\triangle$.

Extend

- Construct $\overleftrightarrow{AB} \parallel \overleftrightarrow{CD}$. Then construct lines $\overleftrightarrow{AC}$ and $\overleftrightarrow{BD}$.
- Construct point E on $\overleftrightarrow{AC}$.
- Construct $\overleftrightarrow{EF} \parallel \overleftrightarrow{AB}$ with point F the intersection of $\overleftrightarrow{EF}$ and $\overleftrightarrow{BD}$.
- Measure $\overline{AC}, \overline{CE}, \overline{BD}$, and $\overline{DF}$.
- Calculate the ratios $\frac{AC}{CE}$ and $\frac{BD}{DF}$.
- Manipulate the locations of A and B and observe the ratios $\frac{AC}{CE}$ and $\frac{BD}{DF}$.

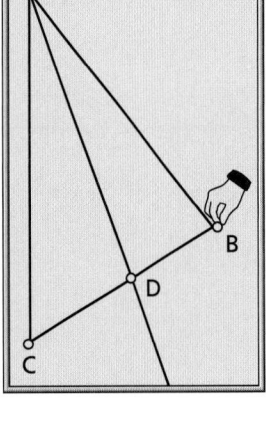

3. Suppose three parallel lines intersect two transversals. Make a conjecture about the segments of the transversals. **The corr. segment ratios are =.**

4. Suppose that four or more parallel lines intersect two transversals. Make a conjecture about the segments of the transversals. **The corr. segment ratios are =.**

Exploring Proportions in Triangles

Students will use geometry software to investigate and make conjectures about the relationships among segments formed by parallel lines and angle bisectors.

Resources

Students may use any geometry software program to explore proportions in triangles.

Teaching Notes

Using geometry software, students will discover proportional relationships formed by parallel lines within triangles, angle bisectors of triangles, and two transversals intersecting a set of three parallel lines. These relationships form the basis of the theorems and corollary in Lesson 8-5.

Teaching Tip
Have students repeat the first Construct and Investigate, using a different parallel line to test their conjectures.

Error Prevention
When students construct their angle bisectors, make sure that they use the bisector feature of their software. Otherwise, the subsequent manipulation of triangle sides will not preserve the given ratios.

Lesson Preview

✔ **Check Skills You'll Need**

Using Similar Figures
Lesson 8-2: Example 3
Exercises 13–16
Extra Practice, p. 697

Lesson Resources

 Teaching Resources
Practice, Reteaching, Enrichment
Checkpoint Quiz 2

👥 **Reaching All Students**
Practice Workbook 8-5
Spanish Practice Workbook 8-5
Reading and Math Literacy 8C
Spanish Reading & Literacy 8C
Spanish Checkpoint Quiz 2
Hands-On Activities 24
Informal Geometry Planning
  Guide 8-5

⏱ **Presentation Assistant Plus!**
Transparencies
• Check Skills You'll Need 8-5
• Additional Examples 8-5
• Student Edition Answers 8-5
• Lesson Quiz 8-5
PH Presentation Pro CD 8-5

PRENTICE HALL
ASSESSMENT SYSTEM

Checkpoint Quiz 2
Computer Test Generator CD

💿 **Technology**
Resource Pro® CD-ROM
Computer Test Generator CD
Prentice Hall Presentation Pro CD

🖥 **www.PHSchool.com**
Student Site
• Teacher Web Code: afk-5500
• Self-grading Lesson Quiz
Teacher Center
• Lesson Planner
• Resources

 Plus 📘 **iTEXT**

 8-5

North Carolina Objectives

Proportions in Triangles

2.03 Apply properties, definitions, and theorems of two-dimensional figures to solve
problems and write proofs: a) Triangles.

Lesson Preview

What You'll Learn

OBJECTIVE 1 To use the Side-Splitter Theorem

OBJECTIVE 2 To use the Triangle-Angle-Bisector Theorem

. . . And Why

To design a sail, as in Example 2

✔ Check Skills You'll Need

(For help, go to Lesson 8-2.)

The two triangles in each diagram are similar. Find the value of x in each.

1.
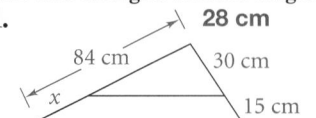
84 cm   28 cm   30 cm x 15 cm

2.
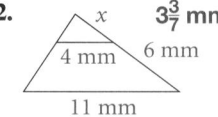
x $3\frac{3}{7}$ mm   4 mm   6 mm   11 mm

3.
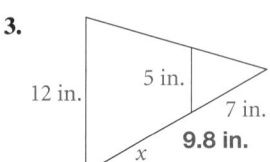
12 in.   5 in.   7 in.   9.8 in. x

4.
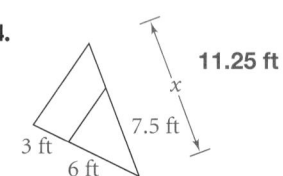
11.25 ft x 3 ft   7.5 ft   6 ft

OBJECTIVE 1

 Interactive lesson includes instant
self-check, tutorials, and activities.

Using the Side-Splitter Theorem

You can use similar triangles to prove the following theorem.

 Key Concepts

Theorem 8-4	Side-Splitter Theorem

If a line is parallel to one side of a triangle and intersects the other two sides,
then it divides those sides proportionally.

Proof **Proof of Theorem 8-4**

Given: $\triangle QXY$ with $\overleftrightarrow{RS} \parallel \overleftrightarrow{XY}$

Prove: $\dfrac{XR}{RQ} = \dfrac{YS}{SQ}$

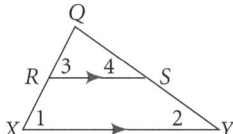

📖 **Reading Math**
For help with reading
the proof of Theorem
8-4, see p. 453.

Statements	Reasons
1. $\overleftrightarrow{RS} \parallel \overleftrightarrow{XY}$	1. Given
2. $\angle 1 \cong \angle 3, \angle 2 \cong \angle 4$	2. If lines are $\parallel$, then corr. $\angle$s are $\cong$.
3. $\triangle QXY \sim \triangle QRS$	3. AA $\sim$ Postulate
4. $\dfrac{XQ}{RQ} = \dfrac{YQ}{SQ}$	4. Corr. sides of $\sim$ $\triangle$s are proportional.
5. $XQ = XR + RQ, YQ = YS + SQ$	5. Segment Addition Postulate
6. $\dfrac{XR + RQ}{RQ} = \dfrac{YS + SQ}{SQ}$	6. Substitute.
7. $\dfrac{XR}{RQ} = \dfrac{YS}{SQ}$	7. A Property of Proportions

---

 Ongoing Assessment and Intervention

Before the Lesson
Diagnose prerequisite skills using:
• Check Skills You'll Need

During the Lesson
Monitor progress using:
• Check Understanding
• Additional Examples
• Standardized Test Prep

After the Lesson
Assess knowledge using:
• Lesson Quiz
• Computer Test Generator CD
• Chapter Checkpoint 2 (p. 452)

1 EXAMPLE Using the Side-Splitter Theorem

Algebra Solve for x.

$$\frac{TS}{SR} = \frac{TU}{UV}$$ Side-Splitter Theorem

$$\frac{x}{16} = \frac{5}{10}$$ Substitute.

$$x = \frac{5}{10} \cdot 16$$ Solve for x.

$$x = 8$$

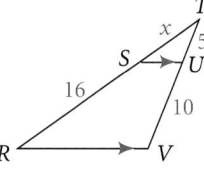

✓ **Check Understanding** ① Use the Side-Splitter Theorem to find the value of x. **1.5**

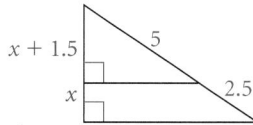

The following corollary to the Side Splitter Theorem says that parallel lines divide all transversals proportionally. You will prove this corollary in Exercise 34.

 Key Concepts

Corollary	Corollary to Theorem 8-4

If three parallel lines intersect two transversals, then the segments intercepted on the transversals are proportional.

$$\frac{a}{b} = \frac{c}{d}$$

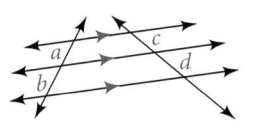

2 EXAMPLE Real-World Connection

Sail Making Sail makers sometimes use a computer to create a pattern for a sail. After they cut out the panels of the sail, they sew them together to form the sail.

The edges of the panels in the sail at the right are parallel. Find the lengths x and y.

$$\frac{2}{x} = \frac{1.7}{1.7}$$ Side-Splitter Theorem

$$x = 2$$

$$\frac{3}{2} = \frac{y}{1.7}$$ Corollary to the Side-Splitter Theorem

$$\frac{3}{2}(1.7) = y$$ Solve for y.

$$2.55 = y$$

Length x is 2 ft and length y is 2.55 ft.

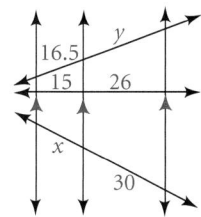

Real-World Connection

You windsurf with a large sail in light winds and a small sail in strong winds.

✓ **Check Understanding** ② Solve for x and y.
$x = \frac{225}{13}; y = 28.6$

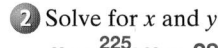

 Reaching All Students

Below Level Review the properties of proportions, especially the Cross-Product Property, before students read the proof of Theorem 8-4 and work through the examples.	**Advanced Learners** Use the Side-Splitter Theorem to prove that, if a line parallel to one side of a triangle intersects the midpoint of another side, then it intersects the midpoint of the third side.	**Visual Learners** See note on page 450. **Error Prevention** See note on page 448.

Math Background

The Side-Splitter Theorem represents a generalization of the Triangle Midsegment Theorem from Chapter 5. The concept of similarity makes possible this generalization. The Side-Splitter Theorem applied to three parallel lines proves the Triangle-Angle Bisector Theorem.

OBJECTIVE

 1 Teaching Notes

Teaching Tip
Discuss as a class the proof of Theorem 8-4. In particular, have students use algebra to show how step 7 follows from step 6.

1 EXAMPLE Alternative Method

ST can be found without using the Side-Splitter Theorem by remembering that sides of similar triangles are proportional. Ask: *What proportion could you write and solve?* $\frac{ST}{ST + 16} = \frac{5}{15}$

2 EXAMPLE Diversity

Some students may be unaware of the different shapes of sails for ancient and modern boats. If possible, show pictures of boats with different kinds of sails.

Additional Examples

① Find y.

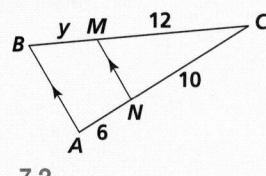

7.2

② The segments joining the sides of trapezoid $RSTU$ are parallel to its bases. Find x and y.

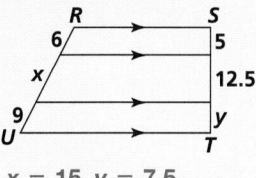

$x = 15, y = 7.5$

Math Tip

After introducing the Triangle-Angle-Bisector Theorem, remind students of the Angle Bisector Theorem in Lesson 5-2. Have them explain how the theorems differ.

Technology Tip

Students can model the proof of Theorem 8-5 using geometry software.

3 **EXAMPLE** **Error Prevention**

Some students looking at the diagram for this example may think they can use the proportions from Lesson 8-4 that apply only to right triangles. Ask: *What must be true to apply the theorems and corollaries from Lesson 8-4?* The triangle must be a right triangle with an altitude to the hypotenuse.

Additional Examples

3 Find the value of *x*.

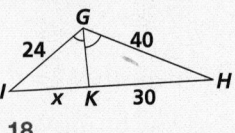

Closure

In △*ABC*, $\overline{QT} \parallel \overline{BC}$ and $\overline{AM}$ bisects ∠*BAC*. Find *x* and *y*.

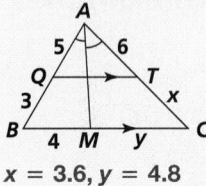

x = 3.6, *y* = 4.8

You can use the Side-Splitter Theorem to prove the following relationship.

 Key Concepts

Theorem 8-5	**Triangle-Angle-Bisector Theorem**

If a ray bisects an angle of a triangle, then it divides the opposite side into two segments that are proportional to the other two sides of the triangle.

Proof **Proof of Theorem 8-5**

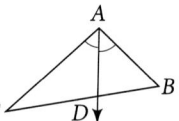

Given: △*ABC*, $\overrightarrow{AD}$ bisects ∠*CAB*.

Prove: $\frac{CD}{DB} = \frac{CA}{BA}$

Draw $\overrightarrow{BE} \parallel \overrightarrow{DA}$. Extend $\overline{CA}$ to meet $\overleftrightarrow{BE}$ at point *F*.

Proof: By the Side-Splitter Theorem, $\frac{CD}{DB} = \frac{CA}{AF}$.
By the Corresponding Angles Postulate, ∠3 ≅ ∠1. Since $\overrightarrow{AD}$ bisects ∠*CAB*, ∠1 ≅ ∠2. By the Alternate Interior Angles Theorem, ∠2 ≅ ∠4. Using the Transitive Property of Congruence, you know that ∠3 ≅ ∠4. By the Converse of the Isosceles Triangle Theorem, *BA* = *AF*. Substituting *BA* for *AF*, $\frac{CD}{DB} = \frac{CA}{BA}$.

 Need Help?

Drawing $\overrightarrow{BE} \parallel \overline{DA}$ sets up △*BCF* for the Side-Splitter Theorem, as well as congruent △1, 2, 3, and 4.

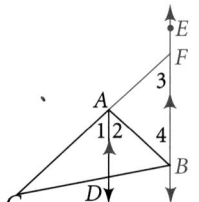

3 **EXAMPLE** **Using the Triangle-Angle-Bisector Theorem**

Algebra Find the value of *x*.

$\frac{PS}{SR} = \frac{PQ}{RQ}$	Triangle-Angle-Bisector Theorem
$\frac{x}{6} = \frac{8}{5}$	Substitute.
$5x = 48$	Cross-Product Property
$x = 9.6$	Solve for *x*.

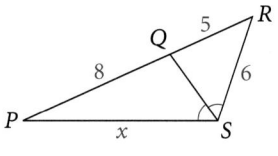

✓ **Check Understanding** 3 Find the value of *y*.
5.76

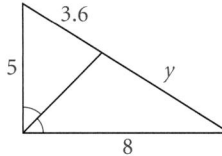

EXERCISES

For more practice, see *Extra Practice*.

Practice and Problem Solving

A **Practice by Example** x^2 **Algebra** **Solve for *x*.**

Example 1
(page 447)

1.

2.

3.

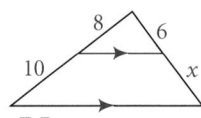

Example 2
(page 447)

Use the figure at the right to complete each proportion.

4. $\frac{a}{b} = \frac{\blacksquare}{e}$ *d*

5. $\frac{b}{\blacksquare} = \frac{e}{f}$ *c*

6. $\frac{f}{e} = \frac{c}{\blacksquare}$ *b*

7. $\frac{a}{b + c} = \frac{\blacksquare}{e + f}$ *d*

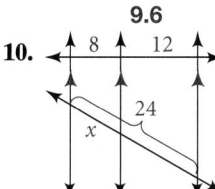

x^2 **Algebra** Solve for *x*.

8.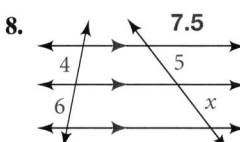
    7.5 · 4 · 5 · 6 · *x*

9.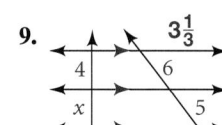
    $3\frac{1}{3}$ · 4 · 6 · *x* · 5

10.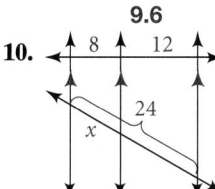
    9.6 · 8 · 12 · *x* · 24

Example 3
(page 448)

x^2 **Algebra** Solve for *x*.

11.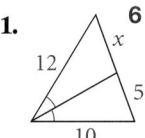
    6 · *x* · 12 · 5 · 10

12.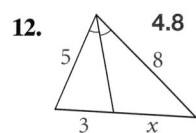
    4.8 · 5 · 8 · 3 · *x*

13.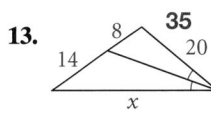
    8 · 35 · 14 · 20 · *x*

14. 3.6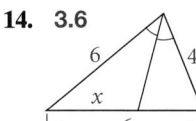
    6 · 4 · *x* · 6

15. $\frac{40}{7}$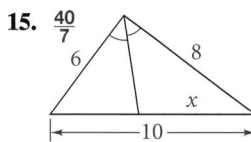
    6 · 8 · *x* · 10

16. 12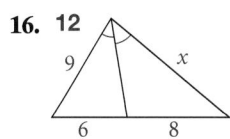
    9 · *x* · 6 · 8

Use the figure at the right to complete each proportion.

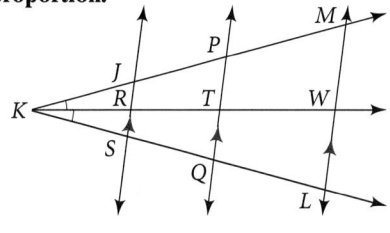

17. $\frac{RS}{\blacksquare} = \frac{JR}{KJ}$ *KS*

18. $\frac{KJ}{JP} = \frac{KS}{\blacksquare}$ *SQ*

19. $\frac{QL}{PM} = \frac{SQ}{\blacksquare}$ *JP*

20. $\frac{PT}{\blacksquare} = \frac{TQ}{KQ}$ *KP*

21. $\frac{KL}{LW} = \frac{\blacksquare}{MW}$ *KM*

22. $\frac{\blacksquare}{KP} = \frac{LQ}{KQ}$ *PM*

23. $\frac{\blacksquare}{SQ} = \frac{JK}{KS}$ *JP*

24. $\frac{KL}{KM} = \frac{\blacksquare}{MW}$ *LW*

B **Apply Your Skills**

Urban Design In Washington, D.C., 17th, 18th, 19th, and 20th Streets are parallel streets that intersect Pennsylvania Avenue and I Street.

25. How long (to the nearest foot) is Pennsylvania Avenue between 19th Street and 18th Street? **559 ft**

26. How long (to the nearest foot) is Pennsylvania Avenue between 18th Street and 17th Street? **671 ft**

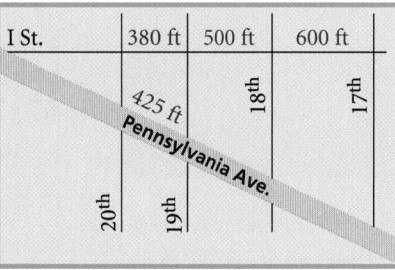

I St. · 380 ft · 500 ft · 600 ft · 425 ft · Pennsylvania Ave. · 20th · 19th · 18th · 17th

27. The legs of a right triangle are 5 cm and 12 cm long. Find the lengths, to the nearest tenth, of the segments into which the bisector of the right angle divides the hypotenuse. **3.8 cm and 9.2 cm**

28. **Open-Ended** In a triangle, the bisector of an angle divides the opposite side into two segments with lengths 6 cm and 9 cm. How long could the other two sides of the triangle be? (*Caution:* Make sure the three sides satisfy the Triangle Inequality Theorem.) **Answers may vary. Sample: 9 cm and 13.5 cm**

Real-World Connection

Careers A master's degree in urban design is good preparation for urban planning.

Assignment Guide

1 **Objective**

A **B** **Core** 1–10, 25, 26, 31, 33–35, 37–39, 47–50

C Extension 51

2 **Objective**

A **B** **Core** 11–24, 27–30, 32, 36, 40–46

Standardized Test Prep 52–55

Mixed Review 56–66

Connection to Algebra

Exercise 3 Use this exercise to check how well students solve complicated proportions. Review solving equations with variables on both sides.

Exercises 14, 15 Have students discuss why the unlabeled segment has length $6 - x$ in Exercise 14 and $10 - x$ in Exercise 15.

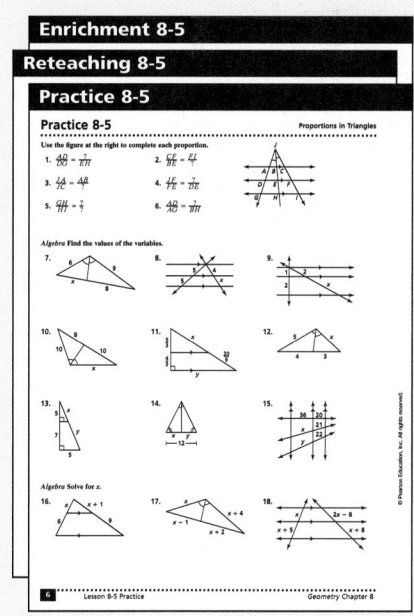

30a.

29. Surveying The perimeter of the triangular lot at the right is 50 m. The surveyor's tape bisects an angle. Find the lengths x and y. $x = 18$ m; $y = 12$ m

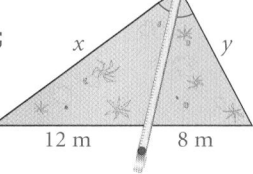

12 m   8 m

30. Critical Thinking Sharell draws $\triangle ABC$. She finds that the bisector of $\angle C$ bisects the opposite side.
  a. Sketch $\triangle ABC$ and the bisector. **See left.**
  b. Writing What type of triangle is $\triangle ABC$? Explain your reasoning. isosceles; $\triangle$-$\angle$ Bisector Thm.

$\boxed{x^2}$ **Algebra** Solve for x.

31. 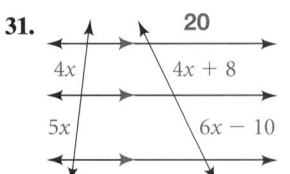   **32.** 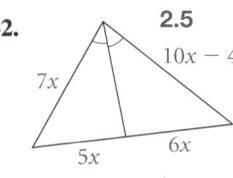   **33.**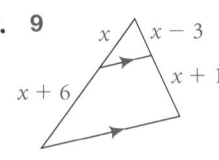

Proof 34. Follow the steps below. Write a proof of the Corollary to the Side-Splitter Theorem found on page 447.

Given: $\overleftrightarrow{AW} \parallel \overleftrightarrow{BX} \parallel \overleftrightarrow{CY}$

Prove: $\frac{AB}{BC} = \frac{WX}{XY}$

Begin by drawing $\overleftrightarrow{WC}$, intersecting $\overline{BX}$ at point Z.
  a. Apply the Side-Splitter Theorem to $\triangle ACW$: $\frac{\blacksquare}{\blacksquare} = \frac{WZ}{ZC} \cdot \frac{AB}{BC}$
  b. Apply the Side-Splitter Theorem to $\triangle CWY$: $\frac{WZ}{ZC} = \blacksquare \cdot \frac{WX}{XY}$
  c. Substitute to prove the corollary. $\frac{AB}{BC} = \frac{WX}{XY}$

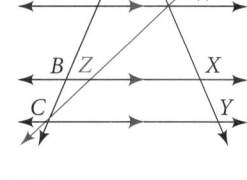

35. Oil Spills Describe how you could use the figure at the right to find the length of the oil spill indirectly. What measurements and calculations would you use? **See margin.**

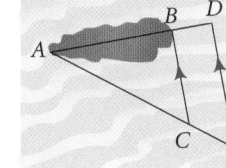

36. An angle bisector of a triangle divides the opposite side of the triangle into segments 5 cm and 3 cm long. A second side of the triangle is 7.5 cm long. Find all possible lengths for the third side of the triangle. **4.5 cm or 12.5 cm**

Geometry in 3 Dimensions In the figure at the right, $\overleftrightarrow{FG} \parallel \overleftrightarrow{AB}, \overleftrightarrow{GH} \parallel \overleftrightarrow{BC}, AF = 2, FE = 4,$ and $BG = 3.$

37. Find GE. **6**

38. If $EH = 5$, find HC. **2.5**

39. If $FG = 3$, find the perimeter of $\triangle ABE$. **19.5**

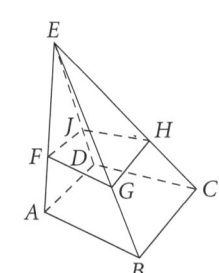

For a right triangle, denote lengths as follows:
ℓ_1 and ℓ_2 the legs, h the hypotenuse, and h_1 and h_2 the hypotenuse segments determined by the bisector of the right angle.
For the two given measures, find the other three to the nearest tenth.

40–45. See margin.

40. $\ell_1 = 6, \ell_2 = 8$ **41.** $h_1 = 4, h_2 = 9$ **42.** $h = 13, \ell_2 = 12$

43. $\ell_1 = 5\sqrt{2}, h_1 = 5$ **44.** $\ell_1 = 15, \ell_2 = 8$ **45.** $h_1 = 4, h = 8$

Proof 46. In a 30°-60°-90° right triangle, the right-angle bisector cuts the hypotenuse into two segments. Prove that one segment is $\sqrt{3}$ times the length of the other. **See margin.**

Real-World Connection

You measure an oil spill to find the size of the boom you'll need to contain it.

35. Measure $\overline{AC}$, $\overline{CE}$, and $\overline{BD}$. Use the Side-Splitter Thm. Write the prop. $\frac{AC}{CE} = \frac{AB}{BD}$ and solve for AB.

40. $h = 10.0, h_1 = 4.3, h_2 = 5.7$

41. $h = 13.0, \ell_1 = 5.3, \ell_2 = 11.9$

42. $\ell_1 = 5.0, h_1 = 3.8, h_2 = 9.2$

43. $\ell_2 = 7.1, h_2 = 5.0, h = 10.0$

44. $h = 17.0, h_1 = 11.1, h_2 = 5.9$

45. $h_2 = 4, \ell_1 = 5.7, \ell_2 = 5.7$

46. The ratio of the legs of a 30°-60°-90° $\triangle$ is $\sqrt{3}$. Let the rt. $\angle$ bisector divide the hyp. into segments x and y. Then by the $\triangle$-$\angle$-bis. Thm., $\frac{x}{y} = \sqrt{3}$, so $x = \sqrt{3}y$.

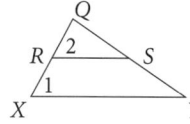

Proof 47. Copy and complete this two-column proof of the Converse of the Side-Splitter Theorem: If a line divides two sides of a triangle proportionally, then it is parallel to the third side.

Given: $\frac{XR}{RQ} = \frac{YS}{SQ}$

Prove: $\overline{RS} \parallel \overline{XY}$

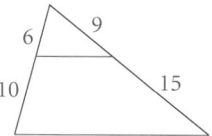

Real-World Connection

In this glass roof, parallel lines divide the sides of triangles proportionally.

Statements	Reasons
1. $\frac{XR}{RQ} = \frac{YS}{SQ}$	a. __?__ Given
2. $\frac{XR + RQ}{RQ} = \frac{YS + SQ}{SQ}$	b. __?__ Prop. of Proportions
3. $\frac{XQ}{RQ} = \frac{YQ}{SQ}$	c. __?__ Segment Add. Post.
4. $\angle Q \cong \angle Q$	d. __?__ Reflexive Prop. of $\cong$
5. $\triangle XQY \sim \triangle RQS$	e. __?__ SAS $\sim$ Thm.
6. $\angle 1 \cong \angle 2$	f. __?__ Corr. $\angle$s of $\sim$ $\triangle$s are $\cong$.
7. $\overline{RS} \parallel \overline{XY}$	g. __?__ If corr. $\angle$s are $\cong$, lines $\parallel$.

Determine whether the red segments are parallel. Explain each answer. You can use the theorem proved in Exercise 47. 48–50. See margin.

48. 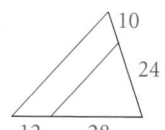   49. 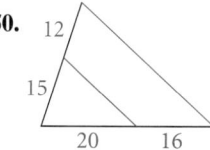   50.

C Challenge Proof 51. Use the definition in part (a) to prove the statements in parts (b) and (c).
  a. Write a definition for a midsegment of a parallelogram.
  b. A parallelogram midsegment is parallel to two sides of the parallelogram.
  c. A parallelogram midsegment bisects the diagonals of a parallelogram.
  a–c. See back of book.

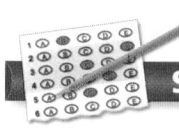

Standardized Test Prep

Multiple Choice

54. [2] $\frac{n + 1}{28} = \frac{20}{35}$;
    $35n + 35 = 560$;
    $n = 15$

    [1] correct proportion solved incorrectly

52. Use the figure at the right. What is x? **D**
    A. 5   B. 10
    C. 15   D. 20

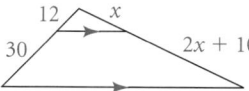

53. The legs of a right triangle have lengths 7 and 24. The bisector of the right angle divides the hypotenuse into two segments. What is the length of the shorter segment of the hypotenuse to the nearest tenth? **F**
    F. 5.6   G. 8.0   H. 19.4   I. 25

Short Response

54. What is n? Show your work.
    See left.

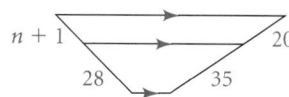

Extended Response

Take It to the NET
Online lesson quiz at
www.PHSchool.com
Web Code: afa-0805

55. The bisectors of an angle of a triangle divide the opposite side of the triangle into segments 4 cm and 5 cm long. A second side of the triangle is 6 cm long.
    a. Draw two diagrams you can use to find the two possible different lengths for the third side. a–b. See back of book.
    b. Use each diagram in part (a) to write a proportion. Solve for each possible length of the third side of the triangle. Show your work.

48. Yes; since $\frac{6}{10} = \frac{9}{15}$, the segments are $\parallel$ by the Converse of the Side-Splitter Thm.

49. No; $\frac{28}{12} \neq \frac{24}{10}$.

50. Yes; since $\frac{15}{12} = \frac{20}{16}$, the segments are $\parallel$ by the Converse of the Side-Splitter Thm.

---

4. Assess

Lesson Quiz 8-5

Solve for x in each diagram.

1.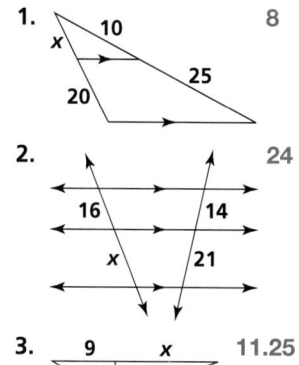

2.

3.

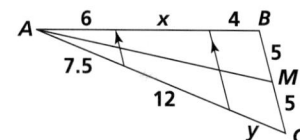

Use the diagram below for Exercises 4–6.

4. Find x. **9.6**

5. Find y. **5**

6. Explain how you know that $\overline{AM}$ is not the angle bisector of $\angle BAC$. If it were, $\frac{AB}{AC}$ would equal $\frac{BM}{MC} = 1$. But $AC > AB$.

Alternative Assessment

Have each student draw two triangles, construct a segment parallel to a side on one triangle and an angle bisector on the other triangle, and then use rulers and calculators to illustrate the Side-Splitter and Triangle-Angle-Bisector Theorems.

Standardized Test Prep

Resources
For additional practice with a variety of test item formats:
● Standardized Test Prep, p. 465
● Test-Taking Strategies, p. 460
● Test-Taking Strategies with Transparencies

Exercise 53 Before students try to write and solve a proportion, they should draw a diagram and apply the Pythagorean Theorem.

451

To check understanding of Lessons 8-3 to 8-5:

Checkpoint Quiz 2 (p. 452)

📁 **Teaching Resources**
Checkpoint Quiz 2 (also in Prentice Hall Assessment System)

👥 **Reaching All Students**
Reading and Math Literacy 8C

Spanish versions available

Mixed Review

Lesson 8-4   Refer to the figure to complete each proportion.

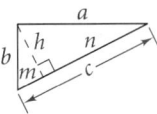

56. $\frac{n}{h} = \frac{h}{\blacksquare}$ m   **57.** $\frac{\blacksquare}{b} = \frac{b}{c}$ m

58. $\frac{n}{a} = \frac{a}{\blacksquare}$ c   **59.** $\frac{m}{h} = \frac{\blacksquare}{n}$ h

Lesson 7-3 x^2 **Algebra** Find the value of each variable. Leave your answer in simplest radical form.

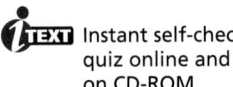

60.   **61.**   **62.**

$x = 24; y = 12\sqrt{3}$ $x = 9; y = 9\sqrt{3}$ $x = 15; y = 30$

Lesson 6-4 x^2 **Algebra** $RSTV$ is a rectangle. Find the lengths of the diagonals $\overline{RT}$ and $\overline{SV}$.

63. $RT = SV = 38$ **63.** $RT = 5x + 8, SV = x + 32$ **64.** $RT = 42 - x, SV = 9x - 8$

64. $RT = SV = 37$ **65.** $RT = 8x - 4, SV = 6x + 9$ **66.** $RT = 3x + 5, SV = 5x + 4$
                            $RT = SV = 48$ $RT = SV = 6.5$

✓ Checkpoint Quiz 2   Lessons 8-3 through 8-5

📱 **TEXT** Instant self-check quiz online and on CD-ROM

Determine whether the triangles are similar. If so, write the similarity statement. Also, write the postulate or theorem that proves they are similar.

1. 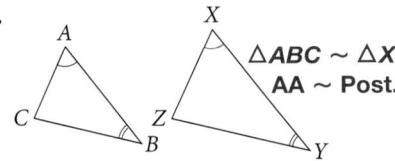   **2.**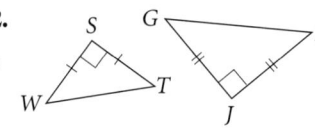

$\triangle ABC \sim \triangle XYZ$; AA $\sim$ Post.

$\triangle WST \sim \triangle HJG$; SAS $\sim$ Thm.

x^2 **Algebra** The polygons are similar. Find the value of each variable.

3. 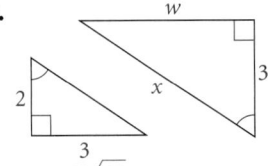   **4.**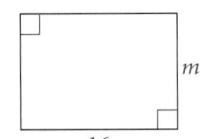

$x = \frac{3\sqrt{13}}{2}$; w = 4.5

x^2 **Algebra** Find the value of each variable.

5. 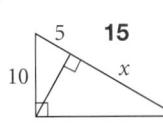   **6.** 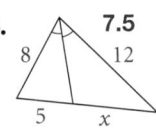   **7.**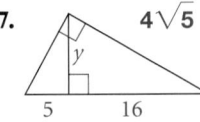

8. 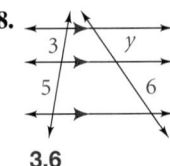   **9.** 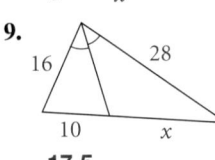   **10.**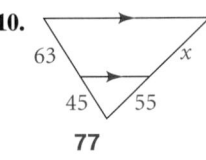

3.6   17.5

Reading Math
Reading a Two-Column Proof

FOR USE WITH PAGE 446, THEOREM 8-4

Reading a two-column proof looks like it should be pretty simple. After all, the statements are numbered and it's clear which reason goes with which statement. The trick is that although the statements are listed in numerical order, it is not always true that each statement follows directly from the preceding statement.

To understand a two-column proof, you may find it helpful to copy the proof and make notes on your copy. Here are things you'll want to do:

1. Mark the diagram to keep track of what you prove.

2. Think of the statement you read as the "then" part of an if-then statement. The reason shown gives a clue to the "if" part. Write in parentheses the step (or steps) that provide the specific information needed to deduce the "then" part.

3. When you see "Substitute," write in parentheses what was substituted where.

Here is the proof of Theorem 8-4, The Side-Splitter Theorem, that a student copied and marked up.

Given: $\triangle QXY$ with $\overleftrightarrow{RS} \parallel \overleftrightarrow{XY}$

Prove: $\dfrac{XR}{RQ} = \dfrac{YS}{SQ}$

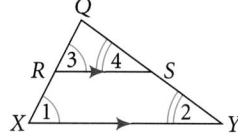

Statements	Reasons
1. $\overleftrightarrow{RS} \parallel \overleftrightarrow{XY}$	1. Given
2. $\angle 1 \cong \angle 3$, $\angle 2 \cong \angle 4$	2. If lines are $\parallel$, then corr. $\angle$s are $\cong$. **(from step 1)**
3. $\triangle QXY \sim \triangle QRS$	3. AA $\sim$ Postulate **(from step 2)**
4. $\dfrac{XQ}{RQ} = \dfrac{YQ}{SQ}$	4. Corr. sides of $\sim$ $\triangle$ are proportional. **(from step 3)**
5. $XQ = XR + RQ$, $YQ = YS + SQ$	5. Segment Addition Postulate
6. $\dfrac{XR + RQ}{RQ} = \dfrac{YS + SQ}{SQ}$	6. Substitute. **(the two sums from step 5, into step 4)**
7. $\dfrac{XR}{RQ} = \dfrac{YS}{SQ}$	7. A Property of Proportions **(from step 6)**

In conclusion, a two-column proof has a more organized structure than a flow proof. On the other hand, the flow of logic can be harder to follow. Marking a diagram and keeping notes can be helpful.

EXERCISE

Copy the two-column proof from p. 199, Exercise 29. Fill in the missing statements and reasons. Mark your diagram and proof. **See margin.**

Reading a Two-Column Proof

A two-column proof format organizes each statement and its justification. Unlike a flow proof, however, it does not make clear each logical connection. This feature helps students understand how to identify the logic flow and missing links when reading a two-column proof.

Teaching Notes

By reading the parenthetical annotations in the two-column proof, students can better understand the logic of the reasons. After they read the proof, ask students why the steps in the proof could or could not be interchanged.

Teaching Tip

Have volunteers state the AA Similarity and Segment Addition Postulates.

Exercise

Have students work independently to complete the proof. Then have volunteers share with the class what they were thinking as they completed each step of the proof.

3. $\angle Q \cong \angle S$ (All right $\angle$s are $\cong$; from step 2.)

4. $\angle QTP \cong \angle STR$ (Vert. $\angle$s are $\cong$.)

5. T is the midpoint of $\overline{PR}$. (Given)

6. $\overline{PT} \cong \overline{RT}$ (Def. of midpt.; from step 5)

7. $\triangle PQT \cong \triangle RST$ (AAS; from steps 3, 4, and 6)

---

page 453 **Check Understanding**

Given: $\overline{PQ} \perp \overline{QS}$, $\overline{RS} \perp \overline{QS}$, T is the midpoint of $\overline{PR}$.

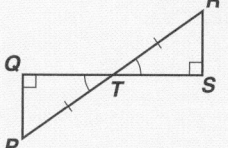

Prove: $\triangle PQT \cong \triangle RST$

1. $\overline{PQ} \perp \overline{QS}$, $\overline{RS} \perp \overline{QS}$, (Given)

2. $\angle Q$ and $\angle S$ are right $\angle$s. (Def. of $\perp$; from step 1)

1. Plan

Lesson Preview

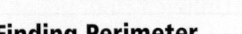 **Check Skills You'll Need**

Finding Perimeter
Lesson 1-7: Example 1
Exercises 1–7
Extra Practice, p. 690

Finding Area
Lesson 1-7: Example 4
Exercises 20–26
Extra Practice, p. 690

Lesson Resources

📁 **Teaching Resources**
Practice, Reteaching, Enrichment

👥 **Reaching All Students**
Practice Workbook 8-6
Spanish Practice Workbook 8-6
Informal Geometry Planning
   Guide 8-6

🕐 **Teacher's Time Savers!**
Transparencies
• Check Skills You'll Need 8-6
• Additional Examples 8-6
• Student Edition Answers 8-6
• Lesson Quiz 8-6
PH Presentation Pro CD 8-6

(ASSESSMENT SYSTEM)

Computer Test Generator CD

💿 **Technology**
Resource Pro® CD-ROM
Computer Test Generator CD
Prentice Hall Presentation Pro CD

🖥 **www.PHSchool.com**
Student Site
• Teacher Web Code: afk-5500
• Self-grading Lesson Quiz
Teacher Center
• Lesson Planner
• Resources

Plus

454

 **8-6**

Perimeters and Areas of Similar Figures

 North Carolina Objectives

2.03 Apply properties, definitions, and theorems of two-dimensional figures to solve problems and write proofs: a) Triangles. b) Quadrilaterals. c) Other polygons.

Lesson Preview

What You'll Learn

OBJECTIVE 1 To find the perimeters and areas of similar figures

. . . And Why

To find the expected yield of a garden, as in Example 3

✓ Check Skills You'll Need

(For help see Lesson 1-7.)

Find the perimeter and area of each figure.

1.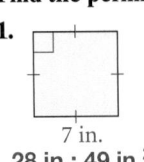
7 in.
28 in.; 49 in.²

2.
4 m
8 m
24 m; 32 m²

3.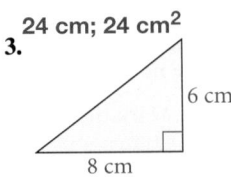
24 cm; 24 cm²
6 cm
8 cm

Find the perimeter and area of each rectangle with the given base and height.

4. $b = 1$ cm, $h = 3$ cm
8 cm; 3 cm²

5. $b = 2$ cm, $h = 6$ cm
16 cm; 12 cm²

6. $b = 3$ cm, $h = 9$ cm
24 cm; 27 cm²

 Interactive lesson includes instant self-check, tutorials, and activities.

OBJECTIVE 1 **Finding Perimeters and Areas of Similar Figures**

Investigation: Perimeters and Areas of Similar Rectangles

• On a piece of grid paper, draw a 3-unit by 4-unit rectangle.

• Draw three different rectangles, each similar to the original rectangle. Label them I, II, and III.

1. Use your drawings to complete a chart like this. **Check students' work.**

Centimeter Grid Paper

Rectangle	Perimeter	Area
Original		
I		
II		
III		

2. Use the information from the first chart to complete a chart like this.
Check students' work.

Rectangle	Similarity Ratio	Ratio of Perimeters	Ratio of Areas
I to Original			
II to Original			
III to Original			

3. The ratio for perimeters is the same, but the ratio for areas is the similarity ratio squared.

3. How do the ratios of perimeters and the ratios of areas compare with the similarity ratios? **See left.**

454 Chapter 8 Similarity

Ongoing Assessment and Intervention

Before the Lesson **Diagnose prerequisite skills using:**	**During the Lesson** **Monitor progress using:**	**After the Lesson** **Assess knowledge using:**
• Check Skills You'll Need	• Check Understanding • Additional Examples • Standardized Test Prep	• Lesson Quiz • Computer Test Generator CD

To compare areas of similar figures, you can square the similarity ratio.

 Key Concepts

Theorem 8-6	Perimeters and Areas of Similar Figures

If the similarity ratio of two similar figures is $\frac{a}{b}$, then
(1) the ratio of their perimeters is $\frac{a}{b}$ and
(2) the ratio of their areas is $\frac{a^2}{b^2}$.

1 EXAMPLE Finding Ratios in Similar Figures

The trapezoids at the right are similar. The ratio of the lengths of corresponding sides is $\frac{6}{9}$, or $\frac{2}{3}$.

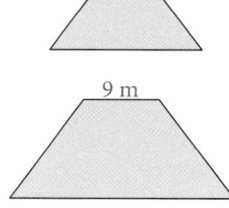
6 m

9 m

a. Find the ratio (smaller to larger) of the perimeters.

The ratio of the perimeters is the same as the ratio of corresponding sides, which is $\frac{2}{3}$.

b. Find the ratio (smaller to larger) of the areas.

The ratio of the areas is the square of the ratio of corresponding sides, which is $\frac{2^2}{3^2}$, or $\frac{4}{9}$.

✔ **Check Understanding** ① Two similar polygons have corresponding sides in the ratio 5 : 7.
a. Find the ratio of their perimeters. **5:7**
b. Find the ratio of their areas. **25:49**

When you know the area of one of two similar polygons, you can use a proportion to find the area of the other polygon.

2 EXAMPLE Finding Areas Using Similar Figures

The area of the smaller regular pentagon is about 27.5 cm^2. Find the area A of the larger regular pentagon.

All regular pentagons are similar. Here the ratio of the lengths of the corresponding sides is $\frac{4}{10}$, or $\frac{2}{5}$. The ratio of the areas is $\frac{2^2}{5^2}$, or $\frac{4}{25}$.

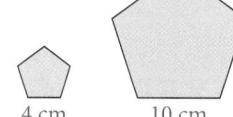
4 cm   10 cm

$\frac{4}{25} = \frac{27.5}{A}$ **Write a proportion.**

$4A = 687.5$ **Cross-Product Property**

$A = \frac{687.5}{4} = 171.875$ **Solve for A.**

● The area of the larger pentagon is about 172 cm^2.

Need Help?

Regular pentagons are similar because all angles measure 108 and all sides in each are congruent.

✔ **Check Understanding** ② The corresponding sides of two similar parallelograms are in the ratio $\frac{3}{4}$. The area of the larger parallelogram is 96 in.^2. Find the area of the smaller parallelogram. **54 in.²**

You can apply what you know about the ratios of the areas of similar figures to real-world problems.

 **Reaching All Students**

Below Level Before you go over Theorem 8-6, have students draw a triangle and three midsegments. Discuss how the four congruent triangles relate to Theorem 8-6(2).	**Advanced Learners** After Example 2, have students prove that the ratio of the areas of two similar regular polygons equals the square of the ratios of their sides.	**Visual Learners** See note on page 456. **Error Prevention** See note on page 455.

---

2. Teach

Professional Development

Math Background

The Distributive Property readily proves that the ratio of the perimeters of two similar figures with the similarity ratio $a : b$ is also $a : b$. To prove that the ratio of the areas of two similar triangles with the similarity ratio $a : b$ is $a^2 : b^2$, draw altitudes to corresponding sides and prove that the right triangles thus formed are similar. The Transitive Property allows the proportional relationship of the triangles' sides to be extended to their altitudes.

OBJECTIVE
① Teaching Notes

Investigation (Optional)
Because all rectangles have four right angles, remind students that all rectangles with a 3 : 4 ratio of sides are similar.

① EXAMPLE **Math Tip**

Point out that the ratios of the perimeters and areas were found without calculating the perimeter or area of either trapezoid. In fact, those measurements cannot be found for the given figures because only one side length of each is known.

② EXAMPLE **Error Prevention**

Remind students not to use the similarity ratio as the ratio of the areas. Point out that area is measured in *square* units, so the ratio of the areas is the *square* of the similarity ratio.

Teaching Tip
After students finish Example 2, ask: *How do you know that all regular pentagons are similar?* All regular figures are equilateral and equiangular. So, all angles of regular pentagons are congruent, and the ratio of the sides of any two regular pentagons is constant.

455

3 EXAMPLE Visual Learners

Have students draw a rectangle for each plot of land to help them visualize the descriptions.

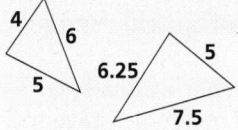
4 EXAMPLE Connection to Algebra

Students are used to solving an equation for one variable but not for the ratio of two variables. Discuss why taking the square root of a ratio is like solving two equations.

Additional Examples

❶ The triangles below are similar. Find the ratio (larger to smaller) of their perimeters and of their areas.

4, 6, 5, 6.25, 5, 7.5

perimeters: $\frac{5}{4}$; areas: $\frac{25}{16}$

❷ The ratio of the lengths of the corresponding sides of two regular octagons is $\frac{8}{3}$. The area of the larger octagon is 320 ft². Find the area of the smaller octagon. **45 ft²**

❸ Benita plants the same crop in two rectangular fields, each with side lengths in a ratio of 2 : 3. Each dimension of the larger field is $3\frac{1}{2}$ times the dimension of the smaller field. Seeding the smaller field costs $8. How much money does seeding the larger field cost? **$98**

❹ The areas of two similar pentagons are 32 in.² and 72 in.² What is their similarity ratio? What is the ratio of their perimeters? **2 : 3; 2 : 3**

Closure

The similarity ratio of two similar triangles is 5 : 3. The perimeter of the smaller triangle is 36 cm, and its area is 18 cm². Find the perimeter and area of the larger triangle. **perimeter: 60 cm; area: 50 cm²**

Real-World Connection

Many cities make city land available to the community for gardening.

3 EXAMPLE Real-World Connection

Community Service During the summer, a group of high school students used a plot of city land and harvested 13 bushels of vegetables that they gave to a food pantry. Their project was so successful that next summer the city will let them use a larger, similar plot of land.

In the new plot, each dimension is 2.5 times the corresponding dimension of the original plot. How many bushels can they expect to harvest next year?

The ratio of the dimensions is 2.5 : 1. So, the ratio of the areas is $(2.5)^2$: 1^2, or 6.25 : 1. With 6.25 times as much land next year, the students can expect to harvest 6.25(13), or about 81 bushels.

✔ **Check Understanding** ❸ The similarity ratio of the dimensions of two similar pieces of window glass is 3 : 5. The smaller piece costs $2.50. What should be the cost of the larger piece? **$6.94**

When you know the ratio of the areas of two similar figures, you can work backward to find the ratio of their perimeters.

4 EXAMPLE Finding Similarity and Perimeter Ratios

The areas of two similar triangles are 50 cm² and 98 cm². What is the similarity ratio? What is the ratio of their perimeters?

Find the similarity ratio $a : b$.

$\frac{a^2}{b^2} = \frac{50}{98}$ **The ratio of the areas is $a^2 : b^2$.**

$\frac{a^2}{b^2} = \frac{25}{49}$ **Simplify.**

$\frac{a}{b} = \frac{5}{7}$ **Take square roots.**

The ratio of the perimeters equals the similarity ratio 5 : 7.

✔ **Check Understanding** ❹ The areas of two similar rectangles are 1875 ft² and 135 ft². Find the ratio of their perimeters. **$5\sqrt{5}$:3**

EXERCISES

For more practice, see *Extra Practice*.

Practice and Problem Solving

Ⓐ **Practice by Example**

Example 1
(page 455)

The figures in each pair are similar. Compare the first figure to the second. Give the ratio of the perimeters and the ratio of the areas.

1. **1:2; 1:4**

2 in.   4 in.

2. **4:3; 16:9**

8 cm   6 cm

3.

14 m   21 m
2:3; 4:9

4.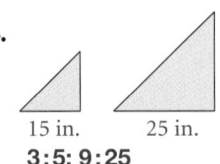

15 in.   25 in.
3:5; 9:25

Example 2
(page 455)

The figures in each pair are similar. The area of one figure is given. Find the area of the other figure to the nearest whole number.

5. 24 in.^{2}

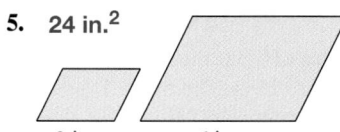

3 in.   6 in.
Area of smaller parallelogram = 6 in.^{2}

6. 54 m^2

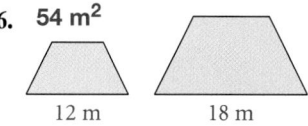

12 m   18 m
Area of larger trapezoid = 121 m^2

7. 59 ft^2

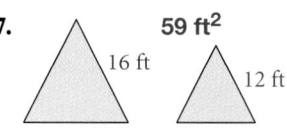

16 ft   12 ft
Area of larger triangle = 105 ft^2

8.

439 m^2

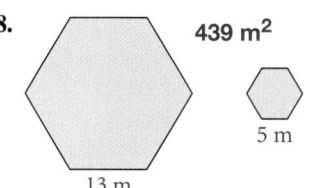

5 m

13 m
Area of smaller hexagon = 65 m^2

Example 3
(page 456)

9. **Remodeling** It costs a family $216 to have a 9 ft-by-12 ft wooden floor refinished. At that rate, how much would it cost them to have a 12 ft-by-16 ft wooden floor refinished? **$384**

10. **Decorating** An embroidered placemat costs $2.95. An embroidered tablecloth is similar to the placemat, but four times as long and four times as wide. How much would you expect to pay for the tablecloth? **$47.20**

Example 4
(page 456)

Find the similarity ratio and the ratio of perimeters for each pair of similar figures.

11. two regular octagons with areas 4 ft^2 and 16 ft^2 **1:2; 1:2**

12. two triangles with areas 75 m^2 and 12 m^2 **5:2; 5:2**

13. two trapezoids with areas 49 cm^2 and 9 cm^2 **7:3; 7:3**

14. two parallelograms with areas 18 in.^{2} and 32 in.^{2} **3:4; 3:4**

15. two equilateral triangles with areas $16\sqrt{3}$ ft^2 and $\sqrt{3}$ ft^2 **4:1; 4:1**

16. two circles with areas 2π cm^2 and 200π cm^2 **1:10; 1:10**

B **Apply Your Skills**

The similarity ratio of two similar polygons is given. Find the ratio of their perimeters and the ratio of their areas.

17. 3 : 1   **3:1; 9:1**

18. 2 : 5   **2:5; 4:25**

19. $\frac{2}{3}$ **2:3; 4:9**

20. $\frac{7}{4}$ **7:4; 49:16**

21. 6 : 1   **6:1; 36:1**

22. The area of a regular decagon is 50 cm^2. What is the area of a regular decagon with sides four times the length of the smaller decagon? **800 cm^2**

23. **Error Analysis** A reporter used the graphic below to show that the number of houses with more than two televisions had doubled in the past few years. Explain why this graphic is misleading. **While the ratio of lengths is 2 : 1, the ratio of areas is 4 : 1.**

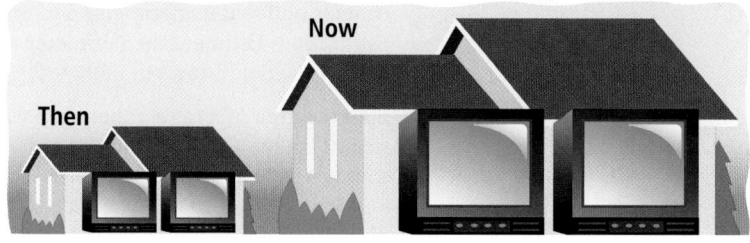

Now

Then

Connection to Statistics

Exercise 23 Misleading graphs often are found in magazines and newspapers, so everyone needs to know how to analyze graphs critically. Have students suggest how they would draw a more appropriate graph.

Exercises 26–31 If necessary, remind students of the formula for the area of a triangle.

Exercise 38 Ask students to share their answers as a way to highlight the importance of proportional reasoning in everyday activities.

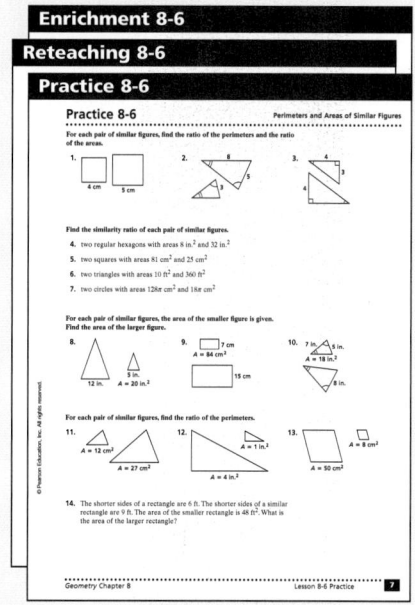

Enrichment 8-6
Reteaching 8-6
Practice 8-6

Lesson Quiz 8-6

1. For the similar rectangles, give the ratios (smaller to larger) of the perimeters and of the areas.

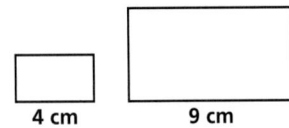

4 cm   9 cm

perimeters: $\frac{4}{9}$; areas: $\frac{16}{81}$

2. The triangles below are similar. The area of the larger triangle is 48 ft². Find the area of the smaller triangle.

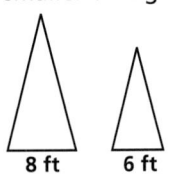

8 ft   6 ft

27 ft²

3. The similarity ratio of two regular octagons is 5 : 9. The area of the smaller octagon is 100 in.² Find the area of the larger octagon.
324 in.²

4. The areas of two equilateral triangles are 27 yd² and 75 yd². Find their similarity ratio and the ratio of their perimeters. **3 : 5; 3 : 5**

5. Mulch to cover an 8-ft by 16-ft rectangular garden costs $48. At the same rate, what would be the cost of mulch to cover a 12-ft by 24-ft rectangular garden?
$108

Alternative Assessment

Have students work in pairs and use rulers and graph paper to estimate the area of a map of your state. Then have them use the map scale and Theorem 8-6 to estimate the actual area of the state.

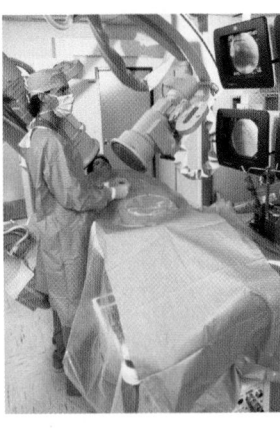

Real-World 🌐 Connection

Careers Doctors use enlarged images to aid in certain medical procedures.

Need Help?

For Exercise 34, recall the length of a diagonal of a square with 2-in. sides.

38. Answers may vary. Sample: The proposed playground is more than adequate. The number of students has approximately doubled. The proposed playground would be four times larger than the original playground.

39b. 114 mm; 475 mm²

24. **Medicine** For some medical imaging, the scale of the image is 3 : 1. That means that if an image is 3 cm long, the corresponding length on the person's body is 1 cm. Find the actual area of a lesion if its image has area 2.7 cm². **0.3 cm²**

25. The longer sides of a parallelogram are 5 m. The longer sides of a similar parallelogram are 15 m. The area of the smaller parallelogram is 28 m². What is the area of the larger parallelogram? **252 m²**

x^2 **Algebra** **Find the values of *x* and *y* when the smaller triangle shown here has the given area.**

26. 3 cm²   **27.** 6 cm²   **28.** 12 cm²

29. 16 cm²   **30.** 24 cm²   **31.** 48 cm²

26–31. See margin.

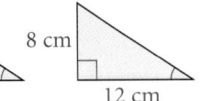

32. Two similar rectangles have areas 27 in.² and 48 in.². The length of one side of the larger rectangle is 16 in. What are the dimensions of both rectangles?
$2\frac{1}{4}$ in. by 12 in., 3 in. by 16 in.

33. In $\triangle RST$, $RS = 20$ m, $ST = 25$ m, and $RT = 40$ m.
  a. Open-Ended Choose a convenient scale. Then use a ruler and compass to draw $\triangle R'S'T' \sim \triangle RST$. **Check students' work.**
  b. Constructions Construct an altitude of $\triangle R'S'T'$ and measure its length. Find the area of $\triangle R'S'T'$. **Check students' work.**
  c. Estimation Estimate the area of $\triangle RST$. **Estimates may vary. Sample: 205 m²**

34. **Drawing** Draw a square with an area of 8 in.². Draw a second square with an area that is four times as large. What is the ratio of their perimeters?
Ratio of small to large is 1:2.

Compare the blue figure to the red figure. Find the ratios of (a) their perimeters and (b) their areas.

35.
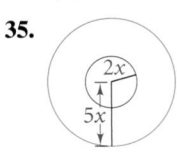
$\frac{5}{2}$, $\frac{25}{4}$

36. $\frac{8}{3}$; $\frac{64}{9}$
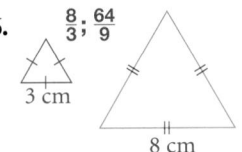
3 cm
8 cm

37. $\frac{2}{1}$; $\frac{4}{1}$
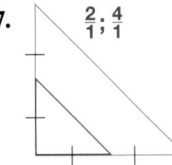

38. **Writing** The enrollment at an elementary school is going to increase from 200 students to 395 students. A parents' group is planning to increase the 100 ft-by-200 ft playground area to a larger area that is 200 ft by 400 ft. What would you tell the parents' group when they ask your opinion about whether the new playground will be large enough? **See left.**

39. a. Surveying A surveyor measured one side and two angles of a field as shown in the diagram. Use a ruler and a protractor to draw a similar triangle. **See margin.**
  b. Measure the sides and altitude of your triangle and find its perimeter and area.
  c. Estimation Estimate the perimeter and area of the field. **456 yd; 7600 yd²**

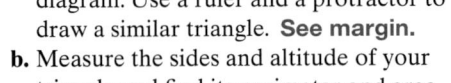
30°   50°
200 yd

40. a. Find the area of a regular hexagon with sides 2 cm long. Leave your answer in simplest radical form. **$6\sqrt{3}$ cm²**
  b. Use your answer to part (a) and Theorem 8-6 to find the areas of the regular polygons shown at the right.
  $54\sqrt{3}$ cm²; $13.5\sqrt{3}$ cm²; $96\sqrt{3}$ cm²

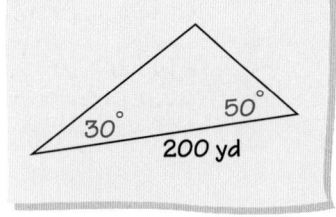
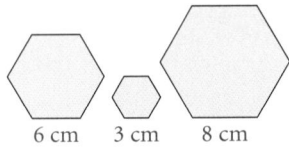
6 cm   3 cm   8 cm

pages 456–459 **Exercises**

26. $x = 2$ cm, $y = 3$ cm

27. $x = 2\sqrt{2}$ cm, $y = 3\sqrt{2}$ cm

28. $x = 4$ cm, $y = 6$ cm

29. $x = \frac{8\sqrt{3}}{3}$ cm, $y = 4\sqrt{3}$ cm

30. $x = 4\sqrt{2}$ cm, $y = 6\sqrt{2}$ cm

31. $x = 8$ cm, $y = 12$ cm

C Challenge   Complete each statement with *sometimes*, *always*, or *never*. Justify your answers.

41. Two similar rectangles with the same perimeter are ___?___ congruent.

42. Two rectangles with the same area are ___?___ similar.   **41–43. See margin.**

43. Two rectangles with the same area and different perimeters are ___?___ similar.

44. Similar figures ___?___ have the same area.
Sometimes; if they are ≅, they are ~ and have = areas.

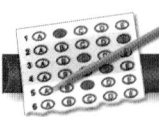

Standardized Test Prep

Gridded Response

45. Two regular hexagons have sides in the ratio 3 : 5. The area of the smaller hexagon is 81 m². In square meters, what is the area of the larger hexagon? **225**

46. Two similar polygons have areas in the ratio 9 : 16. The perimeter of the larger polygon is 900. What is the perimeter of the smaller polygon? **675**

47. The two triangles are similar. Their perimeters have the ratio 1 : 3. In square feet, what is the area of the larger triangle? **54**

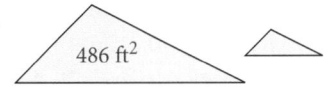

486 ft²

48. A rectangle has a perimeter of 192 in. A similar rectangle has a perimeter of 528 in. The area of the smaller rectangle is 2288 in.². In square inches, what is the area of the larger rectangle? **17303**

49. The area of a polygon is 3267 cm². The area of a similar polygon is 9075 cm². The perimeter of the larger polygon is 270.5 cm. In centimeters, what is the perimeter of the smaller one? **162.3**

Take It to the NET
Online lesson quiz at
www.PHSchool.com
Web Code: afa-0806

Mixed Review

Lesson 8-5 $x = 45; y = 107.5$
50. Solve for x and y in the diagram at the right.

51. An angle bisector divides the opposite side of a triangle into segments 4 cm and 6 cm long. A second side of the triangle is 8 cm long. Find all possible lengths for the third side of the triangle.
$5\frac{1}{3}$ cm; 12 cm

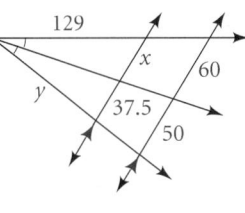

129

x
60
y
37.5
50

Lesson 7-5   **Find the area of each regular polygon.**

52. a square with a **50 cm²**
10-cm diagonal

53. a pentagon with apothem 13.8 and side length 20 **690 units²**

54. an octagon with apothem 12 and side length 10 **480 units²**

55. a 12-sided polygon with apothem 3.7 and side length 2.0 **44.4 units²**

Lesson 3-5 x^2 Algebra   **Write the equation in slope-intercept form, and graph the line.**
56–59. See margin.

56. $6x - 2y = 8$ **57.** $x + y = -2$ **58.** $3x = 4y$ **59.** $2x + \frac{1}{2}y = \frac{5}{2}$

x^2 Algebra   **Write the equation of the line described.**
60–61. Eq. forms may vary. Samples are given.

60. has slope -3 and contains point $(1, -2)$ $y = -3x + 1$

61. contains points $(3, 7)$ and $(0, -1)$ $y + 1 = \frac{8}{3}x$

Lesson 8-6   Perimeters and Areas of Similar Figures   **459**

39. Answers may vary.
Sample:

a.

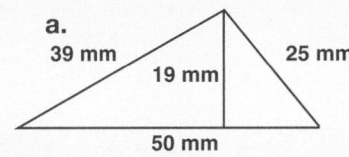

39 mm
19 mm
25 mm
50 mm

41. Always; ~ rectangles with = perimeters have a similarity ratio of 1, so they are ≅.

42. Sometimes; a 1-by-8 rect. and 2-by-4 rect. have the same areas, but are not ~.

Standardized Test Prep (right margin)

A sheet of blank grids is available in the Test-Taking Strategies with Transparencies booklet. Give this sheet to students for practice with filling in the grids.

📁 **Resources**
For additional practice with a variety of test item formats:
• Standardized Test Prep, p. 465
• Test-Taking Strategies, p. 460
• Test-Taking Strategies with Transparencies

Exercises 45–49 Remind students that ratios can be written as fractions, decimals, or percents. Whether students solve these exercises using proportions or some other method depends on how they express the ratios.

43. Never; if they were ≅, both measures would be the same. If they were ~, but not ≅, their areas would not be =.

56. $y = 3x - 4;$

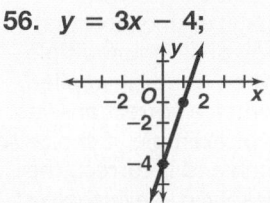

57. $y = -x - 2;$

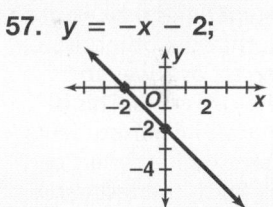

58. $y = \frac{3}{4}x;$

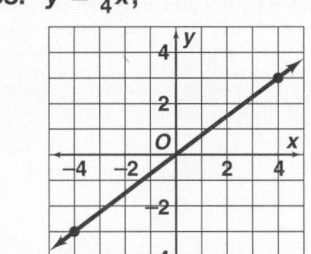

59.
$y = -4x + 5;$

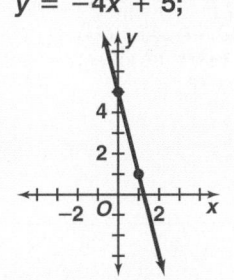

459

Testing Multiple Choices

Assessment tests almost always include multiple-choice questions. This feature reminds students that a guess-and-test strategy is effective in testing answers to multiple-choice questions.

Resources

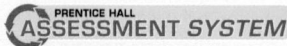
PRENTICE HALL
ASSESSMENT SYSTEM

Test-Taking Strategies with Transparencies
• Transparency 8
• Practice sheet p. 20

Teaching Notes

Help students understand that the strategy of testing multiple choices, when correctly applied, succeeds when a correct answer is found. For example, if choice A is tested first and is correct, the problem is solved. Nevertheless, students sometimes may want to make sure that the other choices are *not* correct as a way to confirm their answers. This is especially useful when students are unsure of their answers or when they finish the test early.

Test-Taking Strategies with Transparencies

Test-Taking Strategy: Testing Multiple Choices

When you take a multiple-choice test, one of the answer choices is always correct. You can solve a problem by testing the answer choices to find the correct one.

Solve $5^x + 12 = 637$.

   A. 2   B. 3   C. 4   D. 5

Work backward by substituting each answer choice for x.

$5^2 + 12 = ?$
$25 + 12 = 37$ not correct

$5^3 + 12 = ?$
$125 + 12 = 137$ not correct

$5^4 + 12 = ?$
$625 + 12 = 637$ correct

You do not have to continue substituting answer choices once you find the correct choice.

The answer is C, 4.

Solve these problems by working backward.

1. Solve $4^x - 7 = 4089$.
   A. 5   B. 6   C. 7   D. 8

2. Solve $y^4 - 24 = 57$.
   A. 7   B. 5   C. 3   D. 1

Solutions

1. B
2. C

Transparency 8

460

Your choices in a multiple-choice question include a correct answer. A strategy is to test each choice in the original problem. You may find mental math to be particularly useful for this.

EXAMPLE

Algebra What is the value of x in the diagram at the right?

   A. 0   **B.** 3
   C. 6   **D.** 10

The triangles are similar. The proportion $\frac{3}{5} = \frac{x}{x + 4}$ is apparent in the diagram. You can test the four answer choices using mental math.

Let $x = 0$.
$$\frac{x}{x + 4} = \frac{0}{0 + 4} = 0 \neq \frac{3}{5}$$
A is not the answer.

Let $x = 3$.
$$\frac{x}{x + 4} = \frac{3}{3 + 4} = \frac{3}{7} \neq \frac{3}{5}$$
B is not the answer.

Let $x = 6$.
$$\frac{x}{x + 4} = \frac{6}{6 + 4} = \frac{6}{10} = \frac{3}{5}$$
Yes! C is likely the answer.

To help make sure, let $x = 10$.
$$\frac{x}{x + 4} = \frac{10}{10 + 4} = \frac{10}{14} = \frac{5}{7} \neq \frac{3}{5}$$
D is not the answer.

● You write or mark C as your answer.

EXERCISES

1. What number is a solution to $\frac{x}{12} = \frac{x - 3}{8}$?   **D**
   A. 1   **B.** 3
   C. 6   **D.** 9

2. What number is a solution to $\frac{8}{13} = \frac{20}{a + 12}$?   **F**
   F. 20.5   **G.** 31
   H. 34   **I.** 44.5

x^2 **3. Algebra** What is the value of x?   **B**
   A. 4   **B.** 6
   C. 8   **D.** 10

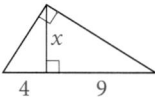

x^2 **4. Algebra** What is the value of y?   **F**
   F. 2   **G.** 4
   H. 6   **I.** 10

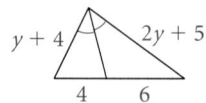

5. $AB = 2$, $CD = 4$, $FE = 10$, and $AE = 20$. What is AC?   **B**
   A. 2   **B.** 4
   C. 6   **D.** 8

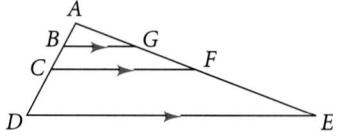

Chapter Review

Vocabulary

Cross-Product Property (p. 417)
extended proportion (p. 417)
geometric mean (p. 440)
golden ratio (p. 425)

golden rectangle (p. 425)
indirect measurement (p. 434)
proportion (p. 417)
scale (p. 418)

scale drawing (p. 418)
similar (p. 423)
similarity ratio (p. 423)

 Reading Math
Understanding
Vocabulary

Choose the correct term to complete each sentence.

1. Two polygons are __?__ if corresponding angles are congruent and corresponding sides are proportional. **similar**

2. The __?__ states that the product of the extremes is equal to the product of the means. **Cross-Product Property**

3. A __?__ is a rectangle that can be divided into a square and a rectangle that is similar to the original rectangle. **golden rectangle**

4. The ratio of the lengths of corresponding sides of two similar figures is the __?__. **4. similarity ratio**

5. A __?__ is a statement that two ratios are equal. **proportion**

6. Finding distances using similar triangles is called __?__. **indirect measurement**

7. The length and width of a golden rectangle are in the __?__. **golden ratio**

Take It to the NET
Online vocabulary quiz
at www.PHSchool.com
Web Code: afj-0851

Skills and Concepts

8-1 Objectives

▼ To write ratios and solve proportions

A ratio is a comparison of two quantities by division. You can write the ratio of a to b or $a : b$ as the quotient $\frac{a}{b}$ when $b \neq 0$.

A **proportion** is a statement that two ratios are equal. According to the **Properties of Proportions,** $\frac{a}{b} = \frac{c}{d}$ is equivalent to

(1) $ad = bc$ (2) $\frac{b}{a} = \frac{d}{c}$ (3) $\frac{a}{c} = \frac{b}{d}$ (4) $\frac{a+b}{b} = \frac{c+d}{d}$

Property 1, above, illustrates the **Cross-Product Property,** which states that the product of the extremes is equal to the product of the means.

When three or more ratios are equal, you can write an **extended proportion.**

In a **scale drawing,** the **scale** compares each length in the drawing to the actual length being represented.

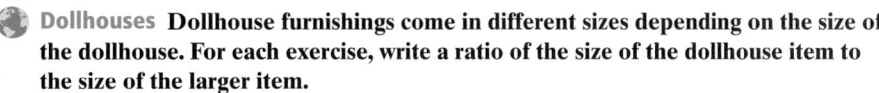 **Dollhouses** Dollhouse furnishings come in different sizes depending on the size of the dollhouse. For each exercise, write a ratio of the size of the dollhouse item to the size of the larger item.

8. dollhouse sofa: $1\frac{1}{2}$ in. long;
real sofa: 6 ft long **1:48**

9. dollhouse piano: $1\frac{3}{4}$ in. high
real piano: 3 ft 6 in. high **1:24**

If $\frac{p}{q} = \frac{2}{5}$, tell whether each equation must be true. Explain. 10–13. See margin.

10. $2q = 5p$ **11.** $\frac{5}{2} = \frac{q}{p}$ **12.** $5q = 2p$ **13.** $\frac{p}{2} = \frac{q}{5}$

---

pages 461–463 Chapter Review

10. True; use the Cross-Product Prop.

11. True; the cross product eq. is equivalent to the original proportion.

12. False; the cross product eq. is *not* equivalent to the original proportion.

13. True; the cross product eq. is equivalent to the original proportion.

Resources

8-2 and 8-3 Objectives

▼ To identify and apply similar polygons

▼ To use AA, SAS, and SSS similarity statements

▼ To apply AA, SAS, and SSS similarity statements

Similar polygons have congruent corresponding angles and proportional corresponding sides. The ratio of the lengths of corresponding sides is the **similarity ratio.**

A **golden rectangle** is a rectangle that can be divided into a square and a rectangle that is similar to the original rectangle. In any golden rectangle, the length and the width are in the **golden ratio,** which is about 1.618 : 1.

If two angles of one triangle are congruent to two angles of another triangle, then the triangles are similar by the **Angle-Angle Similarity Postulate** (AA ~). If an angle of one triangle is congruent to an angle of a second triangle, and the sides including the two angles are proportional, then the triangles are similar by the **Side-Angle-Side Similarity Theorem** (SAS ~). If the corresponding sides of two triangles are proportional, then the triangles are similar by the **Side-Side-Side Similarity Theorem** (SSS ~).

Methods of **indirect measurement** use similar triangles and measurements to find distances that are difficult to measure directly.

14. $\angle M \cong \angle R$, $\angle N \cong \angle S$, $\angle P \cong \angle T$; $\frac{MN}{RS} = \frac{MP}{RT} = \frac{NP}{ST}$

14. If $\triangle MNP \sim \triangle RST$, which angles are congruent? Write an extended proportion to indicate the proportional corresponding sides of the triangles.

15. Art An artist is creating a stained glass window and wants it to be a golden rectangle. To the nearest inch, what should be the length if the width is 24 in.? **39 in. or 15 in.**

The triangles are similar. Find the similarity ratio of the first to the second.

16. **2:3**

17. **2.5:1 or 5:2**

x^2 **Algebra** **The polygons are similar. Find the value of each variable.**

18.

19. **x = 12; y = 15**

Are the triangles similar? If so, write the similarity statement and name the postulate or theorem you used. If not, explain.

20. $\triangle XYZ \sim \triangle JKL$; SAS ~ Thm.

21. Not ~ ; Corr. sides are not prop.

20.

21.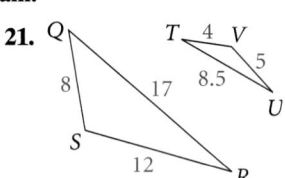

22. Two right triangles have an acute angle with the same measure. Name the theorem or postulate that is the most direct way to prove the triangles similar. **AA ~ Post.**

23. Indirect Measurement A crate is 1.5 ft high and casts a 2-ft shadow. At the same time, an apple tree casts an 18-ft shadow. How tall is the tree? **13.5 ft**

462 Chapter 8 Chapter Review

8-4 Objective

▼ To find and use relationships in similar right triangles

The **geometric mean** of two positive numbers a and b is the positive number x such that $\frac{a}{x} = \frac{x}{b}$.

When the altitude is drawn to the hypotenuse of a right triangle:

- the two triangles formed are similar to the original triangle and to each other;
- the length of the altitude is the geometric mean of the lengths of the segments of the hypotenuse; and
- the length of each leg is the geometric mean of the length of the adjacent hypotenuse segment and the length of the hypotenuse.

x^2 **Algebra Find the values of the variables. When an answer is not a whole number, leave it in simplest radical form.** $\quad x = 2\sqrt{21}; y = 4\sqrt{3}; z = 4\sqrt{7}$

24.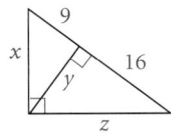

25.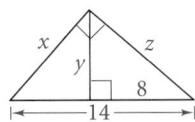

26.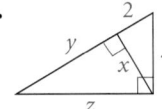

$x = 15; y = 12; z = 20 \qquad\qquad\qquad\qquad x = 2\sqrt{3}; y = 6; z = 4\sqrt{3}$

8-5 Objectives

▼ To use the Side-Splitter Theorem

▼ To use the Triangle-Angle-Bisector Theorem

The Side-Splitter Theorem states that if a line is parallel to one side of a triangle and intersects the other two sides, then it divides those sides proportionally. If three parallel lines intersect two transversals, then the segments intercepted on the transversals are proportional. The **Triangle-Angle-Bisector Theorem** states that if a ray bisects an angle of a triangle, then it divides the opposite side into two segments that are proportional to the other two sides of the triangle.

x^2 **Algebra Find the value of x.**

27. 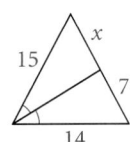 7.5

28.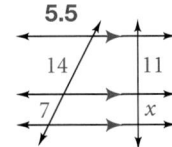

29.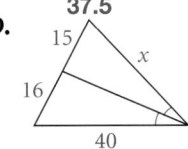

8-6 Objective

▼ To find the perimeters and areas of similar figures

If the similarity ratio of two similar figures is $\frac{a}{b}$, then the ratio of their perimeters is $\frac{a}{b}$, and the ratio of their areas is $\frac{a^2}{b^2}$.

For each pair of similar figures, find the ratio of the area of the first figure to the area of the second.

30.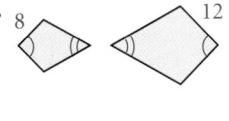

4:9

31.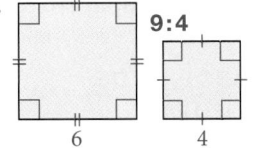

9:4

32.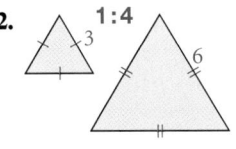

1:4

33. If the ratio of areas of two similar hexagons is 8 : 25, what is the ratio of their perimeters? $2\sqrt{2} : 5$

34. The similarity ratio of two similar triangles is 3 : 7. The area of the smaller triangle is 36 cm². What is the area of the larger triangle? **196 cm²**

Chapter 8   Chapter Review   **463**

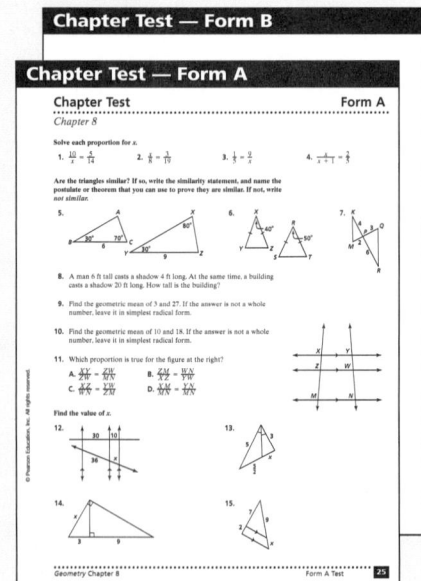

Chapter Test — Form B

Chapter Test — Form A

Chapter 8

Chapter Test

💻 **Take It to the NET**
Online chapter test at
www.PHSchool.com
Web Code: afa-0852

x^2 **Algebra** Solve each proportion.

1. $\frac{4}{5} = \frac{x}{20}$ **16**   **2.** $\frac{6}{x} = \frac{10}{7}$ **4.2**   **3.** $\frac{x}{3} = \frac{8}{12}$ **2**

x^2 **Algebra** The figures in each pair are similar. Find the value of each variable.

4. $x = 42; y = 138; z = 9$

5. **4**

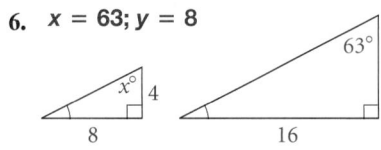

6. $x = 63; y = 8$

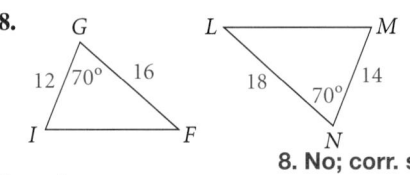

Are the triangles similar? If *yes*, write the similarity statement and name the postulate or theorem you can use to prove they are similar. If *no*, explain.

7. $\triangle PRQ \sim \triangle TWV$; SSS ~ Thm.

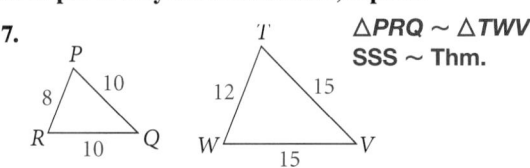

8.

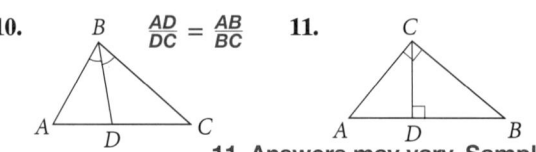

8. No; corr. sides are not in prop.

9. $\triangle ABC \sim \triangle FDE$; AA ~ Thm.

Use the information shown in the diagram and write a proportion for each triangle.

10. $\frac{AD}{DC} = \frac{AB}{BC}$ **11.**

11. Answers may vary. Sample: $\frac{AD}{CD} = \frac{CD}{DB}$

12. Indirect Measurement A meter stick is held perpendicular to the ground. It casts a shadow 1.5 m long. At the same time, a telephone pole casts a shadow that is 9 m long. How tall is the telephone pole? **6 m**

13. Photography A photographic negative is 3 cm by 2 cm. If a similar print from the negative is 9 cm long on its shorter side, what is the length of its longer side? **13.5 cm**

Find the geometric mean of each pair of numbers. If the answer is not a whole number, write it in simplest radical form.

14. 10, 15 $5\sqrt{6}$ **15.** 4, 9 **6**   **16.** 6, 12 $6\sqrt{2}$

17. Open-Ended Draw an isosceles triangle, $\triangle ABC$. Then draw $\triangle DEF$ so that $\triangle ABC \sim \triangle DEF$. State the similarity ratio of $\triangle ABC$ to $\triangle DEF$.
Check students' work.

x^2 **Algebra** Find the value of x.

18. $16\frac{2}{3}$

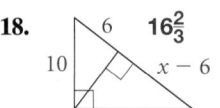

19. **10**

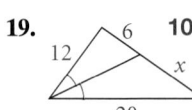

20. $5\frac{5}{11}$

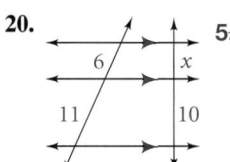

21. **10**

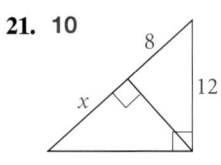

22. Writing Describe an object whose height or length would be difficult to measure directly. Then describe a method for measuring the object that involves using similar triangles. **See margin.**

For each pair of similar figures, find the ratio of the area of the first figure to the area of the second.

23. **49 : 64**

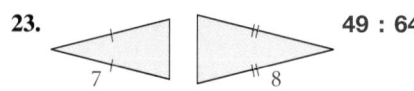

24. **9 : 4**

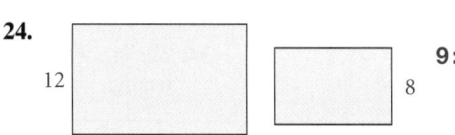

page 464 Chapter Test

22. Answers may vary. Sample: To measure the height of a tree on a sunny day, measure the length of the shadow it casts. Then measure the length of the shadow that you cast. Since you already know your height, you can use ~ △ to write and solve a proportion.

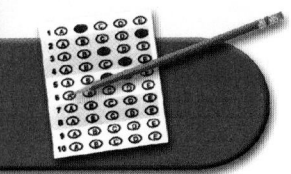

Standardized Test Prep

Multiple Choice

For Exercises 1–7, choose the correct letter.

1. What is the center of the circle that circumscribes △OMN? **D**
   A. (0, 0)
   B. (0, −1)
   C. (−1, 0)
   D. (−1, −1)

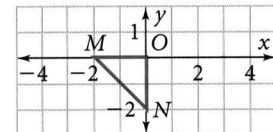

2. Which quadrilateral cannot contain four right angles? **G**
   F. square
   G. trapezoid
   H. rectangle
   I. rhombus

3. The lengths of the hypotenuse and one leg of a right triangle are 15 and 10. What is the length of the other leg to the nearest whole number? **D**
   A. 8   B. 9   C. 10   D. 11

4. **Algebra** For which value of x are lines g and h parallel? **I**
   F. 12
   G. 15
   H. 18
   I. 25

$(2x + 10)°$ g
$(5x − 5)°$ h

5. Which is an equation of the line that has slope 3 and contains point P(2, 5)? **D**
   A. $y = x + 3$ B. $y = x − 3$
   C. $y = 3x + 1$ D. $y = 3x − 1$

6. **Algebra** What is the value of x for this kite? **I**
   F. 48
   G. 52
   H. 62
   I. 68

$22°$ $x°$

7. **Algebra** What is the value of x? **A**
   A. 3.75
   B. 3.9
   C. 4
   D. 4.25

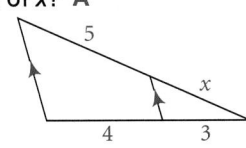

8. △ABC has AB = 7, BC = 24, and CA = 25. Which statement is true? **G**
   F. △ABC is an isosceles triangle.
   G. △ABC is a right triangle.
   H. ∠A is the largest angle.
   I. ∠B is the smallest angle.

Quantitative Comparison

Compare the boxed quantity in Column A with the boxed quantity in Column B. Choose the best answer.

   A. The quantity in Column A is greater.
   B. The quantity in Column B is greater.
   C. The two quantities are equal.
   D. The relationship cannot be determined from the information given.

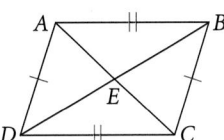

Column A	Column B
C 9. AE	EC
D 10. $m\angle ACD$	$m\angle CAD$
C 11. $m\angle ADB$	$m\angle CBD$

Gridded Response

12. What is the area in square centimeters of a rhombus with diagonals of lengths 20 cm and 14.2 cm? **142**

Short Response

13. **Constructions** Draw line m with point A on it. Construct a line perpendicular to m at A.
   See back of book.

Extended Response

14. In the diagram, $AB = FE$, $BC = ED$, and $AE = FB$.
   a. Is there enough information to prove △BCG ≅ △EDG?
   b. What one additional piece of information would allow you to prove △BCD ≅ △EDC?   **a–d. See margin.**
   c. What can you conclude from the diagram that would help you prove △BAF ≅ △EFA?
   d. In part (c), is △BAF ≅ △EFA by SAS or SSS?

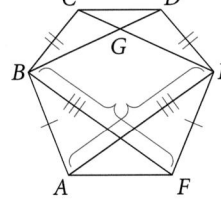

Resources

📁 **Teaching Resources**
Cumulative Review

👥 **Reaching All Students**
Spanish Cumulative Review

PRENTICE HALL
ASSESSMENT SYSTEM

Standardized Test Prep Workbook
• Ch. 8 standardized test practice
Assessment Masters
• Cumulative Review
Computer Test Generator CD
• Standardized Test Practice

💻 **www.PHSchool.com**
• Standardized test practice
• Resources

Plus **iTEXT**

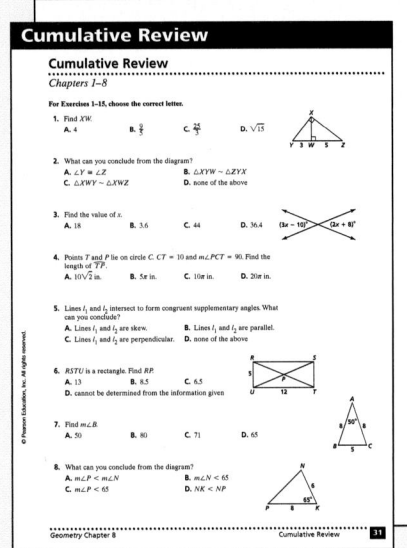

Item	Lesson	Item	Lesson
1	5-3	8	7-2
2	6-1	9	6-2
3	7-2	10	6-2
4	3-2	11	6-2
5	3-5	12	7-4
6	6-5	13	3-7
7	8-5	14	4-2

page 465   **Standardized Test Prep**

14. [4] a. no
   b. $m\angle BCD = m\angle EDC$
      or $BD = EC$
   c. $AF = AF$
   d. SSS
   [3] any 3 answers correct
   [2] any 2 answers correct
   [1] any 1 answer correct

465

How Far Can You See?

In these activities students apply their knowledge of circles, tangents to circles, and the Pythagorean Theorem.

Connecting to Prior Knowledge

Have students brainstorm how artists, architects, and engineers might have used mathematics to design and build the buildings shown here.

Teaching Notes

After students read the first paragraph, have them relate their own experiences of seeing "endless" distances from a ship, a beach, or a mountain. Encourage them to estimate how far they actually could see from that point.

English Learners

Relate the word *curvature* to the word *curve.* Point out that *curvature* refers to the spherical shape of Earth.

Engineering Connection

Tell students that the invention of the elevator helped make tall buildings feasible. People would have been unwilling to climb many flights of stairs each day to reach their homes or places of work.

466

Real-World Snapshots

How Far Can You See?

Applying the Pythagorean Theorem Imagine that you're standing on an ocean beach looking out across the water. The deep blue sky is clearer than you've ever seen it, and it seems as though you can see forever! Well, you know that isn't really possible on Earth. The extent of your vision is limited by Earth's curvature. You can see to the horizon—and perhaps slightly beyond.

The Empire State Building in New York City is 1250 ft tall, not including its mast. 7000 people visit the building each day.

The Bank of China Building in Hong Kong is 1033 ft tall.

The CN Tower in Toronto is 1815 ft tall.

The Chrysler Building in New York City is 1046 ft tall.

A chain of 8000 paper clips dangled from the top floor of 1 Canada Square in London would reach the ground, 797 ft below.

The KTHI-TV tower in North Dakota rises to 2063 ft.

The Eiffel Tower in Paris is 1052 ft tall, which is 16 times as tall as a four-story town house.

Four-story town house, 66 ft tall

The *Saturn V* rocket is 364 ft tall.

Activity 1
Answers depend on structure chosen.

- KTHI-TV tower: about 55.7 mi
- CN Tower: about 52.2 mi
- Empire State Building: about 43.3 mi
- Chrysler Building: about 39.6 mi
- Eiffel Tower: about 39.7 mi
- Bank of China building: about 39.4 mi
- 1 Canada Square: about 34.6 mi
- Saturn V rocket: about 23.4 mi
- St. Peter's Basilica: about 26.0 mi
- Great Pyramid: about 26.9 mi
- Cologne Cathedral: about 27.8 mi
- Leaning Tower of Pisa: about 16.4 mi
- Four-story town house: about 10.0 mi

Activity 1

Choose one of the structures on these pages. Imagine climbing to the very top to get a good view of the horizon. Assume that Earth is spherical and has a radius of 3963 mi. Also assume that you see a smooth horizon such as that of an ocean or desert. Find the distance from the top of the structure to the horizon. (*Hint:* Use a calculator and the Pythagorean Theorem.)

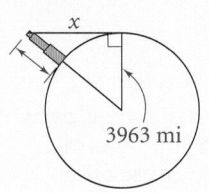

3963 mi

Take It to the NET For more information about buildings, go to www.PHSchool.com.
Web Code: afe-0853

Crow's nest, lookout post for land and ships

Flag indicates ship's origin.

Galleon
Galleons were fighting ships, with 40 to 50 cannons on board.

Activity 2

Sailors used to climb into the crow's nest on a ship's mast so they could spot land and other ships at a greater distance than was possible on deck. Imagine that you are on watch in a crow's nest so that your eyes are 40 ft above the water.

a. Determine the farthest distance from which you could spot the top of a 50-ft tree on a sea-level island.

b. Determine the farthest distance from which you could spot the tree if you were standing on deck with your eyes 15 ft above the water.

c. Compare your answers from parts (a) and (b).

With a spyglass, distant objects appear closer.

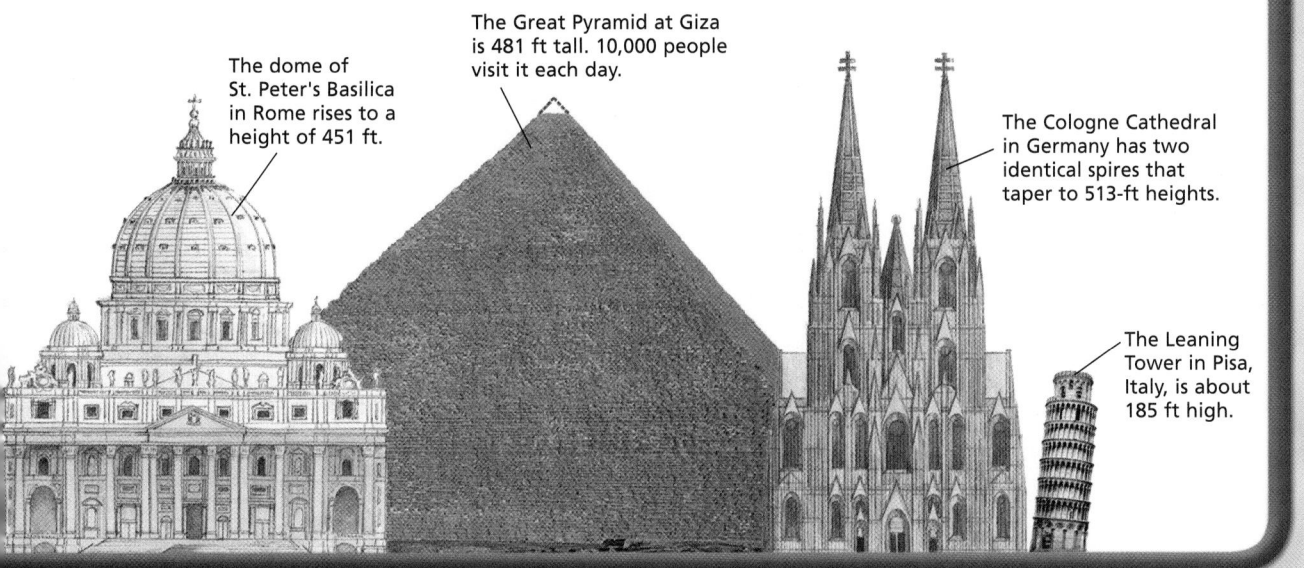

The dome of St. Peter's Basilica in Rome rises to a height of 451 ft.

The Great Pyramid at Giza is 481 ft tall. 10,000 people visit it each day.

The Cologne Cathedral in Germany has two identical spires that taper to 513-ft heights.

The Leaning Tower in Pisa, Italy, is about 185 ft high.

467

Teaching Tip
Students can do Activity 1 for all the buildings by writing and graphing an equation on a graphing calculator. For Activity 2, students will need to use the right angle method twice, once for the crow's nest and once for the tree.

Activity 1

Materials paper and pencil

Teaching Tip
If necessary, remind students that a tangent is perpendicular to the radius containing the point of tangency.

Activity 2

Materials paper and pencil

Visual Learners
It is essential that students begin their work by drawing an accurate representation of the situation. Students may want to start by discussing how to interpret the given information in light of what they learned in Activity 1.

Scoring Rubric

This scoring rubric applies to both activities. Share this scoring rubric with students before they begin work.
4   Calculations are accurate. Drawings are neat and accurate and clearly reflect the problem situations. Explanations are thorough.
3   Calculations are mostly accurate. Drawings are neat and mostly accurate. Explanations lack detail or are not completely accurate.
2   Calculations are often inaccurate. Explanations lack clarity. Drawings, if included, are not accurate.
1   Calculations are inaccurate. No work is shown.

Activity 2

a. about 16.4 mi

b. about 13.4 mi

c. From the crow's nest, you can spot the top of the tree from about 3 miles farther away.

Right Triangle Trigonometry

Chapter at a Glance

North Carolina Objectives

9-1	The Tangent Ratio	1.01

NCTM 3, 6, 7, 8, 9, 10
- ▽ Using Tangents in Triangles

9-2	Sine and Cosine Ratios	1.01

NCTM 3, 6, 8, 9, 10
- ▽ Using Sine and Cosine in Triangles

9-3	Angles of Elevation and Depression	1.01

NCTM 2, 3, 4, 6, 7, 8, 9, 10
- ▽ Using Angles of Elevation and Depression

9-4	Vectors	1.01

NCTM 1, 2, 3, 6, 8, 9, 10
- ▽ Describing Vectors
- ▽ Adding Vectors

9-5	Trigonometry and Area	1.01

NCTM 2, 3, 4, 6, 8, 9, 10
- ▽ Finding the Area of a Regular Polygon
- ▽ Finding the Area of a Triangle

NCTM STANDARDS 2000

1 Number and Operations
2 Algebra
3 Geometry
4 Measurement
5 Data Analysis and Probability
6 Problem Solving
7 Reasoning and Proof
8 Communication
9 Connections
10 Representation

Pacing Options

This chart suggests pacing only for the lessons and their parts. It is provided as a possible guide. It will help you determine how much time you have in your schedule to cover other components, such as the features, Chapter Review and Chapter Test.

Day	Traditional 45 min.	Two-Year 45 min.	Block 90 min.
1	9-1 ▽	9-1 ▽	9-1 ▽
2	9-1 ▽	9-1 ▽	9-2 ▽
3	9-2 ▽	9-1 ▽	9-3 ▽
4	9-2 ▽	9-2 ▽	9-4 ▽ ▽
5	9-3 ▽	9-2 ▽	9-5 ▽ ▽
6	9-3 ▽	9-2 ▽	
7	9-4 ▽	9-3 ▽	
8	9-4 ▽	9-3 ▽	
9	9-4 ▽	9-3 ▽	
10	9-5 ▽	9-4 ▽	
11	9-5 ▽	9-4 ▽	
12	9-5 ▽	9-4 ▽	
13		9-4 ▽	
14		9-4 ▽	
15		9-5 ▽	
16		9-5 ▽	
17		9-5 ▽	
18		9-5 ▽	
19		9-5 ▽	
20			
21			
22			

NAEP Correlation (National Assessment of Educational Progress 2000 Mathematics Objectives)

9-1	9-2	9-3	9-4	9-5
G6b, A14a, c	G6e, A14a, c	G6e, A14a, c	G9c; A14a, c	M4a; A14a, c

N = Number Sense, Properties, and Operations; **M** = Measurement; **G** = Geometry and Spatial Sense; **D** = Data Analysis, Statistics, and Probability; **A** = Algebra and Functions

Math Background

Chapter Overview

The trigonometric ratios *sine, cosine,* and *tangent* are defined and then used to solve problems involving right triangles, to find areas of polygons, and to determine directions of vectors. Vectors and vector addition are described.

The Tangent Ratio   9-1

Astronomy, navigation, surveying, and other real-world applications have used trigonometric ratios to measure indirectly for over 2000 years.

Some students may know the meaning of *tangent* from the Latin *tangere,* to touch. Others may know its geometric definition as a line, ray, or segment that intersects a circle exactly once. The definition can be expanded to include lines that intersect a portion of a curve exactly once.

The tangent ratio in a right triangle is related to the tangent to a circle. Place a unit circle with its center at the origin *O* of a coordinate plane. Draw central angle *POQ* in the first quadrant, with *Q* at (1, 0) and *P* on the segment tangent to the circle at *Q*. Students probably will be willing to assume $\overline{OQ} \perp \overline{PQ}$, but this really needs to be proved. The proof is provided in Lesson 11-1, but it is not too difficult for students to read now. Because the radius of the circle is 1, the tangent ratio for ∠*POQ* is the length of the tangent segment *PQ.*

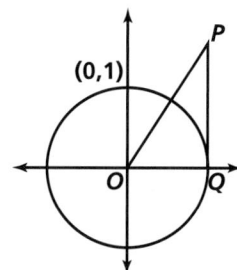

Students may enjoy extending this connection to 90° angles and to obtuse angles.

Students usually recognize that triangles with side lengths that are multiples of 3, 4, and 5 are right triangles, so finding the angle whose tangent is $\frac{3}{4}$, or 0.75, in a table of the values of trigonometric functions may help them understand the inverse tangent function. Although the exact angle whose tangent is 0.75 is not listed in the table, students can see that it lies between 36° and 37°. The inverse tangent function key on a calculator may be introduced at this point. A calculator can determine the angle with accuracy not possible using a textbook table of trigonometric values.

Sine and Cosine Ratios   9-2

The classic mnemonic device to help students remember the trigonometric ratios is "SOH-CAH-TOA," representing "**S**ine is **O**pposite leg over **H**ypotenuse; **C**osine is **A**djacent leg over **H**ypotenuse; and **T**angent is **O**pposite leg over **A**djacent leg."

Calculators can easily be used to find the values of trigonometric ratios, but a table shows the range of these values, and how a value changes as an angle measure increases. Point out that the table's values for 0° and 90° angles agree with the limits students determined in "Exploring Trigonometric Ratios" before this lesson. Later courses apply trigonometry to angles that are greater than 90°. Students should recognize that any table can describe only a discrete set of values, but the angles from 0° to 90° are a continuous set of real numbers. Many tables are organized with the angle measures increasing down the left column and decreasing down the right column, exhibiting cofunction relationships such as sin *A* = cos (90° − *A*) across the same row. A table can be used to find the inverse trigonometric function by locating the approximate value in the column for that trigonometric function and reading across to find the measure of the angle.

Angles of Elevation and Depression   9-3

The vertex of an angle of elevation or depression is always at the endpoint of a horizontal ray and a ray along the line of sight (below the horizontal for an angle of depression or above it for an angle of elevation).

Vectors   9-4

The usefulness of vectors can be illustrated by the distinction between speed (a number) and velocity (a number and a direction). This lesson on vectors touches only on representations of velocity and motion, which students will see again in a physics class. There they also may use vectors to describe lines and planes and to solve systems. In subsequent math courses students may expand applications and learn to operate in vector spaces. Some students may be aware that the use of vectors may easily be extended to three or more dimensions.

Trigonometry and Area   9-5

The formula Area = $\frac{1}{2}bc$(sin *A*) still holds if *A* is a right angle. A calculator can because sin 90° = 1.

Ongoing Assessment and Intervention

Tools for Monitoring Student Progress

The Prentice Hall *Geometry* program provides you with many options for assessment in the Student Edition, the Teacher's Edition and the teaching resources. From these options, you may choose instructional materials and techniques that are appropriate for your students and support your district's curriculum requirements.

Instant Check System™ in Chapter 9

Allows students to check their own learning before, during, and after each lesson.

Diagnosing Readiness before the chapter (p. 468)

Check Skills You'll Need exercises in each lesson (pp. 470, 477, 482, 490, 498)

Check Understanding questions with each Example (pp. 471, 472, 477, 478, 482, 483, 489, 491, 492, 493, 498, 499, 500)

Checkpoint Quiz (p. 488)

 Test Prep in Chapter 9

Teaches students strategies and gives them practice with all the test item formats they will encounter on state tests and standardized national exams.

Standardized Test Prep exercises in each lesson (pp. 475, 481, 487, 497, 502)

Test-Taking Strategies (p. 504: Eliminating Answers)

Standardized Test Prep (p. 509: Reading Comprehension)

All your assessment needs in one place!

Program Assessment

Assess student progress throughout the *Geometry* text with blackline masters and CD-ROM.

Assessment Resources

- Checkpoint Quiz 1
- Chapter Test, Forms A & B
- Chapter Alternative Assessment

Spanish versions available. Tests for Informal Geometry also available.

Computer Test Generator

- Unlimited questions of varying difficulty for every lesson objective.
- Create your own practice sheets, quizzes, and tests, or use the pre-made Chapter Tests.
- Diagnose readiness with questions on prerequisite skills.
- Prepare students by making tests based on standardized test objectives.
- Access Algebra 1, Geometry, and Algebra 2 content—all on one CD-ROM.

Test Preparation

A three-step approach to preparing students for high stakes, national, and state exams.

❶ Diagnose & Prescribe

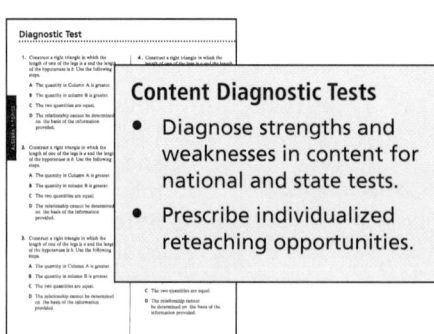

Content Diagnostic Tests
- Diagnose strengths and weaknesses in content for national and state tests.
- Prescribe individualized reteaching opportunities.

❷ Review & Reteach

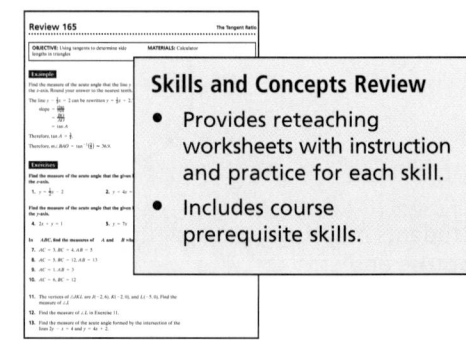

Skills and Concepts Review
- Provides reteaching worksheets with instruction and practice for each skill.
- Includes course prerequisite skills.

❸ Practice & Assess

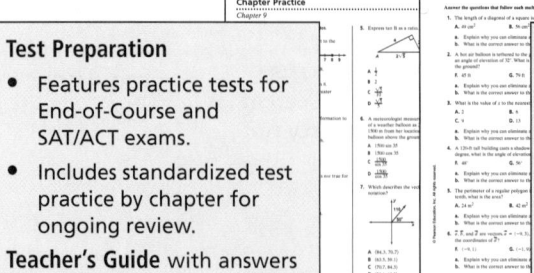

Test Preparation
- Features practice tests for End-of-Course and SAT/ACT exams.
- Includes standardized test practice by chapter for ongoing review.

Teacher's Guide with answers and correlations.

Test-Taking Strategies with Transparencies
- Support the Test-Taking Strategies pages in the Student Edition.
- Provide a teaching transparency and a practice worksheet for each strategy.

 # Reaching All Students

Support in the Student Text and Additional Resources

The textbook, the iText, and other technology components provide numerous opportunities to reach students of various ability levels and learning styles. Each Teacher's Edition lesson suggests how you can help *all* your students be successful and understand the mathematics in Chapter 9.

Below Level

Student Edition
- Diagnosing Readiness*: p. 468
- Check Skills You'll Need*: pp. 470, 477, 482, 490, 498

Reteaching
Chapter 9 Support File: pp. 6–10

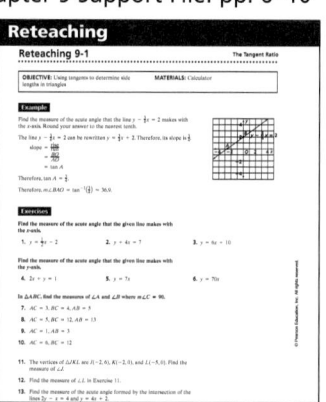

Informal Geometry Planning Guide
Chapter 9 Lesson Plans: pp. 53–57
Chapter 9 Tests: pp. 111–114

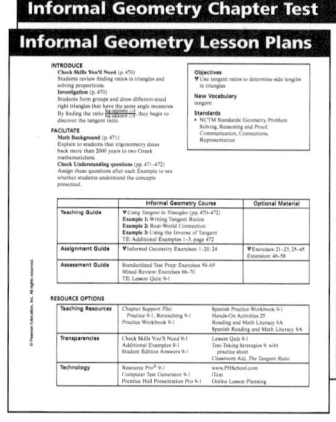

* Can be used with all ability levels to ensure mastery of prerequisite skills.

Advanced Learners

Student Edition
- Challenge exercises: pp. 474, 480, 486, 496, 502

Enrichment
Chapter 9 Support File: pp. 11–15

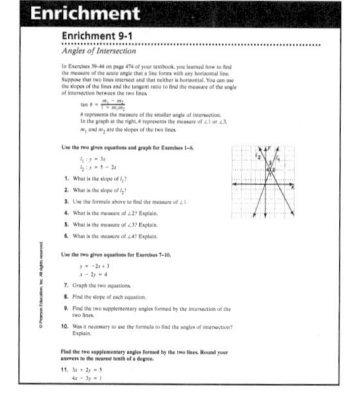

Reading and Math Literacy

Student Edition
- Vocabulary: pp. 469, 505, *plus* in every Lesson Preview
- Reading Math: pp. 470, 472, 478, 480, 485, 489, 490, 499, 505
- Illustrated Glossary: pp. 741–777

Reading and Math Literacy Masters
Chapter 9: pp. 33–36

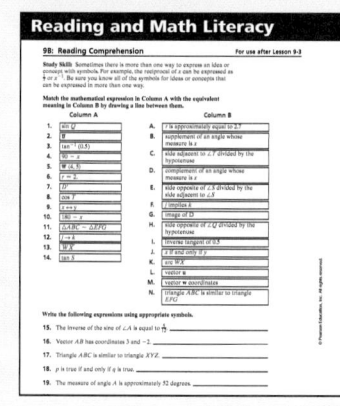

English Learners

Student Edition
- English/Spanish Illustrated Glossary: pp. 741–777

Workbook and Masters
Spanish Practice Workbook: pp. 53–57
Spanish Reading and Math Literacy Masters: pp. 33–36

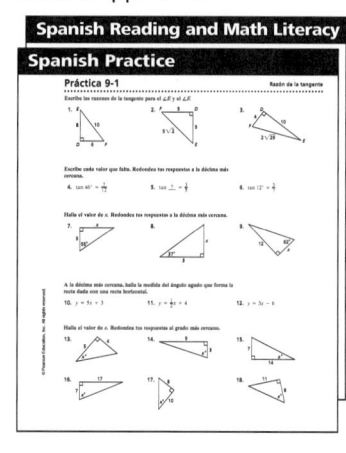

Learning Styles

Student Edition
- Investigation: p. 470
- Technology: pp. 471, 472, 474, 476, 478, 480, 483, 489, 490, 491, 493, 498, 499, 500, 502
- Writing: pp. 473, 474, 480, 485, 488, 495, 496, 497, 501, 506, 508

Activity Masters
Hands-On Activities: 25, 26, 27

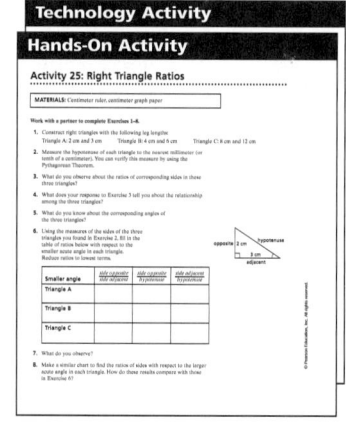

Program Resources

	Teaching Resources in Grab & Go™ Files				Resources for Reaching All Students				Spanish Resources			Transparencies				Prentice Hall Presentation Pro CD-ROM
	Practice	Reteach	Enrich	Checkpoint Quiz	Reading & Math Literacy	Technology Activities	Hands-On Activities	Informal Geometry Lesson Plans	Practice	Reading & Math Literacy	Checkpoint Quiz	Skills Check	Additional Examples	Answers to Exercises	Lesson Quiz	
9-1	■	■	■		■		■	■	■	■		■	■	■	■	■
9-2	■	■	■				■	■	■			■	■	■	■	■
9-3	■	■	■	■	■		■	■	■		■	■	■	■	■	■
9-4	■	■	■				■	■	■	■		■	■	■	■	■
9-5	■	■	■		■		■	■	■	■		■	■	■	■	■
For the chapter	Chapter Tests, Alternative Assessment, Cumulative Review, Cumulative Assessment				Informal Geometry Chapter Tests				Spanish Chapter Tests, Alternative Assessment, Cumulative Review, Cumulative Assessment			Classroom Aid Transparencies				

Also available for use with the chapter:

 *see page 468C.*

- Practice Workbook
- Solution Key

- For teacher support and access to student Web site materials, use Web Code afk-5500.
- For additional online and technology resources, see below.

Technology

iTEXT Online and on CD-ROM

Complete Interactive Student Text online and on CD-ROM—with instant feedback assessment, tutorial help, dynamic activities, instructional and real-world videos, audio, and additional practice.

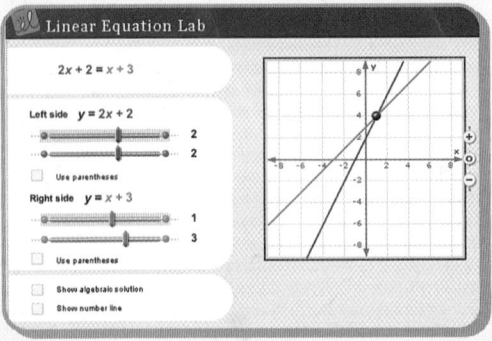

www.PHSchool.com For Students

Use **Web Codes** for easy access to online activities, chapter projects, self-grading lesson quizzes and chapter tests, vocabulary quizzes, updated data sources, graphing calculator procedures, and more.

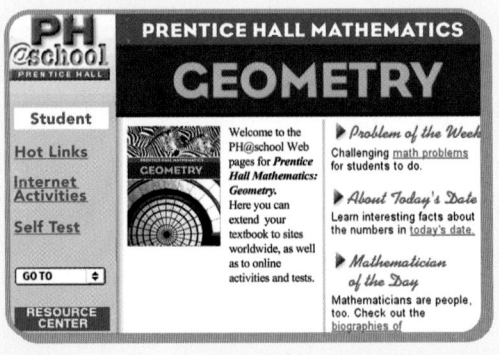

PH SuccessNet For Teachers

Online lesson planning with built-in state correlations, all the teaching resources, complete reference library, your own calendar and Teacher Web page, professional development, and more.

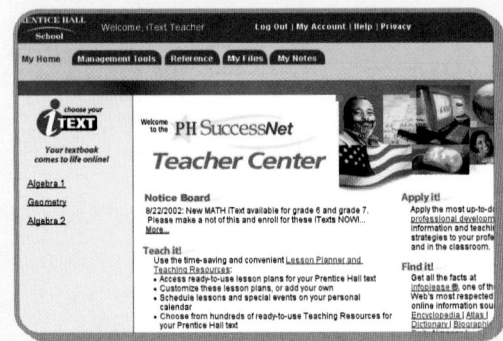

468E

Presentation Assistant Plus!

The Prentice Hall *Presentation Assistant Plus!* provides you with the material you need to teach a lesson from beginning to end. Two easy-to-use formats—Transparencies and CD-ROM—allow you to present a lesson the way you are most comfortable.

Transparencies

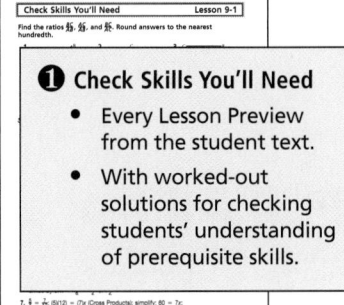

❶ Check Skills You'll Need
- Every Lesson Preview from the student text.
- With worked-out solutions for checking students' understanding of prerequisite skills.

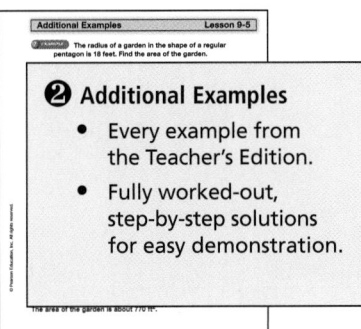

❷ Additional Examples
- Every example from the Teacher's Edition.
- Fully worked-out, step-by-step solutions for easy demonstration.

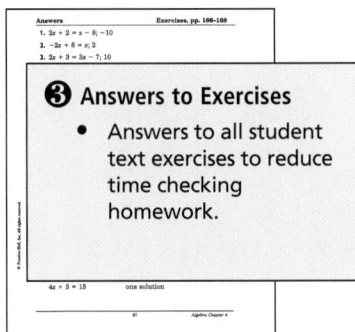

❸ Answers to Exercises
- Answers to all student text exercises to reduce time checking homework.

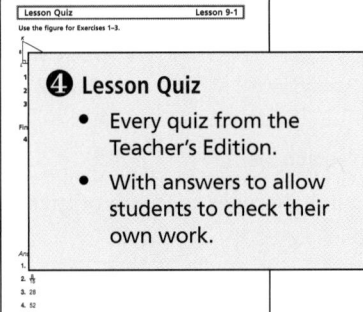

❹ Lesson Quiz
- Every quiz from the Teacher's Edition.
- With answers to allow students to check their own work.

 Throughout the Teacher's Edition, this symbol indicates material that is available on transparency in the Presentation Assistant Plus!

Prentice Hall Presentation Pro CD-ROM

- Includes all Transparencies.
- Conveniently organized by lesson so you can easily ❶ Introduce, ❷ Teach, ❸ Check Homework, and ❹ Assess each lesson.
- Animated examples allow step-by-step instruction at your own pace.
- Easy to edit so you can create custom presentations.

Teaching Chapter 9 Using Presentation Assistant Plus!

	❶ Introduce	❷ Teach	❸ Check Homework	❹ Assess
	Check Skills You'll Need	Additional Examples	Student Edition Answers	Lesson Quiz
9-1	p. 53	pp. 140–141	✔	p. 128
9-2	p. 54	pp. 141–143	✔	p. 129
9-3	p. 55	pp. 144–145	✔	p. 130
9-4	p. 55	pp. 146–149	✔	p. 131
9-5	p. 56	pp. 150–152	✔	p. 132

Prentice Hall Presentation Pro

CD-ROM with dynamic PowerPoint® presentations for every lesson. Helps you introduce and develop concepts, check homework, and assess progress. Part of Presentation Assistant Plus! *(See above.)*

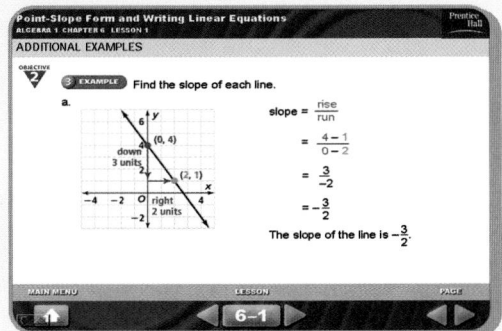

Computer Test Generator

CD-ROM to create practice sheets and tests for course objectives and standardized tests. Includes Instant Chapter Tests™, online testing, and student reports. Part of the PH Assessment System. *(See page 468C.)*

Resource Pro® with Planning Express®

CD-ROM with a lesson planning tool that allows you to import state and local objectives. Includes electronic versions of all the teaching resources.

Right Triangle Trigonometry

✓ **Diagnosing Readiness**

Students will find answers to these exercises in the back of their textbooks.

For intervention, direct students to:

Solving Proportions
Lesson 8-1: Example 3
Exercises 12–20
Extra Practice, p. 697

Proving Triangles Similar
Lesson 8-3: Examples 1 and 2
Exercises 1–9
Extra Practice, p. 697

Similarity in Right Triangles
Lesson 8-4: Example 2
Exercises 15–20
Extra Practice, p. 697

Where You've Been

● In Chapter 7, you learned how to use the Pythagorean Theorem to solve right triangles and to find relationships among the sides of special right triangles.

● In Chapter 8, you learned how to prove triangles similar and that corresponding sides of similar triangles are in proportion.

● In Chapter 7, you learned how to find the area of a triangle. In Chapter 8, you learned how areas of similar triangles are related.

 Instant self-check online and on CD-ROM

Diagnosing Readiness   (For help, go to the Lesson in green.)

Solving Proportions (Lesson 8-1)

x^2 **Algebra** Solve for x. Round answers to the nearest thousandth.

1. $0.2734 = \frac{x}{17}$
4.648

2. $0.5858 = \frac{24}{x}$
40.970

3. $0.8572 = \frac{5271}{x}$
6149.090

4. $0.5 = \frac{x}{3x + 5}$
−5

Proving Triangles Similar (Lesson 8-3)

Name the postulate or theorem that proves each pair of triangles similar.

5. $\overline{CD} \parallel \overline{AB}$ AA~ Post.

6.

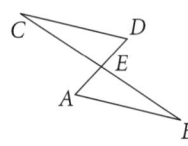

SSS~ Thm.

7. $\overline{JK} \perp \overline{ML}$ SAS~ Thm.

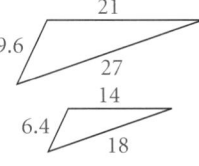

Similarity in Right Triangles (Lesson 8-4)

x^2 **Algebra** Find the unknown quantity in $\triangle ABC$ with right $\angle C$ and altitude $\overline{CD}$.

8.

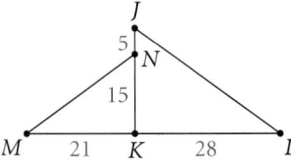

9.

10. $2\sqrt{13}$

11.

Right Triangle Trigonometry

Chapter 9

Key Vocabulary

- angle of depression (p. 482)
- angle of elevation (p. 482)
- cosine (p. 477)
- identity (p. 478)
- initial point (p. 490)
- magnitude (p. 490)
- resultant (p. 492)
- sine (p. 477)
- tangent (p. 470)
- terminal point (p. 490)
- vector (p. 490)

Chapter 9 Overview

The sine, cosine, and tangent trigonometric ratios are developed as applications of right triangle geometry. Students use the ratios to find unknown lengths and angle measures in diagrams and real-world scenarios involving angles of elevation, angles of depression, and vectors. Finally, they apply new formulas that use trigonometry to find the areas of regular polygons and triangles in real-world applications.

Reading Math
Reading for Problem Solving, p. 489

Vocabulary
A complete list of terms, plus vocabulary exercises, appears in the Chapter Review, p. 505.

Illustrated Glossary
Examples for each vocabulary term, plus definitions in both English and Spanish, appear starting on p. 741.

Test-Taking Strategies
Eliminating Answers, p. 504

Real-World Connections
Some of the applications you will find in this chapter are astronomy (9-2), aviation (9-3), navigation (9-4), and surveying (9-5).

www.PHSchool.com
Internet support for this chapter includes:
- Self-grading Vocabulary and Chapter 9 Tests
- Chapter Project
- Chapter Planner
- Ch. 9 Resources

Plus 📘TEXT

Where You're Going

- In this chapter, you will use similar right triangles to define the sine, cosine, and tangent ratios.

- With these ratios, you will solve height and distance problems using angles of elevation and angles of depression.

- You will also learn how to use vectors as a tool in other applications of trigonometry.

Real-World Connection Applying what you learn, you will find the height of a cloud layer on page 486.

469

1. Plan

Lesson Preview

✓ **Check Skills You'll Need**

Solving Proportions
Lesson 8-1: Example 3
Exercises 12–20
Extra Practice, p. 697

Using 45°-45°-90° Triangles
Lesson 7-3: Example 1
Exercises 1–3
Extra Practice, p. 696

Using 30°-60°-90° Triangles
Lesson 7-3: Example 5
Exercises 15–20
Extra Practice, p. 696

Lesson Resources

📁 **Teaching Resources**
Practice, Reteaching, Enrichment

👥 **Reaching All Students**
Practice Workbook 9-1
Spanish Practice Workbook 9-1
Reading and Math Literacy 9A
Spanish Reading & Literacy 9A
Hands-On Activities 25
Informal Geometry Planning
   Guide 9-1

⏰ **Presentation Assistant Plus!**
Transparencies
• Check Skills You'll Need 9-1
• Additional Examples 9-1
• Student Edition Answers 9-1
• Lesson Quiz 9-1
PH Presentation Pro CD 9-1

ⒶSSESSMENT *SYSTEM*

Computer Test Generator CD

💿 **Technology**
Resource Pro® CD-ROM
Computer Test Generator CD
Prentice Hall Presentation Pro CD

💻 **www.PHSchool.com**
Student Site
• Teacher Web Code: afk-5500
• Self-grading Lesson Quiz
Teacher Center
• Lesson Planner
• Resources

Plus ⒾTEXT

470

9-1

The Tangent Ratio

1.01   Use the trigonometric ratios to model and solve problems involving right triangles.

 North Carolina Objectives

Lesson Preview

What You'll Learn

▼ OBJECTIVE
1
To use tangent ratios to determine side lengths in triangles

. . . And Why

To use the tangent ratio to estimate distance to a distant object, as in Example 2

✓ Check Skills You'll Need   (For help, go to Lessons 7-3 and 8-1.)

Find the ratios $\frac{BC}{AB}$, $\frac{AC}{AB}$, and $\frac{BC}{AC}$. Round answers to the nearest hundredth.

1. 0.71; 0.71; 1   **2.**   **3.**

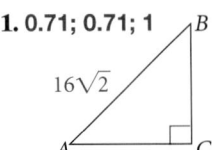

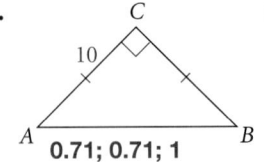
0.71; 0.71; 1

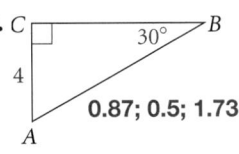
0.87; 0.5; 1.73

x^2 **Algebra** Solve each proportion.

4. $\frac{x}{3} = \frac{4}{7}$ $\frac{12}{7}$ **5.** $\frac{6}{11} = \frac{x}{9}$ $\frac{54}{11}$ **6.** $\frac{8}{15} = \frac{4}{x}$ $\frac{15}{2}$ **7.** $\frac{5}{x} = \frac{7}{12}$ $\frac{60}{7}$

New Vocabulary   • tangent

ⒾTEXT **Interactive lesson includes instant self-check, tutorials, and activities.**

OBJECTIVE
1   **Using Tangents in Triangles**

Investigation: Tangent Ratios

Work in groups of three or four.

• Have your group select one angle measure from {10°, 20°, . . . , 80°}. Then have each member of your group draw a right triangle, △ABC, where ∠A has the selected measure. Make the triangles different sizes.

• Measure the legs of each △ABC to the nearest millimeter.
Check students' work.
1. Compute the ratio $\frac{\text{leg opposite } \angle A}{\text{leg adjacent to } \angle A}$ and round to two decimal places.

2. Compare the ratios in your group. Make a conjecture. **See left.**

2. Answers may vary. Sample: For each ∠, the ratio is the same no matter how large or small the △.

📖 **Reading Math**

Trigonometry comes from the Greek words *trigonon* and *metria* meaning "triangle measurement."

In a right triangle, △ABC, the ratio of the length of the leg opposite ∠A to the length of the leg adjacent to ∠A is constant, no matter what lengths are chosen for the sides of the triangles. This trigonometric ratio is called the tangent ratio.

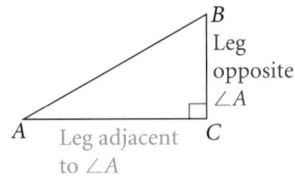

tangent of $\angle A = \dfrac{\text{length of leg opposite } \angle A}{\text{length of leg adjacent to } \angle A}$

You can abbreviate this equation as $\tan A = \dfrac{\text{opposite}}{\text{adjacent}}$.

INSTANT CHECK SYSTEM **Ongoing Assessment and Intervention**

Before the Lesson
Diagnose prerequisite skills using:
• Check Skills You'll Need

During the Lesson
Monitor progress using:
• Check Understanding
• Additional Examples
• Standardized Test Prep

After the Lesson
Assess knowledge using:
• Lesson Quiz
• Computer Test Generator CD

1 EXAMPLE Writing Tangent Ratios

Write the tangent ratios for $\angle T$ and $\angle U$.

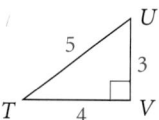

$$\tan T = \frac{\text{opposite}}{\text{adjacent}} = \frac{UV}{TV} = \frac{3}{4}$$

$$\tan U = \frac{\text{opposite}}{\text{adjacent}} = \frac{TV}{UV} = \frac{4}{3}$$

✔ **Check Understanding** 1 **a.** Write the tangent ratios for $\angle K$ and $\angle J$. $\frac{3}{7}$; $\frac{7}{3}$

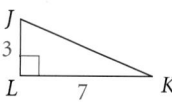

b. How is $\tan K$ related to $\tan J$?
They are reciprocals.

As stated on the facing page, the tangent ratio for an acute angle does not depend on leg lengths of a right triangle. To see why this is so, consider the congruent angles, $\angle T$ and $\angle T'$, in the two right triangles shown here.

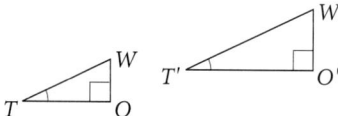

$\triangle TOW \sim T'O'W'$ **AA Similarity Postulate**

$\dfrac{OW}{TO} = \dfrac{O'W'}{T'O'}$ **Corresponding sides of ~ triangles are proportional.**

$\tan T = \tan T'$ **Substitute.**

You can use the tangent ratio to measure distances that would be difficult to measure directly.

2 EXAMPLE Real-World Connection

Cross-Country Skiing Your goal in Bryce Canyon National Park is the distant cliff. About how far away is the cliff?

Step 1 Point your compass at a distinctive feature of the cliff and note the reading.

Step 2 Turn 90° and stride 50 ft in a straight path.

Step 3 Turn and point the compass again at the same feature seen in Step 1. Take a reading.

Suppose in Step 3, you find that $m\angle 1 = 86$. The distance you walked in Step 2 was 50 ft. To find the distance to the cliff use the tangent ratio.

$\tan 86° = \frac{x}{50}$ **Use the tangent ratio.**

$x = 50(\tan 86°)$ **Solve for x.**

50 [TAN] 86 [ENTER] 715.03331 **Use a calculator.**

The cliff is about 715 ft away.

✔ **Check Understanding** 2 Find the value of w to the nearest tenth.

a. **13.8**   **b.** **1.9**   **c.** **3.8**

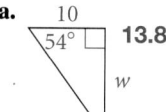
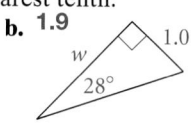
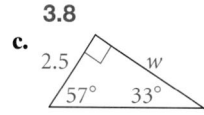

not to scale   1   50 ft

2. Teach

Math Background

The Greek mathematicians Hipparchus of Nicaea and Claudius Ptolemy created the discipline of trigonometry more than 2000 years ago, primarily to study astronomy. Subsequent Indian and Arabic mathematicians also developed trigonometry.

OBJECTIVE
1 Teaching Notes

Investigation (Optional)
Because of measurement errors and rounding, students in a group may find that their ratios are close but not equal. If this occurs, ask students to explain why the ratios vary.

Math Tip
Point out that this definition of the tangent of an angle cannot be used to find tan 90° because a right angle has no opposite leg.

Teaching Tip
After students complete Example 1, ask: *What can you conclude about the tangents of complementary angles?* They are reciprocals.

2 EXAMPLE English Learners

Point out that a directional compass is different from the compass used in geometric constructions. If possible, display a directional compass and demonstrate its use.

👥 Reaching All Students

Below Level Have students use all the ratios from the Investigation to make a table of tangent values.	**Advanced Learners** Have students explain how to find tan 30° and tan 60° without using a calculator, and then confirm the values with a calculator.	**English Learners** See note on page 471. **Error Prevention** See note on page 472.

Students may confuse the angle whose tangent is 5, $\tan^{-1} 5$, with $\tan 5^{-1}$. Point out that $\tan 5^{-1} = \tan \frac{1}{5}$, but $\tan^{-1} 5$ represents the inverse trigonometric function, or *the angle whose tangent is 5.*

③ EXAMPLE

Students should repeat the example on their own calculators to determine their correct key sequences.

Additional Examples

① Write the tangent ratios for ∠A and ∠B.

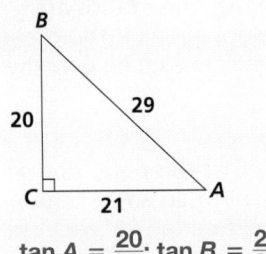

$$\tan A = \frac{20}{21}; \tan B = \frac{21}{20}$$

② To measure the height of a tree, Alma walked 125 ft from the tree and measured a 32° angle from the ground to the top of the tree. Estimate the height of the tree.

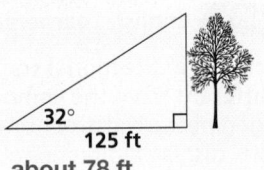

about 78 ft

③ Find $m\angle R$ to the nearest degree.

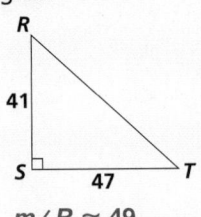

$m\angle R \approx 49$

Closure

Without using a calculator, find the angle whose tangent equals 1. Explain. **Sample: 45°; by the Converse of the Isosceles Triangle Theorem, a 45°-45°-90° triangle has congruent legs, so $\tan 45° = \frac{1}{1} = 1$.**

472

If you know leg lengths for a right triangle, you can find the tangent ratio for each acute angle. Conversely, if you know the tangent ratio for an angle, you can use inverse of tangent, $\tan^{-1}$, to find the measure of the angle.

③ EXAMPLE **Using the Inverse of Tangent**

The lengths of the sides of △BHX are given. Find $m\angle X$ to the nearest degree.

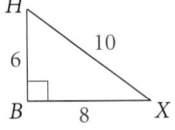

$\tan X = \frac{6}{8} = 0.75$ **Find the tangent ratio.**

$m\angle X = \tan^{-1}(0.75)$ **Use the inverse of tangent.**

TAN 0.75 ENTER 36.869898 **Use a calculator.**

● So $m\angle X \approx 37$.

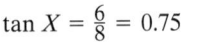 **Reading Math**

Think of $\tan^{-1}(0.75)$ as "the angle whose tangent is 0.75."

✓ Check Understanding **③** Find $m\angle Y$ to the nearest degree.
68

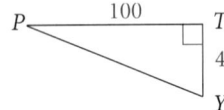

EXERCISES

For more practice, see *Extra Practice*.

Practice and Problem Solving

Ⓐ **Practice by Example**

Write the tangent ratios for ∠A and ∠B.

Example 1
(page 471)

1. $\frac{1}{2}$; 2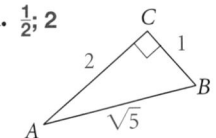

2. $\frac{2}{3}$; $\frac{3}{2}$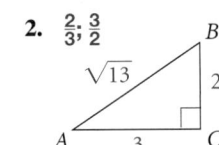

3. 1; 1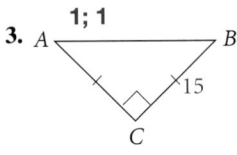

Example 2
(page 471)

Find the value of *x* to the nearest tenth.

4. 11.2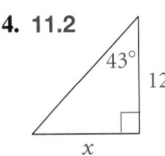

5. 12.3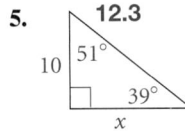

6. 14.4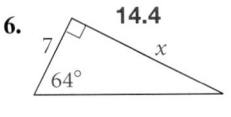

7. 2.5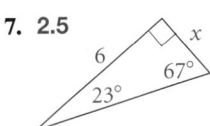

8. 1.6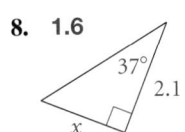

9. 21.4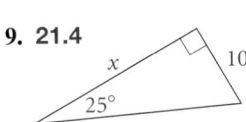

10. Surveying To find the distance from the boathouse on shore to the cabin on the island, a surveyor measures from the boathouse to point *X* as shown. He then finds $m\angle X$ with an instrument called a transit. Use the surveyor's measurements to find the distance from the boathouse to the cabin. **about 50 yd**

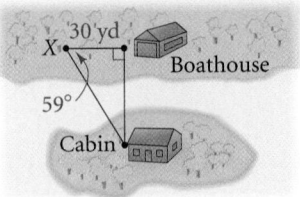

472 Chapter 9 Right Triangle Trigonometry

pages 472–475 Exercises

24. Consider a 30-60-90 △. Let the length of the shorter side be *a*. Then the length of the longer side, opposite the 60°∠, is $a\sqrt{3}$. Thus, $\tan 60° = \frac{a\sqrt{3}}{a} = \sqrt{3}$.

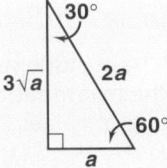

Example 3
(page 472)

Find the value of *x* to the nearest degree.

11. 32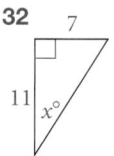

12. 58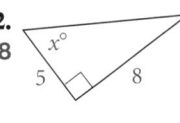

13. 48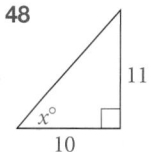

14. 65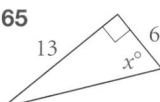

15. 63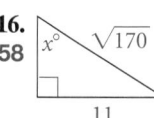

16. 58

Find each missing value to the nearest tenth.

17. $\tan \blacksquare° = 3.5$
74.1

18. $\tan 34° = \dfrac{\blacksquare}{20}$
13.5

19. $\tan 2° = \dfrac{4}{\blacksquare}$
114.5

20. $\tan \blacksquare° = 90$
89.4

B Apply Your Skills

21. The lengths of the diagonals of a rhombus are 2 in. and 5 in. Find the measures of the angles of the rhombus to the nearest degree. **44 and 136**

 22. **Pyramids** All but two of the pyramids built by the ancient Egyptians have faces inclined at 52° angles. Suppose an archaeologist discovers the ruins of a pyramid. Most of the pyramid has eroded, but she is able to determine that the length of a side of the square base is 82 m. How tall was the pyramid, assuming its faces were inclined at 52°? Round your answer to the nearest meter. **52 m**

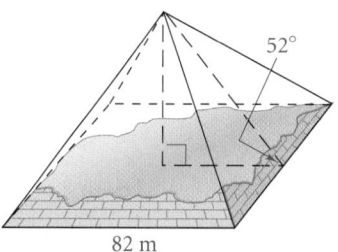
52°
82 m

? ......
Need Help?

A Pythagorean triple is a set of three nonzero whole numbers, *a*, *b*, and *c*, for which $a^2 + b^2 = c^2$ (p. 357).

23. **Open-Ended** Select a Pythagorean triple other than a multiple of 3, 4, 5. Find the measures of the acute angles of the right triangle associated with your Pythagorean triple. Round each measure to the nearest tenth. **See left.**

 24. **Writing** Explain why $\tan 60° = \sqrt{3}$. Include a diagram with your explanation.

25. Explain why $\tan^{-1} \dfrac{\sqrt{2}}{\sqrt{2}} = 45°$. **24–25. See margin.**

23. Answers may vary.
Sample: 5, 12, 13;
22.6 and 67.4

26. A rectangle is 80 cm long and 20 cm wide. To the nearest degree, find the measures of the angles formed by the diagonals at the center of the rectangle. **152 and 28**

Find the value of *w*, then *x*. Round lengths of segments to the nearest tenth. Round angle measures to the nearest degree.

27.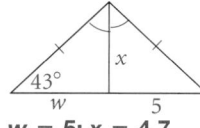
43°
w
5
x
w = 5; *x* = 4.7

28.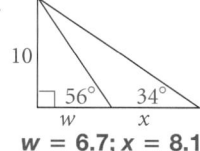
10
56° 34°
w *x*
w = 6.7; *x* = 8.1

29.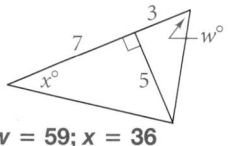
3
7
5
x°
w°
w = 59; *x* = 36

30a. 0; 1; 0.2; 0.3; 0.4;
0.5; 0.6; 0.7; 0.8; 1;
1.2; 1.4; 1.7; 2.1; 2.7;
3.7; 5.7; 11.4

30c. approaches 0;
increases to infinity

30d. Answers may vary.
Samples: 82; 2.5; 74

30. a. **Coordinate Geometry** Complete the table of values at the right. Give table entries to the nearest tenth.
b. Plot the points $(x, \tan x°)$ on the coordinate plane. Connect the points with a smooth curve. **See margin.**
c. What happens to the tangent ratio as the angle measure *x* approaches 0? Approaches 90?
d. Use your graph to estimate each value. **a, c–d. See left.**
$\tan \blacksquare° = 7$ $\tan 68° = \blacksquare$ $\tan \blacksquare° = 3.5$

x	tan *x*°
5	▓
10	▓
⋮	⋮
85	▓

Lesson 9-1   The Tangent Ratio   **473**

25. $\dfrac{\sqrt{2}}{\sqrt{2}} = 1$, so we have to show $\tan^{-1} 1 = 45°$. This is equivalent to showing $1 = \tan 45°$.

Consider a 45-45-90 △. Let the lengths of the shorter sides be *a*. Thus, $\tan 45° = \dfrac{a}{a} = 1$.

30. b.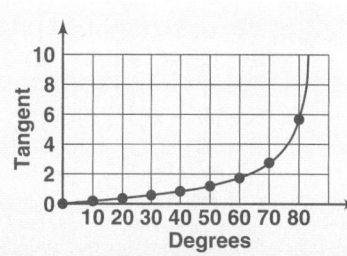
Tangent
10 8 6 4 2 0
10 20 30 40 50 60 70 80
Degrees

3. Practice

Assignment Guide

1 Objective
Ⓐ Ⓑ Core 1–45
Ⓒ Extension 46–58

Standardized Test Prep 59–65

Mixed Review 66–70

Technology Tip
Make sure that students set their calculators in degree mode.

Alternative Method

Exercise 9 Point out that students can solve a simpler equation by using the ratio $\tan(90 - 25)° = \frac{x}{10}$.

Exercises 15, 16 Students need to apply the Pythagorean Theorem before they can find the value of *x*.

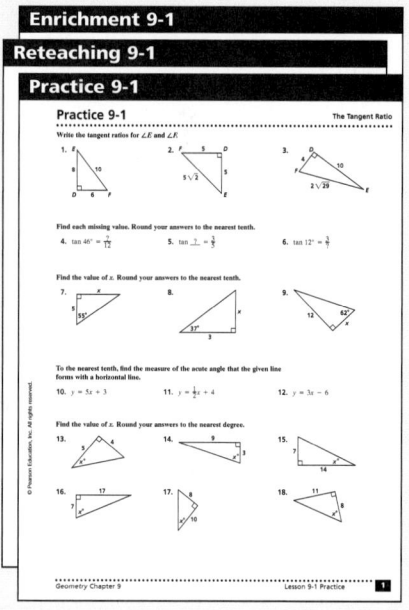

473

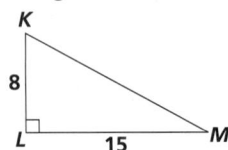
Lesson Quiz 9-1

Use the figure for Exercises 1–3.

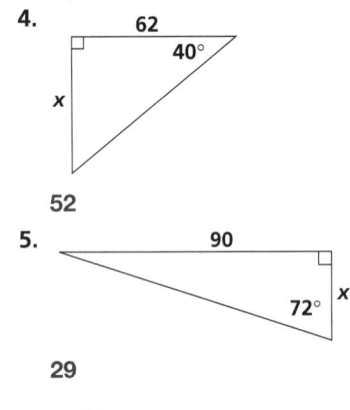

1. Write the tangent ratio for ∠K. $\frac{15}{8}$

2. Write the tangent ratio for ∠M. $\frac{8}{15}$

3. Find $m\angle M$ to the nearest degree. **28**

Find x to the nearest whole number.

4. **62**

5. **29**

Alternative Assessment

Have students draw a right triangle, measure one acute angle and the leg adjacent to it, and then use the tangent function to estimate the length of the other leg. Have students draw another right triangle, measure each leg, and use the inverse tangent function to estimate both acute angles of the triangle.

Real-World Connection

The world's steepest railway is the Katoomba Scenic Railway in Australia's Blue Mountains.

Take It to the NET
Graphing Calculator procedures online at
www.PHSchool.com
Web Code: afe-2111

C Challenge

46c. **Conjecture:**
$\tan x° \cdot \tan(90 - x)° = 1$.
Proof: Let x be an acute ∠ measure in a rt. △. Then the other acute ∠ measures $(90 - x)$.
So $\tan x° = \frac{\text{opp.}}{\text{adj.}}$, and $\tan (90 - x)° = \frac{\text{adj.}}{\text{opp.}}$.
Therefore,
$\tan x° \cdot \tan(90 - x)° = \frac{\text{opp.}}{\text{adj.}} \cdot \frac{\text{adj.}}{\text{opp.}} = 1$.

Engineering The grade of a road or a railway road bed is the ratio $\frac{\text{rise}}{\text{run}}$, usually expressed as a percent. For example, a railway with a grade of 5% rises 5 ft for every 100 ft of horizontal distance.

31. The Katoomba Railway, pictured at left, has a grade of 122%. What angle does its roadbed make with the horizontal? **about 51°**

32. The Johnstown, Pennsylvania, inclined railway was built as a "lifesaver" after the Johnstown flood of 1889. It has a 987-ft run at a 71% grade. How high does this railway lift its passengers? **about 701 ft**

33. The Fenelon Place Elevator railway in Dubuque, Iowa, lifts passengers 189 ft to the top of a bluff. It has an 83% grade. How long is this railway? **about 296 ft**

34. The Duquesne Incline Plane Company's roadway in Pittsburgh, Pennsylvania, climbs Mt. Washington, located above the mouth of the Monongahela River. It reaches a height of 400 ft with a 793-ft incline. What is its grade? **about 58.4%**

Find the missing value to the nearest tenth.

35. $x = 2, y = $ ■ **71.6**   36. $x = 2\sqrt{3}, y = $ ■ **60.0**   37. $x = 6, y = $ ■ **45.0**

38. $x = 6\sqrt{3}, y = $ ■ **30.0**   39. $x = $ ■$, y = 15$ **22.4**   40. $x = $ ■$, y = 30$ **10.4**

41. $x = $ ■$, y = 45$ **6.0**   42. $x = $ ■$, y = 60$ **3.5**   43. $x = $ ■$, y = 75$ **1.6**

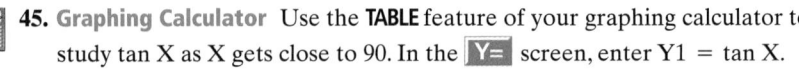

44. a. **Critical Thinking** Does $\tan A + \tan B = \tan (A + B)$ when $A + B < 90$? Explain. **a–b. See margin.**
   b. **Reasoning** Does $\tan A - \tan B = \tan (A - B)$ when $A - B > 0$? Use part (a) and indirect reasoning to explain.

45. **Graphing Calculator** Use the **TABLE** feature of your graphing calculator to study tan X as X gets close to 90. In the **Y=** screen, enter Y1 = tan X.
   a. Use the **TBLSET** feature so that X starts at 80 and changes by 1. Access the **TABLE**. From the table, what is tan X for X = 89? **57.290**
   b. Perform a "numerical zoom in." Use the **TBLSET** feature, so that X starts with 89 and changes by 0.1. What is tan X for X = 89.9? **572.96**   **c. See margin.**
   c. Continue to numerically zoom in on values close to 90. What is the greatest value you can get for tan X on your calculator? How close is X to 90?
   d. **Writing** Use right triangles to explain the behavior of tan X found above. **See margin.**

46. **Graphing Calculator** Use the **TABLE** and graphing features of your graphing calculator to study the product tan X · tan (90 − X). In the **Y=** screen, enter Y1 = tan X · tan (90 − X).
   a. Use the **TBLSET** feature so that X starts at 1 and changes by 1. Access the **TABLE**. What do you notice? **Every Y₁ value = 1.**
   b. Press **GRAPH**. What do you notice? **The graph is that of Y₁ = 1.**
   Proof c. Make a conjecture about tan X · tan (90 − X) based on parts (a) and (b). Write a paragraph proof of your conjecture. **See left.**

Use the given information and $\tan^{-1}$ to find $m\angle A$ to the nearest whole number.

47. $\tan 2A = 9.5144$ **42**   48. $\tan \frac{A}{3} = 0.4663$ **75**

49. $(\tan 5A)^2 = 0.3333$ **6**   50. $\frac{\tan A}{1 + \tan A} = 0.5437$ **50**

Simplify each expression. (*Hint:* Recall from p. 472 how to think of $\tan^{-1} x$.)

51. $\tan (\tan^{-1} x)$ **x**   52. $\tan^{-1} (\tan X)$ **$m\angle X$**

---

pages 472–475 Exercises

44. a. No; Answers may vary. Sample: tan 45° + tan 30° ≈ 1 + 0.6 = 1.6, but tan(45 + 30)° = tan 75° ≈ 3.7

b. No; assume tan A° − tan B° = tan(A − B)°, or tan A° = tan B° + tan (A − B)°. Let A = B + C, so by subst., tan(B + C)° = tan B° + tan C°. This is false by part (a).

45. c. Answers may vary. Sample: tan X° ≈ 572,958 for X = 89.9999

d. Answers may vary. Sample: In a rt. △, as an acute ∠ approaches 90°, the opp. side gets longer.

Coordinate Geometry You can use the slope of a line to find the measure of the acute angle that the line forms with any horizontal line.

$$\text{slope} = \frac{\text{rise}}{\text{run}} = 3$$

$$\tan A = \frac{\text{opposite}}{\text{adjacent}} = 3$$

$$m\angle A = \tan^{-1}(3) \approx 71.6$$

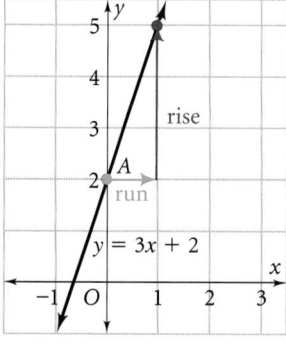

To the nearest tenth, find the measure of the acute angle that the line forms with a horizontal line.

53. $y = \frac{1}{2}x + 6$ **26.6**

54. $y = 6x - 1$ **80.5**

55. $y = 5x - 7$ **78.7**

56. $y = \frac{4}{3}x - 1$ **53.1**

57. $3x - 4y = 8$ **36.9**

58. $-2x + 3y = 6$ **33.7**

Gridded Response

59. What is tan 84° to the nearest tenth? **9.5**

60. What is the whole number value of $\tan^{-1}\sqrt{3}$? **60**

In Exercises 61–64 what is the value of *x* to the nearest tenth?

61.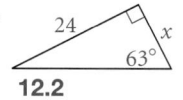
12.2

62.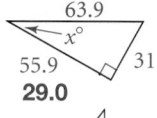
29.0

63.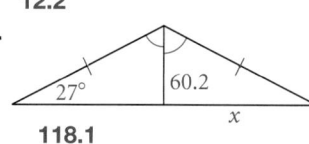
118.1

64.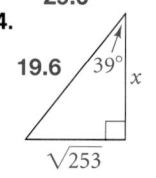
19.6

Take It to the NET
Online lesson quiz at
www.PHSchool.com
Web Code: afa-0901

65. The tangent of an angle is 7.5. What is the measure of the angle to the nearest tenth? **82.4**

Mixed Review

Lesson 8-6

66. The area of a regular octagon is 100 cm². Another regular octagon has sides that are three times as long. What is its area? **900 cm²**

Lesson 7-2

The lengths of the sides of a triangle are given. Classify each triangle as *acute*, *right*, or *obtuse*.

67. 5, 8, 4
     obtuse

68. 15, 15, 20
     acute

69. 0.5, 1.2, 1.3
     right

Lesson 6-7

70. For the kite pictured at the right, give the coordinates of the midpoints of its sides.
$R(a, b)$; $S(a, -b)$; $T(c, -b)$; $V(c, b)$

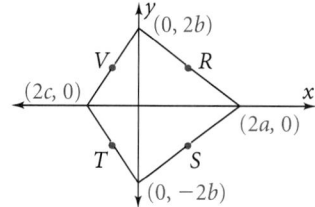

Standardized Test Prep

A sheet of blank grids is available in the Test-Taking Strategies with Transparencies booklet. Give this sheet to students for practice with filling in the grids.

Resources
For additional practice with a variety of test item formats:
• Standardized Test Prep, p. 509
• Test-Taking Strategies, p. 504
• Test-Taking Strategies with Transparencies

Exercise 64 Students can use either the 39° angle or the 51° angle to write and solve an equation to find *x*.

 **Technology**

Exploring Trigonometric Ratios

Exploring Trigonometric Ratios

Students will use geometry software to investigate the tangent, sine, and cosine ratios.

Resources

Students may use any geometry software program to explore trigonometric ratios.

Teaching Notes

This exploration extends the Investigation in Lesson 9-1. Using geometric software, students can dynamically manipulate right triangles to examine trigonometric ratios. Students should make these observations:

- Trigonometric ratios remain the same for angles having the same measure, regardless of the lengths of the legs and the hypotenuse.
- The ratios seem to have limits as the angle measures approach 0 or 90 (except for the tangent ratio).

Visual Learners

Trigonometry can be overly abstract and frustrating for students who are not grounded in a visual understanding of right triangle relationships. Encourage students to use this activity as a starting point in designing their own ways to model the relationships in Chapter 9.

Auditory Learners

Have students discuss their discoveries while they work through the investigation. Suggest that they ask questions of one another and answer one another's questions. Encourage them to form conjectures as a class.

Construct

Use geometry software to construct $\overrightarrow{AB}$ and $\overrightarrow{AC}$ so that $\angle A$ is acute. Through a point D on $\overrightarrow{AB}$ construct a line perpendicular to $\overrightarrow{AB}$ that intersects $\overrightarrow{AC}$ in point E. Moving point D enlarges or reduces $\triangle ADE$. Moving point C changes the size of $\angle A$.

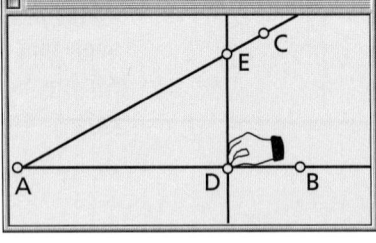

EXERCISES

1. • Measure $\angle A$.
   - Find the lengths of the sides of $\triangle ADE$.
   - Calculate the ratio $\frac{\text{leg opposite } \angle A}{\text{hypotenuse}}$, which is $\frac{ED}{AE}$.
   - Move point D to change the size of the right triangle without changing the size of $\angle A$.

   What do you observe about the ratio as the size of $\triangle ADE$ changes? **It doesn't change.**

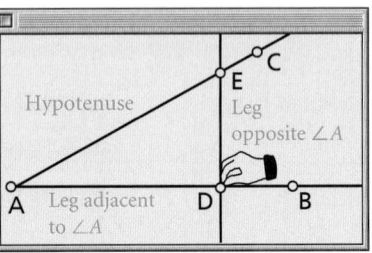

2. • Move point C to change the size of $\angle A$.
   a. What do you observe about the ratio as the size of $\angle A$ changes? **The ratio becomes larger as the angle becomes larger.**
   b. What value does the ratio approach as $m\angle A$ approaches 0? As $m\angle A$ approaches 90? **0; 1**

3. • Make a table that shows values for $m\angle A$ and the ratio $\frac{\text{leg opposite } \angle A}{\text{hypotenuse}}$. In your table, include $10, 20, 30, \ldots, 80$ for $m\angle A$.
   - Compare your table with the table of trigonometric ratios on page 731.

   Do your values for $\frac{\text{leg opposite } \angle A}{\text{hypotenuse}}$ match the values in one of the columns of the table? What is the name of this ratio in the table? **yes; sine**

Extend

4. Repeat Exercises 1–3 for the ratio $\frac{\text{leg adjacent to } \angle A}{\text{hypotenuse}}$, which is $\frac{AD}{AE}$.

5. Repeat Exercises 1–3 for the ratio $\frac{\text{leg opposite } \angle A}{\text{leg adjacent to } \angle A}$, which is $\frac{ED}{AD}$.

6. • Choose a measure for $\angle A$ and determine the ratio $r = \frac{\text{leg opposite } \angle A}{\text{hypotenuse}}$. Record $m\angle A$ and this ratio.
   - Manipulate the triangle so that $\frac{\text{leg adjacent to } \angle A}{\text{hypotenuse}}$ has the same value r. Record this $m\angle A$ and compare it with your first value of $m\angle A$.
   - Repeat this procedure several times.
   - Look for a pattern in the two measures of $\angle A$ that you found for the different values of r.

   Make a conjecture.

4. It doesn't change; the ratio becomes smaller as the angle becomes larger; 1; 0; the values match cosine.

5. It doesn't change; the ratio becomes larger as the angle becomes larger; 0; a large number; the values match tangent.

6. When these two ratios are equal, the two angles are complementary.

Sine and Cosine Ratios

North Carolina Objectives

1.01   Use the trigonometric ratios to model and solve problems involving right triangles.

Lesson Preview

What You'll Learn

OBJECTIVE 1
To use sine and cosine to determine side lengths in triangles

. . . And Why

To use the sine ratio to estimate astronomical distances indirectly, as in Example 2

✓ **Check Skills You'll Need**   (For help, go to Lesson 9-1.)

For each triangle, find (a) the length of the leg opposite ∠B and (b) the length of the leg adjacent to ∠B.

1. 9; 12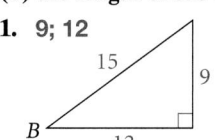

2.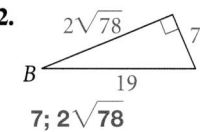
    7; 2√78

3.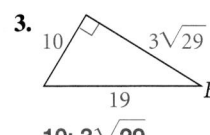
    10; 3√29

New Vocabulary • sine • cosine • identity

OBJECTIVE
1 Using Sine and Cosine in Triangles

The tangent ratio, as you have seen, involves both legs of a right triangle. The sine and cosine ratios involve one leg and the hypotenuse.

sine of ∠A = $\dfrac{\text{leg opposite } \angle A}{\text{hypotenuse}}$

cosine of ∠A = $\dfrac{\text{leg adjacent to } \angle A}{\text{hypotenuse}}$

These equations can be abbreviated:

$$\sin A = \dfrac{\text{opposite}}{\text{hypotenuse}} \qquad \cos A = \dfrac{\text{adjacent}}{\text{hypotenuse}}$$

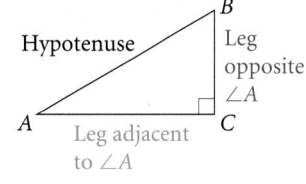

Real-World Connection

For an angle of a given size, the sine and cosine ratios are constant, no matter where the angle is located.

1 EXAMPLE   Writing Sine and Cosine Ratios

Use the triangle to write each ratio.

a. sin T $\sin T = \dfrac{\text{opposite}}{\text{hypotenuse}} = \dfrac{8}{17}$

b. cos T $\cos T = \dfrac{\text{adjacent}}{\text{hypotenuse}} = \dfrac{15}{17}$

c. sin G $\sin G = \dfrac{\text{opposite}}{\text{hypotenuse}} = \dfrac{15}{17}$

d. cos G $\cos G = \dfrac{\text{adjacent}}{\text{hypotenuse}} = \dfrac{8}{17}$

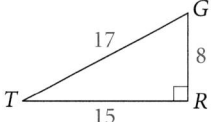

1a. $\sin X = \dfrac{64}{80}; \cos X = \dfrac{48}{80};$
$\sin Y = \dfrac{48}{80}; \cos Y = \dfrac{64}{80}$

✓ **Check Understanding** ❶ **a.** Write the sine and cosine ratios for ∠X and ∠Y. **See right.**

b. **Critical Thinking** In general, how are sin X and cos Y related? Explain.
sin X = cos Y when ∠X and ∠Y are complementary.

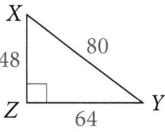

Lesson 9-2   Sine and Cosine Ratios   **477**

Lesson Preview

✓ **Check Skills You'll Need**

Writing Tangent Ratios
Lesson 9-1: Example 1
Exercises 1–3
Extra Practice, p. 698

Lesson Resources

📁 **Teaching Resources**
Practice, Reteaching, Enrichment

👥 **Reaching All Students**
Practice Workbook 9-2
Spanish Practice Workbook 9-2
Hands-On Activities 26
Informal Geometry Planning
    Guide 9-2

🕐 **Presentation Assistant Plus!**
Transparencies
• Check Skills You'll Need 9-2
• Additional Examples 9-2
• Student Edition Answers 9-2
• Lesson Quiz 9-2
PH Presentation Pro CD 9-2

 **ASSESSMENT SYSTEM**

Computer Test Generator CD

💿 **Technology**
Resource Pro® CD-ROM
Computer Test Generator CD
Prentice Hall Presentation Pro CD

🖥 **www.PHSchool.com**
Student Site
• Teacher Web Code: afk-5500
• Self-grading Lesson Quiz
Teacher Center
• Lesson Planner
• Resources

Plus

Ongoing Assessment and Intervention

Before the Lesson
Diagnose prerequisite skills using:
• Check Skills You'll Need

During the Lesson
Monitor progress using:
• Check Understanding
• Additional Examples
• Standardized Test Prep

After the Lesson
Assess knowledge using:
• Lesson Quiz
• Computer Test Generator CD

Math Background

A *unit circle* has radius 1 and center (0,0) in the coordinate plane. For all real values of θ, the point that is reached by traveling θ radians from point (1,0) in a counterclockwise direction has coordinates (cos θ, sin θ).

OBJECTIVE 1 Teaching Notes

Visual Learners

Have students display a poster listing the trigonometric ratios.

 **Additional Examples**

① Use the triangle to find sin *T*, cos *T*, sin *G*, and cos *G*.

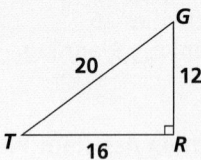

$\sin T = \frac{12}{20}$, $\cos T = \frac{16}{20}$,
$\sin G = \frac{16}{20}$, $\cos G = \frac{12}{20}$

② A 20-ft wire supporting a flagpole forms a 35° angle with the flagpole. To the nearest foot, how high is the flagpole?

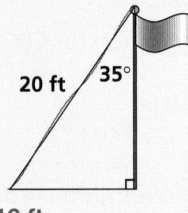

③ A right triangle has a leg 1.5 units long and a hypotenuse 4.0 units long. Find the measures of its acute angles to the nearest degree. **22, 68**

Closure

A right triangle whose hypotenuse is 18 cm long contains a 65° angle. Find the lengths of its legs to one decimal place. **16.3 cm, 7.6 cm**

One way to describe the relationship of sine and cosine is to say that $\sin x° = \cos (90 - x)°$ for values of x between 0 and 90. This type of equation is called an **identity** because it is true for all the allowed values of the variable. You will discover other identities in the exercises.

② **EXAMPLE** **Real-World** 🌎 **Connection**

Astronomy The trigonometric ratios have been known for centuries by peoples in many cultures. The Polish astronomer Nicolaus Copernicus (1473–1543) developed a method for determining the sizes of orbits of planets closer to the sun than Earth. The key to his method was determining when the planets were in the position shown in the diagram, and then measuring the angle to find *a*.

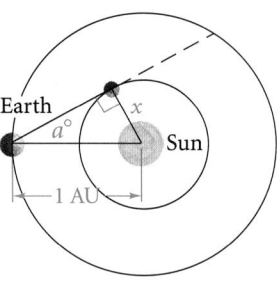

not to scale

If $a = 22.3$ for Mercury, how far is Mercury from the sun in astronomical units (AU)? One astronomical unit is defined as the average distance from Earth to the center of the sun, about 93 million miles.

$$\sin 22.3° = \frac{x}{1} \qquad \text{Use the sine ratio.}$$
$$x = \sin 22.3° \qquad \text{Solve for } x.$$

[SIN] 22.3 [ENTER] $.37945616$ **Use a calculator.**

● Mercury is about 0.38 AU from the sun.

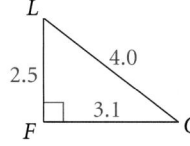 **Check Understanding** **②** **a.** If $a = 46$ for Venus, how far is Venus from the sun in AU? **about 0.72 AU**
b. About how many miles from the sun is Venus? Mercury?
66,960,000 mi; 35,340,000 mi

When you know the leg and hypotenuse lengths of a right triangle, you can use inverse of sine and inverse of cosine to find the measures of the acute angles.

③ **EXAMPLE** **Using the Inverse of Cosine and Sine**

Find $m\angle L$ to the nearest degree.

Reading Math

Think of $\cos^{-1}\left(\frac{5}{8}\right)$ as "the angle whose cosine is $\frac{5}{8}$," and $\sin^{-1}\left(\frac{3.1}{4.0}\right)$ as "the angle whose sine is the quotient $\frac{3.1}{4.0}$."

Method 1

$\cos L = \frac{2.5}{4.0} = \frac{5}{8}$ ← Find the trigonometric ratio. → $\sin L = \frac{3.1}{4.0}$

$m\angle L = \cos^{-1}\left(\frac{5}{8}\right)$ ← Use the inverse. → $m\angle L = \sin^{-1}\left(\frac{3.1}{4.0}\right)$

[COS⁻¹] 5 [÷] 8 [ENTER] ← Use a calculator. → [SIN⁻¹] 3.1 [÷] 4.0 [ENTER]
51.317813 50.805033

● $m\angle L \approx 51$ $m\angle L \approx 51$

Method 2

Check Understanding **③** Find the value of x. Round your answer to the nearest degree.
a. **41**   **b.** **68**

👥 Reaching All Students

Below Level Have students draw and measure right triangles to make a table of sine and cosine values for the angles in the set {10°, 20°, ... , 80°}.	**Advanced Learners** Encourage students to make conjectures about the values of sin 0°, cos 0°, sin 90°, and cos 90°, defend their conjectures, and then check the values on a calculator.	**Visual Learners** See note on page 478. **Error Prevention** See note on page 479.

EXERCISES

Practice and Problem Solving

A **Practice by Example**

Example 1
(page 477)

Write the ratios for sin M and cos M.

1.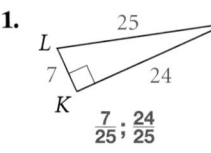
$\frac{7}{25}; \frac{24}{25}$

2.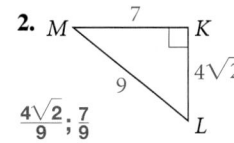
$\frac{4\sqrt{2}}{9}; \frac{7}{9}$

3.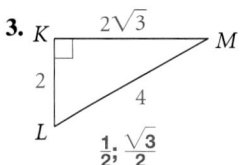
$\frac{1}{2}, \frac{\sqrt{3}}{2}$

Example 2
(page 478)

Find the value of x. Round answers to the nearest tenth.

4. 11.5

5. 8.3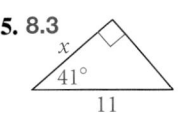

6. 17.9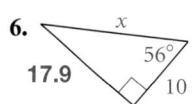

7. 17.0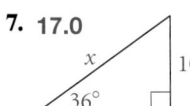

8. 4.3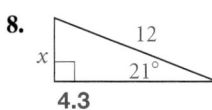

9. 106.5

10. Escalators An escalator in the subway system of St. Petersburg, Russia, has a vertical rise of 195 ft 9.5 in., and rises at an angle of 10.4°. How long is the escalator? Round your answer to the nearest foot. **1085 ft**

Example 3
(page 478)

Find the value of x. Round answers to the nearest degree.

11.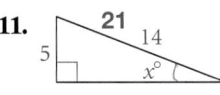

12.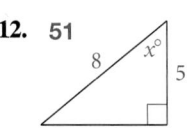

13.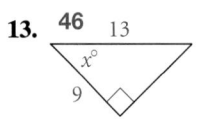

14.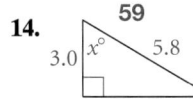

15.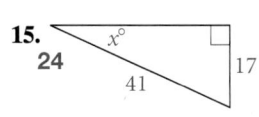

16.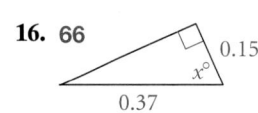

B **Apply Your Skills**

Real-World Connection

Corn that fills the bin in Exercise 17 would make 28,500 gallons of ethanol.

17. Construction Carlos is planning to build a grain bin with a radius of 15 ft. He reads that the recommended slant of the roof is 25°. He wants the roof to overhang the edge of the bin by 1 ft. What should the length x be? Give your answer in feet and inches. **about 17 ft 8 in.**

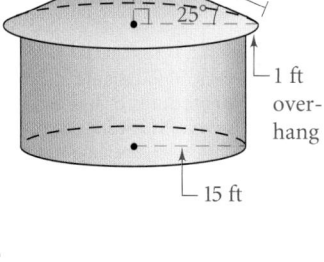
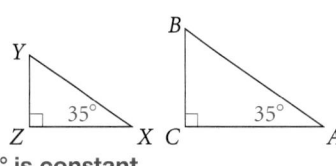

Use what you know about trigonometric ratios (and other identities) to show that each equation is an identity. **18–20. See margin.**

18. $\tan X = \frac{\sin X}{\cos X}$ **19.** $\sin X = \cos X \cdot \tan X$ **20.** $\cos X = \frac{\sin X}{\tan X}$

21. Error Analysis A student states that $\sin A > \sin X$ because the lengths of the sides of $\triangle ABC$ are greater than the lengths of the sides of $\triangle XYZ$. Is the student correct? Explain.
No; the △ are ∼ and the sine ratio for 35° is constant.

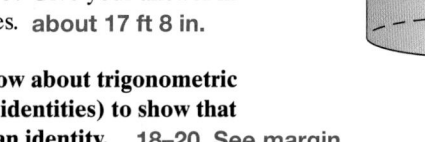

Lesson 9-2 Sine and Cosine Ratios   **479**

Assignment Guide

1 Objective
   A B Core 1–30
   C Extension 31–36

Standardized Test Prep 37–40

Mixed Review 41–47

Error Prevention

Exercises 6, 7 Some students may need help solving equations with the variable in the denominator. Review techniques such as cross-multiplication and taking the reciprocal of each side.

Exercise 25 Tell students that there is also a cotangent ratio. Ask: *What do you think is the cotangent ratio?* $\frac{\text{adjacent}}{\text{opposite}}$

Alternative Method

Exercises 33, 34 Students can divide both sides of the Pythagorean Theorem by a^2 or b^2 to derive these identities.

Exercise 36 Point out that Copernicus's method depends on the sun, Earth, and outer planets' being in a line at one point in time and forming a right angle at the other point in time.

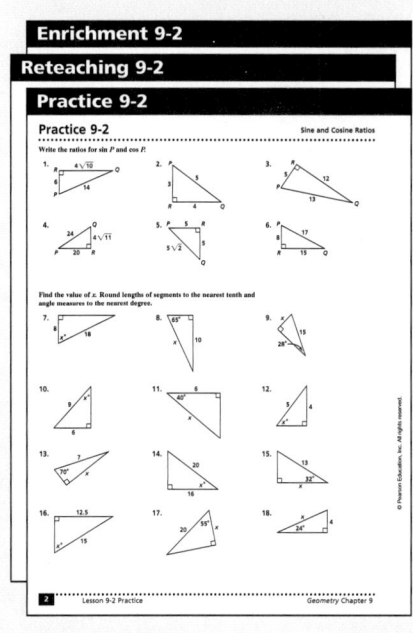

479

Use this figure for Exercises 1 and 2.

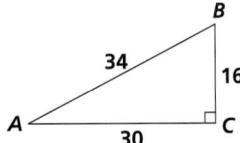

1. Write the ratios for sin A and sin B. $\sin A = \frac{16}{34}$, $\sin B = \frac{30}{34}$

2. Write the ratios for cos A and cos B. $\cos A = \frac{30}{34}$, $\cos B = \frac{16}{34}$

Use this figure for Exercises 3 and 4.

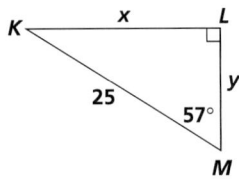

3. Find x to the nearest tenth. 21.0

4. Find y to the nearest tenth. 13.6

Use this figure for Exercises 5 and 6.

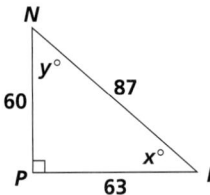

5. Find x to the nearest degree. 44

6. Find y to the nearest degree. 46

Alternative Assessment

Have students write two measurement problems involving distances in your school. Students also should show how to solve one problem using the sine ratio and the other problem using the cosine ratio.

480

25a. They are equal; yes; The sine and cosine of complementary ∆ are =.

25c. Sample: cosine of ∠A = sine of the compl. of ∠A.

27. Yes; use any trig. function and the known measures to find one other side. Use the Pythagorean Thm. to find the 3rd side. Subtract the acute ∠ measure from 90 to get the other ∠ measure.

Reading Math

In Exercise 27, Leona could say, "Given a side and an acute angle of a right triangle, I can solve the triangle."

28e. $\cos 30° = \sqrt{3} \sin 30°$

28f. $\sin 60° = \sqrt{3} \cos 60°$

30b–d. Answers may vary. Samples are given.

30c. $\sin X = 1$ for $X = 89.9$; no

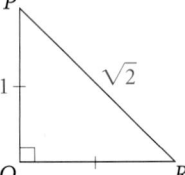

Take It to the NET

Graphing Calculator procedures online at www.PHSchool.com

Web Code: afe-2111

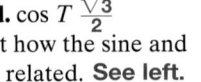

Find the values of w and then x. Round lengths to the nearest tenth and angle measures to the nearest degree.

22.
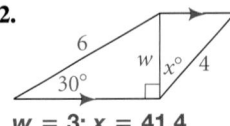
$w = 3; x = 41.4$

23.
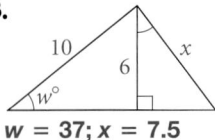
$w = 37; x = 7.5$

24.
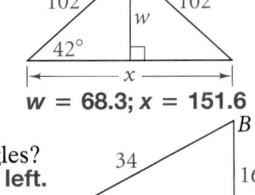
$w = 68.3; x = 151.6$

25. **a.** In $\triangle ABC$, how does sin A compare to cos B? Is this true for the acute angles of other right triangles? **See left.**
   b. Reading Math The word cosine is derived from the words *complement's sine* (see page 614). Which angle in $\triangle ABC$ is the complement of ∠A? Of ∠B? ∠B; ∠A
   c. Explain why the derivation of the word cosine makes sense. **See left.**

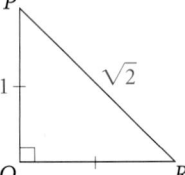

26. Find each ratio.
   a. sin P a. $\frac{\sqrt{2}}{2}$ c. $\frac{\sqrt{2}}{2}$ **b.** cos P b. $\frac{\sqrt{2}}{2}$ d. $\frac{\sqrt{2}}{2}$
   c. sin R
   d. cos R
   e. Make a conjecture about how the sine and cosine of a 45° angle are related. **They are equal.**

27. **Writing** Leona said that if she had a diagram that showed the measure of one acute angle and the length of one side of a right triangle, she could find the measure of the other acute angle and the lengths of the other sides. Is she correct? Explain. **See left.**

28. Find each ratio.
   a. sin S a. $\frac{\sqrt{3}}{2}$ c. $\frac{1}{2}$ **b.** cos S $\frac{1}{2}$
   c. sin T
   d. cos T $\frac{\sqrt{3}}{2}$
   e. Make a conjecture about how the sine and cosine of a 30° angle are related. **See left.**
   f. Make a conjecture about how the sine and cosine of a 60° angle are related. **See left.**

$\overset{Proof}{\longrightarrow}$ 29. Write a paragraph to prove that sin $A < 1$, no matter how large ∠A is in right $\triangle ABC$. **See margin.**

30. **Graphing Calculator** Use the **TABLE** feature of your graphing calculator to study sin X as X gets close (but ≠) to 90. In the **Y=** screen, enter Y1 = sin X.
   a. Use the **TBLSET** feature so that X starts at 80 and changes by 1. Access the **TABLE**. From the table, what is sin X for X = 89? **0.99985**
   b. Perform a "numerical zoom in." Use the **TBLSET** feature, so that X starts with 89 and changes by 0.1. What is sin X for X = 89.9? **1**
   c. Continue to numerically zoom in on values close to 90. What is the greatest value you can get for sin X on your calculator? How close is X to 90? Does your result contradict what you are asked to prove in Exercise 29? **See left.**
   d. Writing Use right triangles to explain the behavior of sin X found above. **See margin.**

Show that each equation is an identity by showing that each expression on the left simplifies to 1. 31–34. See margin.

31. $(\sin A)^2 + (\cos A)^2 = 1$ 32. $(\sin B)^2 + (\cos B)^2 = 1$

33. $\frac{1}{(\cos A)^2} - (\tan A)^2 = 1$ 34. $\frac{1}{(\sin A)^2} - \frac{1}{(\tan A)^2} = 1$

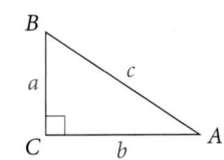

35. Show that $(\tan A)^2 - (\sin A)^2 = (\tan A)^2 (\sin A)^2$ is an identity. **See margin.**

---

pages 479–481 Exercises

29. Answers may vary. Sample: Since $\sin A = \frac{\text{opp.}}{\text{hyp.}}$, if $\sin A \geq 1$, then opp. $\geq$ hyp., which is impossible.

30. **d.** For ∆ that approach 90, the opp. side gets close to the hyp. in length, so $\frac{\text{opp.}}{\text{hyp.}}$ approaches 1.

31. $(\sin A)^2 + (\cos A)^2 = \left(\frac{a}{c}\right)^2 + \left(\frac{b}{c}\right)^2 = \frac{a^2}{c^2} + \frac{b^2}{c^2} = \frac{a^2 + b^2}{c^2} = \frac{c^2}{c^2} = 1$

Real-World ☉ Connection

Poland honored Copernicus with this 1000-zloty note, last used in 1995.

36. Astronomy Copernicus devised a method different from the one in Example 2 in order to find the sizes of the orbits of planets farther from the sun than Earth. His method involved noting the number of days between the times that a planet was in the positions labeled A and B in the diagram. Using this time and the number of days in each planet's year, he calculated c and d.

    a. For Mars, $c = 55.2$ and $d = 103.8$. How far is Mars from the sun in astronomical units (AU)? **about 1.5 AU**

    b. For Jupiter, $c = 21.9$ and $d = 100.8$. How far is Jupiter from the sun in astronomical units? **about 5.2 AU**

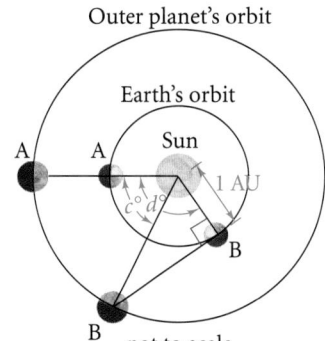

Outer planet's orbit

Earth's orbit

Sun

1 AU

A   A

c° d°

B

B   not to scale

Standardized Test Prep

Multiple Choice

37. What is the value of x to the nearest whole number? **A**
    A. 2   **B.** 3
    C. 4   **D.** 6

38. What is the value of y to the nearest tenth? **H**
    F. 5.4   **G.** 5.5
    H. 5.6   **I.** 5.7

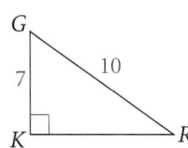

x $\sqrt{37}$ 23° y

Take It to the NET

Online lesson quiz at
www.PHSchool.com
Web Code: afa-0902

39. What is the value of x to the nearest whole number? **A**
    A. 53   **B.** 47
    C. 43   **D.** 37

35.1   46.8 $x°$ 58.5

Short Response

40. Use the figure at the right.
    a. Find $m\angle G$. Show your work. **a–b. See margin.**
    b. Find $m\angle R$ by two different methods. Show your work.

G 10   7 K R

Mixed Review

Lesson 9-1   **Find the value of x. Round answers to the nearest tenth.**

41.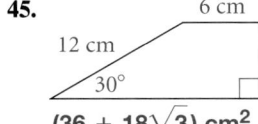
6.9   4   30° x

42.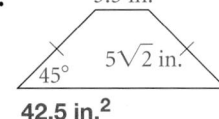
3.3   7   65° x

43.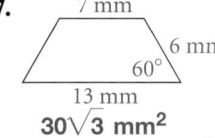
18   18   45° x

Lesson 8-2   **44.** The wall of a room is in the shape of a golden rectangle. If the height of the wall is 8 ft, what are the possible lengths of the wall to the nearest tenth?
12.9 ft or 4.9 ft

Lesson 7-4   **Find the area of each trapezoid. Leave your answer in simplest radical form.**

45.
6 cm   12 cm   30°
$(36 + 18\sqrt{3})$ cm^2

46.
3.5 in.   45° $5\sqrt{2}$ in.
42.5 in.^{2}

47.
7 mm   6 mm   60°   13 mm
$30\sqrt{3}$ mm^2

Lesson 9-2 Sine and Cosine Ratios **481**

Standardized Test Prep

📁 **Resources**

For additional practice with a variety of test item formats:
• Standardized Test Prep, p. 509
• Test-Taking Strategies, p. 504
• Test-Taking Strategies with Transparencies

Exercise 39 Because x is opposite the longer leg, $x > 45$, so choices C and D can be eliminated.

Exercise 40 There is often more than one way to solve a problem. Here students could use the inverse of the sine of $\angle R$ or the inverse of the cosine of $\angle G$.

32. $(\sin B)^2 + (\cos B)^2 =$
$$\left(\frac{b}{c}\right)^2 + \left(\frac{a}{c}\right)^2 = \frac{b^2}{c^2} + \frac{a^2}{c^2} =$$
$$\frac{b^2 + a^2}{c^2} = \frac{c^2}{c^2} = 1$$

33. $\dfrac{1}{(\cos A)^2} - (\tan A)^2$
$$= \left(1 \div \frac{b^2}{c^2}\right) - \frac{a^2}{b^2}$$
$$= \frac{c^2}{b^2} - \frac{a^2}{b^2} =$$
$$\frac{c^2 - a^2}{b^2} = \frac{b^2}{b^2} = 1$$

34. $\dfrac{1}{(\sin A)^2} - \dfrac{1}{(\tan A)^2} =$
$$\frac{1}{\left(\frac{a}{c}\right)^2} - \frac{1}{\left(\frac{a}{b}\right)^2} = \frac{c^2}{a^2} - \frac{b^2}{a^2} =$$
$$\frac{c^2 - b^2}{a^2} = \frac{a^2}{a^2} = 1$$

35. $(\tan A)^2 - (\sin A)^2 =$
$$\left(\frac{a}{b}\right)^2 - \left(\frac{a}{c}\right)^2 = \frac{a^2}{b^2} - \frac{a^2}{c^2} =$$
$$\frac{a^2 c^2}{b^2 c^2} - \frac{a^2 b^2}{b^2 c^2} =$$
$$\frac{a^2 c^2 - a^2 b^2}{b^2 c^2} =$$
$$\frac{a^2(c^2 - b^2)}{b^2 c^2} = \frac{a^2 \cdot a^2}{b^2 c^2} =$$
$$\left(\frac{a}{b}\right)^2\left(\frac{a}{c}\right)^2 =$$
$$(\tan A)^2(\sin A)^2$$

40. [2] a. $\cos G = \frac{7}{10}$
$$m\angle G =$$
$$\cos^{-1}\left(\frac{7}{10}\right) \approx 46$$

    b. $m\angle R \approx 90 - 46 = 44$ OR $m\angle R = \sin^{-1}\left(\frac{7}{10}\right) \approx 44$

[1] one angle found correctly

481

Lesson Preview

✓ **Check Skills You'll Need**

Finding Measures of Angles
Lesson 3-1: Examples 4 and 5
Exercises 11–16
Extra Practice, p. 692

**Applying the Triangle
Angle-Sum Theorem**
Lesson 3-3: Example 1
Exercises 1–3
Extra Practice, p. 692

Lesson Resources

📁 **Teaching Resources**
Practice, Reteaching, Enrichment

👥 **Reaching All Students**
Practice Workbook 9-3
Spanish Practice Workbook 9-3
Reading and Math Literacy 9B
Spanish Reading & Literacy 9B
Spanish Checkpoint Quiz 1
Informal Geometry Planning
 Guide 9-3

⏰ **Presentation Assistant Plus!**
Transparencies
• Check Skills You'll Need 9-3
• Additional Examples 9-3
• Student Edition Answers 9-3
• Lesson Quiz 9-3
PH Presentation Pro CD 9-3

ASSESSMENT SYSTEM

Computer Test Generator CD

💿 **Technology**
Resource Pro® CD-ROM
Computer Test Generator CD
Prentice Hall Presentation Pro CD

🖥 **www.PHSchool.com**
Student Site
• Teacher Web Code: afk-5500
• Updated Data
• Self-grading Lesson Quiz
Teacher Center
• Lesson Planner
• Resources

Plus

9-3 Angles of Elevation and Depression

 North Carolina Objectives

1.01   Use the trigonometric ratios to model and solve problems involving right triangles.

Lesson Preview

What You'll Learn

OBJECTIVE 1
To use angles of elevation and depression to solve problems

. . . And Why

To use the angle of elevation to calculate the height of a natural wonder, as in Example 2

✓ Check Skills You'll Need

(For help, go to Lesson 6-1.)

Refer to rectangle *ABCD* to complete the statements.

1. $\angle 1 \cong \blacksquare \angle 7$ **2.** $\angle 5 \cong \blacksquare \angle 11$

3. $\angle 3 \cong \blacksquare \angle 6$ **4.** $m\angle 1 + m\angle 5 = \blacksquare\ 90$

5. $m\angle 10 + m\angle 3 = \blacksquare\ 180$ **6.** $\angle 10 \cong \blacksquare \angle 8$

New Vocabulary   • angle of elevation   • angle of depression

OBJECTIVE

1   Using Angles of Elevation and Depression

🖥 **Interactive lesson** includes instant self-check, tutorials, and activities.

Suppose a person on the ground sees a hot-air balloon gondola at a 38° angle above a horizontal line.

This angle is the **angle of elevation.**

At the same time, a person in the hot-air balloon sees the person on the ground at a 38° angle below a horizontal line.

This angle is the **angle of depression.**

Examine the diagram. The angle of elevation is congruent to the angle of depression because they are alternate interior angles.

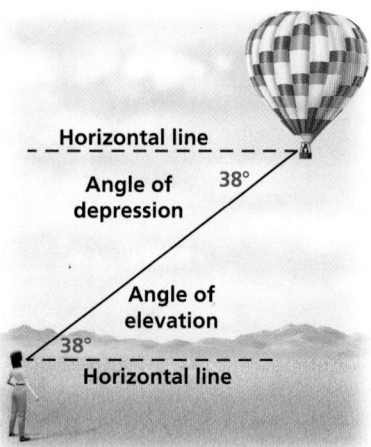
Horizontal line
Angle of depression   38°
Angle of elevation
38°
Horizontal line

1 EXAMPLE   **Identifying Angles of Elevation and Depression**

Describe each angle as it relates to the situation shown.

a. $\angle 1$ $\angle 1$ is the angle of depression from the peak to the hiker.

b. $\angle 4$ $\angle 4$ is the angle of elevation from the hut to the hiker.

✓ **Check Understanding** 1 Describe each angle as it relates to the situation in Example 1.
a. $\angle 2$ **b.** $\angle 3$ ∠ of depression from hiker to hut
∠ of elevation from hiker to peak

Ongoing Assessment and Intervention

Before the Lesson	**During the Lesson**	**After the Lesson**
Diagnose prerequisite skills using:	Monitor progress using:	Assess knowledge using:
• Check Skills You'll Need	• Check Understanding	• Lesson Quiz
	• Additional Examples	• Computer Test Generator CD
	• Standardized Test Prep	• Chapter Checkpoint 1 (p. 488)

Surveyors use two instruments, the transit and the theodolite, to measure angles of elevation and depression. On both instruments, the surveyor sets the horizon line perpendicular to the direction of gravity. Using gravity to find the horizon line ensures accurate measures even on sloping surfaces.

Horizon line

Pull of gravity

Math Background

Indirect measurement has been used since antiquity to measure distances that could not be measured directly. For example, Eratosthenes measured the Earth's circumference more than 2000 years ago, assuming the Earth to be round although subsequent scholars assumed it to be flat.

2 EXAMPLE **Real-World Connection**

Surveying To find the height of Delicate Arch in Arches National Park in Utah, a surveyor levels a theodolite with the bottom of the arch. From there, she measures the angle of elevation to the top of the arch. She then measures the distance from where she stands to a point directly under the arch. Her results are shown in the diagram. What is the height of the arch?

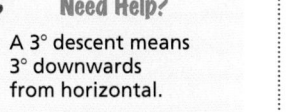
x ft
48°
36 ft
5 ft
not to scale

$\tan 48° = \frac{x}{36}$ Use the tangent ratio.

$x = 36(\tan 48°)$ Solve for *x*.

36 TAN 48 ENTER *39.982051*   Use a calculator.

So $x \approx 40$. To find the height of the arch, add the height of the theodolite. Since $40 + 5 = 45$, Delicate Arch is about 45 feet high.

OBJECTIVE 1 **Teaching Notes**

2 EXAMPLE **Careers**

Have students research the work description and tools of surveyors, including electronic distance measurement devices (EDMs).

✔ **Check Understanding** **2** You sight a rock climber on a cliff at a 32° angle of elevation. The horizontal ground distance to the cliff is 1000 ft. Find the line-of-sight distance to the rock climber. **about 1179 ft**

Rock Climber
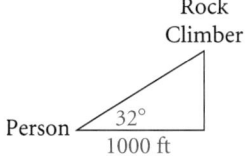
Person 32°
1000 ft

Additional Examples

1 Describe ∠1 and ∠2 as they relate to the situation shown.

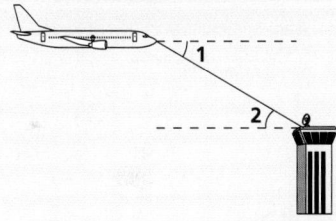
1
2

∠1 is the angle of depression; ∠2 is the angle of elevation.

3 EXAMPLE **Real-World Connection**

? **Need Help?**

A 3° descent means 3° downwards from horizontal.

Aviation To approach runway 17 of the Ponca City Municipal Airport in Oklahoma, the pilot must begin a 3° descent starting from an altitude of 2714 ft. The airport altitude is 1007 ft. How many miles from the runway is the airplane at the start of this approach?

3° Angle of descent
2714 ft
not to scale   Altitude of airport: 1007 ft

The airplane is $2714 - 1007$, or 1707 ft above the level of the airport. Use trigonometry to find the desired distance.

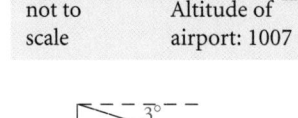
1707 ft
3°
x
3°

$\sin 3° = \frac{1707}{x}$ Use the sine ratio.

$x = \frac{1707}{\sin 3°}$ Solve for *x*.

1707 ÷ SIN 3 ENTER *32616.2*   Use a calculator.

÷ 5280 ENTER *6.1773105*   Divide by 5280 to convert feet to miles.

The airplane is about 6.2 mi from the runway at the start of the approach.

2 A surveyor stands 200 ft from a building to measure its height with a 5-ft tall theodolite. The angle of elevation to the top of the building is 35°. How tall is the building? **about 145 ft**

3 An airplane flying 3500 ft above ground begins a 2° descent to land at an airport. How many miles from the airport is the airplane when it starts its descent? **about 19 mi**

✔ **Check Understanding** **3** An airplane pilot sights a life raft at a 26° angle of depression. The airplane's altitude is 3 km. What is the airplane's surface distance *d* from the raft? **about 6.2 km**

Closure

Two buildings are 30 ft apart. The angle of elevation from the top of one to the top of the other is 19°. What is their difference in height? **about 10 ft**

👥 Reaching All Students

| **Below Level** Highlight the importance of parallel lines by having students copy the diagrams in Examples 1 and 3 and marking pairs of congruent angles in different colors. | **Advanced Learners** Challenge students to solve Example 3 using the cosine ratio. | **English Learners** See note on page 486. **Error Prevention** See note on page 485. |

Assignment Guide

▼ **Objective**

Ⓐ Ⓑ Core 1–33

Ⓒ Extension 34–36

Standardized Test Prep 37–44

Mixed Review 45–55

Teaching Tip

Exercises 14, 15 Check that students relate the angle of depression to its alternate interior angle in the triangle. Ask: *How do you know that the angle of depression and the angle of elevation are congruent?* They are alternate interior angles formed by parallel lines.

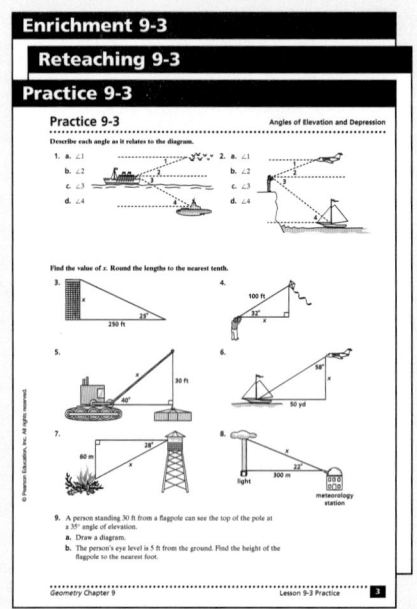

EXERCISES

For more practice, see *Extra Practice*.

Practice and Problem Solving

Ⓐ **Practice by Example**

Example 1
(page 482)

Describe each angle as it relates to the situation in the diagram. 1–8. See margin.

1. ∠1 **2.** ∠2 **3.** ∠3 **4.** ∠4 **5.** ∠5 **6.** ∠6 **7.** ∠7 **8.** ∠8

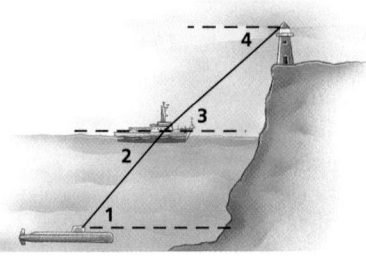

Jim   Kelley

Example 2
(page 483)

Find the value of *x*. Round the lengths to the nearest tenth.

9. 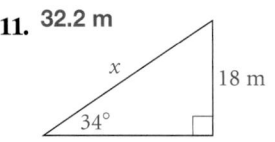 34.2 ft, 100 ft, x, 20°

10. 502.4 m 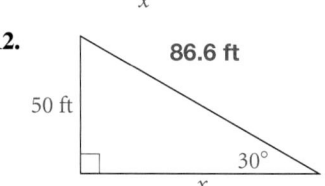 203 m, 22°, x

11. 32.2 m, x, 18 m, 34°

12. 86.6 ft, 50 ft, 30°, x

13. **Meteorology** A meteorologist measures the angle of elevation of a weather balloon as 41°. A radio signal from the balloon indicates that it is 1503 m from his location. To the nearest meter, how high above the ground is the balloon? **about 986 m**

Example 3
(page 483)

Find the value of *x*. Round lengths to the nearest tenth of a unit.

14. 26°, 25 ft, 51.3 ft, x

15. 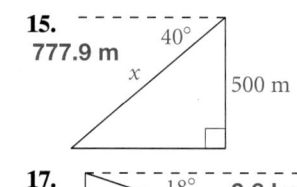 40°, 777.9 m, x, 500 m

16. 27°, 263.3 yd, 580 yd, x

17. 18°, x, 0.6 km, 2 km

18. **Indirect Measurement** Miguel looks out from the crown of the Statue of Liberty approximately 250 ft above ground. He sights a ship coming into New York harbor and measures the angle of depression as 18°. Find the distance from the base of the statue to the ship to the nearest foot. **769 ft**

Ⓑ **Apply Your Skills** 🌐 **19.** **Flagpole** The world's tallest unsupported flagpole is a 282-ft-tall steel pole in Surrey, British Columbia. The shortest shadow cast by the pole during the year is 137 ft long. To the nearest degree, what is the angle of elevation of the sun when the shortest shadow is cast? **64°**

pages 484–488 Exercises

1. ∠ of elevation from sub to boat

2. ∠ of depression from boat to sub

3. ∠ of elevation from boat to lighthouse

4. ∠ of depression from lighthouse to boat

5. ∠ of elevation from Jim to waterfall

6. ∠ of elevation from Kelley to waterfall

7. ∠ of depression from waterfall to Jim

8. ∠ of depression from waterfall to Kelley

20. **Engineering** The Americans with Disabilities Act states that wheelchair ramps can have a slope no greater than $\frac{1}{12}$. Find the angle of elevation of a ramp with this slope. Round your answer to the nearest tenth. **4.8°**

21. **Construction** Two office buildings are 51 m apart. The height of the taller building is 207 m. The angle of depression from the top of the taller building to the top of the shorter building is 15°. Find the height of the shorter building to the nearest meter. **about 194 m**

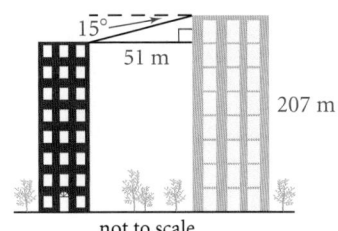
15°
51 m
207 m
not to scale

22. **a. Open-Ended** Draw and label a diagram that shows your own real-world example of an angle of elevation and an angle of depression.

 b. Writing Write a word problem that uses the angle of depression from your diagram. Include a detailed solution to your problem. **a–b. Check students' work.**

23. **Aerial Television** A blimp is providing aerial television views of a football game. The television camera sights the stadium at a 7° angle of depression. The blimp's altitude is 400 m. What is the line-of-sight distance from the TV camera to the stadium, to the nearest hundred meters? **3300 m**

x^2 **Algebra** The angle of elevation e from A to B and the angle of depression d from B to A are shown below. Find the measure of each angle.

24. e: $(7x - 5)°$, d: $4(x + 7)°$ **72, 72** 25. e: $(3x + 1)°$, d: $2(x + 8)°$ **46, 46**

26. e: $(x + 21)°$, d: $3(x + 3)°$ **27, 27** 27. e: $5(x - 2)°$, d: $(x + 14)°$ **20, 20**

28. **Hydromechanics** An engineer is 980 ft from the base of a fountain at Fountain Hills, Arizona. The angle of elevation to the top of the column of water is 29.7°. The surveyor's angle measuring device is at the same level as the base of the fountain.

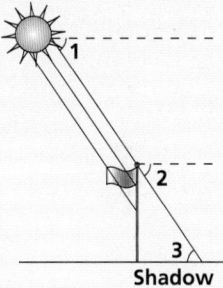
29.7°
980 ft

 a. Find the height of the column of water to the nearest 10 ft. **560 ft**

 b. When the top of the column of water is just half as high as in part (a), find the angle of elevation to its top. **about 15.9°**

29. **Writing** A communications tower is located on a plot of flat land. The tower is supported by several guy wires. Assume that you are able to measure distances along the ground, as well as angles formed by the guy wires and the ground. Explain how you could estimate each of the following measurements.

 a. the length of any guy wire **a–b. See left.**

 b. how high on the tower each wire is attached

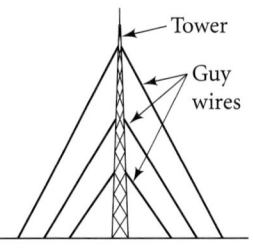
Tower
Guy wires

Flying An airplane at altitude a flies distance d towards you with velocity v. You watch for time t and measure its angles of elevation, $\angle E_1$ and $\angle E_2$, at the start and end of your watch. Find the missing information.

30. $a = $ ▨ mi, $v = 5$ mi/min, $t = 1$ min, $m\angle E_1 = 45$, $m\angle E_2 = 90$ **5**

31. $a = 2$ mi, $v = $ ▨ mi/min, $t = 15$ s, $m\angle E_1 = 40$, $m\angle E_2 = 50$ **about 2.8**

32. $a = 4$ mi, $d = 3$ mi, $v = 6$ mi/min, $t = $ ▨ min, $m\angle E_1 = 50$, $m\angle E_2 = $ ▨ **0.5; about 84.9**

Lesson 9-3 Angles of Elevation and Depression **485**

Reading Math

For help with Exercise 23, see Reading Math on p. 489.

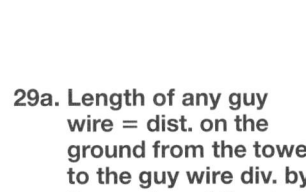

Real-World Connection

The TV blimp can be $\frac{2}{3}$ the length of a football field.

29a. Length of any guy wire = dist. on the ground from the tower to the guy wire div. by the cosine of the ∠ formed by the guy wire and the ground.

29b. Height of attachment = dist. on the ground from the tower to the guy wire times the tangent of the ∠ formed by the guy wire and the ground.

Error Prevention

Exercise 18 Some students may think the angle of depression is the angle between the vertical segment to the ground and the ship. Ask each student to draw a diagram that represents the situation in the exercise and then compare diagrams with a partner. Emphasize that one side of an angle of depression or of an angle of elevation must be horizontal.

Connection to Physics

Exercise 19 The sun's great distance from Earth explains why its rays are considered to be parallel. Copy the diagram below on the board to clarify how the angle of depression from the sun to the top of the flagpole relates to the angle of elevation from the end of the shadow to the top of the flagpole. Point out that as the position of the sun changes during the day, the angle of depression from the sun to the top of the flagpole changes. Discuss how the length of the shadow is longer when the sun is lower in the sky and shortest when the sun is highest in the sky.

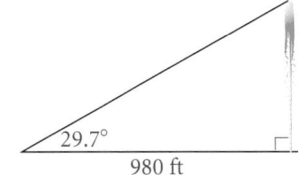
1
2
3
Shadow

485

Diversity

Exercise 20 This is a good opportunity to discuss disabilities with students. They may be surprised to learn that although some people are born with disabilities, about three fourths of the disabilities in America are caused by accidents, disease, or war.

Connection to Language Arts

Exercise 21 Ask students to use what they learned about similarity in Chapter 8 to explain what the label *not to scale* means.

English Learners

Exercise 29 Have students familiar with guy wires explain their purpose and give examples of other uses for these wires, such as to stabilize telephone poles.

Exercise 35 If students do not make the necessary connection, point out that a shadow is shortest when the sun is directly over head —sometimes called *high noon.*

Real-World Connection

Careers Atmospheric scientists specialize by linking meteorology with another field such as agriculture.

35. **Measure the length of the stick and the shortest shadow. The tangent of the angle of elevation is the ratio of the length of the stick to the length of the shadow. Then use inverse tangent.**

33. **Meteorology** One method that meteorologists could use to find the height of a layer of clouds above the ground is to shine a bright spotlight directly up onto the cloud layer and measure the angle of elevation from a known distance away. Find the height of the cloud layer in the diagram to the nearest 10 m. **370 m**

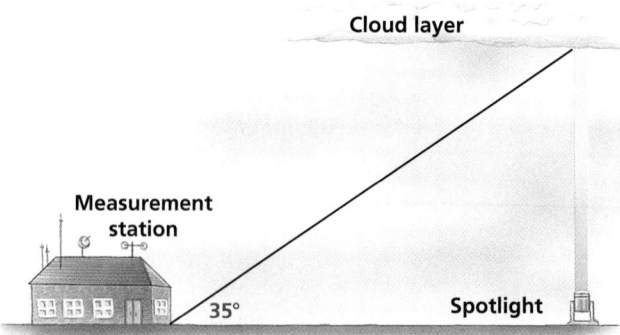

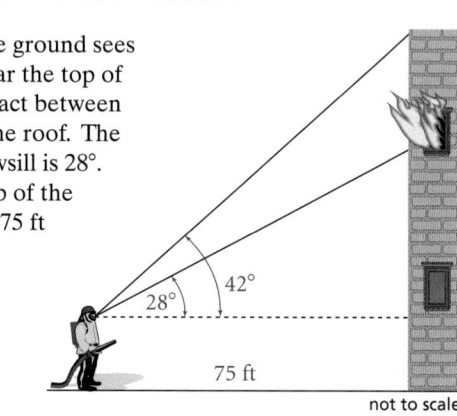

C Challenge 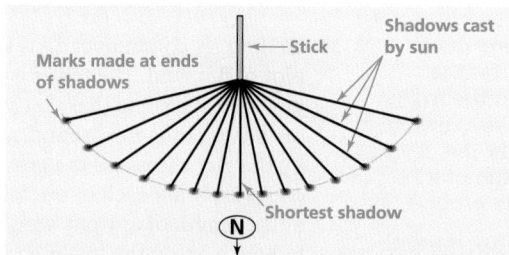 **34.** **Firefighting** A firefighter on the ground sees fire break through a window near the top of the building. There is voice contact between the ground and firefighters on the roof. The angle of elevation to the windowsill is 28°. The angle of elevation to the top of the building is 42°. The firefighter is 75 ft from the building and her eyes are 5 ft above the ground. What roof-to-windowsill distance can she report to the firefighters on the roof? **about 28 ft**

35. **Indirect Measurement** Here is a simple method for finding a north-south line.

Put a stick in the ground before noon and regularly mark the end of its shadow. When the shadow begins to lengthen, stop marking. The mark closest to the stick is directly north of the stick.

Explain how you could use this method to find the angle of elevation of the sun at noon (when the sun is highest in the sky). **See left.**

36. **Geography** For locations in the United States, the relationship between the latitude ℓ and the greatest angle of elevation a of the sun at noon on the first day of summer is $a = 90° - \ell + 23\frac{1}{2}°$. Find the latitude of your town. Then determine the greatest angle of elevation of the sun for your town on the first day of summer. **Check students' work.**

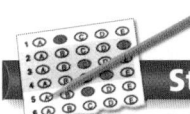
Multiple Choice

37. A 107-ft-tall building casts a shadow of 90 ft. To the nearest whole degree, what is the angle of elevation to the sun? **C**

   A. 33°   **B.** 40°   **C.** 50°   **D.** 57°

38. The angle of depression of a submarine from another Navy ship is 28°. **F** The submarine is 791 ft from the ship. About how deep is the submarine?

   F. 371 ft   **G.** 421 ft   **H.** 563 ft   **I.** 698 ft

39. A kite on a 100-ft string has an angle of elevation of 18°. The hand holding the string is 4 ft from the ground. How high above the ground is the kite?

   A. 95 ft   **B.** 35 ft   **C.** 31 ft   **D.** 22 ft **B**

Quantitative Comparison

Compare the boxed quantity in Column A with the boxed quantity in Column B. Choose the best answer.

   A. The quantity in Column A is greater.
   B. The quantity in Column B is greater.
   C. The two quantities are equal.
   D. The relationship cannot be determined from the information given.

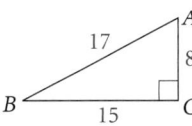

	Column A	Column B
A **40.**	$\sin A$	$\cos A$
C **41.**	$\sin A$	$\cos B$
A **42.**	$\tan A$	$\cos B$
C **43.**	$\dfrac{\sin A}{15}$	$\dfrac{\sin B}{8}$

Short Response

44. A 6-ft-tall man is viewing the top of a tree with an angle of elevation of 83°. He is standing 12 ft from the base of the tree. **a–b. See back of book.**

   a. Draw a sketch of the situation. Show a stick figure for the man. Label the angle of elevation, the height of the man, and the distance the man is standing from the tree.

   b. Write and solve an equation to find the height of the tree. Round your answer to the nearest foot.

Take It to the NET
Online lesson quiz at
www.PHSchool.com
Web Code: afa-0903

Lesson 9-2

Find the value of *x*. Round answers to the nearest tenth.

45.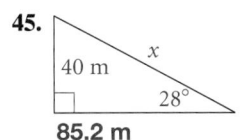

46.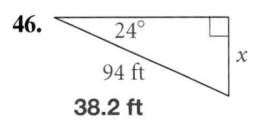

47.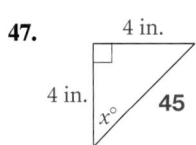

Lesson 9-3 Angles of Elevation and Depression **487**

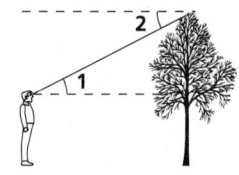

Lesson Quiz 9-3

Use the diagram for Exercises 1 and 2.

1. Describe how ∠1 relates to the situation. **angle of elevation from man's eyes to treetop**

2. Describe how ∠2 relates to the situation. **angle of depression from treetop to man's eyes**

A 6-ft man stands 12 ft from the base of a tree. The angle of elevation from his eyes to the top of the tree is 76°.

3. About how tall is the tree? **about 54 ft**

4. If the man releases a pigeon that flies directly to the top of the tree, about how far will it fly? **about 50 ft**

5. What is the angle of depression from the tree-top to the man's eyes? **76°**

Alternative Assessment

Have students work in pairs to plan how to measure the height of your school building using angles of elevation and depression and trigonometric functions. Then have them carry out their plans.

Standardized Test Prep

Resources
For additional practice with a variety of test item formats:
• Standardized Test Prep, p. 509
• Test-Taking Strategies, p. 504
• Test-Taking Strategies with Transparencies

Exercises 38, 39 Students should draw each situation to help them understand the relationships.

To check understanding of
Lessons 9-1 to 9-3:

Checkpoint Quiz 1 (p. 488)

📁 **Teaching Resources**
Checkpoint Quiz 1 (also in
Prentice Hall Assessment
System)

👥 **Reaching All Students**
Reading and Math Literacy 9B

Spanish versions available

---

page 488 Checkpoint Quiz 1

1. $\tan A = \frac{5}{4}$; $\sin A = \frac{25}{32}$;
   $\cos A = \frac{5}{8}$; $\tan B = \frac{4}{5}$;
   $\sin B = \frac{5}{8}$; $\cos B = \frac{25}{32}$

2. $\tan A = \frac{5}{12}$; $\sin A = \frac{5}{13}$;
   $\cos A = \frac{12}{13}$; $\tan B = \frac{12}{5}$;
   $\sin B = \frac{12}{13}$; $\cos B = \frac{5}{13}$

3. $\tan A = \frac{57}{40}$; $\sin A = \frac{57}{70}$;
   $\cos A = \frac{4}{7}$; $\tan B = \frac{40}{57}$;
   $\sin B = \frac{4}{7}$; $\cos B = \frac{57}{70}$

Lesson 7-6   Find the measure of each arc in $\odot C$. $\overline{PQ}$ is a diameter.

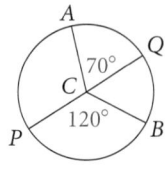

48. $\widehat{AQ}$ 70   49. $\widehat{AP}$ 110   50. $\widehat{BQ}$ 60

51. $\widehat{AQB}$ 130   52. $\widehat{PAB}$ 240   53. $\widehat{BPA}$ 230

Lesson 6-1 x^2 **Algebra** Find the value of each variable. Then find the length of each side.

54.
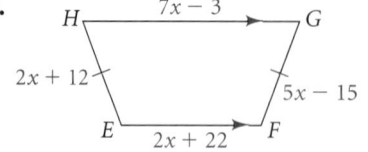

55.
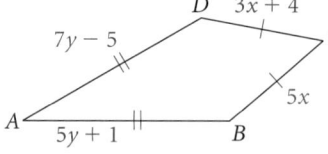

$x = 9$; 60, 30, 40, 30 $y = 3, x = 2$; 16, 10, 10, 16

✓ **Checkpoint Quiz 1**   **Lessons 9-1 through 9-3**

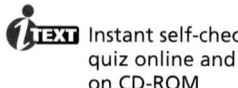 Instant self-check
quiz online and
on CD-ROM

Write the tangent, sine, and cosine ratios for $\angle A$ and $\angle B$.   1–3. See margin.

1.
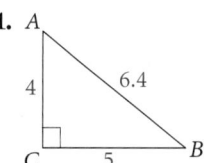

2.
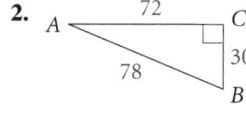

3.
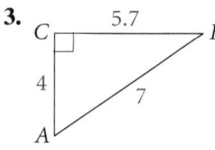

x^2 **Algebra** Find the value of x. Round each segment length to the nearest tenth and each angle measure to the nearest whole number.

4.
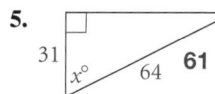
x 15.0

5.
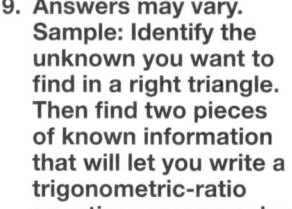
61

6.   20.8
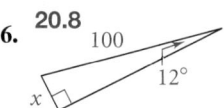

🌐 7. **Landmarks** The Leaning Tower of Pisa, shown at the right, reopened in 2001 after a 10-year project reduced its tilt from vertical by 0.5°. How far from the base of the tower will an object land if it is dropped the 150 ft shown in the photo? **about 13.1 ft**

🌐 8. **Navigation** A captain of a sailboat sights the top of a lighthouse at a 17° angle of elevation. A navigation chart shows the height of the lighthouse to be 120 m. How far is the sailboat from the lighthouse? **about 393 m**

9. Answers may vary.
Sample: Identify the
unknown you want to
find in a right triangle.
Then find two pieces
of known information
that will let you write a
trigonometric-ratio
equation you can solve
for the unknown.

✏️ 9. **Writing** How do you decide which   **See left.** trigonometric ratio to use to solve a problem?

🌐 10. **Hang Gliding** Students in a hang gliding class stand on the top of a cliff 70 m high. They watch a hang glider land on the beach below. The angle of depression to the hang glider is 72°. How far is the hang glider from the base of the cliff? **about 22.7 m**

488   Chapter 9   Right Triangle Trigonometry

Reading for Problem Solving

Read the problem. Then follow along with what Curtis thinks as he solves it. Check your understanding by solving the exercise at the bottom of the page.

A blimp is providing aerial television views of a football game. The television camera sights the stadium at a 7° angle of depression. The blimp's altitude is 400 m. What is the line-of-sight distance from the TV camera to the stadium, to the nearest hundred meters?

Reading for Problem Solving

Real-world problems usually do not have diagrams attached. Students need to be able to translate relevant information into useful diagrams. This feature helps students analyze and solve problems using diagrams.

Teaching Notes

After reading the introductory paragraph, have volunteers draw diagrams on the board to represent the situation. Then have students compare their diagrams with those that Curtis drew.

What Curtis Thinks	What Curtis Writes
To start, I'll draw and label a sketch. Angle of depression = 7° Altitude of blimp = 400 m	
I'm supposed to find the line-of-sight distance from the TV camera to the stadium. That's the diagonal segment from the blimp's gondola to the 50-yd line. I'll label it x.	
To find x, I'll probably need a trig ratio. I've labeled a leg and the hypotenuse of a right triangle 400 m and x. I can use a *sine* or *cosine* ratio if I can find one of the acute angles. Because alternate interior angles must be congruent, the smaller acute angle is 7°.	

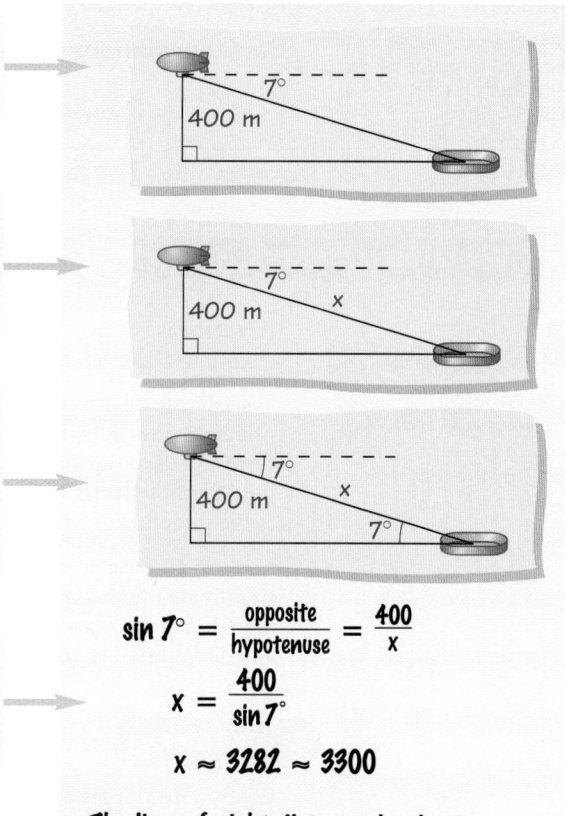

$$\sin 7° = \frac{\text{opposite}}{\text{hypotenuse}} = \frac{400}{x}$$

Now I'll write an equation.

I'll solve the equation for x.

I'll use a calculator and round.

$$x = \frac{400}{\sin 7°}$$

$$x \approx 3282 \approx 3300$$

Now I can state the answer.

The line-of-sight distance is about 3300 m.

English Learners

The derivation of the word *depress* is the Latin *depressus,* which means "pressed down." As students read the solution to the example, reinforce the meanings of the phrases *angle of depression* and *line-of-sight distance.*

Exercise

Have students work independently to solve the problem, showing the steps they used. Then have volunteers share with the class what they were thinking as they wrote each step. Elicit the fact that there are often different ways to arrive at the solution of a problem.

EXERCISE

A pedestrian sights the top of a building at an angle of elevation of 75°. She is standing 50 ft from the base of the building. How high above her eye level is the top of the building to the nearest foot?   **187 ft**

1. Plan

Lesson Preview

✔ **Check Skills You'll Need**

Skill
Lesson 7-2: Example 1
Exercises 1–6
Extra Practice, p. 696

Lesson Resources

📁 **Teaching Resources**
Practice, Reteaching, Enrichment

👥 **Reaching All Students**
Practice Workbook 9-4
Spanish Practice Workbook 9-4
Hands-On Activities 27
Informal Geometry Planning
   Guide 9-4

⏱ **Presentation Assistant Plus!**
Transparencies
• Check Skills You'll Need 9-4
• Additional Examples 9-4
• Student Edition Answers 9-4
• Lesson Quiz 9-4
PH Presentation Pro CD 9-4

PRENTICE HALL ASSESSMENT SYSTEM

Computer Test Generator CD

💿 **Technology**
Resource Pro® CD-ROM
Computer Test Generator CD
Prentice Hall Presentation Pro CD

💻 **www.PHSchool.com**
Student Site
• Teacher Web Code: afk-5500
• Self-grading Lesson Quiz
Teacher Center
• Lesson Planner
• Resources

Plus **iTEXT**

9-4

Vectors

1.01   Use the trigonometric ratios to model and solve problems involving right triangles.

North Carolina Objectives

Lesson Preview

What You'll Learn

OBJECTIVE 1 To describe vectors

OBJECTIVE 2 To solve problems that involve vector addition

. . . And Why

To use vectors to describe the distance and direction of an airplane flight, as in Example 3

✔ **Check Skills You'll Need**   (For help, go to Lesson 7-2.)

x^2 **Algebra** Find the value of x. Leave your answers in simplest radical form.

1.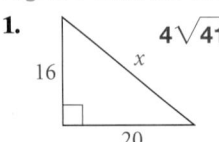

2.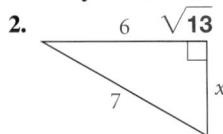

3.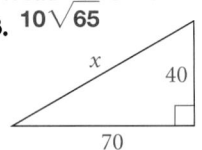

New Vocabulary   • vector   • magnitude   • initial point   • terminal point   • resultant

---

iTEXT **Interactive lesson includes instant self-check, tutorials, and activities.**

OBJECTIVE 1

Describing Vectors

📖 **Reading Math**

You distinguish between $\overline{KW}$ and $\overrightarrow{KW}$, and between $\langle x, y \rangle$ and (x, y) by the context in which each is used.

A **vector** is any quantity with magnitude (size) and direction. There are many models for a vector.

You can use an arrow for a vector as shown by the velocity vector $\overrightarrow{KW}$ in the photo. The **magnitude** corresponds to the distance from **initial point** K to the **terminal point** W. The direction corresponds to the direction in which the arrow points.

You can also use an ordered pair $\langle x, y \rangle$ in the coordinate plane for a vector. The magnitude and direction of the vector correspond to the distance and direction of $\langle x, y \rangle$ from the origin.

Magnitude 25 mi/h

1 EXAMPLE **Describing a Vector**

Coordinate Geometry Describe $\overrightarrow{OL}$ as an ordered pair. Give the coordinates to the nearest tenth.

Use the sine and cosine ratios to find the values of x and y.

$\cos 50° = \dfrac{x}{65}$ $\sin 50° = \dfrac{y}{65}$ **Use sine and cosine.**

$x = 65(\cos 50°)$ $y = 65(\sin 50°)$ **Solve for the variable.**

≈ 41.78119463 ≈ 49.7928888 **Use a calculator.**

● L is in the fourth quadrant so the y-coordinate is negative. $\overrightarrow{OL} \approx \langle 41.8, -49.8 \rangle$.

⚡ **Ongoing Assessment and Intervention**

Before the Lesson **Diagnose prerequisite skills using:**	**During the Lesson** **Monitor progress using:**	**After the Lesson** **Assess knowledge using:**
• Check Skills You'll Need	• Check Understanding • Additional Examples • Standardized Test Prep	• Lesson Quiz • Computer Test Generator CD

✓ **Check Understanding** **①** Describe the vector at the right as an ordered pair. Give the coordinates to the nearest tenth.
⟨−21.6, 46.2⟩

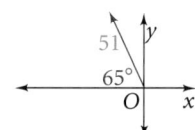

Real-World 🌐 Connection

A velocity vector for a "bullet train" can have magnitude 275 km/h paired with any direction point on a compass.

In many applications of vectors, you use the compass directions north, south, east, and west to describe the direction of a vector.

② EXAMPLE **Describing a Vector Direction**

Use compass directions to describe the direction of each vector.

a.
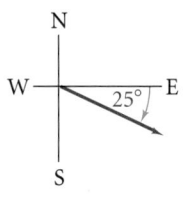
25° south of east

b.
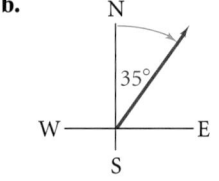
35° east of north

2a.
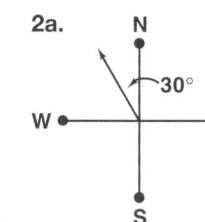

✓ **Check Understanding** **②** **a.** Sketch a vector that has the direction 30° west of north.
b. Critical Thinking Give a second description for the direction of this vector.
2b. 60° north of west

Example 3 shows how to describe a vector's magnitude and direction when you are given its description as an ordered pair.

③ EXAMPLE **Real-World 🌐 Connection**

Aviation An airplane lands 40 km west and 25 km south from where it took off. The result of the trip can be described by the vector ⟨−40, −25⟩. Use distance (for magnitude) and direction to describe this vector a second way.

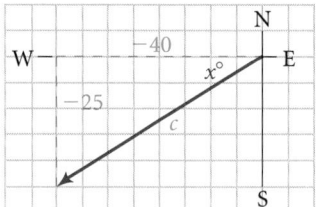

To find the distance, use the Distance Formula:

$d = \sqrt{(-40 - 0)^2 + (-25 - 0)^2}$
$d = \sqrt{1600 + 625}$ **Simplify.**
$d = \sqrt{2225}$
$d \approx 47.169906$ **Use a calculator to find the square root.**

To find the direction of the flight, find the angle of the vector south of west.

$\tan x° = \frac{25}{40}$ **Find the tangent ratio.**
$x = \tan^{-1}\left(\frac{25}{40}\right)$ **Use the inverse of tangent.**
TAN⁻¹ 25 ÷ 40 ENTER *32.005383* **Use a calculator.**

The airplane flew about 47 km at 32° south of west.

✓ **Check Understanding** **③** A small airplane lands at a point 246 mi east and 76 mi north of the point from which it took off. Describe the magnitude and the direction of its flight vector.
about 257 mi at 17° N of E

Lesson 9-4 Vectors **491**

👥 **Reaching All Students**

| **Below Level** Have students use centimeter graph paper to confirm the distance in Example 3 and use rulers and protractors to compare methods of describing the vector. | **Advanced Learners** After learning how to add vectors, students can investigate whether vector addition is commutative and associative. | **English Learners** See note on page 491. **Inclusion** See note on page 495. |

---

2. Teach

Professional Development

Math Background

Scientific descriptions need to be precise and concise. Because vectors describe quantities with both magnitude and direction, they are especially useful in science. For example, the study of physics employs vectors extensively to describe force and velocity.

OBJECTIVE
▼ 1 Teaching Notes

② EXAMPLE English Learners

In finding *35° east of north,* students should focus first on *due north* and then move 35° *east.* Encourage students to use a compass diagram when finding vector directions.

🏋 Additional Examples

① Describe $\overrightarrow{OM}$ as an ordered pair. Give coordinates to the nearest tenth.

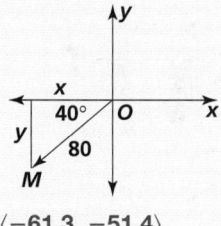

⟨−61.3, −51.4⟩

② Use compass directions to describe the direction of the vector.

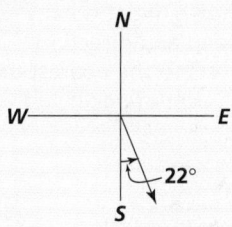

22° east of south

③ A boat sailed 12 mi east and 9 mi south. The trip can be described by the vector ⟨12, −9⟩. Use distance and direction to describe this vector a second way.
The boat sailed 15 mi at about 37° south of east.

491

Technology Tip
Have students check to see whether their calculators perform vector addition.

4 EXAMPLE **Connection to Physics**

Point out that vectors are used extensively in physics to find the resultant of several velocities (as in Example 5), accelerations, or forces.

5 EXAMPLE **Alternative Method**

Point out that this example uses the Pythagorean Theorem, whereas Example 3 used the Distance Formula. Have students discuss how the two approaches are alike and how they are different.

Additional Examples

4 Vectors $\vec{v}$ ⟨4, 3⟩ and $\vec{w}$ ⟨4, −3⟩ are shown below. Write $\vec{s}$, their sum, as an ordered pair.

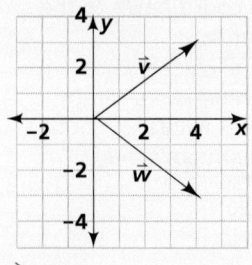

$\vec{s}$ ⟨8, 0⟩

5 An airplane's speed is 250 mi/h in still air. The wind is blowing due east at 20 mi/h. If the airplane heads due north, what is its resultant speed and direction? Round answers to the nearest unit. 251 mi/h, 5° east of north

Closure

Sketch a vector with magnitude 50 and direction 30° west of north. Describe it as an ordered pair with coordinates rounded to the nearest tenth. ⟨−25, 43.3⟩; check that vectors are drawn from (0, 0) to (−25, 43.3).

You can also use a single lowercase letter, such as $\vec{u}$, to name a vector.

This map shows vectors representing a flight from Houston to Memphis with a stopover in New Orleans. The vector from Houston to Memphis is called the sum, or **resultant,** of the other two vectors. You write this as

$$\vec{w} = \vec{u} + \vec{v}.$$

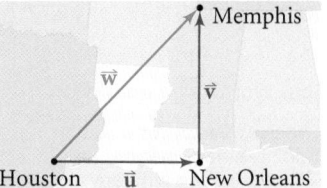

You can add vectors by adding their coordinates. You can also show the sum geometrically.

🔑 **Key Concepts**

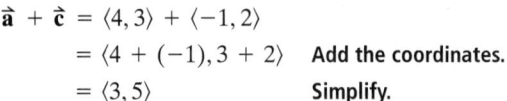

Property	Adding Vectors

For $\vec{a}$ = ⟨x_1, y_1⟩ and $\vec{c}$ = ⟨x_2, y_2⟩, $\vec{a}$ + $\vec{c}$ = ⟨$x_1 + x_2, y_1 + y_2$⟩.

4 **EXAMPLE** **Adding Vectors**

Vectors $\vec{a}$ ⟨4, 3⟩ and $\vec{c}$ ⟨−1, 2⟩ are shown in the diagram. Write the sum of the two vectors as an ordered pair. Then draw $\vec{e}$, the sum of $\vec{a}$ and $\vec{c}$.

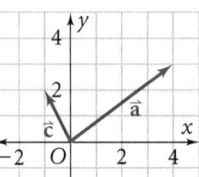

$$\vec{a} + \vec{c} = \langle 4, 3 \rangle + \langle -1, 2 \rangle$$
$$= \langle 4 + (-1), 3 + 2 \rangle \quad \textbf{Add the coordinates.}$$
$$= \langle 3, 5 \rangle \quad \textbf{Simplify.}$$

⟨3, 5⟩ is the resultant.

Draw $\vec{a}$ with its initial point at the origin. Then draw $\vec{c}$ with its initial point at the terminal point of $\vec{a}$. Finally, draw the resultant $\vec{e}$ from the initial point of $\vec{a}$ to the terminal point of $\vec{c}$.

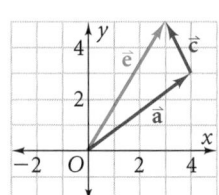

✓ **Check Understanding** 4 Write the sum of the two vectors ⟨2, 3⟩ and ⟨−4, −2⟩ as an ordered pair. ⟨**−2, 1**⟩

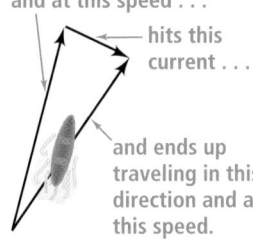

A canoe traveling in this direction and at this speed . . .
← hits this current . . .
and ends up traveling in this direction and at this speed.

A vector sum can show the result of vectors that occur in sequence, such as in the airplane flight described above.

A vector sum can also show the result of vectors that act at the same time, such as when you row in a direction different from that of the current. See diagram at left.

The velocity of the canoe is the vector sum of the velocities of the paddlers and the stream.

492 Chapter 9 Right Triangle Trigonometry

pages 493–497
Exercises

7.
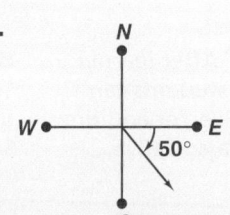

8.
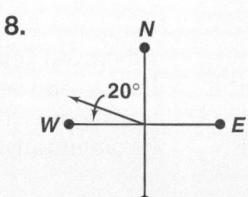

9.
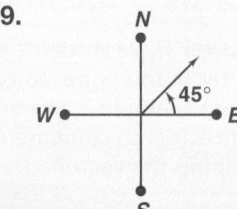

5 EXAMPLE **Real-World** **Connection**

Navigation A ferry shuttles people from one side of a river to the other. The speed of the ferry in still water is 25 mi/h. The river flows directly south at 7 mi/h. If the ferry heads directly west, what are the ferry's resultant speed and direction?

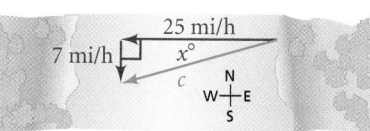

The diagram shows the sum of the two vectors. To find the ferry's resultant speed, use the Pythagorean Theorem.

$c^2 = 25^2 + 7^2$ **The lengths of the legs are 25 and 7.**

$c^2 = 674$ **Simplify.**

$c \approx 25.961510$ **Use a calculator.**

To find the ferry's resultant direction, use trigonometry.

$\tan x° = \frac{7}{25}$ **Use the tangent ratio.**

$x = \tan^{-1}\left(\frac{7}{25}\right)$ **Use the inverse of the tangent.**

$x \approx 15.642246$ **Use a calculator.**

● The ferry's speed is about 26 mi/h. Its direction is about 16° south of west.

Real-World **Connection**

Ferry service is essential in remote regions such as on the Mackenzie River in Canada's Northwest Territories.

✓ **Check Understanding**

5 Critical Thinking Use the diagram to find the angle at which the ferry must head upriver in order to travel directly across the river.
about 16° north of west

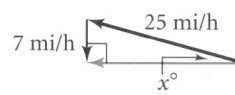

EXERCISES

For more practice, see Extra Practice.

Practice and Problem Solving

A **Practice by Example**

Example 1
(page 490)

Describe each vector as an ordered pair. Give the coordinates to the nearest tenth.

1.

900
48°
$\langle 602.2,\ 668.8 \rangle$

2.
10°
312
$\langle -307.3,\ -54.2 \rangle$

3.
30°
75
$\langle 37.5,\ -65.0 \rangle$

Example 2
(page 491)

Use compass directions to describe the direction of each vector.

4.
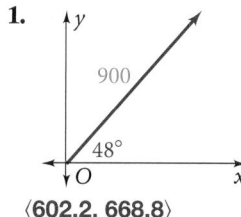
15°
15° south of west

5.
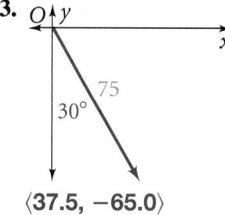
20°
20° west of south

6.
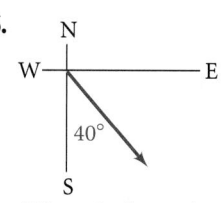
40°
40° east of south

Sketch a vector that has the given direction. 7–12. See margin.

7. 50° south of east   **8.** 20° north of west   **9.** 45° northeast

10. 70° west of north   **11.** 45° southwest   **12.** 10° east of south

Lesson 9-4   Vectors   **493**

10.
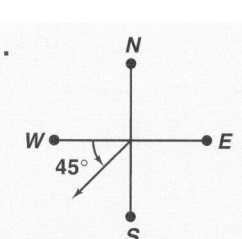
70°

11.
45°

12.
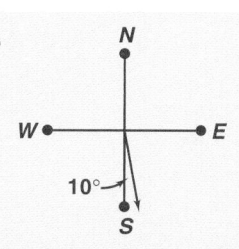
10°

3. Practice

Assignment Guide

1 Objective
A B Core 1–16, 29, 30, 32, 33, 40, 45, 46
C Extension 49

2 Objective
A B Core 17–28, 31, 34–39, 41–44, 47, 48
C Extension 50–52

Standardized Test Prep 53–55

Mixed Review 56–60

Error Prevention

Exercises 2, 3 Students may forget to determine the signs of the coordinates. Remind students to check which quadrant contains the vector in the diagram.

Auditory Learners

Exercises 4–6 Have students work in small groups to name the direction of each vector using both the given angle and its complement.

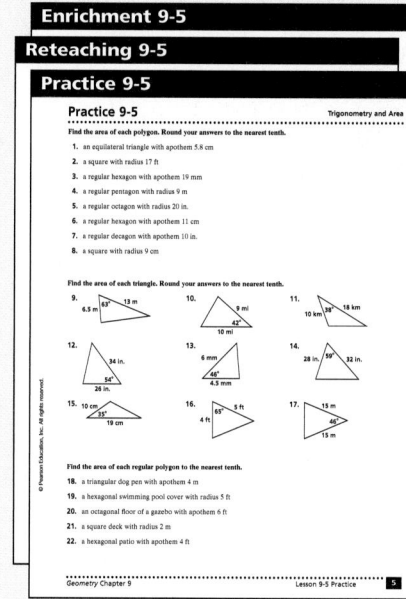

Alternative Method

Exercise 14 Ask: *If m represents magnitude, what equation would you write to find* m *using the Distance Formula?* $m = \sqrt{300^2 + 640^2}$ *What equation would you write to find* m *using the Pythagorean Theorem?* $m^2 = 300^2 + 640^2$ Display the two equations, and have students explain why they are equivalent.

Tactile Learners

Exercises 17–22 Have students use pencils, straws, or other straight objects to model the vectors and their sums.

Diversity

Exercises 26, 27 Although there are many mathematics problems about boats and currents, many students are unfamiliar with the idea of forces pushing in different directions. Help students relate the problem to walking in a strong wind or swimming against a current.

Connection to Algebra

Exercise 31 Ask: *What algebraic property does the Parallelogram Rule establish?* **Commutative Property of Vector Addition**

Exercise 35 Point out that this exercise can be solved and analyzed without drawing a diagram.

pages 493–497 Exercises

17. a. $\langle -9, -9 \rangle$ b.
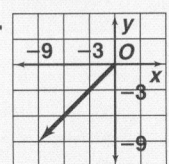

18. a. $\langle -6, 2 \rangle$ b.
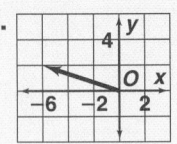

19. a. $\langle -1, 0 \rangle$ b.
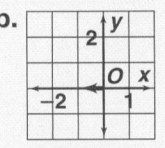

494

Example 3
(page 491)

14. about 707 mi; 65° south of west

15. about 54 mi/h; 22° north of east

16. 4805 km; 12° north of west

Example 4
(page 492)

Example 5
(page 493)

26. 35.9 mi/h; 12.9° south of west

27. about 13.2° north of west

B **Apply Your Skills**

29. Yes; both vectors have the same direction, but could have diff. mag.

---

13. **History** Homing pigeons have the ability or instinct to find their way home when released hundreds of miles away from home. Homing pigeons carried news of Olympic victories to various cities in ancient Greece. Suppose one such pigeon took off from Athens and landed in Sparta, which is 73 mi west and 64 mi south of Athens. Find the distance and direction of its flight.
about 97 mi at 41° south of west

Find the magnitude and direction of each vector. 14–16. See left.

14.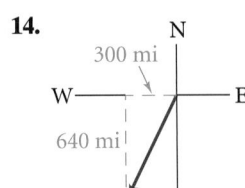
15.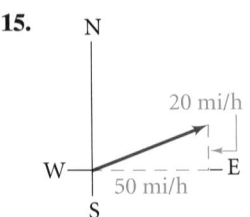
16.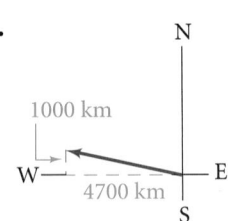

In Exercises 17–22, (a) write the resultant as an ordered pair and (b) draw the resultant. 17–22. See margin.

17.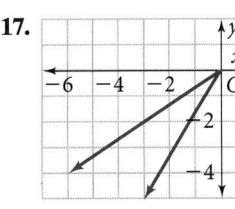
18.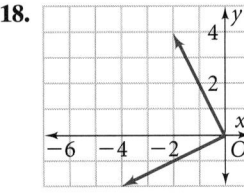
19.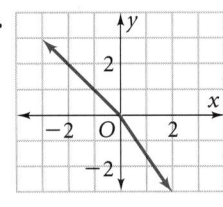

20.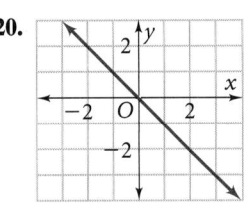
21.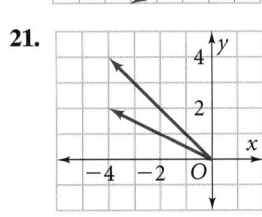
22.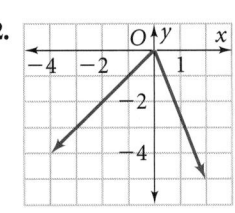

Write the sum of the two vectors as an ordered pair.

23. $\langle 2, 1 \rangle$ and $\langle -3, 2 \rangle$ 24. $\langle 0, 0 \rangle$ and $\langle 4, -6 \rangle$ 25. $\langle -1, 1 \rangle$ and $\langle -1, 2 \rangle$
$\langle -1, 3 \rangle$ $\langle 4, -6 \rangle$ $\langle -2, 3 \rangle$

Navigation **The speed of a powerboat in still water is 35 mi/h. It is traveling on a river that flows directly south at 8 mi/h.**

26. The boat heads directly west across the river. What are the resulting speed and direction of the boat? Round answers to the nearest tenth. **See left.**

27. At what angle should the boat head upriver in order to travel directly west?

28. **Aviation** A twin-engine airplane has a speed of 300 mi/h in still air. Suppose this airplane heads directly south and encounters a 50 mi/h wind blowing due east. Find the resulting speed and direction of the plane. Round your answers to the nearest unit. **304 mi/h; 9° east of south**

29. **Critical Thinking** Valerie described the direction of a vector as 35° south of east. Pablo described it as 55° east of south. Could the two be describing the same vector? Explain. **See left.**

30. **Error Analysis** Ely says that the magnitude of vector $\langle 6, 1 \rangle$ is 3 times that of vector $\langle 2, 1 \rangle$ since 6 is 3 times 2. Explain why Ely's statement is incorrect.
$\langle 6, 1 \rangle$ has mag. $\sqrt{37}$, but $\langle 2, 1 \rangle$ has mag. $\sqrt{5}$.

20. a. $\langle 1, -1 \rangle$ b.
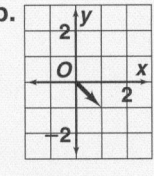

21. a. $\langle -8, 6 \rangle$ b.
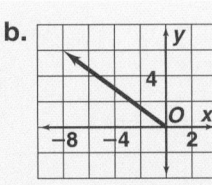

22. a. $\langle -2, -9 \rangle$ b.
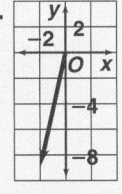

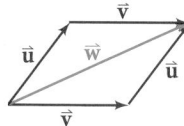

Need Help?

You can also model vector addition with the *Triangle Rule* as shown in Example 4, and by either triangular half of the diagram above.

31. The diagram at the left shows that you can add vectors in any order. That is, $\vec{u} + \vec{v} = \vec{v} + \vec{u}$. Notice also that the four vectors shown in red form a parallelogram. The resultant $\vec{w}$ is the diagonal of the parallelogram. This representation of vector addition is called *The Parallelogram Rule*. **See margin.**

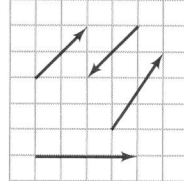

  a. Copy the diagram at the right. Draw a parallelogram that has the given vectors as adjacent sides.
  b. Find the magnitude and direction of the resultant. **about 173 due east**

32. Use the diagrams below to write a definition of *equal vectors*.

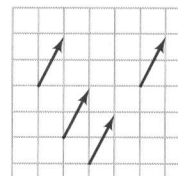

Equal vectors have the same mag. and direction.

These vectors are equal.   No two of these vectors are equal.

33. Use the diagrams below to write a definition of *parallel vectors*.

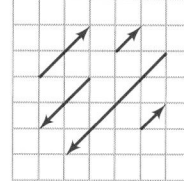 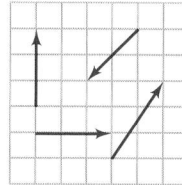

Vectors are ∥ if they have the same or opp. directions.

These vectors are parallel.   No two of these vectors are parallel.

34. Aviation A Red Cross helicopter takes off and flies 75 km at 20° south of west. There, it drops off some relief supplies. It then flies 125 km at 10° west of north to pick up three medics. **a–b. See back of book.**
  a. Make an accurate drawing of the two vectors described.
  b. Draw the resultant and measure it to find the helicopter's distance from its point of origin and the direction it should head to get back.

35b. $\vec{a}$ and $\vec{c}$ have = mag. and opp. direction.

 35. a. Find the sum of $\vec{a}$ and $\vec{c}$, where $\vec{a} = \langle 45, -60 \rangle$ and $\vec{c} = \langle -45, 60 \rangle$. **⟨0, 0⟩**
  b. Writing Based on your answer to part (a), how can you describe $\vec{a}$ and $\vec{c}$?

36. Aviation In still air, the WP-3D (see below) flies at 374 mi/h. Suppose that a WP-3D flies due west and meets a hurricane wind blowing due south at 95 mi/h. What are the resultant speed and direction of the airplane to the nearest unit? **about 386 mi/h at 14° south of west**

Flying into a Hurricane

When most pilots hear a forecast for gale force winds, they don't think, "Time to fly." Then again, most pilots don't work for the National Oceanic and Atmospheric Administration. NOAA fly their four-engine WP-3D turboprops directly into hurricanes. These aircraft carry eight crew members, up to ten scientists, and a load of data-collection equipment. Some of this equipment is in the WP-3D's long "snout," which also serves as a lightning rod. In a routine flight, the WP-3D is struck by lightning three or four times. Surprisingly, small burn holes are the only damage from these strikes. To help overcome temporary blindness caused by lightning flashes, the pilot sets the cockpit lights at the brightest level.

31. a.

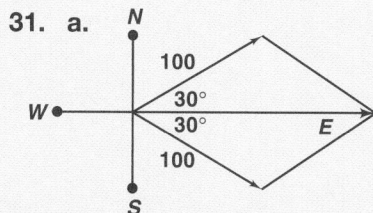

Math Tip

Exercise 33 After students write their definitions, point out that parallel vectors can have opposite directions.

Exercise 34 Have students work with partners. In part a, each student should draw a diagram, and then partners should compare them to make sure that the diagrams represent the situation accurately. In part b, students should discuss and agree on a strategy before beginning their work.

Inclusion

Exercise 40 Visually-impaired students may describe the vectors verbally to partners who compare the oral descriptions with the diagrams.

Exercise 45 Ask: *Suppose $\overrightarrow{AB}$ describes walking due east at 3 mi/h. What does $\overrightarrow{BA}$ describe?* **walking due west at 3 mi/h** Have the class calculate the sum of $\overrightarrow{AB}$ and $\overrightarrow{BA}$. **0**

Visual Learners

Exercise 49 Students may need help extending the Distance Formula to find the magnitude of a vector in three dimensions. If possible, provide a physical model to help explain the formula.

Use the diagram for Exercises 1 and 2.

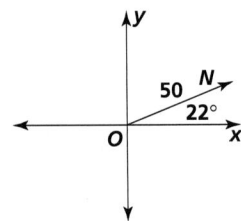

1. Describe the vector as an ordered pair. Round coordinates to the nearest tenth. **⟨46.4, 18.7⟩**

2. Use compass directions to describe the direction of $\overrightarrow{ON}$. **22° north of east**

3. Iris rode her bike 30 mi south and 16 mi west of her home. Her trip can be described by the vector ⟨−16, −30⟩. Use distance and direction to describe the vector a second way. **34 mi at about 28° west of south**

4. Write the vector $\vec{v} = \vec{a} + \vec{b}$ as an ordered pair.

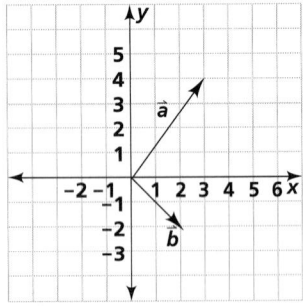

⟨5, 2⟩

5. An airplane has a speed of 240 mi/h in still air. The plane heads due north and encounters a 30-mi/h wind blowing due east. Find the resultant speed and direction. Round to the nearest unit. **242 mi/h at 7° east of north**

496

?
Need Help?

In Exercise 40, remember that any vector is equal to one whose initial point is the origin.

42. ⟨−3, −7⟩

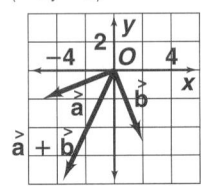

43. ⟨0, −4⟩

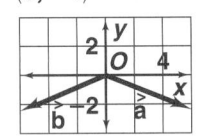

44. ⟨3, −3⟩

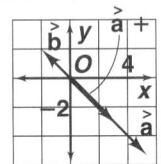

45. The vectors have the same mag.; the vectors have opp. directions.

46. Answers may vary. Sample: ⟨7, 24⟩, ⟨−7, 24⟩, ⟨7, −24⟩, ⟨24, 7⟩

47a. about 15° south of west

  b. about 6.7 h

C Challenge

The vector ⟨−5, 5⟩ can be written as the *column matrix* $\begin{bmatrix} -5 \\ 5 \end{bmatrix}$. Find the sum of the vectors in column matrix form.

37. $\begin{bmatrix} 2 \\ -4 \end{bmatrix} + \begin{bmatrix} -3 \\ 2 \end{bmatrix}\begin{bmatrix} -1 \\ -2 \end{bmatrix}$ **38.** $\begin{bmatrix} 8 \\ -1 \end{bmatrix} + \begin{bmatrix} 3 \\ -4 \end{bmatrix}\begin{bmatrix} 11 \\ -5 \end{bmatrix}$ **39.** $\begin{bmatrix} 4 \\ -5 \end{bmatrix} + \begin{bmatrix} -5 \\ 5 \end{bmatrix}\begin{bmatrix} -1 \\ 0 \end{bmatrix}$

🌐 **40. Aviation** An airplane takes off from a runway in the direction 10° east of south. When it reaches 5000 ft, it turns right 45°. It cruises at this altitude for 60 mi. Then it turns left 160°, descends, and lands. Match each vector with the appropriate portion of the flight.

I.   II.   III.

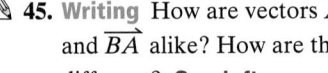

III   II   I
A. The plane takes off.   B. The plane cruises.   C. The plane lands.

🌐 **41. Aviation** The cruising speed of a Boeing 767 in still air is 530 mi/h. Suppose that a 767 is cruising directly east when it encounters an 80 mi/h wind blowing 40° south of west. **a. See back of book.** **b. ⟨530, 0⟩; ⟨−61.3, −51.4⟩**
  a. Sketch the vectors for the velocities of the airplane and the wind.
  b. Express both vectors from part (a) in ordered pair notation.
  c. Find the sum of the vectors from part (b). **⟨468.7, −51.4⟩**
  d. Find the magnitude and direction of the vector from part (c).
    471.5 mi/h at 6.3° south of east

Give the sum of $\vec{a}$ and $\vec{b}$. Show $\vec{a}$ and $\vec{b}$ and their sum in the coordinate plane.

42. $\vec{a}$ ⟨−5, −2⟩, $\vec{b}$ ⟨2, −5⟩   **43.** $\vec{a}$ ⟨5, −2⟩, $\vec{b}$ ⟨−5, −2⟩   **44.** $\vec{a}$ ⟨5, −5⟩, $\vec{b}$ ⟨−2, 2⟩
42–44. See left.

✏ **45. Writing** How are vectors $\overrightarrow{AB}$ and $\overrightarrow{BA}$ alike? How are they different? **See left.**

46. Open-Ended Name four other vectors with the same magnitude as ⟨−7, −24⟩. **See left.**

🌐 **47. Navigation** A fishing boat leaves its home port and travels 150 mi directly east. It then changes course and travels 40 mi due north. **See left.**
  a. In what direction should the boat head to return to home port?
  b. How long will the return trip take if the boat averages 23 mi/h?

🌐 **48. Navigation** A boat left dock A, traveled north for 10 miles, then 45° east of north for 20 miles, and docked at B.
  a. How far north did the boat travel? How far east did it travel? **about 24.1 mi;**
  b. Find the magnitude and direction of the direct-path vector $\overrightarrow{AB}$. **about 14.1 mi**
    about 28 mi at about 30° east of north

🌐 **49. Geometry in 3 Dimensions** A hot-air balloon traveled 2000 ft north and 900 ft east, while rising 400 ft. This trip can be described with the three-coordinate vector ⟨2000, 900, 400⟩. What is the magnitude of the vector? What is the angle of elevation of the balloon from its starting point? **about 2229 ft; about 10°**

THE FAR SIDE By GARY LARSON

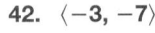

"Well, lemme think. ... You've stumped me, son. Most folks only wanna know how to go the other way."

Exercise 45

50. a. Probability You choose two of the vectors at the right at random. Find the probability that the magnitude of their resultant vector is greater than that of the third vector. $\frac{2}{3}$

b. Open-Ended Draw three vectors of your own. Then do part (a) for your vectors.
Check students' work.

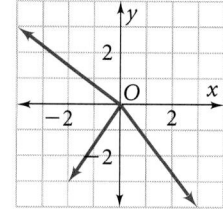

51. Answers may vary. Sample: zero vector = ⟨0, 0⟩; it has mag. 0 and no direction.

 51. Writing Think of the number zero and its properties. Define a *zero vector* and justify your definition. **See left.**

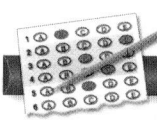 **52. Aviation** A helicopter starts at $(0, 0)$ and makes three parts of a flight represented by the vectors $⟨10, 10⟩$, $⟨5, -4⟩$, and $⟨-3, 5⟩$, in that order.

a. If another helicopter starts at $(0, 0)$ and flies the same three parts in a different order, would it end in the same place? Justify your answer.

b. If yet another helicopter flew the three parts of the flight in a different order from the original trip, could the second part of the flight end at the same place as the second part of the original trip? Justify your answer.
a–b. See margin.

Standardized Test Prep

Multiple Choice

53. $\vec{c}$, $\vec{s}$, and $\vec{u}$ are vectors. $\vec{c} = ⟨-8, 10⟩$, $\vec{s} = ⟨0, -3⟩$, and $\vec{u} = \vec{c} + \vec{s}$. What are the coordinates of $\vec{u}$? **D**

A. $⟨7, -8⟩$ B. $⟨-7, 8⟩$ C. $⟨8, -7⟩$ D. $⟨-8, 7⟩$

Short Response

54. A boat heads due south directly across a river at 30 ft/min. The river is flowing east at 20 ft/min.
a. What is the resultant speed of the boat? **a–b. See margin.**
b. What is the resultant direction of the boat?

Extended Response

55. A small aircraft is traveling east at 400 mi/h. It encounters a 50 mi/h wind blowing 30° west of south. **a–d. See margin.**
a. Sketch and label vectors for the velocities of the aircraft and the wind.
b. Express both vectors in ordered pair notation.
c. Find the sum of the vectors.
d. Find the magnitude and direction of the vector from part (c).

Mixed Review

Lesson 9-3

56. Indirect Measurement A hot-air balloon pilot sights the landing field from a height of 2000 ft. The angle of depression is 24°. To the nearest foot, what is the ground distance from the hot-air balloon to the landing field? **4492 ft**

Lesson 7-8 **Games** You toss a dart at each dartboard and hit at a random point. Find the probability that the dart hits in the red region.

57.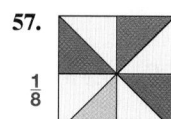
$\frac{1}{8}$

58.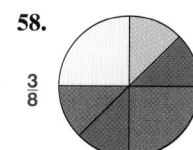
$\frac{3}{8}$

59.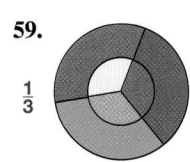
$\frac{1}{3}$

Lesson 7-1 **60.** Find the area of $\square ABCD$ with vertices $A(-1, -5)$, $B(6, -5)$, $C(9, 3)$, and $D(2, 3)$. **56 units²**

Lesson 9-4   Vectors   **497**

Standardized Test Prep

 **Resources**
For additional practice with a variety of test item formats:
• Standardized Test Prep, p. 509
• Test-Taking Strategies, p. 504
• Test-Taking Strategies with Transparencies

Exercise 53 Give students these tips for adding vectors:
• If coordinates for the vectors are given, you don't need to draw a diagram to find the resultant.
• If vectors already are drawn in a diagram, the name *Parallelogram Rule* reminds you how to rearrange the vectors to find their sum, with the initial point of one vector touching the terminal point of the other vector.

pages 493–497   Exercises

52. a. yes; when you add integers, which are the coordinates of the vectors, order is not important.

b. yes; if the first two vectors are the same, but in the opp. order

54. [2] **a.** about 36 ft/min
b. about 34° east of south
[1] correct speed OR correct direction

55. [4] **a.**

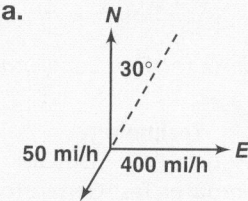

b. aircraft: $⟨400, 0⟩$
wind: $⟨-25, -43.3⟩$

c. $⟨375, -43.3⟩$

d. about 377 mi/h, 6.6° south of east

[3] appropriate methods, but with one computational error

[2] correct speed of aircraft OR correct speed of wind

[1] correct speed of aircraft OR correct speed of wind without work shown

497

Lesson Preview

 **Check Skills You'll Need**

Finding the Area of a Regular Polygon
Lesson 7-5: Example 2
Exercises 4–9
Extra Practice, p. 696

Lesson Resources

498

9-5

Trigonometry and Area

 North Carolina Objectives   1.01   Use the trigonometric ratios to model and solve problems involving right triangles.

Lesson Preview

What You'll Learn

OBJECTIVE 1
To find the area of a regular polygon using trigonometry

OBJECTIVE 2
To find the area of a triangle using trigonometry

. . . And Why

To find the area of a courtyard, as in Example 2

✔ Check Skills You'll Need

(For help, go to Lesson 7-5.)

Find the area of each regular polygon.

1.
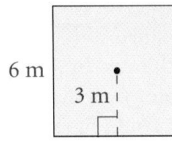
6 m
3 m
36 m²

2.
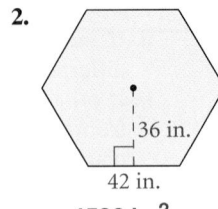
36 in.
42 in.
4536 in.²

3.
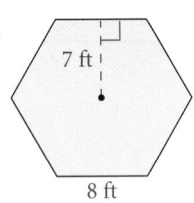
7 ft
8 ft
168 ft²

 Interactive lesson includes instant self-check, tutorials, and activities.

OBJECTIVE

1   Finding the Area of a Regular Polygon

In Chapter 7, you learned to find the area of a regular polygon by using the formula $A = \frac{1}{2}ap$, where a is the apothem and p is the perimeter. By using this formula and trigonometric ratios, you can solve other types of problems.

? Need Help?

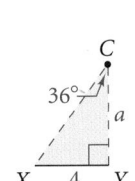
Center
Apothem
Central angle
Radius

1 EXAMPLE   Finding Area

Find the area of a regular pentagon with 8-cm sides.

To use the formula $A = \frac{1}{2}ap$, you need the apothem and perimeter. The perimeter is 5 · 8, or 40 cm.

To find the apothem, use trigonometry.
The measure of the central angle $\angle XCZ$ is $\frac{360}{5}$, or 72.
$m\angle XCY = \frac{1}{2}m\angle XCZ = 36$.
$XY = \frac{1}{2}XZ$, so $XY = 4$.

$\tan 36° = \frac{4}{a}$ **Use the tangent ratio.**

$a = \frac{4}{\tan 36°}$ **Solve for a.**

Now substitute into the area formula.

$A = \frac{1}{2}ap$

$= \frac{1}{2} \cdot \frac{4}{\tan 36°} \cdot 40$ **Substitute for a and p.**

$= \frac{80}{\tan 36°}$ **Simplify.**

80 ÷ [TAN] 36 [ENTER] *110.11055*   **Use a calculator.**

● The area of the regular pentagon is about 110 cm².

8 cm
C
a
X   Y   Z

C
36°
a
X   4   Y

✔ **Check Understanding** 1 Find the area of a regular octagon with a perimeter of 80 in. Give the area to the nearest tenth.   **482.8 in.²**

Ongoing Assessment and Intervention

Before the Lesson
Diagnose prerequisite skills using:
• Check Skills You'll Need

During the Lesson
Monitor progress using:
• Check Understanding
• Additional Examples
• Standardized Test Prep

After the Lesson
Assess knowledge using:
• Lesson Quiz
• Computer Test Generator CD

Sometimes you can use trigonometry to find both apothem and perimeter.

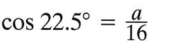

Architecture The Castel del Monte, built on a hill in southern Italy circa 1240, makes extraordinary use of regular octagons. One regular octagon, the inner courtyard, has radius 16 m. Find the area of the courtyard.

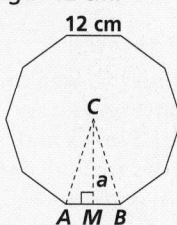

The measure of a central angle of the octagon is $\frac{360}{8}$, or 45.

So $m\angle C = \frac{1}{2}(45) = 22.5$.

Use the cosine ratio to find the apothem.

$\cos 22.5° = \frac{a}{16}$

$\quad a = 16(\cos 22.5°)$

Use the sine ratio to find the perimeter.

$\sin 22.5° = \frac{x}{16}$

$\quad\quad x = 16(\sin 22.5°)$

$\quad\quad p = 8 \cdot \text{length of a side}$

$\quad\quad\quad = 8 \cdot 2x$ **The length of each side is 2x.**

$\quad\quad\quad = 8 \cdot 2 \cdot 16(\sin 22.5°)$ **Substitute for x.**

$\quad\quad\quad = 256(\sin 22.5°)$ **Simplify.**

Substitute into the area formula, $A = \frac{1}{2}ap$.

$\quad A = \frac{1}{2} \cdot 16(\cos 22.5°) \cdot 256(\sin 22.5°)$ **Substitute for a and p.**

$\quad\quad \approx 724.07734$ **Use a calculator.**

● The area of the courtyard is about 724 m².

✓ Check Understanding ② **Critical Thinking** If the radius of the main structure is twice the radius of the inner courtyard, how does the area it covers compare to the area of the courtyard? **It is 4 times as large.**

OBJECTIVE

2 **Finding the Area of a Triangle**

Reading Math

Before going on, learn to read the last equation as "the area of a triangle is half the product of two sides and the sine of their included angle."

Suppose you want to find the area of $\triangle ABC$, but you know only $m\angle A$ and the lengths b and c. To use the formula Area $= \frac{1}{2}bh$, you need to know the height. You can find the height by using the sine ratio.

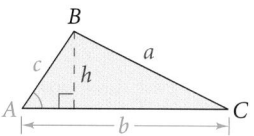

$\quad \sin A = \frac{h}{c}$ **Use the sine ratio.**

$\quad\quad h = c(\sin A)$ **Solve for h.**

Now substitute for h in the formula Area $= \frac{1}{2}bh$.

$\quad \text{Area} = \frac{1}{2}bc(\sin A)$

 Reaching All Students

Below Level Before beginning this lesson, review how to find the area of a regular polygon (in Lesson 7-5), focusing on a specific regular figure, such as a hexagon.	**Advanced Learners** Have students discuss whether the area formula at the bottom of page 499 can be used as is or needs to be modified when $\angle A$ is obtuse.	**Tactile Learners** See note on page 500. **Error Prevention** See note on page 499.

---

2. Teach

Math Background

Let θ be the angle between consecutive radii r in a regular n-gon. Then using $A = \frac{1}{2}ab\sin\theta$ for the area of the triangle, $A = \frac{n}{2}r^2\sin\left(\frac{180}{n}\right)$ is the area of the n-gon.

OBJECTIVE
1 **Teaching Notes**

Error Prevention

Students may confuse the radius with the apothem. Point out that the apothem is always perpendicular to a side and that one endpoint of a radius is always a vertex.

② **EXAMPLE** **Math Tip**

The area of a regular polygon with radius r and apothem a is less than πr^2, the area of the circumscribed circle, and greater than πa^2, the area of the inscribed circle. Students can use these upper and lower bounds to check their answers.

Additional Examples

❶ Find the area of a regular polygon with 10 sides and side length 12 cm.

12 cm

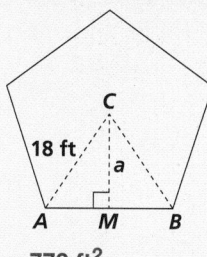

≈ 1108 cm²

❷ The radius of a garden in the shape of a regular pentagon is 18 ft. Find the area of the garden.

≈ 770 ft²

499

OBJECTIVE 2 Teaching Notes

Alternative Method

Proving a theorem from a different but related point of view helps students strengthen their mastery of geometry. Have students prove Theorem 9-1 again, this time using an altitude drawn from C to base $\overline{AB}$ where $\sin A = \frac{h}{b}$.

 **3 EXAMPLE** Tactile Learners

Have each student draw a large triangle on graph paper and estimate its area by counting squares and partial squares. Then have them cut out the triangle and use a protractor and the formula Area $= \frac{1}{2}bc(\sin A)$ to find its area.

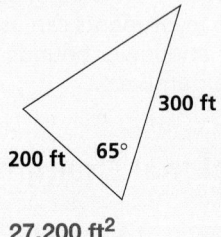 **Additional Examples**

3 A triangular park has two sides that measure 200 ft and 300 ft and form a 65° angle. Find the area of the park to the nearest hundred square feet.

300 ft
200 ft 65°

27,200 ft²

Closure

Explain how to find the area of a regular polygon if you know only the length of a side s and the number of sides n. **Sample:** Divide 360 by n to find the measure of the central angle, and then divide by 2 to find the angle measure inside a right triangle. Use the tangent ratio to find the apothem, and then use the formula $A = \frac{1}{2}ap$, where $p = ns$.

Your work at the bottom of page 499 completes a proof of the following theorem for the case in which $\angle A$ is acute.

 Key Concepts

Theorem 9-1	Area of a Triangle Given SAS

The area of a triangle is one half the product of the lengths of two sides and the sine of the included angle.

$$\text{Area of } \triangle ABC = \tfrac{1}{2}bc(\sin A)$$

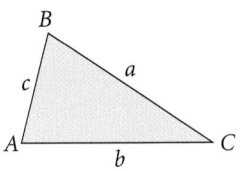

3 EXAMPLE Real-World Connection

Surveying The surveyed lengths of two adjacent sides of a triangular plot of land are 412 ft and 386 ft. The angle between the sides is 71°. Find the area of the plot.

Area $= \frac{1}{2} \cdot$ side length $\cdot$ side length $\cdot$ sine of included angle

$= \frac{1}{2} \cdot 412 \cdot 386 \cdot \sin 71°$ **Substitute.**

≈ 75183.855 **Use a calculator.**

The area of the plot is approximately 75,200 ft².

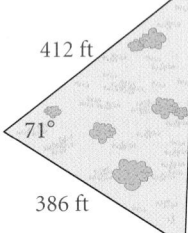

412 ft

71°

386 ft

✓ **Check Understanding** **3** Two sides of a triangular building plot are 120 ft and 85 ft long. They include an angle of 85°. Find the area of the building plot to the nearest square foot. **5081 ft²**

EXERCISES

For more practice, see *Extra Practice*.

Practice and Problem Solving

A Practice by Example

Example 1 (page 498)

Find the area of each regular polygon. Give answers to the nearest tenth.

1. octagon with side length 6 cm
173.8 cm²

2. pentagon with side length 7 in.
84.3 in.²

3. hexagon with perimeter 60 m
259.8 m²

4. 15-gon with perimeter 180 yd
2540.5 yd²

5. *PQRST* is a regular pentagon with center O and radius 10 in.
   a. Find $m\angle POQ$. **72**   **b.** Find $m\angle POX$. **36**
   c. Find OX. **about 8.1 in.**   **d.** Find PQ. **about 11.8 in.**
   e. Find the perimeter. **about 58.8 in.**   **f.** Find the area. **about 238 in.²**

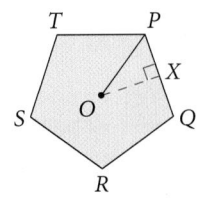

Example 2 (page 499)

Find the area of each regular polygon. Give answers to the nearest tenth.

6. hexagon with radius 10 ft **259.8 ft²**   **7.** decagon with radius 4 in. **47.0 in.²**

8. octagon with radius 20 cm **1131.4 cm²** **9.** square with radius 2 ft **8 ft²**

10. Architecture Each of the eight small towers around Castel del Monte (page 499) is a regular octagon. The radius is 7.3 m. Find the area each tower covers to the nearest square meter. **151 m²**

Example 3
(page 500)

Find the area of each triangle. Give answers to the nearest tenth.

11. 27.7 m²
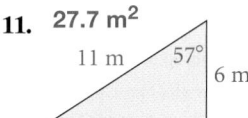
11 m 57° 6 m

12.
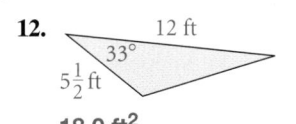
12 ft 33° $5\frac{1}{2}$ ft
18.0 ft²

13. 104 m 7554.0 m²
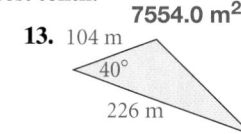
40° 226 m

14.
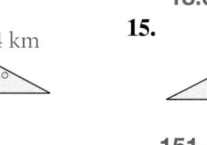
34 km 28° 39 km
311.3 km²

15.
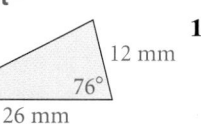
12 mm 76° 26 mm
151.4 mm²

16.
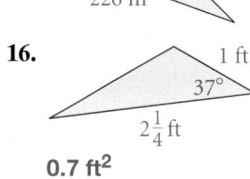
1 ft 37° $2\frac{1}{4}$ ft
0.7 ft²

17. **Surveying** A surveyor marks off a triangular parcel of land. One side of the triangle extends 80 yd. A second side of 150 yd forms an angle of 67° with the first side. Determine the area of the parcel of land to the nearest square yard.
5523 yd²

B Apply Your Skills 18. **Industrial Design** Refer to the diagram of the regular hexagonal nut. Round each answer to the nearest unit.
   a. Find the area of the circular hole in the hexagonal nut. **50 mm²**
   b. Find the area of the hexagonal face. **116 mm²**

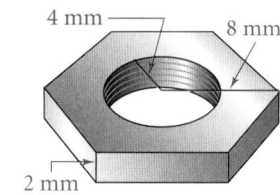
4 mm 8 mm 2 mm

19. **Writing** Describe two ways to find the area of an equilateral triangle that has a 1-in. radius. **See margin.**

20. **Architecture** The Pentagon, in Arlington, Virginia, is one of the world's largest office buildings. It is a regular pentagon, and the length of each of its sides is 921 ft. Find the area of this pentagon to the nearest thousand square feet.
1,459,000 ft²

21. **Windows** Replacement glass for more energy efficient windows costs $5/ft². Approximately how much will you pay for replacement glass for a regular hexagonal window with a radius of 2 ft? **$51.96**

Find the perimeter and area of each regular polygon to the nearest tenth.

22. 20.8 m; 20.8 m²
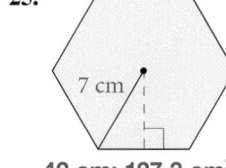
4 m

23.
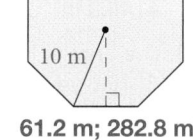
8 in.
45.3 in.; 128 in.²

24. 17.6 ft; 21.4 ft²
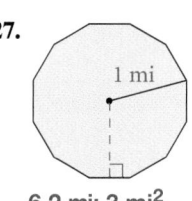
3 ft

25.

7 cm
42 cm; 127.3 cm²

26.
10 m
61.2 m; 282.8 m²

27.
1 mi
6.2 mi; 3 mi²

Regular polygons A and B are similar. Compare their areas. 28–32.
See margin.

28. The radius of square A is twice the radius of square B.

29. The apothem of pentagon A equals the radius of pentagon B.

30. The length of a side of hexagon A equals the radius of hexagon B.

31. The radius of octagon A equals the apothem of octagon B.

32. The perimeter of decagon A equals the length of a side of decagon B.

Assignment Guide

1 Objective
  A B Core 1–10, 18, 20–34
  C Extension 35, 37

2 Objective
  A B Core 11–17, 19
  C Extension 36

Standardized Test Prep 38–42

Mixed Review 43–51

Connection to Calculus
Exercise 34 Students will need calculators to evaluate the expression in part d for large values of *n*. As *n* increases, the sides of the *n*-gon come closer and closer to the inscribed circle. Thus, its area gets closer and closer to π.

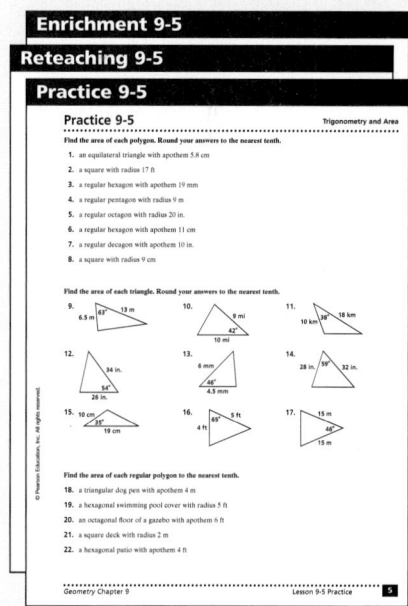

Enrichment 9-5
Reteaching 9-5
Practice 9-5

Real-World Connection
The length of each side of the Pentagon courtyard is 356 ft. A football field is 360 ft.

pages 500–503 Exercises

19. Answers may vary. Sample: 1. Find the apothem and the side ⊥ to apothem using a 30-60-90 △ with hyp. 1. Then use the formula $A = \frac{1}{2}ap$.
2. After finding the apothem and the ⊥ side, the height of the equil. △ is apothem + 1. Then use the formula $A = \frac{1}{2}bh$.

28. (area of sq. A) = 4 · (area of sq. B)

29. (area of pent. A) ≈ 1.53 · (area of pent. B)

30. (area of hex. A) = (area of hex. B)

31. (area of oct. B) ≈ 1.17 · (area of oct. A)

32. (area of dec. A) = 0.01 · (area of dec. B)

501

Lesson Quiz 9-5

Find the area of each figure. Give answers to the nearest square unit.

1. regular hexagon with perimeter 90 ft 585 ft^2

2. regular pentagon with radius 12 m 342 m^2

3. regular polygon with 12 sides of length 1 in. 11 in.^{2}

4.

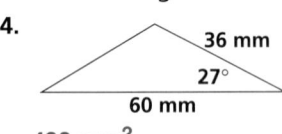

490 mm^2

5.

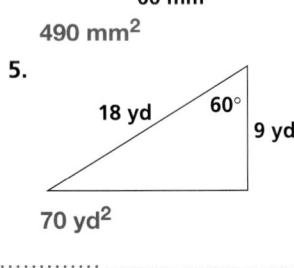

70 yd^2

Alternative Assessment

Have students use a compass and a straightedge to construct a large, regular hexagon; use a ruler to measure the length of a side; and use trigonometry to calculate the area of the hexagon.

pages 500–503 Exercises

34. a. Each central ∠ measures $(360 \div n)$ and $m\angle C = \frac{1}{2}$ that measure or $(180 \div n)$.
   b. $\tan C = \frac{s}{1} = s$
   c. $s = \tan C$, so $p = n \cdot 2(\tan C)$ or $2n(\tan C)$.
   d. Since $a = 1$ and $p = 2n(\tan C)$, $A = \frac{1}{2}ap = \frac{1}{2}(1)(2n \tan C) = n(\tan C) = n\left(\tan \frac{180}{n}\right)$.

   g. Answers may vary. Sample: 425; as X increases, Y_1 approaches π, so the first 4 viewable decimal places become fixed; the n-gons start to look like a circle of radius 1.

502

34f. X increases by 1 and Y_1 approaches π.

C Challenge

35. Using steps similar to Ex. 34, $A = n(\cos \frac{180}{n})(\sin \frac{180}{n})$, which also appr. π as n increases.

33. **Road Signs** The length of a side of the standard stop sign shown at left is 1 ft $\frac{1}{4}$ in. Find the area of the stop sign to the nearest tenth of a square foot.
   5.0 ft^2

34. Suppose a circle is inscribed in a regular n-gon with center C and apothem 1, as shown in the diagram. In parts (a)–(d), explain why each statement is true.
   a. $m\angle C = \frac{1}{2}\left(\frac{360}{n}\right) = \frac{180}{n}$ **a–d. See margin.**
   b. $s = \tan C$
   c. The perimeter of the n-gon is $2n(\tan C)$.
   d. The area of the n-gon is $n\left(\tan \frac{180}{n}\right)$.
   e. **Graphing Calculator** Use the TABLE feature of your graphing calculator to study the areas of regular n-gons of apothem 1 as n increases. What should you enter as Y1?   **X tan(180/X)**
   f. Use the **TBLSET** feature so that X starts at 3 and changes by 1. Access the **TABLE**. Tell what happens in the X and Y1 columns as you scroll down. **See left.**
   g. For what value of X does Y1 take on a new value for the last time? Explain why this is so. Also, in terms of the circle and the circumscribing regular n-gons, interpret what you observe. **See margin.**

35. Suppose a circle is circumscribed about a regular n-gon with center C and radius 1. Proceed with steps similar to those in Exercise 34 to study the areas of regular n-gons inscribed in a circle as n increases. **See left.**

36. **Surveying** A surveyor wants to mark off a triangular parcel with an area of 1 acre (1 acre = 43,560 ft^2). One side of the triangle extends 300 ft along a straight road. A second side extends at an angle of 65° from one end of the first side. Draw a triangle to represent the piece of land. Determine the length of the second boundary line to the nearest foot. **See margin.**

37. Segments are drawn between the midpoints of consecutive sides of a regular pentagon to form another regular pentagon. Find, to the nearest hundredth, the ratio of the area of the smaller pentagon to the area of the larger pentagon.
   0.65

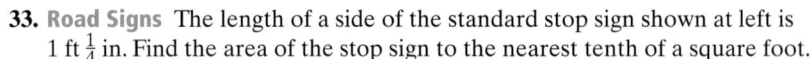

Standardized Test Prep

Multiple Choice   In Exercises 38–40, the polygons are regular.

38. The perimeter is 54 m. The apothem is $3\sqrt{3}$ m. To the nearest tenth, what is the area? **B**
   A. 46.8 m^2 B. 140.3 m^2 C. 243.0 m^2 D. 280.6 m^2

39. The area is 1623.8 yd^2. The perimeter is 150 yd. What is the apothem? **G**
   F. 10.8 yd   G. 21.7 yd   H. 32.5 yd   I. 43.3 yd

40. The area is 100 cm^2. The apothem is 5 m. What is the perimeter? **B**
   A. 20 cm   B. 40 cm   C. 50 cm   D. 100 cm

Short Response

41. Sketch all possible right triangles ABC with $m\angle A = 40$ and $AC = 10$. Find the area of each. **See margin.**

Extended Response

Take It to the NET
Online lesson quiz at
www.PHSchool.com
Web Code: afa-0905

42. a. In the regular pentagon, find x. Then use x to find a.
   b. Explain how you can use the perimeter of a regular polygon to find the area of the polygon.
   c. Use the perimeter of the pentagon shown here to find the area to the nearest tenth. Show your work.
   a–c. See margin.

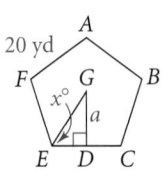

36.   **320 ft**

Mixed Review

Lesson 9-4

43. Find the sum $\vec{a} + \vec{c}$. Give your answer as an ordered pair. $\langle -2, -9 \rangle$

44. Describe a vector $\vec{d}$ such that $\vec{a} + \vec{d} = \vec{c}$. $\langle 6, 1 \rangle$

45. Describe a vector $\vec{e}$ such that $\vec{c} + \vec{e} = \vec{a}$. $\langle -6, -1 \rangle$

46. Which two vectors have $\vec{c}$ as their sum?

$\langle -2, -2 \rangle$ $\qquad$ $\langle 2, -4 \rangle$ $\qquad$ $\langle 4, -2 \rangle$

$\langle -2, -2 \rangle$ and $\langle 4, -2 \rangle$

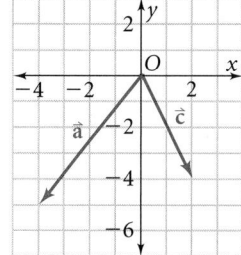

Lesson 7-7 **Find the area of each shaded sector of a circle. Leave your answer in terms of π.**

47.

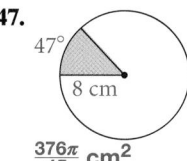

47° 8 cm

$\frac{376\pi}{45}$ cm^2

48.

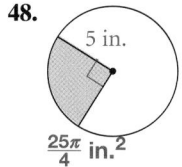

5 in.

$\frac{25\pi}{4}$ in.^{2}

49.

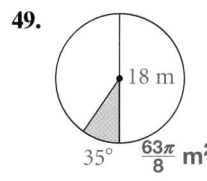

18 m 35°

$\frac{63\pi}{8}$ m^2

Lesson 6-6 **Coordinate Geometry** **Find the coordinates of the midpoint of $\overline{WZ}$. Then find WZ.**

50. rectangle

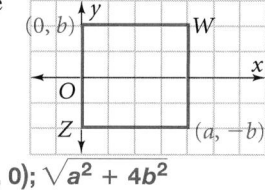

$(\frac{a}{2}, 0)$; $\sqrt{a^2 + 4b^2}$

51. kite

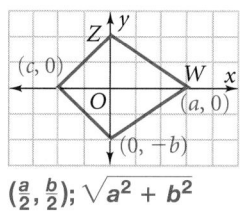

$(\frac{a}{2}, \frac{b}{2})$; $\sqrt{a^2 + b^2}$

Geometry at Work

·······Surveyor

Surveyors calculate the locations, shapes, and areas of plots of land. A survey begins with a benchmark, a reference point whose latitude, longitude, and elevation are known. The surveyor uses a device called a transit to measure the boundary angles for the plot of land and the distances of key points from the benchmark. Using trigonometry, the surveyor finds the latitude, longitude, and elevation of each key point in the survey. These points are located on a map and an accurate sketch of the plot is drawn. Finally, the area is calculated.

One method involves dividing the plot into triangles and measuring the lengths of two sides and the included angle of each. The formula $A = \frac{1}{2}ab(\sin C)$ gives the area of each triangle. The area of the entire plot is the sum of the areas of the triangles.

 **Take It to the NET** For more information about surveying, go to **www.PHSchool.com**. Web Code: afb-2031

Lesson 9-5 Trigonometry and Area **503**

Standardized Test Prep

📁 **Resources**

For additional practice with a variety of test item formats:
- Standardized Test Prep, p. 509
- Test-Taking Strategies, p. 504
- Test-Taking Strategies with Transparencies

Exercises 38–40 Each exercise can be solved without a diagram by using the formula $A = \frac{1}{2}ap$.

Exercise 41 Warn students not to assume too much because either $\angle B$ or $\angle C$ could be the right angle.

41. [2]

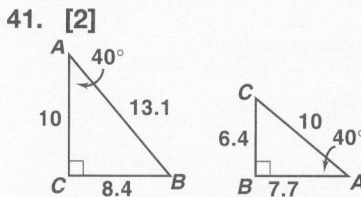

A 40° 10 13.1 C 8.4 B

C 6.4 10 40° B 7.7 A

42 units^2, 24.6 units^2

[1] correct drawings OR correct solutions OR one correct drawing with solution

42. [4] a. $x = 54$; $\tan 54° = \frac{a}{10}$ so $a = 10 \tan 54° \approx 13.8$ yd

b. Use the formula $A = \frac{1}{2}ap$ where A represents the area, a represents the apothem, and p represents the perimeter.

c. The perimeter is (20)(5), or 100 yd. $A = \frac{1}{2}ap$

$A = \frac{1}{2}(10 \tan 54°)(100) \approx 688.2$ yd^2

[3] appropriate methods, but with one computational error

[2] correct answer but with no work shown

[1] correct answer to (a)

Eliminating Answers

Mental math often can help students eliminate some of the incorrect answer choices for multiple-choice questions. This feature helps students understand the importance of using estimation to eliminate some of the incorrect answer choices.

Resources

 **PRENTICE HALL**
ASSESSMENT SYSTEM

Test-Taking Strategies with Transparencies
- Transparency 9
- Practice sheet p. 21

Teaching Notes

Discuss as a class that only two answer choices in Example 2 are eliminated using mental math, so the correct answer must still be found. Emphasize that eliminating answers is only a time-saving strategy.

Test-Taking Strategies with Transparencies

Test-Taking Strategy: Eliminating Answers

The easiest way to narrow down the answer choices in a multiple-choice item is to eliminate obviously wrong answers.

Solve $\frac{|2x + 16|}{x - 8} = 10$.

A. –4   B. 8   C. 10   D. 12

Look at each answer choice to see if it can be eliminated.

–4 If –4 is substituted then the denominator would be negative which would make the quotient negative. The given quotient is positive, so this answer choice can be eliminated.

8 If 8 is substituted, the denominator would be zero and division by zero is undefined. This answer choice can be eliminated.

The answer choice is either C or D. Substitute these choices for x to select the correct one. D is correct.

Solve these problems by eliminating answer choices.

1. Solve $\frac{625}{y} = -125$.

   A. –25   B. –5   C. 5   D. 25

2. Solve $\frac{1295}{b} = 259$.

   A. 5   B. 8   C. 10   D. 12

Solutions
1. B
2. A

Transparency 9

Before you begin working a problem in earnest, or if you do not know how to do a problem, you usually can eliminate some answer choices. Cross out the answers you eliminate. But do this in the test booklet, not on the answer sheet.

1 EXAMPLE

The length of a diagonal of a square is 12 cm. What is the area of the square?

A. 49 cm^2 **B.** 72 cm^2 **C.** 145 cm^2 **D.** 225 cm^2

The area of a square with side length s is s^2. Since the length of the side of the square is less than the length of the diagonal, you can eliminate answers C and D. Those areas are both larger than $12^2 = 144$. Answer A is the area of a square whose side is 7 cm, and this square does not have a diagonal whose length is 12 cm.
● B is the correct answer.

2 EXAMPLE

A kite at the end of a 100-ft string has an angle of elevation of 28°. The end of the string is staked to the ground. Which is the best estimate of the kite's height?

F. 38 ft   **G.** 47 ft   **H.** 52 ft   **I.** 65 ft

Draw a diagram. Since 28° is a little less than 30°, you can estimate the answer by using a 30°-60°-90° triangle. If the angle of elevation were 30°, then the height of the kite would be 50 ft. Since the actual angle is less than 30°, you know the actual height is less than 50 ft. You can eliminate answers H and I since they are greater than 50 ft.
● The correct answer must be either F or G.

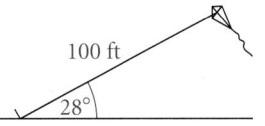
100 ft
28°

EXERCISES

1. If d is the length of a diagonal of a square, what is the area of the square in terms of d? $\frac{d^2}{2}$

2. Use the sine ratio to find the height of the kite above the ground in Example 2. **about 47 ft**

Use the following question for Exercises 3–5.

The lengths of the diagonals of a rhombus are 6 cm and 10 cm. What is the measure of each acute angle of the rhombus?

A. 31.0   **B.** 45   **C.** 61.9   **D.** 118.1

3. Explain why you can immediately eliminate answer D. **It is not an acute angle.**

4. The diagonals of a rhombus are perpendicular and bisect each other. Draw a diagram of the rhombus and its diagonals. Use the three sides of a right triangle to explain why you can eliminate answer A. **See margin.**

5. Explain how you now choose between B and C.
   61.9 is closest to 60.

page 504   Test-Taking Strategies

4. **The half of the rhombus with the acute ∠ has sides**
   $\sqrt{34} \approx 6$ **by the Pythagorean Thm., so it is**
   approx. equilateral. 31.0 is too small.

Chapter Review

Vocabulary

angle of depression (p. 482)
angle of elevation (p. 482)
cosine (p. 477)
identity (p. 478)

initial point (p. 490)
magnitude (p. 490)
resultant (p. 492)
sine (p. 477)

tangent (p. 470)
terminal point (p. 490)
vector (p. 490)

Reading Math
Understanding
Vocabulary

Choose the correct term to complete each sentence.

1. Any quantity that has magnitude and direction is called a(n) _?_. **vector**

2. The _?_ is the angle formed by a horizontal line and the line of sight to an object above that horizontal line. **angle of elevation**

3. The _?_ of $\angle A$ is $\dfrac{\text{leg adjacent } \angle A}{\text{hypotenuse}}$. **cosine**

4. The _?_ of $\angle A$ is $\dfrac{\text{leg opposite } \angle A}{\text{hypotenuse}}$. **sine**

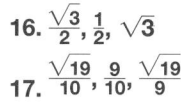
Take It to the NET
Online vocabulary quiz
at www.PHSchool.com
Web Code: afj-0951

5. An equation that is true for all allowed values of the variable is called a(n) _?_. **identity**

6. The sum of two vectors is the _?_. **resultant vector**

7. The _?_ of a vector modeled by an arrow is the distance from its _?_ to its _?_. **magnitude; initial point; terminal point**

Skills and Concepts

9-1 and 9-2 Objectives

▼ To use tangent ratios to determine side lengths in triangles

▼ To use sine and cosine to determine side lengths in triangles

In right $\triangle ABC$,

$$\textbf{sine of } \angle A = \sin A = \frac{\text{leg opposite } \angle A}{\text{hypotenuse}}$$

$$\textbf{cosine of } \angle A = \cos A = \frac{\text{leg adjacent to } \angle A}{\text{hypotenuse}}$$

and $\textbf{tangent of } \angle A = \tan A = \dfrac{\text{leg opposite } \angle A}{\text{leg adjacent to } \angle A}$

You can use the inverses of sine, cosine, and tangent to find the measures of the acute angles of a right triangle.

A trigonometric **identity** is an equation that is always true for all the allowed values of the variable.

Find each missing value to the nearest whole number.

8. $\tan \blacksquare^{\circ} = 0.9$ **42**   **9.** $\sin 17^{\circ} = \dfrac{\blacksquare}{7}$ **2**   **10.** $\tan 27^{\circ} = \dfrac{1}{\blacksquare}$ **2**   **11.** $\cos \blacksquare^{\circ} = 0.39$ **67**

12. $\sin \blacksquare^{\circ} = 0.39$ **23**   **13.** $\sin \blacksquare^{\circ} = \dfrac{2}{3}$ **42**   **14.** $\tan 76^{\circ} = \dfrac{\blacksquare}{3}$ **12**   **15.** $\cos 83^{\circ} = \dfrac{1}{\blacksquare}$ **8**

Express $\sin A$, $\cos A$, and $\tan A$ as ratios. 16–18. See left.

16. $\dfrac{\sqrt{3}}{2}, \dfrac{1}{2}, \sqrt{3}$

17. $\dfrac{\sqrt{19}}{10}, \dfrac{9}{10}, \dfrac{\sqrt{19}}{9}$

18. $\dfrac{4}{5}, \dfrac{3}{5}, \dfrac{4}{3}$

16.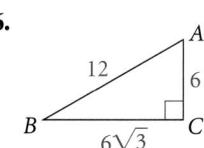

17.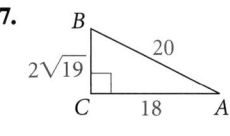

18.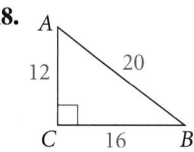

Find the value of *x*. Round lengths of segments to the nearest tenth. Round angle measures to the nearest degree.

19.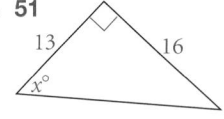

20.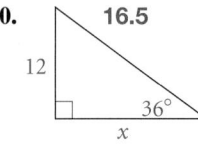

21.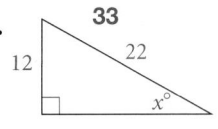

9-3 Objective

▼ To use angles of elevation and depression to solve problems

A horizontal line and the line of sight to an object above the horizontal line form an **angle of elevation.** A horizontal line and the line of sight to an object below that horizontal line form an **angle of depression.**

Solve each problem.

 22. Elevation Two hills are 2 mi apart. The taller hill is 2707 ft high. The angle of depression from the top of the taller hill to the top of the shorter hill is 7°. Find the height of the shorter hill to the nearest foot. (1 mi = 5280 ft) **1410 ft**

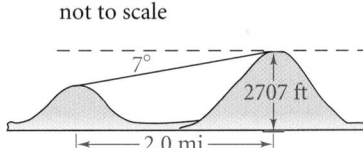

 23. Surveying A surveyor is 305 ft from the base of the new courthouse. Her angle measuring device is 5 ft above the ground. The angle of elevation to the top of the courthouse is 42°. Find the height of the courthouse to the nearest foot. **280 ft**

24. Indirect Measurement Linda is flying a kite. She lets out 45 yd of string and anchors it to the ground. She determines that the angle of elevation of the kite is 58°. What is the height of the kite from the ground? **about 38.2 yd**

25. Writing Explain why in this diagram the angle of depression, ∠1, and the angle of elevation, ∠2, are congruent.
They are alt. int. ∕s to ‖ lines.

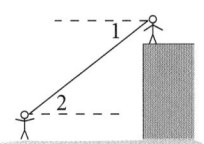

9-4 Objective

▼ To describe vectors

▼ To solve problems that involve vector addition

A **vector** is any quantity that has magnitude and direction. You can describe a vector by its horizontal and vertical change (ordered pair) or by its size and direction. Direction is often described in relation to north, south, east, and west.

The sum of two vectors is the **resultant.** Vector sums can show the result of vector actions that take place one after the other. Additionally, vector sums can show the result of two vector actions that occur at the same time. You can add vectors by adding their coordinates. You can also show the sum geometrically.

Describe each vector using ordered pair notation.

26.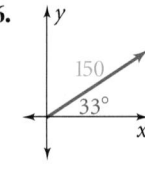

⟨125.8, 81.7⟩

27.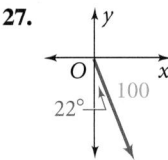

⟨37.5, −92.7⟩

28.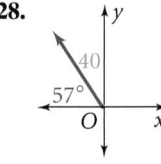

⟨−21.8, 33.5⟩

29. about 167.7 mi; about 26.6° east of south

30. about 206.2 km; about 14.0° west of south

31. about 503.1 mi/h; about 26.6° north of west

32. ⟨6, 8⟩, ⟨9, 12⟩, ⟨30, 40⟩; ⟨x, y⟩ and ⟨nx, ny⟩ have the same direction for n > 0.

Find the magnitude and direction of each vector. 29–31. See left.

29.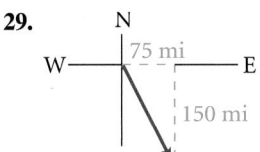

30.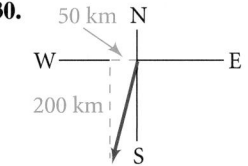

31.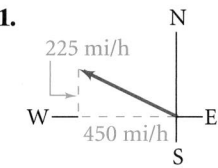

32. Open-Ended Write three vectors with the same direction as ⟨3, 4⟩. Explain how you found your answers. **See left.**

Sketch a vector that has the given direction. 33–35. See margin.

33. 25° east of north   **34.** 45° north of east   **35.** 60° west of south

Find the sum of each pair of vectors. Give your answers in ordered pair notation.

36.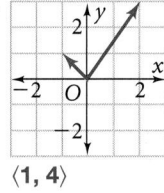

⟨1, 4⟩

37.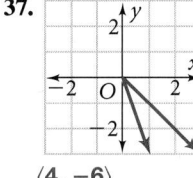

⟨4, −6⟩

38.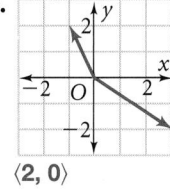

⟨2, 0⟩

 39. Navigation A whale-watching tour leaves port and travels 12 mi directly north. The tour then travels 5 mi due east. **39a. about 67.4° south of west**
a. In what direction should the boat head to return directly to port?
b. How long will the return trip take if the boat averages 20 mi/h?
    about 39 min

9-5 Objectives

▼ To find the area of a regular polygon using trigonometry

▼ To find the area of a triangle using trigonometry

You can use trigonometry to find the areas of regular polygons.

You can also use trigonometry to find the area of a triangle when you know the lengths of two sides and the measure of the included angle.

Area of triangle $= \frac{1}{2} \cdot$ side length $\cdot$ side length $\cdot$ sine of included angle

Area of $\triangle ABC = \frac{1}{2}bc(\sin A)$

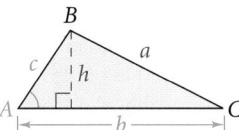

Find the area of each polygon. Round your answers to the nearest tenth.

40. regular decagon with radius 5 ft **73.5 ft²**

41. regular pentagon with apothem 8 cm **232.5 cm²**

42. regular hexagon with apothem 6 in. **124.7 in.²**

43. regular quadrilateral with radius 2 m **8 m²**

44.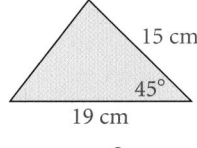

100.8 cm²

45.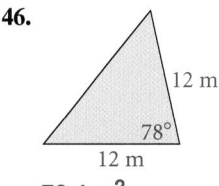

88.4 ft²

46.

70.4 m²

Chapter 9 Chapter Review   **507**

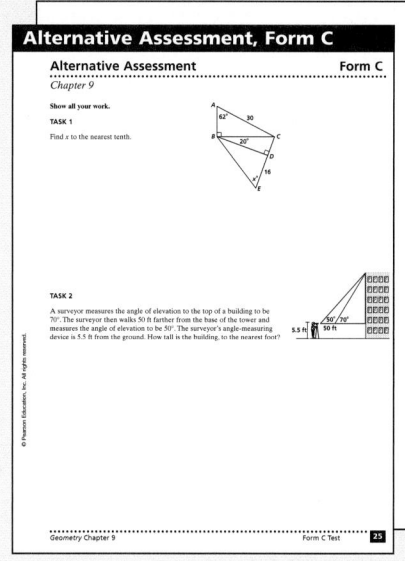
pages 505–507   Chapter Review

33.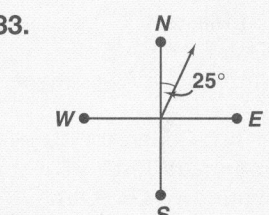

34.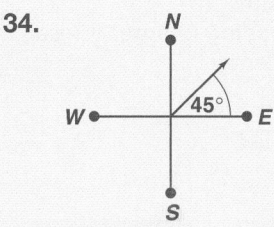

35.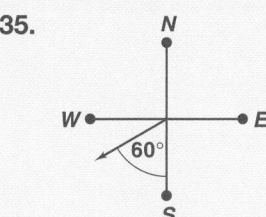

Chapter Test

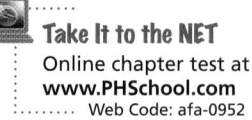
····· **Take It to the NET**
Online chapter test at
www.PHSchool.com
····· Web Code: afa-0952

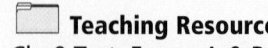

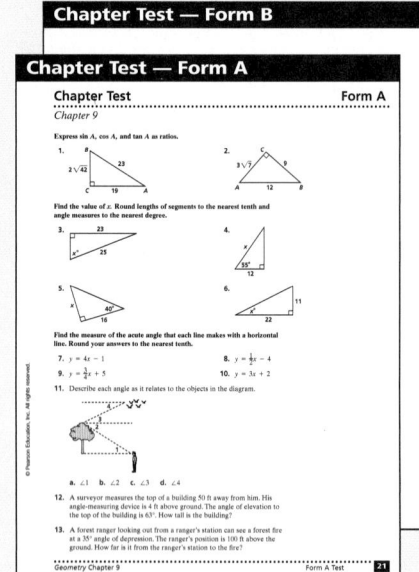

Express sin B, cos B, and tan B as ratios.

1.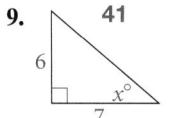
$\frac{\sqrt{57}}{11}, \frac{8}{11}, \frac{\sqrt{57}}{8}$

2.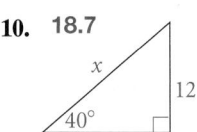
$\frac{\sqrt{33}}{7}, \frac{4}{7}, \frac{\sqrt{33}}{4}$

Find each missing value to the nearest tenth.

3. tan ■° = 1.11 **48.0**

4. tan 18° = $\frac{■}{87}$ **28.3**

5. sin 34° = $\frac{5}{■}$ **8.9**

6. sin ■° = 0.996 **84.9**

7. cos ■° = $\frac{12}{15}$ **36.9**

8. cos 76° = $\frac{■}{24}$ **5.8**

Find the value of x. Round lengths to the nearest tenth and angle measures to the nearest degree.

9. 41 **6.0**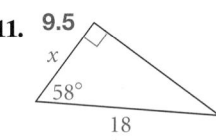

10. 18.7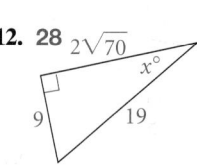

11. 9.5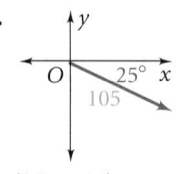

12. 28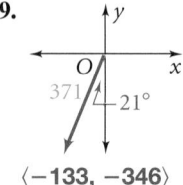

Indirect Measurement Solve each problem.

13. A surveyor measuring the tallest tree in a park is 100 ft from the tree. His angle-measuring device is 5 ft above the ground. The angle of elevation to the top of the tree is 48°. How tall is the tree?
about 116 ft

14. Twenty minutes after being launched, a hot-air balloon has risen to an altitude of 300 m. The pilot can still see the starting point on the ground at a 25° angle of depression. How many meters is the balloon from the starting point? **about 710 m**

15. A 5-foot-tall woman stands 15 ft from a statue. She must look up at an angle of 60° to see the top of the statue. How tall is the statue? **about 31 ft**

16. A family vacationed at a beach 120 mi east and 30 mi south of their home. Find the distance and the direction from their home to the beach.
about 123.7 mi; about 14° south of east

17. Writing Explain why sin $x°$ = cos (90 − x)°. Include a diagram with your explanation.
See margin.

Describe each vector using ordered pair notation. Round the coordinates to the nearest unit.

18.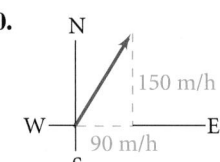
⟨95, −44⟩

19.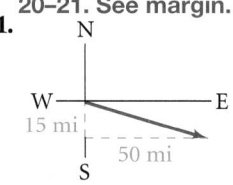
⟨−133, −346⟩

Find the magnitude and direction of each vector.
20–21. See margin.

20.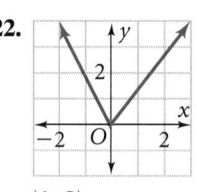

21.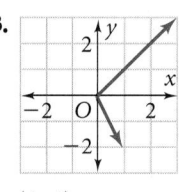

Describe the resultant as an ordered pair.

22.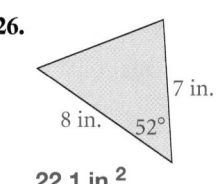
⟨1, 8⟩

23.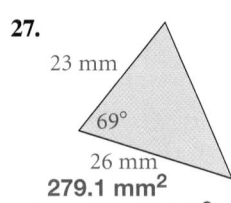
⟨4, 1⟩

24. A canoe heading 30° west of north is being paddled at a rate of 7 mi/h. The current is pushing the canoe 20° south of west at a rate of 3 mi/h. Find the resulting speed and direction of the canoe.
8.1 mph at 39° north of west

25. Open-Ended Draw two vectors with different directions on a coordinate grid. Then draw their resultant and describe it as an ordered pair.
Check students' work.

Find the area of each polygon to the nearest tenth.

26.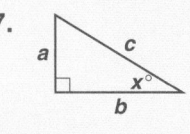
22.1 in.²

27. 23 mm, 69°, 26 mm
279.1 mm²

28. a regular hexagon with apothem 5 ft **86.6 ft²**

29. a regular pentagon with radius 3 cm **21.4 cm²**

page 508   Chapter Test

17.
a, c, $x°$, b

$\sin x° = \frac{a}{c}$

$\cos(90 − x)° = \frac{a}{c}$

It follows that sin $x°$ = cos(90 − x)° by subst.

20. about 174.9 mi/h at about 59° north of east

21. about 52.2 mi at about 73° east of south

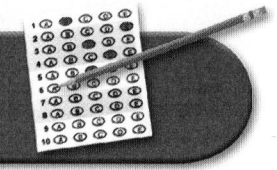

Standardized Test Prep

Reading Comprehension **Read the passage below. Then answer the questions on the basis of what is *stated* or *implied* in the passage.**

In Balance To suspend a mobile so that it balances, you need to know how to find the center of mass. If a figure has a "nice" geometric shape, you can find the center of mass, or centroid, using geometric methods. There are alternative ways to find centers of mass in figures without "nice" shapes.

Here is how one artist found the center of mass for the irregularly shaped flat sheet of metal shown at the right.

1. She suspended the shape from a point at its edge. She also suspended a *plumb line* (a weight on a string) from the same point. She traced the plumb line onto the shape.
2. She suspended the shape from another point, and again traced the plumb line. She found the center of mass of the shape at the intersection *M* of the two traced lines.

This method works because each traced plumb line passes through the center of mass. If you place the metal shape horizontally with a traced plumb line along the thin edge of a ruler, the shape will balance on the ruler. Since the shape balances along each traced plumb line, it will balance at the point of intersection of two such lines.

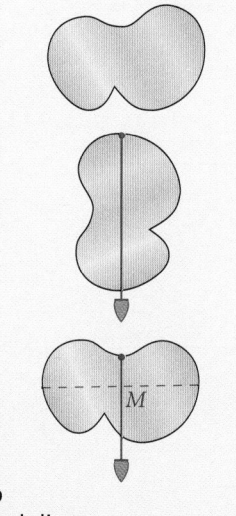

1. What should you learn how to do from the passage? **C**
   A. suspend a mobile
   B. find a center of mass using geometric methods
   C. find the center of mass of any flat shape
   D. attach a plumb line to any flat shape

2. Why is a plumb line necessary? **G**
   F. to show a straight line
   G. to find a vertical line
   H. to split the shape into two equal halves
   I. to suspend the shape at its center of mass

3. What geometric fact is applied in the passage? **B**
   A. Two nonparallel planes determine a line.
   B. Two intersecting lines lie in one plane.
   C. Two nonparallel lines determine a point.
   D. Two points lie in one line.

4. Why does the shape balance when you place it on the edge of a ruler along a traced plumb line? **F**
   F. The center of mass of the shape rests on the edge of the ruler.
   G. The traced plumb line is longer than the edge of the ruler.
   H. The shape is placed horizontally on the edge of the ruler.
   I. Half the mass of the shape is on each side of the edge of the ruler.

5. If the metal shape were an isosceles triangle, what would be other names for some traced plumb lines? Justify your answer. **See margin.**

6. If the metal shape were a circular ring with its inner circle cut out, where would you find the center of mass? **at the center of the inner circle**

page 509   Standardized Test Prep

5. **Answers may vary. Sample: The plumb line through the vertex would be an ∠ bis., a median,** an altitude, and the ⊥ bis. of the opposite side. In an isosc. △, these 4 segments are the same.

Students must be able to extract information from reading passages, answer multiple-choice questions, and construct responses, in order to be successful on current state and national assessments.

To answer the questions, students apply skills and concepts from this chapter and previous chapters.
Multiple Choice: Items 1–4
Extended Response: Items 5, 6

Resources

Teaching Resources
Cumulative Review
Quarter 3 Test, Forms A & B

Reaching All Students
Spanish Cumulative Review
Spanish Quarter 3 Tests

ASSESSMENT SYSTEM
PRENTICE HALL

Standardized Test Prep Workbook
• Ch. 9 Standardized Test Practice
Assessment Masters
• Cumulative Review
• Quarter 3 Test, Forms A & B
Computer Test Generator CD
• Standardized Test Practice

www.PHSchool.com
• Standardized Test Practice
• Resources

Plus **iTEXT**

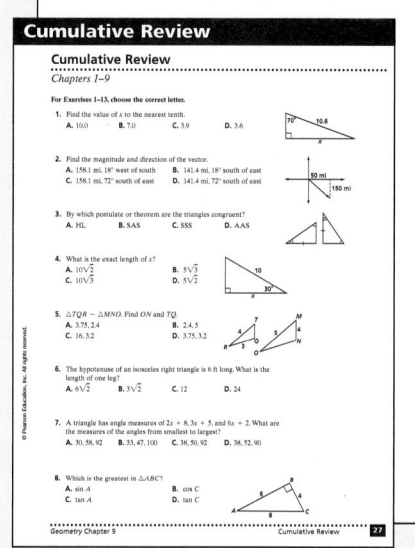

Chapter 10

Surface Area and Volume

Chapter at a Glance

North Carolina Objectives

10-1	Space Figures and Nets	2.04
NCTM 2, 3, 6, 8, 9, 10	▼ Identifying Nets of Space Figures	

10-2	Space Figures and Drawings	2.04
NCTM 3, 5, 6, 8, 9, 10	▼ Drawing Isometric and Orthographic Views ▼ Describing Cross Sections	

10-3	Surface Areas of Prisms and Cylinders	1.02, 2.04
NCTM 2, 3, 4, 6, 8, 9, 10	▼ Finding Surface Area of a Prism ▼ Finding Surface Area of a Cylinder	

10-4	Surface Areas of Pyramids and Cones	1.02, 2.04
NCTM 2, 3, 4, 6, 8, 9, 10	▼ Finding Surface Area of a Pyramid ▼ Finding Surface Area of a Cone	

10-5	Volumes of Prisms and Cylinders	1.02, 2.04
NCTM 2, 3, 4, 6, 7, 8, 9, 10	▼ Finding Volume of a Prism ▼ Finding Volume of a Cylinder	

10-6	Volumes of Pyramids and Cones	1.02, 2.04
NCTM 2, 3, 4, 6, 7, 8, 9, 10	▼ Finding Volume of a Pyramid ▼ Finding Volume of a Cone	

10-7	Surface Areas and Volumes of Spheres	1.02, 2.04
NCTM 2, 3, 4, 6, 8, 9, 10	▼ Finding Surface Area and Volume of a Sphere	

10-8	Areas and Volumes of Similar Solids	1.02, 2.04
NCTM 2, 3, 4, 6, 8, 9, 10	▼ Finding Relationships in Area and Volume	

NCTM STANDARDS 2000

1	Number and Operations	6	Problem Solving
2	Algebra	7	Reasoning and Proof
3	Geometry	8	Communication
4	Measurement	9	Connections
5	Data Analysis and Probability	10	Representation

Pacing Options

This chart suggests pacing only for the lessons and their parts. It is provided as a possible guide. It will help you determine how much time you have in your schedule to cover other components, such as the features, Chapter Review and Chapter Test.

Day	Traditional 45 min.	Two-Year 45 min.	Block 90 min.
1	10-1 ▼	10-1 ▼	10-1 ▼
2	10-2 ▼	10-1 ▼	10-2 ▼▼
3	10-2 ▼	10-2 ▼	10-3 ▼▼
4	10-2 ▼	10-2 ▼	10-4 ▼▼
5	10-3 ▼	10-2 ▼	10-5 ▼▼
6	10-3 ▼	10-3 ▼	10-6 ▼▼
7	10-4 ▼	10-3 ▼	10-7 ▼
8	10-4 ▼	10-3 ▼	10-8 ▼
9	10-5 ▼	10-4 ▼	
10	10-5 ▼	10-4 ▼	
11	10-6 ▼	10-4 ▼	
12	10-6 ▼	10-4 ▼	
13	10-7 ▼	10-5 ▼	
14	10-7 ▼	10-5 ▼	
15	10-8 ▼	10-5 ▼	
16		10-5 ▼	
17		10-6 ▼	
18		10-6 ▼	
19		10-6 ▼	
20		10-6 ▼	
21		10-7 ▼	
22		10-7 ▼	
23		10-8 ▼	
24		10-8 ▼	

NAEP Correlation (National Assessment of Educational Progress 2000 Mathematics Objectives)

10-1	10-2	10-3	10-4	10-5	10-6	10-7	10-8
G1a, b; G2	G1a, b; G4b	N3c, M4b, M5	N3d, M4b, M5	M4b, M5, G4b	N4a, M4b, M5	N4a, M4b, M5	M4b, M5, G6c

N = Number Sense, Properties, and Operations; **M** = Measurement; **G** = Geometry and Spatial Sense;
D = Data Analysis, Statistics, and Probability; **A** = Algebra and Functions

Math Background

Chapter Overview

Nets and isometric, orthographic, and foundation drawings are useful two-dimensional representations of three-dimensional figures. They enhance students' understanding of prisms, pyramids, cylinders, cones, and spheres, and prepare them for the volume formulas and lateral- and surface-area formulas that are developed and applied.

Space Figures, Nets, and Drawings   10-1, 10-2

Many students have difficulty interpreting diagrams of three-dimensional figures and drawing two-dimensional representations of them. These lessons focus on developing these spatial visualization skills. Students with art experience may be familiar with isometric or orthographic drawing, but foundational drawing is likely to be new to all students. Both lessons make the surface-area formulas for three-dimensional figures much easier to understand and remember.

The Four-Color Map Theorem solved a famous but seemingly trivial question about the minimum number of colors needed to color a map so that no two adjoining regions are the same color. It was solved in 1976 only with the aid of a computer, after about 125 years of mathematical endeavor. Encourage students to investigate some of the mathematical discoveries with important practical applications that resulted from the search for a proof of this theorem. For example, graph theory was established as a mathematical discipline, making possible, among other things, high-speed, efficient telephone systems.

In hyperbolic geometry, Euler's Formula becomes $F + V = E + 1$.

Surface Areas of Prisms and Cylinders   10-3

Students will become more comfortable with these formulas as they recognize the similarities: Lateral area is the product of height and "distance around," whether "distance around" is perimeter or circumference. Surface area is the area of the bases added to the lateral area.

Students may enjoy developing the formula for the lateral area of an oblique prism (one with some lateral faces that are nonrectangular parallelograms).

Surface Areas of Pyramids and Cones   10-4

There are similarities in the formulas for the lateral areas of pyramids and cones. Here, lateral area is the product of slant height and "distance around." Surface area is the sum of the area of the base and the lateral area.

This is a practical opportunity for students to review areas of sectors of circles by computing, for example, the lateral area of a cone formed by a 120° sector cut from a circle with a 4-in. radius. Make sure that they realize why the lateral area of this cone is equal to $\frac{1}{3}$ the area of the original circle.

Volumes of Prisms, Cylinders, Pyramids, and Cones   10-5, 10-6

Because both prisms and cylinders have the same cross-sectional area at every distance from the base, their volume formulas are similar. The same principle (Cavalieri's Principle) applies to the volume formulas for pyramids and cones.

Surface Areas and Volumes of Spheres   10-7

The approximation techniques used to justify the formulas for the surface area and volume of a sphere anticipate those in calculus. Students will benefit from seeing approximation used in this way.

Of all his discoveries, Archimedes was most proud of his discovery that a sphere has $\frac{2}{3}$ the volume of its circumscribed cylinder. He asked that an inscribed sphere be carved on his headstone when he died. In 1965 such a headstone was found among ruins in Syracuse, Greece, the city where Archimedes died.

Areas and Volumes of Similar Solids   10-8

The relationships between linear, area, and volume measures of similar solids are nonintuitive but easily verified algebraically. It may help students who expect all to be linear relationships to create graphs of the changes in diameter, surface area, and volume of a sphere as the radius increases in increments of 1 unit. The graphs may be compared to help students understand the different proportional relationships for linear, area, and volume measurements in three-dimensional figures.

Platonic and Archimedean solids are named for the Greek philosopher Plato and the Greek mathematician and inventor Archimedes. Plato used the five regular solids in his system of cosmology: The tetrahedron represented fire; the octahedron, air; the icosahedron, water; the cube, earth; and the dodecahedron, as the perfect solid, represented the entire universe. Archimedean solids are semiregular polyhedrons composed of at least two regular polygons with identical arrangements of the polygons at each vertex. There are 13 distinct Archimedean solids. They can be viewed and manipulated on various Web sites.

 # Ongoing Assessment and Intervention

Tools for Monitoring Student Progress

The Prentice Hall *Geometry* program provides you with many options for assessment in the Student Edition, the Teacher's Edition and the teaching resources. From these options, you may choose instructional materials and techniques that are appropriate for your students and support your district's curriculum requirements.

Instant Check System™ in Chapter 10

Allows students to check their own learning before, during, and after each lesson.

Diagnosing Readiness before the chapter (p. 510)

Check Skills You'll Need exercises in each lesson (pp. 512, 520, 528, 537, 544, 551, 558, 566)

Check Understanding questions with each Example (pp. 512, 513, 517, 520, 521, 522, 529, 531, 538, 539, 540, 545, 546, 547, 552, 553, 554, 559, 560, 566, 567, 568)

Checkpoint Quiz (pp. 535 and 564)

 Test Prep in Chapter 10

Teaches students strategies and gives them practice with all the test item formats they will encounter on state tests and standardized national exams.

Standardized Test Prep exercises in each lesson (pp. 516, 526, 534, 543, 550, 556, 563, 571)

Test-Taking Strategies (p. 572: Choosing "Cannot Be Determined")

Standardized Test Prep (p. 577: Cumulative Review)

 PRENTICE HALL ASSESSMENT *SYSTEM*

All your assessment needs in one place!

Program Assessment

Assess student progress throughout the *Geometry* text with blackline masters and CD-ROM.

Assessment Resources

- Checkpoint Quizzes 1 & 2
- Chapter Test, Forms A & B
- Chapter Alternative Assessment

Spanish versions available. Tests for Informal Geometry also available.

 ### Computer Test Generator

- Unlimited questions of varying difficulty for every lesson objective.
- Create your own practice sheets, quizzes, and tests, or use the pre-made Chapter Tests.
- Diagnose readiness with questions on prerequisite skills.
- Prepare students by making tests based on standardized test objectives.
- Access Algebra 1, Geometry, and Algebra 2 content—all on one CD-ROM.

Test Preparation

A three-step approach to preparing students for high stakes, national, and state exams.

❶ Diagnose & Prescribe

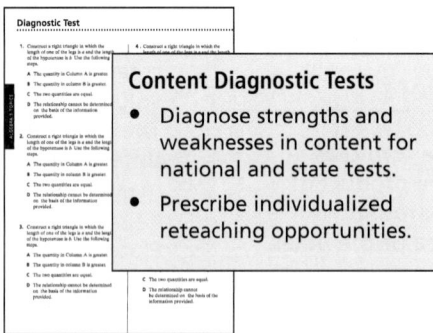

Content Diagnostic Tests
- Diagnose strengths and weaknesses in content for national and state tests.
- Prescribe individualized reteaching opportunities.

❷ Review & Reteach

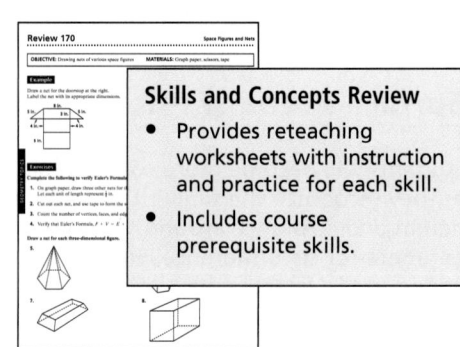

Skills and Concepts Review
- Provides reteaching worksheets with instruction and practice for each skill.
- Includes course prerequisite skills.

❸ Practice & Assess

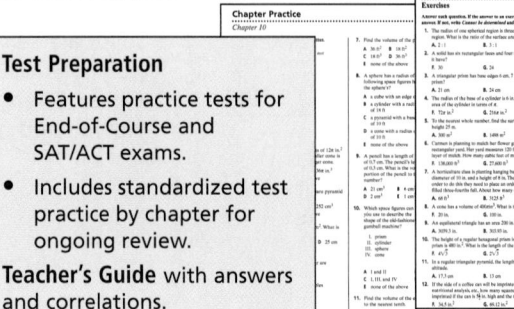

Test Preparation
- Features practice tests for End-of-Course and SAT/ACT exams.
- Includes standardized test practice by chapter for ongoing review.

Teacher's Guide with answers and correlations.

Test-Taking Strategies with Transparencies
- Support the Test-Taking Strategies pages in the Student Edition.
- Provide a teaching transparency and a practice worksheet for each strategy.

Reaching All Students

Support in the Student Text and Additional Resources

The textbook, the iText, and other technology components provide numerous opportunities to reach students of various ability levels and learning styles. Each Teacher's Edition lesson suggests how you can help *all* your students be successful and understand the mathematics in Chapter 10.

Below Level

Student Edition
- Diagnosing Readiness*: p. 510
- Check Skills You'll Need*: pp. 512, 520, 528, 537, 544, 551, 558, 566

Reteaching
Chapter 10 Support File: pp. 10–17

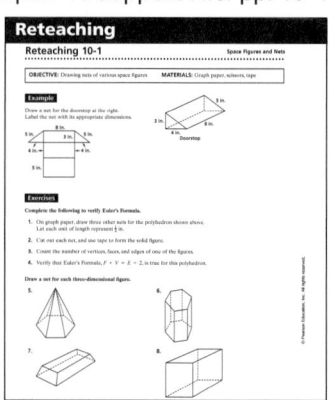

Informal Geometry Planning Guide
Chapter 10 Lesson Plans: pp. 58–65
Chapter 10 Tests: pp. 115–118

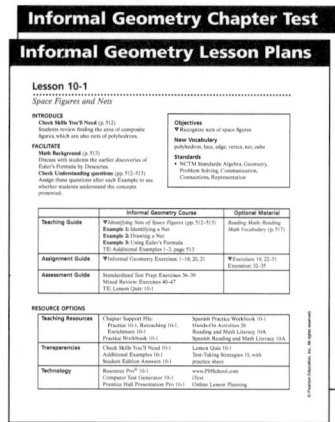

* Can be used with all ability levels to ensure mastery of prerequisite skills.

Advanced Learners

Student Edition
- Challenge exercises: pp. 516, 525, 533, 542, 549, 556, 562, 570
- Extension: pp. 518–519

Enrichment
Chapter 10 Support File: pp. 18–25

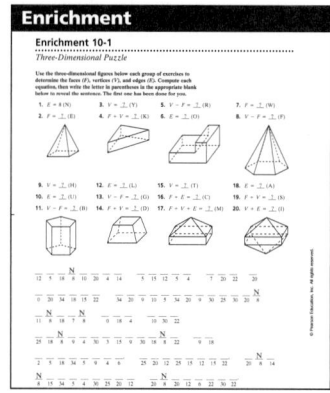

Reading and Math Literacy

Student Edition
- Vocabulary: pp. 511, 573, *plus* in every Lesson Preview
- Reading Math: pp. 512, 515, 517, 520, 567, 573
- Illustrated Glossary: pp. 741–777

Reading and Math Literacy Masters
Chapter 10: pp. 37–40

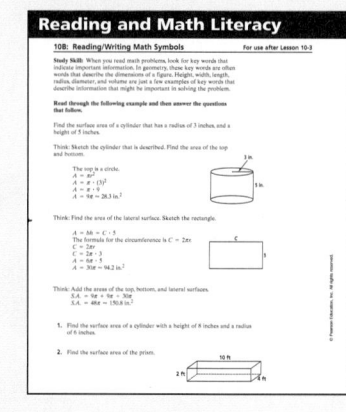

English Learners

Student Edition
- English/Spanish Illustrated Glossary: pp. 741–777

Workbook and Masters
Spanish Practice Workbook: pp. 58–65
Spanish Reading and Math Literacy Masters: pp. 37–40

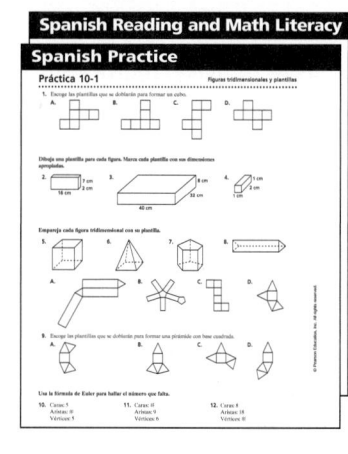

Learning Styles

Student Edition
- Investigation: pp. 544, 551
- Technology: pp. 531, 536, 538, 540, 553, 554, 556, 559, 560, 562, 565, 567
- Writing: pp. 515, 524, 532, 535, 541, 548, 555, 562, 570, 576
- DK Activities: pp. 578–579

Activity Masters
Hands-On Activities: 28, 29, 30
Technology Activities: 51

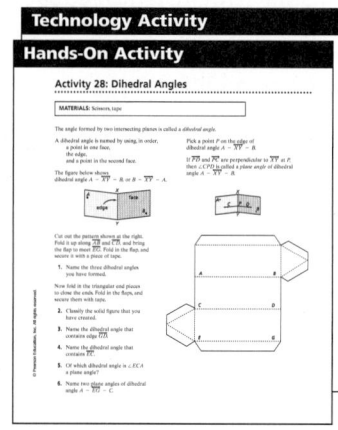

Program Resources

	Teaching Resources in Grab & Go™ Files				Resources for Reaching All Students				Spanish Resources			Transparencies				Prentice Hall Presentation Pro CD-ROM
	Practice	Reteach	Enrich	Checkpoint Quiz	Reading & Math Literacy	Technology Activities	Hands-On Activities	Informal Geometry Lesson Plans	Practice	Reading & Math Literacy	Checkpoint Quiz	Skills Check	Additional Examples	Answers to Exercises	Lesson Quiz	
10-1	■	■	■		■		■	■	■	■		■	■	■	■	■
10-2	■	■	■						■			■	■	■	■	■
10-3	■	■	■	■	■			■	■	■	■	■	■	■	■	■
10-4	■	■	■				■	■	■			■	■	■	■	■
10-5	■	■	■			■		■	■			■	■	■	■	■
10-6	■	■	■					■	■			■	■	■	■	■
10-7	■	■	■	■	■		■	■	■	■	■	■	■	■	■	■
10-8	■	■	■					■	■			■	■	■	■	■
For the chapter	Chapter Tests, Alternative Assessment, Cumulative Review, Cumulative Assessment				Informal Geometry Chapter Tests				Spanish Chapter Tests, Alternative Assessment, Cumulative Review, Cumulative Assessment			Classroom Aid Transparencies				

Also available for use with the chapter:

 *see page 510C.*

- Practice Workbook
- Solution Key

- For teacher support and access to student Web site materials, use Web Code afk-5500.
- For additional online and technology resources, see below.

Technology

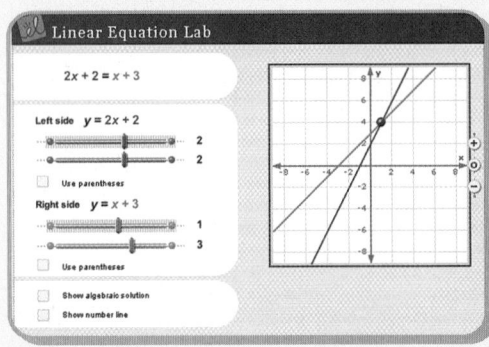

iTEXT Online and on CD-ROM

Complete Interactive Student Text online and on CD-ROM—with instant feedback assessment, tutorial help, dynamic activities, instructional and real-world videos, audio, and additional practice.

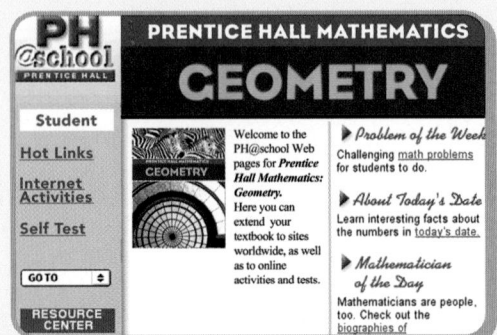

www.PHSchool.com
For Students

Use **Web Codes** for easy access to online activities, chapter projects, self-grading lesson quizzes and chapter tests, vocabulary quizzes, updated data sources, graphing calculator procedures, and more.

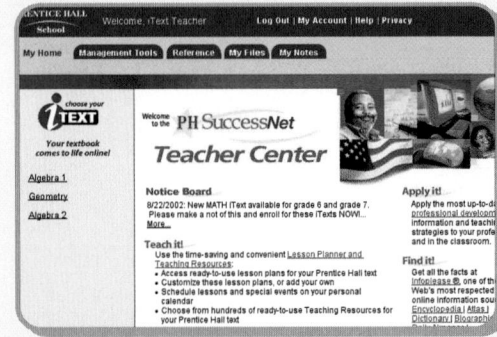

PH SuccessNet **For Teachers**

Online lesson planning with built-in state correlations, all the teaching resources, complete reference library, your own calendar and Teacher Web page, professional development, and more.

Presentation Assistant Plus!

The Prentice Hall *Presentation Assistant Plus!* provides you with the material you need to teach a lesson from beginning to end. Two easy-to-use formats—Transparencies and CD-ROM—allow you to present a lesson the way you are most comfortable.

Transparencies

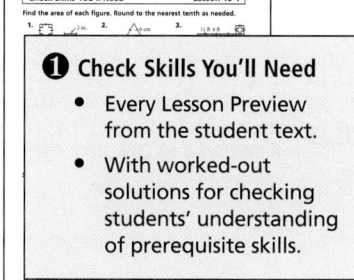

❶ Check Skills You'll Need
- Every Lesson Preview from the student text.
- With worked-out solutions for checking students' understanding of prerequisite skills.

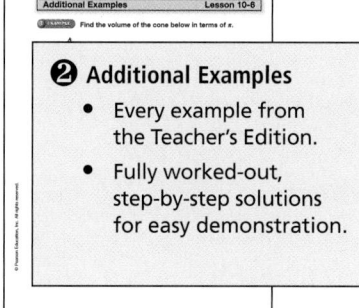

❷ Additional Examples
- Every example from the Teacher's Edition.
- Fully worked-out, step-by-step solutions for easy demonstration.

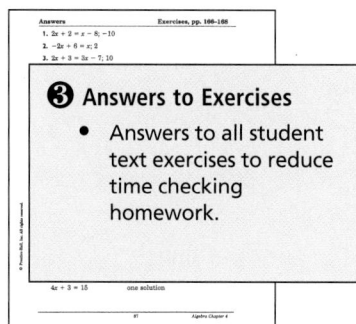

❸ Answers to Exercises
- Answers to all student text exercises to reduce time checking homework.

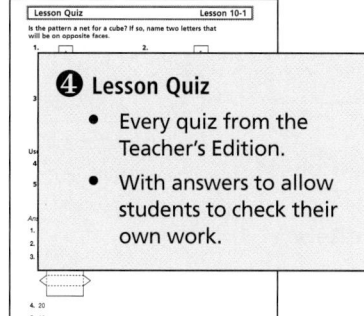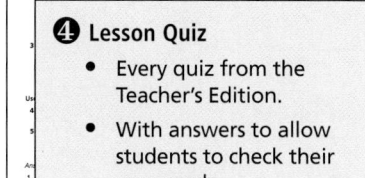

❹ Lesson Quiz
- Every quiz from the Teacher's Edition.
- With answers to allow students to check their own work.

 Throughout the Teacher's Edition, this symbol indicates material that is available on transparency in the Presentation Assistant Plus!

Prentice Hall Presentation Pro CD-ROM

- Includes all Transparencies.
- Conveniently organized by lesson so you can easily ❶ Introduce, ❷ Teach, ❸ Check Homework, and ❹ Assess each lesson.
- Animated examples allow step-by-step instruction at your own pace.
- Easy to edit so you can create custom presentations.

Teaching Chapter 10 Using Presentation Assistant Plus!

	❶ Introduce	❷ Teach	❸ Check Homework	❹ Assess
	Check Skills You'll Need	Additional Examples	Student Edition Answers	Lesson Quiz
10-1	p. 57	pp. 153–154	✔	p. 133
10-2	p. 58	pp. 155–158	✔	p. 134
10-3	p. 59	pp. 159–161	✔	p. 135
10-4	p. 60	pp. 162–165	✔	p. 136
10-5	p. 60	pp. 166–169	✔	p. 137
10-6	p. 61	pp. 170–172	✔	p. 138
10-7	p. 61	pp. 173–175	✔	p. 139
10-8	p. 62	pp. 176–178	✔	p. 140

Prentice Hall Presentation Pro

CD-ROM with dynamic PowerPoint® presentations for every lesson. Helps you introduce and develop concepts, check homework, and assess progress. Part of Presentation Assistant Plus! *(See above.)*

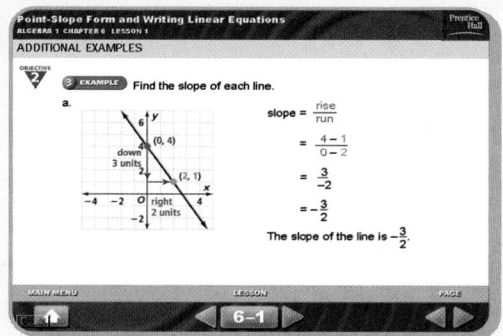

Computer Test Generator

CD-ROM to create practice sheets and tests for course objectives and standardized tests. Includes Instant Chapter Tests™, online testing, and student reports. Part of the PH Assessment System. *(See page 510C.)*

Resource Pro® with Planning Express®

CD-ROM with a lesson planning tool that allows you to import state and local objectives. Includes electronic versions of all the teaching resources.

Surface Area and Volume

 Diagnosing Readiness

Students will find answers to these exercises in the back of their textbooks.

For intervention, direct students to:

Area
Lesson 7-1: Example 4
Exercises 11–13
Lesson 7-2: Example 6
Exercises 24–35
Lesson 7-4: Example 1
Exercises 1–3
Lesson 7-5: Example 3
Exercises 10–12
Extra Practice, p. 696

The Pythagorean Theorem
Lesson 7-2: Examples 1, 2
Exercises 1–6, 10–15
Extra Practice, p. 696

Special Right Triangles
Lesson 7-3: Examples 3, 4, 6
Exercises 9, 12–14, 21
Extra Practice, p. 696

Perimeters and Areas of Similar Figures
Lesson 8-6: Examples 1, 3
Exercises 1–4, 9, 10
Extra Practice, p. 697

Where You've Been

● In Chapter 1, you learned that geometric figures can lie in a plane or be three-dimensional.

● In Chapters 7 and 9, you learned how to find the areas of certain plane figures such as triangles, special quadrilaterals, and regular polygons.

● In Chapter 8, you learned how perimeters and areas of similar figures are related.

iTEXT Instant self-check online and on CD-ROM

Diagnosing Readiness (For help, go to the Lesson in green.)

Area (Lessons 7-1, 7-4, 7-5)

Find the area of each figure. Leave your answers in simplest radical form.

1.

44 units^2

2.

$14\sqrt{3}$ units^2

3.
234 units^2

4.
$54\sqrt{3}$ units^2

The Pythagorean Theorem (Lesson 7-2)

x^2 **Algebra** Solve for a, b, or c in right $\triangle ABC$ where a and b are the lengths of the legs and c is the length of the hypotenuse.

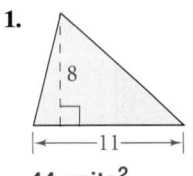 **5.** $a = 8; b = 15; c = \underline{\ ?\ }$ 17

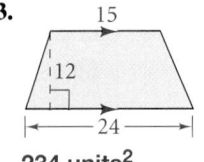 **6.** $a = \underline{\ ?\ }; b = 4; c = 12$ $8\sqrt{2}$

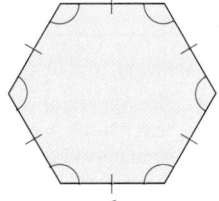 **7.** $a = 2\sqrt{3}; b = 2\sqrt{6}; c = \underline{\ ?\ }$ 6

Special Right Triangles (Lesson 7-3)

8. Find the length of the shorter leg of a 30°-60°-90° right triangle with hypotenuse $8\sqrt{5}$. $4\sqrt{5}$

9. Find the length of the diagonal of a square whose perimeter is 24. $6\sqrt{2}$

10. Find the height of an equilateral triangle with sides of length 8. $4\sqrt{3}$

Perimeters and Areas of Similar Figures (Lesson 8-6)

11. Two similar triangles have corresponding sides in a ratio of 3:5. Find the perimeter of the smaller triangle if the larger triangle has perimeter 40. 24

12. Two regular hexagons have areas of 8 and 25. Find the ratio of corresponding sides. $2\sqrt{2}:5$

Surface Area and Volume

Where You're Going

- In this chapter, you will learn about special three-dimensional figures built from two-dimensional figures such as triangles and rectangles.

- To help you work with these space figures, you will learn how to create three-dimensional drawings on a two-dimensional sheet of paper.

- You will use what you know about finding perimeter and area to help you find surface area and volume.

Real-World Snapshots Applying what you learn, you will solve problems on pages 578 and 579 involving shapes of colossal size.

Key Vocabulary

- altitude (pp. 528, 530, 537, 539)
- base(s) (pp. 528, 537)
- cone (p. 539)
- cross section (p. 522)
- cylinder (p. 530)
- foundation drawing (p. 521)
- height (pp. 528, 530, 537, 539)
- isometric drawing (p. 520)
- net (p. 512)
- orthographic drawing (p. 521)
- prism (p. 528)
- pyramid (p. 537)
- similar solids (p. 566)
- sphere (p. 558)
- surface area (pp. 528, 530, 538)
- volume (p. 544)

511

Chapter 10 Overview

In this chapter, students will draw nets of solids and develop skill in three drawing techniques that represent solids in two dimensions. Then students will focus on prisms, cylinders, pyramids, cones, and spheres. For each figure, they will develop and apply formulas, first for surface area, and then for volume. Finally, students will look at the ratios of lengths, surface areas, and volumes of similar solids, and how each ratio relates to the similarity ratio of the solids.

📖 **Reading Math**
Reading Math Vocabulary, p. 517

📖 **Vocabulary**
A complete list of terms, plus vocabulary exercises, appears in the Chapter Review, p. 573.

📖 **Illustrated Glossary**
Examples for each vocabulary term, plus definitions in both English and Spanish, appear starting on p. 741.

Test-Taking Strategies
Choosing "Cannot Be Determined," p. 572

Real-World Snapshots
See pages 578–579 for a real-world application of ratios, proportions, and volume that utilizes Dorling Kindersley's (DK) unique graphic presentation.

🌐 **Real-World Connections**
Some of the applications you will find in this chapter are packaging (10-1), machinery (10-3), chemistry (10-4), landscaping (10-5), and geography (10-7).

💻 **www.PHSchool.com**
Internet support for this chapter includes:
- Self-grading Vocabulary and Chapter 10 Tests
- Chapter Project
- Chapter Planner
- Ch. 10 Resources

Plus

1. Plan

Lesson Preview

 **Check Skills You'll Need**

Finding Areas
Lesson 1-7: Examples 4, 6
Exercises 20–26, 37–40
Extra Practice, p. 690

Areas of Regular Polygons
Lesson 7-5: Example 4
Exercises 13–18
Extra Practice, p. 696

Lesson Resources

📁 **Teaching Resources**
Practice, Reteaching, Enrichment

👥 **Reaching All Students**
Practice Workbook 10-1
Spanish Practice Workbook 10-1
Reading and Math Literacy 10A
Spanish Reading & Literacy 10A
Hands-On Activities 28
Informal Geometry Planning
    Guide 10-1

⏱ **Presentation Assistant Plus!**
Transparencies
• Check Skills You'll Need 10-1
• Additional Examples 10-1
• Student Edition Answers 10-1
• Lesson Quiz 10-1
PH Presentation Pro CD 10-1

PRENTICE HALL ASSESSMENT *SYSTEM*

Computer Test Generator CD

💿 **Technology**
Resource Pro® CD-ROM
Computer Test Generator CD
Prentice Hall Presentation Pro CD

💻 **www.PHSchool.com**
Student Site
• Teacher Web Code: afk-5500
• Self-grading Lesson Quiz
Teacher Center
• Lesson Planner
• Resources

Plus *iTEXT*

512

Space Figures and Nets

2.04 Develop and apply properties of solids to solve problems.

Lesson Preview

North Carolina Objectives

What You'll Learn

OBJECTIVE 1 To recognize nets of space figures

... And Why

To see the structure of a package, as in Example 2

✔ **Check Skills You'll Need** (For help, go to Lessons 1-7 and 7-5.)

Find the area of each figure. Round to the nearest tenth as needed.

1. 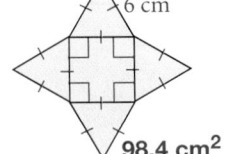 2 in.

24 in.^{2}

2. 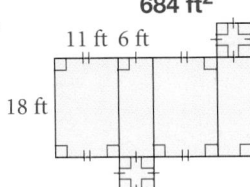 6 cm

98.4 cm^2

3. 684 ft^2 11 ft 6 ft

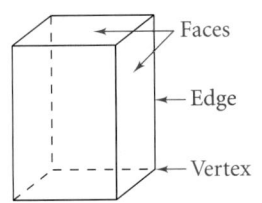

18 ft

New Vocabulary • polyhedron • face • edge • vertex • net • cube

iTEXT **Interactive lesson includes instant self-check, tutorials, and activities.**

OBJECTIVE 1 **Identifying Nets of Space Figures**

📖 **Reading Math**

"Polyhedron" comes from the Greek *poly* for "many" and *hedron* for "side."

A **polyhedron** is a three-dimensional figure whose surfaces are polygons. Each polygon is a **face** of the polyhedron. An **edge** is a segment that is formed by the intersection of two faces. A **vertex** is a point where three or more edges intersect.

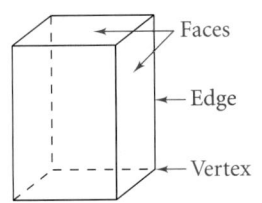
Faces
Edge
Vertex

A **net** is a two-dimensional pattern that you can fold to form a three-dimensional figure. One of the simplest such figures is a **cube**—a polyhedron with six faces, each of which is a square.

① **EXAMPLE** **Identifying a Net**

Is the pattern a net for a cube? If so, name the letters that will appear on opposite faces.

1.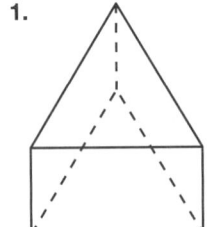

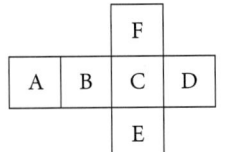 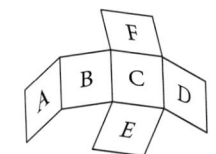 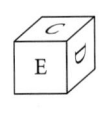

Yes, the pattern is a net because you can fold it to form a cube.
● A and C, B and D, and E and F are on opposite faces.

✔ **Check Understanding** ① Sketch the three-dimensional figure that corresponds to the net at the right.
See left.

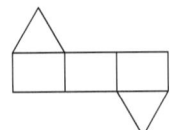

512 Chapter 10 Surface Area and Volume

🔄 **Ongoing Assessment and Intervention**

Before the Lesson
Diagnose prerequisite skills using:
• Check Skills You'll Need

During the Lesson
Monitor progress using:
• Check Understanding
• Additional Examples
• Standardized Test Prep

After the Lesson
Assess knowledge using:
• Lesson Quiz
• Computer Test Generator CD

Package designers can use nets to help design containers.

2 EXAMPLE Drawing a Net

Packaging Draw a net for the graham cracker box. Label the net with its dimensions.

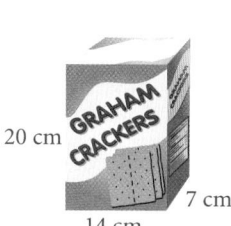

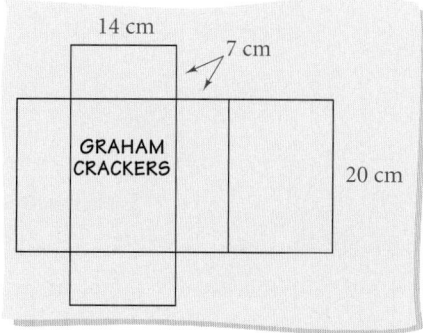

✔ **Check Understanding** 2 Draw a different net for this box. Show the dimensions in your diagram. **See back of book.**

Leonhard Euler, a Swiss mathematician, discovered a relationship among the numbers of faces, vertices, and edges of any polyhedron. The result is known as Euler's Formula.

 Key Concepts

Formula	Euler's Formula

The numbers of faces (F), vertices (V), and edges (E) of a polyhedron are related by the formula $F + V = E + 2$.

3 EXAMPLE Using Euler's Formula

Count faces and edges. Then use Euler's Formula to find the number of vertices in the polyhedron at the right.

The polyhedron has 2 hexagons and 6 rectangles for a total of 8 faces.

The 2 hexagons have a total of 12 edges.
The 6 rectangles have a total of 24 edges.
If the hexagons and rectangles are joined to form a polyhedron, each edge is shared by two faces. Therefore, the number of edges in the polyhedron is one half of the total of 36, or 18.

Real-World Connection

Euler's Formula applies to the polyhedron suggested by the panels on a volleyball.

$F + V = E + 2$ **Euler's Formula**
$8 + V = 18 + 2$ **Substitute.**
$V = 12$ **Simplify.**

Count the number of vertices in the figure to verify the result.

✔ **Check Understanding** 3 Use Euler's Formula to find the number of edges on a polyhedron with eight triangular faces. **12 edges**

👥 Reaching All Students

Below Level Have students reproduce the net in Example 1 using scissors and graph paper.	**Advanced Learners** Have students determine if values of *F*, *V*, and *E* satisfy Euler's Formula to see if such a polyhedron can exist.	**Tactile Learners** See note on page 514. **Error Prevention** See note on page 514.

OBJECTIVE

① Teaching Notes

The references to plane figures are somewhat informal. Explain, for example, that a base of a cylinder is not technically a circle; it is a circle together with the circle's interior. Similarly, a face of a polyhedron is not actually a polygon; it is a polygon together with its interior.

🔨 Additional Examples

① Is the pattern a net for a cube? If so, name two letters that will be on opposite faces.

A			
B	D	E	F
C			

yes; *A* and *C*, *B* and *E*, *D* and *F*

② Draw a net for the figure with a square base and four isosceles triangular faces. Label the net with its dimensions.

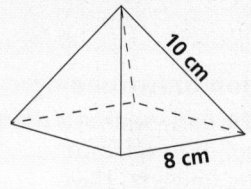

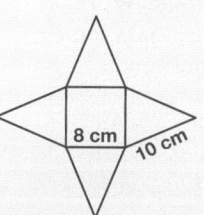

③ Use Euler's Formula to find the number of edges of a polyhedron with 6 faces and 8 vertices. **12 edges**

Closure

Two faces of a polyhedron are pentagonal, and five are rectangular. Draw a net for the solid, and use Euler's Formula to find the values of *F*, *V*, and *E*. Sample:

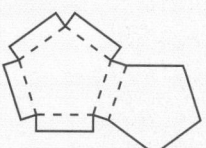

$F = 7, E = 15, V = 10$ **513**

3. Practice

Assignment Guide

▼ **Objective**

Ⓐ Ⓑ **Core** 1–31

Ⓒ **Extension** 32–35

Standardized Test Prep 36–39

Mixed Review 40–47

Tactile Learners

Exercises 1–6 Have students copy and cut out each net and then try to fold it into a cube.

Error Prevention

Exercises 10–12 Remind students that a polyhedron may have many nets.

Connection to Calculus

Exercises 26–28 Formulas for the volumes of more complicated solids of revolution are developed in calculus.

Connection to Astronomy

Exercise 29 Early scientists used Platonic solids to attempt to explain the universe. Have students investigate some of these explanations.

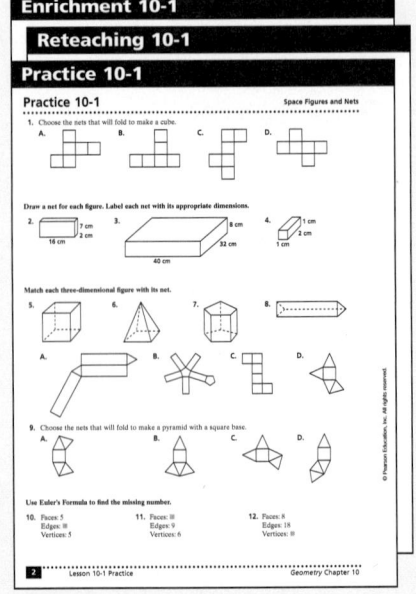

EXERCISES

For more practice, see *Extra Practice*.

Practice and Problem Solving

Ⓐ **Practice by Example**

Example 1
(page 512)

Is each pattern below a net for a cube? If so, name the letters that will appear on opposite faces. If not, explain.

1.

F yes; *E* and *C*, *B* and *D*, *A* and *F*

2.

No; four squares share a vertex.

3.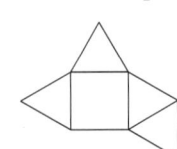

yes; *A* and *C*, *B* and *E*, *D* and *F*

Is each pattern below a net for the three-dimensional figure at the left? Explain.

4.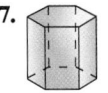

Yes; the faces only share one edge.

5.

Yes; the faces only share one edge.

6.

Yes, the faces only share one edge.

Match each three-dimensional figure with its net.

7. 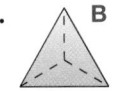 C

8. A

9. B

A.

B.

C.

Example 2
(page 513)

Draw a net for each figure. Label the net with its dimensions.

10–12. See back of book.

10.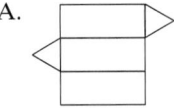

2 in.

2 in.   4 in.

11.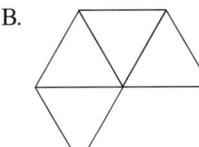

7 m

8 m

6 m

12.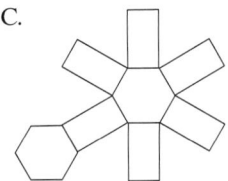

30 mm

36 mm   12 mm

Example 3
(page 513)

Use Euler's Formula to find the missing number.

13. Faces: ■   8
Edges: 15
Vertices: 9

14. Faces: 8   12
Edges: ■
Vertices: 6

15. Faces: 20   12
Edges: 30
Vertices: ■

Use Euler's Formula to find the number of vertices in each polyhedron described below.

16. 6 square faces   8

17. 5 faces: 1 rectangle and 4 triangles   5

18. 9 faces: 1 octagon and 8 triangles   9

Ⓑ **Apply Your Skills**

19. a. Open-Ended Sketch a polyhedron whose faces are all rectangles. Label the lengths of its edges. **a–b. See back of book.**

b. Use graph paper to draw two different nets for the polyhedron.

514   Chapter 10   Surface Area and Volume

pages 514–516   **Exercises**

24. a. Answers may vary.
Sample:

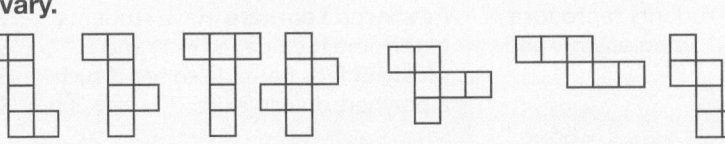

Visualization Think about how each net can be folded to form a cube. What is the color of the face that will be opposite the red face?

20. 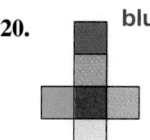 blue
21.  green
22. 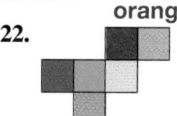 orange
23. 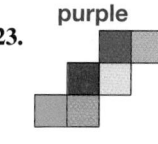 purple

24b. **Answers may vary. Sample: the net shown in Exercise 20; it is easy to cut and fold.**

24. There are eleven different nets for a cube. Four of them are shown above.
   a. Draw as many of the other seven as you can. (*Hint:* Two nets are the same if you can rotate or flip one to match the other.) **See margin p. 514.**
   b. **Writing** If you were going to make 100 cubes for a mobile, which of the eleven nets would you use? Explain why. **See left.**

25. There are eight different nets for a pyramid with a square base. Draw as many of them as you can. **See margin.**

Visualization A plane region that revolves completely about a line sweeps out a *solid of revolution*. Use the sample to help you describe the solid of revolution you get by revolving each region about line ℓ.

Sample: Revolve the rectangular region about the line ℓ and you get a cylinder as a solid of revolution.

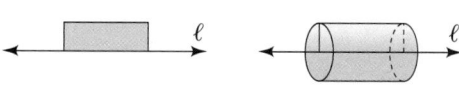

cylinder attached to a cone

26.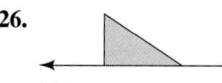
cone

27.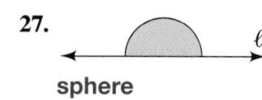
sphere

28.

Reading Math

For help with Exercise 29, see p. 517.

29. There are five regular polyhedrons. They are called *regular* because all their faces are congruent regular polygons, and the same number of faces meet at each vertex. They are also called Platonic Solids after the Greek philosopher Plato (427–347 B.C.).

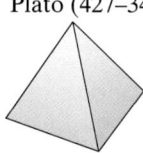
Tetrahedron

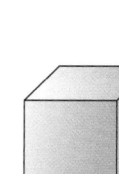
Hexahedron

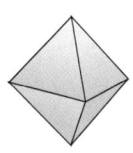
Octahedron

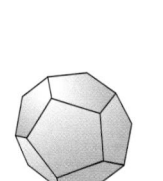
Dodecahedron

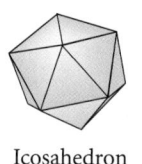
Icosahedron

   a. Match each net below with a Platonic Solid.

A.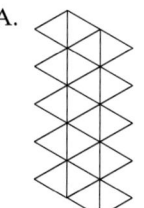
B.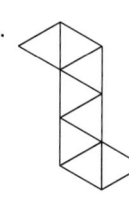
C.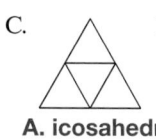
D.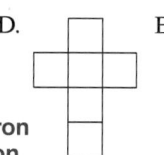
E.

   A. icosahedron
   B. octahedron
   C. tetrahedron
   D. hexahedron
   E. dodecahedron

Real-World Connection

A fluorite crystal forms as a regular octahedron.

29b. **regular triangular pyramid, cube**
   b. The first two Platonic solids have more familiar names. What are they?
   c. Verify that Euler's Formula is true for the first three Platonic solids. **See below.**
30. A cube has a net with area 216 in.². How long is an edge of the cube? **6 in.**
   29c. 4 + 4 = 6 + 2, 6 + 8 = 12 + 2, 8 + 6 = 12 + 2

Lesson 10-1 Space Figures and Nets **515**

25.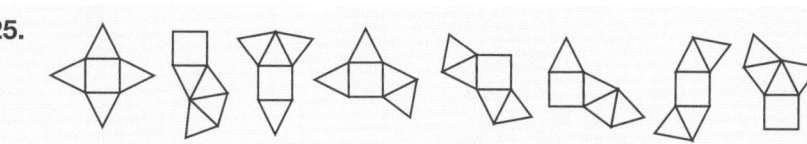

4. Assess

Lesson Quiz 10-1

Is the pattern a net for a cube? If so, name two letters that will be on opposite faces.

1.
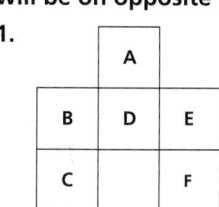
no

2.
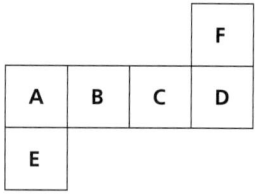
yes; *A* and *C*, *B* and *D*, *E* and *F*

3. Draw a net for the figure.
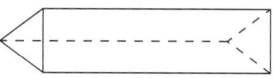

Sample:
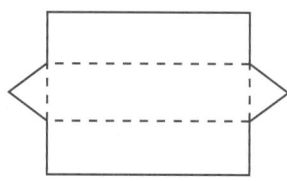

Use Euler's Formula to solve.

4. A polyhedron with 12 vertices and 30 edges has how many faces? **20**

5. A polyhedron with 2 octagonal faces and 8 rectangular faces has how many vertices? **16**

Alternative Assessment

Have each student bring a real-world polyhedron to class and draw a net for the solid. Have them use Euler's Formula to calculate the number of edges and vertices and then verify their results by actually counting the number of faces, edges, and vertices.

515

Resources

For additional practice with a variety of test item formats:
- Standardized Test Prep, p. 577
- Test-Taking Strategies, p. 572
- Test-Taking Strategies with Transparencies

Exercise 38 Drawing a figure is sometimes too complicated. Encourage students to consider that each face has 5 sides and each edge is shared by 2 faces, so the number of edges of the solid is half the total number of sides.

pages 514–516 Exercises

33.

$12 + 20 = 30 + 2$

34. Answers may vary. Sample:

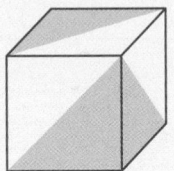

39. [2] correct net and labels

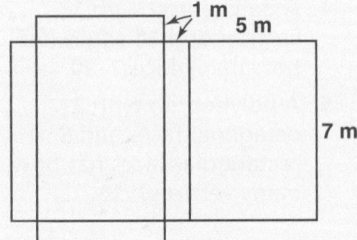

[1] mislabeled net

 Sports Equipment Some balls are made from panels that suggest polygons. The ball then suggests a polyhedron to which Euler's Formula, $F + V = E + 2$, applies.

31. A soccer ball suggests a polyhedron with 20 regular hexagons and 12 regular pentagons. How many vertices does this polyhedron have? **60**

 **Challenge**

32. Show how Euler's Formula applies to the polyhedron suggested by the volleyball pictured on page 513. (*Hint:* It has 6 sets of 3 panels.)
$$18 + 32 = 48 + 2$$

33. Some older volleyballs have 6 sets of 2 panels. (See Exercise 32.) Sketch this type of volleyball and show how Euler's Formula applies. **See margin.**

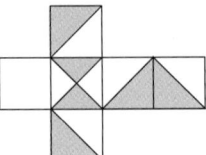

34. The net at the left is folded into a cube. Sketch the cube so that its front face is shaded as shown at the right.
See margin.

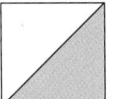

35. Refer to the Platonic Solids shown in Exercise 29.
  a. Explain why there cannot be a Platonic Solid with six equilateral triangles at each vertex. **See below.**
  b. Explain why no Platonic Solid is made of polygons with more than 5 sides.
  35a. 6 × 60° = 360° at each vertex, a flat figure
    b. 6 or more sides would require ≥360° at each vertex.

Standardized Test Prep

Multiple Choice

For Exercises 36–38, you may need Euler's Formula, $F + V = E + 2$.

B

36. A polyhedron has four vertices and six edges. How many faces does it have?
  A. 2   **B.** 4   **C.** 5   **D.** 10

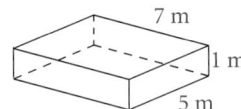 **Take It to the NET**
Online lesson quiz at **www.PHSchool.com**
Web Code: afa-1001

37. A polyhedron has three rectangular faces and two triangular faces. How many vertices does it have? **G**
  F. 5   **G.** 6   **H.** 10   **I.** 12

38. A polyhedron has 12 pentagonal faces. How many edges does it have? **C**
  A. 12   **B.** 20   **C.** 30   **D.** 60

Short Response

39. Draw a net for the rectangular box. Label the net with its dimensions.
See margin.

Mixed Review

Lesson 9-5

40. Find the area of a regular 12-gon with perimeter 24 cm. Give the area to the nearest tenth of a square centimeter. **44.8 cm²**

Lesson 7-2

Find the length of the hypotenuse of a right triangle with the given leg lengths. Leave your answer in simplest radical form.

41. 8 cm, 9 cm $\sqrt{145}$ **cm**   **42.** 3 in., 5 in. $\sqrt{34}$ **in.**

43. 10 mm, 5 mm $5\sqrt{5}$ **mm** **44.** 9 ft, 12 ft **15 ft**

Lesson 6-5

Find each value for the kite at the right.

45. x **20**   **46.** $m\angle JML$ **50** **47.** $m\angle JKL$ **100**

Reading Math Vocabulary

FOR USE WITH PAGE 515, EXERCISE 29

There are five regular polyhedrons. They are called *regular* because all their faces are congruent regular polygons, and the same number of faces meet at each vertex. They are also called Platonic Solids after the Greek philosopher Plato (427–347 B.C.).

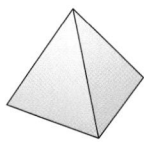
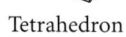
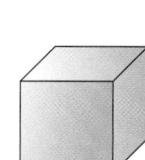
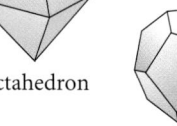
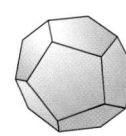

Tetrahedron   Octahedron   Icosahedron

Hexahedron   Dodecahedron

Many math vocabulary words you see in geometry have their origins in Greek. Does this mean you have to study Greek to understand these words? Of course not. Some of the terms you will learn about solids correspond to terms you already know about figures in a plane.

Plane Figures		Solid Figures	
Many angles	Polygon	Polyhedron	Many faces
All sides are ≅. All angles are ≅.	Regular Polygon	Regular Polyhedron	All faces are ≅ regular polygons. Same number of faces meet at each vertex.
? sides six sides eight sides ? sides	Tetragon Hexagon Octagon Dodecagon	Tetrahedron Hexahedron Octahedron Dodecahedron	four faces six faces eight faces ? faces

EXERCISES

1. A tetrahedron has four faces.
   a. How many sides does a tetragon have? **4**
   b. What is another name for a tetragon? **quadrilateral**

2. Dodeca comes from a combination of the Greek words "duo," meaning "two," and "deca," meaning "ten." Dodeca = duo + deca.
   a. Find two other words that begin with "deca." **Answers may vary. Sample: decade, decathlon, decagram**
   b. How many sides does a dodecagon have? **12**
   c. How many faces does a dodecahedron have? **12**

3. Icosa, as in icosahedron, comes from the Greek "eikosi." What number does "eikosi" stand for? **20**

Reading Math

Reading Math Vocabulary

Students must be able to understand and use many new math vocabulary words as they study geometry. This feature helps them identify common prefixes and roots and relate those they already use to new vocabulary.

Teaching Notes

Many students do not know that their textbooks contain a glossary and index in the back. Have all students locate the glossary and index. Ask volunteers to explain when each might be useful.

Tactile Learners
Have students examine models of all five regular polyhedrons.

Teaching Tip
Ask: *What is another name for a hexahedron?* **cube**

Exercises
Have students work independently to solve the problems. Then have volunteers share with the class what they were thinking as they answered each question.

Extension

Perspective Drawing

Students will learn how to draw prisms in one-point and two-point perspective and then apply these techniques to draw their own prisms and identify the perspective used in a drawing. In Lesson 10-2, students will draw isometric and orthographic views of space figures.

Resources

Technology
Computer Test Generator CD-ROM: Chapter 0, Extension Topics

Teaching Notes

Techniques of perspective drawing usually are taught in an art class. Point out that students can use these techniques whenever they want their drawings to appear three-dimensional.

Technology Tip
Have students investigate how to draw Examples 1 and 2 using geometry software.

Connection to Art
Although ancient Greeks and Romans used perspective drawing, it was not fully developed until the Renaissance. Bring an art textbook to class that shows both nonperspective and perspective drawings for students to compare. Jacopo Bellini's sketchbook drawings, such as *The Palace of Herod,* are excellent examples of perspective drawing.

You can create a three-dimensional space figure with a two-dimensional *perspective drawing.* Suppose two lines are parallel in three dimensions but recede from the viewer. You draw them—and create perspective—so that they meet at a *vanishing point* on a *horizon line.*

1 EXAMPLE

Draw a cube in one-point perspective.

Step 1: Draw a square. Then draw a horizon line and a vanishing point on the line.

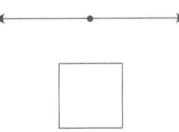

Step 2: Lightly draw segments from the vertices of the square to the vanishing point.

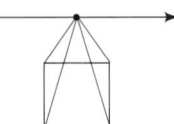

Step 3: Draw a square for the back of the cube. Each vertex should lie on a segment you drew in Step 2.

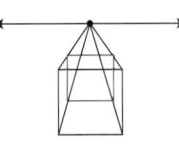

Step 4: Complete the figure by using dashes for hidden edges of the cube. Erase unneeded lines.

Two-point perspective involves the use of two vanishing points.

2 EXAMPLE

Draw a box in two-point perspective.

Step 1: Draw a vertical segment. Then draw a horizon line and two vanishing points on the line.

Step 2: Lightly draw segments from the endpoints of the vertical segment to each vanishing point.

Step 3: Draw two vertical segments between the segments of Step 2.

Step 4: Draw segments from the endpoints of the segments you drew in Step 3 to the vanishing points.

Step 5: Complete the figure by using dashes for hidden edges of the figure. Erase unneeded lines.

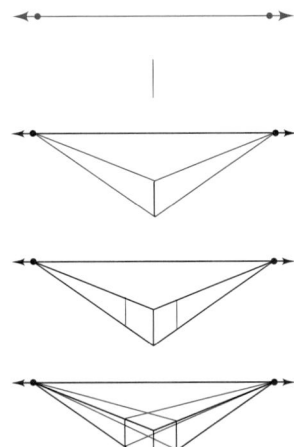

page 519   Extension

11.

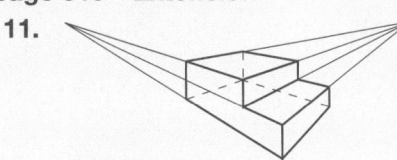

12.

EXERCISES

Is each object drawn in one- or two-point perspective?

1.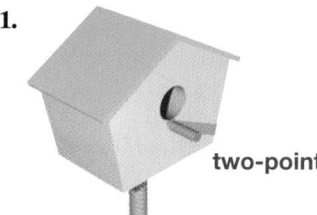
two-point

2. **two-point**

3. **one-point**

4.
two-point

5.
one-point

6. **two-point**

Draw each object in one-point perspective and then in two-point perspective. 7–8. See back of book.

7. a shoe box

8. a building in your town that sits on a street corner

Draw each container using one-point perspective. Show a base at the front. 9–10. See back of book.

9. triangular carton

10. hexagonal box

Copy each figure and locate the vanishing point(s). 11–13. See margin pp. 518–519.

11.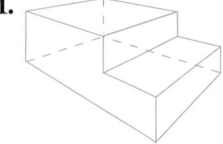

12.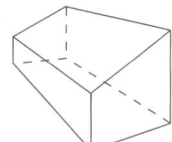

13.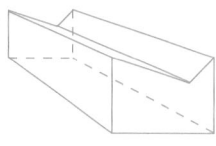

Optical Illusions **What is the optical illusion? Explain how each illusion relates to concepts on these pages.** 14–15. Answers may vary. Samples are given.

14.  **See margin.**

15. 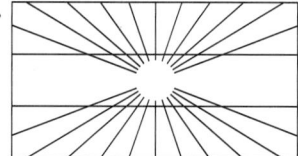 The horizontal lines appear to be curved; the slanted lines that would meet at the vanishing pt. create a cylinder effect.

16. **Open Ended** You can draw block letters in either one-point perspective or two-point perspective. Write your initals in block letters using one-point perspective and two-point perspective. **Check students' work.**

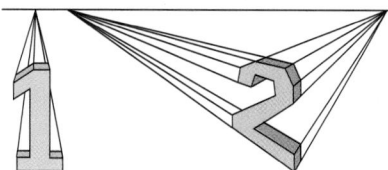

13.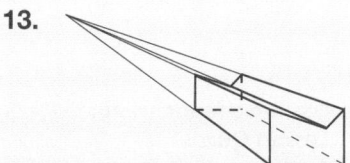

14. The horizontal segments appear to be different lengths; the 4 non-horizontal lines appear to converge at the vanishing pt. So the upper horizontal line appears to be longer.

Exercises 1–6 After students complete these exercises, have them explain how to tell whether an object is drawn in one-point or two-point perspective. Students should mention that a face of a prism appears parallel to the paper in one-point perspective and does not in two-point perspective.

Exercises 11–13 These exercises help students understand that the placement of the horizon line and vanishing point affect the appearance of the prism.

Exercises 14, 15 Students who are new to English may not be familiar with the expression *optical illusion*. Encourage other students to explain what the expression means.

Lesson Preview

✓ **Check Skills You'll Need**

Identifying Planes
Lesson 1-2: Example 4
Exercises 24–28
Extra Practice, p. 690

Lesson Resources

📁 **Teaching Resources**
Practice, Reteaching, Enrichment

👥 **Reaching All Students**
Practice Workbook 10-2
Spanish Practice Workbook 10-2
Informal Geometry Planning
   Guide 10-2

⏰ **Presentation Assistant Plus!**
Transparencies
• Check Skills You'll Need 10-2
• Additional Examples 10-2
• Student Edition Answers 10-2
• Lesson Quiz 10-2
PH Presentation Pro CD 10-2

PRENTICE HALL ASSESSMENT SYSTEM

Computer Test Generator CD

💿 **Technology**
Resource Pro® CD-ROM
Computer Test Generator CD
Prentice Hall Presentation Pro CD

🖥️ **www.PHSchool.com**
Student Site
• Teacher Web Code: afk-5500
• Self-grading Lesson Quiz
Teacher Center
• Lesson Planner
• Resources

Plus **iTEXT**

10-2

Space Figures and Drawings

North Carolina Objectives   2.04   Develop and apply properties of solids to solve problems.

Lesson Preview

What You'll Learn

OBJECTIVE 1
To make isometric and orthographic drawings

OBJECTIVE 2
To describe cross sections of three-dimensional figures

. . . And Why

To make a foundation drawing, as in Example 3

✓ Check Skills You'll Need

(For help, go to Lesson 1-2.)

For each exercise, make a copy of the cube at the right. Shade the plane that contains the indicated points. 1–7. See back of book.

1. A, B, and C 2. A, B, and G

3. A, C, and G 4. A, D, and G

5. F, D, and G 6. B, D, and G

7. the midpoints of $\overline{AD}$, $\overline{CD}$, $\overline{EH}$, and $\overline{GH}$

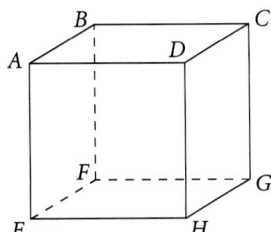

New Vocabulary   • isometric drawing   • orthographic drawing
                   • foundation drawing   • cross section

---

iTEXT Interactive lesson includes instant self-check, tutorials, and activities.

OBJECTIVE 1

Drawing Isometric and Orthographic Views

There are different ways to show a three-dimensional figure on a two-dimensional surface. On a computer screen, you can manipulate the figure for a virtual view of it from any direction. On isometric dot paper, you can make an **isometric drawing** to show three sides of the figure from a corner view.

📖 **Reading Math**

In Greek, *isos* means "equal" and *metron* means "measure." In an isometric drawing, all 3-D measurements are scaled equally.

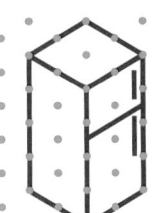 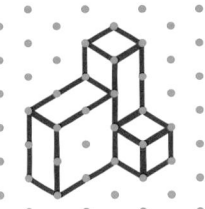

1 EXAMPLE   Isometric Drawing

Make an isometric drawing of the cube structure at the left.

Isometric drawing:

  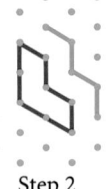 

Step 1   Step 2   Step 3

1. Answers may vary. Sample:

✓ **Check Understanding**   1 Make an isometric drawing of a structure that can be made using 4 cubes. See left.

520   Chapter 10   Surface Area and Volume

Ongoing Assessment and Intervention

Before the Lesson Diagnose prerequisite skills using:	**During the Lesson** Monitor progress using:	**After the Lesson** Assess knowledge using:
• Check Skills You'll Need	• Check Understanding • Additional Examples • Standardized Test Prep	• Lesson Quiz • Computer Test Generator CD

An **orthographic drawing** is another way to show a three-dimensional figure. It shows a top view, front view, and right-side view.

2 EXAMPLE Orthographic Drawing

Make an orthographic drawing from the isometric drawing at the left.

Isometric drawing:

Front   *Right*

Orthographic drawing:

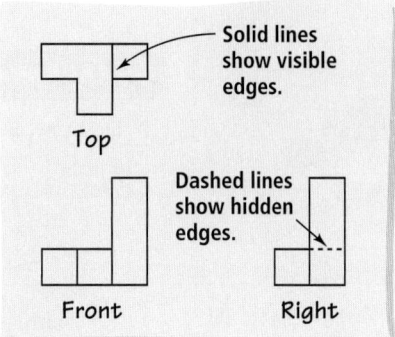

Solid lines show visible edges.

Top

Dashed lines show hidden edges.

Front   **Right**

? Need Help?

Use dashed segments for "hidden" edges.

✓ **Check Understanding** ② Make an orthographic drawing from this isometric drawing.

Isometric drawing:

Front *Right*

2.

Front   **Top**   **Right**

A **foundation drawing** shows the base of a structure and the height of each part. A foundation drawing of the Sears Tower is shown at the right.

49	89	65
109	109	89
65	89	49

The Sears Tower is made up of nine sections. The numbers tell how many stories tall each section is.

3 EXAMPLE Foundation Drawing

Make a foundation drawing for the isometric drawing at the left.

Isometric drawing:

Front   *Right*

Foundation drawing:

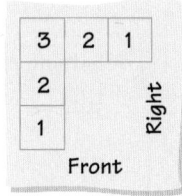

3	2	1
2		
1		

Front   Right

Real-World 🌐 Connection

The foundation drawing shows four heights in the nine sections of the Sears Tower in Chicago, Illinois.

✓ **Check Understanding** ③ **a.** How many cubes would you use to make the structure in Example 3? **9 cubes**
b. Critical Thinking Which drawing did you use to answer part (a), the foundation drawing or the isometric drawing? Explain.
Answers may vary. Sample: The foundation drawing; you can just add the five numbers.

Lesson 10-2 Space Figures and Drawings **521**

👫 **Reaching All Students**

Below Level Provide cubes for students to examine as they work through Examples 1–3.	**Advanced Learners** After Example 4b, have students describe how a plane could intersect a prism to form each of the following cross sections: rectangle, line, point.	**Visual Learners** See note on page 522. **Error Prevention** See note on page 524.

---

2. Teach

Professional Development

Math Background

Geometric principles are the basis of drawing techniques. For example, isometric dot paper is a pattern of the vertices of equilateral triangles and can easily be used to draw equilateral triangles and hexagons that tesselate a plane. Cross sections take on added meaning in analytic geometry, when conic sections are studied.

OBJECTIVE
① Teaching Notes

1 EXAMPLE

Point out that the isometric drawing does not show all the edges of the cubes.

2 EXAMPLE Careers

Architects use orthographic drawings for floor plans. Ask: *A floor plan of your school building would show which view?* **top**

3 EXAMPLE Error Prevention

Because a foundation drawing shows the base, students may think there is a bottom view. Remind them that the top view shows the base.

🔧 Additional Examples

① Make an isometric drawing of the cube structure below.

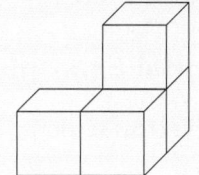

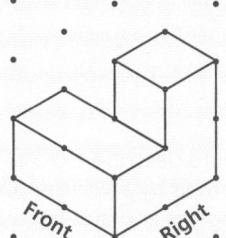

Front   *Right*

② Make an orthographic drawing from the isometric drawing in Additional Example 1.

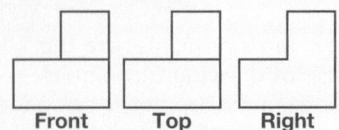

Front   Top   Right

③ Create a foundation drawing for the isometric drawing in Additional Example 1.

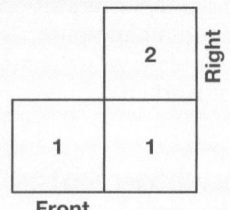

Error Prevention

Students may think the plane of a cross section must be horizontal or vertical. Show a cross section of an apple or orange cut along a plane that is neither horizontal nor vertical.

⑤ EXAMPLE Teaching Tip

Point out that the example assumes that the bottom face of the cube is horizontal. Ask: *If the cube were tilted slightly, what might the cross section look like?* **Sample: parallelogram**

Visual Learners

Encourage students to slice cubes of butter, ice cream, or modeling clay at home to investigate how planes may intersect cubes.

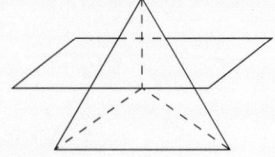 **Additional Examples**

④ Describe this cross section.

triangle

⑤ Draw and describe a cross section formed by a vertical plane intersecting the top and bottom faces of a cube. **Check students' work; square or rectangle.**

522

Real-World 🌐 Connection

A cross section of a cylinder can be a circle.

A **cross section** is the intersection of a solid and a plane. You can think of a cross section as a very thin slice of the solid.

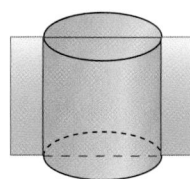

④ EXAMPLE Describing a Cross Section

Describe each cross section.

a.

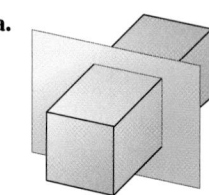

The cross section is a square.

b.

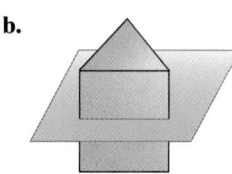

The cross section is a triangle.

✔ **Check Understanding** ④ Describe this cross section of a sphere. **circle**

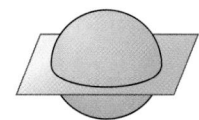

To draw a cross section, you can sometimes use the idea from Postulate 1-3 that the intersection of two planes is exactly one line.

⑤ EXAMPLE Drawing a Cross Section

Visualization Draw and describe a cross section formed by a vertical plane intersecting the front and right faces of the cube.

A vertical plane cuts the vertical faces of the cube in parallel segments.

Draw the parallel segments.

Join their endpoints. Shade the cross section.

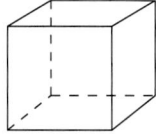

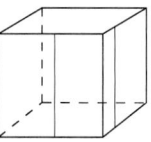

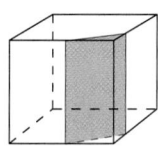

The cross section is a rectangle.

✔ **Check Understanding** ⑤ Draw and describe the cross section formed by a horizontal plane intersecting the left and right faces of the cube. **See left.**

5. square

Closure

Explain how isometric, orthographic, and foundation drawings are alike and how they are different. **Sample: All show three-dimensional figures on a two-dimensional surface; isometric drawings show three faces, orthographic drawings show the outlines of three views, and foundation drawings use the top view of orthographic drawings to show the height of each part of the figure.**

EXERCISES

Practice and Problem Solving

For more practice, see *Extra Practice*.

 Practice by Example

Example 1
(page 520)

Make an isometric drawing of each cube structure. 1–3. See margin.

1.

2.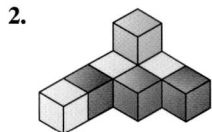

3.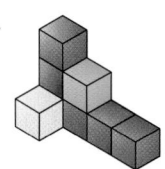

Example 2
(page 521)

Match each isometric drawing with the correct orthographic drawing.

4.
B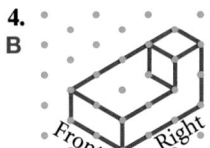

5.
C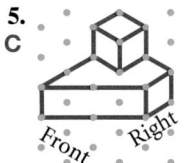

6.
A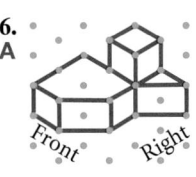

A.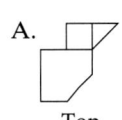

B.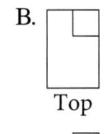

C.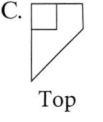

8.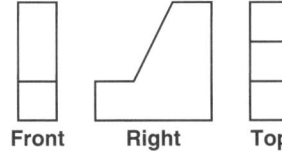

Front   Right   Top

9.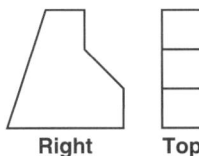

Front   Right   Top

Make an orthographic drawing for each isometric drawing.

7.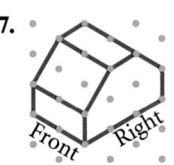

8.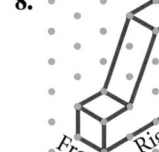

8–9.
See left.

9.

See back of book.

Examples 2, 3
(page 521)

For each figure, make (a) a foundation drawing, and
(b) an orthographic drawing. 10–12. See back of book.

10.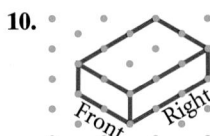

11.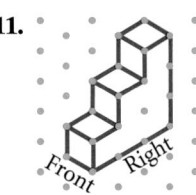

12.

How many cubes would you use to make each of the following?

13. the structure in Exercise 10 **6**

14. the structure in Exercise 11 **6**

15. the structure in Exercise 12 **8**

16. a model of the Sears Tower on page 521 **713**

Assignment Guide

1 Objective
Ⓐ Ⓑ **Core** 1–16, 23–36
Ⓒ **Extension** 52

2 Objective
Ⓐ Ⓑ **Core** 17–22, 37–42
Ⓒ **Extension** 43–51

Standardized Test Prep 53–56

Mixed Review 57–64

Exercises 1–3 If possible, provide wooden cubes so that students can model each cube structure.

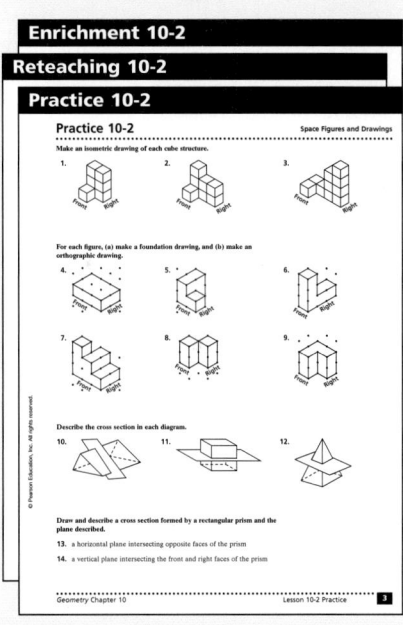

---

pages 523–526 **Exercises**

1.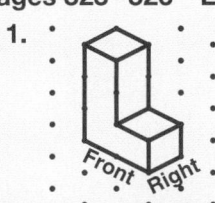

2.

3.

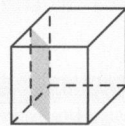
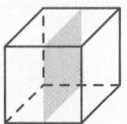
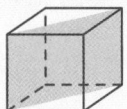
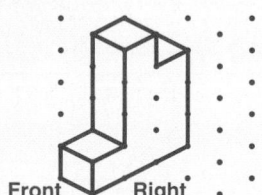
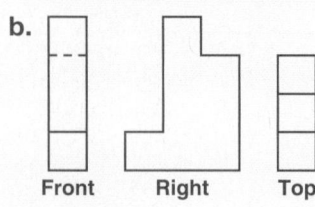
Example 4 (page 522)

Describe each cross section.   17. regular hexagon with hexagonal hole

17.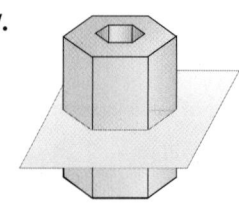

18.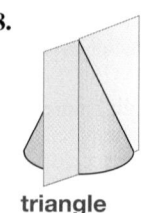
triangle

19.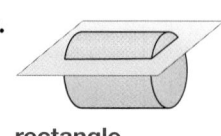
rectangle

Example 5 (page 522)

Visualization Draw and describe a cross section formed by a vertical plane intersecting the cube as follows.

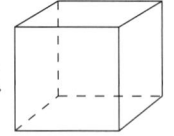

20–22. See margin.

20. The vertical plane intersects the front and left faces of the cube.

21. The vertical plane intersects opposite faces of the cube.

22. The vertical plane contains opposite edges of the cube.

B **Apply Your Skills**

23c.
3	Right
4	
1	
Front

23. a. **Open-Ended** Make an isometric drawing of a structure that can be built using 8 cubes. **a–b. See margin.**
   b. Make an orthographic drawing of this structure.
   c. Make a foundation drawing for this structure. **See left.**

For each foundation drawing, make (a) an isometric drawing on dot paper, and (b) an orthographic drawing. 24–26. See back of book.

24.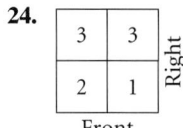
| 3 | 3 |
| 2 | 1 |
Front · Right

25.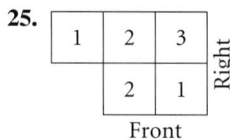
| 1 | 2 | 3 |
| | 2 | 1 |
Front · Right

26.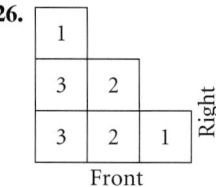
1		
3	2	
3	2	1
Front · Right

A two-by-two foundation drawing shows a positive integer in each of its four squares. How many different cube structures are possible if the sum of the numbers is as given?

27. 4   1   28. 5   1   29. 6   3   30. 7   5

? **Need Help?**
Two cube stuctures are the same if you can rotate one to match the other.

Read the comic strip and complete Exercises 31 and 32.

SHOE by Jeff MacNelly

31. What type of drawing that you've studied in this lesson is a "bird's-eye view"? **See left.**

32. **Writing** Photographs of the Washington Monument are typically not taken from a bird's-eye view. Describe a situation in which you would want a photo showing a bird's-eye view. **See left.**

43.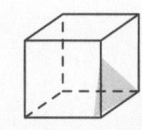

44.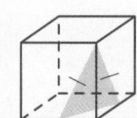

45.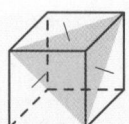

33. Engineering Engineers use engineering layouts to describe structures. A complete layout includes three orthographic views and an isometric view. Make a complete engineering layout for a cube structure suggested by the foundation plan below.

See back of book.

4	3	2
3	2	1
2	1	

Right

Front

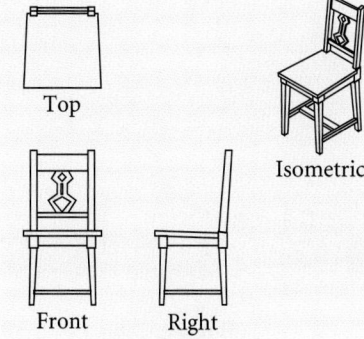

Top

Isometric

Front   Right

34. Probability Mark made the structure at the left using 27 wooden cubes. He painted four of the faces blue and left the top and bottom unpainted. Then he took the structure apart and placed the cubes in a bag.

Leah closes her eyes, reaches into the bag, and pulls out a cube.
a. What is the probability that the cube is unpainted? $\frac{1}{9}$
b. What is the probability that two of its faces are blue? $\frac{4}{9}$
c. What is the probability that only one of its faces is blue? $\frac{4}{9}$

For each figure, make (a) a foundation drawing and (b) an orthographic drawing. Assume there are no cubes hidden behind the structures. **35–36. See back of book.**

35.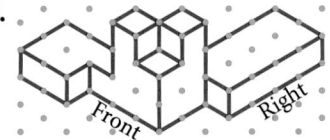

36.

37–39. Drawings may vary. Samples are given.
Visualization **Draw and describe a cross section formed by a plane intersecting the cube as follows.** **37–39. See left.**

37. rectangle
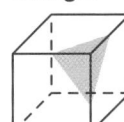

38. rectangle

39. triangle

37. The plane is tilted and intersects the left and right faces of the cube.

38. The plane contains opposite horizontal edges of the cube.

39. The plane cuts off a corner of the cube.

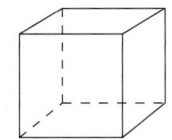

Describe the cross section shown.

triangle
40.

circle
41.

2 trapezoids
42.

C Challenge

Visualization **Draw a plane intersecting a cube to get the cross section indicated.**

43. scalene triangle   **44.** isosceles triangle   **45.** equilateral triangle

46. trapezoid   **47.** isosceles trapezoid   **48.** parallelogram

49. rhombus   **50.** pentagon   **51.** hexagon
43–51. See margin pp. 524–525.

Lesson 10-2 Space Figures and Drawings **525**

46. 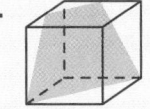   **47.** 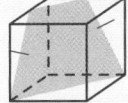   **48.** 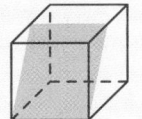   **49.** 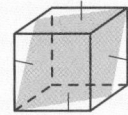   **50.**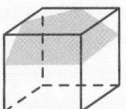

525

 Lesson Quiz 10-2

Use the figure below for Exercises 1–3.

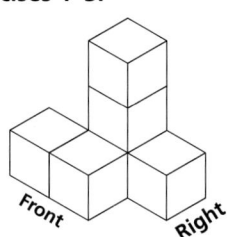

Front   Right

1. Make an isometric drawing of the cube structure.

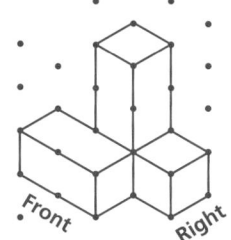

Front   Right

2. Make an orthographic drawing.

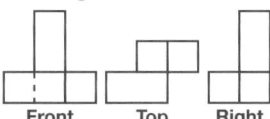

Front   Top   Right

3. Make a foundation drawing.

3	1
1	1

Right

Front

4. Describe the cross section.

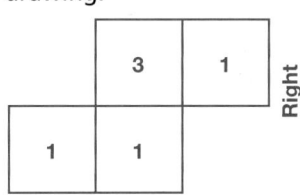

circle

5. Draw and describe a cross section formed by a vertical plane cutting the left and back faces of a cube.
Check students' drawings; rectangle.

51.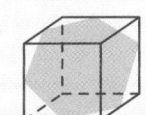

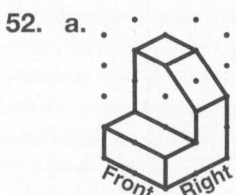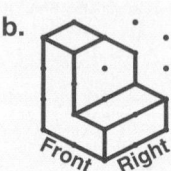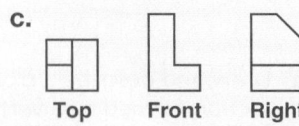
52. Visualization Use the orthographic drawing at the right.
   a. Make an isometric drawing of the structure.
   b. Make an isometric drawing of the structure from part (a) after it has been turned on its base 90° counterclockwise.
   c. Make an orthographic drawing of the stucture from part (b).
   d. Turn the structure from part (a) 180°. Repeat parts (b) and (c).
   a–c. See margin.   d. See back of book.

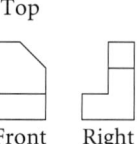
Top
Front   Right

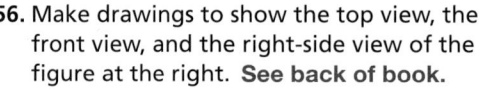
Standardized Test Prep

Multiple Choice

53. The plane is horizontal. What best describes the shape of the cross section? **D**
   A. rhombus   **B.** trapezoid
   C. parallelogram   **D.** square

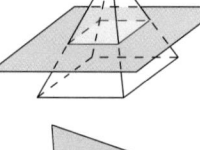

 **Take It to the NET**
Online lesson quiz at
www.PHSchool.com
········ Web Code: afa-1002

54. The plane is vertical. What best describes the shape of the cross section? **I**
   F. pentagon   **G.** square
   H. rectangle   **I.** triangle

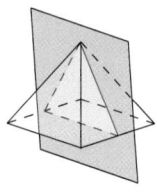

Short Response

55. Draw and describe a cross section formed by a plane intersecting a cube as follows.
   a. The plane is parallel to a horizontal face of the cube.
   b. The plane cuts off two corners of the cube.
      a–b. See margin.

Extended Response

56. Make drawings to show the top view, the front view, and the right-side view of the figure at the right. **See back of book.**

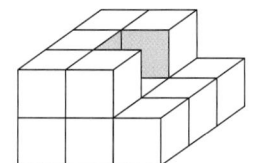

Mixed Review

Lesson 10-1   **Draw a net for each space figure. Label the net with its dimensions.**

57. a rectangular box with height 5 cm and a base 3 cm by 4 cm
58. a cube with 2-in. sides
      57–58. See back of book.

Lesson 9-1   **Find the value of *x* to the nearest tenth.**

59.
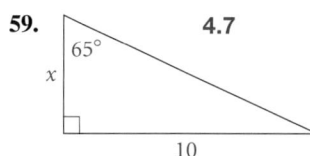
4.7
65°
x
10

60. 8.3
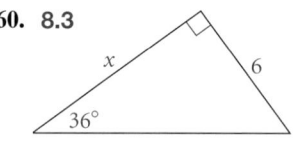
x
6
36°

61. The lengths of the diagonals of a rhombus are 4 cm and 6 cm. Find the measures of the angles of the rhombus to the nearest degree. **67 and 113**

Lesson 7-5   **Find the area of each equilateral triangle with the given measure. Leave answers in simplest radical form.**

62. side 2 ft
$\sqrt{3}$ ft^2
63. apothem 8 cm
$192\sqrt{3}$ cm^2
64. radius 100 in.
$7500\sqrt{3}$ in.^{2}

55. **[2] a. square**
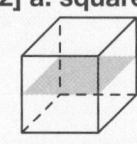

b. Answers may vary. Sample: trapezoid
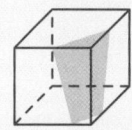

[1] only 1 correct drawing

Literal Equations

A *literal equation* is an equation involving two or more variables. A formula is a special type of literal equation. You can transform a formula by solving for one variable in terms of the others.

1 EXAMPLE

Algebra The formula for the volume of a cylinder is $V = \pi r^2 h$. Find a formula for the height in terms of the radius and volume.

$$V = \pi r^2 h$$

$$\frac{V}{\pi r^2} = \frac{\pi r^2 h}{\pi r^2} \quad \text{Divide each side by } \pi r^2, r \neq 0.$$

$$\frac{V}{\pi r^2} = h \quad \text{Simplify.}$$

The formula for the height is $h = \dfrac{V}{\pi r^2}$.

Solving literal equations also allows you to build other formulas.

2 EXAMPLE

Algebra Find a formula for the area of a square in terms of its perimeter.

$$P = 4s \quad \text{Use the formula for perimeter.}$$

$$\frac{P}{4} = s \quad \text{Solve for } s \text{ in terms of } P.$$

$$A = s^2 \quad \text{Use the formula for area.}$$

$$A = \left(\frac{P}{4}\right)^2 \quad \text{Substitute.}$$

$$A = \frac{P^2}{16} \quad \text{Simplify.}$$

The formula for the area is $A = \dfrac{P^2}{16}$.

EXERCISES

x^2 Algebra Solve each equation for the variable in red.

1. $C = 2\pi r$ $r = \frac{C}{2\pi}$

2. $A = \frac{1}{2}bh$ $b = \frac{2A}{h}$

3. $A = \pi r^2$ $r = \sqrt{\frac{A}{\pi}}$

x^2 Algebra Solve for the variable in red. Then solve for the variable in blue.

4. $P = 2w + 2\ell$
   $w = \frac{P - 2\ell}{2}; \ell = \frac{P - 2w}{2}$
   Find a formula as stated.

5. $\tan A = \frac{y}{x}$
   $y = x \tan A; x = \frac{y}{\tan A}$

6. $A = \frac{1}{2}(b_1 + b_2)h$
   $h = \frac{2A}{b_1 + b_2}; b_1 = \frac{2A}{h} - b_2$

7. the circumference of a circle in terms of its area $C = 2\sqrt{\pi A}$

8. the area of an isosceles right triangle in terms of the hypotenuse $A = \frac{1}{4}h^2$

9. the apothem of a regular hexagon in terms of the area of the hexagon
   $a = \frac{\sqrt{6A\sqrt{3}}}{6}$ or $\frac{\sqrt{6A} \cdot \sqrt[4]{3}}{6}$

Literal Equations

Students will review working with literal equations because they will use this skill in Lessons 10-3 through 10-7.

Resources

 **Technology**
Geometry Resource Pro® CD-ROM:
   Algebra 1 Review Resources
Computer Test Generator CD-ROM,
   Chapter 0, Extension Topics

Teaching Notes

Teaching Tip
When students solved systems of linear equations, each equation had two variables, and two equations were necessary to solve the system. Explain that a literal equation is an equation whose solution for one variable is an expression involving one or more other variables.

1 EXAMPLE

Point out that r is not equal to zero or there would be no cylinder.

Exercise 8 Remind students that the area of a right triangle can be expressed in terms of the lengths of its perpendicular legs.

Surface Areas of Prisms and Cylinders

North Carolina Objectives

1.02 Use length, area, and volume of geometric figures to solve problems.
2.04 Develop and apply properties of solids to solve problems.

Lesson Preview

✔ Check Skills You'll Need

Finding Area
Lesson 1-7: Examples 4–6
Exercises 20–40
Extra Practice, p. 690

Areas of Regular Polygons
Lesson 7-5: Example 2
Exercises 4–9
Extra Practice, p. 696

Lesson Resources

📁 Teaching Resources
Practice, Reteaching, Enrichment
Checkpoint Quiz 1

👥 Reaching All Students
Practice Workbook 10-3
Spanish Practice Workbook 10-3
Reading and Math Literacy 10B
Spanish Reading & Literacy 10B
Spanish Checkpoint Quiz 1
Informal Geometry Planning
  Guide 10-3

⏰ Presentation Assistant Plus!
Transparencies
• Check Skills You'll Need 10-3
• Additional Examples 10-3
• Student Edition Answers 10-3
• Lesson Quiz 10-3
PH Presentation Pro CD 10-3

PRENTICE HALL **ASSESSMENT SYSTEM**

Checkpoint Quiz 1
Computer Test Generator CD

💿 Technology
Resource Pro® CD-ROM
Computer Test Generator CD
Prentice Hall Presentation Pro CD

💻 www.PHSchool.com
Student Site
• Teacher Web Code: afk-5500
• Self-grading Lesson Quiz
Teacher Center
• Lesson Planner
• Resources

Plus *📖 TEXT*

528

Lesson Preview

What You'll Learn

OBJECTIVE 1 To find the surface area of a prism

OBJECTIVE 2 To find the surface area of a cylinder

. . . And Why

To find the area covered by a drum on a roller used in road construction, as in Example 4

✔ Check Skills You'll Need

(For help, go to Lessons 1-7 and 7-5.)

Find the area of each net.

1. 96 cm²
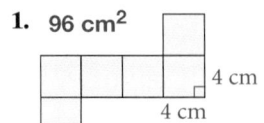
4 cm
4 cm

2. 40π cm²
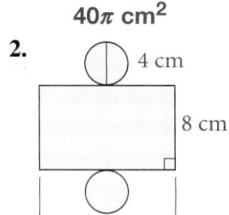
4 cm
8 cm
← 4π cm →

3. 36√3 m²

6 m

New Vocabulary
• prism • bases, lateral faces, altitude, height, lateral area, surface area (of a prism) • right prism • oblique prism • cylinder • bases, altitude, height, lateral area, surface area (of a cylinder) • right cylinder • oblique cylinder

---

📖 TEXT **Interactive lesson includes instant self-check, tutorials, and activities.**

OBJECTIVE 1

Finding Surface Area of a Prism

Real-World 🌎 Connection

A triangular prism breaks white light into rainbow colors.

A **prism** is a polyhedron with exactly two congruent, parallel faces, called **bases.** Other faces are **lateral faces.** You name a prism by the shape of its bases.

An **altitude** of a prism is a perpendicular segment that joins the planes of the bases. The **height** *h* of the prism is the length of an altitude.

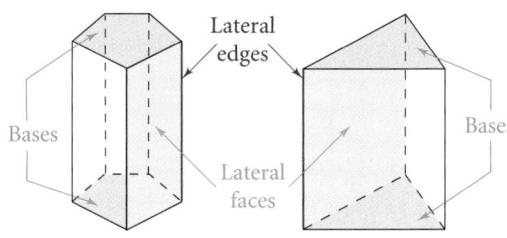

Lateral edges
Lateral faces
Bases
Bases
Pentagonal prism   Triangular prism

A prism may either be right or oblique.

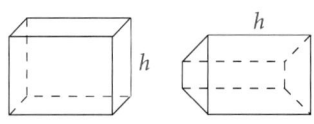
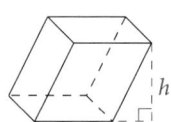
h
h
h

right prisms   **oblique prism**

In a right prism the lateral faces are rectangles and a lateral edge is an altitude. In this book you may assume that a prism is a right prism unless stated or pictured otherwise.

The **lateral area** of a prism is the sum of the areas of the lateral faces. The **surface area** is the sum of the lateral area and the area of the two bases.

528 Chapter 10 Surface Area and Volume

🔄 Ongoing Assessment and Intervention

Before the Lesson
Diagnose prerequisite skills using:
• Check Skills You'll Need

During the Lesson
Monitor progress using:
• Check Understanding
• Additional Examples
• Standardized Test Prep

After the Lesson
Assess knowledge using:
• Lesson Quiz
• Computer Test Generator CD
• Chapter Checkpoint 1 (p. 535)

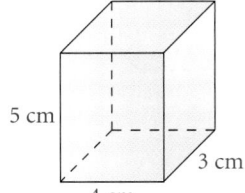

① EXAMPLE Finding Surface Area of a Prism

Use a net to find the surface area of the prism at the left.

Surface Area = Lateral Area + area of bases

= sum of areas of lateral faces + area of bases

$= (5 \cdot 4 + 5 \cdot 3 + 5 \cdot 4 + 5 \cdot 3) + 2(3)(4)$

$= 70 + 24$

$= 94$

● The surface area of the prism is 94 cm².

✓ Check Understanding ① Use a net to find the surface area of the triangular prism. **See left.**

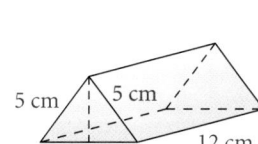

1. 216 cm²

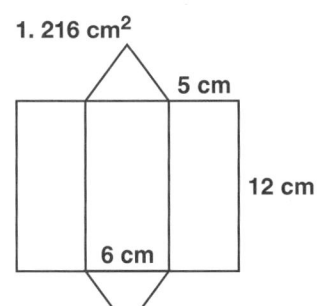

You can find formulas for lateral and surface areas by looking at a net for a prism.

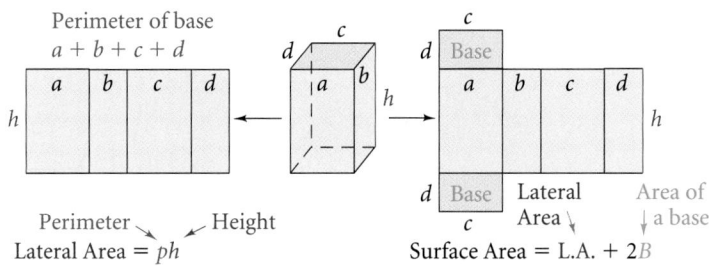

Perimeter of base
$a + b + c + d$

Perimeter ↘   ↙ Height

Lateral Area = ph

Surface Area = L.A. + $2B$

You can use the formulas with any right prism.

② EXAMPLE Using Formulas to Find Surface Area

Use formulas to find the lateral area and surface area of the prism.

By the Pythagorean Theorem, the hypotenuse of the triangular base is 5 cm.

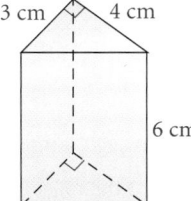

L.A. $= ph$ **Use the formula for lateral area.**

$= 12 \cdot 6$ **$p = 3 + 4 + 5 = 12$ cm**

$= 72$

The lateral area of the prism is 72 cm².

Now use the formula for surface area.

S.A. $=$ L.A. $+ 2B$

$= 72 + 2(6) = 84$ **$B = \frac{1}{2}(3 \cdot 4) = 6$ cm²**

● The surface area of the prism is 84 cm².

✓ Check Understanding ② Use formulas to find the lateral area and surface area of the prism.
432 m²; about 619 m²

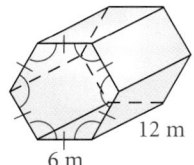

The formulas are summarized at the top of the next page.

Lesson 10-3 Surface Areas of Prisms and Cylinders   **529**

Professional Development

Math Background

This lesson uses the area formulas from Chapter 7 and nets to develop formulas for the lateral and surface areas of prisms and cylinders. Nets especially simplify finding these areas for nonright prisms, such as parallelepipeds. The key idea is that the lateral faces of any prism are parallelograms.

OBJECTIVE
▼ ① Teaching Notes

English Learners

Have students prepare a class poster to display examples of the new vocabulary in the lesson.

Error Prevention

Some students may think that a right prism must contain a right angle in its base. Point out that the right angle is formed by the lateral faces meeting the base.

② EXAMPLE Alternative Method

Have students calculate the sum of the areas of the lateral faces to help them understand why the formula L.A. = ph makes sense.

Additional Examples

① Use a net to find the surface area of the cube.

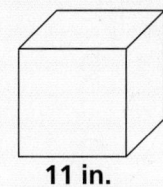

11 in.

726 in.²

🎓 Reaching All Students

Below Level Making nets of rectangular prisms may help students understand and remember Theorem 10-1.	**Advanced Learners** After Example 2, ask students to write a formula for the surface area of a rectangular prism with edges of length ℓ, w, and h. **S.A. $= 2(h\ell + hw + \ell w)$**	**English Learners** See note on page 529. **Visual Learners** See note on page 533.

Additional Examples

❷ Find the surface area of a 10-cm high right prism with triangular bases having 18-cm edges. Round to the nearest whole number. **821 cm²**

OBJECTIVE

2 **Teaching Notes**

Tactile Learners

Have students tape the sides of a sheet of paper together (without overlapping) to form a cylinder. Ask: *What is the lateral area of the cylinder?* the area of the paper

Connection to Algebra

The formula for the surface area of a cylinder is sometimes written as S.A. = $2\pi r(r + h)$. Have students show that this formula is equivalent to the formula S.A. = $2\pi rh + 2\pi r^2$.

 **Diversity**

Some students may never have seen a steamroller. Have other students explain how steamrollers work.

 Additional Examples

❸ The radius of the base of a cylinder is 6 ft, and its height is 9 ft. Find its surface area in terms of π. **180π ft²**

 Key Concepts

Theorem 10-1	Lateral and Surface Areas of a Prism

The lateral area of a right prism is the product of the perimeter of the base and the height.

$$\text{L.A.} = ph$$

The surface area of a right prism is the sum of the lateral area and the areas of the two bases.

$$\text{S.A.} = \text{L.A.} + 2B$$

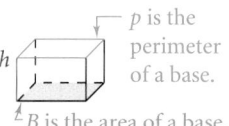

p is the perimeter of a base.

B is the area of a base.

OBJECTIVE

2 **Finding Surface Area of a Cylinder**

Like a prism, a **cylinder** has two congruent parallel **bases.** However, the bases of a cylinder are circles. An **altitude** of a cylinder is a perpendicular segment that joins the planes of the bases. The **height** h of a cylinder is the length of an altitude.

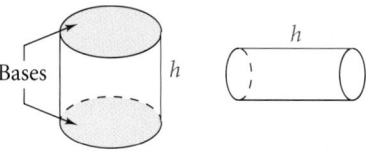

Bases

right cylinders   **oblique cylinder**

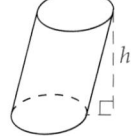

In this book you may assume that a cylinder is a right cylinder unless stated or pictured otherwise.

To find the area of the curved surface of a cylinder, visualize "unrolling" it. The area of the resulting rectangle is the **lateral area** of the cylinder. The **surface area** of a cylinder is the sum of the lateral area and the areas of the two circular bases. You can find formulas for these areas by looking at a net for a cylinder.

Real-World Connection

A full turn of the roller inks a rectangle with area equal to the roller's lateral area.

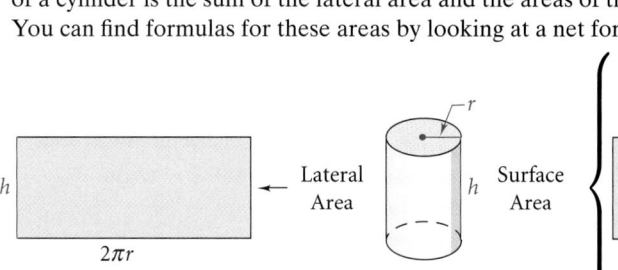

h Lateral Area h Surface Area

$2\pi r$

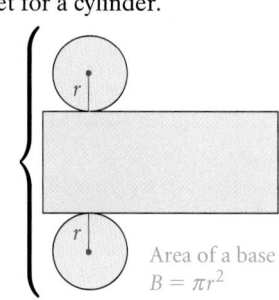

r

Area of a base

$B = \pi r^2$

 Key Concepts

Theorem 10-2	Lateral and Surface Areas of a Cylinder

The lateral area of a right cylinder is the product of the circumference of the base and the height of the cylinder.

$$\text{L.A.} = 2\pi rh, \text{ or L.A.} = \pi dh$$

The surface area of a right cylinder is the sum of the lateral area and the areas of the two bases.

$$\text{S.A.} = \text{L.A.} + 2B, \text{ or S.A.} = 2\pi rh + 2\pi r^2$$

B is the area of a base.

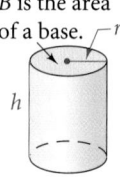

530 Chapter 10 Surface Area and Volume

④ A company sells cornmeal and barley in cylindrical containers. The diameter of the base of the 6-in. high cornmeal container is 4 in. The diameter of the base of the 4-in. high barley container is 6 in. Which container has the greater surface area? **barley container**

3 EXAMPLE Finding Surface Area of a Cylinder

The radius of the base of a cylinder is 4 in. and its height is 6 in. Find the surface area of the cylinder in terms of π.

S.A. $= $ L.A. $+ 2B$	Use the formula for surface area of a cylinder.
$= 2\pi rh + 2(\pi r^2)$	Substitute the formulas for lateral area and area of a circle.
$= 2\pi(4)(6) + 2\pi(4^2)$	Substitute 4 for r and 6 for h.
$= 48\pi + 32\pi$	Simplify.
$= 80\pi$	

● The surface area of the cylinder is 80π in.^{2}.

✓ **Check Understanding** ❸ Find the surface area of a cylinder with height 10 cm and radius 10 cm in terms of π. **400π cm^2**

4 EXAMPLE Real-World  Connection

Machinery The drums of the roller at the left are cylinders of length 3.5 ft. The diameter of the large drum is 4.2 ft. What area does the large drum cover in one full turn? Round your answer to the nearest square foot.

The area covered is the lateral area of a cylinder that has a diameter of 4.2 ft and a height of 3.5 ft.

L.A. $= \pi dh$	Use the formula for lateral area of a cylinder.
$= \pi(4.2)(3.5)$	Substitute.
$= 46.181412$	Use a calculator.

● In one full turn, the large drum covers about 46 ft^2.

✓ **Check Understanding** ❹ The small drum has diameter 3 ft. **33 ft^2**
 a. To the nearest square foot, what area does the small drum cover in one turn?
 b. **Critical Thinking** What area does the small drum cover in one turn of the large drum? **same as large drum (about 46 ft^2)**

Closure

Explain why the factor 2 appears in both terms of the formula for the surface area of a cylinder S.A. $= 2\pi rh + 2\pi r^2$. **$2\pi rh$ is the lateral area, which is the area of a rectangle with one side equal to $2\pi r$, the circumference of the base of the cylinder. The term $2\pi r^2$ is the sum of the areas of the two circular bases of the cylinder.**

EXERCISES

For more practice, see *Extra Practice*.

Practice and Problem Solving

Ⓐ Practice by Example

Example 1
(page 529)

Use a net to find the surface area of each prism. **1–3. See margin for drawings.**

1.
29 cm
6.5 cm
19 cm
1726 cm^2

2.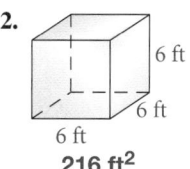
6 ft
6 ft
6 ft
216 ft^2

3.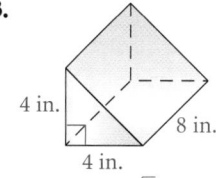
4 in.
8 in.
4 in.
$80 + 32\sqrt{2}$ in.^{2} or about 125.3 in.^{2}

4. a. Classify the prism. **right hexagonal prism**
 b. Find the lateral area of the prism. **240 cm^2**
 c. The bases are regular hexagons. Find the sum of their areas. **$48\sqrt{3}$ cm^2**
 d. Find the surface area of the prism. **$(240 + 48\sqrt{3})$ cm^2**

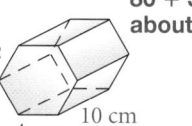
4 cm
10 cm

Lesson 10-3 Surface Areas of Prisms and Cylinders **531**

pages 531–535 Exercises

1.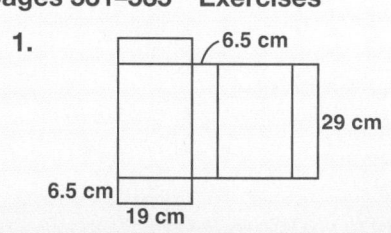
6.5 cm
29 cm
6.5 cm
19 cm

2.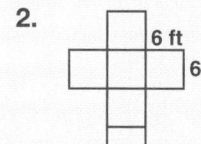
6 ft
6 ft
6 ft

3.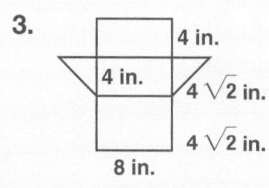
4 in.
4 in.
$4\sqrt{2}$ in.
$4\sqrt{2}$ in.
8 in.

Assignment Guide

 **Objective**

Ⓐ Ⓑ **Core** 1–7, 16, 17, 19–24, 26

Ⓒ **Extension** 37

 **Objective**

Ⓐ Ⓑ **Core** 8–15, 18, 25, 27–32

Ⓒ **Extension** 33–36

Standardized Test Prep 38–44

Mixed Review 45–50

Connection to Algebra

Exercise 2 After students finish the exercise, ask: *What formula gives the surface area of a cube with sides of length s?* **S.A. = 6s²**

Exercise 4 Remind students that the area of a regular polygon with apothem *a* and perimeter *p* is given by the formula $A = \frac{1}{2}ap$. This formula also will be needed in Exercise 7.

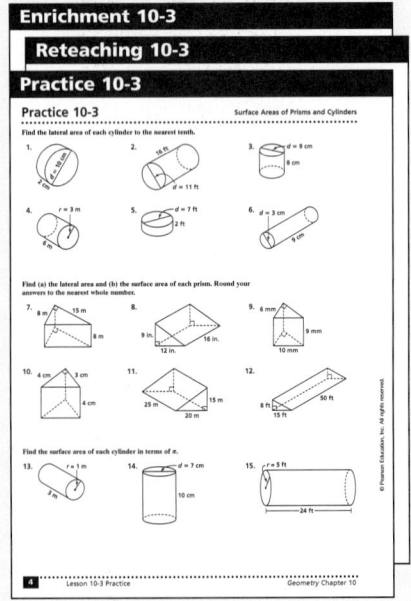

Example 2
(page 529)

Use formulas to find the lateral area and surface area of each prism. Show your answer to the nearest whole number.

5.
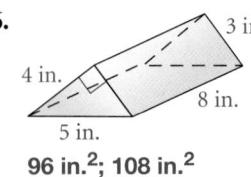
4 ft
10 ft   5 ft
120 ft²; 220 ft²

6.
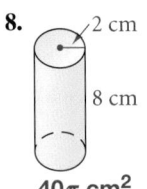
3 in.
4 in.
5 in.   8 in.
96 in.²; 108 in.²

7. **880 cm²; 1121 cm²**
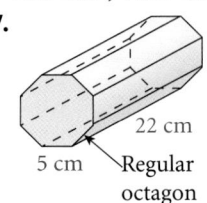
22 cm
5 cm   Regular octagon

Example 3
(page 531)

Find the surface area of each cylinder in terms of π.

8.
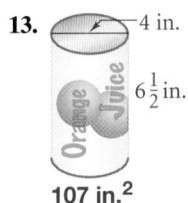
2 cm
8 cm
40π cm²

9.
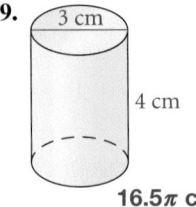
3 cm
4 cm
16.5π cm²

10.
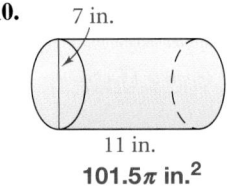
7 in.
11 in.
101.5π in.²

11. A standard drinking straw is 19.5 cm long and has a diameter of 0.6 cm. How many square centimeters of plastic are used in one straw? Round your answer to the nearest tenth. **36.8 cm²**

Example 4
(page 531)

12. Packaging A cylindrical carton of oatmeal with radius 3.5 in. is 9 in. tall. If all surfaces except the top are made of cardboard, how much cardboard is used to make the oatmeal carton? Round your answer to the nearest square inch. **236.4 in.²**

Find the surface area of each cylinder to the nearest whole number.

13.
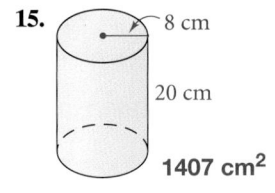
4 in.
$6\frac{1}{2}$ in.
107 in.²

14.
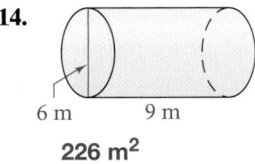
6 m   9 m
226 m²

15.
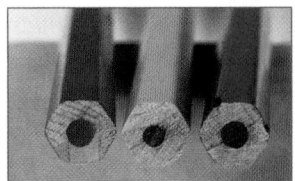
8 cm
20 cm
1407 cm²

Ⓑ Apply Your Skills

16. A triangular prism has base edges 4 cm, 5 cm, and 6 cm long. Its lateral area is 300 cm². What is the height of the prism? **20 cm**

17. Estimation Estimate the surface area of a cube with edges 4.95 cm long. **150 cm²**

18. A cylinder and a prism both have two ≅ ∥ bases and lateral faces that are rectangular. The bases of a cylinder are circles and the bases of a prism are polygons.

 18. Writing Explain how a cylinder and a prism are alike and how they are different. **See left.**

19. A hexagonal pencil is a hexagonal prism. A base edge of the pencil has length 4 mm. The pencil (without eraser) has height 170 mm. How much surface area of a hexagonal pencil gets painted? **4080 mm²**

20. Open-Ended Draw a net for a rectangular prism with a surface area of 220 cm². **See margin.**

21. Consider a box with dimensions 3, 4, and 5.
  a. Find its surface area. **94 units²**
  b. Double each dimension and then find the new surface area. **376 units²**
  c. Find the ratio of the new surface area to the original surface area. **4 : 1**
  d. Repeat parts (a)–(c) for a box with dimensions 6, 9, and 11. **See left.**

21d. **438 units²; 1752 units²; 4 : 1**

  e. Make a Conjecture How does doubling the dimensions of a rectangular prism affect the surface area? **The surface area becomes 4 times as large.**

532 Chapter 10 Surface Area and Volume

pages 531–535   **Exercises**
20. **Answers may vary. Sample:**

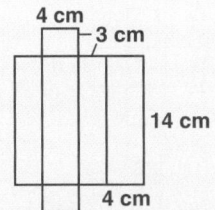
4 cm
3 cm
14 cm
4 cm

22. The surface area of a cube is 726 in.^{2}. What is the length of each lateral edge of the cube? **11 in.**

23. Pest Control A flour moth trap has the shape of a triangular prism that is open on both ends. An environmentally safe chemical draws the moth inside the prism, which is lined with an adhesive. Find the surface area of the trap. **47.5 in.^{2}**

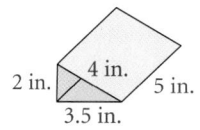

2 in.   4 in.   5 in.   3.5 in.

24. Packaging A typical box for a videocassette tape is open on one side as pictured at the left. How many square inches of cardboard are in a typical box for a videocassette tape? **about 75.5 in.^{2}**

25. Suppose that a cylinder has a radius of r units, and that the height of the cylinder is also r units. The lateral area of the cylinder is 98π square units.

x^2 **a. Algebra** Find the value of r. **7 units**
    b. Find the surface area of the cylinder. **196π units^2**

26. a. Geometry in 3 Dimensions Find the three coordinates of each vertex $A, B, C,$ and D of the rectangular prism. **A(3, 0, 0); B(3, 5, 0); C(0, 5, 0); D(0, 5, 4)**
    b. Find AB. **5**
    c. Find BC. **3**
    d. Find CD. **4**
    e. Find the surface area of the prism. **94 units^2**

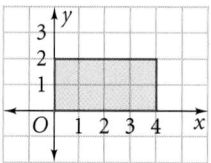

Visualization The plane region is revolved completely about the given line to sweep out a solid of revolution. Describe the solid and find its surface area in terms of π. **27–30. See left.**

27. the y-axis   **28.** the x-axis

29. the line $y = 2$ **30.** the line $x = 4$

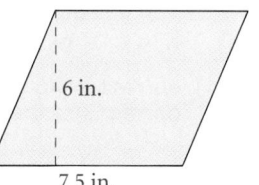

31. a. Critical Thinking Suppose you double the radius of a right cylinder. How does that affect the lateral area? **Lateral area is doubled.**
    b. How does that affect the surface area? **b-c. See left below.**
    c. Use the formula for surface area of a right cylinder to explain why the surface area in part (b) was not doubled.

32. a. Packaging The wrapper for a container of biscuits is a parallelogram with base 7.5 in. and height 6 in. Find the radius and height of the container. **$r \approx$ 1.2 in.; h = 6 in.**
    b. Find the surface area of the container of biscuits. **about 54.0 in.^{2}**

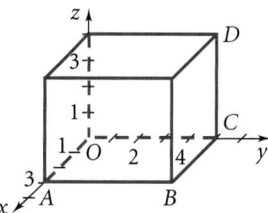

6 in.   7.5 in.

Judging by appearances, what is the surface area of each solid?

33.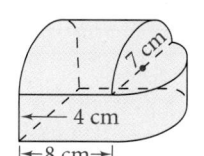
7 cm   4 cm |← 8 cm →|
(148 + 66.5π) cm^2

34.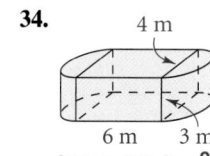
4 m   6 m   3 m
(84 + 20π) m^2

35.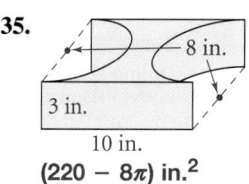
8 in.   3 in.   10 in.
(220 − 8π) in.^{2}

x^2 **36. Algebra** The sum of the height and radius of a cylinder is 9 m. The surface area of the cylinder is 54π m^2. Find the height and the radius. **h = 6 m; r = 3 m**

Exercise 24

1 in. $7\frac{1}{2}$ in.   4 in.

SUPER VHS VIDEOCASSETTE   2 HOURS ST-120

27. cylinder of radius 4 and height 2; 48π units^2

28. cylinder of radius 2 and height 4; 24π units^2

29. cylinder of radius 2 and height 4; 24π units^2

30. cylinder of radius 4 and height 2; 48π units^2

Need Help?

In Exercise 32, the slanted sides of the parallelogram form a spiral seam about the biscuit cylinder. The horizontal sides form circular bases.

C Challenge

31b. Surface area is more than doubled.
c. S.A. $= 2\pi r^2 + 2\pi rh$; if r doubles: S.A. $= 2(4\pi r^2 + 2\pi rh)$. Since r is squared, surface area is more than doubled.

Connection to Coordinate Geometry
Exercise 26 Point out that the coordinates are listed in the order (x, y, z).

Visual Learners
Exercises 27–30 Students may revolve an index card about fixed lines to help them visualize the cylinders formed in these exercises.

Exercise 34 Students should recognize that the curved ends of the solid form a cylinder with a 2-m radius.

Connection to Algebra
Exercise 36 This exercise is easily solved if students use the Distributive Property to write the formula for surface area as S.A. $= 2\pi r(r + h)$.

Use the prism below for Exercises 1 and 2.

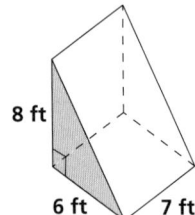

8 ft

6 ft   7 ft

1. Use a net to find the surface area.

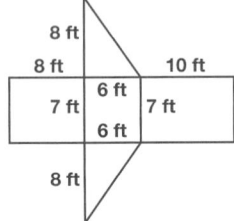

8 ft

8 ft   10 ft

6 ft

7 ft   7 ft

6 ft

8 ft

S.A. = 216 ft²

2. Use a formula to find the surface area.
S.A. = L.A. + 2B =
168 + 48 = 216; **216 ft²**

3. The height of a prism is 5 cm. Its rectangular bases have 3-cm and 9-cm sides. Find its surface area.
174 cm²

4. The radius of the base of a cylinder is 16 in., and its height is 4 in. Find its surface area in terms of π.
640π in.²

5. A contractor paints all but the bases of a 28-ft high cylindrical water tank. The diameter of the base is 22 ft. How many square feet are painted? Round to the nearest hundred. **1900 ft²**

Alternative Assessment

Have partners design and label two different prisms, each having a surface area of 200 cm².

37. Each edge of the large cube at the right is 12 inches long. The cube is painted on the outside, and then cut into 27 smaller cubes. Answer these questions about the 27 cubes.
  a. How many are painted on 4, 3, 2, 1, and 0 faces?
  b. What is the total surface area that is unpainted?
  a. 0, 8, 12, 6, 1   **b. 1728 in.²**

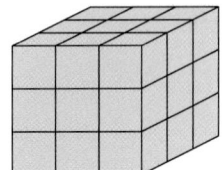

 **Standardized Test Prep**

Multiple Choice

38. What is the surface area of the figure to the nearest tenth? **C**
  A. 335.7 m²   **B.** 411.6 m²
  C. 671.5 m²   **D.** 721.2 m²

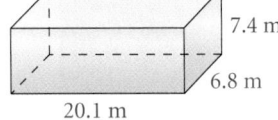

7.4 m

6.8 m

20.1 m

39. If the radius and height of a cylinder are both doubled, then the surface area is __?__ . **I**
  F. the same   **G.** doubled   **H.** tripled   **I.** quadrupled

40. A cylinder of radius r sits snugly inside a cube. Which expression represents the difference of their lateral areas? **D**
  A. $2r^2(8 - \pi)$ **B.** $2r(\pi - 2)$ **C.** $2r(4 - \pi)$ **D.** $4r^2(4 - \pi)$

Quantitative Comparison

Compare the boxed quantity in Column A with the boxed quantity in Column B. Choose the best answer.
  A. The quantity in Column A is greater.
  B. The quantity in Column B is greater.
  C. The two quantities are equal.
  D. The relationship cannot be determined from the information given.

44. [2] a. Lateral area is the perimeter times height. Since the lateral area is 48 in.² and the perimeter of the △ is 24 in., h = 2 in.
  b. S.A. = 96 in.²

[1] correct explanation correct surface area

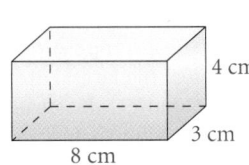

4 cm

3 cm

8 cm

Figure 1

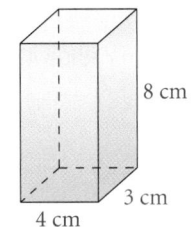

8 cm

4 cm

3 cm

Figure 2

Column A	Column B
A **41.** perimeter of the base in Figure 1	perimeter of the base in Figure 2
B **42.** lateral area in Figure 1	lateral area in Figure 2
C **43.** surface area in Figure 1	surface area in Figure 2

Take It to the NET
Online lesson quiz at
www.PHSchool.com
Web Code: afa-1003

Short Response

44. The sides of a base of a right triangular prism are 6 in., 8 in., and 10 in. The lateral area of the prism is 48 in.². **a–b. See left.**
  a. Find the height of the prism. Explain your reasoning.
  b. What is the surface area of the prism?

534   Chapter 10   Surface Area and Volume

pages 531–535   **Exercises**   **47.**

46.

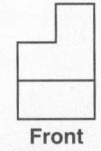   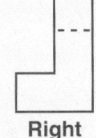   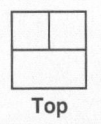

Front   Right   Top

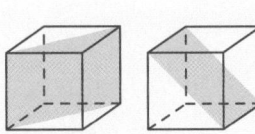   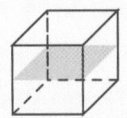

Mixed Review

Lesson 10-2

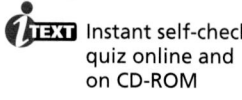

45. an isometric drawing **See left.**

Front Right

Make each type of drawing from the foundation drawing at the right.

2	3
1	1

Front

Right

45. an isometric drawing **See left.**

46. an orthographic drawing **See margin p. 534.**

47. Draw sketches to show how three planes can intersect a cube to form three different rectangular cross sections. **See margin p. 534.**

Lesson 7-7

Find the area of each part of the circle to the nearest tenth.

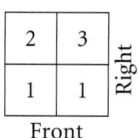

48. sector QOP **37.7 cm²**

49. the segment of the circle bounded by $\overline{QP}$ and $\overparen{QP}$ **22.1 cm²**

Lesson 6-7

50. In the kite at the right $AB = AD$ and $CB = CD$. Points $P, Q, R,$ and S are midpoints.
   a. Determine the coordinates of the midpoints. **$R(c, b), S(c, -b), P(a, -b), Q(a, b)$**
   b. $RQ = \blacksquare$; $SP = \blacksquare$; $PQ = \blacksquare$; $SR = \blacksquare$ **$a - c$; $a - c$; $2b$; $2b$**
   c. Use your answers to part (b) to explain why $PQRS$ must be a parallelogram. **Opposite sides are $\cong$.**

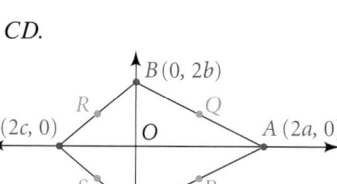

✓ Checkpoint Quiz 1

Lessons 10-1 through 10-3

📱TEXT Instant self-check quiz online and on CD-ROM

1.

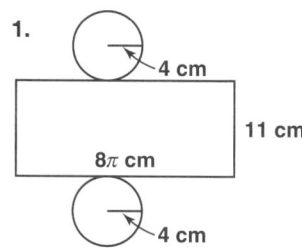
11 cm
4 cm
8π cm
4 cm

Draw a net for each figure. Label the net with its dimensions.

1. **See left.**

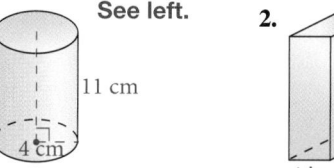
11 cm
4 cm

2.

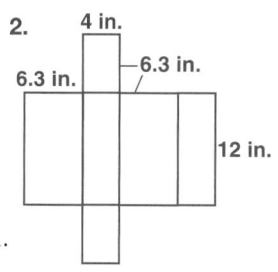
12 in.
6.3 in.
4 in.

2.
4 in.
6.3 in.
6.3 in.
12 in.

3. **120π cm²**

3. Find the surface area of the cylinder in Exercise 1.

4. Find the surface area of the prism in Exercise 2. **297.6 in.²**

🌐 5. **Space Exploration** A space shuttle brings a docking module to a space station. The module is a cylinder with a 24-m diameter and a 46-m height. What is the surface area of the docking module to the nearest tenth? **4373.1 m²**

✏️ 6. **Open-Ended** Draw a net for a regular hexagonal prism. **See margin.**

7. Both formulas involve multiplying perimeter of the base by the height. For a cylinder, the base is a circle so π is always in the formula.

✏️ 7. **Writing** Explain how the formulas for the lateral area of a prism and the lateral area of a cylinder are alike and how they are different. **See left.**

8. Create an isometric drawing of a figure that can be constructed with 5 cubes. **See margin.**

Draw a cube. Shade the cube to show each cross section. 9–10. See margin.

9. a rectangle   10. a trapezoid

Lesson 10-3 Surface Areas of Prisms and Cylinders **535**

page 535 Checkpoint Quiz 1

6. Answers may vary.
   Sample:

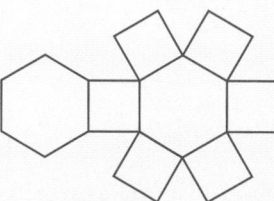

Standardized Test Prep

📄 **Resources**

For additional practice with a variety of test item formats:
- Standardized Test Prep, p. 577
- Test-Taking Strategies, p. 572
- Test-Taking Strategies with Transparencies

Exercise 39 Suggest that students who cannot solve this exercise by examining the formula substitute numbers for r and h and then compare the surface areas before and after doubling the radius and height.

✓ Chapter Checkpoint 1

To check understanding of Lessons 10-1 to 10-3:

Checkpoint Quiz 1 (p. 535)

📁 **Teaching Resources**

Checkpoint Quiz 1 (also in Prentice Hall Assessment System)

👥 **Reaching All Students**

Reading and Math Literacy 10B

Spanish versions available

8–10. **Answers may vary. Samples are given:**

8.

9.

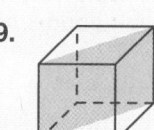

10.

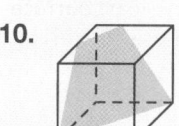

Technology

Exploring Surface Area

Exploring Surface Area

Students use a graphing calculator to investigate how the surface area of a square prism with fixed volume changes as the length of each side of a base changes.

Resources

Students may use any calculator that can create lists to explore surface area relationships.

Teaching Notes

By considering a 1-L square prism, students can see how surface area changes as the length of each side of a base changes. Because S.A. $= 2s^2 + \frac{4V}{s}$, the change in surface area is nonlinear.

Inclusion

Have students who are unfamiliar with making calculator lists work with partners who have done this.

Technology Tip

Students may substitute 1000 for V and graph the function S.A. $= 2s^2 + \frac{4V}{s}$ on graphing calculators. They will need to determine appropriate parameters for the viewing window first. Graphing provides a visual complement to the lists and helps summarize the pattern of the relationship between s and S.A.

Connection to Calculus

Point out that techniques of differential calculus can prove that a cube has the least surface area of all square prisms of fixed volume.

At room temperature, 1 L, 1000 mL, and 1000 cm^3 all represent the same amount of water. Thus, one type of model for a liter is any square prism that holds 1000 cm^3. The best model, perhaps, is a 10-cm cube as shown here. But there are many others.

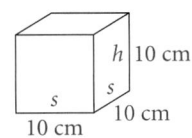

You can use graphing calculator lists to study how height (h) and surface area (S.A.) of a 1-L square prism change as the length (s) of each side of a base changes.

The volume of a prism equals the area of a base times its height ($V = Bh$ or $V = s^2h$). You can solve for h in each equation to find $h = \frac{V}{B} = \frac{V}{s^2}$. The surface area equals two times the area of a base plus four times the area of a face, or

$$\begin{aligned} \text{S.A.} = 2B + 4sh &= 2s^2 + 4sh \\ &= 2s^2 + 4s\frac{V}{s^2} \quad \textbf{Substitute.} \\ &= 2s^2 + \frac{4V}{s} \quad \textbf{Simplify.} \end{aligned}$$

Use the commands shown on the screens below to create lists L_1, L_2, and L_3, for s, h, and S.A., respectively. The fourth screen shows the lists after they have been created.

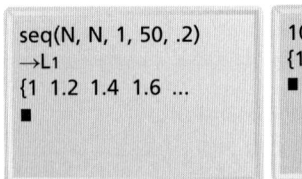

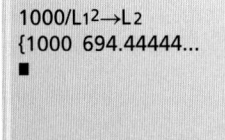

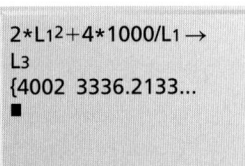

L1	L2	L3	1
1	1000	4002	
1.2	694.44	3336.2	
1.4	510.2	2861.1	
1.6	390.63	2505.1	
1.8	308.64	2228.7	
2	250	2008	
2.2	206.61	1827.9	
L1(1)=1			

EXERCISES

Create the lists (shown above) on your graphing calculator. Scroll down to study them.

1. How small can the surface area be? How large can it be? **600 cm^2; 5080 cm^2**

2. a. Which dimensions give a very large surface area? **large values of either s or h**
   b. Which dimensions give the smallest surface area? **$s = h = 10$**
   c. How do s and h compare in the prism with the smallest surface area? **They are =.**
   d. What is the shape of the prism that has the smallest surface area? **cube**

Extend

3. If a square prism must have a volume of 100 cm^3, what dimensions would give the smallest surface area? **about 4.64 cm by 4.64 cm by 4.64 cm**

4. A cereal manufacturer is designing a cereal box that has a capacity of 3000 cm^3. Surface area should be large to provide space for advertising. What else should be considered for the box design? Use a graphing calculator as needed to support your conclusions. **Answers may vary. Sample: the box should be stable, but fit as many as possible on a shelf.**

536 Technology Exploring Surface Area

10-4 Surface Areas of Pyramids and Cones

North Carolina Objectives
1.02 Use length, area, and volume of geometric figures to solve problems.
2.04 Develop and apply properties of solids to solve problems.

Lesson Preview

What You'll Learn

OBJECTIVE 1 To find the surface area of a pyramid

OBJECTIVE 2 To find the surface area of a cone

. . . And Why

To find the lateral area of the Great Pyramid of Egypt, as in Example 2

✔ **Check Skills You'll Need** (For help, go to Lesson 7-2.)

Find the length of the hypotenuse in simplest radical form.

1.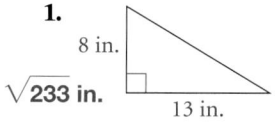

2.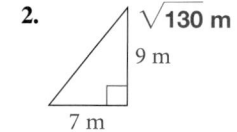

3.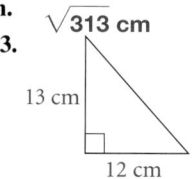

New Vocabulary • pyramid • base, lateral faces, vertex, altitude, height, slant height, lateral area, surface area (of a pyramid) • regular pyramid • cone • base, altitude, vertex, height, slant height, lateral area, surface area (of a cone) • right cone

 Interactive lesson includes instant self-check, tutorials, and activities.

OBJECTIVE 1

Finding Surface Area of a Pyramid

Need Help?

If the base is a hexagon, the pyramid is a hexagonal pyramid.

A **pyramid** is a polyhedron in which one face (the **base**) can be any polygon and the other faces (the **lateral faces**) are triangles that meet at a common vertex (called the **vertex** of the pyramid).

You can name a pyramid by the shape of its base. The **altitude** of a pyramid is the perpendicular segment from the vertex to the plane of the base. The length of the altitude is the **height** h of the pyramid.

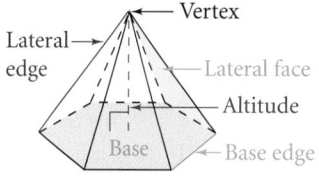

A **regular pyramid** is a pyramid whose base is a regular polygon and whose lateral faces are congruent isosceles triangles. The **slant height** ℓ is the length of the altitude of a lateral face of the pyramid.

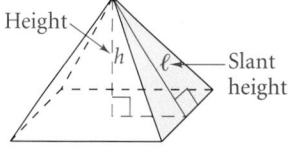

In this book, you can assume that a pyramid is regular unless stated otherwise.

The **lateral area** of a pyramid is the sum of the areas of the congruent lateral faces. You can find a formula for the lateral area of a pyramid by looking at its net.

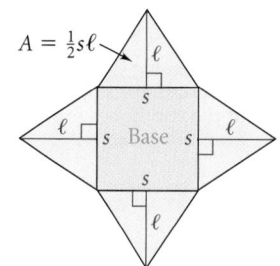

$$\text{L.A.} = 4\left(\tfrac{1}{2}s\ell\right) \quad \text{The area of each lateral face is } \tfrac{1}{2}s\ell.$$

$$= \tfrac{1}{2}(4s)\ell \quad \text{Commutative and Associative Properties of Multiplication}$$

$$= \tfrac{1}{2}p\ell \quad \text{The perimeter } p \text{ of the base is } 4s.$$

10-4

North Carolina Objectives
1.02, 2.04

1. Plan

Lesson Preview

✔ **Check Skills You'll Need**

Simplest Radical Form
Lesson 7-2: Example 2
Exercises 10–15
Extra Practice, p. 696

Lesson Resources

 **Teaching Resources**
Practice, Reteaching, Enrichment

Reaching All Students
Practice Workbook 10-4
Spanish Practice Workbook 10-4
Hands-On Activities 29
Informal Geometry Planning Guide 10-4

Presentation Assistant Plus!
Transparencies
• Check Skills You'll Need 10-4
• Additional Examples 10-4
• Student Edition Answers 10-4
• Lesson Quiz 10-4
PH Presentation Pro CD 10-4

 PRENTICE HALL ASSESSMENT SYSTEM

Computer Test Generator CD

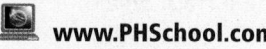 **Technology**
Resource Pro® CD-ROM
Computer Test Generator CD
Prentice Hall Presentation Pro CD

 **www.PHSchool.com**
Student Site
• Teacher Web Code: afk-5500
• Self-grading Lesson Quiz
Teacher Center
• Lesson Planner
• Resources

Plus **iTEXT**

Ongoing Assessment and Intervention

Before the Lesson
Diagnose prerequisite skills using:
• Check Skills You'll Need

During the Lesson
Monitor progress using:
• Check Understanding
• Additional Examples
• Standardized Test Prep

After the Lesson
Assess knowledge using:
• Lesson Quiz
• Computer Test Generator CD

2. Teach

Math Background

 Professional Development

The fact that the lateral area of both a pyramid and cone equals $\frac{1}{2}p\ell$ is not coincidental. A cone can be thought of as the limiting case of a regular pyramid, just as a circle can be thought of as the limiting case of a regular *n*-gon.

OBJECTIVE ① Teaching Notes

English Learners

Have students add examples of the new vocabulary to the poster they made for Lesson 10-3.

Error Prevention

Students may confuse the height h and slant height ℓ of a pyramid. Suggest that students use the word *slant* as a cue that the height being measured is along a slanted triangular face.

Tactile Learners

Have models of pyramids and cones for students to touch as you discuss the definitions and theorems in this lesson.

① EXAMPLE Teaching Tip

Make sure that students remember how to use a 30°-60°-90° triangle to find $3\sqrt{3}$, the apothem of the hexagonal base.

🏠 Additional Examples

① Find the surface area of a square pyramid with base edges 7.5 ft and slant height 12 ft. **236.25 ft²**

② Find the lateral area of the hexagonal pyramid below. Round to the nearest whole number.

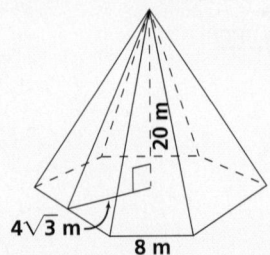

about 508 m²

538

To find the **surface area** of a pyramid, add the area of its base to its lateral area.

🔑 **Key Concepts**

Theorem 10-3	Lateral and Surface Areas of a Regular Pyramid

The lateral area of a regular pyramid is half the product of the perimeter of the base and the slant height.

$$\text{L.A.} = \tfrac{1}{2}p\ell$$

The surface area of a regular pyramid is the sum of the lateral area and the area of the base.

$$\text{S.A.} = \text{L.A.} + B$$

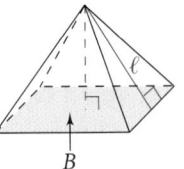

① EXAMPLE Finding Surface Area of a Pyramid

Find the surface area of the hexagonal pyramid at the left.

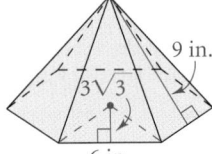

9 in.
$3\sqrt{3}$
6 in.

$$\text{S.A.} = \text{L.A.} + B \qquad \text{Use the formula for surface area.}$$
$$= \tfrac{1}{2}p\ell + \tfrac{1}{2}ap \qquad \text{Substitute the formulas for L.A. and } B.$$
$$= \tfrac{1}{2}(36)(9) + \tfrac{1}{2}(3\sqrt{3})(36) \quad \text{Substitute.}$$
$$\approx 255.53074 \qquad \text{Use a calculator.}$$

● The surface area of the pyramid is about 256 in.²

✓ **Check Understanding** ① Find the surface area of a square pyramid with base edges 5 m and slant height 3 m. **55 m²**

Sometimes the slant height of a pyramid is not given. You must calculate it before you can find the lateral or surface area.

② EXAMPLE Real-World 🌐 Connection

Social Studies The Great Pyramid at Giza, Egypt, pictured at the left, was built about 2580 B.C. as a final resting place for Pharaoh Khufu. At the time it was built, its height was about 481 ft. Each edge of the square base was about 756 ft long. What was the lateral area of the Great Pyramid?

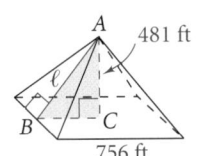

A
481 ft
B   C
756 ft

The legs of right $\triangle ABC$ are the height of the pyramid and the apothem of the base. The height of the pyramid was 481 ft. The apothem of the base was $\frac{756}{2}$, or 378 ft. You can use the Pythagorean Theorem to find the slant height ℓ.

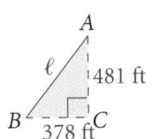

A
481 ft
B 378 ft C

$$\text{L.A.} = \tfrac{1}{2}p\ell \qquad \text{Use the formula for lateral area.}$$
$$= \tfrac{1}{2}(4s)\sqrt{a^2 + b^2} \qquad \text{Substitute the formulas for } p \text{ and } \ell.$$
$$= \tfrac{1}{2}(4 \cdot 756)\sqrt{378^2 + 481^2} \quad \text{Substitute.}$$
$$\approx 924974.57 \qquad \text{Use a calculator.}$$

● The lateral area of the Great Pyramid was about 925,000 ft².

Real-World 🌐 Connection

Today, most casing stones (used to smooth the sides) and some of the top stones are gone from this pyramid.

✓ **Check Understanding** ② Find the surface area of the Great Pyramid to the nearest square foot. **1,496,511 ft²**

538   Chapter 10   Surface Area and Volume

👫 Reaching All Students

Below Level Have students construct and label a net for a hexagonal pyramid to use with Example 1.	**Advanced Learners** How much greater is the surface area of a cylinder than the surface area of a cone if the base radius of each is 6 in. and their heights are 10 in.? **108π in.**	**English Learners** See note on page 538. **Visual Learners** See note on page 541.

Finding Surface Area of a Cone

A **cone** is "pointed" like a pyramid, but its **base** is a circle. In a **right cone**, the **altitude** is a perpendicular segment from the **vertex** to the center of the base. The **height** h is the length of the altitude. The **slant height** ℓ is the distance from the vertex to a point on the edge of the base.

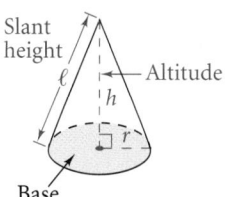

As with a pyramid, the **lateral area** is $\frac{1}{2}$ the perimeter (circumference) of the base times the slant height. The formulas for the lateral area and **surface area** of a cone are similar to those for a pyramid.

Key Concepts

Need Help?

Circumference of base = $2\pi r$

Theorem 10-4	Lateral and Surface Areas of a Cone

The lateral area of a right cone is half the product of the circumference of the base and the slant height.

$$\text{L.A.} = \frac{1}{2} \cdot 2\pi r \cdot \ell, \text{ or L.A.} = \pi r \ell$$

The surface area of a right cone is the sum of the lateral area and the area of the base.

$$\text{S.A.} = \text{L.A.} + B$$

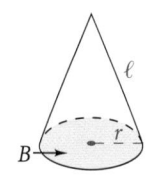

In this book, you can assume that a cone is a right cone unless stated or pictured otherwise.

3 EXAMPLE **Finding Surface Area of a Cone**

Find the surface area of the cone in terms of π.

S.A. = L.A. + B	Use the surface area formula.
$= \pi r \ell + \pi r^2$	Substitute the formulas for L.A. and B.
$= \pi(15)(25) + \pi(15)^2$	Substitute.
$= 375\pi + 225\pi$	Simplify.
$= 600\pi$	

• The surface area of the cone is 600π cm².

 **✓ Check Understanding** ❸ The radius of the base of a cone is 22 m. Its slant height is 10 m. Find the surface area in terms of π. **704π m²**

By cutting a cone and laying it out flat, you can see how the formula for lateral area of a cone $\left(\text{L.A.} = \frac{1}{2} \cdot C_{\text{base}} \cdot \ell\right)$ resembles that for the area of a triangle $\left(A = \frac{1}{2} bh\right)$.

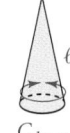 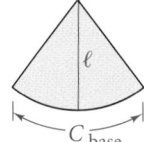

Math Tip
Have students compare the lateral areas $\frac{1}{2}p\ell$ and $\frac{1}{2}2\pi r \cdot \ell$. Ask: *How are the formulas similar?* The perimeter of a pyramid's base is like the circumference of a cone's base.

3 EXAMPLE **Connection to Algebra**

Challenge students to justify why the formula for the surface area of a cone can be written S.A. = $\pi r(r + \ell)$.

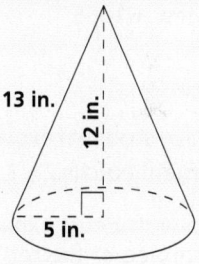 **Additional Examples**

❸ Find the surface area of the cone in terms of π.

13 in. / 12 in. / 5 in.

90π in.²

❹ Leandre uses paper cones to cover her plants in the early spring. The diameter of each cone is 1 ft, and its height is 1.5 ft. How much paper is in the cone? Round to the nearest tenth. **about 2.5 ft²**

Closure

How is finding the surface area of a pyramid like finding the surface area of a prism? How is it different? **Sample: S.A. is the sum of the areas of the lateral faces and bases; the faces of a prism are rectangular and there are two bases, but the faces of a pyramid are triangular and there is one base.**

Assignment Guide

1 Objective
  A **B** Core 1–11, 21–27, 29, 31, 33, 36–39
  C Extension 45, 50, 53

2 Objective
  A **B** Core 12–20, 28, 30, 32, 34, 35, 40–44
  C Extension 46–49, 51, 52, 54

Standardized Test Prep 55–60

Mixed Review 61–65

Exercise 2 Have students explain why the apothem equals $2\sqrt{3}$ m.

Exercise 4 Have students explain why the shorter leg of the red triangle has length 30 m.

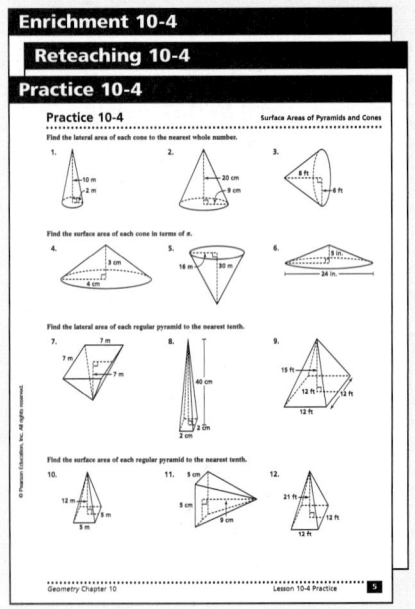

Careers Successful chemists attend to detail, persevere, and work independently.

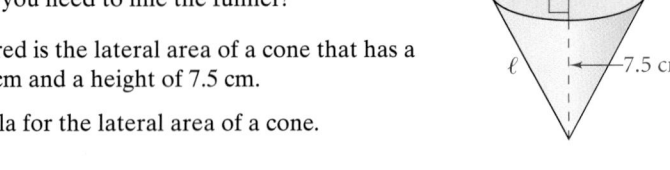

4 **EXAMPLE** Real-World Connection

Chemistry The funnel is in the shape of a cone. How much filter paper do you need to line the funnel?

The area covered is the lateral area of a cone that has a diameter of 8 cm and a height of 7.5 cm.

Use the formula for the lateral area of a cone.

$$L.A. = \pi r\ell$$
$$= \pi r(\sqrt{a^2 + b^2})$$ **To find the slant height use the Pythagorean Theorem.**
$$= \pi(4)(\sqrt{4^2 + 7.5^2})$$ **Substitute. If $d = 8$, then $r = 4$.**
$$= 106.81415$$ **Use a calculator.**

You need about 107 cm² of filter paper to line the funnel.

✓ **Check Understanding** **4** Find the lateral area of a cone with radius 15 in. and height 20 in. **1178 in.²**

EXERCISES

For more practice, see *Extra Practice*.

Practice and Problem Solving

A Practice by Example

Example 1
(page 538)

Find the surface area of each pyramid to the nearest whole number.

1. 11 in. / 12 in. **408 in.²**

2. 138 m² / 8 m / $2\sqrt{3}$ / 4 m

3. 179 in.² / 7.2 in. / 8 in.

Example 2
(page 538)

Find the slant height ℓ of each pyramid to the nearest whole number.

4. 40 m / ℓ / 60 m / 60 m / **50 m**

5. 11 in. / ℓ / 11 in. / 11 in. / **12 in.**

6. 4 m / ℓ / 4 m / $\sqrt{3}$ m / 2 m

Find the lateral area of each pyramid to the nearest whole number.

7. **204 m²** / 6 m / 12 m

8. 8 cm / ℓ / 10 cm / $5\sqrt{3}$ cm / **354 cm²**

9. 51 m² / 6 m / 4 m / 4 m

10. Social Studies The original height of the pyramid built for Khafre, next to the Great Pyramid, was about 471 ft. Each side of its square base was about 708 ft. What is the lateral area to the nearest foot of a pyramid with those dimensions? **834,308 ft²**

11. Construction The roof of a tower is a square pyramid with side length 10 ft. The height of the pyramid is 6 ft. To the nearest square foot, find the area of the roofing material needed to cover the roof. **156 ft²**

Example 3 (page 539)

Find the surface area of each cone in terms of π.

12. 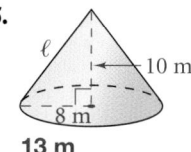 144π cm²

18 cm

12 cm

13.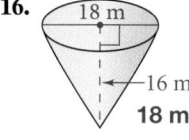

8 ft

6 ft

33π ft²

14. 119π cm²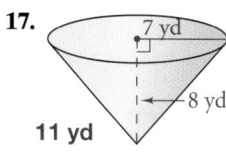

10 cm

7 cm

Example 4 (page 540)

Find the slant height ℓ of each cone to the nearest whole number.

15.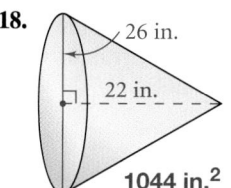

ℓ

10 m

8 m

13 m

16.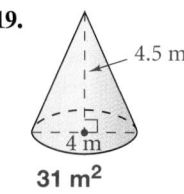

18 m

16 m

18 m

17.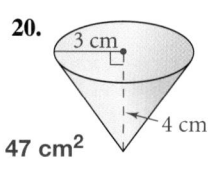

7 yd

8 yd

11 yd

Find the lateral area of each cone to the nearest whole number.

18.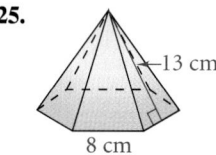

26 in.

22 in.

1044 in.²

19.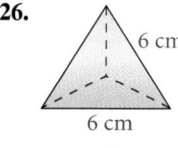

4.5 m

4 m

31 m²

20.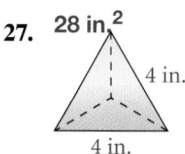

3 cm

4 cm

47 cm²

21. Answers may vary. Sample: PT < PR since PR is a hyp. in △PTR. m∠PCR = m∠PBR (since △PCB is isosc.) and m∠PBR < m∠PRC, so m∠PCR < m∠PRC. Therefore, PR < PC. By the Trans. Prop., PT < PC. Since PA = PB = PC = PD, PT < each edge length.

 Apply Your Skills

Need Help?

In Exercise 21, explain why $\overline{PT}$ is shorter than $\overline{PR}$, and then why $\overline{PR}$ is shorter than $\overline{PC}$.

22. Altitude; altitude; the altitude is shorter because it is one leg of a right △ with the lateral edge as the hyp., and is steeper because it rises the same vert. distance over less horiz. distance.

23. 228.1 in.²

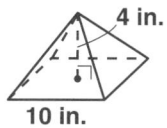

4 in.

10 in.

21. Writing Explain why the altitude $\overline{PT}$ in the pyramid at the right must be shorter than each edge $\overline{PA}$, $\overline{PB}$, $\overline{PC}$, and $\overline{PD}$. **See left.**

22. Reasoning Suppose you could climb to the top of the Great Pyramid in Egypt. Which route would be shorter, a route along a lateral edge or along the altitude of a side? Which of these routes is steeper? Explain your answers. **See left.**

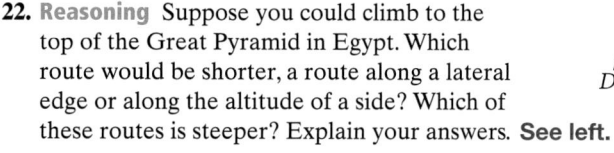

P

A B

T R

D C

23. A square pyramid has base edges 10 in. long and height 4 in. Sketch the pyramid and find its surface area. Round your answer to the nearest tenth. **See left.**

$\boxed{x^2}$ **24. Algebra** The lateral area of a pyramid with a square base is 240 ft². Its base edges are 12 ft long. Find the height of the pyramid. **8 ft**

Find the surface area to the nearest whole number.

25.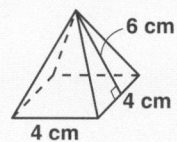

13 cm

8 cm

478 cm²

26.

6 cm

6 cm

62 cm²

27. 28 in.²

4 in.

4 in.

4 in.

28. The lateral area of a cone is 48π in.². The radius is 12 in. Find the slant height.

29. Open-Ended Draw a square pyramid with a lateral area of 48 cm². Label its dimensions. Then find its surface area. **See margin.**

pages 540–543 Exercises

29. Answers may vary. Sample:

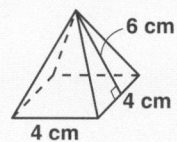

6 cm

4 cm

4 cm

64 cm²

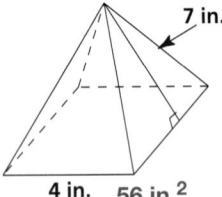

Lesson Quiz 10-4

1. Find the slant height of a square pyramid with base edges 12 cm and altitude 8 cm. **10 cm**

2. Find the lateral area of the regular square pyramid below.

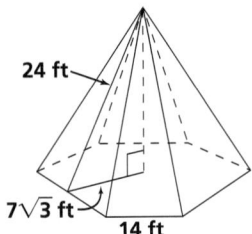

7 in.

4 in. **56 in.²**

3. Find the surface area of the pyramid whose base is a regular hexagon. Round to the nearest whole number.

24 ft

$7\sqrt{3}$ ft

14 ft

1517 ft²

4. Find the surface area of a cone with radius 8 cm and slant height 17 cm in terms of π. **200π cm²**

5. The roof of a building is shaped like a cone with diameter 40 ft and height 20 ft. Find the surface area of the roof. Round to the nearest whole number. **1777 ft²**

Alternative Assessment

Pair students, and have one draw a pyramid and label its dimensions and the other draw a cone and label its dimensions. Each student should calculate the surface area on a separate sheet of paper. Then have students exchange drawings, calculate the surface areas, and compare their answers for both figures.

Exercise 30

34. Cylinder: the lateral area of the 2 cones is 30π in.² and the lateral area of the cylinder is 48π in.².

35. $(\ell + r)r\pi = \pi r\ell + \pi r^2$, which is the lateral area plus the circular base area. This formula may require fewer keystrokes and doesn't use exponents.

36. L.A. = 30 in.², $h = 4.8$ in., $\ell = 5$ in.

40. $\ell = 2.3$ ft, $C = 18.8$ ft, L.A. = 21.7 ft

46. cone with $r = 4$ and $h = 3$; 36π

47. cone with $r = 3$ and $h = 4$; 24π

48. cylinder with cone-shaped hole; 60π

49. cylinder with cone-shaped hole; 48π

C Challenge

30. **Architecture** The roof of a tower in a castle is shaped like a cone. The height of the roof is 30 ft and the radius of the base is 15 ft. What is the area of the roof? Round your answer to the nearest tenth. **1580.6 ft²**

Find the surface area to the nearest whole number.

31.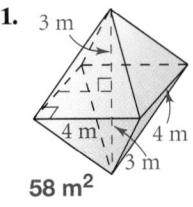
3 m
4 m 4 m
3 m
58 m²

32.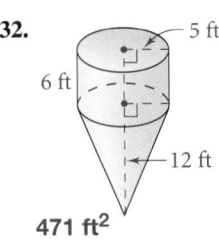
5 ft
6 ft
12 ft
471 ft²

33.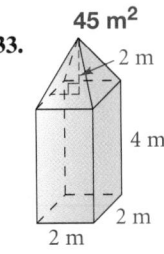
45 m²
2 m
4 m
2 m
2 m

34. The hourglass shown at the right is made by connecting two glass cones inside a glass cylinder. Which has more glass, the two cones or the cylinder? Explain. **See left.**

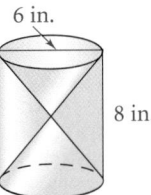
6 in.
8 in.

35. You can use the formula S.A. $= (\ell + r) r\pi$ to find the surface area of a cone. Explain why this formula works. Also, explain why you may prefer to use this formula when finding surface area with a calculator. **See left.**

The length of a side of the base (*s*), slant height, height, lateral area, and surface area are measurements of a square pyramid. Given two of the measurements, find the other three to the nearest tenth.

36. $s = 3$ in., S.A. = 39 in.² **See left.**

37. $h = 8$ m, $\ell = 10$ m
$s = 12$ m, L.A. = 240 m², S.A. = 384 m²

38. $\ell = 5$ ft, L.A. = 20 ft²
$s = 2$ ft, $h = 4.9$ ft, S.A. = 24 ft²

39. L.A. = 118 cm², S.A. = 182 cm²
$s = 8$ cm, $\ell = 7.4$ cm, $h = 6.2$ cm

Circumference, radius, slant height, lateral area, and surface area are measurements of a cone. Given two of the measurements, find the other three to the nearest tenth.

40. $r = 3$ ft, S.A. = 50 ft² **See left.**

41. $r = 4$ m, L.A. = 81.7 m²
$\ell = 6.5$ m, $C = 25.1$ m, S.A. = 132.0 m²

42. $C = 44$ in., L.A. = 176 in.²
$r = 7.0$ in., $\ell = 8.0$ in., S.A. = 330.1 in.²

43. $\ell = 10.6$ ft, L.A. = 33.3 ft²
$r = 1.0$ ft, S.A. = 36.4 ft² $C = 6.3$ ft

44. A cone with radius 9 cm has the same surface area as a cylinder with radius 6 cm and height 18 cm. What is the height of the cone to the nearest tenth? **21.2 cm**

45. Find the surface area of the hexagonal pyramid at the right. **about 613.5 cm²**

8 cm
ℓ
10 cm
$5\sqrt{3}$ cm

Visualization The plane region is revolved completely about the given line to sweep out a solid of revolution. Describe the solid. Then find its surface area in terms of π. 46–49. **See left.**

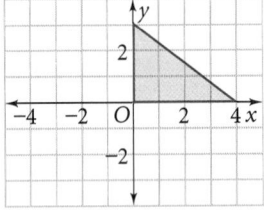

46. about the *y*-axis

47. about the *x*-axis

48. about the line $x = 4$

49. about the line $y = 3$

The given figure fits inside a 10-cm cube. The figure's base is in one face of the cube and is as large as possible. The figure's vertex is in the opposite face of the cube. Draw a sketch and find the lateral and surface areas of the figure.

50. a square pyramid
$100\sqrt{5}$ cm²; $100\sqrt{5} + 100$ cm²

51. a cone $25\pi\sqrt{5}$ cm²; $25\pi\sqrt{5} + 25\pi$ cm²

59. [2] Use the formula for surface area of a pyramid: S.A. $= \frac{1}{2}p\ell + B$. Subst. the surface area, perimeter, and base: $240 = 16\ell + 64$. Solve: $\ell = 11$.

[1] correct formula with one computational error

52. A sector has been cut out of the disk. The radii of the part that remains are taped together, without overlapping, to form the cone. The cone has a lateral area of 64π cm^2. Find the measure of the central angle of the cut-out sector. **129.6**

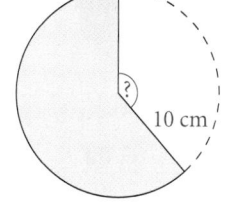

10 cm

53. Archaeology Find out about ancient Mexican and Egyptian pyramids. How are they alike and different? Summarize your findings in a short report. **Check students' work.**

54. The lateral area of a cone is three fifths the surface area. Find the ratio of the radius to the slant height. **2:3**

Standardized Test Prep

Resources
For additional practice with a variety of test item formats:
- Standardized Test Prep, p. 577
- Test-Taking Strategies, p. 572
- Test-Taking Strategies with Transparencies

Exercises 55–60 Students should begin by sketching each figure that is described. Translating the given information into a diagram is a good way to make sure that necessary information is used and that no information is misinterpreted.

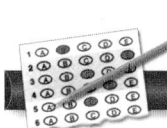

Standardized Test Prep

Multiple Choice

55. To the nearest whole number, what is the surface area of a cone with diameter 27 m and slant height 19 m? **A**
A. 1378 m^2 B. 1951 m^2 C. 2757 m^2 D. 3902 m^2

56. To the nearest whole number, what is the surface area of a cone with radius 14 cm and slant height 18 cm? **I**
F. 448 cm^2 G. 836 cm^2 H. 1012 cm^2 I. 1407 cm^2

57. To the nearest whole number, what is the surface area of a square pyramid with each side of the base 30 yd and slant height 42 yd? **C**
A. 900 yd^2 B. 2520 yd^2 C. 3420 yd^2 D. 3600 yd^2

Take It to the NET
Online lesson quiz at **www.PHSchool.com**
Web Code: afa-1004

58. A cylinder and a cone each have height 1 and radius $\sqrt{3}$. How does the cylinder's lateral area x compare with the cone's lateral area y? **F**
F. $x = y$ G. $x = 2y$ H. $x > 2y$ I. $x < 2y$

Short Response

59. A square pyramid is 8 m on each side. Its surface area is 240 m^2. What is its slant height? Show your work and explain your reasoning. **See above left.**

Extended Response

60. The lateral area of a cone is twice the area of its base.
a. What is its slant height in terms of the radius r? Show your work.
b. What is the lateral area to the nearest tenth if the radius is 6 centimeters? Show your work. **a–b. See margin.**

Mixed Review

Lesson 10-3

61. How much cardboard do you need to make a closed box that is 4 ft by 5 ft by 2 ft? **76 ft^2**

62. How much posterboard do you need to make a cylinder, open at each end, with height 9 in. and diameter $4\frac{1}{2}$ in.? Round your answer to the nearest square inch. **127 in.^{2}**

Lesson 9-3

63. A TV camera views a tall building 400 m away with a 35° angle of elevation to the top. How tall is the building if the camera lens is 160 cm off the ground? **about 281.7 m**

Lesson 7-4

64. The area of a rhombus is 714 cm^2. One diagonal is 42 cm long. Find the length of the other diagonal. **34 cm**

65. A kite with area 195 in.^{2} has a 15-in. diagonal. How long is the other diagonal? **26 in.**

Lesson 10-4   Surface Areas of Pyramids and Cones   **543**

---

pages 540–543   Exercises

60. [4] a. L.A. $= 2B$
$\pi r\ell = 2\pi r^2$
$\ell = 2r$
b. L.A. $= \pi r\ell$
L.A. $= \pi(6)(12)$
L.A. $= 226.2$ cm^2

[3] one computational error

[2] correct methods in (a) and (b) but incorrect relationship between ℓ and r

[1] correct lateral area without any work shown

Lesson Preview

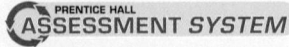
✓ Check Skills You'll Need

Areas of Rectangles and Circles
Lesson 1-7: Examples 4, 5
Exercises 20–32
Extra Practice, p. 690

Area of a Triangle
Lesson 7-1: Example 4
Exercises 11–13
Extra Practice, p. 696

Lesson Resources

📁 **Teaching Resources**
Practice, Reteaching, Enrichment

👥 **Reaching All Students**
Practice Workbook 10-5
Spanish Practice Workbook 10-5
Technology Activities 51
Informal Geometry Planning
  Guide 10-5

⏱ **Presentation Assistant Plus!**
Transparencies
• Check Skills You'll Need 10-5
• Additional Examples 10-5
• Student Edition Answers 10-5
• Lesson Quiz 10-5
PH Presentation Pro CD 10-5

PRENTICE HALL
ASSESSMENT SYSTEM

Computer Test Generator CD

💿 **Technology**
Resource Pro® CD-ROM
Computer Test Generator CD
Prentice Hall Presentation Pro CD

🖥 **www.PHSchool.com**
Student Site
• Teacher Web Code: afk-5500
• Self-grading Lesson Quiz
Teacher Center
• Lesson Planner
• Resources

Plus 📘**TEXT**

544

Volumes of Prisms and Cylinders

 North Carolina Objectives

1.02 Use length, area, and volume of geometric figures to solve problems.
2.04 Develop and apply properties of solids to solve problems.

Lesson Preview

What You'll Learn

OBJECTIVE 1 To find the volume of a prism

OBJECTIVE 2 To find the volume of a cylinder

. . . And Why

To estimate the volume of a backpack, as in Example 4

✓ Check Skills You'll Need

(For help, go to Lessons 1-7 and 7-1.)

Find the area of each figure. For answers that are not whole numbers, round to the nearest tenth.

1. a square with side length 7 cm **49 cm²**
2. a circle with diameter 15 in. **176.7 in.²**
3. a circle with radius 10 mm **314.2 mm²**
4. a rectangle with length 3 ft and width 1 ft **3 ft²**
5. a rectangle with base 14 in. and height 11 in. **154 in.²**
6. a triangle with base 11 cm and height 5 cm **27.5 cm²**
7. an equilateral triangle that is 8 in. on each side **27.7 in.²**

New Vocabulary • volume • composite space figure

OBJECTIVE
1 **Finding Volume of a Prism**

📘**TEXT** Interactive lesson includes instant self-check, tutorials, and activities.

Investigation: Finding Volume

Explore the volume of a prism with unit cubes.

• Make a one-layer rectangular prism that is 4 cubes long and 2 cubes wide. The prism will be 4 units by 2 units by 1 unit.

1. How many cubes are in the prism? **8 cubes**

2. Add a second layer to your prism to make a prism 4 units by 2 units by 2 units. How many cubes are in this prism? **16 cubes**

3. Add a third layer to your prism to make a prism 4 units by 2 units by 3 units. How many cubes are in this prism? **24 cubes**

4. How many cubes would be in the prism if you added two additional layers of cubes for a total of 5 layers? **40 cubes**

5. How many cubes would be in the prism if there were 10 layers? **80 cubes**

Volume is the space that a figure occupies. It is measured in cubic units such as cubic inches (in.³), cubic feet (ft³), or cubic centimeters (cm³). The volume of a cube is the cube of the length of its edge, or $V = e^3$.

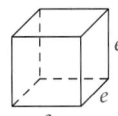

🔄 **Ongoing Assessment and Intervention**

Before the Lesson	**During the Lesson**	**After the Lesson**
Diagnose prerequisite skills using:	**Monitor progress using:**	**Assess knowledge using:**
• Check Skills You'll Need	• Check Understanding	• Lesson Quiz
	• Additional Examples	• Computer Test Generator CD
	• Standardized Test Prep	

Example 4
(page 554)

14. Chemistry In a chemistry lab you use a filter paper cone to filter a liquid. The diameter of the cone is 6.5 cm and its height is 6 cm. How much liquid will the cone hold when it is full? **about 66.4 cm³**

15. Chemistry This funnel has a filter that was being used to remove impurities from a solution but became clogged and stopped draining. The remaining solution is represented by the shaded region. How many cubic centimeters of the solution remain in the funnel?
about 4.7 cm³

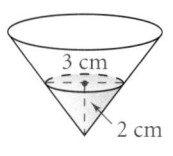
3 cm
2 cm

B **Apply Your Skills**   **Find the volume to the nearest whole number.**

16.   123 in.³
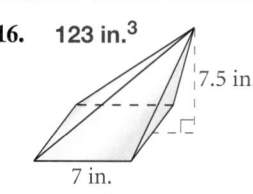
7.5 in.
7 in.
Square base

17.   312 cm³
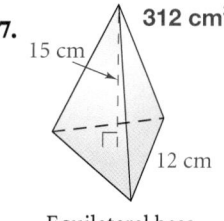
15 cm
12 cm
Equilateral base

18.   10,368 ft³
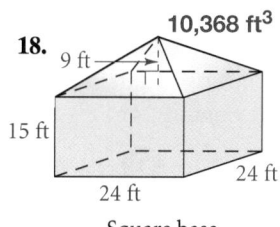
9 ft
15 ft
24 ft
24 ft
Square base

19. They are equal; both volumes are $\frac{1}{3}\pi r^2 h$.

19. Writing The two cylinders pictured at the right are congruent. How does the volume of the larger cone compare to the total volume of the two smaller cones? Explain. **See left.**

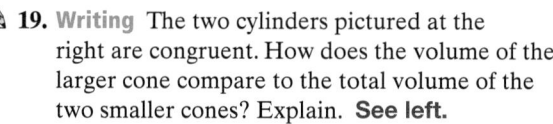

20. Architecture The Transamerica Pyramid in San Francisco (see photo at left) is 853 ft tall with a square base that is 149 ft on each side.
 a. What is its volume to the nearest thousand cubic feet? **6,312,000 ft³**
 b. Imagine, in place of the Transamerica Pyramid, a building in the shape of a prism with the same square base as the Pyramid. How tall would this building have to be to have the same volume as the Pyramid?
about 284 ft

Exercise 20

x^2 **Algebra** **Find the value of the variable in each figure. Leave answers in simplest radical form. The diagrams are not to scale.**

21.   6
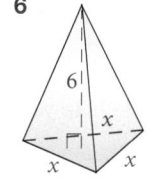
6
x
x   x
Volume = 18√3

22.   3
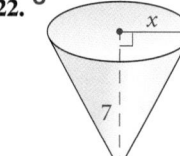
x
7
Volume = 21π

23.   3√2
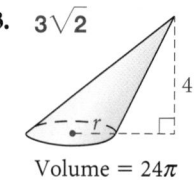
4
r
Volume = 24π

24. Hardware Builders use a plumb bob to find a vertical line. The plumb bob shown combines a regular hexagonal prism with a pyramid. Find its volume to the nearest cubic centimeter.
73 cm³

2 cm
6 cm
3 cm

25. Answers may vary. Sample: h = 50 in., r = 6 in.; h = 18 in., r = 10 in.

25. Open-Ended A cone has a volume of 600π in.³. Find two possible sets of dimensions for its height and radius. **See left.**

26. cube: 8 units³, cone: $\frac{2}{3}\pi$ units³, pyramid: $\frac{8}{3}$ units³

26. A cone with radius 1 fits snugly inside a square pyramid which fits snugly inside a cube. What are the volumes of the three figures? **See left.**

27. A cone with radius 3 ft and height 10 ft has a volume of 30π ft³. What is the volume of the cone formed when the following happens to the original cone?
 a. The radius is doubled. **120π ft³**   **b.** The height is doubled. **60π ft³**
 c. The radius and the height are both doubled. **240π ft³**

Exercise 18 Students must find the volumes of two space figures. Ask: *What figure is on the bottom?* rectangular prism *What figure is on the top?* pyramid

Connection to Mental Math
Exercise 20 Do part b as a class exercise. Write the formulas for the volume of a prism and the volume of a pyramid side by side. Then challenge students to solve the problem using mental math and explain their methods.

Careers
Exercise 24 Builders must know how to construct level floors and vertical walls. Have students investigate how carpentry tools such as plumb bobs and levels use principles of geometry to do this.

Exercise 27 The answer to part c will be generalized to all similar cones in Lesson 10-8.

Visual Learners
Exercise 33 Have students with strong visual skills explain to the rest of the class what the solid looks like, then cut off the tip of a conical ice cream cone to illustrate it.

Lesson Quiz 10-6

Find the volume of each figure. When appropriate, leave your answer in terms of π.

1.

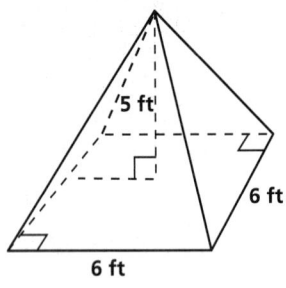

60 ft^3

2.

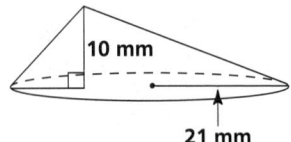

1470π mm^3

3. square pyramid with base edges 24 in. long and slant height 15 in. 1728 in.^{3}

4. cone with diameter 3 m and height 4 m 3π m^3

5.

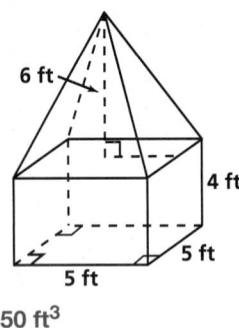

150 ft^3

Alternative Assessment

Have partners solve the following exercise and show their work in detail: A cone and a square pyramid each have height 12 cm. The perimeter of the base of the pyramid and the circumference of the base of the cone are each 24 cm. Which has the greater volume?

---

29. cone with $r = 4$ and $h = 3$; 16π

30. cone with $r = 3$ and $h = 4$; 12π

31. cylinder with $r = 4$, $h = 3$, with a cone of $r = 4$, $h = 3$ removed from it; 32π

32. cone with $r = 4$, $h = 5\frac{1}{3}$, with a cone of $r = 1$, $h = 1\frac{1}{3}$ cut off the top, and a cylinder of $r = 1$ cut out of its center; 24π

 Challenge

28. List the volumes of the cone, prism, and pyramid in order from least to greatest. cone: 234.6 in.^{3}; prism: 240 in.^{3}; pyramid: 256 in.^{3}

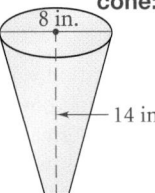
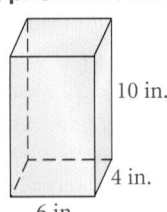
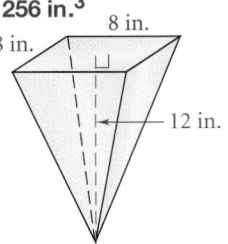

Visualization The plane region is revolved completely about the given line to sweep out a solid of revolution. Describe the solid. Then find its volume in terms of π. **29–32. See left.**

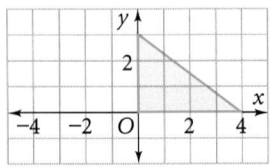

29. the y-axis

30. the x-axis

31. the line $x = 4$

32. the line $y = -1$

33a. See margin.

33. A *frustum* of a cone is the part that remains when the vertex is cut off by a plane parallel to the base.
  a. Explain how to use the formula for the volume of a cone to find the volume of a frustum of a cone.
  b. Containers A 9-in. tall popcorn container is the frustum of a cone. Its small radius is 4.5 in. and its large radius is 6 in. What is its volume? **about 784.6 in.^{3}**

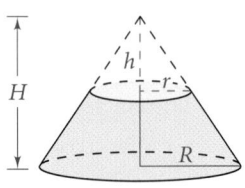

Frustum of cone

34. A disk has radius 10 m. A 90° sector is cut away, and a cone is formed. **47.1 m**
  a. What is the circumference of the base of the cone?
  b. What is the area of the base of the cone? **176.7 m^2**
  c. What is the volume of the cone? (*Hint:* Use the slant height and the radius of the base to find the height.) **389.6 m^3**

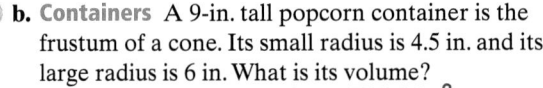

Graphing Calculator In Exercises 35 and 36, the volume of the solid is 1000 cm^3. Use the Exploration on page 536 to help you complete each exercise.

35. For a square pyramid, find the length of a side of the base for which the lateral area is as small as possible. **about 16.2 cm**

36. For a cone, find the radius for which the lateral area is as small as possible. **about 8.8 cm**

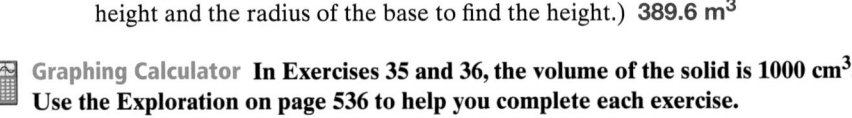

Standardized Test Prep

Multiple Choice

37. What is the volume of a 6-ft high square pyramid with base edges 8 ft? **A**
  A. 128 ft^3 **B.** 192 ft^3 **C.** 256 ft^3 **D.** 384 ft^3

38. What is the volume of a cone with diameter 21 m and height 4 m? **F**
  F. 147π m^3 **G.** 220.5π m^3 **H.** 294π m^3 **I.** 441π m^3

39. What is the volume of an oblique cone with radius 9 cm and height 12 cm?
  A. 324π cm^3 **B.** 486π cm^3 **C.** 648π cm^3 **D.** 972π cm^3 **A**

pages 554–557 Exercises
33. a. The frustum has vol.
$V = \frac{1}{3}\pi R^2 H - \frac{1}{3}\pi r^2 h = \frac{1}{3}\pi(R^2 H - r^2 h)$. Now if $h_1 = H - h$ is the frustum's height,

$V = \frac{1}{3}\pi(R^2(h_1 + h) - r^2 h) = \frac{1}{3}\pi(R^2 h_1 + h(R^2 - r^2))$.

By similar $\triangle$, $\frac{h}{r} = \frac{h_1 + h}{R}$,

or $h = \frac{rh_1}{R - r}$.

Simplifying, $V = \frac{1}{3}\pi h_1(r^2 + rR + R^2)$.

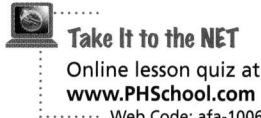

Take It to the NET
Online lesson quiz at
www.PHSchool.com
Web Code: afa-1006

40. What is the volume of the square pyramid at the right? **F**
F. 1568 m³   G. 1633 m³
H. 2352 m³   I. 2450 m³

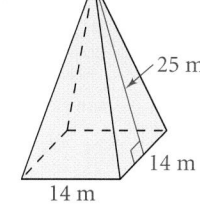

25 m
14 m
14 m

41. What is the volume of an oblique square pyramid
with base edges 25 in. and height 24 in.? **A**
A. 5000 in.³   B. 7500 in.³
C. 10,000 in.³   D. 15,000 in.³

Short Response

42. The volume of a cone is 82,418π cm³. Its diameter is 203 cm. What is its
height? Show all your work, including any formulas that you use.
See margin.

Mixed Review

Lesson 10-5

43. Sports A cylindrical hockey puck is 1 in. high and 3 in. in diameter. What is its
volume in cubic inches? Round your answer to the nearest tenth. **7.1 in.³**

44. A triangular prism has height 30 cm. Its base is a right triangle with legs 10 cm
and 24 cm. Find the volume of the prism. **3600 cm³**

Lesson 9-5

45. Find the area of a regular pentagon with a radius 5 in. Give your answer to the
nearest tenth of a square inch. **59.4 in.²**

Lesson 7-3

Find the area of each equilateral triangle to the nearest tenth of a square unit.
57.7 in.²
46. The triangle has 12 cm sides. **62.4 cm²47.** The triangle has 10-in. altitudes.

48. Find the area of a 30°-60°-90° triangle with shorter leg of length 4 cm. **13.9 cm²**

Geometry at Work

·······················**Package Designer**

Each year, more than one trillion dollars in manufactured goods are
packaged in containers. To create each new box, bag, or carton,
package designers must balance such factors as safety, environmental
impact, and attractiveness against cost of production.

Consider the three boxes
of dishwasher detergent. All
three boxes have standard
volumes of 108 in.³. The
boxes have different shapes,
however, and different surface
areas. The box on the left has
the greatest surface area and therefore costs the most to produce. Despite the
higher cost, the box on the left has become standard. In this case, the least
expensive package on the right is too difficult for a consumer to pick up and pour.

9 in.
6 in.
6 in.
2 in.

6 in.
6 in.
3 in.

6 in.
4½ in.
4 in.

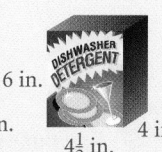

Take It to the NET For more information about
package design, go to **www.PHSchool.com**.
Web Code: afb-2031

Lesson 10-6   Volumes of Pyramids and Cones   **557**

42. [2] ½d = r;
    r = ½(203) = 101.5;
    V = ⅓πr²h, so

82,418π =
⅓π(101.5)²h, and
h = 24 cm.

[1] one computational
error

Standardized Test Prep

 **Resources**
For additional practice with a
variety of test item formats:
• Standardized Test Prep, p. 577
• Test-Taking Strategies, p. 572
• Test-Taking Strategies with
  Transparencies

Exercise 40 Remind students that
slant height is not the height of
the pyramid but may be used in
the Pythagorean Theorem to find
the height.

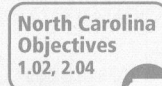
1. Plan

Lesson Preview

 **Check Skills You'll Need**

Finding Circumference of a Circle
Lesson 1-7: Example 2
Exercises 8–15
Extra Practice, p. 690

Finding Area of a Circle
Lesson 1-7: Example 5
Exercises 27–36
Extra Practice, p. 690

Lesson Resources

 Teaching Resources
Practice, Reteaching, Enrichment
Checkpoint Quiz 2

Reaching All Students
Practice Workbook 10-7
Spanish Practice Workbook 10-7
Reading and Math Literacy 10C
Spanish Reading & Literacy 10C
Spanish Checkpoint Quiz 2
Hands-On Activities 30
Informal Geometry Planning
  Guide 10-7

Presentation Assistant Plus!
Transparencies
• Check Skills You'll Need 10-7
• Additional Examples 10-7
• Student Edition Answers 10-7
• Lesson Quiz 10-7
PH Presentation Pro CD 10-7

 PRENTICE HALL
ASSESSMENT SYSTEM

Checkpoint Quiz 2
Computer Test Generator CD

 Technology
Resource Pro® CD-ROM
Computer Test Generator CD
Prentice Hall Presentation Pro CD

 **www.PHSchool.com**
Student Site
• Teacher Web Code: afk-5500
• Self-grading Lesson Quiz
Teacher Center
• Lesson Planner
• Resources

Plus **iTEXT**

558

10-7 Surface Areas and Volumes of Spheres

 North Carolina Objectives

1.02 Use length, area, and volume of geometric figures to solve problems.
2.04 Develop and apply properties of solids to solve problems.

Lesson Preview

What You'll Learn

OBJECTIVE 1 To find the surface area and volume of a sphere

... And Why

To approximate the surface area of Earth, as in Example 2

✓ Check Skills You'll Need
(For help, go to Lesson 1-7.)

Find the area and circumference of a circle with the given radius. Round your answers to the nearest tenth.
                                                                    19.6 ft²; 15.7 ft
1. 6 in. 113.1 in.²; 37.7 in.   **2.** 5 cm 78.5 cm²; 31.4 cm   **3.** 2.5 ft
4. 1.2 m 4.5 m²; 7.5 m   **5.** 15 yd 706.9 yd²; 94.2 yd   **6.** 12 mm
                                                                    452.4 mm²; 75.4 mm

New Vocabulary • sphere • center, radius, diameter, circumference (of a sphere) • great circle • hemisphere

 Interactive lesson includes instant self-check, tutorials, and activities.

OBJECTIVE 1 Finding Surface Area and Volume of a Sphere

Real-World Connection

The diameter of the Hayden Sphere in New York City is 87 ft.

A **sphere** is the set of all points in space equidistant from a given point called the **center**. A **radius** is a segment that has one endpoint at the center and the other endpoint on the sphere. A **diameter** is a segment passing through the center with endpoints on the sphere.

When a plane and a sphere intersect in more than one point, the intersection is a circle. If the center of the circle is also the center of the sphere, the circle is called a **great circle** of the sphere. The circumference of a great circle is the **circumference** of the sphere. A great circle divides a sphere into two **hemispheres**.

A baseball is a model of a sphere. To approximate its surface area, you can take apart its covering. Each of the two sections suggests a pair of circles with radius r approximately the radius of the ball. The area of the four circles, $4\pi r^2$, suggests the surface area of the ball.

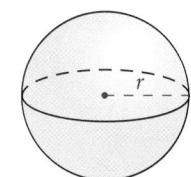
The *length r* is *the* radius of the sphere. 2*r* is *the* diameter.

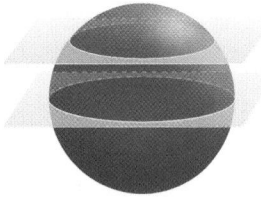

πr^2

 Key Concepts

Theorem 10-10 **Surface Area of a Sphere**
The surface area of a sphere is four times the product of π and the square of the radius of the sphere. $$\text{S.A.} = 4\pi r^2$$ 

 **Ongoing Assessment and Intervention**

Before the Lesson
Diagnose prerequisite skills using:
• Check Skills You'll Need

During the Lesson
Monitor progress using:
• Check Understanding
• Additional Examples
• Standardized Test Prep

After the Lesson
Assess knowledge using:
• Lesson Quiz
• Computer Test Generator CD
• Chapter Checkpoint 2 (p. 564)

558

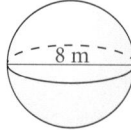 **EXAMPLE** Finding Surface Area

Find the surface area of this sphere. Leave your answer in terms of π.

$$S.A. = 4\pi r^2 \qquad \text{Use the formula for surface area.}$$
$$= 4\pi 4^2 \qquad \text{Substitute } r = \tfrac{8}{2} = 4.$$
$$= 64\pi \qquad \text{Simplify.}$$

- The surface area is 64π m^2.

 **Check Understanding** ❶ Find the surface area of a sphere with $d = 14$ in. Give your answer two ways, in terms of π and rounded to the nearest square inch. **196π in.^{2}; 616 in.^{2}**

You can use spheres to approximate the surface areas of real-world objects.

❷ **EXAMPLE** Real-World 🌐 Connection

Geography Earth's equator is about 24,902 mi long. Approximate the surface area of Earth by finding the surface area of a sphere with circumference 24,902 mi.

Step 1 Find the radius.

$$C = 2\pi r \qquad \text{Use the formula for circumference.}$$
$$24{,}902 = 2\pi r \qquad \text{Substitute.}$$
$$\frac{24{,}902}{2\pi} = r \qquad \text{Solve for } r.$$
$$r = 3963.2764 \qquad \text{Use a calculator.}$$

Step 2 Use the radius to find the surface area.

$$S.A. = 4\pi r^2 \qquad \text{Use the formula for surface area.}$$
$$= 4\pi \text{ ANS } \boxed{x^2} \boxed{\text{ENTER}} \qquad \text{Use a calculator.}$$
$$= 197387020$$

- The surface area of Earth is about 197,400,000 mi^2.

 **Check Understanding** ❷ Find the surface area of a melon with circumference 18 in. Round your answer to the nearest ten square inches. **100 in.^{2}**

The following model suggests a formula for the volume of a sphere.

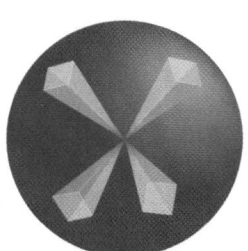

Fill a sphere with a large number n of small pyramids. The vertex of each pyramid is the center of the sphere. The height of each pyramid is approximately the radius r of the sphere. The sum of the areas of the bases of the n pyramids approximates the surface area of the sphere. The sum of the volumes of the n pyramids should approximate the volume of the sphere.

Volume of each pyramid $= \frac{1}{3}Bh$

$$\text{Sum of the volumes of } n \text{ pyramids} \approx n \cdot \tfrac{1}{3}Br \qquad \text{Substitute } r \text{ for } h.$$
$$= \tfrac{1}{3} \cdot (nB) \cdot r$$
$$\approx \tfrac{1}{3} \cdot (4\pi r^2) \cdot r \qquad \text{Replace } nB \text{ with the surface area of a sphere.}$$
$$= \tfrac{4}{3}\pi r^3$$

It is reasonable to conjecture that the volume of a sphere is $\frac{4}{3}\pi r^3$.

Take It to the NET
Graphing Calculator procedures online at **www.PHSchool.com**
Web Code: afe-2101

Math Background

We can thank Archimedes for the formulas for the surface area and volume of a sphere. His clever proofs using the *method of exhaustion* anticipate calculus methods developed nearly 2000 years later. Although neither formula can be proved at this level, illustrations will show that each formula is reasonable.

OBJECTIVE
▼ **Teaching Notes**

English Learners
Have students add examples of the vocabulary to the poster they made for Lesson 10-3.

Careers
Airplane pilots and the men and women who plan airline routes use great circles for the shortest routes between distant cities on Earth.

❷ **EXAMPLE** Connection to Algebra

Have students practice manipulating literal equations by showing that surface area can be expressed in terms of circumference using the formula $S.A. = \frac{C^2}{\pi}$.

Connection to Calculus
Point out that the formula for the volume of a sphere is treated informally at this point. In a calculus course, the formula can be proved using integration.

Error Prevention
The formulas for surface area and volume resemble each other closely enough to cause confusion for some students. Have them focus on the exponents to help differentiate the formulas, remembering that area and volume are measured in square and cubic units, respectively.

👥 Reaching All Students

Below Level Before introducing Theorems 10-10 and 10-11, write only the words on the board. Then ask students to write the words as an algebraic formula.	**Advanced Learners** Have students prove or disprove that the surface area of a sphere equals the square of its circumference.	**English Learners** See note on page 559. **Inclusion** See note on page 562.

4 EXAMPLE
Technology Tip

Remind students that $\sqrt[3]{x}$ also can be expressed as $x^{\frac{1}{3}}$, which may be easier for students to compute on their calculators.

Additional Examples

1 Find the surface area of the sphere. Leave your answer in terms of π.

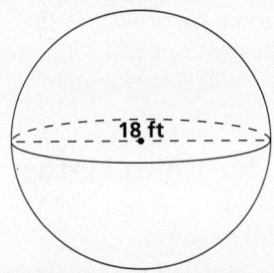

18 ft

324π ft^2

2 The circumference of a rubber ball is 13 cm. Approximate its surface area to the nearest whole number. **54 cm^2**

3 Find the volume of the sphere. Leave your answer in terms of π.

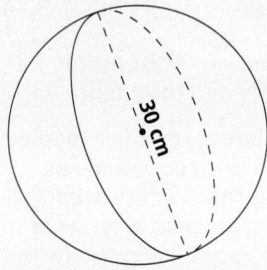

30 cm

4500π cm^3

4 The volume of a sphere is 1 in.^{3} Find its surface area to the nearest tenth. **4.8 in.^{2}**

Closure

The surface area of a sphere is 125 in.^{2} Find its volume to the nearest whole number. **131 in.^{3}**

 Key Concepts

Theorem 10-11	Volume of a Sphere

The volume of a sphere is four thirds the product of π and the cube of the radius of the sphere.

$$V = \tfrac{4}{3}\pi r^3$$

3 EXAMPLE Finding Volume

Find the volume of the sphere. Leave your answer in terms of π.

$V = \tfrac{4}{3}\pi r^3$ **Use the formula for volume.**

$= \tfrac{4}{3}\pi 6^3$ **Substitute.**

$= 288\pi$

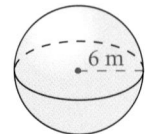
6 m

● The volume of the sphere is 288π m^3.

✓ **Check Understanding** **3** Find the volume to the nearest cubic inch of a sphere with diameter 60 in.
113,097 in.^{3}

If you know the volume of a sphere, you can find its surface area.

4 EXAMPLE Using Volume to Find Surface Area

The volume of a sphere is 5000 m^3. What is the surface area of the sphere?

Step 1 Find the radius r.

$V = \tfrac{4}{3}\pi r^3$ **Use the formula for volume of a sphere.**

$5000 = \tfrac{4}{3}\pi r^3$ **Substitute.**

$5000\left(\tfrac{3}{4\pi}\right) = r^3$ **Solve for r^3.**

$\sqrt[3]{5000\left(\tfrac{3}{4\pi}\right)} = r$ **Take cube roots.**

$r = 10.607844$ **Use a calculator.**

 Need Help?

The cube root of x, $\sqrt[3]{x}$, is the number whose third power is x.

Step 2 Find the surface area of the sphere.

S.A. $= 4\pi r^2$ **Use the formula for the surface area of a sphere.**

$= 4\pi$ ANS $\boxed{x^2}$ $\boxed{\text{ENTER}}$ **Use a calculator.**

$= 1414.0479$

● The surface area of the sphere is about 1414 m^2.

✓ **Check Understanding** **4** The volume of a sphere is 4200 ft^3. Find the surface area to the nearest tenth.
1258.9 ft^2

EXERCISES

For more practice, see *Extra Practice*.

Practice and Problem Solving

A Practice by Example

Example 1
(page 559)

Find the surface area of the sphere with the given diameter or radius. Leave your answer in terms of π.

1. $d = 30$ m   **2.** $r = 10$ in.   **3.** $d = 32$ mm   **4.** $r = 100$ yd
     900π m^2 400π in.^{2} 1024π mm^2 $40{,}000\pi$ yd^2

Find the surface area of each ball. Leave each answer in terms of π.

5.

$d = 68$ mm
4624π mm^2

6.

$d = 24$ cm
576π cm^2

7. $\frac{121}{16}\pi$ in.^{2}

$d = 2\frac{3}{4}$ in.

Example 2
(page 559)

Use the given circumference to find the surface area of each spherical object. Round your answer to the nearest whole number.

232 in.^{2}

8. a grapefruit with $C = 14$ cm **62 cm^2** **9.** a bowling ball with $C = 27$ in.

10. a pincushion with $C = 8$ cm **20 cm^2** **11.** a head of lettuce with $C = 22$ in.
154 in.^{2}

Example 3
(page 560)

Find the volume of each sphere. Give each answer in terms of π and rounded to the nearest cubic unit.

288π cm^3; 905 cm^3 $\frac{1125}{2}\pi$ in.^{3}; 1767 in.^{3}

12. $\frac{500}{3}\pi$ ft^3; **13.** **14.**
524 ft^3

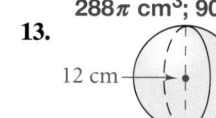
5 ft

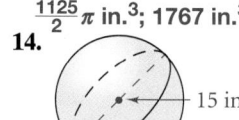
12 cm

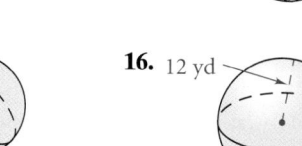
15 in.

15. **16.** 12 yd **17.** 8.4 m

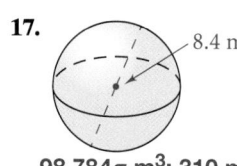
8 cm

$\frac{2048}{3}\pi$ cm^3; 2145 cm^3

2304π yd^3; 7238 yd^3 98.784π m^3; 310 m^3

Example 4
(page 560)

A sphere has the volume given. Find its surface area to the nearest whole number.

18. $V = 900$ in.^{3} **451 in.^{2}** **19.** $V = 3000$ m^3 **1006 m^2** **20.** $V = 140$ cm^3 **130 cm^2**

B Apply Your Skills

21. Mental Math Use $\pi \approx 3$ to estimate the surface area and volume of a sphere with radius 3 cm. **S.A. $\approx$ 108 cm^2, $V \approx$ 108 cm^3**

22. Visualization The region enclosed by the semicircle at the right is revolved completely about the x-axis. **sphere of radius 4**
a. Describe the solid of revolution that is formed.
b. Find its volume in terms of π. $\frac{256}{3}\pi$ units^3
c. Find its surface area in terms of π. 64π units^2

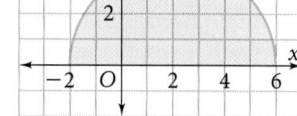

23. Yes; the volume of the frozen yogurt is $\frac{256}{3}\pi$ cm^3, and the volume of the cone is 64π cm^3.

23. Food A sphere of frozen yogurt was pressed into the cone as shown at the left. If the yogurt melts into the cone, would the cone overflow? Explain. **See left.**

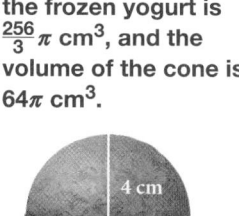

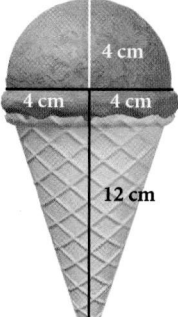

4 cm

4 cm   4 cm

12 cm

Exercise 23

24. The sphere at the right fits snugly inside a cube with 6-in. edges.
a. What is the radius of the sphere? **3 in.**
b. What is the volume of the space between the sphere and cube, to the nearest tenth? **102.9 in.^{3}**

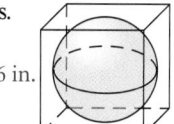
6 in.

Geometry in 3 Dimensions A sphere has center $(0, 0, 0)$ and radius 5.
Answers may vary. Sample: (5, 0, 0), (0, 5, 0), (0, 0, 5),
25. Name the coordinates of six points on the sphere.$(-5, 0, 0), (0, -5, 0), (0, 0, -5)$

26. Tell whether each of the following points is inside, outside, or on the sphere.
$A(0, -3, 4), B(1, -1, -1), C(4, -6, -10)$ **A: on; B: inside; C: outside**

Lesson 10-7 Surface Areas and Volumes of Spheres **561**

Assignment Guide

1 Objective
Ⓐ Ⓑ Core 1–44
Ⓒ Extension 45–51

Standardized Test Prep 52–59

Mixed Review 60–67

Exercise 6 As students examine the photograph, ask: *What mathematical term describes two of the black circles on the basketball?* great circles

Connection to Algebra
Exercises 18–20 Before assigning these exercises, review how to solve $V = \frac{4}{3}\pi r^3$ for r.

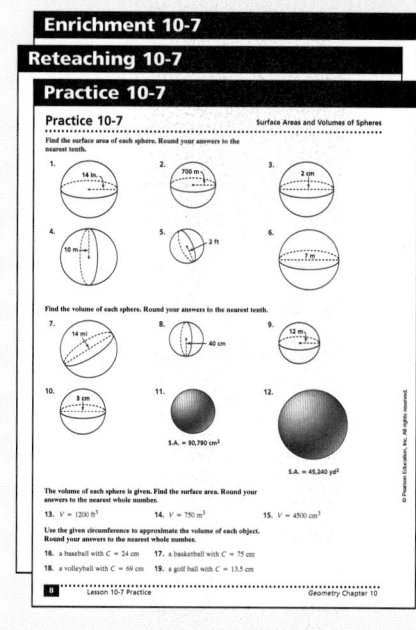

Enrichment 10-7

Reteaching 10-7

Practice 10-7

Practice 10-7   Surface Areas and Volumes of Spheres

Find the surface area of each sphere. Round your answers to the nearest tenth.

Find the volume of each sphere. Round your answers to the nearest tenth.

The volume of each sphere is given. Find the surface area. Round your answers to the nearest whole number.
13. $V = 1200$ ft^3 14. $V = 780$ m^3 15. $V = 4500$ cm^3

Use the given circumference to approximate the volume of each object. Round your answers to the nearest whole number.
16. a baseball with $C = 24$ cm   17. a basketball with $C = 75$ cm
18. a volleyball with $C = 69$ cm   19. a golf ball with $C = 13.5$ cm

Lesson 10-7 Practice   Geometry Chapter 10

562

Inclusion

Exercise 22 For students who find visualizing the solid of revolution difficult, discuss ways to model it, such as drawing a semicircle on an index card, cutting it out, attaching it to a pencil along its diameter, and then revolving the pencil.

Math Tip

Exercise 24 Have students calculate the percent of space inside the cube that is *not* taken up by the sphere. They may be surprised to discover that it is almost 50 percent.

Connection to Coordinate Geometry

Exercise 26 After students complete this exercise, challenge them to find the distance between the center of the sphere and points *A, B,* and *C*.

Diversity

Exercise 38 Students who have not played golf may not know that golf balls are dimpled. If possible, bring in golf balls for students to examine.

Connection to Physics

Exercise 43 In physics, *density* is the ratio of the mass of an object to its volume. Discuss how the concept of density explains why a piece of wood floats in water but a rock with the same dimensions sinks.

Exercise 44 Students need to apply the Pythagorean Theorem twice to find the length of the cube's diagonal.

Real-World  **Connection**

Hail with diameter about an inch larger than shown here broke this windshield.

38b. The answer is less than the actual surface area since the dimples on the golf ball add to the surface area.

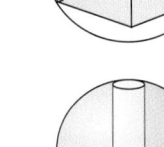 **Challenge**

43. Answers may vary. Sample: You could lift the small ball because it weighs about 75 lb. The big ball would be much harder to lift since it weighs about 253 lb.

48a. Cube; explanations may vary. Sample:
If $s^3 = \frac{4}{3}\pi r^3$,
then $s = \sqrt[3]{\frac{4\pi}{3}} \, r$.
So $6s^2 = 6\left(\sqrt[3]{\frac{4\pi}{3}} \, r\right)^2$
$\approx 15.6 \, r^2 > 4\pi r^2$.

27. Meteorology On September 3, 1970, a hailstone with diameter 5.6 in. fell at Coffeyville, Kansas. It weighed about 0.018 lb/in.³ compared to the normal 0.033 lb/in.³ for ice. About how heavy was this Kansas hailstone? **1.7 lb**

28. Critical Thinking Which is greater, the total volume of three spheres, each of which has diameter 3 in., or the volume of one sphere that has diameter 8 in.? **See margin.**

Find the volume in terms of π of each sphere with the given surface area. $\frac{500}{3}\pi$ mm³

29. 4π m² $\frac{4}{3}\pi$ m³   **30.** 36π in.² 36π in.³ **31.** 9π ft² $\frac{9}{2}\pi$ ft³   **32.** 100π mm²

33. 25π yd²   **34.** 144π cm²   **35.** 49 m² $\frac{343}{6}\pi$ m³ **36.** 225π mi²
 $\frac{125}{6}\pi$ yd³ 288π cm³ $\frac{1125}{2}\pi$ mi³

37. A balloon has a 14-in. diameter when it is fully inflated. Half of the air is let out of the balloon. Assume that the balloon is a sphere.
  a. Find the volume of the fully-inflated balloon in terms of π. $457\frac{1}{3}\pi$ in.³
  b. Find the volume of the half-inflated balloon in terms of π. $228\frac{2}{3}\pi$ in.³
  c. What is the diameter of the half-inflated balloon to the nearest inch? **11 in.**

38. Sports Equipment The golf ball diameter is 1.68 in.
  a. Approximate the surface area of the golf ball. **about 8.9 in.²**
  b. Critical Thinking Do you think that the value you found in part (a) is greater or less than the actual surface area of the golf ball? Explain. **See left.**

39. Open-Ended Give the dimensions of a cylinder and a sphere that have the same volume. **Answers may vary. Sample: sphere radius 3 in.; cylinder radius 3 in., height 4 in.**

Find the surface area and volume of each figure.

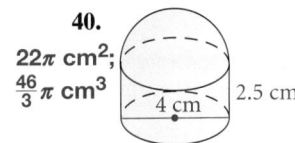 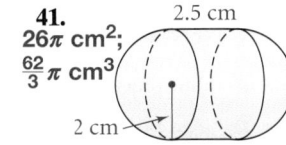 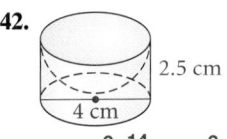

40.
22π cm²;
$\frac{46}{3}\pi$ cm³
4 cm   2.5 cm

41.
26π cm²;
$\frac{62}{3}\pi$ cm³
2.5 cm
2 cm

42.
2.5 cm
4 cm
22π cm²; $\frac{14}{3}\pi$ cm³

43. Science The density of steel is about 0.28 lb/in.³. Could you lift a solid steel ball with radius 4 in.? With radius 6 in.? Explain. **See left.**

44. A cube with edges 6 in. long fits snugly inside the sphere. The diagonal of the cube is the diameter of the sphere.
  a. Find the length of the diagonal and the radius of the sphere. Leave your answers in simplest radical form.
  b. What is the volume of the space between the sphere and the cube to the nearest tenth? **371.7 in.³**
  44a. $6\sqrt{3}$ in.; $3\sqrt{3}$ in.

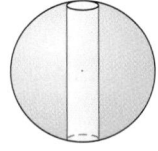 **Graphing Calculator** The sphere has a 10-cm radius. Of all the cylinders that fit snugly inside the sphere, such as the one shown here, find the dimensions of the one with the greatest measure indicated. (*Hint:* Use the Exploration on page 536.)

45. lateral area   **46.** volume
$r \approx 7.1$ cm, $h \approx 14.1$ cm $r \approx 8.2$ cm, $h \approx 11.4$ cm

47. A plane intersects a sphere to form a circular cross section. The radius of the sphere is 17 cm and the plane comes to within 8 cm of the center. Draw a sketch and find the area of the cross section, to the nearest whole number.
  707 cm²

48. Suppose a cube and a sphere have the same volume.
  a. Which has the greater surface area? Explain. **See left.**
  b. Writing Explain why spheres are rarely used for packaging.
     Answers may vary. Sample: Spheres are difficult to stack.

562 Chapter 10 Surface Area and Volume

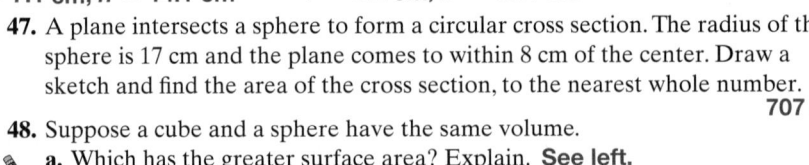

pages 560–564 Exercises

28. 8 in. sphere; the volume of the three spheres is 13.5π and of the large sphere is $85\frac{1}{3}\pi$.

Find the radius of a sphere with the given property.

49. The number of square meters of surface area equals the number of cubic meters of volume. **3 m**

50. The ratio of surface area in square meters to volume in cubic meters is 1 : 5.

51. **History** The sphere fits snugly inside the cylinder. Archimedes (c. 287–212 B.C.) asked that such a figure be put on his gravestone along with the ratio of their volumes, a finding that he regarded as his greatest. What is that ratio? **2:3**

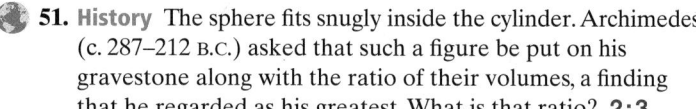

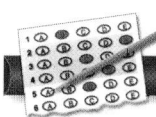

Standardized Test Prep

Reading Comprehension

Read the passage below, then answer Exercises 52–54 based on what is stated in the passage.

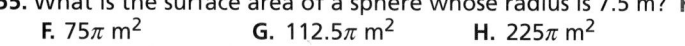

Believe It Or Not

J.C. Payne, a Texas farmer, is the world champion string collector. The ball of string he wound over a three-year period has a circumference of 41.5 ft. It weighs 13,000 lb.

Listed in the Guinness Book of World Records, the ball of string is now in a museum devoted to oddities. It took almost a dozen men with fork-lift trucks to load the ball onto a truck to move it there.

52. What is the radius of the ball of string to the nearest tenth of a foot? **B**
A. 3.3 ft   **B.** 6.6 ft   **C.** 13.2 ft   **D.** 20.75 ft

53. Which is the best approximation of the volume of the ball of string? **H**
F. 300 ft^3 **G.** 600 ft^3 **H.** 1200 ft^3 **I.** 2400 ft^3

54. If Mr. Payne wound the same amount of string each year, which is the best estimate of the radius after one year? **D**
A. 2.2 ft   **B.** 2.3 ft   **C.** 4.4 ft   **D.** 4.6 ft

Multiple Choice

55. What is the surface area of a sphere whose radius is 7.5 m? **H**
F. 75π m^2 **G.** 112.5π m^2 **H.** 225π m^2 **I.** 562.5π m^2

56. What is the volume of a sphere whose radius is 6 ft? **C**
A. 48π ft^3 **B.** 144π ft^3 **C.** 288π ft^3 **D.** 324π ft^3

57. The volume of a sphere is 26,244π cm^3. What is its surface area? **I**
F. 1070π cm^2 **G.** 1402π cm^2 **H.** 2448π cm^2 **I.** 2916π cm^2

58. The surface area of a sphere is 576π in.^{2}. What is its diameter? **C**
A. 1 ft   **B.** 1.7 ft   **C.** 2 ft   **D.** 3.5 ft

Short Response

59. The surface area of a sphere is 36π ft^2. **a–b. See margin p. 564.**
     a. What is the radius of the sphere? Show your work.
     b. What is the volume of the sphere? Show your work.

Take It to the NET
Online lesson quiz at
www.PHSchool.com
Web Code: afa-1007

Lesson 10-7 Surface Areas and Volumes of Spheres **563**

---

59. [2] a. S.A. = $4\pi r^2$
     36π = $4\pi r^2$
     9 = r^2
     r = 3 ft

b. $V = \frac{4}{3}\pi r^3$
     $V = \frac{4}{3}\pi 3^3$
     $V = 36\pi$ ft^3

[1] one computational
error

 Lesson Quiz 10-7

For Exercises 1–3, find the surface area. Leave your answer in terms of π.

1. a sphere whose diameter is 13 cm **169π cm^2**

2. a ball whose circumference is 19π mm **361π mm^2**

3. a sphere whose volume is 288π in.^{3} **144π in.^{2}**

For Exercises 4 and 5, find the volume. Round your answer to the nearest whole number.

4. sphere with radius 5 m **524 m^3**

5. sphere with diameter 7 yd **180 yd^3**

Alternative Assessment

Have students work in pairs to solve the following problem and write a full explanation: A spherical ornament is snugly packaged inside a cube-shaped box with 2-in. edges so that it touches all six sides. Find the volume and surface areas of the box and of the ornament. Round to the nearest tenth.

Standardized Test Prep

 Resources

For additional practice with a variety of test item formats:
- Standardized Test Prep, p. 577
- Test-Taking Strategies, p. 572
- Test-Taking Strategies with Transparencies

Exercises 52–54 Whenever a problem has text preceding it, instruct students to read the text carefully before and after reading the problem to extract the information necessary to solve it.

To check understanding of Lessons 10-4 to 10-7:

Checkpoint Quiz 2 (p. 564)

📁 **Teaching Resources**
Checkpoint Quiz 2 (also in Prentice Hall Assessment System)

👥 **Reaching All Students**
Reading and Math Literacy 10C

Spanish versions available

Mixed Review

Lesson 10-6   **Find the volume of each figure to the nearest cubic unit.**

60. 3 m   **16 m³**   4 m   4 m

61. 2 in.   5 in.   **19 in.³**

62. **19,396 mm³**   42 mm   21 mm

Lesson 9-2   **63.** A leg of a right triangle measures 4 cm and the hypotenuse measures 7 cm. Find the measure of each acute angle of the triangle to the nearest degree. **35, 55**

64. The length of each side of a rhombus is 16. The longer diagonal has length 26. Find the measures of the angles of the rhombus to the nearest degree. **109, 109, 71, 71**

Lesson 8-6   **The similarity ratio of a pair of similar isosceles trapezoids is 2 : 3. A diagonal of the smaller figure has length 7 cm.**

65. Find the length of a diagonal in the larger trapezoid. **10.5 cm**

66. The perimeter of the larger trapezoid is 40.5 cm. What is the perimeter of the smaller trapezoid? **27 cm**

67. The area of the smaller trapezoid is 30 cm². What is the area of the larger trapezoid? **67.5 cm²**

✓ Checkpoint Quiz 2   Lessons 10-4 through 10-7

📱 Instant self-check quiz online and on CD-ROM

Find the surface area and volume of each figure to the nearest tenth.

1. 3 ft   5 ft   **60.2 ft²; 22.5 ft³**

2. 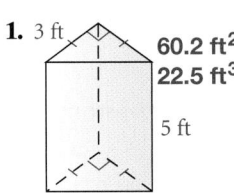 10 in.   6 in.   **332.9 in.²; 377.0 in.³**

3. 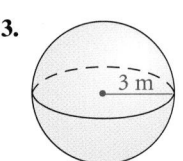 3 m   **113.1 m²; 113.1 m³**

4. 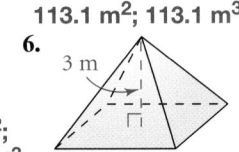 5 cm   9 cm   **439.8 cm²; 706.9 cm³**

5. 7 yd   9 yd   **207 yd²; 144.8 yd³**

6. 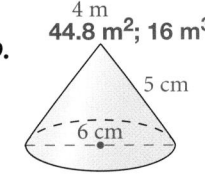 3 m   4 m   **44.8 m²; 16 m³**

7. 20 m   16 m   **1181.7 m²; 2217.0 m³**

8. 3 ft   2 ft   **32 ft²; 12 ft³**

9. 5 cm   6 cm   **75.4 cm²; 37.7 cm³**

10. The balls; the volume of the space is $2\pi r^3$ and the volume of the balls is $4\pi r^3$.

10. Critical Thinking Tennis balls fit snugly inside a cylinder as shown. Which is greater, the volume of the three tennis balls or the volume of the space around the balls? Explain. **See left.**

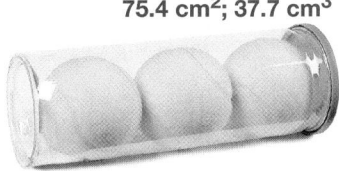

 **Technology**

Exploring Similar Solids

 **Technology**

Exploring Similar Solids

Students use geometry software to investigate how the similarity ratio of similar solids is related to the ratio of their surface areas and the ratio of their volumes.

To explore the surface areas and volumes of similar rectangular prisms, you can set up a spreadsheet like the one below. You choose the numbers for the length, width, height, and similarity ratio. The computer will use formulas to calculate all the other numbers.

	A	B	C	D	E	F	G	H	I
1					Surface		Similarity		
2		Length	Width	Height	Area	Volume	Ratio (II : I)	Ratio of	Ratio of
3	Rectangular Prism I	6	4	23	508	552	2	Surface	Volumes
4								Areas (II : I)	(II : I)
5	Similar Prism II	12	8	46	2032	4416		4	8

In cell E3 enter the formula =2*(B3*C3+B3*D3+C3*D3).
This will calculate the sum of the areas of the six faces of Prism I.
In cell F3 enter the formula =B3*C3*D3. This will calculate the volume of Prism I.

In cells B5, C5, and D5 enter the formulas =G3*B3, =G3*C3, and =G3*D3, respectively. These will calculate the dimensions of similar Prism II. Copy the formulas from E3 and F3 into E5 and F5 to calculate the surface area and volume of Prism II.

In cell H5 enter the formula =E5/E3 and in cell I5 enter the formula =F5/F3. These will calculate the ratios of the surface areas and volumes.

Investigate

In row 3, enter numbers for the length, width, height, and similarity ratio. Change those numbers to investigate how the ratio of the surface areas and the ratio of the volumes are each related to the similarity ratio.

EXERCISES

Make a Conjecture **State a relationship that seems to be true about the similarity ratio and each given ratio.**

2. The ratio of surface areas is the similarity ratio squared.

1. the ratio of volumes   2. the ratio of surface areas
The ratio of volumes is the similarity ratio cubed.

Extend

Set up spreadsheets that allow you to investigate the following ratios. State a conclusion from each investigation. 3–8. See margin.

3. the volumes of similar cylinders   4. the lateral areas of similar cylinders

5. the surface areas of similar cylinders   6. the volumes of similar square pyramids

7. the lateral areas of similar square pyramids   8. the surface areas of similar square pyramids

Resources

Students may use any spreadsheet software to explore the surface areas and volumes of similar solids.

Teaching Notes

By using a spreadsheet that calculates the surface areas and volumes of prisms, students are able to focus on the relationship of similarity, surface area, and volume ratios for many different prisms. This exploration will prepare students for the Areas and Volumes of Similar Solids Theorem in Lesson 10-8.

Connection to Algebra

Have students use their knowledge of surface area and volume to explain what function the symbol * represents.

Teaching Tip

By starting with similarity ratios whose numerators and denominators are whole numbers, students are more likely to see how the ratio of surface areas and ratio of volumes are related to the similarity ratio.

page 565   Technology

3. **The ratio of volumes is the similarity ratio cubed.**

4. **The ratio of lateral areas is the similarity ratio squared.**

5. **The ratio of surface areas is the similarity ratio squared.**

6. **The ratio of volumes is the similarity ratio cubed.**

7. **The ratio of lateral areas is the similarity ratio squared.**

8. **The ratio of the surface areas is the similarity ratio squared.**

1. Plan

Lesson Preview

✔ **Check Skills You'll Need**

Determining Similarity
Lesson 8-2: Example 2
Exercises 7–12
Extra Practice, p. 697

Finding Volumes of Prisms and Cylinders
Lesson 10-5: Examples 1, 3
Exercises 1–3, 9–11
Extra Practice, p. 699

Lesson Resources

📁 **Teaching Resources**
Practice, Reteaching, Enrichment

👥 **Reaching All Students**
Practice Workbook 10-8
Spanish Practice Workbook 10-8
Informal Geometry Planning
  Guide 10-8

⏰ **Presentation Assistant Plus!**
Transparencies
• Check Skills You'll Need 10-8
• Additional Examples 10-8
• Student Edition Answers 10-8
• Lesson Quiz 10-8
PH Presentation Pro CD 10-8

PRENTICE HALL
ASSESSMENT SYSTEM

Computer Test Generator CD

💿 **Technology**
Resource Pro® CD-ROM
Computer Test Generator CD
Prentice Hall Presentation Pro CD

💻 **www.PHSchool.com**
Student Site
• Teacher Web Code: afk-5500
• Self-grading Lesson Quiz
Teacher Center
• Lesson Planner
• Resources

Plus 📘**iTEXT**

566

10-8

Areas and Volumes of Similar Solids

North Carolina Objectives

1.02   Use length, area, and volume of geometric figures to solve problems.
2.04   Develop and apply properties of solids to solve problems.

Lesson Preview

What You'll Learn

OBJECTIVE 1
To find relationships between the ratios of the areas and volumes of similar solids

. . . And Why

To use similarity ratios to find the weight of an object, as in Example 4

✔ Check Skills You'll Need   (For help, go to Lessons 8-2 and 10-5.)

Are the figures similar? Explain. Include the similarity ratio as appropriate.

1. two squares, one with 3-in. sides and the other with 1-in. sides **See back of book.**
2. two isosceles right triangles, one with a 3-cm hypotenuse and the other with a 1-cm leg **Yes; all corr. ⚟ are ≅ and corr. sides are prop.; 3 : √2.**

Find the volume of each space figure.

3. a cube with a 3-in. edge **27 in.³**
4. a 3 m-by-5 m-by-9 m rectangular prism **135 m³**
5. a cylinder with radius 4 cm and height 8 cm **about 402.1 cm³**

New Vocabulary   • similar solids   • similarity ratio

---

iTEXT Interactive lesson includes instant self-check, tutorials, and activities.

OBJECTIVE

1   Finding Relationships in Area and Volume

Similar solids have the same shape, and all their corresponding dimensions are proportional. The ratio of corresponding linear dimensions of two similar solids is the **similarity ratio.** Any two cubes are similar, as are any two spheres.

Real-World 🌐 Connection

These Russian nesting dolls suggest similar solids.

① EXAMPLE Identifying Similar Solids

Are the two rectangular prisms similar? If so, give the similarity ratio.

a.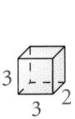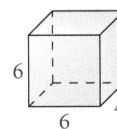
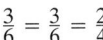

$$\frac{3}{6} = \frac{3}{6} = \frac{2}{4}$$

The rectangular prisms are similar because the ratios of the corresponding linear dimensions are equal.

The similarity ratio is $\frac{1}{2}$.

b.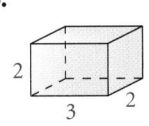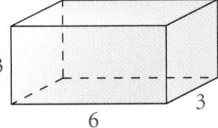

$$\frac{2}{3} \neq \frac{3}{6}$$

The rectangular prisms are not similar because the ratios of corresponding linear dimensions are not equal.

✔ Check Understanding

① Are the two cylinders similar? If so, give the similarity ratio.
yes; 6 : 5

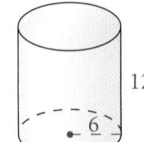 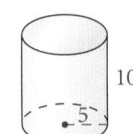

566   Chapter 10   Surface Area and Volume

INSTANT CHECK SYSTEM
🔄 Ongoing Assessment and Intervention

Before the Lesson
Diagnose prerequisite skills using:
• Check Skills You'll Need

During the Lesson
Monitor progress using:
• Check Understanding
• Additional Examples
• Standardized Test Prep

After the Lesson
Assess knowledge using:
• Lesson Quiz
• Computer Test Generator CD

The two similar prisms shown here suggest two important relationships for similar solids.

The ratio of the side lengths is 1 : 2.
The ratio of the surface areas is 22 : 88, or 1 : 4.
The ratio of the volumes is 6 : 48, or 1 : 8.

The ratio of the surface areas equals the square of the similarity ratio. The ratio of the volumes equals the cube of the similarity ratio. These two facts apply to all similar solids.

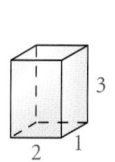
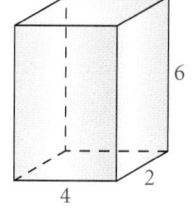

S.A. = 22 m^2 S.A. = 88 m^2
V = 6 m^3 V = 48 m^3

 Key Concepts

Theorem 10-12	Areas and Volumes of Similar Solids

If the similarity ratio of two similar solids is $a : b$, then
(1) the ratio of their corresponding areas is $a^2 : b^2$, and
(2) the ratio of their volumes is $a^3 : b^3$.

2 EXAMPLE Finding the Similarity Ratio

Find the similarity ratio of two cubes with volumes of 729 cm^3 and 1331 cm^3.

$\dfrac{a^3}{b^3} = \dfrac{729}{1331}$ **The ratio of the volumes is $a^3 : b^3$.**

$\dfrac{a}{b} = \dfrac{9}{11}$ **Take cube roots.**

● The similarity ratio is 9 : 11.

 **Check Understanding** **2** Find the similarity ratio of two similar prisms with surface areas 144 m^2 and 324 m^2.
2 : 3

3 EXAMPLE Using a Similarity Ratio

Paint Cans The lateral areas of two similar paint cans are 1019 cm^2 and 425 cm^2. The volume of the small can is 1157 cm^3. Find the volume of the large can.

First find the similarity ratio $a : b$.

$\dfrac{a^2}{b^2} = \dfrac{1019}{425}$ **The ratio of the surface areas is $a^2 : b^2$.**

$\dfrac{a}{b} = \dfrac{\sqrt{1019}}{\sqrt{425}}$ **Take square roots.**

 Reading Math

V_{large} and V_{small} are the volumes of the large and small cans, respectively.

Use the similarity ratio to find the volume.

$\dfrac{V_{large}}{V_{small}} = \dfrac{\sqrt{1019}^3}{\sqrt{425}^3}$ **The ratio of the volumes is $a^3 : b^3$.**

$\dfrac{V_{large}}{1157} = \dfrac{\sqrt{1019}^3}{\sqrt{425}^3}$ **Substitute 1157 for V_{small}.**

$V_{large} = 1157 \cdot \dfrac{\sqrt{1019}^3}{\sqrt{425}^3}$ **Solve for V_{large}.**

$V_{large} \approx 4295$ **Use a calculator.**

● The volume of the large paint can is about 4295 cm^3.

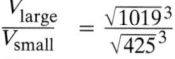 **Check Understanding** **3** The volumes of two similar solids are 128 m^3 and 250 m^3. The surface area of the larger solid is 250 m^2. What is the surface area of the smaller solid? **160 m^2**

Lesson 10-8   Areas and Volumes of Similar Solids   **567**

 **Reaching All Students**

Below Level Bring in sample 8-oz. and 26-oz. cans of tomato sauce. Have students calculate the similarity ratio, and measure the volumes. The ratio of the volumes will illustrate Theorem 10-12 (2).	**Advanced Learners** After Example 4, have students discuss ways to estimate the weight of the water in a swimming pool, given the shape and dimensions.	**Tactile Learners** See note on page 567. **Auditory Learners** See note on page 567.

Math Background

The surface areas and volumes of similar solids are directly proportional, respectively, to the square and cube of their similarity ratios. The weight of a prism is twice the weight of a similar prism made of the same material when the ratio of corresponding lengths is $\sqrt[3]{2} : 1 \approx 5 : 4$.

OBJECTIVE
1 Teaching Notes

Teaching Tip
Remind students that when the similarity ratio of two similar plane figures is $a : b$, the ratio of their perimeters is $a : b$ and the ratio of their areas is $a^2 : b^2$.

Tactile Learners
Students can build similar rectangular prisms with cubes to investigate the Areas and Volumes of Similar Solids Theorem.

Auditory Learners
Have students suggest ways to remember whether the ratio of surface areas or volumes is the square of or the cube of the similarity ratio.

 **2 EXAMPLE** Connection to Algebra

Students are accustomed to solving an equation for a single variable but not for a ratio. Point out that only the ratio $\frac{a}{b}$ is needed, not a value of a or b.

 **3 EXAMPLE**

Review the four properties of proportions in Lesson 8-1, especially the Cross-Product Property.

4 EXAMPLE Alternative Method

Ask: *How can you find the weight without using a variable or proportion?* Sample: The volume and weight of the similar paperweight are 27 times the volume and weight of the original, so multiply the weight of the original by 27.

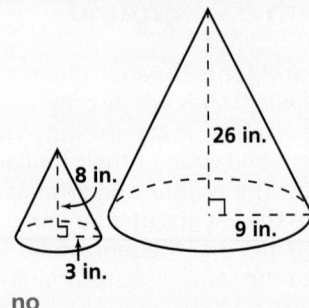

no

❷ Find the similarity ratio of two similar cylinders with surface areas of 98π ft^2 and 2π ft^2. **7 : 1**

❸ Two similar square pyramids have volumes of 48 cm^3 and 162 cm^3. The surface area of the larger pyramid is 135 cm^2. Find the surface area of the smaller pyramid. **60 cm^2**

❹ A box of detergent shaped like a rectangular prism is 6 in. high and holds 3.25 lb of detergent. How much detergent would a similar box that is 8 in. high hold? Round your answer to the nearest tenth. **7.7 lb**

Closure

The volumes of two similar solids are 81 m^3 and 375 m^3. The height of the smaller solid is 6 m. The surface area of the larger solid is 325 m^2. Find the height of the larger solid and the surface area of the smaller solid. **height: 10 m; surface area: 117 m^2**

The weights of solid objects made of the same material are proportional to their volumes.

4 EXAMPLE   **Real-World 🌐 Connection**

Paperweights A marble paperweight shaped like a pyramid weighs 0.15 lb. How much does a similarly shaped marble paperweight weigh if each dimension is three times as large?

The similarity ratio is 1 : 3. The ratio of the volumes, and hence the ratio of the weights, is $1^3 : 3^3$, or 1 : 27.

$\frac{1}{27} = \frac{0.15}{x}$ **Let x = the weight of the larger paperweight.**

$x = 27(0.15)$ **Use the Cross Product Property.**

$x = 4.05$

● The larger paperweight weighs about 4 lb.

✓ **Check Understanding** ❹ Find the weight of a marble bead that is similar to the paperweight in Example 4 but has dimensions half as large. **0.01875 lb**

EXERCISES

For more practice, see Extra Practice.

Practice and Problem Solving

Ⓐ **Practice by Example**

Example 1 (page 566)

Are the two figures similar? If so, give the similarity ratio.

1. no

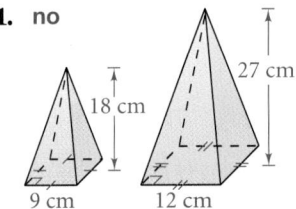

2.   **yes; 3 : 2**

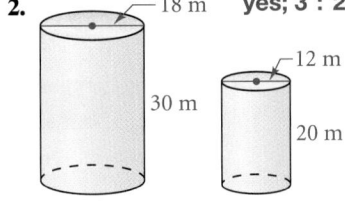

3.

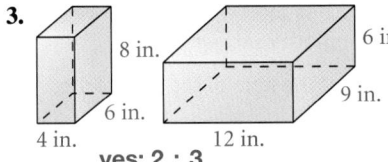

yes; 2 : 3

4.   **no**

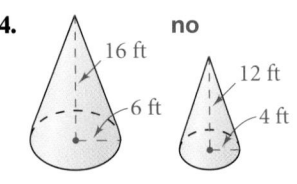

5. two cubes, one with 3-cm edges, the other with 4.5-cm edges **yes; 2 : 3**

6. a cylinder and a square prism each with 3-in. radii and 1-in. heights **no**

Example 2 (page 567)

Each pair of figures is similar. Use the given information to find the similarity ratio of the smaller figure to the larger figure.

7. 5 : 6

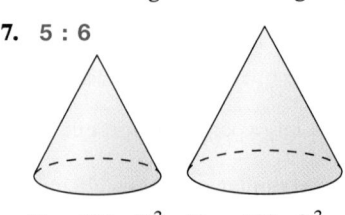

$V = 250\pi$ ft^3 $V = 432\pi$ ft^3

8.   **6 : 7**

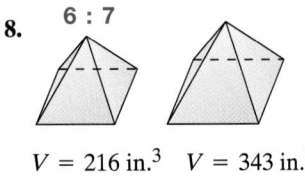

$V = 216$ in.^{3} $V = 343$ in.^{3}

568   Chapter 10   Surface Area and Volume

9. 3 : 4

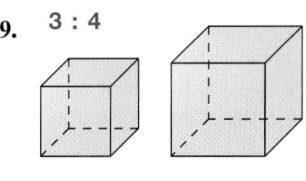

S.A. = 18 m²   S.A. = 32 m²

10. 2 : 5

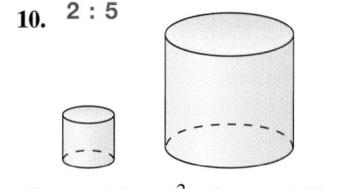

S.A. = 20π yd²   S.A. = 125π yd²

Example 3
(page 567)

The surface areas of two similar figures are given. The volume of the larger figure is given. Find the volume of the smaller figure.

11. S.A. = 18 in.²
S.A. = 98 in.²
V = 343 in.³
27 in.³

12. S.A. = 192 m²
S.A. = 1728 m²
V = 4860 m³
180 m³

13. S.A. = 52 ft²
S.A. = 208 ft²
V = 192 ft³
24 ft³

The volumes of two similar figures are given. The surface area of the smaller figure is given. Find the surface area of the larger figure.

14. V = 27 in.³
V = 125 in.³
S.A. = 63 in.²
175 in.²

15. V = 5 m³
V = 40 m³
S.A. = 4 m²
16 m²

16. V = 54 yd³
V = 128 yd³
S.A. = 18 yd²
32 yd²

Example 4
(page 568)

17. Packaging There are 750 toothpicks in a regular-sized box. If a jumbo box is made by doubling all the dimensions of the regular-sized box, how many toothpicks will the jumbo box hold? **6000 toothpicks**

18. Packaging A cylinder 4 in. in diameter and 6 in. high holds 1 lb of oatmeal. To the nearest ounce, how much oatmeal will a similar 10-in.-high cylinder hold? (*Hint:* 1 lb = 16 oz) **74 oz**

19a. It is 64 times the smaller prism.
b. It is 64 times the smaller prism.

19. A regular pentagonal solid prism has 9-cm base edges. A larger, similar solid prism of the same material has 36-cm base edges. How does each indicated measurement for the larger prism compare to the same measurement for the smaller prism? **a–b. See left.**
  a. the volume   **b.** the weight

B Apply Your Skills

20. Two similar prisms have heights 4 cm and 10 cm.
  a. What is their similarity ratio? **2 : 5**
  b. What is the ratio of their surface areas? **4 : 25**
  c. What is the ratio of their volumes? **8 : 125**

21. Atomic Clock A company announced that it had developed the technology to reduce the size of its atomic clock, which is used in electronic devices that transmit data. The company claims that the smaller clock will be similar to the existing clock made of the same material. It will be $\frac{1}{10}$ the size of its existing atomic clocks and $\frac{1}{100}$ the weight. Do these ratios make sense? Explain. **See margin.**

22. Is there a value of x for which the rectangular prisms below are similar? Explain. **Yes; 60;** $\frac{80}{60} = \frac{40}{30} = \frac{60}{45} = \frac{4}{3}$.

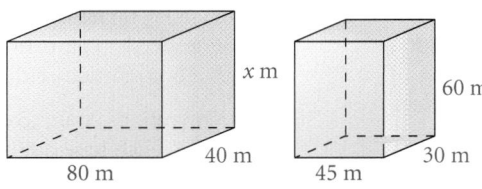

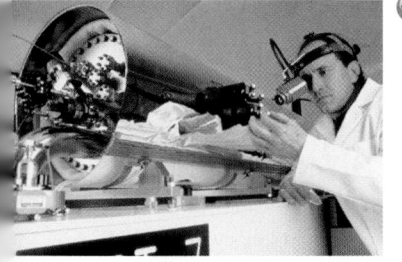

Real-World Connection

The time scale of an atomic clock is based on vibrations of atoms and molecules.

23. The volume of a spherical balloon with radius 3.1 cm is about 125 cm³. Estimate the volume of a similar balloon with radius 6 cm. **about 1000 cm³**

pages 568–571 Exercises

21. No; explanations may vary. Sample: If "size" refers to the vol., then the new clock should be at $\frac{1}{10}$ the weight.

Assignment Guide

1 Objective
  Ⓐ Ⓑ Core 1–34
  Ⓒ Extension 35–37

Standardized Test Prep 38–42

Mixed Review 43–50

Error Prevention

Exercises 7–10 Students may forget to take the square or cube root to find the similarity ratio. Suggest that they write the measurement units as part of the ratio to help them remember the correct relationship.

Exercise 22 Do this exercise as a class to help correct the common misconception that similar prisms must be shown in the same orientation.

Connection to Biology

Exercise 35 The Areas and Volumes of Similar Solids Theorem has dramatic implications for the scale and size of animals. Recommend that interested students read J.B.S. Haldane's classic essay *On Being the Right Size.*

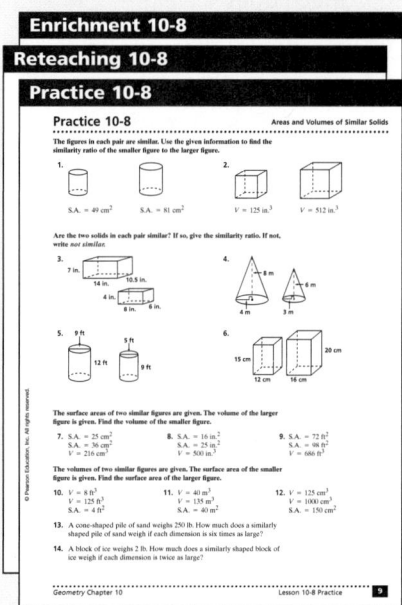

Lesson Quiz 10-8

For Exercises 1 and 2, are the two solids similar? If so, give the similarity ratio of the smaller figure to the larger figure.

1.

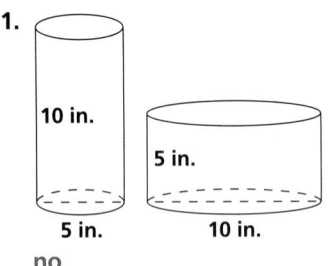

10 in.

5 in.

5 in.   10 in.

no

2.

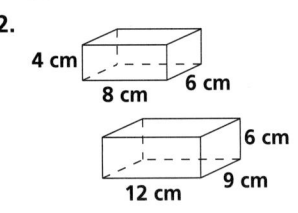

4 cm

8 cm   6 cm

6 cm

12 cm   9 cm

yes; 2 : 3

3. Find the similarity ratio of two spheres with volumes of 20π m^3 and 160π m^3. **1 : 2**

4. The volumes of two similar solids are 54 ft^3 and 250 ft^3. The surface area of the smaller solid is 45 ft^2. Find the surface area of the larger solid. **125 ft^2**

5. A solid chocolate rabbit is 6 in. high and weighs 0.25 lb. A similar chocolate rabbit is 12 in. high. How much does it weigh? **2 lb**

Alternative Assessment

Assign students to groups of three or four. Have each student find one set of possible dimensions for two similar rectangular prisms whose volumes are 288 cm^3 and 972 cm^3, draw the prisms, and list the similarity ratio, ratio of surface areas, and ratio of volumes. Students then should compare their drawings to see the number of different figures that are represented.

---

24. No; an increase in the lengths of sides does not create prop. ratios unless the box is a cube.

25. Answers may vary. Sample: A sphere has only one measure, r, so there's only one possible ratio.

Challenge

35c. His weight is 1000 times the weight of an average person, but his bones can only support 600 times the weight.

---

24. **Critical Thinking** A carpenter is making a blanket chest based on an antique chest. Both chests have the shape of a rectangular prism. The length, width, and height of the new chest will all be 4 in. greater than the respective dimensions of the antique. Will the chests be similar? Explain. **See left.**

25. **Writing** Explain why all spheres are similar. **See left.**

26. Two similar pyramids have lateral area 8 ft^2 and 18 ft^2. The volume of the smaller pyramid is 32 ft^3. Find the volume of the larger pyramid. **108 ft^3**

27. The volumes of two spheres are 729 in.^{3} and 27 in.^{3}.
    a. Find the ratio of their radii. **3 : 1**
    b. Find the ratio of their surface areas. **9 : 1**

28. The volumes of two similar pyramids are 1331 cm^3 and 2744 cm^3.
    a. Find the ratio of their heights. **11 : 14**
    b. Find the ratio of their surface areas. **121 : 196**

29. A clown's face on a balloon is 4 in. high when the balloon holds 108 in.^{3} of air. How much air must the balloon hold for the face to be 8 in. high? **864 in.^{3}**

Copy and complete the table for the similar solids.

	Similarity Ratio	Ratio of Surface Areas	Ratio of Volumes	
30.	1 : 2	▦ : ▦	▦ : ▦	1 : 4; 1 : 8
31.	3 : 5	▦ : ▦	▦ : ▦	9 : 25; 27 : 125
32.	▦ : ▦	49 : 81	▦ : ▦	7 : 9; 343 : 729
33.	▦ : ▦	▦ : ▦	125 : 512	5 : 8; 25 : 64

34. **Literature** In *Gulliver's Travels* by Jonathan Swift, Gulliver first traveled to Lilliput. The Lilliputian average height was one twelfth of Gulliver's height.
    a. How many Lilliputian coats could be made from the material in Gulliver's coat? (*Hint:* Use the ratio of surface areas.) **144 coats**
    b. How many Lilliputian meals would be needed to make a meal for Gulliver? (*Hint:* Use the ratio of volumes.) **1728 meals**

35. **Indirect Reasoning** Some stories say that Paul Bunyan was ten times as tall as the average human. Assume that Paul Bunyan's bone structure was proportional to that of ordinary people.
    a. Strength of bones is proportional to the area of their cross section. How many times as strong as the average person's bones would Paul Bunyan's bones be? **100 times**
    b. Weights of objects made of like material are proportional to their volumes. How many times the average person's weight would Paul Bunyan's weight be? **1000 times**
    c. Human leg bones can support about 6 times the average person's weight. Use your answers to parts (a) and (b) to explain why Paul Bunyan could not exist with a bone structure that was proportional to that of ordinary people.

36. Square pyramids A and B are similar. In pyramid A, each base edge is 12 cm. In pyramid B, each base edge is 3 cm and the volume is 6 cm^3.
    a. Find the volume of pyramid A. **384 cm^3**
    b. Find the ratio of the surface area of A to the surface area of B. **16 : 1**
    c. Find the surface area of each pyramid.
    pyramid A: 384 cm^2; pyramid B: 24 cm^2

37. The cone is cut by a plane parallel to its base. The small cone on top is similar to the large cone. The ratio of the slant heights of the cones is 1 : 2. Find the ratio indicated.

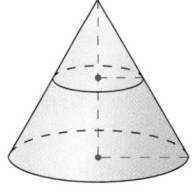

    a. the surface area of the large cone to that of the small cone; the volume of the large cone to that of the small cone **4 : 1; 8 : 1**

    b. the surface area of the frustum to that of the large cone; to that of the small cone **See below left.**

    c. the volume of the frustum to that of the large cone; to that of the small cone **7 : 8; 7 : 1**

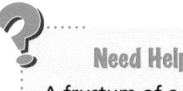

Need Help?

A frustum of a cone is defined on page 556.

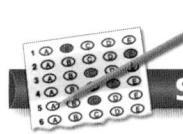

Standardized Test Prep

Gridded Response

37b. Let r = radius, ℓ = slant height of small cone. $3\ell + 5r : 4\ell + 4r$; $3\ell + 5r : \ell + r$

38. The slant heights of two similar pyramids are in the ratio 1 : 5. The volume of the smaller pyramid is 60 m³. What is the volume in cubic meters of the larger pyramid? **7500**

39. A lawn chair weighs 8 lb. A child's lawn chair has dimensions exactly one half those of the larger chair. How many pounds does the child's chair weigh? **1**

40. A model of a historical home has dimensions that are one fifteenth the dimensions of the actual home. The area of a window in the model is 2 cm². What is the area in square centimeters of the corresponding window in the actual home? **450**

41. The volumes of two similar rectangular prisms are 64 cm³ and 1000 cm³. The surface area of the smaller figure is 112 cm². What is the surface area in square centimeters of the larger figure? **700**

42. The surface areas of two similar cylinders are 54 ft² and 96 ft². The volume of the smaller cylinder is 216 ft³. What is the volume in cubic feet of the larger cylinder? **512**

Take It to the NET

Online lesson quiz at
www.PHSchool.com

Web Code: afa-1008

Mixed Review

Lesson 10-7   **43. Sports Equipment** The circumference of a regulation basketball is between 75 cm and 78 cm. What are the smallest and the largest surface areas that a basketball can have? Give your answers to the nearest whole unit.
     1790 cm² and 1937 cm²

Find the volume and surface area of each sphere to the nearest tenth.

44. diameter = 6 in.   **45.** circumference = 2.5π m   **46.** radius = 6 in.
113.1 in.³; 113.1 in.²   **8.2 m³; 19.6 m²**   **904.8 in.³; 452.4 in.²**

Lesson 8-4   **47.** The altitude to the hypotenuse of a right triangle ABC divides the hypotenuse into 12-mm and 16-mm segments. Find the length of each of the following.
    a. the altitude to the hypotenuse $8\sqrt{3}$ **mm**
    b. the shorter leg of $\triangle ABC$ $4\sqrt{21}$ **mm**
    c. the longer leg of $\triangle ABC$ $8\sqrt{7}$ **mm**

Lesson 8-1 x^2 **Algebra** **Solve each proportion.**

48. $\frac{25}{16} = \frac{x}{16}$ **25**   **49.** $\frac{21}{x} = \frac{8}{5}$ **13.125**   **50.** $\frac{3}{8} = \frac{n}{n+4}$ **2.4**

Standardized Test Prep

A sheet of blank grids is available in the Test-Taking Strategies with Transparencies booklet. Give this sheet to students for practice with filling in the grids.

📁 **Resources**

For additional practice with a variety of test item formats:
- Standardized Test Prep, p. 577
- Test-Taking Strategies, p. 572
- Test-Taking Strategies with Transparencies

Exercises 40–42 Students should examine the measurement units given to help them remember which ratio to use. For example, they may remember that the ratio of volumes is $\frac{a^3}{b^3}$ because volume is measured in cubic units.

Choosing "Cannot Be Determined"

Many assessment tests include multiple-choice questions in which the final answer choice is a form of "cannot be determined." This feature helps students understand how to evaluate whether enough information is given to answer the question.

Resources

PRENTICE HALL ASSESSMENT SYSTEM

Test-Taking Strategies with Transparencies
- Transparency 10
- Practice sheet 22

Teaching Notes

Help students understand that if they cannot determine to their satisfaction that an answer is correct, or if they can establish that there is more than one possible answer, the correct answer choice is probably "cannot be determined."

Connection to Algebra

Quite often, thinking algebraically is the key to choosing "cannot be determined." Discuss as a class how algebra is used to reason through the example and exercises in this feature.

Test-Taking Strategies with Transparencies

Test-Taking Strategy: Choosing "Cannot Be Determined"

When you are not given enough information, you may not be able to determine the answer.

Example The area of a rectangle is 12. What is its perimeter?
A. 14   B. 16   C. 26   D. cannot be determined

12 factors into 3 × 4, 2 × 6, and 1 × 12.
The rectangle could have perimeter
3 + 4 + 3 + 4 = 14,
2 + 6 + 2 + 6 = 16, or
1 + 12 + 1 + 12 = 26.
There is not enough information to decide the correct answer.
The answer choice must be **D**, cannot be determined.

Choose the correct answer. If your choice is "cannot be determined," explain.
1. In isosceles △*ABC, AB* = 5. How does *BC* compare to 5?
   A. *BC* > 5   B. *BC* = 5
   C. *BC* < 5   D. cannot be determined
2. In right △*DEF, DE* = 3 and *EF* = 4. What is *DF*?
   F. √7   G. 5   H. 7   I. cannot be determined
3. What is the solution of the inequality *ay* + 3 > *x*?
   A. $y > \frac{x-3}{a}$ B. $y > \frac{x}{a} - 3$
   C. $y < \frac{x-3}{a}$ D. cannot be determined

Solutions
1. D; the congruent sides are not known.
2. D; the sides that are the legs are not known.
3. D; it is not known whether *a* is positive or negative.

Transparency 10

Some multiple-choice questions do not contain enough information. In such cases, you will not be able to find an answer, and one of the answer choices should be "cannot be determined." If, however, you see "cannot be determined" before reading the question, don't assume that you cannot answer the question. You still have to try to answer it on its own merits.

EXAMPLE

The rectangular prism is inscribed in the cylinder. The diameter and height of the cylinder are both *s*. What is the ratio of the volume of the prism to the volume of the cylinder?

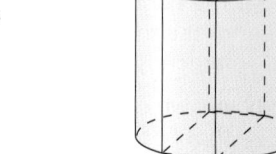

A. $\frac{2}{\pi}$ **B.** $\frac{1}{\pi}$

C. $\frac{1}{2}$ **D.** cannot be determined

To find the ratio of the volumes, you need to find the volume of each solid. The volume of a cylinder is $V = \pi r^2 h$. You know that the height of this cylinder is *s* and its radius is one half the diameter, or $\frac{s}{2}$. The volume of this cylinder is $V = \pi r^2 h = \pi\left(\frac{s}{2}\right)^2 \cdot s = \frac{\pi s^3}{4}$.

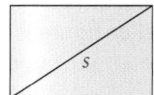

The volume of the prism is $V = Bh$ where *B* is the area of the base and *h* is the height. The height of the prism is *s*, but what is the area of the base? The only thing you know about the base is that it is a rectangle whose diagonal is *s*. Since the length of the diagonal of a rectangle does not fix the dimensions of the rectangle, there is not enough information about the base to find its area.

There is not enough information to determine the volume of the prism.
The correct answer choice is D, "cannot be determined."

> **2a.** No; radius is not given.
> **b.** about 27.4 cm³

EXERCISES

Can the answer to each exercise be determined? If *yes*, state the answer. If *no*, explain.

1. The sum of the circumference and height of a cylinder is 20 cm. What is the surface area of the cylinder? **No; radius and height can vary.**

2. **a.** The surface area of a cylinder is 44 cm². What is the volume of the cylinder? **a–b.**
   b. The surface area of a sphere is 44 cm². What is the volume of the sphere?   **See above.**

3. A polyhedron has 10 faces and the number of edges is 8 more than the number of vertices. What is the number of edges of the polyhedron? **No; number of vertices can vary.**

4. An equilateral triangle has an area of 100 in.². What is the length of a side? **about 15.2 in.**

Chapter Review

Vocabulary

altitude (pp. 528, 530, 537, 539)
base(s) (pp. 528, 530, 537, 539)
center of a sphere (p. 558)
circumference of a sphere (p. 558)
composite space figure (p. 547)
cone (p. 539)
cross section (p. 522)
cube (p. 512)
cylinder (p. 530)
diameter of a sphere (p. 558)
edge (p. 512)
face (p. 512)
foundation drawing (p. 521)

great circle (p. 558)
height (pp. 528, 530, 537, 539)
hemisphere (p. 558)
isometric drawing (p. 520)
lateral area (pp. 528, 530, 537, 539)
lateral faces (pp. 528, 537)
net (p. 512)
oblique cylinder (p. 530)
oblique prism (p. 528)
orthographic drawing (p. 521)
polyhedron (p. 512)
prism (p. 528)
pyramid (p. 537)

radius of a sphere (p. 558)
regular pyramid (p. 537)
right cone (p. 539)
right cylinder (p. 530)
right prism (p. 528)
similar solids (p. 566)
similarity ratio (p. 566)
slant height (p. 537, 539)
sphere (p. 558)
surface area (pp. 528, 530, 538, 539)
vertex (pp. 512, 537, 539)
volume (p. 544)

Reading Math
Understanding
Vocabulary

Take It to the NET
Online vocabulary quiz
at **www.PHSchool.com**
Web Code: afj-1051

Choose the correct term to complete each sentence.

1. A set of points in space equidistant from a given point is called a (*circle, sphere*). **sphere**

2. A(n) (*orthographic drawing, net*) is a two-dimensional pattern that you can fold to form a three-dimensional figure. **net**

3. A (*pyramid, prism*) is a polyhedron in which one face can be any polygon and the lateral faces are triangles that meet at a common vertex. **pyramid**

4. If you slice a prism with a plane, the intersection of the prism and the plane is a (*lateral area, cross section*) of the prism. **cross section**

5. In a(n) (*right, oblique*) prism, the lateral faces are rectangles and a lateral edge is an altitude. **right**

Skills and Concepts

10-1 and 10-2 Objectives

▼ To recognize nets of space figures

▼ To make isometric and orthographic drawings

▼ To describe cross sections of three-dimensional figures

A **polyhedron** is a three-dimensional figure whose surfaces are polygons. The polygons are **faces** of the polyhedron. An **edge** is a segment that is the intersection of two faces. A **vertex** is a point where three or more edges intersect. A **net** is a two-dimensional pattern that folds to form a three-dimensional figure.

Draw a net for each three-dimensional figure.

6–8. Nets may vary. Samples are given. See margin.

6. 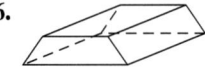   7.    8.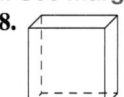

The number of faces (*F*), vertices (*V*), and edges (*E*) of a polyhedron are related by Euler's Formula $F + V = E + 2$.

Use Euler's Formula to find the missing number.

9. $F = 5, V = 5, E = $ ■ 8

10. $F = 6, V = $ ■, $E = 12$ 8

pages 573–575   **Chapter Review**

6. 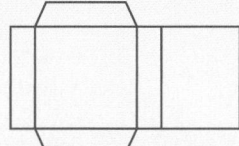   7. 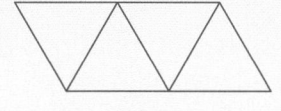   8.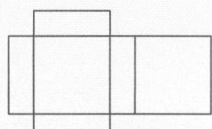

Resources

An **isometric drawing** is a two-dimensional drawing of a three-dimensional object that shows three sides of the object in one drawing. An **orthographic drawing** shows the top, front, and right-side views of an object. A **foundation drawing** shows the base of a structure and the height of each part. A **cross section** is the intersection of a solid and a plane.

12.

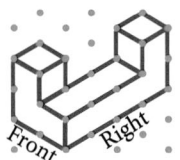

11. a. Use the isometric drawing at the right to make an orthographic drawing.
  b. Make a foundation drawing. **a–b. See back of book.**
12. Sketch a cube with an equilateral triangle cross section. **See left.**

10-3 and 10-5 Objectives

▼ To find the surface area of a prism

▼ To find the surface area of a cylinder

▼ To find the volume of a prism

▼ To find the volume of a cylinder

The **lateral area** of a **right prism** is the product of the perimeter of the base and the height. The **lateral area** of a **right cylinder** is the product of the circumference of the base and the height of the cylinder. The **surface area** of each solid is the sum of the lateral area and the areas of the bases.

The **volume** of a space figure is the space that the figure occupies. Volume is measured in cubic units. The **volume** of a **prism** and the **volume** of a **cylinder** are the product of the area of a base and the height of the solid.

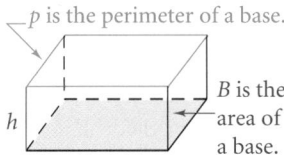

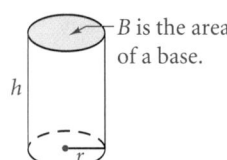

L.A. (prism) $= ph$

S.A. $=$ L.A. $+ 2B$

$V = Bh$

L.A. (cylinder) $= 2\pi rh$ or πdh

S.A. $=$ L.A. $+ 2B$

$V = Bh$

Find the surface area and volume of each figure. Leave your answers in terms of π.

13.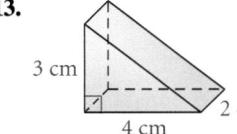

3 cm

2 cm

4 cm

36 cm^2; 12 cm^3

14.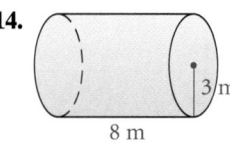

3 m

8 m

66π m^2; 72π m^3

15.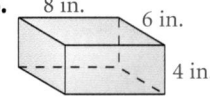

8 in.

6 in.

4 in.

208 in.^{2}; 192 in.^{3}

10-4 and 10-6 Objectives

▼ To find the surface area of a pyramid

▼ To find the surface area of a cone

▼ To find the volume of a pyramid

▼ To find the volume of a cone

The **lateral area** of a **regular pyramid** is half the product of the perimeter of the base and the slant height.

The **surface area** of a pyramid is the sum of the lateral area and the area of the base.

The **volume** of a pyramid is one third the product of the area of the base and the height of the solid.

L.A. (pyramid) $= \frac{1}{2}p\ell$

S.A. $=$ L.A. $+ B$

$V = \frac{1}{3}Bh$

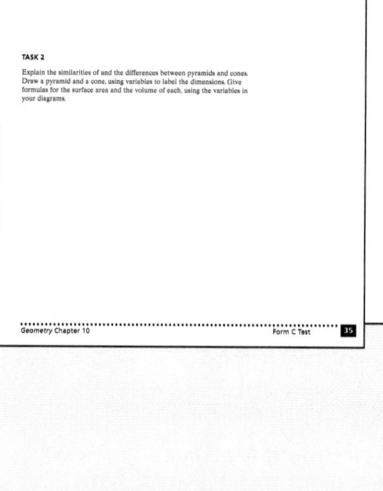
The **lateral area** of a **right cone** is half the product of the circumference of the base and the slant height.

The **surface area** of a cone is the sum of the lateral area and the area of the base.

The **volume** of a cone is one third the product of the area of the base and the height of the solid.

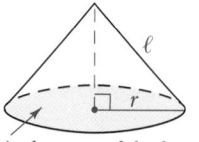

B is the area of the base.

$$\text{L.A. (cone)} = \pi r \ell$$

$$\text{S.A.} = \text{L.A.} + B$$

$$V = \tfrac{1}{3}Bh$$

Find the surface area and volume of each figure. Leave your answers in terms of π.

16.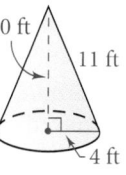
10 ft
11 ft
4 ft

60π ft^2; $\frac{160}{3}\pi$ ft^3

17.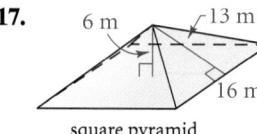
6 m   13 m
16 m
square pyramid

672 m^2; 512 m^3

18.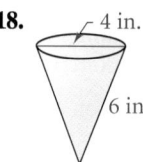
4 in.
6 in.

16π in.^{2}; $\frac{16\sqrt{2}}{3}\pi$ in.^{3}

10-7 Objectives

▼ To find the surface area and volume of a sphere

The **surface area of a sphere** is four times the product of π and the square of the radius of the sphere. The **volume of a sphere** is $\frac{4}{3}$ the product of π and the cube of the radius of the sphere.

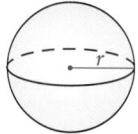

Find the surface area and volume of a sphere with the given radius or diameter. Round answers to the nearest tenth.

50.3 ft^2; 33.5 ft^3

19. $r = 5$ in.
314.2 in.^{2}; 523.6 in.^{3}

20. $d = 7$ cm
153.9 cm^2; 179.6 cm^3

21. $d = 4$ ft

22. $r = 0.8$ ft
8.0 ft^2; 2.1 ft^3

 23. Sports Equipment The circumference of a lacrosse ball is 8 in. Find its volume to the nearest tenth of a cubic inch. **8.6 in.^{3}**

10-8 Objectives

▼ To find relationships between the ratios of the areas and volumes of similar solids

Similar solids have the same shape and all their corresponding dimensions are proportional.

If the **similarity ratio** of two similar solids is $a : b$, then the ratio of their corresponding surface areas is $a^2 : b^2$, and the ratio of their volumes is $a^3 : b^3$.

24. Open-Ended Sketch two similar solids whose surface areas are in the ratio 16 : 25. Include dimensions. **See margin.**

For each pair of similar solids, find the ratio of the volume of the first figure to the volume of the second.

25. 27 : 64
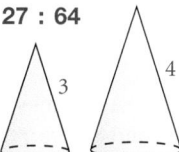
3   4

26. 64 : 27
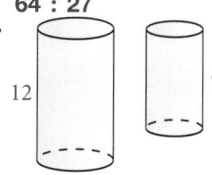
12   9

pages 573–575   Chapter Review

24.   Answers may vary.

Sample:
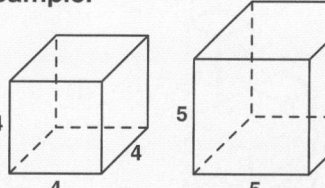
4   4   4   5   5   5

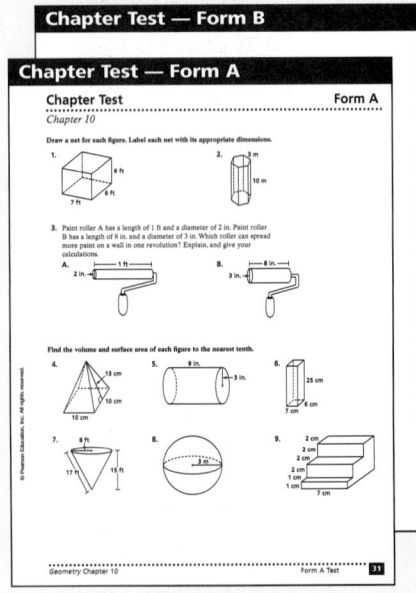

Chapter Test

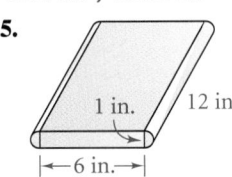 **Take It to the NET**
Online chapter test at
www.PHSchool.com
Web Code: afa-1052

Draw a net for each figure. Label the net with appropriate dimensions. 1–2. See margin.

1. 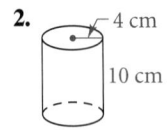 6 in. / 6 in.

2. 4 cm / 10 cm

1–4. Drawings may vary. Samples are given.

Use the foundation drawing at the right for Exercises 3 and 4.

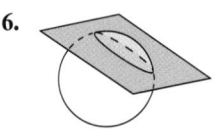

3. Create an isometric drawing. 3–4. See margin.

4. Create an orthographic drawing.

5. Find the number of edges in a pyramid with seven faces. **12**

Describe the cross section formed in each diagram.

6.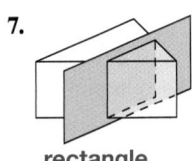

circle

7.

rectangle

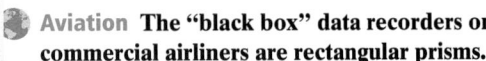 **Aviation** The "black box" data recorders on commercial airliners are rectangular prisms.

8. The base of a recorder is 15 in. by 8 in. Its height ranges from 15 in. to 22 in. What are the largest and smallest possible volumes for the recorder?
2640 in.³; 1800 in.³

9. New flight data recorders are smaller and record more data. A new recorder might be 8 in. by 8 in. by 13 in. What is its volume? **832 in.³**

Find the volume and surface area of each figure to the nearest tenth.

10. 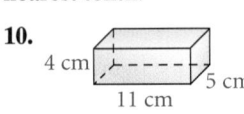 4 cm / 5 cm / 11 cm
220 cm³; 238 cm²

11. 4 ft
268.1 ft³; 201.1 ft²

12. 6 m / 5 m
157.1 m³; 201.2 m²

13. 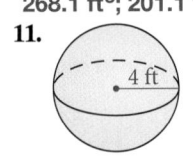 8 cm / 3 cm
226.2 cm³; 207.3 cm²

576 Chapter 10 Chapter Test

14. 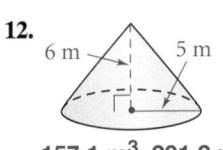 9 in. / 8 in. / 8 in.
172.0 in.³; 208 in.²

15. 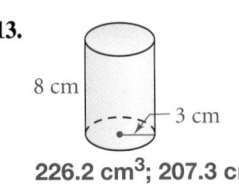 1 in. / 12 in. / 6 in.
81.4 in.³; 195.3 in.²

16. Open-Ended Draw two different space figures that have a volume of 100 in.³. Label the dimensions of each figure. **See back of book.**

17. Visualization The triangle is revolved completely about the *y*-axis.
a. Describe the solid of revolution that is formed. **cone with r = 4, h = 3**
b. Find its lateral area and volume in terms of π. **20π units²; 16π units³**

18. Painting The floor of a bedroom is 12 ft by 15 ft and the walls are 7 ft high. One gallon of paint covers about 450 ft². How many gallons of paint do you need to paint the walls of the bedroom? **1 gal**

19. List these space figures in order from the one with least volume to the one with greatest volume.
A. cube with an edge of 5 cm **C, A, E, D, B**
B. cylinder with radius 4 cm and height 4 cm
C. square pyramid with base sides of 6 cm and height 6 cm
D. cone with radius 4 cm and height 9 cm
E. rectangular prism with a 5 cm-by-5 cm base and height 6 cm

20. Writing Describe a real-world situation in which you would need to know the volume of an object. Then describe another situation in which you would need to know the lateral area of an object. **See margin p. 577.**

21. The two solids are similar. Find the ratio of the volume of the first figure to the volume of the second. **64 : 125**

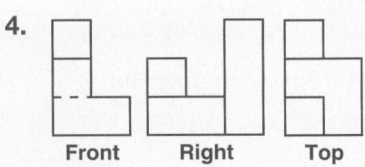 4 / 4 / 4 / 5 / 5 / 5

22. The volumes of two spheres are 327π mm³ and 8829π mm³. What is the ratio of their surface areas? **1 : 9**

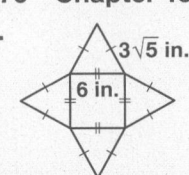
page 576 Chapter Test

1. 3√5 in. / 6 in.

2. 10 cm / 4 cm

3. Front Right

4. Front Right Top
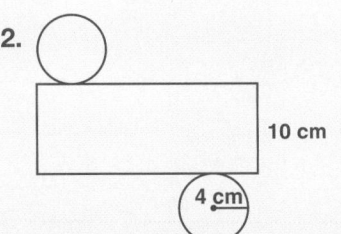

576

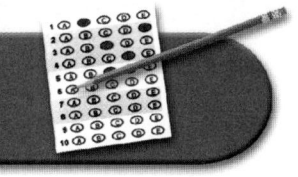

Standardized Test Prep

Multiple Choice

For Exercises 1–7, choose the correct letter.

1. One leg of an isosceles right triangle is 3 in. long. What is the length of the hypotenuse? **B**
   A. 3 in.   **B.** $3\sqrt{2}$ in.   **C.** $3\sqrt{3}$ in.   **D.** 6 in.

2. What is the ratio of the volumes of similar solids whose similarity ratio is 4 : 9? **I**
   F. 2 : 3   **G.** 8 : 27   **H.** 16 : 81   **I.** 64 : 729

3. What is the most precise name of the figure? **C**

   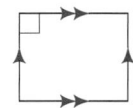

   A. quadrilateral   **B.** parallelogram
   C. rectangle   **D.** square

4. For what value of x will the two triangles be similar? **I**

   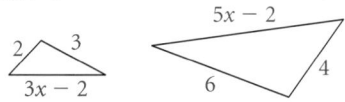

   F. 10   **G.** 8   **H.** 4   **I.** 2

5. What is the surface area of the cylinder? **B**

   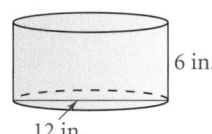

   A. 96π in.^{2} **B.** 144π in.^{2}
   C. 192π in.^{2} **D.** 216π in.^{2}

6. Find the surface area of a sphere with radius 6 in.
   F. 36π in.^{2} **G.** 144π in.^{2} **G**
   H. 216π in.^{2} **I.** 288π in.^{2}

7. Which ordered pair describes the vector? **C**
   A. $\langle 50\sqrt{2}, 50 \rangle$
   B. $\langle 50, 50\sqrt{2} \rangle$
   C. $\langle 50, 50\sqrt{3} \rangle$
   D. $\langle 50\sqrt{3}, 50 \rangle$

   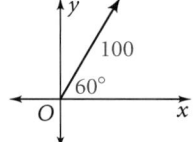

Quantitative Comparison

Compare the boxed quantity in Column A with the boxed quantity in Column B. Choose the best answer.

   A. The quantity in Column A is greater.
   B. The quantity in Column B is greater.
   C. The two quantities are equal.
   D. The relationship cannot be determined from the information given.

   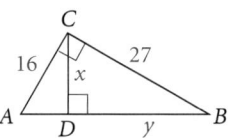

Column A	Column B
B 8. x	y
C 9. $m\angle ACD$	$m\angle B$

Gridded Response

10. Find the area in square centimeters of a regular pentagon with side length 4 cm. Round your answer to the nearest tenth. **27.5**

Short Response

11. Find the circumference of the circle shown below and then the length of $\overline{AB}$. Leave your answers in terms of π. **See back of book.**

   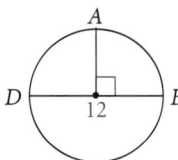

Extended Response

12. Find the area of the shaded figure. Leave your answer in terms of π. Explain your work.
   See back of book.

   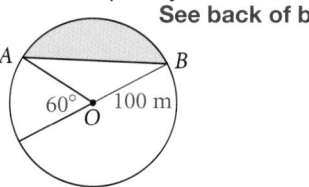

20. **Answers may vary. Sample: You need to know the volume of a planter to fill it with soil. You need to know the lateral area of a planter to paint its exterior sides.**

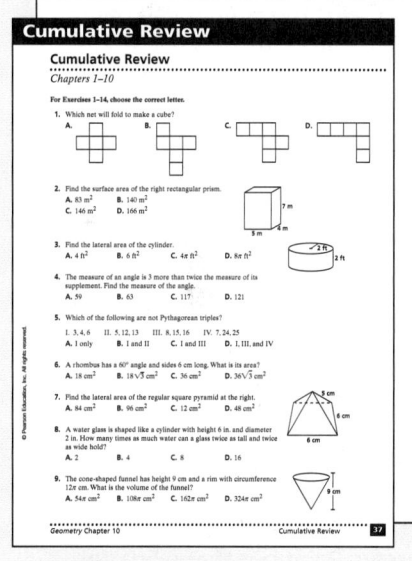

Item	Lesson
1	7-3
2	10-8
3	6-1
4	8-3
5	10-3
6	10-7
7	9-4
8	8-4
9	8-4
10	7-5
11	7-6
12	7-7

577

 **Real-World Snapshots**

A Colossal Task

In these activities students apply their knowledge of similarity, scale drawing, ratio, and proportion.

Connecting to Prior Knowledge

Have students brainstorm how artists draw human beings accurately and relate their own experiences in drawing the human form. Elicit the fact that artists use ratio and proportion extensively to represent images accurately.

Teaching Notes

After students read the introductory paragraph, ask how many have visited the Statue of Liberty. Invite students to relate their impressions of its size and proportions.

History Connection

The Colossus of Rhodes was a statue of the Greek god Apollo. The historian Pliny claimed that it was 70 cubits high. A cubit is the length of one's forearm from elbow to fingertips. Have students use their own forearms to calculate Pliny's estimate of the height of the Colossus.

Chemistry Connection

Students may think that the Statue of Liberty has always been green. Point out that oxidation turns copper green as it ages.

Teaching Tip

Have students work in pairs or in small groups to complete the activities. Have each team read through all the activities before beginning to work. If time is limited, allow each team to choose which of the three activities it will complete.

 **Real-World Snapshots**

A Colossal Task

Applying Volume The Statue of Liberty stands in New York harbor, welcoming people to the United States. A similar giant statue once stood at the entrance to the harbor of the Greek island of Rhodes. A stone base and an iron framework supported the bronze statue, which took 12 years to construct. The statue remained standing for only about 66 years, falling to the ground after a violent earthquake weakened its knees.

The Colossus of Rhodes

The Colossus is believed to have included 12.9 tons of bronze and 7.7 tons of iron. Some historians believe that the sculptor modeled the head of the Colossus on that of Alexander the Great.

Activity 1

Materials: ruler, paper and pencil

a. Measure the height of one person attaching bronze plates to the shin of the Colossus. Estimate the probable height of the finished statue.

b. Using the painting of the Colossus (above left) as a guide, sketch the statue. Use proportions to determine at least eight dimensions on the statue. Add these dimensions to your sketch.

The Sculptor

Chares of Lindos (in red robes) probably made small models and scaled them up to get correct proportions.

Artist's rendition

pages 578–579	**Real-World Snapshots**	**Activity 1**	**Activity 2**
		a–b. Answers may vary. Check students' work.	a. 8:1
			b. 1000:1

Activity 2

a. The dimensions of the larger block are twice the dimensions of the smaller block. Calculate the ratio of the larger block's volume to the smaller block's volume.

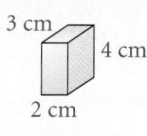

3 cm
4 cm
2 cm

b. Determine what the volume ratio would be if the larger block's dimensions were 10 times the smaller block's dimensions.

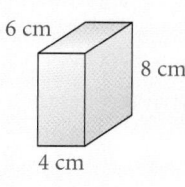

6 cm
8 cm
4 cm

The Statue of Liberty

French sculptor Frederic-Auguste Bartholdi used his mother as the model for the Statue of Liberty. The statue was built in France and shipped to New York in 350 pieces. The seven spikes on the crown symbolize the seven seas and seven continents.

Light Lady Liberty

From heel to top of head, the Statue of Liberty is about 1.3 times as long as a mature blue whale but only about 1.6 times as heavy. The statue weighs less than you'd think because, rather than being solid, it is a thin layer of copper over an iron framework.

The Statue of Liberty weighs 225 tons.

A fully grown blue whale weighs about 143 tons.

Activity 3

Materials: newspaper or Internet

Suppose the residents in your area have decided to honor you, a friend, or a local hero by building a 100-ft solid-gold statue in the center of town. Draw a sketch of the statue. Estimate the weight and cost.

Hints:

- Use what you learned in Activity 2 to estimate the ratio of the statue's volume to its subject's volume.
- Think about how the weight ratio relates to the volume ratio.
- You'll need to find the density of gold. You'll also need to compare the density of gold to that of a person. Keep in mind that our bodies are mostly water.
- Research the current price of gold.

Take It to the NET For more information about statues, go to **www.PHSchool.com.**
Web Code: afe-1053

579

Activity 1

Materials ruler, paper and pencil

Teaching Tip

Point out that estimates will vary. Students may want to use a whole number, such as 5 or 6 ft, for the average height of a man. The worker holding the mallet is standing fairly upright, so that is a good place to start measuring. Measure his foot and the foot of the Colossus to begin your proportions.

Activity 2

Materials paper and pencil

Tactile Learners

Students can use same-sized blocks to model the activity. Letting one block represent the smaller prism, they can build the larger prism and see why its volume is eight times the volume of one block.

Activity 3

Materials paper and pencil

Error Prevention

Students may initially think that the ratio of weights equals the ratio of heights. Emphasize that this is only true when the densities of the objects are the same.

Scoring Rubric

This scoring rubric applies to all activities. Share this scoring rubric with students before they begin work.

4   Measurements and estimates are reasonable. Drawings are neat and accurate and clearly reflect the situations. Explanations are thorough.

3   Measurements and estimates are mostly reasonable. Drawings are neat and mostly accurate. Explanations lack detail or are not completely accurate.

2   Drawings are not accurate. Explanations lack clarity.

1   Satisfactory answers are given, but no work is shown.

Activity 3

Answers may vary. Check students' work.

(*Hints:* 1. Sample: If the subject is 5 ft tall, the volume ratio would be $\frac{8000}{1}$.

2. They are the same.

3. density of gold ≈ 19.3 g/cm^3 ≈ 1200 lb/ft^3)

Circles

Chapter at a Glance

 North Carolina Objectives

11-1 **Tangent Lines** 2.03d

NCTM ▽ Using the Radius-Tangent Relationship
2, 3, 6, ▽ Using Multiple Tangents
7, 8, 9,
10

11-2 **Chords and Arcs** 2.03d

NCTM ▽ Using Congruent Chords, Arcs, and Central Angles
2, 3, 6, ▽ Lines Through the Center of a Circle
7, 8, 9,
10

11-3 **Inscribed Angles** 2.03d

NCTM ▽ Finding the Measure of an Inscribed Angle
2, 3, 4, ▽ The Angle Formed by a Tangent and a Chord
6, 7, 8,
9, 10

11-4 **Angle Measures and Segment Lengths** 2.03d

NCTM ▽ Finding Angle Measures
2, 3, 4, ▽ Finding Segment Lengths
6, 7, 8,
9, 10

11-5 **Circles in the Coordinate Plane** 2.03d

NCTM ▽ Writing an Equation of a Circle
2, 3, 4, ▽ Finding the Center and Radius of a Circle
6, 7, 8,
9, 10

11-6 **Locus: A Set of Points** 2.02

NCTM ▽ Drawing and Describing a Locus
3, 6, 8,
9, 10

NCTM STANDARDS 2000

1 Number and Operations	6 Problem Solving
2 Algebra	7 Reasoning and Proof
3 Geometry	8 Communication
4 Measurement	9 Connections
5 Data Analysis and Probability	10 Representation

Pacing Options

This chart suggests pacing only for the lessons and their parts. It is provided as a possible guide. It will help you determine how much time you have in your schedule to cover other components, such as the features, Chapter Review and Chapter Test.

Day	Traditional 45 min.	Two-Year 45 min.	Block 90 min.
1	11-1 ▽	11-1 ▽	11-1 ▽ ▽
2	11-1 ▽	11-1 ▽	11-2 ▽ ▽
3	11-1 ▽	11-1 ▽	11-3 ▽ ▽
4	11-2 ▽	11-1 ▽	11-4 ▽ ▽
5	11-2 ▽	11-2 ▽	11-5 ▽ ▽
6	11-3 ▽	11-2 ▽	11-6 ▽
7	11-3 ▽	11-2 ▽	
8	11-3 ▽	11-2 ▽	
9	11-3 ▽	11-3 ▽	
10	11-4 ▽	11-3 ▽	
11	11-4 ▽	11-3 ▽	
12	11-5 ▽	11-3 ▽	
13	11-5 ▽	11-4 ▽	
14	11-5 ▽	11-4 ▽	
15	11-6 ▽	11-4 ▽	
16		11-4 ▽	
17		11-5 ▽	
18		11-5 ▽	
19		11-5 ▽	
20		11-5 ▽	
21		11-6 ▽	
22		11-6 ▽	
23			

NAEP Correlation (National Assessment of Educational Progress 2000 Mathematics Objectives)

11-1	11-2	11-3	11-4	11-5	11-6
M9, G1a, G6b	M9, G6b, G8	A5e	A5e	G9b, A3a	G1a, G8

N = Number Sense, Properties, and Operations; **M** = Measurement; **G** = Geometry and Spatial Sense;
D = Data Analysis, Statistics, and Probability; **A** = Algebra and Functions

Math Background

Chapter Overview

Chapter 11 applies deductive methods to establish relationships among and between angles, arcs, chords, secants, and tangents. In many ways, this chapter is a grand summary using the geometry presented up to now. Triangle congruence and triangle similarity are used extensively to prove the theorems in this chapter. The chapter concludes with a discussion of circles in an analytic geometry context and an introduction to loci.

Tangent Lines   11-1

Have students imagine and describe spinning and then releasing a ball attached to a string. The released ball will follow a path (easy to see because of the string) influenced by gravity, but its direction at the point of release is along the line tangent to its original orbit at the point of release. Point out that the law of physics it obeys is related to the geometry theorems in this lesson.

Chords and Arcs   11-2

Theorem 11-4 appears to contain three statements. Careful analysis reveals that it actually contains six. For example, statements (1) and (2) taken together with the Law of Syllogism allow students to conclude the converse of statement (3): *Congruent central angles have congruent arcs.* Starting with the first diagram below that summarizes Theorem 11-4, students can establish three related statements by using logical reasoning.

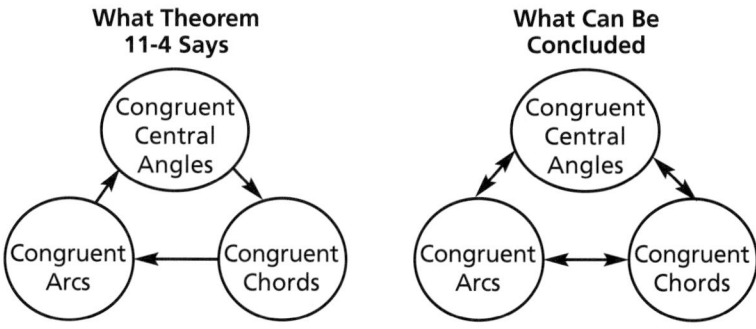

Inscribed Angles   11-3

The measure of a central angle equals the measure of its intercepted arc. The measure of an *inscribed* angle equals one half the measure of its intercepted arc. Students might relate this idea to situations in sports. They already know that the angle within which a shot will be successful becomes smaller and smaller as a shooter moves farther from a hockey or soccer goal. Now, thanks to Corollary 1 to the Inscribed Angle Theorem, they can prove that shooting positions are equivalent if they are vertices of inscribed angles on the same circle with the same intercepted arc (the goal).

The proof of the Inscribed Angle Theorem uses a divide-and-conquer strategy. It is important for students to see because it illustrates a complex situation broken into simpler situations that are easier to prove.

Angle Measures and Segment Lengths   11-4

Theorem 11-11 combines statements that often are given as individual theorems. Linking statements about angles formed by lines intersecting both inside and outside a circle focuses attention on the similarities and differences between the two related situations. Similarly, Theorem 11-12's combining the three "Power Theorems" emphasizes the similarities and differences between these related theorems in a manner that will help students relate and recall them.

Circles in the Coordinate Plane   11-5

Much time is spent in algebra simplifying expressions and equations. A student might wonder initially why the equation $(x - h)^2 + (y - k)^2 = r^2$ is written in such a complicated form instead of expanding and rewriting it. Help students understand that the center-radius form immediately displays the key aspects of a circle. Circles, ellipses, hyperbolas, and parabolas are all conic sections and the equation of each can be written in a way that makes its graph obvious.

Locus   11-6

The word *locus* is used in this lesson in the context of characterization theorems. Angle bisectors and perpendicular bisectors were originally defined in terms of the measures of the angles and lengths of the segments formed. Here, each is recast in terms of equidistance. One type of characterization theorem occurs when a figure can be characterized by a condition that its points and no other points satisfy.

# Ongoing Assessment and Intervention

Tools for Monitoring Student Progress

The Prentice Hall *Geometry* program provides you with many options for assessment in the Student Edition, the Teacher's Edition and the teaching resources. From these options, you may choose instructional materials and techniques that are appropriate for your students and support your district's curriculum requirements.

Instant Check System™ in Chapter 11

Allows students to check their own learning before, during, and after each lesson.

Diagnosing Readiness before the chapter (p. 580)

Check Skills You'll Need exercises in each lesson (pp. 582, 590, 598, 607, 615, 621)

Check Understanding questions with each Example (pp. 583, 584, 585, 590, 591, 593, 597, 599, 600, 601, 608, 609, 610, 615, 616, 617, 621, 622)

Checkpoint Quiz (pp. 605 and 620)

Test Prep in Chapter 11

Teaches students strategies and gives them practice with all the test item formats they will encounter on state tests and standardized national exams.

Standardized Test Prep exercises in each lesson (pp. 589, 596, 604, 613, 619, 625)

Test-Taking Strategies (p. 626: Using Estimation)

Standardized Test Prep (p. 631: Reading Comprehension)

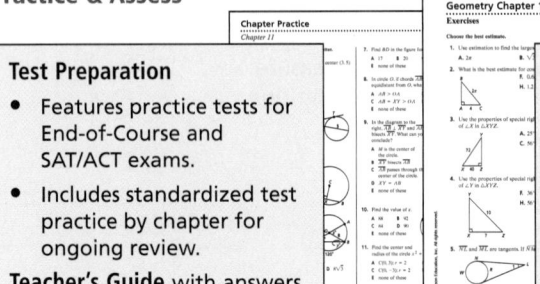
All your assessment needs in one place!

Program Assessment

Assess student progress throughout the *Geometry* text with blackline masters and CD-ROM.

Assessment Resources

- Checkpoint Quizzes 1 & 2
- Chapter Test, Forms A & B
- Chapter Alternative Assessment

Spanish versions available. Tests for Informal Geometry also available.

 Computer Test Generator

- Unlimited questions of varying difficulty for every lesson objective.
- Create your own practice sheets, quizzes, and tests, or use the pre-made Chapter Tests.
- Diagnose readiness with questions on prerequisite skills.
- Prepare students by making tests based on standardized test objectives.
- Access Algebra 1, Geometry, and Algebra 2 content—all on one CD-ROM.

Test Preparation

A three-step approach to preparing students for high stakes, national, and state exams.

❶ Diagnose & Prescribe

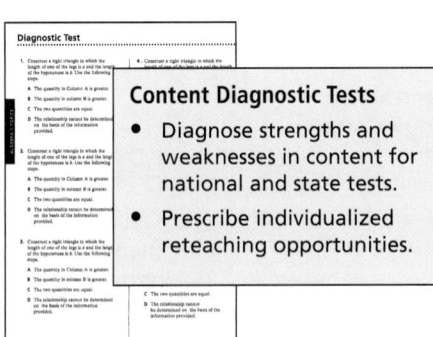

Content Diagnostic Tests

- Diagnose strengths and weaknesses in content for national and state tests.
- Prescribe individualized reteaching opportunities.

❷ Review & Reteach

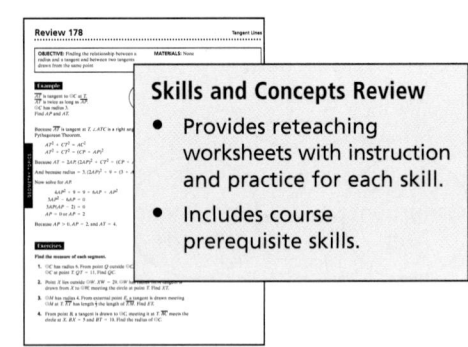

Skills and Concepts Review

- Provides reteaching worksheets with instruction and practice for each skill.
- Includes course prerequisite skills.

❸ Practice & Assess

Test Preparation

- Features practice tests for End-of-Course and SAT/ACT exams.
- Includes standardized test practice by chapter for ongoing review.

Teacher's Guide with answers and correlations.

Test-Taking Strategies with Transparencies

- Support the Test-Taking Strategies pages in the Student Edition.
- Provide a teaching transparency and a practice worksheet for each strategy.

Reaching All Students

Support in the Student Text and Additional Resources

The textbook, the iText, and other technology components provide numerous opportunities to reach students of various ability levels and learning styles. Each Teacher's Edition lesson suggests how you can help *all* your students be successful and understand the mathematics in Chapter 11.

Below Level

Student Edition
- Diagnosing Readiness*: p. 580
- Check Skills You'll Need*: pp. 582, 590, 598, 607, 615, 621

Reteaching
Chapter 11 Support File: pp. 8–13

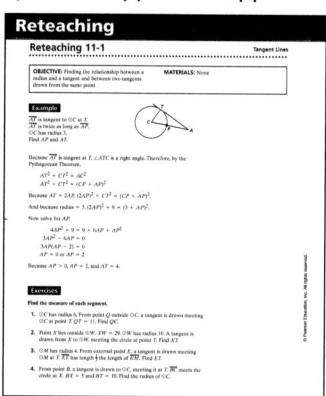

Informal Geometry Planning Guide
Chapter 11 Lesson Plans: pp. 66–71
Chapter 11 Tests: pp. 119–122

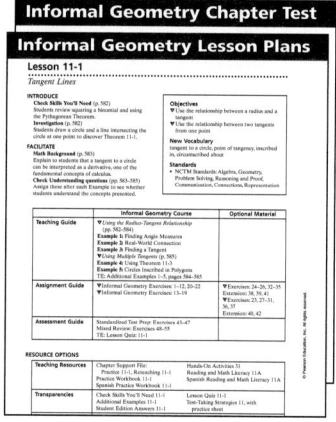

* Can be used with all ability levels to ensure mastery of prerequisite skills.

Advanced Learners

Student Edition
- Challenge exercises: pp. 588, 595, 603, 612, 619, 625
- Extension: p. 614

Enrichment
Chapter 11 Support File: pp. 14–19

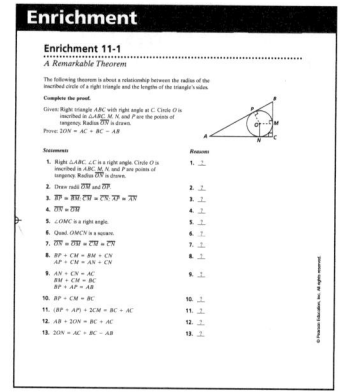

Reading and Math Literacy

Student Edition
- Vocabulary: pp. 581, 627, *plus* in every Lesson Preview
- Reading Math: pp. 582, 586, 595, 597, 599, 607, 609, 622, 627
- Illustrated Glossary: pp. 741–777

Reading and Math Literacy Masters
Chapter 11: pp. 41–44

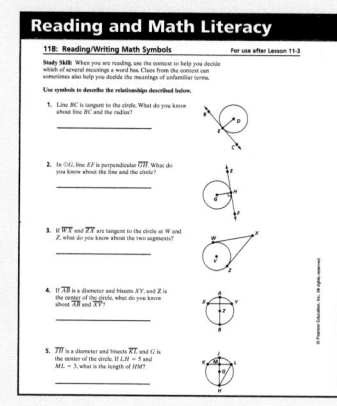

English Learners

Student Edition
- English/Spanish Illustrated Glossary: pp. 741–777

Workbook and Masters
Spanish Practice Workbook: pp. 66–71
Spanish Reading and Math Literacy Masters: pp. 41–44

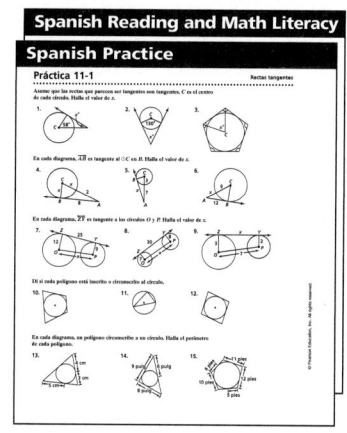

Learning Styles

Student Edition
- Investigation: pp. 582, 598
- Technology: pp. 584, 597, 602, 603, 606, 619
- Writing: pp. 587, 595, 602, 612, 618, 619, 620, 624, 630

Activity Masters
Hands-On Activities: 31, 32, 33

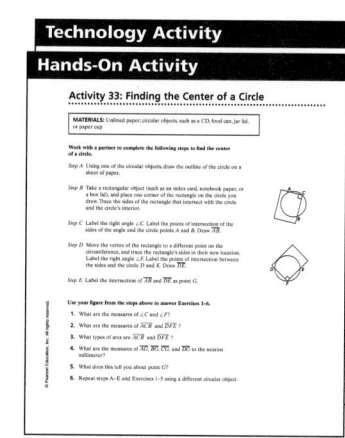

Program Resources

	Teaching Resources in Grab & Go™ Files				Resources for Reaching All Students				Spanish Resources			Transparencies				Presentation Assistant Plus!
	Practice	Reteach	Enrich	Checkpoint Quiz	Reading & Math Literacy	Technology Activities	Hands-On Activities	Informal Geometry Lesson Plans	Practice	Reading & Math Literacy	Checkpoint Quiz	Skills Check	Additional Examples	Answers to Exercises	Lesson Quiz	Prentice Hall Presentation Pro CD-ROM
11-1	■	■	■		■		■	■	■	■		■	■	■	■	■
11-2	■	■	■				■		■			■	■	■	■	■
11-3	■	■	■	■	■		■	■	■	■	■	■	■	■	■	■
11-4	■	■	■					■	■			■	■	■	■	■
11-5	■	■	■		■			■	■			■	■	■	■	■
11-6	■	■	■					■	■			■	■	■	■	■
For the chapter	Chapter Tests, Alternative Assessment, Cumulative Review, Cumulative Assessment				Informal Geometry Chapter Tests				Spanish Chapter Tests, Alternative Assessment, Cumulative Review, Cumulative Assessment			Classroom Aid Transparencies				

Also available for use with the chapter:

PRENTICE HALL **ASSESSMENT SYSTEM** *see page 580C.*

- Practice Workbook
- Solution Key

- For teacher support and access to student Web site materials, use Web Code afk-5500.
- For additional online and technology resources, see below.

Technology

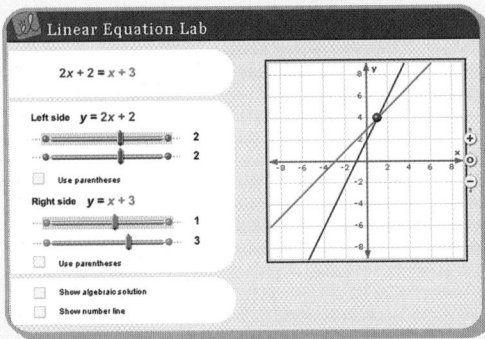

iTEXT — Online and on CD-ROM

Complete Interactive Student Text online and on CD-ROM—with instant feedback assessment, tutorial help, dynamic activities, instructional and real-world videos, audio, and additional practice.

www.PHSchool.com — For Students

Use **Web Codes** for easy access to online activities, chapter projects, self-grading lesson quizzes and chapter tests, vocabulary quizzes, updated data sources, graphing calculator procedures, and more.

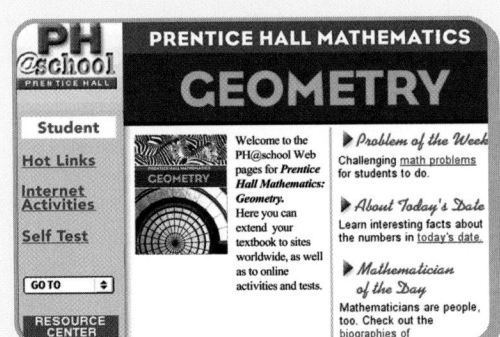

PH SuccessNet — For Teachers

Online lesson planning with built-in state correlations, all the teaching resources, complete reference library, your own calendar and Teacher Web page, professional development, and more.

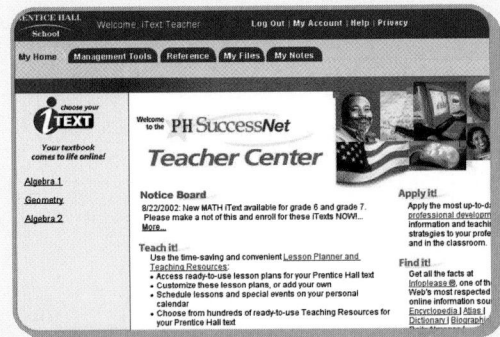

Presentation Assistant Plus!

The Prentice Hall *Presentation Assistant Plus!* provides you with the material you need to teach a lesson from beginning to end. Two easy-to-use formats—Transparencies and CD-ROM—allow you to present a lesson the way you are most comfortable.

Transparencies

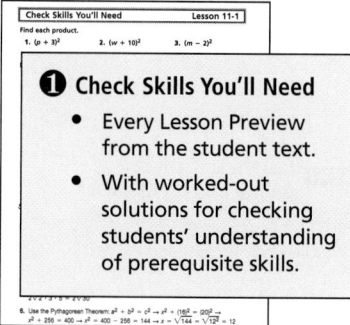

❶ Check Skills You'll Need

- Every Lesson Preview from the student text.
- With worked-out solutions for checking students' understanding of prerequisite skills.

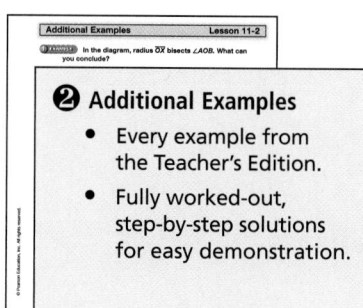

❷ Additional Examples

- Every example from the Teacher's Edition.
- Fully worked-out, step-by-step solutions for easy demonstration.

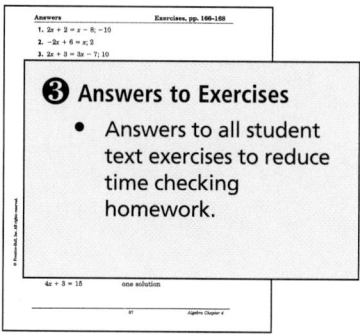

❸ Answers to Exercises

- Answers to all student text exercises to reduce time checking homework.

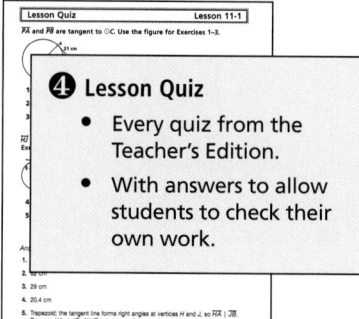

❹ Lesson Quiz

- Every quiz from the Teacher's Edition.
- With answers to allow students to check their own work.

 Throughout the Teacher's Edition, this symbol indicates material that is available on transparency in the Presentation Assistant Plus!

Prentice Hall Presentation Pro CD-ROM

- Includes all Transparencies.
- Conveniently organized by lesson so you can easily ❶ Introduce, ❷ Teach, ❸ Check Homework, and ❹ Assess each lesson.
- Animated examples allow step-by-step instruction at your own pace.
- Easy to edit so you can create custom presentations.

Teaching Chapter 11 Using Presentation Assistant Plus!

	❶ Introduce	❷ Teach	❸ Check Homework	❹ Assess
	Check Skills You'll Need	Additional Examples	Student Edition Answers	Lesson Quiz
11-1	p. 63	pp. 179–183	✔	p. 141
11-2	p. 64	pp. 184–185	✔	p. 142
11-3	p. 65	pp. 186–188	✔	p. 143
11-4	p. 66	pp. 189–192	✔	p. 144
11-5	p. 67	pp. 193–194	✔	p. 145
11-6	p. 68	pp. 195–196	✔	p. 146

Prentice Hall Presentation Pro

CD-ROM with dynamic PowerPoint® presentations for every lesson. Helps you introduce and develop concepts, check homework, and assess progress. Part of Presentation Assistant Plus! *(See above.)*

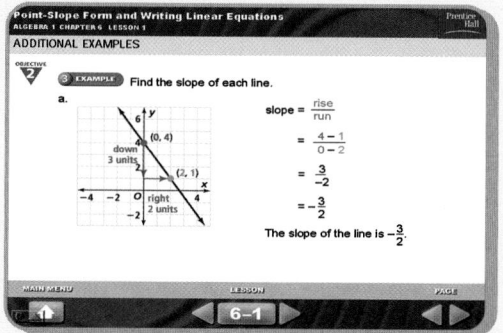

Computer Test Generator

CD-ROM to create practice sheets and tests for course objectives and standardized tests. Includes Instant Chapter Tests™, online testing, and student reports. Part of the PH Assessment System. *(See page 580C.)*

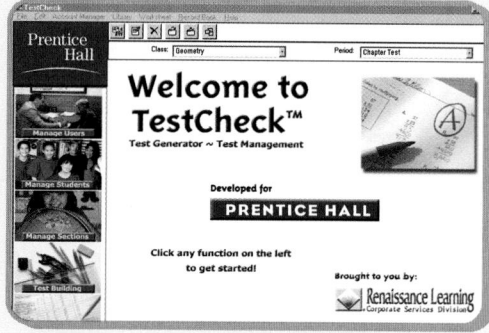

Resource Pro® with Planning Express®

CD-ROM with a lesson planning tool that allows you to import state and local objectives. Includes electronic versions of all the teaching resources.

Circles

 Diagnosing Readiness

Students will find answers to these exercises in the back of their textbooks.

For intervention, direct students to:

The Pythagorean Theorem
Lesson 7-2: Examples 1 and 2
Exercises 1–6, 10–15
Extra Practice, p. 696

Isosceles and Equilateral Triangles
Lesson 4-5: Example 3
Exercises 7–16
Extra Practice, p. 693

Solving Equations
Skills Handbook: p. 720

Distance Formula
Lesson 1-6: Example 1
Exercises 1–9
Extra Practice, p. 690

Where You've Been

● In Chapters 1 and 7, you learned how to find the circumference and area of a circle.

● In Chapters 4 and 5, you learned relationships involving congruent triangles, corresponding parts of congruent triangles, and special segments within a triangle.

● In Chapter 7, you learned special properties of right triangles, including the Pythagorean Theorem.

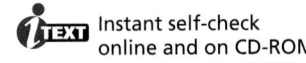
Instant self-check online and on CD-ROM

 **Diagnosing Readiness**   (For help, go to the Lesson in green.)

Solving Equations (Skills Handbook Page 720)

x^2 **Algebra** Solve for x.

1. $\frac{1}{2}(x + 42) = 62$ **2.** $(5 + 3)8 = (4 + x)6$ **3.** $(9 + x)2 = (12 + 4)3$
     82 $6\frac{2}{3}$ **15**

Distance Formula (Lesson 1-6)

Find the distance between each pair of points.

4. $(13, 7), (6, 31)$ **5.** $(-4, 4), (2, -4)$ **6.** $(-3, -1), (0, 3)$ **7.** $(2\sqrt{3}, 5), (-\sqrt{3}, 2)$
   25   **10**   **5**   **6**

Isosceles and Equilateral Triangles (Lesson 4-5)

x^2 **Algebra** Find the value of x.

8.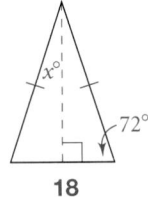
18

9.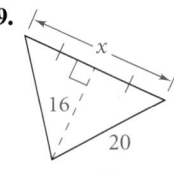
24

10.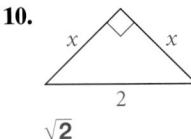

11.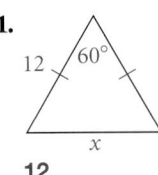
12

The Pythagorean Theorem (Lesson 7-2)

x^2 **Algebra** Find the value of x. Leave your answer in simplest radical form.

12.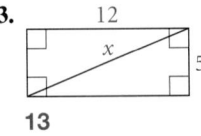
4√2

13.
13

14.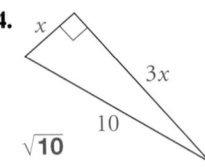
√10

15.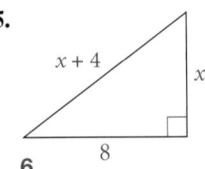
6

Circles

Key Vocabulary

- chord (p. 590)
- circumscribed about (p. 585)
- inscribed angle (p. 598)
- inscribed in (p. 585)
- intercepted arc (p. 598)
- locus (p. 621)
- point of tangency (p. 582)
- secant (p. 607)
- standard form of an equation of a circle (p. 615)
- tangent to a circle (p. 582)

Chapter 11 Overview

In this chapter, students will build on their knowledge of circles by studying properties of tangents, secants, chords, and arcs. They will prove properties of tangents and establish properties of chords and their relationships to arcs. Then they will study angles formed by chords, tangents, and secants, their relationships to intercepted arcs, and the relationships among segments of intersecting chords, tangents, and secants. Students will use coordinate geometry to describe the standard form of an equation of a circle and apply the concept of locus to the geometry they have studied up to this point.

 Reading Math
Reading for Problem Solving, p. 597

Vocabulary
A complete list of terms, plus vocabulary exercises, appears in the Chapter Review, p. 627.

Illustrated Glossary
Examples for each vocabulary term, plus definitions in both English and Spanish, appear starting on p. 741.

 Test-Taking Strategies
Using Estimation, p. 626

Real-World Connections
Some of the applications you will find in this chapter are bicycles (11-1), archaeology (11-2), photography (11-4), and communications (11-5).

www.PHSchool.com
Internet support for this chapter includes:
- Self-grading Vocabulary and Chapter 11 Tests
- Chapter Project
- Chapter Planner
- Ch. 11 Resources

Where You're Going

- In this chapter, you will learn the many properties of circles and of lines and segments that intersect circles.

- When these lines and segments meet to form angles, you will learn how the angles are related to the arcs they intercept on a circle.

- You will also learn how to describe a set of points as a locus.

 Real-World Connection Applying what you learn, you will describe on page 625 the locus of points in space that are equidistant from the points of a circle.

581

Plus

1. Plan

Lesson Preview

 Check Skills You'll Need

For help use
Skills Handbook, p. 716

The Pythagorean Theorem
Lesson 7-2: Example 2
Exercises 10–15
Extra Practice, p. 696

Lesson Resources

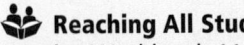 **Teaching Resources**
Practice, Reteaching, Enrichment

 Reaching All Students
Practice Workbook 11-1
Spanish Practice Workbook 11-1
Reading and Math Literacy 11A
Spanish Reading & Literacy 11A
Hands-On Activities 31
Informal Geometry Planning
    Guide 11-1

Presentation Assistant Plus!
Transparencies
• Check Skills You'll Need 11-1
• Additional Examples 11-1
• Student Edition Answers 11-1
• Lesson Quiz 11-1
PH Presentation Pro CD 11-1

PRENTICE HALL
ASSESSMENT SYSTEM

Computer Test Generator CD

 **Technology**
Resource Pro® CD-ROM
Computer Test Generator CD
Prentice Hall Presentation Pro CD

www.PHSchool.com
Student Site
• Teacher Web Code: afk-5500
• Self-grading Lesson Quiz
Teacher Center
• Lesson Planner
• Resources

Plus **iTEXT**

582

Tangent Lines

 North Carolina Objectives
2.03 Apply properties, definitions, and theorems of two-dimensional figures to solve problems and write proofs: d) Circles.

Lesson Preview

What You'll Learn

 OBJECTIVE 1
To use the relationship between a radius and a tangent

 OBJECTIVE 2
To use the relationship between two tangents from one point

. . . And Why

To find the distance between the centers of two dirt bike gears, as in Example 2

✔ Check Skills You'll Need

(For help, go to Skills Handbook page 716 and Lesson 7-2.)

Find each product.

1. $(p + 3)^2$ $p^2 + 6p + 9$
$w^2 + 20w + 100$
2. $(w + 10)^2$
$m^2 - 4m + 4$
3. $(m - 2)^2$

$\boxed{x^2}$ **Algebra** **Find the value of x. Leave your answer in simplest radical form.**

4.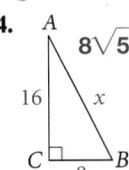

5.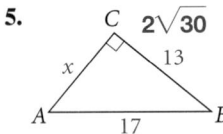

6. 12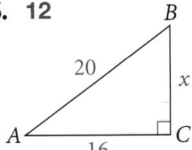

New Vocabulary
• tangent to a circle
• point of tangency
• inscribed in
• circumscribed about

OBJECTIVE

1 Using the Radius-Tangent Relationship

 Interactive lesson includes instant self-check, tutorials, and activities.

> **Investigation: Exploring Properties of Tangents**
>
> • Use a compass to draw a circle. Label the center O.
>
> • Use a straightedge to draw a line (not a line segment) that intersects the circle in only one point. Label the point A.
>
> • Draw $\overline{OA}$.
>
> 1. What seems to be true about the angles with side $\overline{AO}$? **They are rt. ∠s.**
>
> 2. Compare your results with others in your class. Make a conjecture about the relationship between a line that intersects a circle in only one point and the radius to that point. **They are ⊥.**

In Chapter 9, you studied the tangent ratio in right triangles. The tangents you will study here relate to circles.

Reading Math

The word "tangent" may refer to a line, ray, or segment.

A tangent to a circle is a line in the plane of the circle that intersects the circle in exactly one point.

The point where a circle and a tangent intersect is the point of tangency.

$\overrightarrow{BA}$ is a tangent ray and $\overline{BA}$ is a tangent segment.

Theorem 11-1 relates a tangent and a radius in a given circle.

Ongoing Assessment and Intervention

Before the Lesson	**During the Lesson**	**After the Lesson**
Diagnose prerequisite skills using:	**Monitor progress using:**	**Assess knowledge using:**
• Check Skills You'll Need	• Check Understanding	• Lesson Quiz
	• Additional Examples	• Computer Test Generator CD
	• Standardized Test Prep	

 **Key Concepts**

If a line is tangent to a circle, then the line is perpendicular to the radius drawn to the point of tangency.

$$\overleftrightarrow{AB} \perp \overline{OP}$$

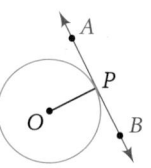

Proof → **Indirect Proof of Theorem 11-1**

Given: line n is tangent to $\odot O$ at P.

Prove: line $n \perp \overline{OP}$

Step 1 Assume the opposite.
Assume that line n is not perpendicular to $\overline{OP}$.

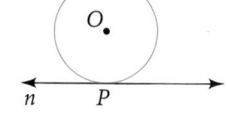

Step 2 Find a contradiction.
If line n is not perpendicular to $\overline{OP}$, some other segment $\overline{OL}$ must be perpendicular to line n. Also there is a point K on $\overrightarrow{PL}$ as shown in the diagram such that $\overline{LK} \cong \overline{LP}$. $\angle OLK$ and $\angle OLP$ are right angles by the definition of perpendicular. $\angle OLK \cong \angle OLP$ and $\overline{OL} \cong \overline{OL}$. $\triangle OLK \cong \triangle OLP$ by SAS, so $\overline{OK} \cong \overline{OP}$ by CPCTC. Thus, both K and P are on $\odot O$. For two points of line n to also be on $\odot O$ contradicts the given fact that line n is tangent to $\odot O$ at P.

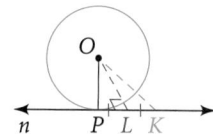

Step 3 State a conclusion.
The assumption that line n is not perpendicular to $\overline{OP}$ must be false. Therefore, line $n \perp \overline{OP}$ must be true.

You can use Theorem 11-1 to solve problems involving tangents to circles.

1 **EXAMPLE** **Finding Angle Measures**

Algebra $\overline{ML}$ and $\overline{MN}$ are tangent to $\odot O$. Find the value of x.

Since $\overline{ML}$ and $\overline{MN}$ are tangent to $\odot O$, $\angle L$ and $\angle N$ are right angles. $LMNO$ is a quadrilateral whose angle measures have a sum of 360.

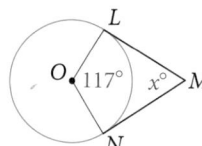

$$m\angle L + m\angle M + m\angle N + m\angle O = 360$$
$$90 + x + 90 + 117 = 360 \quad \textbf{Substitute.}$$
$$297 + x = 360 \quad \textbf{Simplify.}$$
$$x = 63 \quad \textbf{Solve.}$$

✓ **Check Understanding** ① $\overline{ED}$ is tangent to $\odot O$. Find the value of x. **52**

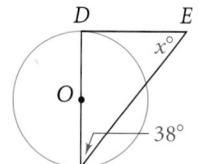

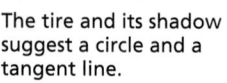

Real-World 🌐 **Connection**

The tire and its shadow suggest a circle and a tangent line.

Math Background

A tangent to a circle is related to the geometric interpretation of a derivative, the fundamental concept of differential calculus. A derivative measures the rate of change of a function at any point and corresponds to the slope of the tangent to the graph of the function at that point.

OBJECTIVE
1 **Teaching Notes**

Investigation (Optional)
To draw a line that intersects a circle at only one point, suggest that students pivot the straight-edge about a point outside the circle until it appears to touch the circle at only one point.

Connection to Language Arts
The term *tangent* is derived from the Latin verb *tangere*, which means "to touch."

Math Tip
For a ray or segment to be tangent to a circle, the line containing the ray or segment must be tangent to the circle. Note that a radius is never tangent to a circle.

Teaching Tip
Students may need to review the method of indirect proof before reading the proof of Theorem 11-1.

👪 **Reaching All Students**

| **Below Level** Have students use a protractor to check their Investigation conjectures. | **Advanced Learners** After Example 5, have students write an equation for the radius of a circle inscribed in an equilateral triangle with sides of length s. | **English Learners** See note on page 585. **Inclusion** See note on page 587. |

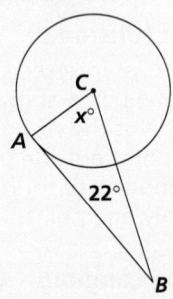
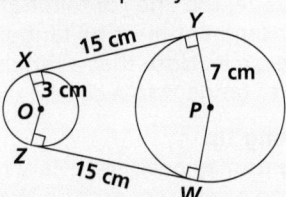
2 EXAMPLE Real-World Connection

Dirt Bikes A dirt bike chain fits tightly around two gears. The chain and gears form a figure like the one at the right. Find the distance between the centers of the gears.

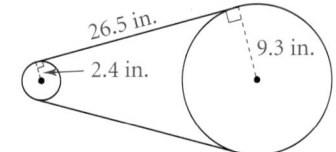

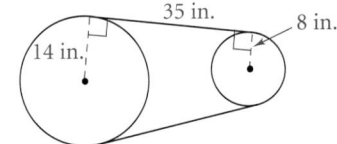

Label the diagram.

Draw $\overline{AE}$ parallel to $\overline{BC}$.

ABCE is a rectangle. $\triangle AED$ is a right triangle with $AE = 26.5$ in. and $ED = 9.3 - 2.4 = 6.9$ in.

$$AD^2 = AE^2 + ED^2 \qquad \text{Pythagorean Theorem}$$
$$AD^2 = 26.5^2 + 6.9^2 \qquad \text{Substitute.}$$
$$AD^2 = 749.86 \qquad \text{Simplify.}$$
$$AD \approx 27.383572 \qquad \text{Use a calculator to find the square root.}$$

● The distance between the centers is about 27.4 in.

Real-World Connection

This motorcycle and many other two-wheeled vehicles have chain-drive systems like the one shown in Example 2.

✓ **Check Understanding** **2** A belt fits tightly around two circular pulleys, as shown at the right. Find the distance between the centers of the pulleys. **about 35.5 in.**

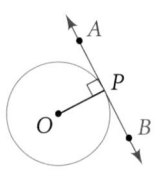

Theorem 11-2 is the converse of Theorem 11-1. You can use it to prove that a segment is tangent to a circle. You can also use Theorem 11-2 to construct a tangent to a circle (see Exercise 32). You will prove this theorem in Exercise 38.

Key Concepts

Theorem 11-2

If a line in the plane of a circle is perpendicular to a radius at its endpoint on the circle, then the line is tangent to the circle.

$\overleftrightarrow{AB}$ is tangent to $\odot O$.

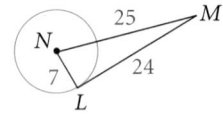

3 EXAMPLE Finding a Tangent

Is $\overline{ML}$ tangent to $\odot N$ at *L*? Explain.

$$NL^2 + LM^2 \stackrel{?}{=} NM^2 \qquad \text{Is } \triangle MLN \text{ a right triangle?}$$
$$7^2 + 24^2 \stackrel{?}{=} 25^2 \qquad \text{Substitute.}$$
$$625 = 625 \checkmark \qquad \text{Simplify.}$$

By the Converse of the Pythagorean Theorem, $\triangle MLN$ is a right triangle with right ● ∠*L*. Therefore $\overline{ML} \perp \overline{NL}$, and $\overline{ML}$ is tangent to $\odot N$ at *L* by Theorem 11-2.

✓ **Check Understanding** **3** If $NL = 4$, $LM = 7$, and $NM = 8$, is $\overline{ML}$ tangent to $\odot N$ at *L*? Explain. **No; $4^2 + 7^2 \neq 8^2$.**

In Chapter 5 you learned that a circle is circumscribed about a triangle if all vertices of the triangle lie on the circle. In that case, the triangle is **inscribed in** the circle.

Similarly, when a circle is inscribed in a triangle, as in the diagram at the right, the triangle is **circumscribed about** the circle. Each side of the triangle is tangent to the circle.

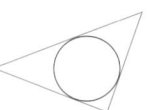

Theorem 11-3 will help you solve problems about polygons that circumscribe circles. You will prove this theorem in Exercise 40.

 Key Concepts

> **Theorem 11-3**
>
> The two segments tangent to a circle from a point outside the circle are congruent.
>
> $\overline{AB} \cong \overline{CB}$

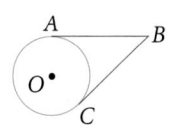

4 **EXAMPLE** **Using Theorem 11-3**

The diagram represents a chain drive system on a bicycle. Give a convincing argument that $BC = GF$.

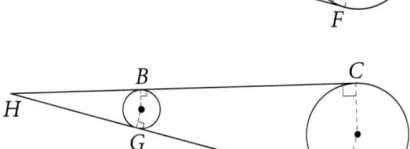

Extend $\overline{BC}$ and $\overline{GF}$ to intersect in point H. By Theorem 11-3, $HC = HF$, or $HB + BC = HG + GF$. By Theorem 11-3 again, $HB = HG$, so by the Subtraction Property of Equality, $BC = GF$.

 **Check Understanding** **4** **Critical Thinking** Give a convincing argument that $BC = GF$ above if you know that $\overleftrightarrow{BC}$ and $\overleftrightarrow{GF}$ never intersect.
If $\overleftrightarrow{BC}$ and $\overleftrightarrow{GF}$ never intersect, then $BCFG$ is a rectangle.

5 **EXAMPLE** **Circles Inscribed in Polygons**

$\odot O$ is inscribed in $\triangle ABC$. Find the perimeter of $\triangle ABC$.

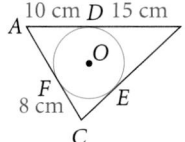

$AD = AF = 10$ cm   **The two segments tangent to a**
$BD = BE = 15$ cm   **circle from a point outside the**
$CF = CE = 8$ cm   **circle are congruent.**

$p = AB + BC + CA$	**Definition of perimeter p**
$= AD + DB + BE + EC + CF + FA$	**Segment Addition Postulate**
$= 10 + 15 + 15 + 8 + 8 + 10$	**Substitute.**
$= 66$	

The perimeter is 66 cm.

 **Check Understanding** **5** $\odot O$ is inscribed in $\triangle PQR$. $\triangle PQR$ has a perimeter of 88 cm. Find QY. **12 cm**

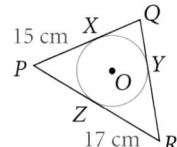

Math Tip
Point out that this lesson provides another way to define an inscribed circle: A circle is inscribed in a polygon if it is tangent to each side of the polygon.

English Learners
Students may remember the meaning of *circumscribed* more easily if they know that the prefix *circum-* means "around."

 Additional Examples

4 $\overline{QS}$ and $\overline{QT}$ are tangent to $\odot O$ at points S and T, respectively. Give a convincing argument that the diagonals of quadrilateral $QSOT$ are perpendicular.

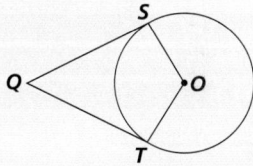

$QSOT$ is a kite or a rhombus, so its diagonals are perpendicular.

5 $\odot C$ is inscribed in quadrilateral $XYZW$. Find the perimeter of $XYZW$.

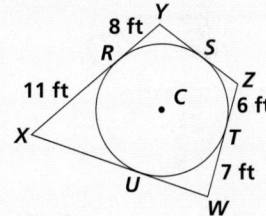

64 ft

Closure

Find the radius of the circle inscribed in the right triangle below.

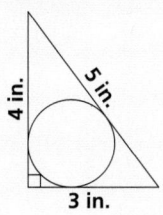

1 in.

EXERCISES For more practice, see *Extra Practice*.

Assignment Guide

1 Objective
- Ⓐ Ⓑ **Core** 1–12, 20–22, 24–26, 32–35
- Ⓒ **Extension** 38, 39, 41

2 Objective
- Ⓐ Ⓑ **Core** 13–19, 23, 27–31, 36, 37
- Ⓒ **Extension** 40, 42

Standardized Test Prep 43–47

Mixed Review 48–55

Enrichment 11-1

Reteaching 11-1

Practice 11-1

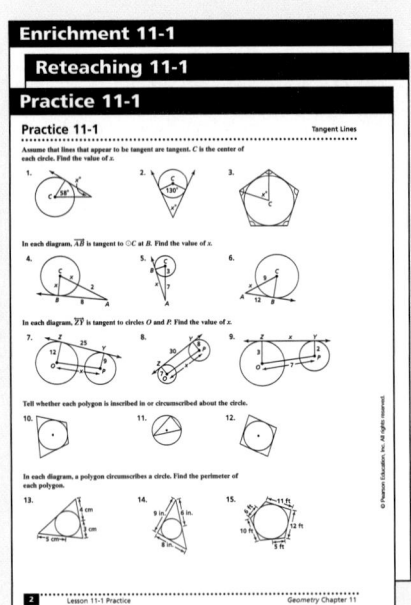

Ⓐ **Practice by Example**

Example 1
(page 583)

x^2 **Algebra** Assume that lines that appear to be tangent are tangent. O is the center of each circle. Find the value of x.

1.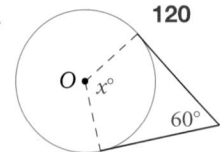
120
60°

2.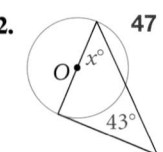
47
43°

3. 30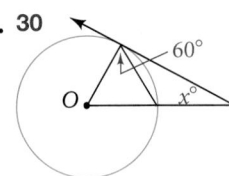
60°

Examples 2, 4
(pages 584, 585)

A belt fits snugly around the two circular pulleys shown.

4. Find the distance between the centers of the pulleys. Round to the nearest hundredth. **14.04 in.**

5. Give a convincing argument why the belt lengths RS and QP are equal. **See margin.**

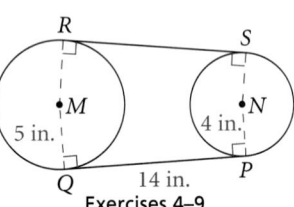
Exercises 4–9

📖 **Reading Math**
$\overline{RS}$ and $\overline{QP}$ are common tangents.

For the pulley system shown, use the lengths given below. Find the missing length to the nearest tenth.

6. $MQ = 10$ cm, $NP = 4$ cm, **15.2 cm** $QP = 14$ cm, $MN = \blacksquare$ cm

7. $MQ = 5$ in., $NP = 4$ in., **20.0 in.** $QP = 20$ in., $MN = \blacksquare$ in.

8. $MQ = 5$ in., $NP = 4$ in., **14.0 in.** $MN = 14$ in., $QP = \blacksquare$ in.

9. $MQ = 10$ cm, $NP = 4$ cm, $MN = 14$ cm, $RS = \blacksquare$ cm **19.1 cm**

Example 3
(page 584)

Determine whether a tangent line is shown in each diagram. Explain. 10–12. **See left.**

10. No; $5^2 + 16^2 \neq 16^2$.
11. Yes; $2.5^2 + 6^2 = 6.5^2$.
12. Yes; $6^2 + 8^2 = 10^2$.

10. 5, 15, 16

11. 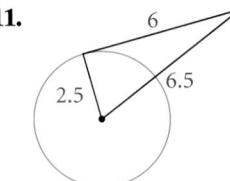 6, 2.5, 6.5

12. 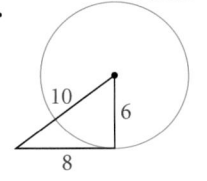 10, 6, 8

Example 5
(page 585)

Tell whether each polygon is inscribed in or circumscribed about the circle.

13. **inscribed in**

14. **circumscribed about**

15. **circumscribed about**

Each polygon circumscribes a circle. Find the perimeter of the polygon.

16. 8 cm, 16 cm, 78 cm, 6 cm, 9 cm

17. 1.9 in. **14.2 in.** 3.7 in. 3.4 in. 3.6 in.

pages 586–589 Exercises

5. Extend $\overline{RS}$ and $\overline{QP}$ until they meet at a point, H. By Thm. 11-3, $RH = QH$, or $SH + RS = QP + PH$. By 11-3 again, $SH = PH$. Thus, $RS = QP$.

18.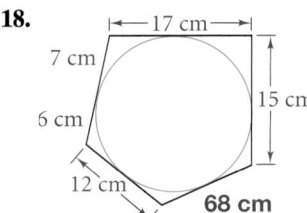
17 cm
7 cm
6 cm
15 cm
12 cm
68 cm

19.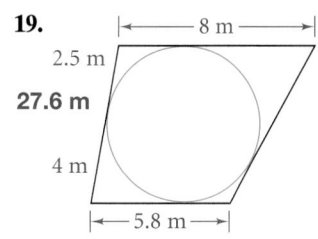
8 m
2.5 m
27.6 m
4 m
5.8 m

B Apply Your Skills

23a. external
b. external
c. internal

x^2 **Algebra** Assume that lines that appear to be tangent are tangent. **O** is the center of each circle. Find the value of *x* to the nearest tenth.

8 in.

20.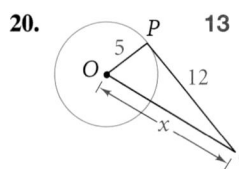
P 13
5
O
12
x
Q

21.
10 cm
x
7 cm x
3.6 cm

22.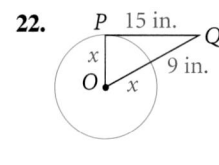
P 15 in. Q
x
O x 9 in.

Real-World Connection

This "diamond ring" effect in a solar eclipse may be seen by a person on Earth at the end of a common external tangent of the sun and moon. (See diagram at right.)

23. Solar Eclipse Common tangents to two circles may be *internal* or *external*. If you draw a segment joining the centers of the circles, a common internal tangent will intersect the segment. A common external tangent will not.

For this cross-sectional diagram of the sun, moon, and Earth during a solar eclipse, use the terms above to describe the types of tangents of each color. **a–c. See left.**
a. red **b.** blue **c.** green
d. Which tangents show the extent **blue lines; green lines** on Earth's surface of total eclipse? Of partial eclipse?
e. Reasoning In general, does every pair of circles have common tangents of both types? Explain. **No; explanations may vary. Sample: Two circles that have a common center have no common tangents.**

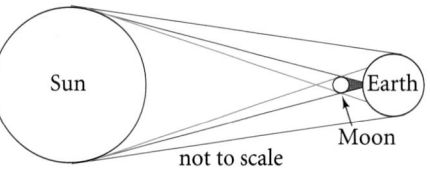
Sun
Earth
Moon
not to scale

Earth The circle at the right represents Earth. The radius of Earth is about 6400 km. Find the distance *d* that a person can see on a clear day from each of the following heights *h* above Earth. Round your answer to the nearest tenth of a kilometer.

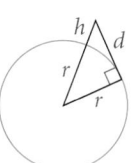
h d
r
r

24. 100 m
35.8 km

25. 500 m
80.0 km

26. 1 km
113.1 km

27. $\overline{BD}$ and $\overline{CK}$ at the right are diameters of $\odot A$.**57.5** $\overline{BP}$ and $\overline{QP}$ are tangents to $\odot A$. What is $m\angle CDA$?

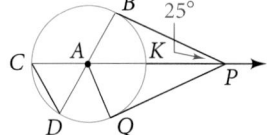
B 25°
C A K
P
D Q

? **Need Help?**

For Exercise 28(a), you must make a sketch for what da Vinci meant, *not* merely for what he said.

28. History Leonardo da Vinci wrote, "When each of two squares touch the same circle at four points, one is double the other." **a–b. See margin.**
✏ **a.** Sketch a figure that illustrates this statement.
✏ **b. Writing** Explain why the statement is true.

29. Clocks A regular hexagon is circumscribed about the ring surrounding the clock face. The diameter of the ring is 10 in. Find the perimeter of the hexagon. **about 34.6 in.**

30c. Kites; two pairs of adj. sides are ≅ but no opp. sides are ≅. (Special case: for a rt. isosc. △, one kite is a square.)

30. a. Open-Ended Draw a triangle circumscribed about a circle. Then draw the radius to each point of tangency. **See margin.**
b. How many quadrilaterals are in the figure you drew in part (a)? **3**
c. Classify these special quadrilaterals. Explain. **See left.**

Lesson 11-1 Tangent Lines **587**

28. a.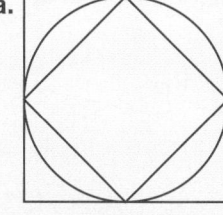

b. Answers may vary. Sample: If you draw 2 diagonals for both squares, 8 ≅ △ are formed in the entire figure with 4 in the small square.

30. a.

Connection to Astronomy

Exercise 23 As the diagram suggests, a solar eclipse occurs when the moon blocks sunlight from reaching Earth. A *total* eclipse occurs when the moon completely blocks the sun's rays, as in the region between the moon and Earth bounded by the common internal tangents to the sun and the moon.

Tactile Learners

Exercise 31 Have students manipulate a nickel, a dime, and a quarter to show how three circles can be mutually tangent.

Inclusion

Exercise 32 Students with motor difficulties can give step-by-step instructions to partners who then do the actual constructions.

Connection to Coordinate Geometry

Exercise 35 Before drawing a tangent segment, students must find its length, 4, using the Pythagorean Theorem. Then they can place a compass point at (0, 5), swing an arc of length 4 until it intersects the circle, and join either point of intersection and (0, 5).

Exercises 38–42 You may want students to work with partners or in small groups. Suggest that they begin each proof by writing a plan.

587

4. Assess

Lesson Quiz 11-1

$\overline{PA}$ and $\overline{PB}$ are tangent to $\odot C$. Use the figure for Exercises 1–3.

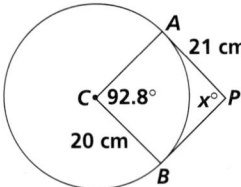

A
21 cm
C 92.8° $x°$ P
20 cm
B

1. Find the value of x. **87.2**

2. Find the perimeter of quadrilateral *PACB*. **82 cm**

3. Find *CP*. **29 cm**

$\overleftrightarrow{HJ}$ is tangent to $\odot A$ and to $\odot B$. Use the figure for Exercises 4 and 5.

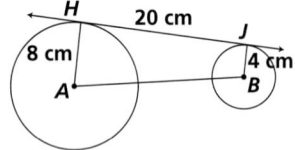

H 20 cm J
8 cm   4 cm
A   B

4. Find *AB* to the nearest tenth. **20.4 cm**

5. What type of special quadrilateral is *AHJB*? Explain how you know. **Trapezoid; the tangent line forms right angles at vertices *H* and *J*, so $\overline{HA} \parallel \overline{JB}$. Because $HA \neq JB$, *AHJB* is not a parallelogram but a trapezoid.**

Alternative Assessment

- Have students use compass and straightedge to construct a circle and then construct a line through a point on the circle perpendicular to a radius of the circle.
- Have students repeat the construction using a different radius and then find the intersection of the two lines they constructed.
- After constructing each line and finding the intersection, students should state a conclusion based on a theorem in this lesson.

588

---

31. All four are ≅; the two tangents to each coin from *A* are ≅, so by the Trans. Prop., all are ≅.

34. $90 - \left(\frac{180 - x}{2}\right)$ or $\frac{x}{2}$; $m \angle 4$ is $\frac{1}{2} m \angle 1$.

Real-World Connection

Careers HVAC technicians often specialize in either installation or maintenance and repair of heating, ventilation, and air conditioning systems.

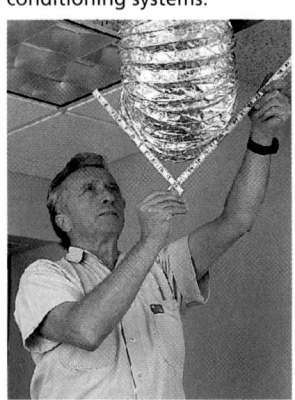

Challenge Proof 38.

37d. $\overline{AB} \parallel \overline{CD}$; arguments may vary.

---

31. **Critical Thinking** A nickel, a dime, and a quarter are touching as shown. Tangents are drawn from point *A* to both sides of each coin. What can you conclude about the four tangent segments? Explain. **See left.**

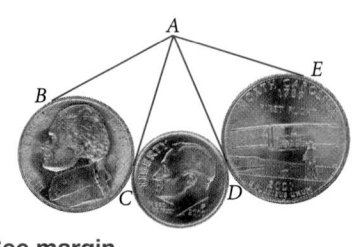

32. **Constructions** Draw a circle. Label the center *T*. Locate a point on the circle and label it *R*. Construct a tangent to $\odot T$ at *R*. **See margin.**

$\overline{AC}$ **is tangent to** $\odot O$ **at** *A*, **and** $m\angle 1 = 70$.

33. Find $m\angle 4$. **35**

34. Let $m\angle 1 = x$. Find $m\angle 4$ in terms of *x*. What is the relationship between $\angle 1$ and $\angle 4$? **See left.**

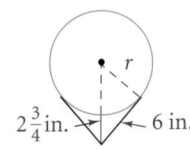

35. **Coordinate Geometry** Graph the equation $x^2 + y^2 = 9$. Then draw a segment from $(0, 5)$ tangent to the circle. Find the length of the segment. **See back of book.**

36. **Maintenance** Mr. Gonzales is replacing a cylindrical air-conditioning duct. He estimates the radius of the duct by folding a ruler to form two 6-in. tangents to the duct. The tangents form an angle. Mr. Gonzales measures the angle bisector from the vertex to the duct. It is about $2\frac{3}{4}$ in. long. What is the radius of the duct? **about 5.2 in.**

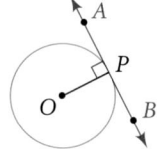

37. a. Construct two nonintersecting circles, $\odot O$ and $\odot P$, of different sizes on the same sheet of paper. Neither circle should be inside the other.
    b. Carefully draw tangents from the center of $\odot O$ to $\odot P$. Label the points of intersection of the tangent lines with $\odot P$ as *A* and *B*. **a–c. See margin.**
    c. Carefully draw tangents from the center of $\odot P$ to $\odot O$. Label the points of intersection of the tangent lines with $\odot O$ as *C* and *D*.
    d. **Make a Conjecture** What seems to be true about $\overline{AB}$ and $\overline{CD}$? Give a convincing argument to support your conjecture. (*Hint:* Draw $\overline{OP}$.) **See left.**

38. Write an indirect proof of Theorem 11-2.

Given: $\overleftrightarrow{AB} \perp \overline{OP}$ at *P*.
Prove: $\overleftrightarrow{AB}$ is tangent to $\odot O$.
See back of book.

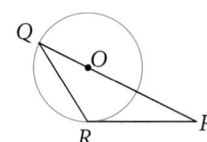

39. $\overline{PR}$ is tangent to $\odot O$ at *R*, $OP = 17$ cm, and $RP = 15$ cm. Find the area of $\triangle QPR$ to the nearest tenth of a square centimeter. **88.2 cm²**

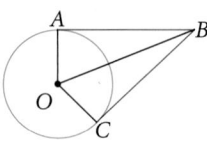

Proof **In Exercises 40–42, write a two-column proof, paragraph proof, or flow proof.**

40. Prove Theorem 11-3.

Given: $\overline{BA}$ and $\overline{BC}$ are tangent to $\odot O$ at *A* and *C*, respectively.
Prove: $\overline{BA} \cong \overline{BC}$ **See margin p. 589.**

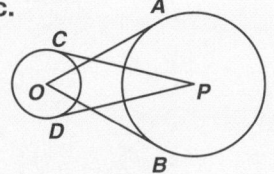

pages 586–589 **Exercises**

32.

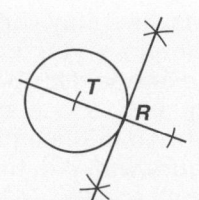

37. a–c.

41. Given: $\overline{BC}$ is tangent to $\odot A$ at D.
$\overline{DB} \cong \overline{DC}$

Prove: $\overline{AB} \cong \overline{AC}$ See margin.

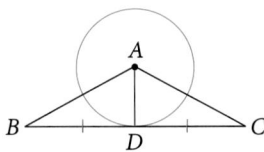

42. Given: $\odot A$ and $\odot B$ with common tangents $\overline{DF}$ and $\overline{CE}$

Prove: $\triangle GDC \sim \triangle GFE$ See margin.

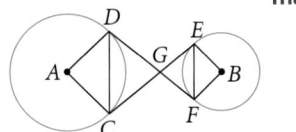

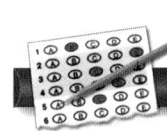

Standardized Test Prep

Standardized Test Prep

📁 **Resources**

For additional practice with a variety of test item formats:
• Standardized Test Prep, p. 631
• Test-Taking Strategies, p. 626
• Test-Taking Strategies with Transparencies

Error Prevention

Exercise 46 Be careful that students do not think that $(x + 8)^2$ equals $x^2 + 8^2$. If necessary, review how to find $(x + 8)^2$.

Exercise 47 Students can prove that triangles are similar by SSS.

Multiple Choice

Point O is the center of each circle. Assume the lines that appear tangent are tangent. What is the value of the variable?

43. C

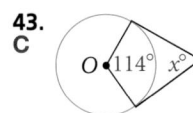

    A. 26
    B. 57
    C. 66
    D. 114

44. F

    F. 22
    G. 28
    H. 34
    I. 40

45. C

    A. 8
    B. 9
    C. 15
    D. 17

46. I

    F. 2
    G. 3
    H. 4
    I. 5

47. [2] $\frac{2}{3} = \frac{3}{x}$
$2x = 9$
$x = 4.5$
OR equivalent solution

[1] correct eq. solved incorrectly

Short Response

47. Find the value of x. Show your work. See left.

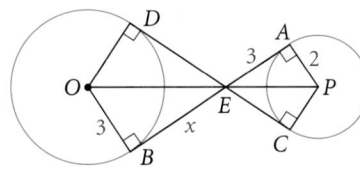

Take It to the NET
Online lesson quiz at
www.PHSchool.com
Web Code: afa-1101

41. 1. $\overline{BC}$ is tangent to $\odot A$ at D. (Given)
2. $\overline{DB} \cong \overline{DC}$ (Given)
3. $\overline{AD} \perp \overline{BC}$ (If a line is tan. to a circle, it is $\perp$ to the radius.) 4. $\angle ADB$ and $\angle ADC$ are rt. $\angle$s (Def. of $\perp$) 5. $\angle ADB \cong \angle ADC$ (rt. $\angle$s are $\cong$) 6. $\overline{AD} \cong \overline{AD}$ (Refl. Prop. of $\cong$)
7. $\triangle ADB \cong \triangle ADC$ (SAS)
8. $\overline{AB} \cong \overline{AC}$ (CPCTC)

42. 1. $\odot A$ and $\odot B$ with common tangents $\overline{DF}$ and $\overline{CE}$ (Given)
2. $PG = GC$ and $GE = GF$ (Two tan. segments from a pt. to a circle are $\cong$.)

3. $\frac{GD}{GC} = 1$, $\frac{GF}{GE} = 1$ (Div. Prop. of =)

4. $\frac{GD}{GC} = \frac{GF}{GE}$ (Trans. Prop. of =)
5. $\angle DGC \cong \angle EGF$ (Vert. $\angle$s are $\cong$.) 6. $\triangle GDC \sim \triangle GFE$ (SAS $\sim$ Thm.)

Mixed Review

Lesson 10-8   **Two cubes have heights 6 in. and 8 in. Find each ratio.**

48. similarity ratio
   3 : 4

49. ratio of surface areas
   9 : 16

50. ratio of volumes
   27 : 64

Lesson 9-1 x^2 **Algebra**   **Find the value of x. Round answers to the nearest tenth.**

51.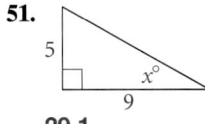
      29.1

52. 28.1

53. 68.2

Lesson 8-2   **The polygons are similar. (a) State the similarity ratio and (b) find the values of the variables.**   a. 10 : 17   b. $m = 1.82$; $n = 3.78$

54.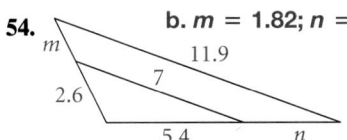

55. a. 4 : 1

$a = 1.625$; $b = 1.75$; $c = 3$

40. 1. $\overline{BA}$ and $\overline{BC}$ are tangent to $\odot O$ at A and C (Given)
2. $\overline{AB} \perp \overline{OA}$ and $\overline{BC} \perp \overline{OC}$ (If a line is tan. to a circle, it is $\perp$ to the radius.) 3. $\triangle BAO$ and $\triangle BCO$ are right $\angle$s. (Def. of rt. $\triangle$) 4. $\overline{AO} \cong \overline{OC}$ (Radii of a circle are $\cong$.)
5. $\overline{BO} \cong \overline{BO}$ (Refl. Prop. of $\cong$) 6. $\triangle BAO \cong \triangle BCO$ (HL Thm.) 7. $\overline{BA} \cong \overline{BC}$ (CPCTC)

1. Plan

Lesson Preview

 Check Skills You'll Need

Using 45°-45°-90° Triangles
Lesson 7-3: Example 2
Exercises 4–9
Extra Practice, p. 696

Using 30°-60°-90° Triangles
Lesson 7-3: Example 5
Exercises 15–20
Extra Practice, p. 696

Lesson Resources

 Teaching Resources
Practice, Reteaching, Enrichment

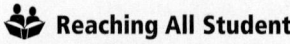 **Reaching All Students**
Practice Workbook 11-2
Spanish Practice Workbook 11-2
Hands-On Activities 32
Informal Geometry Planning
  Guide 11-2

 **Presentation Assistant Plus!**
Transparencies
• Check Skills You'll Need 11-2
• Additional Examples 11-2
• Student Edition Answers 11-2
• Lesson Quiz 11-2
PH Presentation Pro CD 11-2

 PRENTICE HALL
ASSESSMENT SYSTEM

Computer Test Generator CD

 Technology
Resource Pro® CD-ROM
Computer Test Generator CD
Prentice Hall Presentation Pro CD

 **www.PHSchool.com**
Student Site
• Teacher Web Code: afk-5500
• Self-grading Lesson Quiz
Teacher Center
• Lesson Planner
• Resources

Plus **iTEXT**

590

 # 11-2

Chords and Arcs

North Carolina Objectives

2.03 Apply properties, definitions, and theorems of two-dimensional figures to solve problems and write proofs: d) Circles.

Lesson Preview

What You'll Learn

OBJECTIVE 1 To use congruent chords, arcs, and central angles

OBJECTIVE 2 To recognize properties of lines through the center of a circle

. . . And Why

To see how an archaeologist finds the center and radius of the rim of a jar, as in Exercise 20

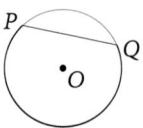 **Check Skills You'll Need**   (For help, go to Lesson 7-3.)

Find the value of each variable. Leave your answer in simplest radical form.

1.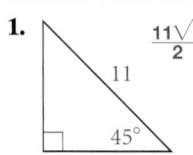

2. 5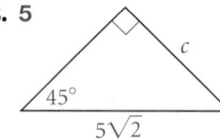

3.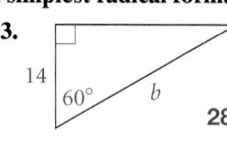

New Vocabulary • chord

 Interactive lesson includes instant self-check, tutorials, and activities.

OBJECTIVE 1

Using Congruent Chords, Arcs, and Central Angles

A segment whose endpoints are on a circle is called a **chord**. The diagram shows the related chord and arc, $\overline{PQ}$ and $\overparen{PQ}$.

The following theorem is about related central angles, chords, and arcs. It says, for example, that if two central angles in a circle are congruent, then so are the two chords and two arcs that the angles intercept.

Key Concepts

> **Theorem 11-4**
>
> Within a circle or in congruent circles
>
> (1) Congruent central angles have congruent chords.
>
> (2) Congruent chords have congruent arcs.
>
> (3) Congruent arcs have congruent central angles.

You will prove Theorem 11-4 in Exercises 23, 24, and 35.

1 EXAMPLE Using Theorem 11-4

In the diagram, $\odot O \cong \odot P$. Given that $\overparen{BC} \cong \overparen{DF}$, what can you conclude?

By Theorem 11-4, $\angle O \cong \angle P$ and $\overline{BC} \cong \overline{DF}$.

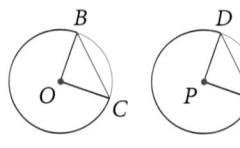

Check Understanding ① If you are instead given that $\overline{BC} \cong \overline{DF}$, what can you conclude?
$\angle O \cong \angle P$; $\overparen{BC} \cong \overparen{DF}$

590 Chapter 11 Circles

 ## Ongoing Assessment and Intervention

Before the Lesson	During the Lesson	After the Lesson
Diagnose prerequisite skills using:	**Monitor progress using:**	**Assess knowledge using:**
• Check Skills You'll Need	• Check Understanding • Additional Examples • Standardized Test Prep	• Lesson Quiz • Computer Test Generator CD

The following theorem shows a relationship between two chords and their distances from the center of a circle. A proof of part (1) is given below. You will prove part (2) in Exercise 37.

 Key Concepts

> **Theorem 11-5**
>
> Within a circle or in congruent circles
>
> (1) Chords equidistant from the center are congruent.
>
> (2) Congruent chords are equidistant from the center.

 **Proof**

Proof of Theorem 11-5, Part (1)

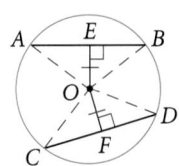

Given: $\odot O, \overline{OE} \cong \overline{OF}$, $\overline{OE} \perp \overline{AB}, \overline{OF} \perp \overline{CD}$

Prove: $\overline{AB} \cong \overline{CD}$

Need Help?

In a circle, the distance from the center to a chord is the length of the perpendicular segment from the center to the chord.

Statements	Reasons
1. $\overline{OA} \cong \overline{OB} \cong \overline{OC} \cong \overline{OD}$	1. Radii of a circle are congruent.
2. $\overline{OE} \cong \overline{OF}, \overline{OE} \perp \overline{AB}, \overline{OF} \perp \overline{CD}$	2. Given
3. $\angle AEO$ and $\angle CFO$ are right angles.	3. Def. of perpendicular segments
4. $\triangle AEO \cong \triangle CFO$	4. HL Theorem
5. $\angle A \cong \angle C$	5. CPCTC
6. $\angle B \cong \angle A, \angle C \cong \angle D$	6. Isosceles Triangle Theorem
7. $\angle B \cong \angle D$	7. Transitive Property of Congruence
8. $\angle AOB \cong \angle COD$	8. If two ∠ of a △ are ≅ to two ∠ of another △, then the third ∠ are ≅.
9. $\overline{AB} \cong \overline{CD}$	9. ≅ central angles have ≅ chords.

You can use Theorem 11-5 to find missing lengths in circles.

Real-World Connection

Steel beams model congruent chords equidistant from the center to give the illusion of a circle.

2 EXAMPLE Using Theorem 11-5

Find the value of a in the circle.

$PQ = QR = 12.5$ **Given**

$PQ + QR = PR$ **Segment Addition Postulate**

$25 = PR$ **Substitute.**

$a = PR$ **Chords equidistant from the center of a circle are congruent.**

$a = 25$ **Substitute.**

✔ **Check Understanding** ② Find the value of x in the circle. **16**

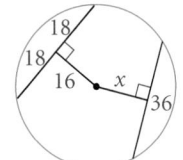

👥 **Reaching All Students**

Below Level Have students draw diagrams for Theorems 11-6, 11-7, and 11-8 that accurately represent the given information.	**Advanced Learners** Have students write a paragraph to explain why the phrase *that is not a diameter* is necessary in Theorem 11-7.	**English Learners** See note on page 594. **Visual Learners** See note on page 591.

Math Background

Theorem 11-8 can be used to prove the theorem of analytic geometry that states that any three noncollinear points determine a unique circle. It also can be used to justify a method of constructing the circle. Construct the perpendicular bisectors of two of the three possible segments. Construct a circle whose center is the point of intersection of the perpendicular bisectors and whose radius is the distance from the center to any of the three points.

OBJECTIVE

1 Teaching Notes

Visual Learners

On the board, copy the diagram below that summarizes Theorem 11-4.

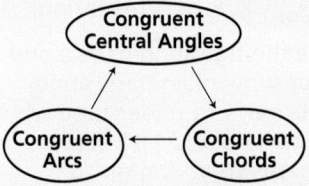

Ask: *Can you conclude that congruent chords have congruent central angles? If so, how?* yes; by the Law of Syllogism

Alternative Method

An alternate proof of part 1 of Theorem 11-5 would use the HL Theorem to prove $\triangle AOE \cong \triangle BOE \cong \triangle COF \cong \triangle DOF$ and then use CPCTC and the Segment Addition Postulate. This method also could be used to prove Theorem 11-6.

Additional Examples

1 In the diagram, radius $\overline{OX}$ bisects $\angle AOB$. What can you conclude?

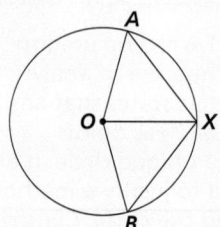

$\angle AOX \cong \angle BOX$; $\overline{AX} \cong \overline{BX}$; $\overset{\frown}{AX} \cong \overset{\frown}{BX}$

2 Find AB.

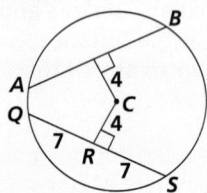

14

OBJECTIVE
2 Teaching Notes

3 **EXAMPLE** Error Prevention

Because the figures in parts a and b do not show diameters, some students may not understand why Theorems 11-6 and 11-7 apply. Have them reread the section above Theorem 11-6 to reinforce that the theorems apply to lines or segments that contain the center of the circle.

Additional Examples

3 P and Q are points on $\odot O$. The distance from O to $\overline{PQ}$ is 15 in., and $PQ = 16$ in. Find the radius of $\odot O$. **17 in.**

Closure

$\overline{XY}$ and $\overline{YZ}$ are perpendicular chords within $\odot C$ that are also equidistant from center C. What is the most precise name for quadrilateral $MYNC$? Explain.

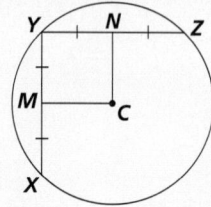

Square; congruent chords are equidistant from the center, and a diameter that bisects a chord is $\perp$ to the chord.

592

OBJECTIVE
2 Lines Through the Center of a Circle

The Converse of the Perpendicular Bisector Theorem from Lesson 5-2 has special applications to a circle and its diameters, chords, and arcs.

Key Concepts

> **Theorem 11-6**
>
> In a circle, a diameter that is perpendicular to a chord bisects the chord and its arcs.
>
> **Theorem 11-7**
>
> In a circle, a diameter that bisects a chord (that is not a diameter) is perpendicular to the chord.
>
> **Theorem 11-8**
>
> In a circle, the perpendicular bisector of a chord contains the center of the circle.

Proof

Proof of Theorem 11-7

Given: $\odot T$ with diameter $\overline{QR}$ bisecting $\overline{SU}$ at V.

Prove: $\overline{QR} \perp \overline{SU}$

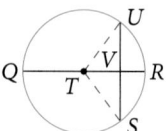

Proof: $TS = TU$ because the radii of a circle are congruent. $VS = VU$ by the definition of bisect. Thus, T and V are equidistant from S and U. By the Converse of the Perpendicular Bisector Theorem, T and V are on the perpendicular bisector of $\overline{SU}$. Since two points determine one line, $\overleftrightarrow{TV}$ is the perpendicular bisector of $\overline{SU}$. Another name for $\overleftrightarrow{TV}$ is $\overleftrightarrow{QR}$. Thus, $\overline{QR} \perp \overline{SU}$.

You will prove Theorems 11-6 and 11-8 in Exercises 25 and 36, respectively.

3 **EXAMPLE** Using Diameters and Chords

Algebra Find each missing length to the nearest tenth.

a.

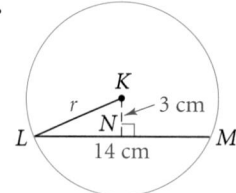

$LN = \frac{1}{2}(14) = 7$ A diameter $\perp$ to a chord bisects the chord.

$r^2 = 3^2 + 7^2$ Use the Pythagorean Theorem.

$r \approx 7.6$ Find the square root of each side.

b.

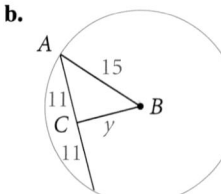

$\overline{BC} \perp \overline{AC}$ A diameter that bisects a chord that is not a diameter is $\perp$ to the chord.

$y^2 + 11^2 = 15^2$ Use the Pythagorean Theorem.

$y^2 = 104$ Solve for y^2.

$y \approx 10.2$ Find the square root of each side.

592 Chapter 11 Circles

Real-World **Connection**

The center of the tire is located on the perpendicular bisector of the flat part.

✓ **Check Understanding** ③ Use the circle at the right.
  a. Find the length of the chord. **about 11**
  b. Find the distance from the midpoint of the chord to the midpoint of its minor arc.
  2.8

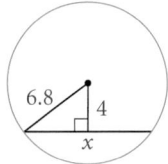

EXERCISES

For more practice, see *Extra Practice*.

Practice and Problem Solving

Ⓐ **Practice by Example**

Example 1
(page 590)

In Exercises 1 and 2, the circles are congruent. What can you conclude?

1. 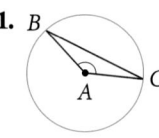 **1–2.** **2.**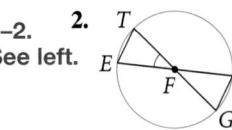
See left.
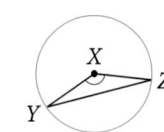 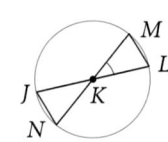

1. $\overparen{BC} \cong \overparen{YZ}$; $\overline{BC} \cong \overline{YZ}$

2. $\overparen{ET} \cong \overparen{GH} \cong \overparen{JN} \cong$ $\overparen{ML}$; $\overline{ET} \cong \overline{GH} \cong \overline{JN} \cong$ $\overline{ML}$; $\angle TFE \cong \angle HFG$; $\angle JKN \cong \angle MKL$

Example 2
(page 591)

Find the value of *x*.

3. **14**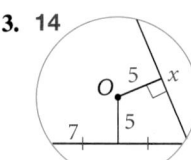

4. **2**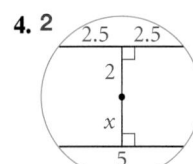

5. **7**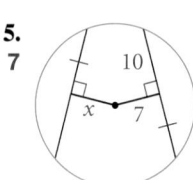

6. **50**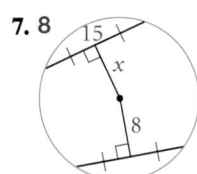

7. **8**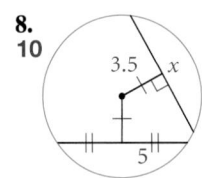

8. **10**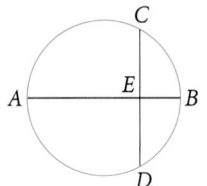

Example 3
(page 592)

9. Answers may vary.
Samples are given.
  a. $\overline{CE}$
  b. $\overline{DE}$
  c. $\angle CEB$
  d. $\angle DEA$

Use the diagram at the right to complete Exercises 9 and 10.

9. Given that $\overline{AB}$ is a diameter of the circle and $\overline{AB} \perp \overline{CD}$, then **a.** ___?___ ≅ **b.** ___?___ and **c.** ___?___ ≅ **d.** ___?___. **a-d. See left.**

10. Given that $\overline{AB}$ is the perpendicular bisector of $\overline{CD}$, then $\overline{AB}$ contains ___?___. **the center of the circle**

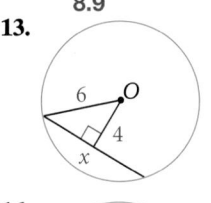

Algebra Find the value of *x* to the nearest tenth.

11. **6**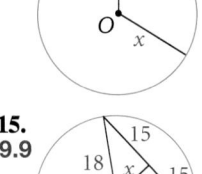

12. **5.4**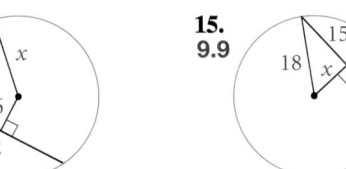

13. **8.9**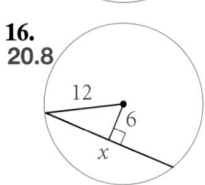

14. **12.5**

15. **9.9**

16. **20.8**

Assignment Guide

▼ ① **Objective**
  Ⓐ Ⓑ **Core** 1–8, 17, 23, 24, 27, 29–32, 35
  Ⓒ **Extension** 37

▼ ② **Objective**
  Ⓐ Ⓑ **Core** 9–16, 18–22, 25, 26 ,28, 33, 34, 36
  Ⓒ **Extension** 38–40

Standardized Test Prep 41–46

Mixed Review 47–50

Teaching Tip

Exercise 19 Students will need to find $\cos^{-1}\left(\frac{15}{17}\right)$ or $\sin^{-1}\left(\frac{15}{17}\right)$.

Exercises 12, 14 Students may find it helpful to draw and label the third side of the triangle, using the fact that all radii are congruent.

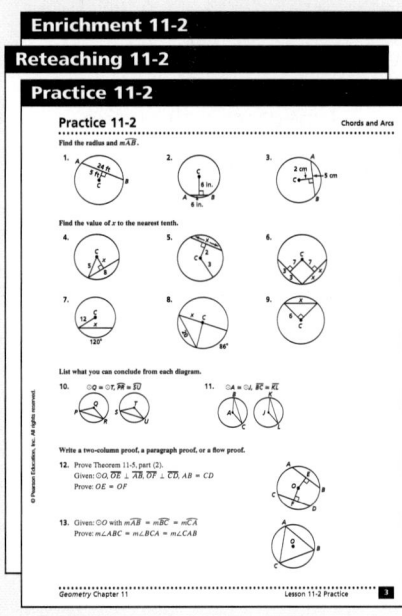

pages 593–596 **Exercises**

20. She can draw 2 chords, and their ⊥ bisectors, of the partial circle. The intersection pt. of the ⊥ bisectors will be the center and she can then measure the radius.

24. a. All radii of a circle are ≅.

b. $\overline{AB} \cong \overline{CD}$

c. Given

d. SSS

e. $\angle AEB \cong \angle CED$

f. ≅ central ∠ have ≅ arcs.

36. *X* is equidist. from *W* and *Y*, since $\overline{XW}$ and $\overline{XY}$ are radii. So *X* is on the ⊥ bis. of $\overline{WY}$ by the Conv. of the ⊥ Bis. Thm. But ℓ is the ⊥ bis. of $\overline{WY}$, so ℓ contains *X*.

594

B Apply Your Skills

Find $m\widehat{AB}$. (*Hint:* You will need to use trigonometry in Exercise 19.) about 123.9

17. 108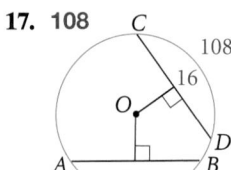

18. 90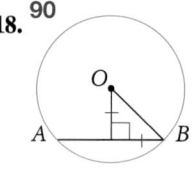

19.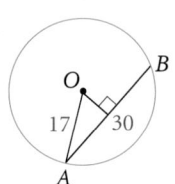

20. **Archaeology** An archaeologist found several jar fragments including a large piece of the circular rim. How can she find the center and radius of the rim to help her reconstruct the jar? **See margin.**

21. **Geometry in 3 Dimensions** In the figure at the right, sphere *O* with radius 13 cm is intersected by a plane 5 cm from center *O*. Find the radius of cross section ⊙*A*. **12 cm**

22. **Geometry in 3 Dimensions** A plane intersects a sphere that has radius 10 in. forming cross section ⊙*B* with radius 8 in. How far is the plane from the center of the sphere? **6 in.**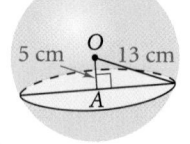

23. Complete the paragraph proof of Theorem 11-4, Part (1).

Given: ⊙*P* with $\angle KPM \cong \angle LPN$

Prove: $\overline{KM} \cong \overline{LN}$ a–c. $\overline{PL}; \overline{PM};$ All radii of a circle are ≅.

Proof: $\overline{KP} \cong$ a. __?__ ≅ b. __?__ ≅ $\overline{NP}$ because c. __?__. △*KPM* ≅ d. __?__ by e. __?__. $\overline{KM} \cong \overline{LN}$ by f. __?__.
  d–f. △*LPN*; SAS; CPCTC

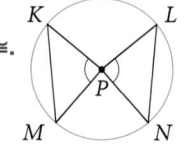

24. Complete the flow proof of Theorem 11-4, Part (2).

Given: ⊙*E* with congruent chords $\overline{AB}$ and $\overline{CD}$

Prove: $\overline{AB} \cong \overline{CD}$ **See margin.**

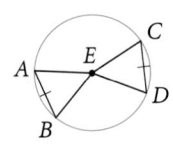

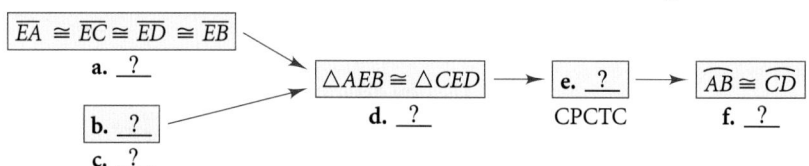

$$\boxed{\overline{EA} \cong \overline{EC} \cong \overline{ED} \cong \overline{EB}}$$
a. __?__
b. __?__
c. __?__
→ $\boxed{\triangle AEB \cong \triangle CED}$
d. __?__
→ $\boxed{\text{e. __?__}}$
CPCTC
→ $\boxed{\overline{AB} \cong \overline{CD}}$
f. __?__

25. Complete the two-column proof of Theorem 11-6.

Given: ⊙*O* with diameter $\overline{ED} \perp \overline{AB}$ at *C*

Prove: $\overline{AC} \cong \overline{BC}$ and $\widehat{AD} \cong \widehat{BD}$

Begin by drawing $\overline{OA}$ and $\overline{OB}$.

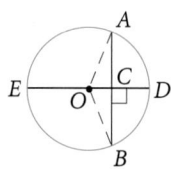

Statements	Reasons
1. $\overline{OA} \cong \overline{OB}$	a. __?__ All radii of a ⊙ are ≅.
2. $\overline{ED} \perp \overline{AB}$	b. __?__ Given
3. $\angle ACO$ and $\angle BCO$ are right angles.	c. __?__ Def. of ⊥
4. $\overline{OC} \cong \overline{OC}$	d. __?__ Reflexive Prop. of ≅
5. △*AOC* ≅ △*BOC*	e. __?__ HL Thm.
6. $\overline{AC} \cong \overline{BC}$	f. __?__ CPCTC
7. $\angle AOC \cong \angle BOC$	g. __?__ CPCTC
8. $\widehat{AD} \cong \widehat{BD}$	h. __?__ ≅ central ∠ have ≅ arcs.

594 Chapter 11 Circles

Reading Math

For help with reading and solving Exercise 26, see p. 597.

27. He doesn't know that the chords are equidistant from the center.

35. 1. ⊙P with $\overset{\frown}{QS} \cong \overset{\frown}{RT}$ (Given) **2.** $m\overset{\frown}{QS} = m\angle QPS$ and $m\overset{\frown}{RT} = m\angle RPT$ (Arc measure = central ∠measure.)
3. $m\overset{\frown}{QS} = m\overset{\frown}{RT}$ (Def. of ≅) **4.** $\angle QPS \cong \angle RPT$ (Subst.)

26. Two concentric circles have radii of 4 cm and 8 cm. A segment tangent to the smaller circle is a chord of the larger circle. What is the length of the segment? **about 13.9 cm**

27. Error Analysis Scott looks at this figure and concludes that $\overline{ST} \cong \overline{PR}$. What is wrong with Scott's conclusion? **See left.**

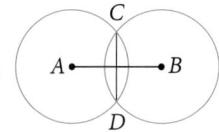

28. Open-Ended Use a circular object such as a can or a saucer to draw a circle. Construct the center of the circle. **Check students' work.**

29. Writing Theorems 11-4 and 11-5 both begin with the phrase "Within a circle or in congruent circles." Explain why "congruent" is essential for both theorems.
Circles can have ≅ chords or ≅ central ∡ without having both. ⊙A and ⊙B are congruent. $\overline{CD}$ is a chord of both circles.

30. $AB = 8$ in., $CD = 6$ in. How long is a radius? **5 in.**

31. $AB = 24$ cm, radius = 13 cm. How long is $\overline{CD}$? **10 cm**

32. radius = 13 ft, $CD = 24$ ft. How long is $\overline{AB}$? **10 ft**

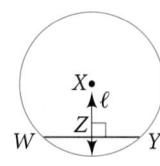

33. Coordinate Geometry Find the length of the chord of the circle $x^2 + y^2 = 25$ that is formed by the line $x = 3$. **8**

34. Critical Thinking The diameter of a circle is 20 cm. Two chords parallel to the diameter are 6 cm and 16 cm long. What are the possible distances between the chords to the nearest tenth of a centimeter? **3.5 cm, 15.5 cm**

Proof **Write a two-column proof, paragraph proof, or flow proof.** **See margin p. 594.**

35. Prove Theorem 11-4, Part (3).
Given: ⊙P with $\overset{\frown}{QS} \cong \overset{\frown}{RT}$
Prove: $\angle QPS \cong \angle RPT$ **See left.**

36. Prove Theorem 11-8.
Given: ℓ is the ⊥ bisector of $\overline{WY}$.
Prove: ℓ contains the center of ⊙X.

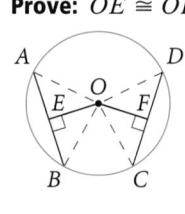 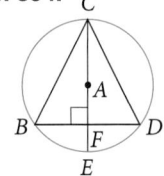

C Challenge Proof **Write a two-column proof, paragraph proof, or flow proof.**

37. Prove Theorem 11-5, Part (2).
Given: ⊙O with $\overline{AB} \cong \overline{CD}$
Prove: $\overline{OE} \cong \overline{OF}$ **37-38. See margin p. 594.**

38. Given: ⊙A with $\overline{CE} \perp \overline{BD}$
Prove: $\overset{\frown}{BC} \cong \overset{\frown}{DC}$

Real-World Connection

The cylinders used on milk tank trucks lie on the lateral surface and have a vertical base at each end.

39. Dairy The diameter of the base of a cylindrical milk tank is 59 in. The length of the tank is 470 in. You estimate that the depth of the milk in the tank is 20 in. Find the number of gallons of milk in the tank to the nearest gallon. (1 gal = 231 in.³) **1661 gal**

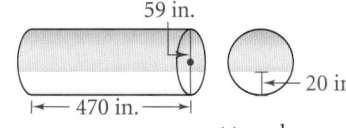
not to scale

40. If two circles are concentric and a chord of the larger circle is tangent to the smaller circle, prove that the point of tangency is the midpoint of the chord. **See margin.**

40. Let O be the center of the circles, and P be the pt. of tangency of the larger circle's chord to the smaller circle. Then $\overline{OP}$ is ⊥ to the chord, and therefore bisects it. So P is the midpt. of the chord.

 Lesson Quiz 11-2

For Exercises 1–5, use the diagram of ⊙L below.

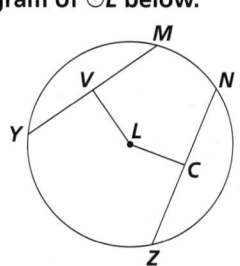

1. If $\overline{YM}$ and $\overline{ZN}$ are congruent chords, what can you conclude?
$\overset{\frown}{YM} \cong \overset{\frown}{ZN}$; $\angle YLM \cong \angle ZLN$

2. If $\overline{YM}$ and $\overline{ZN}$ are congruent chords, explain why you cannot conclude that $LV = LC$. **You do not know whether $\overline{LV}$ and $\overline{LC}$ are perpendicular to the chords.**

3. Suppose that $\overline{YM}$ has length 12 in., and its distance from point L is 5 in. Find the radius of ⊙L to the nearest tenth. **7.8 in.**

For Exercises 4 and 5, suppose that $\overline{LV} \perp \overline{YM}$, $YV = 11$ cm, and ⊙L has a diameter of 26 cm.

4. Find YM. **22 cm**

5. Find LV to the nearest tenth. **6.9 cm**

Alternative Assessment

Have students use only pictures and mathematical symbols to express each theorem in this lesson. Then have each student exchange their work with a partner who writes a paragraph below the picture evaluating the presentation for accuracy and clarity. Use the drawings and paragraphs to assess students' understanding.

Standardized Test Prep

Multiple Choice

41. The diameter of a circle is 25 cm and a chord of the same circle is 16 cm. To the nearest tenth, what is the distance of the chord from the center of the circle? **B**

A. 9.0 cm   B. 9.6 cm   C. 18.0 cm   D. 19.2 cm

42. In the figure at the right, what is the value of x to the nearest tenth? **G**

F. 3.0   G. 6.2
H. 6.8   I. 9.0

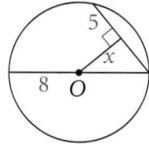

Quantitative Comparison

Compare the boxed quantity in Column A with the boxed quantity in Column B. Choose the best answer.

A. The quantity in Column A is greater.
B. The quantity in Column B is greater.
C. The two quantities are equal.
D. The relationship cannot be determined from the information given.

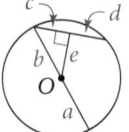

	Column A	Column B
43. C	a	b
44. D	d	e
45. C	b + d	a + c

Short Response

46. Circles M and N are congruent with radii measuring 13 cm. $\overline{PQ}$ is a chord of both circles and $PQ = 18$ cm. To the nearest tenth, find MN. Justify your answer.

See margin.

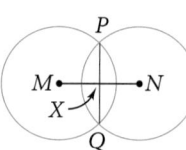

Mixed Review

Lesson 11-1

Assume that lines that appear to be tangent are tangent. O is the center of each circle. Find the value of x to the nearest tenth.

47.

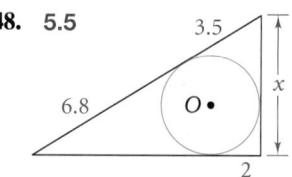

40

48. **5.5**

Lesson 9-3

49. From the top of a building you look down at an object on the ground. If your eyes are 50 feet above the ground and the angle of depression is 50°, how far is the object on the ground from the base of the building? **about 42 ft**

Lesson 8-5

50. The legs of a right triangle are 10 in. and 24 in. long. Find the lengths, to the nearest tenth, of the segments into which the bisector of the right angle divides the hypotenuse. **18.4 in. and 7.6 in.**

596 Chapter 11 Circles

pages 593–596 Exercises

46. [2] $\overline{PN}$ is a radius of ⊙N. Thus, $PN = 13$ cm.
$PX = \frac{1}{2}PQ = 9$,
$\triangle PNX$ is a rt. $\triangle$, so

$NX \approx 9.38$ cm. Thus, $MN = 18.8$ cm, to the nearest tenth.

[1] incorrect length OR incorrect explanation

Read the problem below and then follow along with what Jamal thinks as he solves the problem. Check your understanding by solving the exercise at the bottom of the page.

x^2 **Algebra** Two concentric circles have radii of 4 cm and 8 cm. A segment tangent to the smaller circle is a chord of the larger circle. What is the length of the segment?

What Jamal Thinks

I need a picture to understand what this is about. I'll make a sketch.

Concentric circles have the same center, like circles in a bull's eye. The larger circle has radius 8 cm. The smaller circle has radius 4 cm.

I need to draw a segment tangent to the smaller circle with both ends on the larger circle.

Now I need to find a relationship between these segments. I'll redo my sketch; move things around. Is a right triangle possible for my sketch so I can use the Pythagorean Theorem? Yes! Theorem 11-1 says a tangent to a circle and the radius to the point of tangency are perpendicular.

I'll use the Pythagorean Theorem . . .

. . . and a calculator to find $\sqrt{48}$.

To find the length of the chord, I multiply 6.9 by 2 because Theorem 11-6 says that a diameter perpendicular to a chord bisects the chord.

What Jamal Writes

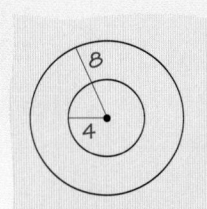

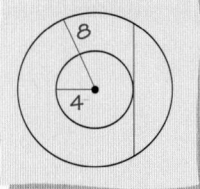

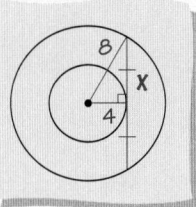

$$4^2 + x^2 = 8^2$$
$$x^2 = 64 - 16$$
$$x = \sqrt{48} \approx 6.9$$

The chord is about 13.8 cm long.

Reading for Problem Solving

When problems are difficult for students to understand, drawing a diagram may be key to their understanding what is being described and asked. This feature helps students understand the sequential reasoning that precedes drawing step-by-step diagrams to solve complicated problems.

Teaching Notes

As students examine the diagrams, have volunteers identify each segment. Ask: *Why can the two segments of the chord be marked congruent in the third diagram?* A radius perpendicular to a chord bisects the chord.

Technology Tip

Have students use geometry software to model and solve the problem. Using the measurement tools of their software, they should be able to draw both circles and estimate the length of the chord.

Exercise

Have students work independently to solve the problem, showing the steps they used. Then have volunteers share with the class what they were thinking as they wrote each step. Elicit the fact that there are often different ways to arrive at the solution of a problem.

EXERCISE

x^2 **Algebra** Two parallel chords of a circle are each 24 cm long. The distance between them is 10 cm. Find the circumference of the circle. **26π cm or about 81.7 cm**

1. Plan

Lesson Preview

 Check Skills You'll Need

Central Angles and Arcs
Lesson 7-6: Examples 2, 3
Exercises 9–26
Extra Practice, p. 696

Lesson Resources

 Teaching Resources
Practice, Reteaching, Enrichment
Checkpoint Quiz 1

Reaching All Students
Practice Workbook 11-3
Spanish Practice Workbook 11-3
Reading and Math Literacy 11B
Spanish Reading & Literacy 11B
Spanish Checkpoint Quiz 1
Hands-On Activities 33
Informal Geometry Planning
 Guide 11-3

Presentation Assistant Plus!
Transparencies
• Check Skills You'll Need 11-3
• Additional Examples 11-3
• Student Edition Answers 11-3
• Lesson Quiz 11-3
PH Presentation Pro CD 11-3

 **ASSESSMENT SYSTEM**

Checkpoint Quiz 1
Computer Test Generator CD

 Technology
Resource Pro® CD-ROM
Computer Test Generator CD
Prentice Hall Presentation Pro CD

 www.PHSchool.com
Student Site
• Teacher Web Code: afk-5500
• Self-grading Lesson Quiz
Teacher Center
• Lesson Planner
• Resources

Plus **TEXT**

598

11-3

Inscribed Angles

2.03 Apply properties, definitions, and theorems of two-dimensional figures to solve problems and write proofs: d) Circles.

Lesson Preview

What You'll Learn

OBJECTIVE 1 To find the measure of an inscribed angle

OBJECTIVE 2 To find the measure of an angle formed by a tangent and a chord

. . . And Why

To use theorems and corollaries to find missing lengths in circles, as in Example 3

✓ **Check Skills You'll Need**

1–4. Answers may vary. Samples are given. (For help, go to Lesson 7-6.)

Identify the following in ⊙*P* at the right.

1. a semicircle $\widehat{STQ}$ 2. a minor arc $\widehat{SR}$
3. a major arc $\widehat{RTQ}$ 4. a central angle ∠*TPQ*

Find the measure of each arc in ⊙*P*.

5. $\widehat{ST}$ 86   6. $\widehat{STQ}$ 180
7. $\widehat{RST}$ 121   8. $\widehat{TQ}$ 94

New Vocabulary • inscribed angle • intercepted arc

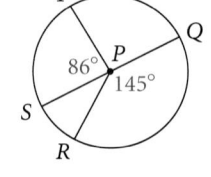

OBJECTIVE 1

Finding the Measure of an Inscribed Angle

TEXT Interactive lesson includes instant self-check, tutorials, and activities.

1. a. Check students' work.
 b. $m\angle 1 = \frac{1}{2}m\widehat{AB}$
 c. $m\angle 1 = m\angle 2 = m\angle 3$

2. a. Check students' work.
 b. The measure of an ∠ whose vertex is on a circle and whose sides intersect the endpts. of a diameter of the circle is 90.

Investigation: Exploring Inscribed Angles

• Draw two large circles with a compass. Label the centers *X* and *Y*.

• On the circles, use a straightedge and copy the diagrams shown.

1. a. **Patterns** In ⊙*X*, use a protractor to measure ∠*AXB* and each numbered angle. Determine $m\widehat{AB}$. Record your results and look for patterns. Compare your results with others. **a–c. See left.**
 b. Write a conjecture about the relationship between $m\angle 1$ and $m\widehat{AB}$.
 c. Write a conjecture about the measures of ∠1, ∠2, and ∠3.

2. a. **Patterns** Use a protractor to measure the numbered angles in ⊙*Y*. Record your results and look for patterns. Compare your results.
 b. Write a conjecture about an angle whose vertex is on a circle and whose sides intersect the endpoints of a diameter of the circle. **a–b. See left.**

At the right, the vertex of ∠*C* is on ⊙*O*, and the sides of ∠*C* are chords of the circle. ∠*C* is an **inscribed angle**. $\widehat{AB}$ is the **intercepted arc** of ∠*C*.

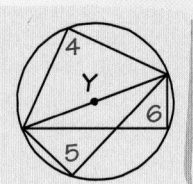

Intercepted arc

Inscribed angle

Ongoing Assessment and Intervention

Before the Lesson	**During the Lesson**	**After the Lesson**
Diagnose prerequisite skills using:	**Monitor progress using:**	**Assess knowledge using:**
• Check Skills You'll Need	• Check Understanding	• Lesson Quiz
	• Additional Examples	• Computer Test Generator CD
	• Standardized Test Prep	• Chapter Checkpoint 1 (p. 605)

Theorem 11-9 describes the relationship between an inscribed angle and its intercepted arc.

 Key Concepts

Theorem 11-9	Inscribed Angle Theorem

The measure of an inscribed angle is half the measure of its intercepted arc.

$$m\angle B = \frac{1}{2}m\overset{\frown}{AC}$$

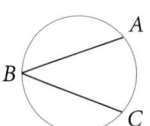

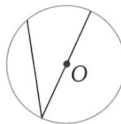 **Reading Math**

When different conditions are possible, each possibility can be called a case. You can prove a theorem by proving it for all possible cases.

To prove Theorem 11-9, there are three cases to consider.

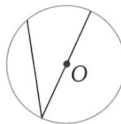 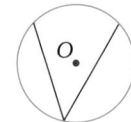 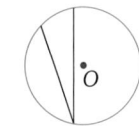

I: The center is on   II: The center is   III: The center is
a side of the angle.   inside the angle.   outside the angle.

A proof of Case I is below. You will prove Cases II and III in Exercises 40 and 41.

Proof   **Proof of Theorem 11-9, Case I**

Given: $\odot O$ with inscribed $\angle B$ and diameter $\overline{BC}$
Prove: $m\angle B = \frac{1}{2}m\overset{\frown}{AC}$

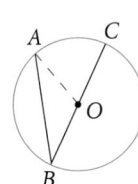

Draw radius $\overline{OA}$ to form isosceles $\triangle AOB$ with $OA = OB$ and, hence, $m\angle A = m\angle B$.

$m\overset{\frown}{AC} = m\angle AOC$	Definition of $m\overset{\frown}{AC}$
$= m\angle A + m\angle B$	Triangle Exterior Angle Theorem
$= 2m\angle B$	Substitute and simplify.
$\frac{1}{2}m\overset{\frown}{AC} = m\angle B$	Solve for $m\angle B$.

You can use the Inscribed Angle Theorem to find missing measures in circles.

1 EXAMPLE   **Using the Inscribed Angle Theorem**

Find the values of a and b.

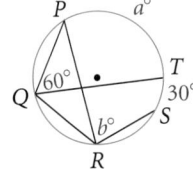

$m\angle PQT = \frac{1}{2}m\overset{\frown}{PT}$	Inscribed Angle Theorem
$60 = \frac{1}{2}a$	Substitute.
$120 = a$	Solve for a.
$m\angle PRS = \frac{1}{2}m\overset{\frown}{PS}$	Inscribed Angle Theorem
$b = \frac{1}{2}\left(m\overset{\frown}{PT} + m\overset{\frown}{TS}\right)$	Arc Addition Postulate
$= \frac{1}{2}(120 + 30)$	Substitute.
$b = 75$	Simplify.

✓ Check Understanding ● **1** Find $m\angle PQR$ if $m\overset{\frown}{RS} = 60$. **105**

Lesson 11-3 Inscribed Angles   **599**

 **Reaching All Students**

Below Level The Investigation can be done using geometry software. For part 1, fix points A and B and move point C on $\odot O$. The measures of $\angle ACB$ and $\overset{\frown}{AB}$ as point C moves illustrate Theorem 11-9.	**Advanced Learners** Have students use a right triangle inscribed in a circle to prove that the median drawn to the hypotenuse of a right triangle forms two isoceles triangles.	**Tactile Learners** See note on page 603. **Error Prevention** See note on page 599.

 Professional Development

Math Background

Corollary 2 to the Inscribed Angle Theorem suggests this method of constructing a right angle: Construct a circle of any radius with any center, then use a straightedge to draw a diameter. Any angle with vertex on the circle whose sides intersect the endpoints of the diameter is a right angle.

OBJECTIVE
1 **Teaching Notes**

Investigation (Optional)

Students will measure and make conjectures about the relationships between inscribed angles and their intercepted arcs. Point out that the placement of the vertices in $\odot Y$ is unimportant when copying the diagrams but that the sides of angles 4, 5, and 6 must intersect the endpoints of the diameter.

Math Tip

The Inscribed Angle Theorem must be proved for three mutually exclusive cases: the center of the circle on a side of the angle, in the interior of the angle, and exterior to, or outside the angle.

1 EXAMPLE

Ask students to restate the Arc Addition Postulate. Remind them of its similarity to the Angle Addition Postulate.

2 EXAMPLE Technology Tip

Have students use geometry software to explore the corollaries.

Error Prevention

Students may carelessly apply the Inscribed Angle Theorem to angles whose vertices are not on the circle. Remind them that the theorem applies only to angles whose vertices are on a circle and whose sides contain chords of the circle.

599

1 Find the values of x and y.

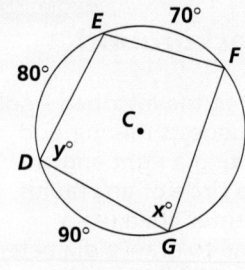

$x = 75; y = 95$

2 Find the values of a and b.

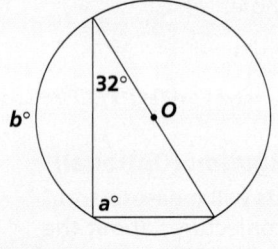

$a = 90; b = 116$

3 EXAMPLE Alternative Method

Students can find the value of x by applying Corollary 2 to the Inscribed Angle Theorem and then using the Triangle Angle-Sum Theorem to find the value of y.

Additional Examples

3 $\overline{RS}$ and $\overline{TU}$ are diameters of $\odot A$. $\overleftrightarrow{RB}$ is tangent to $\odot A$ at point R. Find $m\angle BRT$ and $m\angle TRS$.

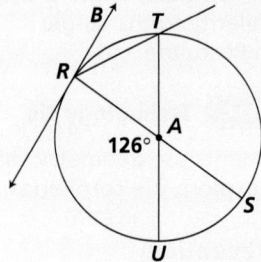

$m\angle BRT = 27; m\angle TRS = 63$

Closure

In the diagram, $\overline{TA}$ is tangent to $\odot O$ at point A, and $\overline{TB}$ is tangent to $\odot O$ at point B. Find $m\widehat{AB}$.

600

You will use three corollaries to the Inscribed Angle Theorem to find measures of angles in circles. You will justify these corollaries in Exercises 42, 43, and 44.

Key Concepts

Corollaries   **Corollaries to the Inscribed Angle Theorem**

1. Two inscribed angles that intercept the same arc are congruent.
2. An angle inscribed in a semicircle is a right angle.
3. The opposite angles of a quadrilateral inscribed in a circle are supplementary.

2 EXAMPLE Using Corollaries to Find Angle Measures

Find the measure of the numbered angle.

a.

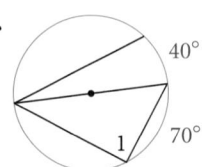

b.

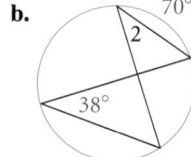

∠1 is inscribed in a semicircle. By Corollary 2, ∠1 is a right angle. $m\angle 1 = 90$

∠2 and the 38° angle intercept the same arc. By Corollary 1, the angles are congruent, so $m\angle 2 = 38$.

✔ **Check Understanding** **2** For the diagram at the right, find the measure of each numbered angle.

$m\angle 1 = 90, m\angle 2 = 110,$
$m\angle 3 = 90, m\angle 4 = 70.$

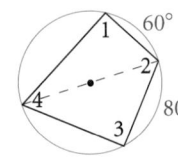

In the diagram, B and C are fixed points, and point A moves along the circle. From the Inscribed Angle Theorem, you know that as A moves, $m\angle A$ remains the same and is $\frac{1}{2}m\widehat{BC}$. As the last diagram suggests, this is also true when A and C coincide.

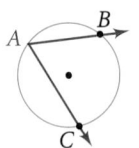 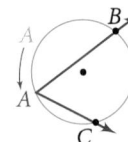 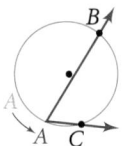 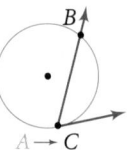

Key Concepts

Theorem 11-10

The measure of an angle formed by a tangent and a chord is half the measure of the intercepted arc.

$$m\angle C = \tfrac{1}{2}m\widehat{BDC}$$

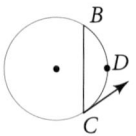 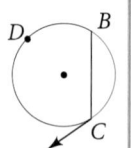

You will prove Theorem 11-10 in Exercise 45.

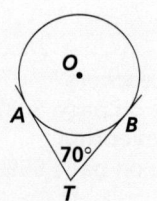

3 **EXAMPLE** Using Theorem 11-10

In the diagram at the right, $\overrightarrow{KJ}$ is tangent to the circle at J. Find the values of x and y.

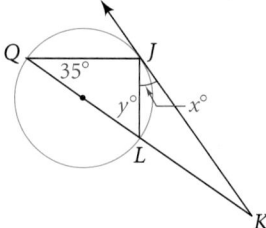

$x = \frac{1}{2}m\widehat{JL}$ **Theorem 11-10**

   $= m\angle Q$ **Inscribed Angle Theorem**

   $= 35$ **Substitution**

$y = \frac{1}{2}m\widehat{QJ}$ **Theorem 11-10**

   $= \frac{1}{2}\left(m\widehat{QL} - m\widehat{JL}\right)$ **Arc Addition Postulate**

   $= \frac{1}{2}(180 - 70)$ **Substitute.**

   $= 55$ **Simplify.**

✓ **Check Understanding** **3** Describe two ways to find $m\angle QJK$ using Theorem 11-10.

$m\angle QJK = m\angle LJK + m\angle QJL = 35 + 90 = 125$
$m\angle QJK = \frac{1}{2}m\widehat{QLJ} = \frac{1}{2}(70 + 180) = 125$

EXERCISES

For more practice, see *Extra Practice*.

Practice and Problem Solving

A Practice by Example

Example 1
(page 599)

Identify the inscribed angle and its intercepted arc.

4a. $\angle BAD$ and $\widehat{BCD}$;
$\angle ABC$ and $\widehat{ADC}$;
$\angle DCB$ and $\widehat{DAB}$;
$\angle ADC$ and $\widehat{ABC}$

$\angle MPN$; $\widehat{MN}$

1.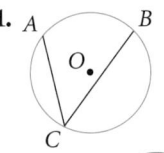
$\angle ACB$; $\widehat{AB}$

2.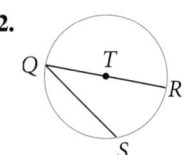
$\angle RQS$; $\widehat{RS}$

3.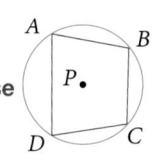

4. a. Name the four inscribed angles and their intercepted arcs.
   b. Which angles appear to intercept major arcs? What kind of angles do these appear to be? $\angle ABC$ and $\angle BCD$; obtuse

8. $a = 54$; $b = 30$; $c = 96$

9. $a = 112$; $b = 120$; $c = 38$

10. $a = 101$; $b = 67$; $c = 84$; $d = 80$

11. $x = 36$; $y = 36$

12. $a = 85$; $b = 47.5$; $c = 90$

13. $a = 50$; $b = 90$; $c = 90$

14. $p = 90$; $q = 122$

Find the value of each variable. 8–14. See left.

5.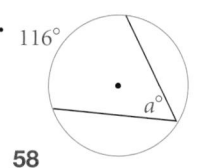
58

6.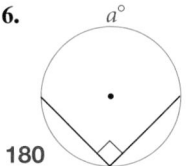
180

7.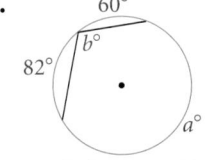
$a = 218$; $b = 109$

8.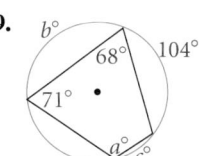

9.

10.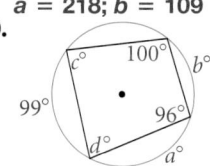

Example 2
(page 600)

11.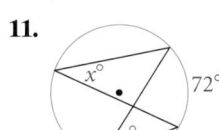

12.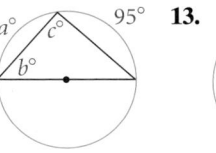

13.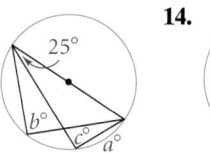

14.

Lesson 11-3   Inscribed Angles   **601**

3. Practice

Assignment Guide

1 Objective
  A **B** Core 1–14, 21–23, 25–35, 37–39
  C Extension 40–44

2 Objective
  A **B** Core 15–20, 24, 36
  C Extension 45

Standardized Test Prep 46–50

Mixed Review 51–58

Exercise 4 Review the definitions of *semicircle*, *minor arc*, and *major arc* and how to name these arcs.

Exercise 8 Students who focus on theorems from this lesson to answer the exercises may overlook the Vertical Angles Theorem. Use this exercise as an opportunity to remind them that it is often necessary to integrate earlier work.

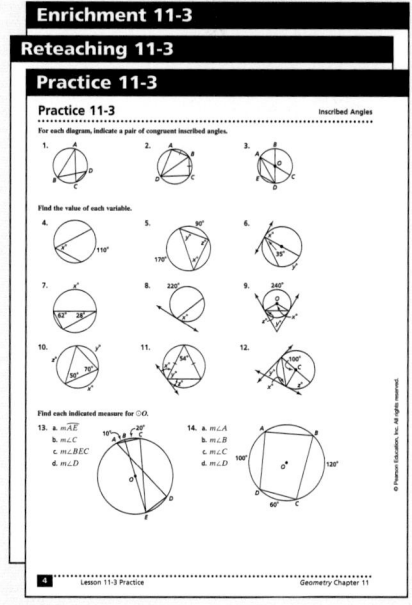

601

Example 3
(page 601)

18. *a* = 26; *b* = 64; *c* = 42

19. *a* = 22; *b* = 78; *c* = 156

20. *a* = 30; *b* = 60; *c* = 62; *d* = 124; *e* = 60

Find the value of each variable. You may assume that rays that appear to be tangent are tangent.

15. 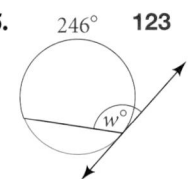 123

16.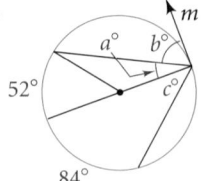

x = 65; *y* = 130

17.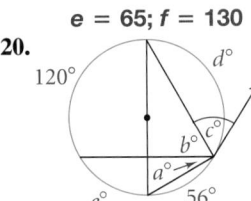

e = 65; *f* = 130

18.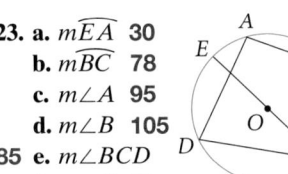

19.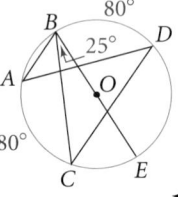

20.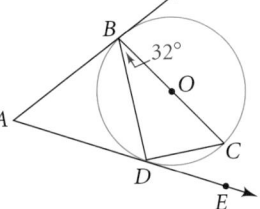

18-20. See left.

B Apply Your Skills

Find each indicated measure for ⊙O.

21. a. $m\overparen{BC}$ 96
   b. $m\angle B$ 55
   c. $m\angle C$ 77
   d. $m\overparen{AB}$ 154

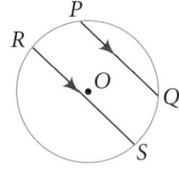

22. a. $m\angle A$ 40
   b. $m\overparen{CE}$ 50
   c. $m\angle C$ 40
   d. $m\angle D$ 40
   e. $m\angle ABE$ 65

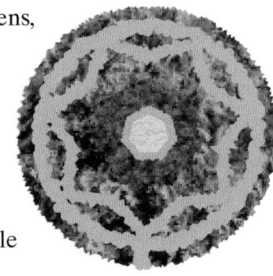

25. ∠*PQR* ≅ ∠*QRS* since they are alt. int. ⫨. Since ≅ inscribed ⫨ intercept ≅ arcs, $m\overparen{PR} = m\overparen{QS}$.

26a. Check students' work.

29. about 7.1 cm by 7.1 cm

30. about 4.3 cm for each side

31. about 7.1 cm legs, and a 10 cm base

23. a. $m\overparen{EA}$ 30
   b. $m\overparen{BC}$ 78
   c. $m\angle A$ 95
   d. $m\angle B$ 105
   e. $m\angle BCD$ 85
   f. $m\angle D$ 75

24. a. $m\overparen{DC}$ 64
   b. $m\overparen{BD}$ 116
   c. $m\angle BCD$ 58
   d. $m\angle BDC$ 90
   e. $m\angle ABC$ 90
   f. $m\angle ADB$ 58

 25. **Writing** Copy the diagram at the right on your paper. Draw chord $\overline{RQ}$. Explain why $m\overparen{PR} = m\overparen{QS}$. **See left.**

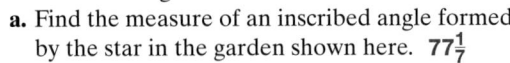

26. a. **Open-Ended** Sketch a trapezoid inscribed in a circle. Repeat several times using different circles. **See left.**
   b. **Make a Conjecture** What kind of trapezoid can be inscribed in a circle? Justify your response. **See margin.**

27. **Landscape Architecture** Some circular English gardens, like the one shown here, have paths in the shape of an inscribed regular star.
   a. Find the measure of an inscribed angle formed by the star in the garden shown here. $77\frac{1}{7}$
   b. What is the measure of an inscribed angle in a garden with a five-pointed star? 36

28. **Critical Thinking** A parallelogram inscribed in a circle must be what kind of parallelogram? Explain. **See margin.**

Graphing Calculator The diameter of a circle is 10 cm. Find the dimensions of the largest figure of each type that can be inscribed in the circle. (*Hint:* Use techniques demonstrated in the Exploration on page 536.) 29-31. See above left.

29. a rectangle   30. a triangle   31. a right triangle

pages 601–605 Exercises

26.b. isosc. trapezoid; justifications may vary. Sample: Arcs between two ∥ chords are ≅.

28. Rectangle; all adjacent ⫨ must be supp. and opp.

⫨ must be supp., so all ⫨ are 90°.

32. Answers may vary. Sample:
   a. If the cameras' lenses open at = ⫨, then in the positions shown

they share the same arc of the scene.

b. No; the distances from each position of the scene to each camera affect the look of the scene.

Real-World Connection

A big red "tally light" on each camera tells this anchorman which camera is "hot" (on the air).

32. Television The director of a telecast wants the option of showing the same scene from three different views. **a-b. See margin p. 602.**
  a. Explain why cameras in the positions shown in the diagram will transmit the same scene.
  b. Critical Thinking Will the scenes look the same to the director when she views them on the control room monitors? Explain.

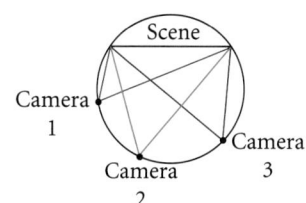

Critical Thinking **Decide whether each statement is true or false. Give a counterexample for each false statement.**
See margin.

33. If two angles inscribed in a circle are congruent, then they intercept the same arc.

34. If an inscribed angle is a right angle, then it is inscribed in a semicircle. **true**

35. A circle can always be circumscribed about a quadrilateral whose opposite angles are supplementary. **true**

36. Constructions The diagrams below show the construction of a tangent to a circle from a point outside the circle. Explain why $\overleftrightarrow{BC}$ must be tangent to ⊙A. (*Hint:* Copy the third diagram and draw $\overline{AC}$.) **See margin.**

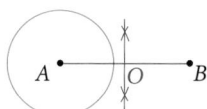 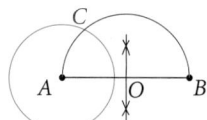 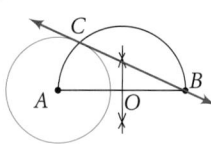

Given: ⊙A and point B. Construct the midpoint of $\overline{AB}$. Label the point O. 　Construct a semicircle with radius OA and center O. Label its intersection with ⊙A as C. 　Draw $\overleftrightarrow{BC}$.

37. Technology Construct ⊙A and the chords shown with geometry software.
  a. As you move E on $\overset{\frown}{CED}$ between C and D, which inscribed angles remain congruent? **∠CEF, ∠FEG, and ∠GED**
  b. Which inscribed angle remains a right angle? **∠CED**
  c. Which inscribed angles remain supplementary in quadrilateral EFGD? **∠EFG and ∠EDG; ∠FED and ∠FGD**

38. Constructions Use Corollary 2 of Theorem 11-9 to construct a right triangle given one leg and the hypotenuse. **See margin.**

39. Constructions Draw two segments. Label their lengths x and y. Construct the geometric mean of x and y. (*Hint:* Construct a circle with diameter x + y. Then find a right triangle whose altitude to the hypotenuse has the length you seek.) **See margin.**

C **Challenge** *Proof* **Write a two-column proof, paragraph proof, or flow proof.** **40-41. See margin.**

40. Inscribed Angle Theorem, Case II
  Given: ⊙O with inscribed ∠ABC
  Prove: $m\angle ABC = \frac{1}{2}m\overset{\frown}{AC}$

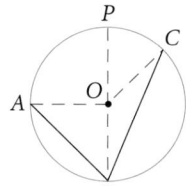

Hint: Use the Inscribed Angle Theorem, Case I.

41. Inscribed Angle Theorem, Case III
  Given: ⊙S with inscribed ∠PQR
  Prove: $m\angle PQR = \frac{1}{2}m\overset{\frown}{PR}$

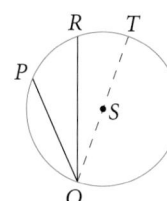

Hint: Use the Inscribed Angle Theorem, Case I.

Lesson 11-3 Inscribed Angles **603**

33. false

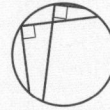

36. ∠ACB is a rt. ∠ because it is inscribed in semicircle $\overset{\frown}{ACB}$, and if a line is ⊥ to a radius at its endpoint, it is tangent to the circle.

38.

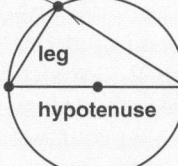

leg

hypotenuse

39. In the construction below, RS = x, ST = y, O is the mdpt. of $\overline{RT}$, and $\overline{QS} \perp \overline{RT}$.

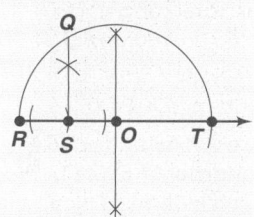

40. 1. ⊙O with inscribed ∠ABC (Given)
2. $m\angle ABO = \frac{1}{2}m\overset{\frown}{AP}$; $m\angle OBC = \frac{1}{2}m\overset{\frown}{PC}$ (Inscribed ∠ Thm., Case I) 3. $m\angle ABO + m\angle OBC = m\angle ABC$ (∠ Add. Post.) 4. $\frac{1}{2}m\overset{\frown}{AP} + \frac{1}{2}m\overset{\frown}{PC} = m\angle ABC$ (Subst.) 5. $\frac{1}{2}(m\overset{\frown}{AP} + m\overset{\frown}{PC}) = m\angle ABC$ (Distr. Prop.) 6. $\frac{1}{2}m\overset{\frown}{AC} = m\angle ABC$ (Arc Add. Post.)

41. 1. ⊙S with inscribed ∠PQR (Given)
2. $m\angle PQT = \frac{1}{2}m\overset{\frown}{PT}$ (Inscribed ∠ Thm., Case I)
3. $m\angle RQT = \frac{1}{2}m\overset{\frown}{RT}$ (Inscr. ∠ Thm., Case I)
4. $m\overset{\frown}{PR} = m\overset{\frown}{PT} - m\overset{\frown}{RT}$ (Arc Add. Post.)
5. $m\angle PQR = m\angle PQT - m\angle RQT$ (∠ Add. Post.)
6. $m\angle PQR = \frac{1}{2}m\overset{\frown}{PT} - \frac{1}{2}m\overset{\frown}{RT}$ (Subst.)
7. $m\angle PQR = \frac{1}{2}m\overset{\frown}{PR}$ (Subst.)

603

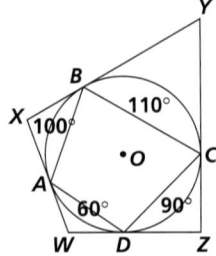

4. Assess

Lesson Quiz 11-3

In the diagram below, ⊙O circumscribes quadrilateral ABCD and is inscribed in quadrilateral XYZW.

1. Find the measure of each inscribed angle.
   m∠A = 100; m∠B = 75; m∠C = 80; m∠D = 105

2. Find m∠DCZ. 45

3. Are ∠XAB and ∠XBA congruent? Explain. Yes; each is formed by a tangent and a chord, and they intercept the same arc.

4. Find the angle measures in quadrilateral XYZW.
   m∠X = 80; m∠Y = 70; m∠Z = 90; m∠W = 120

5. Does a diagonal of quadrilateral ABCD intersect the center of the circle? Explain how you can tell. No; the diagonal would be a diameter of ⊙O and the inscribed angle would be a right angle, which was not found in Exercise 1 above.

Alternative Assessment

Give each student a compass and straightedge. Have students use the theorems in Lesson 11-3 to plan, justify, and execute a method for constructing a right angle.

pages 601–605 Exercises

43. 1. ⊙O with inscribed ∠CAB in a semicircle (Given) 2. m∠CAB = $\frac{1}{2}m\widehat{BDC}$ (Inscr. ∠ Thm.)
3. $m\widehat{BDC}$ = 180 (Meas. of semicircle = 180.)
4. m∠CAB = 90 (Subst.)
5. ∠CAB is a rt. ∠. (Def. of rt. ∠)

604

---

42. 1. ⊙O, ∠A intercepts $\widehat{BC}$, and ∠D intercepts $\widehat{BC}$ (Given) 2. m∠A = $\frac{1}{2}m\widehat{BC}$ and m∠D = $\frac{1}{2}m\widehat{BC}$ (Inscr. ∠ Thm.)
3. m∠A = m∠D (Subst.)
4. ∠A ≅ ∠D (Def. of ≅)

Need Help?

In Exercise 45, let $\overline{GH}$ first be a diameter.

---

42. Inscribed Angle Theorem, Cor. 1
Given: ⊙O; ∠A intercepts $\widehat{BC}$, and ∠D intercepts $\widehat{BC}$.
Prove: ∠A ≅ ∠D See left.

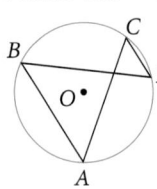

44. Inscribed Angle Theorem, Cor. 3
Given: quadrilateral ABCD inscribed in ⊙O
Prove: ∠A and ∠C are supplementary. ∠B and ∠D are supplementary. **See back of book.**

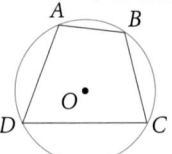

---

43. Inscribed Angle Theorem, Cor. 2
Given: ⊙O with ∠CAB inscribed in a semicircle **See margin.**
Prove: ∠CAB is a right angle.

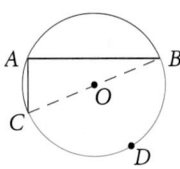

45. Theorem 11-10
Given: $\overline{GH}$ and tangent ℓ intersecting at H on ⊙E
Prove: $m∠GHI = \frac{1}{2}m\widehat{GFH}$
See margin.

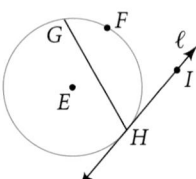

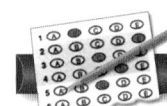

Standardized Test Prep

Multiple Choice   In Exercises 46 and 47, what is the value of each variable?

46.
A
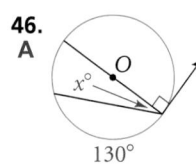
130°

   A. 25
   B. 35
   C. 45
   D. 65

47.
I

   F. 20
   G. 30
   H. 50
   I. 60

Take It to the NET
Online lesson quiz at
www.PHSchool.com
Web Code: afa-1103

48. In the figure at the right, a square is circumscribed about ⊙A. What is the area of the square? C
   A. 64 in.²
   B. 192 in.²
   C. 256 in.²
   D. (256 + 16√3) in.²

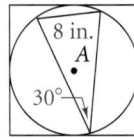

Short Response

49. a. Explain how you can find m∠XYZ.
    b. Find m∠XYZ. a-b. See margin p. 605.

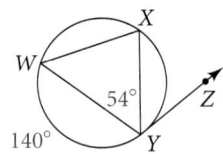

Extended Response

50. Use the figure at the right. a-c. See margin p. 605.
    a. What is m∠D? Explain.
    b. What is m∠ACB? Explain.
    c. Use an equation to find the value of x.

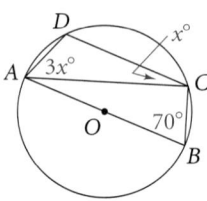

---

45. 1. $\overline{GH}$ and tangent ℓ intersecting at H on ⊙E (Given) 2. Construct diameter $\overline{HD}$ intersecting circle E at D. (Constr.)
3. ∠DHI is a rt. ∠.
(Tangent and radius are ⊥.) 4. $\widehat{DGH}$ is a semicircle of measure 180. (Def. of semicircle) 5. m∠DHG + m∠GHI = m∠DHI (∠ Add. Post.) 6. $m\widehat{DG}$ + $m\widehat{GFH}$ = $m\widehat{DGH}$ (Arc
Add. Post.) 7. 90 = m∠DHG + m∠GHI (Subst.) 8. 180 = $m\widehat{DG}$ + $m\widehat{GFH}$ (Subst.)
9. 90 = $\frac{1}{2}(m\widehat{DG}$ + $m\widehat{GFH})$ (Div. Prop.)

Mixed Review

Lesson 11-2 x^2 **Algebra Find the value of x to the nearest tenth.**

51.
17.3

52.
34.6

53.
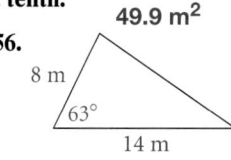
17.5

Lesson 9-5 **Find the area of each triangle. Give answers to the nearest tenth.**

54.
14 in.
26°
16 in.
49.1 in.²

55.
22 cm
23°
15 cm
64.5 cm²

56.
49.9 m²
8 m
63°
14 m

Lesson 8-3 **Indirect Measurement** To find the width of a river, you have made the measurements shown in the sketch.

d
750 ft
2400 ft 300 ft

57. Both have rt. ∠ and the vertical ∠ are ≅, so △ are ~ by AA ~ Post.

57. Explain why the triangles are similar.

58. a. Find the width of the river in feet. **960 ft**
   b. Find the width of the river in miles. **about 0.18 mi**

✓ Checkpoint Quiz 1

Lessons 11-1 through 11-3

🔲TEXT Instant self-check quiz online and on CD-ROM

Each polygon below circumscribes the circle. Find the perimeter of the polygon.

1. 76 cm
9 cm
13 cm 16 cm

2.
|←13 in.→|
10 in. 14 in.
8 in.
48 in.

3.
51 m
5 m
11 m 7.5 m
5 m
7 m

7. $w = 104$; $x = 22$; $y = 108$

8. $a = 30$; $b = 42$; $c = 80$; $d = 116$

9. $w = 105$; $x = 75$; $y = 210$

10. $a = 140$; $b = 70$; $c = 47.5$

x^2 **Algebra Find the value of x.**

4.
24
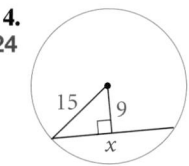
15 9
x

5.
5
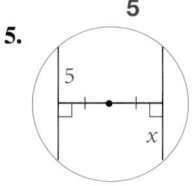
5
x

6.
8
30
x
17

7-10. See left.

x^2 **Algebra Find the value of each variable. Lines that appear to be tangent are tangent.**

7.
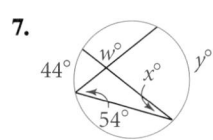
44°
$w°$ $x°$ $y°$
54°

8.
100°
60°
$a°$ $b°$
$c°$ $d°$
84°

9.
$y°$
$w°$
$x°$
150°

10.
125°
$a°$ $b°$
$c°$
140°

Lesson 11-3 Inscribed Angles **605**

10. $m\angle DHG + m\angle GHI = \frac{1}{2}m\widehat{DG} + \frac{1}{2}m\widehat{GFH}$ (Subst. and Distr. Prop.)
11. $m\angle DHG = \frac{1}{2}m\widehat{DG}$ (Inscr. ∠ Thm.)

12. $m\angle GHI = \frac{1}{2}m\widehat{GFH}$ (Subtr. Prop.)

49. [2] a. $m\widehat{WY} = 140$;
   $m\widehat{WX} = 2 \cdot 54 = 108$;
   $m\widehat{XY} = 112 = 2m\angle XYZ$.
   Thus, $m\angle XYZ = 56$.

b. 56

[1] incorrect answer OR incorrect explanation

Standardized Test Prep

🔲 Resources

For additional practice with a variety of test item formats:
- Standardized Test Prep, p. 631
- Test-Taking Strategies, p. 626
- Test-Taking Strategies with Transparencies

Exercise 46 When a problem looks complicated, students should copy the diagram and fill in all angle measures and arc measures they can figure out as they copy. Students also may find it helpful to write each equation that relates the measure of an inscribed angle to half the measure of its intercepted arc.

✓ Chapter Checkpoint 1

To check understanding of Lessons 11-1 to 11-3:

Checkpoint Quiz 1 (p. 605)

🔲 Teaching Resources

Checkpoint Quiz 1 (also in Prentice Hall Assessment System)

👥 Reaching All Students

Reading and Math Literacy 11B

Spanish versions available

50. [4] a. $m\widehat{ADC} = 140$, so $m\widehat{ABC} = 220$, and $\angle D = 110$.

   b. $m\angle ACB = 90$, because it is inscribed in a semicircle.

   c. $180 = 110 + 4x$. Thus, $70 = 4x$ and $x = 17.5$.

   [3] appropriate methods, but with one computational error

   [2] incorrect methods solved correctly OR correct methods solved incorrectly

   [1] correct answers to a–c, without work shown

605

Technology

Exploring Chords and Secants

FOR USE WITH LESSON 11-4

Exploring Chords and Secants

Students will use geometry software to investigate the relationships formed by chords that intersect in the interior of a circle and by secants that intersect outside a circle.

Resources

Students may use any geometry software program to explore relationships between chords and between secants.

Teaching Notes

Intersecting chords and secants form proportional relationships that can be expressed as the products of their lengths. By using the dynamic features of geometry software and calculating the products on the computer, students will discover these relationships for themselves.

Alternative Method

The diagrams show points *E* and *D* being manipulated. Tell students that any point can be manipulated to change the measures of the segments that are drawn.

Visual Learners

Before students begin Exercise 3, have them manipulate a secant until it no longer intersects the circle at two points. In this way, they can see one relationship between secants and tangents.

Construct

Construct a circle with center *A* and two chords $\overline{BC}$ and $\overline{DE}$ that intersect each other at *F*.

Investigate

Measure $\overline{BF}, \overline{FC}, \overline{EF},$ and $\overline{FD}$. Use the calculator program of your software to find the products $BF \cdot FC$ and $EF \cdot FD$. Manipulate your construction and observe the products. What do you discover? Use your discovery to answer Exercise 1.

Construct

A *secant* is a line that intersects a circle in two points. Construct another circle and two secants that intersect in a point outside the circle. Label your construction as shown in the diagram.

Investigate

Measure $\overline{DG}, \overline{DF}, \overline{DE},$ and $\overline{DB}$. Calculate the products $DG \cdot DF$ and $DE \cdot DB$. Manipulate your construction and observe the products. What do you discover? Use your discovery to answer Exercise 2.

EXERCISES

Use results from your two investigations above. Make conjectures about the products of the lengths of the segments to a circle from the point of intersection of the figures given below. 1–2. See margin.

1. two chords inside a circle

2. two secants outside a circle

Extend

3. Construct circle *A* with radius $\overline{AG}$ as shown. Construct a segment $\overline{DG}$ perpendicular to radius $\overline{AG}$. Then construct a secant $\overline{DE}$ that does not cross $\overline{AG}$. Hide $\overline{AG}$. Measure $\overline{DG}, \overline{DE},$ and $\overline{DB}$. Calculate DG^2 and the product $DE \cdot DB$. What is true about the products you calculated? Can you explain how this special case is related to the case of two secants? **See margin.**

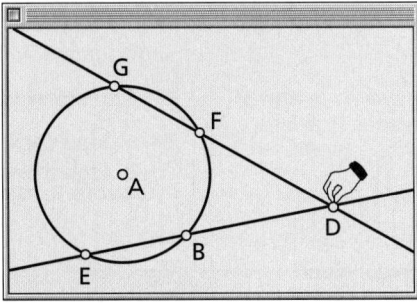

4. Combine conjectures from Exercises 1–3 into a conjecture about any two intersecting lines, each of which also intersects a circle. **The prod. of the two segments from the intersection to the circle on one line = the prod. of the two segments from the intersection to the circle on the other line.**

page 606   Technology

1. The prod. of the lengths of the segments of one chord = the prod. of the lengths of the segments of the other chord.

2. The prod. of the lengths of one secant segment and its external segment = the prod. of the lengths of the other secant segment and its external segment.

3. The products are =. For $\overline{DG}$, the secant segment and its external segment are the same.

Angle Measures and Segment Lengths

 North Carolina Objectives

2.03 Apply properties, definitions, and theorems of two-dimensional figures to solve problems and write proofs: d) Circles.

Lesson Preview

What You'll Learn

 OBJECTIVE 1 To find the measures of angles formed by chords, secants, and tangents

OBJECTIVE 2 To find the lengths of segments associated with circles

. . . And Why

To find the measure of an arc of a circular basin, as in Example 2

✓ **Check Skills You'll Need** (For help, go to Lessons 11-1 and 11-3.)

In the diagram at the right, $\overline{FE}$ and $\overline{FD}$ are tangents to ⊙*C*. Find each arc measure, angle measure, or length.

1. $m\widehat{DE}$ 57 2. $m\widehat{AED}$ 180 3. $m\widehat{EBD}$ 303
4. $m\angle EAD$ 28.5 5. $m\angle AEC$ 28.5 6. *CE* 4
7. *DF* 2   8. *CF* about 4.5 9. $m\angle EFD$ 123

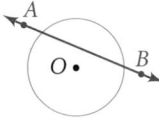

New Vocabulary • secant

OBJECTIVE 1 **Finding Angle Measures**

 Reading Math

The word "secant" may refer to a line, ray, or segment.

A **secant** is a line that intersects a circle at two points. $\overrightarrow{AB}$ is a secant ray, and $\overline{AB}$ is a secant segment.

Angles formed by secants, tangents and chords intercept arcs on circles. The measures of the intercepted arcs can help you find the measures of the angles.

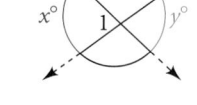

 Key Concepts

> **Theorem 11-11**
>
> The measure of an angle formed by two lines that
>
> (1) intersect inside a circle is half the sum of the measures of the intercepted arcs.
>
> $$m\angle 1 = \tfrac{1}{2}(x + y)$$
>
> (2) intersect outside a circle is half the difference of the measures of the intercepted arcs.
>
> $$m\angle 1 = \tfrac{1}{2}(x - y)$$
>
>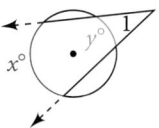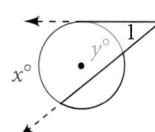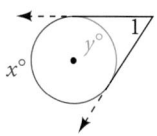

Part (1) is proved on the next page. The three cases of Part (2) are proved in Exercises 29 and 30.

 Ongoing Assessment and Intervention

Before the Lesson
Diagnose prerequisite skills using:
• Check Skills You'll Need

During the Lesson
Monitor progress using:
• Check Understanding
• Additional Examples
• Standardized Test Prep

After the Lesson
Assess knowledge using:
• Lesson Quiz
• Computer Test Generator CD

Math Background

The Inscribed Angle Theorem establishes the relationships that are summarized below.

Angle Vertex	Measure
Center	$m(\text{arc})$
On circle	$\frac{1}{2} \cdot m(\text{arc})$
Inside circle	$\frac{1}{2} \cdot$ sum of $m(\text{arcs})$
Outside circle	$\frac{1}{2} \cdot$ difference of $m(\text{arcs})$

One consequence of triangle similarity is the proportionality of the lengths of segments formed by chords, secants, or tangents, which is often stated using the Cross-Product Property of Proportions.

OBJECTIVE
1 Teaching Notes

English Learners
Use the diagrams for Theorem 11-11 to help students distinguish between lines that *intersect* and *intercepted* arcs.

1 EXAMPLE Auditory Learners

Suggest that students use the phrase *interior add, exterior subtract* to remember when to add and when to subtract the measures of intercepted arcs.

Careers

Photographers use mathematics to relate the opening of a camera's lens and its shutter speed and to photograph subjects from pleasing angles. Encourage interested students to find more applications of mathematics in photography.

Proof

Proof of Theorem 11-11, Part (1)

Given: $\odot O$ with intersecting chords $\overline{AC}$ and $\overline{BD}$

Prove: $m\angle 1 = \frac{1}{2}\left(m\widehat{AB} + m\widehat{CD}\right)$

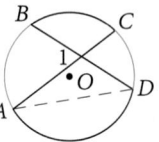

Begin by drawing $\overline{AD}$ as shown in the diagram.

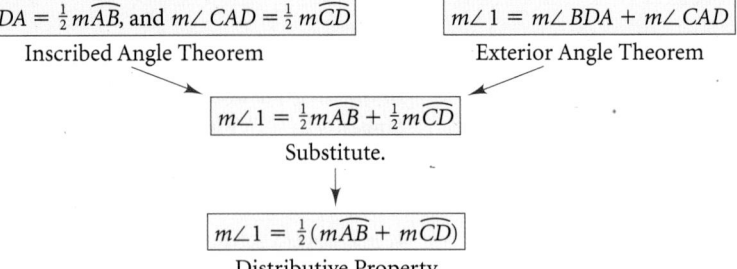

$m\angle BDA = \frac{1}{2}m\widehat{AB}$, and $m\angle CAD = \frac{1}{2}m\widehat{CD}$
Inscribed Angle Theorem

$m\angle 1 = m\angle BDA + m\angle CAD$
Exterior Angle Theorem

$m\angle 1 = \frac{1}{2}m\widehat{AB} + \frac{1}{2}m\widehat{CD}$
Substitute.

$m\angle 1 = \frac{1}{2}\left(m\widehat{AB} + m\widehat{CD}\right)$
Distributive Property

You can use Theorem 11-11 to find the measures of angles and intercepted arcs.

1 EXAMPLE Finding Angle Measures

Algebra Find the value of each variable.

a.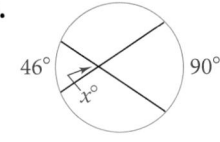

b. 95°

$x = \frac{1}{2}(46 + 90)$ **Theorem 11-11 (1)**
$x = 68$ **Simplify.**

$20 = \frac{1}{2}(95 - z)$ **Theorem 11-11 (2)**
$40 = 95 - z$ **Solve for z.**
$z = 55$

✓ Check Understanding 1 Find the value of each variable.

a. 250

b. 40

2 EXAMPLE Real-World Connection

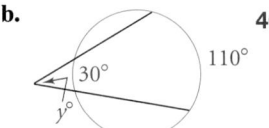

Real-World Connection

Line-of-sight tangents to this fountain basin form a larger angle than do those to the distant basin.

Photography You focus your camera on a fountain. Your camera is at the vertex of the angle formed by tangents to the fountain. You estimate that this angle is 40°.

What is the measure of the arc of the circular basin of the fountain that will be in the photograph?

Let $m\widehat{AB} = x$.
Then $m\widehat{AEB} = 360 - x$.

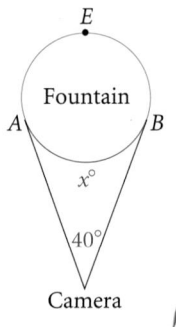

608   Chapter 11 Circles

Reaching All Students

Below Level As students read Theorem 11-11, they should copy the diagrams and clearly label each intercepted arc. Then have the class identify the intercepted arcs.	**Advanced Learners** After Example 2, have students show that an angle whose sides are tangent to a circle and intercept a minor arc of measure x has measure $180 - x$.	**English Learners** See note on page 608. **Auditory Learners** See note on page 608.

$$40 = \frac{1}{2}\left(m\overset{\frown}{AEB} - m\overset{\frown}{AB}\right)$$ **Theorem 11-11 (2)**

$$40 = \frac{1}{2}[(360 - x) - x]$$ **Substitute.**

$$40 = \frac{1}{2}(360 - 2x)$$ **Simplify.**

$$40 = 180 - x$$ **Distribute.**

$$x = 140$$ **Solve for x.**

● A 140° arc will be in the photograph.

 **Check Understanding** ❷ **Critical Thinking** To photograph a 160° arc of the basin, should you move towards or away from the fountain? What angle should the tangents form?
away; 20°

From a given point P, you can draw two segments to a circle along infinitely many lines. For example, $\overline{PA_1}$ and $\overline{PB_1}$ lie along one such line. Theorem 11-12 states the surprising result that, no matter which line you use, the product $PA \cdot PB$ remains constant.

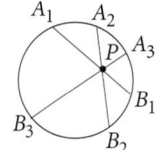

$PA_i \cdot PB_i$ is constant.

 Key Concepts

Theorem 11-12

For a given point and circle, the product of the lengths of the two segments from the point to the circle is constant along any line through the point and circle.

 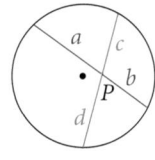

I.

II.

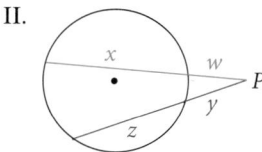

III.

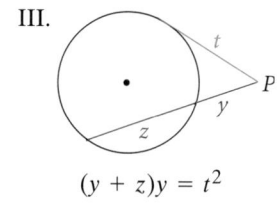

$$a \cdot b = c \cdot d$$ $$(w + x)w = (y + z)y$$ $$(y + z)y = t^2$$

 Reading Math

The two segments to a circle along a secant are called *secant segments*.

Note in Case III that the tangent segment is used twice.

Here is a proof for Case I. You will prove II and III in Exercises 31 and 32.

Proof **Proof of Theorem 11-12 (I)**

Given: a circle with chords $\overline{AB}$ and $\overline{CD}$ intersecting at P

Prove: $a \cdot b = c \cdot d$

Draw $\overline{AC}$ and $\overline{BD}$. $\angle A \cong \angle D$ and $\angle C \cong \angle B$ because they are inscribed angles and each pair intercept the same arc. Thus, $\triangle APC \sim \triangle DPB$ by the Angle-Angle Similarity Postulate. The lengths of corresponding sides of similar triangles are proportional, so $\frac{a}{d} = \frac{c}{b}$. Therefore, $a \cdot b = c \cdot d$.

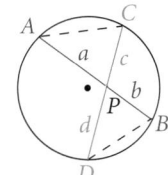

❶ Find the value of the variable.

a.

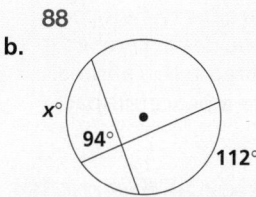

88

b.

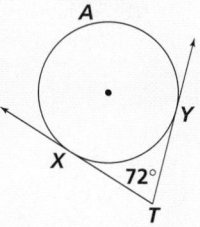

76

❷ An advertising agency wants a frontal photo of a "flying saucer" ride at an amusement park. The photographer stands at the vertex of the angle formed by tangents to the "flying saucer." What is the measure of the arc that will be in the photograph?

108

OBJECTIVE
2 **Teaching Notes**

Math Tip
Discuss the proof of Theorem 11-12 (1). If students forget how chord segments are related, suggest that they reproduce the proof to derive the proportion resulting from triangle similarity.

❸ **EXAMPLE**

Make sure that students add only like terms and correctly apply the Distributive Property. You may want to pair students so that they can help each other with the algebra.

609

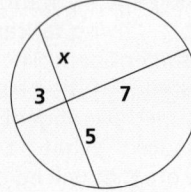
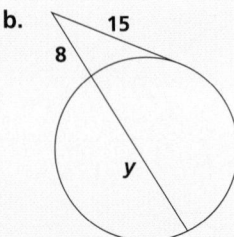
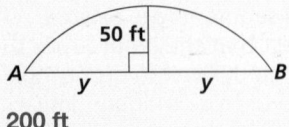
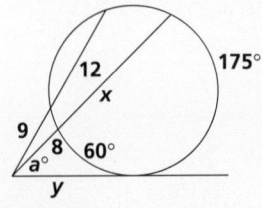
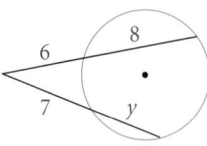
You can use Theorem 11-12 to find lengths of segments in circles.

3 EXAMPLE Finding Segment Lengths

Algebra Find the value of the variable. If the answer is not a whole number, round to the nearest tenth.

a.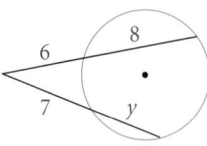

b.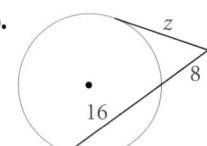

a.	
$(6 + 8)6 = (7 + y)7$	**Thm. 11-12 (II)**
$84 = 49 + 7y$	**Solve for y.**
$35 = 7y$	
$5 = y$	

b.	
$(8 + 16)8 = z^2$	**Thm. 11-12 (III)**
$192 = z^2$	**Solve for z.**
$13.9 \approx z$	

✓ **Check Understanding** **3** Find the value of the variable to the nearest tenth.

a.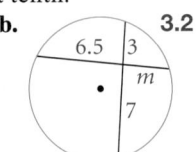

b.

4 EXAMPLE Real-World Connection

Bridge Design The arch of the Taiko Bashi is an arc of a circle. A 14-ft chord is 4.8 ft from the edge of the circle. Find the radius of the circle.

Draw a diagram that shows a 14-ft chord 4.8 ft below the top of a circle. Let *x* represent the length of the part of the diameter from the chord to the bottom of the circle. Use *x* and Theorem 11-12 to find the radius.

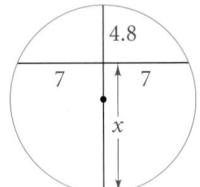

$4.8x = 7 \cdot 7$	**Theorem 11-12 (I)**
$4.8x = 49$	**Solve for x.**
$x \approx 10.2$	
diameter $\approx 10.2 + 4.8 = 15$ ft	**Add the segment lengths.**
radius ≈ 7.5 ft	

The radius is about 7.5 ft.

✓ **Check Understanding** **4** The basis of a design of a rotor for a Wankel engine is an equilateral triangle. Each side of the triangle is a chord to an arc of a circle. The opposite vertex of the triangle is the center of the arc. In the diagram at the right, each side of the equilateral triangle is 8 in. long.

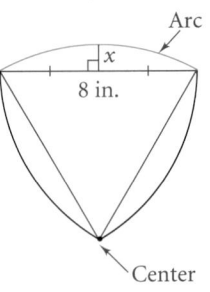

a. Use what you know about equilateral triangles and find the value of *x*. **(8 − 4√3) in.**

b. **Critical Thinking** Copy the diagram and complete the circle with the given center. Then use Theorem 11-12 to find the value of *x*. Show that your answers to parts (a) and (b) are equal. $\frac{16}{8 + 4\sqrt{3}}$ **in.**

EXERCISES

Practice and Problem Solving

For more practice, see *Extra Practice*.

Ⓐ Practice by Example $\boxed{x^2}$ **Algebra Find the value of each variable.**

Example 1
(page 608)

1. 46
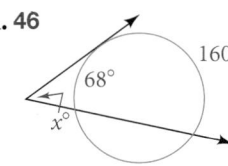

2. 50
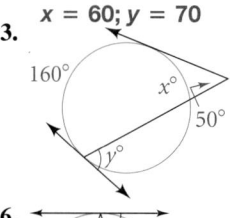

3. $x = 60; y = 70$
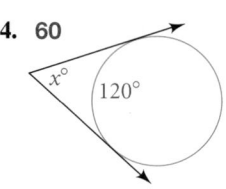

4. 60
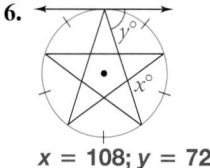

5. $x = 115; y = 74$
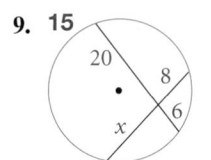

6. $x = 108; y = 72$
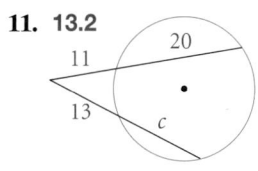

Example 2
(pages 608–609)

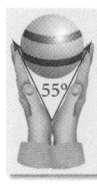

7. Astroscience A departing space probe sends back a picture of Earth as it crosses the plane of Earth's equator. The angle formed by the two tangents to the equator is 20°. What arc of the equator is visible to the space probe? **160°**

8. At the left, the cross section of the ball is a circle. About how many degrees is the arc of the circle that is below the points of contact with the hands? **125**

Example 3
(page 610)

$\boxed{x^2}$ **Algebra Find the value of each variable using the given chord, secant, and tangent lengths. If the answer is not a whole number, round to the nearest tenth.**

9. 15
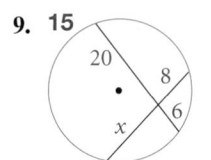

10. 11.5
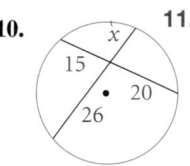

11. 13.2
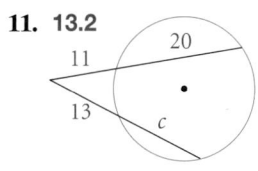

12. 3.5
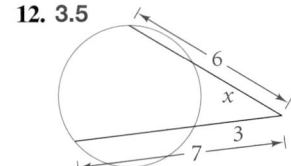

13. $x = 25.8; y \approx 12.4$
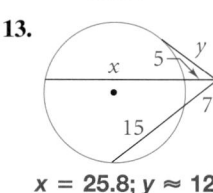

14. $x \approx 5.3; y \approx 2.9$
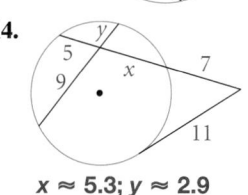

Example 4
(page 610)

Geology This natural arch, in Arches National Park, Utah, is an arc of a circle.

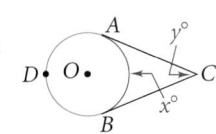

15. Find the diameter of the circle.
about 270.8 ft

16. The chord length shown is rounded. It could range from 165 ft to 175 ft. Find the corresponding range for the diameter.
It could range from 256.9 ft to 285.2 ft.

Ⓑ Apply Your Skills $\boxed{x^2}$ **Algebra** $\overline{CA}$ and $\overline{CB}$ are tangents to $\odot O$. Write an expression for each arc or angle in terms of the given variable.

17. $m\overset{\frown}{ADB}$ using x
360 − x

18. $m\angle C$ using x
180 − x

19. $m\overset{\frown}{AB}$ using y
180 − y

Lesson 11-4 Angle Measures and Segment Lengths **611**

Assignment Guide

▼1 Objective
Ⓐ Ⓑ **Core** 1–8, 17–19, 27–33
Ⓒ **Extension** 34, 35

▼2 Objective
Ⓐ Ⓑ **Core** 9–16, 20–26
Ⓒ **Extension** 36, 37

Standardized Test Prep 38–42

Mixed Review 43–48

Error Prevention

Exercise 5 Remind students not to assume from the diagram that the triangles are isosceles.

Connection to Algebra

Exercise 13 You may want to review solving the quadratic equation $x^2 = a$ before assigning this exercise.

Exercise 28 Relate the Inscribed Angle Theorem and Theorem 11-11 visually by pointing out that the possible angle measures depend on the ships' positions relative to the circle.

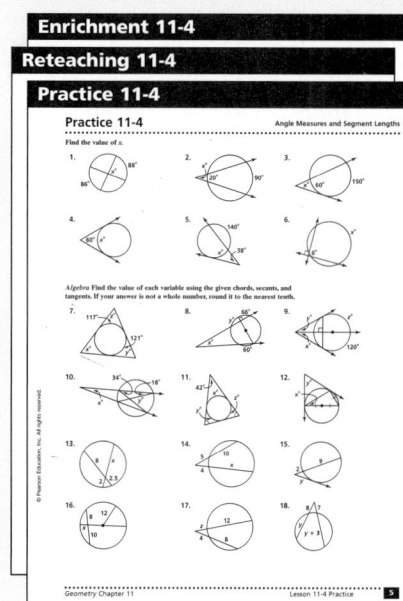

4. Assess

Lesson Quiz 11-4

Use ⊙M for Exercises 1 and 2.

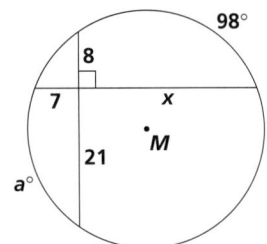

1. Find a. **82**

2. Find x. **24**

Use ⊙O for Exercises 3–5.

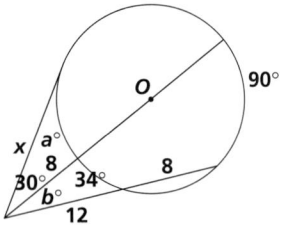

3. Find a and b. **a = 60; b = 28**

4. Find x to the nearest tenth. **15.5**

5. Find the diameter of ⊙O. **22**

Alternative Assessment

Have each student design three problems with art whose solutions depend on a different theorem or part of a theorem from this lesson. After students find the solutions, have them exchange problems with partners, solve, compare their solutions, and discuss their methods.

pages 611–613   Exercises

29. Answers may vary. Sample: Since they are inscribed ∠s: $m\angle BED = \frac{1}{2}m\widehat{BD}$ and $m\angle ABE = \frac{1}{2}m\widehat{AE}$. Apply the Ext. ∠ Thm. to △BCE to prove that $m\angle C = \frac{1}{2}(m\widehat{AE} - m\widehat{BD})$.

612

Find the diameter of ⊙O. If your answer is not a whole number, round it to the nearest tenth.

20. 26.7 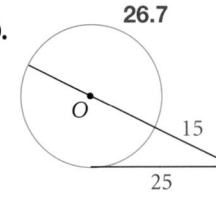 **21.** 16.7 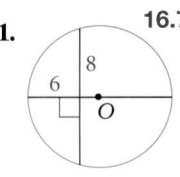 **22.** 14.1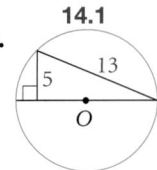

x^2 **Algebra** Find the values of x and y using the given chord, secant, and tangent lengths. If your answer is not a whole number, round it to the nearest tenth.

23. 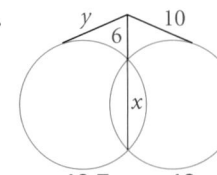 **24.** 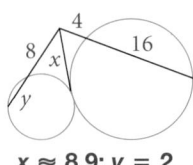 **25.**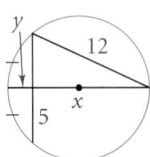

$x \approx 10.7; y = 10$ $x \approx 8.9; y = 2$ $x \approx 10.9; y \approx 2.3$

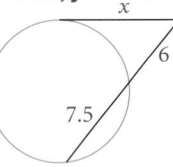

26. You must use (7.5 + 6)6, or the entire segment length.

27. 95, 104, 86, 75

26. Error Analysis To find the value of x, a student wrote the equation $(7.5)6 = x^2$. What error did the student make? **See left.**

27. A circle is inscribed in a quadrilateral whose four angles have measures 85, 76, 94, and 105. Find the measures of the four arcs between consecutive points of tangency. **See left.**

Exercise 26

28. Navigation The map at the left shows that the waters within $\widehat{AXB}$, a 300° arc, are unsafe. Here are what the letters represent.

A: a lighthouse   B: a lighthouse   X: locations of a ship on ⊙O
Y: locations of a ship inside ⊙O   Z: locations of a ship outside ⊙O

a. Critical Thinking What measures are possible for ∠X? For ∠Y? For ∠Z?
b. Writing Using the angles a ship makes with the lighthouses (like angles X, Y, and Z), explain how a navigator can be sure the ship is in safe waters.
a–b. See left.

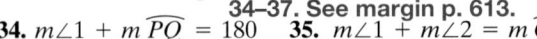

28a. 30; 30 < m∠Y < 180; 0 < m∠Z < 30

b. If the ∠ measure is ≤ 30, the ship is safe.

29. Write a plan for a proof for Theorem 11-11, Part (2) as it applies to two secants that intersect outside a circle.

Given: ⊙O with secants $\overline{CA}$ and $\overline{CE}$ intersecting at C
Prove: $m\angle ACE = \frac{1}{2}(m\widehat{AE} - m\widehat{BD})$ **See margin.**

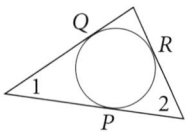

Proof **30.** Prove the other two cases of Theorem 11-11, Part (2). (See Exercise 29.) **See back of book.**

Proof **For Exercises 31 and 32, write proofs that use similar triangles.**

31. Prove Theorem 11-12 (II). **See margin.**
32. Prove Theorem 11-12 (III). **See back of book.**

33. Explain why Theorem 11-12 is true when the given point is on the circle. **See back of book.**

Ⓒ **Challenge** *Proof* **In Exercises 34–37, prove each statement or theorem.**
34–37. See margin p. 613.
34. $m\angle 1 + m\widehat{PQ} = 180$ **35.** $m\angle 1 + m\angle 2 = m\widehat{QR}$

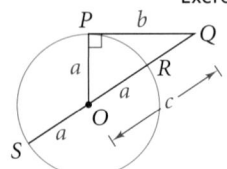

Exercises 34, 35

36. the Pythagorean Theorem (Use the diagram at the right and the theorems of this lesson.)

37. The tangents to a circle at the vertices of an inscribed equilateral triangle form an equilateral triangle.

612   Chapter 11   Circles

31. Given: a circle with secant segments $\overline{XV}$ and $\overline{ZV}$; Prove: $XV \cdot WV = ZV \cdot YV$.

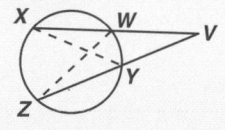

1. Construct $\overline{XY}$ and $\overline{ZW}$. **2.** $\angle XVY \cong \angle ZVW$ (Reflexive Prop. of ≅) **3.** $\angle VXY \cong \angle WZV$ (2 inscribed ∠ that intercept the same arc are ≅.)

4. △XVY ~ △ZVW (AA~) **5.** $\frac{XV}{ZV} = \frac{YV}{WV}$ (In similar figures, corr. sides are proport.) **6.** $XV \cdot WV = YV \cdot ZV$ (Prop. of Proport.)

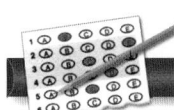

Gridded Response

Take It to the NET
Online lesson quiz at
www.PHSchool.com
Web Code: afa-1104

38. If $m\overset{\frown}{AE}$ = 86 and $m\overset{\frown}{BD}$ = 40, find $m\angle BKD$. **63**

39. If AK = 14, EK = 17, and BK = 7, find DK. **8.5**

40. If BC = 6, DC = 5, and CE = 12, find AC. **10**

41. If $m\angle C$ = 14 and $m\overset{\frown}{AE}$ = 140, find $m\overset{\frown}{BD}$. **112**

42. If $m\overset{\frown}{AB}$ = 110 and $m\overset{\frown}{DE}$ = 130, find $m\angle AKE$. **60**

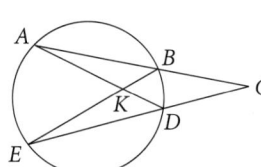

Mixed Review

Lesson 11-3

Find the value of each variable.

43.

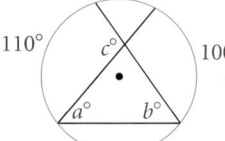

$a = 55; b = 35; c = 30$

44.

$a = 50; b = 55; c = 105$

Lesson 9-2 **Find the value of x to the nearest degree.**

45. **30**

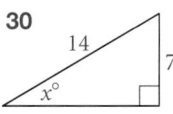

46. **42**

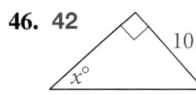

47.

57
5.5
$x°$
3

Lesson 8-6

48. The areas of two similar parallelograms are 20 cm^2 and 3.2 cm^2. Find the similarity ratio of the larger parallelogram to the smaller parallelogram. **5 : 2**

Geometry at Work

.... Aerospace Engineer

Aerospace engineers design and build all types of spacecraft, from the low-orbit space shuttle to interplanetary probes. Much of today's work involves communications satellites that relay television, telephone, computer, and other signals all over the world. The portion of Earth's surface that can communicate with a satellite increases as the height of the orbit increases.

Earth has a radius of about 3960 miles. The figure at the right shows a satellite 12,000 miles above Earth. $\overset{\frown}{AB}$ is the arc of Earth that is in the range of the satellite. You can find $m\overset{\frown}{AB}$ by finding $m\angle AEB$, which is twice $m\angle AES$.

$$m\overset{\frown}{AB} = m\angle AEB = 2m\angle AES = 2 \cdot \cos^{-1}\left(\frac{3960}{3960 + 12,000}\right) \approx 151.3$$

The measure of the arc of Earth in the range of the satellite is about 151.3.

S

12,000 mi

A
3960 mi
E
B

Earth

Take It to the NET For more information about aerospace careers, go to **www.PHSchool.com**.
Web Code: afb-2031

Lesson 11-4 Angle Measures and Segment Lengths **613**

34. 1. $m\angle 1 = \frac{1}{2}m\overset{\frown}{QRP} - \frac{1}{2}m\overset{\frown}{PQ}$ (Thm. 11-11)
2. $m\angle 1 + m\overset{\frown}{PQ} = \frac{1}{2}m\overset{\frown}{QRP} + \frac{1}{2}m\overset{\frown}{PQ}$ (Add. Prop. of = and Distr. Prop.)

3. $m\angle 1 + m\overset{\frown}{PQ} = \frac{1}{2}(m\overset{\frown}{QRP} + m\overset{\frown}{PQ})$ (Distr. Prop.)
4. $m\angle 1 + m\overset{\frown}{PQ} = \frac{1}{2}(360)$ (A circle has 360°.)

5. $m\angle 1 + m\overset{\frown}{PQ} = 180$ (Multiply.)

Standardized Test Prep

A sheet of blank grids is available in the Test-Taking Strategies with Transparencies booklet. Give this sheet to students for practice with filling in the grids.

📁 **Resources**
For additional practice with a variety of test item formats:
• Standardized Test Prep, p. 631
• Test-Taking Strategies, p. 626
• Test-Taking Strategies with Transparencies

Exercises 38–42 For each exercise advise students to copy the diagram and highlight the parts that are used.

35. 1. $m\angle 1 = \frac{1}{2}m\overset{\frown}{QRP} - \frac{1}{2}m\overset{\frown}{PQ}$ (Thm. 11-11)
2. $m\angle 2 = \frac{1}{2}m\overset{\frown}{RQP} - \frac{1}{2}m\overset{\frown}{RP}$ (Thm. 11-11)
3. $m\angle 1 + m\angle 2 = \frac{1}{2}m\overset{\frown}{QRP} + \frac{1}{2}m\overset{\frown}{RQP} - \frac{1}{2}m\overset{\frown}{PQ} - \frac{1}{2}m\overset{\frown}{RP}$ (Subst.)
4. $m\angle 1 + m\angle 2 = \frac{1}{2}m\overset{\frown}{QR} + \frac{1}{2}m\overset{\frown}{RP} + \frac{1}{2}m\overset{\frown}{QR} + \frac{1}{2}m\overset{\frown}{PQ} - \frac{1}{2}m\overset{\frown}{PQ} - \frac{1}{2}m\overset{\frown}{RP}$ (Arc Add. Post. and Distr. Prop.)
5. $m\angle 1 + m\angle 2 = m\overset{\frown}{QR}$ (Distr. Prop.)

36. 1. $(PQ)^2 = (QS)(QR)$ (Thm. 11-12 [3])
2. $b^2 = (c + a)(c - a)$ (Subst.)
3. $b^2 = c^2 - a^2$ (Distr. Prop.)
4. $b^2 + a^2 = c^2$ (Add. Prop. of =)

37.

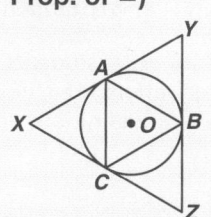

$m\overset{\frown}{AB} = m\overset{\frown}{BC} = m\overset{\frown}{AC} = 120$, since chords $\overline{AB}$, $\overline{BC}$, and $\overline{CA}$ are all $\cong$. So the measures of $\angle X$, $\angle Y$, and $\angle Z$ are $\frac{1}{2}(240 - 120) = 60$, and $\triangle XYZ$ is equilateral.

613

Extension

Tangent Lines, Tangent Ratios

Students will relate the six trigonometric functions defined by ratios of pairs of sides of a right triangle with segments in a unit circle and use the ratios to prove trigonometric identities.

Resources

Technology
Computer Test Generator CD-ROM, Chapter 0, Extension Topics

Teaching Notes

When students understand the relationships between chords, tangents, and secants to a circle, the sine, cosine, and tangent ratios defined in Chapter 9 can be applied to a unit circle and extended to all six trigonometric ratios.

Visual Learners

Exercises 2, 3 Have students point to *adjacent, opposite,* and *hypotenuse* on the unit circle as they explain the terms. Suggest that students will find it easier to memorize the ratios than to reconstruct the circles.

Math Tip

Reinforce the reciprocal relationship between sine A and cosecant A, cosine A and secant A, and tangent A and cotangent A.

Exercises 7, 10 Have students show that these equations are true by using both ratio definitions and a unit circle.

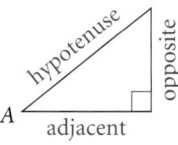

Extension
Tangent Lines, Tangent Ratios

You learned about tangent ratios in Chapter 9 and tangent lines in this chapter. Are the two related? Yes, indeed! In fact, there are six trigonometric ratios that you can study in advanced mathematics.

$$\text{sine } \angle A = \frac{\text{opposite}}{\text{hypotenuse}} \qquad \text{cosine } \angle A = \frac{\text{adjacent}}{\text{hypotenuse}} \qquad \text{tangent } \angle A = \frac{\text{opposite}}{\text{adjacent}}$$

$$\text{cosecant } \angle A = \frac{\text{hypotenuse}}{\text{opposite}} \qquad \text{secant } \angle A = \frac{\text{hypotenuse}}{\text{adjacent}} \qquad \text{cotangent } \angle A = \frac{\text{adjacent}}{\text{opposite}}$$

Each of these is related to the geometry of a unit circle, the circle shown in both figures below. Sine A, tangent A, and secant A are the segment lengths highlighted in Figure 1. Cosine A, cotangent A, and cosecant A are highlighted in Figure 2.

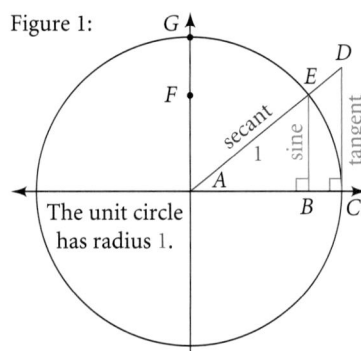

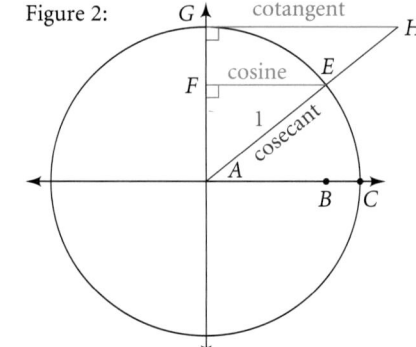

4. On the unit circle, tangent $A = \frac{\text{opp.}}{1} =$ opp. = length of $\overline{DC}$, the tangent segment.

5. On the unit circle, secant $A = \frac{\text{hyp.}}{1} =$ hyp. = length of $\overline{DA}$, the secant segment.

EXERCISES

1. For the four triangles shown above, complete these similarity statements:
$\triangle ABE \sim \triangle\ \underline{?}\ \sim \triangle\ \underline{?}\ \sim \triangle\ \underline{?}$. **ACD; HGA; EFA**

2. Explain why the sine A, tangent A, and secant A ratios have the same values as the segment lengths highlighted in Figure 1.
2–3. The radius of the circle is 1, which is the denominator in each of the ratios.

3. Explain why the cosine A, cotangent A, and cosecant A ratios have the same values as the segment lengths highlighted in Figure 2.

Describe the connection between each of the following. **4–5. See above.**

4. the tangent A ratio and a tangent segment

5. the secant A ratio and a secant segment

6. $\angle EAB$ in Figure 1 and $\angle EAF$ in Figure 2; what are the first two letters in a word that is commonly used to describe this connection?
They are complementary; *co*

Show that each equation is true. **7–12. See margin.**

7. $(\text{tangent } A)^2 = (\text{secant } A)^2 - 1$

8. $\text{tangent } A = \frac{\text{sine } A}{\text{cosine } A}$

9. $\text{cotangent } A = \frac{1}{\text{tangent } A}$

10. $(\text{sine } A)^2 + (\text{cosine } A)^2 = 1$

11. $\text{secant } A = \frac{1}{\text{cosine } A}$

12. $\text{cosecant } A = \frac{1}{\text{sine } A}$

---

page 614 Extension

7.
$(\text{tangent } A)^2 = \left(\frac{DC}{CA}\right)^2 = \left(\frac{EB}{BA}\right)^2 =$
$\frac{(EB)^2}{(BA)^2} = \frac{(EA)^2 - (BA)^2}{(BA)^2} =$
$\frac{(EA)^2}{(BA)^2} - 1 = (\text{secant } A)^2 - 1$

8. $\text{tangent } A = \frac{DC}{CA} =$
$\frac{EB}{BA} = \frac{EB}{EF} = \frac{\text{sine } A}{\text{cosine } A}$

9. $\text{cotangent } A = \frac{HG}{GA} =$
$\frac{CA}{CD} = \frac{1}{\frac{CD}{CA}} = \frac{1}{\text{tangent } A}$

10. $(\text{sine } A)^2 + (\text{cosine } A)^2 =$
$(EB)^2 + (EF)^2 =$
$(EB)^2 + (BA)^2 =$
$(EA)^2 = 1$

11. $\text{secant } A = \frac{EA}{AB} =$
$\frac{EA}{EF} = \frac{1}{\frac{EF}{EA}} = \frac{1}{\text{cosine } A}$

12. $\text{cosecant } A = \frac{HA}{GA} =$
$\frac{DA}{DC} = \frac{1}{\frac{DC}{DA}} = \frac{1}{\text{sine } A}$

11-5

Circles in the Coordinate Plane

 11-5 | North Carolina Objectives 2.03d

1. Plan

North Carolina Objectives

2.03 Apply properties, definitions, and theorems of two-dimensional figures to solve problems and write proofs: d) Circles.

Lesson Preview

What You'll Learn

OBJECTIVE 1 To write an equation of a circle

OBJECTIVE 2 To find the center and radius of a circle

. . . And Why

To describe the position and range of three cellular telephone towers, as in Example 4

 Check Skills You'll Need (For help, go to Lesson 1-6.)

Find the length of each segment to the nearest tenth.

1. 5.8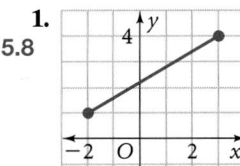

2. 12.8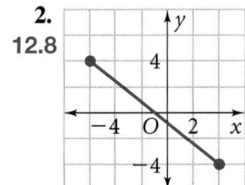

3. 5.8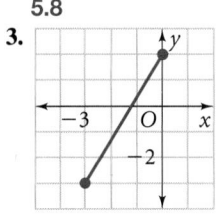

 New Vocabulary • standard form of an equation of a circle

OBJECTIVE 1

Writing an Equation of a Circle

 Interactive lesson includes instant self-check, tutorials, and activities.

You can use the Distance Formula to find an equation of a circle with center (h, k) and radius r. Let (x, y) be any point on the circle. Then the radius r is the distance from (h, k) to (x, y).

$r = \sqrt{(x - h)^2 + (y - k)^2}$ **Distance Formula**

$r^2 = (x - h)^2 + (y - k)^2$ **Square both sides.**

This essentially proves the following theorem.

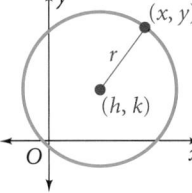

Key Concepts

Theorem 11-13

An equation of a circle with center (h, k) and radius r is $(x - h)^2 + (y - k)^2 = r^2$.

The equation $(x - h)^2 + (y - k)^2 = r^2$ is in **standard form.** You may also call it the *standard equation* of a circle.

1 EXAMPLE Writing the Equation of a Circle

Write the standard equation of the circle with center $(5, -2)$ and radius 7.

$(x - h)^2 + (y - k)^2 = r^2$ **Use standard form.**

$(x - 5)^2 + [y - (-2)]^2 = 7^2$ **Substitute (5, −2) for (h, k), and 7 for r.**

$(x - 5)^2 + (y + 2)^2 = 49$ **Simplify.**

Check Understanding **1** Write the standard equation of each circle.

a. center $(3, 5)$; radius 6
$(x - 3)^2 + (y - 5)^2 = 36$

b. center $(-2, -1)$; radius $\sqrt{2}$
$(x + 2)^2 + (y + 1)^2 = 2$

Lesson 11-5 Circles in the Coordinate Plane **615**

Lesson Preview

 Check Skills You'll Need

Finding Distance on the Coordinate Plane
Lesson 1-6: Example 1
Exercises 1–9
Extra Practice, p. 690

Lesson Resources

 Teaching Resources
Practice, Reteaching, Enrichment
Checkpoint Quiz 2

Reaching All Students
Practice Workbook 11-5
Spanish Practice Workbook 11-5
Reading and Math Literacy 11C
Spanish Reading & Literacy 11C
Spanish Checkpoint Quiz 2
Informal Geometry Planning Guide 11-5

 Presentation Assistant Plus!
Transparencies
• Check Skills You'll Need 11-5
• Additional Examples 11-5
• Student Edition Answers 11-5
• Lesson Quiz 11-5
PH Presentation Pro CD 11-5

ASSESSMENT SYSTEM

Checkpoint Quiz 2
Computer Test Generator CD

Technology
Resource Pro® CD-ROM
Computer Test Generator CD
Prentice Hall Presentation Pro CD

 **www.PHSchool.com**
Student Site
• Teacher Web Code: afk-5500
• Self-grading Lesson Quiz
Teacher Center
• Lesson Planner
• Resources

Plus **iTEXT**

Ongoing Assessment and Intervention

Before the Lesson
Diagnose prerequisite skills using:
• Check Skills You'll Need

During the Lesson
Monitor progress using:
• Check Understanding
• Additional Examples
• Standardized Test Prep

After the Lesson
Assess knowledge using:
• Lesson Quiz
• Computer Test Generator CD
• Chapter Checkpoint 2 (p. 620)

615

2. Teach

Professional Development

Math Background

The equation of a circle is used extensively in analytic geometry and trigonometry. The equation of a unit circle with center at the origin leads to the fundamental trigonometric relationship $\sin^2 x + \cos^2 x = 1$, whose importance in finding formulas for derivatives and integrals in calculus cannot be understated.

OBJECTIVE

1 Teaching Notes

Teaching Tip
Students may be overwhelmed by the five variables used to derive the standard form of an equation of a circle. Instead of using radius r and center (h, k), you may want to specify natural-number values for r, h, and k before introducing the theorem.

1 EXAMPLE Error Prevention

Review subtraction of negative numbers to help students simplify correctly after substituting a negative coordinate of a center in the standard equation.

2 EXAMPLE

Point out that r, h, and k replace d, x_2, and y_2 in the Distance Formula $d = \sqrt{(x_1 - x_2)^2 + (y_1 - y_2)^2}$ because of their special meanings in a circle and that the standard equation cannot be found without first finding the radius.

Additional Examples

1 Write the standard equation of a circle with center $(-8, 0)$ and radius $\sqrt{5}$. $(x + 8)^2 + y^2 = 5$

2 Write the standard equation of a circle with center $(5, 8)$ that passes through the point $(-15, -13)$. $(x - 5)^2 + (y - 8)^2 = 841$

If you know the center of a circle and a point on the circle, you can write the standard equation of the circle.

2 EXAMPLE Using the Center and a Point on a Circle

Write the standard equation of the circle with center $(1, -3)$ that passes through the point $(2, 2)$.

$r = \sqrt{(x - h)^2 + (y - k)^2}$ **Use the Distance Formula to find r.**

$ = \sqrt{(2 - 1)^2 + (2 - (-3))^2}$ **Substitute $(1, -3)$ for (h, k), and $(2, 2)$ for (x, y).**

$ = \sqrt{1 + 25} = \sqrt{26}$ **Simplify.**

$(x - h)^2 + (y - k)^2 = r^2$ **Use standard form.**

$(x - 1)^2 + [y - (-3)^2] = (\sqrt{26})^2$ **Substitute $(1, -3)$ for (h, k), and $\sqrt{26}$ for r.**

$(x - 1)^2 + (y + 3)^2 = 26$ **Simplify.**

✓ **Check Understanding** **2** Write the standard equation of the circle with center $(2, 3)$ that passes through the point $(-1, 1)$. $(x - 2)^2 + (y - 3)^2 = 13$

OBJECTIVE

2 Finding the Center and Radius of a Circle

If you know the standard equation of a circle, you can describe the circle by naming its center and radius. Then you can use this information to graph the circle.

3 EXAMPLE Graphing a Circle Given its Equation

Find the center and radius of the circle with equation $(x - 7)^2 + (y + 2)^2 = 64$. Then graph the circle.

$(x - 7)^2 + (y + 2)^2 = 64$

$(x - 7)^2 + (y - (-2))^2 = 8^2$ **Use standard form.**

$\underset{h}{\uparrow}\underset{k}{\uparrow}\underset{r}{\uparrow}$

The center is $(7, -2)$ and the radius is 8.

Need Help?

Standard form requires that $y + 2$ be written with a minus sign.

3. center: $(2, 3)$; radius: 10

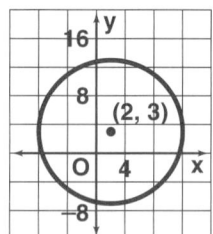

To graph the circle, place the compass point at the center $(7, -2)$ and draw a circle with radius 8.

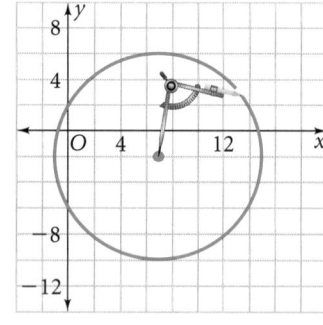

✓ **Check Understanding** **3** Find the center and radius of the circle with equation $(x - 2)^2 + (y - 3)^2 = 100$. Then graph the circle. **See left.**

You can use equations of circles to model real-world situations.

616   Chapter 11   Circles

Reaching All Students

Below Level Display the graphs of the circles in Examples 1 and 2. Then have students check that several points on the graphs satisfy the equations.	**Advanced Learners** After Example 3, challenge students to graph the inequalities $(x - 7)^2 + (y + 2)^2 < 64$ and $(x - 7)^2 + (y + 2)^2 > 64$.	**Inclusion** See note on page 617. **Visual Learners** See note on page 618.

Real-World Connection

To blend into the landscape, cellular phone towers can be disguised as trees.

4 EXAMPLE Real-World 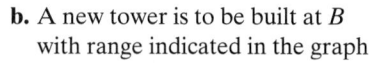 Connection

Communications When you make a call on a cellular phone, a tower receives the call. In the diagram, the centers of circles O and A are locations of cellular telephone towers.

a. The equation
$(x - 16)^2 + (y - 10)^2 = 100$
models the position and range of Tower A. Describe the position and range of Tower A.

$(x - 16)^2 + (y - 10)^2 = 10^2$
is in standard form. It shows that tower A is located at $(16, 10)$ and has a range of 10 units.

b. A new tower is to be built at B with range indicated in the graph. Write an equation that describes the position and range of this tower.

$\odot B$ has center $(4, 20)$ and radius 10. Substitute these into the standard equation.

$(x - h)^2 + (y - k)^2 = r^2$
$(x - 4)^2 + (y - 20)^2 = 10^2$ **Substitute.**
$(x - 4)^2 + (y - 20)^2 = 100$ **This is an equation for Tower B.**

✓ **Check Understanding** **4** Write an equation that describes the position and range of Tower O.
$(x - 0)^2 + (y - 0)^2 = x^2 + y^2 = 144$

EXERCISES

For more practice, see *Extra Practice*.

Practice and Problem Solving

A **Practice by Example**

Write the standard equation of each circle. 1–9. See margin.

Example 1
(page 615)

even only

1. center $(2, -8); r = 9$ **2.** center $(0, 3); r = 7$ **3.** center $(0.2, 1.1); r = 0.4$

4. center $(5, -1); r = 12$ **5.** center $(-6, 3); r = 8$ **6.** center $(-9, -4); r = \sqrt{5}$

7. center $(0, 0); r = 4$ **8.** center $(-4, 0); r = 3$ **9.** center $(-1, -1); r = 1$

Example 2
(page 616)

Write the standard equation of the circle with the given center that passes through the given point. 10–15. See margin.

10. center $(-2, 6);$ point $(-2, 10)$ **11.** center $(1, 2);$ point $(0, 6)$

12. center $(7, -2);$ point $(1, -6)$ **13.** center $(-10, -5);$ point $(-5, 5)$

14. center $(6, 5);$ point $(0, 0)$ **15.** center $(-1, -4);$ point $(-4, 0)$

16–21. See back of book.

Example 3
(page 616)

Find the center and radius of the circle with the given equation. Then graph the circle.

16. $(x + 7)^2 + (y - 5)^2 = 16$ **17.** $(x - 3)^2 + (y + 8)^2 = 100$

18. $(x + 4)^2 + (y - 1)^2 = 25$ **19.** $x^2 + y^2 = 36$

20. $(x - 0.3)^2 + y^2 = 0.04$ **21.** $(x + 5)^2 + (y + 2)^2 = 48$

Lesson 11-5 Circles in the Coordinate Plane   **617**

pages 617–620   Exercises

1. $(x - 2)^2 + (y + 8)^2 = 81$

2. $x^2 + (y - 3)^2 = 49$

3. $(x - 0.2)^2 + (y - 1.1)^2 = 0.16$

4. $(x - 5)^2 + (y + 1)^2 = 144$

5. $(x + 6)^2 + (y - 3)^2 = 64$

6. $(x + 9)^2 + (y + 4)^2 = 5$

7. $x^2 + y^2 = 16$

8. $(x + 4)^2 + y^2 = 9$

9. $(x + 1)^2 + (y + 1)^2 = 1$

10. $(x + 2)^2 + (y - 6)^2 = 16$

11. $(x - 1)^2 + (y - 2)^2 = 17$

3 EXAMPLE **Inclusion**

Have students with motor difficulties identify the center and radius, and have partners actually graph the circle.

4 EXAMPLE

Ask: *How can you tell quickly that Tower B's circle has radius 10?* Count the units from the center along a horizontal or vertical radius.

Additional Examples

3 Find the center and radius of the circle with equation $(x + 4)^2 + (y - 1)^2 = 25$. Then graph the circle.

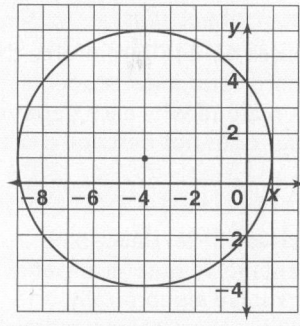

$(-4, 1); r = 5$

4 A diagram locates a radio tower at $(6, -12)$ on a coordinate grid where each unit represents 1 mi. The radio signal's range is 80 mi. Find an equation that describes the position and range of the tower.
$(x - 6)^2 + (y + 12)^2 = 6400$

Closure

The point $(-1, 4)$ is on a circle with center $(5, -2)$. Find the standard equation and diameter of the circle. Leave your answer in simplest radical form.
$(x - 5)^2 + (y + 2)^2 = 72; d = 12\sqrt{2}$

12. $(x - 7)^2 + (y + 2)^2 = 52$

13. $(x + 10)^2 + (y + 5)^2 = 125$

14. $(x - 6)^2 + (y - 5)^2 = 61$

15. $(x + 1)^2 + (y + 4)^2 = 25$

617

Assignment Guide

 **Objective**

A B Core 1–15, 27–39,
41–44, 46, 48

C Extension 63

2 Objective

A B Core 16–26, 40, 45,
47, 49–61

C Extension 62, 64

Standardized Test Prep 65–69

Mixed Review 70–81

Auditory Learners

Exercises 42–44 To reinforce the standard form, have students explain aloud why each equation does or does not describe a circle.

Visual Learners

Exercises 53–58 Have some students solve graphically and others solve algebraically, and then have them compare their methods and solutions.

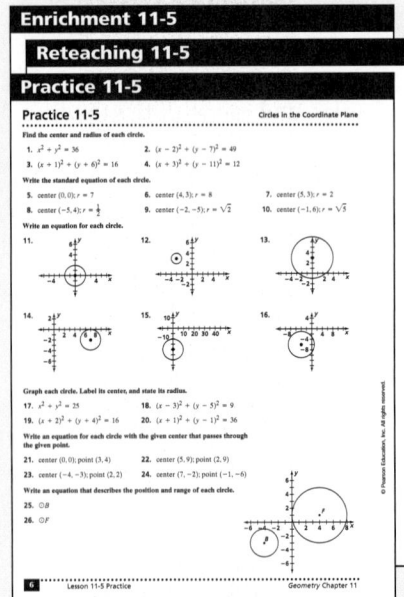

B Apply Your Skills

27. $x^2 + y^2 = 4$

28. $x^2 + y^2 = 9$

29. $x^2 + (y - 3)^2 = 4$

30. $(x - 2)^2 + y^2 = 9$

31. $(x - 2)^2 + (y - 2)^2 = 16$

32. $(x + 1)^2 + (y - 1)^2 = 4$

33. $(x - 4)^2 + (y - 3)^2 = 25$

34. $(x - 5)^2 + (y - 3)^2 = 13$

? **Need Help?**

In Exercises 33–38, use the Midpoint Formula (p. 45) to find centers.

35. $(x - 3)^2 + (y - 3)^2 = 8$

36. $(x + 3)^2 + (y + 1.5)^2 = 6.25$

37. $(x + 1.5)^2 + (y - 5)^2 = 18.25$

38. $(x - 2)^2 + (y + 2)^2 = 41$

39. $x^2 + y^2 = 1$

40. The graph is the point (0, 0).

42. yes

43. No; the x and y terms are not squared.

48. $(x - h)^2 + (y - k)^2 = r^2$
$(y - k)^2 = r^2 - (x - h)^2$
$y - k = \pm\sqrt{r^2 - (x - h)^2}$
$y = \pm\sqrt{r^2 - (x - h)^2} + k$

Example 4
(page 617)

Use the diagram at the right. Write an equation that describes the position and radius of each circle.

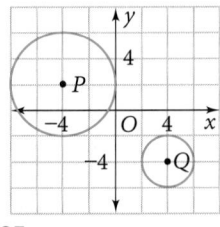

22. ⊙P
$(x + 4)^2 + (y - 2)^2 = 16$

23. ⊙Q
$(x - 4)^2 + (y + 4)^2 = 4$

24. **Communications** The plotted location of a cellular phone tower on a coordinate grid is $(-3, 2)$ and the range is 5 units. Write an equation that describes the position and range of the tower. $(x + 3)^2 + (y - 2)^2 = 25$

Each equation models the position and range of a tornado alert siren. Describe the position and range of each.

position: (−4, 9); range: 12 units

25. $(x - 5)^2 + (y - 7)^2 = 81$
position: (5, 7); range: 9 units

26. $(x + 4)^2 + (y - 9)^2 = 144$

Write the standard equation of each circle. 27–32. See left.

27.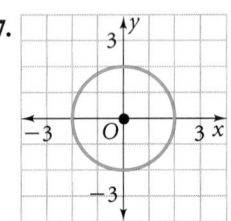

28.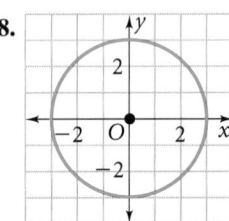

29.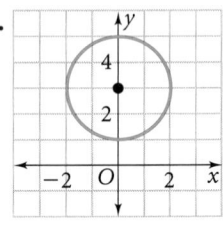

30.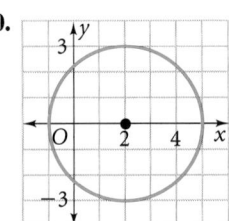

31.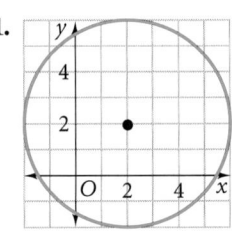

32.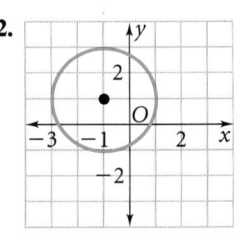

Write an equation of a circle with diameter $\overline{AB}$. 33–38. See left.

33. $A(0, 0), B(8, 6)$ 34. $A(3, 0), B(7, 6)$ 35. $A(1, 1), B(5, 5)$

36. $A(-1, 0), B(-5, -3)$ 37. $A(-3, 1), B(0, 9)$ 38. $A(-2, 3), B(6, -7)$

39. The *unit circle* has center $(0, 0)$ and radius 1. Write an equation for this circle.
39–40. See left.

40. **Critical Thinking** Describe the graph of $x^2 + y^2 = r^2$ when $r = 0$.

41. **Open-Ended** On graph paper, make a design that includes at least three circles. Write the standard equations of your circles. **Check students' work.**

Determine whether each equation is an equation of a circle. If not, explain.

42. $(x - 1)^2 + (y + 2)^2 = 9$ 43. $x + y = 9$ 44. $x + (y - 3)^2 = 9$
                                     See left.   No; the x term is not squared.

45. Find the circumference and area of the circle whose equation is $(x - 9)^2 + (y - 3)^2 = 64$. Leave your answers in terms of π. 16π; 64π

46. Write an equation of a circle with area 36π and center $(4, 7)$.
$(x - 4)^2 + (y - 7)^2 = 36$

47. What are the x- and y-intercepts of the line tangent to the circle $(x - 2)^2 + (y - 2)^2 = 5^2$ at the point $(5, 6)$? x-int. = 13, y-int. = $\frac{39}{4}$

48. For $(x - h)^2 + (y - k)^2 = r^2$, show that $y = \sqrt{r^2 - (x - h)^2} + k$, or $y = -\sqrt{r^2 - (x - h)^2} + k$. **See left.**

Take It to the NET
Graphing Calculator
procedures online at
www.PHSchool.com
Web Code: afe-2110

 Graphing Calculator Use a graphing calculator to graph each circle. (*Hint:* See Exercise 48.) View the plotting in both sequential mode and simultaneous mode. **49–52. See back of book.**

49. $(x - 3)^2 + (y - 2)^2 = 9$

50. $(x + 5)^2 + (y - 8)^2 = 1$

51. circle with center $(0, 0)$ and radius 7

52. circle with center $(-6, -3)$ and radius 2

Find all points of intersection of each pair of graphs. Make a sketch.
53–58. See back of book.

53. $x^2 + y^2 = 13$
$y = -x + 5$

54. $x^2 + y^2 = 17$
$y = -\frac{1}{4}x$

55. $x^2 + y^2 = 8$
$y = 2$

56. $x^2 + y^2 = 20$
$y = -\frac{1}{2}x + 5$

57. $(x + 1)^2 + (y - 1)^2 = 18$
$y = x + 8$

58. $(x - 2)^2 + (y - 2)^2 = 10$
$y = -\frac{1}{3}x + 6$

 Graphing Calculator Use a graphing calculator to convince yourself that the given line is not tangent to the circle $x^2 + y^2 = 25$. Explain what you did.

59. $y = -5x + 26$

60. $3x + 5y = 29$ **59–60. See margin.**

 61. Writing Explain why it is not possible to conclude that a line and a circle are tangent by viewing their graphs. **See margin.**

 Challenge

62. Lines $y = \frac{2}{3}x + 3$ and $y = 5$ cut the ring formed by circles $(x - 3)^2 + (y - 5)^2 = 64$ and $(x - 3)^2 + (y - 5)^2 = 25$ into four parts. Find the area of each part.
about 11.5, 11.5, 49.8, 49.8

63. Nautical Distance The radius of Earth's equator is about 3960 miles. **See margin.**
a. Write the equation of the equator with the center of Earth as the origin.
b. Find the length of a 1° arc on the equator to the nearest tenth of a mile. **69.1 mi**
c. A 1° arc along the equator is 60 nautical miles long. How many miles are in a nautical mile? Round to the nearest tenth. **1.2 mi**
d. History Columbus planned his trip to the East by going west. He thought each 1° arc was 45 miles long. He estimated that the trip would take 21 days. Use your answer to part (b) to find a better estimate. **about 32 days**

64. Geometry in 3 Dimensions The equation of a sphere is similar to the equation of a circle. The equation of a sphere with center (h, j, k) and radius r is
$(x - h)^2 + (y - j)^2 + (z - k)^2 = r^2$.
a. $M(-1, 3, 2)$ is the center of a sphere passing through $T(0, 5, 1)$. What is the radius of the sphere? $\sqrt{6}$
b. Write an equation of the sphere.
$(x + 1)^2 + (y - 3)^2 + (z - 2)^2 = 6$

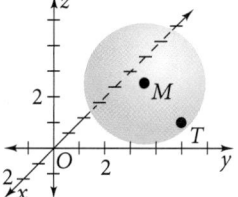

Real-World Connection
In 2001, Ellen MacArthur, age 24, sailed solo around the world in 94.2 days.

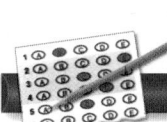
Standardized Test Prep

Multiple Choice

65. What is an equation of a circle with radius 16 and center $(2, -5)$? **D**
A. $(x - 2)^2 + (y + 5)^2 = 16$
B. $(x + 2)^2 + (y - 5)^2 = 256$
C. $(x + 2)^2 + (y - 5)^2 = 4$
D. $(x - 2)^2 + (y + 5)^2 = 256$

66. What are the coordinates of the center of the circle whose equation is $(x - 9)^2 + (y + 4)^2 = 1$? **I**
F. $(3, -2)$
G. $(-3, 2)$
H. $(-9, 4)$
I. $(9, -4)$

Take It to the NET
Online lesson quiz at
www.PHSchool.com
Web Code: afa-1105

67. What is the diameter of the circle with equation $(x - 1)^2 + (y + 1)^2 = 4$? **C**
A. 1
B. 2
C. 4
D. 16

Lesson 11-5 Circles in the Coordinate Plane **619**

pages 617–620 **Exercises**

59–60. Explanations may vary. Sample: Solve the circle and line eqs. for y, enter in the calc., and use the zooming feature.

61. Answers may vary. Sample: Lines can appear tangent on a graph, but may not be.

63. a. $x^2 + y^2 = 15,681,600$

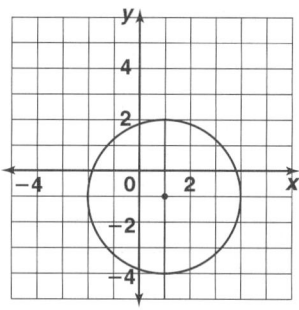
Lesson Quiz 11-5

1. Find the center and radius of the circle with equation $(x - 1)^2 + (y + 1)^2 = 9$. Then graph the circle.

$(1, -1); r = 3$

2. A cellular phone tower with a range of 25 units is located on a coordinate grid at $(10, 35)$. Write an equation that describes its position and range.
$(x - 10)^2 + (y - 35)^2 = 625$

Write the standard equation of each circle.

3. center $(0, -6)$; radius $\sqrt{11}$
$x^2 + (y + 6)^2 = 11$

4. center $(3, 2)$; diameter 18
$(x - 3)^2 + (y - 2)^2 = 81$

5. center $(-9, 5)$; passing through $(-7, 1)$
$(x + 9)^2 + (y - 5)^2 = 20$

Alternative Assessment

Have students graph a circle that contains a diameter with endpoints $(-2, -3)$ and $(4, 5)$ and then write the standard equation of the circle. Have them explain how this can be done using a compass and the standard form of an equation of a circle.

Exercise 69 Remind students that they may need to apply theorems they learned early in the course. To write the equation of the circle, students need to remember that a tangent is perpendicular to the radius at the point of tangency and that the product of the slopes of perpendicular lines is −1.

✓ **Chapter Checkpoint 2**

To check understanding of Lessons 11-4 to 11-5:

Checkpoint Quiz 2 (p. 620)

📁 **Teaching Resources**
Checkpoint Quiz 2 (also in Prentice Hall Assessment System)

👥 **Reaching All Students**
Reading and Math Literacy 11C

Spanish versions available

---

pages 617–620 Exercises

68. **[2]** This equation is in the standard form of an equation of a circle. This means that $r^2 = 25$. Taking the sq. root of each side, $r = 5$. Thus, the radius is 5.

   [1] incorrect answer OR incorrect explanation

69. **[4]** The slope of the radius through (6, 3) is $\frac{3}{4}$, so the line containing this radius is $y = \frac{3}{4}x - \frac{3}{2}$. Since $y = 0$, $x = 2$, and the center is (2, 0), $r = \sqrt{(2-6)^2 + (0-3)^2} = 5$. $(x-2)^2 + y^2 = 25$

   [3] appropriate methods, but with one computational error

Short Response

68. Show how to find the radius of the circle whose equation is $x^2 + (y + 8)^2 = 25$. **See margin.**

Extended Response

69. The line represented by the equation $y = -\frac{4}{3}x + 11$ is tangent to a circle at (6, 3). The center of the circle is on the *x*-axis. Write an equation of the circle. Show your work. **See margin.**

Mixed Review

Lesson 11-4 Find the value of each variable. Assume that lines that appear tangent are tangent.

70.

71. **38**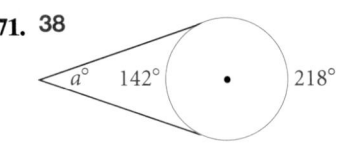

$x = 25; y = 75$

Lesson 9-4 For the given vectors $\vec{a}$ and $\vec{c}$, write the sum $\vec{a} + \vec{c}$ as an ordered pair.

72. $\vec{a} = \langle -2, 5 \rangle$ and $\vec{c} = \langle 8, 7 \rangle$ $\langle 6, 12 \rangle$

73. $\vec{a} = \langle -3, -4 \rangle$ and $\vec{c} = \langle -2, 6 \rangle$ $\langle -5, 2 \rangle$

74. $\vec{a} = \langle 3, 1 \rangle$ and $\vec{c} = \langle 1, 3 \rangle$ $\langle 4, 4 \rangle$

75. $\vec{a} = \langle 9, -6 \rangle$ and $\vec{c} = \langle 2, -1 \rangle$ $\langle 11, -7 \rangle$

Lesson 8-4 Find the geometric mean of each pair of numbers in simplest radical form.

76. 3 and 12 **6**

77. 9 and 27 $9\sqrt{3}$

78. 4 and 18 $6\sqrt{2}$

79. $\sqrt{3}$ and $\sqrt{27}$ **3**

80. $\sqrt{3}$ and $\sqrt{12}$ $\sqrt{6}$

81. $\frac{3}{8}$ and $\frac{3}{2}$ $\frac{3}{4}$

✓ Checkpoint Quiz 2   Lessons 11-4 through 11-5

🔲 **iTEXT** Instant self-check quiz online and on CD-ROM

Find the value of each variable. Assume that lines that appear tangent are tangent.

1. **58**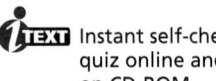

2.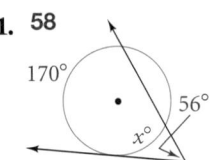
   226

3.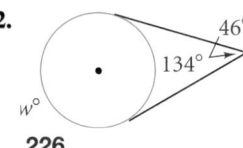
   30

4.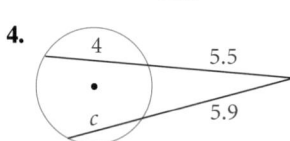
   about 3.0

5.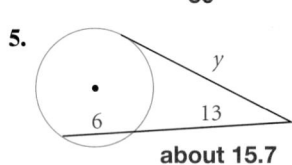
   about 15.7

6. In the circle at the right, what is $m\overset{\frown}{BF}$? **40**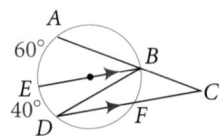

✏️ 7. **Writing** Explain the difference between a chord and a secant. Include a diagram. **See margin.**

The endpoints of a diameter are given. Write an equation of the circle.
8–10. See left.

8. (3, 1) and (0, 0)

9. (−2, 5) and (9, −3)

10. (−4, −8) and (1, 0)

8. $(x - 1.5)^2 + (y - 0.5)^2 = 2.5$

9. $(x - 3.5)^2 + (y - 1)^2 = 46.25$

10. $(x + 1.5)^2 + (y + 4)^2 = 22.25$

620 Chapter 11 Circles

---

[2] incorrect equation OR correct equation found incorrectly

[1] correct equation, without work shown

page 620 Checkpoint Quiz 2

7. A chord is a segment whose endpoints are on the circle. A secant is a line, ray, or segment that intersects a circle at two points.

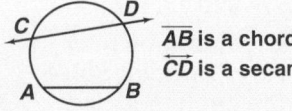

$\overline{AB}$ is a chord
$\overleftrightarrow{CD}$ is a secant

11-6

Locus: A Set of Points

North Carolina Objectives

2.02 Apply properties, definitions, and theorems of angles and lines to solve problems and write proofs.

1. Plan

Lesson Preview

What You'll Learn

OBJECTIVE 1 To draw and describe a locus

. . . And Why

To interpret a locus description of a geometric figure, as in Example 3

✔ **Check Skills You'll Need**

(For help, go to Lessons 1-5 and 3-7.)

Sketch each of the following. 1–3. See back of book.

1. the perpendicular bisector of $\overline{CD}$

2. $\angle EFG$ bisected by $\overrightarrow{FH}$

3. line k parallel to line m and perpendicular to line w, all in plane N

New Vocabulary • locus

Lesson Preview

✔ **Check Skills You'll Need**

Constructing Parallel and Perpendicular Lines
Lesson 3-7: Examples 1, 4
Exercises 1–4, 10–13
Extra Practice, p. 692

Constructing the Angle Bisector
Lesson 1-5: Example 5
Exercises 13, 14
Extra Practice, p. 690

Lesson Resources

📁 **Teaching Resources**
Practice, Reteaching, Enrichment

👥 **Reaching All Students**
Practice Workbook 11-6
Spanish Practice Workbook 11-6
Informal Geometry Planning Guide 11-6

⏱ **Presentation Assistant Plus!**
Transparencies
• Check Skills You'll Need 11-6
• Additional Examples 11-6
• Student Edition Answers 11-6
• Lesson Quiz 11-6
PH Presentation Pro CD 11-6

ASSESSMENT SYSTEM
Computer Test Generator CD

💿 **Technology**
Resource Pro® CD-ROM
Computer Test Generator CD
Prentice Hall Presentation Pro CD

💻 **www.PHSchool.com**
Student Site
• Teacher Web Code: afk-5500
• Self-grading Lesson Quiz
Teacher Center
• Lesson Planner
• Resources

Plus

OBJECTIVE

1 ▼ **Drawing and Describing a Locus**

iTEXT Interactive lesson includes instant self-check, tutorials, and activities.

A **locus** is a set of points, all of which meet a stated condition. To sketch a locus, draw points of the locus until you see a pattern.

1 EXAMPLE Describing a Locus in a Plane

a. Draw and describe the locus: In a plane, the points 1 cm from a given point C.

Draw a point C.
Sketch several points 1 cm from C.
Keep doing so until you see a pattern.
Draw the figure the pattern suggests.

The locus is a circle with center C and radius 1 cm.

b. Draw and describe the locus: In a plane, the points 1 cm from a segment $\overline{AB}$.

The locus is
• two segments parallel to $\overline{AB}$ and
• two semicircles centered at A and B

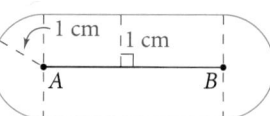

Real-World 🌐 Connection

The locus of footprints of children pushing the merry-go-round is a circle.

✔ **Check Understanding**

1 Draw and describe the locus: In a plane, the points 2 cm from a line $\overleftrightarrow{XY}$. See left.

1.Two lines ∥ to $\overleftrightarrow{XY}$, each 2 cm from $\overleftrightarrow{XY}$.

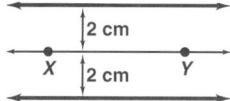

You can use locus descriptions for geometric terms.

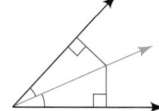

An angle bisector: The points in the interior of the angle that are equidistant from the sides of the angle.

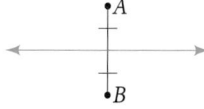

A perpendicular bisector of a segment: In a plane, the points that are equidistant from the segment endpoints.

Ongoing Assessment and Intervention

Before the Lesson
Diagnose prerequisite skills using:
• Check Skills You'll Need

During the Lesson
Monitor progress using:
• Check Understanding
• Additional Examples
• Standardized Test Prep

After the Lesson
Assess knowledge using:
• Lesson Quiz
• Computer Test Generator CD

2. Teach

Math Background

A locus is the set of all the points, and only those points, that satisfy a stated condition. The word *locus* signals that the characterization of a set will follow.

OBJECTIVE

1 Teaching Notes

3 EXAMPLE Math Tip

Have students compare these space loci with the analogous plane loci in Example 1.

Additional Examples

For Exercises 1–3, check students' drawings.

1 Draw and describe the locus: In a plane, the points 3 cm from ⊙C with radius 3 cm. **center *C* and a concentric circle with radius 6 cm**

2 Point *P* is 10 in. from point *Q*. Draw and describe the locus: In a plane, the points 6 in. from point *P* and 8 in. from point *Q*. **intersection of ⊙*P* with radius 6 in. and ⊙*Q* with radius 8 in.**

3 Describe the locus: In space, the points 4 cm from a plane *M*. **two distinct planes, each 4 cm from and parallel to plane *M***

Closure

Point *A* lies on line ℓ in plane *P*. Draw and describe the locus: In a plane, the points 5 cm from point *A*
• on line ℓ.
• in plane *P*.
• in space.
Check students' drawings; two collinear points 5 cm each side of *A*; circle of radius 5 cm with center *A*; sphere of radius 5 cm with center *A*.

622

Reading Math

The word "locus" comes from the Latin word for "location." Its plural is *loci* (LOH sy).

2.

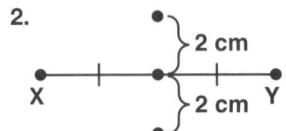

✓ **Check Understanding** **2** Draw the locus: In a plane, the points equidistant from two points *X* and *Y* and 2 cm from the midpoint of $\overline{XY}$. **See left.**

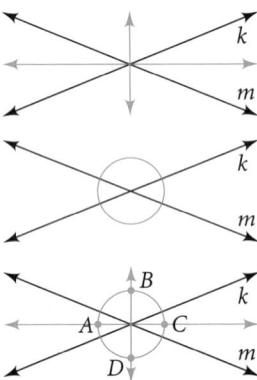

Real-World Connection

A soap bubble is a sphere, a locus of points in space that are a given distance from a given point.

✓ **Check Understanding**

Sometimes a locus is described by two conditions. You can draw the locus by first drawing the points that satisfy each condition. Then find their intersection.

2 EXAMPLE Drawing a Locus for Two Conditions

Draw the locus: In a plane, the points equidistant from two lines *k* and *m* and 5 cm from the point where *k* and *m* intersect.

The points in a plane equidistant from lines *k* and *m* are two lines that bisect the vertical angles formed by *k* and *m*.

The points in a plane 5 cm from the point where *k* and *m* intersect is a circle.

The locus that satisfies both conditions is the set of points *A*, *B*, *C*, and *D*.

A locus in a plane and a locus in space can be quite different.

3 EXAMPLE Describing a Locus in Space

a. Draw and describe the locus: In space, the points that are *c* units from a point *D*.

The locus is a sphere with center at point *D* and radius *c*.

b. Draw and describe the locus: In space, the points that are 3 cm from a line ℓ.

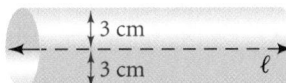

The locus is an endless cylinder with radius 3 cm and center-line ℓ.

3 Draw and describe each locus. **a–b. See back of book.**
a. In a plane, the points that are equidistant from two parallel lines.
b. In space, the points that are equidistant from two parallel planes.

You can also think of a locus as a path. For example, the locus of the tip of a hand of a clock each day is the circle traced by the tip as it travels around the clock face. The locus of a point on the handle of a sliding-glass door when you enter a room is the line segment along which the point travels as the door slides back and forth.

Reaching All Students

| **Below Level** Students should have compasses and rulers available as they work through Examples 1 and 2. | **Advanced Learners** After students complete Example 3, have them draw and describe the set of points in space that are equidistant from each of the points on ⊙*O*. | **Error Prevention** See note on page 623. |

EXERCISES

Practice and Problem Solving

For more practice, see *Extra Practice*.

A **Practice by Example**

Example 1
(page 621)

Draw and describe each locus in a plane. 1–8. See back of book.

1. points 4 cm from a point X

2. points 2 in. from a segment $\overline{UV}$

3. points 3 mm from a line $\overleftrightarrow{LM}$

4. points 1 in. from a circle with radius 3 in.

5. points equidistant from the endpoints of $\overline{PQ}$

6. points in the interior of $\angle ABC$ and equidistant from the sides of $\angle ABC$

7. points equidistant from two perpendicular lines

8. midpoints of radii of a circle with radius 2 cm

Example 2
(page 622)

In a plane, draw the locus whose points satisfy the given conditions.

9. equidistant from points M and N and on a circle with center M and radius $= \frac{1}{2}MN$ **See left.**

10. 3 cm from $\overline{GH}$ and 5 cm from G, where $GH = 4.5$ cm

10–13. See back of book.

11. equidistant from the sides of $\angle PQR$ and on a circle with center P and radius PQ

9. the single pt. L

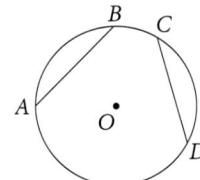
M   L   N

12. equidistant from both points A and B and points C and D

13. equidistant from the sides of $\angle JKL$ and on $\odot C$

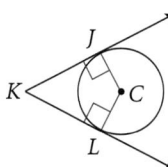

Example 3
(page 622)

Draw and describe each locus in space. 14–17. See back of book.

14. points 3 cm from a point F

15. points 4 cm from a line $\overleftrightarrow{DE}$

16. points 1 in. from plane M

17. points 5 mm from $\overrightarrow{PQ}$

B **Apply Your Skills**

Describe the locus that each blue figure represents. 18–20. See margin.

18.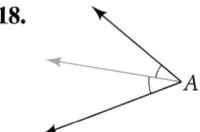

19.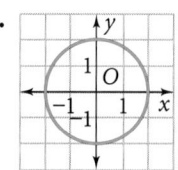

20.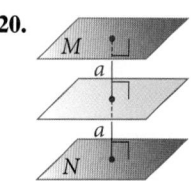

21. Open-Ended Give two examples of loci from everyday life, one in a plane and one in space. **Check students' work.**

22. Reasoning Rosie says that it is impossible to find a point equidistant from three collinear points. Is she correct? Explain. **See margin.**

Real-World 🌐 **Connection**

A fingertip of the skater traces a locus as she twirls.

Coordinate Geometry Write an equation for the locus: In the plane, the points equidistant from the two given points.

23. $A(0, 2)$ and $B(2, 0)$
$y = x$

24. $P(1, 3)$ and $Q(5, 1)$
$y = 2x - 4$

25. $T(2, -3)$ and $V(6, 1)$
$y = -x + 3$

Lesson 11-6   Locus: A Set of Points   **623**

---

pages 623–625   Exercises

18. the set of all points on the bisector of $\angle A$

19. the set of all points 2 units from the origin

20. the set of all points a units from planes M and N

22. Yes; if the collinear pts. are A, B, and C, then the locus of pts. equidist. from A and B is a plane M, $\perp$ to AB at its midpt.

Similarly, pts. equidist. from B and C are on plane N, $\perp$ at the midpt. of BC. But $M \parallel N$.

Assignment Guide

1 **Objective**
A **B** Core 1–44
C Extension 45–50

Standardized Test Prep 51–53

Mixed Review 54–61

Exercises 1–13 Suggest that students use compass and straightedge when appropriate.

Teaching Tip

Exercises 14–17 Have students compare each locus with the locus in a plane that meets the stated conditions.

Error Prevention

Exercise 17 Students who correctly describe the cylinder may overlook the points 5 mm from the endpoint P. Remind them to consider point P separately to help them see that part of the locus is a hemisphere.

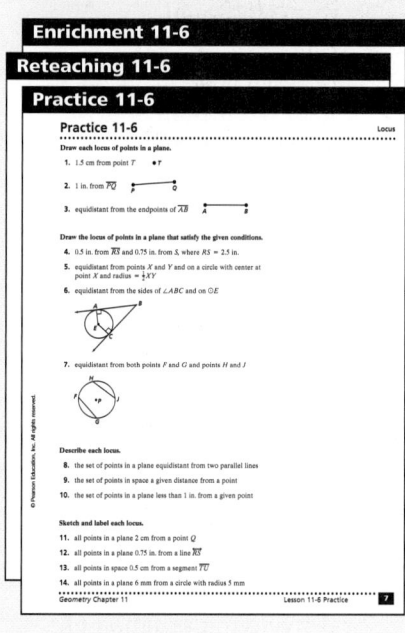

Lesson Quiz 11-6

In Exercises 1–3 draw and describe each locus in a plane.

1. 2 cm from ⊙*O* with radius 4 cm

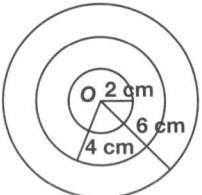

two concentric circles with radii 2 cm and 6 cm

2. equidistant from the vertices of rectangle *ABCD*

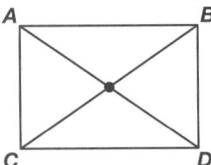

point of intersection of the diagonals of *ABCD*

3. 3 cm from line *m* and 4 cm from point *P*, where *P* is 6 cm from line *m*

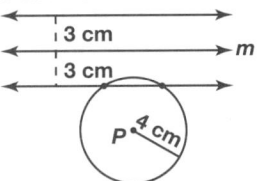

two points where ⊙*P* with radius 4 cm intersects a line parallel to and 3 cm from line *m*

4. Draw and describe the locus: In space, the points 10 in. from a segment 30 in. long.

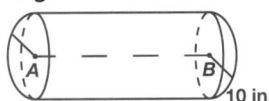

the lateral surface of a cylinder of radius 10 in. and two hemispheres of radius 10 in. with centers at the segment's endpoints

5. Describe the locus of points satisfying the equation of a circle $(x - 2)^2 + (y + 8)^2 = 25$.

the set of points in a coordinate plane 5 units from the point $(2, -8)$

26. Coordinate Geometry Complete the following locus description of the points highlighted in blue at the right: in the coordinate plane, the points 2 units from the __?__ and 1 unit from the __?__-axis. **origin; x**

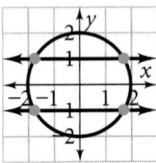

Make a drawing of each locus. 27–30. See margin.

27. the path of a doorknob as a door opens

28. the path of a knot in the middle of a jump rope as it is being used

29. the path of the tip of your nose as you turn your head

30. the path of a fast-pitched softball

31. Draw a circle with center downtown and radius 3 mi. Connect Jack's and Julie's offices with a segment and construct the ⊥ bis. Locations will lie on the ⊥ bis. and on or inside the circle.

32. yes; 2 points

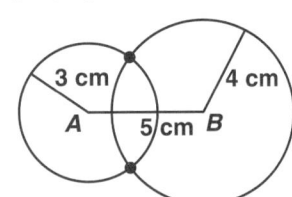

31. Jack and Julie Wilson take new jobs in Shrevetown and need a place to live. Jack says, "Let's try to move somewhere equidistant from both of our offices." Julie says, "Let's try to stay within three miles of downtown." Where on the map should the Wilsons look for a home? **See left.**

32. Critical Thinking Points *A* and *B* are 5 cm apart. Do the following loci in a plane have any points in common?

the points 3 cm from *A*

the points 4 cm from *B*

Illustrate with a sketch. **See left.**

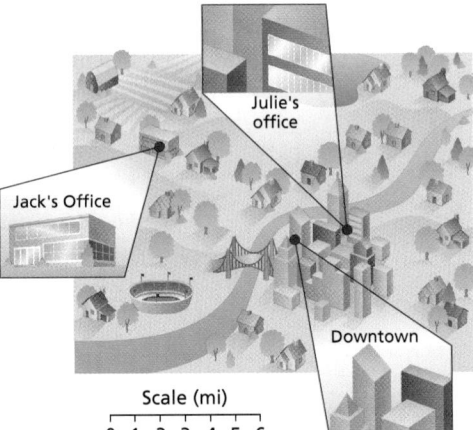

Julie's office

Jack's Office

Downtown

Scale (mi)

0 1 2 3 4 5 6

33–40. See back of book.

Coordinate Geometry Draw each locus on the coordinate plane.

33. all points 3 units from the origin

34. all points 2 units from $(-1, 3)$

35. all points 4 units from the *y*-axis

36. all points 5 units from $x = 2$

37. all points equidistant from $y = 3$ and $y = -1$

38. all points equidistant from $x = 4$ and $x = 5$

39. all points equidistant from the *x*- and *y*-axes

40. all points equidistant from $x = 3$ and $y = 2$

Spinning cup   Axis

🌐 **Meteorology** **In an anemometer, there are three cups mounted on an axis. Imagine a point on the edge of one of the cups.**

41. Describe the locus that this point traces as the cup spins in the wind. **a circle**

42. Suppose the distance of the point from the axis of the anemometer is 2 in. Write an equation for the locus of part (a). Use the axis as the origin. $x^2 + y^2 = 4$

43. Robert draws a segment to use as the base of an isosceles triangle.
  a. Draw a segment to represent Robert's base. Locate three points that could be the vertex of the isosceles triangle. **a–c. See margin p. 625.**
  b. Describe the locus of possible vertices for Robert's isosceles triangle.
  ✏ **c. Writing** Explain why points in the locus you described are the only possibilities for the vertex of Robert's triangle.

Real-World 🌐 **Connection**

An anemometer measures wind speed.

624 Chapter 11 Circles

pages 623–625 **Exercises**

27.

28.

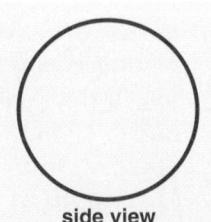

top view   side view

29.

top view

30.

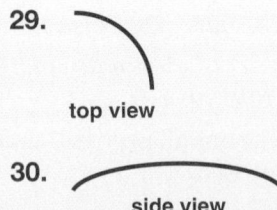

side view

44. Describe the locus: The points in space equidistant from the points of a circle. **See left.**

44. a line through the center of the circle, ⊥ to the plane of the circle

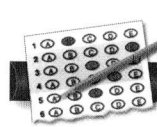 **Challenge** 🌐 **Playground Equipment** **Think about the path of a child on each piece of playground equipment. Draw the path from (a) a top view, (b) a front view, and (c) a side view. 45–49. See margin.**

45. a swing   **46.** a straight slide   **47.** a corkscrew slide

48. a merry-go-round   **49.** a firefighters' pole

50. In the diagram, three students are seated at uniform distances around a circular table. Copy the diagram. Shade the points on the table that are closer to Moesha than to Jan or Leandra. **See margin.**

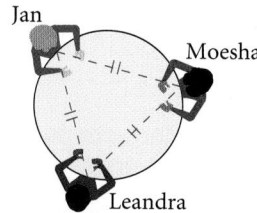

Standardized Test Prep

Multiple Choice

53. [2] no

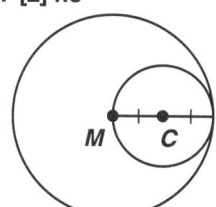

Take It to the NET
Online lesson quiz at
www.PHSchool.com
Web Code: afa-1106
Short Response

51. Which graph shows the locus: The points in a plane 1 unit from the intersection of the lines $x + y = 2$ and $x - y = 4$? **B**

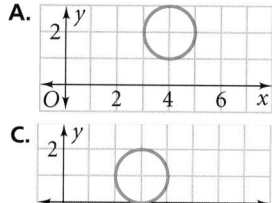

52. Which equation describes the locus: The points in the coordinate plane that are 5 units from the y-axis? **G**

F. $|y| = 5$ **G.** $|x| = 5$ **H.** $x + y = 5$ **I.** $x^2 + y^2 = 25$

53. Margie's cordless telephone can transmit up to 0.5 mile from her home. Carol's cordless telephone can transmit up to 0.25 mile from her home. Carol and Margie live 0.25 mile from each other. Can Carol's telephone work in a region that Margie's cannot? Sketch and label a diagram. **[2] See left. [1] incorrect answer OR incorrect diagram.**

Mixed Review

Lesson 11-5

Write an equation of the circle with center C and radius r. 54–56. See left.

54. $C(6, -10), r = 5$ **55.** $C(1, 7), r = 6$ **56.** $C(-8, 1), r = \sqrt{13}$

54. $(x - 6)^2 + (y + 10)^2 = 25$
55. $(x - 1)^2 + (y - 7)^2 = 36$
56. $(x + 8)^2 + (y - 1)^2 = 13$

Lesson 10-3

Find the surface area of each figure to the nearest tenth.

57.
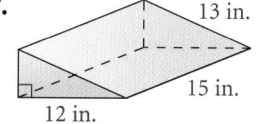
13 in.
15 in.
12 in.
510 in.²

58.
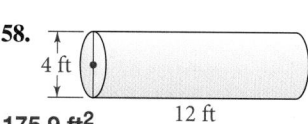
4 ft
12 ft
175.9 ft²

Lesson 7-7

In ⊙O, find the area of sector AOB. Leave your answer in terms of π.

59. $OA = 4, m\widehat{AB} = 90$ **60.** $OA = 8, m\widehat{AB} = 72$ **61.** $OA = 10, m\widehat{AB} = 36$
4π $\dfrac{64\pi}{5}$ 10π

43. a.
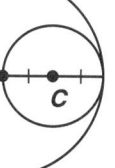
Base

b. ⊥ bis. of the base, except the pt. on the base

c. The vertex must be equidist. from the endpoints of the base. These points lie only on the ⊥ bis.

45.

side view   front view
top view

Alternative Assessment

Have each student write a locus problem with a condition that must be met in a plane and another with a condition that must be met in space, draw the loci, and describe the loci in writing. Then have students exchange problems with partners, solve the problems, and compare their solutions.

Standardized Test Prep

Resources
For additional practice with a variety of test item formats:
• Standardized Test Prep, p. 631
• Test-Taking Strategies, p. 626
• Test-Taking Strategies with Transparencies

Exercise 52 Remind students that the equation that describes the y-axis is $x = 0$, not $y = 0$.

46.
front | top
side

47.
top view ○
side view   front view

48.
side view   front view
○ top view

49.
front | side
• top

50.
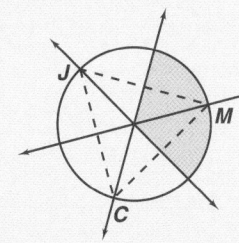

625

Using Estimation

This feature helps students understand how to use estimation on assessment tests to eliminate incorrect choices, to choose correct answer choices, and to write short-response or extended-response answers.

Resources

PRENTICE HALL
ASSESSMENT *SYSTEM*

Test-Taking Strategies with Transparencies
• Transparency 11
• Practice sheet p. 22

Teaching Notes

Point out that part of the estimation process in finding the answer to the example was assigning a value of 1 to the radius of the smaller circle. Discuss how the arbitrary choice of 1 simplified the calculations.

Technology Tip

Point out that good estimation skills go hand-in-hand with calculator use. Students should always compare answers found using a calculator with a mental estimate to check their calculator work.

Test-Taking Strategies with Transparencies

Test-Taking Strategy: Using Estimation

Sometimes you can estimate to find the answer.

Example Shannon used a calculator to find 7.95 × 13. Which is a reasonable number to see in the calculator display?

A. 1.0335   B. 10.335   C. 103.35   D. 1033.5

Estimate: Round to the nearest whole number.

7.95 × 13

8 × 13 = 104

Only C is near 104.

The answer is 103.35, or choice C.

Estimate to find the answer.

1. A pair of shoes is on sale for 33% off the original price of $47.99. About how much will the shoes cost on sale?

   A. $64   B. $48   C. $32   D. $16

2. The circumference of a circle with radius 5 in. is about

   F. 29 in.   G. 31 in.   H. 33 in.   I. 35 in.

3. Estimate the value of $2x^2 + 5$ when $x = 4.1$.

   A. 69   B. 37   C. 23   D. 21

Solutions

1. C
2. G
3. B

Transparency 11

626

Estimation may help you find answers, check an answer, or eliminate one or more answer choices. Here are some decimal approximations that can be helpful. The symbol ≈ means "is approximately equal to."

$$\pi \approx 3 \qquad \frac{1}{\pi} \approx \frac{1}{3} \approx 0.3 \qquad \sqrt{2} \approx 1.4 \qquad \sqrt{3} \approx 1.7$$

EXAMPLE

Two circles have the same center O. The radius of the larger circle is twice the radius of the smaller circle, and chord $\overline{DB}$ is tangent to the smaller circle at C. Which of the following is the greatest?

A. DB
B. OA
C. length of $\overparen{XCY}$
D. length of $\overparen{AB}$

Let $OY = 1$ and $YA = 1$. Therefore $OA = 2$.

The length of $\overparen{XCY}$ is one-half the circumference of the small circle.
The length of $\overparen{XCY} = \frac{1}{2}(2\pi r) = \pi \approx 3$. Thus, choice C is greater than choice B.

Draw $\overline{OC}$. $\triangle ODC$ has a right angle at C with $OD = 2$ and $OC = 1$.
By the Pythagorean Theorem, $DC = \sqrt{3}$. Therefore $DB = 2\sqrt{3} \approx 2(1.7) = 3.4$.
So, choice A is greater than choice C.

$\triangle OCD$ is a 30°-60°-90° triangle, so $m\overparen{AB} = 60$.

Thus, the length of $\overparen{AB}$ is $\frac{1}{6}$ the circumference of the larger circle.
The length of $\overparen{AB} = \frac{1}{6}(2\pi r) = \frac{1}{6}(4\pi) = \frac{2}{3}\pi \approx 2$, which is less than DB (choice A).

● Therefore the greatest quantity is DB. The correct answer is A.

EXERCISES

1a–e. Answers may vary. Samples are given.

1. Use the approximations above to estimate the value of each number.
   a. 2π **6**   b. $\frac{\pi}{2}$ **1.5**   c. $\frac{1}{\sqrt{2}}$ **0.7**   d. $\frac{1}{\sqrt{3}}$ **0.6**   e. $\sqrt{8}$ **2.8**

2. Which number is greatest? (*Hint:* Use estimation.) **C**
   A. π B. $2\sqrt{3}$ C. $3\sqrt{2}$ D. $\sqrt{3} + \sqrt{2}$

3. A student used a calculator to find the value of $\sqrt{8} + \sqrt{15}$ and got 4.796. Use estimation to explain why this answer is incorrect. $\sqrt{8} + \sqrt{15} \approx \sqrt{9} + \sqrt{16} = 3 + 4 = 7$

4. Which is the best estimate for sin A? **A**
   A. 0.32   B. 0.42   C. 0.52   D. 0.62

5. Which is the best estimate for tan A? **C**
   A. 0.14   B. 0.24   C. 0.34   D. 0.44

6. Use properties of special triangles to estimate the measures of $\angle X$ and $\angle Y$ in $\triangle XYZ$. $m\angle X \approx 30, m\angle Y \approx 60$

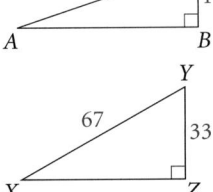

Chapter Review

Vocabulary

chord (p. 590)
circumscribed about (p. 585)
inscribed angle (p. 598)
inscribed in (p. 585)

intercepted arc (p. 598)
locus (p. 621)
point of tangency (p. 582)
secant (p. 607)

standard form of an equation of a circle (p. 615)
tangent to a circle (p. 582)

Reading Math
Understanding Vocabulary

Take It to the NET
Online vocabulary quiz at **www.PHSchool.com**
Web Code: afj-1151

Use the figure to choose the correct term to complete each sentence.

1. $\overline{CB}$ is (*a secant of, tangent to*) $\odot X$. **tangent to**

2. $\overline{DF}$ is a (*chord, locus*) of $\odot X$. **chord**

3. $\triangle DEF$ is (*inscribed in, circumscribed about*) $\odot X$.
   inscribed in

4. $\angle DEF$ is an (*intercepted arc, inscribed angle*) of $\odot X$. **inscribed angle**

5. The set of "all points equidistant from the endpoints of $\overline{CB}$" is a (*locus, tangent*). **locus**

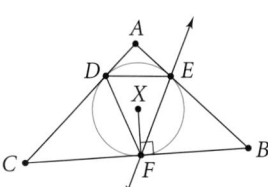

Skills and Concepts

11-1 Objectives

▼ To use the relationship between a radius and a tangent

▼ To use the relationship between two tangents from one point

A **tangent to a circle** is a line, ray, or segment in the plane of the circle that intersects the circle in exactly one point, the **point of tangency**. Two segments tangent to a circle from a point outside the circle are congruent. If a line is tangent to a circle, then the line is perpendicular to the radius drawn to the point of tangency. The converse is also true.

Tangent
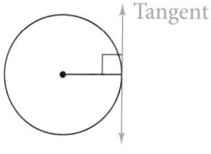

A triangle is **inscribed in** a circle if all of the vertices lie on the circle. When a triangle is **circumscribed about** a circle, each side is tangent to the circle.

Each polygon circumscribes a circle. Find the perimeter of the polygon.

6.
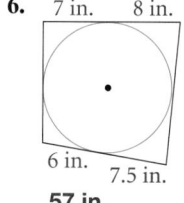
7 in.   8 in.
6 in.   7.5 in.
57 in.

7.
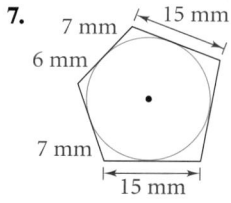
7 mm   15 mm
6 mm
7 mm
15 mm
72 mm

8.
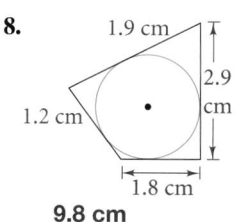
1.9 cm
2.9 cm
1.2 cm
1.8 cm
9.8 cm

11-2 Objectives

▼ To use congruent chords, arcs, and central angles

▼ To recognize properties of lines through the center of a circle

Segments with endpoints on a circle are called **chords**. Within a circle or in congruent circles,

• congruent central angles have congruent chords.

• congruent chords have congruent arcs.

• congruent arcs have congruent central angles.

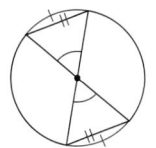

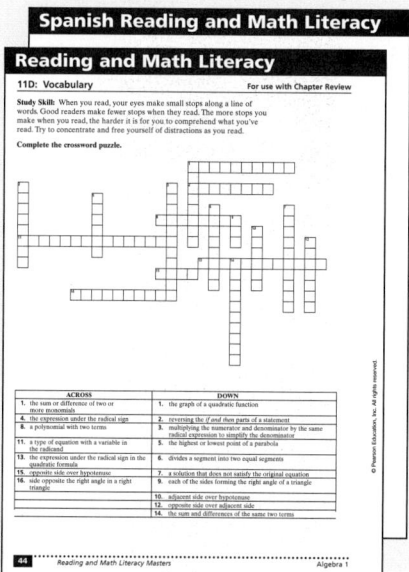

- chords equidistant from the center are congruent.
- congruent chords are equidistant from the center.

A diameter that is perpendicular to a chord bisects the chord and its arcs. A diameter that bisects a chord that is not a diameter is perpendicular to the chord. The perpendicular bisector of a chord contains the center of the circle.

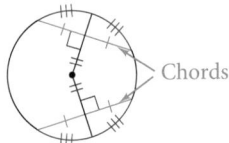

Chords

Find the value of x to the nearest tenth.

9.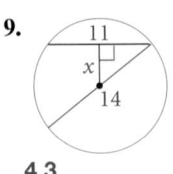
11
x
14

4.3

10.
12
7
x

19.5

11. 45°
x
9

6.4

12.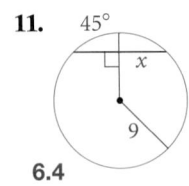
9
5
x
5

4.5

11-3 Objectives

▼ To find the measure of an inscribed angle

▼ To find the measure of an angle formed by a tangent and a chord

An angle is an **inscribed angle** if the vertex is on a circle and sides of the angle are chords of the circle. Its **intercepted arc** is the arc whose endpoints are on the sides of the angle and whose remaining points lie in the interior of the angle.

The measure of an inscribed angle is half the measure of its intercepted arc. The measure of an angle formed by a tangent and a chord that intersect on a circle is half the measure of the intercepted arc.

Two inscribed angles that intercept the same arc are congruent. An angle inscribed in a semicircle is a right angle. The opposite angles of a quadrilateral inscribed in a circle are supplementary.

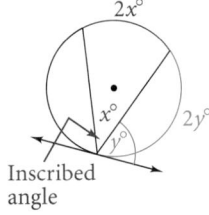

$2x°$
$x°$
$y°$
$2y°$

Inscribed angle

Assume that lines that appear tangent are tangent. Find the value of each variable.

13.
$b°$
$a°$
$20°$
$c°$

$a = 40; b = 140; c = 90$

14.
$c°$
$b°$
$a°$
$59°$ $72°$
$d°$

$a = 118; b = 49;$
$c = 144; d = 98$

15.
$b°$
$a°$
$45°$
$d°$ $c°$
140°

$a = 90; b = 90;$
$c = 70; d = 65$

11-4 Objectives

▼ To find the measures of angles formed by chords, secants, and tangents

▼ To find the lengths of segments associated with circles

A **secant** is a line, ray, or segment that intersects a circle at two points.

The measure of an angle formed by two chords that intersect in a circle is half the sum of the measures of the intercepted arcs.

The measure of an angle formed by two secants, two tangents, or a secant and a tangent drawn from a point outside the circle is half the difference of the measures of the intercepted arcs.

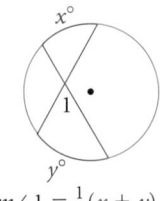

$x°$
1
$y°$

$m\angle 1 = \frac{1}{2}(x + y)$

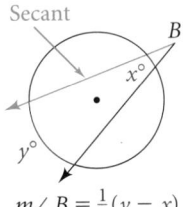

Secant
B
$x°$
$y°$

$m\angle B = \frac{1}{2}(y - x)$

For a given point and circle, the product of the lengths of the two segments from the point to the circle is constant along any line through the point and circle.

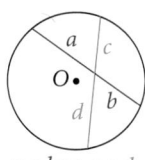

$$a \cdot b = c \cdot d$$

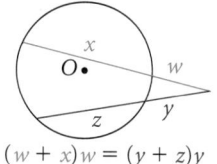

$$(w + x)w = (y + z)y$$

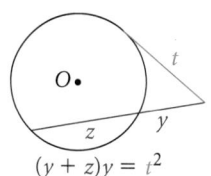

$$(y + z)y = t^2$$

Assume that lines that appear tangent are tangent. Find the value of each variable.

16.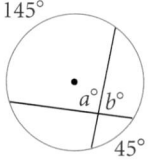

17.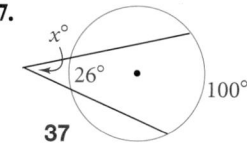

18.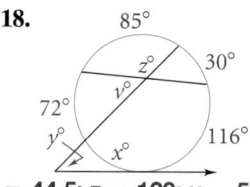

$a = 95; b = 85$

$x = 57; y = 44.5; z = 129; v = 51$

x^2 **Algebra** **Find the value of each variable using the given chords, secants, and tangents. If your answer is not an integer, round to the nearest tenth.**

19.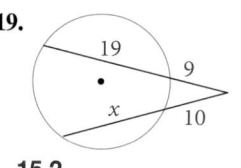

15.2

20.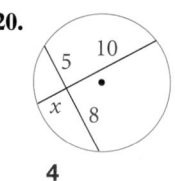

4

21.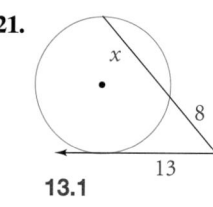

13.1

11-5 and 11-6 Objectives

▼ To write an equation of a circle

▼ To find the center and radius of a circle

▼ To draw and describe a locus

The equation $(x - h)^2 + (y - k)^2 = r^2$ is in **standard form.** You may also call it the *standard equation* of a circle.

If you know the center and a point on a circle, you can write the standard equation of the circle. Use the Distance Formula to find the radius. Then substitute the coordinates of the center for (h, k) and the radius for r in the equation of a circle. If you know the equation of a circle, you can identify the center and radius.

A set of points that meet a stated condition is a **locus.** Sometimes you can describe a figure as a locus.

22–24.

22. $(x - 2)^2 + (y - 5)^2 = 12.25$

23. $(x + 3)^2 + (y - 1)^2 = 5$

24. $(x - 9)^2 + (y + 4)^2 = 16$

25. $x^2 + (y - 1)^2 = 80$

26. $(x + 2)^2 + (y - 3)^2 = 85$

27. $(x - 10)^2 + (y - 7)^2 = 468$

28. center $= (0, 8); r = 7$

29. center $= (5, -9); r = 2\sqrt{10}$

30. center $= (-1, 0); r = 3$

Write the standard equation of the circle with center C and radius r. See left.

22. $C(2, 5); r = 3.5$ **23.** $C(-3, 1); r = \sqrt{5}$ **24.** $C(9, -4); r = 4$

Write the standard equation of the circle with center C passing through point P.

25. $C(0, 1); P(4, 9)$ **26.** $C(-2, 3); P(4, -4)$ **27.** $C(10, 7); P(-8, -5)$

25–27. See left.

Describe the circle with the given equation. 28–30. See left.

28. $x^2 + (y - 8)^2 = 49$ **29.** $(x - 5)^2 + (y + 9)^2 = 40$ **30.** $(x + 1)^2 + y^2 = 9$

Sketch and label each locus. 31–33. See margin.

31. all points in a plane 2 cm from a circle with radius 1 cm

32. all points in a plane equidistant from two points

33. all points in space a distance a from $\overline{DS}$

pages 627–629   **Chapter Review**

31. a circle of radius 3 cm

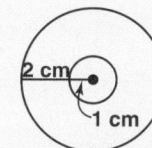

2 cm
1 cm

32. the ⊥ bis. of the segment between the pts.

33. a cylinder with hemispherical ends

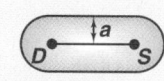

Chapter 11

Chapter Test

Take It to the NET
Online chapter test at
www.PHSchool.com
Web Code: afa-1152

Resources

Teaching Resources
Ch. 11 Test, Forms A & B
Ch. 11 Alternative Assessment, Form C

Reaching All Students
Spanish Ch. 11 Test, Forms A & B
Spanish Ch. 11 Alternative Assessment, Form C
Informal Geometry Ch. 11 Test, Forms D & E

PRENTICE HALL ASSESSMENT SYSTEM

Assessment Masters
• Ch. 11 Test, Forms A & B
• Ch. 11 Alternative Assessment, Form C
Computer Test Generator CD
• Ch. 11 pre-made Test
• Make your own Ch. 11 test

www.PHSchool.com
Student Site
• Self-grading Chapter 11 Test
Teacher Center
• Resources

Plus **iTEXT**

Chapter Test — Form B

Chapter Test — Form A

---

x^2 **Algebra** Assume that lines that appear tangent are tangent. Find the value of x.

1. 94

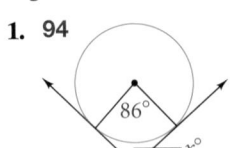

2. 8

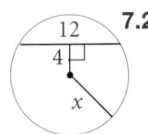

3. a. Open-Ended Draw a circle with two congruent chords that form an inscribed angle. **See margin.**
  b. Constructions Construct the bisector of the inscribed angle. What do you notice? **Answers may vary. Sample: The center lies on the ∠ bisector.**

x^2 **Algebra** Find the value of x. If your answer is not an integer, round to the nearest tenth.

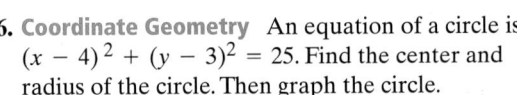

4. 7.2

5. 9.8

6. Coordinate Geometry An equation of a circle is $(x - 4)^2 + (y - 3)^2 = 25$. Find the center and radius of the circle. Then graph the circle. **See back of book.**

Find $m\overset{\frown}{AB}$.

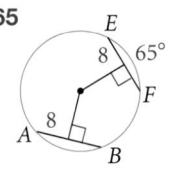

7. 65

8. 120

9. Find the value of z. 60

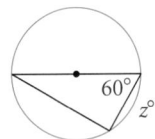

10. Writing What is special about a rhombus inscribed in a circle? Justify your answer. **See margin.**

11. A chord of a circle has length 4.2 cm and is 8 cm from the center of the circle. What is the radius of the circle to the nearest hundredth? **8.27 cm**

Find the center and radius of each circle.

12. $(x + 3)^2 + (y - 2)^2 = 9$
  (−3, 2); 3

13. $x^2 + (y - 9)^2 = 225$
  (0, 9); 15

630 Chapter 11 Chapter Test

---

x^2 **Algebra** For Exercises 14–19, lines that appear tangent are tangent. Find the value of each variable. If your answer is not an integer, round to the nearest tenth.

14. 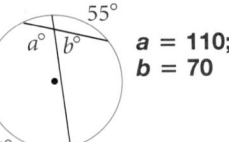 $a = 110; b = 70$

15. 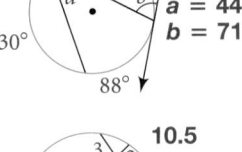 $a = 44; b = 71$

16. 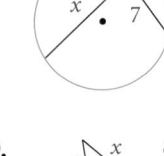 $x = 26; y = 41.5$

17. 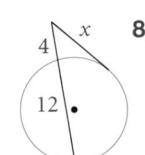 10.5

18. 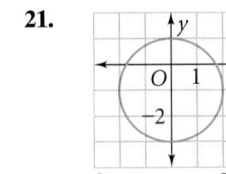 6.5

19. x 8

Write the standard equation of each circle.

20. $(x - 2)^2 + (y - 4)^2 = 4$

21. $x^2 + (y + 1)^2 = 4$

22. Write the equation of the circle with center $(3, 0)$ that passes through point $(-2, -4)$. $(x - 3)^2 + y^2 = 41$

23. Find the circumference and area of the circle whose equation is $(x - 2)^2 + (y - 7)^2 = 81$. Round to the nearest tenth. **56.5 units; 254.5 units²**

24. Write an equation for the locus: Points in the coordinate plane that are 4 units from $(-5, 2)$. $(x + 5)^2 + (y - 2)^2 = 16$

Coordinate Geometry Sketch each locus on a coordinate plane. **25–28. See back of book.**

25. all points 6 units from the origin

26. all points 3 units from the line $y = -2$

27. all points equidistant from points $(2, 4)$ and $(0, 0)$

28. all points equidistant from the axes

---

page 630 Chapter Test

3. a.

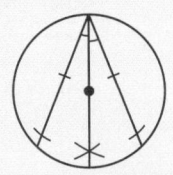

10. It's a square; justifications may vary. Sample: Since opp. ∠ of an inscr. quad. are suppl., and opp. ∠ of a rhombus are ≅, all 4 ∠ are rt. ∠.

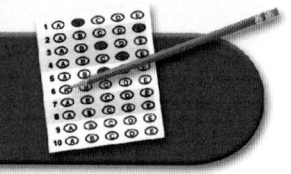

Standardized Test Prep

Reading Comprehension Read the passage below. Then answer the questions on the basis of what is *stated* or *implied* in the passage.

Packaging In the cosmetics section of a department store you can see many unusual and eye-catching geometric shapes. There are star-shaped perfume sprayers, gourd-shaped bath-oil bottles, and hexagonal jars of skin cream. In general, the easiest way to package and ship such items is to use rectangular boxes.

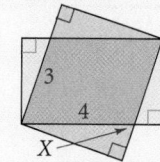

Suppose a bar of soap has a "footprint" that is a parallelogram with sides of lengths 3 and 4. There are two ways to "box" the parallelogram (shown in red and blue at the right) so that the box aligns with one side of the parallelogram and otherwise wastes no space.

The red box has base $4 \cdot \sin X$ and height $3 + 4 \cdot \cos X$. Its area is $4 \cdot \sin X \cdot (3 + 4 \cdot \cos X)$, or $12 \cdot \sin X + 16 \cdot \sin X \cdot \cos X$.

The blue box has base $4 + 3 \cdot \cos X$ and height $3 \cdot \sin X$. Its area is $3 \cdot \sin X \cdot (4 + 3 \cdot \cos X)$, or $12 \cdot \sin X + 9 \cdot \sin X \cdot \cos X$.

Thus the area of the red box is $7 \cdot \sin X \cdot \cos X$ greater than the area of the blue box. This value is greatest when $X = 45$.

It can also be shown that the perimeter of the red box exceeds the perimeter of the blue box by $2 \cdot \sin X + 2 \cdot \cos X - 2$, which is also greatest when $X = 45$.

Clearly the blue box is a better design for packaging the parallelogram.

---

1. Why is it important to design rectangular boxes for packages with unusual shapes? **C**
  A. for easy arrangement on store shelves
  B. to disguise the contents
  C. for easy shipment
  D. so the packages don't rattle around inside

2. In the passage, why is the blue box a better design for packaging the parallelogram? **I**
  F. In the blue box the parallelogram has base 4.
  G. The blue box is horizontal.
  H. The parallelogram fits perfectly inside the blue box.
  I. The blue box requires less package materials.

3. With how many different rectangles can you box an equilateral triangle so that the box contains one side of the triangle and otherwise wastes no space? **A**
  A. 1   **B.** 2   **C.** 3   **D.** infinitely many

With how many different rectangles can you box the given shape so that the box contains at least one side of the shape and otherwise wastes no space? Justify each answer. 4–7. See back of book.

4. a scalene triangle   **5.** a rhombus

6. an isosceles trapezoid   **7.** a regular hexagon

8. Which fact below allows you to express the dimensions of both rectangles in terms of X? **G**
  F. The red and blue triangles are congruent.
  G. Sine equals cosine of the complement.
  H. Vertical angles are congruent.
  I. All right angles are congruent.

9. Explain how you can check that $7 \cdot \sin X \cdot \cos X$ is greatest when $X = 45$. **See margin.**

10. For the boxes above, the red box has the greater perimeter. Show that it exceeds the perimeter of the blue box by $2 \cdot \sin X + 2 \cdot \cos X - 2$. **See margin.**

Students must be able to extract information from reading passages, answer multiple-choice questions, and construct responses in order to be successful on current state and national assessments.

To answer the questions, students apply skills and concepts from this chapter and previous chapters.
Multiple Choice: Items 1–3, 8
Extended Response: Items 4–7, 9, 10

Resources

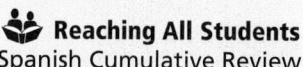 **Teaching Resources**
Cumulative Review

 **Reaching All Students**
Spanish Cumulative Review

 PRENTICE HALL
ASSESSMENT SYSTEM

Standardized Test Prep
• Ch. 11 Standardized Test Practice
Assessment Masters
• Cumulative Review
Computer Test Generator CD
• Standardized Test Practice

 **www.PHSchool.com**
• Standardized Test Practice
• Resources

Plus **iTEXT**

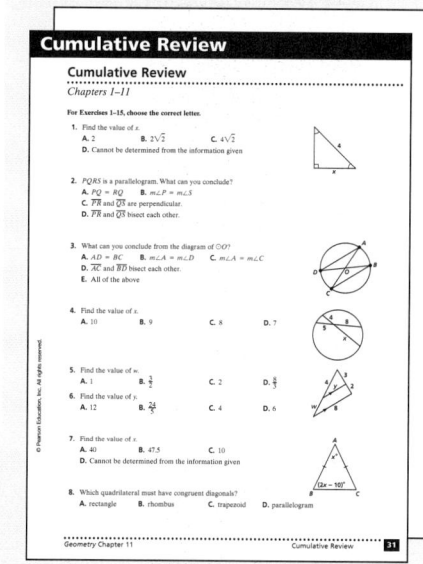

---

page 631   Standardized Test Prep

9. Answers may vary.
Sample: Use a graphing calculator and examine the graph.

10. $2(3 + 4 \cos X) + 2(4 \sin X) = 6 + 8 \cos X + 8 \sin X$
$2(4 + 3 \cos X) + 2(3 \sin X) = 8 + 6 \cos X + 6 \sin X$

$$\begin{array}{r} 6 + 8\cos X + 8\sin X \\ -\ 8 + 6\cos X + 6\sin X \\ \hline -2 + 2\cos X + 2\sin X = 2\sin X + 2\cos X - 2 \end{array}$$

Transformations

Chapter at a Glance

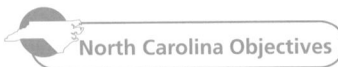
North Carolina Objectives

12-1	Reflections	3.01
NCTM 3, 6, 8, 9, 10	∇ Identifying Isometries ∇ Finding Reflection Images	
12-2	Translations	3.01, 3.02
NCTM 1, 3, 6, 8, 9, 10	∇ Translations Using Vectors ∇ Translations Using Matrix and Vector Sums	
12-3	Rotations	3.01
NCTM 3, 6, 8, 9, 10	∇ Drawing and Identifying Rotation Images	
12-4	Compositions of Reflections	3.01
NCTM 3, 6, 8, 9, 10	∇ Compositions of Reflections ∇ Glide Reflections	
12-5	Symmetry	
NCTM 3, 6, 8, 9, 10	∇ Identifying Types of Symmetry in Figures	
12-6	Tessellations	3.01
NCTM 2, 3, 6, 8, 9, 10	∇ Identifying Transformations in Tessellations ∇ Identifying Symmetries in Tessellations	
12-7	Dilations	3.01, 3.02
NCTM 1, 3, 4, 6, 8, 9, 10	∇ Locating Dilation Images	

NCTM STANDARDS 2000

1	Number and Operations	6	Problem Solving
2	Algebra	7	Reasoning and Proof
3	Geometry	8	Communication
4	Measurement	9	Connections
5	Data Analysis and Probability	10	Representation

Pacing Options

This chart suggests pacing only for the lessons and their parts. It is provided as a possible guide. It will help you determine how much time you have in your schedule to cover other components, such as the features, Chapter Review and Chapter Test.

Day	Traditional 45 min.	Two-Year 45 min.	Block 90 min.
1	12-1 ∇	12-1 ∇	12-1 ∇ ∇
2	12-1 ∇	12-1 ∇	12-2 ∇ ∇
3	12-1 ∇	12-1 ∇	12-3 ∇
4	12-1 ∇	12-1 ∇	12-4 ∇ ∇
5	12-2 ∇	12-2 ∇	12-5 ∇
6	12-2 ∇	12-2 ∇	12-6 ∇ ∇
7	12-2 ∇	12-2 ∇	12-7 ∇
8	12-2 ∇	12-2 ∇	
9	12-3 ∇	12-3 ∇	
10	12-3 ∇	12-3 ∇	
11	12-4 ∇	12-4 ∇	
12	12-4 ∇	12-4 ∇	
13	12-4 ∇	12-4 ∇	
14	12-4 ∇	12-4 ∇	
15	12-5 ∇	12-5 ∇	
16	12-6 ∇	12-5 ∇	
17	12-6 ∇	12-6 ∇	
18	12-7 ∇	12-6 ∇	
19		12-6 ∇	
20		12-6 ∇	
21		12-7 ∇	
22			

NAEP Correlation (National Assessment of Educational Progress 2000 Mathematics Objectives)

12-1	12-2	12-3	12-4	12-5	12-6	12-7
G3a, G3b	G3a, b	G1a, b; G3b	G1a, b; G3a	G1b, G3a	G2; G3a, b	G3b, G6c

N = Number Sense, Properties, and Operations; M = Measurement; G = Geometry and Spatial Sense;
D = Data Analysis, Statistics, and Probability; A = Algebra and Functions

Math Background

Chapter Overview

The concluding chapter of the book discusses the four isometric transformations: reflections, translations, rotations, and glide reflections. As part of the presentation of these transformations, applications are made to symmetry and tessellations. The chapter ends with a discussion of dilations, a nonisometric transformation.

Reflections 12-1

Students can relate the topic of reflections to the use of a mirror to form reflections. However, some practical differences should be examined. On paper, students can reflect a two-dimensional figure using paper folding or more analytic procedures. The result is an image every bit as tangible as the original object. Reflection of a three-dimensional object is different. Although a mirror can show a reflection, the image is not tangible in the same sense.

Translations 12-2

Matrices and vectors are used to represent and solve translation problems in this lesson and are used extensively in advanced mathematics and science courses. Matrices allow for the systematic analysis of systems of equations and provide a way for computers to handle data. Vectors are as fundamental to the study of group theory, ring theory, and physics as algebraic expressions are to the study of mathematics. Interested students might explore whether combinations of translations are commutative.

Rotations 12-3

Regular polygons can provide a useful perspective on rotations. For a regular n-gon, a rotation of $\frac{360}{n}$ degrees or any multiple of $\frac{360}{n}$ degrees about the center of the n-gon will create an isometry. A rotation of 360° about the center will create the identity isometry. If the center of rotation is on the figure, the rotation image is more difficult to find. Interested students might explore whether combinations of rotations are commutative.

Compositions of Reflections 12-4

The introduction of the glide reflection completes all the possible isometric transformations, as made clear by the Isometry Classification Theorem. The theorems in this lesson are sophisticated, and their proofs are too complicated for students at this point. Nevertheless, their inclusion is warranted because the theorems themselves are easily understood and applied. Students who pursue geometry at the college level will consider the proofs of these theorems at that point. Interested students might explore whether a glide reflection is 'commutative' (whether a glide followed by a reflection is equivalent to a reflection followed by a glide).

Symmetry 12-5

Symmetry is a familiar topic to most students and one that is strongly intuitive because of that familiarity. It relates to aesthetic considerations in art, architecture, and music as well as physical considerations in biology and chemistry.

Finding and describing symmetries in solid figures can be challenging. Lines of symmetry in a cube include the major diagonals and the segments joining the centers of opposite faces. Lines of symmetry in a tetrahedron include the altitudes and segments joining the midpoint of an edge and the midpoint of the nonintersecting edge. Students may use models of the Platonic solids to explore further.

Tessellations 12-6

Dutch artist M. C. Escher is the world's most famous creator of tessellations. Students will be able to find many examples of his work on the Internet. You might have students explore Penrose tiles. These are two shapes that will tile a plane without any general pattern to the tessellation. The word tessellation is derived from the Latin word *tesserae*, which were small glass pieces used by Roman artists to produce mosaic works of art.

Dilations 12-7

In ordinary usage, dilation occurs when an object is enlarged or widened, as when the pupil of an eye dilates. In geometry, dilation refers to an enlargement or a reduction, with the restrictions that the image be similar to the original and that there be a center of dilation. Thus, for any dilation, the preimage and image are similar. The converse is false: Two similar objects are not necessarily related by dilation if there is no center of dilation.

Students might want to examine the relationship between the perimeters and areas of a figure and its image under dilation. Dilation is an excellent topic for students to study using geometry software.

Ongoing Assessment and Intervention

Tools for Monitoring Student Progress

The Prentice Hall *Geometry* program provides you with many options for assessment in the Student Edition, the Teacher's Edition and the teaching resources. From these options, you may choose instructional materials and techniques that are appropriate for your students and support your district's curriculum requirements.

 ### Instant Check System™ in Chapter 12

Allows students to check their own learning before, during, and after each lesson.

Diagnosing Readiness before the chapter (p. 632)

Check Skills You'll Need exercises in each lesson (pp. 634, 641, 647, 654, 662, 667, 674)

Check Understanding questions with each Example (pp. 634, 635, 636, 641, 642, 643, 648, 649, 653, 654, 655, 656, 657, 662, 663, 667, 668, 669, 675)

Checkpoint Quiz (pp. 652 and 673)

Test Prep in Chapter 12

Teaches students strategies and gives them practice with all the test item formats they will encounter on state tests and standardized national exams.

Standardized Test Prep exercises in each lesson (pp. 639, 646, 651, 660, 666, 672, 679)

Test-Taking Strategies (p. 680: Answering the Question Asked)

Standardized Test Prep (pp. 685–687: Cumulative Review)

PRENTICE HALL
ASSESSMENT *SYSTEM*

All your assessment needs in one place!

Program Assessment

Assess student progress throughout the *Geometry* text with blackline masters and CD-ROM.

Assessment Resources

- Checkpoint Quizzes 1 & 2
- Chapter Test, Forms A & B
- Chapter Alternative Assessment

Spanish versions available. Tests for Informal Geometry also available.

 Computer Test Generator

- Unlimited questions of varying difficulty for every lesson objective.
- Create your own practice sheets, quizzes, and tests, or use the pre-made Chapter Tests.
- Diagnose readiness with questions on prerequisite skills.
- Prepare students by making tests based on standardized test objectives.
- Access Algebra 1, Geometry, and Algebra 2 content—all on one CD-ROM.

Test Preparation

A three-step approach to preparing students for high stakes, national, and state exams.

❶ **Diagnose & Prescribe**

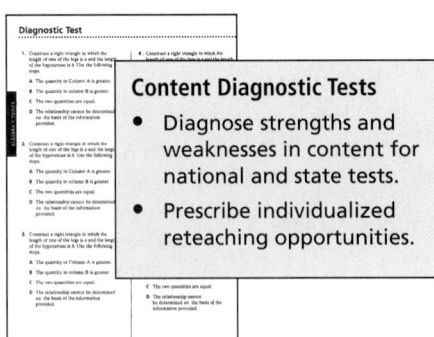

Content Diagnostic Tests
- Diagnose strengths and weaknesses in content for national and state tests.
- Prescribe individualized reteaching opportunities.

❷ **Review & Reteach**

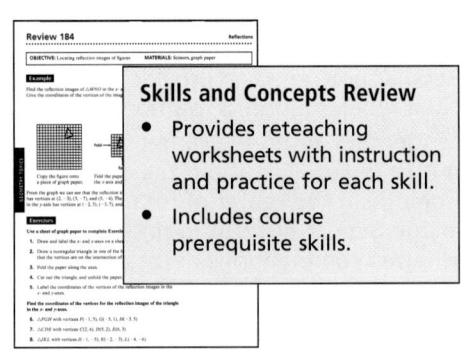

Skills and Concepts Review
- Provides reteaching worksheets with instruction and practice for each skill.
- Includes course prerequisite skills.

❸ **Practice & Assess**

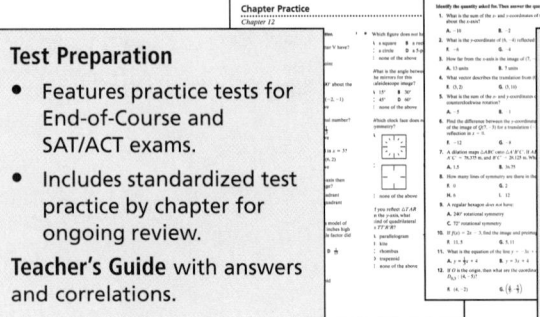

Test Preparation
- Features practice tests for End-of-Course and SAT/ACT exams.
- Includes standardized test practice by chapter for ongoing review.

Teacher's Guide with answers and correlations.

Test-Taking Strategies with Transparencies
- Support the Test-Taking Strategies pages in the Student Edition.
- Provide a teaching transparency and a practice worksheet for each strategy.

Reaching All Students

Support in the Student Text and Additional Resources

The textbook, the iText, and other technology components provide numerous opportunities to reach students of various ability levels and learning styles. Each Teacher's Edition lesson suggests how you can help *all* your students be successful and understand the mathematics in Chapter 12.

Below Level

Student Edition
- Diagnosing Readiness*: p. 632
- Check Skills You'll Need*: pp. 634, 641, 647, 654, 662, 667, 674

Reteaching
Chapter 12 Support File: pp. 8–14

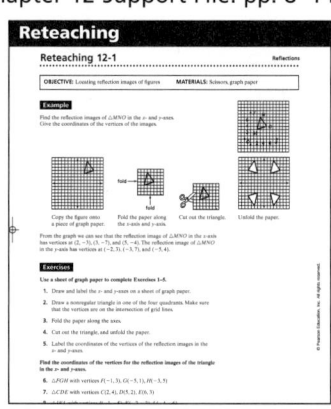

Informal Geometry Planning Guide
Chapter 12 Lesson Plans: pp. 72–78
Chapter 12 Tests: pp. 123–126

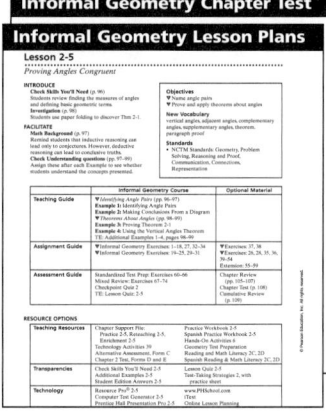

* Can be used with all ability levels to ensure mastery of prerequisite skills.

Advanced Learners

Student Edition
- Challenge exercises: pp. 638, 646, 651, 659, 665, 671, 678

Enrichment
Chapter 12 Support File: pp. 15–21

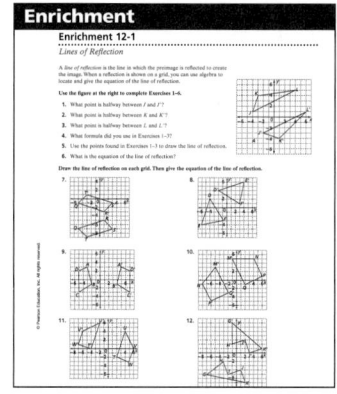

Reading and Math Literacy

Student Edition
- Vocabulary: pp. 633, 681, *plus* in every Lesson Preview
- Reading Math: pp. 634, 635, 648, 651, 653, 662, 663, 667, 681
- Illustrated Glossary: pp. 741–777

Reading and Math Literacy Masters
Chapter 12: pp. 45–48

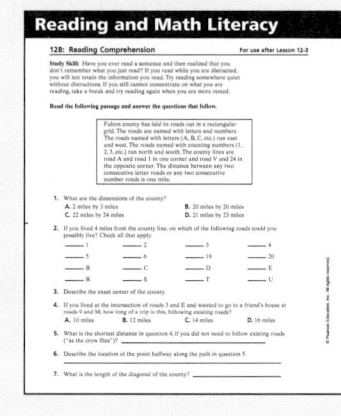

English Learners

Student Edition
- English/Spanish Illustrated Glossary: pp. 741–777

Workbook and Masters
Spanish Practice Workbook: pp. 72–78
Spanish Reading and Math Literacy Masters: pp. 45–48

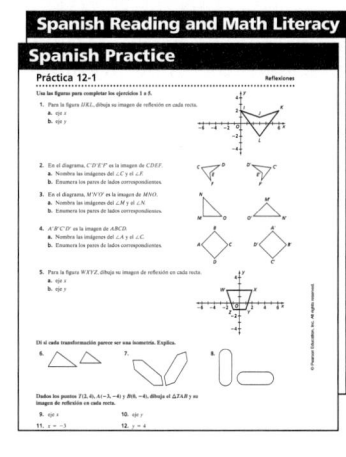

Learning Styles

Student Edition
- Investigation: pp. 647, 669
- Technology: pp. 661, 677
- Writing: pp. 638, 645, 646, 651, 658, 665, 671, 677, 679, 684
- DK Activities: pp. 688–689

Activity Masters
Hands-On Activities: 34, 35, 36
Technology Activities: 52

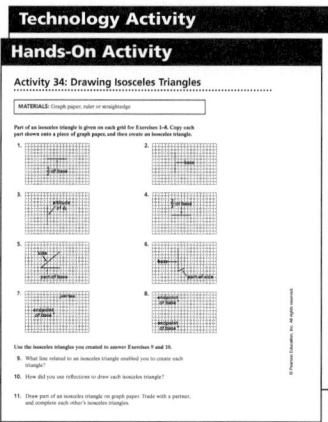

Program Resources

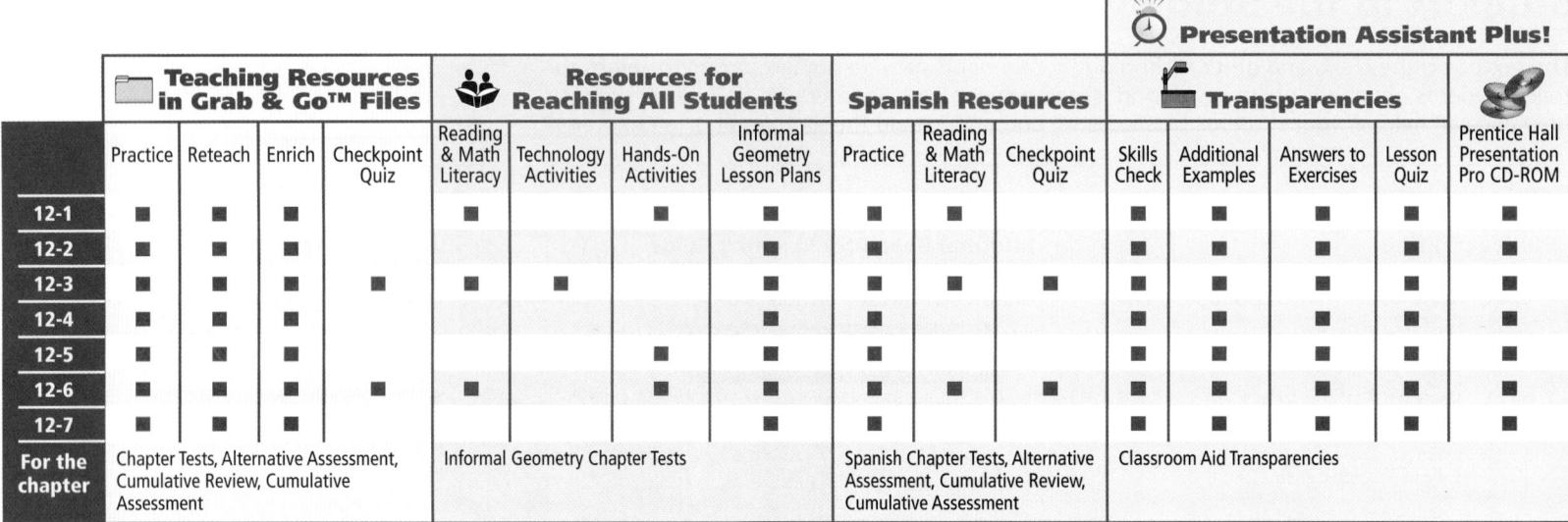

	Teaching Resources in Grab & Go™ Files				Resources for Reaching All Students				Spanish Resources			Transparencies				Presentation Assistant Plus!
	Practice	Reteach	Enrich	Checkpoint Quiz	Reading & Math Literacy	Technology Activities	Hands-On Activities	Informal Geometry Lesson Plans	Practice	Reading & Math Literacy	Checkpoint Quiz	Skills Check	Additional Examples	Answers to Exercises	Lesson Quiz	Prentice Hall Presentation Pro CD-ROM
12-1	■	■	■		■				■	■		■	■	■	■	■
12-2	■	■	■					■	■			■	■	■	■	■
12-3	■	■	■	■	■	■		■	■	■	■	■	■	■	■	■
12-4	■	■	■					■	■			■		■	■	■
12-5	■	■	■				■	■	■			■	■	■	■	■
12-6	■	■	■	■	■		■	■	■	■	■	■	■	■	■	■
12-7	■	■	■					■	■			■	■	■	■	■
For the chapter	Chapter Tests, Alternative Assessment, Cumulative Review, Cumulative Assessment				Informal Geometry Chapter Tests				Spanish Chapter Tests, Alternative Assessment, Cumulative Review, Cumulative Assessment			Classroom Aid Transparencies				

Also available for use with the chapter:

 *see page 632C.*

- Practice Workbook
- Solution Key

- For teacher support and access to student Web site materials, use Web Code afk-5500.
- For additional online and technology resources, see below.

 Technology

 Online and on CD-ROM

Complete Interactive Student Text online and on CD-ROM—with instant feedback assessment, tutorial help, dynamic activities, instructional and real-world videos, audio, and additional practice.

www.PHSchool.com For Students

Use **Web Codes** for easy access to online activities, chapter projects, self-grading lesson quizzes and chapter tests, vocabulary quizzes, updated data sources, graphing calculator procedures, and more.

PH SuccessNet For Teachers

Online lesson planning with built-in state correlations, all the teaching resources, complete reference library, your own calendar and Teacher Web page, professional development, and more.

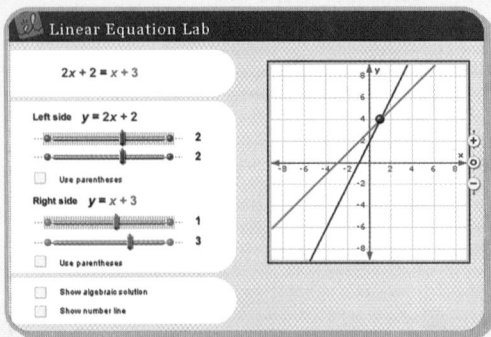

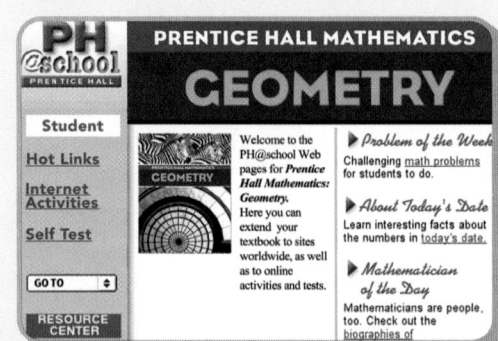

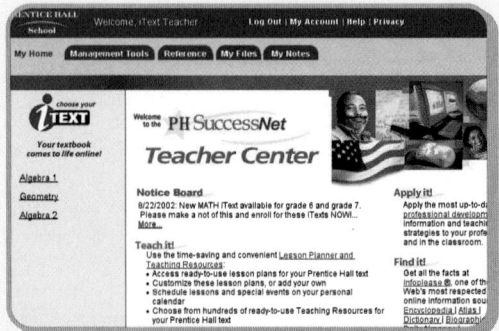

Presentation Assistant Plus!

The Prentice Hall *Presentation Assistant Plus!* provides you with the material you need to teach a lesson from beginning to end. Two easy-to-use formats—Transparencies and CD-ROM—allow you to present a lesson the way you are most comfortable.

Transparencies

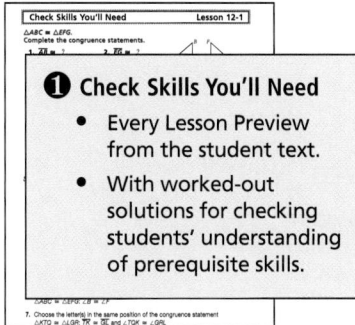

❶ Check Skills You'll Need
- Every Lesson Preview from the student text.
- With worked-out solutions for checking students' understanding of prerequisite skills.

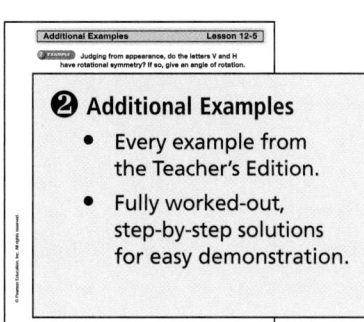

❷ Additional Examples
- Every example from the Teacher's Edition.
- Fully worked-out, step-by-step solutions for easy demonstration.

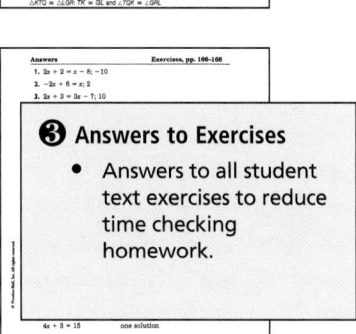

❸ Answers to Exercises
- Answers to all student text exercises to reduce time checking homework.

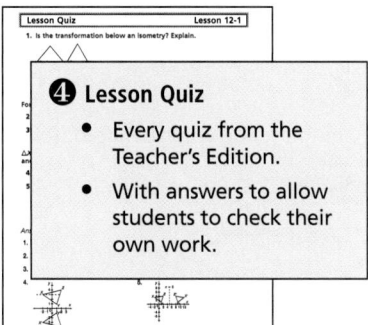

❹ Lesson Quiz
- Every quiz from the Teacher's Edition.
- With answers to allow students to check their own work.

 Throughout the Teacher's Edition, this symbol indicates material that is available on transparency in the Presentation Assistant Plus!

Prentice Hall Presentation Pro CD-ROM

- Includes all Transparencies.
- Conveniently organized by lesson so you can easily ❶ Introduce, ❷ Teach, ❸ Check Homework, and ❹ Assess each lesson.
- Animated examples allow step-by-step instruction at your own pace.
- Easy to edit so you can create custom presentations.

Teaching Chapter 12 Using Presentation Assistant Plus!

	❶ Introduce	❷ Teach	❸ Check Homework	❹ Assess
	Check Skills You'll Need	Additional Examples	Student Edition Answers	Lesson Quiz
12-1	p. 69	pp. 197–198	✔	p. 147
12-2	p. 70	pp. 199–201	✔	p. 148
12-3	p. 71	pp. 202–204	✔	p. 149
12-4	p. 72	pp. 204–208	✔	p. 150
12-5	p. 73	pp. 208–209	✔	p. 151
12-6	p. 74	pp. 210–211	✔	p. 152
12-7	p. 75	pp. 212–213	✔	p. 153

Prentice Hall Presentation Pro

CD-ROM with dynamic PowerPoint® presentations for every lesson. Helps you introduce and develop concepts, check homework, and assess progress. Part of Presentation Assistant Plus! *(See above.)*

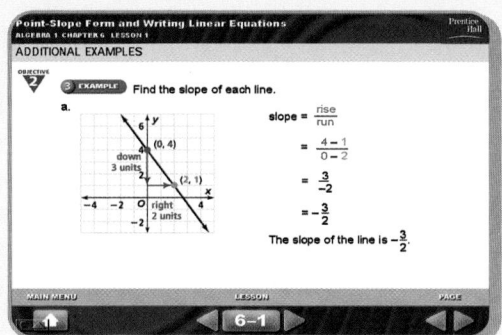

Computer Test Generator

CD-ROM to create practice sheets and tests for course objectives and standardized tests. Includes Instant Chapter Tests™, online testing, and student reports. Part of the PH Assessment System. *(See page 632C.)*

Resource Pro® with Planning Express®

CD-ROM with a lesson planning tool that allows you to import state and local objectives. Includes electronic versions of all the teaching resources.

Transformations

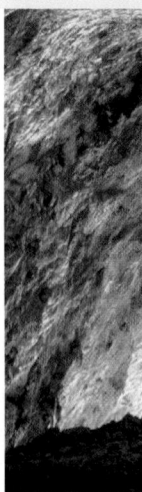

Where You've Been

- In Chapter 4, you learned that you can move one of two congruent figures so that it can fit exactly on the other one.

- In Chapter 9, you learned how vectors can be used to represent distance and direction.

- In Chapter 11, you learned to use the relationship between central angles and arcs on a circle.

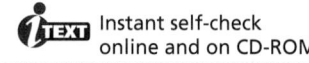 Instant self-check online and on CD-ROM

 **Diagnosing Readiness**   (For help, go to the Lesson in green.)

Regular Polygons (Lesson 3-4)

Determine the measure of an angle of the given regular polygon.

1. pentagon **108**   **2.** octagon **135**   **3.** decagon **144**   **4.** 18-gon **160**

Congruent Figures (Lesson 4-1)

The triangles are congruent. Complete the congruence statement, $\triangle ABC \cong \underline{\ ?\ }$.

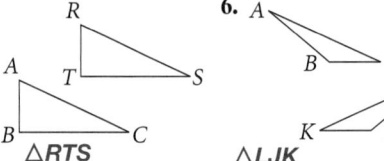

5. △RTS   **6.** △LJK   **7.** △ADC   **8.** △LHC

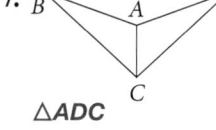

Quadrilaterals (Lessons 6-2, 6-4, and 6-5)

Determine whether a diagonal of the given quadrilateral *always*, *sometimes*, or *never* produces congruent triangles.

9. rectangle **always**   **10.** isosceles trapezoid **never**   **11.** kite **sometimes**   **12.** parallelogram **always**

Similar Figures (Lesson 8-6)

Determine the similarity ratio for each pair of similar polygons.

13. triangles with perimeters 45 and 72 **5 : 8**   **14.** squares with areas 16 and 64 **1 : 2**

Vectors (Lesson 9-4)

Write the sum of the two vectors as an ordered pair.

15. $\langle 3, 1 \rangle$ and $\langle -2, 4 \rangle$ **16.** $\langle -1, 2 \rangle$ and $\langle -5, 0 \rangle$ **17.** $\langle 0, 0 \rangle$ and $\langle -6, 3 \rangle$
$\langle 1, 5 \rangle$ $\langle -6, 2 \rangle$ $\langle -6, 3 \rangle$

Transformations

Chapter 12

Key Vocabulary

- composition (p. 642)
- dilation (p. 674)
- enlargement (p. 674)
- glide reflection (p. 656)
- glide reflectional symmetry (p. 668)
- image (p. 634)
- isometry (p. 634)
- line symmetry (p. 662)
- point symmetry (p. 663)
- preimage (p. 634)
- reduction (p. 674)
- reflection (p. 635)
- reflectional symmetry (p. 662)
- rotation (p. 648)
- rotational symmetry (p. 663)
- scalar multiplication (p. 675)
- symmetry (p. 662)
- tessellation (p. 667)
- tiling (p. 667)
- transformation (p. 634)
- translation (p. 641)
- translational symmetry (p. 668)

Where You're Going

- In this chapter, you will learn how to use transformations known as reflections, translations, and rotations to create a congruent image of a given shape.

- You will learn to use transformations for relating two given congruent shapes to each other.

- You will learn the effects of applying two transformations, one after the other.

- By learning about transformations, you will understand such terms as *symmetry* and *tessellation*.

Real-World Snapshots Applying what you learn, you will do activities on pages 688 and 689 involving transformations in three dimensions.

Chapter 12 Overview

In this chapter, students will name and examine transformations on a plane. They will identify and perform reflections, translations, and rotations, and then combine them as compositions of transformations and glide reflections. They then will apply the Fundamental Theorem of Isometries and the Isometry Classification Theorem to symmetry and tessellations. Finally, students will study dilations as non-isometric similarity transformations.

📖 **Reading Math**
Reading for Problem Solving, p. 653

📖 **Vocabulary**
A complete list of terms, plus vocabulary exercises, appears in the Chapter Review, p. 681.

📖 **Illustrated Glossary**
Examples for each vocabulary term, plus definitions in both English and Spanish, appear starting on p. 741.

▦ **Test-Taking Strategies**
Answering the Question Asked, p. 680

Real-World Snapshots
See pages 688–689 for a real-world application of translations and rotations that utilizes Dorling Kindersley's (DK) unique graphic presentation.

🌐 **Real-World Connections**
Some of the applications you will find in this chapter are engineering (12-1), football (12-2), Native American art (12-3), logos (12-5), and scale models (12-7).

💻 **www.PHSchool.com**
Internet support for this chapter includes:
- Self-grading Vocabulary and Chapter 12 Tests
- Chapter Project
- Chapter Planner
- Ch. 12 Resources

Plus

1. Plan

Lesson Preview

✓ **Check Skills You'll Need**

Congruent Figures
Lesson 4-1: Example 1
Exercises 1–15
Extra Practice, p. 693

Lesson Resources

Teaching Resources
Practice, Reteaching, Enrichment

Reaching All Students
Practice Workbook 12-1
Spanish Practice Workbook 12-1
Reading and Math Literacy 12A
Spanish Reading & Literacy 12A
Hands-On Activities 34
Informal Geometry Planning
   Guide 12-1

Presentation Assistant Plus!
Transparencies
• Check Skills You'll Need 12-1
• Additional Examples 12-1
• Student Edition Answers 12-1
• Lesson Quiz 12-1
PH Presentation Pro CD 12-1

ASSESSMENT SYSTEM

Computer Test Generator CD

Technology
Resource Pro® CD-ROM
Computer Test Generator CD
Prentice Hall Presentation Pro CD

www.PHSchool.com
Student Site
• Teacher Web Code: afk-5500
• Self-grading Lesson Quiz
Teacher Center
• Lesson Planner
• Resources

Plus **iTEXT**

634

12-1

Reflections

Lesson Preview

What You'll Learn

OBJECTIVE **1** To identify isometries

OBJECTIVE **2** To find reflection images of figures

. . . And Why

To minimize distances in construction, as in Example 4

✓ **Check Skills You'll Need**   (For help, go to Lesson 4-1.)

$\triangle ABC \cong \triangle EFG$.
Complete the congruence statements.
1. $\overline{AB} \cong$? $\overline{EF}$ 2. $\overline{EG} \cong$? $\overline{AC}$
3. $\overline{FG} \cong$? $\overline{BC}$4. $\angle C \cong$? $\angle G$
5. $\angle E \cong$? $\angle A$6. $\angle B \cong$? $\angle F$
7. Complete: If $\triangle KTQ \cong \triangle LGR$, then $\overline{TK} \cong$? and $\angle TQK \cong$? .
$\overline{GL}; \angle GRL$

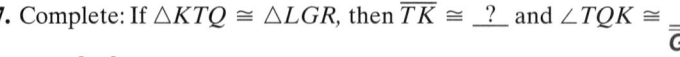

New Vocabulary • transformation • preimage • image
• isometry • reflection

---

iTEXT Interactive lesson includes instant self-check, tutorials, and activities.

Reading Math

In general, the word *transformation* can refer to any kind of change in appearance.

A **transformation** of a geometric figure is a change in its position, shape, or size. When you assemble a jigsaw puzzle, you often move the puzzle pieces by flipping them, sliding them, or turning them. Each move is a type of transformation. The photos below illustrate some basic transformations that you will study.

The figure flips.   The figure slides.   The figure turns.

The original figure is the **preimage.** The resulting figure is an **image.** An **isometry** is a transformation in which the preimage and image are congruent. Each transformation above is an isometry.

1 EXAMPLE **Identifying Isometries**

Does the transformation appear to be an isometry? Explain.

No, this transformation involves a change in size. The sides of the preimage square and the sides of its image are not congruent.

Preimage   Image

✓ **Check Understanding** ❶ Does the transformation appear to be an isometry? Explain.

a.

Preimage   Image

Yes; the figures are ≅ by a flip.

b. Preimage

Image

Yes; the figures are ≅ by a flip and a slide.

Ongoing Assessment and Intervention

Before the Lesson
Diagnose prerequisite skills using:
• Check Skills You'll Need

During the Lesson
Monitor progress using:
• Check Understanding
• Additional Examples
• Standardized Test Prep

After the Lesson
Assess knowledge using:
• Lesson Quiz
• Computer Test Generator CD

Reading Math

Read $K \rightarrow K'$ as "K maps onto K prime."

A transformation maps a figure onto its image and may be described with arrow ($\rightarrow$) notation. Prime (') notation is sometimes used to identify image points. In the diagram at the right, K' is the image of K ($K \rightarrow K'$).

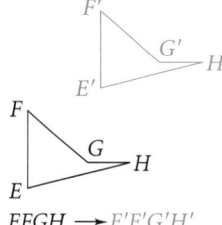

$\triangle JKQ \longrightarrow \triangle J'K'Q'$
$\triangle JKQ$ maps onto $\triangle J'K'Q'$.

Notice that you list corresponding points of the preimage and image in the same order, as you do for corresponding points of congruent or similar figures.

2 EXAMPLE **Naming Images and Corresponding Parts**

In the diagram, $E'F'G'H'$ is an image of $EFGH$.

a. Name the images of $\angle F$ and $\angle H$.

$\angle F'$ is the image of $\angle F$.
$\angle H'$ is the image of $\angle H$.

b. List all pairs of corresponding sides.

$\overline{EF}$ and $\overline{E'F'}$; $\overline{FG}$ and $\overline{F'G'}$;
$\overline{EH}$ and $\overline{E'H'}$; $\overline{GH}$ and $\overline{G'H'}$

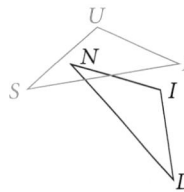

$EFGH \longrightarrow E'F'G'H'$

✓ Check Understanding **2** In the diagram, $NID \rightarrow SUP$.
a. Name the images of $\angle I$ and point D. $\angle U$; P
b. List all pairs of corresponding sides.
$\overline{NI}$ and $\overline{SU}$; $\overline{ID}$ and $\overline{UP}$; $\overline{ND}$ and $\overline{SP}$

OBJECTIVE

2 **Finding Reflection Images**

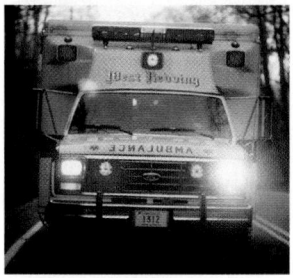

Real-World Connection

In your rear-view mirror you see the reflection "AMBULANCE."

A reflection (or *flip*) is an isometry in which a figure and its image have opposite orientations. Thus, a reflected image in a mirror appears "backwards." In the diagram at the right, $\triangle BUG$ is reflected in a line to produce $\triangle B'U'G'$. Since the reflection is an isometry, $\triangle BUG \cong \triangle B'U'G'$.

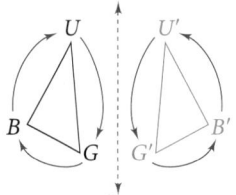

Using the diagram below, a **reflection** in line r is a transformation for which the following are true.

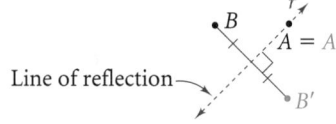

Line of reflection

- If a point A is on line r, then the image of A is A itself (that is, $A' = A$).
- If a point B is not on line r, then r is the perpendicular bisector of $\overline{BB'}$.

You can use these properties to find and draw reflection images.

Professional Development

Math Background

A geometric transformation in a plane is a one-to-one correspondence between two sets of points. An isometry is a rigid-motion transformation that preserves length so that if A and B are the preimages of A' and B', respectively, then $AB = A'B'$.

OBJECTIVE
1 **Teaching Notes**

English Learners

Have students fill half a poster with definitions and illustrations of the new vocabulary, leaving room to add more vocabulary from subsequent lessons. They can refer to it as needed.

1 EXAMPLE **Teaching Tip**

Ask: *What do you call figures whose corresponding angles are congruent and whose corresponding sides are proportional?* similar

Additional Examples

1 Does the transformation appear to be an isometry? Explain.

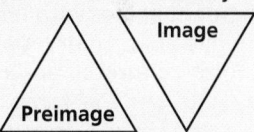

Yes; corresponding parts appear to be congruent.

2 In the diagram, $\triangle XYZ$ is an image of $\triangle ABC$.

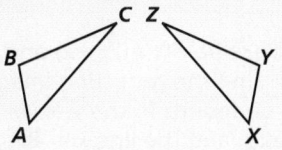

a. Name the images of $\angle B$ and $\angle C$. $\angle Y$ and $\angle Z$
b. List all pairs of corresponding sides. $\overline{AB}$ and $\overline{XY}$; $\overline{AC}$ and $\overline{XZ}$; $\overline{BC}$ and $\overline{YZ}$

🌐 Reaching All Students

Below Level Give examples of familiar figures that illustrate isometries, such as the congruent triangles formed by a diagonal of a parallelogram or a circle and its diameter.	**Advanced Learners** Have students write rules for finding the coordinates of the image of point (x, y) reflected in the line $x = 1$ and reflected in the line $y = 1$.	**English Learners** See note on page 635. **Visual Learners** See note on page 636.

Tactile Learners

Have students explore how they can use paper folding to draw and identify reflection images.

3 EXAMPLE

Review the definition of a perpendicular bisector.

4 EXAMPLE Visual Learners

Discuss as a class why $WP + PD'$ is smallest when W, P, and D' are collinear. Have students pick other possible locations for P and apply the Triangle Inequality Theorem.

Additional Examples

3 $\triangle XYZ$ has vertices $X(0, 3)$, $Y(2, 0)$, and $Z(4, 2)$. Draw $\triangle XYZ$ and its reflection image in the line $x = 4$.

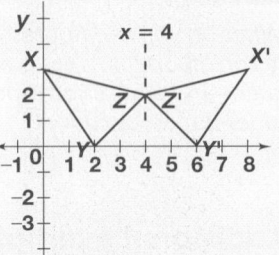

4 Use the diagram from Example 4. Show that $\overline{PD}$ and $\overline{PW}$ form congruent angles with line ℓ. A reflection is an isometry, so $\overline{PD}$ and $\overline{PD'}$ form congruent angles with line ℓ. $\overline{PD'}$ and $\overline{PW}$ form congruent vertical angles with line ℓ. Therefore, $\overline{PD}$ and $\overline{PW}$ form congruent angles with line ℓ by the Transitive Property.

Closure

$\overline{AB}$ has endpoints $A(2, -2)$ and $B(5, 3)$. Find the reflection image of the endpoints in the y-axis, the x-axis, and the line $x = 8$.
y-axis: $A'(-2, -2)$, $B'(-5, 3)$;
x-axis: $A'(2, 2)$, $B'(5, -3)$; $x = 8$:
$A'(14, -2)$, $B'(11, 3)$

pages 636–639 Exercises

4. a. Answers may vary.
Sample: $\angle Q \rightarrow \angle Q'$

b. $\overline{QR}$ and $\overline{Q'R'}$; $\overline{RS}$ and $\overline{R'S'}$; $\overline{SP}$ and $\overline{S'P'}$; $\overline{QP}$ and $\overline{Q'P'}$

636

3.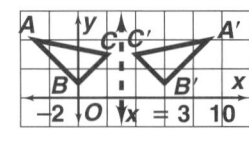

3 EXAMPLE Drawing Reflection Images

Coordinate Geometry Given points $A(-3, 4)$, $B(0, 1)$, and $C(2, 3)$, draw $\triangle ABC$ and its reflection image in each line.

a. the x-axis

b. the y-axis

Locate points A', B', and C' such that the line of reflection is the perpendicular bisector of $\overline{AA'}$, $\overline{BB'}$, and $\overline{CC'}$.

✓ Check Understanding 3 Draw $\triangle ABC$ of Example 3. Then draw its reflection image in the line $x = 3$.
See left.

You can use the properties of reflections to solve real-world problems.

4 EXAMPLE Real-World Connection

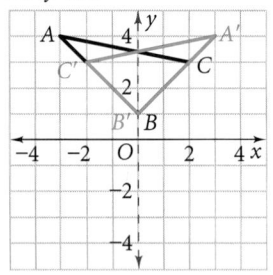

Engineering Town officials in Waterville and Drighton (see aerial view at left) are planning to construct a water pumping station along the Franklin Canal. The station will provide both towns with water. Where along the canal should the officials build the pumping station to minimize the amount of pipe needed?

You need to find the point P on ℓ such that $WP + PD$ is as small as possible. Locate D', the reflection image of D in ℓ. Because a reflection is an isometry, $PD = PD'$, and $WP + PD = WP + PD'$. By the Triangle Inequality Theorem, the sum $WP + PD'$ is smallest when W, P, and D' are collinear. So, the pump should be located at the point P where $\overline{WD'}$ intersects ℓ.

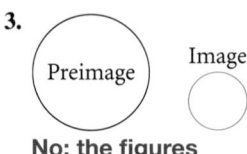

✓ Check Understanding 4 **Critical Thinking** Angela began to solve the problem above by reflecting point W in line ℓ. Will her method work? Explain.
Yes; the intersection of $\overline{DW'}$ and ℓ is the same point P.

EXERCISES

For more practice, see *Extra Practice*.

Practice and Problem Solving

A Practice by Example

Example 1
(page 634)

State whether the transformation appears to be an isometry. Explain.

1. Image
Preimage
Yes; the trans. is a slide.

2. Preimage Image
Yes; the trans. is a flip.

3. Preimage Image
No; the figures are not ≅.

5. a. Answers may vary.
Sample: $\angle R \rightarrow \angle R'$

b. $\overline{RI}$ and $\overline{R'I'}$; $\overline{IT}$ and $\overline{I'T'}$; $\overline{RT}$ and $\overline{R'T'}$

6. a. Answers may vary.
Sample: $\angle A \rightarrow \angle A'$

b. $\overline{AB}$ and $\overline{A'B'}$; $\overline{BC}$ and $\overline{B'C'}$; $\overline{AC}$ and $\overline{A'C'}$

18. Reflect the point for Balance Rock over the line for Summit Trail. Connect this point and

Overlook. The trails will connect at the intersection of the segment and Summit Trail.

Example 2
(page 635)

7a. Answers may vary.
Sample: $G \rightarrow M$
 b. $\overline{GW}$ and $\overline{MR}$;
 $\overline{WP}$ and $\overline{RT}$;
 $\overline{PN}$ and $\overline{TX}$;
 $\overline{NB}$ and $\overline{XS}$;
 $\overline{BG}$ and $\overline{SM}$

8a. Answers may vary.
Sample: $Z \rightarrow L$
 b. $\overline{ZO}$ and $\overline{LF}$;
 $\overline{OW}$ and $\overline{FM}$;
 $\overline{WE}$ and $\overline{MA}$;
 $\overline{EZ}$ and $\overline{AL}$

In each diagram, the blue figure is an image of the black figure.
(a) Choose an angle or point from the preimage and name its image.
(b) List all pairs of corresponding sides.

4. 4–6.
See margin
p. 636.

7–9. See left.

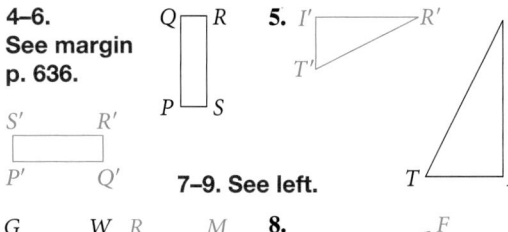

5.

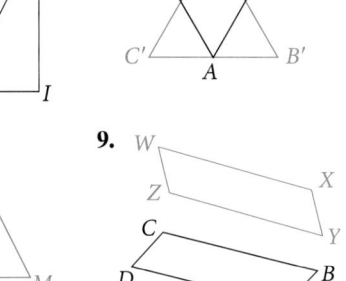

6.

7.

8.

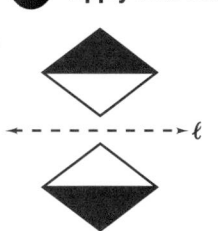

9.

Example 3
(page 636)

9a. Answers may vary.
Sample: $W \rightarrow D$
 b. $\overline{WZ}$ and $\overline{DC}$;
 $\overline{ZY}$ and $\overline{CB}$;
 $\overline{YX}$ and $\overline{BA}$;
 $\overline{XW}$ and $\overline{AD}$

Coordinate Geometry Given points $J(1, 4)$, $A(3, 5)$, and $R(2, 1)$, draw $\triangle JAR$ and its reflection image in each line. 10–17. See back of book.

10. the x-axis   **11.** the y-axis   **12.** $y = 2$ **13.** $y = 5$

14. $x = -1$ **15.** $x = 2$ **16.** $y = -x$ **17.** $y = x - 3$

Example 4
(page 636)

19. Reflect point D over
the mirrored wall.
Connect this point
and C. The
intersection of the
segment and the wall
is the point to focus
the camera.

18. Trail Building A hiking club is building
a new trail system. They want to build
trails to the Overlook and Balance Rock
that will connect at a point on Summit
Trail. Working under a tight budget, they
want to minimize the total length of these
trails. If the trails cover similar terrain,
at what point should they meet on
Summit Trail? **See margin p. 636.**

19. Security You are installing a security
camera. At what point on the mirrored
wall should you aim camera C in order
to videotape door D? **See left.**

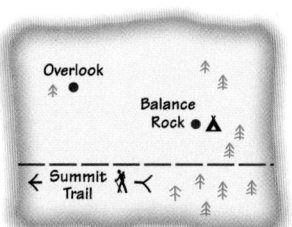

Mirrored wall

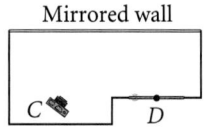

B Apply Your Skills

20.

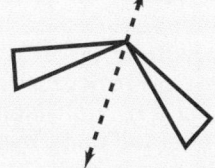

21.

Copy each figure and line ℓ. Then draw each figure's reflection image in line ℓ.

20.

20–21. See left.

21.

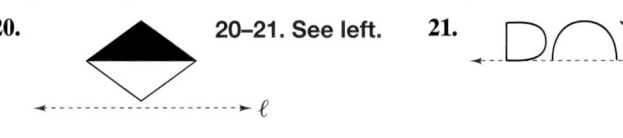

Copy each pair of figures. Then draw the line of reflection you can use to map one figure onto the other. 22–24. See margin.

22.

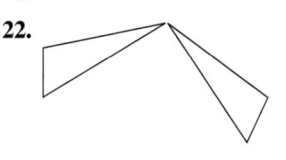

23.

24.

Lesson 12-1 Reflections **637**

22.

23.

24.

Assignment Guide

1 Objective
 Ⓐ Ⓑ **Core** 1–9, 37–46

2 Objective
 Ⓐ Ⓑ **Core** 10–36
 Ⓒ **Extension** 47–55

Standardized Test Prep 56–61

Mixed Review 62–64

Error Prevention
Exercises 16, 17 Suggest that
students construct a line through
each vertex that is perpendicular
to the line of reflection and mark
the reflection of the vertex an
equal distance from the line of
reflection.

Connection to Physics
Exercise 19 Point out that the
angle of incidence formed by
the camera, mirror, and door
equals the angle of reflection.

Diversity
Exercise 25 Ask left-handed
students to relate experiences
with objects designed for right-
handed use that have no left-
handed versions.

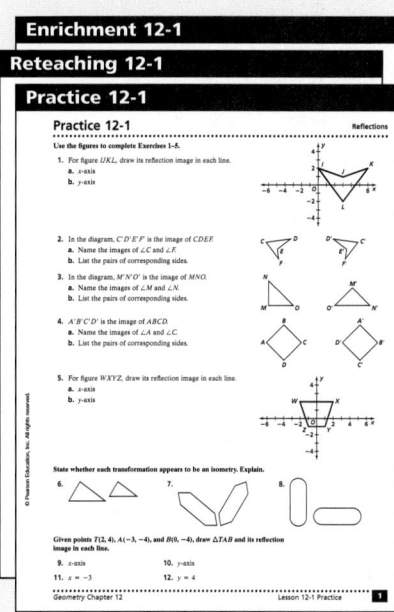

637

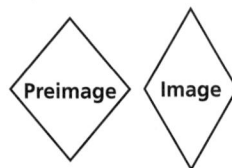

Lesson Quiz 12-1

1. Is the transformation below an isometry? Explain.

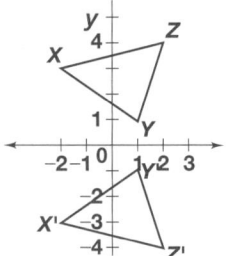

No; the angles are not congruent.

For Exercises 2 and 3, *ABCD* is an image of *KLMN*.

2. Name the images of $\angle L$ and $\angle N$. $\angle B$ and $\angle D$

3. Name the sides that correspond to $\overline{KL}$ and $\overline{NK}$. $\overline{AB}$ and $\overline{DA}$

$\triangle XYZ$ has vertices $X(-2, 3)$, $Y(1, 1)$, and $Z(2, 4)$. Draw $\triangle XYZ$ and its reflection image in each line.

4. the *x*-axis

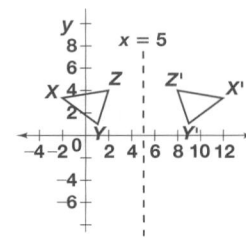

5. the line $x = 5$

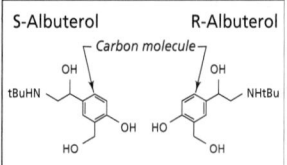

Albuterol's Structure

S-Albuterol   R-Albuterol

Carbon molecule

tBuHN   NHtBu

SOURCE: *Wall Street Journal*

The *R-isomer* of the drug albuterol relieves asthma. Its twin has been shown to increase the chances of having future attacks.

30a. Leonardo da Vinci was left-handed.

30b. Answers may vary. Sample: His writing hand would not cover what was written so far.

31. $x^2 + y^2 = 49$

32. $x^2 + (y - 4)^2 = 4$

33. $x^2 + (y + 3)^2 = 9$

34. $(x + 3)^2 + (y - 4)^2 = 16$

35. $x^2 + (y + 3)^2 = 36$

36. $(x - 5)^2 + (y + 1)^2 = 25$

Challenge

54. for $b \neq d$, $y = \left(\dfrac{a - c}{d - b}\right)x$
$- \dfrac{a^2 + b^2 - c^2 - d^2}{2(d - b)}$;
for $b = d$, $x = \dfrac{a + c}{2}$

---

25. Pharmaceuticals Most drugs are made of two versions of the same molecule, each a mirror image of the other. One version is known as an *R-isomer* and the other as an *S-isomer*. While one isomer can help with what ails you, the other can create unwanted side effects. Models of two isomers are shown above. For this drug to cure an illness, it needs to fit into the "receptor molecule." Which isomer will cure the illness? **S-Isomer**

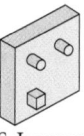 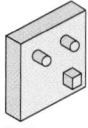
S-Isomer   R-Isomer   Receptor Molecule

26. Open-Ended Give three examples from everyday life of objects that come in a left-handed version and a right-handed version.
    Answers may vary. Sample: scissors, a baseball glove, a guitar

Coordinate Geometry A point is reflected in the given line. How are the coordinates of the point and its image related? Explain.

27. *x*-axis
(x, y) has image $(x, -y)$.

28. *y*-axis
(x, y) has image $(-x, y)$.

29. the line $y = x$
(x, y) has image (y, x).

30. History The work of artist and scientist Leonardo da Vinci (1452–1519) has an unusual characteristic. His handwriting is a mirror image of normal handwriting.
a. Write the mirror image of the sentence, "Leonardo da Vinci was left-handed." Use a mirror to check how well you did.
b. Explain why the fact about da Vinci in part (a) might have made mirror writing seem natural to him. **a–b. See left.**

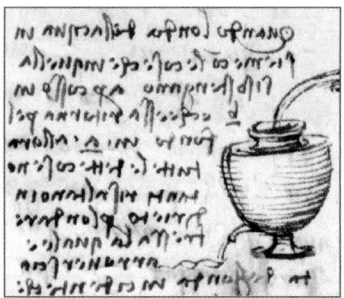

Write an equation for the image of the given circle after a reflection in line ℓ.

31. $x^2 + y^2 = 49$, ℓ: *y*-axis

32. $x^2 + y^2 = 4$, ℓ: $y = 2$

33. $(x - 2)^2 + (y + 3)^2 = 9$, ℓ: $x = 1$

34. $(x + 3)^2 + (y + 4)^2 = 16$, ℓ: *x*-axis

35. $x^2 + (y + 3)^2 = 36$, ℓ: $y = -3$

36. $(x + 1)^2 + (y - 5)^2 = 25$, ℓ: $y = x$

Find the image of $O(0, 0)$ after two reflections, first in ℓ_1 and then in ℓ_2. **(0, 0)**

37. ℓ_1: $y = 3$, ℓ_2: *x*-axis
    (0, −6)

38. ℓ_1: $x = -2$, ℓ_2: *y*-axis
    (4, 0)

39. ℓ_1: *x*-axis, ℓ_2: *y*-axis

40. ℓ_1: $x = -2$, ℓ_2: $y = 3$
    (−4, 6)

41. ℓ_1: $y = 3$, ℓ_2: $x = -2$
    (−4, 6)

42. ℓ_1: $x = -2$, ℓ_2: $y = x$
    (0, −4)

43. ℓ_1: $x = a$, ℓ_2: $y = b$
    (2a, 2b)

44. ℓ_1: $x = a$, ℓ_2: $y = x$
    (0, 2a)

45. ℓ_1: $y = b$, ℓ_2: $y = x$
    (2b, 0)

46. Critical Thinking Given that the transformation $\triangle ABC \rightarrow \triangle A'B'C'$ is an isometry, list everything you know about the two figures. **See margin.**

 **Challenge**

Writing Can the given type of quadrilateral be described in terms of reflections? Explain.   47–52. See margin pp. 638–639.

47. parallelogram

48. isosceles trapezoid

49. kite

50. rhombus

51. rectangle

52. square

53. Coordinate Geometry Show that $B(b, a)$ is the reflection image of $A(a, b)$ in the line $y = x$. (*Hint:* Show that $y = x$ is the perpendicular bisector of $\overleftrightarrow{AB}$.)
    See margin p. 639

54. Coordinate Geometry Find the line of reflection that maps $A(a, b)$ to $C(c, d)$.
    See left.

pages 636–639 Exercises

46. $\overline{AB} \cong \overline{A'B'}$; $\overline{BC} \cong \overline{B'C'}$; $\overline{AC} \cong \overline{A'C'}$; $A \rightarrow A'$; $B \rightarrow B'$; $C \rightarrow C'$; $\angle A \cong \angle A'$; $\angle B \cong \angle B'$; $\angle C \cong \angle C'$

47. yes; a $\triangle$ reflected in any side and then reflected in the $\perp$ bis. of that side

48. yes; a trap. with one leg $\perp$ to the $\parallel$ sides, reflected in that side

49. yes; a scalene, acute, or obtuse $\triangle$ reflected in any side, or an isosc., non-rt. $\triangle$ reflected in a leg, or a rt., non-isosc. $\triangle$ reflected in its hyp.

55b. (−2, −4)
 c. (−4, −2)

55. Use the diagram at the right. Find the coordinates of the given point in the given line. **a. (4, 2)**
 a. A', the reflection image of A in the line $y = x$
 b. A'', the reflection image of A' in the line $y = -x$
 c. A''', the reflection image of A'' in the line $y = x$
 d. A'''', the reflection image of A''' in the line $y = -x$ **(2, 4)**
 e. How are A and A'''' related? **They are the same point.**

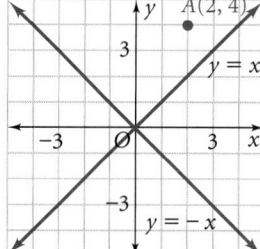

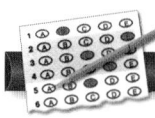

Standardized Test Prep

Multiple Choice

56. What is the reflection image of $(5, -3)$ in the y-axis? **C**
 A. $(5, 3)$ **B.** $(-5, 3)$ **C.** $(-5, -3)$ **D.** $(-3, 5)$

57. What is the reflection image of $(5, -3)$ in the line $y = -x$? **H**
 F. $(-3, 5)$ **G.** $(-3, -5)$ **H.** $(3, -5)$ **I.** $(3, 5)$

Quantitative Comparison

Compare the boxed quantity in Column A with the boxed quantity in Column B. Choose the best answer.
 A. The quantity in Column A is greater.
 B. The quantity in Column B is greater.
 C. The two quantities are equal.
 D. The relationship cannot be determined from the information given.

$(-7, -1)$ reflected in the x-axis has image (x_1, y_1).
$(-7, -1)$ reflected in the y-axis has image (x_2, y_2).

Column A	Column B
B 58. x_1	x_2
A 59. y_1	y_2
C 60. $\lvert y_1 \rvert$	$\lvert y_2 \rvert$

Take It to the NET
Online lesson quiz at
www.PHSchool.com
Web Code: afa-1201

Short Response

61. A point is reflected in the line $y = x$. Its image is in Quadrant III. In which quadrant is the preimage? Explain. **See margin.**

Mixed Review

$y = \frac{2}{3}x - 1$

Lesson 11-6 62. Write an equation for the locus: The points equidistant from $(1, 4)$ and $(5, -2)$.

Lesson 10-8 63. **Sports Equipment** The circumference of a softball is 12 in. and the circumference of a field hockey ball is 9 in.
 a. Find the similarity ratio of the softball to the field hockey ball. **4 : 3**
 b. Find the ratio of the volumes: softball to field hockey ball. **64 : 27**

Lesson 8-1 64. **Maps** A map of Alberta, Canada, is drawn to the scale 1 cm = 25 km. On the map, the distance from Calgary to Edmonton is about 11.1 cm.
 a. About how far apart are the two cities? **277.5 km**
 b. If 1 km = 0.62 mi, about how many miles apart are the cities? **about 172 mi**

Lesson 12-1 Reflections **639**

50. yes; an isosc. △ reflected in its base

51. yes; a rt. △ reflected in its hyp. and then reflected in the ⊥ bis. of the hypotenuse

52. yes; an isosc. rt. △ reflected in its hyp.

Alternative Assessment

Have students title two columns on a sheet of paper "Reflection in a vertical line" and "Reflection in a horizontal line." Have them examine which letters of the alphabet can be formed by a reflection and write those letters in the appropriate column. Have students write several words using letters from one of the columns, such as THAT and COB, and determine whether the reflections are also words.

Standardized Test Prep

📁 **Resources**
For additional practice with a variety of test item formats:
• Standardized Test Prep, p. 685
• Test-Taking Strategies, p. 680
• Test-Taking Strategies with Transparencies

Exercises 56–61 Advise students to sketch each preimage and image when asked to find a reflection image in a coordinate plane.

53. The slope of $\overleftrightarrow{AB}$ is $\frac{a - b}{b - a}$
 $= \frac{a - b}{-1(a - b)} = -1$.
 The slope of $y = x$ is 1.
 Since $(1)(-1) = -1$, the lines are ⊥. The midpoint of $\overline{AR} =$
 $\left(\frac{b + a}{2}, \frac{a + b}{2}\right)$, which is a pt. on $y = x$.

61. **[2]** The preimage is also in Quadrant III. If x and y are positive numbers, an image in Quadrant III would be the point $(-x, -y)$. That point's preimage, reflected in the line $y = x$, was $(-y, -x)$, which is still in Quadrant III.

 [1] correct quadrant with insufficient explanation

Algebra 1 Review

Matrices

Students will use the skill of matrix addition and subtraction to find images in Lesson 12-2.

Resources

Technology
Geometry Resource Pro® CD-ROM:
   Algebra Review Resources
Computer Test Generator CD-ROM,
   Chapter 0, Extension Topics

Teaching Notes

Technology Tip
Have students investigate how to use a graphing calculator to perform matrix addition and subtraction.

Alternative Method
Have students enter the matrices into a graphing calculator, and then add or subtract the appropriate matrices.

A *matrix* is a rectangular arrangement of numbers. You can display a matrix by writing it between brackets as shown at the right. You identify the size of a matrix by how many rows and columns it has. This matrix has two rows and three columns, so it is a 2×3 (two-by-three) matrix. Each number in a matrix is called an *entry*. This matrix has six entries.

$$\begin{bmatrix} -1 & 4 & 9 \\ 3 & -5 & 7 \end{bmatrix}$$

You can add or subtract matrices if they are the same size. You do this by adding or subtracting corresponding entries.

EXAMPLE

Add $\begin{bmatrix} 6 & -5 \\ 0 & 3 \end{bmatrix} + \begin{bmatrix} 1 & 8 \\ -2 & 10 \end{bmatrix}$.

$$\begin{bmatrix} 6 & -5 \\ 0 & 3 \end{bmatrix} + \begin{bmatrix} 1 & 8 \\ -2 & 10 \end{bmatrix} = \begin{bmatrix} 6+1 & -5+8 \\ 0+(-2) & 3+10 \end{bmatrix}$$

$$= \begin{bmatrix} 7 & 3 \\ -2 & 13 \end{bmatrix}$$

EXERCISES

Add or subtract each pair of matrices.

1. $\begin{bmatrix} 3 & 8 \\ 1 & 5 \end{bmatrix} + \begin{bmatrix} 8 & 2 \\ 0 & 7 \end{bmatrix}$ $\begin{bmatrix} 11 & 10 \\ 1 & 12 \end{bmatrix}$

2. $\begin{bmatrix} -6 & 3 \\ -8 & 1 \end{bmatrix} - \begin{bmatrix} -4 & -9 \\ 3 & 5 \end{bmatrix}$ $\begin{bmatrix} -2 & 12 \\ -11 & -4 \end{bmatrix}$

3. $\begin{bmatrix} 1 & -6 \\ 2 & -7 \end{bmatrix} + \begin{bmatrix} \frac{1}{2} & -1 \\ \frac{2}{3} & -2 \end{bmatrix}$ $\begin{bmatrix} 1\frac{1}{2} & -7 \\ 2\frac{2}{3} & -9 \end{bmatrix}$

4. $\begin{bmatrix} \frac{1}{3} & \frac{3}{4} \\ \frac{1}{2} & \frac{2}{5} \end{bmatrix} - \begin{bmatrix} -\frac{1}{6} & \frac{1}{4} \\ -\frac{3}{5} & \frac{2}{3} \end{bmatrix}$ $\begin{bmatrix} \frac{1}{2} & \frac{1}{2} \\ \frac{11}{10} & -\frac{4}{15} \end{bmatrix}$

5. $\begin{bmatrix} 2 & 9 \\ 6 & 7 \end{bmatrix} + \begin{bmatrix} 6 & 2.3 \\ 9 & 4.1 \end{bmatrix}$ $\begin{bmatrix} 8 & 11.3 \\ 15 & 11.1 \end{bmatrix}$

6. $\begin{bmatrix} 3 & -7 & 4 \\ 0 & -4 & 9 \end{bmatrix} + \begin{bmatrix} -9 & 4 & 10 \\ 3 & -11 & 2 \end{bmatrix}$ **See above.**

   $\begin{bmatrix} -6 & -3 & 14 \\ 3 & -15 & 11 \end{bmatrix}$

7. $\begin{bmatrix} 5 & -3.5 \\ 10 & 14 \\ -5 & 4.7 \end{bmatrix} + \begin{bmatrix} -6.1 & 0.8 \\ 7 & -5 \\ 8.3 & 9 \end{bmatrix}$ $\begin{bmatrix} -1.1 & -2.7 \\ 17 & 9 \\ 3.3 & 13.7 \end{bmatrix}$

8. $\begin{bmatrix} 4 & 2 & 9 \\ -11 & 20 & 5 \\ -18 & 21 & -2 \end{bmatrix} - \begin{bmatrix} 8 & 17 & 4 \\ -34 & 26 & -9 \\ 3 & 0 & 17 \end{bmatrix}$ **See above.**

   $\begin{bmatrix} -4 & -15 & 5 \\ 23 & -6 & 14 \\ -21 & 21 & -19 \end{bmatrix}$

9. Use matrix addition to find the total number of Greenfield students per grade involved in each activity. **See margin.**

	Greenfield High School North		
	Sports	Drama	Debate
9th	146	5	11
10th	201	15	4
11th	205	11	7
12th	176	19	13

	Greenfield High School South		
	Sports	Drama	Debate
9th	301	13	9
10th	345	8	6
11th	245	11	11
12th	220	11	9

page 640 Algebra 1 Review

9.	Sports	Drama	Debate
	447	18	20
	546	23	10
	450	22	18
	396	30	22

Translations

 North Carolina Objectives

3.01 Describe the transformation of polygons in the coordinate plane in simple algebraic terms.
3.02 Use matrix operations to describe the transformations.

Lesson Preview

What You'll Learn

OBJECTIVE 1
To describe translations using vectors

OBJECTIVE 2
To find translation images using matrix and vector sums

. . . And Why

To determine a position after a composition of translations, as in Example 4

✔ **Check Skills You'll Need**   (For help, go to Lesson 9-4 and page 640.)

Write the sum of the two vectors as an ordered pair.

1. $\langle 12, -3 \rangle$ and $\langle -8, 6 \rangle$ $\langle 4, 3 \rangle$ **2.** $\langle -1, -5 \rangle$ and $\langle -6, 10 \rangle$ $\langle -7, 5 \rangle$

Add each pair of matrices.

3. $\begin{bmatrix} -2 & 3 \\ 1 & 8 \end{bmatrix} + \begin{bmatrix} -5 & 0 \\ -2 & 5 \end{bmatrix}$ $\begin{bmatrix} -7 & 3 \\ -1 & 13 \end{bmatrix}$ **4.** $\begin{bmatrix} -1 & -2 & -3 \\ -7 & -6 & -5 \end{bmatrix} + \begin{bmatrix} 2 & 2 & 2 \\ 3 & 3 & 3 \end{bmatrix}$

New Vocabulary   • translation   • composition $\begin{bmatrix} 1 & 0 & -1 \\ -4 & -3 & -2 \end{bmatrix}$

OBJECTIVE 1

Translations Using Vectors

Real-World Connection

It is easier to check parts when each is a translation image of the others.

A translation (or *slide*) is an isometry that maps all points of a figure the same distance in the same direction. Thus you can use a vector to describe a translation.

Using the diagram at the right, a **translation** described by $\overrightarrow{VV'}$ is a transformation that maps point A to A' so that the following are true.

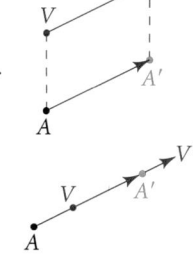

• $AA'V'V$ is a parallelogram if A, V, and V' are noncollinear.
• $AA' = VV'$ and $AV = A'V'$ if A, V, and V' are collinear.

For the coordinate plane, recall that you use an ordered pair $\langle x, y \rangle$ for a vector. In this notation, x represents horizontal change and y represents vertical change from the initial point to the terminal point.

TEXT Interactive lesson includes instant self-check, tutorials, and activities.

1 EXAMPLE **Translations Using Vectors**

a. Find the image of T under the translation described by the vector $\langle 2, 3 \rangle$.

$\langle 2, 3 \rangle$ is a translation right 2 units and up 3 units. The image of T under $\langle 2, 3 \rangle$ is R.

b. Find the vector that describes the translation $S \rightarrow U$.

To go from S to U, you move left 4 units and down 5 units. The translation vector is $\langle -4, -5 \rangle$.

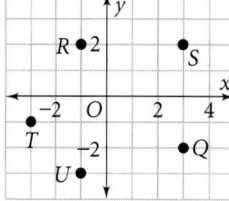

✔ **Check Understanding** **1** Refer to the diagram in Example 1.
a. Find the image of Q under the translation described by the vector $\langle -4, 4 \rangle$. *R*
b. Find the vector that describes the translation $T \rightarrow S$. $\langle 6, 3 \rangle$

Ongoing Assessment and Intervention

Before the Lesson
Diagnose prerequisite skills using:
• Check Skills You'll Need

During the Lesson
Monitor progress using:
• Check Understanding
• Additional Examples
• Standardized Test Prep

After the Lesson
Assess knowledge using:
• Lesson Quiz
• Computer Test Generator CD

Lesson Preview

✔ **Check Skills You'll Need**

Adding Vectors
Lesson 9-4: Example 4
Exercises 17–22
Extra Practice, p. 698

Matrices
Algebra Review, p. 640
Exercises 1–9

Lesson Resources

📁 **Teaching Resources**
Practice, Reteaching, Enrichment

🌱 **Reaching All Students**
Practice Workbook 12-2
Spanish Practice Workbook 12-2
Informal Geometry Planning
   Guide 12-2

⏱ **Presentation Assistant Plus!**
Transparencies
• Check Skills You'll Need 12-2
• Additional Examples 12-2
• Student Edition Answers 12-2
• Lesson Quiz 12-2
PH Presentation Pro CD 12-2

ASSESSMENT SYSTEM

Computer Test Generator CD

Technology
Resource Pro® CD-ROM
Computer Test Generator CD
Prentice Hall Presentation Pro CD

💻 **www.PHSchool.com**
Student Site
• Teacher Web Code: afk-5500
• Self-grading Lesson Quiz
Teacher Center
• Lesson Planner
• Resources

Plus **TEXT**

Professional
Development

Math Background

A translation is an isometry in which no point, in general, is its own image. A translation can be determined by its length and direction. A composition of transformations is simply a composition of functions. Composition of translations is commutative and associative, but this is not generally true for transformations.

OBJECTIVE

1 Teaching Notes

1 EXAMPLE Math Tip

Point out that the vector describing a translation goes from preimage to image. After students finish part b, ask: *Which vector describes the translation* $U \rightarrow S$? $\langle 4, 5 \rangle$

Additional Examples

1 Use the diagram below.

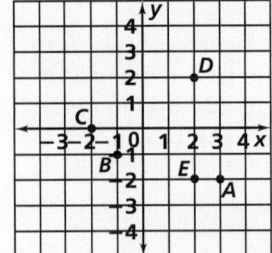

a. Find the image of A under the translation described by the vector $\langle -1, 4 \rangle$. **D**

b. Find the vector that describes the translation $B \rightarrow E$. $\langle 3, -1 \rangle$

2 Write a rule to describe the translation $\triangle ABC \rightarrow \triangle A'B'C'$.

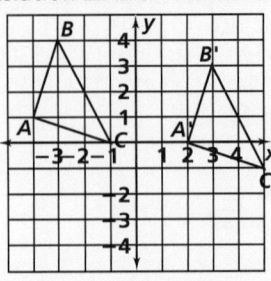

$(x, y) \rightarrow (x + 6, y - 1)$

Using variables, you can say that the vector $\langle a, b \rangle$ maps each (x, y) pair to $(x + a, y + b)$. Symbolically, $(x, y) \rightarrow (x + a, y + b)$.

2 EXAMPLE Writing a Rule to Describe a Translation

Write a rule to describe the translation $PQRS \rightarrow P'Q'R'S'$.

Use $P(-1, -2)$ and its image $P'(-5, -1)$.

Horizontal change: $-5 - (-1) = -4$
Vertical change: $-1 - (-2) = 1$

The vector is $\langle -4, 1 \rangle$.

The rule is $(x, y) \rightarrow (x - 4, y + 1)$.

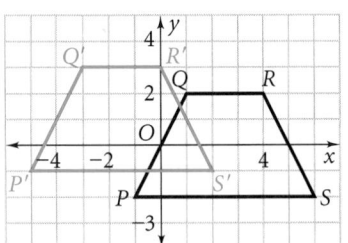

✓ **Check Understanding** **2** Use the rule $(x, y) \rightarrow (x + 7, y - 1)$ to find the translation image of $\triangle LMN$.
L′ (1, −2), M′(3, −4), N′(6, −2)

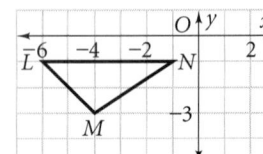

OBJECTIVE

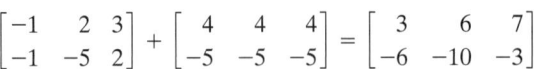

2 Translations Using Matrix and Vector Sums

You can use matrices to find translation images of several points at once. To translate a triangle, you need a matrix for the three vertices and a matrix that shows the translation vector three times.

3 EXAMPLE Using Matrices to Find Images

Use matrices to find the image of $\triangle MFH$ under the translation $\langle 4, -5 \rangle$.

$$\begin{array}{c} \\ x\text{-coordinate} \\ y\text{-coordinate} \end{array} \begin{array}{ccc} M & F & H \\ \begin{bmatrix} -1 & 2 & 3 \\ -1 & -5 & 2 \end{bmatrix} \end{array} \quad \text{Write a matrix for } \triangle MFH.$$

$$\begin{bmatrix} 4 & 4 & 4 \\ -5 & -5 & -5 \end{bmatrix} \quad \text{Write the translation matrix.}$$

$$\begin{bmatrix} -1 & 2 & 3 \\ -1 & -5 & 2 \end{bmatrix} + \begin{bmatrix} 4 & 4 & 4 \\ -5 & -5 & -5 \end{bmatrix} = \begin{bmatrix} 3 & 6 & 7 \\ -6 & -10 & -3 \end{bmatrix} \quad \text{Add the matrices.}$$

The image of $\triangle MFH$ is $\triangle M'F'H'$ with $M'(3, -6)$, $F'(6, -10)$, and $H'(7, -3)$.

✓ **Check Understanding** **3** Use matrices to find the image of $\triangle MFH$ under the translation $\langle 2, 8 \rangle$.
M′ (1, 7), F′ (4, 3), H′ (5, 10)

A **composition** of transformations is a combination of two or more transformations. In a composition, each transformation is performed on the image of the preceding transformation.

In a knight's move on a chessboard, the translation indicated in blue is the composition of two translations indicated in red.

642 Chapter 12 Transformations

Reaching All Students

| **Below Level** Have students copy the diagram in Example 1 on graph paper and draw the vectors that describe the translations. | **Advanced Learners** After students read about the composition of transformations, have them investigate whether composition of translations is commutative. | **Diversity** See note on page 644. **Error Prevention** See note on page 644. |

In general, the composition of any two translations is a translation.

4 EXAMPLE Real-World Connection

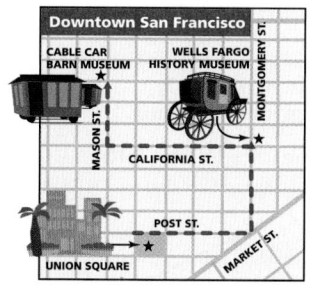

Tourism Yolanda Perez is visiting San Francisco. From her hotel near Union Square, she walks 4 blocks east and 4 blocks north to the Wells Fargo History Museum to see a stagecoach and relics of the Gold Rush. Then she walks 5 blocks west and 3 blocks north to the Cable Car Barn Museum. Now how many blocks is she from her hotel?

The vector $\langle 4, 4 \rangle$ represents a walk of 4 blocks east and 4 blocks north. The vector $\langle -5, 3 \rangle$ represents her second walk. Yolanda's current position is the sum of the vectors. $\langle 4, 4 \rangle + \langle -5, 3 \rangle = \langle -1, 7 \rangle$, so Yolanda is 1 block west and 7 blocks north of her hotel.

✓ **Check Understanding** ④ Yolanda next walks to a restaurant 2 blocks east and 4 blocks south of the Cable Car Barn Museum. Now how many blocks is she from her hotel? **1 block east and 3 blocks north of her hotel**

EXERCISES

For more practice, see *Extra Practice*.

Practice and Problem Solving

A Practice by Example

Example 1 (page 641)

Describe in words the translation represented by each vector. **1–5. See margin.**

1. $\langle 2, 5 \rangle$ **2.** $\langle 4, 1 \rangle$ **3.** $\langle -3, 8 \rangle$ **4.** $\langle 7, -2 \rangle$ **5.** $\langle -1, -6 \rangle$

Describe each translation using an ordered pair.

6. 0 units to the right, 4 units up $\langle 0, 4 \rangle$ **7.** 2 units to the left, 1 unit down $\langle -2, -1 \rangle$

8. 3 units to the left, 6 units down $\langle -3, -6 \rangle$ **9.** 8 units to the right, 10 units up $\langle 8, 10 \rangle$

In the diagram, find the image of F under the translation described by the given vector.

10. $\langle -1, 4 \rangle$ **C**   **11.** $\langle 4, -1 \rangle$ **H**   **12.** $\langle 4, 1 \rangle$ **G**

13. $\langle 1, 4 \rangle$ **E**   **14.** $\langle 5, 5 \rangle$ **I**   **15.** $\langle -4, -1 \rangle$ **B**

16. $\langle 0, -2 \rangle$
17. $\langle 5, 5 \rangle$
18. $\langle -6, -1 \rangle$

Find the vector that describes each translation.

16. $G \rightarrow H$ **17.** $B \rightarrow E$ **18.** $I \rightarrow C$

19. $H \rightarrow G$ $\langle 0, 2 \rangle$ **20.** $E \rightarrow B$ $\langle -5, -5 \rangle$ **21.** $C \rightarrow I$ $\langle 6, 1 \rangle$

Example 2 (page 642)

In Exercises 22–25, the blue figure is a translation image of the red figure. Write a rule to describe each translation.

22.

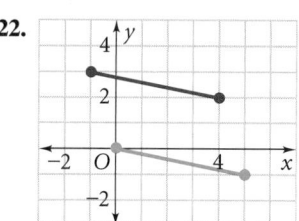

$(x, y) \rightarrow (x + 1, y - 3)$

23.

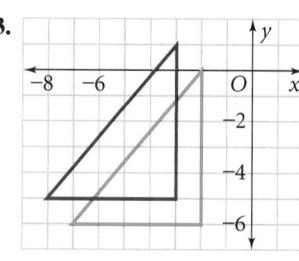

$(x, y) \rightarrow (x + 1, y - 1)$

Lesson 12-2 Translations   **643**

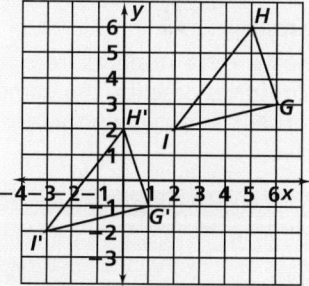

OBJECTIVE
2 Teaching Notes

4 EXAMPLE

Ask: *Why is a negative number used for Yolanda's walk west?* Vectors represent distance and direction, and left and down both are negative directions on a coordinate grid.

Additional Examples

3 $\overline{XY}$ has endpoints $X(-8, 11)$ and $Y(0, -4)$. Use matrices to find the image of $\overline{XY}$ under the translation $\langle 6, -5 \rangle$. $\overline{X'Y'}$ with $X'(-2, 6)$ and $Y'(6, -9)$

4 Tritt rides his bicycle 3 blocks north and 5 blocks east of a pharmacy to deliver a prescription. Then he rides 4 blocks south and 8 blocks west to make a second delivery. How many blocks is he now from the pharmacy? **1 block south and 3 blocks west**

Closure

$\triangle GHI \rightarrow \triangle G'H'I'$. Find the vector, rule, and 2×3 matrix that describe the translation. Then find the image $\triangle G''H''I''$ of $\triangle G'H'I'$ under the translation $\langle 8, 6 \rangle$.

vector: $\langle -5, -4 \rangle$;
rule: $(x, y) \rightarrow (x - 5, y - 4)$;
matrix: $\begin{bmatrix} -5 & -5 & -5 \\ -4 & -4 & -4 \end{bmatrix}$;
$\triangle G''H''I''$ with vertices $G''(9, 5)$, $H''(8, 8)$, and $I''(5, 4)$

Assignment Guide

1 Objective
 Ⓐ Ⓑ Core 1–25, 36–41, 47–49
 Ⓒ Extension 51

2 Objective
 Ⓐ Ⓑ Core 26–35, 42–46, 50
 Ⓒ Extension 52

Standardized Test Prep 53–58

Mixed Review 59–66

Error Prevention

Exercise 23 Suggest that students who are confused by overlapping figures focus on each vertex and its image separately.

Exercise 25 Remind students who think that the figures are not identical that the arrows indicate that both parabolas extend without bound.

Exercise 34 Discuss why 3 km southwest corresponds to the vector $\left\langle \frac{3}{2}\sqrt{2}, \frac{3}{2}\sqrt{2} \right\rangle$.

Diversity

Exercise 46 Have students from other countries describe the game of "football" as played in their countries.

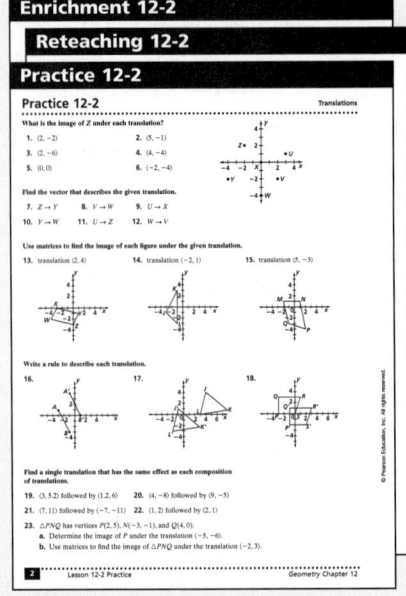

24.

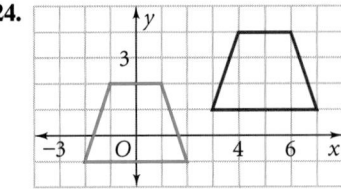

$(x, y) \rightarrow (x - 5, y - 2)$

25.

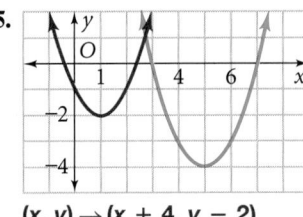

$(x, y) \rightarrow (x + 4, y - 2)$

Example 3 (page 642)

Use matrices to find the image of each figure under the given translation.

26. translation $\langle 3, 2 \rangle$ (−6, 5), (−3, 1), (2, 4) 27. translation $\langle 5, -1 \rangle$ **See left.**

27. (1, −2), (4, 1), (10, −2), (7, −5)

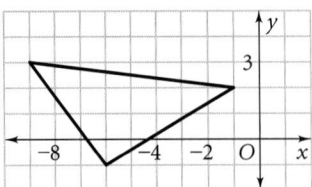   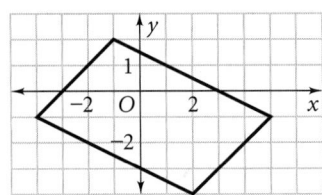

28. translation $\langle -2, 5 \rangle$ 29. translation $\langle -4, 3 \rangle$

30. A′(−2, 6), C′(−17, 9), E′(−9, −2)

31. P′(12, −13), U′(15, −7), N′(6, −5)

32. P′(−1, 0), L′(0, 1), A′(1, 1), T′(0, 0)

33. N′(−1, −9), I′(−1, −2), L′(−6, 0), E′(−6, −7)

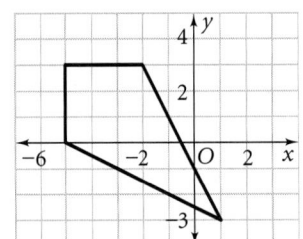   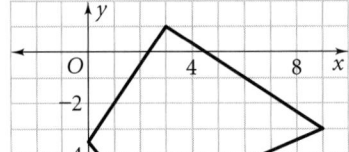

(−7, 5), (−7, 8), (−4, 8), (−1, 2)   (−4, −0.5), (−2, −3), (−1, 4), (5, 0)

30. $\triangle ACE$ with vertices $A(7, 2)$, $C(-8, 5)$, $E(0, -6)$; translation: $\langle -9, 4 \rangle$ **30–33.**

31. $\triangle PUN$ with vertices $P(1, 0)$, $U(4, 6)$, $N(-5, 8)$; translation: $\langle 11, -13 \rangle$ **See left.**

32. $\square PLAT$ with vertices $P(-2, 0)$, $L(-1, 1)$, $A(0, 1)$, $T(-1, 0)$; translation: $\langle 1, 0 \rangle$

33. $\square NILE$ with vertices $N(2, -5)$, $I(2, 2)$, $L(-3, 4)$, $E(-3, -3)$; translation: $\langle -3, -4 \rangle$

Example 4 (page 643)

34b. about 7.1 km west, 1.9 km north

34. Emily left Galveston Bay at the east jetty and sailed 4 km north to an oil rig. She then sailed 5 km west to Redfish Island. Finally, she sailed 3 km southwest to Spinnaker Restaurant.
 a. Draw vectors on graph paper that show her journey. **See back of book.**
 b. Describe where Spinnaker Restaurant is from where Emily started. **See left.**

35. Nakesha and her parents are visiting colleges. They leave their home in Enid, Oklahoma, and drive to Tulsa, which is 107 mi east and 18 mi south of Enid. From Tulsa, they go to Norman, 83 mi west and 63 mi south of Tulsa. Draw a diagram to show their trip. Then, tell where Norman is in relation to Enid. **See margin.**

Ⓑ Apply Your Skills

The orange figure is a translation image of the red figure. Write a rule to describe each translation.

36.

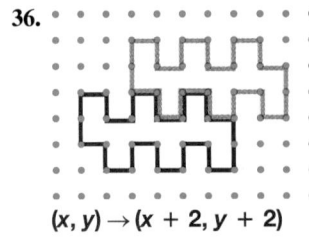

$(x, y) \rightarrow (x + 2, y + 2)$

37.

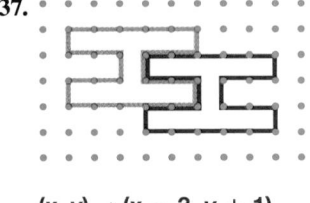

$(x, y) \rightarrow (x - 3, y + 1)$

644 Chapter 12 Transformations

pages 643–646 Exercises

35.

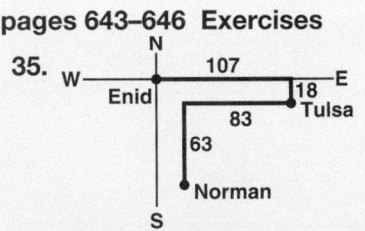

Norman is 24 mi east and 81 mi south of Enid.

Real-World Connection

A time-lapse photo captures translations of different points of the truck.

38. Photography When you snap a photograph, a shutter opens to expose the film to light. The amount of time that the shutter remains open is known as the shutter speed. For the photograph at the left, the photographer used a long shutter speed. It created an image that suggests a translation. Draw a picture of your own that suggests a translation. **Check students' work.**

39. Coordinate Geometry $\triangle MUG$ has coordinates $M(2, -4)$, $U(6, 6)$, and $G(7, 2)$. A translation maps point M to $M'(-3, 6)$. Find the coordinates of U' and G' under this translation. **U'(1, 16), G'(2, 12)**

40. Coordinate Geometry $\square ABCD$ has vertices $A(3, 6)$, $B(5, 5)$, $C(4, 2)$, and $D(2, 3)$. The figure is translated so that the image of point C is the origin.
a. Find the vector that describes the translation. **⟨−4, −2⟩**
b. Graph $\square ABCD$ and its image. **See back of book.**

41. Writing Is the transformation at the right, $\triangle HYP \rightarrow \triangle H'Y'P'$, a translation? Explain.
No; it is a reflection.

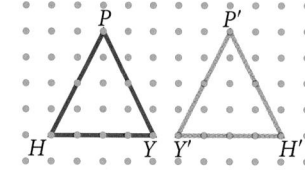

Find a single translation that has the same effect as each composition of translations.

42. ⟨2, 5⟩ followed by ⟨−4, 9⟩ **⟨−2, 14⟩**　　**43.** ⟨−3, 7⟩ followed by ⟨3, −7⟩ **⟨0, 0⟩**

44. ⟨1, −3⟩ followed by ⟨5, 2⟩ **⟨6, −1⟩**　　**45.** ⟨12, 0.5⟩ followed by ⟨1, −3⟩
　　　　　　　　　　　　　　　　　　　　　　⟨13, −2.5⟩

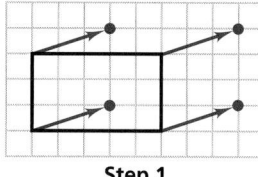

46. Football The play chart at the left shows routes that a wide receiver (WR) can choose to run when the team is in the "red zone" (within 20 yards of the goal line). The quarterback (QB) drops back two steps to make the pass to the wide receiver. **a–b. See left below.**
a. Suppose a wide receiver runs a slant. Describe the two translations involved and the composition of those two translations.
b. Describe the two intended translations of the football during the play, and the composition of the translations.
c. What is the intended outcome of the two compositions in parts (a) and (b)?
The WR catches the football passed by the QB.

46a. A slant involves one translation straight downfield and then another diagonally towards the middle of the field; the composition is one translation.

b. The ball drops straight back with the QB and is then thrown to the receiver downfield; the composition is one translation.

Geometry in 3 Dimensions Use each figure, graph paper, and the given vector to draw a three-dimensional figure.

SAMPLE Use the rectangle and vector ⟨3, 1⟩ to draw a box.

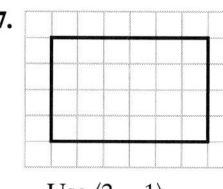

Step 1　　　　　　　　Step 2

47.
Use ⟨2, −1⟩.

48.
Use ⟨−2, 2⟩.

49.
Use ⟨−3, −5⟩.

47–49. See margin.

50. Open-Ended You work for a company that specializes in creating unique, artistic designs for business stationery. One of your clients is Totter Toy Co. You have been assigned to create a border design for the top of their stationery. Create a design that involves translations to present to your client.
Check students' work.

Lesson 12-2 Translations　**645**

47.

48.
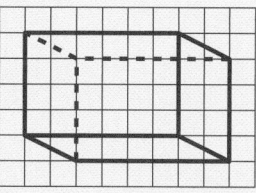

Lesson Quiz 12-2

Use the diagram below.

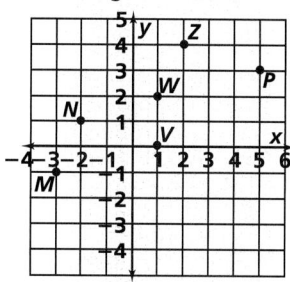

1. Find the image of N under the translation described by the vector ⟨−1, −2⟩. **M**

2. Find the vector that describes the translation $M \rightarrow Z$. **⟨5, 5⟩**

3. Find the image of Z under the composition of transformations described by the vectors ⟨−3, −4⟩, ⟨1, 5⟩, and ⟨2, −1⟩. **Z**

4. Write a rule to describe the translation $\triangle MNV \rightarrow \triangle WZP$.
$(x, y) \rightarrow (x + 4, y + 3)$

5. Write a matrix that you could use to find the image of $\triangle MNV$ under a translation of 2 units to the left and 5 units up.
$$\begin{bmatrix} -2 & -2 & -2 \\ 5 & 5 & 5 \end{bmatrix}$$

Alternative Assessment

Have each student draw a quadrilateral and its image under a translation in a coordinate grid. Then have students exchange papers with partners and find a vector, matrix, and rule to describe the translation shown.

49.
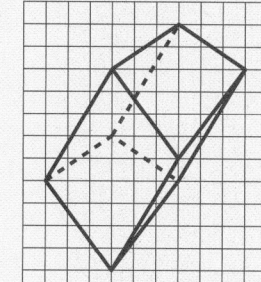

645

pages 643–646 Exercises

51. b. midpoint of $\overline{AB}$ = (−3, 2); midpoint of $\overline{BC}$ = (−1, −2); midpoint of $\overline{AC}$ = (0, 1); midpoint of $\overline{A'B'}$ = (1, 4); midpoint of $\overline{B'C'}$ = (3, 0); midpoint of $\overline{A'C'}$ = (4, 3); image of (−3, 2) = (1, 4) = midpoint of $\overline{A'B'}$; image of (−1, −2) = (3, 0) = midpoint $\overline{B'C'}$; image of (0, 1) = (4, 3) = midpoint of $\overline{A'C'}$

52. Translate a line segment in a direction different than along the segment. Then connect the endpoints of the line segment and its image to form a ▱.

59.
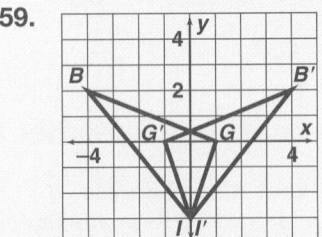

60.
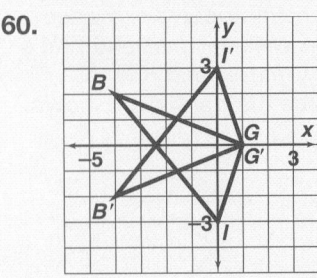

61.
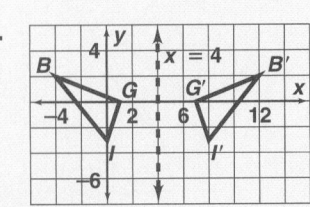

646

🅒 **Challenge**

51. **a.** △ABC has vertices $A(-2, 5)$, $B(-4, -1)$, and $C(2, -3)$. Find the image of △ABC under the translation $\langle 4, 2 \rangle$. **A'(2, 7), B'(0, 1), C'(6, −1)**

   b. Show that the images of the midpoints of the sides of △ABC are the midpoints of △A'B'C'. **See margin.**

✏️ 52. **Writing** Explain how a parallelogram could be defined in terms of translations. **See margin.**

Standardized Test Prep

Multiple Choice

53. What is the image of (6, −2) under the translation $\langle -5, -8 \rangle$? **D**
   A. (14, 3)   B. (−2, −7)   C. (11, 6)   D. (1, −10)

54. The point (5, −9) is the image under the translation $\langle 3, 2 \rangle$. What is the preimage? **F**
   F. (2, −11)   G. (8, −7)   H. (2, −7)   I. (8, −11)

55. What vector describes the translation of 4 units up and 12 units left? **B**
   A. $\langle 12, 4 \rangle$ B. $\langle -12, 4 \rangle$ C. $\langle -12, -4 \rangle$ D. $\langle 12, -4 \rangle$

56. What vector describes the translation from (0, −3) to (9, 5)? **I**
   F. $\langle -9, -8 \rangle$ G. $\langle -9, 8 \rangle$ H. $\langle 9, -8 \rangle$ I. $\langle 9, 8 \rangle$

57. △XYZ has vertices $X(-5, 2)$, $Y(0, -4)$, and $Z(3, 3)$. What are the vertices of the image of △XYZ under the translation $\langle 7, -5 \rangle$? **A**
   A. X'(2, −3), Y'(7, −9), Z'(10, −2)   B. X'(−12, 7), Y'(−7, 1), Z'(−4, 8)
   C. X'(−12, −3), Y'(−7, −9), Z'(−4, −2)   D. X'(2, −3), Y'(10, −2), Z'(7, −9)

Short Response

58. △ABC has coordinates $A(0, -3)$, $B(-4, -2)$, and $C(2, 1)$. A translation maps point B to (10, −3).
   a. What vector describes the translation? **a–b. See left.**
   b. What are the images of A and C under this translation?

Mixed Review

Lesson 12-1 △BIG has vertices $B(-4, 2)$, $I(0, -3)$, and $G(1, 0)$. Draw △BIG and then its reflection image in the given line. **59–61. See margin.**

59. the y-axis   60. the x-axis   61. $x = 4$

Lesson 10-5 Find the volume of each cylinder in terms of π.

62.
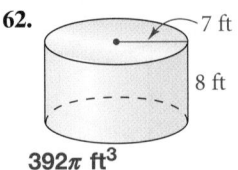
7 ft
8 ft
392π ft³

63.
10 cm
25 cm
2500π cm³

64.
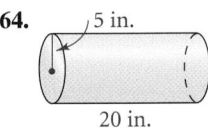
5 in.
20 in.
500π in.³

Lesson 8-5 Solve for x.

65.
x
6
5   16   **19.2**

66.
x 4.5
8.5   9
17

Rotations

 North Carolina Objectives

3.01 Describe the transformation (translation, reflection, rotation, dilation) of polygons in the coordinate plane in simple algebraic terms.

Lesson Preview

What You'll Learn

 OBJECTIVE 1
To draw and identify rotation images of figures

. . . And Why

To identify rotation images in art designs, as in Example 3

✓ Check Skills You'll Need

(For help, go to Lesson 7-5.)

Find the measure of the angle formed by two consecutive radii in each regular polygon.

1. triangle **120**   2. quadrilateral **90**   3. pentagon **72**

4. hexagon **60**   5. octagon **45**   6. decagon **36**

New Vocabulary • rotation

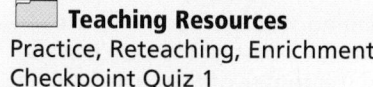

1. Plan

Lesson Preview

✓ Check Skills You'll Need

Finding Angle Measures
Lesson 7-5: Example 1
Exercises 1–3
Extra Practice, p. 696

Lesson Resources

Teaching Resources
Practice, Reteaching, Enrichment
Checkpoint Quiz 1

Reaching All Students
Practice Workbook 12-3
Spanish Practice Workbook 12-3
Reading and Math Literacy 12B
Spanish Reading & Literacy 12B
Spanish Checkpoint Quiz 1
Technology Activities 52
Informal Geometry Planning
   Guide 12-3

Presentation Assistant Plus!
Transparencies
• Check Skills You'll Need 12-3
• Additional Examples 12-3
• Student Edition Answers 12-3
• Lesson Quiz 12-3
PH Presentation Pro CD 12-3

 **ASSESSMENT SYSTEM**

Checkpoint Quiz 1
Computer Test Generator CD

Technology
Resource Pro® CD-ROM
Computer Test Generator CD
Prentice Hall Presentation Pro CD

 **www.PHSchool.com**
Student Site
• Teacher Web Code: afk-5500
• Self-grading Lesson Quiz
Teacher Center
• Lesson Planner
• Resources

Plus **iTEXT**

OBJECTIVE

1 **Drawing and Identifying Rotation Images**

 Interactive lesson includes instant self-check, tutorials, and activities.

Investigation: Making Designs With Rotations

You will need at least three pieces of tracing paper for this Investigation.

Step 1 Place a piece of paper over the figure at the right. Trace the six points on the circle, the center of the circle, and the triangle.

Step 2 Place the point of your pencil on the center of the circle and then rotate the paper until the six points align again. Trace the triangle in its new location.

Step 3 Repeat Step 2 until there are six triangles on your paper. Compare your drawings to others to be sure that your results look the same.

Check students' work.

Step 4 Now it's your turn to be creative. Place a piece of paper over the figure above, trace the six points on the circle and the center of the circle, and then draw your own triangle on the paper.

Step 5 Place the paper from Step 4 on your desk. On a blank piece of paper, repeat Steps 1–3. Color your drawing to make a design.

Turn the above diagram 60° about the center of the circle and each dot on the circle maps to the next dot on the circle. This is an example of a type of transformation known as a rotation (or *turn*).

Ongoing Assessment and Intervention

Before the Lesson
Diagnose prerequisite skills using:
• Check Skills You'll Need

During the Lesson
Monitor progress using:
• Check Understanding
• Additional Examples
• Standardized Test Prep

After the Lesson
Assess knowledge using:
• Lesson Quiz
• Computer Test Generator CD
• Chapter Checkpoint 1 (p. 652)

Math Background

A rotation is an isometry in which exactly one point is its own image, the center of rotation. A rotation function is uniquely determined by its center of rotation and its angle of rotation. The consideration of rotational symmetry in Lesson 12-5 presupposes a basic understanding of rotation.

OBJECTIVE
1 Teaching Notes

Investigation (Optional)

Remind students to make sure that the point of the pencil stays on the center of the circle as they rotate their papers. When their designs are complete, ask: *What toy displays patterns like this?* Sample: kaleidoscope

English Learners

Have students use an analog clock to explain the meanings of *clockwise* and *counterclockwise*.

1 EXAMPLE Inclusion

Students who have physical or visual difficulty using protractors may give directions to partners who do the actual drawing.

2 EXAMPLE

Discuss how to use a protractor to identify an angle greater than 180°. Point out that angles of rotation can be any positive number.

3 EXAMPLE

Point out that each counter-clockwise rotation also can be described as a clockwise rotation about another angle.

Technology Tip

Geometry software programs are ideal vehicles for exploring rotations. Students can rotate a figure any number of degrees and still keep the preimage in place.

Reading Math

Clockwise

Counterclockwise

1.

To describe a rotation, you need to know the center of rotation (a point), the angle of rotation (a positive number of degrees), and whether the rotation is clockwise or counterclockwise. Unless stated otherwise, rotations in this book are counterclockwise.

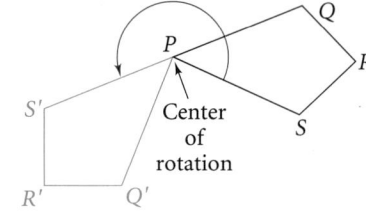

In general, a **rotation** of $x°$ about a point R is a transformation for which the following are true.

- The image of R is itself (that is, $R' = R$).
- For any point V, $RV' = RV$ and $m\angle VRV' = x$.

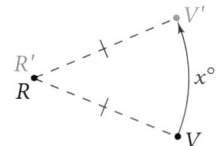

1 EXAMPLE Drawing a Rotation Image

Draw the image of $\triangle LOB$ for a 100° rotation about C.

Step 1
Use a protractor to draw a 100° angle with vertex C and side $\overline{CO}$.

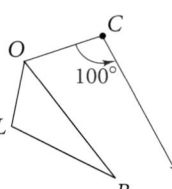

Step 2
Use a compass to construct $\overline{CO'} \cong \overline{CO}$.

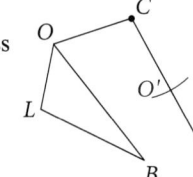

Step 3
Locate B' and L' in a similar manner. Draw $\triangle L'O'B'$.

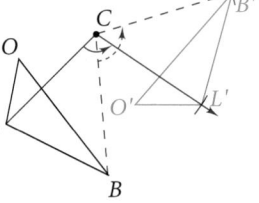

✓ Check Understanding **1** Draw the image of $\triangle LOB$ from Example 1 for a 50° rotation about B. Label the vertices of the image. **See left.**

You can use what you know about regular polygons to identify images for a given angle of rotation.

2 EXAMPLE Identifying a Rotation Image

Regular pentagon *PENTA* is divided into five congruent triangles.

a. Name the image of E for a 72° rotation about X.

b. Name the image of P for a 216° rotation about X.

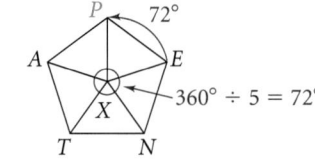

P is the image of E.

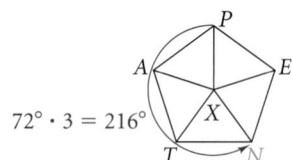

N is the image of P.

✓ Check Understanding **2** Name the image of T for a 144° rotation about X. **E**

648 Chapter 12 Transformations

🌟 Reaching All Students

| **Below Level** Students can investigate rotations of regular polygons by cutting them out of construction paper and anchoring them on cardboard with pins through their centers. | **Advanced Learners** After students complete Example 2, have them determine rules for rotating regular *n*-gons so that the rotation images and the preimages are identical. | **English Learners** See note on page 648. **Inclusion** See note on page 648. |

Figures that are rotation images of themselves have a special beauty that you will study more closely in Lesson 12-5.

3 EXAMPLE Real-World 🌎 Connection

Native American Art You can find circular designs with rotation images in some types of Native American art. In the design pictured, find the angle of rotation about *C* that maps *Q* to *X*.

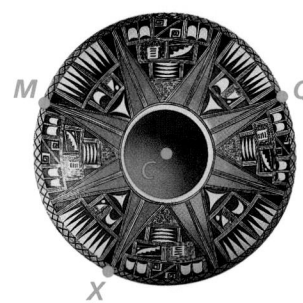

The eight-pointed star in the design divides the circle into eight congruent parts. $360 \div 8 = 45$, so each part has a 45° central angle. The angle of rotation that maps *Q* to *X* is $5 \cdot 45$, or 225°.

✓ **Check Understanding** **3** In the design above, find the angle of rotation about *C* that maps *Q* to *M*. **135°**

A composition of rotations about the same point is itself a rotation about that point. To sketch the image, add the angles of rotation to find the total rotation.

4 EXAMPLE Compositions of Rotations

Draw the image of the kite at the left for a composition of a 30° rotation and a 60° rotation, both about point *K*.

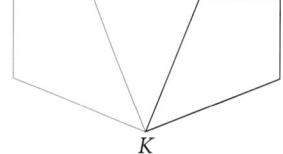

The total rotation is 90°. Draw the kite. Locate image points of the vertices for a 90° rotation. Use the image points to sketch the entire image.

✓ **Check Understanding** **4** Draw the kite at the left. Then draw its image for a composition of two 90° rotations about point *K*.
See margin.

1 Copy △*LOB*, and draw its image under a 60° rotation about *C*.
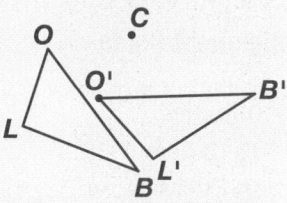

2 Regular hexagon *ABCDEF* is divided into six equilateral triangles.
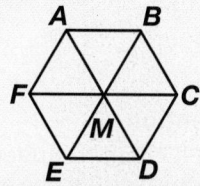

a. Name the image of *B* for a 240° rotation about *M*. **D**
b. Name the image of *M* for a 60° rotation about *F*. **A**

3 A regular 12-sided polygon can be formed by stacking congruent square sheets of paper rotated about the same center on top of each other. Find the angle of rotation about *M* that maps *W* to *B*.
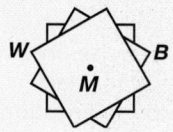
210°

4 Describe the image of quadrilateral *XYZW* for a composition of a 145° rotation and then a 215° rotation, both about point *X*. **The image is the preimage *XYZW*.**

Closure

BCDE is a square. Name three different rotations for which the image of point *C* is point *E*.
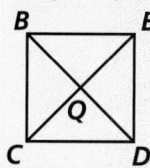

Sample: a 90° rotation about point *B*; a 180° rotation about point *Q*; a 270° rotation about point *D*

EXERCISES

For more practice, see *Extra Practice*.

Practice and Problem Solving

🅐 **Practice by Example**

Example 1
(page 648)

Copy each figure and point *P*. Draw the image of each figure for the given rotation about *P*. Label the vertices of the image. 1–5. See back of book.

1. 60°
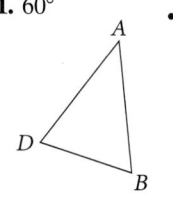

2. 90°
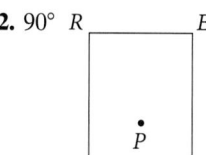

3. 90°
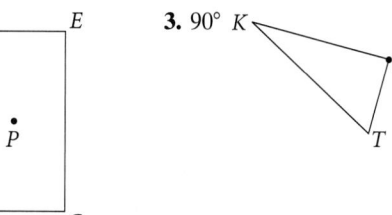

4. 180°
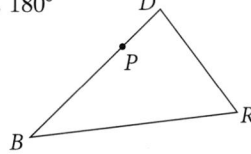

5. 140°
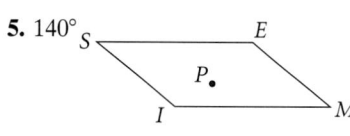

page 649   Check Understanding
4.
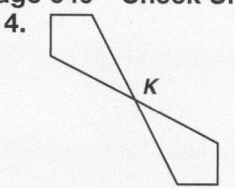

Assignment Guide

1 **Objective**
  Ⓐ Ⓑ **Core** 1–33
  Ⓒ **Extension** 34

Standardized Test Prep 35–39

Mixed Review 40–43

Error Prevention

Exercises 10–17 Before students begin, have the class list the angle measures of a regular triangle, quadrilateral, and hexagon and the measures of the central angles formed by the angle bisectors of their vertices. Have students discuss how to use this information to solve each exercise.

Exercises 28–30 There are many such rotations, each 360° more than the other.

Teaching Tip

Exercise 32 This exercise provides a good opportunity for class discussion and experimentation. Let students suggest ideas and test them. Focus the discussion by drawing a segment and its rotation and then erasing the center of rotation.

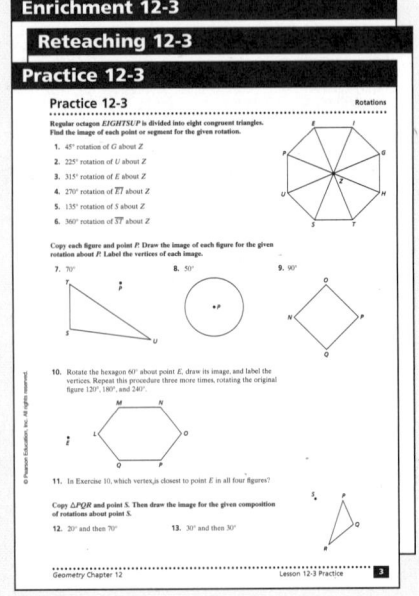

Copy each figure. Then draw the image of $\overline{JK}$ for a 180° rotation about P.

6. $J \quad P \quad K$

$K' \quad\quad J'$
$J \quad P \quad K$

7. $\quad K$
J
$\quad P$

7–9. See back of book.

8. J
$\quad\quad K$
$\quad P$

9. K
$\quad\quad J = P$
$\quad\quad P$

Example 2
(page 648)

The large triangle, quadrilateral, and hexagon are regular. Find the image of each point or segment for the given rotation. (*Hint:* Green segments form 30° angles.)

10. 120° rotation of B about O **H**

11. 270° rotation of L about O **M**

12. 60° rotation of E about O **C**

13. 300° rotation of $\overline{IB}$ about O **$\overline{BC}$**

14. 240° rotation of G about O **A**

15. 180° rotation of $\overline{JK}$ about O **$\overline{LM}$**

16. 120° rotation of F about H **I**

17. 270° rotation of M about L **K**

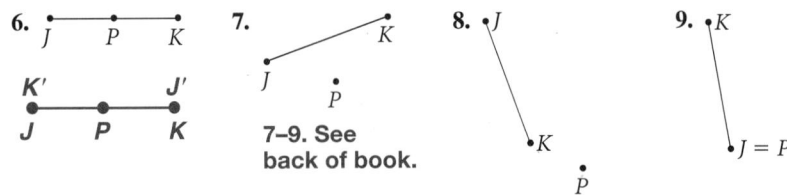

Example 3
(page 649)

Native American Art Find the angle of rotation about C that (a) maps Q to X and (b) maps X to Q.

18. **90°; 270°**

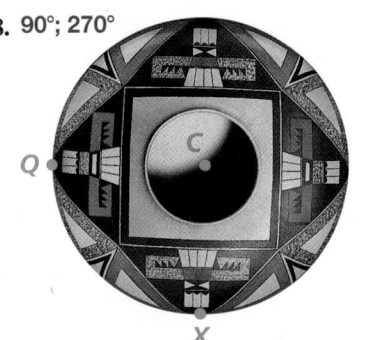

19. **108°; 252°**

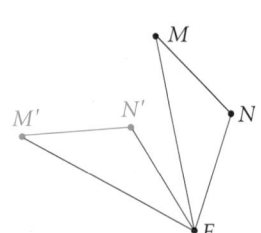

Example 4
(page 649)

For each of Exercises 20–25, copy $\triangle XYZ$. Draw the image of $\triangle XYZ$ for the given composition of rotations about the given point. **20–25. See back of book.**

20. 45°, then 45°; X

21. 45°, then 45°; Y

22. 30°, then 30°; Z

23. 20°, then 160°; Z

24. 135°, then 135°; Y

25. 180°, then 180°; X

Ⓑ **Apply Your Skills**

26. $\overline{M'N'}$ is the rotation image of $\overline{MN}$ about point E. Name all pairs of congruent angles and all pairs of congruent segments in the diagram. **See margin.**

27. **Language Arts** The symbol ə is called a *schwa*. It is used in dictionaries to represent neutral vowel sounds such as *a* in *ago*, *i* in *sanity*, and *u* in *focus*. What transformation maps a ə to a lowercase e? **180° rotation about its center**

pages 649–652 **Exercises**

26. $\overline{MN} \cong \overline{M'N'}$; $\overline{EN} \cong \overline{EN'}$; $\overline{ME} \cong \overline{M'E}$; $\angle M \cong \angle M'$; $\angle N \cong \angle N'$; $\angle MEN \cong \angle M'EN'$; $\angle MEM' \cong \angle NEN'$

Find the angle of rotation about C that maps the black figure onto the blue figure.

28. 180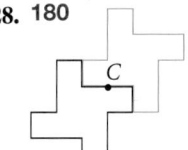

29.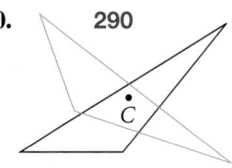

110

•C

30. 290

29–30. Answers may vary. Samples are given.

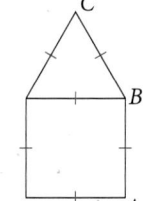

31. Sketch the figure at the right. Then draw three images of the figure for rotations of 90° about each of *A*, *B*, and *C*. **See back of book.**

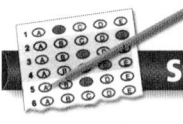

Reading Math

For help with reading and solving Exercise 32, see p. 653.

32. **Reasoning** If you are given a figure and a rotation image of the figure, how can you find the center and angle of rotation? **See margin.**

33. **Writing** Describe compositions of rotations that have the same effect as a 360° rotation about a point *X*. **See left.**

C Challenge

33. Answers may vary. Sample: a 90° and a 270° rotation

34. **a. Coordinate Geometry** Graph *A*(5, 2). Then graph *B*, the image of *A* for a 90° rotation about the origin *O*. (*Hint:* Consider the slope of $\overline{OA}$.)
 b. Graph *C*, the image of *A* for a 180° rotation about *O*. **a–c. See**
 c. Graph *D*, the image of *A* for a 270° rotation about *O*. **back of book.**
 d. What type of quadrilateral is *ABCD*? Explain.
  Square; all sides are ≅ and all ∠ are 90°.

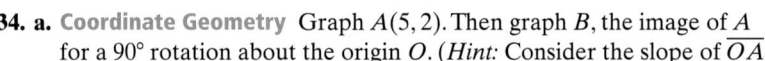

Standardized Test Prep

Multiple Choice

35. Name the image of *X* for a 240° counterclockwise rotation about the center of the regular hexagon. **B**
 A. *A*   **B.** *G*   **C.** *O*   **D.** *H*

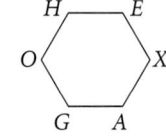

36. What is the image of (1, −6) for a 90° counterclockwise rotation about the origin? **F**
 F. (6, 1)   **G.** (−1, 6)   **H.** (−6, −1)   **I.** (−1, −6)

Reading Comprehension

Read the passage below. Then answer the questions on the basis of what is stated or implied in the passage.

The same hemisphere of the moon always faces Earth. Thus, the motion of the moon about Earth for a given time interval can be modeled by a rotation. The center of the rotation is the center of Earth. The angle of rotation is determined by the time interval, given that one journey of the moon around Earth takes about $27\frac{1}{3}$ days.

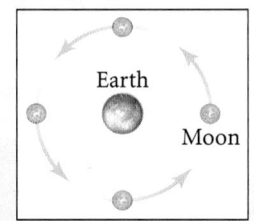

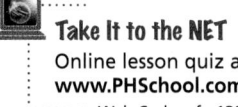

Take It to the NET

Online lesson quiz at **www.PHSchool.com**
Web Code: afa-1203

37. What rotation is modeled by the motion of the moon? **B**
 A. a circle rotating about its center   **B.** a circle rotating about a point
 C. 2 circles rotating around each other   **D.** a circle rotating around a circle

38. In how many days does the moon complete a 90° angle of rotation? **G**
 F. about 4   **G.** about 7   **H.** about 14   **I.** about 27

Short Response

39. △*XYZ* has vertices *X*(1, 2), *Y*(0, 5), and *Z*(−8, 0). **a–b. See back of book.**
 a. Graph △*XYZ* and its image after a 270° rotation about the origin.
 b. Name the coordinates of each vertex of the image.

Lesson 12-3 Rotations **651**

32. Draw two segments connecting preimage pts. *A* and *B* to image pts. *A'* and *B'*. Construct the ⊥ bis. of $\overline{AA'}$ and $\overline{BB'}$ to find *C*, the center of rotation. *m∠ACA'* is the ∠ of rotation.

Lesson Quiz 12-3

Copy △RST and point C. Draw the image for the given transformation about point C. Label the vertices of the image.

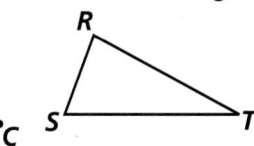

1. 75° rotation

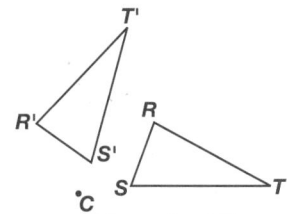

2. composition of a 30° rotation and then a 150° rotation

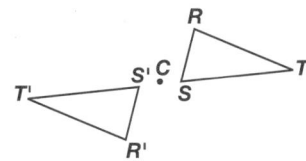

ABCDEFGH is a regular octagon. Name the image for the given rotation.

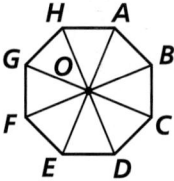

3. 135° rotation of *A* about *O*
 F

4. 270° rotation of $\overline{DE}$ about *O* $\overline{FG}$

5. 135° rotation of *B* about *O*
 G

Alternative Assessment

Have each student pick a point in a coordinate plane and find the coordinates of its images after a 90°, 180°, and 270° rotation about the origin. Then have them guess what the coordinates of the image of (*x, y*) are under the rotations above.

Mixed Review

Lesson 12-2

In each diagram, the blue figure is the translation image of the red figure. Write a rule to describe each translation.

40.

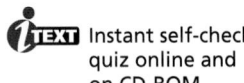

$(x, y) \rightarrow (x + 4, y - 2)$

41.

$(x, y) \rightarrow (x - 5, y - 1)$

Lesson 10-7 🌐 **42. Geography** The United States has about 3,540,000 mi² of land. Earth is approximately a sphere with radius 3960 miles. What percent, to the nearest tenth, of the surface area of Earth is the land area of the United States? **1.8%**

Lesson 9-4 🌐 **43. Navigation** An airplane lands at a point 100 km east and 420 km south from where it took off. Describe the magnitude and the direction of its flight vector. **about 431.7 mi at 76.6° south of east**

✓ Checkpoint Quiz 1   Lessons 12-1 through 12-3

📱 **TEXT** Instant self-check quiz online and on CD-ROM

1. No; the figures are not ≅.

2. Yes; the figures are ≅ and the transf. is a translation.

3. Yes; the figures are ≅ and the transf. is a translation or reflection.

4. ⟨−3, 5⟩ is a translation of 3 units to the left and 5 units up.

State whether the transformation appears to be an isometry. Explain.

1.

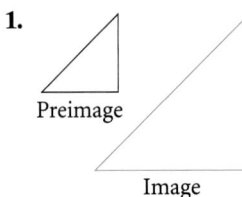

Preimage

Image

2. Image

Preimage

3. Image

Preimage

1–4. See left.

4. Describe in words the translation represented by the vector ⟨−3, 5⟩.

5. Use an ordered pair to describe a translation 5 units left and 10 units up. **⟨−5, 10⟩**

6. Describe in words the result of the translation ⟨7, −2⟩ followed by the translation ⟨−3, 2⟩. **⟨4, 0⟩, a translation of 4 units to the right**

Sketch each figure and point A. Draw the image of each figure for the given angle of rotation about A. Label the vertices of the image. **7–9. See margin.**

7. 40°

8. 90°

9. 180°

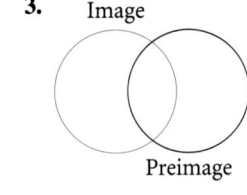

10. △WXY has vertices $W(-4, 1)$, $X(2, -7)$, and $Y(0, -3)$. Find its image for the translation ⟨−2, 5⟩. **$W'(-6, 6)$, $X'(0, -2)$, $Y'(-2, 2)$**

page 652 **Checkpoint Quiz 1**

7.

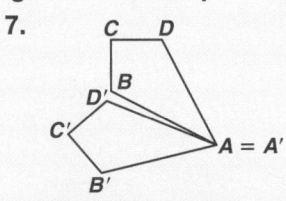

8.

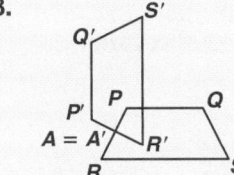

9.

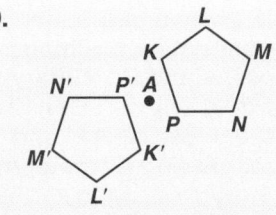

Reading for Problem Solving

FOR USE WITH PAGE 651, EXERCISE 32

Read the problem below and then follow along with what Kate thinks as she solves the problem. Check your understanding by solving the exercise at the bottom of the page.

If you are given a figure and a rotation image of the figure, how can you find the center and angle of rotation?

What Kate Thinks	What Kate Draws
I'll use tracing paper and draw two congruent figures that have the same orientation. I like the letter K, so I think I'll use it. I'll tilt one K so that it's not a translation image.	
I think I see a rotation. It will rotate the left K counterclockwise onto the right K. It will rotate point A to point A' and point B to point B'.	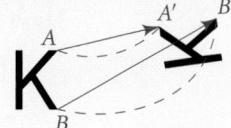
That means that A and A' are on a circle whose center is the center of rotation. The same is true for B and B'. The perpendicular bisectors of both $\overline{AA'}$ and $\overline{BB'}$ go through the center. I'll use blue to construct the perpendicular bisectors.	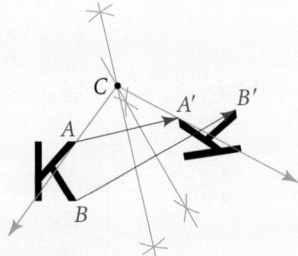
Point C must be a center of rotation.	
I can check this using tracing paper.	
To find the angle of rotation, I just have to draw $\angle ACA'$ and measure it.	The center of rotation is C. The angle of rotation is 98°.

EXERCISE

In a newspaper or magazine that you can cut, find two large identical letters that are the same size and type. Cut them out and place them at random on a large piece of paper. Then find the center and angle of rotation that maps one onto the other. **Check students' work.**

Reading for Problem Solving

Mathematics problems sometimes ask generalized questions that can be answered by examining any example that a student chooses. This feature helps students think how to represent a problem and how to reason through its solution.

Teaching Notes

Before students begin to answer the question, have them rotate a triangle 90° and 180° about different centers of rotation.

Tactile Learners

Have students use a compass and straightedge to model the problem as they read through the solution.

Exercise

Have students work independently to solve the problem, showing the steps they used. Then have volunteers share with the class what they were thinking as they wrote each step. Elicit the fact that there are often different ways to arrive at the solution of a problem.

1. Plan

Lesson Preview

✓ **Check Skills You'll Need**

Drawing Reflection Images
Lesson 12-1: Example 3
Exercises 10–17
Extra Practice, p. 701

Compositions of Translations
Lesson 12-2: Example 4
Exercises 33, 34
Extra Practice, p. 701

Lesson Resources

📁 **Teaching Resources**
Practice, Reteaching, Enrichment

👥 **Reaching All Students**
Practice Workbook 12-4
Spanish Practice Workbook 12-4
Informal Geometry Planning
   Guide 12-4

⏱ **Presentation Assistant Plus!**
Transparencies
• Check Skills You'll Need 12-4
• Additional Examples 12-4
• Student Edition Answers 12-4
• Lesson Quiz 12-4
PH Presentation Pro CD 12-4

ASSESSMENT SYSTEM (PRENTICE HALL)

Computer Test Generator CD

💿 **Technology**
Resource Pro® CD-ROM
Computer Test Generator CD
Prentice Hall Presentation Pro CD

🖥 **www.PHSchool.com**
Student Site
• Teacher Web Code: afk-5500
• Self-grading Lesson Quiz
Teacher Center
• Lesson Planner
• Resources

Plus 🄸TEXT

654

12-4

Compositions of Reflections

North Carolina Objectives    3.01   Describe the transformation (translation, reflection, rotation, dilation) of polygons in the coordinate plane in simple algebraic terms.

Lesson Preview

What You'll Learn

OBJECTIVE **1** To use a composition of reflections

OBJECTIVE **2** To identify glide reflections

. . . And Why

To classify isometries, as in Example 5

✓ **Check Skills You'll Need**   (For help, go to Lessons 12-1 and 12-2.)

Given points $R(-1, 1)$, $S(-4, 3)$, and $T(-2, 5)$, draw $\triangle RST$ and its reflection image in each line. 1–3. See back of book.

1. the y-axis   **2.** the x-axis   **3.** $y = 1$

Draw $\triangle RST$ described above and its translation image for each translation vector.

4. $\langle 0, -3 \rangle$ 4–6. See back of book.   **5.** $\langle 4, 0 \rangle$ **6.** $\langle 2, -5 \rangle$

7. Copy the figure. Draw images of the figure for a reflection in $\overleftrightarrow{DG}$ and for the translation vector $\overrightarrow{FG}$.
See back of book.

New Vocabulary   • glide reflection

[figure: trapezoid with vertices labeled E, F (top), D, G (bottom)]

OBJECTIVE **1**

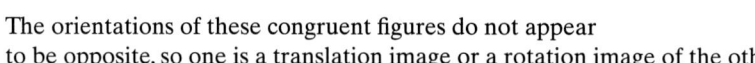
Compositions of Reflections

🄸TEXT **Interactive lesson includes instant self-check, tutorials, and activities.**

Need Help?
You know a reflection is involved if a figure and its image have opposite orientations.

If two figures are congruent, there is a transformation that maps one onto the other. If no reflection is involved, then the figures are either translation or rotation images of each other.

1 EXAMPLE   **Recognizing the Transformation**

The two figures are congruent. Is one figure a translation image of the other, a rotation image, or neither? Explain.

The orientations of these congruent figures do not appear to be opposite, so one is a translation image or a rotation image of the other.
• Clearly, it's not a translation image, so it must be a rotation image.

✓ **Check Understanding**   **1** The two figures are congruent. Is one figure a translation image of the other, a rotation image, or neither? Explain.
Neither; the figures do not have the same orientation.

Any translation or rotation can be expressed as the composition of two reflections.

Key Concepts

Theorem 12-1

A translation or rotation is a composition of two reflections.

The examples that illustrate Theorems 12-2 and 12-3 suggest a proof of Theorem 12-1 (how to find two reflections for a given translation or rotation).

Ongoing Assessment and Intervention

Before the Lesson
Diagnose prerequisite skills using:
• Check Skills You'll Need

During the Lesson
Monitor progress using:
• Check Understanding
• Additional Examples
• Standardized Test Prep

After the Lesson
Assess knowledge using:
• Lesson Quiz
• Computer Test Generator CD

Theorems 12-2 and 12-3 together form the converse of Theorem 12-1.

 Key Concepts

> **Theorem 12-2**
>
> A composition of reflections in two parallel lines is a translation.

> **Theorem 12-3**
>
> A composition of reflections in two intersecting lines is a rotation.

Real-World 🌐 **Connection**

Each mirror shows a reverse image. But bend the mirrors like this ╱‾╲ and you get compositions of reflections.

2 EXAMPLE **Composition of Reflections in Parallel Lines**

Find the image of R or a reflection in line ℓ followed by a reflection in line *m*. Describe the resulting translation.

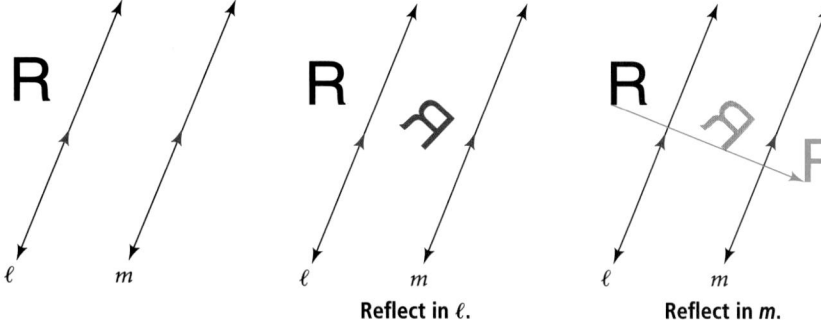

Reflect in ℓ.   Reflect in *m*.

R is translated the distance and direction shown by the green arrow. The arrow is perpendicular to lines ℓ and *m* with length equal to twice the distance from ℓ to *m*.

✓ **Check Understanding** ❷ Draw lines ℓ and *m* as shown above. Draw R between ℓ and *m*. Find the image of R for a reflection in line ℓ and then in line *m*. Describe the resulting translation. **See back of book.**

3 EXAMPLE **Composition of Reflections in Intersecting Lines**

Lines *a* and *b* intersect in point *C* and form acute ∠1 with measure 35. Find the image of R for a reflection in line *a* and then a reflection in line *b*. Describe the resulting rotation.

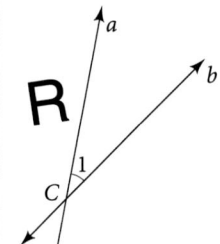 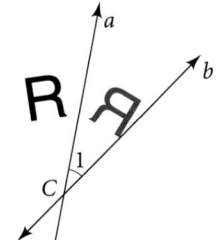 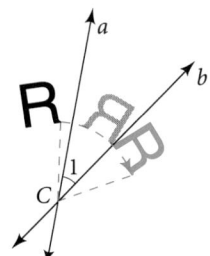

Reflect in *a*.   Reflect in *b*.

R rotates clockwise through the angle shown by the green arrow. The center of rotation is *C* and the measure of the angle is twice *m*∠1, or 70.

✓ **Check Understanding** ❸ Repeat Example 3, but begin with R in a different position. **See back of book.**

Lesson 12-4 Compositions of Reflections **655**

 Reaching All Students

| **Below Level** Before students read the theorems in this lesson, have them try compositions of reflections using geometry software or paper and pencil. | **Advanced Learners** After Example 2, have students find the image of R reflected in line ℓ and then in line *m*, when ℓ ⊥ *m*, and develop a theorem for this composition of reflections. | **Tactile Learners** See note on page 658. **Auditory Learners** See note on page 658. |

2. Teach

 Professional Development

Math Background

The four distinct isometry types can be divided into two sets: the direct, or sense-preserving, set that contains translations and rotations; and the opposite, or sense-reversing, set that contains reflections and glide reflections. The theorems in this lesson summarize the abstract algebra group properties of these isometries.

OBJECTIVE
1 **Teaching Notes**

2 EXAMPLE **Error Prevention**

Students may think that each R should look like a translation of the original R. Have them copy the diagram and use paper folding to see why the orientation of the second R must be different from that of the first and third Rs.

Math Tip
Copy the composition of reflections in Example 2 on the board. Label the distance between R and line ℓ "*x*" and the distance between line *m* and the reflection in line *m* "*y*". Have students use algebra to compare the length of the arrow with the distance between lines ℓ and *m*.

3 EXAMPLE **Technology Tip**

Have students use geometry software to carry out the composition of reflections and then show that a counter-clockwise rotation of 294° about point *C* creates the same image.

Additional Examples

1 Judging by appearances, is one figure a translation image or a rotation image of the other? Explain.

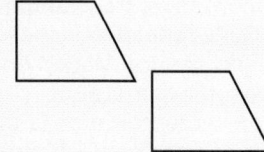

translation; congruent with same orientation

655

Additional Examples

2 Find the image of the figure for a reflection in line ℓ and then line *m.*

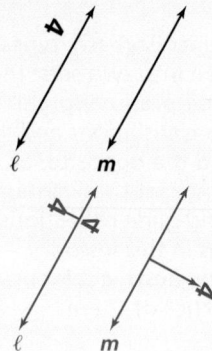

3 The letter D is reflected in line *x* and then in line *y.* Describe the resulting rotation.

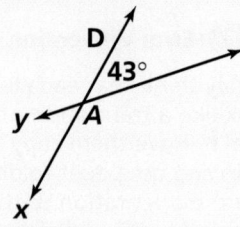

D rotates 86° clockwise about the center of rotation *A.*

Additional Examples

4 △*ABC* has vertices *A*(−4, 5), *B*(6, 2), and *C*(0, 0). Find the image of △*ABC* for a glide reflection where the glide is ⟨0, 2⟩ and the reflection line is *x* = 1. *A'*(6, 7), *B'*(−4, 4), and *C'*(2, 2)

5 Tell whether the orientations are the same or opposite. Then classify the isometry.

opposite; reflection in vertical line

Closure

Name four isometries. Then choose two, and explain which composition of transformations results in each. **Glide reflection, reflection, rotation, translation; sample: Glide reflection is the composition of a translation and a reflection in a line ∥ to the translation vector; rotation is the composition of two reflections.**

656

Two plane figures A and B can be congruent with opposite orientations. Reflect A and you get a figure A′ that has the same orientation as B. Thus, B is a translation or rotation image of A′. By Theorem 12-1, two reflections map A′ to B. The net result is that three reflections map A to B.

This is summarized in what is sometimes called the Fundamental Theorem of Isometries.

Key Concepts

Theorem 12-4	Fundamental Theorem of Isometries

In a plane, one of two congruent figures can be mapped onto the other by a composition of at most three reflections.

If two figures are congruent and have opposite orientations (but are not simply reflections of each other), then there is a slide and a reflection that will map one onto the other. A **glide reflection** is the composition of a glide (translation) and a reflection in a line parallel to the glide vector.

4 **EXAMPLE** **Finding a Glide Reflection Image**

Coordinate Geometry Find the image of △*TEX* for a glide reflection where the glide vector is ⟨0, −5⟩ and the reflection line is *x* = 0.

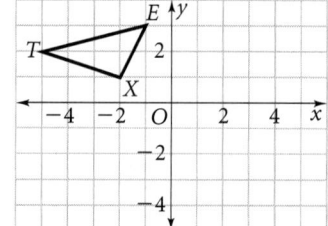

Real-World Connection

A computer can translate an image and then reflect it, or vice versa. The two rabbit images are glide reflection images of each other.

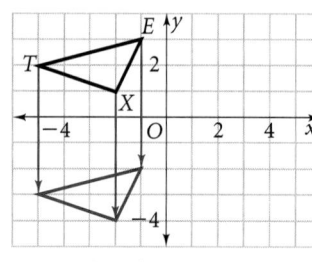

Translate △*TEX* by ⟨0, −5⟩.   Reflect the image in *x* = 0.

4a.
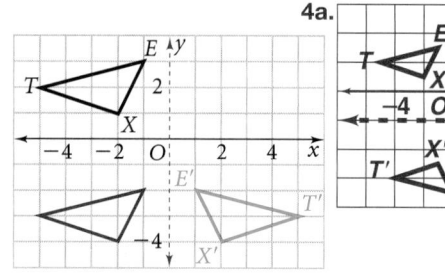

Check Understanding **4** Use △*TEX* from Example 4 above.
   a. Find the image of △*TEX* under a glide reflection where the glide vector is ⟨1, 0⟩ and the reflection line is *y* = −2. **See above.**
   b. **Critical Thinking** Would the result of part (a) be the same if you reflected △*TEX* first, and then translated it? Explain. **Yes; if you reflected it and then moved it right, the result would be the same.**

You can map one of any two congruent figures onto the other by a single reflection, translation, rotation, or glide reflection. Thus, you are able to classify any isometry.

 **Key Concepts**

Theorem 12-5 Isometry Classification Theorem

There are only four isometries. They are the following.

Reflection	Translation	Rotation	Glide reflection
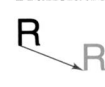			

5 EXAMPLE Classifying Isometries

Each figure is an isometry image of the figure at the left. Tell whether their orientations are the same or opposite. Then classify the isometry.

a.

b.

c.

d.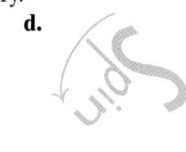

opposite;
a reflection

opposite;
a glide reflection

same;
a translation

same;
a rotation

✓ **Check Understanding** **5** Classify the isometry.
rotation

EXERCISES

For more practice, see *Extra Practice*.

Practice and Problem Solving

A Practice by Example

Example 1
(page 654)

The two figures in each pair are congruent. Is one figure a translation image of the other, a rotation image, or neither? Explain. 1–3. See margin.

1.

2.

3.

Example 2
(page 655)

Find the image of each letter through a reflection in line ℓ and then a reflection in line *m*. Describe the resulting translation or rotation. 4–5. See margin.

4.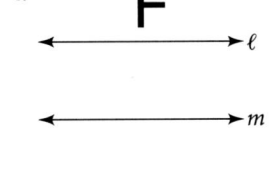

5.

6.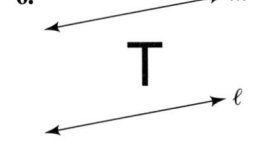

6–9. See back of book.

Example 3
(page 655)

7.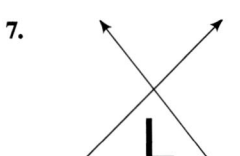

8.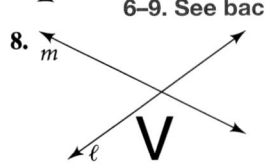

9.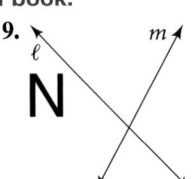

Assignment Guide

1 Objective
  A B Core 1–9, 26, 27, 32–37
  C Extension 49–51, 53

2 Objective
  A B Core 10–25, 28–31, 38–47
  C Extension 48, 52, 54–57

Standardized Test Prep 58–61

Mixed Review 62–69

Exercises 4–6 Before students begin, ask: *How can you tell that the composition of reflections will result in a translation?* Lines ℓ and *m* are parallel.

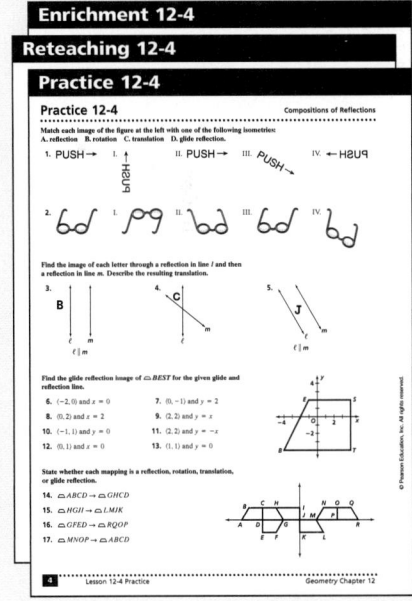

5.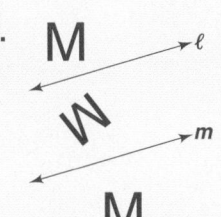

M is translated across line *m* twice the distance between ℓ and *m*.

---

pages 657–660 Exercises

1. rotation

2. translation

3. Neither; the figures do not have the same orientation.

4.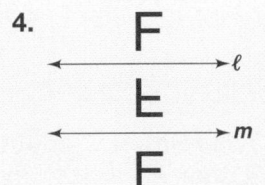

F is translated down twice the distance between ℓ and *m*.

657

Example 4
(page 656)

Find the glide reflection image of △PNB for the given glide vector and reflection line. 10–17. See back of book.

10. ⟨2, 0⟩ and y = 3   11. ⟨0, −3⟩ and x = 0

12. ⟨0, 3⟩ and x = −2   13. ⟨−2, 0⟩ and y = −1

14. ⟨2, 2⟩ and y = x   15. ⟨−1, 1⟩ and y = −x

16. ⟨0, −2⟩ and x = 2   17. ⟨−2, −2⟩ and y = x

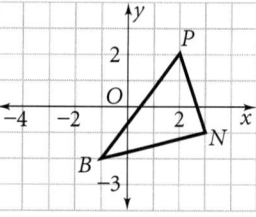

Example 5
(page 657)

Each figure is an isometry image of the figure at the left. Tell whether their orientations are the same or opposite. Then classify the isometry. same; rotation

18.   19.   20.   21.

opp.; reflection   same; translation

19. opp.; glide reflection   25. opp.; glide reflection

22.   23.   24.   25.

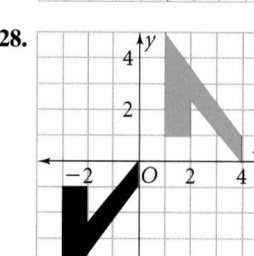
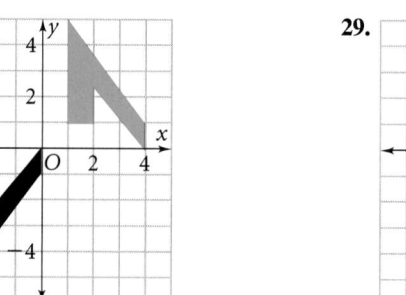
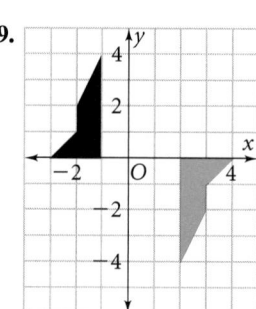

same; rotation   same; translation   opp.; reflection

B Apply Your Skills

The two figures are congruent. Name the isometry that maps one onto the other.

26., 28–29. Isometries map black fig. to blue fig.

26. glide reflection; glide ⟨−2, −2⟩, refl. in y = x − 1

28. glide reflection; glide ⟨0, 4⟩, refl. in y = 0

29. rotation; 180° about the pt. (0, ½)

26.   27. reflection; refl. in y = −½

28.   29.

30. Odd isometries can be expressed as the composition of an odd number of reflections. Even isometries are the composition of an even number of reflections.

32. Yes; a rotation of x° followed by a rotation of y° is equivalent to a rotation of (x + y)°.

30. **Writing** Reflections and glide reflections are *odd isometries*, while translations and rotations are *even isometries*. Use what you learned in this lesson to explain why these categories make sense. **See left.**

31. **Open-Ended** Draw △ABC. Then, describe a reflection, a translation, a rotation, and a glide reflection, and draw the image of △ABC for each transformation. **Check students' work.**

32. For center of rotation P, does an x° rotation followed by a y° rotation give the same image as a y° rotation followed by an x° rotation? Explain. **See left.**

33. Does an x° rotation about a point P followed by a reflection in a line ℓ give the same image as a reflection in ℓ followed by an x° rotation about P? Explain. **No; explanations may vary.**

658   Chapter 12 Transformations

pages 657–660   **Exercises**

49. If $\overline{XY}$ is reflected in line ℓ, then ℓ is the ⊥ bis. of $\overline{XX'}$ and $\overline{YY'}$, so $\overline{XX'} \parallel \overline{YY'}$ and $XX'YY'$ is an isosc. trap. Therefore $\overline{XY} \cong \overline{X'Y'}$.

50. $\overline{XX'} \parallel \overline{YY'}$ and $\overline{XX'} \cong \overline{YY'}$, so $XX'Y'Y$ is a ▱. Therefore, $\overline{XY} \cong \overline{X'Y'}$.

51. If $\overline{XY}$ is rotated x° about pt. R, then $\overline{RX} \cong \overline{RX'}$ and $\overline{RY} \cong \overline{RY'}$. Also, $m\angle XRY$

$+ m\angle YRX' = m\angle YRX'$ $+ m\angle X'RY' = x°$, so $\angle XRY \cong \angle X'RY'$. So $\triangle XRY \cong \triangle X'RY'$ by SAS and $\overline{XY} \cong \overline{X'Y'}$ by CPCTC.

Need Help?
To learn more
about kaleidoscopes,
see p. 661.

Kaleidoscopes The vibrant images of a kaleidoscope are produced by compositions of reflections in intersecting mirrors. Determine the angle between the mirrors in each kaleidoscope image.

34. 60°

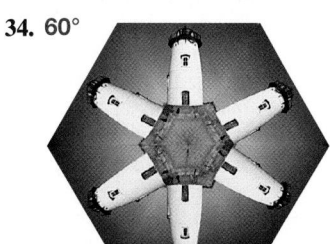

35. 60°

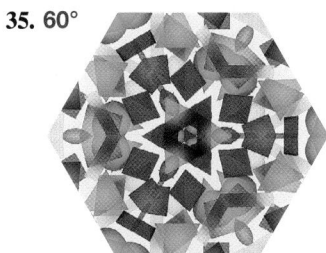

36. $51\frac{3}{7}$°

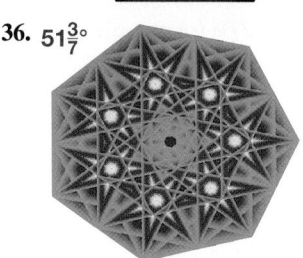

37. 30°

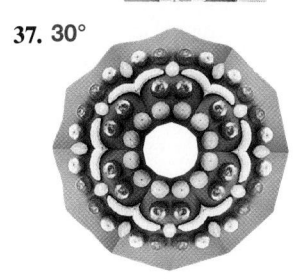

38. rotation; center *C*,
∠ of rotation 180°
39. glide reflection;
⟨11, 0⟩, *y* = 0
40. translation; ⟨−9, 0⟩
41. reflection; *y* = 0
42. reflection; *x* = 4
43. reflection; *x* = −$\frac{1}{2}$
44. rotation; center (3, 0),
∠ of rotation 180°
45. glide reflection;
⟨0, 4⟩, *x* = 4
46. translation; ⟨−11, −4⟩
47. rotation; center (0, 2),
∠ of rotation 180°

Identify each mapping as a reflection, translation, rotation, or glide reflection. Find the reflection line, translation vector, center and angle of rotation, or glide vector and reflection line. 38–47. See left.

38. △*ABC* → △*EDC*

39. △*EDC* → △*PQM*

40. △*MNJ* → △*EDC*

41. △*HIF* → △*HGF*

42. △*PQM* → △*JLM*

43. △*MNP* → △*EDC*

44. △*JLM* → △*MNJ*

45. △*PQM* → △*KJN*

46. △*KJN* → △*ABC*

47. △*HGF* → △*KJN*

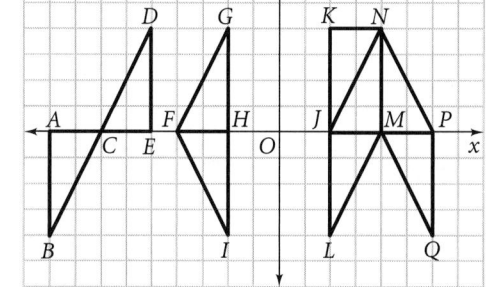

C Challenge

48. The glide involves a translation to the right and the reflection is in a line with a positive slope passing between each R.

48. Describe a glide and a reflection that maps the red R to the blue R. **See left.**

For the given transformation mapping $\overline{XY}$ to $\overline{X'Y'}$, give a convincing argument why $\overline{XY} \cong \overline{X'Y'}$. 49–51. See margin p. 658.

49. a reflection   **50.** a translation   **51.** a rotation

52. The definition states that a glide reflection is the composition of a translation and a reflection. Explain why these can occur in either order. **See margin.**

53. For lines of reflection *r* and *s*, does a reflection in *r* followed by a reflection in *s* give the same image as a reflection in *s* followed by a reflection in *r*? Explain. **See margin.**

P → *P′*(3, −1) **for the given glide vector and reflection line. Find the coordinates of *P*.**

54. glide ⟨−3, 0⟩, reflection line *y* = 2
(6, 5)
55. glide ⟨0, −3⟩, reflection line *x* = 2
(1, 2)
56. glide ⟨−3, −3⟩, reflection line *y* = *x*
(2, 6)
57. glide ⟨4, −4⟩, reflection line *y* = −*x*
(−3, 1)

Lesson 12-3 Compositions of Reflections **659**

Lesson Quiz 12-4

Use the diagram for Exercises 1–3.

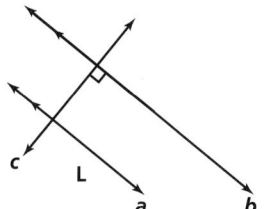

1. Find the image of L for a reflection in line *a* and then in line *b*.

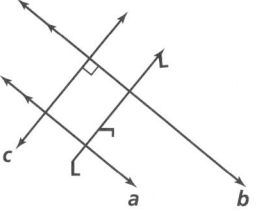

2. Find the image of L for a reflection in line *a* and then in line *c*.

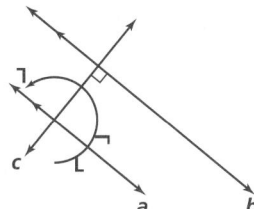

3. Describe the rotation in Exercise 2. **180° rotation with center of rotation at the intersection of lines *a* and *c***

4. $\overline{PQ}$ has endpoints *P*(4, 15) and *Q*(−6, 10). Find the image of $\overline{PQ}$ for a glide reflection where the glide is ⟨0, −8⟩ and the reflection line is *x* = 0. **Check that students' images have endpoints *P′*(-4, 7) and *Q′*(6, 2).**

5. Name the four types of isometries. **glide reflection, reflection, rotation, translation**

52. Answers may vary. Sample: since a reflection moves a pt. in the direction ⊥ to the translation, the order does not matter.

53. No; explanations may vary. Sample: If (1, 1) is reflected over the line *y* = *x* and then the *x*-axis, the image is (1, −1). **If the reflections are reversed, the image is** (−1, 1).

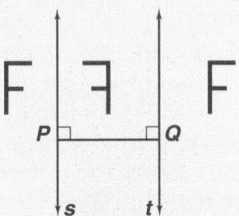
660

Standardized Test Prep

58. Find the image of $P(11, -5)$ for the translation $\langle -12, -6 \rangle$ followed by a reflection in $x = 0$. **A**
   A. $(1, -11)$ **B.** $(-1, 11)$ **C.** $(1, 11)$ **D.** $(-1, -11)$

59. A reflection in the y-axis followed by a reflection in the x-axis does NOT give the same result as which of the following transformations? **H**
   F. a reflection in the x-axis followed by a reflection in the y-axis
   G. a rotation of 180°
   H. a rotation of 90° followed by a reflection in the x-axis
   I. a reflection in the line $y = x$ followed by a reflection in the line $y = -x$

60. Find the image of $\triangle VTY$ for the given glide reflection. Show all your steps.
   glide vector: $\langle 3, -3 \rangle$
   reflection line: $y = -x$ **See margin.**

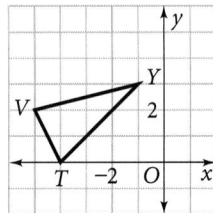

61. Copy the diagram with $s \parallel t$.
   a. Draw the image of F for a composition of two reflections. Reflect first in line s and then in line t. **a–b. See margin.**
   b. Explain why the resulting image is the same image as found by translating F in a direction parallel to $\overline{PQ}$ through a distance $2 \cdot PQ$.

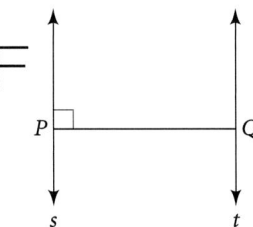

Mixed Review

62. Which capital letters of the alphabet are rotation images of themselves? Draw each letter and give an angle of rotation ($< 360°$).
   H-180; I-180, O-any rotation; X-180; N-180; S-180; Z-180

Find the value of a.

63. 123
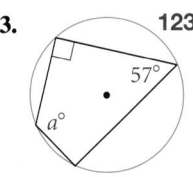

64. 90
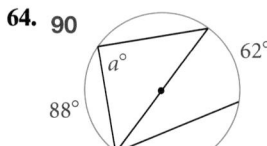

65. 60°   87
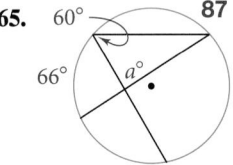

66. Diameter $\overline{AB}$ and chord $\overline{AC}$ of $\odot O$ form an inscribed angle with measure 48.
   a. How many arcs do A, B, and C determine on the circle? **6**
   b. What is the measure of each arc? **84, 96, 180, 180, 264, 276**

Find the slant height of each cone.

67.
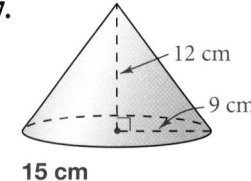
15 cm

68.
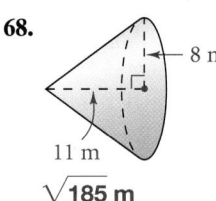
11 m
$\sqrt{185}$ m

69. cone with a base radius of 4 m and a lateral area of 22π m²
   5.5 m

Kaleidoscopes

FOR USE WITH LESSON 12-4

The mirrors in a kaleidoscope provide compositions of reflections to create a *symmetrical* design. You can create your own kaleidoscope.

Construct

- Use geometry software. Draw a line and construct a point on the line. Rotate the line 60° about the point and repeat to get a third line.

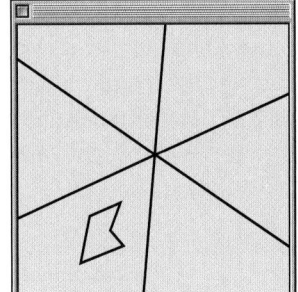 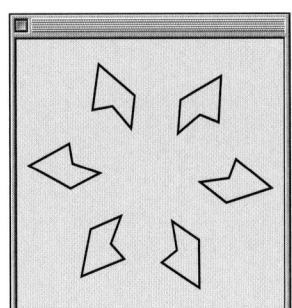

- Construct a polygon in the interior of an angle, as shown. Reflect the polygon in the closest line, then in the next line, and so on until the kaleidoscope is filled and you have a symmetrical design. Then hide the lines of reflection.

Investigate

- Manipulate the original figure by dragging any of its vertices or selecting and moving it. As you manipulate the figure, what happens to the images? Does the design remain symmetrical? Continue manipulating the original figure until you are satisfied with your design. Print the design and color it.

- Now add other figures beside the original polygon. Reflect these figures to create a more interesting design, as shown at the right. (You may need to temporarily show the lines of reflection.) Print your design and color it.

EXERCISES

1. Create a kaleidoscope with four lines of reflection. Draw a line and construct a point on the line. Rotate the line 45° about the point and repeat two more times to get four lines. Add a figure to the interior of an angle and reflect it as described above. **Check students' work.**

A *tessellation* is another type of interesting design that can be constructed using geometry software. An example is shown in Exercise 2 and tessellations are explained more fully in Lesson 12-6.

2. Construct a regular hexagon. Translate the hexagon several times to create the tessellation shown. Can you make a similar tessellation with other regular polygons? Can you find two or more polygons that, when placed together repeatedly, form a tessellation? **Answers may vary. Sample: Yes; you can use squares or equilateral ▵; yes; hexagons and equilateral ▵.**

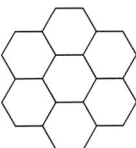

 **Technology**

Kaleidoscopes

Students will use geometry software to simulate and investigate kaleidoscopes. Kaleidoscopes illustrate that *a composition of reflections in two intersecting lines is a rotation* (Theorem 12-3). Students will create figures displaying different symmetries that will be studied in Lesson 12-5.

Resources

Students may use any geometry software program to explore kaleidoscopes.

Teaching Notes

Technology Tip
When rotating lines or reflecting figures, remind students to set their programs so that the original figures remain in place.

Tactile Learners
Encourage students to print and color other interesting patterns they create and to display their designs in class.

Lesson Preview

✓ **Check Skills You'll Need**

Finding Reflection Images
Lesson 12-1: Example 3
Exercises 10–17
Extra Practice, p. 701

Drawing and Identifying Rotation Images
Lesson 12-3: Example 2
Exercises 10–17
Extra Practice, p. 701

Lesson Resources

📁 **Teaching Resources**
Practice, Reteaching, Enrichment

👥 **Reaching All Students**
Practice Workbook 12-5
Spanish Practice Workbook 12-5
Hands-On Activities 35
Informal Geometry Planning
　Guide 12-5

⏲ **Presentation Assistant Plus!**
Transparencies
• Check Skills You'll Need 12-5
• Additional Examples 12-5
• Student Edition Answers 12-5
• Lesson Quiz 12-5
PH Presentation Pro CD 12-5

◇ PRENTICE HALL
ASSESSMENT SYSTEM

Computer Test Generator CD

💿 **Technology**
Resource Pro® CD-ROM
Computer Test Generator CD
Prentice Hall Presentation Pro CD

🖥 **www.PHSchool.com**
Student Site
• Teacher Web Code: afk-5500
• Self-grading Lesson Quiz
Teacher Center
• Lesson Planner
• Resources

Plus

Symmetry

Lesson Preview

What You'll Learn

OBJECTIVE 1
To identify the type of symmetry in a figure

. . . And Why

To identify types of symmetry in real-life objects, as in Example 3

✓ **Check Skills You'll Need**　(For help, go to Lessons 12-1 and 12-3.)

The regular octagon at the right is divided into eight congruent triangles. Find the image of the given point or segment for the given rotation or reflection.

1. point A; a 90° rotation about the center　**G**

2. point H; a 180° rotation about the center　**D**

3. $\overline{AB}$; a reflection in $\overleftrightarrow{AE}$　$\overline{AH}$

4. $\overline{GH}$; a reflection in $\overleftrightarrow{AE}$　$\overline{CB}$

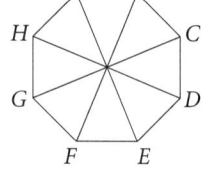

New Vocabulary　• symmetry　• reflectional symmetry　• line symmetry
　　• rotational symmetry　• point symmetry

 Interactive lesson includes instant self-check, tutorials, and activities.

OBJECTIVE

1　**Identifying Types of Symmetry in Figures**

Reading Math
If a figure maps onto itself by some type of isometry, the figure has that type of symmetry.

A figure has **symmetry** if there is an isometry that maps the figure onto itself. If the isometry is the reflection of a plane figure, the figure has **reflectional symmetry** or **line symmetry.** One half of the figure is a mirror image of its other half. Fold the figure along the line of symmetry and the halves match exactly.

The image of the Inuit sculpture at the right has reflectional symmetry about a vertical line down the middle of the face.

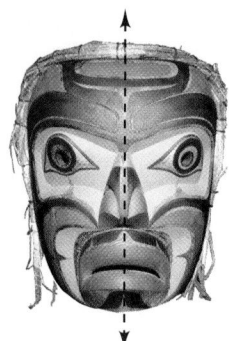

It is possible for a figure to have more than one line of symmetry.

1 EXAMPLE　**Identifying Lines of Symmetry**

Draw all lines of symmetry for a regular hexagon.

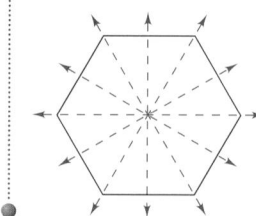

Draw a regular hexagon.

Then draw lines on the hexagon that make mirror-image congruent halves.

There are 6 lines of symmetry.

✓ **Check Understanding**　① Draw a rectangle and all of its lines of symmetry.

1.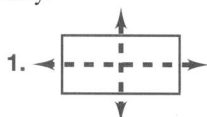

Ongoing Assessment and Intervention

Before the Lesson	**During the Lesson**	**After the Lesson**
Diagnose prerequisite skills using:	**Monitor progress using:**	**Assess knowledge using:**
• Check Skills You'll Need	• Check Understanding	• Lesson Quiz
	• Additional Examples	• Computer Test Generator CD
	• Standardized Test Prep	

A figure that has **rotational symmetry** is its own image for some rotation of 180° or less. A figure that has **point symmetry** has 180° rotational symmetry. A square has 90° and 180° rotational symmetry with the center of rotation at the center of the square. Thus, a square also has point symmetry.

Reading Math
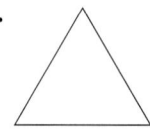

The angle of rotation for rotational symmetry is the smallest angle needed for the figure to rotate onto itself.

2 EXAMPLE Identifying Rotational Symmetry

Judging from appearance, tell whether each triangle has rotational symmetry. If so, give the angle of rotation.

a.

120°

The equilateral triangle has rotational symmetry. The angle of rotation is 120°.

b.

This isosceles triangle does not have rotational symmetry.

✔ **Check Understanding** **2 a.** Judging from appearance, tell whether the figure at the right has rotational symmetry. If so, give the angle of rotation. **yes; 180°**
b. Does the figure have point symmetry? **yes**

Three-dimensional objects can have various types of symmetry, including rotational symmetry about a line and reflectional symmetry in a plane.

3 EXAMPLE Real-World 🌐 Connection

Symmetric Design Tell whether each object has rotational symmetry about a line and/or reflectional symmetry in a plane.

a.

The paddle has both rotational and reflectional symmetry.

b.

The cup has reflectional symmetry.

✔ **Check Understanding** **3** Tell whether the umbrella has rotational symmetry about a line and/or reflectional symmetry in a plane.
rotational and reflectional symmetry

👥 **Reaching All Students**

Below Level Examine patterns of symmetry for regular polygons. Use inductive reasoning to show that a regular *n*-gon has *n* lines of symmetry and $\left(\frac{360}{n}\right)°$ rotational symmetry.	**Advanced Learners** Have students investigate how many shapes can be made with four congruent, nonoverlapping squares, and classify them by their symmetries.	**Diversity** See note on page 664. **Error Prevention** See note on page 664.

---

2. Teach

Professional Development

Math Background

A figure has symmetry when isometries other than the identity isometry leave it unchanged while permuting its parts. These are called the *symmetry group* of the figure.

OBJECTIVE
1 Teaching Notes

3 EXAMPLE **Connection to Physical Science**
Have students name other objects in nature that have symmetry, such as insects, amoebas, starfish, and minerals.

Additional Examples

1 Draw all lines of symmetry for an isosceles trapezoid.

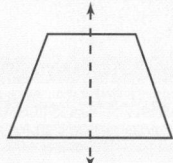

2 Judging from appearance, does V or H have rotational symmetry? If so, give an angle of rotation. **V: no; H: 180° rotational symmetry**

3 A nut holds a bolt in place. Some nuts have square faces, like the top view shown below. Tell whether the nut has rotational symmetry about a line and/or reflectional symmetry in a plane.

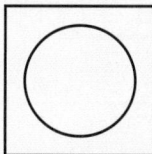

four lines of symmetry and 90° rotational symmetry

Closure

Tell whether a regular octagon has reflectional and/or rotational symmetry. **eight lines of reflectional symmetry and 45° rotational symmetry**

▼ **Objective**
   Ⓐ Ⓑ **Core** 1–44
   Ⓒ **Extension** 45–50

Standardized Test Prep 51–56

Mixed Review 57–62

Error Prevention

Exercises 1–12 Students can copy the figures and rotate them or use paper folding.

Diversity

Exercise 21 Ask whether anyone can name the Greek letters or list the letters of other alphabets.

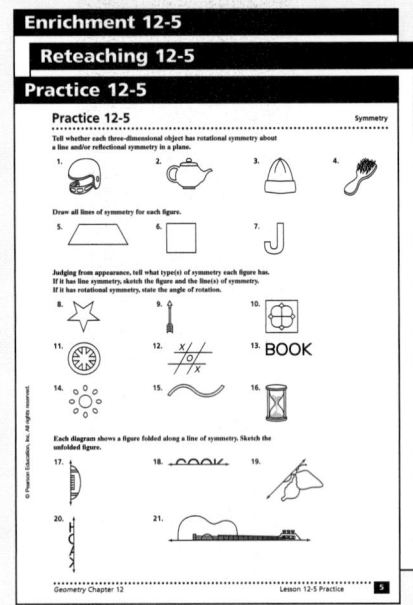

EXERCISES

For more practice, see *Extra Practice*.

Practice and Problem Solving

Ⓐ **Practice by Example**

Examples 1, 2
(pages 662, 663)

Tell what type(s) of symmetry each figure has. If it has line symmetry, sketch the figure and the line(s) of symmetry. If it has rotational symmetry, state the angle of rotation. 1–12. See back of book.

1. 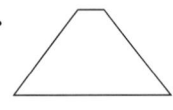 2.  3. 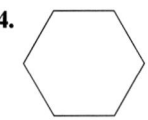 4.

5. 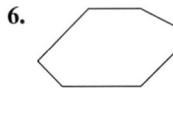 6. 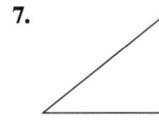 7. 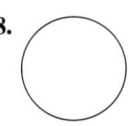 8.

9. 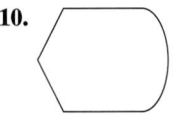 10. 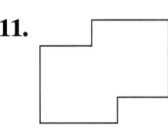 11. 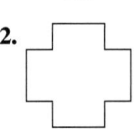 12.

Draw each quadrilateral. Then draw all of its lines of symmetry.

13–16. See margin.

13. rhombus   14. kite   15. square   16. parallelogram

Example 3
(page 663)

Tell whether each three-dimensional object has rotational symmetry about a line and/or reflectional symmetry in a plane.

17. 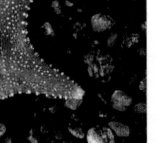 18.

rotational and reflectional   reflectional

19–20. Answers may vary. Samples are given

19. CODE, HOOD, DOCK

20. TOMATO, HOAX, WAXY

Ⓑ **Apply Your Skills**

19. **Open-Ended** The word **CHECKBOOK** has a horizontal line of symmetry. Find two other words for which this is true. 19–20. See left.

20. **Open-Ended** Stack the letters of **MATH** vertically and upright, and you can find a vertical line of symmetry. Find two other words for which this is true.

21b. Sample: Greek; Greek alphabet has more letters with at least one kind of symmetry and more letters with multiple symmetries.

21. **a.** **Alphabets** Copy the chart. Use it to classify the letters of the English and Greek alphabets below. You will list some letters in more than one category.
   b. Which alphabet can you say is more symmetrical? Explain.

21a. See back of book.

Type of Symmetry

Language	Horizontal Line	Vertical Line	Point
English			
Greek			

English: ABCDEFGHIJKLMNOPQRSTUVWXYZ

Greek: ΑΒΓΔΕΖΗΘΙΚΛΜΝΞΟΠΡΣΤΥΦΧΨΩ

pages 664–665
Exercises

13.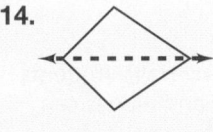

14.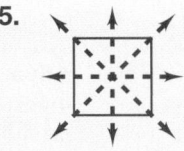

15.

16.

Tell what type(s) of symmetry each image has. For line symmetry, sketch the image and the line(s) of symmetry. For rotational symmetry, state the angle of rotation.
22–23. Check students' sketches.

22.
reflectional

23.
rotational: 90°; reflectional

24. Answers may vary.
Sample: $30 \div 10 = 3$;
$|8 - 1| = |1 - 8|$,
$80 + 3 < 88$; $\frac{80}{80} = \frac{33}{33}$

24. **Open-Ended** The equation $\frac{10}{10} - 1 = 0 \div \frac{83}{83}$ is not only true, but also symmetrical (horizontally). Write four other equations or inequalities that are both true and symmetrical. **See left.**

 Logos Describe the types of symmetry, if any, of each automobile logo.

25. reflectional; rotational
26. reflectional
29. reflectional; rotational
31. reflectional, rotational

25.

26.

27.
point

28.
none

29.

30.
reflectional

31.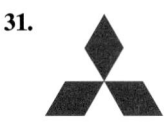

32.
reflectional

33. Is the line that contains the bisector of an angle a line of symmetry of the angle? Explain. **See margin.**

34. Is the line that contains the bisector of an angle of a triangle a line of symmetry of the triangle? Explain. **See left.**

35. Is a bisector of a segment a line of symmetry of the segment? Explain. See margin.

 36. **Writing** Use what you learned in Lesson 12-4 to explain why a figure with two or more lines of symmetry also has rotational symmetry. **See margin.**

Need Help?

In Exercises 33–35, you can conclude a statement is false by finding a counterexample.

34. Not necessarily; the △ would need the two other ∠s to be ≅.

Coordinate Geometry A figure has a vertex at (3, 4). If the figure has the given type of symmetry, state the coordinates of another vertex of the figure.

37. line symmetry about the *y*-axis (−3, 4)   38. line symmetry about the *x*-axis (3, −4)

39. point symmetry about the origin (−3, −4)   40. line symmetry about the line $y = x$ (4, 3)

Coordinate Geometry Graph each equation. Describe the symmetry of each graph.

41. $y = x$ 42. $y = x^2$ 43. $x = y^2$ 44. $x^2 + y^2 = 9$

45. $y = (x + 2)^2$ 46. $y = x^3$ 47. $y = |x|$ 48. $x = |y|$
41–48. See back of book.

For each three-dimensional figure, draw a net that has rotational symmetry and a net that has 1, 2, or 4 lines of symmetry. 49–50. See back of book.

Ⓒ Challenge

49.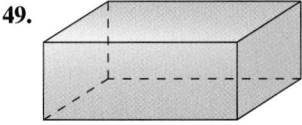

50.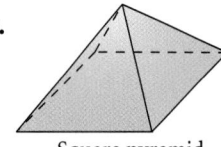
Square pyramid

Lesson 12-5   Symmetry   **665**

33. Yes; the bisector divides the ∠ into 2 ≅ ∠s with one side of the ∠ being the reflection of the other.

35. Not necessarily; the bisector divides the segment into 2 ≅ parts but one part cannot be the reflection of the other unless the bisector is the ⊥ bisector.

36. Answers may vary. Sample: The composition of reflections in two intersecting lines (the lines of symmetry) is a rotation.

665

4. Assess

📋 **Lesson Quiz 12-5**

Tell what type(s) of symmetry each figure has.

1. D horizontal line of symmetry

2. O horizontal and vertical lines of symmetry; point symmetry

Draw each figure and all its lines of symmetry.

3. isosceles right triangle

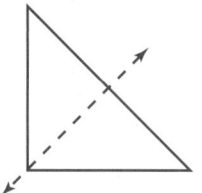

4. rhombus that is not a square

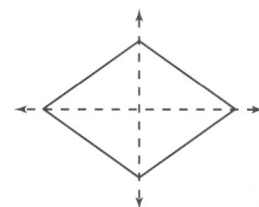

5. The star below appears on the United States flag. If the star has line symmetry, sketch it and draw the line(s) of symmetry. If it has rotational symmetry, state the angle of rotation.

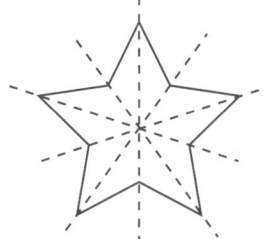

72° rotational symmetry

Alternative Assessment

Have each student design a logo for a new company that manufactures solar-powered automobiles. The logos should contain both line symmetry and rotational symmetry. Students should include a written description of all the symmetries of their designs.

Standardized Test Prep

 **Resources**

For additional practice with a variety of test item formats:
• Standardized Test Prep, p. 685
• Test-Taking Strategies, p. 680
• Test-Taking Strategies with Transparencies

Exercise 51 Students can check for rotational symmetry by rotating their books. If the figure looks the same in a half-turn or less, it has rotational symmetry.

Standardized Test Prep

Multiple Choice

51. Which figure does NOT have rotational symmetry? **B**
   A. [rectangle]   B. [triangle]   C. N   D. I

52. Which figure, in general, has exactly two lines of symmetry? **I**
   F. pentagon   G. circle   H. square   I. rectangle

Quantitative Comparison

Compare the boxed quantity in Column A with the boxed quantity in Column B. Choose the best answer.
   A. The quantity in Column A is greater.
   B. The quantity in Column B is greater.
   C. The two quantities are equal.
   D. The relationship cannot be determined from the information given.

 **Take It to the NET**
Online lesson quiz at
www.PHSchool.com
Web Code: afa-1205

Column A	Column B
A 53. the smallest angle of rotational symmetry for an equilateral triangle	the smallest angle of rotational symmetry for a regular hexagon
D 54. the number of lines of symmetry for a nonrectangular parallelogram	the number of lines of symmetry for a nonrectangular quadrilateral
B 55. the number of lines of symmetry for a regular pentagon	the number of lines of symmetry for a regular octagon

Short Response

56. Use the figure at the right to answer the questions below.
   a. Does the figure have rotational symmetry? If so, identify the angle of rotation. **a–b. See margin.**
   b. Does the figure have reflectional symmetry? If so, how many lines of symmetry does it have?

Mixed Review

Lesson 12-4

57. A triangle has vertices $A(3, 2)$, $B(4, 1)$, and $C(4, 3)$. Find the coordinates of the images of A, B, and C for a glide reflection with glide vector $\langle 0, 1 \rangle$ and reflection line $x = 0$. **$A'(-3, 3)$, $B'(-4, 2)$, $C'(-4, 4)$**

Lesson 11-4

Find the value of each variable using the given chords, secants, and tangents. If your answer is not an integer, round it to the nearest tenth.

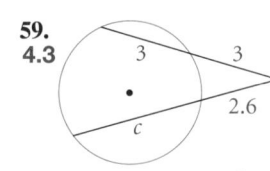

58. 8   **59.** 4.3   **60.** 8.7

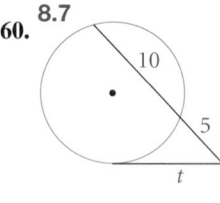

61. $66\frac{2}{3}$ cm³

Lesson 10-6

61. Find the volume of a square pyramid with height 8 cm and base edges 5 cm.

62. Find the volume of a cone with radius 7 in. and height 10 in.
   $\frac{490\pi}{3}$ in.³ ≈ 513.13 in.³

page 666 **Standardized Test Prep**

56. **[2]** a. no
      b. yes; 1
   [1] incorrect response
      OR incorrect number

12-6

Tessellations

3.01 Describe the transformation (translation, reflection, rotation, dilation) of polygons in the coordinate plane in simple algebraic terms.

Lesson Preview

What You'll Learn

OBJECTIVE 1
To identify transformations in tessellations, and figures that will tessellate

OBJECTIVE 2
To identify symmetries in tessellations

. . . And Why

To identify a tessellation in art, as in Example 1

✓ Check Skills You'll Need

(For help, go to Lesson 3-4.)

Classify the polygon with the given number of sides.

1. five **pentagon**
2. eight **octagon**
3. twelve **dodecagon**

Find the measure of an angle of each regular polygon.

4. triangle **60**
5. quadrilateral **90**
6. hexagon **120**
7. octagon **135**
8. decagon **144**
9. 14-gon **154$\frac{2}{7}$**

New Vocabulary

- tessellation
- tiling
- translational symmetry
- glide reflectional symmetry

OBJECTIVE 1

Identifying Transformations in Tessellations

 Interactive lesson includes instant self-check, tutorials, and activities.

 Reading Math

A figure that creates a tessellation is said *to tessellate*.

A **tessellation,** or **tiling,** is a repeating pattern of figures that completely covers a plane, without gaps or overlaps. You can create tessellations with translations, rotations, and reflections. You can find tessellations in art (see below), nature (cells in a honeycomb), and everyday life (tiled floors).

1 EXAMPLE Identifying the Transformation in a Tessellation

Art Identify a transformation and the repeating figures in this tessellation.

Repeating figures

SOURCE: © 1996 M. C. Escher Heirs/Cordon Art, Baarn, Holland. All rights reserved.

● The arrow shows a translation.

✓ Check Understanding

1 Identify a transformation and the repeating figures in each tessellation below.

a–b. See left.

1a. rotation; one fish

b. translation; horse and rider

a.

SOURCE: © 1996 M. C. Escher Heirs/Cordon Art, Baarn, Holland. All rights reserved.

b.
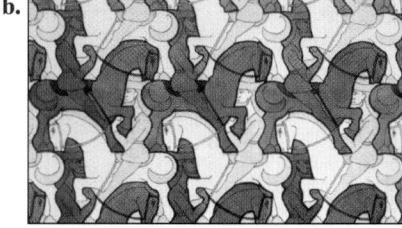
SOURCE: © 1996 M. C. Escher Heirs/Cordon Art, Baarn, Holland. All rights reserved.

Ongoing Assessment and Intervention

Before the Lesson
Diagnose prerequisite skills using:
- Check Skills You'll Need

During the Lesson
Monitor progress using:
- Check Understanding
- Additional Examples
- Standardized Test Prep

After the Lesson
Assess knowledge using:
- Lesson Quiz
- Computer Test Generator CD
- Chapter Checkpoint 2 (p. 673)

12-6

 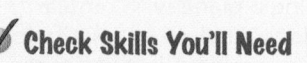
1. Plan

Lesson Preview

✓ Check Skills You'll Need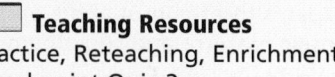

Classifying Polygons
Lesson 3-4: Example 2
Exercises 8–10
Extra Practice, p. 692

Polygon Angle-Sums
Lesson 3-4: Examples 3, 5
Exercises 11–15, 22–25
Extra Practice, p. 692

Lesson Resources

📁 **Teaching Resources**
Practice, Reteaching, Enrichment
Checkpoint Quiz 2

👥 **Reaching All Students**
Practice Workbook 12-6
Spanish Practice Workbook 12-6
Reading and Math Literacy 12C
Spanish Reading & Literacy 12C
Spanish Checkpoint Quiz 2
Hands-On Activities 36
Informal Geometry Planning
  Guide 12-6

⏱ **Presenation Assistant Plus!**
Transparencies
- Check Skills You'll Need 12-6
- Additional Examples 12-6
- Student Edition Answers 12-6
- Lesson Quiz 12-6
PH Presentation Pro CD 12-6

PRENTICE HALL
ASSESSMENT *SYSTEM*

Checkpoint Quiz 2
Computer Test Generator CD

💿 **Technology**
Resource Pro® CD-ROM
Computer Test Generator CD
Prentice Hall Presentation Pro CD

🖥 **www.PHSchool.com**
Student Site
- Teacher Web Code: afk-5500
- Self-grading Lesson Quiz
Teacher Center
- Lesson Planner
- Resources

Plus

667

Math Background

The astronomer Johannes Kepler is believed to have been the first to investigate the possible ways of covering a plane with regular polygons. Analysis of tessellations using more complicated figures requires understanding of isometry and symmetry.

OBJECTIVE

1 **Teaching Notes**

Careers

A tile setter uses tessellations to design floors and other surfaces. Although most tiles are square, other shapes also are used. Have students locate unusual tile or mosaic patterns and copy them to show the class.

1 EXAMPLE

Ask students to name the simplest transformation, not a composition of two reflections.

2 EXAMPLE **Visual Learners**

To help students see why the angle measure of a regular polygon must be a factor of 360 for the polygon to tessellate a plane, have them use geometry drawing software or a protractor to construct adjacent 35° angles with the same vertex. They will find that ten 35° angles leave a gap of 10°, and eleven adjacent 35° angles overlap.

Additional Examples

1 Identify the repeating figures and a transformation in the tessellation.

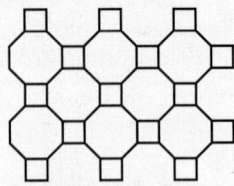

regular octagon and square; translation

Because the figures in a tessellation do not overlap or leave gaps, the sum of the measures of the angles around any vertex must be 360°. If the angles around a vertex are all congruent, then the measure of each angle must be a factor of 360.

2 EXAMPLE **Determining Figures That Will Tessellate**

Determine whether a regular 18-gon tessellates a plane.

$a = \dfrac{180(n-2)}{n}$ **Use the formula for the measure of an angle of a regular polygon.**

$a = \dfrac{180(18-2)}{18}$ **Substitute 18 for n.**

$a = 160$ **Simplify.**

Since 160 is not a factor of 360, the 18-gon will not tessellate.

 Check Understanding **2** Explain why you can tessellate a plane with an equilateral triangle.
The interior ⊿ of an equilateral △ measure 60.
60 divides 360, so it will tessellate.

A figure does not have to be a regular polygon to tessellate.

Key Concepts

Theorem 12-6	
Every triangle tessellates.	
Theorem 12-7	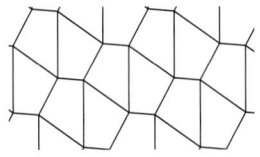
Every quadrilateral tessellates.	

OBJECTIVE

2 **Identifying Symmetries in Tessellations**

Real-World Connection

Careers Physicists apply the symmetries of tessellations to study subatomic particles. Here they use a particle detector to study quarks.

The tessellation with regular hexagons at the right has reflectional symmetry in each of the blue lines. It has rotational symmetry centered at each of the red points. The tessellation also has translational symmetry and glide reflectional symmetry, as shown below.

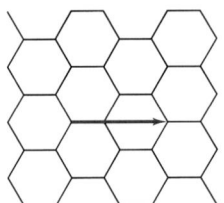

Translational Symmetry

A translation maps the tessellation onto itself.

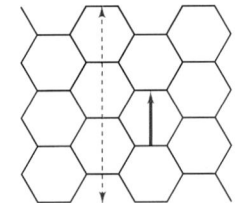

Glide Reflectional Symmetry

A glide reflection maps the tessellation onto itself.

Reaching All Students

Below Level Have students search the classroom for tessellations. Discuss their findings and whether they meet the criteria for tessellations.	**Advanced Learners** After students complete Example 2, have them determine which regular *n*-gons tessellate a plane, and prove their findings.	**English Learners** See note on page 669. **Visual Learners** See note on page 668.

3 EXAMPLE Identifying Symmetries in Tessellations

List the symmetries in the tessellation.

Rotational symmetry centered at each red point
Translational symmetry (blue arrow)

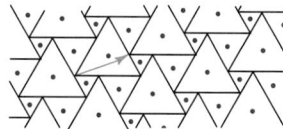

✓ Check Understanding ❸ List the symmetries in the tessellation at the right.

line symmetry, rotational symmetry, glide reflectional symmetry, translational symmetry

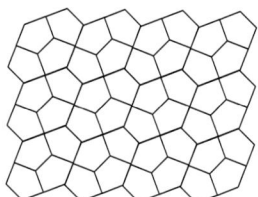

The following Investigation shows the steps for making creative tessellations.

Investigation: Creating Tessellations

- Draw a 1.5-inch square on a blank piece of paper and cut it out.

- Draw a curve joining two consecutive vertices.

- Cut along the curve you drew and slide the cutout piece to the opposite side of the square. Tape it in place.

  Check students' work.
- Repeat this process using the other two opposite sides of the square.

- Rotate the resulting figure. What does your imagination suggest it looks like? Is it a penguin wearing a hat or a knight on horseback? Could it be a dog with floppy ears? Draw the image on your figure.

- Create a tessellation using your figure.

Lesson 12-6 Tessellations **669**

Additional Examples

❷ Determine whether a regular 15-gon tessellates a plane. Explain.
No; 156 is not a factor of 360.

OBJECTIVE 2 Teaching Notes

3 EXAMPLE

Remind students that a drawing can only suggest that tessellations, like planes, extend without bound in all directions.

English Learners

Students new to English may have trouble describing symmetries. Pair them with partners who can help them express the relationships they observe.

Investigation (Optional)

After students have designed their figures, have them trace the outlines on lightweight cardboard, cut out the figures, and trace around the cutouts to create their tessellations.

Additional Examples

❸ List the symmetries in the tessellation.

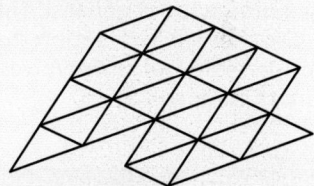

point symmetry centered at any vertex, translational symmetry

Closure

Use angle measures to explain how an arrangement of regular 12-gons and equilateral triangles tessellates a plane. An angle of an equilateral triangle measures 60, and an angle of a regular 12-gon measures 150. Because 60 + 150 + 150 = 360, two 12-gons share a vertex with each vertex of the triangles.

3. Practice

Assignment Guide

1 Objective
- Ⓐ Ⓑ Core 1–10, 17–23
- Ⓒ Extension 28–37

2 Objective
- Ⓐ Ⓑ Core 11–16, 24–27
- Ⓒ Extension 38, 39

Standardized Test Prep 40–44

Mixed Review 45–54

Error Prevention

Exercises 11–16 Encourage students to trace the tessellations, place dots at the center of figures or "spaces," and then test for rotational symmetry by turning their tracings. Encourage them to draw lines through vertices and midpoints of figures to test for reflectional symmetry.

Exercise 15 The text definition of tessellation is that of a *periodic tessellation*. The idea of tessellation is more general. This exercise shows a tessellation that is not periodic, but still involves a figure that repeats.

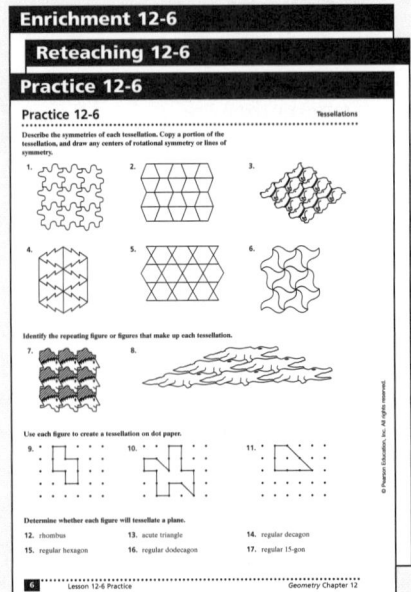

Ⓐ **Practice by Example**

Example 1
(page 667)

1–4. Answers may vary. Samples are given.

1. yes; translation; two ⊥ rectangles

2. yes; translation; two ▱ and a rhombus with a flower in it

3. yes; translation; four rectangles in a square shape (see overlay)

4. no

Does the picture show a tessellation of repeating figures? If so, identify a transformation and the repeating figure.

1.    2.

3.    4.

Example 2
(page 668)

Determine whether each figure will tessellate a plane.

5. equilateral triangle **yes**   6. square **yes**   7. regular pentagon **no**

8. regular heptagon **no**   9. regular octagon **no**   10. regular nonagon **no**

Example 3
(page 669)

List the symmetries in each tessellation.   11–16. See margin.

11. 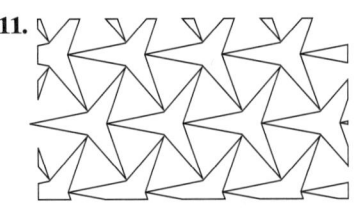   12.

13. 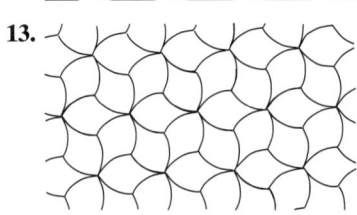   14.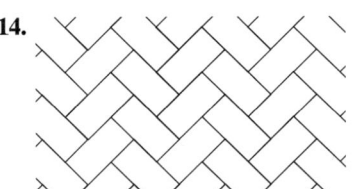

15. 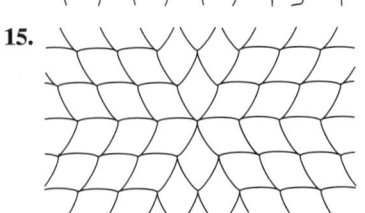   16.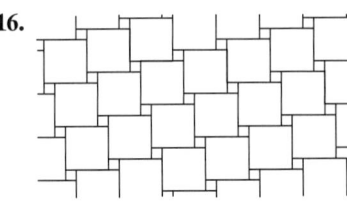

pages 670–672   Exercises

11. rotational, reflectional, glide reflectional, and translational

12. rotational, point, reflectional, glide reflectional, and translational

13. rotational, reflectional, glide reflectional, and translational

14. rotational, point, and translational

15. rotational and reflectional

16. rotational, point, and translational

670

B Apply Your Skills

23. A regular polygon with more than 6 sides must have ∠ measures greater than 120, and at least 3 polygons must meet at each vertex. The sum of 3 or more ∠s with measures greater than 120 > 360. So the 3 regular polygons are 3-, 4-, and 6-sided, since their int. ∠ measures divide 360.

Use each figure to create a tessellation on dot paper. 17–19. See margin.

17. 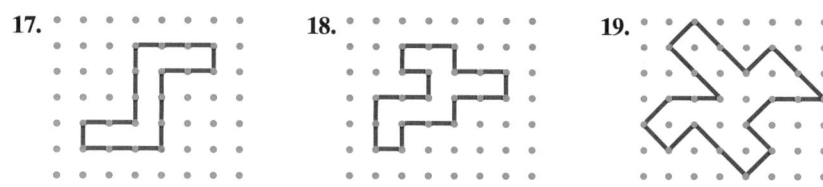 **18.** **19.**

Show how to tessellate with each figure described below. Try to draw two different tessellations. If you think that two are not possible, explain.

20. a scalene triangle **21.** the pentagon at the right 20–22. See back of book.

22. a quadrilateral with no sides parallel or congruent

23. Writing A *pure tessellation* is a tessellation made up of congruent copies of one figure. Explain why there are three, and only three, pure tessellations that use regular polygons. (*Hint:* See Exercises 5–10.) **See left.**

A *semiregular tessellation* is made from two or more regular polygons.

Decide whether a semiregular tessellation (see photo) is possible using the given pair of regular polygons. If so, draw a sketch.

24. 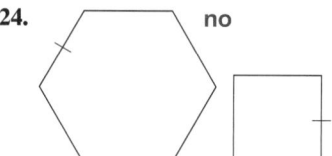 no **25.** 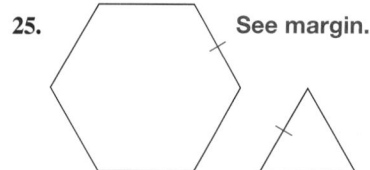 See margin.

Can each set of polygons be used to create a tessellation? If so, draw a sketch.

26. 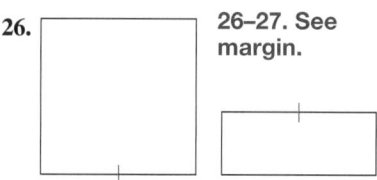 26–27. See margin. **27.**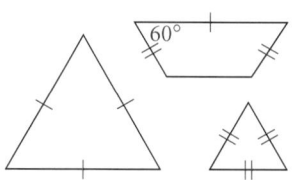

C Challenge

Copy the Venn diagram. Write each exercise number in the correct region of the diagram.

28. scalene triangle **29.** obtuse triangle
30. equilateral △ **31.** isosceles △
32. kite **33.** rhombus 28–37. See margin.
34. square **35.** regular pentagon
36. regular hexagon **37.** regular octagon

Regular figures   Polygons

Figures that tessellate

38d. Yes, *ABCD* tessellates; the sum of the measures of the ∠s of a quad. is 360. Copies of the quad. can be arranged so that the four ∠s share a vertex. The quad. fills the plane.

38. On graph paper, draw quadrilateral *ABCD* with no two sides congruent. Locate *M*, the midpoint of $\overline{AB}$, and *N*, the midpoint of $\overline{BC}$.
  a. Draw the image of *ABCD* under a 180° rotation about *M*. a–c.
  b. Draw the image of *ABCD* under a 180° rotation about *N*. See margin.
  c. Draw the image of *ABCD* under the translation that maps *D* to *B*.
  d. Make a conjecture about whether your quadrilateral tessellates, using the pattern in parts (a)–(c). Justify your answer. **See left.**

Lesson 12-6 Tessellations **671**

Diversity
Ukrainian Easter eggs, or *pysanky,* have tessellations painted on their surfaces. The world's largest *pysanka* is in Vegreville, Canada.

Exercise 23 Point out that these three examples are called *regular tessellations.* Compare this exercise with Exercises 24 and 25, which investigate semiregular tessellations.

Exercise 25 Challenge students to find more semiregular tessellations.

Alternate Method
Exercise 38 Have students use geometry software to perform the translation and rotations. Challenge them to use their observations to explain why every quadrilateral tessellates.

25. yes;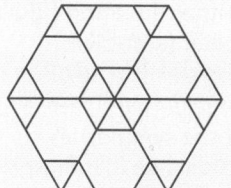

26. yes;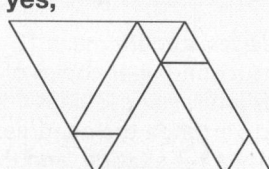

27. yes;

28–37.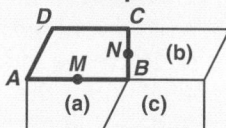

Regular Figures   Polygons

    35 37
   30 36
    34   28
         29 31
         32 33

Figures that tessellate

38. a–c. Drawings may vary. Sample:

17. 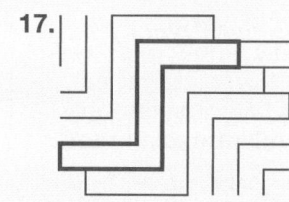 **18.**  **19.**

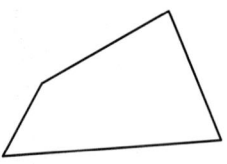

Lesson Quiz 12-6

Determine whether each figure will tessellate a plane.

1. regular octagon no

2. regular hexagon yes

3.

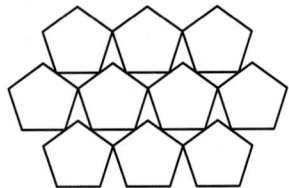

yes

Use the tessellation below for Exercises 4 and 5.

4. List the repeating figures.
   regular pentagon,
   isosceles triangle,
   concave quadrilateral

5. List the symmetries.
   vertical line symmetry,
   translational symmetry

Alternative Assessment

Have each student make 12 construction-paper copies of a quadrilateral whose sides differ in length, arrange the quadrilaterals to form a tessellation, and then explain in writing what a tessellation is and what theorem guarantees that the figure will tessellate the plane.

pages 670–672   **Exercises**

39. **Answers may vary. Sample:**
    Draw △ABC. Locate M, the mdpt. of $\overline{AB}$, and N, the mdpt. of $\overline{BC}$. Draw the images of △ABC under 180° rotations about M and N. Draw the image of △ABC under the translation that maps A to C. 2nd way: Draw △ABC. Draw the reflection image

672

39. List steps (like those in Exercise 38) that suggest a way to tessellate with any scalene triangle. Then list a second set of steps that suggest another way.
    See margin.

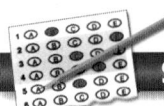

Standardized Test Prep

Multiple Choice

40. Which figure will NOT tessellate a plane? **B**

    A.    B. 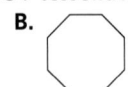   C.   D.

Take It to the NET
Online lesson quiz at
www.PHSchool.com
Web Code: afa-1206

41. You can tessellate a plane using a regular octagon together with which other type of regular polygon? **G**
    F. triangle   G. square   H. pentagon   I. hexagon

42. Which is NOT a symmetry for the tessellation? **C**
    A. line symmetry
    B. translational symmetry
    C. rotational symmetry
    D. glide reflectional symmetry

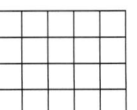

Short Response

43. Is it possible to tile a plane with regular pentagons? Justify your answer.
    See left below.

Extended Response

44. Unit squares form this tessellation. Tell whether this tessellation has each type of symmetry (line, point, rotational, translational, or glide reflectional). Explain. **See margin pp. 672–673.**

Mixed Review

Lesson 12-5

Coordinate Geometry A figure has a vertex at (−2, 7). If the figure has the given type of symmetry, state the coordinates of another vertex of the figure.

45. line symmetry about the x-axis
    (−2, −7)

46. line symmetry about the y-axis
    (2, 7)

47. point symmetry about the origin
    (2, −7)

48. line symmetry about the line $y = x$
    (7, −2)

Lesson 11-5

Write the standard equation of each circle.

43. [2] No; the int. $\angle$s of a pentagon measure 108. 108 is not a factor of 360, so a pentagon cannot tessellate the plane. (OR equivalent explanation)
    [1] correct answer with no explanation

49. 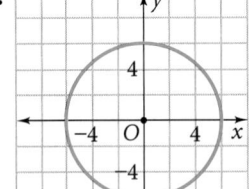 $x^2 + y^2 = 36$

50. 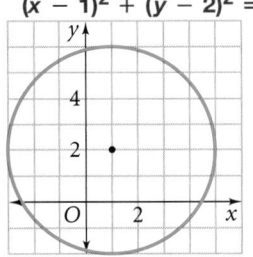 $(x - 1)^2 + (y - 2)^2 = 16$

51. the circle with center (−1, 0) and radius 3 $(x + 1)^2 + y^2 = 9$

Lesson 10-1

Use Euler's Formula, $F + V = E + 2$, to find the missing number.

52. Faces: ■ 9
    Edges: 16
    Vertices: 9

53. Faces: 12 30
    Edges: ■
    Vertices: 20

54. Faces: 7 7
    Edges: 12
    Vertices: ■

of pt. C over $\overline{AB}$, C'. Now use the steps from Ex. 38 for quad. ACBC'.

44. [4] line symmetry: any vert. or horiz. line, a

diag. line drawn through a square's corners, or a line drawn through the ⊥ bis. of a square's side; rotational symmetry: 90° and point about any square's center;

translational: vertically or horizontally 1 unit; glide refl.: translate 1 unit and reflect through a line of symmetry. (OR equivalent explanation)

 Instant self-check quiz online and on CD-ROM

3. line, point

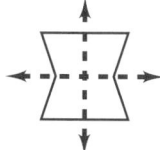

5. line, rotational: 120

7. rotational, reflectional, glide reflectional, and translational

8. rotational, point, reflectional, glide reflectional, and translational

9. reflectional, glide reflectional, and translational

10. rotational, point, reflectional, glide reflectional, and translational

The two figures in each pair are congruent. Is one figure a translation image, a rotation image, or a reflection image of the other? Explain.

1. 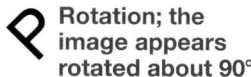 Rotation; the image appears rotated about 90°.

2.  Reflection; the orientation is reversed.

Tell what type(s) of symmetry (line, rotational, or point) each figure has. For line symmetry, sketch the figure and the line(s) of symmetry. For rotational symmetry, state the angle of rotation.

3.  See left.

4. 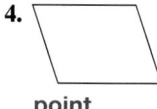 point

5.  See left.

6. 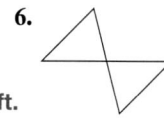 point

List the symmetries of each tessellation. 7–10. See left.

7.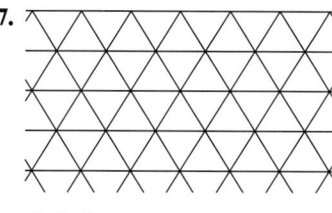

8.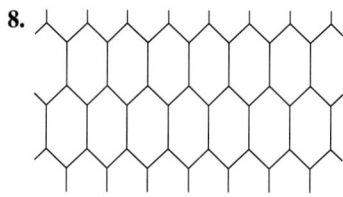

9.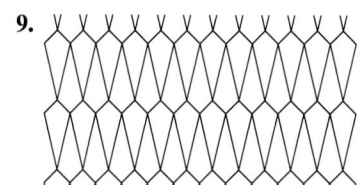

10.

Standardized Test Prep

📁 **Resources**

For additional practice with a variety of test item formats:
- Standardized Test Prep, p. 685
- Test-Taking Strategies, p. 680
- Test-Taking Strategies with Transparencies

Exercises 40, 41, 43 Students can use the formula for the angle measure of a regular polygon, $a = \frac{180\,(n-2)}{n}$, to determine whether a regular polygon tessellates a plane alone or in combination with another polygon.

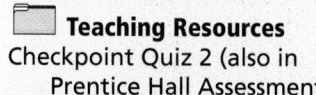 **Chapter Checkpoint 2**

To check understanding of Lessons 12-4 to 12-6:

Checkpoint Quiz 2 (p. 673)

📁 **Teaching Resources**
Checkpoint Quiz 2 (also in Prentice Hall Assessment System)

👥 **Reaching All Students**
Reading and Math Literacy 12C

Spanish versions available

A Point in Time

1500 1600 1700 1800 1900 2000

A mosaic is a picture or design made by setting tiny pieces of glass, stone, or other materials in clay or plaster. A mosaic may be a tessellation. Most mosaics, however, do not have a repeating pattern of figures. Mosaics go back at least 6000 years to the Sumerians, who used tiles to both decorate and reinforce walls.

During 100 and 200 A.D., Roman architects used two million tiles to create the magnificent mosaic of Dionysus in Germany. In the years 1941–1951 Mexican artist Juan O'Gorman covered all four sides of a 10-story library in Mexico with 7.5 million stones—the largest mosaic ever. It depicts Mexico's cultural history.

Take It to the NET For more information about mosaics, go to **www.PHSchool.com**.
Web Code: afe-2032

Lesson 12-6 Tessellations **673**

[3] 2 or 3 correct answers and explanations OR 3 or 4 correct answers with 2 or 3 incorrect explanations

[2] 1 or 2 correct answers and explanations OR 2 or 3 correct answers with 1 or 2 incorrect explanations

[1] incorrect explanations and answers

 **Check Skills You'll Need**

Ratios and Proportions
Lesson 8-1: Examples 3, 4
Exercises 12–25
Extra Practice, p. 697

Lesson Resources

📁 **Teaching Resources**
Practice, Reteaching, Enrichment

👥 **Reaching All Students**
Practice Workbook 12-7
Spanish Practice Workbook 12-7
Informal Geometry Planning
   Guide 12-7

⏰ **Presentation Assistant Plus!**
Transparencies
• Check Skills You'll Need 12-7
• Additional Examples 12-7
• Student Edition Answers 12-7
• Lesson Quiz 12-7
PH Presentation Pro CD 12-7

(PRENTICE HALL **ASSESSMENT SYSTEM**)

Computer Test Generator CD

💿 **Technology**
Resource Pro® CD-ROM
Computer Test Generator CD
Prentice Hall Presentation Pro CD

💻 **www.PHSchool.com**
Student Site
• Teacher Web Code: afk-5500
• Self-grading Lesson Quiz
Teacher Center
• Lesson Planner
• Resources

Plus

 12-7

Dilations

Lesson Preview

3.01 Describe the transformation of polygons in the coordinate plane in simple algebraic terms.
3.02 Use matrix operations to describe the transformations.

What You'll Learn

OBJECTIVE 1
To locate dilation images of figures

...And Why

To find the dimensions of a car using the dimensions of its model, as in Example 2

✓ **Check Skills You'll Need**

(For help, go to Lesson 8-1.)

Determine the scale drawing dimensions of a room using a scale of $\frac{1}{4}$ in. = 1 ft.

1. kitchen: 12 ft by 16 ft **3 in. by 4 in.**
2. bedroom: 8 ft by 10 ft **2 in. by $2\frac{1}{2}$ in.**
3. laundry room: 6 ft by 9 ft **$1\frac{1}{2}$ in. by $2\frac{1}{4}$ in.**
4. bathroom: 5 ft by 7 ft **$1\frac{1}{4}$ in. by $1\frac{3}{4}$ in.**

New Vocabulary • dilation • enlargement • reduction • scalar multiplication

---

 Interactive lesson includes instant self-check, tutorials, and activities.

OBJECTIVE
1 **Locating Dilation Images**

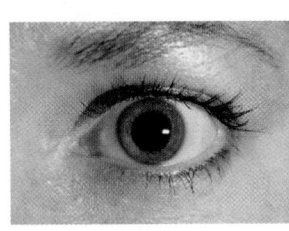

Real-World 🌐 Connection

Look closely at your pupil in a mirror, and you can watch it dilate.

A dilation is a transformation whose preimage and image are similar. Thus, a dilation is a similarity transformation. It is *not*, in general, an isometry.

Every dilation has a center and a scale factor $n, n > 0$. The scale factor describes the size change from the original figure to the image.

In general, a **dilation** with center C and scale factor n is a transformation for which the following are true.

• The image of C is itself (that is, $C' = C$).

• For any point R, R' is on $\overrightarrow{CR}$ and $CR' = n \cdot CR$.

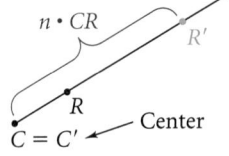

The dilation is an **enlargement** if the scale factor is greater than 1. The dilation is a **reduction** if the scale factor is between 0 and 1.

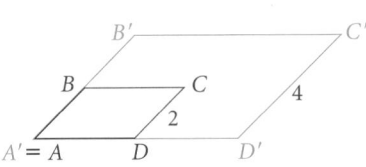

Enlargement
Center A, scale factor 2

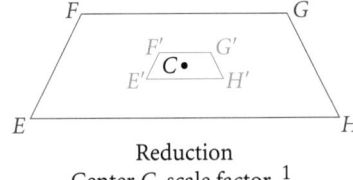

Reduction
Center C, scale factor $\frac{1}{4}$

1 EXAMPLE **Finding a Scale Factor**

The blue triangle is a dilation image of the red triangle. Describe the dilation.

The center is X. The image is larger than the preimage, so the dilation is an enlargement.

$$\frac{X'T'}{XT} = \frac{4 + 8}{4} = 3$$

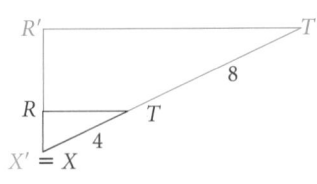

● The dilation has center X and scale factor 3.

Ongoing Assessment and Intervention

Before the Lesson	During the Lesson	After the Lesson
Diagnose prerequisite skills using:	**Monitor progress using:**	**Assess knowledge using:**
• Check Skills You'll Need	• Check Understanding • Additional Examples • Standardized Test Prep	• Lesson Quiz • Computer Test Generator CD

✓ **Check Understanding**   ❶ The blue quadrilateral is a dilation image of the red quadrilateral. Describe the dilation.
The dilation is a reduction with center (0, 0) and scale factor $\frac{1}{2}$.

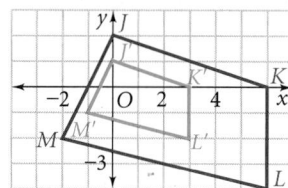

Scale factors help you understand scale models, both large and small.

❷ **EXAMPLE** 🌐 **Real-World Connection**

Scale Models The packaging lists a model car's length as 7.6 cm. It also gives the scale as 1 : 63. What is the length of the actual car?

To "enlarge" the model car to the actual car, use the scale factor 63. Multiply 7.6 cm by 63 to get 478.8 cm, or about 4.8 m, for the length of the actual car.

✓ **Check Understanding**   ❷ The height of a tractor-trailer truck is 4.2 m. The scale factor for a model of the truck is $\frac{1}{54}$. Find the height of the model to the nearest centimeter.   **8 cm**

Suppose a dilation is centered at the origin. You can find the dilation image of a point by multiplying its coordinates by the scale factor.

Scale factor 4, $(x, y) \longrightarrow (4x, 4y)$ Scale factor $\frac{1}{3}$, $(x, y) \longrightarrow \left(\frac{1}{3}x, \frac{1}{3}y\right)$

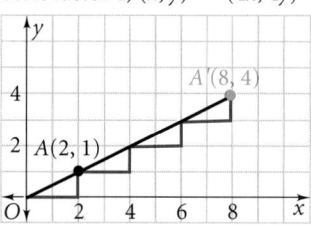   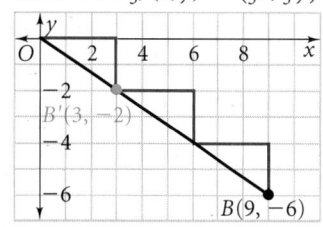

3. $P'(1, 0)$, $Z'\left(-\frac{1}{2}, \frac{1}{4}\right)$,
    $G'\left(\frac{1}{2}, -1\right)$

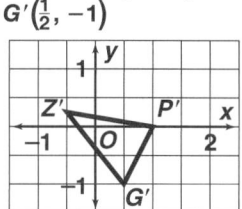

To dilate a triangle from the origin, find the dilation images of its vertices. Enter all six vertex coordinates in a matrix, and then multiply each matrix entry by the scale factor. Multiplying a matrix by a *scalar* in this way is called **scalar multiplication**.

❸ **EXAMPLE**   **Using Scalar Multiplication**

$\triangle PZG$ has vertices $P(2, 0)$, $Z\left(-1, \frac{1}{2}\right)$, and $G(1, -2)$. Use scalar multiplication to find the image of $\triangle PZG$ for a dilation with center $(0, 0)$ and scale factor 3. Draw the enlargement.

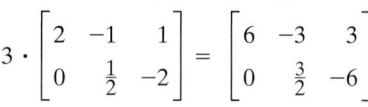

$$\begin{array}{c} \quad\quad\quad P \quad\ Z \quad\ G \\ \begin{array}{l} x\text{-coordinate} \\ y\text{-coordinate} \end{array} \begin{bmatrix} 2 & -1 & 1 \\ 0 & \frac{1}{2} & -2 \end{bmatrix} \end{array}$$ **Write a matrix for $\triangle PZG$.**

$$3 \cdot \begin{bmatrix} 2 & -1 & 1 \\ 0 & \frac{1}{2} & -2 \end{bmatrix} = \begin{bmatrix} 6 & -3 & 3 \\ 0 & \frac{3}{2} & -6 \end{bmatrix}$$ **Multiply entries by the scale factor 3.**

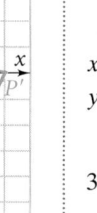

The vertices of the enlargement at the left are $P'(6, 0)$, $Z'\left(-3, \frac{3}{2}\right)$, and $G'(3, -6)$.

✓ **Check Understanding**   ❸ Use scalar multiplication to find the image of $\triangle PZG$ for a dilation with center $(0, 0)$ and scale factor $\frac{1}{2}$. Draw the reduction.   **See left above.**

Lesson 12-7   Dilations   **675**

👥 **Reaching All Students**

| **Below Level** Before presenting dilations, review the definition of similar polygons and the postulates and theorems about similar triangles. | **Advanced Learners** Students can use the definition of dilation, and triangle similarity postulates and theorems, to prove that the trapezoids above Example 1 are similar. | **Visual Learners** See note on page 677. **Error Prevention** See note on page 676. |

---

2. Teach

Professional Development

Math Background

Dilations map figures onto similar figures. A dilation may or may not have an invariant point that maps onto itself but is uniquely determined by its effect on any two given points.

OBJECTIVE
❶ Teaching Notes

Connection to Biology
Ask: *When your pupil dilates, is the dilation an enlargement or a reduction?* **enlargement**

❸ **EXAMPLE** **Math Tip**

Scalar multiplication is used only for dilations centered at the origin. Have students try to find the image with center P to see why this is so.

✍ Additional Examples

❶ Circle A with a 3-cm diameter and center C is a dilation of concentric circle B with an 8-cm diameter. Describe the dilation. **reduction with center C and scale factor $\frac{3}{8}$**

❷ The scale factor on a museum's floor plan is 1 : 200. The length and width on the drawing are 8 in. and 6 in. Find the actual dimensions in feet and inches. **133 ft, 4 in. by 100 ft**

❸ $\triangle ABC$ has vertices $A(-2, -3)$, $B(0, 4)$, and $C(6, -12)$. Use scalar multiplication to find the coordinates of the image of $\triangle ABC$ for a dilation with center $(0, 0)$ and scale factor 0.75. **$A'(-1.5, -2.25)$, $B'(0, 3)$, $C'(4.5, -9)$**

Closure

Draw square $ABCD$, a dilation image of $ABCD$ with center A and scale factor 3, and a dilation image of $ABCD$ with center C and scale factor $\frac{1}{2}$. **Check students' drawings.**

675

EXERCISES

For more practice, see *Extra Practice*.

Practice and Problem Solving

Assignment Guide

Objective

Ⓐ Ⓑ **Core** 1–61

Ⓒ **Extension** 62–66

Standardized Test Prep 67–71

Mixed Review 72–79

Error Prevention

Exercises 1–9 Students should be careful not to describe dilations as "as big as" or "bigger than" but to give the precise scale factor.

Exercises 10–14 Ask students who have model railroads to bring cars to class to show other students. You can use the cars to create exercises like these.

Alternative Method

Exercises 15–17 Organize the class into two groups. Have one group copy the graphs and draw segments to find the images and the other group use scalar multiplication to find the images. Discuss the advantages of each method.

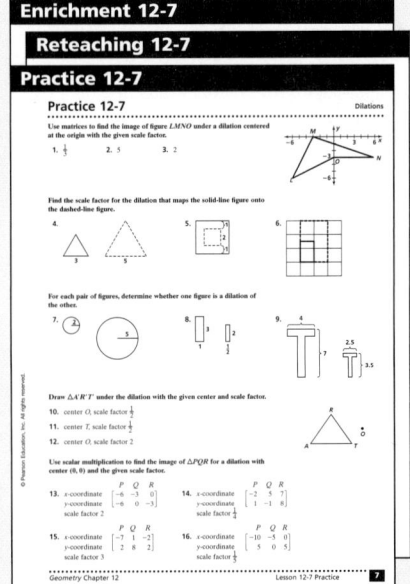

Ⓐ **Practice by Example**

Example 1
(page 674)

1. enlargement; center A, scale factor $\frac{3}{2}$

2. enlargement; center C, scale factor 3

3. enlargement; center R, scale factor $\frac{3}{2}$

4. reduction; center K, scale factor $\frac{1}{3}$

5. reduction; center L, scale factor $\frac{1}{3}$

6. enlargement; center M, scale factor 2

7. reduction; center (0, 0), scale factor $\frac{1}{2}$

8. enlargement; center (0, 0), scale factor 2

9. enlargement; center (0, 0), scale factor $\frac{3}{2}$

The blue figure is a dilation image of the red figure. Describe the dilation.
1–9. See left.

1.
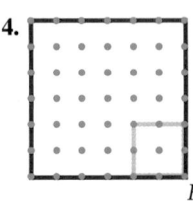

2.
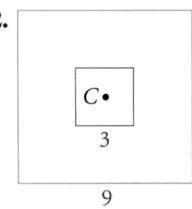

3.
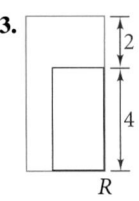

4.
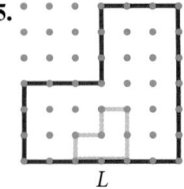

5.

6.
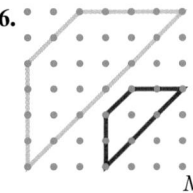

7.
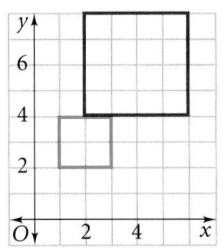

8.
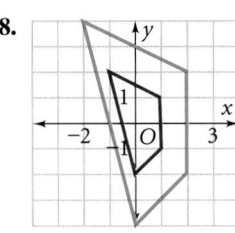

9.
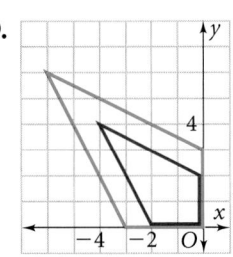

Example 2
(page 675)

Model Railroads The table shows scales for different types of model railroads. For each model in Exercises 10–12, what would be the actual measurement?
121.94 in.

10. An HO-scale tank car is 1.4 in. high.

11. An S-scale boxcar has length 8 in. **512 in.**

12. A model of an engineer in a G-scale model train layout is 3 in. tall. **67.5 in.**

13. A diesel engine is 60 feet long. How long is its O-scale model? **1.25 ft**

14. Actual railroad tracks are 4 ft 8.5 in. apart. How far apart are N-scale tracks? **0.35 in.**

Model Railroad Scales

Scale Name	Scale Ratio
N	1 : 160
HO	1 : 87.1
S	1 : 64
O	1 : 48
G	1 : 22.5

Example 3
(page 675)

Use a matrix and scalar multiplication. Find the image of △PQR for a dilation with center (0, 0) and the scale factor given. Draw the image. 15–17. See back of book.

15.
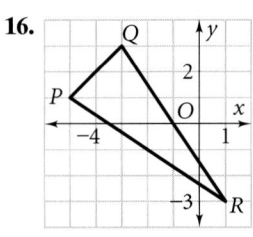
scale factor 3

16.
scale factor 10

17.
scale factor $\frac{3}{4}$

A dilation has center (0, 0). Find the image of each point for the scale factor given.

18. $D(1, -5); 2$ **D'(2, -10)** 19. $L(-3, 0); 5$ **L'(-15, 0)** 20. $A(-6, 2); 1.5$ **A'(-9, 3)**

21. $T(0, 6); 3$ **T'(0, 18)** 22. $M(0, 0); 10$ **M'(0, 0)** 23. $N(-4, -7); 0.1$
N'(-0.4, -0.7)

Use scalar multiplication to find the image of $\triangle ABC$ for a dilation with center (0, 0) and the scale factor given. Draw $\triangle ABC$ and its image.

24.
$$\begin{array}{c c c c} & A & B & C \\ x\text{-coordinate} & \begin{bmatrix} 1 & 3 & 5 \\ 0 & 2 & 1 \end{bmatrix} \\ y\text{-coordinate} & \end{array}$$
scale factor 2

24–27. See back of book.

25.
$$\begin{array}{c c c c} & A & B & C \\ x\text{-coordinate} & \begin{bmatrix} -2 & 1 & 1 \\ -2 & 1 & -1 \end{bmatrix} \\ y\text{-coordinate} & \end{array}$$
scale factor $\frac{1}{4}$

26.
$$\begin{array}{c c c c} & A & B & C \\ x\text{-coordinate} & \begin{bmatrix} 3 & -6 & 12 \\ 1 & -9 & -3 \end{bmatrix} \\ y\text{-coordinate} & \end{array}$$
scale factor $\frac{1}{3}$

27.
$$\begin{array}{c c c c} & A & B & C \\ x\text{-coordinate} & \begin{bmatrix} -2 & -4 & -3 \\ 0 & -3 & 0 \end{bmatrix} \\ y\text{-coordinate} & \end{array}$$
scale factor 5

 **Apply Your Skills**

Use scalar multiplication to find the image of $QRTW$ for a dilation with center (0, 0) and the scale factor given.

28. 3 29. 2 30. $\frac{1}{2}$ 31. $\frac{1}{4}$

32. 0.6 33. 0.9 34. 10 35. 100
28–35. See margin.

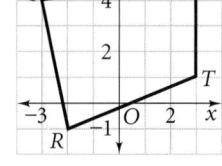

36. **Writing** An equilateral triangle has 4-in. sides. Describe its image for a dilation with scale factor 2.5. Explain.
The image has side lengths 10 in. and $\angle$ measures 60.

Coordinate Geometry Graph $MNPQ$ and its image $M'N'P'Q'$ for a dilation with center (0, 0) and the scale factor given. **37–40. See back of book.**

37. $M(-1, -1), N(1, -2), P(1, 2), Q(-1, 3)$; scale factor 2

38. $M(1, 3), N(-3, 3), P(-5, -3), Q(-1, -3)$; scale factor 3

39. $M(0, 0), N(4, 0), P(6, -2), Q(-2, -2)$; scale factor $\frac{1}{2}$

40. $M(2, 6), N(-4, 10), P(-4, -8), Q(-2, -12)$; scale factor $\frac{1}{4}$

41. **Open-Ended** Use the dilation command in geometry software or drawing software to create a design that involves repeated dilations. The software will prompt you to specify a center of dilation and a scale factor. Print your design and color it. Feel free to use other transformations along with dilations.
Check students' work.

42. **Copy Reduction** Your copy of your family crest is 4.5 in. wide. You need a reduced copy for the front page of the family newsletter. The copy must fit in a space 1.8 in. wide. What scale factor should you use on the copy machine?
Use a scale factor of $\frac{2}{5}$.

A dilation maps $\triangle HIJ$ to $\triangle H'I'J'$. Find the missing values.

43. $HI = 8$ in.
$IJ = 5$ in.
$HJ = 6$ in.
$H'I' = 16$ in.
$I'J' = \blacksquare$ in. **10**
$H'J' = \blacksquare$ in. **12**

44. $HI = 7$ cm
$IJ = 7$ cm
$HJ = \blacksquare$ cm **12**
$H'I' = 5.25$ cm
$I'J' = \blacksquare$ cm **5.25**
$H'J' = 9$ cm

45. $HI = \blacksquare$ ft **32**
$IJ = 30$ ft
$HJ = 24$ ft
$H'I' = 8$ ft
$I'J' = \blacksquare$ ft **7.5**
$H'J' = 6$ ft

46. **Error Analysis** Brendan says that when a rectangle with length 6 cm and width 4 cm is dilated by a scale factor of 2, the perimeter and area of the rectangle are doubled. Explain what is incorrect about Brendan's statement.
The perimeter is doubled but the area is multiplied by 4.

Lesson 12-7 Dilations **677**

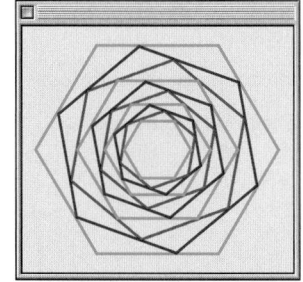
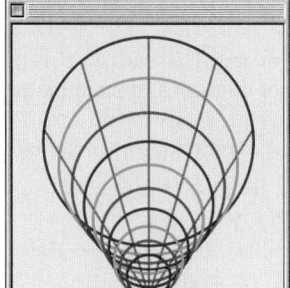
Exercise 41

pages 676–679 **Exercises**

28. **Q'(-9, 12), W'(9, 15), T'(9, 3), R'(-6, -3)**

29. **Q'(-6, 8), W'(6, 10), T'(6, 2), R'(-4, -2)**

30. **Q'($-\frac{3}{2}$, 2), W'($\frac{3}{2}$, $\frac{5}{2}$), T'($\frac{3}{2}$, $\frac{1}{2}$), R'(-1, $-\frac{1}{2}$)**

31. **Q'($-\frac{3}{4}$, 1), W'($\frac{3}{4}$, $\frac{5}{4}$), T'($\frac{3}{4}$, $\frac{1}{4}$), R'($-\frac{1}{2}$, $-\frac{1}{4}$)**

Teaching Tip

Exercise 41 Before students begin, discuss how to create each figure using dilations, rotations, and translations.

Diversity

Exercise 42 Students unfamiliar with heraldry may not know what a family crest or coat of arms is. Internet genealogy sites provide many such examples for students to examine.

Exercise 46 If necessary, review Theorem 8-6: *If the similarity ratio of two similar figures is a : b, then (1) the ratio of their perimeters is a : b and (2) the ratio of their areas is a² : b².*

Exercises 49–52 Exercises 49, 50, and 52 can be done with compass and straightedge. Exercise 51 requires a ruler.

Exercises 57–61 Use these exercises for class discussion to assess students' understanding of the lesson. If answers vary, have students explain their reasons to one another.

Connection to Film

Exercise 62 The ratio of the perimeters of the similar triangles is also 3 in. : 1 ft. Point out that the flashlight models a film projector, the small rectangle models a film slide, and the large rectangle models its projection on a screen.

Visual Learners

Exercise 63 Suggest that students place a tracing of $\overline{AB}$ and $\overline{A'B'}$ over a coordinate grid.

32. **Q'(-1.8, 2.4), W'(1.8, 3), T'(1.8, 0.6), R'(-1.2, -0.6)**

33. **Q'(-2.7, 3.6), W'(2.7, 4.5), T'(2.7, 0.9), R'(-1.8, -0.9)**

34. **Q'(-30, 40), W'(30, 50), T'(30, 10), R'(-20, -10)**

35. **Q'(-300, 400), W'(300, 500), T'(300, 100), R'(-200, -100)**

677

Lesson Quiz 12-7

1. A model is a reduction of a real tractor by the scale factor of 1 : 16. Its dimensions are 1.2 ft by 0.6 ft by 0.625 ft. Find the actual dimensions of the tractor. **19.2 ft by 9.6 ft by 10 ft**

For Exercises 2 and 3, $\triangle XYZ$ has vertices $X(3, 1)$, $Y(2, -4)$, and $Z(-2, 0)$.

2. Use scalar multiplication to find the image of $\triangle XYZ$ for a dilation with center $(0, 0)$ and scale factor 2.5. **$X'(7.5, 2.5)$, $Y'(5, -10)$, $Z'(-5, 0)$**

3. Draw and label the preimage and image.

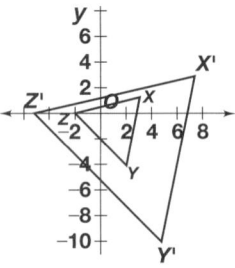

For Exercises 4 and 5, $\triangle DIL$ is a dilation image of $\triangle DAT$.

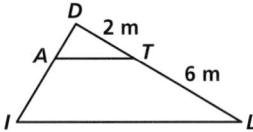

4. Identify the center of dilation. **D**

5. Find the scale factor. **4**

Alternative Assessment

Have each student draw and label a triangle with vertices A, B, and C; choose a scale factor; and then exchange papers with a partner and draw the dilation image of the partner's triangle, using A as the center. After drawing the images, have partners compare the pre-images and images and check each other's work.

678

49.

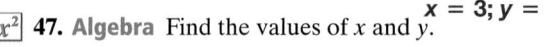

51.

Real-World Connection

An overhead projection is a dilation only when the mirror in the head is tilted at a 45° angle. Turning the head distorts the images.

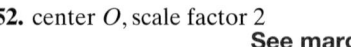

Challenge

62. Each vertex is 1 ft from the light.

63. Connect corresponding points A and A' and B and B'. Extend $\overline{AA'}$ and $\overline{BB'}$ until they intersect at the center of dilation. The scale factor is the length of $\overline{A'B'}$ divided by the length of $\overline{AB}$.

The diagram at the right shows $\triangle LMN$ and its image $\triangle L'M'N'$ for a dilation with center P.

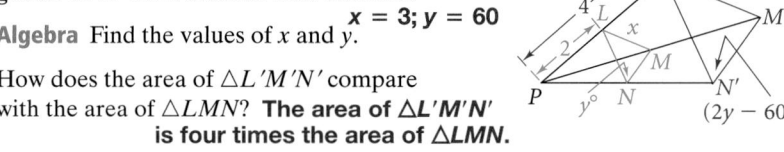

47. Algebra Find the values of x and y. $x = 3; y = 60$

48. How does the area of $\triangle L'M'N'$ compare with the area of $\triangle LMN$? **The area of $\triangle L'M'N'$ is four times the area of $\triangle LMN$.**

Copy $\triangle TBA$ and point O for each of Exercises 49–52. Draw the dilation image $\triangle T'B'A'$ for the given center and scale factor.

49. center O, scale factor $\frac{1}{2}$ **See left.**

50. center B, scale factor 3 **See back of book.**

51. center T, scale factor $\frac{1}{3}$ **See left.**

52. center O, scale factor 2 **See margin.**

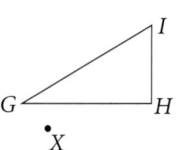

53. Constructions Copy $\triangle GHI$ and point X onto your paper. Use a compass and straightedge to construct the image of $\triangle GHI$ for a dilation with center X and scale factor 2. **See margin.**

Overhead Projection An overhead projector can dilate figures on transparencies.

54. A segment on a transparency is 2 in. long. Its image on the screen is 2 ft long. What is the scale factor of the dilation? **12**

55. The height of a parallelogram on the transparency is 4 cm. The scale factor is 15. What is the height of the parallelogram on the screen? **60 cm**

56. The area of a triangle on the screen is 9 ft². The scale factor is 16. What is the area of the triangle on the transparency? **$\frac{9}{256}$ ft²**

Write *true* or *false* for Exercises 57–61. Explain your answers. **57–61. See margin p. 679.**

57. A dilation is an isometry.

58. A dilation changes orientation.

59. A dilation with a scale factor greater than 1 is a reduction.

60. For a dilation, corresponding angles of the image and preimage are congruent.

61. A dilation image cannot have any points in common with its preimage.

62. A flashlight projects an image of rectangle $ABCD$ on a wall so that each vertex of $ABCD$ is 3 ft away from the corresponding vertex of $A'B'C'D'$. The length of $\overline{AB}$ is 3 in. The length of $\overline{A'B'}$ is 1 ft. **See left.** How far from each vertex of $ABCD$ is the light?

63. Critical Thinking You are given $\overline{AB}$ and its dilation image $\overline{A'B'}$ with A, B, A', and B' noncollinear. Explain how to find the center of dilation and scale factor. **See left.**

Coordinate Geometry In the coordinate plane you can extend dilations to include scale factors that are negative numbers. **a–c. See back of book.**

64. a. Graph $\triangle PQR$ with vertices $P(1, 2)$, $Q(3, 4)$, and $R(4, 1)$.
b. For a dilation centered at the origin with a scale factor of -3, multiply the coordinates in part (a) by -3. List the results as P', Q', and R'.
c. Graph $\triangle P'Q'R'$ on the same set of axes.

pages 676–679 **Exercises**

52.

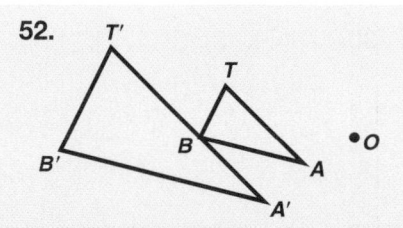

53.

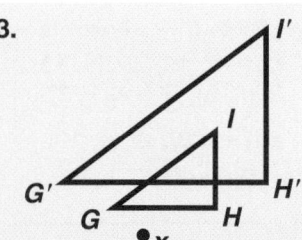

Need Help?

For Exercise 65(b), recall the meaning of reflection in a line.

65. a. A dilation with center at the origin and scale factor −1 (see Exercise 64) may be called a *reflection in a point.* For △*PQR* of Exercise 64, find the image △*P′Q′R′* for such a dilation. **P′(−1, −2), Q′(−3, −4), R′(−4, −1)**

 **b. Writing** Explain why the dilation described in part (a) may be called a *reflection in a point.* Extend your explanation to a new definition of point symmetry. Compare your new definition with the definition given on page 663. **See margin.**

66. Constructions Draw acute △*ABC*. Construct square *DEFG* so that $\overline{DG}$ is on $\overline{AC}$, and *E* and *F* are on the other two sides of △*ABC*. (*Hint:* First, try the special case with a right angle at *A* and use a dilation.) **See margin.**

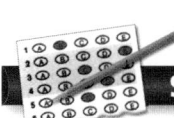

Standardized Test Prep

Gridded Response

67. A dilation maps △*ABC* onto △*A′B′C′* with a scale factor of 0.3. If *A′B′* = 3126 m, what is *AB* in meters? **10420**

68. A dilation maps △*CDE* onto △*C′D′E′*. If *CD* = 7.5 ft, *CE* = 15 ft, *D′E′* = 3.75 ft, and *C′D′*= 2.5 ft, what is *DE* in feet? **11.25**

69. A dilation maps △*XYZ* onto △ *X′Y′Z′*. If *XY* = 24 m, *YZ* = 29 m, *X′Z′* = 8.7 m, and *Y′Z′* = 29.145 m, what is *X′Y′* in meters? **24.12**

Take It to the NET

Online lesson quiz at **www.PHSchool.com**

Web Code: afa-1207

70. The center of dilation of quadrilateral *ABCD* is point *X*, as shown at the right. The length of a side of quadrilateral *A′B′C′D′* is what percent of the length of the corresponding side of quadrilateral *ABCD*? **50**

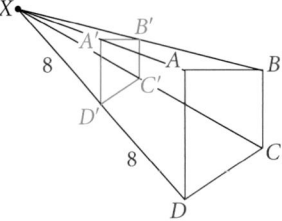

71. A dilation maps △*JKL* onto △*J′K′L′*. If *JK* = 28 cm, *KL* = 52 cm, *JL* = 40.2 cm, and *J′K′* = 616 cm, what is the scale factor? **22**

Mixed Review

Lesson 12-6 **Determine whether the polygons described could tessellate a plane.**

72. congruent regular hexagons **yes**   **73.** squares and regular triangles **yes**

74. congruent regular octagons **no**   **75.** congruent kite figures **yes**

Lesson 11-6 **Give another description of each locus.** **76–77. See margin.**

76. all points in a plane equidistant from three noncollinear points

77. all points in space 3 inches from a sphere with a 3-inch radius

Lesson 11-2 $\boxed{x^2}$ **Algebra Find the value of *a*.**

78. **4**

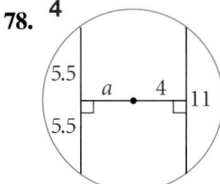

79. **30**

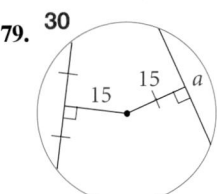

A sheet of blank grids is available in the Test-Taking Strategies with Transparencies booklet. Give this sheet to students for practice with filling in the grids.

📁 **Resources**

For additional practice with a variety of test item formats:
- Standardized Test Prep, p. 685
- Test-Taking Strategies, p. 680
- Test-Taking Strategies with Transparencies

Exercises 68, 69 Each exercise contains more information than is needed to find the missing length. Drawing a rough sketch will help students use the appropriate data.

65. b. Each point of the △ is reflected in the origin, which is the point of reflection. Two figures are symmetrical with respect to a pt. *P* if *P* is the midpoint of each segment that connects two corr. points of the figure.

66. Construct small square *D′E′F′G′* so that $\overline{D′G′}$ is on $\overline{AC}$ (with *D′* between *A* and *G′*), *E′* is on $\overline{AB}$, and *F′* is inside △*ABC*. Draw $\overrightarrow{AF′}$ to meet $\overline{BC}$ at *F*. Through *F* construct the line ∥ to $\overline{AC}$. Label its point of intersection with $\overline{AB}$ as *E*. Through *E* and *F* construct the lines ⊥ to $\overline{AC}$. Label their points of intersection with $\overline{AC}$ as *D* and *G* respectively. *DEFG* is the desired square.

76. the point that is the intersection of the ⊥ bisectors of the segments connecting the 3 noncollinear points

77. a sphere with a 6-in. radius, concentric with the given sphere, and the center of the spheres

---

57. False; a dilation doesn't map a segment to a ≅ segment unless the scale factor is 1.

58. False; a dilation does not change orientation.

59. False; a dilation with a scale factor greater than 1 is an enlargement.

60. True; the image and preimage are similar, so the △ are ≅.

61. False; if the center of dilation is on the preimage, it is also on the image.

Test-Taking Strategies

Answering the Question Asked

Multiple-choice questions often include answers that are distractors, that is, answers to closely related questions. Students who misread the question or fail to identify what is asked may actually answer a related question. This feature helps students understand the importance of focusing on and answering the question that is asked.

Resources

Test-Taking Strategies with Transparencies
- Transparency 12
- Practice sheet p. 24

Teaching Notes

Help students understand that the answer choices listed in multiple-choice questions are not arbitrarily chosen. They are specifically designed as answers that reflect common errors and common misconceptions.

Teaching Tip

Students might examine the answer choices for these exercises and discuss why the test maker selected the answer choices shown.

Test-Taking Strategies with Transparencies

Test-Taking Strategy: Answering the Question Asked

Incorrect choices may answer related questions.

Example A savings account earns interest compounded annually at a rate of 7%. If $1000 is deposited, what is the account balance after 1 year?

A. $1000   B. $70   C. $1070   D. $7000

Calculate the interest earned: 0.07 × 1000 = $70

Choice B is $70, but this is the interest earned, not the account balance.

Calculate the account balance: 1000 + 70 = $1070

The answer is $1070, or choice C.

Answer the question asked. Explain your reasoning.

1. Seven friends went bowling. Here are their scores.

78 110 99 81 104 84 81

Find the mean of the scores.

A. 81   B. 84   C. 78   D. 91

2. If 3x − 7 = 8, what is the value of 4x? Write your response on the grid.

3. Write in standard form the equation of the line perpendicular to y = x − 6 through (−2, 3).

A. −x + y = 5   B. x + y = 1   C. −x + y = −6
D. x + y = −1

Solutions

1. D
2. 5
3. A

Transparency 12

680

When answering a question, be sure to answer the question that is asked. Read the question carefully and identify the quantity that you are asked to find. Some answer choices are answers to related questions, so you have to be careful.

1 EXAMPLE

The point $L(a, b)$ in Quadrant I is rotated 90° about the origin and is then reflected in the y-axis. What is the x-coordinate of the image?

  A. a **B.** $-b$ **C.** b **D.** $-a$

The question asks for the x-coordinate of the image. The x-coordinate of the preimage is a. After the 90° rotation about the origin, the x-coordinate is $-b$. After a reflection in the y-axis, the x-coordinate of the image is b.

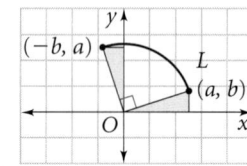 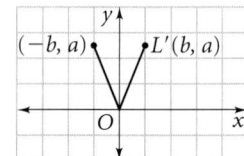

The correct answer is C. Choice A is the y-coordinate of the image, but that is not what is asked for.

2 EXAMPLE

What is the image of $M(4, 3)$ for the translation $\langle -2, 1 \rangle$ followed by a reflection in the line $x = -1$?

  F. $(2, -6)$ **G.** $(-4, 4)$ **H.** $(0, 4)$ **I.** $(-8, 4)$

The translation $\langle -2, 1 \rangle$ puts the point at $(2, 4)$. A reflection in $x = -1$ then puts the point at $(-4, 4)$. The correct answer is G.

Answers F and H result from the translation $\langle -2, 1 \rangle$ followed by a reflection in a line other than $x = -1$. In fact, if you reflect $(2, 4)$ in $x = 1$, which is one unit in the negative direction from $(2, 4)$, you get $(0, 4)$, or choice H, as your answer. If you do the steps in the wrong order, you will get answer I.

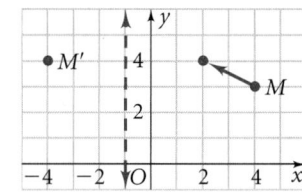

EXERCISES

Answer the question. Then ask a related question that would lead to an incorrect choice. 1–3. See margin.

1. The point $K(4, 3)$ is rotated 90° about the origin. What is the sum of the x- and y-coordinates of the image?
  A. -7 **B.** -1 **C.** 1 **D.** 7

2. The point $P(1, 3)$ is rotated 180° about the origin, and then reflected in the line $y = 0$. What is the y-coordinate of the image?
  F. -3 **G.** -1 **H.** 1 **I.** 3

3. The point $T(5, -1)$ is reflected in the y-axis. What is the distance between the image and the preimage?
  A. 1 **B.** 2 **C.** $\sqrt{26}$ **D.** 10

---

page 680 Test-Taking Strategies

1–3. Related questions may vary. Samples are given.

1. C; what is the sum of the pre-image's coordinates?

2. I; what is the y-coordinate after the rotation only?

3. D; what is the distance if T were reflected in the x-axis?

Chapter Review

Vocabulary

composition (p. 642)
dilation (p. 674)
enlargement (p. 674)
glide reflection (p. 656)
glide reflectional symmetry (p. 668)
image (p. 634)
isometry (p. 634)
line symmetry (p. 662)

point symmetry (p. 663)
preimage (p. 634)
reduction (p. 674)
reflection (p. 635)
reflectional symmetry (p. 662)
rotation (p. 648)
rotational symmetry (p. 663)
scalar multiplication (p. 675)

symmetry (p. 662)
tessellation (p. 667)
tiling (p. 667)
transformation (p. 634)
translation (p. 641)
translational symmetry (p. 668)

Reading Math
Understanding Vocabulary

To complete each definition, find the appropriate word in the second column.

1. A(n) _?_ is a change in position, shape, or size of a figure. **F**

2. A(n) _?_ is a transformation in which the preimage and its image are congruent. **D**

3. A _?_ is an isometry in which a figure and its image have opposite orientations. **E**

4. A _?_ is an isometry in which all points of a figure move the same distance in the same direction. **G**

5. A(n) _?_ is a translation followed by a reflection in a line parallel to the translation vector. **B**

6. A(n) _?_ is a repeating pattern of figures that completely covers a plane, without gaps or overlaps. **C**

7. A(n) _?_ is a transformation that proportionally reduces or enlarges a figure. **A**

A. dilation

B. glide reflection

C. tessellation

D. isometry

E. reflection

F. transformation

G. translation

Take It to the NET
Online vocabulary quiz at www.PHSchool.com
Web Code: afj-1251

Skills and Concepts

12-1 and 12-2 Objectives

▼ To identify isometries

▼ To find reflection images of figures

▼ To describe translations using vectors

▼ To find translation images using matrix and vector sums

A **transformation** of a geometric figure is a change in its position, shape, or size. An **isometry** is a transformation in which the **preimage** and **image** are congruent. A transformation maps a figure onto its image. The diagram shows a **reflection** of B to B' in line r. A reflection is an isometry in which a figure and its image have opposite orientations.

A **translation** is an isometry that maps all points of a figure the same distance in the same direction. A translation is an isometry that does not change orientation. You can use vectors and matrices to describe a translation.

A **composition** of transformations is a combination of two or more transformations. Each transformation is performed on the image of the preceding transformation.

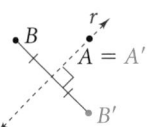

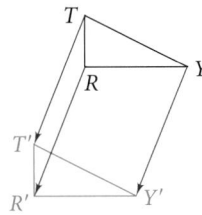

8.

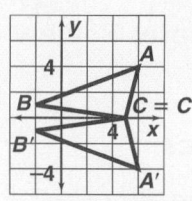

9.

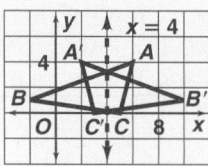

10.

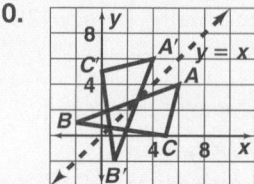

23. same; rotation

24. opposite; reflection

25. same; translation

26. opposite; glide reflection

27. same; translation

28. opposite; glide reflection

29. same; rotation

30. opposite; reflection

11. $A'(7, 12)$, $B'(8, 6)$, $C'(3, 5)$

12. $R'(-4, 3)$, $S'(-6, 6)$, $T'(-10, 8)$

Given points $A(6, 4)$, $B(-2, 1)$, and $C(5, 0)$, draw $\triangle ABC$ and its reflection image in each line.   8–10. See margin.

8. the x-axis   **9.** $x = 4$ **10.** $y = x$

Use matrices to find the image of each triangle for the given translation. 11–12. See left.

11. $\triangle ABC$ with vertices $A(5, 9)$, $B(6, 3)$, $C(1, 2)$; translation: $\langle 2, 3 \rangle$

12. $\triangle RST$ with vertices $R(0, -4)$, $S(-2, -1)$, $T(-6, 1)$; translation: $\langle -4, 7 \rangle$

Find a single translation that has the same effect as each composition of translations.

13. $\langle -5, -7 \rangle$ followed by $\langle 3, 6 \rangle$
$\langle -2, -1 \rangle$

14. $\langle 10, -9 \rangle$ followed by $\langle 1, 5 \rangle$
$\langle 11, -4 \rangle$

12-3 and 12-4 Objectives

▼ To draw and identify rotation images of figures

▼ To use a composition of reflections

▼ To identify glide reflections

The diagram shows a rotation of point V about point R through $x°$. A **rotation** is an isometry that does not change orientation.

A composition of reflections in two parallel lines is a translation. A composition of reflections in two intersecting lines is a rotation. A **glide reflection** is the composition of a glide (translation) and a reflection in a line parallel to the translation vector. The only four isometries are reflection, translation, rotation, and glide reflection.

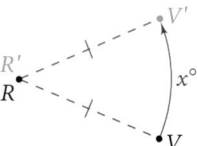

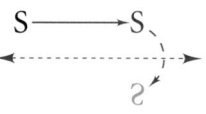

Copy each figure and point P. Draw the image of each figure for the given rotation about P. Label the vertices of the image.   15–17. See left.

15.

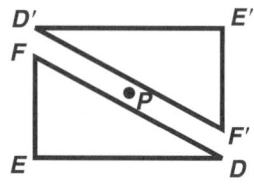

16.

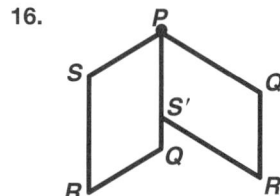

17.

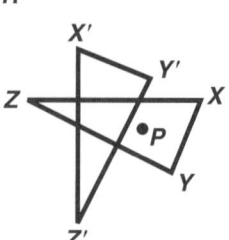

15. 180°

16. 60°

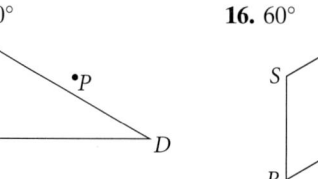

17. 90°

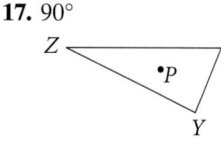

Find the image of each point for a 90° rotation about the origin.

18. $(5, 2)$ $(-2, 5)$ **19.** $(0, 3)$ $(-3, 0)$ **20.** $(-4, 1)$ $(-1, -4)$ **21.** $(7, 0)$ $(0, 7)$ **22.** $(-2, -8)$ $(8, -2)$

For each figure at the left below, four isometry images are shown. Tell whether orientations are the same or opposite. Then classify the isometry.   23–30. See margin.

23.

24.

25.

26.

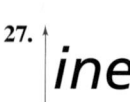

27.

28.

29.

30.

31. $\triangle TAM$ has vertices $T(0, 5)$, $A(4, 1)$, and $M(3, 6)$. Find the image of $\triangle TAM$ where the glide vector is $\langle -4, 0 \rangle$ and the reflection is in the line $y = -2$.
$T'(-4, -9)$, $A'(0, -5)$, $M'(-1, -10)$

12-5 and 12-6 Objectives

▼ To identify the type of symmetry in a figure

▼ To identify transformations in tessellations and figures that will tessellate

▼ To identify symmetries of tessellations

A figure has **symmetry** if there is an isometry that maps the figure onto itself. A plane figure has **reflectional symmetry,** or **line symmetry,** if one half of the figure is a mirror image of its other half. A figure that has **rotational symmetry** is its own image for some rotation of 180° or less. A figure that has **point symmetry** has 180° rotational symmetry.

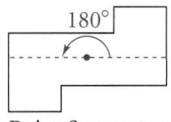
180°

Point Symmetry

Tell what type(s) of symmetry each figure has. If it has rotational symmetry, state the angle of rotation.

32.

reflectional

33. rotational; 72°

34a.

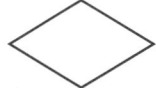

b. rotational, point, reflectional, translational, glide reflectional

35a.

 and

b. rotational, point, reflectional, translational, glide reflectional

A **tessellation,** or **tiling,** is a repeating pattern of figures that completely covers a plane, without gaps or overlaps. A tessellation can have **translational symmetry** if there is a translation that maps the tessellation onto itself. If a tessellation can be mapped onto itself by a glide reflection, then the tessellation has **glide reflectional symmetry.**

For each tessellation, (a) identify a transformation and the repeating figures, and (b) list the symmetries. 34–35. See left.

34.

35.

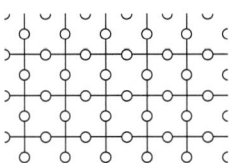

12-7 Objective

▼ To locate dilation images of figures

The diagram shows a **dilation** with center C and scale factor n. A dilation is a similarity transformation because its preimage and image are similar figures. When the scale factor is greater than 1, the dilation is an **enlargement.** When the scale factor is between 0 and 1, the dilation is a **reduction.** In the coordinate plane, you can use **scalar multiplication** to find the image of a figure under a dilation centered at the origin.

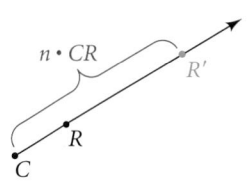
$n \cdot CR$
R'
R
C

A dilation has center $(0, 0)$. Find the image of each point for the scale factor given.

36. $A(0, 3); 4$
$A'(0, 12)$

37. $B(-2, 6); 0.5$
$B'(-1, 3)$

38. $C(1.5, -2); 10$
$C'(15, -20)$

Use matrices to find the image of each set of points for a dilation with center at the origin and the scale factor given. $M'(-15, 20), A'(-30, -5), T'(0, 0), H'(15, 10)$

39. $M(-3, 4), A(-6, -1), T(0, 0), H(3, 2)$; scale factor 5

40. $F(-4, 0), U(5, 0), N(-2, -5)$; scale factor $\frac{1}{2}$
$F'(-2, 0), U'\left(\frac{5}{2}, 0\right), N'\left(-1, -\frac{5}{2}\right)$

Chapter 12 Chapter Review **683**

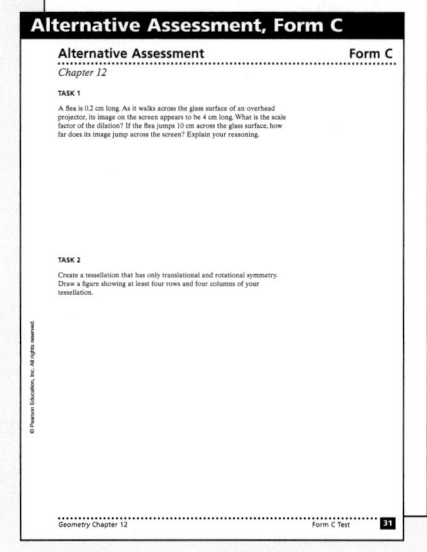

Resources

📁 **Teaching Resources**
Ch. 12 Test, Forms A & B
Ch. 12 Alternative Assessment,
Form C

👥 **Reaching All Students**
Spanish Ch. 12 Test, Forms A & B
Spanish Ch. 12 Alternative
Assessment, Form C
Informal Geometry Ch. 12 Test,
Forms D & E

 **ASSESSMENT SYSTEM**

Assessment Masters
• Ch. 12 Test, Forms A & B
• Ch. 12 Alternative Assessment,
Form C
Computer Test Generator CD
• Ch. 12 pre-made Test
• Make your own Ch. 12 test

 www.PHSchool.com
Student Site
• Self-grading Chapter 12 Test
Teacher Center
• Resources

Plus  **TEXT**

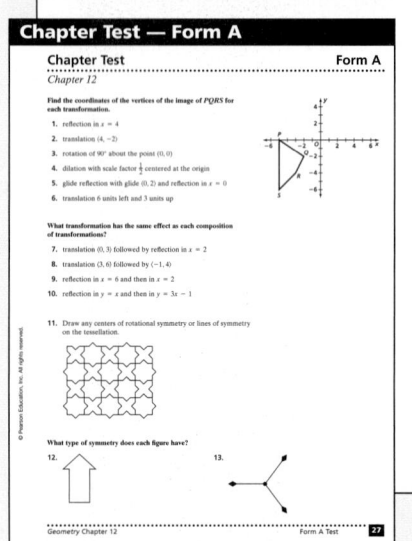

Chapter
12

Chapter Test

🖥 **Take It to the NET**
Online chapter test at
www.PHSchool.com
.... Web Code: afa-1252

Find the coordinates of the vertices of the image of
ABCD **for each transformation.**
1–10. See margin.

1. reflection in
the line $x = -4$

2. translation $\langle -6, 8 \rangle$

3. rotation of 90° about
the point $(0, 0)$

4. dilation centered at
$(0, 0)$ with scale factor $\frac{2}{3}$

5. glide reflection with glide vector $\langle 0, 3 \rangle$ and
reflection in the line $x = 0$

6. reflection in the line $y = x$

7. rotation of 270° about $(0, 0)$

8. dilation centered at the origin with scale factor 5

9. glide reflection with glide vector $\langle -2, 0 \rangle$ and
reflection in the line $y = 5$

10. translation 3 units right and 1 unit down

**What type of transformation has the same effect as
each composition of transformations?**

11. translation $\langle 4, 0 \rangle$ followed by a reflection
in the line $y = -4$ **glide reflection**

12. translation $\langle 4, 8 \rangle$ followed by $\langle -2, 9 \rangle$ **translation**

13. reflection in the line $y = 7$, and then in the
line $y = 3$ **translation**

14. reflection in the line $y = x$, and then in the
line $y = 2x + 5$ **rotation**

**Open-Ended Draw a figure that has each
type of symmetry. 15–17. See margin p. 685.**

15. reflectional   **16.** rotational   **17.** point

What type(s) of symmetry does each figure have?

18.

rotational, reflectional

19.

rotational, point,
reflectional

20. Writing Line *m* intersects $\overline{UH}$ at *N*, and
$UN = NH$. Must *H* be the reflection image
of *U* in line *m*? Explain.   **See back of book.**

21. Describe the symmetries of this tessellation. Copy a
portion of the tessellation and draw any centers of
rotational symmetry or lines of symmetry.

**See back
of book.**

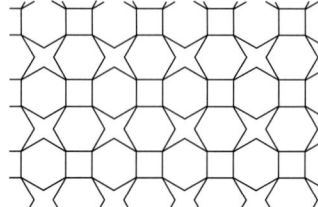

**Does each letter tessellate? If so, sketch a tessellation.
If not, explain why it cannot tessellate. 22–24. See
back of book.**

22. V   **23.** H   **24.** K

**Find the image of △ABC for a dilation with
center (0, 0) and the scale factor given. See back
of book.**

25. $A(-2, 2)$, $B(2, -2)$, $C(3, 4)$; scale factor 3

26. $A(0, 0)$, $B(-3, 2)$, $C(1, 7)$; scale factor $\frac{1}{2}$
$A'(0, 0)$, $B'\left(-1\frac{1}{2}, 1\right)$, $C'\left(\frac{1}{2}, 3\frac{1}{2}\right)$

27. The blue figure is a
translation image of the
red figure. Write a rule to
describe the translation.
$(x, y) \rightarrow (x + 3, y - 3)$

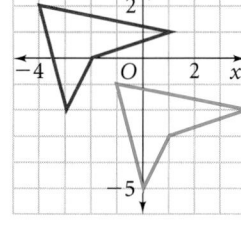

28. 10, −25
28. A dilation with center $(0, 0)$ and scale factor 2.5
maps $(4, -10)$ to (a, b). Find the values of *a* and *b*.

29. A dilation maps $\triangle LMN$ to $\triangle L'M'N'$. Find the
missing values. $6\frac{1}{2}$; $11\frac{1}{4}$; $\frac{1}{4}$

$LM = 36$ ft, $LN = 26$ ft, and $MN = 45$ ft;
$L'M' = 9$ ft, $L'N' = $ ■ ft, and $M'N' = $ ■ ft;
scale factor = ■

30. A dilation with scale factor 4 maps square A onto
square B. The area of square B is 25. Find the area
of square A.   **1.5625 units²**

Chapter Test — Form B

Chapter Test — Form A

Chapter Test   Form A
Chapter 12

Find the coordinates of the vertices of the image of *PQRS* for
each transformation.

1. reflection in $x = 4$
2. translation $\langle 4, -2 \rangle$
3. rotation of 90° about the point $(0, 0)$
4. dilation with scale factor $\frac{1}{2}$ centered at the origin
5. glide reflection with glide $\langle 0, 2 \rangle$ and reflection in $x = 1$
6. translation 6 units left and 3 units up

What transformation has the same effect as each composition
of transformations?

7. translation $\langle 0, 3 \rangle$ followed by reflection in $x = 2$
8. translation $\langle 3, 6 \rangle$ followed by $\langle -1, 4 \rangle$
9. reflection in $x = 6$ and then in $x = 2$
10. reflection in $y = x$ and then in $y = 3x - 1$

11. Draw any centers of rotational symmetry or lines of symmetry
on the tessellation.

What type of symmetry does each figure have?
12.   13.

Geometry Chapter 12   Form A Test   27

---

1. $A'(-11, 0)$, $B'(-9, -2)$,
$C'(-11, -5)$, $D'(-15, -1)$

2. $A'(-3, 8)$, $B'(-5, 6)$,
$C'(-3, 3)$, $D'(1, 7)$

3. $A'(0, 3)$, $B'(2, 1)$, $C'(5, 3)$,
$D'(1, 7)$

4. $A'(2, 0)$, $B'\left(\frac{2}{3}, -1\frac{1}{3}\right)$,
$C'\left(2, -3\frac{1}{3}\right)$, $D'\left(4\frac{2}{3}, -\frac{2}{3}\right)$

5. $A'(-3, 3)$, $B'(-1, 1)$,
$C'(-3, -2)$, $D'(-7, 2)$

6. $A'(0, 3)$, $B'(-2, 1)$,
$C'(-5, 3)$, $D'(-1, 7)$

7. $A'(0, -3)$, $B'(-2, -1)$,
$C'(-5, -3)$, $D'(-1, -7)$

8. $A'(15, 0)$, $B'(5, -10)$,
$C'(15, -25)$, $D'(35, -5)$

9. $A'(1, 10)$, $B'(-1, 12)$,
$C'(1, 15)$, $D'(5, 11)$

10. $A'(6, -1)$, $B'(4, -3)$,
$C'(6, -6)$, $D'(10, -2)$

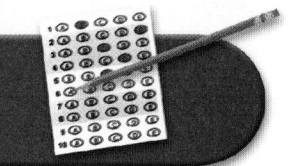

Standardized Test Prep

CUMULATIVE REVIEW
CHAPTERS 1–12

Take It to the NET
Online end-of-course test
at www.PHSchool.com
Web Code: afa-1354

Multiple Choice

For Exercises 1–31, choose the correct letter.

1. Which word(s) best describes the triangle at the right? **D**
A. equilateral
B. isosceles
C. right
D. isosceles right

2. What are the coordinates of the midpoint of $\overline{QS}$ with endpoints $Q(-2, -5)$ and $S(3, -8)$? **H**
F. $(-2.5, 1.5)$ G. $(-2.5, 6.5)$
H. $(0.5, -6.5)$ I. $(0.5, 1.5)$

3. What is the volume of the figure? **D**
A. 72 ft^3
B. $72\pi \text{ ft}^3$
C. $(18 + 72\pi) \text{ ft}^3$
D. $(72 + 18\pi) \text{ ft}^3$

3 ft
6 ft
4 ft

4. Which of the following statements can be derived from the biconditional statement "The day is long if and only if it is summer"? **I**
F. If the day is long, then it is summer.
G. If it is summer, then the day is long.
H. If the day is not long, then it is not summer.
I. all of the above

5. Which line or lines are perpendicular to the line $y = 4x - 1$? **D**
I. $y = 4x + 7$ II. $y = \frac{1}{4}x + 3$
III. $y = -\frac{1}{4}x - 5$ IV. $x + 4y = 16$
A. I only   B. II only
C. III only   D. III and IV

6. Which solid has the least volume? **H**
F.
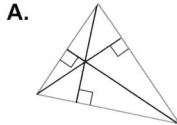
6 cm
6 cm
G.
6 cm
3 cm
H.
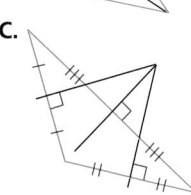
6 cm
2 cm
I.
3 cm

7. Which figure below is the reflection in the x-axis of the figure at the right? **B**
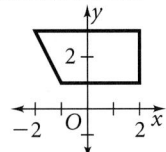

A.
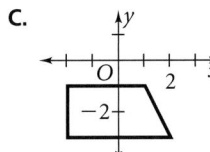
B.
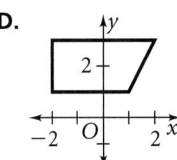

C.
D.

8. Which conditions allow you to conclude that a quadrilateral is a parallelogram? **H**
F. one pair of sides congruent, the other pair parallel
G. perpendicular congruent diagonals
H. congruent bisecting diagonals
I. one diagonal bisecting opposite angles

9. Which triangle is drawn with its medians? **B**
A.
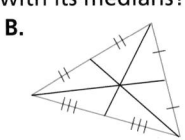
B.
C.
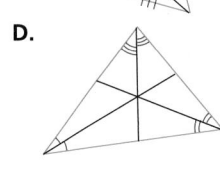
D.

10. What kind of symmetry does the figure have? **H**
F. 60° rotational symmetry
G. 90° rotational symmetry
H. line symmetry
I. point symmetry

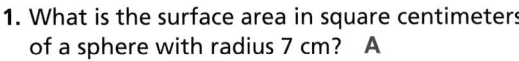

11. What is the surface area in square centimeters of a sphere with radius 7 cm? **A**
A. 196π B. $\frac{196}{3}\pi$ C. 49π D. 14π

15–16. Answers may vary. Samples are given.

15.
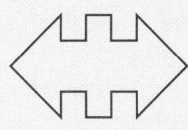

16.
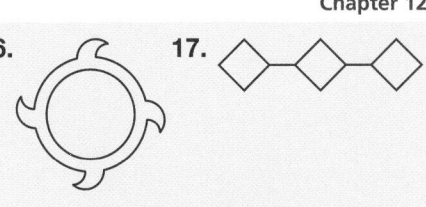

17.
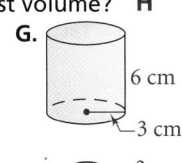 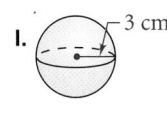

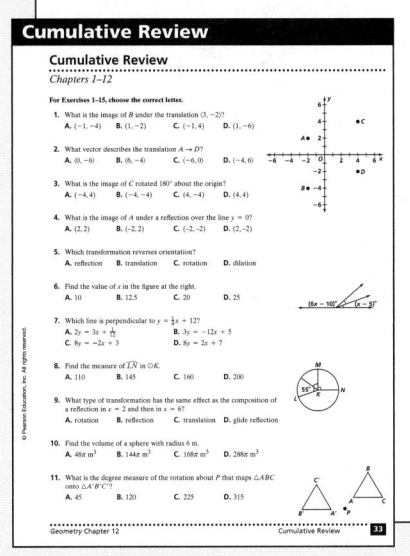

Item	Lesson	Item	Lesson
1	3-3	7	12-1
2	1-6	8	6-4
3	10-5	9	5-3
4	2-2	10	12-5
5	3-6	11	10-7
6	10-7		

12. In $\triangle RST$, $RS = 4$, $ST = 5$, and $RT = 6$. Which angle is largest? **G**
  F. $\angle R$ **G.** $\angle S$ **H.** $\angle T$
  I. cannot be determined

13. Which is true for both a rhombus and a kite? **C**
  A. The diagonals are congruent.
  B. Opposite sides are congruent.
  C. The diagonals are perpendicular.
  D. Opposite sides are parallel.

14. To the nearest tenth, what is the value of x? **G**
  F. 9.2
  G. 13.6
  H. 15.0
  I. 20.6

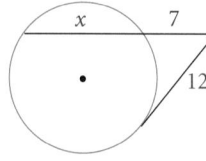

15. If $\frac{m}{n} = \frac{1}{3}$, which of the following must be true? **C**

  I. $3m = n$ II. $m = 3n$
  III. $m + 1 = \frac{n + 3}{3}$ IV. $mn = 3$

  A. I only   **B.** I and II only
  C. I and III only   **D.** I and IV only

16. The length of the hypotenuse of an isosceles right triangle is 8 in. What is the length of one leg? **G**
  F. $8\sqrt{2}$ in.   **G.** $4\sqrt{2}$ in.   **H.** 4 in.   **I.** 2 in.

17. Which equation is that of a line that contains the point $P(5, 6)$ and has slope $-\frac{1}{3}$? **D**
  A. $y = -\frac{1}{3}x + \frac{3}{23}$ **B.** $y = -\frac{1}{3}x - \frac{3}{23}$
  C. $y = -\frac{1}{3}x - \frac{23}{3}$ **D.** $y = -\frac{1}{3}x + \frac{23}{3}$

18. Which of the following must be true? **H**
  I. $\angle BAC \cong \angle B$
  II. $\angle B \cong \angle C$
  III. $\overline{AD} \cong \overline{AB}$
  IV. $\overline{BD} \cong \overline{CD}$

  F. I and II only   **G.** I and III only
  H. II and IV only   **I.** III and IV only

19. What is the area of the trapezoid? **C**
  A. 75 in.^{2}
  B. 43 in.^{2}
  C. 79.5 in.^{2}
  D. 159 in.^{2}

20. $\overleftrightarrow{AB}$ is tangent to $\odot C$ at point B. Which of the following can you NOT conclude is true? **F**
  F. $m\angle CAB < m\angle ACB$
  G. $AB^2 + BC^2 = AC^2$
  H. $\angle CAB$ and $\angle ACB$ are complements.
  I. $\overleftrightarrow{AB} \perp \overleftrightarrow{BC}$

21. Sphere B has 4 times the surface area of sphere A. How many times the volume of sphere A is the volume of sphere B? **B**
  A. 4   **B.** 8   **C.** 4π **D.** 8π

22. What is the value of x? **I**
  F. $\sqrt{30}$
  G. $\sqrt{39}$
  H. $3\sqrt{13}$
  I. $\sqrt{130}$

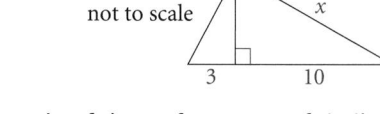
not to scale

23. What is the ratio of the surface areas of similar solids whose similarity ratio is 3 : 5? **C**
  A. 6 : 10   **B.** 9 : 15   **C.** 9 : 25   **D.** 27 : 125

24. What are the values of x and y? **H**
  F. $x = 56$, $y = 68$
  G. $x = 68$, $y = 56$
  H. $x = 57$, $y = 66$
  I. $x = 66$, $y = 57$

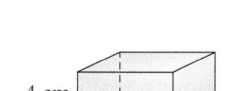

25. What is the volume of the prism in cubic centimeters? **B**
  A. 202   **B.** 180
  C. 99   **D.** 81

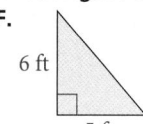

26. What is the circumference of a circle with radius 9? **H**
  F. 4.5π **G.** 9π **H.** 18π **I.** 81π

27. Which information CANNOT be used to prove that two triangles are congruent? **D**
  A. SAS   **B.** ASA   **C.** AAS   **D.** AAA

28. Which figure does NOT have an area of 15 ft^2? **I**

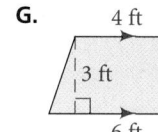
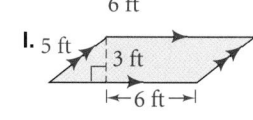
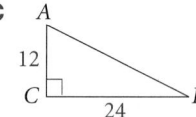

29. Which is greatest in $\triangle ABC$? **C**
  A. $\sin A$ **B.** $\cos A$
  C. $\tan A$ **D.** $\tan B$

30. What is the surface area in square centimeters of a rectangular prism 9 cm by 8 cm by 10 cm? **H**
  F. 240   **G.** 242   **H.** 484   **I.** 720

31. What is the standard equation of a circle with center $(-2, 0)$ and radius 4? **B**
  A. $(x - 2)^2 + y^2 = 4$ **B.** $(x + 2)^2 + y^2 = 16$
  C. $x^2 + (y - 2)^2 = 2^2$ **D.** $x^2 + (y + 2)^2 = 16$

pages 685–687   Standardized Test Prep

43. [2] area $= \frac{1}{2}b \cdot h =$ 12.5 m^2
  [1] one computational error

Quantitative Comparison

Compare the boxed quantity in Column A with the boxed quantity in Column B. Choose the best answer.

A. The quantity in Column A is greater.
B. The quantity in Column B is greater.
C. The two quantities are equal.
D. The relationship cannot be determined from the information given.

Column A	Column B
32. **A** the magnitude of $\langle 5, 1 \rangle$	the magnitude of $\langle 4, -2 \rangle$
33. **C** the distance between (7, 3) and (10, −2)	the distance between (3, −1) and (0, 4)
34. **B** in a circle, the measure of an inscribed angle that intercepts a 78° arc	in a circle, the measure of a central angle that intercepts a 78° arc
35. **B** the number of pairs of corresponding angles formed by two parallel lines and a transversal	the number of pairs of alternate interior angles formed by three parallel lines and a transversal

∠R is a supplement of ∠S.

36. **D** $m\angle R$	$m\angle S$

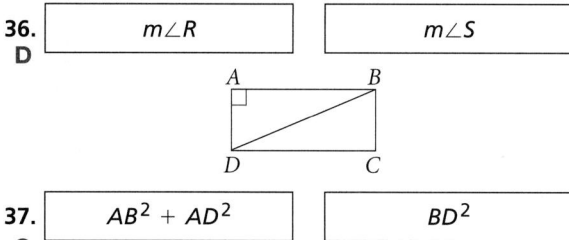

37. **C** $AB^2 + AD^2$	BD^2

Gridded Response

38. A diagonal of a rectangular field makes a 70° angle with a side of the field that is 100 ft long. To the nearest whole number of square feet, what is the area of the rectangle?   **27475**

39. You are making a scale model of a building. The front of the actual building is 60 ft wide and 100 ft tall. The front of your model is 3 ft by 5 ft. What is the scale factor of the reduction? $\frac{1}{20}$

40. You are 5 ft 6 in. tall. When your shadow is 6 ft long, the shadow of a sculpture is 30 ft long. How tall is the sculpture?   **27.5**

41. What is the surface area in square centimeters of a right cone with slant height 5 cm and radius 3 cm? Use 3.14 for π.   **75.36**

42. At 8 o'clock, what is the degree measure of the angle formed by the two hands of the clock?   **120**

Short Response

Show your work.   43–46. See margin pp. 686–687.

43. What is the area of an isosceles right triangle whose hypotenuse is $5\sqrt{2}$ m long?

44. The coordinates of the endpoints of $\overline{CD}$ are C(5, 2.5) and D(0, −9.5). Find the length of $\overline{CD}$ and the coordinates of the midpoint of $\overline{CD}$.

45. Write an equation of a line parallel to the line $y = 6x + 4$. Then write an equation of a line perpendicular to the line $y = 6x + 4$.

46. $\triangle DEB$ has vertices D(3, 7), E(1, 4), and B(−1, 5). In which quadrant(s) is the image of $\triangle DEB$ for a 90° rotation about the origin?

Extended Response

Show your work.   47–49. See margin.

47. Draw an angle. Then construct another angle congruent to the first.

48. Quadrilateral ABCD has vertices A(−1, −3), B(4, −2), C(3, 7), and D(−7, 0). Find the vertices of the image of quadrilateral ABCD under the translation $\langle -4, -1 \rangle$.

49. When airplane pilots make a visual sighting of an object outside the airplane, they often refer to the face of a dial clock to help locate the object. For example, an object at 12 o'clock is straight ahead, an object at 3 o'clock is 90° to the right, and so on.

Suppose that two pilots flying two airplanes in the same direction spot the same object. One pilot reports the object at 1 o'clock; the other pilot reports the object at 2 o'clock. At the same time the first pilot reports seeing the other airplane at 9 o'clock.

Draw a diagram showing the possible locations of the two planes and the object.

Item	Lesson
32	9-4
33	1-6
34	11-3
35	3-1
36	6-1
37	7-2
38	9-1
39	12-7
40	8-3
41	10-4
42	7-6
43	7-3
44	1-6
45	3-6
46	12-3
47	1-5
48	12-2
49	9-3

[3] ∠ drawn but the second ∠ is not ≅

[2] ∠ drawn but second ∠ is not constructed

[1] no second ∠

48. [4] A′(−5, −4), B′(0, −3), C′(−1, 6), D′(−11, −1)

[3] appropriate methods, but with one computational error

[2] appropriate methods, but with more than one computational error

[1] correct vertices with no work shown OR incorrect method

49. [4]

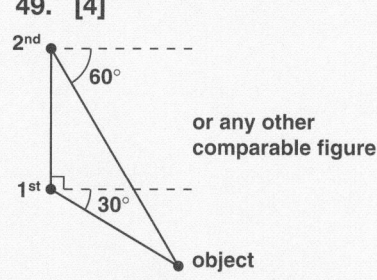

or any other comparable figure

[3] correct positions, but with no mention of alternate locations

[2] 1 or 2 incorrect positions

[1] incorrect positions

---

44. [2] length = 13; midpoint = $\left(\frac{5}{2}, -\frac{7}{2}\right)$

[1] length or midpoint correct

45. [2] $y = 6x + 1$ (OR any different line with slope 6);

$y = -\frac{1}{6}x + 1$ (OR any line with slope $-\frac{1}{6}$)

[1] one correct equation

46. [2] II and III

[1] sketch shown

47. [4]

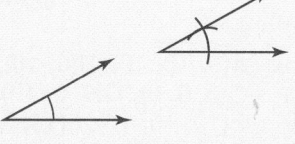

How'd They Do That?

In these activities students apply their knowledge of coordinate geometry and transformations.

Connecting to Prior Knowledge

Have students discuss how computer-generated animation makes the imaginary seem real. Encourage volunteers to describe what they know about animation and computer-generated images.

Teaching Notes

Have a volunteer read aloud the introductory paragraph. Ask: *Did you realize that engineers help create computer graphics? What else do engineers do?* Have students share their ideas about the scope of an engineering career.

Geography Connection

Ancient maps often included interesting illustrations. For example, maps of Europe made in medieval times sometimes included dragons, or sea serpents, patrolling the Mediterranean Sea.

 **Real-World Snapshots**

How'd They Do That?

Applying Translations and Rotations To create computer-generated characters and objects, computer animators and designers first define every point of a wire-frame model within a three-dimensional coordinate system. To make the model move and rotate, the animators must move and rotate its points.

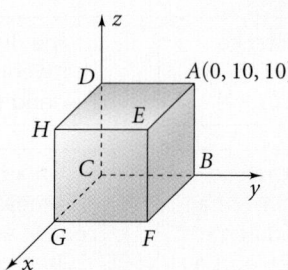

Wire-frame wings stretch out in flight or fold in close to the dragon's body.

Dragon Lore

Unlike European dragons, which breathe fire and wreak havoc across the countryside, Asian dragons are peace-loving protectors of the heavens.

Activity

Use the diagram at the right.

a. Write the coordinates of all eight vertices of the cube.

b. Suppose the cube rotates 90° clockwise about the z-axis (looking down from the positive z-axis). Find the new coordinates of vertices A–H.

c. Starting from the cube's position at the end of part (b), rotate the cube 90° clockwise about the x-axis (looking toward the origin from the positive x-axis). Find the new coordinates of vertices A–H.

d. Describe a composition of rotations that will move point E from its original location to $(-10, -10, -10)$.

e. **Open-Ended** You can also find a composition of translations, each parallel to an axis, to move point E from its original location to the original location of point C, $(0, 0, 0)$. Describe compositions of rotations (about axes) and translations (parallel to axes) that move point E to the locations of two vertices of the cube. Let each composition include at least one translation and one rotation.

f. Suppose the cube returns to its original position and then rotates 30° clockwise about the y-axis (looking toward the origin from the positive y-axis). Find the new coordinates of the eight vertices. (*Hint:* Use trigonometric ratios.)

Tail shape changes as points move and lines stretch.

Muscle structure added to frame

688 All photographs © Dorling Kindersley Limited unless otherwise credited on acknowledgments page

pages 688–689   **Real-World Snapshots**

Activity

a. A(0, 10, 10), B(0, 10, 0), C(0, 0, 0), D(0, 0, 10), E(10, 10, 10), F(10, 10, 0), G(10, 0, 0), H(10, 0, 10)

b. A(10, 0, 10), B(10, 0, 0), C(0, 0, 0), D(0, 0, 10), E(10, −10, 10), F(10, −10, 0), G(0, −10, 0), H(0, −10, 10)

c. A(10, 10, 0), B(10, 0, 0), C(0, 0, 0), D(0, 10, 0), E(10, 10, 10), F(10, 0, 10), G(0, 0, 10), H(0, 10, 10)

Exterior skin detail added and placed within live-action footage

Mouth and snout digitally animated

Eyes are modeled on those of a lizard— they move, blink, open, and close.

Take It to the NET For more information about computer animation, go to **www.PHSchool.com**.
Web Code: afe-1253

d. Answers may vary. Sample: Rotate 90° clockwise about the x-axis, 90° counterclockwise about the y-axis, and 90° counterclockwise about the z-axis (looking toward the origin from the positive axis for each rotation).

e. Answers may vary. Check students' work.

f. $A(-10 \sin 30, 10, 10 \cos 30)$, $B(0, 10, 0)$, $C(0, 0, 0)$, $D(-10 \sin 30, 0, 10 \cos 30)$, $E(10 \cos 30 - 10 \sin 30, 10, 10 \cos 30 + 10 \sin 30)$, $F(10 \cos 30, 10, 10 \sin 30)$, $G(10 \cos 30, 0, 10 \sin 30)$, $H(10 \cos 30 - 10 \sin 30, 0, 10 \cos 30 + 10 \sin 30)$ OR $A(-5, 10, 8.66)$, $B(0, 10, 0)$, $C(0, 0, 0)$, $D(-5, 0, 8.66)$, $E(3.66, 10, 13.66)$, $F(8.66, 10, 5)$, $G(8.66, 0, 5)$, $H(3.66, 0, 13.66)$

23.

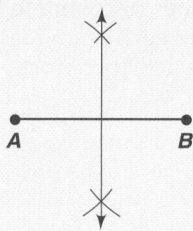

24.

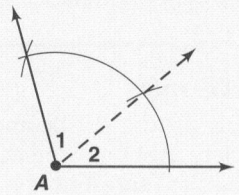

25.

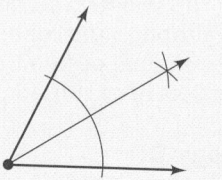

26.

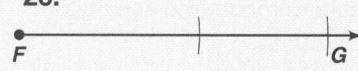

● **Lesson 1-1 Find the next two terms in each sequence.**

1. $12, 17, 22, 27, 32, \ldots$ **37, 42**   **2.** $1, 1.1, 1.11, 1.111, 1.1111, \ldots$ **1.11111, 1.111111**

3. $5000, 1000, 200, 40, \ldots$ **8, $\frac{8}{5}$**   **4.** $1, 12, 123, 1234, \ldots$ **12,345, 123,456**

5. $3, 0.3, 0.03, 0.003, \ldots$ **6.** $1, 4, 9, 16, 25, \ldots$ **36, 49**
     0.0003, 0.00003

● **Lessons 1-2 and 1-3 Write *true* or *false*.**

7. A, D, F are coplanar. **true**   **8.** $\overleftrightarrow{AC}$ and $\overleftrightarrow{FE}$ are coplanar. **false**

9. A, B, E are coplanar. **true**   **10.** D, A, B, E are coplanar. **true**

11. $\overleftrightarrow{FC} \parallel \overleftrightarrow{EF}$ **false**   **12.** plane $ABC \parallel$ plane FDE **true**

13. $\overleftrightarrow{BC}$ and $\overleftrightarrow{DF}$ are skew lines. **true** **14.** $\overleftrightarrow{AD}$ and $\overleftrightarrow{EB}$ are skew lines. **false**

15. $\overleftrightarrow{DE} \parallel \overleftrightarrow{CF}$ **false**   **16.** $D, E,$ and B are collinear. **false**

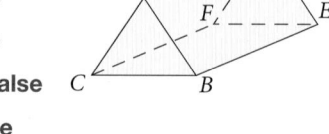

● **Lessons 1-4 and 1-5 Use the figure at the right for Exercises 17–22.**

17. If $BC = 12$ and $CE = 15$, then $BE = \blacksquare$. **27**

18. $\blacksquare$ is the angle bisector of $\blacksquare$. $\overrightarrow{CG}, \angle BCA$

$\boxed{x^2}$ **19. Algebra** $BC = 3x + 2$ and $CD = 5x - 10$. Solve for x. **6**

$\boxed{x^2}$ **20. Algebra** If $AC = 5x - 16$ and $CF = 2x - 4$, then $AF = \blacksquare$. **8**

21. $m\angle BCG = 60, m\angle GCA = \blacksquare$, and $m\angle BCA = \blacksquare$. **60, 120**

22. $m\angle ACD = 60$ and $m\angle DCH = 20$. Find $m\angle HCA$. **40**

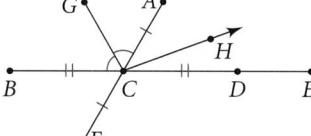

● **Lesson 1-5 Make a diagram larger than the given one. Then do the construction.**

23. Construct the perpendicular bisector of $\overline{AB}$. **23–26.**

24. Construct $\angle A$ so that $m\angle A = m\angle 1 + m\angle 2$. **See margin.**

25. Construct the angle bisector of $\angle 1$.

26. Construct $\overline{FG}$ so that $FG = AB + CD$.

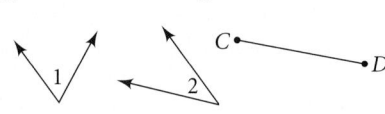

● **Lesson 1-6 (a) Find the distance between the points to the nearest tenth.**
  (b) Find the coordinates of the midpoint of the segments with the given endpoints.

27. $A(2, 1), B(3, 0)$ **1.4; $\left(\frac{5}{2}, \frac{1}{2}\right)$**   **28.** $R(5, 2), S(-2, 4)$ **7.3; $\left(\frac{3}{2}, 3\right)$**

29. $Q(-7, -4), T(6, 10)$ **19.1; $\left(-\frac{1}{2}, 3\right)$** **30.** $C(-8, -1), D(-5, -11)$ **10.4; $\left(-\frac{13}{2}, -6\right)$**

31. $J(0, -5), N(3, 4)$ **9.5; $\left(\frac{3}{2}, -\frac{1}{2}\right)$**   **32.** $Y(-2, 8), Z(3, -5)$ **13.9; $\left(\frac{1}{2}, \frac{3}{2}\right)$**

● **Lesson 1-7 Find the perimeter (or circumference) and area of each figure.**

33. 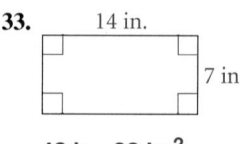 **34.** 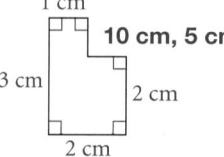 **35.** 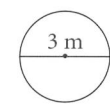 **36.**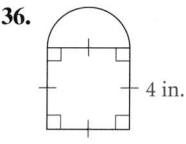

14 in. / 7 in.   1 cm / 10 cm, 5 cm² / 3 cm / 2 cm / 2 cm   3 m / 3π m, $\frac{9}{4}\pi$ m²   4 in.

42 in., 98 in.²   **(12 + 2π) in., (16 + 2π) in.²**

Extra Practice

Lessons 2-1 and 2-2 For each of the statements, write the conditional form and then the converse of the conditional. If the converse is true, combine the statements as a biconditional.   **1–5. See margin.**

1. The number one is the smallest positive square.

2. Rectangles have four sides.

3. A square with area 100 m² has sides that measure 10 m.

4. Two numbers that add up to be less than 12 have a product less than 37.

5. Three points on the same line are collinear.

Lesson 2-2 Is each statement a good definition? If not, find a counterexample.

6. A circle with center O and radius r is defined by the set of points in a plane a distance r from the point O.   **yes**

7. A plane is defined by two lines.   **No; two skew lines are a counterexample.**

8. Segments with the same length are congruent.   **yes**

Lesson 2-3 Using the statements below, apply the Law of Detachment or the Law of Syllogism to draw a conclusion.

9. If Jorge can't raise money, he can't buy a new car. Jorge can't raise money. **Jorge can't buy a new car.**

10. If Shauna is early for her meeting, she will gain a promotion. If Shauna wakes up early, she will be early for her meeting. Shauna wakes up early.   **Shauna will gain a promotion.**

11. If Linda's band wins the contest, they will win $500. If Linda practices, her band will win the contest. Linda practices.   **Linda's band will win $500.**

12. If Brendan learns the audition song, he will be selected for the chorus. If Brendan stays after school to practice, he will learn the audition song. Brendan stays after school to practice.   **Brendan will be selected for the chorus.**

Lesson 2-4 Algebra You are given that $2c^2 = 2bc + \frac{ac}{2}$ with $c \neq 0$. Show that $4b = 4c - a$ by filling in the blanks.

13. a. $2c^2 = 2bc + \frac{ac}{2}$
    b. $4c^2 = 4bc + ac$
    c. $4c = 4b + a$
    d. _?_ $4c - a = 4b$
    e. $4b = 4c - a$

    a. Given
    b. _?_ and _?_   **Mult. Prop. of =, Distr. Prop.**
    c. _?_ and Distributive Property   **Mult. Prop. of =**
    d. Subtraction Property
    e. _?_   **Symm. Prop. of =**

Lesson 2-5 Algebra Find the value of x.

14.
24
$(3x - 14)°$ $(2x + 10)°$
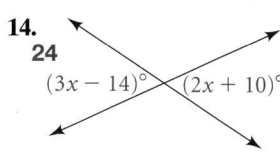

15.
15
$2x°$
$4x°$
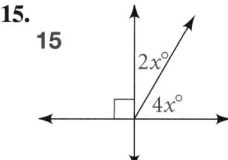

16.
25
$2x°$ $(5x + 5)°$
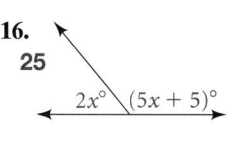

Extra Practice

1. If a number is one, then it is the smallest positive square. If a number is the smallest positive square, then it is one. A number is one if and only if it is the smallest positive square.

2. If a figure is a rectangle, then it has four sides. If a figure has four sides, then it is a rectangle.

3. If a square has an area of 100 m², then it has sides that measure 10 m. If a square has sides that measure 10 m, then it has an area of 100 m². A square has an area of 100 m² if and only if it has sides that measure 10 m.

4. If two numbers add up to be less than 12, then their product is less than 37. If two numbers have a product that is less than 37, then they add up to be less than 12.

5. If three points are on the same line, then they are collinear. If three points are collinear, then they are on the same line. Three points are collinear if and only if they are on the same line.

1. $m\angle 1 = 134$; Same-Side Int. ∠s Thm.
   $m\angle 2 = 46$; Alt. Int. ∠ Thm.

2. $m\angle 1 = 125$; Corr. ∠s Post.
   $m\angle 2 = 55$; Same-Side Int. ∠s Thm.

3. $m\angle 1 = 58$; Alt. Int. ∠ Thm.
   $m\angle 2 = 122$; Same-Side Int. ∠s Thm.

4. $m\angle 1 = 64$; Alt. Int. ∠ Thm.
   $m\angle 2 = 116$; Same-Side Int. ∠s Thm.

21. $y - 2 = -\frac{5}{2}(x - 4)$ or $y + 3 = -\frac{5}{2}(x - 6)$

22. $y + 1 = (x + 1)$ or $y - 1 = (x - 1)$

23. $y + 5 = -1(x - 3)$ or $y - 3 = -1(x + 5)$

24. $y = -\frac{1}{5}(x - 5)$ or $y - 2 = -\frac{1}{5}(x + 5)$

29.
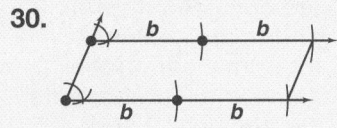

30.
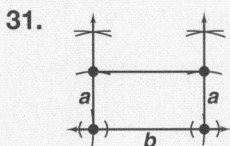

31.

● **Lesson 3-1** Find $m\angle 1$ and then $m\angle 2$. State the theorems or postulates that justify your answers.   1–4. See margin.

1.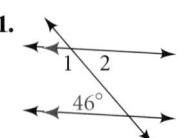

2.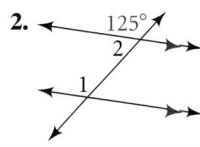

3.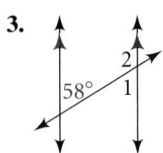

4.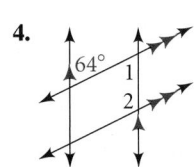

● **Lesson 3-2** Refer to the diagram at the right. Use the given information to determine which lines, if any, must be parallel. If any lines are parallel, use a theorem or postulate to tell why.

7. $c \parallel d$, Conv. of Same-Side Int. ∠s Thm.

$r \parallel s$, Conv. of Corr. ∠s Post.

5. $\angle 9 \cong \angle 14$ none

6. $\angle 1 \cong \angle 9$

7. $\angle 2$ is supplementary to $\angle 3$. **See right.**

8. $\angle 7 \cong \angle 14$ none

9. $m\angle 6 = 60, m\angle 13 = 120$ $r \parallel s$, Vert. ∠ Thm. and Conv. of Same-Side Int. ∠s Thm.

10. $\angle 4 \cong \angle 13$ none

11. $\angle 3$ is supplementary to $\angle 10$. none

12. $\angle 10 \cong \angle 15$ $c \parallel d$, Conv. of Alt. Int. ∠ Thm.

● **Lesson 3-3** Use a protractor and a centimeter ruler to measure the angles and the sides of each triangle. Classify each triangle by its angles and sides.

13.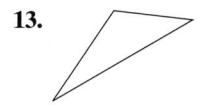
obtuse; scalene

14.
obtuse; isosceles

15.
acute; isosceles

16.
right; scalene

● **Lessons 3-3 and 3-4 Algebra** Find the value of each variable.

17.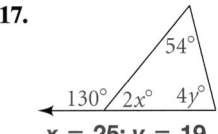
$x = 25; y = 19$

18.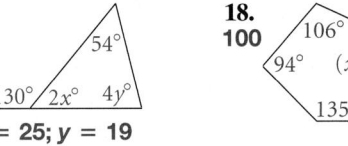
100

19.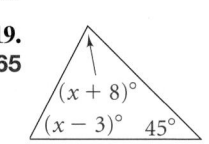
65

20.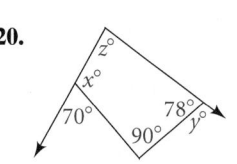
$x = 110; y = 102; z = 82$

● **Lessons 3-5** Write an equation in point-slope form of the line that contains the given points.   21–24. See margin.

21. $A(4, 2), B(6, -3)$

22. $C(-1, -1), D(1, 1)$

23. $F(3, -5), G(-5, 3)$

24. $K(5, 0), L(-5, 2)$

● **Lessons 3-5 and 3-6 Algebra** Graph each pair of lines and state whether they are parallel, perpendicular, or neither. Explain.

neither; not same slope and $m_1 \cdot m_2 \neq -1$

25. $y = 4x - 8$
$y = 4x - 2$
$\parallel$; same slope

26. $13y - x = 7$
$7 - \frac{y}{2} = x$

27. $y = \frac{-4}{3}x + 2$
$\frac{4}{3}y = x - 1$
$\perp$; $m_1 \cdot m_2 = -1$

28. $\frac{3}{5}y = -x + \frac{3}{2}$
$3x - \frac{15}{3}y = 0$
$\perp$; $m_1 \cdot m_2 = -1$

● **Lesson 3-7** Use the segments for each construction.

29. Construct a square with side length $2a$.   **29–31. See margin.**

30. Construct a quadrilateral with one pair of parallel sides each of length $2b$.

31. Construct a rectangle with sides b and a.

a

b

Chapter 4

Extra Practice

● **Lesson 4-1** △*SAT* ≅ △*GRE*. Complete each congruence statement.

1. ∠*S* ≅ _?_ ∠*G* 2. $\overline{GR}$ ≅ _?_ $\overline{SA}$ 3. ∠*E* ≅ _?_ ∠*T*

4. $\overline{AT}$ ≅ _?_ $\overline{RE}$ 5. △*ERG* ≅ _?_
△*TAS*

6. $\overline{EG}$ ≅ _?_ $\overline{TS}$

7. △*REG* ≅ _?_
△*ATS*

8. ∠*R* ≅ _?_ ∠*A*

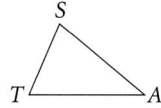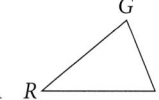

State whether the figures are congruent. Justify each answer. 9–12. See margin.

9. △*ABF*; △*EDC*   10. △*TUV*; △*UVW*   11. □*XYZV*; □*UTZV*   12. △*ABD*; △*EDB*

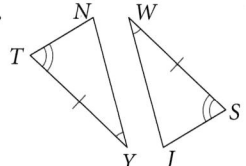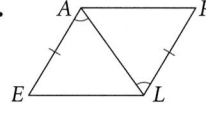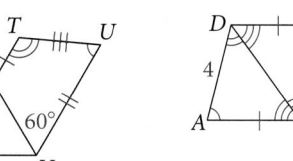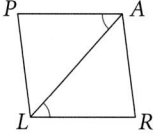

● **Lessons 4-2 and 4-3** Where possible, explain how you would use SSS, SAS, ASA, or AAS to prove the triangles congruent. If not possible, write *not possible*.   13–16. See margin.

13. 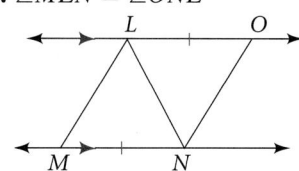   14. 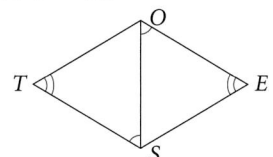   15. 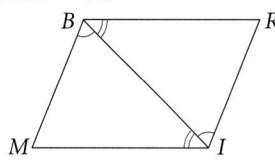   16.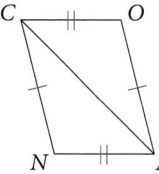

● **Lesson 4-4** Explain how you would use SSS, SAS, ASA, or HL with CPCTC to prove each statement.   17–19. See margin.

17. ∠*MLN* ≅ ∠*ONL*   18. $\overline{TO}$ ≅ $\overline{ES}$ 19. $\overline{MB}$ ≅ $\overline{RI}$

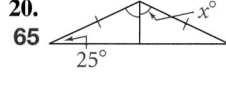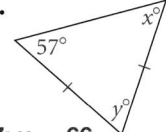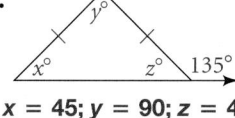

● **Lessons 4-5 and 4-6 Algebra** Find the value of each variable.

20.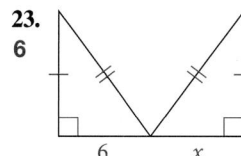
65
25°

21.
57°
x = 57; *y* = 66

22.
x = 45; *y* = 90; *z* = 45

23.
6
6   *x*

● **Lesson 4-7** Name a pair of overlapping congruent triangles in each diagram. State whether the triangles are congruent by SSS, SAS, ASA, AAS, or HL.

24.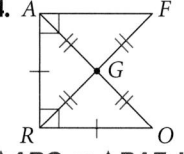
△*ARO* ≅ △*RAF*; HL

25.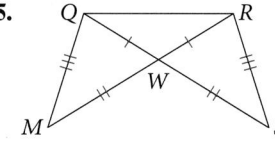
△*RQM* ≅ △*QRS*; SSS

26.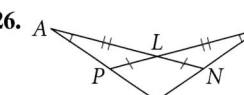
△*AON* ≅ △*MOP*; AAS

9. Yes; corr. sides and corr. ∡ are ≅.

10. No; the only known corr. ≅ part is $\overline{UV}$.

11. Yes; corr. sides and corr. ∡ are ≅.

12. Yes; corr. sides and corr. ∡ are ≅.

13. ∠*T* ≅ ∠*S*, ∠*Y* ≅ ∠*W*, $\overline{TY}$ ≅ $\overline{SW}$; ASA

14. $\overline{EA}$ ≅ $\overline{PL}$, $\overline{AL}$ ≅ $\overline{LA}$, ∠*EAL* ≅ ∠*PLA*; SAS

15. not possible

16. $\overline{CN}$ ≅ $\overline{AO}$, $\overline{NA}$ ≅ $\overline{OC}$, $\overline{AC}$ ≅ $\overline{CA}$; SSS

17. $\overleftrightarrow{OL}$ ∥ $\overleftrightarrow{MN}$, so ∠*OLN* ≅ ∠*MNL*. $\overline{LN}$ ≅ $\overline{LN}$ by the Reflexive Prop. of ≅. Since $\overline{LO}$ ≅ $\overline{MN}$, △*MLN* ≅ △*ONL* by SAS, and ∠*MLN* ≅ ∠*ONL* by CPCTC.

18. $\overline{OS}$ ≅ $\overline{OS}$ by the Reflexive Prop. of ≅. Since ∠*T* ≅ ∠*E* and ∠*TSO* ≅ ∠*EOS*, △*TSO* ≅ △*EOS* by AAS, and $\overline{TO}$ ≅ $\overline{ES}$ by CPCTC.

19. $\overline{BI}$ ≅ $\overline{BI}$ by the Reflexive Prop. of ≅. Since ∠*MBI* ≅ ∠*RIB* and ∠*MIB* ≅ ∠*RBI*, △*MBI* ≅ △*RIB* by ASA, and $\overline{MB}$ ≅ $\overline{RI}$ by CPCTC.

693

17. a. If two ∠s are not vert., then they are not ≅.

   b. If two ∠s are not ≅, then they are not vert.

18. a. If figures are not similar, then their side lengths are not prop.

   b. If their side lengths are not prop., then figures are not similar.

19. a. If a car is not blue, then it has doors.

   b. If a car has doors, then it is not blue.

Chapter 5 Extra Practice

● Lesson 5-1 **Algebra Find the value of x.**

1.
$\frac{25}{7}$
$7x - 1$
48
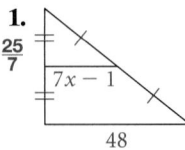

2.
32
48
$3x$
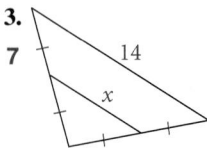

3.
7   14
x
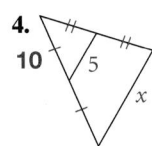

4.
10   5
x
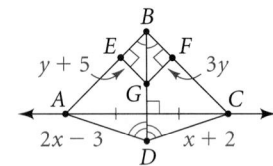

● Lessons 5-1 and 5-2 **Algebra Use the figure at the right.**

5. Find the value of x.   5

6. Find the length of $\overline{AD}$.   7

7. Find the value of y. $\frac{5}{2}$

8. Find the length of $\overline{EG}$. $\frac{15}{2}$

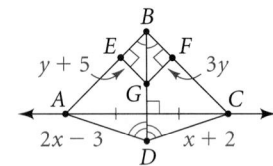

● Lesson 5-3 **Find the center of the circle that you can circumscribe about △ABC.**

9. $A(2, 8)$ **(1, 5)**
   $B(0, 8)$
   $C(2, 2)$

10. $A(-3, 6)$ **(2, 2)**
    $B(-3, -2)$
    $C(7, 6)$

11. $A(4, 3)$ **(0, 0)**
    $B(-4, -3)$
    $C(4, -3)$

12. $A(-10, -2)$
    $B(-2, -2)$
    $C(-2, -10)$
    (−6, −6)

Is $\overline{AB}$ an angle bisector, altitude, median, or perpendicular bisector?

13.
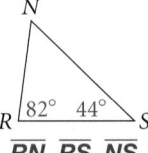
∠ bisector

14.
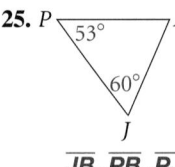
median

15.
altitude
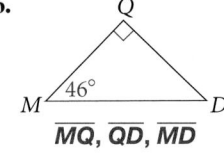

16.
⊥ bisector
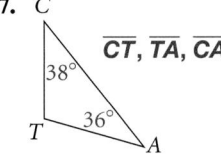

● Lesson 5-4 **Write (a) the inverse and (b) the contrapositive of each statement. 17–19. See margin.**

17. If two angles are vertical, then they are congruent.

18. If figures are similar, then their side lengths are proportional.

19. If a car is blue, then it has no doors.

Write the first step of an indirect proof of each statement.

20. △ABC is a right triangle. **Assume △ABC is not a right △.**

21. Points J, K, and L are collinear. **Assume points J, K, and L are not collinear.**

22. Lines ℓ and m are not parallel. **Assume lines ℓ and m are not ∥.**

23. ▱XYZV is a square. **Assume ▱XYZV is not a square.**

● Lesson 5-5 **List the sides of each triangle in order from shortest to longest.**

24.
N
R 82° 44° S
$\overline{RN}, \overline{RS}, \overline{NS}$

25.
P 53° B
60°
J
$\overline{JB}, \overline{PB}, \overline{PJ}$

26.
Q
M 46° D
$\overline{MQ}, \overline{QD}, \overline{MD}$

27.
C
38°
T 36° A
$\overline{CT}, \overline{TA}, \overline{CA}$

Can a triangle have sides with the given lengths? Explain.

28. 2 in., 3 in., 5 in. **No; 2 + 3 ≯ 5.**

29. 9 cm, 11 cm, 15 cm **Yes; 9 + 11 > 15.**

30. 8 ft, 9 ft, 18 ft **No; 8 + 9 ≯ 18.**

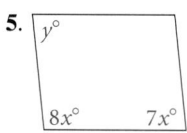

Extra Practice

Lesson 6-1 Graph the given points. Use slope and the Distance Formula to determine the most precise name for quadrilateral *ABCD*.   **1–4. See margin.**

1. $A(3, 5), B(6, 5), C(2, 1), D(1, 3)$

2. $A(-1, 1), B(3, -1), C(-1, -3), D(-5, -1)$

3. $A(2, 1), B(5, -1), C(4, -4), D(1, -2)$

4. $A(-4, 5), B(-1, 3), C(-3, 0), D(-6, 2)$

Lesson 6-2 Algebra Find the values of the variables in each parallelogram.

5.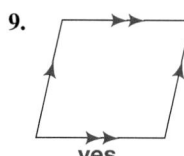
$x = 12; y = 84$

6.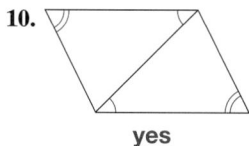
$x = 30; y = 55$

7.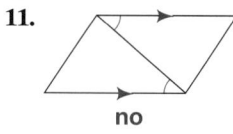
$x = 8; y = 25$

8.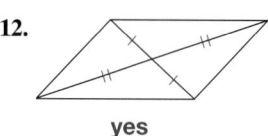
$x = 1; y = 7$

Lesson 6-3 Based on the markings, decide whether each figure must be a parallelogram.

9.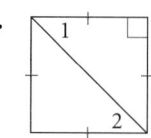
yes

10.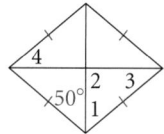
yes

11.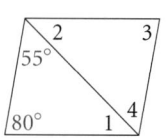
no

12.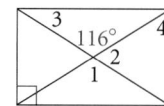
yes

Lesson 6-4 For each parallelogram, determine the most precise name and find the measures of the numbered angles.   **14–16. See margin.**

13.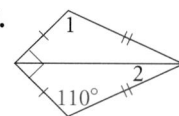
square; $m\angle 1 = 45, m\angle 2 = 45$

14.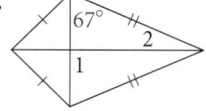

15.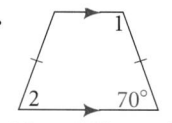

16.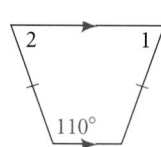

Lesson 6-5 Find $m\angle 1$ and $m\angle 2$.

17.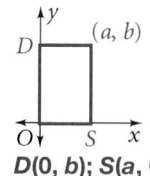
$m\angle 1 = 110, m\angle 2 = 25$

18.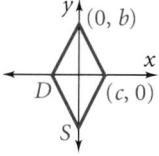
$m\angle 1 = 90, m\angle 2 = 23$

19.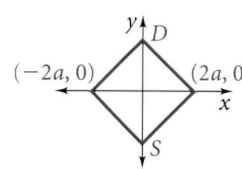
$m\angle 1 = 110, m\angle 2 = 70$

20.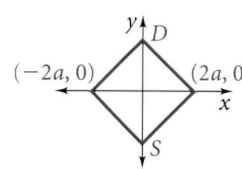
$m\angle 1 = 70, m\angle 2 = 70$

Lesson 6-6 Give coordinates for points *D* and *S* without using any new variables.

21. rectangle
$D(0, b); S(a, 0)$

22. parallelogram
$D(0, b); S(-a, 0)$

23. rhombus
$D(-c, 0); S(0, -b)$

24. square
$D(0, 2a); S(0, -2a)$

Lesson 6-7

25. For the figure in Exercise 24, use coordinate geometry to prove that the midpoints of the sides of a square determine a square.   **See margin.**

page 695
Chapter 6
Extra Practice

1. 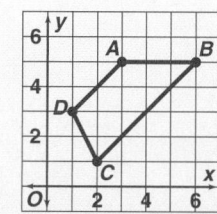   trapezoid

---

2.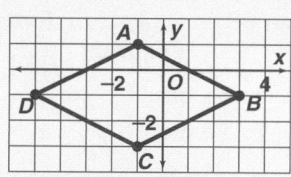

rhombus

3.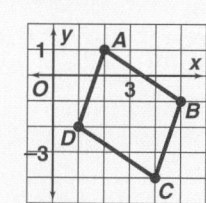

parallelogram

4.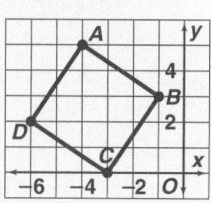

square

14. rhombus; $m\angle 1 = 50$, $m\angle 2 = 90, m\angle 3 = 40$, $m\angle 4 = 40$

15. $\square$; $m\angle 1 = 45, m\angle 2 = 45, m\angle 3 = 80, m\angle 4 = 55$

16. rectangle; $m\angle 1 = 116$, $m\angle 2 = 64, m\angle 3 = 32$, $m\angle 4 = 58$

25. Given: Square *DRSQ* with *K, L, M, N* midpts. of $\overline{DR}, \overline{RS}, \overline{SQ},$ and $\overline{QD}$, respectively. Prove: *KLMN* is a square.

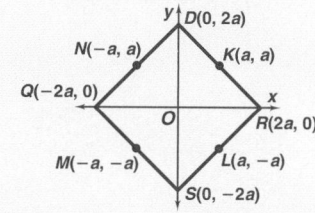

$K(a, a), L(a, -a),$ $M(-a, -a),$ and $N(-a, a)$ are midpts. of the sides of the square. $KL = LM = MN = NK = 2a$. The slopes of $\overline{KL}$ and $\overline{MN}$ are undefined. The slopes of $\overline{LM}$ and $\overline{NK}$ are 0, so adj. sides are $\perp$ to each other. Since all $\angle$s are rt. $\angle$s, the quad. is a rectangle. A rectangle with all $\cong$ sides is a square.

13. a. 6π cm

    b. 2π cm

14. a. 20π ft

    b. $\frac{5}{3}\pi$ ft

15. a. 18π cm

    b. $\frac{9}{2}\pi$ cm

16. a. 10π in.

    b. $\frac{25}{4}\pi$ in.

Chapter 7 Extra Practice

● **Lesson 7-1** Find the perimeter and area of each figure.

1.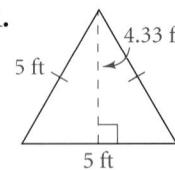
5 ft, 4.33 ft, 5 ft
15 ft; 10.825 ft²

2.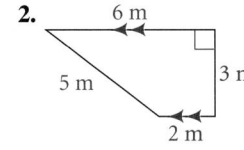
6 m, 5 m, 3 m, 2 m
16 m; 12 m²

3.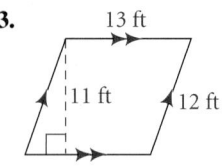
13 ft, 11 ft, 12 ft
50 ft; 143 ft²

4.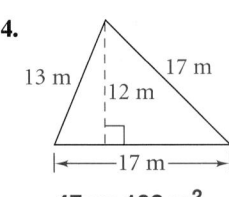
13 m, 17 m, 12 m, 17 m
47 m; 102 m²

● **Lessons 7-2 and 7-3** Find the value of x. If your answer is not a whole number, leave it in simplest radical form.

5.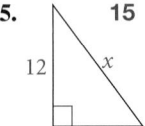
15, 12, x, 9

6.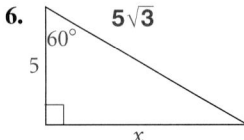
$5\sqrt{3}$, 60°, 5, x

7.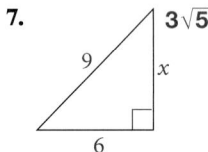
$3\sqrt{5}$, 9, x, 6

8.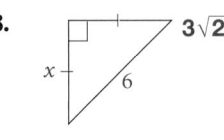
$3\sqrt{2}$, x, 6

● **Lessons 7-4 and 7-5** Find the area of each trapezoid or regular polygon. Leave your answer in simplest radical form.

9.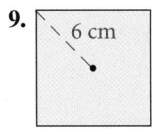
6 cm
72 cm²

10.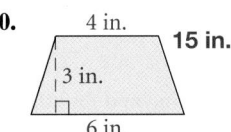
4 in., 15 in.², 3 in., 6 in.

11.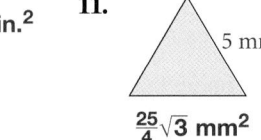
5 mm
$\frac{25}{4}\sqrt{3}$ mm²

12.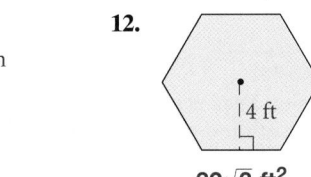
4 ft
$32\sqrt{3}$ ft²

● **Lesson 7-6** (a) Find the circumference of each circle. (b) Find the length of the arc shown in red. Leave your answers in terms of π.   13–16. See margin.

13.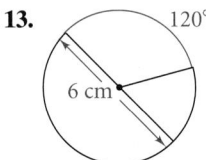
120°, 6 cm

14.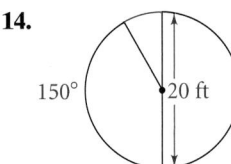
150°, 20 ft

15.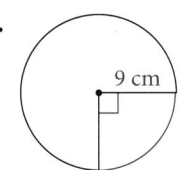
9 cm

16.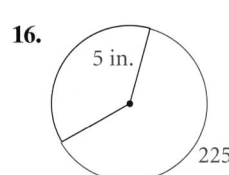
5 in., 225°

● **Lesson 7-7** Find the area of each shaded sector or segment. Leave your answers in terms of π.

17.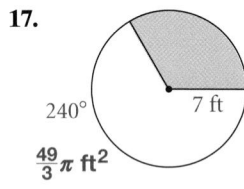
240°, 7 ft
$\frac{49}{3}\pi$ ft²

18.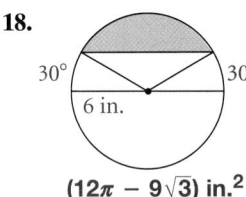
30°, 30°, 6 in.
$(12\pi - 9\sqrt{3})$ in.²

19.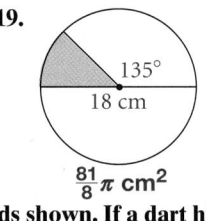
135°, 18 cm
$\frac{81}{8}\pi$ cm²

20.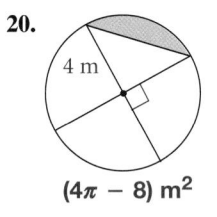
4 m
$(4\pi - 8)$ m²

● **Lesson 7-8** Darts are thrown at random at each of the boards shown. If a dart hits the board, find the probability that it will land in the shaded area.

21.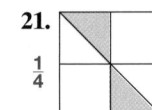
$\frac{1}{4}$

22.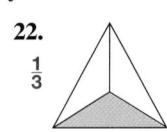
$\frac{1}{3}$

23.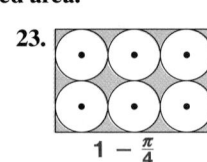
$1 - \frac{\pi}{4}$

24.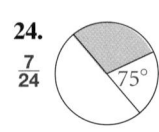
$\frac{7}{24}$, 75°

696

Lesson 8-1 **Algebra** Solve each proportion.

1. $\frac{2}{3} = \frac{x}{15}$ **10**

2. $\frac{4}{9} = \frac{16}{x}$ **36**

3. $\frac{x}{4} = \frac{6}{12}$ **2**

4. $\frac{2}{x} = \frac{3}{9}$ **6**

5. $\frac{3}{4} = \frac{x}{6}$ $\frac{9}{2}$

6. $\frac{3}{7} = \frac{9}{x}$ **21**

Lesson 8-2 **Algebra** The polygons are similar. Find the values of the variables.

7.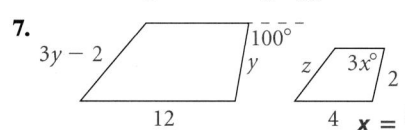

$x = \frac{80}{3}; y = 6; z = \frac{16}{3}$

8.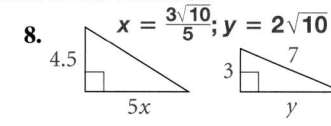

$x = \frac{3\sqrt{10}}{5}; y = 2\sqrt{10}$

9.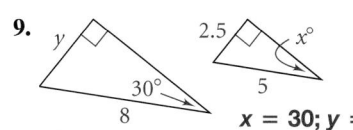

$x = 30; y = 4$

10.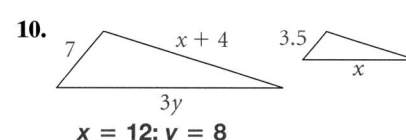

$x = 12; y = 8$

Lesson 8-3 Can you prove that the triangles are similar? If so, write a similarity statement and tell whether you would use AA~, SAS~, or SSS~.

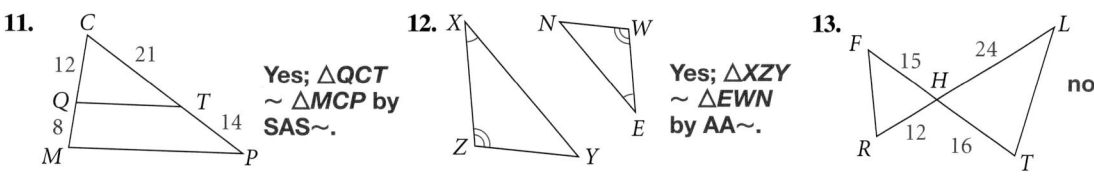

11. Yes; $\triangle QCT \sim \triangle MCP$ by SAS~.

12. Yes; $\triangle XZY \sim \triangle EWN$ by AA~.

13. no

Lessons 8-4 and 8-5 **Algebra** Find the value of each variable. If an answer is not a whole number, leave it in simplest radical form. 14–16. See margin.

14.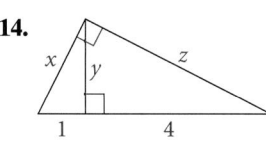

15.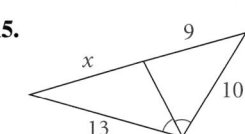

16.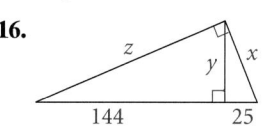

17.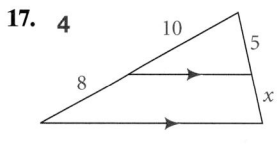

18. $\frac{72}{5}$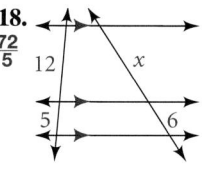

19.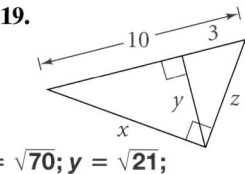

$x = \sqrt{70}; y = \sqrt{21}; z = \sqrt{30}$

20.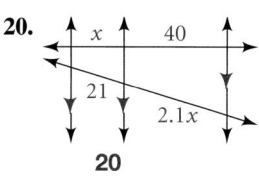

20

21. $\frac{56}{3}$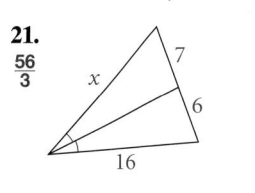

Lesson 8-6 Find the ratio of the perimeters and the ratio of the areas of the blue figure to the red figure.

22.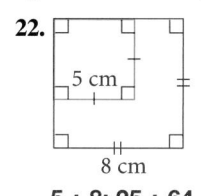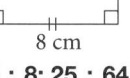

5 : 8; 25 : 64

23.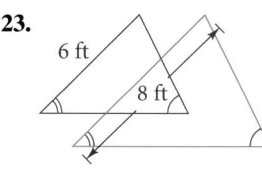

3 : 4; 9 : 16

24.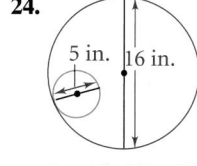

5 : 16; 25 : 256

13. a. ⟨−49, 142⟩, ⟨38, 47⟩

    b. ⟨−11, 189⟩

14. a. ⟨−118, −55⟩, ⟨86, 110⟩

    b. ⟨−32, 55⟩

15. a. ⟨−54, 72⟩, ⟨−95, −33⟩

    b. ⟨−149, 39⟩

16. a. ⟨−21, −56⟩, ⟨27, −64⟩

    b. ⟨6, −120⟩

Chapter 9 Extra Practice

● **Lessons 9-1 and 9-2** Find the value of *x*. Round lengths of segments to the nearest tenth and angle measures to the nearest degree.

1.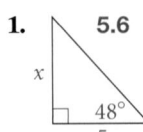

2.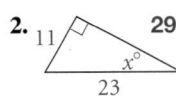

3.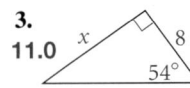

4.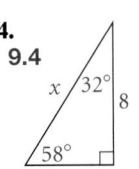

5.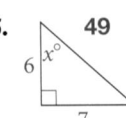

6.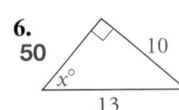

7.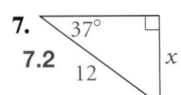

8.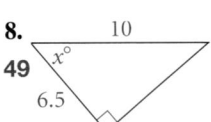

● **Lesson 9-3** Solve each problem. Round your answers to the nearest foot.

9. A couple is taking a balloon ride. After 25 minutes aloft, they measure the angle of depression from the balloon to its launch place as 16°. They are 180 ft above ground. Find the distance from the balloon to its launch place. **653 ft**

10. A surveyor is 300 ft from the base of an apartment building. The angle of elevation to the top of the building is 24°, and her angle-measuring device is 5 ft above the ground. Find the height of the building. **139 ft**

11. Oriana is flying a kite. She lets out 105 ft of string and anchors it to the ground. She determines that the angle of elevation of the kite is 48°. Find the height the kite is from the ground. **78 ft**

12. A plane flying at 10,000 ft spots a hot air balloon in the distance. The balloon is 9000 ft above ground. The angle of depression from the plane to the balloon is 30°. Find the distance from the plane to the balloon. **2000 ft**

● **Lesson 9-4** (a) Describe each vector as an ordered pair. Give the coordinates to the nearest unit. (b) Write the resultant of each pair of vectors as an ordered pair. 13–16. See margin.

13.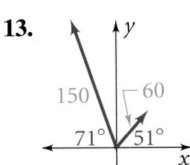

14.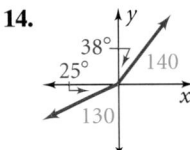

15.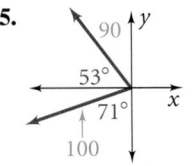

16.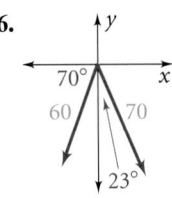

● **Lesson 9-5** Find the area of each polygon. Round your answers to the nearest tenth.

17.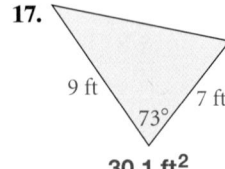
    30.1 ft²

18.
    78.0 in.²

19.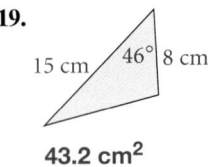
    43.2 cm²

20.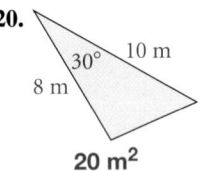
    20 m²

21. a regular hexagon with an apothem of 3 ft **31.2 ft²**   22. a regular octagon with radius 5 ft **70.7 ft²**

Extra Practice

● **Lesson 10-1** Name the space figure that can be formed by folding each net.

1.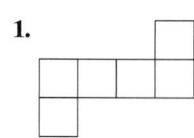
cube

2.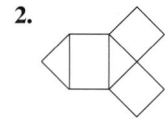
triangular prism

3.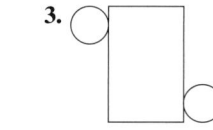
cylinder

4.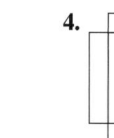
rectangular prism

● **Lesson 10-2** Create (a) an isometric drawing and (b) an orthographic drawing for each foundation drawing. **5–8. See margin.**

5.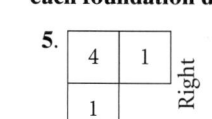
Right
Front

6.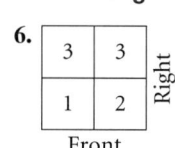
Right
Front

7.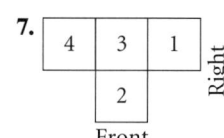
Right
Front

8.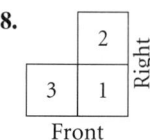
Right
Front

● **Lessons 10-3 and 10-4** Find the (a) lateral area and (b) surface area of each figure. Leave your answers in terms of π or in simplest radical form.

9.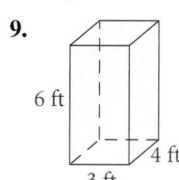
6 ft
4 ft
3 ft
84 ft²; 108 ft²

10.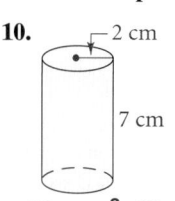
2 cm
7 cm
28π cm²; 36π cm²

11.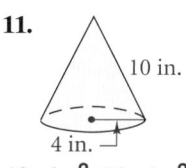
10 in.
4 in.
40π in.²; 56π in.²

12.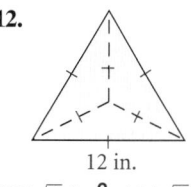
12 in.
108√3 in.²; 144√3 in.²

● **Lessons 10-5 and 10-6** Find the volume of each figure.

13.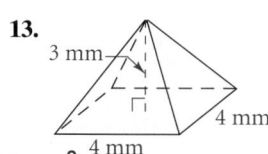
3 mm
4 mm
4 mm
16 mm³

14.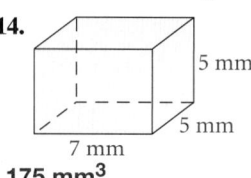
5 mm
5 mm
7 mm
175 mm³

15.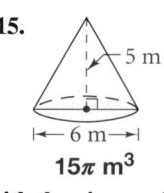
5 m
6 m
15π m³

16.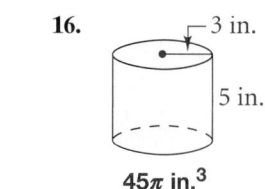
3 in.
5 in.
45π in.³

● **Lesson 10-7** Find the volume and surface area of a sphere with the given radius or diameter. Give each answer in terms of π and rounded to the nearest whole number.

17. $r = 5$ cm

18. $r = 3$ ft

19. $d = 8$ in.

20. $d = 2$ ft

21. $r = 0.5$ in.

22. $d = 9$ m

The surface area of each sphere is given. Find the volume of each sphere in terms of π.

23. 64π m² $\frac{256\pi}{3}$ m³

24. 16π in² $\frac{32\pi}{3}$ in.³

25. 49π ft² $\frac{343\pi}{6}$ ft³

17. $\frac{500\pi}{3}$ cm³, 524 cm³; 100π cm², 314 cm²

18. 36π ft³, 113 ft³; 36π ft², 113 ft²

19. $\frac{256\pi}{3}$ in.³, 268 in.³; 64π in.², 201 in.²

20. $\frac{4\pi}{3}$ ft³, 4 ft³; 4π ft², 13 ft²

21. $\frac{\pi}{6}$ in.³, 1 in.³; π in.², 3 in.²

22. $\frac{243\pi}{2}$ m³, 382 m³; 81π m², 254 m²

● **Lesson 10-8** Copy and complete for three similar solids.

	Similarity Ratio	Ratio of Surface Areas	Ratio of Volumes
26.	2 : 3	4 ■ : ■ 9	8 ■ : ■ 27
27.	5 ■ : ■ 8	25 : 64	125 ■ : ■ 512
28.	3 ■ : ■ 4	9 ■ : ■ 16	27 : 64

5.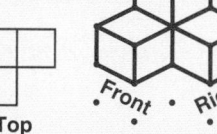
Top
Front   Right

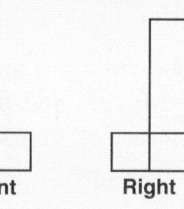
Front   Right

6.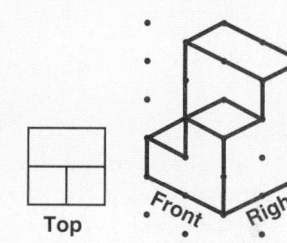
Top
Front   Right
Front   Right

7.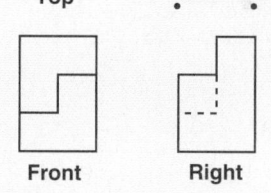
Top
Front   Right
Front   Right

8.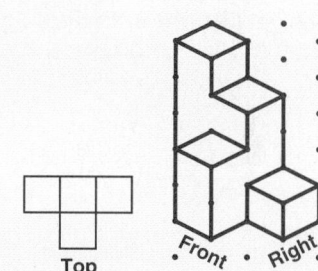
Top
Front   Right
Front   Right

10. $a = 38; b = 52; c = 104;$
    $d = 90$

11. $a = 105; b = 100$

12. $a = 55; b = 72; c = 178;$
    $d = 89$

13. $x = 193; y = 60.5$

14. 5.6

15. ≈ 10.4

16. 70

27. two rays ∥ to and 2 cm
    from $\overrightarrow{AB}$, and the
    semicircle of radius 2 cm
    with center A, opp. pt. B

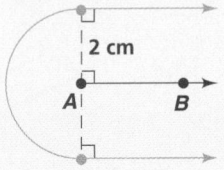

28. a circle of radius 5 cm,
    concentric with the orig.
    circle

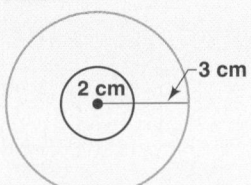

29. a sphere of radius
    1.5 in., and center Q

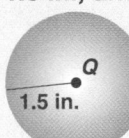

● **Lesson 11-1** Assume that lines that appear to be tangent are tangent. P is the center of each circle. Find the value of x.

1.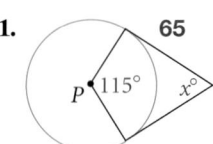

2.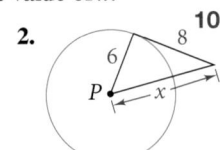

3.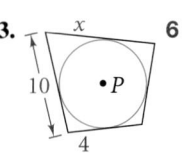

4.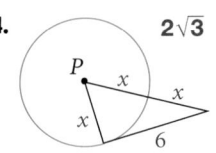

● **Lessons 11-2 and 11-3 Algebra** Find the value of each variable. If your answer is not a whole number, round it to the nearest tenth. **10–12. See margin.**

5.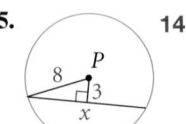

6.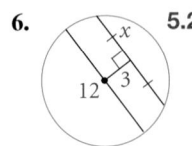

7.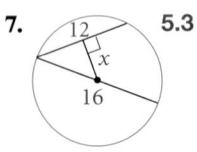

8.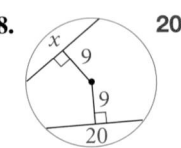

9.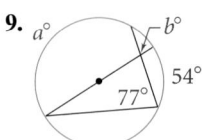

10.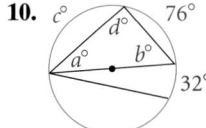

11.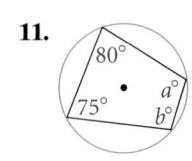

12.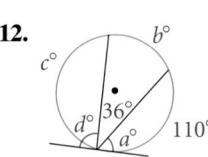

$a = 154; b = 76$

● **Lesson 11-4 Algebra** Assume that lines that appear to be tangent are tangent. Find the value of each variable. If your answer is not a whole number, round it to the nearest tenth. **13–16. See margin.**

13.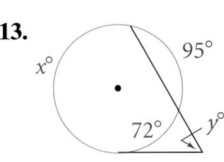

14.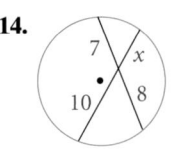

15.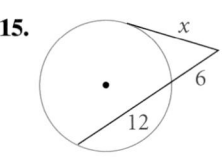

16.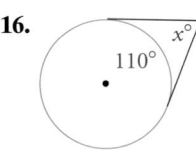

17.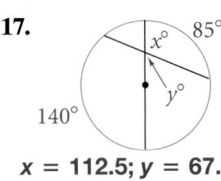

$x = 112.5; y = 67.5$

18.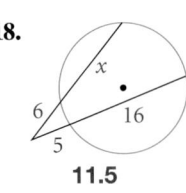

11.5

19.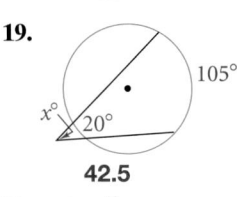

42.5

20.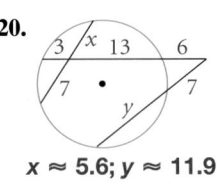

$x \approx 5.6; y \approx 11.9$

● **Lesson 11-5** Write the standard equation for each circle with center P.

21. $P = (0,0); r = 4$ $x^2 + y^2 = 16$

22. $P = (0,5); r = 3$ $x^2 + (y - 5)^2 = 9$

23. $P = (9, -3); r = 7$ $(x - 9)^2 + (y + 3)^2 = 49$

24. $P = (-4, 0);$ through $(2, 1)$ $(x + 4)^2 + y^2 = 37$

25. $P = (-6, -2);$ through $(-8, 1)$
    $(x + 6)^2 + (y + 2)^2 = 13$

26. $P = (-1, -3); r = 3$ $(x + 1)^2 + (y + 3)^2 = 9$

● **Lesson 11-6** Draw and describe each locus.   **27–29. See margin.**

27. all points in a plane 2 cm from $\overrightarrow{AB}$

28. all points in a plane 3 cm from a circle with $r = 2$ cm

29. all points in space 1.5 in. from a point Q

● **Lesson 12-1** Given points $S(6, 1)$, $U(2, 5)$, and $B(-1, 2)$, draw $\triangle SUB$ and its reflection image in each line. **1–8. See back of book.**

1. $y = 5$ **2.** $x = 7$ **3.** $y = -1$ **4.** the x-axis

5. $y = x$ **6.** $x = -1$ **7.** $y = 3$ **8.** the y-axis

● **Lesson 12-2** In Exercises 9–14, refer to the figure at the right.

9. What is the image of C under the translation $\langle 4, -2\rangle$? **E**

10. What vector describes the translation $F \to B$? $\langle\mathbf{-2, 4}\rangle$

11. What is the image of H under the translation $\langle -2, 4\rangle$? **C**

12. What vector describes the translation $D \to H$? $\langle\mathbf{4, -2}\rangle$

13. What is the image of C under the translation $\langle -2, -4\rangle$? **G**

14. What vector describes the translation $B \to A$? $\langle\mathbf{-8, 0}\rangle$

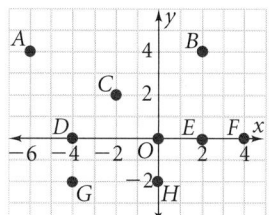

Use matrices to find the image of each figure under the given translation.

15. $\triangle ABC$ with vertices $A(-3, 4)$, $B(-1, -2)$, $C(1, 5)$; translation: $\langle -2, 5\rangle$ **A′(−5, 9), B′(−3, 3), C′(−1, 10)**

16. $\triangle EFG$ with vertices $E(0, 3)$, $F(6, -1)$, $G(4, 2)$; translation: $\langle 1, -3\rangle$ **E′(1, 0), F′(7, −4), G′(5, −1)**

17. $\triangle PQR$ with vertices $P(-9, -4)$, $Q(-5, 1)$, $R(2, 8)$; translation: $\langle -6, -7\rangle$ **P′(−15, −11), Q′(−11, −6), R′(−4, 1)**

● **Lesson 12-3** Copy each figure and point P. Draw the image of each figure for the given rotation about P. Label the vertices of the image. **18–21. See margin.**

18. 60°   **19.** 90°   **20.** 45°   **21.** 180°

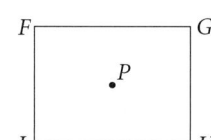 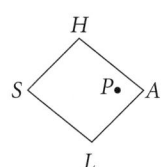 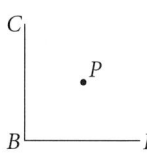

● **Lessons 12-4 and 12-7** The blue figure is the image of the gray figure. State whether the mapping is a reflection, rotation, translation, glide reflection, or dilation.

22.   **23.**   **24.**   **25.**

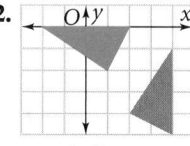 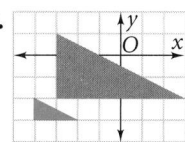 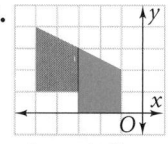 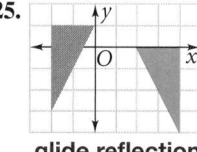

rotation   dilation   translation   glide reflection

● **Lessons 12-5 and 12-6** (a) State what kind of symmetry each figure has.
(b) State whether each figure tessellates. **26–29. See margin.**

26.   **27.**   **28.**   **29.**

   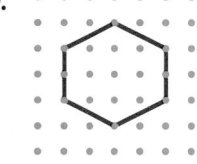

18.

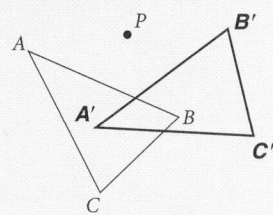

19.

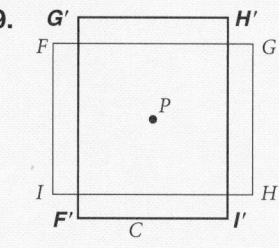

20.

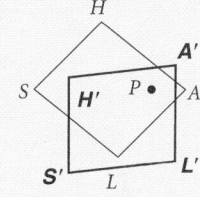

21.

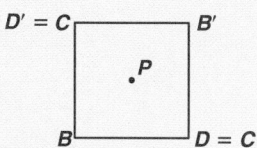

26. a. line, rotation, point
    b. yes

27. a. line
    b. yes

28. a. line
    b. yes

29. a. line, point
    b. yes

 **Skills Handbook**

Problem Solving Strategies

You may find one or more of these strategies helpful in solving a word problem.

Strategy	When to Use it
Draw a Diagram	You need help in visualizing the problem.
Try, Check, Revise	Solving the problem directly is too complicated.
Make a Table	The problem has data that need organizing.
Look for a Pattern	The problem describes a relationship.
Solve a Simpler Problem	The problem is complex or has numbers that are too unmanageable to use at first.
Use Logical Reasoning	You need to reach a conclusion from some given information.
Work Backward	You undo various operations to arrive at the answer.

Problem Solving: Draw a Diagram

> **EXAMPLE**
>
> Antoine is 1.91 m tall. He measures his shadow and finds that it is 2.34 m long. He then measures the length of the shadow of a flagpole and finds that it is 13.2 m long. How tall is the flagpole?
>
> Start by drawing a diagram showing the given information. The diagram shows that you can solve the problem by using a proportion.
>
> $\frac{1.91}{2.34} = \frac{x}{13.2}$ **Write a proportion.**
> $x \approx 10.77$ **Solve for x.**

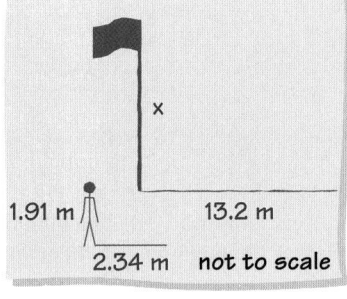

● The flagpole is about 10.8 m tall.

EXERCISES

1. Five people meet and shake hands with one another. How many handshakes are there in all? **10 handshakes**

2. Three tennis balls fit snugly in an ordinary, cylindrical tennis ball container. Which is greater, the circumference of a ball or the height of the container? **circumference**

3. Three lines that all intersect a circle can determine at most 7 regions within the circle, as shown in the diagram. What is the greatest number of regions that can be determined by 5 lines? **16 regions**

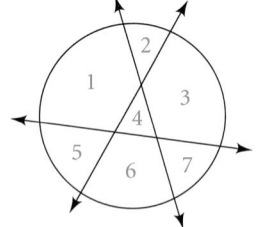

4. A triangle has vertices $(1, 3)$, $(2, 3)$, and $(7, 5)$. Find its area. **1 unit^2**

Problem Solving: Try, Check, Revise

Have you ever weighed yourself on a balance scale at a doctor's office? You start by guessing your weight, and then you see if the scale balances. If it doesn't, you slide the weights back and forth until the scale does balance. This is an example of the *Try, Check, Revise* strategy, a strategy helpful for solving many types of problems.

EXAMPLE

You have 100 ft of fencing and want to build a fence in the shape of a rectangle to enclose the largest possible area. What should be the dimensions of the rectangle?

Try 1: 10 ft wide by 40 ft long   **Make an initial try with a perimeter**
$10 \cdot 40 = 400 \ \text{ft}^2$ **of 100 ft. Find the area.**

Try 2: 20 ft wide by 30 ft long   **Try again and find the area.**
$20 \cdot 30 = 600 \ \text{ft}^2$ **The area is larger than the initial try.**

Try 3: 35 ft wide by 15 ft long   **Continue trying and testing areas.**
$35 \cdot 15 = 525 \ \text{ft}^2$ **This area is smaller than the last try.**

Try 4: 22 ft wide by 28 ft long   **Notice that the areas are larger when the**
$22 \cdot 28 = 616 \ \text{ft}^2$ **width and length are closer together.**

Try 5: 25 ft wide by 25 ft long   **Choose dimensions that are as**
$25 \cdot 25 = 625 \ \text{ft}^2$ **close together as possible.**

● The dimensions of your rectangle should be 25 ft by 25 ft.

EXERCISES

1. The product of three consecutive even integers is 480. Find the integers. **6, 8, 10**

2. The combined ages of a father and his twin daughters are 54 years. The father was 24 years old when the twins were born. How old is each of the three people? **Each daughter is 10 years old; the father is 34 years old.**

3. What numbers can x represent in the rectangle? **any pos. number less than 4** x

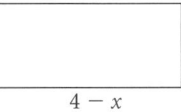

4. Alexandra has a collection of dimes and quarters. The number of dimes equals the number of quarters. She has a total of $2.80. How many of each coin does Alexandra have? **8**

$4 - x$

Use the Try, Check, Revise strategy to find the value of each variable.

5. $2a + 5 = 1$ **−2**   **6.** $10 - 3c = -2$ **4**   **7.** $\frac{w}{-3} + 12 = -6$ **54**

8. $5y - 32 = 28$ **12**   **9.** $12b + 11 = 14$ $\frac{1}{4}$ **10.** $0.5x - 15 = -7$ **16**

11. Ruisa bought 7 rolls of film to take 192 pictures on a field trip. Some rolls had 36 exposures and the rest had 24 exposures. How many of each type did Ruisa buy? **2 rolls of 36 exposures and 5 rolls of 24 exposures**

12. The sum of five consecutive integers is 5. Find the integers. **−1, 0, 1, 2, 3**

13. Paul buys a coupon for $20 from a local theater that allows him to see movies for half price over the course of one year. The cost of seeing a movie is normally $7.50. What is the least number of movies Paul would have to see to pay less than the normal price per movie? **6 movies**

Problem Solving: Make a Table and Look for a Pattern

There are two important ways that making a table can help you solve a problem. First, a table is a handy method of organizing information. Second, once the information is in a table, it is easier for you to find patterns.

EXAMPLE

The squares below are made of toothpicks. How many toothpicks are in the square with 7 toothpicks on a side?

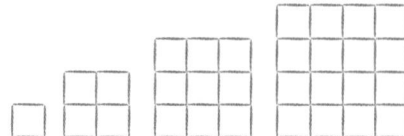

Use a table to organize the information.

Notice the pattern in the increases in the numbers of toothpicks in the squares. For each increase of 1 toothpick on a side, the increase increases by 4. The number of toothpicks in the 5th square is $40 + 20$, or 60. The number in the 6th square is $60 + 24$, or 84, and the number in the 7th square is $84 + 28$, or 112.

Toothpicks on a side	1	2	3	4
Toothpicks in the square	4	12	24	40

$+8$ $+12$ $+16$

EXERCISES

1. The triangles are made of toothpicks. How many toothpicks are in Figure 10?

165 toothpicks

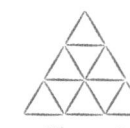

Figure 1   Figure 2   Figure 3

2. In each figure, the vertices of the smallest square are midpoints of the sides of the next larger square. Find the area of the ninth shaded square. $\frac{1}{256}$ **in.²**

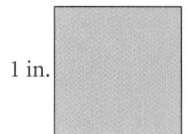 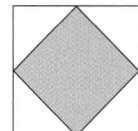 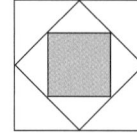

1 in.

3. In each figure, the midpoints of the sides of the unshaded triangles are used as vertices of the shaded triangles. Find the total number of shaded triangles in Figure 8. **3280 triangles**

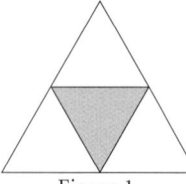 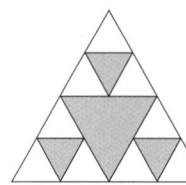 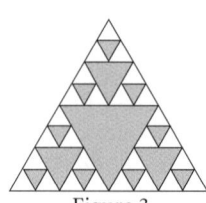

Figure 1   Figure 2   Figure 3

Problem Solving: Solve a Simpler Problem

Looking at a simpler version of a problem can be helpful in suggesting a problem solving approach.

 EXAMPLE

A fence along the highway is 570 m long. There is a fence post every 10 m. How many fence posts are there?

You may be tempted to divide 570 by 10, getting 57 as an answer, but looking at a simpler problem suggests that this answer isn't right. Suppose you have just 10 or 20 m of fencing.

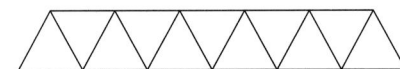

These easier problems suggest that there is always *one more* fence post than one tenth the length. So for a 570-m fence, there are $\frac{570}{10} + 1$, or 58 fence posts.

EXERCISES

1. A farmer wishes to fence in a square lot 70 yards by 70 yards. He will install a fence post every 10 yards. How many fence posts will he need? **28 posts**

2. A snail is trying to escape from a well 10 ft deep. The snail can climb 2 ft each day, but each night it slides back 1 ft. How many days will the snail take to climb out of the well? **9 days**

3. Janette is planning to walk from her house to her friend Barbara's house. How many different paths can she take to get there? Assume that she **84** walks only east and south (along the grid lines). **paths.**

4. A square table can seat four people. For a banquet, a long rectangular table is formed by placing 14 such tables edge to edge in a straight line. How many people can sit at the long table? **30 people**

5. Find the sum of the whole numbers from 1 to 999. **499,500**

6. How many trapezoids are in the figure below? (*Hint:* Solve several simpler problems, and then look for a pattern.) **25 trapezoids**

7. At a business luncheon, 424 handshakes took place. No two people shook hands with each other more than once. What is the least number of people in attendance at the luncheon? **30 people**

8. On the occasion of his 50th birthday, the President was honored with a 21-gun salute. The sound of each gunshot lasted 1 second, and 4 seconds elapsed between shots. How long did the salute last? **101 seconds**

9. In a tennis tournament, each athlete plays one match against each of the other athletes. There are 14 athletes scheduled to play in the tournament. How many matches will be played? **91 matches**

Problem Solving: Use Logical Reasoning

Some problems can be solved without the use of numbers. They can be solved by the use of logical reasoning, given some information.

EXAMPLE

Anna, Bill, Carla, and Doug are siblings. Each lives in a different state beginning with W. Use these clues to determine where each sibling lives:

(1) Neither sister lives in a state containing two words.

(2) Bill lives to the west of his sisters.

(3) Anna doesn't cross the Mississippi River when she visits Doug.

Make a table to organize what you know. Use an initial for each name.

State	A	B	C	D
West Virginia	✗	✗	✗	
Wisconsin		✗		
Wyoming		✗		
Washington	✗	✓	✗	✗

From clue 1, you know that neither Anna nor Carla lives in West Virginia.

Using clues 1 and 2, you know that Bill must live in Washington if he lives to the west of his sisters.

Use logical reasoning to complete the table.

State	A	B	C	D
West Virginia	✗	✗	✗	✓
Wisconsin	✓	✗	✗	✗
Wyoming	✗	✗	✓	✗
Washington	✗	✓	✗	✗

Doug lives in West Virginia because no other sibling does.

From clue 3, you know that Anna must live in Wisconsin.

Carla, therefore, lives in Wyoming.

EXERCISES

1. Harold has a dog, a parrot, a goldfish, and a hamster. Their names are J. T., Izzy, Arf, and Blinky. Izzy has neither feathers nor fins. Arf can't bark. J. T. weighs less than the four-legged pets. Neither the goldfish nor the dog has the longest name. Arf and Blinky don't get along well with the parrot. What is each pet's name? **J.T. is the parrot; Izzy is the dog; Arf is the goldfish; Blinky is the hamster.**

2. At the state basketball championship tournament, 31 basketball games are played to determine the winner of the tournament. After each game, the loser is eliminated from the tournament. How many teams are in the tournament? **32 teams**

3. The sophomore class has 124 students. Of these students, 47 are involved in musical activities: 25 in band and 36 in choir. How many students are involved in both band and choir? **14 students**

4. Tina's height is between Kimiko's and Ignacio's. Ignacio's height is between Jerome's and Kimiko's. Tina is taller than Jerome. List the people in order from shortest to tallest. **Jerome, Ignacio, Tina, Kimiko**

Problem Solving: Work Backward

In some situations it is easier to start with the end result and work backward to find the solution. You work backward in order to solve linear equations. The equation $2x + 3 = 11$ means "double x and add 3 to get 11." To find x, you "undo" those steps in reverse order.

$$2x + 3 = 11$$
$$2x = 8 \quad \textbf{Subtract 3 from each side.}$$
$$x = 4 \quad \textbf{Divide each side by 2.}$$

Another time it is convenient to work backward is when you want to "reverse" a set of directions.

EXAMPLE

Algebra Sandy spent $\frac{1}{10}$ of the money in her purse for lunch. She then spent $23.50 for a gift for her brother, then half of what she had left on a new CD. If Sandy has $13 left in her purse, how much money did she have in it before lunch?

Start with the $13 that Sandy has left in her purse.
She spent half of what she had before the $13 on a new CD, so she must have had twice $13, or $26, before she bought the CD.

She spent $23.50 on a gift for her brother, so add $23.50 to $26. Before buying the gift for her brother, she had $49.50.

She spent $\frac{1}{10}$ of the money for lunch and was left with $49.50. That means $\frac{9}{10}$ of what she had is $49.50. Set up an equation.

$$\frac{9}{10}x = 49.50$$
$$x = 55$$

Sandy had $55 in her purse before lunch.

EXERCISES

1. To go from Bedford to Worcester, take Route 4 south, then Route 128 south, and then Route 90 west. How do you get from Worcester to Bedford?

1. Route 90 east, Route 128 north, Route 4 north

2. Algae are growing on a pond's surface. The area covered doubles each day. It takes 24 days to cover the pond completely. After how many days will the pond be half covered with algae? **23 days**

3. Don sold $\frac{1}{5}$ as many raffle tickets as Carlita. Carlita sold 3 times as many as Ranesha. Ranesha sold 7 fewer than Russell. If Russell sold 12 tickets, how many did Don sell? **3 tickets**

4. At 6% interest compounded annually, the balance in a bank account will double about every 12 years. If such an account has a balance of $16,000 now, how much was deposited when the account was opened 36 years ago? **about $2000**

5. Solve the puzzle that Yuan gave to Inez: I am thinking of a number. If I triple the number and then halve the result, I get 12. What number am I thinking of? **8**

6. Carlos paid a $14.60 taxi fare from a hotel to the airport, including a $2.00 tip. Green Cab Co. charges $1.20 per passenger plus $0.20 for each additional $\frac{1}{5}$ mile. How many miles is the hotel from the airport? **11.4 mi**

1–2. Answers may vary slightly.

1. 35 mm; 46 mm

2. m∠A = 48; m∠B = 97; m∠C = 35

3.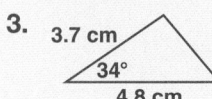
3.7 cm
34°
4.8 cm

4.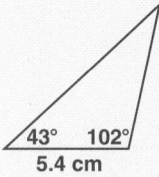
43°   102°
5.4 cm

5.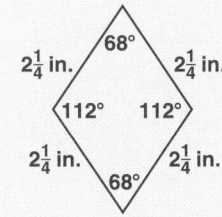
68°
2¼ in.   2¼ in.
112°   112°
2¼ in.   2¼ in.
68°

6.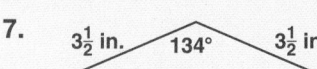
48°   48°
2 in.

7. 3½ in.   134°   3½ in.

Using a Ruler and Protractor

Knowing how to use a ruler and protractor is crucial for success in geometry.

EXAMPLE

Draw a triangle that has sides of length 5.2 cm and 3.0 cm and a 68° angle between these two sides.

The angle opens to the left, so read angle measures from the top scale.

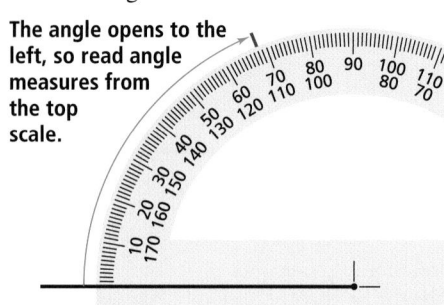

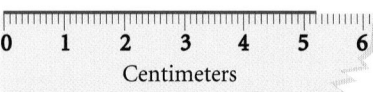
0 1 2 3 4 5 6
Centimeters

Step 1 Use a ruler to draw a segment 5.2 cm long.

Step 2 Place the crosshairs of a protractor at one endpoint of the segment. Make a small mark at the 68° position along the protractor.

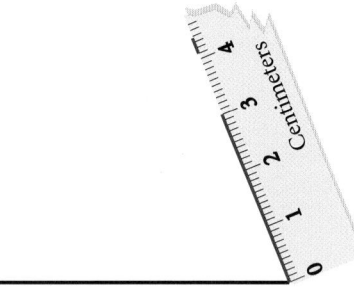

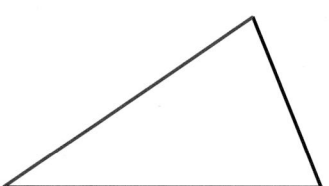

Step 3 Align the ruler along the small mark and the endpoint you used in Step 2. Place the zero point of the ruler at the endpoint. Draw a segment 3.0 cm long.

Step 4 Complete the triangle by connecting the endpoints of the first and second segments.

EXERCISES   1–7. See margin.

1. Measure sides $\overline{AB}$ and $\overline{BC}$ to the nearest millimeter.

2. Measure each angle of △ABC to the nearest degree.

3. Draw a triangle that has sides of length 4.8 cm and 3.7 cm and a 34° angle between these two sides.

4. Draw a triangle that has 43° and 102° angles and a side of length 5.4 cm between these two angles.

5. Draw a rhombus that has sides of length 2¼ in., and 68° and 112° angles.

6. Draw an isosceles trapezoid that has one pair of 48° base angles and a base of length 2 in. between these two base angles.

7. Draw an isosceles triangle that has two congruent sides 3½ in. long and a 134° vertex angle.

B

C

A

Measurement Conversions

To convert from one unit of measure to another, you multiply by a conversion factor in the form of a fraction. The numerator and denominator are in different units, but they represent the same amount. So, you can think of this as multiplying by 1.

An example of a conversion factor is $\frac{1 \text{ ft}}{12 \text{ in.}}$. You can create other conversion factors using the table on page 728.

1 EXAMPLE

Complete each statement.

a. 88 in. = ▓ ft

$$88 \text{ in.} \cdot \frac{1 \text{ ft}}{12 \text{ in.}} = \frac{88}{12} \text{ ft} = 7\frac{1}{3} \text{ ft}$$

b. 5.3 m = ▓ cm

$$5.3 \text{ m} \cdot \frac{100 \text{ cm}}{1 \text{ m}} = 5.3(100) \text{ cm} = 530 \text{ cm}$$

c. 3700 mm = ▓ cm

$$3700 \text{ mm} \cdot \frac{1 \text{ cm}}{10 \text{ mm}} = 370 \text{ cm}$$

d. 90 in. = ▓ yd

$$90 \text{ in.} \cdot \frac{1 \text{ ft}}{12 \text{ in.}} \cdot \frac{1 \text{ yd}}{3 \text{ ft}} = \frac{90}{36} \text{ yd} = 2\frac{1}{2} \text{ yd}$$

Area is always in square units, and volume is always in cubic units.

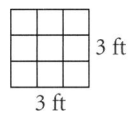

1 yd = 3 ft

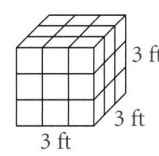

$1 \text{ yd}^2 = 9 \text{ ft}^2$

$1 \text{ yd}^3 = 27 \text{ ft}^3$

2 EXAMPLE

Complete each statement.

a. $300 \text{ in.}^2 = $ ▓ ft^2

$1 \text{ ft} = 12 \text{ in.}$, so $1 \text{ ft}^2 = (12 \text{ in.})^2 = 144 \text{ in.}^2$

$$300 \text{ in.}^2 \cdot \frac{1 \text{ ft}^2}{144 \text{ in.}^2} = 2\frac{1}{12} \text{ ft}^2$$

b. $200{,}000 \text{ cm}^3 = $ ▓ m^3

$1 \text{ m} = 100 \text{ cm}$, so $1 \text{ m}^3 = (100 \text{ cm})^3 = 1{,}000{,}000 \text{ cm}^3$

$$200{,}000 \text{ cm}^3 \cdot \frac{1 \text{ m}^3}{1{,}000{,}000 \text{ cm}^3} = 0.2 \text{ m}^3$$

EXERCISES

Complete each statement.

1. 40 cm = ▓ m **0.4**

2. 1.5 kg = ▓ g **1500**

3. 60 cm = ▓ mm **600**

4. 200 in. = ▓ ft $16\frac{2}{3}$

5. 28 yd = ▓ in. **1008**

6. 1.5 mi = ▓ ft **7920**

7. 42 fl oz = ▓ qt $1\frac{5}{16}$

8. 430 mg = ▓ g **0.43**

9. 34 L = ▓ mL **34,000**

10. 1.2 m = ▓ cm **120**

11. 43 mm = ▓ cm **4.3**

12. 3600 s = ▓ min **60**

13. 15 g = ▓ mg **15,000**

14. 12 qt = ▓ c **48**

15. 0.03 kg = ▓ mg **30,000**

16. 14 gal = ▓ qt **56**

17. 4500 lb = ▓ t $2\frac{1}{4}$

18. 234 min = ▓ h **3.9**

19. 12 mL = ▓ L **0.012**

20. 2 pt = ▓ fl oz **32**

21. 20 m/s = ▓ km/h **72**

22. $3 \text{ ft}^2 = $ ▓ in.^2 **432**

23. $108 \text{ m}^2 = $ ▓ cm^2 **1,080,000**

24. $2100 \text{ mm}^2 = $ ▓ cm^2 **21**

25. $1.4 \text{ yd}^2 = $ ▓ ft^2 **12.6**

26. $0.45 \text{ km}^2 = $ ▓ m^2 **450,000**

27. $1300 \text{ ft}^2 = $ ▓ yd^2 $144\frac{4}{9}$

28. $1030 \text{ in.}^2 = $ ▓ ft^2 $7\frac{11}{72}$

29. $20{,}000{,}000 \text{ ft}^2 = $ ▓ mi^2 $\frac{3125}{4356}$

30. $1000 \text{ cm}^3 = $ ▓ m^3 **0.001**

Measurement, Rounding Error, and Reasonableness

There is no such thing as an *exact* measurement. Measurements are always approximate. No matter how precise it is, a measurement actually represents a range of values.

1 EXAMPLE

Chris's height, to the nearest inch, is 5 ft 8 in. Find the range of values this measurement represents.

The height is given to the nearest inch, so the error is $\frac{1}{2}$ in. Chris's height, then, is between 5 ft $7\frac{1}{2}$ in. and 5 ft $8\frac{1}{2}$ in., or 5 ft 8 in. $\pm \frac{1}{2}$ in. Within this range are all measures which, when rounded to the nearest inch, equal 5 ft 8 in.

As you calculate with measurements, errors can accumulate.

2 EXAMPLE

Jean drives 18 km to work each day. The distance is given to the nearest kilometer.
a. Find the range of values this measurement represents.

The driving distance is between 17.5 and 18.5 km, or 18 ± 0.5 km.

b. Find the error in the round-trip distance.

Double the lower limit, 17.5, and the upper limit, 18.5. Thus, the round trip can be anywhere between 35 and 37 km, or 36 ± 1 km. The error for the round trip is double the error of a single leg of the trip.

So that your answers will be reasonable, keep precision and error in mind as you calculate. For example, in finding AB, the length of the hypotenuse of $\triangle ABC$, it would be inappropriate to give the answer as 9.6566 if the sides are given to the nearest tenth. Round your answer to 9.7.

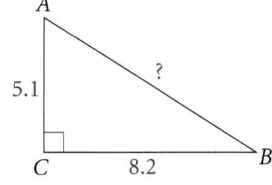

EXERCISES

Each measurement is followed by its unit of greatest precision. Find the range of values that each measurement represents.   **2.** $123\frac{1}{2}$ cm to $124\frac{1}{2}$ cm

1. 24 ft (ft) **$23\frac{1}{2}$ ft to $24\frac{1}{2}$ ft**   **2.** 124 cm (cm)   **3.** 340 mL (mL) **$339\frac{1}{2}$ mL to $340\frac{1}{2}$ mL**

4. $5\frac{1}{2}$ mi. $\left(\frac{1}{2} \text{ mi}\right)$ **5.** 73.2 mm (0.1 mm)   **6.** 34 yd^2 (yd^2) **$33\frac{1}{2}$ yd^2 to $34\frac{1}{2}$ yd^2**
     $5\frac{1}{4}$ mi to $5\frac{3}{4}$ mi   **73.15 mm to 73.25 mm**
7. 5.4 mi (0.1 mi)   **8.** 6 ft 5 in. (0.5 in.)   **9.** $15\frac{1}{2}$ yd $\left(\frac{1}{2} \text{ yd}\right)$ **$15\frac{1}{4}$ yd to $15\frac{3}{4}$ yd**
     5.35 mi to 5.45 mi   **6 ft 4.75 in. to 6 ft 5.25 in.**

10. The lengths of the sides of *TJCM* are given to the nearest tenth of a centimeter. Find the range of values for the figure's perimeter. **8.7 cm to 9.1 cm**

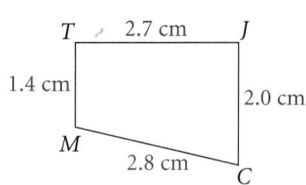

11. To the nearest degree, two angles of a triangle are 49° and 73°. What is the range of values for the measure of the third angle? **57 to 59**

12. The lengths of the legs of a right triangle are measured as 131 m and 162 m. You use a calculator to find the length of the hypotenuse. The calculator display reads 208.33867. What should your answer be? **208 m**

The Effect of Measurement Errors on Calculations

Measurements are always approximate, and calculations with these measurements produce error. Percent error is a measure of accuracy of a measurement or calculation. It is the ratio of the greatest possible error to the measurement.

$$\text{percent error} = \frac{\text{greatest possible error}}{\text{measurement}}$$

EXAMPLE

The dimensions of a box are measured as 18 in., 12 in., and 9 in. Find the percent error in calculating its volume.

The measurements are to the nearest inch, so the greatest possible length error is one half of one inch, or 0.5 in.

as measured	maximum value	minimum value
$V = \ell \cdot w \cdot h$	$V = \ell \cdot w \cdot h$	$V = \ell \cdot w \cdot h$
$= 18 \cdot 12 \cdot 9$	$= 18.5 \cdot 12.5 \cdot 9.5$	$= 17.5 \cdot 11.5 \cdot 8.5$
$= 1944$, or 1944 in.^{3}	≈ 2196.9, or 2196.9 in.^{3}	≈ 1710.6, or 1710.6 in.^{3}

Possible Error:

maximum − measured

2196.9 − 1944 = 252.9

measured − minimum

1944 − 1710.6 = 233.4

$$\text{percent error} = \frac{\text{greatest possible error}}{\text{measurement}}$$
$$= \frac{252.9}{1944}$$
$$\approx 0.1300926$$
$$\approx 13\%$$

● The percent error is about 13%.

EXERCISES

**Find the percent error in calculating the volume of each box given its dimensions.
Round to the nearest percent.**

1. 10 cm by 5 cm by 20 cm **18%**

2. 12 in. by 6 in. by 2 in. **41%**

3. 1.2 mm by 5.7 mm by 2.0 mm **8%**

4. 7.5 m by 6.4 m by 2.7 m **3%**

5. 22.5 cm by 16.4 cm by 26.4 cm **1%**

6. 1.24 cm by 4.45 cm by 5.58 cm **1%**

7. $8\frac{1}{4}$ in. by $17\frac{1}{2}$ in. by 5 in. **5%**

8. $7\frac{3}{4}$ in. by $22\frac{1}{8}$ in. by $6\frac{1}{4}$ in. **2%**

Find the percent error in calculating the perimeter of each figure.

9. 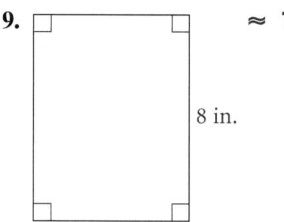 ≈ **7%**

10. 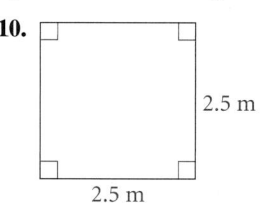 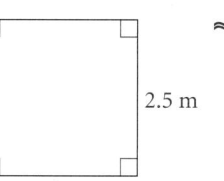 ≈ **2%**

11. 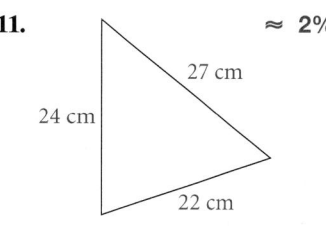 ≈ **2%**

5. Median; the mode does
not represent most of
the data; the mean is
significantly affected by
the single highest salary.

Mean, Median, and Mode

Measures of central tendency, such as mean, median, and mode, are numbers that describe a set of data.

The **mean**, sometimes called the average, is the sum of the data items divided by the number of data items.

The **median** is the middle number when data items are placed in order and there are an odd number of data items. For an even number of data items, the median is the mean of the middle two numbers.

The **mode** is the data item that appears most frequently. A set of data may have more than one mode or no modes.

EXAMPLE

Eighteen students were asked to measure the angle formed by the three objects in the diagram. Their answers, in order from least to greatest, are as follows:

65, 66, 66, 66, 66, 66, 66, 67, 67, 67, 67, 67, 68, 68, 69, 70, 74, 113

Find the mean, median, and mode of the data.

Mean: $\dfrac{\text{sum of the 18 measures}}{18} = \dfrac{1258}{18} = 69\frac{8}{9}$

Median:
This data list is already ordered. The two middle numbers—the ninth and the tenth numbers on the list—are both 67. So the median is 67.

Mode:
There are more 66's than any other number, so the mode is 66.

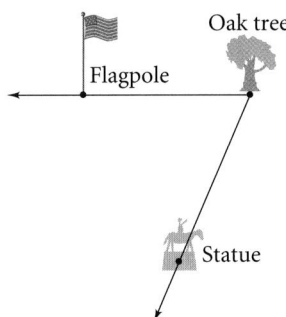

Oak tree

Flagpole

Statue

EXERCISES

Find the mean, median, and mode of each set of data.

1. Numbers of students per school in Newtown: 234, 341, 253, 313, 273, 301, 760 **353.6; 301; no mode**

2. Lunch expenses: $4.50, $3.26, $5.02, $3.58, $1.25, $3.05, $4.24, $3.56, $3.31 **$3.53; $3.56; no mode**

3. Salaries at D. B. Widget & Co.: $15,000; 18,000; $18,000; $21,700; $26,500; $27,000; $29,300; $31,100; $43,000; $47,800; $69,000; $140,000 **$40,533; $28,150; $18,000**

4. Population of towns in Brower County: 567, 632, 781, 902, 1034, 1100, 1598, 2164, 2193, 3062, 3074, 3108, 3800, 3721, 4104 **2123; 2164; no mode**

5. In Exercise 3, which measure or measures of central tendency do you think best represent the data? Explain. **See margin.**

6. Find the mean, median, and mode of the exam scores at the right.

7. In the example, the student who reported the angle measure as 113 most likely made an error. If this measure is dropped from the list, what are the mean, median, and mode of the remaining 17 scores?

8. In the example, if the measurement 65 were instead 51, would the mean decrease? Would the median? Would the mode? **yes; no; no**

9. In the example, if the two students who measured the angle at 68 both reduced their measurements to 67, would the mode be affected? How? **Yes; the mode would be 67.**

Final Exam Scores
34, 47, 53, 56, 57, 62, 62, 64, 67, 70, 74, 74, 74, 78, 82, 85, 85, 85, 85, 86, 88, 92, 93, 93, 94, 95, 97

6. 75.3; 78; 85
7. $67\frac{6}{17}$, 67, 66

Bar Graphs and Line Graphs

Data displayed in a table can be very useful, but a table is not always as easy to interpret as a graph. Bar graphs and line graphs can show the same data, but sometimes one type of graph has advantages over the other.

EXAMPLE

Make a bar graph and a line graph showing the data in the table at the right.

Bar Graph

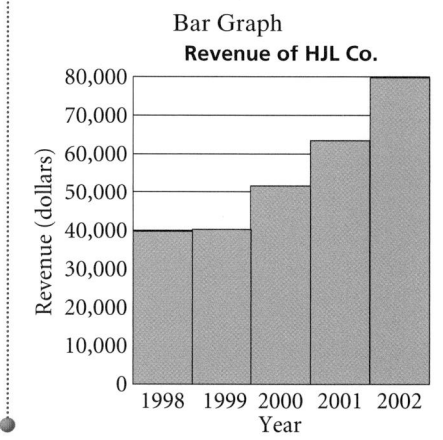

Line Graph

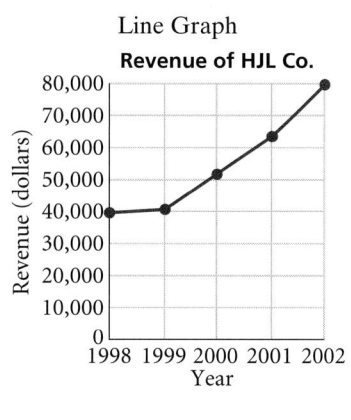

Revenue of HJL Co.

Year	Revenue
1998	$39,780
1999	$40,019
2000	$51,772
2001	$63,444
2002	$79,855

Bar graphs are useful when you wish to compare amounts. In the example above, the tallest bar is clearly twice the height of the shortest bar. At a glance, it is evident that in four years the revenue approximately doubled.

Line graphs allow you to see how a set of data changes over time. In the example, the slope of the line shows that revenue has increased at a steady rate since 1999.

Did revenue increase from 1998 to 1999? It is difficult to tell by looking at either graph; for that information, you should look back at the table.

EXERCISES

1. Create a bar graph and a line graph to display the data in the table below. **See margin.**

Sales of Rock Music (in millions of dollars)

Year	1995	1996	1997	1998	1999	2000
Sales	$4127	$4086	$3977	$3527	$3675	$3552

SOURCE: Recording Industry Association of America.
Go to **www.PHSchool.com** for a data update.
Web Code: afg-2041

For Exercises 2–6, refer to the line graph at the right.

2. What was the lowest temperature recorded between 6 A.M. and 6 P.M.? **10°F**

3. During which time periods did the temperature appear to increase?
8 A.M.–2 P.M.

4. Estimate the temperature at 11 A.M. and at 5 P.M. **28°F; 42°F**

5. Can you tell from the graph what the actual maximum and minimum temperatures were between 6 A.M. and 6 P.M.? Explain. **See above right.**

6. The same data could be presented in a bar graph. Which presentation is better for these data, a line graph or a bar graph? Explain why. **Answers may vary. Sample: A line graph; the line graph shows a change in temperature over time more clearly.**

5. No; you cannot tell how the temperature changed between the measurements.

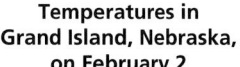

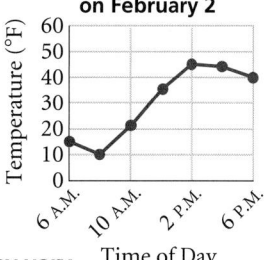

Temperatures in Grand Island, Nebraska, on February 2

Time of Day

page 713 Bar Graphs and Line Graphs

1.

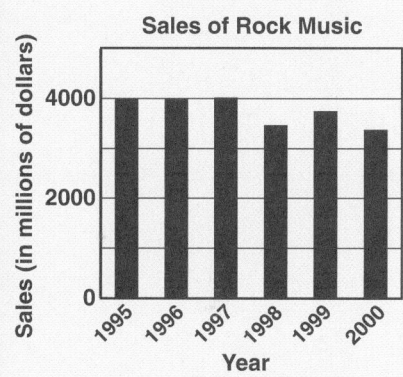

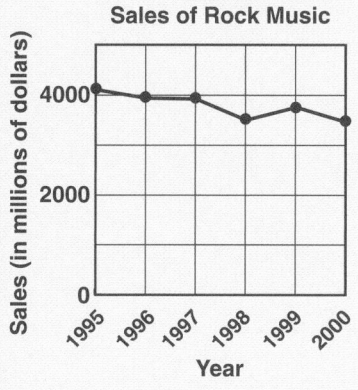

Box-and-Whisker Plots

A *box-and-whisker plot* is a way to display data on a number line. It provides a picture of how tightly the data cluster around the median and how wide a range the data have. The diagram below shows the various points associated with a box-and-whisker plot.

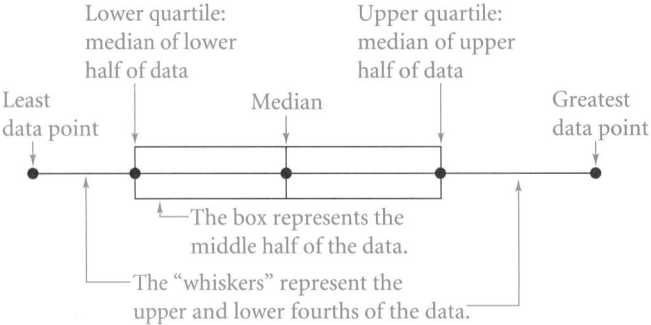

EXAMPLE

The heights, in inches, of 23 geometry students are as follows.

58, 61, 63, 63, 63, 64, 64, 65, 65, 65, 67, 68, 68, 68, 69, 70, 70, 70, 72, 72, 72, 74, 75

Draw a box-and-whisker plot.

The heights range from 58 in. to 75 in. Show 58 and 75 as endpoints on a line segment. The median is 68, so locate 68 in relation to 58 and 75. The lower quartile (the median of the lower eleven heights) is 64. The upper quartile (the median of the upper eleven heights) is 70. Locate 64 and 70 and draw a box enclosing them. Draw a vertical segment inside the box through the median.

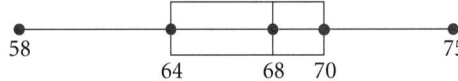

EXERCISES

1. All of the physical education students at Martin Luther King, Jr., High School were timed sprinting the 100-meter dash. The box-and-whisker plot below summarizes the data. Use it to find the following.
   a. median **16.6**   **b.** lower quartile **15.1**   **c.** upper quartile **19.4**

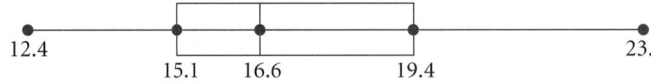

2. Make a box-and-whisker plot for the following data set, which lists the weights, in pounds, of the students trying out for the wrestling team at Benjamin Banneker High School.

   104, 121, 122, 130, 130, 131, 140, 144, 147, 147, 148, 155, 160, 163, 171

2. Wrestlers' Weights

104   130   144   155   171

3. Make a box-and-whisker plot for the following set of data, which lists the numbers of pages in a set of books. (*Hint:* Order the data from smallest to largest.)

   205, 198, 312, 254, 185, 268, 297, 242, 356, 262

3. Pages in Books

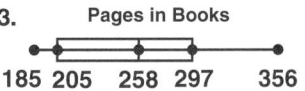

185   205   258   297   356

Squaring Numbers and Finding Square Roots

The square of a number is found by multiplying the number by itself. An exponent of 2 is used to indicate that a number is being squared.

1 EXAMPLE

Simplify.

a. 5^2

$5^2 = 5 \cdot 5$

$= 25$

b. $(-3.5)^2$

$(-3.5)^2 = (-3.5) \cdot (-3.5)$

$= 12.25$

c. $\left(\frac{2}{7}\right)^2$

$\left(\frac{2}{7}\right)^2 = \frac{2}{7} \cdot \frac{2}{7}$

$= \frac{4}{49}$

The square root of a number is itself a number that, when squared, results in the original number. A radical symbol ($\sqrt{}$) is used to represent the positive square root of a number.

2 EXAMPLE

Simplify. Round to the nearest tenth if necessary.

a. $\sqrt{36}$

$\sqrt{36} = 6$ since $6^2 = 36$

b. $\sqrt{174}$

$\sqrt{174} \approx 13.2$ since $13.2^2 \approx 174$

You can solve equations that include squared numbers.

3 EXAMPLE

Algebra Solve.

a. $x^2 = 144$

$x = 12$ or -12

b. $a^2 + 3^2 = 5^2$

$a^2 + 9 = 25$

$a^2 = 16$

$a = 4$ or -4

EXERCISES

Simplify.

1. 11^2 **121**

2. 16^2 **256**

3. $(-14)^2$ **196**

4. $(-21)^2$ **441**

5. 5.1^2 **26.01**

6. $\left(\frac{3}{7}\right)^2$ $\frac{9}{49}$

7. $\left(\frac{8}{5}\right)^2$ $\frac{64}{25}$

8. -6^2 **−36**

$\boxed{x^2}$ **Simplify. Round to the nearest tenth if necessary.**

9. $\sqrt{100}$ **10**

10. $\sqrt{169}$ **13**

11. $\sqrt{74}$ **8.6**

12. $\sqrt{50}$ **7.1**

13. $\sqrt{400}$ **20**

14. $\sqrt{289}$ **17**

15. $\sqrt{\frac{4}{9}}$ $\frac{2}{3}$

16. $\sqrt{\frac{49}{81}}$ $\frac{7}{9}$

Algebra **Solve. Round to the nearest tenth if necessary.**

17. $x^2 = 49$ **±7**

18. $a^2 = 9$ **±3**

19. $y^2 + 7 = 8$ **±1**

20. $5 + x^2 = 11$ **±2.4**

21. $8^2 + b^2 = 10^2$ **±6**

22. $5^2 + 4^2 = c^2$ **±6.4**

23. $p^2 + 12^2 = 13^2$ **±5**

24. $20^2 = 15^2 + a^2$ **±13.2**

22. $-4x^2 + 8x$

23. $x - 5$

24. $-3t^2 + 4t$

25. $r^2 - 2r + 1$

26. $r^2 - 2r + 1$

27. $y^2 - 2y - 3$

Evaluating and Simplifying Expressions

You evaluate an expression with variables by substituting a number for each variable. Then simplify the expression using the order of operations. Be especially careful with exponents and negative signs. For example, the expression $-x^2$ always yields a negative or zero value, and $(-x)^2$ is always positive or zero.

<table>
<tr><td>Order of Operations</td></tr>
<tr><td>1. Perform any operation(s) inside grouping symbols.</td></tr>
<tr><td>2. Simplify any term with exponents.</td></tr>
<tr><td>3. Multiply and divide in order from left to right.</td></tr>
<tr><td>4. Add and subtract in order from left to right.</td></tr>
</table>

1 EXAMPLE

Algebra Evaluate each expression for $r = 4$.

a. $-r^2$

$-r^2 = -(4^2) = -16$

b. $-3r^2$

$-3r^2 = -3(4^2) = -3(16) = -48$

c. $(-3r)^2$

$(-3r)^2 = (-3 \cdot 4)^2 = (-12)^2 = 144$

To simplify an expression, you eliminate any parentheses and combine like terms.

2 EXAMPLE

Algebra Simplify each expression.

a. $5r - 2r + 1$

Combine like terms.
$5r - 2r + 1 = 3r + 1$

b. $\pi(3r - 1)$

Use the distributive property.
$\pi(3r - 1) = 3\pi r - \pi$

c. $(r + \pi)(r - \pi)$

Multiply polynomials.
$(r + \pi)(r - \pi) = r^2 - \pi^2$

EXERCISES

$\boxed{x^2}$ **Algebra** Evaluate each expression for $x = 5$ and $y = -3$.

1. $-2x^2$ **−50**

2. $-y + x$ **8**

3. $-xy$ **15**

4. $(x + 5y) \div x$ **−2**

5. $x + 5y \div x$ **2**

6. $(-2y)^2$ **36**

7. $(2y)^2$ **36**

8. $(x - y)^2$ **64**

9. $\frac{x + 1}{y}$ **−2**

10. $y - (x - y)$ **−11**

11. $-y^x$ **243**

12. $\frac{2(1 - x)}{y - x}$ **1**

13. $x \cdot y - x$ **−20**

14. $x - y \cdot x$ **20**

15. $\frac{y^3 - x}{x - y}$ **−4**

16. $-y(x - 3)^2$ **12**

17. Which expression gives the area of the shaded figure at the right? **B**

A. $\pi(r - s)^2$

B. $\pi(r^2 - s^2)$

C. $\pi(s^2 - r^2)$

D. $\pi r^2 - 2\pi s$

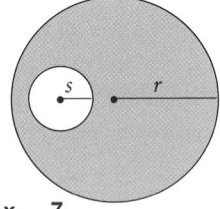

$\boxed{x^2}$ **Algebra** Simplify.

18. $6x - 4x + 8 - 5$ **2x + 3**

19. $2(\ell + w)$ **2ℓ + 2w**

20. $-(4x + 7)$ **−4x − 7**

21. $-4x(x - 2)$ **4x² + 8x**

22. $3x - (5 + 2x)$ **x − 5**

23. $2t^2 + 4t - 5t^2$ **−3t² + 4t**

24. $(r - 1)^2$ **r² − 2r + 1**

25. $(1 - r)^2$ **1 − 2r + r²**

26. $(y + 1)(y - 3)$ **y² − 2y − 3**

27. $4h + 3h - 4 + 3$ **7h − 1**

28. $\pi r - (1 + \pi r)$ **−1**

29. $(x + 4)(2x - 1)$ **2x² + 7x − 4**

30. $2\pi h(1 - r)^2$ **2πhr² − 4πhr + 2πh**

31. $3y^2 - (y^2 + 3y)$ **2y² − 3y**

32. $-(x + 4)^2$ **−x² − 8x − 16**

Simplifying Radicals

A radical expression is in its simplest form when all three of the following statements are true.

1. The expression under the radical sign contains no perfect square factors (other than 1).
2. The expression under the radical sign does not contain a fraction.
3. The denominator does not contain a radical expression.

1 EXAMPLE

Simplify.

a. $\sqrt{\frac{4}{9}}$

$$\sqrt{\frac{4}{9}} = \frac{\sqrt{4}}{\sqrt{9}} = \frac{2}{3}$$

b. $\sqrt{12}$

$$\sqrt{12} = \sqrt{4} \cdot \sqrt{3} = 2\sqrt{3}$$

2 EXAMPLE

Find the length of the diagonal of rectangle *HJKL*.

$c^2 = 7^2 + 1^2$ **Use the Pythagorean Theorem.**

$c^2 = 50$ **Simplify the right side.**

$c = \sqrt{50}$ **Find the square root of each side.**

$\quad = \sqrt{25 \cdot 2}$ **Find a perfect square factor of 50.**

$\quad = 5\sqrt{2}$ **Simplify the radical.**

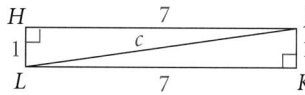

3 EXAMPLE

Simplify $\frac{1}{\sqrt{3}}$.

$$\frac{1}{\sqrt{3}} \cdot \frac{\sqrt{3}}{\sqrt{3}} = \frac{\sqrt{3}}{3}$$ **Multiply by $\frac{\sqrt{3}}{\sqrt{3}}$, or 1, to eliminate the radical in the denominator.**

EXERCISES

Simplify each radical expression.

1. $\sqrt{27}$ $3\sqrt{3}$

2. $\sqrt{24}$ $2\sqrt{6}$

3. $\sqrt{150}$ $5\sqrt{6}$

4. $\sqrt{\frac{1}{9}}$ $\frac{1}{3}$

5. $\sqrt{\frac{72}{9}}$ $2\sqrt{2}$

6. $\frac{\sqrt{228}}{\sqrt{16}}$ $\frac{\sqrt{57}}{2}$

7. $\sqrt{\frac{2}{5}}$ $\frac{\sqrt{10}}{5}$

8. $\sqrt{\frac{27}{75}}$ $\frac{3}{5}$

9. $\frac{3}{\sqrt{8}}$ $\frac{3\sqrt{2}}{4}$

10. $\frac{6\sqrt{18}}{\sqrt{48}}$ $\frac{3\sqrt{6}}{2}$

$\boxed{x^2}$ **Algebra** **Find the value of *x*. Leave your answer in simplest radical form.**

11. 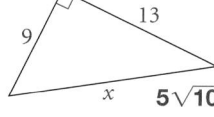 $5\sqrt{10}$

12. 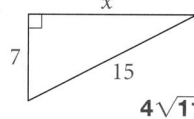 $4\sqrt{11}$

13.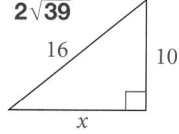

14. 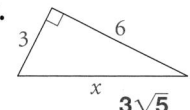 $3\sqrt{5}$

15. 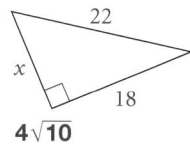 $4\sqrt{10}$

16. 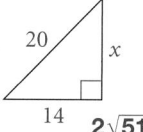 $2\sqrt{51}$

17. 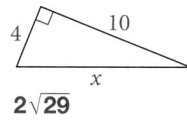 $2\sqrt{29}$

18. 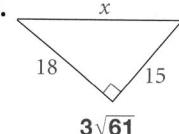 $3\sqrt{61}$

Simplifying Ratios

The ratio of the length of the shorter leg to the length of the longer leg for this right triangle is 4 to 6. This ratio can be written in several ways.

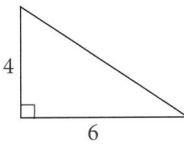

4 to 6 $\frac{4}{6}$ 4 : 6

EXAMPLE

Algebra Simplify each ratio.

a. 4 to 6

$$4 \text{ to } 6 = \frac{4}{6}$$

$$= \frac{2 \cdot 2}{2 \cdot 3}$$ ⟵ Find and remove the common factor. ⟶

$$= \frac{2}{3}$$

b. $3ab : 27ab$

$$3ab : 27ab = \frac{3ab}{27ab}$$

$$= \frac{3ab}{9 \cdot 3ab}$$

$$= \frac{1}{9}$$

c. $\frac{4a + 4b}{a + b}$

$$\frac{4a + 4b}{a + b} = \frac{4(a + b)}{a + b}$$ **Factor the numerator. The denominator cannot be factored. Remove the common factor ($a + b$).**

$$= 4$$

EXERCISES

x^2 **Algebra** **Simplify each ratio.**

1. 25 to 15 $\frac{5}{3}$

2. $6 : 9$ $\frac{2}{3}$

3. $\frac{36}{54}$ $\frac{2}{3}$

4. 0.8 to 2.4 $\frac{1}{3}$

5. $\frac{7}{14x}$ $\frac{1}{2x}$

6. $\frac{12c}{14c}$ $\frac{6}{7}$

7. $22x^2$ to $35x$ $\frac{22x}{35}$

8. $0.5ab : 8ab$ $\frac{1}{16}$

9. $\frac{4xy}{0.25x}$ **16y**

10. $1\frac{1}{2}x$ to $5x$ $\frac{3}{10}$

11. $\frac{x^2 + x}{2x}$ $\frac{x + 1}{2}$

12. $\frac{1}{4}r^2$ to $6r$ $\frac{r}{24}$

13. $0.72t : 7.2t^2$ $\frac{1}{10t}$

14. $(2x - 6) : (6x - 4)$ $\frac{x - 3}{3x - 2}$

15. $12xy : 8xy$ $\frac{3}{2}$

16. $(9x - 9y)$ to $(x - y)$ **9**

17. $\frac{\pi r}{r^2 + \pi r}$ $\frac{\pi}{r + \pi}$

18. $\frac{8ab}{32xy}$ $\frac{ab}{4xy}$

Express each ratio in simplest form.

19. shorter leg : longer leg $\frac{5}{12}$

20. hypotenuse to shorter leg $\frac{13}{5}$

21. $\frac{\text{shorter leg}}{\text{hypotenuse}}$ $\frac{5}{13}$

22. hypotenuse : longer leg $\frac{13}{12}$

23. longer leg to shorter leg $\frac{12}{5}$

24. $\frac{\text{longer leg}}{\text{hypotenuse}}$ $\frac{12}{13}$

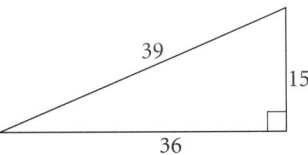

x^2 **Algebra** **Write an expression in simplest form for** $\dfrac{\text{area of shaded figure}}{\text{area of blue figure}}$.

25.
$\frac{2}{\pi}$
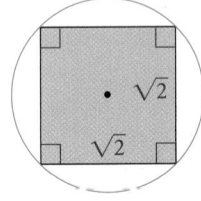

26.
$\frac{5}{14}$
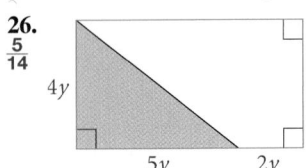

27.
$\frac{1}{9}$
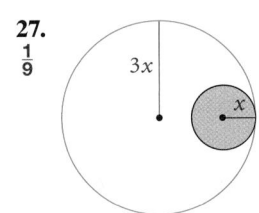

Absolute Value

Absolute value is used to represent the distance of a number from 0 on a number line. Since distance is always referred to as a nonnegative number, the absolute value of an expression is nonnegative.

On the number line at the right, both 4 and −4 are four units from zero. Therefore, $|4|$ and $|-4|$ are both equal to four.

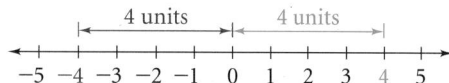

1 EXAMPLE

Simplify each expression.

a. $|-7|$

$|-7| = 7$

b. $|15|$

$|15| = 15$

c. $|4| + |-19|$

$|4| + |-19| = 4 + 19 = 23$

When working with more complicated expressions, always remember to simplify within absolute value symbols first.

2 EXAMPLE

Simplify each expression.

a. $|4 - 8|$

$|4 - 8| = |-4|$

$\quad\quad\quad = 4$

b. $-3|-7 - 4|$

$-3|-7 - 4| = -3|-11|$

$\quad\quad\quad\quad\quad = -3 \cdot 11$

$\quad\quad\quad\quad\quad = -33$

To solve an equation involving absolute value, remember that absolute value symbols cause both negative and positive values to become positive.

3 EXAMPLE

Algebra Solve.

a. $|x| = 7$

$x = 7 \text{ or } -7$

b. $|x| - 3 = 22$

$|x| - 3 = 22$

$\quad\quad |x| = 25$

$\quad\quad\quad x = -25 \text{ or } 25$

EXERCISES

Simplify each expression.

1. $|-8|$ **8**

2. $|11|$ **11**

3. $|16|$ **16**

4. $|-23|$ **23**

5. $|-7| + |15|$ **22**

6. $|-12| - |-12|$ **0**

7. $|5| - |10|$ **−5**

8. $|4| + |2|$ **6**

9. $10 - |-20|$ **−10**

10. $|-9 - 11|$ **20**

11. $2|-21 + 16|$ **10**

12. $-8|-9 + 4|$ **−40**

$\boxed{x^2}$ **Algebra** Solve.

13. $|x| = 16$ **−16 or 16**

14. $2 = |x|$ **−2 or 2**

15. $|x| + 7 = 27$ **−20 or 20**

16. $|x| - 9 = 15$ **−24 or 24**

Solving and Writing Linear Equations

To solve a linear equation, use the properties of equality and properties of real numbers to find the value of the variable that satisfies the equation.

1 EXAMPLE

Algebra Solve each equation.

a. $5x - 3 = 2$

$5x - 3 = 2$

$\quad 5x = 5$ **Add 3 to each side.**

$\quad\quad x = 1$ **Divide each side by 5.**

b. $1 - 2(x + 1) = x$

$1 - 2(x + 1) = x$

$1 - 2x - 2 = x$ **Use the Distributive Property.**

$\quad -1 - 2x = x$ **Simplify the left side.**

$\quad\quad\quad -1 = 3x$ **Add 2x to each side.**

$\quad\quad -\frac{1}{3} = x$ **Divide each side by 3.**

You will sometimes need to translate word problems into equations. Look for words that suggest a relationship or some type of mathematical operation.

2 EXAMPLE

Algebra A student has grades of 80, 65, 78, and 92 on four tests. What is the minimum grade she must earn on her next test to ensure an average of 80?

Relate average of 80, 65, 78, 92, and next test, is 80   **Pull out the key words and numbers.**

Define Let x = the grade on the next test.   **Let a variable represent what you are looking for.**

Write $\dfrac{80 + 65 + 78 + 92 + x}{5} = 80$ **Write an equation.**

$\dfrac{315 + x}{5} = 80$ **Combine like terms.**

$315 + x = 400$ **Multiply each side by 5.**

$x = 85$ **Subtract 315 from each side.**

The student must earn 85 on the next test for an average of 80.

EXERCISES

$\boxed{x^2}$ **Algebra** Solve each equation.

1. $3n + 2 = 17$ **5**

2. $5a - 2 = -12$ **−2**

3. $2x + 4 = 10$ **3**

4. $3(n - 4) = 15$ **9**

5. $4 - 2y = 8$ **−2**

6. $-6z + 1 = 13$ **−2**

7. $6 - (3t + 4) = -17$ **$\frac{19}{3}$**

8. $7 = -2(4n - 4.5)$ **$\frac{1}{4}$**

9. $(w + 5) - (2w + 5) = 5$ **−5**

10. $\frac{5}{7}p - 10 = 30$ **56**

11. $\frac{m}{-2} - 3 = 1$ **−8**

12. $5k + 2(k + 1) = 23$ **3**

$\boxed{x^2}$ **Algebra** Write an equation and solve the problem.

13. Twice a number subtracted from 35 is 9. What is the number? **$35 - 2x = 9$; 13**

14. A new tenant pays the landlord the amount of the first month's rent, the same amount for the last month's rent, and half a month's rent for a security deposit. The total is $2437.50. How much is the monthly rent? **$2.5r = \$2437.50$; $975**

15. The Johnsons pay $9.95 a month plus $0.035 per minute for local phone service. Last month, they paid $12.75. How many minutes of local calls did they make? **$\$9.95 + \$0.035m = \$12.75$; 80 min**

Solving Literal Equations

An equation with two or more variables is called a literal equation. It is often necessary to solve a literal equation for a particular variable.

1 EXAMPLE

Algebra The formula $P = 2(\ell + w)$ gives the perimeter P of a rectangle with length ℓ and width w. Solve the equation for ℓ.

$$P = 2(\ell + w)$$
$$P = 2\ell + 2w \qquad \text{Use the Distributive Property.}$$
$$P - 2w = 2\ell \qquad \text{Subtract } 2w \text{ from each side.}$$
$$\frac{P - 2w}{2} = \ell \qquad \text{Divide each side by 2.}$$

2 EXAMPLE

Algebra The formula $A = \frac{1}{2}(b_1 + b_2)h$ gives the area A of a trapezoid with bases b_1 and b_2 and height h. Solve for h.

$$A = \frac{1}{2}(b_1 + b_2)h$$
$$2A = h(b_1 + b_2) \qquad \text{Multiply each side by 2.}$$
$$\frac{2A}{b_1 + b_2} = h \qquad \text{Divide each side by } (b_1 + b_2).$$

3 EXAMPLE

Algebra The formula for converting from degrees Celsius C to degrees Fahrenheit F is $F = \frac{9}{5}C + 32$. Solve for C.

$$F = \frac{9}{5}C + 32$$
$$F - 32 = \frac{9}{5}C \qquad \text{Subtract 32 from each side.}$$
$$\frac{5}{9}(F - 32) = C \qquad \text{Multiply each side by } \frac{5}{9}.$$

EXERCISES

$\boxed{x^2}$ **Algebra** **Solve each equation for the variable in red.**

1. Perimeter of rectangle: $P = 2w + 2\ell$ $w = \frac{P - 2\ell}{2}$

2. Volume of prism: $V = \ell wh$ $w = \frac{V}{\ell h}$

3. Surface area of sphere: $S = 4\pi r^2$ $r = \frac{1}{2}\sqrt{\frac{S}{\pi}} = \frac{\sqrt{\pi S}}{2\pi}$

4. Lateral area of cylinder: $A = 2\pi rh$ $r = \frac{A}{2\pi h}$

5. Area of kite or rhombus: $A = \frac{1}{2}d_1 d_2$ $d_2 = \frac{2A}{d_1}$

6. Area of circle: $A = \pi r^2$ $r = \sqrt{\frac{A}{\pi}} = \frac{\sqrt{\pi A}}{\pi}$

7. Area of regular polygon: $A = \frac{1}{2}ap$ $a = \frac{2A}{p}$

8. Volume of cylinder: $V = \pi r^2 h$ $h = \frac{V}{\pi r^2}$

9. Area of triangle: $A = \frac{1}{2}bh$ $h = \frac{2A}{b}$

10. Tangent of $\angle A$: $\tan A = \frac{y}{x}$ $x = \frac{y}{\tan A}$

11. Euler's Formula: $F + V = E + 2$ $V = E + 2 - F$

12. Circumference of circle: $C = 2\pi r$ $r = \frac{C}{2\pi}$

13. Cosine of $\angle A$: $\cos A = \frac{b}{c}$ $b = c \cos A$

14. Volume of cone: $V = \frac{1}{3}\pi r^2 h$ $r = \sqrt{\frac{3V}{\pi h}} = \frac{\sqrt{3\pi hV}}{\pi h}$

15. Surface area of right cone: $S = \pi r^2 + \pi r\ell$ **See above.**

16. Area of trapezoid: $A = \frac{1}{2}(b_1 + b_2)h$ **See above.**

17. Volume of pyramid: $V = \frac{1}{3}Bh$ $B = \frac{3V}{h}$

18. Pythagorean Theorem: $a^2 + b^2 = c^2$ $b = \sqrt{c^2 - a^2}$

19. Surface area of regular pyramid: $S = B + \frac{1}{2}p\ell$
$$\ell = \frac{2S - 2B}{p}$$

20. Surface area of right cylinder: $S = 2\pi r^2 + 2\pi rh$
$$h = \frac{S - 2\pi r^2}{2\pi r} = \frac{S}{2\pi r} - r$$

15. $\ell = \frac{S - \pi r^2}{\pi r} = \frac{S}{\pi r} - r$

16. $b_1 = \frac{2A - hb_2}{h} = \frac{2A}{h} - b_2$

Systems of Linear Equations

Normally, there are many ordered pairs that satisfy a given equation. For example, $(3, 4), (4, 5), (5, 6)$, and infinitely many other pairs all satisfy the equation $y = x + 1$. In solving a system of two linear equations, however, you need to find ordered pairs that satisfy both equations at once. Ordinarily, there is just one such ordered pair; it is the point where the graphs of the two lines intersect.

One method you can always use to solve a system of linear equations is the substitution method.

EXAMPLE

Algebra Solve the system.
$$2x - y = -10$$
$$-3x - 2y = 1$$

Solve one of the equations for a variable. Looking at the two equations, it seems easiest to solve the first equation for y.

$$2x - y = -10$$
$\qquad -y = -2x - 10 \qquad$ **Subtract 2x from each side.**
$\qquad y = 2x + 10 \qquad$ **Multiply each side by −1.**

Now substitute $2x + 10$ for y in the other equation.

$\qquad -3x - 2y = 1 \qquad$ **Write the other equation.**
$\qquad -3x - 2(2x + 10) = 1 \qquad$ **Substitute (2x + 10) for y.**
$\qquad -3x - 4x - 20 = 1 \qquad$ **Use the Distributive Property.**
$\qquad -7x = 21 \qquad$ **Simplify and add 20 to each side.**
$\qquad x = -3 \qquad$ **Divide each side by −7.**

So $x = -3$. To find y, substitute -3 for x in either equation.

$\qquad 2x - y = -10 \qquad$ **Write one of the equations.**
$\qquad 2(-3) - y = -10 \qquad$ **Substitute −3 for x.**
$\qquad -6 - y = -10 \qquad$ **Simplify.**
$\qquad -y = -4 \qquad$ **Add 6 to each side.**
$\qquad y = 4 \qquad$ **Multiply each side by −1.**

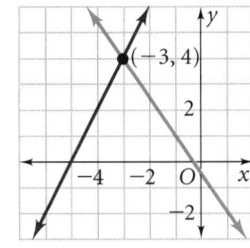

So the solution is $x = -3$ and $y = 4$, or $(-3, 4)$. If you graph $2x - y = -10$ and $-3x - 2y = 1$, you'll find that the lines intersect at $(-3, 4)$.

EXERCISES

x^2 **Algebra** **Solve each system. 5. inf. many solutions: all points on the line $y = \frac{1}{4}x - \frac{3}{4}$**

1. $x + y = 3$ **(4, −1)**
$\quad x - y = 5$

2. $y - x = 4$ **no sol.**
$\quad x + 3 = y$

3. $y = 1$ **(4, 1)**
$\quad 5x - 2y = 18$

4. $3x - y = 5$ **(−2, −11)**
$\quad x = -2$

5. $4y - x = -3$ **See above.**
$\quad 2x - 6 = 8y$

6. $8x - 1 = 4y$ $\left(\frac{3}{4}, \frac{5}{4}\right)$
$\quad 3x = y + 1$

7. $2x + 2y = -4$ **(−3, 1)**
$\quad -x + 3y = 6$

8. $12y - 3x = 11$ $\left(-\frac{1}{3}, \frac{5}{6}\right)$
$\quad x - 2y = -2$

9. $5x + 7y = 1$ **(3, −2)**
$\quad 4x - 2y = 16$

10. Give an example of a system of linear equations with no solution. What do you know about the slopes of the lines of such a system? **Answers may vary. Sample: $y = 2x - 3$, $4x - 2y = 5$. They are equal or they are undefined.**

Percents

A percent is a ratio in which a number is compared to 100. For example, the expression *60 percent* means "60 out of 100." The symbol % stands for "percent."

A percent can be written in decimal form by first writing it in ratio form, and then writing the ratio as a decimal. For example, 25% is equal to the ratio $\frac{25}{100}$ or $\frac{1}{4}$. As a decimal, $\frac{1}{4}$ is equal to 0.25. Note that 25% can also be written directly as a decimal by moving the decimal point two places to the left.

1 EXAMPLE

Convert each percent to a decimal.

a. 42%

$42\% = 0.42$

b. 157%

$157\% = 1.57$

c. 12.4%

$12.4\% = 0.124$

d. 4%

$4\% = 0.04$

To calculate a percent of a number, write the percent as a decimal and multiply.

2 EXAMPLE

Simplify. Where necessary, round to the nearest tenth.

a. 30% of 242

$30\% \text{ of } 242 = 0.3 \cdot 242$

$= 72.6$

b. 7% of 38

$7\% \text{ of } 38 = 0.07 \cdot 38$

$= 2.66 \approx 2.7$

For a percent problem, it is a good idea to check that your answer is reasonable by estimating it.

3 EXAMPLE

Estimate 23% of 96.

$23\% \approx 25\%$ and $96 \approx 100$. $25\% \left(\text{or } \frac{1}{4}\right)$ of $100 = 25$. A reasonable estimate is 25.

EXERCISES

Convert each percent to a decimal.

1. 50% **0.5**

2. 75% **0.75**

3. 27% **0.27**

4. 6% **0.06**

5. 32.5% **0.325**

6. 84.6% **0.846**

7. 9% **0.09**

8. 2.5% **0.025**

Simplify. Where necessary, round to the nearest tenth.

9. 21% of 40 **8.4**

10. 45% of 200 **90**

11. 6% of 120 **7.2**

12. 2% of 54 **1.1**

13. 80.4% of 52 **41.8**

14. 23.8% of 176 **41.9**

15. 7.5% of 32 **2.4**

16. 9.25% of 89 **8.2**

Estimate. Answers may vary. Samples are given.

17. 12% of 70 **7**

18. 48% of 87 **43**

19. 73% of 64 **45**

20. 77% of 42 **32**

Probability

Probability is a measure of the likelihood of an event occurring. All probabilities range from 0 to 1 where 0 is the probability of an event that cannot happen and 1 is the probability of an event that is certain to happen. An event with probability 0.5 or 50% has an equal chance of happening or not happening.

The formula $P(E) = \frac{\text{number of favorable outcomes}}{\text{number of possible outcomes}}$ is used to calculate the probability of event E.

1 EXAMPLE

The numbers 2 through 21 are written on pieces of paper and placed in a hat. One piece of paper is drawn at random. Determine the probability of selecting a perfect square.

The total number of outcomes, $2, 3, 4, \ldots, 21$, for this event is 20.

There are 3 favorable outcomes: $4, 9, 16$.

$P(\text{selecting a perfect square}) = \frac{3}{20}$

2 EXAMPLE

Determine the probability of getting exactly two heads when two coins are tossed.

The total number of outcomes, $(H, H), (H, T), (T, H), (T, T)$, for this event is 4.

There is 1 favorable outcome, (H, H).

$P(\text{two heads}) = \frac{1}{4}$

EXERCISES

A jar contains 3 white balls, 7 red balls, and 4 green balls. A ball is selected at random from the jar. Determine the probability of selecting a ball with the given color.

1. red $\frac{1}{2}$
2. white $\frac{3}{14}$
3. green $\frac{2}{7}$
4. green or white $\frac{1}{2}$

5. A red ball is removed from the jar. Determine the probability that the next ball selected will be green. $\frac{4}{13}$

6. Two green balls are removed from the jar. Determine the probability that the next ball selected will be green. $\frac{1}{6}$

You roll a 12-sided polyhedron with the numbers 1–12 on its congruent faces. Determine the probability of each outcome.

7. rolling a 2 $\frac{1}{12}$
8. rolling a 4 or a 5 $\frac{1}{6}$
9. rolling an even number $\frac{1}{2}$
10. rolling an odd number $\frac{1}{2}$
11. rolling a prime number $\frac{5}{12}$
12. rolling a factor of 8 $\frac{1}{3}$

A coin is flipped three times. Determine the probability of each outcome.

13. exactly two tails $\frac{3}{8}$
14. two heads and one tail $\frac{3}{8}$
15. no more than two tails $\frac{7}{8}$
16. no more than one head $\frac{1}{2}$
17. at least one tail $\frac{7}{8}$
18. all tails or all heads $\frac{1}{4}$

Tables

Table 1 Reading Math Symbols

. . .	and so on	p. 4
=	is equal to, equality	p. 4
×, ·	times (multiplication)	p. 4
n^2	square of n	p. 4
+	plus (addition)	p. 5
$-a$	opposite of a	p. 6
$\overline{AB}$	segment with endpoints A and B	p. 7
$\overrightarrow{AB}$	ray with endpoint A and through point B	p. 7
°	degree(s)	p. 7
( )	parentheses for grouping	p. 8
−	minus (subtraction)	p. 10
$\overleftrightarrow{AB}$	line through points A and B	p. 11
∥	is parallel to	p. 18
AB	length of $\overline{AB}$	p. 25
$|a|$	absolute value of a	p. 25
≅	is congruent to	p. 25
∠A	angle with vertex A	p. 27
∠ABC	angle with sides $\overrightarrow{BA}$ and $\overrightarrow{BC}$	p. 27
$m\angle A$	measure of angle A	p. 27
⌐	right angle symbol	p. 28
⊥	is perpendicular to	p. 35
d	distance	p. 43
(a, b)	ordered pair with x-coordinate a and y-coordinate b	p. 43
A	area	p. 52
s	length of a side	p. 52
b	base length	p. 52
h	height	p. 52
≈	is approximately equal to	p. 52
d	diameter	p. 52
r	radius	p. 52
P	perimeter	p. 52
π	pi, ratio of the circumference of a circle to its diameter	p. 52
C	circumference	p. 52
{ }	set brackets	p. 68
→	maps to	p. 71
>	is greater than	p. 73
<	is less than	p. 73
↔	if and only if	p. 76
≠	is not equal to	p. 90
△	angles	p. 121
△ABC	triangle with vertices A, B, and C	p. 132

n-gon	polygon with n sides	p. 144
m	slope of a linear function	p. 152
b	y-intercept of a linear function	p. 152
[ ]	brackets for grouping	p. 154
≇	is not congruent to	p. 200
△	triangles	p. 220
~	not	p. 265
≥	is greater than or equal to	p. 272
≤	is less than or equal to	p. 272
≯	is not greater than	p. 275
≮	is not less than	p. 275
□$ABCD$	parallelogram with vertices A, B, C, and D	p. 294
▱	parallelograms	p. 294
$\sqrt{x}$	nonnegative square root of x	p. 355
≟	Is this statement true?	p. 359
b_1, b_2	bases of a trapezoid	p. 374
d_1, d_2	lengths of diagonals	p. 375
a	apothem	p. 381
⊙A	circle with center A	p. 386
%	percent	p. 386
$\overarc{AB}$	arc with endpoints A and B	p. 387
$\overarc{ABC}$	arc with endpoints A and C and containing B	p. 387
$m\overarc{AB}$	measure of $\overarc{AB}$	p. 387
P(event)	probability of the event	p. 402
$a : b, \frac{a}{b}$	ratio of a to b	p. 416
±	plus or minus	p. 422
~	is similar to	p. 423
A'	image of A, A prime	p. 432
$\tan A$	tangent of ∠A	p. 470
$\sin A$	sine of ∠A	p. 477
$\cos A$	cosine of ∠A	p. 477
$\overrightarrow{AB}$	vector with initial point A and terminal point B	p. 490
$\langle x, y \rangle$	ordered pair notation for a vector	p. 490
$\vec{v}$	vector $\mathbf{v}$	p. 492
B	area of a base	p. 529
h	length of an altitude	p. 529
L.A.	lateral area	p. 529
S.A.	surface area	p. 529
ℓ	slant height	p. 537
V	volume	p. 544
$\begin{bmatrix} 1 & 2 \\ 3 & 4 \end{bmatrix}$	matrix	p. 640

Tables **725**

Table 2 Formulas

$P = 4s$
$A = s^2$

Square

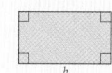

$P = 2b + 2h$
$A = bh$

Rectangle

$A = bh$

Parallelogram

$A = \frac{1}{2}bh$

Triangle

$A = \frac{1}{2}h(b_1 + b_2)$

Trapezoid

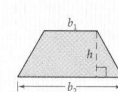

$A = \frac{1}{2}ap$

Regular Polygon

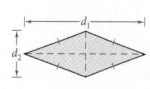

$A = \frac{1}{2}d_1 d_2$

Rhombus

$m\angle A + m\angle B + m\angle C = 180$

Triangle Angle Sum

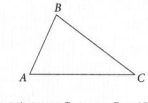

$a^2 + b^2 = c^2$

Pythagorean Theorem

$x\sqrt{2}$

Ratio of sides = $1 : 1 : \sqrt{2}$

45°-45°-90° Triangle

$x\sqrt{3}$, $2x$

Ratio of sides = $1 : \sqrt{3} : 2$

30°-60°-90° Triangle

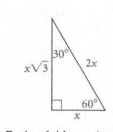

$\tan A = \frac{a}{b}$
$\sin A = \frac{a}{c}$ $\cos A = \frac{b}{c}$

Trigonometric Ratios

726 Tables

$C = \pi d$ or $C = 2\pi r$
$A = \pi r^2$

Circle

Length of $\overarc{AB} = \frac{m\overarc{AB}}{360} \cdot 2\pi r$

Arc

Area of sector $AOB = \frac{m\overarc{AB}}{360} \cdot \pi r^2$

Sector of a Circle

$r^2 = (x - h)^2 + (y - k)^2$

Equation of Circle

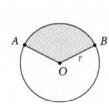

$d = \sqrt{(x_2 - x_1)^2 + (y_2 - y_1)^2}$
$M = \left(\frac{x_1 + x_2}{2}, \frac{y_1 + y_2}{2} \right)$

Distance and Midpoint

$m = \frac{\text{rise}}{\text{run}} = \frac{y_2 - y_1}{x_2 - x_1}$

Slope

$y = mx + b$

Slope-intercept Form of a Linear Equation

L.A. $= ph$
S.A. $=$ L.A. $+ 2B$
$V = Bh$

Right Prism

L.A. $= 2\pi rh$ or L.A. $= \pi dh$
S.A. $=$ L.A. $+ 2B$
$V = Bh$ or $V = \pi r^2 h$

Right Cylinder

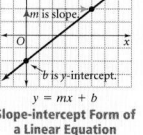

L.A. $= \frac{1}{2} p\ell$
S.A. $=$ L.A. $+ B$
$V = \frac{1}{3} Bh$

Regular Pyramid

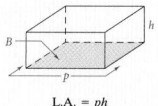

L.A. $= \pi r \ell$
S.A. $=$ L.A. $+ B$
$V = \frac{1}{3} Bh$ or $V = \frac{1}{3} \pi r^2 h$

Right Cone

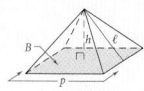

S.A. $= 4\pi r^2$
$V = \frac{4}{3} \pi r^3$

Sphere

Tables **727**

Table 3 Measures

United States Customary	Metric
Length	
12 inches (in.) = 1 foot (ft)	10 millimeters (mm) = 1 centimeter (cm)
36 in. = 1 yard (yd)	100 cm = 1 meter (m)
3 ft = 1 yard	1000 mm = 1 meter
5280 ft = 1 mile (mi)	1000 m = 1 kilometer (km)
1760 yd = 1 mile	
Area	
144 square inches (in.^{2}) = 1 square foot (ft^2)	100 square millimeters (mm^2) = 1 square centimeter (cm^2)
9 ft^2 = 1 square yard (yd^2)	10,000 cm^2 = 1 square meter (m^2)
43,560 ft^2 = 1 acre	10,000 m^2 = 1 hectare (ha)
4840 yd^2 = 1 acre	
Volume	
1728 cubic inches (in.^{3}) = 1 cubic foot (ft^3)	1000 cubic millimeters (mm^3) = 1 cubic centimeter (cm^3)
27 ft^3 = 1 cubic yard (yd^3)	1,000,000 cm^3 = 1 cubic meter (m^3)
Liquid Capacity	
8 fluid ounces (fl oz) = 1 cup (c)	1000 milliliters (mL) = 1 liter (L)
2 c = 1 pint (pt)	1000 L = 1 kiloliter (kL)
2 pt = 1 quart (qt)	
4 qt = 1 gallon (gal)	
Weight or Mass	
16 ounces (oz) = 1 pound (lb)	1000 milligrams (mg) = 1 gram (g)
2000 pounds = 1 ton (t)	1000 g = 1 kilogram (kg)
	1000 kg = 1 metric ton
Temperature	
32°F = freezing point of water	0°C = freezing point of water
98.6°F = normal body temperature	37°C = normal body temperature
212°F = boiling point of water	100°C = boiling point of water

Time	
60 seconds (s) = 1 minute (min)	365 days = 1 year (yr)
60 minutes = 1 hour (h)	52 weeks (approx.) = 1 year
24 hours = 1 day (d)	12 months = 1 year
7 days = 1 week (wk)	10 years = 1 decade
4 weeks (approx.) = 1 month (mo)	100 years = 1 century

728 Tables

Table 4 Properties of Real Numbers

Unless otherwise stated, a, b, c, and d are real numbers.

Identity Properties

Addition $\quad\quad\quad a + 0 = a$ and $0 + a = a$

Multiplication $\quad\quad a \cdot 1 = a$ and $1 \cdot a = a$

Commutative Properties

Addition $\quad\quad\quad a + b = b + a$

Multiplication $\quad\quad a \cdot b = b \cdot a$

Associative Properties

Addition $\quad\quad\quad (a + b) + c = a + (b + c)$

Multiplication $\quad\quad (a \cdot b) \cdot c = a \cdot (b \cdot c)$

Inverse Properties

Addition

The sum of a number and its *opposite*, or *additive inverse*, is zero.

$a + (-a) = 0$ and $-a + a = 0$

Multiplication

The reciprocal, or multiplicative inverse, of a rational number $\frac{a}{b}$ is $\frac{b}{a}$ ($a, b \neq 0$).

$a \cdot \frac{1}{a} = 1$ and $\frac{1}{a} \cdot a = 1$ ($a \neq 0$)

Distributive Properties

$a(b + c) = ab + ac \quad\quad (b + c)a = ba + ca$

$a(b - c) = ab - ac \quad\quad (b - c)a = ba - ca$

Properties of Equality

Addition $\quad\quad$ If $a = b$, then $a + c = b + c$.

Subtraction $\quad\;$ If $a = b$, then $a - c = b - c$.

Multiplication $\;$ If $a = b$, then $a \cdot c = b \cdot c$.

Division $\quad\quad$ If $a = b$ and $c \neq 0$, then $\frac{a}{c} = \frac{b}{c}$.

Substitution $\;\;$ If $a = b$, then b can replace a in any expression.

Reflexive $\quad\quad a = a$

Symmetric $\quad\;$ If $a = b$, then $b = a$.

Transitive $\quad\;\;$ If $a = b$ and $b = c$, then $a = c$.

Properties of Proportions

$\frac{a}{b} = \frac{c}{d}$ ($a, b, c, d \neq 0$) is equivalent to

(1) $ad = bc$ $\quad\quad$ (2) $\frac{b}{a} = \frac{d}{c}$

(3) $\frac{a}{c} = \frac{b}{d}$ $\quad\quad$ (4) $\frac{a + b}{b} = \frac{c + d}{d}$

Zero-Product Property

If $ab = 0$, then $a = 0$ or $b = 0$.

Properties of Inequality

Addition $\quad\quad$ If $a > b$ and $c \geq d$, then $a + c > b + d$.

Multiplication $\;$ If $a > b$ and $c > 0$, then $ac > bc$.
If $a > b$ and $c < 0$, then $ac < bc$.

Transitive $\quad\;\;$ If $a > b$ and $b > c$, then $a > c$.

Comparison $\;\;$ If $a = b + c$ and $c > 0$, then $a > b$.

Properties of Exponents

For any nonzero numbers a and b, any positive number c, and any integers m and n,

Zero Exponent $\quad\quad a^0 = 1$

Negative Exponent $\quad a^{-n} = \frac{1}{a^n}$

Product of Powers $\quad a^m \cdot a^n = a^{m+n}$

Quotient of Powers $\quad \frac{a^m}{a^n} = a^{m-n}$

Power to a Power $\quad (c^m)^n = c^{mn}$

Product to a Power $\quad (ab)^n = a^n b^n$

Quotient to a Power $\quad \left(\frac{a}{b}\right)^n = \frac{a^n}{b^n}$

Properties of Square Roots

For any nonnegative numbers a and b, and any positive number c,

Product of Square Roots $\quad \sqrt{a} \cdot \sqrt{b} = \sqrt{ab}$

Quotient of Square Roots $\quad \frac{\sqrt{a}}{\sqrt{c}} = \sqrt{\frac{a}{c}}$

Table 5 Squares and Square Roots

Number n	Square n^2	Positive Square Root $\sqrt{n}$	Number n	Square n^2	Positive Square Root $\sqrt{n}$	Number n	Square n^2	Positive Square Root $\sqrt{n}$
1	1	1.000	51	2601	7.141	101	10,201	10.050
2	4	1.414	52	2704	7.211	102	10,404	10.100
3	9	1.732	53	2809	7.280	103	10,609	10.149
4	16	2.000	54	2916	7.348	104	10,816	10.198
5	25	2.236	55	3025	7.416	105	11,025	10.247
6	36	2.449	56	3136	7.483	106	11,236	10.296
7	49	2.646	57	3249	7.550	107	11,449	10.344
8	64	2.828	58	3364	7.616	108	11,664	10.392
9	81	3.000	59	3481	7.681	109	11,881	10.440
10	100	3.162	60	3600	7.746	110	12,100	10.488
11	121	3.317	61	3721	7.810	111	12,321	10.536
12	144	3.464	62	3844	7.874	112	12,544	10.583
13	169	3.606	63	3969	7.937	113	12,769	10.630
14	196	3.742	64	4096	8.000	114	12,996	10.677
15	225	3.873	65	4225	8.062	115	13,225	10.724
16	256	4.000	66	4356	8.124	116	13,456	10.770
17	289	4.123	67	4489	8.185	117	13,689	10.817
18	324	4.243	68	4624	8.246	118	13,924	10.863
19	361	4.359	69	4761	8.307	119	14,161	10.909
20	400	4.472	70	4900	8.367	120	14,400	10.954
21	441	4.583	71	5041	8.426	121	14,641	11.000
22	484	4.690	72	5184	8.485	122	14,884	11.045
23	529	4.796	73	5329	8.544	123	15,129	11.091
24	576	4.899	74	5476	8.602	124	15,376	11.136
25	625	5.000	75	5625	8.660	125	15,625	11.180
26	676	5.099	76	5776	8.718	126	15,876	11.225
27	729	5.196	77	5929	8.775	127	16,129	11.269
28	784	5.292	78	6084	8.832	128	16,384	11.314
29	841	5.385	79	6241	8.888	129	16,641	11.358
30	900	5.477	80	6400	8.944	130	16,900	11.402
31	961	5.568	81	6561	9.000	131	17,161	11.446
32	1024	5.657	82	6724	9.055	132	17,424	11.489
33	1089	5.745	83	6889	9.110	133	17,689	11.533
34	1156	5.831	84	7056	9.165	134	17,956	11.576
35	1225	5.916	85	7225	9.220	135	18,225	11.619
36	1296	6.000	86	7396	9.274	136	18,496	11.662
37	1369	6.083	87	7569	9.327	137	18,769	11.705
38	1444	6.164	88	7744	9.381	138	19,044	11.747
39	1521	6.245	89	7921	9.434	139	19,321	11.790
40	1600	6.325	90	8100	9.487	140	19,600	11.832
41	1681	6.403	91	8281	9.539	141	19,881	11.874
42	1764	6.481	92	8464	9.592	142	20,164	11.916
43	1849	6.557	93	8649	9.644	143	20,449	11.958
44	1936	6.633	94	8836	9.695	144	20,736	12.000
45	2025	6.708	95	9025	9.747	145	21,025	12.042
46	2116	6.782	96	9216	9.798	146	21,316	12.083
47	2209	6.856	97	9409	9.849	147	21,609	12.124
48	2304	6.928	98	9604	9.899	148	21,904	12.166
49	2401	7.000	99	9801	9.950	149	22,201	12.207
50	2500	7.071	100	10,000	10.000	150	22,500	12.247

Table 6 Trigonometric Ratios

Angle	Sine	Cosine	Tangent	Angle	Sine	Cosine	Tangent
1°	0.0175	0.9998	0.0175	46°	0.7193	0.6947	1.0355
2°	0.0349	0.9994	0.0349	47°	0.7314	0.6820	1.0724
3°	0.0523	0.9986	0.0524	48°	0.7431	0.6691	1.1106
4°	0.0698	0.9976	0.0699	49°	0.7547	0.6561	1.1504
5°	0.0872	0.9962	0.0875	50°	0.7660	0.6428	1.1918
6°	0.1045	0.9945	0.1051	51°	0.7771	0.6293	1.2349
7°	0.1219	0.9925	0.1228	52°	0.7880	0.6157	1.2799
8°	0.1392	0.9903	0.1405	53°	0.7986	0.6018	1.3270
9°	0.1564	0.9877	0.1584	54°	0.8090	0.5878	1.3764
10°	0.1736	0.9848	0.1763	55°	0.8192	0.5736	1.4281
11°	0.1908	0.9816	0.1944	56°	0.8290	0.5592	1.4826
12°	0.2079	0.9781	0.2126	57°	0.8387	0.5446	1.5399
13°	0.2250	0.9744	0.2309	58°	0.8480	0.5299	1.6003
14°	0.2419	0.9703	0.2493	59°	0.8572	0.5150	1.6643
15°	0.2588	0.9659	0.2679	60°	0.8660	0.5000	1.7321
16°	0.2756	0.9613	0.2867	61°	0.8746	0.4848	1.8040
17°	0.2924	0.9563	0.3057	62°	0.8829	0.4695	1.8807
18°	0.3090	0.9511	0.3249	63°	0.8910	0.4540	1.9626
19°	0.3256	0.9455	0.3443	64°	0.8988	0.4384	2.0503
20°	0.3420	0.9397	0.3640	65°	0.9063	0.4226	2.1445
21°	0.3584	0.9336	0.3839	66°	0.9135	0.4067	2.2460
22°	0.3746	0.9272	0.4040	67°	0.9205	0.3907	2.3559
23°	0.3907	0.9205	0.4245	68°	0.9272	0.3746	2.4751
24°	0.4067	0.9135	0.4452	69°	0.9336	0.3584	2.6051
25°	0.4226	0.9063	0.4663	70°	0.9397	0.3420	2.7475
26°	0.4384	0.8988	0.4877	71°	0.9455	0.3256	2.9042
27°	0.4540	0.8910	0.5095	72°	0.9511	0.3090	3.0777
28°	0.4695	0.8829	0.5317	73°	0.9563	0.2924	3.2709
29°	0.4848	0.8746	0.5543	74°	0.9613	0.2756	3.4874
30°	0.5000	0.8660	0.5774	75°	0.9659	0.2588	3.7321
31°	0.5150	0.8572	0.6009	76°	0.9703	0.2419	4.0108
32°	0.5299	0.8480	0.6249	77°	0.9744	0.2250	4.3315
33°	0.5446	0.8387	0.6494	78°	0.9781	0.2079	4.7046
34°	0.5592	0.8290	0.6745	79°	0.9816	0.1908	5.1446
35°	0.5736	0.8192	0.7002	80°	0.9848	0.1736	5.6713
36°	0.5878	0.8090	0.7265	81°	0.9877	0.1564	6.3138
37°	0.6018	0.7986	0.7536	82°	0.9903	0.1392	7.1154
38°	0.6157	0.7880	0.7813	83°	0.9925	0.1219	8.1443
39°	0.6293	0.7771	0.8098	84°	0.9945	0.1045	9.5144
40°	0.6428	0.7660	0.8391	85°	0.9962	0.0872	11.4301
41°	0.6561	0.7547	0.8693	86°	0.9976	0.0698	14.3007
42°	0.6691	0.7431	0.9004	87°	0.9986	0.0523	19.0811
43°	0.6820	0.7314	0.9325	88°	0.9994	0.0349	28.6363
44°	0.6947	0.7193	0.9657	89°	0.9998	0.0175	57.2900
45°	0.7071	0.7071	1.0000	90°	1.0000	0.0000	

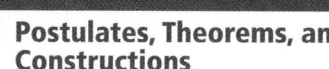

Postulates, Theorems, and Constructions

Chapter 1: Tools of Geometry

Postulate 1-1
Through any two points there is exactly one line. (p. 12)

Postulate 1-2
If two lines intersect, then they intersect in exactly one point. (p. 12)

Postulate 1-3
If two planes intersect, then they intersect in exactly one line. (p. 12)

Postulate 1-4
Through any three noncollinear points there is exactly one plane. (p. 13)

Postulate 1-5
Ruler Postulate
The points of a line can be put into one-to-one correspondence with the real numbers so that the distance between any two points is the absolute value of the difference of the corresponding numbers. (p. 25)

Postulate 1-6
Segment Addition Postulate
If three points A, B, and C are collinear and B is between A and C, then $AB + BC = AC$. (p. 26)

Postulate 1-7
Protractor Postulate
Let $\overrightarrow{OA}$ and $\overrightarrow{OB}$ be opposite rays in a plane. $\overrightarrow{OA}$, $\overrightarrow{OB}$, and all the rays with endpoint O that can be drawn on one side of $\overrightarrow{AB}$ can be paired with the real numbers from 0 to 180 so that
a. $\overrightarrow{OA}$ is paired with 0 and $\overrightarrow{OB}$ is paired with 180.
b. If $\overrightarrow{OC}$ is paired with x and $\overrightarrow{OD}$ is paired with y, then $m\angle COD = |x - y|$. (p. 28)

Postulate 1-8
Angle Addition Postulate
If point B is in the interior of $\angle AOC$, then $m\angle AOB + m\angle BOC = m\angle AOC$.
If $\angle AOC$ is a straight angle, then $m\angle AOB + m\angle BOC = 180$. (p. 28)

The Distance Formula
The distance d between two points $A(x_1, y_1)$ and $B(x_2, y_2)$ is $d = \sqrt{(x_2 - x_1)^2 + (y_2 - y_1)^2}$. (p. 43)
• Proof on p. 362, Exercise 46

The Midpoint Formula
The coordinates of the midpoint M of $\overline{AB}$ with endpoints $A(x_1, y_1)$ and $B(x_2, y_2)$ are the following.
$M\left(\dfrac{x_1 + x_2}{2}, \dfrac{y_1 + y_2}{2}\right)$ (p. 45)

The Distance Formula (Three Dimensions)
In a three-dimensional coordinate system, the distance between two points (x_1, y_1, z_1) and (x_2, y_2, z_2) can be found using this extension of the Distance Formula.
$d = \sqrt{(x_2 - x_1)^2 + (y_2 - y_1)^2 + (z_2 - z_1)^2}$ (p. 48)

Postulate 1-9
If two figures are congruent, then their areas are equal. (p. 54)

Postulate 1-10
The area of a region is the sum of the areas of its nonoverlapping parts. (p. 54)

Chapter 2: Reasoning and Proof

Law of Detachment
If a conditional is true and its hypothesis is true, then its conclusion is true. In symbolic form: If $p \rightarrow q$ is a true statement and p is true, then q is true. (p. 83)

Law of Syllogism
If $p \rightarrow q$ and $q \rightarrow r$ are true statements, then $p \rightarrow r$ is a true statement. (p. 83)

Properties of Congruence
Reflexive Property
$\overline{AB} \cong \overline{AB}$ and $\angle A \cong \angle A$
Symmetric Property
If $\overline{AB} \cong \overline{CD}$, then $\overline{CD} \cong \overline{AB}$.
If $\angle A \cong \angle B$, then $\angle B \cong \angle A$.
Transitive Property
If $\overline{AB} \cong \overline{CD}$ and $\overline{CD} \cong \overline{EF}$, then $\overline{AB} \cong \overline{EF}$.
If $\angle A \cong \angle B$ and $\angle B \cong \angle C$, then $\angle A \cong \angle C$. (p. 91)

Theorem 2-1
Vertical Angles Theorem
Vertical angles are congruent. (p. 98)
• Proof on p. 98, Example 3

Theorem 2-2
Congruent Supplements Theorem
If two angles are supplements of the same angle (or of congruent angles), then the two angles are congruent. (p. 99)
• Proofs on p. 99; p. 102, Exercise 55

Theorem 2-3
Congruent Complements Theorem
If two angles are complements of the same angle (or of congruent angles), then the two angles are congruent. (p. 99)
• Proofs on p. 100, Exercise 19; p. 102, Exercise 56

Theorem 2-4
All right angles are congruent. (p. 99)
• Proof on p. 101, Exercise 31

Theorem 2-5
If two angles are congruent and supplementary, then each is a right angle. (p. 99)
• Proof on p. 101, Exercise 35

Chapter 3: Parallel and Perpendicular Lines

Postulate 3-1
Corresponding Angles Postulate
If a transversal intersects two parallel lines, then corresponding angles are congruent. (p. 116)

Theorem 3-1
Alternate Interior Angles Theorem
If a transversal intersects two parallel lines, then alternate interior angles are congruent. (p. 116)
• Proof on p. 117

Theorem 3-2
Same-Side Interior Angles Theorem
If a transversal intersects two parallel lines, then same-side interior angles are supplementary. (p. 116)
• Proof on p. 117, Example 3

Postulate 3-2
Converse of the Corresponding Angles Postulate
If two lines and a transversal form corresponding angles that are congruent, then the two lines are parallel. (p. 122)

Theorem 3-3
Converse of the Alternate Interior Angles Theorem
If two lines and a transversal form alternate interior angles that are congruent, then the two lines are parallel. (p. 123)
• Proof on p. 123, Example 1

Theorem 3-4
Converse of the Same-Side Interior Angles Theorem
If two lines and a transversal form same-side interior angles that are supplementary, then the two lines are parallel. (p. 123)
• Proofs on p. 126, Exercise 17 and p. 128, Exercise 47

Theorem 3-5
If two lines are parallel to the same line, then they are parallel to each other. (p. 124)
• Proof on p. 127, Exercise 26

Theorem 3-6
In a plane, if two lines are perpendicular to the same line, then they are parallel to each other. (p. 124)
• Proofs on p. 124, Example 3; p. 126, Exercise 16

Theorem 3-7
Triangle Angle-Sum Theorem
The sum of the measures of the angles of a triangle is 180. (p. 131)
• Proof on p. 132

Theorem 3-8
Triangle Exterior Angle Theorem
The measure of each exterior angle of a triangle equals the sum of the measures of its two remote interior angles. (p. 133)
• Proof on p. 137, Exercise 49
Corollary
The measure of an exterior angle of a triangle is greater than the measure of either of its remote interior angles. (p. 274)
• Proof on p. 274

Parallel Postulate
Through a point not on a line, there is one and only one line parallel to a given line. (p. 140)

Spherical Geometry Parallel Postulate
Through a point not on a line, there is no line parallel to the given line. (p. 140)

Theorem 3-9
Polygon Angle-Sum Theorem
The sum of the measures of the angles of an n-gon is $(n - 2)180$. (p. 145)
• Proof on p. 149, Exercise 54

Theorem 3-10
Polygon Exterior Angle-Sum Theorem
The sum of the measures of the exterior angles of a polygon, one at each vertex, is 360. (p. 146)
• Proofs on p. 142 (using a computer) and p. 148, Exercise 46

Slopes of Parallel Lines
If two nonvertical lines are parallel, their slopes are equal. If the slopes of two distinct nonvertical lines are equal, the lines are parallel. Any two vertical lines are parallel. (p. 158)
• Proofs on p. 437, Exercises 42, 43

Slopes of Perpendicular Lines
If two nonvertical lines are perpendicular, the product of their slopes is -1. If the slopes of two lines have a product of -1, the lines are perpendicular. Any horizontal line and vertical line are perpendicular. (p. 159)
• Proofs on p. 329, Exercise 34 and p. 337, Exercise 41

Chapter 4: Congruent Triangles

Theorem 4-1
If the two angles of one triangle are congruent to two angles of another triangle, then the third angles are congruent. (p. 181)
• Proof on p. 184, Exercise 45

Postulate 4-1
Side-Side-Side (SSS) Postulate
If the three sides of one triangle are congruent to the three sides of another triangle, then the two triangles are congruent. (p. 187)

Postulate 4-2
Side-Angle-Side (SAS) Postulate
If two sides and the included angle of one triangle are congruent to two sides and the included angle of another triangle, then the two triangles are congruent. (p. 188)

Postulate 4-3
Angle-Side-Angle (ASA) Postulate
If two angles and the included side of one triangle are congruent to two angles and the included side of another triangle, then the two triangles are congruent. (p. 195)

Theorem 4-2
Angle-Angle-Side (AAS) Theorem
If two angles and a nonincluded side of one triangle are congruent to two angles and the corresponding nonincluded side of another triangle, then the triangles are congruent. (p. 195)
• Proof on p. 196

Theorem 4-3
Isosceles Triangle Theorem
If two sides of a triangle are congruent, then the angles opposite those sides are congruent. (p. 211)
• Proofs on p. 211, Example 1; p. 213, Exercise 2
Corollary
If a triangle is equilateral, then the triangle is equiangular. (p. 212)
• Proof on p. 215, Exercise 32

Theorem 4-4
Converse of the Isosceles Triangle Theorem
If two angles of a triangle are congruent, then the sides opposite the angles are congruent. (p. 211)
• Proofs on p. 211, Question 1; p. 213, Exercise 1
Corollary
If a triangle is equiangular, then the triangle is equilateral. (p. 212)
• Proof on p. 215, Exercise 32

Theorem 4-5
The bisector of the vertex angle of an isosceles triangle is the perpendicular bisector of the base. (p. 211)
• Proof on p. 215, Exercise 41

Theorem 4-6
Hypotenuse-Leg (HL) Theorem
If the hypotenuse and a leg of one right triangle are congruent to the hypotenuse and a leg of another right triangle, then the triangles are congruent. (p. 217)
• Proof on p. 217

Chapter 5: Relationships Within Triangles

Theorem 5-1
Triangle Midsegment Theorem
If a segment joins the midpoints of two sides of a triangle, then the segment is parallel to the third side, and is half its length. (p. 244)
• Proof on p. 244

Theorem 5-2
Perpendicular Bisector Theorem
If a point is on the perpendicular bisector of a segment, then it is equidistant from the endpoints of the segment. (p. 249)
• Proof on p. 253, Exercise 41

Theorem 5-3
Converse of the Perpendicular Bisector Theorem
If a point is equidistant from the endpoints of a segment, then it is on the perpendicular bisector of the segment. (p. 249)
• Proof on p. 253, Exercise 42

Theorem 5-4
Angle Bisector Theorem
If a point is on the bisector of an angle, then the point is equidistant from the sides of the angle. (p. 250)
• Proof on p. 253, Exercise 48

Theorem 5-5
Converse of the Angle Bisector Theorem
If a point in the interior of an angle is equidistant from the sides of the angle, then the point is on the angle bisector. (p. 250)
• Proof on p. 254, Exercise 49

Theorem 5-6
The perpendicular bisectors of the sides of a triangle are concurrent at a point equidistant from the vertices. (p. 257)
• Proof on p. 261, Exercise 30

Theorem 5-7
The bisectors of the angles of a triangle are concurrent at a point equidistant from the sides. (p. 257)
• Proof on p. 261, Exercise 31

Theorem 5-8
The medians of a triangle are concurrent at a point that is two thirds the distance from each vertex to the midpoint of the opposite side. (p. 258)
• Proof on p. 336, Exercise 39

Theorem 5-9
The lines that contain the altitudes of a triangle are concurrent. (p. 259)
• Proof on p. 336, Exercise 40

Comparison Property of Inequality
If $a = b + c$ and $c > 0$, then $a > b$. (p. 273)
• Proof on p. 273

Theorem 5-10
If two sides of a triangle are not congruent, then the larger angle lies opposite the longer side. (p. 274)
• Proof on p. 278, Exercise 33

Theorem 5-11
If two angles of a triangle are not congruent, then the longer side lies opposite the larger angle. (p. 275)
• Proof on p. 275

Theorem 5-12
Triangle Inequality Theorem
The sum of the lengths of any two sides of a triangle is greater than the length of the third side. (p. 276)
• Proof on p. 278, Exercise 40

Chapter 6: Quadrilaterals

Theorem 6-1
Opposite sides of a parallelogram are congruent. (p. 294)
• Proofs on p. 294; p. 299, Exercise 36

Theorem 6-2
Opposite angles of a parallelogram are congruent. (p. 295)
• Proofs on p. 299, Exercises 37, 38

Theorem 6-3
The diagonals of a parallelogram bisect each other. (p. 296)
• Proofs on p. 296; p. 334, Exercise 2

Theorem 6-4
If three (or more) parallel lines cut off congruent segments on one transversal, then they cut off congruent segments on every transversal. (p. 297)
• Proof on p. 300, Exercise 55

Theorem 6-5
If the diagonals of a quadrilateral bisect each other, then the quadrilateral is a parallelogram. (p. 304)
• Proof on p. 304

Theorem 6-6
If one pair of opposite sides of a quadrilateral are both congruent and parallel, then the quadrilateral is a parallelogram. (p. 304)
• Proof on p. 307, Exercise 17

Theorem 6-7
If both pairs of opposite sides of a quadrilateral are congruent, then the quadrilateral is a parallelogram. (p. 305)
• Proof on p. 305

Theorem 6-8
If both pairs of opposite angles of a quadrilateral are congruent, then the quadrilateral is a parallelogram. (p. 305)
• Proof on p. 308, Exercise 19

Theorem 6-9
Each diagonal of a rhombus bisects two angles of the rhombus. (p. 312)
• Proof on p. 312

Theorem 6-10
The diagonals of a rhombus are perpendicular. (p. 313)
• Proof on p. 317, Exercise 54

Theorem 6-11
The diagonals of a rectangle are congruent. (p. 313)
- Proof on p. 313

Theorem 6-12
If one diagonal of a parallelogram bisects two angles of the parallelogram, then the parallelogram is a rhombus. (p. 314)
- Proof on p. 318, Exercise 61

Theorem 6-13
If the diagonals of a parallelogram are perpendicular, then the parallelogram is a rhombus. (p. 314)
- Proof on p. 318, Exercise 62

Theorem 6-14
If the diagonals of a parallelogram are congruent, then the parallelogram is a rectangle. (p. 314)
- Proof on p. 318, Exercise 63

Theorem 6-15
The base angles of an isosceles trapezoid are congruent. (p. 320)
- Proof on p. 324, Exercise 26

Theorem 6-16
The diagonals of an isosceles trapezoid are congruent. (p. 321)
- Proofs on p. 321; p. 334, Exercise 3

Theorem 6-17
The diagonals of a kite are perpendicular. (p. 322)
- Proof on p. 322

Theorem 6-18
(1) The midsegment of a trapezoid is parallel to the bases.
(2) The length of a midsegment of a trapezoid is half the sum of the lengths of the bases. (p. 332)
- Proof on p. 333, Question 1

Chapter 7: Area

Theorem 7-1
Area of a Rectangle
The area of a rectangle is the product of its base and height.
$A = bh$ (p. 349)

Theorem 7-2
Area of a Parallelogram
The area of a parallelogram is the product of a base and the corresponding height.
$A = bh$ (p. 349)

Theorem 7-3
Area of a Triangle
The area of a triangle is half the product of a base and the corresponding height.
$A = \frac{1}{2}bh$ (p. 350)

Theorem 7-4
Pythagorean Theorem
In a right triangle, the sum of the squares of the lengths of the legs is equal to the square of the length of the hypotenuse.
$a^2 + b^2 = c^2$ (p. 357)
- Proofs on p. 356; p. 363, Exercise 60; p. 379; p. 443, Exercise 38; p. 612, Exercise 36

Theorem 7-5
Converse of the Pythagorean Theorem
If the square of the length of one side of a triangle is equal to the sum of the squares of the lengths of the other two sides, then the triangle is a right triangle. (p. 359)
- Proof on p. 364, Exercise 70

Theorem 7-6
If the square of the length of the longest side of a triangle is greater than the sum of the squares of the lengths of the other two sides, the triangle is obtuse. (p. 360)

Theorem 7-7
If the square of the length of the longest side of a triangle is less than the sum of the squares of the lengths of the other two sides, the triangle is acute. (p. 360)

Theorem 7-8
45°-45°-90° Triangle Theorem
In a 45°-45°-90° triangle, both legs are congruent and the length of the hypotenuse is $\sqrt{2}$ times the length of a leg.
longer leg $= \sqrt{2} \cdot$ leg (p. 366)
- Proof on p. 366

Theorem 7-9
30°-60°-90° Triangle Theorem
In a 30°-60°-90° triangle, the length of the hypotenuse is twice the length of the shorter leg. The length of the longer leg is $\sqrt{3}$ times the length of the shorter leg.
hypotenuse $= 2 \cdot$ shorter leg
longer leg $= \sqrt{3} \cdot$ shorter leg (p. 367)
- Proof on p. 368

Theorem 7-10
Area of a Trapezoid
The area of a trapezoid is half the product of the height and the sum of the bases.
$A = \frac{1}{2}h(b_1 + b_2)$ (p. 374)

Theorem 7-11
Area of a Rhombus or a Kite
The area of a rhombus or a kite is half the product of the lengths of its diagonals.
$A = \frac{1}{2}d_1d_2$ (p. 375)
- Proof on p. 375

Theorem 7-12
Area of a Regular Polygon
The area of a regular polygon is half the product of the apothem and the perimeter.
$A = \frac{1}{2}ap$ (p. 381)

Postulate 7-1
Arc Addition Postulate
The measure of the arc formed by two adjacent arcs is the sum of the measures of the two arcs. (p. 387)

Theorem 7-13
Circumference of a Circle
The circumference of a circle is π times the diameter.
$C = \pi d$ or $C = 2\pi r$ (p. 388)

Theorem 7-14
Arc Length
The length of an arc of a circle is the product of the ratio $\frac{\text{measure of the arc}}{360}$ and the circumference of the circle.
length of $\overarc{AB} = \frac{m\overarc{AB}}{360} \cdot 2\pi r$ (p. 389)

Theorem 7-15
Area of a Circle
The area of a circle is the product of π and the square of the radius.
$A = \pi r^2$ (p. 396)

Theorem 7-16
Area of a Sector of a Circle
The area of a sector of a circle is the product of the ratio $\frac{\text{measure of the arc}}{360}$ and the area of the circle.
Area of sector $AOB = \frac{m\overarc{AB}}{360} \cdot \pi r^2$ (p. 396)

Chapter 8: Similarity

Postulate 8-1
Angle-Angle Similarity (AA ~) Postulate
If two angles of one triangle are congruent to two angles of another triangle, then the triangles are similar. (p. 432)

Theorem 8-1
Side-Angle-Side Similarity (SAS ~) Theorem
If an angle of one triangle is congruent to an angle of a second triangle, and the sides including the two angles are proportional, then the triangles are similar. (p. 433)
- Proof on p. 433

Theorem 8-2
Side-Side-Side Similarity (SSS ~) Theorem
If the corresponding sides of two triangles are proportional, then the triangles are similar. (p. 433)
- Proof on p. 433

Theorem 8-3
The altitude to the hypotenuse of a right triangle divides the triangle into two triangles that are similar to the original triangle and to each other. (p. 440)
- Proof on p. 440
  Corollary 1
  The length of the altitude to the hypotenuse of a right triangle is the geometric mean of the lengths of the segments of the hypotenuse. (p. 440)
  - Proof on p. 440
  Corollary 2
  The altitude to the hypotenuse of a right triangle separates the hypotenuse in such a way that the length of each leg of the triangle is the geometric mean of the length of the adjacent hypotenuse segment and the length of the hypotenuse. (p. 441)
  - Proof on p. 441

Theorem 8-4
Side-Splitter Theorem
If a line is parallel to one side of a triangle and intersects the other two sides, then it divides those sides proportionally. (p. 446)
- Proof on p. 446
  Corollary
  If three parallel lines intersect two transversals, then the segments intercepted on the transversals are proportional. (p. 447)
  - Proof on p. 450, Exercise 34
  Converse
  If a line divides two sides of a triangle proportionally, then it is parallel to the third side.
  - Proof on p. 451, Exercise 47

Theorem 8-5
Triangle-Angle-Bisector Theorem
If a ray bisects an angle of a triangle, then it divides the opposite side into two segments that are proportional to the other two sides of the triangle. (p. 448)
- Proof on p. 448

Theorem 8-6
Perimeters and Areas of Similar Figures
If the similarity ratio of two similar figures is $\frac{a}{b}$, then
(1) the ratio of their perimeters is $\frac{a}{b}$ and
(2) the ratio of their areas is $\frac{a^2}{b^2}$. (p. 455)

Chapter 9: Right Triangle Trigonometry

Theorem 9-1
Area of a Triangle Given SAS
The area of a triangle is one half the product of the lengths of two sides and the sine of the included angle.
Area of $\triangle ABC = \frac{1}{2}bc(\sin A)$ (p. 500)
- Proof on p. 499

Chapter 10: Surface Area and Volume

Theorem 10-1
Lateral and Surface Areas of a Prism
The lateral area of a right prism is the product of the perimeter of the base and the height.
L.A. $= ph$
The surface area of a right prism is the sum of the lateral area and the areas of the two bases.
S.A. $=$ L.A. $+ 2B$ (p. 530)

Theorem 10-2
Lateral and Surface Areas of a Cylinder
The lateral area of a right cylinder is the product of the circumference of the base and the height of the cylinder.
L.A. $= 2\pi rh$, or L.A. $= \pi dh$
The surface area of a right cylinder is the sum of the lateral area and the areas of the two bases.
S.A. $=$ L.A. $+ 2B$, or S.A. $= 2\pi rh + 2\pi r^2$ (p. 530)

Theorem 10-3
Lateral and Surface Areas of a Regular Pyramid
The lateral area of a regular pyramid is half the product of the perimeter of the base and the slant height.
L.A. $= \frac{1}{2}p\ell$

The surface area of a regular pyramid is the sum of the lateral area and the area of the base.
S.A. $=$ L.A. $+ B$ (p. 538)

Theorem 10-4
Lateral and Surface Areas of a Cone
The lateral area of a right cone is half the product of the circumference of the base and the slant height.
L.A. $= \frac{1}{2} \cdot 2\pi r\ell$, or L.A. $= \pi r\ell$
The surface area of a right cone is the sum of the lateral area and the area of the base.
S.A. $=$ L.A. $+ B$ (p. 539)

Theorem 10-5
Cavalieri's Principle
If two space figures have the same height and the same cross-sectional area at every level, then they have the same volume. (p. 545)

Theorem 10-6
Volume of a Prism
The volume of a prism is the product of the area of a base and the height of the prism.
$V = Bh$ (p. 545)

Theorem 10-7
Volume of a Cylinder
The volume of a cylinder is the product of the area of the base and the height of the cylinder.
$V = Bh$, or $V = \pi r^2h$ (p. 546)

Theorem 10-8
Volume of a Pyramid
The volume of a pyramid is one third the product of the area of the base and the height of the pyramid.
$V = \frac{1}{3}Bh$ (p. 552)

Theorem 10-9
Volume of a Cone
The volume of a cone is one third the product of the area of the base and the height of the cone.
$V = \frac{1}{3}Bh$, or $V = \frac{1}{3}\pi r^2h$ (p. 553)

Theorem 10-10
Surface Area of a Sphere
The surface area of a sphere is four times the product of π and the square of the radius of the sphere.
S.A. $= 4\pi r^2$ (p. 558)

Theorem 10-11
Volume of a Sphere
The volume of a sphere is four thirds the product of π and the cube of the radius of the sphere.
$V = \frac{4}{3}\pi r^3$ (p. 560)

Theorem 10-12
Areas and Volumes of Similar Solids
If the similarity ratio of two similar solids is $a : b$, then
(1) the ratio of their corresponding areas is $a^2 : b^2$, and
(2) the ratio of their volumes is $a^3 : b^3$. (p. 567)

Chapter 11: Circles

Theorem 11-1
If a line is tangent to a circle, then the line is perpendicular to the radius drawn to the point of tangency. (p. 583)
- Proof on p. 583

Theorem 11-2
If a line in the plane of a circle is perpendicular to a radius at its endpoint on the circle, then the line is tangent to the circle. (p. 584)
- Proof on p. 588, Exercise 38

Theorem 11-3
The two segments tangent to a circle from a point outside the circle are congruent. (p. 585)
- Proof on p. 588, Exercise 40

Theorem 11-4
Within a circle or in congruent circles
(1) Congruent central angles have congruent chords.
(2) Congruent chords have congruent arcs.
(3) Congruent arcs have congruent central angles. (p. 590)
- Proofs on p. 594, Exercises 23, 24; p. 595, Exercise 35

Theorem 11-5
Within a circle or in congruent circles
(1) Chords equidistant from the center are congruent.
(2) Congruent chords are equidistant from the center. (p. 591)
- Proofs on p. 591; p. 595, Exercise 37

Theorem 11-6
In a circle, a diameter that is perpendicular to a chord bisects the chord and its arcs. (p. 592)
- Proof on p. 594, Exercise 25

Theorem 11-7
In a circle, a diameter that bisects a chord (that is not a diameter) is perpendicular to the chord. (p. 592)
- Proof on p. 592

Theorem 11-8
In a circle, the perpendicular bisector of a chord contains the center of the circle. (p. 592)
- Proof on p. 595, Exercise 36

Theorem 11-9
Inscribed Angle Theorem
The measure of an inscribed angle is half the measure of its intercepted arc. (p. 599)
- Proofs on p. 599; p. 603, Exercises 40, 41
  Corollary 1
  Two inscribed angles that intercept the same arc are congruent. (p. 600)
  - Proof on p. 604, Exercise 42
  Corollary 2
  An angle inscribed in a semicircle is a right angle. (p. 600)
  - Proof on p. 604, Exercise 43
  Corollary 3
  The opposite angles of a quadrilateral inscribed in a circle are supplementary. (p. 600)
  - Proof on p. 604, Exercise 44

Theorem 11-10
The measure of an angle formed by a tangent and a chord is half the measure of the intercepted arc. (p. 600)
- Proof on p. 604, Exercise 45

Theorem 11-11
The measure of an angle formed by two lines that
(1) intersect inside a circle is half the sum of the measures of the intercepted arcs.
(2) intersect outside a circle is half the difference of the measures of the intercepted arcs. (p. 607)
- Proofs on p. 608; p. 612, Exercises 29, 30

Theorem 11-12
For a given point and circle, the product of the lengths of the two segments from the point to the circle is constant along any line through the point and circle. (p. 609)
- Proofs on p. 609; p. 612, Exercises 31–33

Theorem 11-13
An equation of a circle with center (h, k) and radius r is $(x - h)^2 + (y - k)^2 = r^2$. (p. 615)

Chapter 12: Transformations

Theorem 12-1
A translation or rotation is a composition of two reflections. (p. 654)

Theorem 12-2
A composition of reflections in two parallel lines is a translation. (p. 655)

Theorem 12-3
A composition of reflections in two intersecting lines is a rotation. (p. 655)

Theorem 12-4
Fundamental Theorem of Isometries
In a plane, one of two congruent figures can be mapped onto the other by a composition of at most three reflections. (p. 656)

Theorem 12-5
Isometry Classification Theorem
There are only four isometries. They are reflection, translation, rotation, and glide reflection. (p. 657)

Theorem 12-6
Every triangle tessellates. (p. 668)

Theorem 12-7
Every quadrilateral tessellates. (p. 668)

Constructions

Construction 1
Congruent Segments
Construct a segment congruent to a given segment. (p. 34)

Construction 2
Congruent Angles
Construct an angle congruent to a given angle. (p. 35)

Construction 3
Perpendicular Bisector
Construct the perpendicular bisector of a segment. (p. 36)

Construction 4
Angle Bisector
Construct the bisector of an angle. (p. 37)

Construction 5
Parallel Through a Point Not on a Line
Construct a line parallel to a given line and through a given point that is not on the line. (p. 165)

Construction 6
Perpendicular Through a Point on a Line
Construct the perpendicular to a given line at a given point on the line. (p. 166)

Construction 7
Perpendicular Through a Point Not on a Line
Construct the perpendicular to a given line through a given point not on the line. (p. 167)

Postulates & Theorems

English/Spanish Illustrated Glossary

A

EXAMPLES

Acute angle (p. 28) An acute angle is an angle whose measure is between 0 and 90.

Ángulo agudo (p. 28) Un ángulo agudo es un ángulo que mide entre 0 y 90 grados.

17°

Acute triangle (p. 133) An acute triangle has three acute angles.

Triángulo acutángulo (p. 133) Un triángulo acutángulo tiene los tres ángulos agudos.

75°
60° 45°

Adjacent angles (p. 96) Adjacent angles are two coplanar angles that have a common side and a common vertex but no common interior points.

Ángulos adyacentes (p. 96) Los ángulos adyacentes son dos ángulos coplanares que tienen un lado común y el mismo vértice, pero no tienen puntos interiores comunes.

∠1 and ∠2 are adjacent. ∠3 and ∠4 are *not* adjacent.

Adjacent arcs (p. 387) Adjacent arcs are on the same circle and have exactly one point in common.

Arcos adyacentes (p. 387) Los arcos adyacentes están en el mismo círculo y tienen exactamente un punto en común.

$\overset{\frown}{AB}$ and $\overset{\frown}{BC}$ are adjacent arcs.

Alternate interior angles (p. 115) Alternate interior angles are nonadjacent interior angles that lie on opposite sides of the transversal.

Ángulos alternos internos (p. 115) Dadas dos rectas y una transversal, los ángulos alternos internos son ángulos internos no adyacentes situados en lados opuestos de la transversal.

∠1 and ∠2 are alternate interior angles, as are ∠3 and ∠4.

Altitude *See* cone; cylinder; parallelogram; prism; pyramid; trapezoid; triangle.

Altura *Ver* cone; cylinder; parallelogram; prism; trapezoid; triangle.

Altitude of a triangle (p. 259) An altitude of a triangle is a perpendicular segment from a vertex to the line containing the side opposite that vertex.

Altura de un triángulo (p. 259) Una altura de un triángulo es el segmento perpendicular que va desde un vértice hasta la recta que contiene el lado opuesto a ese vértice.

Altitude

EXAMPLES

Angle (p. 27) An angle is formed by two rays with the same endpoint. The rays are the *sides* of the angle and the common endpoint is the *vertex* of the angle.

Ángulo (p. 27) Un ángulo está formado por dos rayos que convergen en un mismo punto llamado *vértice*. Los rayos son los *lados* del ángulo.

Vertex Side B
A Side C

This angle could be named ∠A, ∠BAC, or ∠CAB.

Angle bisector (p. 36) An angle bisector is a ray that divides an angle into two congruent angles.

Bisectriz de un ángulo (p. 36) La bisectriz de un ángulo es un rayo que divide al ángulo en dos ángulos congruentes.

$\overrightarrow{LN}$ bisects ∠KLM.
∠KLN ≅ ∠NLM.

Angle of elevation or depression (p. 482) An angle of elevation (depression) is the angle formed by a horizontal line and the line of sight to an object above (below) the horizontal line.

Ángulo de elevación o depresión (p. 482) Un ángulo de elevación (depresión) es el ángulo formado por una línea horizontal y la recta que va de esa línea a un objeto situado arriba (debajo) de ella.

Horizontal line
Angle of depression B
Angle of elevation
A Horizontal line

Apothem (p. 380) The apothem of a regular polygon is the distance from the center to a side.

Apotema (p. 380) La apotema de un polígono regular es la distancia desde el centro hasta un lado.

a ← Apothem

Arc *See* major arc; minor arc. *See also* arc length; measure of an arc; semicircle.

Arco *Ver* major arc; minor arc. *Ver también* arc length; measure of an arc; semicircle.

Arc length (p. 389) The length of an arc of a circle is the product of the ratio $\frac{\text{measure of the arc}}{360}$ and the circumference of the circle.

Longitud de un arco (p. 389) La longitud del arco de un círculo es el producto del cociente $\frac{\text{medida del arco}}{360}$ por la circunferencia del círculo.

D
60°
E
5

Length of $\overset{\frown}{DE} = \frac{60}{360} \cdot 2\pi(5) = \frac{5\pi}{3}$

Area (pp. 348–351, 373–375, 381, 396, 401) The area of a plane figure is the number of square units enclosed by the figure. A list of area formulas is on pp. 726–727.

Área (pp. 348–351, 373–375, 381, 396, 401) El área de una figura plana es de unidades cuadradas que contiene la figura. Una lista de fórmulas para calcular áreas está en las págs. 726–727.

The area of the rectangle is 12 square units, or 12 units².

EXAMPLES

Axes (p. 43) *See* coordinate plane.

Ejes (p. 43) *Ver* coordinate plane.

Axiom (p. 12) *See* postulate.

Axioma (p. 12) *Ver* postulate.

B

Base(s) *See* cone; cylinder; isosceles triangle; parallelogram; prism; pyramid; trapezium; triangle.

Base(s) *See* cone; cylinder; isosceles triangle; parallelogram; prism; pyramid; trapezium; triangle.

Base angles *See* isosceles trapezoid; isosceles triangle.

Ángulos de base *Ver* isosceles trapezoid; isosceles triangle.

Biconditional (p. 75) A biconditional statement is the combination of a conditional statement and its converse. A biconditional contains the words "if and only if."

Bicondicional (p. 75) Un enunciado bicondicional es la combinación de un enunciado condicional y su recíproco. El enunciado bicondicional incluye las palabras "si y solo si".

This biconditional statement is true: Two angles are congruent *if and only if* they have the same measure.

Bisector *See* segment bisector; angle bisector.

Bisectriz *Ver* segment bisector; angle bisector.

C

Center *See* circle; dilation; regular polygon; sphere.

Centro *Ver* circle; dilation; regular polygon; sphere.

Central angle of a circle (p. 386) A central angle of a circle is an angle whose vertex is the center of the circle.

Ángulo central de un círculo (p. 386) Un ángulo central de un círculo es un ángulo cuyo vértice es el centro del círculo.

O R
K

∠ROK is a central angle of ⊙O.

EXAMPLES

Central angle of a regular polygon (p. 498) A central angle of a regular polygon is an angle formed by two consecutive radii.

Ángulo central de un polígono regular (p. 498) Un ángulo central de un polígono regular es el ángulo formado por dos radios consecutivos.

F
E
G

∠EFG is a central angle of the regular pentagon.

Centroid (p. 258) The centroid of a triangle is the point of intersection of the medians of that triangle.

EXAMPLE *P* is the centroid of △ABC.

Centroide (p. 258) El centroide de un triángulo es el punto de intersección de las medianas del triángulo.

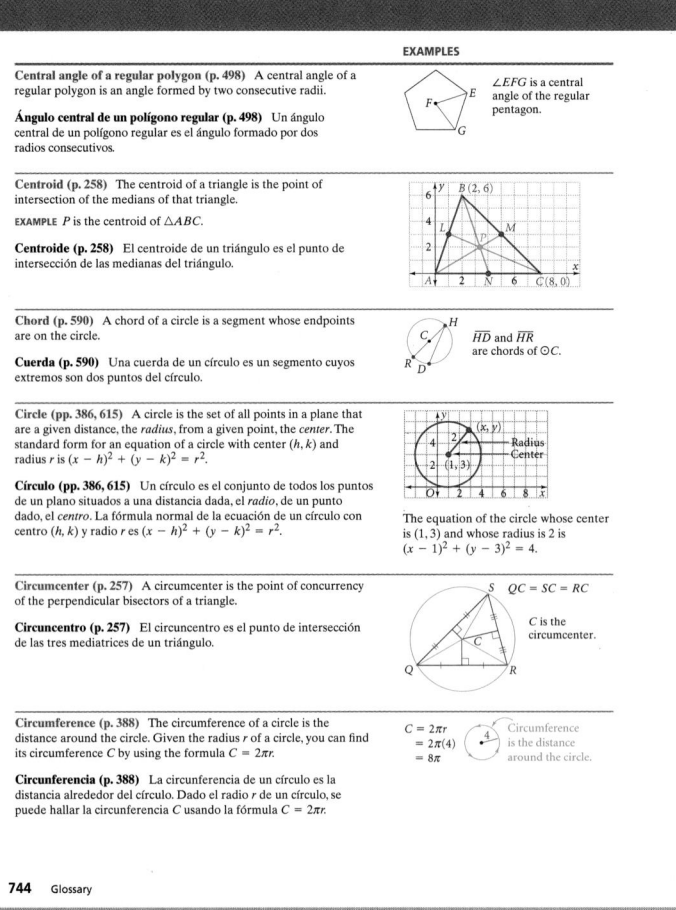

B (2, 6)
M
P
A N C (8, 0)

Chord (p. 590) A chord of a circle is a segment whose endpoints are on the circle.

Cuerda (p. 590) Una cuerda de un círculo es un segmento cuyos extremos son dos puntos del círculo.

C H
R
D

$\overline{HD}$ and $\overline{HR}$ are chords of ⊙C.

Circle (pp. 386, 615) A circle is the set of all points in a plane that are a given distance, the *radius*, from a given point, the *center*. The standard form for an equation of a circle with center (h, k) and radius r is $(x - h)^2 + (y - k)^2 = r^2$.

Círculo (pp. 386, 615) Un círculo es el conjunto de todos los puntos de un plano situados a una distancia dada, el *radio*, de un punto dado, el *centro*. La fórmula normal de la ecuación de un círculo con centro (h, k) y radio r es $(x - h)^2 + (y - k)^2 = r^2$.

(x, y)
Radius
Center
(1, 3)

The equation of the circle whose center is (1, 3) and whose radius is 2 is $(x - 1)^2 + (y - 3)^2 = 4$.

Circumcenter (p. 257) A circumcenter is the point of concurrency of the perpendicular bisectors of a triangle.

Circuncentro (p. 257) El circuncentro es el punto de intersección de las tres mediatrices de un triángulo.

S
QC = SC = RC
C
Q R

C is the circumcenter.

Circumference (p. 388) The circumference of a circle is the distance around the circle. Given the radius r of a circle, you can find its circumference C by using the formula $C = 2\pi r$.

Circunferencia (p. 388) La circunferencia de un círculo es la distancia alrededor del círculo. Dado el radio r de un círculo, se puede hallar la circunferencia C usando la fórmula $C = 2\pi r$.

$C = 2\pi r$
$= 2\pi(4)$
$= 8\pi$

Circumference is the distance around the circle.

Circumference of a sphere (p. 558) *See* sphere.

Circunferencia de una esfera (p. 558) *Ver* sphere.

Circumscribed about (pp. 257, 585) A circle is circumscribed about a polygon if the vertices of the polygon are on the circle. A polygon is circumscribed about a circle if all the sides of the polygon are tangent to the circle.

Circunscrito en (pp. 257, 585) Un círculo está circunscrito en un polígono si los vértices del polígono están en el círculo. Un polígono está circunscrito en un círculo si todos los lados del polígono son tangentes al círculo.

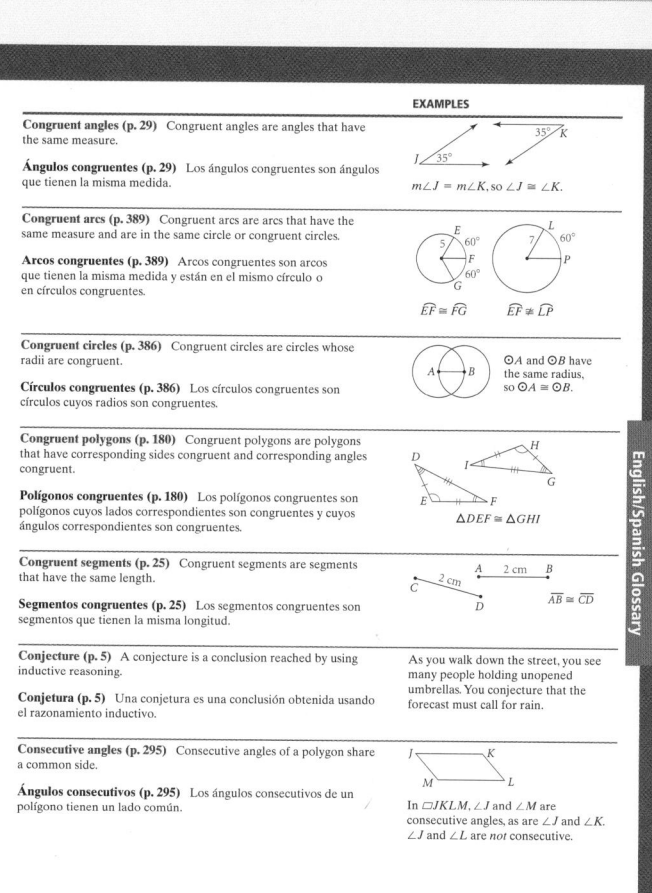

⊙*G* is circumscribed about *ABCD*.

△*XYZ* is circumscribed about ⊙*P*.

Collinear points (p. 11) Collinear points lie on the same line.

Puntos colineales (p. 11) Los puntos colineales son los que están sobre la misma recta.

Points *A*, *B*, and *C* are collinear, but points *A*, *B*, and *Z* are noncollinear.

Compass (p. 34) A compass is a geometric tool used to draw circles and parts of circles, called arcs.

Compás (p. 34) El compás es un instrumento usado para dibujar círculos y partes de círculos, llamados arcos.

Complementary angles (p. 96) Two angles are complementary angles if the sum of their measures is 90.

Ángulos complementarios (p. 96) Dos ángulos son complementarios si la suma de sus medidas es igual a 90.

∠*HKI* and ∠*IKJ* are complementary angles, as are ∠*HKI* and ∠*EFG*.

Composite space figures (p. 547) A composite space figure is the combination of two or more figures into one object.

Figuras geométricas compuestas (p. 547) Una figura geométrica compuesta es la combinación de dos o más figuras en un mismo objeto.

Composition of transformations (p. 642) A composition of two transformations is a transformation in which a second transformation is performed on the image of a first transformation.

Composición de transformaciones (p. 642) Una composición de dos transformaciones es una transformación en la cual una segunda transformación se realiza sobre la imagen de una primera.

If you reflect △*ABC* in line *m* to get △*A′B′C′* and then reflect △*A′B′C′* in line *n* to get △*A″B″C″*, you perform a composition of transformations.

Concave polygon (p. 144) *See* polygon.

Polígono cóncavo (p. 144) *Ver* polygon.

Concentric circles (p. 388) Concentric circles lie in the same plane and have the same center.

Círculos concéntricos (p. 388) Los círculos concéntricos están en el mismo plano y tienen el mismo centro.

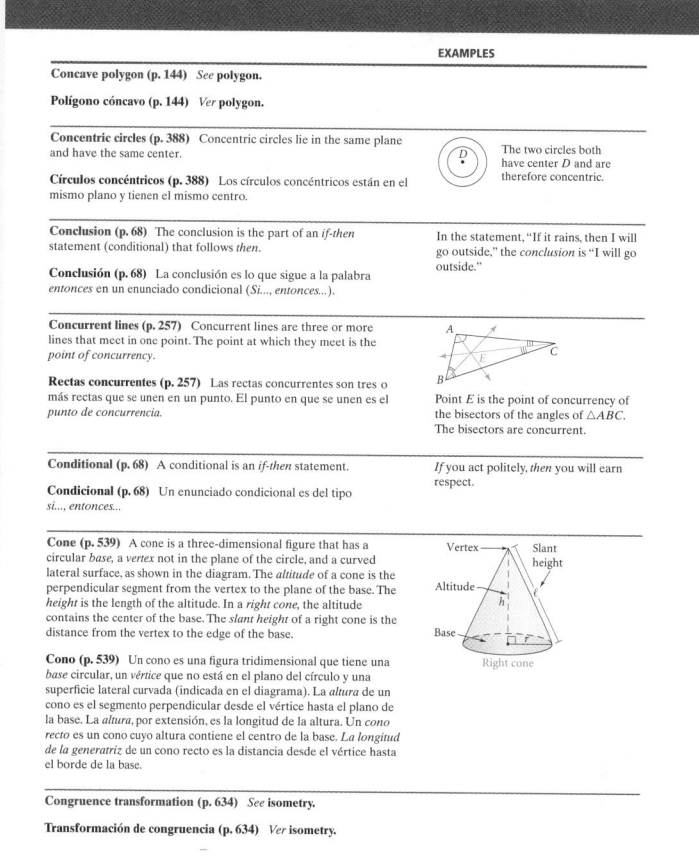

The two circles both have center *D* and are therefore concentric.

Conclusion (p. 68) The conclusion is the part of an *if-then* statement (conditional) that follows *then*.

Conclusión (p. 68) La conclusión es lo que sigue a la palabra *entonces* en un enunciado condicional (*Si..., entonces...*).

In the statement, "If it rains, then I will go outside," the *conclusion* is "I will go outside."

Conditional (p. 68) A conditional is an *if-then* statement.

Condicional (p. 68) Un enunciado condicional es del tipo *si..., entonces...*.

If you act politely, *then* you will earn respect.

Concurrent lines (p. 257) Concurrent lines are three or more lines that meet in one point. The point at which they meet is the *point of concurrency*.

Rectas concurrentes (p. 257) Las rectas concurrentes son tres o más rectas que se unen en un punto. El punto en que se unen es el *punto de concurrencia*.

Point *E* is the point of concurrency of the bisectors of the angles of △*ABC*. The bisectors are concurrent.

Cone (p. 539) A cone is a three-dimensional figure that has a circular *base*, a *vertex* not in the plane of the circle, and a curved lateral surface, as shown in the diagram. The *altitude* of a cone is the perpendicular segment from the vertex to the plane of the base. The *height* is the length of the altitude. In a *right cone*, the altitude contains the center of the base. The *slant height* of a right cone is the distance from the vertex to the edge of the base.

Cono (p. 539) Un cono es una figura tridimensional que tiene una *base* circular, un *vértice* que no está en el plano del círculo y una superficie lateral curvada (indicada en el diagrama). La *altura* de un cono es el segmento perpendicular desde el vértice hasta el plano de la base. La *altura*, por extensión, es la longitud de la altura. Un *cono recto* es un cono cuya altura contiene el centro de la base. *La longitud de la generatriz* de un cono recto es la distancia desde el vértice hasta el borde de la base.

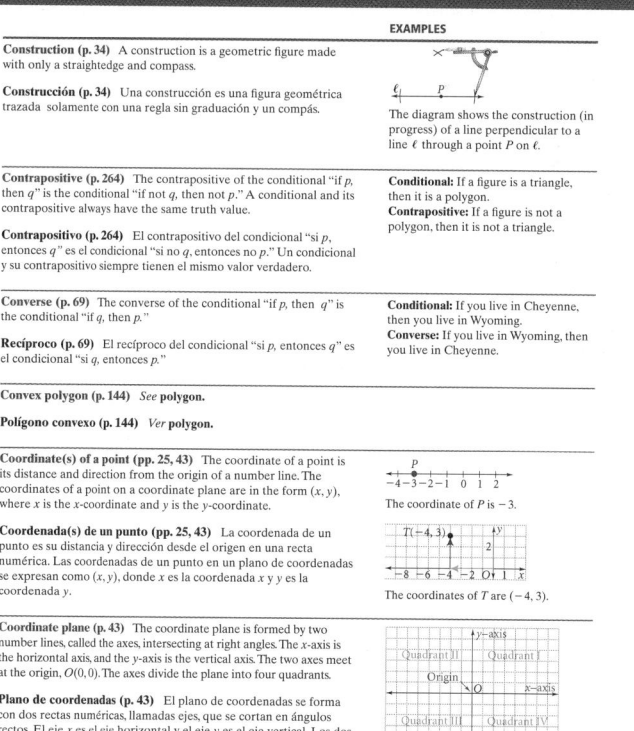

Right cone

Congruence transformation (p. 634) *See* isometry.

Transformación de congruencia (p. 634) *Ver* isometry.

Congruent angles (p. 29) Congruent angles are angles that have the same measure.

Ángulos congruentes (p. 29) Los ángulos congruentes son ángulos que tienen la misma medida.

$m\angle J = m\angle K$, so $\angle J \cong \angle K$.

Congruent arcs (p. 389) Congruent arcs are arcs that have the same measure and are in the same circle or congruent circles.

Arcos congruentes (p. 389) Arcos congruentes son arcos que tienen la misma medida y están en el mismo círculo o en círculos congruentes.

$\overarc{EF} \cong \overarc{FG}$ $\overarc{EF} \cong \overarc{LP}$

Congruent circles (p. 386) Congruent circles are circles whose radii are congruent.

Círculos congruentes (p. 386) Los círculos congruentes son círculos cuyos radios son congruentes.

⊙*A* and ⊙*B* have the same radius, so ⊙*A* ≅ ⊙*B*.

Congruent polygons (p. 180) Congruent polygons are polygons that have corresponding sides congruent and corresponding angles congruent.

Polígonos congruentes (p. 180) Los polígonos congruentes son polígonos cuyos lados correspondientes son congruentes y cuyos ángulos correspondientes son congruentes.

△*DEF* ≅ △*GHI*

Congruent segments (p. 25) Congruent segments are segments that have the same length.

Segmentos congruentes (p. 25) Los segmentos congruentes son segmentos que tienen la misma longitud.

$\overline{AB} \cong \overline{CD}$

Conjecture (p. 5) A conjecture is a conclusion reached by using inductive reasoning.

Conjetura (p. 5) Una conjetura es una conclusión obtenida usando el razonamiento inductivo.

As you walk down the street, you see many people holding unopened umbrellas. You conjecture that the forecast must call for rain.

Consecutive angles (p. 295) Consecutive angles of a polygon share a common side.

Ángulos consecutivos (p. 295) Los ángulos consecutivos de un polígono tienen un lado común.

In ▱*JKLM*, ∠*J* and ∠*M* are consecutive angles, as are ∠*J* and ∠*K*. ∠*J* and ∠*L* are *not* consecutive.

Construction (p. 34) A construction is a geometric figure made with only a straightedge and compass.

Construcción (p. 34) Una construcción es una figura geométrica trazada solamente con una regla sin graduación y un compás.

The diagram shows the construction (in progress) of a line perpendicular to a line *ℓ* through a point *P* on *ℓ*.

Contrapositive (p. 264) The contrapositive of the conditional "if *p*, then *q*" is the conditional "if not *q*, then not *p*." A conditional and its contrapositive always have the same truth value.

Contrapositivo (p. 264) El contrapositivo del condicional "si *p*, entonces *q*" es el condicional "si no *q*, entonces no *p*." Un condicional y su contrapositivo siempre tienen el mismo valor verdadero.

Conditional: If a figure is a triangle, then it is a polygon.
Contrapositive: If a figure is not a polygon, then it is not a triangle.

Converse (p. 69) The converse of the conditional "if *p*, then *q*" is the conditional "if *q*, then *p*."

Recíproco (p. 69) El recíproco del condicional "si *p*, entonces *q*" es el condicional "si *q*, entonces *p*."

Conditional: If you live in Cheyenne, then you live in Wyoming.
Converse: If you live in Wyoming, then you live in Cheyenne.

Convex polygon (p. 144) *See* polygon.

Polígono convexo (p. 144) *Ver* polygon.

Coordinate(s) of a point (pp. 25, 43) The coordinate of a point is its distance and direction from the origin of a number line. The coordinates of a point on a coordinate plane are in the form (x, y), where x is the *x*-coordinate and y is the *y*-coordinate.

Coordenada(s) de un punto (pp. 25, 43) La coordenada de un punto es su distancia y dirección desde el origen en una recta numérica. Las coordenadas de un punto en un plano de coordenadas se expresan como (x, y), donde x es la coordenada x y y es la coordenada y.

The coordinate of *P* is −3.

The coordinates of *T* are (−4, 3).

Coordinate plane (p. 43) The coordinate plane is formed by two number lines, called the axes, intersecting at right angles. The *x*-axis is the horizontal axis, and the *y*-axis is the vertical axis. The two axes meet at the origin, $O(0, 0)$. The axes divide the plane into four quadrants.

Plano de coordenadas (p. 43) El plano de coordenadas se forma con dos rectas numéricas, llamadas ejes, que se cortan en ángulos rectos. El eje *x* es el eje horizontal y el eje *y* es el eje vertical. Los dos ejes se unen en el origen, $O(0, 0)$. Los ejes dividen el plano de coordenadas en cuatro cuadrantes.

English/Spanish Glossary

T731

Coordinate proof (p. 244) *See* **proof.**

Prueba de coordenadas (p. 244) *Ver* **proof.**

Coplanar figures (p. 11) Coplanar figures are figures in the same plane.

Figuras coplanares (p. 11) Las figuras coplanares son las figuras que estan localizados en el mismo plano.

Point C and $\overrightarrow{AB}$ are coplanar but points $A, B, C,$ and Q are noncoplanar.

Corollary (p. 212) A corollary is a statement that follows directly from a theorem.

Corolario (p. 212) Un corolario es un enunciado que procede directamente de un teorema.

Theorem: If two sides of a triangle are congruent, then the angles opposite those sides are congruent.
Corollary: If a triangle is equilateral, then it is equiangular.

Corresponding angles (p. 115) Corresponding angles lie on the same side of the transversal t and in corresponding positions relative to ℓ and m.

Ángulos correspondientes (p. 115) Los ángulos correspondientes están en el mismo lado de la transversal t y en las correspondientes posiciones relativas a ℓ y m.

$\angle 1$ and $\angle 2$ are corresponding angles, as are $\angle 3$ and $\angle 5, \angle 6,$ and $\angle 7$ and $\angle 8.$

Cosine ratio (p. 477) *See* **trigonometric ratios.**

Razón coseno (p. 477) *Ver* **trigonometric ratios.**

Counterexample (pp. 5, 69) A counterexample to a statement is a particular example or instance of the statement that makes the statement false.

Contraejemplo (pp. 5, 69) Un contraejemplo a un enunciado es un ejemplo particular o caso que demuestra que el enunciado no es verdadero.

Statement: If the name of a state begins with W, then that state does not border an ocean.
Counterexample: Washington

CPCTC (p. 203) CPCTC is an abbreviation for "corresponding parts of congruent triangles are congruent."
EXAMPLE By the SAS Congruence Postulate, $\triangle KLM \cong \triangle QPR.$ By CPCTC, you also know that $\angle L \cong \angle P, \angle M \cong \angle R,$ and $\overline{LM} \cong \overline{PR}.$

CPCTC (p. 203) CPCTC es una abreviatura para "partes correspondientes de triángulos congruentes son congruentes."

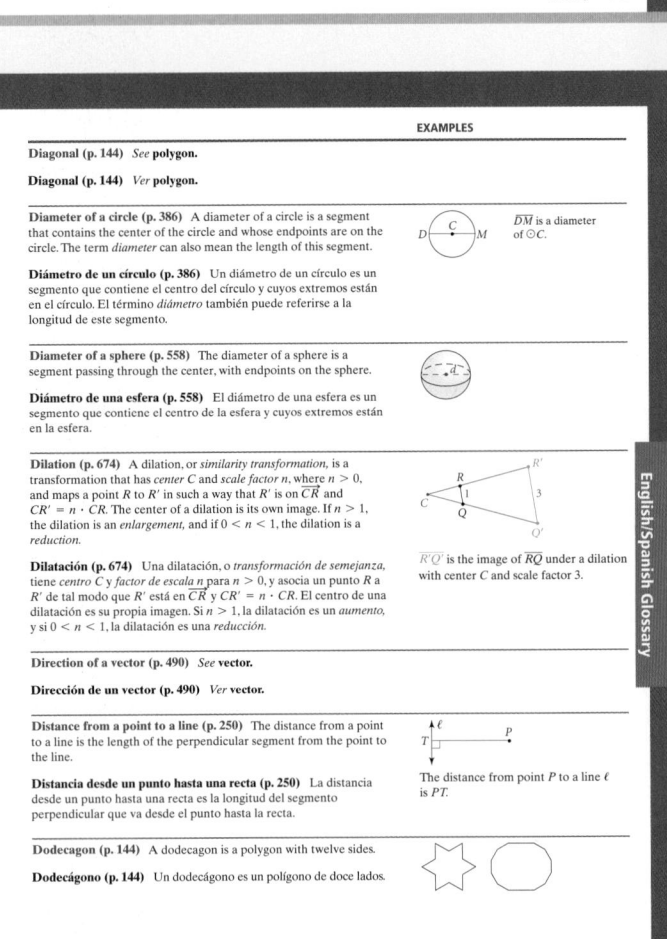

English/Spanish Glossary

Cross-Product Property (p. 417) The product of the extremes of a proportion is equal to the product of the means.

Propiedad del producto en equis (p. 417) El producto de los extremos de una proporción es igual al producto de los medios.

If $\frac{8}{3} = \frac{12}{21},$ then $21x = 3 \cdot 12.$

Cross section (p. 522) A cross section is the intersection of a solid and a plane.

Sección de corte (p. 522) Una sección de corte es la intersección de un plano y un sólido.

The cross section is a circle.

Cube (p. 512) A cube is a polyhedron with six faces, each of which is a square.

Cubo (p. 512) Un cubo es un poliedro de seis caras, cada una de las caras es un cuadrado.

Cylinder (p. 530) A cylinder is a three-dimensional figure with two congruent circular *bases* that lie in parallel planes. An *altitude* of a cylinder is a perpendicular segment that joins the planes of the bases. Its length is the *height* of the cylinder. In a *right cylinder*, the segment joining the centers of the bases is an altitude. In an *oblique cylinder*, the segment joining the centers of the bases is not perpendicular to the planes containing the bases.

Cilindro (p. 530) Un cilindro es una figura tridimensional con dos *bases* congruentes circulares en planos paralelos. Una *altura* de un cilindro es un segmento perpendicular que une los planos de las bases. Su longitud es, por extensión, la *altura* del cilindro. En un *cilindro recto*, el segmento que une los centros de las bases es una altura. En un *cilindro oblicuo*, el segmento que une los centros de las bases no es perpendicular a los planos que contienen las bases.

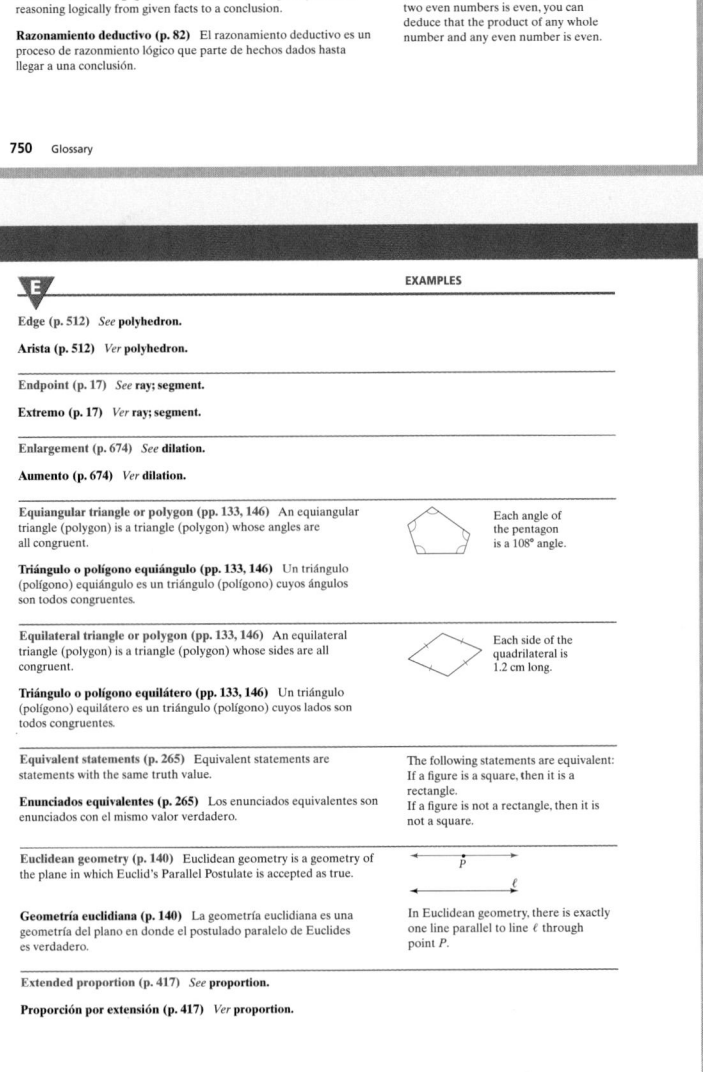

Right cylinder   Oblique cylinder

D

Decagon (p. 144) A decagon is a polygon with ten sides.

Decágono (p. 144) Un decágono es un polígono de diez lados.

Deductive reasoning (p. 82) Deductive reasoning is a process of reasoning logically from given facts to a conclusion.

Razonamiento deductivo (p. 82) El razonamiento deductivo es un proceso de razonamiento lógico que parte de hechos dados hasta llegar a una conclusión.

Based on the fact that the sum of any two even numbers is even, you can deduce that the product of any whole number and any even number is even.

Diagonal (p. 144) *See* **polygon.**

Diagonal (p. 144) *Ver* **polygon.**

Diameter of a circle (p. 386) A diameter of a circle is a segment that contains the center of the circle and whose endpoints are on the circle. The term *diameter* can also mean the length of this segment.

Diámetro de un círculo (p. 386) Un diámetro de un círculo es un segmento que contiene el centro del círculo y cuyos extremos están en el círculo. El término *diámetro* también puede referirse a la longitud de este segmento.

$\overline{DM}$ is a diameter of $\odot C.$

Diameter of a sphere (p. 558) The diameter of a sphere is a segment passing through the center, with endpoints on the sphere.

Diámetro de una esfera (p. 558) El diámetro de una esfera es un segmento que contiene el centro de la esfera y cuyos extremos están en la esfera.

Dilation (p. 674) A dilation, or *similarity transformation*, is a transformation that has *center C* and *scale factor n*, where $n > 0,$ and maps a point R to R' in such a way that R' is on $\overrightarrow{CR}$ and $CR' = n \cdot CR.$ The center of a dilation is its own image. If $n > 1,$ the dilation is an *enlargement*, and if $0 < n < 1,$ the dilation is a *reduction*.

Dilatación (p. 674) Una dilatación, o *transformación de semejanza*, tiene *centro C* y *factor de escala n* para $n > 0,$ y asocia un punto R a R' de tal modo que R' está en $\overrightarrow{CR}$ y $CR' = n \cdot CR.$ El centro de una dilatación es su propia imagen. Si $n > 1,$ la dilatación es un *aumento*, y si $0 < n < 1,$ la dilatación es una *reducción*.

$\overline{R'Q'}$ is the image of $\overline{RQ}$ under a dilation with center C and scale factor 3.

Direction of a vector (p. 490) *See* **vector.**

Dirección de un vector (p. 490) *Ver* **vector.**

Distance from a point to a line (p. 250) The distance from a point to a line is the length of the perpendicular segment from the point to the line.

Distancia desde un punto hasta una recta (p. 250) La distancia desde un punto hasta una recta es la longitud del segmento perpendicular que va desde el punto hasta la recta.

The distance from point P to a line ℓ is $PT.$

Dodecagon (p. 144) A dodecagon is a polygon with twelve sides.

Dodecágono (p. 144) Un dodecágono es un polígono de doce lados.

English/Spanish Glossary

E

Edge (p. 512) *See* **polyhedron.**

Arista (p. 512) *Ver* **polyhedron.**

Endpoint (p. 17) *See* **ray; segment.**

Extremo (p. 17) *Ver* **ray; segment.**

Enlargement (p. 674) *See* **dilation.**

Aumento (p. 674) *Ver* **dilation.**

Equiangular triangle or polygon (pp. 133, 146) An equiangular triangle (polygon) is a triangle (polygon) whose angles are all congruent.

Triángulo o polígono equiángulo (pp. 133, 146) Un triángulo (polígono) equiángulo es un triángulo (polígono) cuyos ángulos son todos congruentes.

Each angle of the pentagon is a 108° angle.

Equilateral triangle or polygon (pp. 133, 146) An equilateral triangle (polygon) is a triangle (polygon) whose sides are all congruent.

Triángulo o polígono equilátero (pp. 133, 146) Un triángulo (polígono) equilátero es un triángulo (polígono) cuyos lados son todos congruentes.

Each side of the quadrilateral is 1.2 cm long.

Equivalent statements (p. 265) Equivalent statements are statements with the same truth value.

Enunciados equivalentes (p. 265) Los enunciados equivalentes son enunciados con el mismo valor verdadero.

The following statements are equivalent:
If a figure is a square, then it is a rectangle.
If a figure is not a rectangle, then it is not a square.

Euclidean geometry (p. 140) Euclidean geometry is a geometry of the plane in which Euclid's Parallel Postulate is accepted as true.

Geometría euclidiana (p. 140) La geometría euclidiana es una geometría del plano en donde el postulado paralelo de Euclides es verdadero.

In Euclidean geometry, there is exactly one line parallel to line ℓ through point $P.$

Extended proportion (p. 417) *See* **proportion.**

Proporción por extensión (p. 417) *Ver* **proportion.**

Exterior angle of a polygon (p. 133) An exterior angle of a polygon is an angle formed by a side and an extension of an adjacent side.

Ángulo exterior de un polígono (p. 133) El ángulo exterior de un polígono es un ángulo formado por un lado y una extensión de un lado adyacente.

$\angle KLM$ is an exterior angle of $\triangle JKL$.

F

Face (p. 512) See **polyhedron.**

Cara (p. 512) Ver **polyhedron.**

Flip (p. 635) See **reflection.**

Flow proof (p. 123) See **proof.**

Prueba de flujo (p. 123) Ver **proof.**

Foundation drawing (p. 521) A foundation drawing shows the base of a structure and the height of each part.

Dibujo de fundación (p. 521) Un dibujo de fundación muestra la base de una estructura y la altura de cada parte.

The first drawing is a foundation drawing, and the second is an isometric drawing based on the foundation drawing.

G

Geometric mean (p. 440) The geometric mean is the number x such that $\frac{a}{x} = \frac{x}{b}$, where a, b and x are positive numbers.

Media geométrica (p. 440) La media geométrica es el número x tanto que $\frac{a}{x} = \frac{x}{b}$, donde a, b y x son números positivos.

The geometric mean of 6 and 24 is 12.
$\frac{6}{x} = \frac{x}{24} \rightarrow x^2 = 144 \rightarrow x = 12$

Geometric probability (p. 402) Geometric probability is a probability that uses a geometric model in which points represent outcomes.

Probabilidad geométrica (p. 402) La probabilidad geométrica es una probabilidad que utiliza un modelo geométrico donde es usan puntos para representar resultados.

Glide reflection (p. 656) A glide reflection is the composition of a translation followed by a reflection in a line parallel to the translation vector.

Reflexión deslizada (p. 656) Una reflexión deslizada es la composición de una traslación seguida de una reflexión en una recta paralela al vector de traslación.

The blue G in the diagram is a glide reflection image of the black G.

Glide reflectional symmetry (p. 668) Glide reflectional symmetry is the type of symmetry for which there is a glide reflection that maps a figure onto itself.

Simetría por reflexión deslizada (p. 668) La simetría por reflexión deslizada es un tipo de simetría en la que una reflexión deslizada vuelve a trazar una figura sobre sí misma.

The tessellation shown can be mapped onto itself by a glide reflection in the given glide vector and reflection line.

Golden rectangle, Golden ratio (p. 425) A *golden rectangle* is a rectangle that can be divided into a square and a rectangle that is similar to the original rectangle. The *golden ratio* is the ratio of the length of a golden rectangle to its width. The value of the golden ratio is $\frac{1 + \sqrt{5}}{2}$, or about 1.62.

Rectángulo áureo, razón áurea (p. 425) Un *rectángulo áureo* es un rectángulo que se puede dividir en un cuadrado y un rectángulo semejante al rectángulo original. La *razón áurea* es la razón de la longitud de un rectángulo áureo en relación a su ancho. El valor de la razón áurea es $\frac{1 + \sqrt{5}}{2}$ o aproximadamente 1.62.

$ABCD$ is a rectangle.
$ADFE$ is a square.
$ABCD \sim BCFE$

Great circle (p. 558) A great circle is the intersection of a sphere and the plane containing the center of the sphere. A great circle divides a sphere into two hemispheres.

Círculo máximo (p. 558) Un círculo máximo es la intersección de una esfera y un plano que contiene el centro de la esfera. Un círculo máximo divide una esfera en dos hemisferios.

Hemispheres Great circle

H

Height See **cone; cylinder; parallelogram; prism; pyramid; trapezoid; triangle.**

Altura Ver **cone; cylinder; parallelogram; prism; pyramid; trapezoid; triangle.**

Hemisphere (p. 558) See **great circle.**

Hemisferio (p. 558) Ver **great circle.**

Heptagon (p. 144) A heptagon is a polygon with seven sides.

Heptágono (p. 144) Un heptágono es un polígono de siete lados.

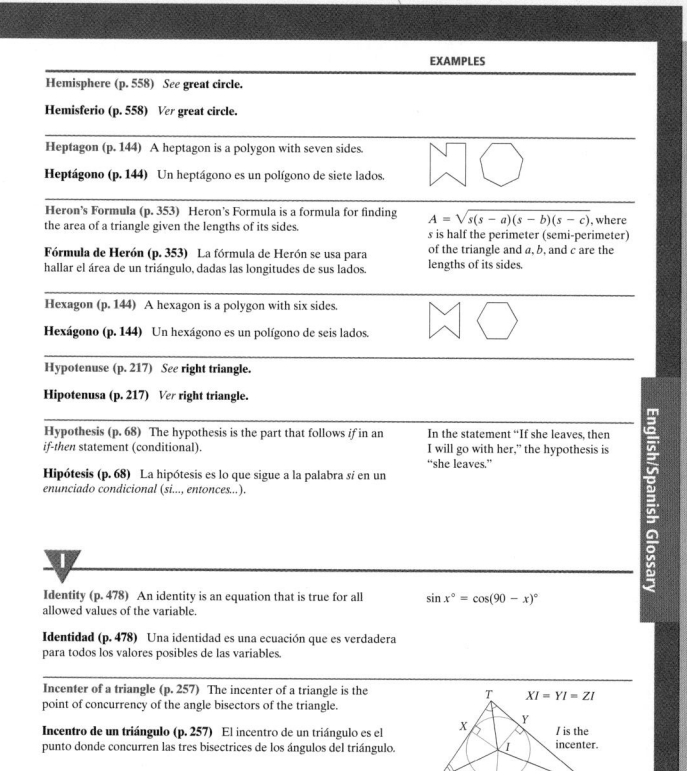

Heron's Formula (p. 353) Heron's Formula is a formula for finding the area of a triangle given the lengths of its sides.

Fórmula de Herón (p. 353) La fórmula de Herón se usa para hallar el área de un triángulo, dadas las longitudes de sus lados.

$A = \sqrt{s(s - a)(s - b)(s - c)}$, where s is half the perimeter (semi-perimeter) of the triangle and a, b, and c are the lengths of its sides.

Hexagon (p. 144) A hexagon is a polygon with six sides.

Hexágono (p. 144) Un hexágono es un polígono de seis lados.

Hypotenuse (p. 217) See **right triangle.**

Hipotenusa (p. 217) Ver **right triangle.**

Hypothesis (p. 68) The hypothesis is the part that follows *if* in an *if-then* statement (conditional).

Hipótesis (p. 68) La hipótesis es lo que sigue a la palabra *si* en un *enunciado condicional* (si..., entonces...).

In the statement "If she leaves, then I will go with her," the hypothesis is "she leaves."

I

Identity (p. 478) An identity is an equation that is true for all allowed values of the variable.

Identidad (p. 478) Una identidad es una ecuación que es verdadera para todos los valores posibles de las variables.

$\sin x° = \cos(90 - x)°$

Incenter of a triangle (p. 257) The incenter of a triangle is the point of concurrency of the angle bisectors of the triangle.

Incentro de un triángulo (p. 257) El incentro de un triángulo es el punto donde concurren las tres bisectrices de los ángulos del triángulo.

$XI = YI = ZI$

I is the incenter.

Indirect measurement (p. 434) Indirect measurement is a way of measuring things that are difficult to measure directly.

EXAMPLE By measuring the distances shown in the diagram and using proportions of similar figures, you can find the height of the taller tower. $\frac{196}{540} = \frac{x}{1300} \rightarrow x \approx 472$ ft

Medición indirecta (p. 434) La medición indirecta es un modo de medir cosas difíciles de medir directamente.

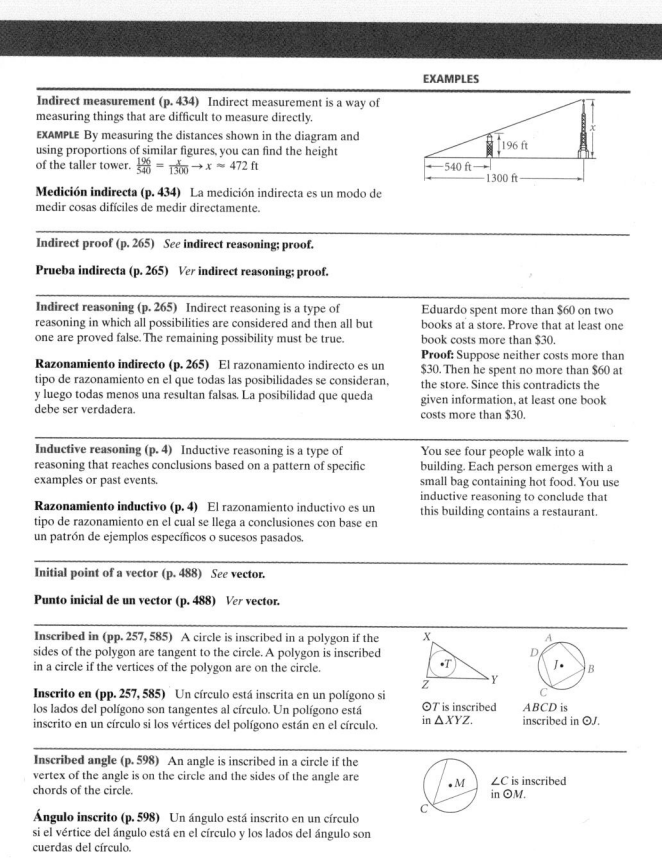

Indirect proof (p. 265) See **indirect reasoning; proof.**

Prueba indirecta (p. 265) Ver **indirect reasoning; proof.**

Indirect reasoning (p. 265) Indirect reasoning is a type of reasoning in which all possibilities are considered and then all but one are proved false. The remaining possibility must be true.

Razonamiento indirecto (p. 265) El razonamiento indirecto es un tipo de razonamiento en el que todas las posibilidades se consideran, y luego todas menos una resultan falsas. La posibilidad que queda debe ser verdadera.

Eduardo spent more than $60 on two books at a store. Prove that at least one book costs more than $30.
Proof: Suppose neither costs more than $30. Then he spent no more than $60 at the store. Since this contradicts the given information, at least one book costs more than $30.

Inductive reasoning (p. 4) Inductive reasoning is a type of reasoning that reaches conclusions based on a pattern of specific examples or past events.

Razonamiento inductivo (p. 4) El razonamiento inductivo es un tipo de razonamiento en el cual se llega a conclusiones con base en un patrón de ejemplos específicos o sucesos pasados.

You see four people walk into a building. Each person emerges with a small bag containing hot food. You use inductive reasoning to conclude that this building contains a restaurant.

Initial point of a vector (p. 488) See **vector.**

Punto inicial de un vector (p. 488) Ver **vector.**

Inscribed in (pp. 257, 585) A circle is inscribed in a polygon if the sides of the polygon are tangent to the circle. A polygon is inscribed in a circle if the vertices of the polygon are on the circle.

Inscrito en (pp. 257, 585) Un círculo está inscrita en un polígono si los lados del polígono son tangentes al círculo. Un polígono está inscrito en un círculo si los vértices del polígono están en el círculo.

$\odot T$ is inscribed in $\triangle XYZ$.

$ABCD$ is inscribed in $\odot J$.

Inscribed angle (p. 598) An angle is inscribed in a circle if the vertex of the angle is on the circle and the sides of the angle are chords of the circle.

Ángulo inscrito (p. 598) Un ángulo está inscrito en un círculo si el vértice del ángulo está en el círculo y los lados del ángulo son cuerdas del círculo.

$\angle C$ is inscribed in $\odot M$.

Intercepted arc (p. 598) An intercepted arc is an arc of a circle having endpoints on the sides of an inscribed angle, and its other points in the interior of the angle.

$\overset{\frown}{UV}$ is the intercepted arc of inscribed angle $\angle T$.

Arco interceptor (p. 598) Un arco interceptor es un arco de un círculo cuyos extremos están en los lados de un ángulo inscrito y los puntos restantes están en el interior del ángulo.

Inverse (p. 264) The inverse of the conditional "if p, then q" is the conditional "if not p, then not q."

Inverso (p. 264) El inverso del condicional "si p, entonces q," es el condicional "si no p, entonces no q."

Conditional: If a figure is a square, then it is a parallelogram.
Inverse: If a figure is not a square, then it is not a parallelogram.

Isometric drawing (p. 520) An isometric drawing of a three-dimensional object shows a corner view of a figure. It is not drawn in perspective and distances are not distorted.

Dibujo isométrico (p. 520) Un dibujo isométrico de un objeto tridimensional muestra una vista desde una esquina de la figura. No se muestra en perspectiva y las distancias no aparecen distorsionadas.

Isometry (p. 634) An isometry, also known as a *congruence transformation*, is a transformation in which an original figure and its image are congruent.

Isometría (p. 634) Una isometría, conocida también como una *transformación de congruencia*, es una transformación en donde una figura original y su imagen son congruentes.

The four isometries are reflections, rotations, translations, and glide reflections.

Isosceles trapezoid (p. 288) An isosceles trapezoid is a trapezoid whose nonparallel opposite sides are congruent.

Trapecio isósceles (p. 288) Un trapecio isósceles es un trapecio cuyos lados opuestos no paralelos son congruentes.

Isosceles triangle (pp. 133, 211) An isosceles triangle is a triangle that has at least two congruent sides. If there are two congruent sides, they are called *legs*. The *vertex angle* is between them. The third side is called the *base* and the other two angles are called the *base angles*.

Triángulo isósceles (pp. 133, 211) Un triángulo isósceles es un triángulo que tiene por lo menos dos lados congruentes. Si tiene dos lados congruentes, éstos se llaman *catetos*. Entre ellos se encuentra el *ángulo de vértice*. El tercer lado se llama *base* y los otros dos ángulos se llaman *ángulos de base*.

Kite (p. 288) A kite is a quadrilateral with two pairs of congruent adjacent sides and no opposite sides congruent.

Cometa (p. 288) Una cometa es un cuadrilátero con dos pares de lados congruentes adyacentes, pero sin lados opuestos congruentes.

Lateral area (pp. 529, 530, 537, 539) The lateral area of a prism or pyramid is the sum of the areas of the lateral faces. The lateral area of a cylinder or cone is the area of the curved surface. A list of lateral area formulas is on p. 727.

Área lateral (pp. 529, 530, 537, 539) El área lateral de un prisma o pirámide es la suma de las áreas de sus caras laterales. El área lateral de un cilindro o de un cono es el área de la superficie curvada. Una lista de las fórmulas de áreas laterales está en la p. 727.

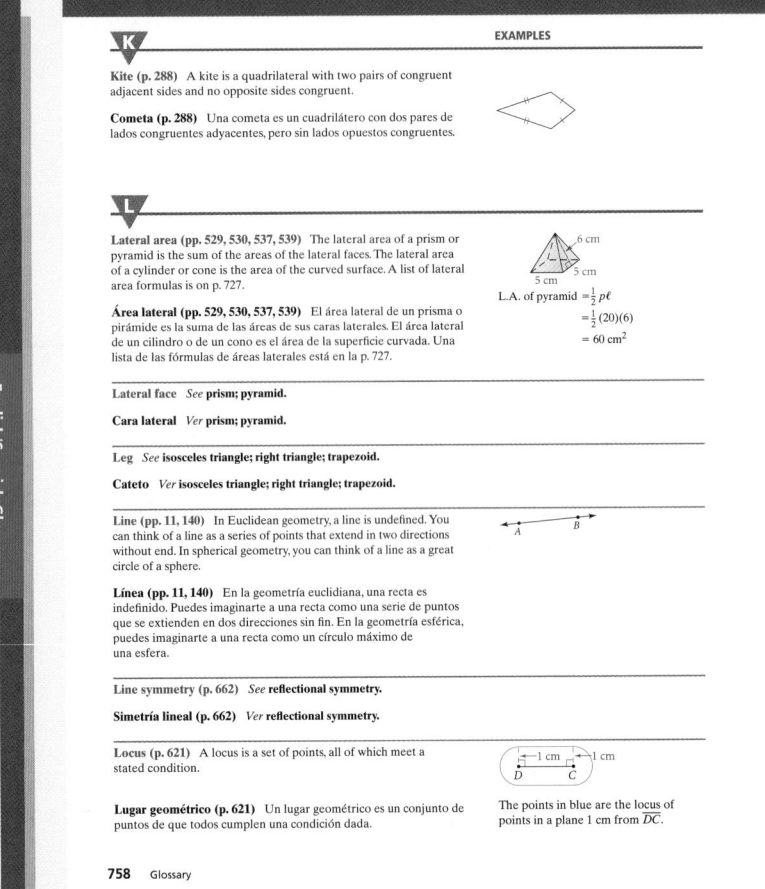

L.A. of pyramid $=\frac{1}{2}p\ell$
$=\frac{1}{2}(20)(6)$
$= 60 \text{ cm}^2$

Lateral face *See* **prism; pyramid.**

Cara lateral *Ver* **prism; pyramid.**

Leg *See* **isosceles triangle; right triangle; trapezoid.**

Cateto *Ver* **isosceles triangle; right triangle; trapezoid.**

Line (pp. 11, 140) In Euclidean geometry, a line is undefined. You can think of a line as a series of points that extend in two directions without end. In spherical geometry, you can think of a line as a great circle of a sphere.

Línea (pp. 11, 140) En la geometría euclidiana, una recta es indefinido. Puedes imaginarte a una recta como una serie de puntos que se extienden en dos direcciones sin fin. En la geometría esférica, puedes imaginarte a una recta como un círculo máximo de una esfera.

Line symmetry (p. 662) *See* **reflectional symmetry.**

Simetría lineal (p. 662) *Ver* **reflectional symmetry.**

Locus (p. 621) A locus is a set of points, all of which meet a stated condition.

Lugar geométrico (p. 621) Un lugar geométrico es un conjunto de puntos de que todos cumplen una condición dada.

The points in blue are the locus of points in a plane 1 cm from $\overline{DC}$.

Magnitude of a vector (p. 490) *See* **vector.**

Magnitud de un vector (p. 490) *Ver* **vector.**

Major arc (p. 387) A major arc of a circle is an arc that is larger than a semicircle.

Arco mayor (p. 387) Un arco mayor de un círculo es cualquier arco más grande que un semicírculo.

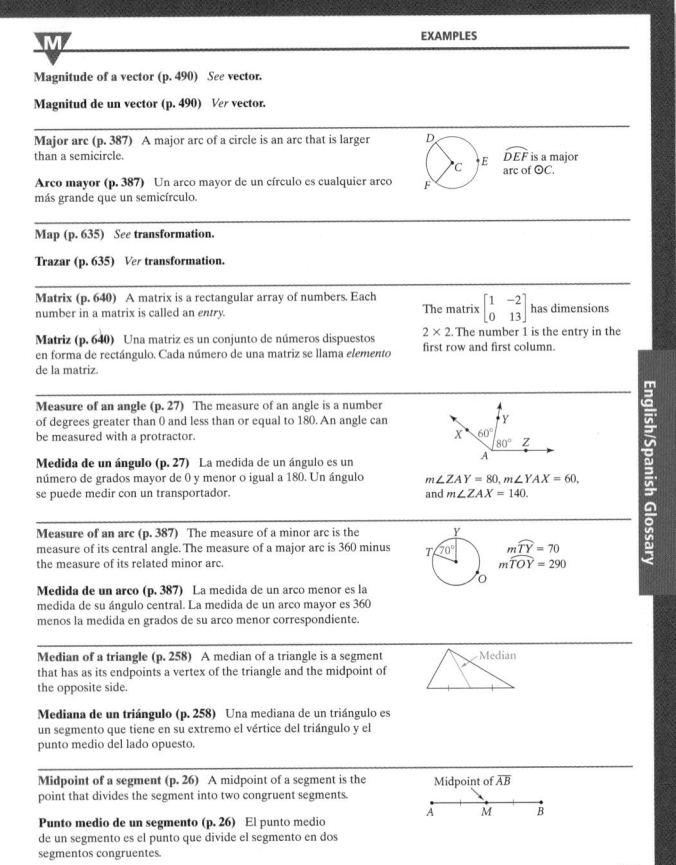

$\overset{\frown}{DEF}$ is a major arc of $\odot C$.

Map (p. 635) *See* **transformation.**

Trazar (p. 635) *Ver* **transformation.**

Matrix (p. 640) A matrix is a rectangular array of numbers. Each number in a matrix is called an *entry*.

Matriz (p. 640) Una matriz es un conjunto de números dispuestos en forma de rectángulo. Cada número de una matriz se llama *elemento* de la matriz.

The matrix $\begin{bmatrix} 1 & -2 \\ 0 & 13 \end{bmatrix}$ has dimensions 2×2. The number 1 is the entry in the first row and first column.

Measure of an angle (p. 27) The measure of an angle is a number of degrees greater than 0 and less than or equal to 180. An angle can be measured with a protractor.

Medida de un ángulo (p. 27) La medida de un ángulo es un número de grados mayor de 0 y menor o igual a 180. Un ángulo se puede medir con un transportador.

$m\angle ZAY = 80$, $m\angle YAX = 60$, and $m\angle ZAX = 140$.

Measure of an arc (p. 387) The measure of a minor arc is the measure of its central angle. The measure of a major arc is 360 minus the measure of its related minor arc.

Medida de un arco (p. 387) La medida de un arco menor es la medida de su ángulo central. La medida de un arco mayor es 360 menos la medida en grados de su arco menor correspondiente.

$m\overset{\frown}{TY} = 70$
$m\overset{\frown}{TOY} = 290$

Median of a triangle (p. 258) A median of a triangle is a segment that has as its endpoints a vertex of the triangle and the midpoint of the opposite side.

Mediana de un triángulo (p. 258) Una mediana de un triángulo es un segmento que tiene en su extremo el vértice del triángulo y el punto medio del lado opuesto.

Median

Midpoint of a segment (p. 26) A midpoint of a segment is the point that divides the segment into two congruent segments.

Punto medio de un segmento (p. 26) El punto medio de un segmento es el punto que divide el segmento en dos segmentos congruentes.

Midpoint of $\overline{AB}$

Midsegment of a trapezoid (p. 332) The midsegment of a trapezoid is the segment that joins the midpoints of the nonparallel opposite sides of a trapezoid.

Segmento medio de un trapecio (p. 332) El segmento medio de trapecio es el segmento que une los puntos medios de los lados paralelos de un trapecio.

Midsegment

Midsegment of a triangle (p. 243) A midsegment of a triangle is the segment that joins the midpoints of two sides of the triangle.

Segmento medio de un triángulo (p. 243) Un segmento medio de un triángulo es el segmento que une los puntos medios de dos lados del triángulo.

Midsegment

Minor arc (p. 387) A minor arc is an arc that is smaller than a semicircle.

Arco menor (p. 387) Un arco menor de un círculo es un arco más corto que un semicírculo.

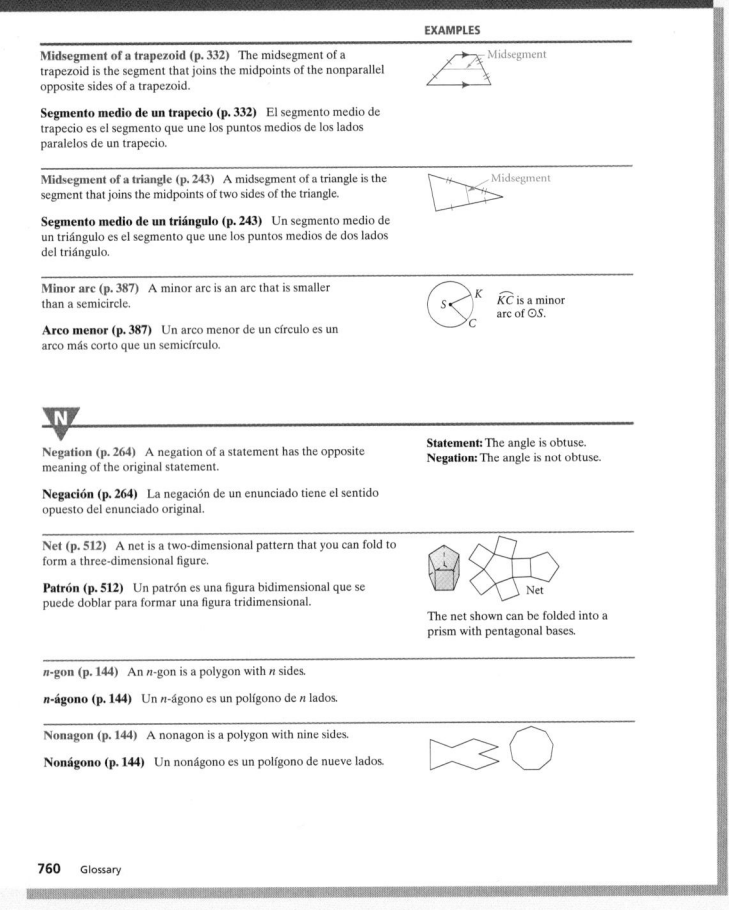

$\overset{\frown}{KC}$ is a minor arc of $\odot S$.

Negation (p. 264) A negation of a statement has the opposite meaning of the original statement.

Negación (p. 264) La negación de un enunciado tiene el sentido opuesto del enunciado original.

Statement: The angle is obtuse.
Negation: The angle is not obtuse.

Net (p. 512) A net is a two-dimensional pattern that you can fold to form a three-dimensional figure.

Patrón (p. 512) Un patrón es una figura bidimensional que se puede doblar para formar una figura tridimensional.

Net

The net shown can be folded into a prism with pentagonal bases.

n-gon (p. 144) An n-gon is a polygon with n sides.

n-ágono (p. 144) Un n-ágono es un polígono de n lados.

Nonagon (p. 144) A nonagon is a polygon with nine sides.

Nonágono (p. 144) Un nonágono es un polígono de nueve lados.

English/Spanish Glossary

Oblique cylinder or prism *See* **cylinder; prism.**

Cilindro oblicuo o prisma *Ver* **cylinder; prism.**

Obtuse angle (p. 28) An obtuse angle is an angle whose measure is between 90 and 180.

Ángulo obtuso (p. 28) Un ángulo obtuso es un ángulo que mide entre 90 y 180.

147°

Obtuse triangle (p. 133) An obtuse triangle has one obtuse angle.

Triángulo obtusángulo (p. 133) Un triángulo obtusángulo tiene un ángulo obtuso.

20° 130° 30°

Octagon (p. 144) An octagon is a polygon with eight sides.

Octágono (p. 144) Un octágono es un polígono de ocho lados.

Opposite rays (p. 18) Opposite rays are collinear rays with the same endpoint. They form a line.

Rayos opuestos (p. 18) Los rayos opuestos son rayos colineales con el mismo extremo. Forman una recta.

T   U   N

$\overrightarrow{UT}$ and $\overrightarrow{UN}$ are opposite rays.

Orientation (p. 635) Two congruent figures have *opposite* orientation if a reflection is needed to map one onto the other. If a reflection is not needed to map one figure onto the other, the figures have the same orientation.

Orientación (p. 635) Dos figuras congruentes tienen orientación *opuesta* si una reflexión es necesaria para trazar una sobre la otra. Si una reflexión no es necesaria para trazar una figura sobre la otra, las figuras tiene la misma orientación.

R Я

The two R's have opposite orientation.

Origin (p. 43) *See* **coordinate plane.**

Origen (p. 43) *Ver* **coordinate plane.**

Orthocenter (p. 259) The orthocenter of a triangle is the point of intersection of the lines containing the altitudes of the triangle.

Ortocentro (p. 259) El ortocentro de un triángulo es el punto donde concurren las tres alturas del triángulo.

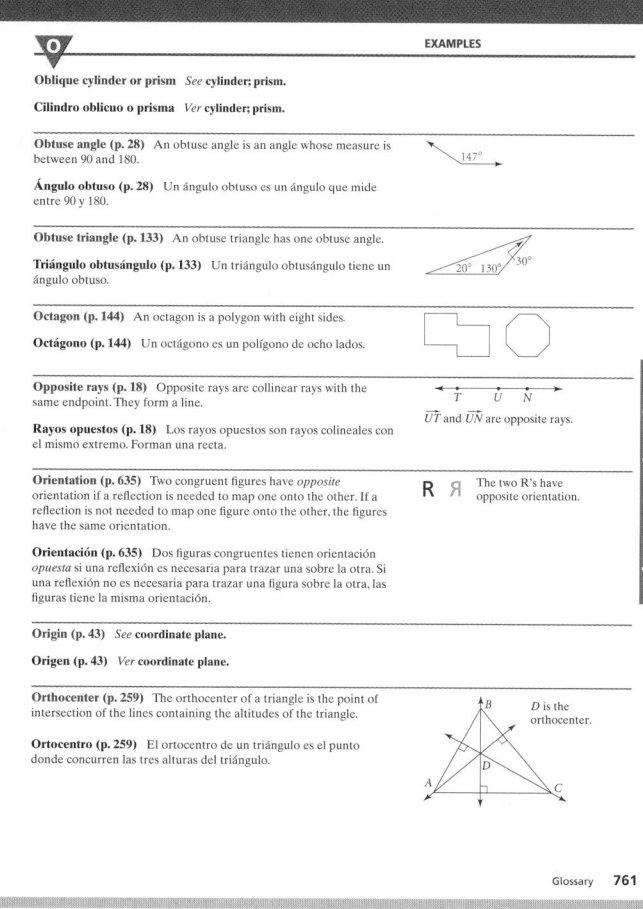

D is the orthocenter.

Orthographic drawing (p. 521) An orthographic drawing is the top view, front view, and right-side view of a three-dimensional figure.

EXAMPLE The diagram shows an isometric drawing (upper right) and the three views that make up an orthographic drawing.

Dibujo ortográfico (p. 521) Un dibujo ortográfico es la vista desde arriba, la vista de frente y la vista del lado derecho de una figura tridimensional.

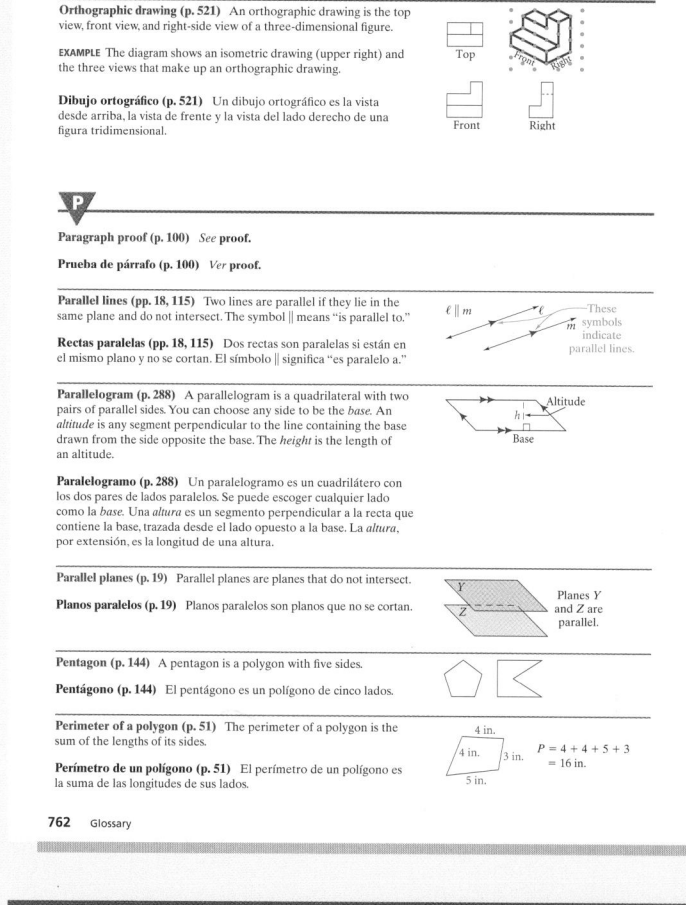

Top   Front   Right

Paragraph proof (p. 100) *See* **proof.**

Prueba de párrafo (p. 100) *Ver* **proof.**

Parallel lines (pp. 18, 115) Two lines are parallel if they lie in the same plane and do not intersect. The symbol ∥ means "is parallel to."

Rectas paralelas (pp. 18, 115) Dos rectas son paralelas si están en el mismo plano y no se cortan. El símbolo ∥ significa "es paralelo a."

$\ell \parallel m$ These symbols indicate parallel lines.

Parallelogram (p. 288) A parallelogram is a quadrilateral with two pairs of parallel sides. You can choose any side to be the *base*. An *altitude* is any segment perpendicular to the line containing the base drawn from the side opposite the base. The *height* is the length of an altitude.

Paralelogramo (p. 288) Un paralelogramo es un cuadrilátero con los dos pares de lados paralelos. Se puede escoger cualquier lado como la *base*. Una *altura* es un segmento perpendicular a la recta que contiene la base, trazada desde el lado opuesto a la base. La *altura*, por extensión, es la longitud de una altura.

Altitude   h   Base

Parallel planes (p. 19) Parallel planes are planes that do not intersect.

Planos paralelos (p. 19) Planos paralelos son planos que no se cortan.

Planes Y and Z are parallel.

Pentagon (p. 144) A pentagon is a polygon with five sides.

Pentágono (p. 144) El pentágono es un polígono de cinco lados.

Perimeter of a polygon (p. 51) The perimeter of a polygon is the sum of the lengths of its sides.

Perímetro de un polígono (p. 51) El perímetro de un polígono es la suma de las longitudes de sus lados.

4 in.   4 in.   3 in.   5 in.
$P = 4 + 4 + 5 + 3$
$= 16$ in.

Perpendicular bisector (p. 35) The perpendicular bisector of a segment is a line, segment, or ray that is perpendicular to the segment at its midpoint.

Mediatriz (p. 35) La mediatriz de un segmento es una recta, segmento, o rayo que es perpendicular al segmento en su punto medio.

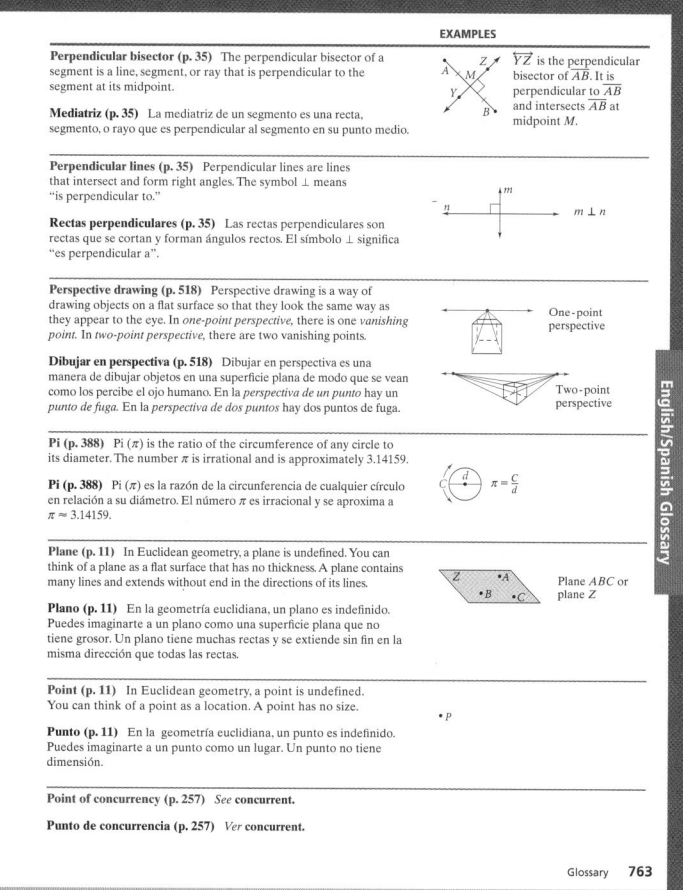

$\overleftrightarrow{YZ}$ is the perpendicular bisector of $\overline{AB}$. It is perpendicular to $\overline{AB}$ and intersects $\overline{AB}$ at midpoint M.

Perpendicular lines (p. 35) Perpendicular lines are lines that intersect and form right angles. The symbol ⊥ means "is perpendicular to."

Rectas perpendiculares (p. 35) Las rectas perpendiculares son rectas que se cortan y forman ángulos rectos. El símbolo ⊥ significa "es perpendicular a".

m   n $m \perp n$

Perspective drawing (p. 518) Perspective drawing is a way of drawing objects on a flat surface so that they look the same way as they appear to the eye. In *one-point perspective*, there is one *vanishing point*. In *two-point perspective*, there are two vanishing points.

Dibujar en perspectiva (p. 518) Dibujar en perspectiva es una manera de dibujar objetos en una superficie plana de modo que se vean como los percibe el ojo humano. En la *perspectiva de un punto* hay un *punto de fuga*. En la *perspectiva de dos puntos* hay dos puntos de fuga.

One-point perspective

Two-point perspective

Pi (p. 388) Pi (π) is the ratio of the circumference of any circle to its diameter. The number π is irrational and is approximately 3.14159.

Pi (p. 388) Pi (π) es la razón de la circunferencia de cualquier círculo en relación a su diámetro. El número π es irracional y se aproxima a π ≈ 3.14159.

d $\pi = \frac{C}{d}$

Plane (p. 11) In Euclidean geometry, a plane is undefined. You can think of a plane as a flat surface that has no thickness. A plane contains many lines and extends without end in the directions of its lines.

Plano (p. 11) En la geometría euclidiana, un plano es indefinido. Puedes imaginarte a un plano como una superficie plana que no tiene grosor. Un plano tiene muchas rectas y se extiende sin fin en la misma dirección que todas las rectas.

Z   A   B   C   Plane ABC or plane Z

Point (p. 11) In Euclidean geometry, a point is undefined. You can think of a point as a location. A point has no size.

Punto (p. 11) En la geometría euclidiana, un punto es indefinido. Puedes imaginarte a un punto como un lugar. Un punto no tiene dimensión.

• P

Point of concurrency (p. 257) *See* **concurrent.**

Punto de concurrencia (p. 257) *Ver* **concurrent.**

Point of tangency (p. 582) *See* **tangent to a circle.**

Punto de tangencia (p. 582) *Ver* **tangent to a circle.**

Point symmetry (p. 663) Point symmetry is the type of symmetry for which there is a rotation of 180° that maps a figure onto itself.

Simetría central (p. 663) La simetría central es un tipo de simetría en la que una figura se ha rotado 180° sobre sí misma.

180° ℓ

Point-slope form (p. 154) The point-slope form for a nonvertical line with slope *m* and through point (x_1, y_1) is $y - y_1 = m(x - x_1)$.

Forma punto-pendiente (p. 154) La forma punto-pendiente para una línea no vertical con pendiente *m* y que pasa por el punto (x_1, y_1) es $y - y_1 = m(x - x_1)$.

$y + 1 = 3(x - 4)$

In this equation, the slope is 3 and (x_1, y_1) is $(4, -1)$.

Polygon (p. 143) A polygon is a closed plane figure with at least three *sides* that are segments. The sides intersect only at their endpoints and no two adjacent sides are collinear. The *vertices* of the polygon are the endpoints of the sides. A *diagonal* is a segment that connects two nonconsecutive vertices. A polygon is *convex* if no diagonal contains points outside the polygon. A polygon is *concave* if a diagonal contains points outside the polygon.

Polígono (p. 143) Un polígono es una figura plana cerrada de, por lo menos, tres *lados*. Los lados se cortan solo en los extremos. No hay dos lados adyacentes que sean colineales. Los *vértices* del polígono son los extremos de los lados. Una *diagonal* es un segmento que une dos vértices no consecutivos. Un polígono es *convexo* si ninguna diagonal contiene puntos fuera del polígono. Un polígono es *cóncavo* si una diagonal contiene puntos fuera del polígono.

Vertices   Diagonal   Sides
Convex   Concave

Polyhedron (p. 512) A polyhedron is a three-dimensional figure whose surfaces, or *faces*, are polygons. The vertices of the polygons are the *vertices* of the polyhedron. The intersections of the faces are the *edges* of the polyhedron.

Poliedro (p. 512) Un poliedro es una figura tridimensional cuyas superficies, o *caras*, son polígonos. Los vértices de los polígonos son los *vértices* del poliedro. Las intersecciones de las caras son las *aristas* del poliedro.

Vertices   Faces   Edges

Postulate (p. 12) A postulate, or *axiom*, is an accepted statement of fact.

Postulado (p. 12) Un postulado, o *axioma*, es un enunciado que se acepta como un hecho.

Postulate: Through any two points there is exactly one line.

Preimage (p. 634) *See* **transformation.**

Preimagen (p. 634) *Ver* **transformation.**

Prime notation (p. 635) *See* **transformation.**

Notación prima (p. 635) *Ver* **transformation.**

Prism (p. 528) A prism is a polyhedron with two congruent and parallel faces, which are called the *bases*. The other faces, which are parallelograms, are called the *lateral faces*. An *altitude* of a prism is a perpendicular segment that joins the planes of the bases. Its length is the *height* of the prism. A *right prism* is one whose lateral faces are rectangular regions and a lateral edge is an altitude. In an *oblique prism*, some or all of the lateral faces are nonrectangular.

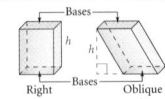
Right prism / Oblique prism

Prisma (p. 528) Un prisma es un poliedro con dos caras congruentes paralelas llamadas *bases*. Las otras caras son paralelogramos llamados *caras laterales*. La *altura* de un prisma es un segmento perpendicular que une los planos de las bases. Su longitud es también la *altura* del prisma. En un *prisma recto*, las caras laterales son rectangulares y una de las aristas laterales es la altura. En un *prisma oblicuo*, algunas o todas las caras laterales no son rectangulares.

Proof (pp. 100, 117, 123, 242, 263) A proof is a convincing argument that uses deductive reasoning. A proof can be written in many forms. In a *two-column proof*, the statements and reasons are aligned in columns. In a *paragraph proof*, the statements and reasons are connected in sentences. In a *flow proof*, arrows show the logical connections between the statements. In a *coordinate proof*, a figure is drawn on a coordinate plane and the formulas for slope, midpoint, and distance are used to prove properties of the figure. An *indirect proof* involves the use of indirect reasoning.

Given: △EFG, with right angle ∠F

Prove: ∠E and ∠G are complementary.

Paragraph Proof: Because ∠F is a right angle, $m\angle F = 90$. By the Triangle Angle-Sum Theorem, $m\angle E + m\angle F + m\angle G = 180$. By substitution, $m\angle E + 90 + m\angle G = 180$. Subtracting 90 from each side yields $m\angle E + m\angle G = 90$. ∠E and ∠G are complementary by definition.

Prueba (pp. 100, 117, 123, 242, 263) Una prueba es un argumento convincente en el cual se usa el razonamiento deductivo. Una prueba se puede escribir de varias maneras. En una *prueba de dos columnas*, los enunciados y las razones se alinean en columnas. En una *prueba de párrafo*, los enunciados y razones están unidos en oraciones. En una *prueba de flujo*, hay flechas que indican las conexiones lógicas entre enunciados. En una *prueba de coordenadas*, se dibuja una figura en un plano de coordenadas y se usan las fórmulas de la pendiente, punto medio y distancia para probar las propiedades de la figura. Una *prueba indirecta* incluye el uso de razonamiento indirecto.

Proportion (p. 417) A proportion is a statement that two ratios are equal. An *extended proportion* is a statement that three or more ratios are equal.

$\frac{4}{5} = \frac{3}{4}$ is a proportion.

$\frac{9}{27} = \frac{3}{9} = \frac{1}{3}$ is an extended proportion.

Proporción (p. 417) Una proporción es un enunciado en el cual dos razones son iguales. Una *proporción extendida* es un enunciado que dice que tres razones o más son iguales.

Pyramid (p. 537) A pyramid is a polyhedron in which one face, the *base*, is a polygon and the other faces, the *lateral faces*, are triangles with a common vertex, called the *vertex* of the pyramid. An *altitude* of a pyramid is the perpendicular segment from the *vertex* to the plane of the base. Its length is the *height* of the pyramid. A *regular pyramid* is a pyramid whose base is a regular polygon and whose lateral faces are congruent isosceles triangles. The *slant height* of a regular pyramid is the length of an altitude of a lateral face.

Vertex / Altitude / Slant height / Base / Regular pyramid

Pirámide (p. 537) Una pirámide es un poliedro en donde una cara, la *base*, es un polígono y las otras caras, las *caras laterales*, son triángulos con un vértice común, llamado el *vértice* de la pirámide. Una *altura* de una pirámide es el segmento perpendicular que va del *vértice* hasta el plano de la base. Su longitud es, por extensión, la *altura* de la pirámide. Una *pirámide regular* es una pirámide cuya base es un polígono regular y cuyas caras laterales son triángulos isósceles congruentes. La *altura de inclinación* de una pirámide regular es la longitud de la altura de la cara lateral.

Pythagorean triple (p. 357) A Pythagorean triple is a set of three nonzero whole numbers a, b, and c, that satisfy the equation $a^2 + b^2 = c^2$.

The numbers 5, 12, and 13 form a Pythagorean triple because $5^2 + 12^2 = 13^2 = 169$.

Triple de Pitágoras (p. 357) Un triple de Pitágoras es un conjunto de tres números enteros positivos a, b, y c que satisfacen la ecuación $a^2 + b^2 = c^2$.

Q

Quadrant (p. 43) *See* **coordinate plane.**

Cuadrante (p. 43) *Ver* **coordinate plane.**

Quadrilateral (p. 144) A quadrilateral is a polygon with four sides.

Cuadrilátero (p. 144) Un cuadrilátero es un polígono de cuatro lados.

R

Radius of a circle (p. 386) A radius of a circle is any segment with one endpoint on the circle and the other endpoint at the center of the circle. *Radius* can also mean the length of this segment.

$\overline{DE}$ is a radius of ⊙D.

Radio de un círculo (p. 386) Un radio de un círculo es cualquier segmento con un extremo en el círculo y el otro extremo en el centro del círculo. *Radio* también se refiere a la longitud de este segmento.

Radius of a regular polygon (p. 380) The radius of a regular polygon is the distance from the center to a vertex.

Radius

Radio de un polígono regular (p. 380) El radio de un polígono regular es la distancia desde el centro hasta un vértice.

Radius of a sphere (p. 558) The radius of a sphere is a segment that has one endpoint at the center and the other endpoint on the sphere.

Radio de una esfera (p. 558) El radio de una esfera es un segmento con un extremo en el centro y otro en la superficie esférica.

Ratio (p. 416) A ratio is the comparison of two quantities by division.

5 to 7

5 : 7

$\frac{5}{7}$

Razón (p. 416) Una razón es la comparación de dos cantidades por medio de una división.

Ray (p. 17) A ray is the part of a line consisting of one *endpoint* and all the points of the line on one side of the endpoint.

Endpoint of $\overrightarrow{AB}$

Rayo (p. 17) Un rayo es una parte de una recta que contiene un *extremo* y todos los puntos de la recta a un lado del extremo.

Rectangle (p. 288) A rectangle is a parallelogram with four right angles.

Rectángulo (p. 288) Un rectángulo es un paralelogramo con cuatro ángulos rectos.

Reduction (p. 674) *See* **dilation.**

Reducción (p. 674) *Ver* **dilation.**

Reflection (p. 635) A reflection in (or *flip across*) line r is a transformation such that if a point A is on line r, then the image of A is itself, and if a point B is not on line r, then its image B' is the point such that r is the perpendicular bisector of $\overline{BB'}$.

Reflexión (p. 635) Una reflexión en la recta r es una transformación tal que si un punto A está en la recta r, entonces la imagen de A es ella misma, y si un punto B no está en la recta r, entonces su imagen B' es el punto tal que r es la mediatriz de $\overline{BB'}$.

Reflectional symmetry (p. 662) Reflectional symmetry, or *line symmetry*, is the type of symmetry for which there is a reflection that maps a figure onto itself. The reflection line is the line of symmetry.

A reflection in the given line maps the figure onto itself.

Simetría por reflexión (p. 662) La simetría por reflexión, o simetría línea, es un tipo de simetría en la que la reflexión vuelve a trazar la figura sobre sí misma. La recta de reflexión es la recta de simetría.

Regular polygon (p. 146) A regular polygon is a polygon that is both equilateral and equiangular. Its *center* is the center of the circumscribed circle.

ABCDEF is a regular hexagon. Point X is its center.

Polígono regular (p. 146) Un polígono regular es un polígono que es equilátero y equiángulo. Su *centro* es el centro del círculo circunscrito.

Regular pyramid (p. 537) *See* **pyramid.**

Pirámide regular (p. 537) *Ver* **pyramid.**

Remote interior angles (p. 133) Remote interior angles are the two nonadjacent interior angles corresponding to each exterior angle of a triangle.

∠1 and ∠2 are remote interior angles of ∠3.

Ángulos interiores remotos (p. 133) Los ángulos interiores remotos son los dos ángulos interiores no adyacentes que corresponden a cada ángulo exterior de un triángulo.

Resultant vector (p. 490) The sum of two vectors is a resultant.

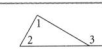
$\vec{w}$ is the resultant of $\vec{u} + \vec{v}$.

Vector resultante (p. 490) La suma de dos vectores es el vector resultante.

Rhombus (p. 288) A rhombus is a parallelogram with four congruent sides.

Rombo (p. 288) Un rombo es un paralelogramo de cuatro lados congruentes.

Right angle (p. 28) A right angle is an angle whose measure is 90.

This symbol indicates a right angle.

Ángulo recto (p. 28) Un ángulo recto es un ángulo que mide 90.

Right cone (p. 539) *See* **cone.**

Cono recto (p. 539) *Ver* **cone.**

Right cylinder (p. 530) *See* **cylinder.**

Cilindro recto (p. 530) *Ver* **cylinder.**

Right prism (p. 528) *See* **prism.**

Prisma recto (p. 528) *Ver* **prism.**

Right triangle (pp. 133, 217) A right triangle contains one right angle. The side opposite the right angle is the *hypotenuse* and the other two sides are the *legs*.

Triángulo rectángulo (pp. 133, 217) Un triángulo rectángulo contiene un ángulo recto. El lado opuesto del ángulo recto es la *hipotenusa* y los otros dos lados son los *catetos*.

Rotation (p. 648) A rotation (*turn*) of $x°$ about a point R is a transformation such that for any point V, its image is the point V', where $RV = RV'$ and $m\angle VRV' = x$. The image of R is itself.

Rotación (p. 648) Una rotación de $x°$ alrededor de un punto R es una transformación de modo que para cualquier punto V, su imagen es el punto V', donde $RV = RV'$ y $m\angle VRV' = x$. La imagen de R es R misma.

Rotational symmetry (p. 663) Rotational symmetry is the type of symmetry for which there is a rotation of 180° or less that maps a figure onto itself.

Simetría rotacional (p. 663) La semetría rotacional es un tipo de simetría en la que una rotación de 180° o menos vuelve a trazar una figura sobre sí misma.

The figure has 120° rotational symmetry.

S

Same-side interior angles (p. 115) Same side interior angles lie on the same side of the transversal t and between ℓ and m.

Ángulos internos del mismo lado (p. 115) Los ángulos internos del mismo lado están en el mismo lado de la transversal t y entre ℓ y m.

$\angle 1$ and $\angle 2$ are same-side interior angles, as are $\angle 3$ and $\angle 4$.

Scalar multiplication (p. 675) Scalar multiplication is the multiplication of each entry in a matrix by the same number, the *scalar*.

Multiplicación escalar (p. 675) La multiplicación escalar es cada elemento de una matriz la multiplicación de por el mismo número, el *escalar*.

$$2 \cdot \begin{bmatrix} 1 & 0 \\ -2 & 3 \end{bmatrix} = \begin{bmatrix} 2(1) & 2(0) \\ 2(-2) & 2(3) \end{bmatrix}$$
$$= \begin{bmatrix} 2 & 0 \\ -4 & 6 \end{bmatrix}$$

Scale (p. 418) A scale is the ratio of any length in a scale drawing to the corresponding actual length. The lengths may be in different units.

Escala (p. 418) Una escala es la razón de cualquier longitud en un dibujo a escala en relación a la correspondiente longitud verdadera.

1 cm to 1 ft
1 cm = 1 ft
1 cm : 1 ft

Scale drawing (p. 418) A scale drawing is a drawing in which all lengths are proportional to corresponding actual lengths.

Dibujo a escala (p. 418) Un dibujo a escala es un dibujo en el que todas las longitudes son proporcionales a las correspondientes longitudes verdaderas.

Living Room | Bedroom | Bath   Scale: 1 in. = 30 ft

Scale factor (p. 674) The scale factor of a dilation is the number that describes the size change from an original figure to its image. *See also* **dilation**.

Factor de escala (p. 674) El factor de escala de una dilatación es el número que describe el cambio de tamaño de una figura original a su imagen. *Ver también* **dilation**.

The scale factor of the dilation that maps $\triangle ABC$ to $\triangle A'B'C'$ is $\frac{1}{2}$.

Scalene triangle (p. 133) A scalene triangle has no sides congruent.

Triángulo escaleno (p. 133) Un triángulo escaleno no tiene lados congruentes.

Secant (p. 607) A secant is a line, ray, or segment that intersects a circle at two points.

Secante (p. 607) Un secante es una recta, rayo o segmento que corta un círculo en dos puntos.

$\overleftrightarrow{AB}$ is a secant of $\odot C$.

Sector of a circle (p. 396) A sector of a circle is the region bounded by two radii and their intercepted arc.

Sector de un círculo (p. 396) Un sector de un círculo es la región limitada por dos radios y el arco abarcado por ellos.

Sector AOB

Segment (p. 17) A segment is the part of a line consisting of two points, called *endpoints*, and all points between them.

Segmento (p. 17) Un segmento es una parte de una recta que consiste en dos puntos, llamados *extremos*, y todos los puntos entre los extremos.

Endpoints of $\overline{DE}$

Segment bisector (p. 26) A segment bisector is a line, segment, ray, or plane that intersects a segment at its midpoint.

Bisectriz de un segmento (p. 26) La bisectriz de un segmento es una recta, segmento, rayo o plano que corta un segmento en su punto medio.

ℓ bisects $\overline{KJ}$.

Segment of a circle (p. 397) A segment of a circle is the part of a circle bounded by an arc and the segment joining its endpoints.

Segmento de un círculo (p. 397) Un segmento de un círculo es la parte de un círculo bordeada por un arco y el segmento que une sus extremos.

Segment of $\odot C$

Semicircle (p. 387) A semicircle is half a circle.

Semicírculo (p. 387) Un semicírculo es la mitad de un círculo.

Semicircle

Side *See* **angle; polygon.**

Lado *Ver* **angle; polygon.**

Similarity ratio (pp. 423, 566) The similarity ratio is the ratio of the lengths of corresponding sides of similar polygons.

Razón de semejanza (pp. 423, 566) La razón de semejanza es la razón de la longitud de los lados correspondientes de polígonos semejantes.

$\frac{AB}{DE} = \frac{BC}{EF} = \frac{CA}{FD}$

$\triangle ABC \sim \triangle DEF$

Similarity transformation (p. 674) *See* **dilation.**

Transformación de semejanza (p. 674) *Ver* **dilation.**

Similar polygons (p. 423) Similar polygons are polygons having corresponding angles congruent and corresponding sides proportional. You denote similarity by $\sim$.

Polígonos semejantes (p. 423) Los polígonos semejantes son polígonos cuyos ángulos correspondientes son congruentes y los lados correspondientes son proporcionales. El símbolo $\sim$ significa "es semejante a".

$\triangle JKL \sim \triangle MNO$

Similarity ratio $= \frac{2}{5}$

Similar solids (p. 566) Similar solids have the same shape and have all their corresponding dimensions proportional.

Cuerpos geométricos semejantes (p. 566) Los cuerpos geométricos semejantes tienen la misma forma y todas sus dimensiones correspondientes son proporcionales.

Sine ratio (p. 477) *See* **trigonometric ratios.**

Razón seno (p. 477) *Ver* **trigonometric ratios.**

Skew lines (p. 18) Skew lines are lines that do not lie in the same plane.

Rectas cruzadas (p. 18) Las rectas cruzadas son rectas que no están en el mismo plano.

$\overleftrightarrow{AB}$ and $\overleftrightarrow{EF}$ are skew.

Slant height *See* **cone; pyramid.**

Altura de inclinación *Ver* **cone; pyramid.**

Slide (p. 641) *See* **translation.**

Slope-intercept form (p. 152) The slope-intercept form of a linear equation is $y = mx + b$, where m is the slope of the line and b is the y-intercept.

Fórmula pendiente-intercepto (p. 152) La fórmula pendiente-intercepto es la ecuación lineal $y = mx + b$, en la que m es la pendiente de la recta y b es el punto de intersección de esa recta con el eje y.

$y = \frac{1}{2}x - 3$
In this equation, the slope is $\frac{1}{2}$ and the y-intercept is -3.

Slope of a line (p. 151) The slope of a line is the ratio of its vertical change in the coordinate plane to the corresponding horizontal change. If (x_1, y_1) and (x_2, y_2) are points on a nonvertical line, then the slope is $\frac{y_2 - y_1}{x_2 - x_1}$. The slope of a horizontal line is 0 and the slope of a vertical line is undefined.

Pendiente de una recta (p. 151) La pendiente de una recta es la razón del cambio vertical en el plano de coordenadas en relación a al cambio horizontal correspondiente. Si (x_1, y_1) y (x_2, y_2) son puntos en una recta no vertical, entonces la pendiente es $\frac{y_2 - y_1}{x_2 - x_1}$. La pendiente de una recta horizontal es 0, y la pendiente de una recta vertical es indefinida.

The line containing $P(-1, -1)$ and $Q(1, -2)$ has slope
$\frac{-2 - (-1)}{1 - (-1)} = \frac{-1}{2} = -\frac{1}{2}$.

Space (p. 11) Space is the set of all points.

Espacio (p. 11) El espacio es el conjunto de todos los puntos.

Sphere (p. 558) A sphere is the set of all points in space a given distance r, the *radius*, from a given point C, the *center*. A *great circle* is the intersection of a sphere with a plane containing the center of the sphere. The *circumference* of a sphere is the circumference of any great circle of the sphere.

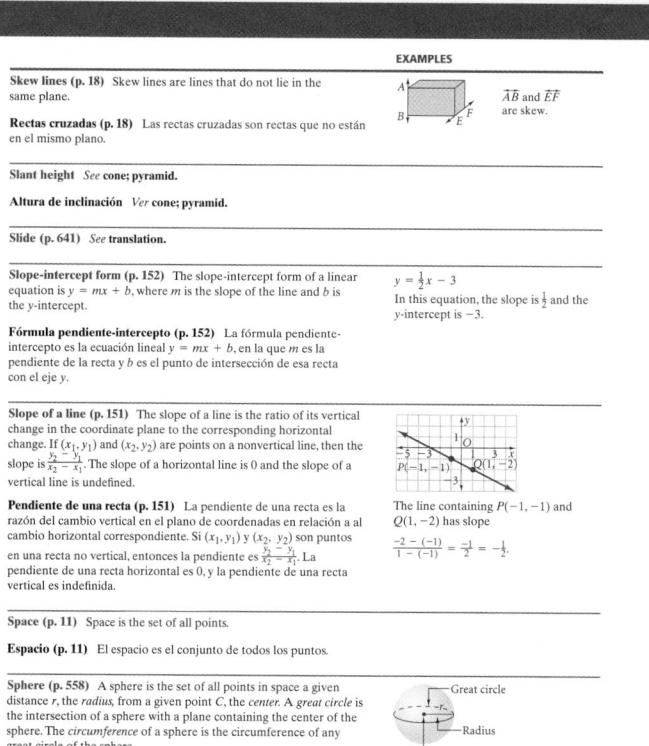

Esfera (p. 558) Una esfera es el conjunto de los puntos del espacio que están a una distancia dada r, el *radio*, de un punto dado C, el *centro*. Un *círculo máximo* es la intersección de una esfera y un plano que contiene el centro de la esfera. La *circunferencia* de una esfera es la circunferencia de cualquier círculo máximo de la esfera.

Spherical geometry (p. 140) In spherical geometry, a plane is considered to be the surface of a sphere and a line is considered to be a great circle of the sphere. In spherical geometry, through a point not on a given line there is no line parallel to the given line.

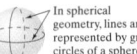

In spherical geometry, lines are represented by great circles of a sphere.

Geometría esférica (p. 140) En la geometría esférica, un plano es la superficie de una esfera y una recta es un círculo máximo de la esfera. En la geometría esférica, a través de un punto que no está en una recta dada, no hay recta paralela a la recta dada.

Square (p. 288) A square is a parallelogram with four congruent sides and four right angles.

Cuadrado (p. 288) Un cuadrado es un paralelogramo con cuatro lados congruentes y cuatro ángulos rectos.

Standard form of a linear equation (p. 153) The standard form of a linear equation is $Ax + By = C$, where A, B, and C are integers and A and B are not both zero.

$6x - y = 3$

Fórmula normal de una ecuación lineal (p. 153) La fórmula normal de una ecuación lineal es $Ax + By = C$, donde A, B, y C son números reales, y donde A y B no son ambos iguales a cero.

Standard form of an equation of a circle (p. 615) The standard form of an equation of a circle is $(x - h)^2 + (y - k)^2 = r^2$, where (h, k) is the center of the circle.

In $(x + 5)^2 + (y + 2)^2 = 48$, $(-5, -2)$ is the center of the circle.

Fórmula normal de la ecuación de un círculo (p. 615) La fórmula normal de la ecuación de un círculo es $(x - h)^2 + (y - k)^2 = r^2$, donde (h, k) son las coordenadas del centro del círculo.

Straight angle (p. 28) A straight angle is an angle whose measure is 180.

$m\angle AOB = 180$

Ángulo llano (p. 28) Un ángulo llano es un ángulo que mide 180.

Straightedge (p. 34) A straightedge is a ruler with no markings on it.

Regla sin graduación (p. 34) Una regla que sólo sirve para trazar rectas.

Supplementary angles (p. 96) Two angles are supplementary if the sum of their measures is 180.

Ángulos suplementarios (p. 96) Dos ángulos son suplementarios cuando sus medidas suman 180.

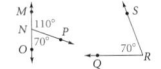

$\angle MNP$ and $\angle ONP$ are supplementary, as are $\angle MNP$ and $\angle QRS$.

Surface area (pp. 529, 530, 538, 539, 558) The surface area of a prism, cylinder, pyramid, or cone is the sum of the lateral area and the areas of the bases. The surface area of a sphere is four times the area of a great circle. A list of surface area formulas is on p. 727.

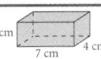

S.A. of prism = L.A. + 2B
= 66 + 2(28)
= 122 cm²

Área (pp. 529, 530, 538, 539, 558) El área de un prisma, pirámide, cilindro o cono es la suma del área lateral y las áreas de las bases. El área de una esfera es igual a cuatro veces el área de un círculo máximo. Una lista de fórmulas de áreas está en la p. 727.

Symmetry (pp. 662, 663, 668) A figure has symmetry if there is an isometry that maps the figure onto itself. *See* **glide reflectional symmetry; point symmetry; reflectional symmetry; rotational symmetry; translational symmetry.**

A regular pentagon has reflectional symmetry and 72° rotational symmetry.

Simetría (pp. 662, 663, 668) Una figura tiene simetría si hay una isometría que traza la figura sobre sí misma. *Ver* **glide reflectional symmetry; point symmetry; reflectional symmetry; rotational symmetry; translational symmetry.**

T

Tangent ratio (p. 470) *See* **trigonometric ratios.**

Razón tangente (p. 470) *Ver* **trigonometric ratios.**

Tangent to a circle (p. 582) A tangent to a circle is a line, segment, or ray in the plane of the circle that intersects the circle in exactly one point. That point is the *point of tangency.*

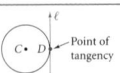

Point of tangency

Tangente de un círculo (p. 582) Un tangente de un círculo es una recta, segmento o rayo en el plano del círculo que corta el círculo en exactamente un punto. Ese punto es el *punto de tangencia.*

Line ℓ is tangent to $\odot C$. Point D is the point of tangency.

Terminal point of a vector (p. 490) *See* **vector.**

Punto terminal de un vector (p. 490) *Ver* **vector.**

Tessellation (p. 667) A tessellation, or *tiling,* is a repeating pattern of figures that completely covers a plane without gaps or overlap. A *pure tessellation* is a tessellation that consists of congruent copies of one figure.

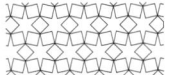

Teselado (p. 667) Un teselado o *reticulado* es un patrón repetitivo de figuras que cubre completamente una superficie plana sin dejar espacios vacíos ni traslaparse. Un *teselado puro* consiste en copias congruentes de una figura.

Theorem (p. 98) A theorem is a conjecture that is proven.

Teorema (p. 98) Un teorema es una conjetura que se demuestra.

The theorem "Vertical angles are congruent" can be proven by using postulates, definitions, properties, and previously stated theorems.

Tiling (p. 667) *See* **tessellation.**

Reticulado (p. 667) *Ver* **tessellation.**

Transformation (p. 634) A transformation is a change in the position, size, or shape of a geometric figure. The given figure is called the *preimage* and the resulting figure is called the *image.* A transformation *maps* a figure onto its image. *Prime notation* is sometimes used to identify image points. In the diagram, X' (read "X prime") is the image of X.

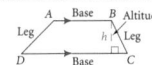

Preimage   Image

$\triangle XYZ \rightarrow \triangle X'Y'Z'$

Transformación (p. 634) Una transformación es un cambio en la posición, tamaño o forma de una figura. La figura dada se llama la *preimagen* y la figura resultante se llama la *imagen.* Una transformación *traza* la figura sobre su propia imagen. La *notación prima* a veces se utiliza para identificar los puntos de la imagen. En el diagrama de la derecha, X' (leído prima X) es la imagen de X.

Translation (p. 641) A translation (*slide*)is a transformation that moves points the same distance and in the same direction. A translation in the coordinate plane is described by a vector.

Traslación (p. 641) Una traslación es la transformación que mueve puntos a la misma distancia y en la misma dirección. Un vector puede describir la traslación en un plano de coordenadas.

The blue triangle is the image of the black triangle under the translation $\langle -5, -2 \rangle$.

Translational symmetry (p. 668) Translational symmetry is the type of symmetry for which there is a translation that maps a figure onto itself.

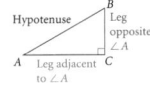

Simetría translacional (p. 668) La simetría translacional es un tipo de simetría en la que la traslación vuelve a trazar la figura sobre sí misma.

The tessellation shown can be mapped onto itself by the given translation.

Transversal (p. 115) A transversal is a line that intersects two coplanar lines in two points.

Transversal (p. 115) Una transversal es una recta que corta dos rectas coplanares en dos puntos.

t is a transversal of ℓ and m.

Trapezoid (pp. 288, 322) A trapezoid is a quadrilateral with exactly one pair of parallel sides, the *bases.* The nonparallel sides are called the *legs* of the trapezoid. Each pair of angles adjacent to a base are *base angles* of the trapezoid. An *altitude* of a trapezoid is a perpendicular segment from one base to the line containing the other base. Its length is called the *height* of the trapezoid.

In trapezoid $ABCD$, $\angle ADC$ and $\angle BCD$ are one pair of base angles, and $\angle DAB$ and $\angle ABC$ are the other.

Trapecio (pp. 288, 322) Un trapecio es un cuadrilátero con exactamente un par de lados paralelos, las *bases.* Los lados no paralelos se llaman los *catetos* del trapecio. Cada par de ángulos adyacentes a la base son *ángulos de base* del trapecio. Una *altura* del trapecio es un segmento perpendicular que va de una base a la recta que contiene la otra base. Su longitud se llama, por extensión, la *altura del trapecio.*

Triangle (p. 143) A triangle is a polygon with three sides. You can choose any side to be a *base.* The *height* is the length of the altitude drawn to the line containing that base.

Triángulo (p. 143) Un triángulo es un polígono con tres lados. Se puede escoger cualquier lado como base. La *altura,* entonces, es la longitud de la altura trazada hasta la recta que contiene la base.

Trigonometric ratios (pp. 470, 477) In right triangle $\triangle ABC$ with acute angle $\angle A$,

$\sin \angle A = \sin A = \dfrac{\text{leg opposite } \angle A}{\text{hypotenuse}}$

$\cos \angle A = \cos A = \dfrac{\text{leg adjacent } \angle A}{\text{hypotenuse}}$

$\tan \angle A = \tan A = \dfrac{\text{leg opposite } \angle A}{\text{leg adjacent } \angle A}$

Razones trigonométricas (pp. 468, 475) En un triángulo rectángulo $\triangle ABC$ con ángulo agudo $\angle A$,

$\text{seno } \angle A = \text{sen } A = \dfrac{\text{cateto opuesto a } \angle A}{\text{hipotenusa}}$

$\text{coseno } \angle A = \cos A = \dfrac{\text{cateto adyacente a } \angle A}{\text{hipotenusa}}$

$\text{tangente } \angle A = \tan A = \dfrac{\text{cateto opuesto a } \angle A}{\text{cateto adyacente a } \angle A}$

Truth value (p. 69) The truth value of a statement is "true" or "false" according to whether the statement is true or false, respectively.

The truth value of the statement "If a figure is a triangle, then it has four sides" is *false.*

Valor verdadero (p. 69) El valor verdadero de un enunciado es "verdadero" o "falso" según el enunciado sea verdadero o falso, respectivamente.

Turn (p. 648) *See* **rotation.**

Two-column proof (p. 117)   *See* **proof.**

Prueba de dos columnas (p. 117)   *Ver* **proof.**

Vector (p. 490)   A vector is any quantity that has magnitude (size) and direction. You can represent a vector as an arrow that starts at one point, the *initial point*, and points to a second point, the *terminal point*. A vector can be described by *ordered pair notation* $\langle x, y \rangle$, where x represents horizontal change from the initial point to the terminal point and y represents vertical change from the initial point to the terminal point.

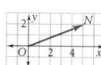

Vector ON has initial point O and terminal point N. The ordered pair notation for the vector is $\langle 5, 2 \rangle$.

Vector (p. 490)   Un vector es cualquier cantidad que tiene magnitud (tamaño) y dirección. Se puede representar un vector como una flecha que empieza en un punto, el *punto inicial,* y se dirige a un segundo punto, el *punto terminal.* Un vector se puede describir mediante la *notación de pares ordenados* $\langle x, y \rangle$, donde x representa el cambio horizontal desde el punto inicial hasta el punto final, y y representa el cambio vertical desde el punto inicial hasta el punto final.

Vertex   *See* **angle; cone; polygon; polyhedron; pyramid.** The plural form of *vertex* is *vertices.*

Vértice   *Ver* **angle; cone; polygon; polyhedron; pyramid.**

Vertex angle (p. 211)   *See* **isosceles triangle.**

Ángulo del vértice (p. 211)   *Ver* **isosceles triangle.**

Vertical angles (p. 96)   Vertical angles are two angles whose sides form two pairs of opposite rays.

$\angle 1$ and $\angle 2$ are vertical angles, as are $\angle 3$ and $\angle 4$.

Ángulos opuestos por el vértice (p. 96)   Dos ángulos son ángulos opuestos por el vértice si sus lados son rayos opuestos.

Volume (p. 544)   Volume is a measure of the space a figure occupies. A list of volume formulas is on p. 727.

The volume of this prism is 24 cubic units, or 24 units³.

Volumen (p. 544)   El volumen es una medida del espacio que ocupa una figura. Una lista de las fórmulas de volumen está en la p. 727.

Answers to Instant Check System™

Chapter 1

Diagnosing Readiness p. 2

1. 9 **2.** 16 **3.** 121 **4.** 37 **5.** 78.5 **6.** 13 **7.** 1 **8.** $-\frac{3}{5}$ **9.** 5 **10.** 8 **11.** 4 **12.** 3 **13.** 3 **14.** 6 **15.** 1

Lesson 1-1 pp. 4–6

Check Skills You'll Need **1.** 2, 4, 6, 8, 10, . . . **2.** 1, 3, 5, 7, 9, . . . **3.** $1^2 = 1, 2^2 = 4, 3^2 = 9, 4^2 = 16, 5^2 = 25, 6^2 = 36, 7^2 = 49, 8^2 = 64, 9^2 = 81, 10^2 = 100$ **4.** It is odd.

Check Understanding **1a.** 29, 37 **b.** Thursday, Friday **c.**

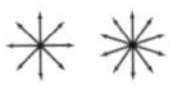

2. The sum of the first 35 odd numbers is 35^2, or 1225.

3. Answers may vary. Sample: True; the product of 5 and any odd number is odd. False; the product of 5 and any number ends in 5. **4a.** 39 skateboards **b.** Not confident; December is too far away.

Lesson 1-2 pp. 10–13

Check Skills You'll Need **1.** (1, 6) **2.** (3, 2) **3.** (5, 10)

4.

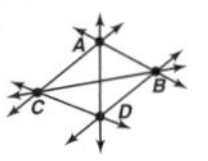

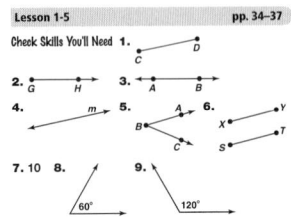

Check Understanding **1a.** no **b.** Answers may vary. Sample: $\overleftrightarrow{EF}$, $\overleftrightarrow{FC}$, $\overleftrightarrow{CE}$ **c.** Arrowheads are used to show that the line extends in opposite directions without end. **2.** Answers may vary. Sample: *HEF, HEFG, FGH* **3.** *ABF* and *CBF* **4a.** *D* **b.** *B*

Lesson 1-3 pp. 17–19, 23

Check Skills You'll Need **1.** no **2.** yes **3.** no **4–9.** Answers may vary. Samples are given. **4.** *NMR* **5.** *PQL* **6.** *NKL* **7.** *PQR* **8.** *PKN* **9.** *LQR*

Check Understanding **1.** No, they do not have the same endpoint. **2a.** $\overrightarrow{HI}$, $\overrightarrow{DN}$ **b.** $\overrightarrow{AB}$, $\overrightarrow{CD}$, $\overrightarrow{CH}$ **c.** $\overrightarrow{DN}$, $\overrightarrow{HI}$; $\overrightarrow{DN}$, $\overrightarrow{HC}$ **3a.** *PSWT* ∥ *RQVU*, *PRUT* ∥ *SQVW*, *PSQR* ∥ *TWVU* **b.** $\overleftrightarrow{TV}$ **c.** Answers may vary. Sample: $\overleftrightarrow{PS}$

Checkpoint Quiz 1 **1.** 29, 31.5 **2.** 3.45678, 3.456789 **3.** For 1: Add 2.5. For 2: Extend the decimal to one more place with a digit that is 1 more than the one to its left. **4.** yes, plane *AEF* **5.** yes, plane *DCEF* **6.** No; *H*, *G*, and *F* are in the front plane, *B* is not. **7.** No; *A*, *E*, and *B* are in the top plane, *C* is not. **8.** $\overline{CD}$, $\overline{AB}$, $\overline{EF}$ **9.** Answers may vary. Sample: $\overleftrightarrow{AE}$ and $\overleftrightarrow{BC}$ **10.** *H*

Lesson 1-4 pp. 25–29

Check Skills You'll Need **1.** 6 **2.** 3.5 **3.** 3 **4.** 6 **5.** 2 **6.** 9 **7.** 4 **8.** 9 **9.** $\frac{1}{3}$

Check Understanding **1a.** $CD = DE$ **b.** yes; $|-5 - (-8)| = |3| = 3$ **2.** 15; $EF = 40$, $FG = 60$ **3.** 13.5 **4a.** ∠2, ∠*DEC* **b.** No; 3 ∠s have *E* for a vertex, so you need more info. in the name to distinguish them from one another. **5a.** 30; acute **b.** 90; right **c.** 140; obtuse **6.** 35

Lesson 1-5 pp. 34–37

Check Skills You'll Need **1.**

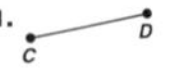

2.

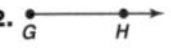

3.

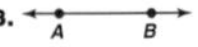

4.

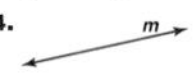

5.

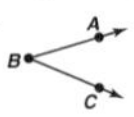

6.

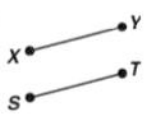

7. 10 **8.**

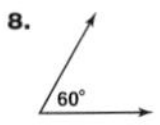

9.

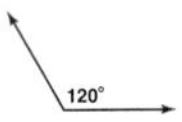

Check Understanding **1.**

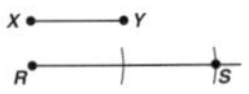

2.

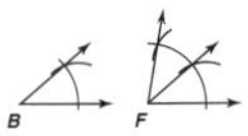

3.

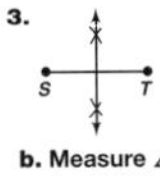

4. 50; 100

5a.

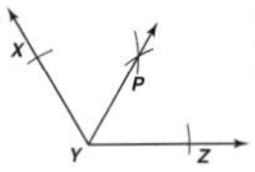

b. Measure ∠*XYP* and ∠*PYZ* to see that they are ≅.

Lesson 1-6 pp. 43–45, 49

Check Skills You'll Need **1.** 5.0 **2.** 4.1 **3.** 11.1 **4.** 100 **5.** 100 **6.** 58 **7.** 196 **8.** 10 **9.** −1

Check Understanding **1a.** 8.6 **b.** Yes; the differences are opposites, and the square of a number and the square of its opposite are the same. **2a.** about 8.9 mi **b.** about 3.2 mi **3.** (4, 4) **4.** (6, −9)

Checkpoint Quiz 2 **1.** 17 **2.** 110 **3.** 140 **4a.** 90 **b.** 60 **5.** ∠*APT* ≅ ∠*RPT* **6.** 45

7.

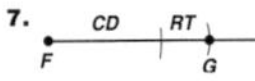

8.

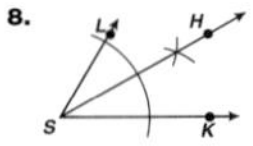

9. 12.2 units **10.** (1, 1.5)

Lesson 1-7 pp. 51–54

Check Skills You'll Need **1.** 4 **2.** 15 **3.** 8 **4.** 6.7 **5.** 3.2 **6.** 7.8 **7.** 4.5 **8.** 13.0 **9.** 7.8

Check Understanding **1a.** 26 in. **b.** 30 in. **2a.** 36π m **b.** 56.5 m **3.**

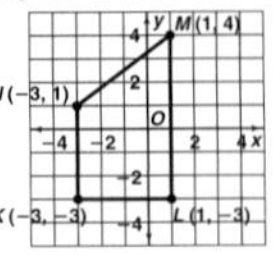

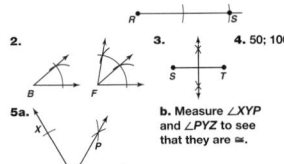

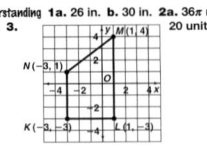

20 units

4. $9\frac{1}{3}$ yd^2; $9\frac{1}{3}$ is one ninth of 84.

5a. $\frac{25}{4}\pi$ ft^2 **b.** 19.6 ft^2

6.

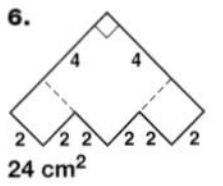

24 cm^2

Chapter 2

Diagnosing Readiness p. 66

1. 50 **2.** −3 **3.** $25\frac{1}{2}$ **4.** 10.5 **5.** 15 **6.** 11 **7.** 20 **8.** −5 **9.** −4 **10.** 5 **11.** 6 **12.** 7 **13.** 18 **14.** ∠*ACD*, ∠*DCA* **15.** C **16.** 3 **17.** ∠*ADB* or ∠*BDA* **18.** $\overline{CD}$ **19.** 45 **20.** 48, 42

Lesson 2-1 pp. 68–70

Check Skills You'll Need **1.** −1 **2.** −2, 2 **3.** 2 **4.** −4, **5.** 0 **6.** −1

Check Understanding **1.** Hypothesis: $y - 3 = 5$, Conclusion: $y = 8$ **2a.** If an integer ends with 0, then it is divisible by 5. **b.** If a figure is a square, then it has 4 congruent sides. **3.** The conditional is false; New Mexico is a counterexample.

4.

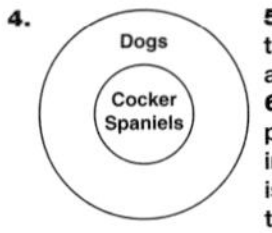

5. If two lines are skew, then they are not parallel and do not intersect. **6a.** If two lines are parallel, then they do not intersect. The conditional is false and the converse is true. **b.** If $|x| = 2$, then $x = 2$. The conditional is true and the converse is false. **7.** Answers may vary. Sample: The statement "I breathe when I sleep" can be rewritten as "If I sleep, then I breathe." The statement "I sleep when I breathe" can be rewritten as "If I breathe, then I sleep." The two statements are converses, and do not have the same meaning.

Lesson 2-2 pp. 75–77

Check Skills You'll Need **1.** Hypothesis: $x > 10$, Conclusion: $x > 5$ **2.** Hypothesis: You live in Milwaukee. Conclusion: You live in Wisconsin. **3.** If a figure is a square, then it has four sides. **4.** If something is a butterfly, then it has wings. **5.** If we go on a picnic, then the sun shines. **6.** If two lines do not intersect, then they are skew. **7.** If $x^3 = -27$, then $x = -3$.

Check Understanding **1.** If three points lie on the same line, then they are collinear. The converse is also true. Three points are collinear if and only if they lie on the same line. **2.** If a number is prime, then it has only two distinct factors, 1 and itself. If a number has only two distinct factors, 1 and itself, then it is prime. **3.** Conditional: If an angle is a right angle, then its measure is 90. Converse: If an angle has measure 90, then it is a right angle. The two statements are true. An angle is a right angle if and only if its measure is 90. **4.** It is not a good definition because a rectangle has four right angles and is not necessarily a square.

Lesson 2-3 pp. 82–84, 88

Check Skills You'll Need **1.** If your grades suffer, then you don't sleep enough. **2.** If you must start early, then you want to arrive on time. **3.** If a year is a leap year, then it has 366 days. **4.** If students do not complete their homework, then they will have lower grades. **5.** If two lines are perpendicular, then they meet to form right angles. **6.** If a person is 16 years old, then that person is a teenager.

Check Understanding **1.** No, there could be other things wrong with the car, such as a faulty starter. **2.** Answers may vary. Sample: Vladimir Nuñez should not pitch a complete game on Tuesday.

3. Not possible; you do not know that the hypothesis is true. **4a.** If a number ends in 0, then it is divisible by 5. **b.** Not possible; the conclusion of one statement is not the hypothesis of the other statement. **5.** The Volga River is less than 2300 miles long. The Volga River is not one of the world's ten longest rivers.

Checkpoint Quiz 1 **1.** Hypothesis: $x > 5$, Conclusion: $x^2 > 25$ **2.** If something is a rose, then it is a beautiful flower. **3.** If an integer is divisible by 2, then the integer ends with 0. **4.** Answers may vary. Sample: 42 is divisible by 2, but it does not end with 0. **5.** If an angle is an acute angle, then its measure is between 0 and 90. If an angle's measure is between 0 and 90, then it is an acute angle. **6.** Points are collinear if and only if they lie on the same line. **7.** Answers may vary. Sample: A graphing calculator has a keyboard and a memory. **8.** Theresa has passing grades. **9.** If a student studies geometry, then the student's mind is expanded. **10.** not possible

Lesson 2-4 pp. 89–91

Check Skills You'll Need **1.** ∠*AOB*, ∠*BOA* **2.** *O* **3.** $\overrightarrow{OB}$ **4.** 45 **5.** $\overrightarrow{OA}$ and $\overrightarrow{OC}$

Check Understanding **1.** Subst. Prop.; Subtr. Prop. of =; Div. Prop. of = **2.** $AB = 12$; $BC = 9$; $AB + BC = 12 + 9 = 21$ **3a.** Reflexive Prop. of ≅ **b.** Transitive or Subst. Prop. of ≅

Lesson 2-5 pp. 96–99

Check Skills You'll Need **1.** 50 **2.** 90 **3.** 35 **4.** right ∠s **5.** vertex

Check Understanding **1a.** Answers may vary. Sample: ∠*AFB* and ∠*BFC*; ∠*BFD* and ∠*DFE* **b.** 153 **2a.** Yes; the ≅ segments are marked. **b.** No; there are no markings. **c.** No; there are no markings. **d.** No; there are no markings. **e.** Yes; the ≅ segments are marked. **3.** No; no; the size of the ∠s does not affect the proof or the truth value of the thm. **4a.** 140 **b.** 40 **c.** 140 + 40 = 180

Chapter 3

Diagnosing Readiness p. 112

1. 72 **2.** 1260 **3.** 2700 **4.** 4 **5.** 15 **6.** −24

7. $2x + x + x = 180$; 45, 45, 90

8. $\frac{1}{2}x + x + x = 180$; 36, 72, 72

9.

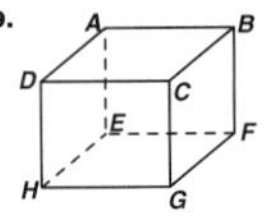

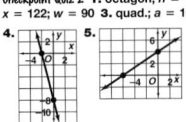

$\overleftrightarrow{AB}$ and $\overleftrightarrow{GH}$; $\overleftrightarrow{AE}$ and $\overleftrightarrow{EF}$

10–12. Check students' work.

Lesson 3-1 pp. 115–118

Check Skills You'll Need **1.** 30 **2.** 30 **3.** 60 **4.** 9 **5.** $m\angle 1 + 2(90 - m\angle 1) = 146$; $m\angle 1 = 34$ **6.** 72 and 108

Check Understanding **1.** ∠5 and ∠4; ∠6 and ∠2; ∠3 and ∠8 **2.** same-side int. ∠s **3.** 1. *a* ∥ *b* (Given) 2. $m\angle 3 + m\angle 2 = 180$ (∠ Add. Post.) 3. $m\angle 1 = m\angle 3$ (Corr. ∠s Post.) 4. $m\angle 1 + m\angle 2 = 180$ (Subst.) 5. ∠1 and ∠2 are suppl. (Def. of Suppl. ∠s) **4a.** 130; corr. ∠s are ≅. **b.** 130; vert. ∠s are ≅. **c.** 50; alt. int. ∠s are ≅. **d.** 50; alt. int. ∠s are ≅. **e.** 130; same-side int. ∠s are suppl. **f.** 50; corr. ∠s are ≅ or vert. ∠s are ≅. **5.** $x = 45$, $y = 115$; 90, 90, 115, 65

Lesson 3-2 pp. 122–125

Check Skills You'll Need **1.** 11 **2.** 4 **3.** 26 **4.** 6 **5.** If a △ has a 90° ∠, then it is a right △; true. **6.** If two ∠s are ≅, then they are vert. ∠s; false. **7.** If two ∠s are suppl., then they are same-side int. ∠s; false.

Check Understanding **1.** If corr. ∠s are ≅, then the lines are ∥. **2.** $\overleftrightarrow{EC} \parallel \overleftrightarrow{DK}$; Conv. of Corr. ∠s Post. **3.** no **4.** 18; $7 \cdot 18 - 8 = 118$, and $62 + 118 = 180$. **5.** By def. of ⊥, all ∠s formed are 90°. So, the sum of the measures of each pair of same-side int. ∠s is 180, making them suppl. By the Conv. of the Same-Side Int. ∠s Thm., the lines are ∥.

Lesson 3-3 pp. 131–134, 139

Check Skills You'll Need **1.** right **2.** acute **3.** acute **4.** 60 **5.** 20 **6.** 32 **7.** 58

Check Understanding **1a.** 32 **b.** The sum of the measures of the ∠s of a △ is 180. If you subtract the measure of the right ∠ from 180, you get 90. The sum of the other two ∠s is 90, so they are compl. **2.** For △*GFH*, $65 + (39 + 21) + z = 180$. Then $125 + z = 180$ and $z = 55$.

3a.

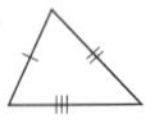

b.

c. Not possible; an equilateral △ has all acute ∠s.

4a. 90 **b.** If the acute ∠s of a △ are compl., then the △ is a right △. True because the two compl. ∠s add to 90, leaving 90 for the third ∠. **5a.** 130 **b.** Answers may vary. Sample: Find the measure of the third ∠ of the △. Subtract this from 180.

Checkpoint Quiz 1 **1.** Corr. ∠s Post. **2.** Conv. of Corr. ∠s Post. **3.** Same-Side Int. ∠s Thm. **4.** Conv. of the Alt. Int. ∠s Thm. **5.** Vert. ∠s Thm. **6.** Alt. Int. ∠s Thm. **7.** Conv. of Corr. ∠s Post. **8.** Corr. ∠s Post. **9.** Conv. of Same-Side Int. ∠s Thm. **10.** 38, 55, 87; acute, 55, 26, 99; obtuse

Lesson 3-4 pp. 143–146

Check Skills You'll Need **1.** $m\angle DAB = 77$; $m\angle B = 65$; $m\angle BCD = 131$; $m\angle D = 87$ **2.** $m\angle D = m\angle B = 60$; $m\angle DAB = m\angle DCB = 120$ **3.** $m\angle A = 70$; $m\angle ABC = 85$; $m\angle C = 125$; $m\angle ADC = 80$

Check Understanding **1.** *ABE*; sides: $\overline{AB}$, $\overline{BE}$, $\overline{EA}$; ∠s: ∠*A*, ∠*ABE*, ∠*BEA*; *BCDE*; sides: $\overline{BC}$, $\overline{CD}$, $\overline{DE}$, $\overline{EB}$; ∠s: ∠*EBC*, ∠*C*, ∠*D*, ∠*DEB*; *ABCDE*; sides: $\overline{AB}$, $\overline{BC}$, $\overline{CD}$, $\overline{DE}$, $\overline{EA}$; ∠s: ∠*A*, ∠*ABC*, ∠*C*, ∠*D*, ∠*AED* **2a.** hexagon; convex **b.** octagon; concave **c.** 24-gon; concave **3a.** 1980 **b.** You can solve the equation $(n - 2)180 = 720$. **4.** 108 **5.** 30; no, it is not formed by extending one side of the polygon.

Lesson 3-5 pp. 152–154

Check Skills You'll Need **1.** $-\frac{2}{3}$ **2.** $\frac{5}{3}$ **3.** 0 **4.** undefined or no slope **5.** $\frac{2}{3}$ **6.** $\frac{3}{2}$ **7.** $\frac{4}{5}$ **8.** −1

Check Understanding

1.

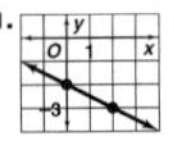

2.

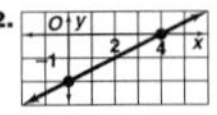

3.

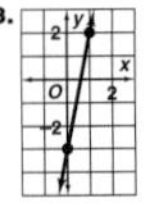

4. $y + 4 = -1(x - 2)$

5. $y - 0 = -\frac{3}{2}(x - 5)$ or $y + 3 = -\frac{3}{2}(x - 7)$

6. $y = -1$; $x = 5$

Lesson 3-6 pp. 158–161, 164

Check Skills You'll Need **1.** $\frac{1}{2}$ **2.** $\frac{5}{2}$ **3.** −5 **4.** 2 **5.** −1 **6.** $\frac{2}{3}$ **7.** 1 **8.** 0 **9.** $\frac{2}{3}$

Check Understanding **1.** No; the slope of $\ell_3 = -\frac{1}{7}$, and the slope of $\ell_4 = -\frac{1}{6}$. **2a.** Yes; each line has a slope of $-\frac{1}{2}$, and the *y*-intercepts are different. **b.** No; the lines have the same slope and *y*-intercept, so they are the same line. **3.** $y - 5 = -1(x + 2)$ **4.** No; the slope of $\ell_3 = \frac{4}{9}$, and the slope of $\ell_4 = -\frac{7}{3}$, and $\frac{4}{9} \cdot -\frac{7}{3} \neq -1$. **5.** $y + 4 = -5(x - 15)$ **6.** $y - 8 = \frac{3}{2}(x - 2)$ or $y = \frac{3}{2}x + 5$

Checkpoint Quiz 2 **1.** octagon; $n = 125$ **2.** hexagon; $x = 122$; $w = 90$ **3.** quad.; $a = 105$; $m = 116$

4.

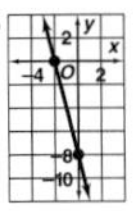

5.

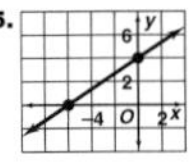

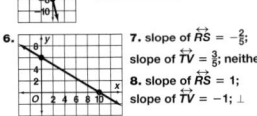

6.

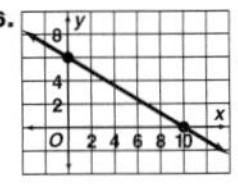

7. slope of $\overleftrightarrow{RS} = -\frac{2}{5}$; slope of $\overleftrightarrow{TV} = \frac{3}{5}$; neither

8. slope of $\overleftrightarrow{RS} = 1$; slope of $\overleftrightarrow{TV} = -1$; ⊥

9. slope of $\overleftrightarrow{RS} = -\frac{5}{4}$; slope of $\overleftrightarrow{TV} = \frac{4}{5}$; ⊥

10. slope of $\overleftrightarrow{RS} = \frac{2}{9}$; slope of $\overleftrightarrow{TV} = \frac{2}{9}$; ∥

Lesson 3-7 pp. 165–167

Check Skills You'll Need **1.**

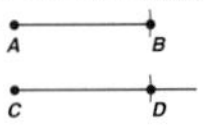

$\overline{AB} \cong \overline{CD}$

2.

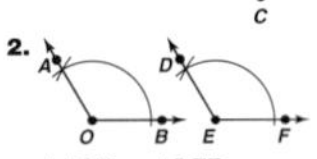

∠*AOB* ≅ ∠*DEF*

3.

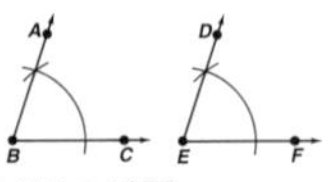

∠*ABC* ≅ ∠*DEF*

4.

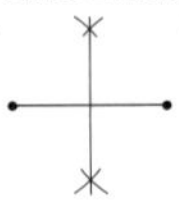

5.

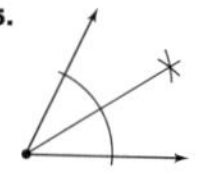

6.

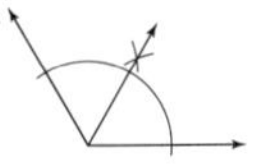

Check Understanding **1.** If corr. ∠s are ≅, the lines are ∥ by the Conv. of Corr. ∠s Post.

2.

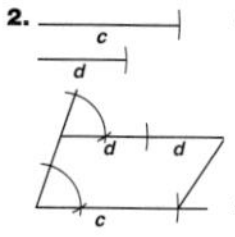

c
d
d
d
c

3.

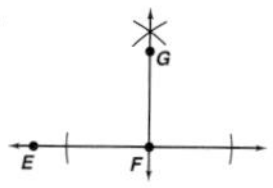

G
E
F

4.

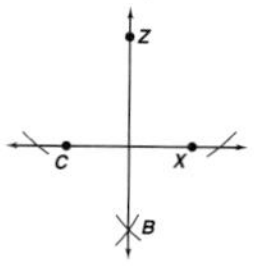

Z
C
X
B

Chapter 4

Diagnosing Readiness p. 178

1. $AB = 4, BC = 3, AC = 5$ **2.** $AB = 8, BC = \sqrt{265}, AC = \sqrt{137}$ **3.** $AB = \sqrt{58}, BC = 4\sqrt{2}, AC = \sqrt{58}$ **4.** $\angle A \cong \angle C$ **5.** $m\angle A = 90 = m\angle B$ or $\angle A$ and $\angle B$ are rt. ⦣s. **6.** $\angle B$ is a rt. $\angle$. **7.** $\angle AFB \cong \angle DFC$ **8.** $\angle A \cong \angle D$ and $\angle B \cong \angle C$ **9.** $\angle ACD \cong \angle CAB$ and $\angle DAC \cong \angle BCA$ **10.** $x = 12$

Lesson 4-1 pp. 180–182

Check Skills You'll Need **1.** 19 **2.** 13 **3.** 108 **4.** 10 **5.** 50

Check Understanding **1.** $\angle WSY \cong \angle MVK$; $\angle SWY \cong \angle VMK$; $\angle WYS \cong \angle MKV$; $\overline{WY} \cong \overline{MK}$; $\overline{WS} \cong \overline{MV}$; $\overline{YS} \cong \overline{KV}$ **2.** $m\angle K = 35$; corr. ⦣s are ≅. **3.** No; corr. sides are not necessarily ≅. **4a.** $\angle A \cong \angle D$; $\angle E \cong \angle C$ (Given) **b.** $\angle ABE \cong \angle DBC$ (Vert. ⦣s are ≅.) **c.** $\overline{AE} \cong \overline{CD}$; $\overline{AB} \cong \overline{BD}$; $\overline{EB} \cong \overline{BC}$ (Given) **d.** $\triangle ABE \cong \triangle DBC$ (Def. of ≅ △s)

Lesson 4-2 pp. 186–188

Check Skills You'll Need **1.** $\overline{AB} \cong \overline{DE}$; $\angle C \cong \angle F$ **2.** $\angle Q \cong \angle S$; $\angle QPR \cong \angle SRP$; $\overline{PR} \cong \overline{PR}$ **3.** $\angle M \cong \angle S$; $\angle MON \cong \angle SVT$; $\overline{TO} \cong \overline{NV}$; $\overline{MO} \parallel \overline{VS}$

Check Understanding **1.** You are given that $\overline{AB} \cong \overline{CB}$ and $\overline{AD} \cong \overline{CD}$. $\overline{BD} \cong \overline{BD}$ by the Refl. Prop. of ≅, so $\triangle ABD \cong \triangle CBD$ by SSS. **2.** $\angle DCA \cong \angle BAC$ or $CB = 8$ **3.** No; you don't know that $\angle E \cong \angle DBC$ or that $\overline{AB} \cong \overline{DC}$.

Lesson 4-3 pp. 194–196, 201

Check Skills You'll Need **1.** $\overline{JH}$ **2.** $\overline{HK}$ **3.** $\angle L$ **4.** $\angle N$ **5.** Reflexive Prop. of ≅ **6.** If 2 ⦣s of a △ are ≅ to 2 ⦣s of another △, the third ⦣s are ≅.

Check Understanding **1.** No; the ≅ side is not the included side. **2.** 1. $\angle CAB \cong \angle DAE$; $\overline{AB} \cong \overline{AE}$ (Given) 2. $\angle ABC$ and $\angle AED$ are right ⦣s. (Given) 3. $\angle ABC \cong \angle AED$ (All right ⦣s are ≅.) 4. $\triangle ABC \cong \triangle AED$ (ASA)

3.

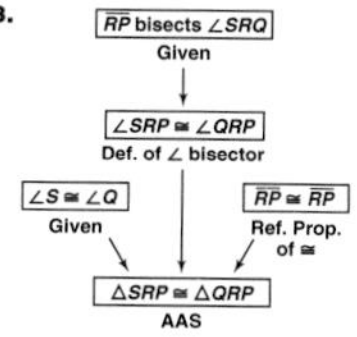

RP bisects ∠SRQ
Given
∠SRP ≅ ∠QRP
Def. of ∠ bisector
∠S ≅ ∠Q
Given
RP ≅ RP
Ref. Prop. of ≅
△SRP ≅ △QRP
AAS

4a. If lines ∥, then alt. int. ⦣s are ≅. **b.** $\triangle XMQ \cong \triangle RMT$ because vert. ⦣s are ≅.

Checkpoint Quiz 1 **1.** $\overline{RS} \cong \overline{JK}$; $\overline{ST} \cong \overline{KL}$; $\overline{RT} \cong \overline{JL}$; $\angle R \cong \angle J$; $\angle S \cong \angle K$; $\angle T \cong \angle L$ **2.** ASA **3.** SSS **4.** SAS **5.** not possible **6.** AAS **7.** not possible **8.** If ∥ lines, then alt. int. ⦣s are ≅. **9.** Vert. ⦣s are ≅. **10.** ASA or AAS

Lesson 4-4 pp. 203–204

Check Skills You'll Need **1.** $\angle J \cong \angle H$; $\angle R \cong \angle V$; $\angle C \cong \angle G$ **2.** $\overline{JR} \cong \overline{HV}$; $\overline{RC} \cong \overline{VG}$; $\overline{JC} \cong \overline{HG}$ **3.** $\angle T \cong \angle L$; $\angle I \cong \angle O$; $\angle C \cong \angle K$ **4.** $\overline{TI} \cong \overline{LO}$; $\overline{IC} \cong \overline{OK}$; $\overline{TC} \cong \overline{LK}$

Check Understanding **1a.** They are ≅ because suppl. of ≅ ⦣s are ≅. **b.** As point S is moved toward point C, $\angle LSC$ and $\angle RSC$ change shape, but they are always ≅ to each other. **2.** 50 ft

Lesson 4-5 pp. 210–212

Check Skills You'll Need **1.** $\angle C$ **2.** $\angle A$ **3.** $\overline{BC}$ **4.** $\overline{BA}$ **5.** 105

Check Understanding **1.** Draw $\overline{XB}$, the bisector of $\angle YXZ$. Then, since $\angle Z \cong \angle Y$ and $\overline{XB} \cong \overline{XB}$ by the Reflexive Prop. of ≅, $\triangle ZXB \cong \triangle YXB$ by AAS. Then $\overline{XZ} \cong \overline{XY}$ by CPCTC. **2.** No; neither $\angle RVU$ nor $\angle RUV$ can be shown ≅ to $\angle R$. **3.** $x = 90$; $y = 47$ **4.** 150

Lesson 4-6 pp. 217–219, 223

Check Skills You'll Need **1.** yes **2.** yes **3.** no **4.** yes **5.** yes **6.** no **7.** yes; SAS **8.** yes; SAS

Check Understanding **1.** $\triangle LMN \cong \triangle OQP$ **2.** $\overline{CB} \cong \overline{EB}$ and $m\angle CBD = m\angle EBA$ because $\overline{AD}$ is the ⊥ bis. of $\overline{CE}$. It is given that $\overline{CD} \cong \overline{EA}$. $\triangle CBD \cong \triangle EBA$ by HL. **3.** The △s are ≅ by SAS.

Checkpoint Quiz 2 **1.** $\overline{PR} \cong \overline{SQ}$; $\angle P \cong \angle S$; $\angle PRQ \cong \angle SQR$ **2a.** Isosc. △ **b.** ≅ **c.** Converse of the Isosc. △ Thm. **3.** $\triangle AED$; $\angle EAB \cong \angle EDC$ (Given), $\triangle EBC$; $\angle EBC \cong \angle ECB$ (Suppl. of ≅ ⦣s are ≅.) **4.** HL **5.** $\triangle GTW \cong \triangle SWT$ by SAS since $\overline{WT} \cong \overline{WT}$, $\angle WTG \cong \angle TWS$, and $\overline{GT} \cong \overline{SW}$. So $\overline{GW} \cong \overline{ST}$ by CPCTC.

Lesson 4-7 pp. 224–226

Check Skills You'll Need **1.** 15; 31 **2a.** yes; SAS **b.** yes; AAS **c.** yes; Trans. Prop. of ≅

Check Understanding **1a.** $\overline{CD}$ **b.** Answers may vary. Sample: $\triangle ABD$ and $\triangle CBD$; $\overline{BD}$ **2.** 1. $\triangle ACD \cong \triangle BDC$ (Given) 2. $\angle ADC \cong \angle BCD$ (CPCTC) 3. $\overline{CE} \cong \overline{DE}$ (If base ⦣s are ≅, the opp. sides are ≅.) **3.** 1. $\overline{PS} \cong \overline{RS}$; $\angle PSQ \cong \angle RSQ$ (Given) 2. $\overline{QS} \cong \overline{QS}$ (Reflexive Prop. of ≅) 3. $\triangle PSQ \cong \triangle RSQ$ (SAS) 4. $\overline{PQ} \cong \overline{RQ}$ (CPCTC) 5. $\angle PQT \cong \angle RQT$ (CPCTC) 6. $\overline{QT} \cong \overline{QT}$ (Reflexive Prop. of ≅) 7. $\triangle PQT \cong \triangle RQT$ (SAS) **4.** 1. $\angle CAD \cong \angle EAD$; $\angle C \cong \angle E$ (Given) 2. $\overline{AD} \cong \overline{AD}$ (Reflexive Prop. of ≅) 3. $\triangle ACD \cong \triangle AED$ (AAS) 4. $\overline{CD} \cong \overline{ED}$ (CPCTC) 5. $\angle BDC \cong \angle FDE$ (Vert. ⦣s are ≅.) 6. $\triangle BDC \cong \triangle FDE$ (ASA) 7. $\overline{BD} \cong \overline{FD}$ (CPCTC)

Chapter 5

Diagnosing Readiness p. 240

1. $x \leq 4$ **2.** $x > \frac{15}{2}$ **3.** $x \leq 1$

4.

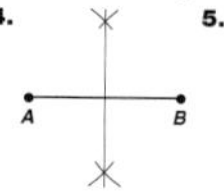

A
B

5.

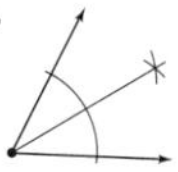

6. 5 **7.** 13 **8.** $4\sqrt{5}$ **9.** (5, 7) **10.** $\left(-3, -\frac{7}{2}\right)$ **11.** $\left(-\frac{9}{2}, \frac{5}{2}\right)$ **12.** −9 **13.** $-\frac{8}{3}$ **14.** 0

Lesson 5-1 pp. 243–245

Check Skills You'll Need **1.** (1, 2) **2.** $\left(\frac{3}{2}, \frac{11}{2}\right)$ **3.** $\left(-\frac{1}{2}, 8\right)$ **4.** (1, 1) **5.** $-\frac{2}{5}$ **6.** $\frac{1}{3}$ **7.** $\frac{4}{7}$ **8.** $\frac{3}{2}$

Check Understanding **1.** $EB = 9$; $BC = 10$; $AC = 20$ **2.** 65; the lines are ∥ so $\angle VUZ$ and $\angle YXZ$ are corr. and ≅. **3a.** 1320 ft **b.** $\frac{1}{4}$ mi

Lesson 5-2 pp. 249–251

Check Skills You'll Need

1.

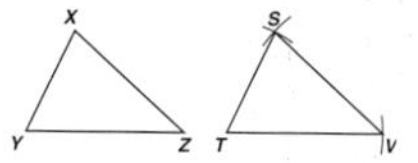

X
Y
Z
S
T
V

2.

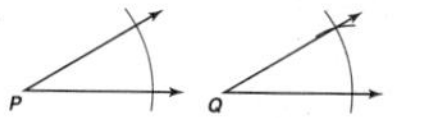

P
Q

3.

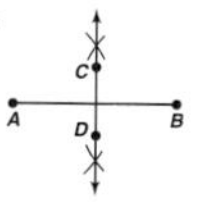

C
A
D
B

4.

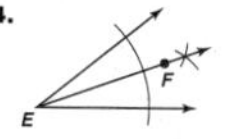

F
E

5. 6 **6.** 68

Check Understanding **1.** $CA = 5$; $DB = 6$; $\overleftrightarrow{CD}$ is the ⊥ bis. of $\overline{AB}$; therefore $CA = CB$ and $DA = DB$. **2a.** 10; 10 **b.** $\overrightarrow{EK}$ is on the ∠ bis. of $\angle DEH$. **c.** 20 **d.** 80

Lesson 5-3 pp. 256–258, 263

Check Skills You'll Need

1–2.

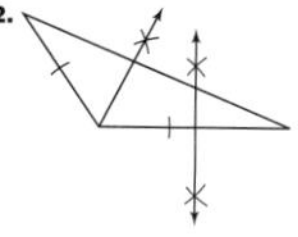

3.

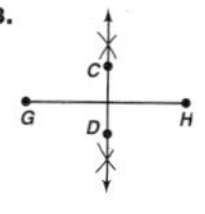

C
G
D
H

4.

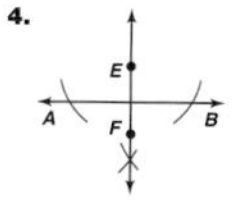

E
A
F
B

Check Understanding **1a.** (−4, 3) **b.** Thm. 5-6: All of the ⊥ bis. of the sides of a △ are concurrent. **2a.** Draw segments connecting the towns. Build the library at the inters. pt. of the ⊥ bisectors of the segments. **b.** The ⊥ bisectors of the sides of a △ are concurrent at a point equidistant from the vertices. **3.** 12 **4.** Median; $\overline{UW}$ is a segment from vertex U to the midpt. of the opp. side.

Checkpoint Quiz 1 **1.** 6 **2.** 3 **3a.** 104 **b.** 228 **4.** right ∠; suppl. to $\angle ADB$ **5.** $\triangle ABD \cong \triangle CBD$; HL **6.** $\overline{AD} \cong \overline{DC}$; CPCTC **7.** $\overrightarrow{XY}$ bisects $\angle ZXW$; Y is equidist. from $\overrightarrow{XZ}$ and $\overrightarrow{XW}$. **8.** 21; $\triangle XYZ \cong \triangle XYW$ by HL, so $XZ = 21$ by CPCTC. **9.** Answers may vary. Sample: Bisect a side of a △. Connect the opp. vertex with the midpt. **10.** Use the procedure for constructing a ⊥ to a line from a point not on the line.

Lesson 5-4 pp. 264–267

Check Skills You'll Need **1.** If we go skiing, then it snows tomorrow. **2.** If 2 lines do not intersect, then they are parallel. **3.** If $x^2 = 1$, then $x = -1$. **4.** If a point is on the bisector of an angle, then it is equidistant from the sides of the angle. If a point is equidistant from the sides of an angle, then it is on the bisector of the angle. **5.** If a point is on the ⊥ bis. of a segment, then it is equidistant from the endpoints of the segment. If a point is equidistant from the endpoints of a segment, then it is on the ⊥ bis. of the segment. **6.** If you will pass a geometry course, then you are successful with your homework. If you are successful with your homework, then you will pass a geometry course.

Check Understanding **1a.** The measure of $\angle XYZ$ is not more than 70. **b.** Today is Tuesday. **2a.** If you stand for something, you won't fall for anything. **b.** If you won't fall for anything, then you stand for something. **3a.** Assume that the shoes cost more than $20. **b.** Assume that $m\angle A \leq m\angle B$. **4.** I and II **5.** $\angle X$ could be a right ∠.

Lesson 5-5 pp. 273–276

Check Skills You'll Need

1.

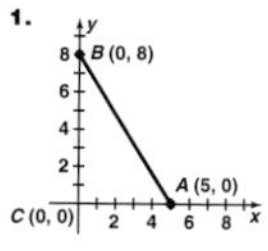

y
B (0, 8)
A (5, 0)
C (0, 0)
x

$\overline{AC}, \overline{BC}, \overline{AB}$

2.

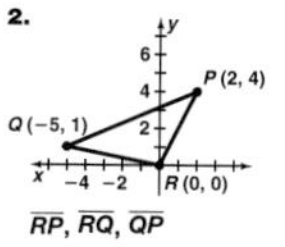

y
P (2, 4)
Q (−5, 1)
R (0, 0)
x

$\overline{RP}, \overline{RQ}, \overline{QP}$

3.

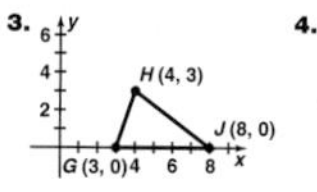

y
H (4, 3)
J (8, 0)
G (3, 0)
x

$\overline{GH}, \overline{HJ}, \overline{JG}$

4.

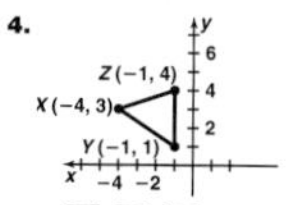

y
Z (−1, 4)
X (−4, 3)
Y (−1, 1)
x

$\overline{ZY}, \overline{XZ}, \overline{XY}$

5. Assume that $m\angle A \leq m\angle B$. **6.** $AB < AC$

Check Understanding **1.** $m\angle OTY > m\angle 2$ by the Comparison Prop. of Ineq. Since it was proven that $m\angle 2 > m\angle 3$, then by the Trans. Prop. $m\angle OTY > m\angle 3$. **2.** $\angle A, \angle C, \angle B$ **3.** $\overline{YZ}, \overline{XY}, \overline{XZ}$; $m\angle Y = 80$. **4a.** No; $2 + 7 \not> 9$. **b.** Yes; $4 + 6 > 9$; $6 + 9 > 4$; $4 + 9 > 6$. **5.** $9 < x < 15$

Chapter 6

Diagnosing Readiness p. 286

1. 30 **2.** 42 **3.** 22 **4.** yes **5.** no **6.** yes **7.** parallel **8.** perpendicular **9.** neither **10.** ASA **11.** SAS **12.** AAS

Lesson 6-1 pp. 288–290

Check Skills You'll Need **1.** 10.8 **2.** 7.8 **3.** 12.7 **4.** $\frac{3}{4}$ **5.** $-\frac{8}{3}$ **6.** 1

Check Understanding **1a.** quad., ▱, rhombus **b.** Rhombus; it is a ▱ and quad. with 4 sides that are ≅. **2.** square **3.** $a = 2, b = 4$; $LN = ST = NT = SL = 14$

Lesson 6-2 pp. 294–297

Check Skills You'll Need **1.** ASA **2a.** $\angle HGE$ **b.** $\angle GHE$ **c.** $\angle HEG$ **d.** $\overline{GH}$ **e.** $\overline{HE}$ **f.** $\overline{EG}$ **3.** They are ∥.

Check Understanding **1.** Yes; by the Converse of the Same-Side Int. ⦣s Thm., both pairs of opp. sides are ∥. **2.** 11; $m\angle E = 70, m\angle G = 70, m\angle F = 110, m\angle H = 110$ **3.** $a = 16, b = 14$ **4.** 7.5

Lesson 6-3 pp. 303–306, 310

Check Skills You'll Need **1.** $\left(\frac{5}{2}, \frac{3}{2}\right), \left(\frac{5}{2}, \frac{3}{2}\right)$; they bisect each other. **2.** Slope of $\overline{BC} = \frac{1}{3}$, slope of $\overline{AD} = \frac{1}{3}$. The slopes are =. **3.** Yes; they are vertical lines. **4.** parallelogram

Check Understanding **1.** 70, 2 **2a.** Yes; a pair of opp. sides are ∥ and ≅. **b.** No; the figure could be a trapezoid. **3.** Once in place, both rulers show the direction and remain ∥. Keep the second ruler in place and move the first ruler to get the compass reading.

Checkpoint Quiz 1 **1.** $m\angle 1 = 59, m\angle 2 = 121, m\angle 3 = 59$ **2.** $m\angle 1 = 43, m\angle 2 = 62, m\angle 3 = 62$ **3.** $m\angle 1 = 106, m\angle 2 = 74, m\angle 3 = 26$ **4.** trapezoid, isos. trapezoid **5.** rectangle, ▱ **6.** rectangle, ▱ **7.** $x = 45, y = 60$ **8.** $x = 1, y = 2$ **9.** 20.6 **10.** kite

Lesson 6-4 pp. 312–315

Check Skills You'll Need **1.** 4.5 **2.** 7 **3.** 109 **4.** 4.75 **5.** 3.5 **6.** 9.5 **7.** 71 **8.** 71

9.

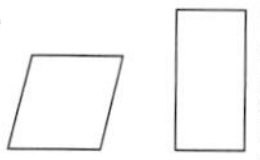

The rhombus is not a square because it has no right ⦣s. The rectangle is not a square because all 4 sides aren't ≅.

Check Understanding **1.** $\angle 1 = 90, \angle 2 = 50, \angle 3 = 50, \angle 4 = 40$ **2.** $8\frac{1}{2}$ **3.** No; if one diagonal bisects two ⦣s, then the figure is a rhombus and cannot have noncongruent sides. **4.** Yes; if the ropes are ⊥ to each other, then the endpoints of the ropes determine a square.

Lesson 6-5 pp. 320–322

Check Skills You'll Need **1.** $a = 5.6, b = 6.8$; 4.5, 4.2, 4.5, 4.2 **2.** 3; 4.8, 16.4, 18, 18 **3.** $m = 5, n = 15$; 15, 15, 21, 21

Check Understanding **1.** 110, 110, 70 **2.** 85, 95 **3.** 90, 46, 44

Lesson 6-6 pp. 326–327, 331

Check Skills You'll Need

1.

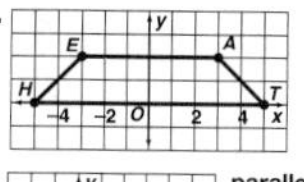

y
E
A
H
T
−4
−2
O
2
4
x

isosc. trapezoid

2.

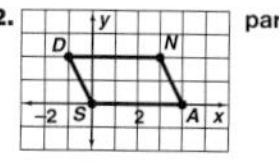

y
D
N
−2
S
2
A
x

parallelogram

3.

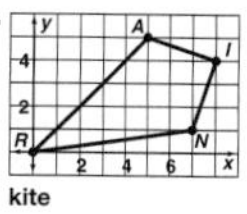

y
A
I
4
2
R
N
2
4
6
x

kite

4.

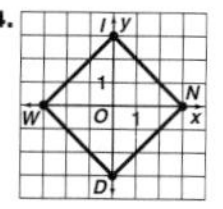

I
y
1
W
O
1
N
x
D

square

Check Understanding **1.** $Q(s + b, c)$ **2.** Midpoint of $\overline{TV} = \left(\frac{a + c + e}{2}, \frac{b + d}{2}\right)$ = midpoint of $\overline{UW}$. So, the diagonals bisect each other and $TWVU$ is a ▱.

Checkpoint Quiz 2 **1.** $x = 51, y = 51$ **2.** $x = 58, y = 32$ **3.** $x = 2, y = 4$ **4.** 3 **5.** $x = \frac{5}{3}, y = \frac{9}{2}, b = 90$ **6–8.** Counterexamples may vary.

6. false;

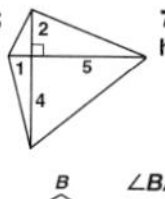

2
1
5
4

7. False; a kite can have ≅ ⊥ diags.

8. false

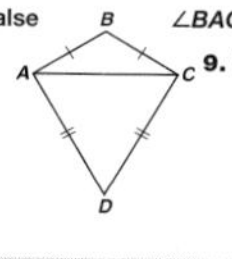

B
A
C
D

$\angle BAC \ncong \angle CAD$

9. (n, m) **10.** $(k, 0)$

Lesson 6-7 pp. 332–333

Check Skills You'll Need **1.** The quad. is a rectangle. **2.** (a, c) **3.** $(-a, 0)$

Check Understanding **1a.** $M(b, c), N(a + d, c)$; by starting with multiples of 2 you eliminate fractions when using the midpoint formula. **b.** 0, 0, 0; they are =. **c.** $MN = d + a - b$, $TP = 2a$, $RA = 2d - 2b$; so $RA + TP = 2d + 2a - 2b$ which is twice MN. So the midsegment is half the sum of the lengths of the bases. **d.** The base along the x-axis allows us to calculate length by subtracting x-values. **2.** Using multiples of 2 in the coordinates for M, N, P, and O eliminates the use of fractions when finding midpoints since finding midpoints requires division by 2.

Chapter 7

Diagnosing Readiness p. 346

1. 9 **2.** 64 **3.** 144 **4.** 225 **5.** 4 **6.** 8 **7.** 10 **8.** 13 **9.** ±6 **10.** ±10.2 **11.** ±6.9 **12.** ±8.1 **13.** $2\sqrt{2}$ **14.** $3\sqrt{3}$ **15.** $4\sqrt{3}$ **16.** $36\sqrt{2}$ **17.** $\frac{3}{5}$ **18.** $\frac{3}{10}$ **19.** 0 **20.** 1 **21.** rhombus **22.** parallelogram **23.** rhombus

Lesson 7-1 pp. 348–351

Check Skills You'll Need **1.** 25 cm^2 **2.** 28 $in.^2$ **3.** 11.5 m^2 **4.** $\frac{3}{2}$ ft^2 **5.** 6 $units^2$ **6.** 2 $units^2$ **7.** 8 $units^2$

Check Understanding **1.** 108 m^2 **2.** 20 $units^2$ **3.** 7.5 cm **4.** 30 cm^2 **5.** The force is doubled.

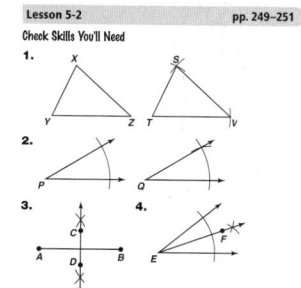

Lesson 7-2 pp. 357–360

Check Skills You'll Need **1.** $3^2 + 4^2 = 5^2$ **2.** $5^2 + 12^2 = 13^2$ **3.** $6^2 + 8^2 = 10^2$ **4.** $4^2 + 4^2 = (4\sqrt{2})^2$

Check Understanding **1.** $5\sqrt{21}$; no **2.** $6\sqrt{3}$ **3.** You want to know the nearest whole number value, which may not be apparent in a radical expression. **4.** 7 cm^2 **5.** no **6.** acute

Lesson 7-3 pp. 366–369, 372

Check Skills You'll Need **1.** 45, 45, 90 **2.** 30, 60, 90 **3.** 45, 45, 90

Check Understanding **1.** $5\sqrt{6}$ **2.** $5\sqrt{2}$ **3.** 141 ft **4.** 6; $6\sqrt{3}$ **5.** $3\sqrt{2}$; $2\sqrt{6}$ **6a.** 50 $in.^2$ **b.** $50\sqrt{3}$ $in.^2$

Checkpoint Quiz 1 **1.** 84 $in.^2$ **2.** 112 cm^2 **3.** 48 m^2 **4.** 12 **5.** $x = 10$; $y = 10\sqrt{2}$ **6.** $x = 12\sqrt{3}$; $y = 24$ **7.** acute **8.** right **9.** obtuse **10.** 28.3 cm

Lesson 7-4 pp. 373–375

Check Skills You'll Need **1.** $A = bh$ or $A = \ell w$ **2.** $A = \frac{1}{2}bh$ **3.** 9 $units^2$ **4.** 7 $units^2$ **5.** 13.5 $units^2$

Check Understanding **1.** 94.5 cm^2 **2.** 12 m^2 **3.** 54 $in.^2$ **4.** $9^2 + 12^2 = 15^2$

Lesson 7-5 pp. 380–382

Check Skills You'll Need **1.** $25\sqrt{3}$ cm^2 **2.** 50 ft^2 **3.** $\frac{100\sqrt{3}}{3}$ m^2 **4.** 24 in. **5.** $16\sqrt{3}$ cm

Check Understanding **1.** $m\angle 1 = 45$; $m\angle 2 = 22.5$; $m\angle 3 = 67.5$ **2.** 232 cm^2 **3.** $384\sqrt{3}$ ft^2 **4.** about 3352 $in.^2$

Lesson 7-6 pp. 386–389

Check Skills You'll Need **1.** 14 cm **2.** 3.2 m **3.** 5 ft **4.** 2.5 in. **5.** 32 **6.** 137 **7.** 180 **8.** 76

Check Understanding **1a.** number of hours spent doing an activity **b.** Each section represents the average of the 3600 participants' answers. **2.** $\overset{\frown}{CEA}$, $\overset{\frown}{DAE}$, $\overset{\frown}{ACD}$, $\overset{\frown}{EDC}$ **3.** 58; 180; 122; 270 **4.** 17 revolutions **5.** 1.3π m

Lesson 7-7 pp. 395–397, 400

Check Skills You'll Need **1.** 4.5 cm **2.** 16 ft **3.** 12π or about 37.7 in. **4.** 6π or about 18.8 m

Check Understanding **1.** about 41 $in.^2$ **2.** 181.5 cm^2 **3.** 13.0 cm^2

Checkpoint Quiz 2 **1.** 135 $in.^2$ **2.** 58.5 m^2 **3.** $72\sqrt{3}$ $in.^2$ **4.** $27\sqrt{3}$ ft^2 **5.** 32 yd^2 **6.** 100π $in.^2$

7. 27π m^2 **8.** $(16\pi - 32)$ cm^2 **9.** 31.4 m **10.** $\frac{9\pi}{2}$ mm

Lesson 7-8 pp. 402–404

Check Skills You'll Need **1.** $\frac{1}{3}$ **2.** $\frac{1}{2}$ **3.** 1 **4.** $\frac{1}{4}$ **5.** $\frac{1}{6}$ **6.** $\frac{1}{2}$ **7.** $\frac{1}{3}$ **8.** $\frac{1}{2}$

Check Understanding **1.** $\frac{2}{5}$ **2.** $\frac{2}{5}$ **3a.** It becomes about 8.7%, or about 4 times greater. **b.** It becomes 19.6%, or about 9 times greater. **4.** Yes; theoretically you should win 1.4 times out of 100.

Chapter 8

Diagnosing Readiness p. 414

1. $\frac{2}{3}$ **2.** 5 **3.** $\frac{4}{3a^3}$ **4.** $\frac{3x - 12}{x^2 - x}$ **5.** $\overline{DL}$ **6.** $\angle A$ **7.** $\angle DLH$ **8.** $\triangle APC$ **9.** 108 **10.** 135 **11.** 144 **12.** $166\frac{2}{3}$ **13.** $10\sqrt{3}$ **14.** $3\sqrt{2}$ **15.** $2\sqrt{3}$ **16.** $24\sqrt{3}$ $units^2$ **17.** 392.4 $units^2$

Lesson 8-1 pp. 416–418

Check Skills You'll Need **1–5.** Answers may vary. Samples are given. **1.** $\frac{1}{2}$ **2.** $\frac{2}{3}$ **3.** $\frac{3}{4}$ **4.** 1 **5.** $\frac{2}{3}$ **6.** 4 **7.** $\frac{1}{4}$ **8.** $\frac{4}{3}$ **9.** Each side of the smaller $\triangle$ is $\frac{1}{2}$ the length of a side of the larger $\triangle$.

Check Understanding **1.** 1 : 3 **2.** Answers may vary. Sample: $\frac{4}{m} = \frac{11}{n}$, $\frac{m+4}{4} = \frac{n+11}{11}$ **3a.** 0.75 **b.** 3 **4.** $3\frac{1}{2}$ in. by $2\frac{1}{2}$ in.

Lesson 8-2 pp. 423–425, 429

Check Skills You'll Need **1.** $\overline{AB} \cong \overline{HI}$; $\overline{BC} \cong \overline{IJ}$; $\overline{AC} \cong \overline{HJ}$ **2.** 6 **3.** 6 **4.** 3 **5.** 5

Check Understanding **1.** $m\angle F = 127$; BC **2.** Yes; corr. ∠s are ≅ and corr. sides are prop. **3.** 3.8 **4.** 7.2 in. by 12 in. **5.** about 32.4 cm

Checkpoint Quiz 1 **1.** 1 : 8 **2.** $\frac{b}{10}$ **3.** no; $\frac{4}{6} \neq \frac{8}{10}$ **4.** 2 **5.** $\frac{34}{7}$ **6.** 12.5 ft **7.** $\angle BDF$ **8.** BF **9.** 3 ft by 2 ft **10.** $3\frac{1}{3}$

Lesson 8-3 pp. 432–435

Check Skills You'll Need **1.** SSS **2.** SAS **3.** ASA

Check Understanding **1.** No; none of the side lengths are known. **2.** $\frac{AC}{EG} = \frac{CB}{GF} = \frac{AB}{EF} = \frac{3}{4}$, so the △s are ~ by SSS ~ Thm.; $\triangle ABC \sim \triangle EFG$. **3.** 9 **4.** 13.5 ft

Lesson 8-4 pp. 439–441

Check Skills You'll Need **1.** 6 **2.** $\frac{14}{3}$ **3.** $\frac{24}{5}$ **4.** 39 **5.** 2 **6.** $\frac{8}{3}$ **7.** $\frac{40}{9}$ **8.** 18 **9.** Sample:

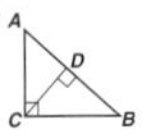

$\triangle ADC$ and $\triangle BCD$

Check Understanding **1.** $10\sqrt{3}$ **2.** $x = 8$; $y = 4\sqrt{3}$ **3.** 240 m

Lesson 8-5 pp. 446–448, 452

Check Skills You'll Need **1.** 28 cm **2.** $3\frac{3}{7}$ mm **3.** 9.8 in. **4.** 11.25 ft

Check Understanding **1.** 1.5 **2.** $x = \frac{225}{13}$; $y = 28.6$ **3.** 5.76

Checkpoint Quiz 2 **1.** $\triangle ABC \sim \triangle XYZ$; AA ~ Post. **2.** $\triangle WST \sim \triangle HJG$; SAS ~ Thm. **3.** $x = \frac{3\sqrt{13}}{2}$; $w = 4.5$ **4.** 12 **5.** 15 **6.** 7.5 **7.** $4\sqrt{5}$ **8.** 3.6 **9.** 17.5 **10.** 77

Lesson 8-6 pp. 454–456

Check Skills You'll Need **1.** 28 in.; 49 $in.^2$ **2.** 24 m; 32 m^2 **3.** 24 cm; 24 cm^2 **4.** 8 cm; 3 cm^2 **5.** 16 cm; 12 cm^2 **6.** 24 cm; 27 cm^2

Check Understanding **1a.** 5 : 7 **b.** 25 : 49 **2.** 54 $in.^2$ **3.** \$6.94 **4.** $5\sqrt{5}$: 3

Chapter 9

Diagnosing Readiness p. 468

1. 4.648 **2.** 40.970 **3.** 6149.090 **4.** −5 **5.** AA~ Post. **6.** SSS~ Thm. **7.** SAS~ Thm. **8.** 12 **9.** 8 **10.** $2\sqrt{13}$ **11.** 9

Lesson 9-1 pp. 470–472

Check Skills You'll Need **1.** 0.71, 0.71, 1 **2.** 0.71; 0.71; 1.00 **3.** 0.87; 0.5; 1.73 **4.** $\frac{12}{7}$ **5.** $\frac{54}{11}$ **6.** $\frac{15}{2}$ **7.** $\frac{60}{7}$

Check Understanding **1a.** $\frac{3}{7}$; $\frac{7}{3}$ **b.** They are reciprocals. **2a.** 13.8 **b.** 1.9 **c.** 3.8 **3.** 68

Lesson 9-2 pp. 477–478

Check Skills You'll Need **1a.** 9 **b.** 12 **2a.** 7 **b.** $2\sqrt{78}$ **3a.** 10 **b.** $3\sqrt{29}$

Check Understanding **1a.** $\sin X = \frac{64}{80}$; $\cos X = \frac{48}{80}$; $\sin Y = \frac{48}{80}$; $\cos Y = \frac{64}{80}$ **b.** $\sin X = \cos Y$ when $\angle X$ and $\angle Y$ are complementary. **2a.** about 0.72 AU **b.** 66,960,000 mi; 35,340,000 mi **3a.** 41 **b.** 68

Lesson 9-3 pp. 482–483, 488

Check Skills You'll Need **1.** $\angle 7$ **2.** $\angle 11$ **3.** $\angle 6$ **4.** 90 **5.** 180 **6.** $\angle 8$

Check Understanding **1a.** ∠ of elevation **b.** ∠ of depression **2.** about 1179 ft **3.** about 6.2 km

Checkpoint Quiz 1 **1.** $\tan A = \frac{5}{4}$; $\sin A = \frac{25}{32}$; $\cos A = \frac{5}{8}$; $\tan B = \frac{4}{5}$; $\sin B = \frac{5}{8}$; $\cos B = \frac{25}{32}$ **2.** $\tan A = \frac{5}{12}$; $\sin A = \frac{5}{13}$; $\cos A = \frac{12}{13}$; $\tan B = \frac{12}{5}$; $\sin B = \frac{12}{13}$; $\cos B = \frac{5}{13}$ **3.** $\tan A = \frac{57}{40}$; $\sin A = \frac{57}{70}$; $\cos A = \frac{4}{7}$; $\tan B = \frac{40}{57}$; $\sin B = \frac{4}{7}$; $\cos B = \frac{57}{70}$ **4.** 15.0 **5.** 61 **6.** 20.8 **7.** about 13.1 ft **8.** about 393 m **9.** Answers may vary. Sample: Identify the unknown you want to find in a right triangle. Then find two pieces of known information that will let you write a trigonometric-ratio equation you can solve for the unknown. **10.** about 22.7 m

Lesson 9-4 pp. 490–493

Check Skills You'll Need **1.** $4\sqrt{41}$ **2.** $\sqrt{13}$ **3.** $10\sqrt{65}$

Check Understanding **1.** $\langle -21.6, 46.2 \rangle$

2a.

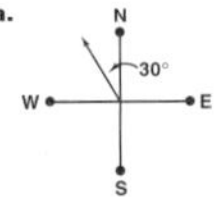

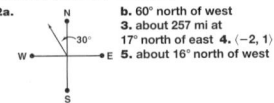

b. 60° north of west **3.** about 257 mi at 17° north of east **4.** $\langle -2, 1 \rangle$ **5.** about 16° north of west

Lesson 9-5 pp. 498–500

Check Skills You'll Need **1.** 36 m^2 **2.** 4536 $in.^2$ **3.** 168 ft^2

Check Understanding **1.** 482.8 $in.^2$ **2.** It is 4 times as large. **3.** 5081 ft^2

Chapter 10

Diagnosing Readiness p. 510

1. 44 $units^2$ **2.** $14\sqrt{3}$ $units^2$ **3.** 234 $units^2$ **4.** $54\sqrt{3}$ $units^2$ **5.** 17 **6.** $8\sqrt{2}$ **7.** 6 **8.** $4\sqrt{5}$ **9.** $6\sqrt{2}$ **10.** $4\sqrt{3}$ **11.** 24 **12.** $2\sqrt{2}$: 5

Lesson 10-1 p. 511–513

Check Skills You'll Need **1.** 24 $in.^2$ **2.** 98.4 cm^2 **3.** 684 ft^2

Check Understanding

1.

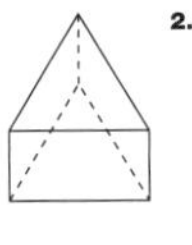

2. Answers may vary. Sample:

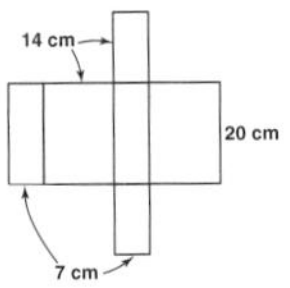

3. 12 edges

Lesson 10-2 pp. 520–522

Check Skills You'll Need

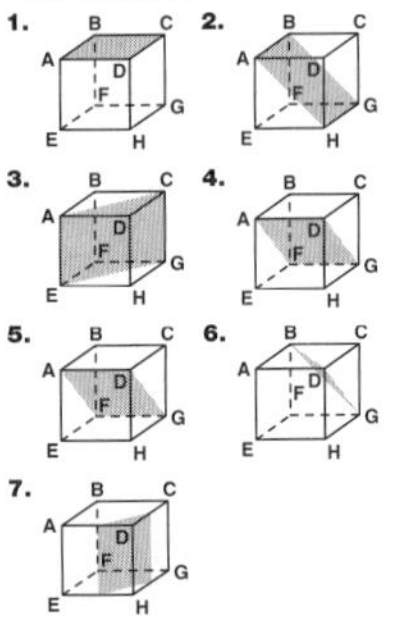

Check Understanding

1. Answers may vary. Sample:

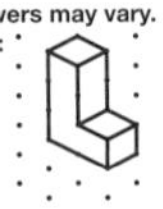

2.

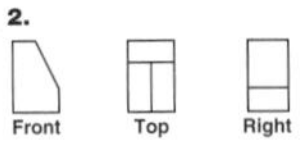

3a. 9 cubes **b.** Answers may vary. Sample: The foundation drawing; you can just add the five numbers. **4.** circle **5.** square

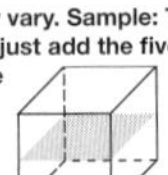

Lesson 10-3 pp. 528–531, 535

Check Skills You'll Need **1.** 96 cm^2 **2.** 40π cm^2 **3.** $36\sqrt{3}$ m^2

Check Understanding

1. 216 cm^2

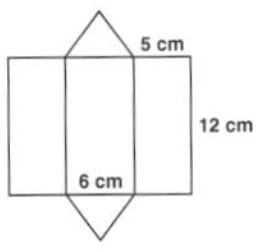

2. 432 m^2; about 619 m^2 **3.** 400π cm^2 **4a.** 33 ft^2 **b.** same as large drum (about 46 ft^2)

Checkpoint Quiz 1

1.

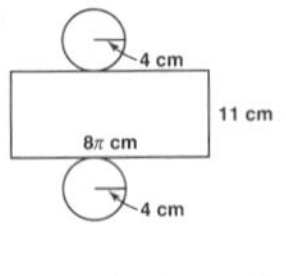

2.

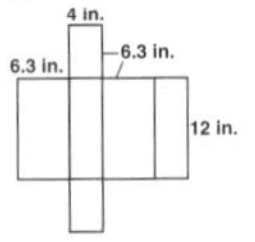

3. 120π cm^2 **4.** 297.6 $in.^2$ **5.** 4373.1 m^2 **6.** Answers may vary. Sample:

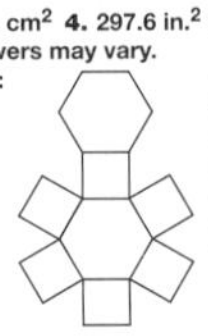

7. Both formulas involve multiplying perimeter of the base by the height. For a cylinder, the base is a circle so π is always in the formula.

8–10. Answers may vary. Samples:

8.

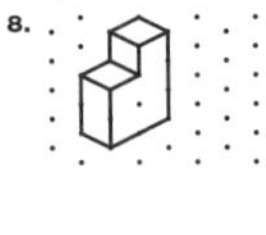

9.

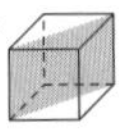

10.

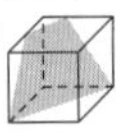

Lesson 10-4 pp. 537–540

Check Skills You'll Need **1.** $\sqrt{233}$ in. **2.** $\sqrt{130}$ m **3.** $\sqrt{313}$ cm

Check Understanding **1.** 55 m^2 **2.** 1,496,511 ft^2 **3.** 704π m^2 **4.** 1178 $in.^2$

Lesson 10-5 pp. 544–547

Check Skills You'll Need **1.** 49 cm^2 **2.** 176.7 $in.^2$ **3.** 314.2 mm^2 **4.** 3 ft^2 **5.** 154 $in.^2$ **6.** 27.5 cm^2 **7.** 27.7 $in.^2$

Check Understanding **1.** Answers may vary. Sample: Multiplication is commutative. **2.** 150 m^3 **3a.** 256π m^3 **b.** 804.2 m^3 **4.** 12 $in.^3$

Lesson 10-6 pp. 551–554

Check Skills You'll Need **1.** 12 cm **2.** 8 in. **3.** 2.5 m

Check Understanding **1.** 384 $in.^3$ **2.** 960 m^3 **3a.** 144π m^3; 452 m^3 **b.** 6174π mm^3; 19,396 mm^3 **4.** 77 ft^3

Lesson 10-7 pp. 558–560, 564

Check Skills You'll Need **1.** 113.1 $in.^2$; 37.7 in. **2.** 78.5 cm^2; 31.4 cm **3.** 19.6 ft^2; 15.7 ft **4.** 4.5 m^2; 7.5 m **5.** 706.9 yd^2; 94.2 yd **6.** 452.4 mm^2; 75.4 mm

Check Understanding **1.** 196π $in.^2$; 616 $in.^2$ **2.** 100 $in.^2$ **3.** 113,097 $in.^3$ **4.** 1258.9 ft^2

Checkpoint Quiz 2 **1.** 60.2 ft^2; 22.5 ft^3 **2.** 332.9 $in.^2$; 377.0 $in.^3$ **3.** 113.1 m^2; 113.1 m^3 **4.** 439.8 cm^2; 706.9 cm^3 **5.** 207 yd^2; 144.8 yd^3 **6.** 44.8 m^2; 16 m^3 **7.** 181.7 m^2; 2217.0 m^3 **8.** 32 ft^2; 12 ft^3 **9.** 75.4 cm^2; 37.7 cm^3 **10.** The balls; the volume of the space is $2\pi r^3$ and the volume of the balls is $4\pi r^3$.

Lesson 10-8 pp. 566–568

Check Skills You'll Need **1.** Yes; all corr. ∠s are ≅ and corr. sides are prop.; 3 : 1. **2.** Yes; all corr. ∠s are ≅ and corr. sides are prop.; $3 : \sqrt{2}$. **3.** 27 $in.^3$ **4.** 135 m^3 **5.** 402.1 cm^3

Check Understanding **1.** yes; 6 : 5 **2.** 2 : 3 **3.** 160 m^2 **4.** 0.01875 lb

Chapter 11

Diagnosing Readiness

1. 82 **2.** $6\frac{2}{3}$ **3.** 15 **4.** 25 **5.** 10 **6.** 5 **7.** 6 **8.** 18 **9.** 24 **10.** $\sqrt{2}$ **11.** 12 **12.** $4\sqrt{2}$ **13.** 13 **14.** $\sqrt{10}$ **15.** 6

Lesson 11-1 pp. 582–585

Check Skills You'll Need **1.** $p^2 + 6p + 9$ **2.** $w^2 + 20w + 100$ **3.** $m^2 - 4m + 4$ **4.** $8\sqrt{5}$ **5.** $2\sqrt{30}$ **6.** 12

Check Understanding **1.** 52 **2.** about 35.5 in. **3.** No; $4^2 + 7^2 \neq 8^2$ **4.** If $\overleftrightarrow{BC}$ and $\overleftrightarrow{GF}$ never intersect, then $BCFG$ is a rectangle. **5.** 12 cm

Lesson 11-2 pp. 590–593

Check Skills You'll Need **1.** $\frac{11\sqrt{2}}{2}$ **2.** 5 **3.** 28

Check Understanding **1.** $\angle O \cong \angle P$; $\overset{\frown}{BC} \cong \overset{\frown}{DF}$ **2.** 16 **3a.** about 11 **b.** 2.8

Lesson 11-3 pp. 598–601, 605

Check Skills You'll Need **1–3.** Answers may vary. Samples are given. **1.** $\overset{\frown}{STQ}$ **3.** $\overset{\frown}{RTQ}$ **5.** 86 **7.** 121

Check Understanding **1.** 90 **2.** $m\angle 1 = 105$, $m\angle 2 = 101$ **3.** $m\angle QJK = m\angle LJK + m\angle QJL = 35 + 90 = 125$ $m\angle QJK + \frac{1}{2}m\overset{\frown}{QLJ} = \frac{1}{2}(70 + 180) = 125$

Checkpoint Quiz 1 **1.** 76 cm **2.** 48 in. **3.** 51 m **4.** 24 **5.** 5 **6.** 8 **7.** $w = 104$; $x = 22$; $y = 108$ **8.** $a = 30$; $b = 42$; $c = 80$; $d = 116$ **9.** $w = 105$; $x = 75$; $y = 210$ **10.** $a = 140$; $b = 70$; $c = 47.5$

Lesson 11-4 pp. 607–610

Check Skills You'll Need **1.** 57 **2.** 180 **3.** 303 **4.** 28.5 **5.** 28.5 **6.** 4 **7.** 2 **8.** about 4.5 **9.** 123

Check Understanding **1a.** 250 **b.** 40 **2.** away; 20° **3a.** 13.8 **b.** 3.2 **4a.** $(8 - 4\sqrt{3})$ in. **b.** $\frac{16}{8 + 4\sqrt{3}}$ in.

Lesson 11-5 pp. 615–617, 620

Check Skills You'll Need **1.** 5.8 **2.** 12.8 **3.** 5.8

Check Understanding **1a.** $(x - 3)^2 + (y - 5)^2 = 36$ **b.** $(x + 2)^2 + (y + 1)^2 = 2$ **2.** $(x - 2)^2 + (y - 3)^2 = 13$ **3.** center: (2, 3); radius: 10

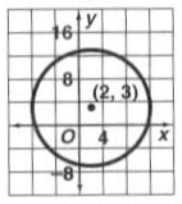

4. $(x - 0)^2 + (y - 0)^2 = x^2 + y^2 = 144$

Checkpoint Quiz 2 **1.** 58 **2.** 226 **3.** 30 **4.** about 3.0 **5.** about 15.7 **6.** 40 **7.** A chord is a segment whose endpoints are on the circle. A secant is a line, ray, or segment that intersects a circle at two points.

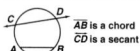

$\overline{AB}$ is a chord
$\overline{CD}$ is a secant

8. $(x - 1.5)^2 + (y - 0.5)^2 = 2.5$
9. $(x - 3.5)^2 + (y - 1)^2 = 46.25$
10. $(x + 1.5)^2 + (y + 4)^2 = 22.25$

Lesson 11-6   pp. 621–622

Check Skills You'll Need

1.   **2.**

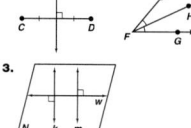

3.

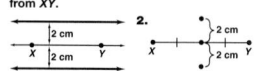

Check Understanding 1. Two lines ∥ to $\overleftrightarrow{XY}$, each 2 cm from $\overleftrightarrow{XY}$.

1.   **2.**

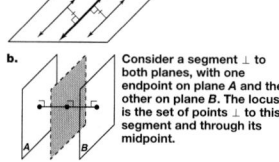

3a. Consider two ∥ lines in a plane. The locus is the line ∥ to and equidist. from the ∥ lines.

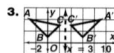

b. Consider a segment ⊥ to both planes, with one endpoint on plane *A* and the other on plane *B*. The locus is the set of points ⊥ to this segment and through its midpoint.

Chapter 12

Diagnosing Readiness   p. 632

1. △RTS **2.** △LJK **3.** △ADC **4.** △LHC
5. always **6.** never **7.** sometimes **8.** always
9. ⟨1, 5⟩ **10.** ⟨−6, 2⟩ **11.** ⟨−6, 3⟩ **12.** 108
13. 135 **14.** 144 **15.** 160 **16.** 5 : 8 **17.** 1 : 2

Lesson 12-1   pp. 634–636

Check Skills You'll Need 1. $\overline{EF}$ **2.** $\overline{AC}$ **3.** $\overline{BC}$ **4.** ∠G
5. ∠A **6.** ∠F **7.** $\overline{GL}$; ∠GRL

Check Understanding 1a. Yes; the figures are ≅ by a flip. **b.** Yes; the figures are ≅ by a flip and a slide. **2a.** ∠U; P **b.** $\overline{NI}$ and $\overline{SU}$; $\overline{ID}$ and $\overline{UP}$; $\overline{ND}$ and $\overline{SP}$

3.

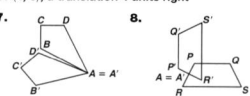

4. Yes; the intersection of $\overline{DW'}$ and *l* is the point for the location of the pump.

Lesson 12-2   pp. 641–643

Check Skills You'll Need 1. ⟨4, 3⟩ **2.** ⟨−7, 5⟩

3. $\begin{bmatrix} -7 & 3 \\ -1 & 13 \end{bmatrix}$ **4.** $\begin{bmatrix} 1 & 0 & -1 \\ -4 & -3 & -2 \end{bmatrix}$

Check Understanding 1a. *R* **b.** ⟨6, 3⟩ **2.** *L'* (1, −2), *M'*(3, −4), *N'*(6, −2) **3.** *M'* (1, 7), *F'* (4, 3), *H'* (5, 10) **4.** 1 block east and 3 blocks north of her hotel

Lesson 12-3   pp. 647–649, 652

Check Skills You'll Need 1. 120 **2.** 90 **3.** 72 **4.** 60
5. 45 **6.** 36

Check Understanding

1.   **2.** *E* **3.** 135°
   4.

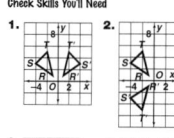

Checkpoint Quiz 1 1. No; the figures are not ≅. **2.** Yes; the figures are ≅ and the transf. is a translation. **3.** Yes; the figures are ≅ and the transf. is a translation or reflection. **4.** (−3, 5) is a translation of 3 units left, 5 units up. **5.** (−5, 10) **6.** ⟨4, 0⟩, a translation 4 units right

7.   **8.**

9. **10.** *W'* (−6, 6), *X'*(0, −2), *Y'*(−2, 2)

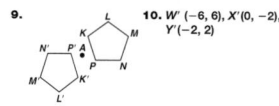
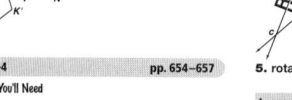

Lesson 12-4   pp. 654–657

Check Skills You'll Need

1.   **2.**

3.   **4.**

5.   **6.**

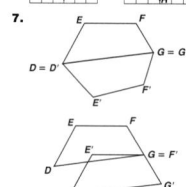

7.

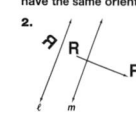

Check Understanding 1. Neither; the figures do not have the same orientation.

2. *R* is translated the distance and direction shown by the arrow. The length of the arrow is twice the distance between *ℓ* and *m*.

3. Answers may vary. Sample:

4a.

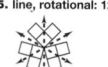

b. Yes; if you reflected it then moved it right, the result would be the same.

5. rotation

Lesson 12-5   pp. 662–663

Check Skills You'll Need 1. *G* **2.** *D* **3.** $\overline{AH}$ **4.** $\overline{CB}$

Check Understanding

1.   **2a.** yes; 180° **b.** yes
   3. rotational and reflectional symmetry

Lesson 12-6   pp. 667–669, 673

Check Skills You'll Need 1. pentagon **3.** dodecagon

Check Understanding 1a. rotation; one fish **b.** translation; horse and rider **2.** The interior △ of an equilateral △ measure 60. 60 divides 360, so it will tessellate. **3.** line symmetry, rotational symmetry, glide reflectional symmetry, translational symmetry

Checkpoint Quiz 2 1. Rotation; the image appears rotated ≈ 90°. **2.** reflection; reverse orientation

3. line, point **4.** point **5.** line, rotational: 120

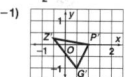

6. point **7.** rotational, reflectional, glide reflectional, and translational **8.** rotational, point, reflectional, glide reflectional, and translational **9.** reflectional, glide reflectional, and translational **10.** rotational, point, reflectional, glide reflectional, and translational

Lesson 12-7   pp. 674–675

Check Skills You'll Need 1. 3 in. by 4 in. **2.** 2 in. by $2\frac{1}{2}$ in. **3.** $1\frac{1}{2}$ in. by $2\frac{1}{4}$ in. **4.** $1\frac{1}{4}$ in. by $1\frac{3}{4}$ in.

Check Understanding 1. The dilation is a reduction with center (0, 0) and scale factor $\frac{1}{2}$. **2.** 8 cm
3. *P'*(1, 0), *Z'*(−$\frac{1}{2}$, $\frac{1}{4}$), *G'*($\frac{1}{2}$, −1)

Selected Answers

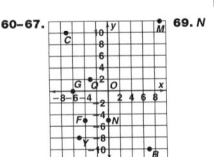

Chapter 1

Lesson 1-1   pp. 7–9
EXERCISES 1. 80, 160 **3.** –3, 4 **17.**

19. The sum of the first 6 pos. even numbers is 6·7, or 42. **21.** The sum of the first 100 pos. even numbers is 100·101, or 10,100. **23.** 555,555,555 **25–27.** Answers may vary. Samples are given. **25.** 8 + (–5) = 3 and 3 ≯ 8 **27.** –6 – (–4) = –2 and –2 ≮ –4 **29.** 75°F **31.** 31, 43
33. 0.0001, 0.00001 **43.**  **45.**

60–67. **69.** N

Lesson 1-2   pp. 13–16
EXERCISES 1. no **3.** yes; line n **11.** ABCD **13.** ABHF **17.** $\overline{RS}$ **19.** $\overleftrightarrow{UV}$ **21.** planes QUX and QUV **23.** planes UXT and WXT
25. **27.**

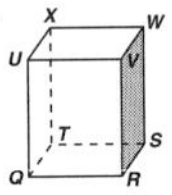

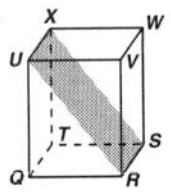

31. X **33.** Q **35.** no **37.** no **39.** coplanar **41.** coplanar **49.** not possible **51.** not possible
53.
yes **61.** never **63.** always

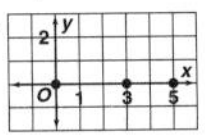

67. Post. 1-4: Through three noncollinear points there is exactly one plane.
69. A, B, and D

73. 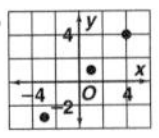
yes **91.** I, K **93.** 1024, 4096 **95.** 34

Lesson 1-3   pp. 19–23
EXERCISES 1. 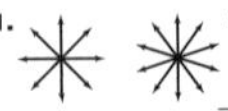 **3.**  A

5. $\overrightarrow{RS}$, $\overrightarrow{RT}$, $\overrightarrow{RW}$, $\overrightarrow{ST}$, $\overrightarrow{SW}$, $\overrightarrow{TW}$ **7a.** $\overrightarrow{TS}$ or $\overrightarrow{TR}$, $\overrightarrow{TW}$ **b.** $\overrightarrow{SR}$, $\overrightarrow{ST}$ **9.** Answers may vary. Sample: 2; $\overrightarrow{YS}$ or $\overrightarrow{YR}$, $\overrightarrow{YT}$ or $\overrightarrow{YW}$ **11.** DF **13.** $\overline{BE}$, $\overline{CF}$ **15.** $\overline{AD}$, $\overline{AB}$, $\overline{AC}$ **17.** ABC ∥ DEF **19.** Answers may vary. Sample: $\overline{CF}$, $\overline{DE}$ **21.** $\overrightarrow{FG}$ **23.** Answers may vary. Sample: $\overrightarrow{BG}$, $\overrightarrow{DH}$, $\overrightarrow{CL}$ **25.** true **27.** true **33.** Yes; both name the segment with endpoints X and Y. **35.** Yes; both are the line through pts. X and Y. **37.** always **39.** always **49a.** Answers may vary. Sample: northeast and southwest, east and west **b.** Answers may vary. Sample: northwest and southeast **53.** Answers may vary. Sample: $\overleftrightarrow{XY}$ and $\overleftrightarrow{ZW}$ intersect at R. **71–73.** Answers may vary. Samples are given. **71.** $\overleftrightarrow{EF}$ **73.** C
79.  **81.**

Lesson 1-4   pp. 29–33
EXERCISES 1. 9; 9; equal **3.** 11; 13; no **5.** XY = ZW **7.** YZ < XW **9.** 25 **11a.** b. RS = 60, ST = 36, RT = 96 **13.** 33 **15.** 130 **17.** ∠MCP, ∠PCM, ∠C, or ∠1 **19.** ∠CBD, ∠DBC **21–23.** Drawings may vary. **21.**

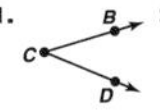

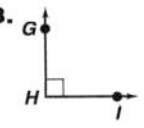

25. 90; right **27.** 34 **29.** Q **31.** –3 **33.** –2.5, 2.5 **35.** –6, –1, 1, 6 **43.** false; BD = 9, CD = 2 **45.** true; AC = 9, CD = 2, AD = 11, and 9 + 2 = 11 **47.** 115 **55.** about 42° **59–61.** Answers may vary. Samples are given. **59.** 180 **61.** 30 **65.** 125 **67–69.** Answers may vary. Samples are given. **67.** ∠QVM and ∠VPN **69.** ∠MQV and ∠PNQ **71.** y = 15; AC = 24, DC = 12 **73a.** Answers may vary. Sample: The two rays come together at a sharp point. **b.** Answers may vary. Sample: Molly had an *acute* pain in her knee. **75.** 12; m∠AOC = 82, m∠AOB = 32, m∠BOC = 50 **77.** 18; m∠AOB = 28, m∠BOC = 52, m∠AOD = 108 **87.** never **89.** always **91.** always **93.** always **95.** 25, 30 **97.** 30, 34

Lesson 1-5   pp. 37–40
EXERCISES 1.

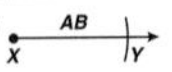

3. 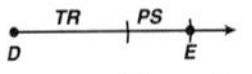 **5.** 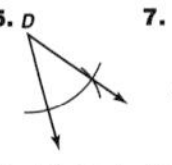 D **7.**

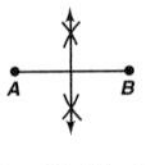

9a. 11; 30 **b.** 30 **c.** 60 **11.** 15; 48 **13.** 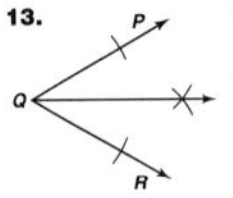 **15.**

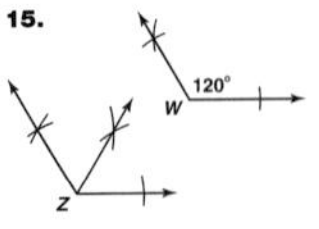

17. Find a segment on $\overrightarrow{SQ}$ so that you can construct $\overrightarrow{SP}$ as its ⊥ bisector. Then bisect ∠PSQ.

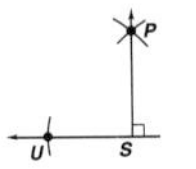

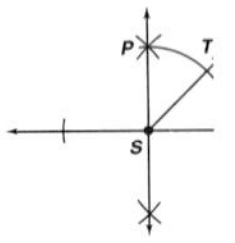

23. 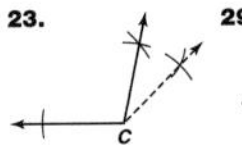 **29.**

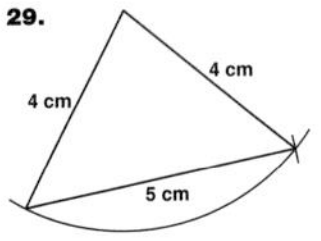

31. impossible; the short segments are not long enough to form a △. **41.** 6 **43.** 4 **49.** No; they do not have the same endpt.

Technology   p. 41
1b. Answers may vary. Sample: Construction is exact and drawing is not. **3b.** no

Lesson 1-6   pp. 46–49
EXERCISES 1. 6 **3.** 8 **11.** about 4.5 mi **13.** 6.4 **15.** 15.8 **19.** (3, 1) **21.** (6, 1) **25.** (5, –1) **27.** (12, –24) **31.** (4, –11) **33.** 5.8; (1.5, 0.5) **41.** IV

45. 10.8 units; (3, –4) **47.** Z; about 12 units **49.** 934 mi **51.** 2693 mi **53–55.** Answers may vary. Samples are given. **53.** (3, 6), (0, 4.5) **55.** (1, 0), (–1, 4)

71. 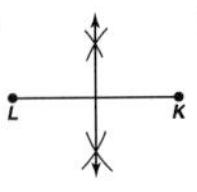 **75.** 10 **77.** ∠TAP, ∠PAT

Lesson 1-7   pp 55–58
EXERCISES 1. 22 in. **3.** 56 in. **5.** 120 m **9.** 10π ft **11.** $\frac{1}{2}\pi$ m **13.** 22.9 m **15.** 351.9 cm
17. 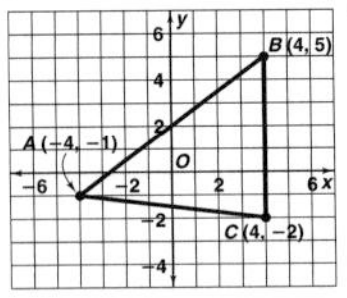 ≈ 25.1 units

21. 4320 in.², or $3\frac{1}{3}$ yd² **23.** 8000 cm², or 0.8 m² **27.** 400π cm² **29.** $\frac{9}{64}\pi$ in.² **33.** 153.9 ft² **35.** 452.4 cm² **37.** 310 m² **39.** 24 cm² **41a.** 144 in.² **b.** 1 ft² **43.** 3289 m² **45–47.** Answers may vary. Check students' work. Samples are given. **45.** 39 in.; 93.5 in.² **47.** 8 ft; 3.75 ft²
55.

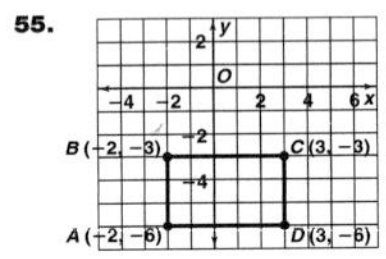

perimeter = 16 units, area = 15 units²
57. 54 units² **59.** 30 m **61.** Area; the wall is a surface. **63.** Perimeter; the fence must fit the perimeter of the garden. **79.** 8.5 units; (5.5, 5) **81.** 13.9 units; (3, 5.5) **85.** 90 **87.** 62 units **89.** 6 units

Technology   p. 59
1. square **3a.** Answers may vary. Sample: 25 ft by 36 ft; P = 122 ft, 30 ft by 30 ft; P = 120 ft, 10 ft by 90 ft; P = 200 ft **b.** 30 ft-by-30 ft square

---

Chapter Review   pp. 61–63
1. coplanar **2.** segment **3.** congruent **4.** midpoint **5.** angle bisector **6.** conjecture **7.** postulate or axiom **8.** Parallel lines **9.** obtuse angle **10.** perpendicular bisector **11.** subtract 5; 20, 15 **12.** Answers may vary. Sample: mult. by –1; 5, –5 **13.** subtr. 7; –1, –8 **14.** mult. by 4; 1536, 6144 **15.** mult. by 2; 64, 128 **16.** alternate adding 1 and 3; 10, 13 **17.** 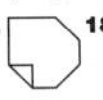 **18–23.** Answers may vary.

Samples are given. **18.** $\overrightarrow{AQ}$ and $\overrightarrow{QR}$ **19.** $\overrightarrow{AQ}$ and $\overrightarrow{BC}$ **20.** A, Q, R **21.** A, Q, R, S **22.** AQTD and BRSC **23.** $\overline{AD}$, $\overline{TD}$, $\overline{CD}$ **24.** always **25.** sometimes **26.** never **27.** never **28.** always **29.** always **30.** –7, 3 **31.** 0.5 **32.** 15 **33.** 31 **34.** $\overline{AB} \cong \overline{CD}$, $\overline{AC} \cong \overline{BD} \cong \overline{CE}$, $\overline{BC} \cong \overline{DE}$ **35.** ∠1: ∠WXY, ∠YXW; ∠2: ∠YXZ, ∠ZXY
36. 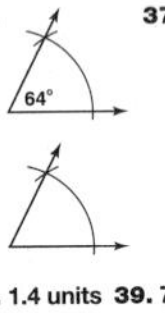 **37a–b.**

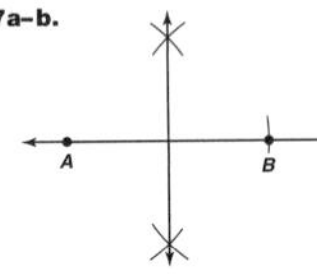

38. 1.4 units **39.** 7.6 units **40.** 14.4 units **41.** (0, 0) **42.** 7.2 units **43.** P = 32 cm, A = 64 cm² **44.** P = 38 ft, A = 78 ft² **45.** P = 32 in., A = 40 in.² **46.** C = 18.85 in., A = 28.27 in.² **47.** C = 47.12 m, A = 176.71 m² **48.** C = 163.36 m, A = 2123.72 m²

Chapter 2

Lesson 2-1   pp. 71–74
EXERCISES 1. Hypothesis: You send in the proof-of-purchase. Conclusion: They send you a get-well card. **3.** Hypothesis: x + 20 = 32, Conclusion: x = 12 **9.** If an object is glass, then it is fragile. **11.** If a whole number has 2 as a factor, then it is even. **15.** Europe **17.** Mexico
19.  **23.** If you grow, then you eat your vegetables.

25. If two segments have the same length, then they are congruent. **27.** Converse: If you have a

passport, then you travel from the United States to Kenya. The original conditional is true and the converse is false. **29.** Converse: If the chemical formula for a substance is H_2O, then it is water. Both statements are true. **33.** If a person is an Olympian, then that person is an athlete. **35.** If something is a whole number, then it is an integer. **37–39.** Answers may vary. Samples are given. **37.** If x = 1, then 2x = 2. **39.** If x = 3, then x² = 6. **41.** If a work is great, then it is made out of a combination of obedience and liberty. **43.** If x = 18, then x – 3 = 15; true. **51.** If a figure has four congruent angles, then it is a square; false; a rectangle that is not a square. **55–57.** Answers may vary. **55.** If two planes intersect, then they meet in exactly one line. **57.** If two planes are given, then there is exactly one line through them. **69.** 21 cm **71.** 23.2 m or 2320 cm **73.** 5 **75.** 9.2 **77.** Subtract 3 from the previous number; –7, –10.

Lesson 2-2   pp. 78–81
EXERCISES 1. If two segments are congruent, then they have the same length. It is true. Two segments have the same length if and only if they are congruent. **3.** If a number is even, then it is divisible by 20. It is false since 4 is even but not divisible by 20. **7.** If a line bisects a segment, then the line intersects the segment only at its midpoint. If a line intersects a segment at its midpoint, then it bisects the segment. **9.** If you live in Washington, D.C., then you live in the capital of the United States. If you live in the capital of the United States, then you live in Washington, D.C. **13.** A line, segment, or ray is a perpendicular bisector of a segment if and only if it is perpendicular to the segment at its midpoint. **15.** not reversible **19–21.** Answers may vary. Samples are given. **19.** No; it is not reversible; a cat is a counterexample. **21.** No; it is not reversible; skew lines are not parallel. **29.** Yes; ∠1 and ∠2 share a side and a vertex, and are suppl. **31.** No; ∠1 and ∠2 do not share a side, and are not suppl. **33.** The converse is false. x = –3 is a counterexample. **35.** x³ = 125 if and only if x = 5. **37.** V is a counterexample. **39.** good definition **41.** Angles are congruent if and only if they have equal measure. **43.** A number is a whole number if and only if it is a nonnegative integer. **45.** If ∠A has measure between 0 and 90, then ∠A is an acute angle. **55.** If a whole number ends in 0, then it is even. **57.** If a day is Sunday, then it is a weekend day.

---

59. 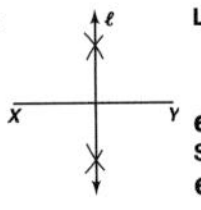
Line ℓ bisects $\overline{XY}$.

63–65. Answers may vary. Samples are given.
63. $\overleftrightarrow{AB}$, $\overleftrightarrow{CG}$ **65.** ABC, EFG

Lesson 2-3   pp. 84–87
EXERCISES 1. Felicia will pass the music theory course. **3.** Line ℓ and line m do not intersect. **5.** Figure ABCD has two pairs of parallel sides. **7.** Points X, Y, and Z are collinear. **11.** If two planes are not parallel, then they intersect in a line. **13.** If you are studying botany, then you are studying a science. **15.** Answers may vary. Sample: If you live in Little Rock, then you live in the 25th state to enter the Union. Since you live in the 25th state to enter the Union, you live in Little Rock. **17.** Must be true; by (E) and (A), it is breakfast time. **19.** Is not true; by (E) and (A), it is breakfast time and nothing else. By (C), Curtis drinks water. **19.** Is not true; by (E) and (A), it is breakfast time and nothing else. **23.** If you are in Key West, Florida, then the temperature is always above 32°F; not possible. **25.** If a figure is a square, then it is a rectangle; ABCD is a rectangle. **27.** No; red cars can never park. **29.** yes **39.** good definition **41.** Answers may vary. Sample: $\frac{1}{2}$ **43.** never

Lesson 2-4   pp. 91–94
EXERCISES 1a. ∠ Add. Post. **b.** Subst. Prop. **c.** Simplify. **d.** Subtr. Prop. **3a.** Mult. Prop. of = **b.** Distr. Prop. **c.** Add. Prop. of = **5.** Reflexive Prop. of ≅ **7.** Div. Prop. of = **17.** 5x **19.** 12 **21.** Given **b.** Def. of midpoint **c.** Subst. Prop. of = **d.** Subtr. Prop. of = **e.** Div. Prop. of = **9a.** m∠GFE + m∠EFI = m∠GFI (∠ Add. Post.) 9x – 2 + 4x = 128 (Subst. Prop.) 13x – 2 = 128 (Simplify.) 13x = 130 (Add. Prop. of =) x = 10 (Div. Prop. of =) **b.** 40 **43.** Elena's teacher is concerned. **45.** 80 **47.** 3.45678, 3.456789 **53.** $\frac{1}{2}$, –$\frac{1}{4}$

Lesson 2-5   pp. 100–103
EXERCISES 1. ∠AOB or ∠DOC **3.** ∠EOC **7.** 30 **9.** 30 **11.** No; there are no markings. **13.** No; there are no markings. **19a.** 90 **b.** 90 **c.** Subst. **d.** m∠3 **21.** x = 25, y = 105 **23.** 60, 60 **25.** 120, 120 **29.** 15; 25, 25 **31a.** rt. ∠ **b.** m∠Y **33.** ∠EIG ≅ ∠FIH since all rt. ∠s are ≅; ∠EIF ≅ ∠HIG since they are compl. of the same ∠. **35a.** V **b.** 180 **c.** Division **d.** right **39.** 9; 36 **41.** 18; 54, 36 **43.** Suppl. of ≅ ∠s are ≅.

45. 45, 45 **47.** m∠A = 72, m∠B = 18 **49.** m∠A = 60, m∠B = 30 **67.** 12 **69.** 3 + NP = 15 **71.** ∠1 and ∠2 are ≅. **73.** If you live south of the equator, then you live in Australia.

Chapter Review   pp. 105–107
1. Reflexive **2.** hypothesis **3.** adjacent **4.** Transitive **5.** complementary **6.** biconditional **7.** vertical angles **8.** converse **9.** Symmetric **10.** supplementary **11a.** If you are younger than 20, then you are a teenager. **b.** conditional: true, converse: false **12a.** If an angle has a measure greater than 90 and less than 180, then it is obtuse. **b.** conditional: true, converse: true **c.** An angle is obtuse if and only if it has measure greater than 90 and less than 180. **13a.** If a figure has four sides, then it is a square. **b.** conditional: true, converse: false **14.** If something is a flower, then it is beautiful. **15.** Rico's definition is not reversible. A magazine is a counterexample. You read a magazine, but it is not a book. **16.** A phrase is an oxymoron if and only if it contains contradictory terms. **17.** If two angles are complementary, then the sum of their measures is 90. If the sum of the measures of two angles is 90, then the angles are complementary. **18.** Lucy will become a better player. **19.** Lines ℓ and m intersect to form right angles. **20.** The sum of the measures of ∠1 and ∠2 is 180. **21.** If Kate studies, then she will graduate. **22.** If a, then c. **23.** If the weather is wet, then Nathan can stop at the ice cream shop. **24a.** Segment Add. Post. **b.** Subst. Prop. **c.** Simplify. **d.** Subtr. Prop. of Equality **e.** Div. Prop. of Equality **25.** 8 **26.** BY **27.** m∠Y **28.** RS = XY **29.** y **30.** 10 **31.** p – 2q **32.** $\overline{NM}$ **33.** 18 **34.** 31 **35.** 20 **36.** m∠KJD + m∠DJH = m∠KJH by the ∠ Add. Post.; m∠KJD = m∠DJH by the markings; $\overline{JD}$ bisects ∠KJH by the def. of ∠ bisector. **37.** AB = CD by the markings; AC = BD by the Add. Prop. of = and the Seg. Add. Post. **38.** ∠1 ≅ ∠4 by the markings; ∠1 ≅ ∠2 and ∠3 ≅ ∠4 because vert. ∠s are ≅; ∠2 ≅ ∠3 by the Trans. Prop. of ≅.

Chapter 3

Technology   p. 114
1. ∠2 ≅ ∠4 ≅ ∠6 ≅ ∠8; ∠1 ≅ ∠3 ≅ ∠5 ≅ ∠7; When a transversal intersects two ∥ lines, the ∠s formed have one of two measures; ∠s between the ∥ lines on opp. sides of the transversal are ≅; ∠s between the ∥ lines on the same side of the transversal are supp. **3.** a. lnear ∠ **5a.** If the same-side int. ∠s are suppl., then the lines are ∥. **b.** The other conjecture is the converse.

Lesson 3-1 pp. 118–121

EXERCISES **1.** $\overleftrightarrow{PQ}$ and $\overleftrightarrow{SR}$ with transversal $\overleftrightarrow{SQ}$; alt. int. ∠s **3.** $\overleftrightarrow{PS}$ and $\overleftrightarrow{QR}$ with transversal $\overleftrightarrow{PQ}$; same-side int. ∠s **5.** ∠1 and ∠2: corr. ∠s, ∠3 and ∠4: alt. int. ∠s, ∠5 and ∠6: corr. ∠s **7.** ∠1 and ∠2: corr. ∠s, ∠3 and ∠4: same-side int. ∠s, ∠5 and ∠6: alt. int. ∠s **9a.** 2 **b.** ∠1 **c.** corr. **11.** m∠1 = 75 because corr. ∠s of ∥ lines are ≅; m∠2 = 105 because same-side int. ∠s of ∥ lines are suppl. **13.** m∠1 = 100 because same-side int. ∠s of ∥ lines are suppl.; m∠2 = 70 because alt. int. ∠s of ∥ lines have = measure. **15.** 25; 65, 65 **17.** m∠1 = m∠3 = m∠6 = m∠8 = m∠9 = m∠11 = m∠13 = m∠15 = 52; m∠2 = m∠4 = m∠5 = m∠7 = m∠10 = m∠12 = m∠14 = 128 **19.** two **21.** two **23.** 32 **25.** x = 135, y = 45 **29a.** alt. int. ∠s **b.** He knew that alt. int. ∠s of ∥ lines are ≅. **43.** 59 **45.** (0.5, 7) **47.** (3, 3) **49.** multiply by −2; 16, −32

Lesson 3-2 pp. 125–129

EXERCISES **1.** $\overleftrightarrow{BE}$ ∥ $\overleftrightarrow{CG}$; Conv. of Corr. ∠s Post. **3.** $\overline{JO}$ ∥ $\overline{LM}$; if two lines and a transversal form same-side int. ∠s that are suppl., then the lines are ∥. **5.** a ∥ b; if two lines and a transversal form same-side int. ∠s that are suppl., then the lines are ∥. **7.** none **17a.** ∠1 **b.** ∠1 **c.** ∠2 **d.** ∠3 **e.** Conv. of Corr. ∠s **19.** 50 **21.** 31 **25.** The corr. ∠s are ≅, so the lines are ∥ by the Conv. of Corr. ∠s Post. **27.** 10; m∠1 = m∠2 = 70 **29.** 2.5; m∠1 = m∠2 = 30 **31.** The corr. ∠s he draws are ≅. **33.** $\overline{PL}$ ∥ $\overline{NA}$ by Conv. of Same-Side Int. ∠s Thm. **35.** $\overline{PN}$ ∥ $\overline{LA}$ by Conv. of Same-Side Int. ∠s Thm. **39.** The corr. ∠s are ≅, and the oars are ∥ by the Conv. of Corr. ∠s Post. **57.** m∠1 = 66 because alt. int. ∠s are ≅. m∠2 = 180 − 94 = 86 because same-side int. ∠s are suppl. **59.** If a circle has a radius of 4 cm, then it has a diameter of 8 cm. Both are true. **61.** If you form the past tense of a verb, then you add *ed* to the verb. Original statement is false, converse is false. **63.** 201.1 in.^{2} **65.** 63.6 ft^2

Lesson 3-3 pp. 134–139

EXERCISES **1.** 30 **3.** 90 **7.** t = 60; w = 60 **9.** 70 **13.** acute, equiangular, equilateral **15.** obtuse, isosceles **17.** Not possible; a right △ will always have one longest side opp. the right ∠.

19.

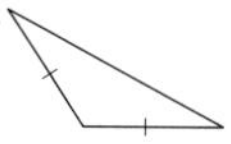

25a. 2 **b.** 6 **27.** 115.5 **29.** x = 147, y = 33 **31.** x = 52.5; 52.5, 52.5, 75; acute **33.** x = 37; 37, 65, 78; acute

37. 60; 180 ÷ 3 = 60 **43a.** 40, 60, 80 **b.** acute **45.** 100 **47.** 32 **53.** 120 or 60 **55.** 90 **71.** 46

73.

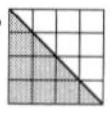

Extension pp. 140–141

1. Answers may vary. Sample:

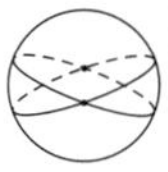

In Euclidean geometry, there is only one line through two points.

3. Answers may vary. Sample:

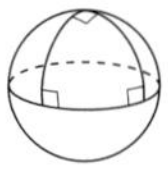

In Euclidean geometry, the only possible equiangular △ has 60° ∠s.

5. Answers may vary. Sample:

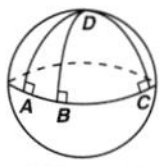

∠ADB ≇ ∠ADC

7. The top circle is not a line, so a piece of the top circle cannot be a line segment. **9.** true

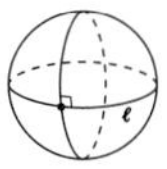

Technology p. 142

1. The sum of the measures of the ext. ∠s of a convex polygon is always 360. **3.** The sum of the measures of the five ∠s meeting at one point is 360.

Lesson 3-4 pp. 147–150

EXERCISES **1.** yes **3.** No; it is not a plane figure. **5.** *MWBFX*; sides: $\overline{MW}$, $\overline{WB}$, $\overline{BF}$, $\overline{FX}$, $\overline{XM}$; ∠s: ∠M, ∠W, ∠B, ∠F, ∠X **7.** *HEPTAGN*; sides: $\overline{HE}$, $\overline{EP}$, $\overline{PT}$, $\overline{TA}$, $\overline{AG}$, $\overline{GN}$, $\overline{NH}$; ∠s: ∠H, ∠E, ∠P, ∠T, ∠A, ∠G, ∠N **9.** decagon; concave **11.** 1080 **13.** 1440 **17.** 103 **19.** 37 **23.** 150; 30 **25.** 176.4; 3.6

27.  90 **29.** 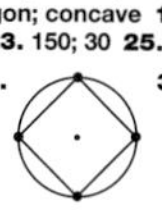 **31.** 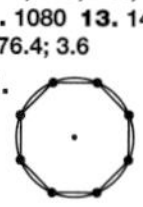

Selected Answers

33. 8 **35.** 18 **37.** octagon; m∠1 = 135; m∠2 = 45 **39.** 20-80-80; 50-50-80 **41.** 144; 10 **43.** 150; 12 **45.** $\frac{4}{5}$ **47.** y = 103; z = 70; quad. **49.** x = 36, 2x = 72, 3x = 108, 4x = 144; quad. **71.** 120, 25 **73.** 104, 76, 35, 69 **75.** Subst. Prop. **77.** Symm. Prop. of ≅ **81.** ∠BRT, ∠BRK **83.** Answers may vary. Sample: ∠BRM

Lesson 3-5 pp. 155–157

EXERCISES

1. 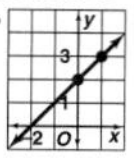 **3.** 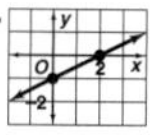

5. 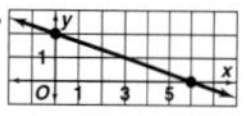

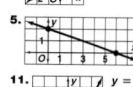

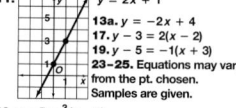

11. 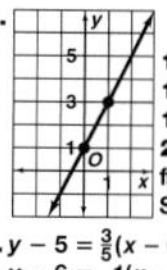

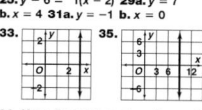

y = 2x + 1

13a. y = −2x + 4 **17.** y − 3 = 2(x − 2) **19.** y − 5 = −1(x + 3) **23–25.** Equations may vary from the pt. chosen. Samples are given.

23. y − 5 = $\frac{3}{8}$(x − 0) **25.** y − 6 = 1(x − 2) **29a.** y = 7 **b.** x = 4 **31a.** y = −1 **b.** x = 0

33. 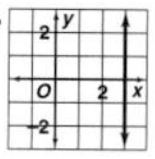 **35.** 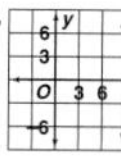

39. No; a line with no slope is a vertical line. 0 slope is a horizontal line. **41a.** Undefined; it is a vertical line. **b.** x = 0

49. 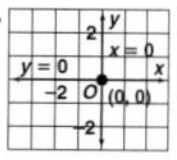 **51.** 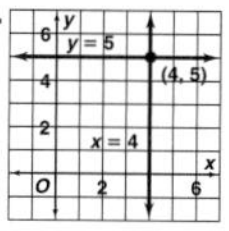

57. Yes; the slope of $\overline{AB}$ = the slope of $\overline{BC}$. **59.** Yes; the slope of $\overline{GH}$ = the slope of $\overline{HI}$. **61.** y − 2 = 3(x + 2); 3x − y = −8 **63.** y − 6 = $\frac{2}{3}$(x − 2); 2x − 3y = −14 **71.** 540 **73.** 2160 **75.** No; ∥ lines never intersect, but they are not skew. **77.** a = 5; m∠MPR = 30 **79.** a = 2; m∠QPR = 8

Lesson 3-6 pp. 161–164

EXERCISES **1.** Yes; both slopes = $-\frac{1}{2}$. **3.** No; the slope of $\ell_1 = \frac{3}{2}$, and the slope of ℓ_2 = 2. **7.** Yes; the lines both have a slope of $\frac{3}{4}$ but different *y*-intercepts. **9.** No; one slope = 7 and the other slope = −7. **13.** y − 0 = $\frac{1}{3}$(x − 6) or y = $\frac{1}{3}$(x − 6) **15.** y + 2 = $-\frac{3}{2}$(x − 6) **17.** Yes; the slope of ℓ_1 = $-\frac{3}{2}$, and the slope of $\ell_2 = \frac{2}{3}$; $-\frac{3}{2}\cdot\frac{2}{3}$ = −1. **19.** Yes; the slope of ℓ_1 = −1, and the slope of ℓ_2 = 1; −1 · 1 = −1. **21–23.** Answers may vary. Samples are given. **21.** y = −2(x − 4) **23.** y = $\frac{4}{3}$x **25.** No; $\frac{1}{2}\cdot 2 \neq -1$. **27.** Yes; one is vertical and the other is horizontal. **31.** slope of $\overline{AB}$ = slope of $\overline{CD}$ = $\frac{2}{3}$; $\overline{AB}$ ∥ $\overline{CD}$ slope of $\overline{BC}$ = slope of $\overline{AD}$ = −3; $\overline{BC}$ ∥ $\overline{AD}$ **33.** slope of $\overline{AB}$ = $\frac{1}{2}$; slope of $\overline{CD}$ = $\frac{1}{4}$; $\overline{AB}$ ∦ $\overline{CD}$; slope of $\overline{BC}$ = −1; slope of $\overline{AD}$ = $-\frac{1}{2}$; $\overline{BC}$ ∦ $\overline{AD}$ **39.** The lines will have the same slope. **41a.** y + 20 = $\frac{3}{4}$(x − 35) **b.** because you are given a point and can quickly find the slope **43.** ⊥ **45.** ⊥ **55.** y − 3 = $-\frac{1}{2}$(x − 0) or y − 3 = $-\frac{1}{2}$x **57.** y + 2 = $\frac{3}{4}$(x − 3) **59.** Mult. Prop. of = **61.** Symm. Prop. of ≅ **63.** If you travel to Switzerland, then you have a passport.

Lesson 3-7 pp. 168–170

1. 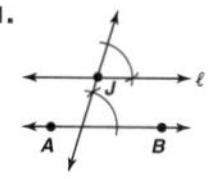

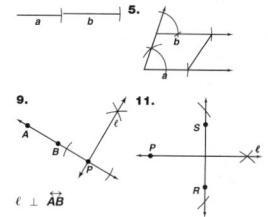

ℓ ∥ $\overleftrightarrow{AB}$

For Exercise 5, constructions may vary. Sample using the following segments is shown:

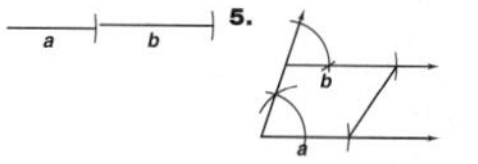

5.

9. 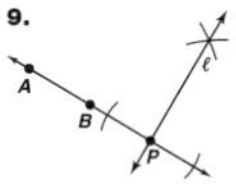

ℓ ⊥ $\overleftrightarrow{AB}$

11. 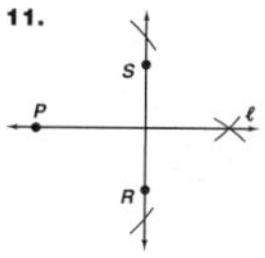

ℓ ⊥ $\overleftrightarrow{RS}$

For Exercises 17–19, constructions may vary. Samples are given.

17. 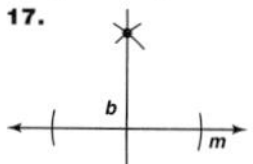 **19.** 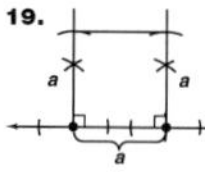

41. No; the slopes are different. **43.** Yes; the slopes are both $-\frac{1}{3}$. **45.** 8.9 **47.** $\overleftrightarrow{DF}$

Chapter Review pp. 173–175

1. acute **2.** obtuse **3.** corr. ∠s **4.** exterior **5.** convex **6.** equiangular **7.** regular **8.** point-slope **9.** slope-int. **10.** alt. int. ∠s **11.** m∠2 = 121, m∠3 = 59, m∠4 = 59 **12.** m∠1 = 120; corr. ∠s are ≅. m∠2 = 120; vert. ∠s are ≅. **13.** m∠1 = 75; same side int. ∠s are suppl. m∠2 = 105; alt. int. ∠s are ≅ or two ∠s that form a straight ∠ are suppl. **14.** m∠1 = 55; same side int. ∠s are suppl. m∠2 = 90; alt. int. ∠s are ≅. **15.** Pairs of consec. ∠s are suppl. because the sides of the quad. are transversals and the int. ∠s are on the same side of a transversal. **16.** 20 **17.** 20 **18.** 24

19. 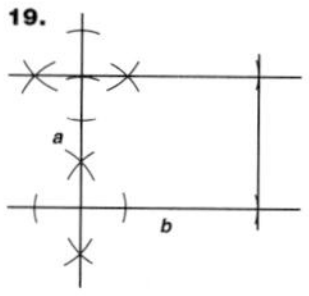 **20.** 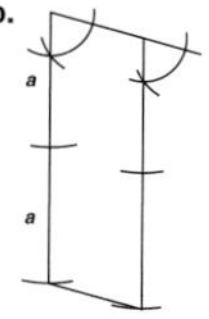

21. ≅ **22.** 61; scalene, acute **23.** x = 60; y = 60; equilateral, acute **24.** x = 45; y = 45; isosc., right **25.** 55; acute **26.** 30; right **27.** 3; acute **28.** 8; obtuse **29.** One ∠ is 90; the remaining 2 ∠s are compl. **30.** 120; 60 **31.** 135; 45 **32.** 144; 36 **33.** 165; 15 **34.** 360

35. m = 2; y-int. = −1 **36.** m = −2; point = (−5, 3)

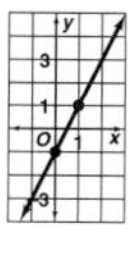 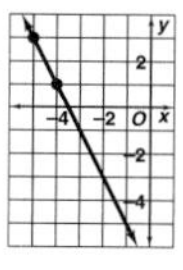

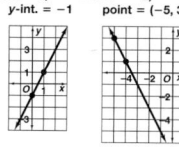

37. 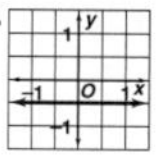 **38.** 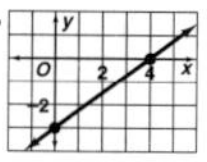

39. x = 6 **40.** neither **41.** ∥ **42.** ⊥ **43.** ∥ **44.** 0; the difference of *y*-coordinates is always zero.

Chapter 4

Lesson 4-1 pp. 182–185

EXERCISES **1.** ∠CAB ≅ ∠DAB; ∠C ≅ ∠D; ∠ABC ≅ ∠ABD; $\overline{AC}$ ≅ $\overline{AD}$; $\overline{AB}$ ≅ $\overline{AB}$; $\overline{CB}$ ≅ $\overline{DB}$ **3.** $\overline{BK}$ **5.** $\overline{ML}$ **9.** △KJB **11.** △JBK **15.** ∠P ≅ ∠S; ∠O ≅ ∠I; ∠L ≅ ∠D; ∠Y ≅ ∠E **17.** 54 in. **19.** 77 **25.** No; the corr. sides are not ≅. **27.** Yes; all corr. sides and ∠s are ≅. **29.** A and H; B and G; C and E; D and F **31.** 5 **33.** m∠B = m∠E = 21 **35.** AC = DF = 19 **39.** △BCE ≅ △ADE **41.** △JLM ≅ △NRZ; ∠JLM ≅ ∠ZRN **53.** Answers may vary. Sample:

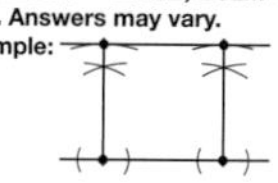

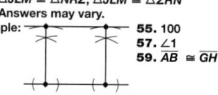

55. 100 **57.** ∠1 **59.** $\overline{AB}$ ≅ $\overline{GH}$

Lesson 4-2 pp. 189–192

EXERCISES **1.** SSS **3.** SAS **5.** Yes; $\overline{OB}$ ≅ $\overline{OB}$ by Refl. Prop.; ∠BOP ≅ ∠BOR since all rt. ∠s are ≅; $\overline{OP}$ ≅ $\overline{OR}$ (Given); the ∠s are ≅ by SAS. **7a.** Given **b.** Reflexive **c.** △JKM **d.** △LMK **9.** ∠W **11.** $\overline{WU}$ **13.** $\overline{XZ}$, $\overline{YZ}$ **15.** ∠T ≅ ∠V or $\overline{RS}$ ≅ $\overline{WU}$ **17.** additional information not needed **19.** Yes; △PVQ ≅ △STR by SSS. **21.** Yes; △NMO ≅ △LOM by SAS. **23.** △KLJ ≅ △MON; SSS **25.** △JEF ≅ △SVF or △JEF ≅ △SFV; SSS **29.** No; you would need ∠H ≅ ∠K or $\overline{GI}$ ≅ $\overline{JL}$.

31. 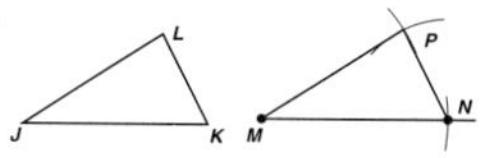

33a. Vertical ∠s are ≅. **b.** Given **c.** Def. of midpt. **d.** Given **e.** Def. of midpt. **f.** SAS **37.** $\overline{IP}$ ≅ $\overline{PO}$; △ISP ≅ △OSP by SSS. **39.** Yes; △ABC ≅ △CDA by SAS; ∠DAC ≅ ∠ACB because if ∥ lines, then alt. int. ∠s are ≅. **49.** ∠E **51.** $\overline{FG}$ **53.** The product of the slopes of two lines is −1 if and only if the lines are ⊥. **55.** If 2x = 6, then x = 3. The statement and the converse are both true.

Selected Answers

Lesson 4-3 pp. 197–201

EXERCISES **1.** △PQR ≅ △VXW **3.** $\overline{RS}$ **5.** yes **7.** yes **9.** AAS **11.** not possible **13a.** ∠UWV **b.** $\overline{UW}$ **c.** right **d.** Reflexive **15.** $\overline{MU}$ ≅ $\overline{UN}$ **17.** ∠WZV ≅ ∠WZY **19.** △PMO ≅ △NMO; ASA **21.** △ZVY ≅ △WVY; AAS **23.** The ∠s are not ≅ because no sides are ≅. **25.** The ∠s are not ≅ because the ≅ ∠s are not included ∠s. **27a.** ∠SRP **b.** $\overline{PR}$ **c.** alt. int. **d.** $\overline{PR}$ **e.** Reflexive **29a.** Def. of ⊥ **b.** All right ∠s are ≅. **c.** ∠QTP ≅ ∠STR **d.** Def. of midpt. **e.** AAS **31.** Yes; by AAS since ∠MON ≅ ∠QOP. **33.** Yes; by ASA, since ∠EAB ≅ ∠DBC because ∥ lines have ≅ corr. ∠s. **47.** not possible **49.** If corr. ∠s are ≅, then the lines are ∥. **51.** 36 photos

Technology p. 202

1. No; there are many noncongruent ∠s with all 3 pairs of ∠s ≅. **3.** No; the circle intersects $\overline{AB}$ just once, so only one △ is formed. If the ≅ ∠s are obtuse, then there could be an SSA congruency since a △ can have only one obtuse ∠.

Lesson 4-4 pp. 204–208

EXERCISES **1.** ∠PSQ ≅ ∠SPR; $\overline{SQ}$ ≅ $\overline{RP}$; $\overline{PQ}$ ≅ $\overline{SR}$ **3.** SAS; △KLJ ≅ △OMN; ∠K ≅ ∠O; ∠J ≅ ∠N; $\overline{KJ}$ ≅ $\overline{ON}$ by CPCTC. **7.** △ABD ≅ △CBD by ASA because $\overline{BD}$ ≅ $\overline{BD}$ by Reflexive Prop. of ≅; $\overline{AB}$ ≅ $\overline{CB}$ by CPCTC. **9.** △SPT ≅ △OPT by SAS because $\overline{TP}$ ≅ $\overline{TP}$ by Refl. Prop. of ≅; ∠S ≅ ∠O by CPCTC. **15.** ∠PKL ≅ ∠QKL by def. of ∠ bisect., and $\overline{KL}$ ≅ $\overline{KL}$ by Refl. Prop. of ≅, so the ∠s are ≅ by SAS. **17.** ∠KLP ≅ ∠KLQ because all rt. ∠s are ≅, $\overline{KL}$ ≅ $\overline{KL}$ by Refl. Prop. of ≅; and ∠PKL ≅ ∠QKL by def. of ∠ bisect; the ∠s are ≅ by ASA. **21.** Prove △ABE ≅ △CDF by SAS since $\overline{AE}$ ≅ $\overline{FC}$ by subtr. **23.** b or e, b or e, d, c, f, a **35.** AAS **37.** The slope of line *m* is the same as the slope of line *n*.

Lesson 4-5 pp. 213–216

EXERCISES **1a.** $\overline{RS}$ **b.** $\overline{RS}$ **c.** Given **d.** Def. of ∠ bisector **e.** Reflexive Prop. of ≅ **f.** AAS **3.** $\overline{VX}$; Conv. of the Isosc. △ Thm. **5.** $\overline{VY}$; VT = VX (Ex. 3) and UT = YX (Ex. 4), so VU = VY by the Subtr. Prop. of =. **7.** x = 80; y = 40 **9.** x = 38; y = 4 **11.** x = 36; y = 36 **13.** 64 **15.** 42 **17.** 150; 15

19a. 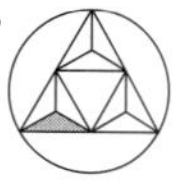

30, 30, 120 **b.** 5; 30, 60, 90, 120, 50 **21.** 50 **23.** 6 **25.** x = 64; y = 71 **27.** Two sides of a △ are ≅ if and only if the ∠s opp. those sides are ≅. **35.** m = 60; n = 30 **51.** AAS **53.** 24 sides

Lesson 4-6 pp. 219–223

EXERCISES **1.** △ABC ≅ △DEF by HL. Both ∠s are rt. ∠s, $\overline{AC}$ ≅ $\overline{DF}$, and $\overline{CB}$ ≅ $\overline{FE}$. **3.** △LMP ≅ △OMN by HL. Both ∠s are rt. ∠s because vert. ∠s are ≅; $\overline{LP}$ ≅ $\overline{NO}$, and $\overline{LM}$ ≅ $\overline{OM}$. **5.** ∠T and ∠Q are rt. ∠s. **7.** $\overline{TY}$ ≅ $\overline{ER}$ or $\overline{RT}$ ≅ $\overline{YE}$ **9.** $\overline{BC}$ ≅ $\overline{FA}$ **11a.** Given **b.** Def. of rt. △ **c.** Reflexive Prop. of ≅ **d.** Given **e.** HL **15.** Yes; $\overline{PM}$ ≅ $\overline{PM}$ and ∠PMW is a rt. ∠ since $\overline{JP}$ ∥ $\overline{MW}$. **17a.** Given **b.** ∠IGH **c.** Def. of rt. △ **d.** *I* is the midpt. of $\overline{HV}$. **e.** Def. of midpt. **f.** △IGH ≅ △ITV **19.** x = 3; y = 2 **21.** whether the 7-yd side is the hyp. or a leg

25. 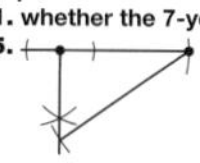 **27.** 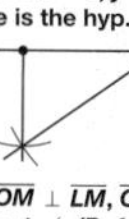

29.1. $\overline{LO}$ bisects ∠MLN, $\overline{OM}$ ⊥ $\overline{LM}$, $\overline{ON}$ ⊥ $\overline{LN}$ (Given) 2. ∠M and ∠N are rt. ∠s (Def. of ⊥) 3. ∠MLO ≅ ∠NLO (Def. of ∠ bis.) 4. ∠M ≅ ∠N (All rt. ∠s are ≅.) 5. $\overline{LO}$ ≅ $\overline{LO}$ (Reflexive Prop. of ≅) 6. △LMO ≅ △LNO (AAS) **39.** isosceles **41.** $\overline{BC}$ ∥ $\overline{AD}$ because each slope = −1. $\overline{BT}$ ⊥ $\overline{BA}$, $\overline{BA}$ ⊥ $\overline{AS}$ because product of slopes is −1. **43.** If two lines are ∥, then same-side int. ∠s are suppl. **45.** If two lines are ∥, then corr. ∠s are ≅.

Lesson 4-7 pp. 226–230

EXERCISES **1.** ∠M **3.** $\overline{XY}$

5. 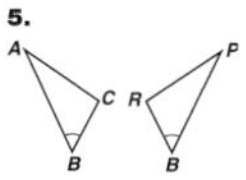 **7.** 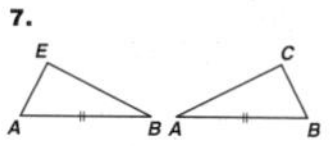

9. 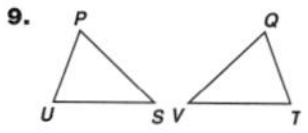

11. △LQP ≅ △PML; HL **13.** △QDA ≅ △UAD; SAS **15.** $\overline{TD}$ ≅ $\overline{RO}$ if △TDI ≅ △ROE by AAS. ∠TID ≅ ∠REO if △TEI ≅ △RIE. △TEI ≅ △RIE by SSS. **17.** ∠QET ≅ ∠QEU by SAS if $\overline{QT}$ ≅ $\overline{QU}$. $\overline{QT}$ and $\overline{QU}$ are corr. parts of △QTB and △QUB which are ≅ by ASA. **19–21.** Answers may vary. Samples are given. **19.** 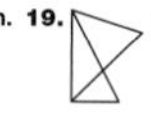 **21a.** 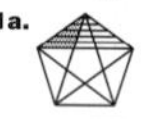 **b.** 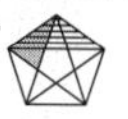

23. △ACE ≅ △BCD by ASA; $\overline{AC}$ ≅ $\overline{BC}$, ∠A ≅ ∠B (Given) ∠C ≅ ∠C (Reflexive Prop. of ≅) △ACE ≅ △BCD (ASA)

Selected Answers

25. $m\angle 1 = 56; m\angle 2 = 56; m\angle 3 = 34; m\angle 4 = 90; m\angle 5 = 22; m\angle 6 = 34; m\angle 7 = 34; m\angle 8 = 68; m\angle 9 = 112$ **29.** Proofs may vary. Sample: It is given that $\angle 1 \cong \angle 2$ and $\angle 3 \cong \angle 4$. Since $\overline{QB} \cong \overline{QB}$ by the Reflexive Prop. of $\cong$, $\triangle QTB \cong \triangle QUB$ by ASA. So $\overline{QT} \cong \overline{QU}$ by CPCTC. Since $\overline{QE} \cong \overline{QE}$ by the Reflexive Prop. of $\cong$, then $\triangle QET \cong \triangle QEU$ by SAS. **39a.** right **b.** $\cong$ **c.** Reflexive **d.** HL

41.

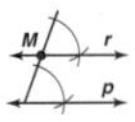

43. $y - 5 = 1(x - 0)$
45. $y - 0 = -\frac{1}{3}(x - 0)$

47. Eq. may vary, depending on pt. chosen. Sample: $y + 5 = \frac{5}{3}(x - 3)$

Chapter Review pp. 233–235

1. legs **2.** vertex angle **3.** CPCTC **4.** hypotenuse **5.** base angles **6.** corollary **7.** legs **8.** Congruent polygons **9.** base **10.** $\overline{ML}$ **11.** $\angle U$ **12.** $\overline{ST}$ **13.** $ONMLK$ **14.** 80 **15.** 3 **16.** 5 **17.** 35 **18.** 100 **19.** SSS **20.** not possible **21.** SAS **22.** not possible **23.** AAS **24.** ASA **25.** $\triangle AWC \cong \triangle RCW$; AAS **26.** $\triangle JKL \cong \triangle UVT$; SAS **27.** $\triangle RGB \cong \triangle DCS$; ASA **28.** $\triangle VTY \cong \triangle WYX$ by AAS so $\overline{TV} \cong \overline{YW}$ by CPCTC. **29.** $\triangle BCE \cong \triangle DCE$ by ASA so $\overline{BE} \cong \overline{DE}$ by CPCTC. **30.** $\triangle KNM \cong \triangle MLK$ by SAS so $\overline{KN} \cong \overline{ML}$ by CPCTC. **31.** $x = 4, y = 65$ **32.** $x = 55, y = 62.5$ **33.** $x = 65, y = 90$ **34.** Since $\overline{PS} \perp \overline{SQ}$ and $\overline{RQ} \perp \overline{QS}$, $\triangle PSQ$ and $\triangle RQS$ are rt. ⊿s. $\overline{PQ} \cong \overline{RS}$ and $\overline{QS} \cong \overline{SQ}$ so $\triangle PSQ \cong \triangle RQS$ by HL. **35.** Since $\overline{LN} \perp \overline{KM}$, $m\angle LNK = m\angle LNM = 90$. $\overline{KL} \cong \overline{ML}$ and $\overline{LN} \cong \overline{LN}$ so $\triangle KLN \cong \triangle MLN$ by HL. **36.** $\triangle AEC \cong \triangle ABD$ by SAS. **37.** $\triangle FIH \cong \triangle GHI$ by SAS. **38.** $\triangle PTS \cong \triangle RTA$ by ASA. **39.** $\triangle CFE \cong \triangle DEF$ by ASA.

Chapter 5

Technology p. 242

1. Midsegments have slopes that are the same as the slopes of the third side, and lengths that are $\frac{1}{2}$ the length of the third side. **3b.** The 4 ⊿s are $\cong$ by Post. 4-1: If 3 sides of one $\triangle$ are $\cong$ to 3 sides of another $\triangle$, the ⊿s are $\cong$. **5a.** The area of $\triangle ABC$ is 4 times the area of each small $\triangle$. **b.** The perimeter of $\triangle ABC$ is 2 times the perimeter of each small $\triangle$.

Lesson 5-1 pp. 246–248

EXERCISES **1.** 9 **3.** 14 **7.** 40 **9.** 160 **11.** $\overline{UW} \parallel \overline{TX}$; $\overline{UY} \parallel \overline{VX}$; $\overline{YW} \parallel \overline{TV}$ **13a.** $\overline{ST} \parallel \overline{PR}$; $\overline{SU} \parallel \overline{QR}$; $\overline{UT} \parallel \overline{PQ}$ **b.** $m\angle QPR = 40$ **15.** $\overline{FG}$ **17.** $\overline{EG}$

21a. 114 ft 9 in. **b.** Answers may vary. Sample: The highlighted segment is a midsegment of the triangular face of the building. **23.** 45 **25.** 55 **27.** $18\frac{1}{2}$ **29.** 60 **31.** 10 **35.** $x = 3$; $DF = 24$ **47.** $\triangle SXT \cong \triangle TYS$; SAS **49.** $\triangle KLQ \cong \triangle PNR$; HL

51.

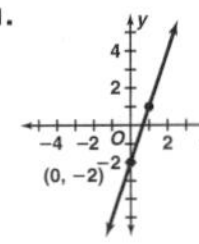

$y = 3x - 2$
53. $46\frac{2}{3}$
55. 40

Lesson 5-2 pp. 251–254

EXERCISES **1.** $\overline{AC}$ is the $\perp$ bis. of $\overline{BD}$. **3.** 18 **7.** $y = 3$; $ST = 15$; $TU = 15$ **9.** $y = 9$; $m\angle FHL = 54$; $m\angle KHL = 54$ **11.** Point E is on the bisector of $\angle KHF$. **13.** 10 **15.** Isosceles; it has 2 $\cong$ sides. **19.** 4 **21.** 16 **27.** Answers may vary. Sample: The student needs to know that $\overline{QS}$ bisects $\overline{PR}$. **31.** the pitcher's plate **35.** $C(3, 2), D(3, 0)$; $AC = BC = 3, AD = BD = \sqrt{13}$ **37.** $C(0, 0), D(1, 1)$; $AC = BC = 3, AD = BD = \sqrt{5}$ **41.** bisector; right; Reflexive; SAS; CPCTC **55.** 8 **57.** 6 **59.** Div. Prop. of = **61.** Distr. Prop. **65.** $C\left(0, \frac{7}{2}\right)$; $AB = \sqrt{97}$, $AC = BC = \frac{\sqrt{97}}{2}$

Technology p. 255

1. Each set of 3 lines intersect in one point. **3.** Each set of 3 lines, $\angle$ bisectors, $\perp$ bisectors, lines containing altitudes, and the medians of a $\triangle$ meet in one point. **5.** Since isosc. ⊿s can be acute, right, or obtuse, the special segments are as seen in the table. Since all equil. ⊿s are acute, all special segments intersect inside.

Lesson 5-3 pp. 259–263

EXERCISES **1.** $(-2, -3)$ **3.** $\left(1\frac{1}{2}, 1\right)$ **9.** Z **11.** $TY = 18$; $TW = 27$ **13.** $VY = 6$; $YX = 3$ **15.** Neither; it's not a segment drawn from a vertex.

17.

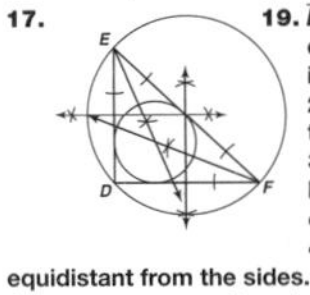

19. $\overline{BE}$ **21.** $\overrightarrow{CA}$ **23.** 1 : 2 or 2 : 1 **27.** $\angle$ bisector; it bisects an $\angle$. **29.** Altitude; $\overline{AB}$ is $\perp$ to a side from a vertex. **31a.** $\angle$ Bis. Thm. **b.** $\angle$ Bis. Thm. **c.** Trans. **d.** $\angle$ Bis. **43.** Yes; point B is equidistant from the sides. **45.** right **47–49.** Answers may vary. Samples are given.

47. $\overleftrightarrow{AB}$ **49.** ABC and ADE

Lesson 5-4 pp. 267–270

EXERCISES **1.** Two angles are not congruent. **3.** The angle is obtuse. **7a.** If you don't eat all of your vegetables, then you won't grow. **b.** If you won't grow, then you don't eat all of your vegetables. **9a.** If a figure isn't a rectangle, then it doesn't have four sides. **b.** If a figure doesn't have four sides, then it isn't a rectangle. **11.** Assume that $\angle J$ is a right angle. **13.** Assume that none of the angles is obtuse. **17.** I and II **19.** II and III **21a.** right angle **b.** right angles **c.** 90 **d.** 180 **e.** 90 **f.** 90 **g.** 0 **h.** more than one right angle **i.** at most one right angle **23a.** If four points aren't collinear, then they aren't coplanar; false **b.** If four points aren't coplanar, then they aren't collinear; true **25–27.** Answers may vary. Samples are given. **25.** If today is Sunday, then tomorrow is Monday. **27.** If two sides of a triangle are congruent, then the triangle is isosceles. **33.** If the animal is a kitten, then it is a cat. If the animal isn't a cat, then it's not a kitten. **35.** If a number is a whole number, then it is an integer. If a number isn't an integer, then it isn't a whole number. **37a.** Earl proves that it's later than 5:00. **b.** He starts with the assumption that it is before 5:00. **c.** It is not noisy. **51.** same-side int. ⊿s **53.** corr. ⊿s **55.** $45 = m\angle ABC$

Lesson 5-5 pp. 273–276

EXERCISES **1.** $\angle 3 \cong \angle 2$ because they are vertical ⊿s and $m\angle 1 > m\angle 3$ by Corollary to the Ext. $\angle$ Thm. So, $m\angle 1 > m\angle 2$ by subst. **3.** $m\angle 1 > m\angle 4$ by Corollary to the Ext. $\angle$ Thm. and $\angle 4 \cong \angle 2$ because if $\parallel$ lines, then alt. int. ⊿s are $\cong$. **5.** $\angle D, \angle C, \angle E$ **7.** $\angle A, \angle B, \angle C$ **9.** $\angle Z, \angle X, \angle Y$ **11.** $\overline{FH}, \overline{GF}, \overline{GH}$ **13.** $\overline{AC}, \overline{AB}, \overline{CB}$ **17.** Yes; $11 + 12 > 15$; $12 + 15 > 11$; $11 + 15 > 12$. **19.** Yes; $1 + 15 > 15$; $15 + 15 > 1$. **23.** $11 < s < 21$ **25.** $5 < s < 41$ **31.** Answers may vary. Sample: The shortcut across the grass is shorter than the sum of the two paths. **35.** $\overline{CD}$ **49.** $m\angle X \le m\angle B$ **51.** The triangle is obtuse. **53.** 35 **55.** 55 **57.** 962.1 mm^2 **59.** 314.2 mi^2

Chapter Review pp. 281–283

1. median of a $\triangle$ **2.** distance from the point to the line **3.** $\perp$ Bis. Thm. **4.** altitude **5.** contrapositive **6.** indirect proof **7.** $\triangle$ Ineq. Thm. **8.** incenter **9.** $\angle$ Bis. Thm. **10.** point of concurrency **11.** 15 **12.** 11 **13.** 40 **14.** 7 **15.** 14 **16.** 80 **17.** $(-1, 0)$ **18.** $(0, -1)$ **19.** $(2, -3)$ **20.** $\angle$ bisector, it bisects an $\angle$. **21.** altitude; it is $\perp$ to a side. **22.** median; it goes through a midpoint. **23.** Inverse: If it is not snowing, then it is not cold outside. Contrapositive: If it is not cold outside, then it is not snowing. **24.** Inverse: If an angle is not obtuse, then its measure is not greater than 90 and less than 180. Contrapositive: If an angle's measure is not greater than 90 and less than 180, then it is not obtuse. **25.** Inverse: If a figure is not a square, then its sides are not congruent. Contrapositive: If a figure's sides are not congruent, then it is not a square. **26.** Inverse: If you are not in Australia, then you are not south of the equator. Contrapositive: If you are not south of the equator, then you are not in Australia. **27.** Assume that both numbers are odd. The product of 2 odd numbers is always odd, which contradicts that the product is even. Therefore, at least one number must be even. **28.** Assume a right $\angle$ can be formed by non-perp. lines. Then by the def. of $\perp$, the lines are $\perp$. Therefore, the assumption is false. **29.** Assume that an $\triangle$ has 2 obtuse ⊿s. Then these ⊿s by def. are greater than 90, which makes their sum greater than 180. But the sum of the measures of the ⊿s of a $\triangle$ = 180, so the assumption must be false. **30.** Assume an $\angle$ is obtuse, and therefore has measure greater than 90. Since the $\triangle$ is equilateral, it is equiangular, and each $\angle$ measures 60. **31.** $\angle T, \angle R, \angle S$; $\overline{RS}, \overline{TS}, \overline{TR}$ **32.** $\angle G, \angle O, \angle F$; $\overline{OF}, \overline{FG}, \overline{OG}$ **33.** No; $5 + 8 \ngtr 15$. **34.** Yes; each pair > 3rd. **35.** Yes; each pair > 3rd. **36.** Yes; each pair > 3rd. **37.** No; $1 + 1 \ngtr 3$. **38.** Yes; each pair > 3rd. **39.** $3 < x < 11$ **40.** $7 < x < 23$ **41.** $6 < x < 10$ **42.** $1 < x < 25$

Chapter 6

Lesson 6-1 pp. 288–293

EXERCISES **1.** ▱, rectangle, rhombus, square **3.** trapezoid **7.** rhombus **9.** rhombus **13.** rhombus

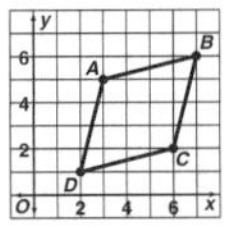

15. trapezoid **19.** $x = 11, y = 29$; 13, 13, 23, 23 **21.** $x = 2, y = 6$; 2, 7, 7, 2 **25.** 40, 40, 140, 140; 11, 11, 15, 32 **27.** rectangle, square, trapezoid

29–31. Answers may vary. Samples are given.

29.

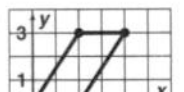

31. Impossible; a trapezoid with one rt. $\angle$ must have another, since two sides are $\parallel$.

37. True; a square is both a rectangle and a rhombus. **39.** False; a kite does not have $\cong$ opp. sides. **43.** Rhombus; all 4 sides are $\cong$ because they come from the same cut. **51.** rectangle, ▱, kite **53.** square, rhombus, ▱ **65.** Yes; the sum of the lengths of any 2 sides is greater than the third side. **67.** No; $3 + 5 \ngtr 8$. **69.** 16 mm **71.** 82

Lesson 6-2 pp. 297–301

EXERCISES **1.** 127 **3.** 76 **7.** $\frac{3}{4}$ **9.** 4 **11.** 22; 18.5, 23.6, 23.6 **13.** 18 **15.** 12; $m\angle Q = m\angle S = 36$, $m\angle P = m\angle R = 144$ **17.** $x = 6, y = 8$ **19.** $x = 7, y = 10$ **25.** 3 **27.** 6 **35.** $BC = AD = 33$ cm; $AB = CD = 13$ cm **37a.** Given **b.** Def. of ▱ **c.** If 2 lines are $\parallel$, then alt. int. ⊿s are $\cong$. **d.** If 2 lines are $\parallel$, then alt. int. ⊿s are $\cong$. **e.** Reflexive Prop. of $\cong$ **f.** ASA **g.** ASA **h.** CPCTC **i.** CPCTC **39.** 38, 32, 110 **41.** 95, 37, 37 **43.** 18, 162 **45.** $x = 15, y = 45$ **47.** $x = 25, y = 115$ **57.** Answers may vary. Sample: In ▱s $LENS$ and $NGTH$, $\overline{GT} \parallel \overline{EH}$ and $\overline{EH} \parallel \overline{LS}$ by the def. of a ▱. Therefore $\overline{LS} \parallel \overline{GT}$ because if 2 lines are $\parallel$ to the same line then they are $\parallel$ to each other. **71.** parallelogram **73.** 49 **75.** 49

Lesson 6-3 pp. 307–310

EXERCISES **1.** 5 **3.** $x = 1.6, y = 1$ **7.** Yes; both pairs of opp. sides are $\cong$. **9.** Yes; both pairs of opp. ⊿s are $\cong$. **17a.** bisect **b.** $\overline{XR}$ **c.** $\triangle XYR$ **d.** ASA **e.** alt. interior **21.** No; the figure could be a kite. **23.** No; the figure could be a trapezoid. **27.** $x = 3, y = 11$ **29.** $k = 9, m = 23.4$ **31.** $\frac{1}{6}$ **33.** (6, 6) **47.** $e = 13, f = 11, c = 204$ **49.** If a quad. is a ▱, then the diagonals bisect each other; if the diagonals of a quad. bisect each other, then it is a ▱. **51.** If the prod. of the slopes of two nonvertical lines is -1, then they are $\perp$; if two nonvertical lines are $\perp$, then the prod. of their slopes is -1.

Technology p. 311

1. Diagonals of a rectangle are $\cong$. **3.** Diagonals of a square are both $\cong$ and $\perp$, and bisect the ⊿s. **5.** Diagonals that are $\cong$ yield a rectangle.

Lesson 6-4 pp. 315–318

EXERCISES **1.** 38, 38, 38, 38 **3.** 118, 31, 31 **11.** 3; $LN = MP = 7$ **13.** 9; $LN = MP = 67$ **17.** Yes; $\cong$ diagonals in a ▱ mean it can be a rectangle with 2 opp. sides 2 cm long. **19.** Impossible; if the figure is a ▱, then the $\angle$ opp. the bisected $\angle$ is also bisected, and the figure is a rhombus. But the sides are not $\cong$. **23.** After measuring the sides, she can measure the diagonals. If the diagonals are $\cong$, then the figure is a rectangle by Thm. 6-14. **25–27.** Symbols may vary. Sample: parallelogram: ▱; rhombus: (R); rectangle: ▭; square: (S) **25.** (R), (S) **27.** ▱, (R), ▭, (S)

37.

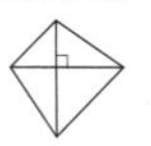

Diag. are $\cong$, diag. are $\perp$. **39–41.** Answers may vary. Samples are given. **39.** Draw diag. 1, and construct its midpt. Draw a line through the midpt. Construct segments of length diag. 2 in opp. directions from mdpt. Then, bisect these segments. Connect these mdpts. with the endpoints of diag. 1. **41.** Same as 39, but construct a $\perp$ line at the midpt. of diag. 1. **45.** Yes; since all right ⊿s are $\cong$, the opp. ⊿s are $\cong$ and it is a ▱. Since it has all right ⊿s, it is a rectangle. **47.** Yes; a quad. with 4 $\cong$ sides is a ▱ and a ▱ with 4 $\cong$ sides and 4 right ⊿s is a square. **49.** $x = 5, y = 32, z = 7.5$ **57.** 16, 16 **59.** 1, 1 **61.** 4. $\triangle ABC \cong \triangle ADC$ (ASA) 5. $\overline{AB} \cong \overline{AD}$ (CPCTC) 6. $\overline{AB} \cong \overline{DC}, \overline{AD} \cong \overline{BC}$ (Opp. sides of a ▱ are $\cong$.) 7. $\overline{AB} \cong \overline{BC} \cong \overline{CD} \cong \overline{AD}$ (Trans. Prop. of $\cong$) **67.** Yes; both pairs of opp. sides are $\cong$. **69.** Yes; the diag. bisect each other. **71.** 16 **73.** $\overline{RQ}$

Technology p. 319

3. For $MNOP$ and $EFGH$, the ratio of the sides and perimeters is 1 : 2 and the ratios of the areas is 1 : 4. The sides of $MNOP$ and $EFGH$ are $\parallel$.

Lesson 6-5 pp. 322–325

EXERCISES **1.** 77, 103, 103 **3.** 49, 131, 131 **7a.** isosc. trapezoids **b.** 69, 69, 111, 111 **9.** 90, 45, 45 **11.** 90, 26, 90 **19.** No; explanations may vary. Sample: If both ⊿s are bisected, then this combined with $\overline{KM} \cong \overline{KM}$ by the Reflexive Prop. means $\triangle KLM \cong \triangle KNM$ by SAS. So by CPCTC, opp. ⊿s L and N are $\cong$, so it is not an isos. trapezoid. **21.** 15 **23.** 3 **27.** 28 **29.** $x = 18, y = 108$ **31.** 112, 68, 68 **33.** Yes, the $\cong$ ⊿s can be obtuse, as well as one other $\angle$. **37.** No; if two consecutive ⊿s were compl., then the kite would be concave. **51.** 126 **53.** 27 **55a.** 3 **b.** 30 **c.** 30

Lesson 6-6 pp. 328–330

EXERCISES **1.** $W(0, h)$; $Z(b, 0)$ **3.** $W(-b, b)$; $Z(-b, -b)$ **7.** $\left(\frac{b}{2}, \frac{h}{2}\right)$; $-\frac{h}{b}$ **9.** $(-b, 0)$; undefined **13a.** $(2a, 0)$ **b.** $(0, 2b)$ **c.** (a, b) **d.** $\sqrt{b^2 + a^2}$ **e.** $\sqrt{b^2 + a^2}$ **f.** $\sqrt{b^2 + a^2}$ **g.** $MA = MB = MC$ **15–17.** Answers may vary. Samples are given.

15. B, D, H, F **17.** A, C, G, E **21.** $W(2a, 2a)$; $Z(2a, 0)$ **23.** $W(0, b)$; $Z(2a, 0)$ **29.** $(a, 0)$

31a.

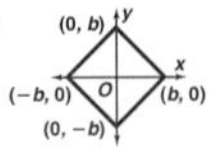

b. $(-b, 0), (0, b), (b, 0), (0, -b)$ **c.** $b\sqrt{2}$ **d.** 1, -1 **e.** Yes, because the product of the slopes is -1. **43.** (3, 2) **45a.** Reflexive **b.** AAS

Lesson 6-7 pp. 333–337

EXERCISES **1a.** $W\left(\frac{a}{2}, \frac{b}{2}\right)$; $Z\left(\frac{c + e}{2}, \frac{d}{2}\right)$ **b.** $W(a, b)$; $Z(c + e, d)$ **c.** $W(2a, 2b)$; $Z(2c + 2e, 2d)$; c; it uses multiples of 2 to name the coordinates of W and Z. **3a.** y-axis **b.** Distance **5a.** isos. **b.** x-axis **c.** y-axis **d.** Midpoints **e.** $\cong$ sides **f.** slopes **g.** the Distance Formula **7a.** $\sqrt{a^2 + b^2}$ **b.** $2\sqrt{a^2 + b^2}$ **9a.** (a, b) **b.** (a, b) **c.** the same point **11a.** $\cong$ **b.** midpts. **c.** $(-2b, 2c)$ **d.** $L(b, a + c), M(b, c), N(-b, c), K(-b, a + c)$ **e.** 0 **f.** vertical lines **g.** $\parallel$ **h.** $\perp$ **13–15.** Answers may vary. Samples are given. **13.** yes; same slope **15.** no; may not have intersection pt. **25.** 1, 4, 7 **27.** $-0.8, 0.4, 1.6, 2.8, 4, 5.2, 6.4, 7.6, 8.8$ **31.** $\left(-1, 6\frac{2}{3}\right), \left(1, 8\frac{1}{3}\right), (3, 10), \left(5, 11\frac{2}{3}\right), \left(7, 13\frac{1}{3}\right)$ **33.** $(-2.76, 5.2), (-2.52, 5.4), (-2.28, 5.6), \ldots, (8.52, 14.6), (8.76, 14.8)$ **47a.** If the sum of the ⊿s of a polygon is 360°, then the polygon is a quad. **b.** If a polygon is a quad., then the sum of its ⊿s is 360°. **49a.** If $a \neq 5$, then $a^2 \neq 25$. **b.** If $a^2 \neq 25$, then $a \neq 5$. **53.** $\overline{HE} \cong \overline{FG}, \overline{EF} \cong \overline{GH}$, and $\overline{HF} \cong \overline{HF}$ by the Reflexive Prop. of $\cong$, so $\triangle HEF \cong \triangle FGH$ by SSS. Then by CPCTC $\angle 1 \cong \angle 2$.

Chapter Review pp. 339–341

1. F **2.** H **3.** G **4.** B **5.** I **6.** J **7.** A **8.** C **9.** E **10.** D

11.

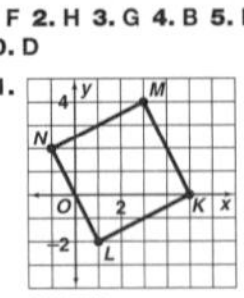

square

12.

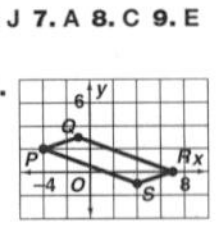

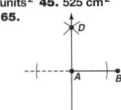

parallelogram

13. $x = 8$; 9, 14, 9, 7 **14.** $m = 4, t = 5$; 7, 14, 14, 7 **15.** 101, 79, 101 **16.** 38, 43, 99 **17.** 37, 26, 26 **18.** yes **19.** yes **20.** no **21.** yes **22.** $x = 29, y = 28$ **23.** $x = 4, y = 5$ **24.** 124, 28, 62 **25.** 60, 90, 30 **26.** 90, 25 **27.** 26 in. **28.** 20 cm **29.** 19 ft **30.** (a, b) **31.** $(0, c)$ **32.** $(a - b, c)$ **33a.** -1 **b.** 1 **c.** The prod. of the slopes is -1. **34a.** a **b.** $(0, b)$ **c.** $\sqrt{a^2 + b^2}$ **d.** $\sqrt{a^2 + b^2}$ **e.** BD

Chapter 7

Lesson 7-1 pp. 351–354

EXERCISES **1.** 240 cm^2 **3.** 26.79 $in.^2$ **5.** 9 $units^2$ **7.** 6 $units^2$ **9.** 0.24 **11.** 14 m^2 **13.** 3 ft^2 **15.** 15 $units^2$ **17.** 6 $units^2$ **23.** 14 cm

25a.

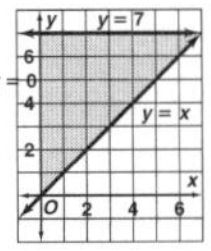

b. 24.5 $units^2$ **27b.** 16 $units^2$ **29.** The area does not change; the height and base AB do not change. **31.** 9 $units^2$ **33.** 4200 yd^2 **35a.** Blank grid; area is 84 $units^2$ while figures are 36 $units^2$. **b.** No; the figures have the same area. **37.** 28 $units^2$ **39.** 9 $units^2$ **45.** 525 cm^2 **57.** (a, a) **59.** 108 **61.** 72 **65.**

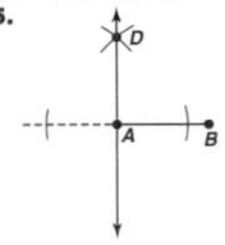

Lesson 7-2 pp. 360–364

EXERCISES **1.** 10 **3.** 34 **5.** 65 **7.** No; $4^2 + 5^2 \neq 6^2$. **9.** Yes; $15^2 + 20^2 = 25^2$. **11.** $\sqrt{33}$ **13.** $2\sqrt{89}$ **17.** 17.0 m **19.** $12\sqrt{7}$ cm^2 **21.** No; $19^2 + 20^2 \neq 28^2$. **23.** Yes; $33^2 + 56^2 = 65^2$. **25.** right **27.** right **37.** $8\sqrt{5}$ **41.** 168 ft^2 **43.** 32 $in.^2$ **45.** Yes; $7^2 + 24^2 = 25^2$, so $\angle RST$ is a rt. $\angle$. **49.** 50 **51.** 35 **53–55.** Answers may vary. Samples are given. **53.** 4; 5 **55.** 11; 12 **61.** 2830 km **63.** 12.5 cm **77.** 15 ft **79.** 3; 20 **81.** 3 **83.** 7

Lesson 7-3 pp. 369–372

EXERCISES **1.** $x = 8$; $y = 8\sqrt{2}$ **3.** $y = 60\sqrt{2}$ **5.** $4\sqrt{2}$ **7.** $\sqrt{3}$ **11.** 25.5 ft **13.** $x = \sqrt{3}$; $y = 3$ **15.** $x = 24$; $y = 12\sqrt{3}$ **17.** $x = 4\sqrt{3}$; $y = 6$ **21.** 43.3 cm^2 **23.** 101.8 m^2 **25.** $a = 6$; $b = 6\sqrt{2}$; $c = 2\sqrt{3}$; $d = 6$ **27.** $a = 4$; $b = 4$ **33a.** 8.5 m **b.** 3.1 m **35.** 110.9 cm^2 **37.** 11.3 yd^2 **47.** $4\sqrt{21}$ cm

49. no

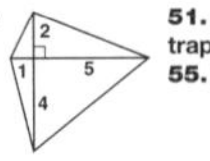

51. no; an isosceles trapezoid **53.** no **55.** yes; ASA Post.

Lesson 7-4 pp. 376–379

EXERCISES **1.** 472 in.^{2} **3.** 108 ft^2 **5.** 150 cm^2 **7.** about 43,290 mi^2 **9.** 72 m^2 **11.** $52\sqrt{3}$ ft^2 **15.** 18 m^2 **17.** 56 ft^2 **19.** 96 in.^{2} **21.** 20 in.^{2} **25.** 19.5 cm^2 **27.** 49.9 ft^2 **29.** 18 units^2 **31.** 15 units^2 **33.** 135 m^2 **35.** 18 cm^2 **37.** $\frac{128\sqrt{3}}{3}$ in.^{2} **49.** $5\sqrt{2}$ units **51.** always **53.** never

Lesson 7-5 pp. 382–385

EXERCISES **1.** $m\angle 1 = 120; m\angle 2 = 60; m\angle 3 = 30$ **3.** $m\angle 7 = 60; m\angle 8 = 30; m\angle 9 = 60$ **5.** 2851.8 ft^2 **7.** 2475 in.^{2} **11.** 27.7 in.^{2} **13.** 72 cm^2 **15.** $300\sqrt{3}$ ft^2 **19a.** 72 **b.** 54 **21a.** 40 **b.** 70 **23.** 310.4 ft^2 **25.** $m\angle 1 = 36; m\angle 2 = 18; m\angle 3 = 72$ **27.** 73 cm^2 **29.** 27 m^2 **31.** 220 cm^2 **33.** $600\sqrt{3}$ m^2 **35.** 128 cm^2 **37.** $900\sqrt{3}$ m^2; 1558.8 m^2 **41a.** $b = s; h = \frac{\sqrt{3}}{2}s; A = \frac{1}{2}bh = \frac{1}{2}s \cdot \frac{\sqrt{3}}{2}s = \frac{1}{4}s^2\sqrt{3}$ **b.** apothem $= \frac{s\sqrt{3}}{6}$; $A = \frac{1}{2}ap = \frac{1}{2}\left(\frac{s\sqrt{3}}{6}\right)(3s) = \frac{1}{4}s^2\sqrt{3}$ **51.** 46 m^2 **53.** 8 m **55.** $\triangle ACG$ and $\triangle BDF$ **57a.** 7.1 mi^2 **b.** about 8 mi

Lesson 7-6 pp. 389–393

EXERCISES **1.** 25 **3.** 32 **9–11.** Answers may vary. Samples are given. **9.** $\overset{\frown}{ED}$ **11.** $\overset{\frown}{BFE}$ **15.** 128 **17.** 218 **27.** 20π cm **29.** 8.4π m **33.** 25 in. **35.** 8π ft **37.** 33π in. **43.** 180 **45.** 55 **49a.** 6 **b.** 30 **c.** 120 **51.** 100 **53.** 40 **55.** 100 in. **57.** $\frac{100\pi}{3}$ in. **59.** 105 ft **61.** (2.5, 5) **63.** 5.125π ft **65.** 3π m **69.** 12.6 units **77.** 18.6 mm **79.** No; it could be an isosc. trap. **81.** Yes; if one pair of sides is both ≅ and ∥, it is a ▱. **83.** never

Lesson 7-7 pp. 397–400

EXERCISES **1.** 9π m^2 **3.** 0.7225π ft^2 **5.** about 86,394 ft^2 **7.** 40.5π yd^2 **9.** $\frac{169\pi}{6}$ m^2 **13.** $\frac{25\pi}{4}$ m^2 **15.** 24π in.^{2} **17.** 22.1 cm^2 **19.** 3.3 m^2 **21.** 120.4 cm^2 **23.** $(54\pi + 20.25\sqrt{3})$ cm^2 **25.** $(4 - \pi)$ ft^2 **31.** 15.7 in.^{2} **35.** $(49\pi - 73.5\sqrt{3})$ m^2 **37.** 4π m^2 **45.** 2π m **47.** $11\frac{1}{4}$ in., $11\frac{1}{4}$ in., $11\frac{1}{4}$ in., $15\frac{1}{4}$ in.

Technology p. 401

1. Each ratio will approach 1. **3.** about 63 cm; about 314 cm^2

Lesson 7-8 pp. 404–407

EXERCISES **1.** $\frac{1}{2}$ **3.** $\frac{3}{5}$ **7.** $\frac{2}{5}$ or 40%

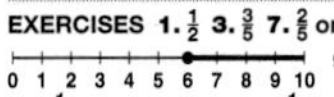

0 1 2 3 4 5 6 7 8 9 10

9. $\frac{4}{15}$ or about 27% **11.** $\frac{1}{3}$ or about 33% **15.** $\frac{1}{4}$ or 25% **17.** $\frac{2}{5}$ or 40% **21.** 4% **23.** $\frac{\pi}{4}$ **25.** $\frac{\pi}{4}$ **27a.** 14 prizes **b.** \$110 **29.** 36 s **31a.**

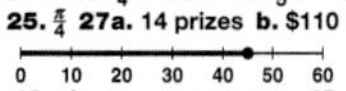

0 10 20 30 40 50 60

If it starts after 45 min, you cannot erase 15 min of a 60 min tape. **b.** $\frac{7}{45}$ or about 16% **33.** $\frac{3}{10}$ **35.** 0 **41.** about 36% **43.** about 46% **53.** 12π cm^2 **55.** $x = 36; y = 144$ **57a.** $D(3, 1); E(1, 4)$ **b.** slope $\overline{DE} = -\frac{3}{2}$; slope $\overline{AC} = -\frac{3}{2}$

Chapter Review pp. 409–411

1. base **2.** sector **3.** diameter **4.** apothem **5.** adjacent arcs **6.** 10 m^2 **7.** 90 in.^{2} **8.** 33 ft^2 **9.** $96\sqrt{3}$ mm^2 **10.** 96 ft^2 **11.** 117 cm^2

12. 20.8 in.^{2}

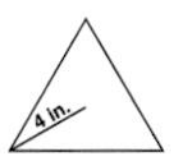

4 in.

13. 128 mm^2

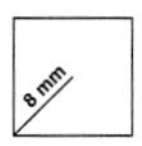

8 mm

14. 127.3 cm^2

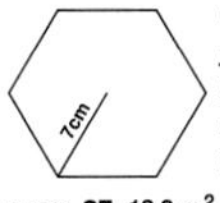

7cm

15. 16 **16.** $2\sqrt{113}$ **17.** 17 **18.** $x = 9\sqrt{3}; y = 18$ **19.** $12\sqrt{2}$ **20.** $x = \frac{20\sqrt{3}}{3}; y = \frac{40\sqrt{3}}{3}$ **21.** 30 **22.** 120 **23.** 330 **24.** 120 **25.** $\frac{22}{9}\pi$ in. **26.** π mm **27.** 18.3 m^2 **28.** 41.0 cm^2 **29.** $\frac{1}{2}$ or 50% **30.** $\frac{3}{8}$ or 37.5% **31.** $\frac{1}{6}$ or about 16.7%

Chapter 8

Lesson 8-1 pp. 418–421

EXERCISES **1.** 1 : 1000 **3–5.** Answers may vary. Samples are given. **3.** $3b$ **5.** $\frac{b}{4}$ **13.** $1\frac{2}{3}$ **15.** 6.875 **21.** 125 mi **23.** about 135 mi **27.** 5 : 4 **29.** $\frac{5}{48}$ **31.** $\frac{9}{4}$ **33.** $\frac{b}{2}$ **35.** 6 **37.** 16.5 **45.** 9; 18 **47.** 8; 21 **49–51.** Answers may vary. Samples are given.

49.

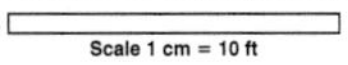

Scale 1 cm = 10 ft

51.

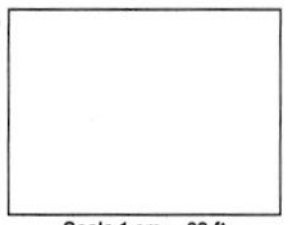

Scale 1 cm = 32 ft

53. $\frac{b}{d}$ or $\frac{a}{c}$ **55.** $\frac{c + 2d}{d}$ **67.**

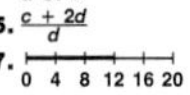

0 4 8 12 16 20

60%

69.

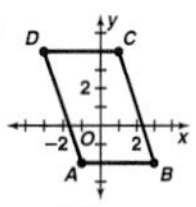

y
D
C
2
-2
O
2
x
A
B

parallelogram

71.

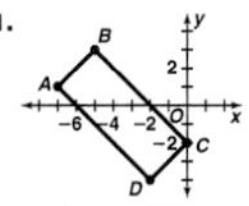

y
B
A
2
-6
-4
-2
O
x
-2
C
D

rectangle, parallelogram

73. I and III **75a.** If an ∠ is not acute, then it does not have measure between 0 and 90. **b.** If an ∠ does not have measure between 0 and 90, then it is not acute. **77a.** If two ∠s are not compl., then the ∠s are not both acute. **b.** If two ∠s are not both acute, then they are not compl.

Lesson 8-2 pp. 425–429

EXERCISES **1.** $\angle JHY$ **3.** $\angle JXY$ **7.** no; $\frac{20}{30} \neq \frac{36}{52}$ **9.** yes; $KLMJ \sim PQNO$; $\frac{3}{5}$ **11.** No; corr. ∠s are not ≅. **13.** $x = 4; y = 3$ **15.** $x = 16; y = 4.5; z = 7.5$ **17.** 3.6 in. by 6 in. **19.** 70 mm **21.** 2 : 3 **33.** 2.6 cm **35.** 3 : 1 **37.** 1 : 2 **39.** 2 : 3 **41.** sides of 2 cm; ∠s of 60° and 120° **43.** sides of 0.8 cm; ∠s of 60° and 120° **47.** 6.2 in. **57.** $7y$ **59.** $\frac{y + 9}{9}$ **61.** no; only one pair of ∥ sides **63.** $\triangle CEA, \triangle FED, \triangle BCD$ **65.** 8

Extension pp. 430–431

1.

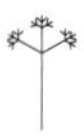

3. $\frac{64}{27}; \frac{256}{81}$ **5.**

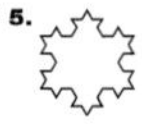

9.

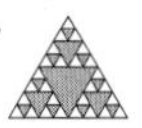

Lesson 8-3 pp. 435–438

EXERCISES **1.** Yes; $\triangle ABC \sim \triangle FED$; SSS ~ Thm. **3.** Ex. 1: $\frac{2}{3}$ (for $\triangle ABC$ to $\triangle FED$); Ex. 2: Not possible; the △s aren't similar. **5.** No; $\frac{6}{3} \neq \frac{10}{4}$. **7.** Yes; $\triangle APJ \sim \triangle ABC$; SSS ~ Thm. or SAS ~ Thm. **11.** AA ~ Post.; 2.5 **13.** AA ~ Post.; 12 **17.** AA ~ Post.; 220 yd **19.** AA ~ Post.; 90 ft **21.** 151 m **23a.** No; the corr. ∠s may not be ≅. **b.** Yes; every isosc. rt. △ is a 45°-45°-90° △. Therefore, by AA ~ Thm. they are all ~. **25.** Yes; $\triangle AWV \sim \triangle AST$; SAS ~ Thm. **27.** No; there is only one pair of ≅ ∠s. **31.** 2 : 1 **33.** 4 : 3 **41a.** 98 m; 98 m **b.** 420 m^2; 420 m^2 **c.** No; the △s given are a counterexample to this conjecture, since the sides are not in proportion. **49.** $\angle E$ **51.** $\angle Y$ **55.** x-values may vary. Sample: $W(-b, c)$; $Z(-b, -c)$ **57.** $6 < x < 24$

Lesson 8-4 pp. 442–444

EXERCISES **1.** 6 **3.** $4\sqrt{3}$ **9.** s **11.** c **15.** 9 **17.** 10 **21a.** 18 mi **b.** 24 mi **23a.** 4 cm

23b.

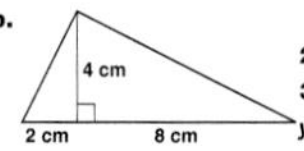

4 cm
2 cm
8 cm

25. (10, 6), (−2, 6) **27.** 14 **29.** $\sqrt{14}$ **35.** $x = 12\sqrt{5}; y = 12; z = 6\sqrt{5}$ **37.** $12\sqrt{2}$ **39.** about 6.5 m **41.** $h = 5, a = \frac{12}{5}, h_1 = \frac{9}{5}, h_2 = \frac{16}{5}$ **43.** $\ell_1 = \ell_2 = 6\sqrt{2}, h = 12, h_2 = 6$ **63a.** $\triangle PRQ \sim \triangle ACB$ **b.** SSS ~ Thm. **65.** 7.5 **67.** $x = 5; y = 8$ **69.** $x = 3; y = 4$

Technology p. 445

1. It divides the sides into prop. segments. **3.** The corr. segment ratios are =.

Lesson 8-5 pp. 448–452

EXERCISES **1.** 7.5 **3.** 5.2 **5.** c **7.** d **9.** $3\frac{1}{3}$ **11.** 6 **13.** 35 **19.** JP **21.** KM **25.** 559 ft **27.** 3.8 cm and 9.2 cm **29.** $x = 18$ m; $y = 12$ m **31.** 20 **33.** 9 **37.** 6 **39.** 19.5 **41.** $h = 13.0, \ell_1 = 5.3, \ell_2 = 11.9$ **43.** $\ell_2 = 7.1, h_2 = 5.0, h = 10.0$ **49.** No; $\frac{28}{12} \neq \frac{24}{10}$. **57.** m **59.** h **61.** $x = 9; y = 9\sqrt{3}$ **63.** $RT = SV = 38$ **65.** $RT = SV = 48$

Lesson 8-6 pp. 456–459

EXERCISES **1.** 1 : 2; 1 : 4 **3.** 2 : 3; 4:9 **5.** 24 in.^{2} **7.** 59 ft^2 **9.** \$384 **11.** 1 : 2; 1 : 2 **13.** 7 : 3; 7 : 3 **17.** 3 : 1; 9 : 1 **19.** 2 : 3; 4 : 9 **27.** $x = 2\sqrt{2}$ cm, $y = 3\sqrt{2}$ cm **29.** $x = \frac{8\sqrt{3}}{3}$ cm, $y = 4\sqrt{3}$ cm **35a.** $\frac{5}{2}$ **b.** $\frac{25}{4}$ **37a.** $\frac{2}{1}$ **b.** $\frac{4}{1}$ **51.** $5\frac{1}{3}$ cm; 12 cm **53.** 690 units^2 **55.** 44.4 units^2

57. $y = -x - 2$;

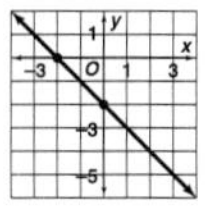

y
1
x
-3
O
1
3
-3
-5

61. Answers may vary. Sample: $y + 1 = \frac{8}{3}x$

Chapter Review pp. 461–463

1. similar **2.** Cross-Product Property **3.** golden rectangle **4.** similarity ratio **5.** proportion **6.** indirect measurement **7.** golden ratio **8.** 1 : 48 **9.** 1 : 24 **10.** True; use the Cross-Product Prop. **11.** True; the cross product is equivalent to the original proportion. **12.** False; the cross product is *not* equivalent to the original proportion. **13.** True; the cross product is equivalent to the original proportion. **14.** $\angle M \cong \angle R, \angle N \cong \angle S, \angle P \cong \angle T; \frac{MN}{RS} = \frac{MP}{RT} = \frac{NP}{ST}$ **15.** 39 in. **16.** 2 : 3 **17.** 2.5 : 1 or 5 : 2 **18.** 9 **19.** $x = 12; y = 15$ **20.** $\triangle XYZ \sim \triangle JKL$; SAS ~ Thm. **21.** No; corr. sides are not in prop. **22.** AA ~ Post. **23.** 13.5 ft **24.** $x = 15; y = 12; z = 20$ **25.** $x = 2\sqrt{21}; y = 4\sqrt{3}; z = 4\sqrt{7}$ **26.** $x = 2\sqrt{3}; y = 6; z = 4\sqrt{3}$ **27.** 7.5 **28.** 5.5 **29.** 37.5 **30.** 4 : 9 **31.** 9 : 4 **32.** 1 : 4 **33.** $2\sqrt{2}$: 5 **34.** 196 cm^2

Chapter 9

Lesson 9-1 pp. 472–475

EXERCISES **1.** $\frac{1}{2}$; 2 **3.** 1; 1 **5.** 12.3 **7.** 2.5 **9.** 21.4 **11.** 32 **13.** 48 **17.** 74.1 **19.** 114.5 **21.** 44 and 136 **27.** $w = 5; x = 4.7$ **29.** $w = 59; x = 36$ **31.** about 51° **33.** about 296 ft **35.** 71.6 **37.** 45.0 **47.** 42 **49.** 6 **51.** x **53.** 26.6 **55.** 78.7 **67.** obtuse **69.** right

Technology p. 476

1. It doesn't change. **3.** yes; sine **5.** It doesn't change; the ratio becomes larger as the angle becomes larger; 0; a large number; the values match tangent.

Lesson 9-2 pp. 479–481

EXERCISES **1.** $\frac{7}{25}; \frac{24}{25}$ **3.** $\frac{1}{2}; \frac{\sqrt{3}}{2}$ **5.** 8.3 **7.** 17.0 **11.** 21 **13.** 46 **19.** $\cos X \cdot \tan X = \frac{\text{adj.}}{\text{hyp.}} \cdot \frac{\text{opp.}}{\text{adj.}} = \frac{\text{opp.}}{\text{hyp.}} = \sin X$ **21.** No; the △s are ~ and the sine ratio for 35° is constant. **23.** $w = 37; x = 7.5$ **41.** 6.9 **43.** 18 **45.** $(36 + 18\sqrt{3})$ cm^2 **47.** $30\sqrt{3}$ mm^2

Lesson 9-3 pp. 484–488

EXERCISES **1.** ∠ of elevation from sub to boat **3.** ∠ of elevation from boat to lighthouse **9.** 34.2 ft **11.** 32.2 m **15.** 777.9 m **17.** 0.6 km **19.** 64° **21.** about 194 m **23.** 3300 m **25.** 46, 46 **27.** 20, 20 **31.** about 2.8 **33.** 370 m **45.** 85.2 m **47.** 45 **49.** 110 **55.** $y = 3, x = 2$; 16, 10, 10, 16

Lesson 9-4 pp. 493–497

EXERCISES **1.** ⟨602.2, 668.8⟩ **3.** ⟨37.5, −65.0⟩ **5.** 20° west of south

7.

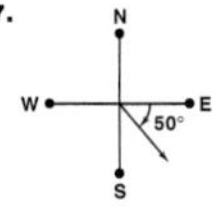

N
W
E
50°
S

13. about 97 mi at 41° south of west **15.** about 54 mi/h; 22° north of east

17a. ⟨−9, −9⟩

b.

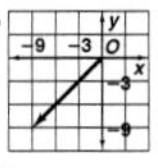

y
-9
-3
O
x
-3
-9

23. ⟨−1, 3⟩ **25.** ⟨−2, 3⟩ **27.** about 13.2° north of west **29.** Yes; both vectors have the same direction, but could have diff. mag.

31a.

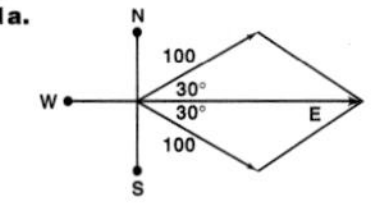

N
100
30°
W
30°
E
100
S

b. about 173 due east **33.** Vectors are ∥ if they have the same or opp. directions. **35a.** ⟨0, 0⟩ **b.** $\vec{a}$ and $\vec{c}$ have = mag. and opp. direction. **37.** $\begin{bmatrix} -1 \\ -2 \end{bmatrix}$ **39.** $\begin{bmatrix} -1 \\ 0 \end{bmatrix}$ **43.** ⟨0, −4⟩

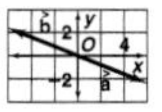

45. The vectors have the same mag.; the vectors have opp. directions. **47a.** 15° south of west **b.** about 6.7 h **57.** $\frac{1}{8}$ **59.** $\frac{1}{3}$

Lesson 9-5 pp. 500–503

EXERCISES **1.** 173.8 cm^2 **3.** 259.8 m^2 **7.** 47.0 in.^{2} **9.** 8 ft^2 **11.** 27.7 m^2 **13.** 7554.0 m^2 **17.** 5523 yd^2 **21.** \$51.96 **23.** 45.3 in.; 128 in.^{2} **29.** (area of pent. A) ≈ 1.53 · (area of pent. B) **31.** (area of oct. B) ≈ 1.17 · (area of oct. A) **33.** 5.0 ft^2 **43.** ⟨−2, −9⟩ **45.** ⟨−6, −1⟩ **47.** $\frac{376\pi}{45}$ cm^2 **49.** $\frac{63\pi}{8}$ m^2 **51.** $\left(\frac{a}{2}, \frac{b}{2}\right)$; $\sqrt{a^2 + b^2}$

Chapter Review pp. 505–507

1. vector **2.** angle of elevation **3.** cosine **4.** sine **5.** identity **6.** resultant vector **7.** magnitude; initial point; terminal point **8.** 42 **9.** 2 **10.** 2 **11.** 67 **12.** 23 **13.** 42 **14.** 12 **15.** 8 **16.** $\frac{\sqrt{3}}{2}, \frac{1}{2}, \sqrt{3}$ **17.** $\frac{\sqrt{19}}{10}, \frac{9}{10}, \frac{\sqrt{19}}{9}$ **18.** $\frac{4}{5}, \frac{3}{5}, \frac{4}{3}$ **19.** 51 **20.** 16.5 **21.** 33

22. 1410 ft **23.** 280 ft **24.** about 38.2 yd **25.** They are alt. int. ∠s to ∥ lines. **26.** ⟨125.8, 81.7⟩ **27.** ⟨37.5, −92.7⟩ **28.** ⟨−21.8, 33.5⟩ **29.** about 167.7 mi; about 26.6° east of south **30.** about 206.2 km; about 14.0° west of south **31.** about 503.1 mi/h; about 26.6° north of west **32.** ⟨6, 8⟩, ⟨9, 12⟩, ⟨30, 40⟩; ⟨x, y⟩ and ⟨nx, ny⟩ have the same direction for $n > 0$.

33.

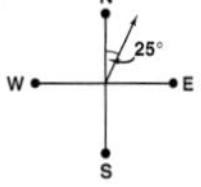

N
25°
W
E
S

34.

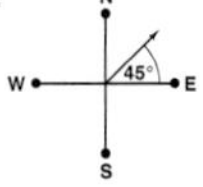

N
45°
W
E
S

35.

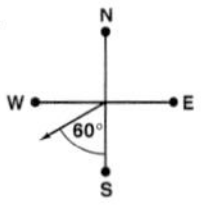

N
W
E
60°
S

36. ⟨1, 4⟩ **37.** ⟨4, −6⟩ **38.** ⟨2, 0⟩ **39a.** about 67.4° south of west **b.** about 39 min **40.** 73.5 ft^2 **41.** 232.5 cm^2 **42.** 124.7 in.^{2} **43.** 8 m^2 **44.** 100.8 cm^2 **45.** 88.4 ft^2 **46.** 70.4 m^2

Chapter 10

Lesson 10-1 pp. 514–516

EXERCISES **1.** yes; E and C, B and D, A and F **3.** yes; A and C, B and E, D and F **5.** Yes; the faces only share one edge. **7.** C **9.** B **11.** Answers may vary. Sample:

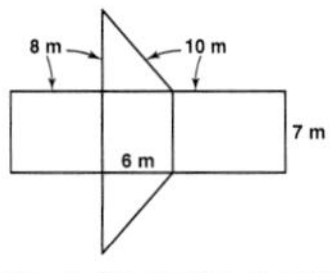

8 m
10 m
7 m
6 m

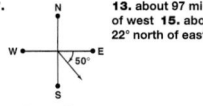

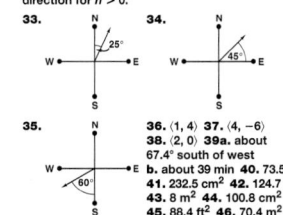

13. 8 **15.** 12 **17.** 5 **21.** green **23.** purple **27.** sphere **29a.** A. icosahedron B. octahedron C. tetrahedron D. hexahedron E. dodecahedron **b.** reg. triangular pyramid, cube **c.** $4 + 4 = 6 + 2$; $6 + 8 = 12 + 2$; $8 + 6 = 12 + 2$ **31.** 60 **41.** $\sqrt{145}$ cm **43.** $5\sqrt{5}$ mm **45.** 20 **47.** 105

Extension p. 519

1. two-point **3.** one-point

7.

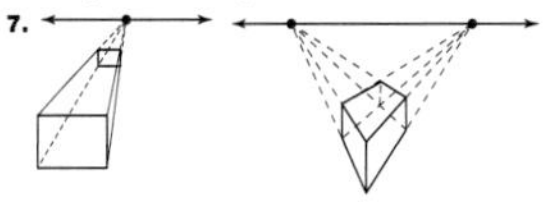

9.

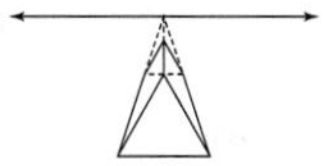

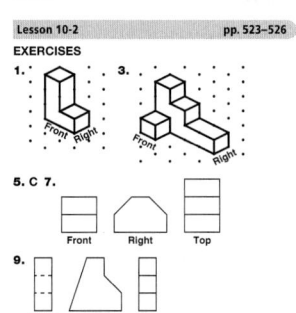

15. Answer may vary. Sample: The horizontal lines appear to be curved; the slanted lines that would meet at the vanishing pt. create a cylinder effect.

Lesson 10-2 pp. 523–526

EXERCISES

1.

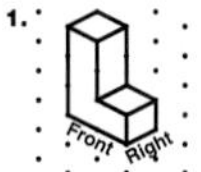

Front
Right

3.

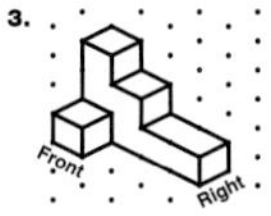

Front
Right

5. C **7.**

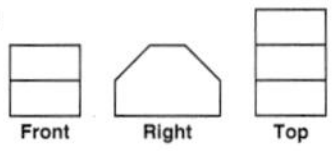

Front
Right
Top

9.

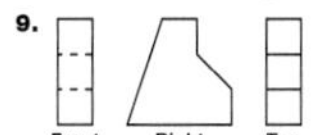

Front
Right
Top

11a.

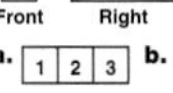

1
2
3

b.

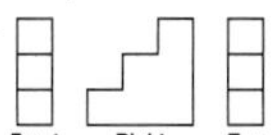

Front
Right
Top

13. 6 **15.** 8 **17.** regular hexagon with hexagonal hole **19.** rectangle **21.** square

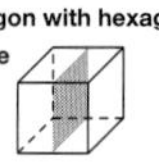

25a.

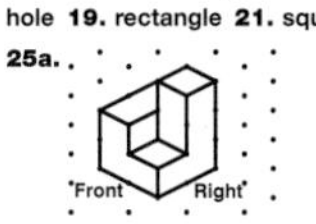

Front
Right

b.

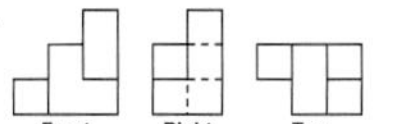

Front
Right
Top

27. 1 **29.** 3 **31.** orthographic top view

33.

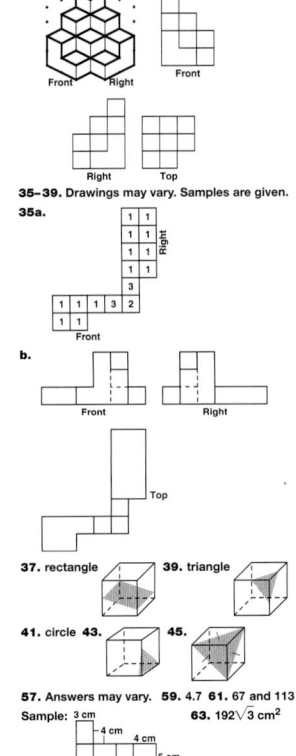

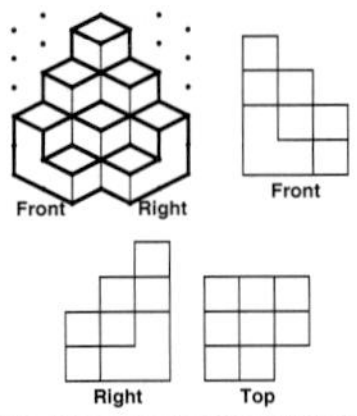
Front
Right
Front
Right
Top

35–39. Drawings may vary. Samples are given.

35a.

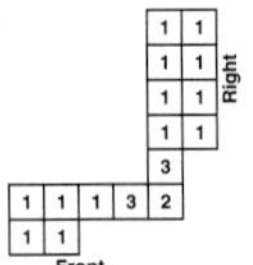
Right
Front

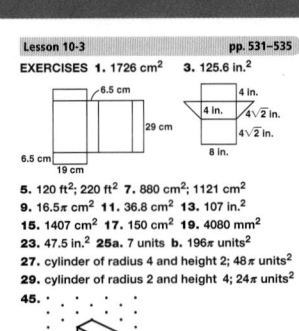

b.

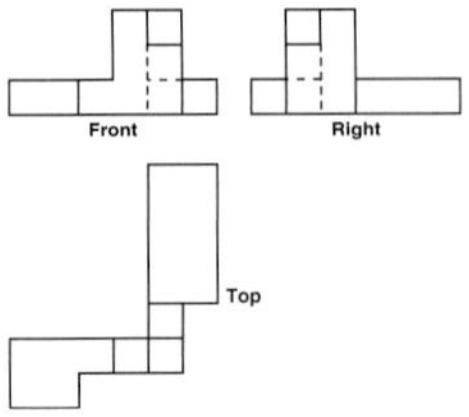
Front
Right
Top

37. rectangle

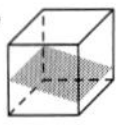

39. triangle

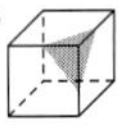

41. circle **43.**

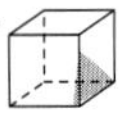

45.

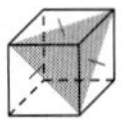

57. Answers may vary. Sample:

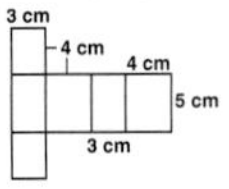
3 cm
4 cm
4 cm
5 cm
3 cm

59. 4.7 **61.** 67 and 113 **63.** $192\sqrt{3}$ cm^2

Lesson 10-3 — pp. 531–535

EXERCISES **1.** 1726 cm^2 **3.** 125.6 in.^{2}

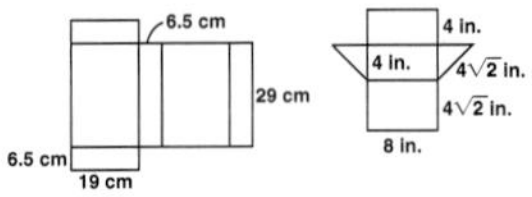
6.5 cm
29 cm
6.5 cm
19 cm
4 in.
4 in.
$4\sqrt{2}$ in.
$4\sqrt{2}$ in.
8 in.

5. 120 ft^2; 220 ft^2 **7.** 880 cm^2; 1121 cm^2 **9.** 16.5π cm^2 **11.** 36.8 cm^2 **13.** 107 in.^{2} **15.** 1407 cm^2 **17.** 150 cm^2 **19.** 4080 mm^2 **23.** 47.5 in.^{2} **25a.** 7 units **b.** 196π units^2 **27.** cylinder of radius 4 and height 2; 48π units^2 **29.** cylinder of radius 2 and height 4; 24π units^2

45.

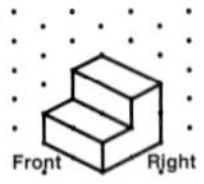
Front
Right

47.

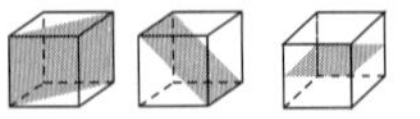

49. 22.1 cm^2

Technology — p. 536

1–3. Answers may vary. Samples are given. **1.** 600 cm^2; 5080 cm^2 **3.** about 4.64 cm by 4.64 cm by 4.64 cm

Lesson 10-4 — pp. 540–543

EXERCISES **1.** 408 in.^{2} **3.** 179 in.^{2} **5.** 12 in. **7.** 204 m^2 **9.** 51 m^2 **11.** 156 ft^2 **13.** 33π ft^2 **15.** 13 m **17.** 11 yd **19.** 31 m^2 **23.** 228.1 in.^{2}

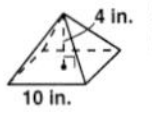
4 in.
10 in.

25. 478 cm^2 **27.** 28 in.^{2} **31.** 58 m^2 **33.** 45 m^2

37. $s = 12$ m, L.A. = 240 m^2, S.A. = 384 m^2 **39.** $s = 8$ cm, $\ell = 7.4$ cm, $h = 6.2$ cm **41.** $\ell = 6.5$ m, $C = 25.1$ m, S.A. = 132.0 m^2 **43.** $r = 1.0$ ft, S.A. = 36.4 ft^2, $C = 6.3$ ft **47.** cone with $r = 3$ and $h = 4$; 24π **61.** 76 ft^2 **63.** about 281.7 m **65.** 26 in.

Lesson 10-5 — pp. 547–550

EXERCISES **1.** 216 ft^3 **3.** 180 m^3 **5.** about 280.6 cm^3 **7.** 720 mm^3 **9.** 288π in.^{3}, 904.8 in.^{3} **11.** 37.5π m^3, 117.8 in.^{3} **13.** 3445 in.^{3} **15.** 501 in.^{3} **17.** $\frac{26}{9}$ cm **19.** 6 ft **21.** 28–42 pots **25.** 80 units^3 **27.** 3 cm **29.** cylinder with $r = 2$ and $h = 4$; 16π units^3 **31.** cylinder with $r = 2$ and $h = 4$; 16π units^3 **33.** 125.7 cm^3 **47.** 469.2 ft^2 **49.** 70; 110, 70 **51.** 50; 14, 144, 148, 54

Lesson 10-6 — pp. 554–557

EXERCISES **1.** about 233,333 ft^3 **3.** 1296 in.^{3} **5.** about 443.7 cm^3 **7.** 2048 m^3 **9.** about 3714.5 mm^3 **11.** $\frac{16}{3}\pi$ ft^3; 17 ft^3 **13.** 36.75π in.^{3}; 115 in.^{3} **15.** ≈ 4.7 cm^3 **17.** 312 cm^3 **19.** They are equal; both volumes are $\frac{1}{3}\pi r^2 h$. **21.** 6 **23.** $3\sqrt{2}$ **27a.** 120π ft^3 **b.** 60π ft^3 **c.** 240π ft^3 **29.** cone with $r = 4$ and $h = 3$; 16π **43.** 7.1 in.^{3} **45.** 59.4 in.^{2} **47.** 57.7 in.^{2}

Lesson 10-7 — pp. 560–564

EXERCISES **1.** 900π m^2 **3.** 1024π mm^2 **5.** 4624π mm^2 **7.** $\frac{121}{16}\pi$ in.^{2} **9.** 232 in.^{2} **11.** 154 in.^{2} **13.** 288π cm^3; 905 cm^3 **15.** $\frac{2048}{3}\pi$ cm^3; 2145 cm^3 **19.** 1006 m^2 **21.** S.A. ≈ 108 cm^2, V ≈ 108 cm^3 **27.** 1.7 lb **29.** $\frac{4}{3}\pi$ m^3 **31.** $\frac{9}{2}\pi$ ft^3 **41.** 26π cm^2; $\frac{62}{3}\pi$ cm^3 **61.** 19 in.^{3} **63.** 35, 55 **65.** 10.5 cm **67.** 67.5 cm^2

Technology — p. 565

1. The ratio of volumes is the similarity ratio cubed. **3.** The ratio of volumes is the similarity ratio cubed. **5.** The ratio of surface areas is the similarity ratio squared.

Lesson 10-8 — pp. 568–571

EXERCISES **1.** no **3.** yes; 2 : 3 **7.** 5 : 6 **9.** 3 : 4 **11.** 27 in.^{3} **13.** 24 ft^3 **15.** 16 m^2 **17.** 6000 toothpicks **19a.** It is 64 times the smaller prism. **b.** It is 64 times the smaller prism. **23.** about 1000 cm^3 **27a.** 3 : 1 **b.** 9 : 1 **29.** 864 in.^{3} **31.** 9 : 25; 27 : 125 **33.** 5 : 8; 25 : 64 **43.** 1790 cm^2 and 1937 cm^2 **45.** 8.2 m^2 ; 19.6 m^2 **47a.** $8\sqrt{3}$ mm 809 **b.** $4\sqrt{21}$ mm **c.** $8\sqrt{7}$ mm **49.** 13.125

Chapter Review — pp. 573–575

1. sphere **2.** net **3.** pyramid **4.** cross section **5.** right

6.

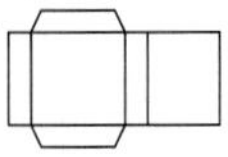

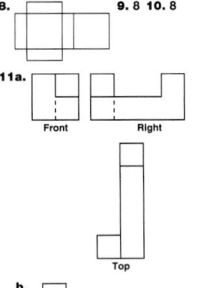

7.

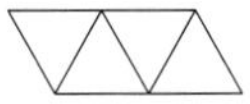

8.

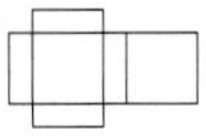

9. 8 **10.** 8

11a.

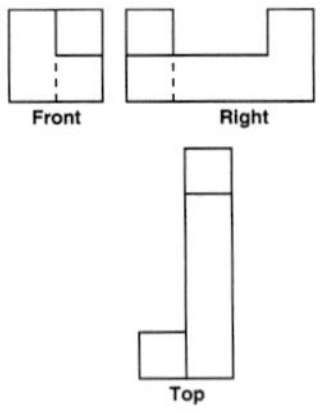
Front
Right
Top

b.

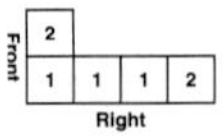
2
1
1
1
2
Front
Right

12.

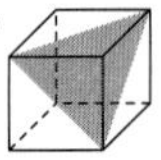

13. 36 cm^2; 12 cm^3 **14.** 66π m^2; 72π m^3 **15.** 208 in.^{2}; 192 in.^{3} **16.** 60π ft^2; $\frac{160}{3}\pi$ ft^3

17. 672 m^2; 512 m^3 **18.** 16π in.^{2}; $\frac{16\sqrt{2}}{3}\pi$ in.^{3} **19.** 314.2 in.^{2}; 523.6 in.^{3} **20.** 153.9 cm^2; 179.6 cm^3 **21.** 50.3 ft^2; 33.5 ft^3 **22.** 8.0 ft^2; 2.1 ft^3 **23.** 8.6 in.^{3} **24.** Answers may vary. Sample:

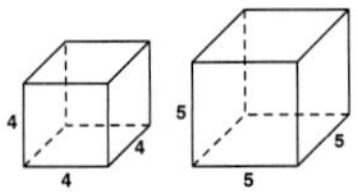
4
4
4
5
5
5

25. 27 : 64 **26.** 64 : 27

Chapter 11

Lesson 11-1 — pp. 586–589

EXERCISES **1.** 120 **3.** 30 **7.** 20.0 in. **9.** 19.1 cm **11.** Yes; $2.5^2 + 6^2 = 6.5^2$ **13.** inscribed in **15.** circumscribed about **17.** 14.2 in. **21.** 3.6 cm **25.** 80.0 km **27.** 57.5 **29.** about 34.6 in. **33.** 35 **37.** a–c.

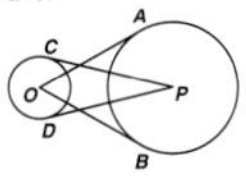
A
C
O
P
D
B

d. $\overline{AB} \parallel \overline{CD}$; arguments may vary.

49. 9:16 **51.** 29.1 **53.** 68.2 **55a.** 4:1 **b.** $a = 1.625$; $b = 1.75$, $c = 3$

Lesson 11-2 — pp. 593–596

EXERCISES **1.** $\widehat{BC} \cong \widehat{YZ}$; $\overline{BC} \cong \overline{YZ}$ **3.** 14 **5.** 7 **9.** Answers may vary. Samples are given. **a.** $\overline{CE}$ **b.** $\overline{DE}$ **c.** ∠CEB **d.** ∠DEA **11.** 6 **13.** 8.9 **17.** 108 **19.** about 123.9 **21.** 12 cm **31.** 10 cm **33.** 8 **47.** 40 **49.** about 42 ft

Lesson 11-3 — pp. 601–605

EXERCISES **1.** ∠ACB; $\widehat{AB}$ **3.** ∠MPN; $\widehat{MN}$ **5.** 58 **7.** $a = 218$; $b = 109$ **11.** $x = 36$; $y = 36$ **13.** $a = 50$; $b = 90$; $c = 90$ **15.** $w = 123$ **17.** $e = 65$; $f = 130$ **21a.** 96 **b.** 55 **c.** 77 **d.** 154 **23a.** 30 **b.** 78 **c.** 95 **d.** 105 **e.** 85 **f.** 75 **27a.** $77\frac{1}{7}°$ **b.** 36° **29.** about 7.1 cm by 7.1 cm **31.** about 7.1 cm legs, and a 10 cm base

33. false

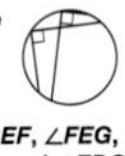

35. true

37a. ∠CEF, ∠FEG, ∠GFD and ∠GED **b.** ∠CED **c.** ∠EFG and ∠EDG; ∠FED and ∠FGD **51.** 17.3 **53.** 17.5 **55.** 64.5 cm^2 **57.** Both have rt. ∠s and the vertical ∠s are ≅, so △s are ~ by AA ~ Post.

Technology — pp. 606

1. The prod. of the lengths of the segments of one chord = the prod. of the lengths of the segments of the other chord.

3. The products are =. For $\overline{DG}$, the secant segment and its external segment are the same.

Lesson 11-4 — pp. 611–613

EXERCISES **1.** 46 **3.** $x = 60$; $y = 70$ **7.** 160° **9.** 15 **11.** 13.2 **15.** about 270.8 ft **17.** $360 - x$ **19.** $180 - y$ **21.** 16.7 **23.** $x \approx 10.7$; $y = 10$ **25.** $x \approx 10.9$; $y \approx 2.3$ **27.** 95, 104, 86, 75 **29.** Answers may vary. Sample: Since they are inscribed ∠s: $m\angle BED = \frac{1}{2}m\widehat{BD}$ and $m\angle ABE = \frac{1}{2}m\widehat{AE}$. Apply the Ext. ∠ Thm. to △BCE to prove that $m\angle C = \frac{1}{2}(m\widehat{AE} - m\widehat{BD})$. **31.** Given: a circle with secant segments $\overline{XV}$ and $\overline{ZV}$; Prove: $XV \cdot WV = ZV \cdot YV$.

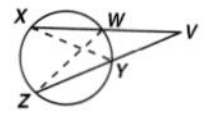
X
W
V
Y
Z

1. Construct $\overline{XY}$ and $\overline{ZW}$. **2.** ∠XVY ≅ ∠ZVW (Reflexive Prop. of ≅) **3.** ∠VXY ≅ ∠WZV (2 inscribed ∠s that intercept the same arc are ≅.) **4.** △XVY ~ △ZVW (AA~) **5.** $\frac{XV}{ZV} = \frac{YV}{WV}$ (In similar figures, corr. sides are proport.) **6.** $XV \cdot WV = YV \cdot ZV$ (Prop. of Proport.) **43.** $a = 50$; $b = 55$; $c = 105$ **45.** 30 **47.** 57

Extension — p. 614

1. ACD; HGA; EFA **3.** The radius of the circle is 1, which is the denominator in each of the ratios. **5.** On the unit circle, secant $A = \frac{\text{hyp.}}{1}$ = hyp. = length of $\overline{DA}$, the secant segment.

7. $(\text{tangent } A)^2 = \left(\frac{DC}{CA}\right)^2 = \left(\frac{EB}{BA}\right)^2 = \frac{(EB)^2}{(BA)^2} = \frac{(EA)^2 - (BA)^2}{(BA)^2} = \frac{(EA)^2}{(BA)^2} - 1 = (\text{secant } A)^2 - 1$

9. $\text{cotangent } A = \frac{HG}{GA} = \frac{CA}{CD} = \frac{1}{\frac{CD}{CA}} = \frac{1}{\text{tangent } A}$

11. $\text{secant } A = \frac{EA}{AB} = \frac{EA}{EF} = \frac{1}{\frac{EF}{EA}} = \frac{1}{\text{cosine } A}$

Lesson 11-5 — pp. 617–620

EXERCISES **1.** $(x - 2)^2 + (y + 8)^2 = 81$ **3.** $(x - 0.2)^2 + (y - 1.1)^2 = 0.16$ **11.** $(x - 1)^2 + (y - 2)^2 = 17$ **13.** $(x + 10)^2 + (y + 5)^2 = 125$ **17.** center: (3, −8); radius: 10

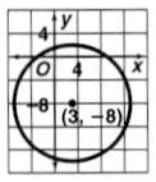
y
4
O
4
x
−8
(3, −8)

23. $(x - 4)^2 + (y + 4)^2 = 4$ **25.** position: (5, 7); range: 9 units **27.** $x^2 + y^2 = 4$ **29.** $x^2 \pm (y - 3)^2 \neq 4$ **33.** $(x - 4)^2 + (y - 3)^2 = 25$

35. $(x - 3)^2 + (y - 3)^2 = 8$ **39.** $x^2 + y^2 = 1$ **43.** No; the x and y terms are not squared. **45.** circumference: 16π; area: 64π

49.

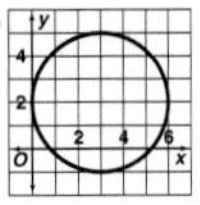

53. (3, 2); (2, 3)

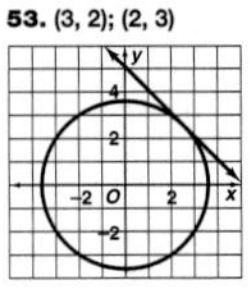

71. 38 **73.** ⟨−5, 2⟩ **75.** ⟨11, −7⟩ **77.** $9\sqrt{3}$ **79.** 3

Lesson 11-6 — pp. 623–625

EXERCISES **1.** a circle of radius 4 cm with center X

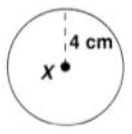
4 cm
X

3. two distinct lines ∥ to $\overleftrightarrow{LM}$ and 3 mm from $\overleftrightarrow{LM}$

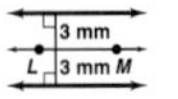
3 mm
L
3 mm
M

9. the single pt. L **11.** the single pt. N

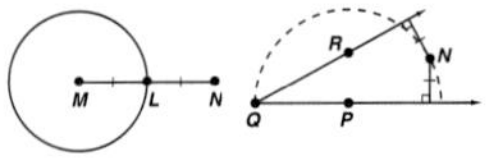
M
L
N
R
N
Q
P

15. an endless cylinder with radius 4 cm and center-line $\overleftrightarrow{DE}$

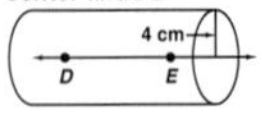
4 cm
D
E

17. an endless cylinder with radius 5 mm and center-ray $\overrightarrow{PQ}$ and a hemisphere of radius 5 mm centered at P

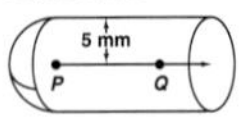
5 mm
P
Q

19. the set of all points 2 units from the origin **23.** $y = x$ **25.** $y = -x + 3$

27. **29.**

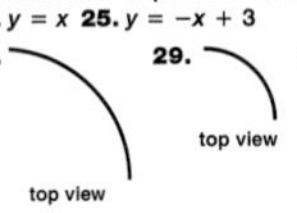
top view
top view

33.

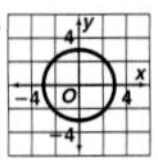

35.

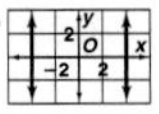

41. a circle **55.** $(x - 1)^2 + (y - 7)^2 = 36$ **57.** 510 in.^{2} **59.** 4π **61.** 10π

Chapter Review — pp. 627–629

1. tangent to **2.** chord **3.** inscribed in **4.** inscribed angle **5.** locus **6.** 57 in. **7.** 72 mm **8.** 9.8 cm **9.** 4.3 **10.** 19.5 **11.** 6.4 **12.** 4.5 **13.** $a = 40$; $b = 140$; $c = 90$ **14.** $a = 118$; $b = 49$; $= 144$; $d = 98$ **15.** $a = 90$; $b = 90$; $c = 70$; $d = 65$ **16.** $a = 95$; $b = 85$ **17.** 37 **18.** $x = 57$; $y = 44.5$; $z = 129$; $v = 51$ **19.** 17.1 **20.** 4 **21.** 21.1 **22.** $(x - 2)^2 + (y - 5)^2 = 12.25$ **23.** $(x + 3)^2 + (y - 1)^2 = 5$ **24.** $(x - 9)^2 + (y + 4)^2 = 16$ **25.** $x^2 + (y - 1)^2 = 80$ **26.** $(x + 2)^2 + (y - 3)^2 = 85$ **27.** $(x - 10)^2 + (y - 7)^2 = 468$ **28.** center = (0, 8); $r = 7$ **29.** center = (5, −9); $r = 2\sqrt{10}$ **30.** center = (−1, 0); $r = 3$

31. a circle of radius 3 cm **32.** the ⊥ bis. of the segment between the pts.

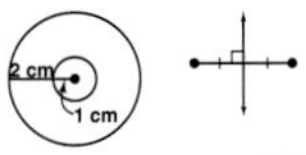
2 cm
1 cm

33. a cylinder with hemispherical ends

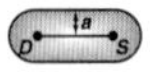

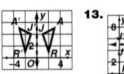

Chapter 12

Lesson 12-1 — pp. 636–639

EXERCISES **1.** Yes; the trans. is a slide. **3.** No; the figures are not ≅. **5a.** Answers may vary. Sample: ∠R → ∠R' **b.** $\overline{RI}$ and $\overline{R'I'}$; $\overline{IT}$ and $\overline{I'T'}$; $\overline{RT}$ and $\overline{R'T'}$ **7a.** Answers may vary. Sample: $G \rightarrow M$ **b.** $\overline{GW}$ and $\overline{MR}$; $\overline{WP}$ and $\overline{RT}$; $\overline{PN}$ and $\overline{TX}$; $\overline{NB}$ and $\overline{XS}$; $\overline{BG}$ and $\overline{SM}$

11.

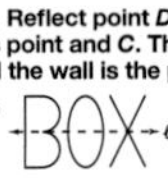

13.

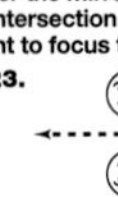

19. Reflect point D over the mirrored wall. Connect this point and C. The intersection of the segment and the wall is the point to focus the camera.

21. **23.**

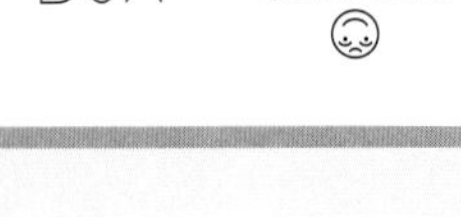
BOX

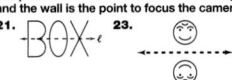

25. S-Isomer **27.** (x, y) has image $(x, -y)$. **29.** (x, y) has image (y, x). **31.** $x^2 + y^2 = 49$ **33.** $x^2 + (y + 3)^2 = 9$ **37.** $(0, -6)$ **39.** $(0, 0)$ **63a.** 4 : 3 **b.** 64 : 27

Lesson 12-2 pp. 643–646

EXERCISES **1.** $\langle 2, 5\rangle$ is a translation of 2 units to the right and 5 units up. **3.** $\langle -3, 8\rangle$ is a translation of 3 units to the left and 8 units up. **7.** $\langle -2, -1\rangle$ **9.** $\langle 8, 10\rangle$ **11.** *H* **13.** *E* **17.** $\langle 5, 5\rangle$ **19.** $\langle 0, -2\rangle$ **23.** $(x, y) \to (x + 1, y - 1)$ **25.** $(x, y) \to (x + 4, y - 2)$ **27.** $(1, -2), (4, 1), (10, -2), (7, -5)$ **29.** $(-4, -0.5), (-2, -3), (-1, 4), (5, 0)$

35.
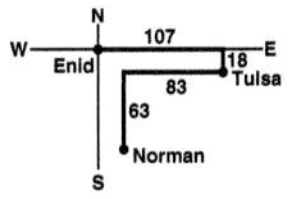

Norman is 24 mi east and 81 mi south of Enid.

37. $(x, y) \to (x - 3, y + 1)$ **39.** $U'(1, 16), G'(2, 12)$ **43.** $\langle 0, 0\rangle$ **45.** $\langle 13, -2.5\rangle$

47.
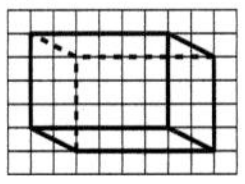

49.
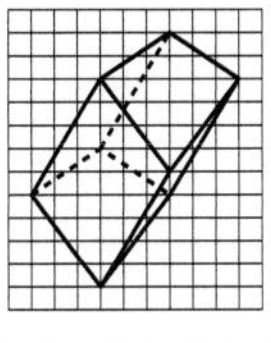

Lesson 12-3 pp. 649–652

EXERCISES

1.
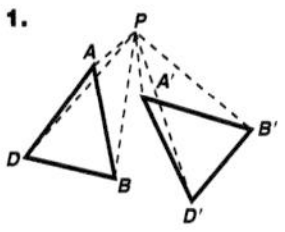

3.
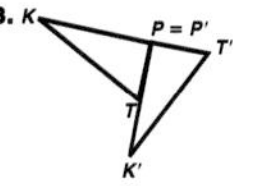

5.
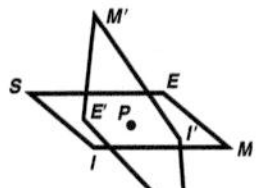

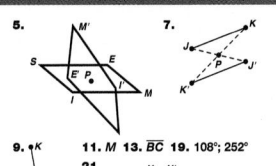

7.
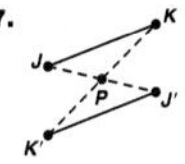

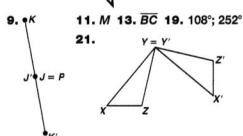

9.
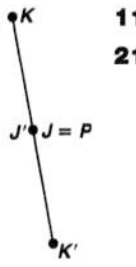

11. *M* **13.** $\overline{BC}$ **19.** 108°; 252°

21.
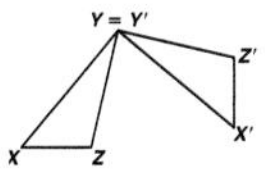

23.
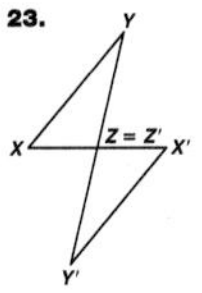

27. 180° rotation about its center **29.** Answers may vary. Sample: 110

31.
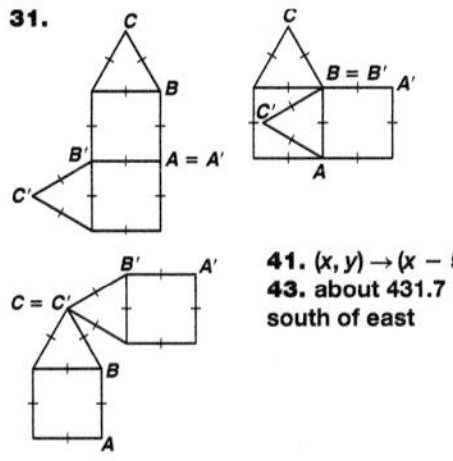

41. $(x, y) \to (x - 5), (y - 1)$ **43.** about 431.7 mi at 76.6° south of east

Lesson 12-4 pp. 657–660

EXERCISES **1.** rotation **3.** Neither; the figures do not have the same orientation.

5.
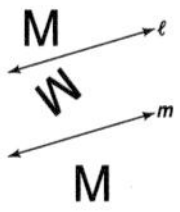

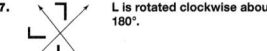

M is translated across line *m* twice the distance between ℓ and *m*.

7.
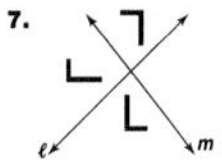

L is rotated clockwise about 180°.

9.
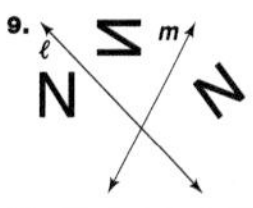

N is rotated clockwise about 160°.

11.
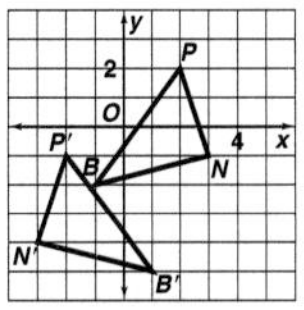

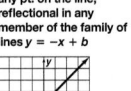

13.
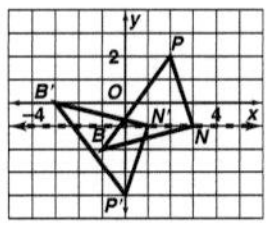

19. opp.; glide reflection **21.** same; rotation **27.** reflection **29.** rotation **35.** 60 **37.** 30 **39.** glide reflection; $\langle 11, 0\rangle$, $y = 0$ **41.** reflection; $y = 0$ **63.** 123 **65.** 87 **67.** 15 cm **69.** 5.5 m

Lesson 12-5 pp. 664–666

EXERCISES

1. line
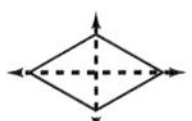

3. rotational: 90°

13.
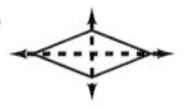

15.
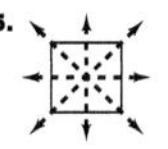

17. rotational and reflectional **19.** Answer may vary. Samples: CODE, HOOD, DOCK

21a.

Language	Horiz. line	Vert. line	Point
English	B, C, D, E, H, I, K, O, X	A, H, I, M, O, T, U, V, W, X, Y	H, I, N, O S, X, Z
Greek	B, E, H, Θ I, K, Ξ, O, Σ, Φ, X	A, Δ, H, Θ, I, Λ, M, Ξ, O, Π, T, Υ, Φ, X, Ψ, Ω	Z, H, Θ, I, N, Ξ, O, Φ, X

b. Sample: Greek; Greek alphabet has more letters with at least one kind of symmetry and more letters with multiple symmetries. **23.** rotational, reflectional **25.** reflectional; rotational **27.** point **29.** reflectional; rotational **33.** Yes; the bisector divides the ∠ into 2 ≅ △s with one side of the ∠ being the reflection of the other. **35.** Not necessarily; the bisector divides the segment into 2 ≅ parts but one part cannot be the reflection of the other unless the bisector is the ⊥ bisector. **37.** $(-3, 4)$ **39.** $(-3, -4)$

41. point symmetry about any pt. on the line; reflectional in any member of the family of lines $y = -x + b$
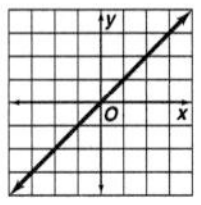

43. reflectional in *x*-axis
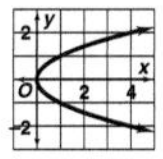

45. reflectional in $x = -2$ **47.** reflectional in *y*-axis
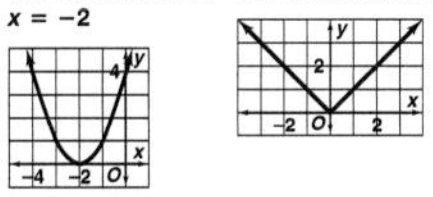

49. Sample:
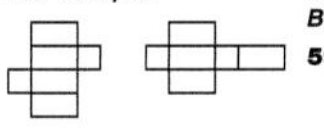

57. $A'(-3, 3)$, $B'(-4, 2)$, $C'(-4, 4)$ **59.** 4.3 **61.** $66\frac{2}{3}$ cm^3

Lesson 12-6 pp. 670–672

EXERCISES **1–3.** Answers may vary. Samples are given. **1.** yes; translation; two ⊥ rectangles **3.** rotation; four rectangles in a square shape **5.** yes **7.** no **11.** rotational, reflectional, glide reflectional, and translational **13.** rotational, reflectional, glide reflectional, and translational

17. **19.**
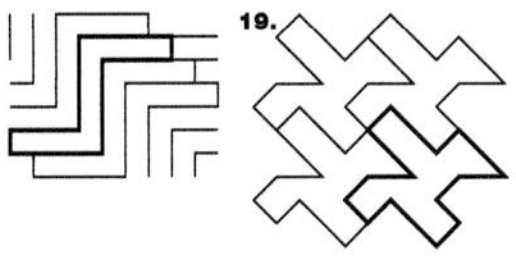

21. Answers may vary. Sample is given.
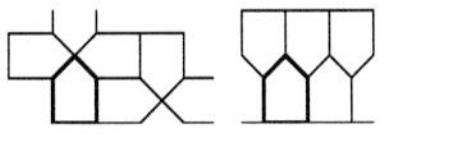

25. yes;
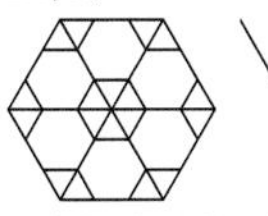

27. yes;
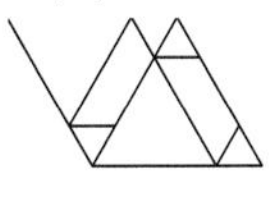

45. $(-2, -7)$ **47.** $(2, -7)$ **49.** $x^2 + y^2 = 36$ **51.** $(x + 1)^2 + y^2 = 9$ **53.** 30

Lesson 12-7 pp. 676–679

EXERCISES **1.** enlargement; center *A*, scale factor $\frac{3}{2}$ **3.** enlargement; center *R*, scale factor $\frac{3}{2}$ **11.** 512 in. **13.** 1.25 ft **15.** $P'(6, -3), Q'(6, 12), R'(12, -3)$

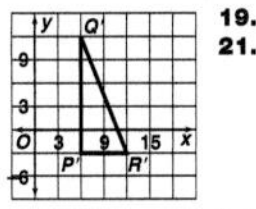

19. $L'(-15, 0)$ **21.** $T'(0, 18)$

25. $A'\left(-\frac{1}{2}, -\frac{1}{2}\right), B'\left(\frac{1}{4}, \frac{1}{4}\right), C'\left(\frac{1}{4}, -\frac{1}{4}\right)$

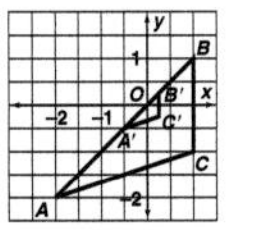

29. $Q'(-6, 8), W'(6, 10), T'(6, 2), R'(-4, -2)$ **31.** $Q'\left(-\frac{3}{4}, 1\right), W'\left(\frac{3}{4}, \frac{5}{4}\right), T'\left(\frac{3}{4}, \frac{1}{4}\right), R'\left(-\frac{1}{2}, -\frac{1}{4}\right)$

37.
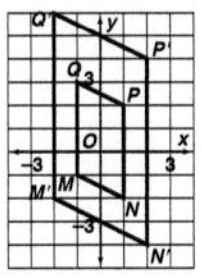

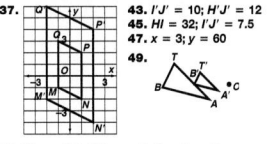

43. $I'J' = 10$; $H'J' = 12$ **45.** $HI = 32$; $I'J' = 7.5$ **47.** $x = 3$; $y = 60$

49.
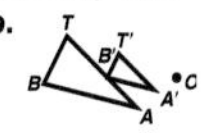

55. 60 cm **57.** False; a dilation doesn't map a segment to a ≅ segment unless the scale factor is 1. **59.** False; a dilation with a scale factor greater than 2 is an enlargement. **73.** yes **75.** yes **77.** a sphere with a 6-in. radius, concentric with the given sphere, and the center of the spheres **79.** 30

Chapter Review pp. 681–683

1. F **2.** D **3.** E or B **4.** G **5.** B **6.** C **7.** A

8. **9.**
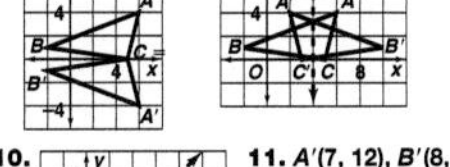

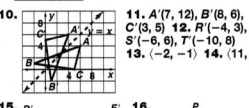

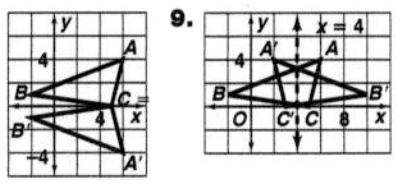

10.
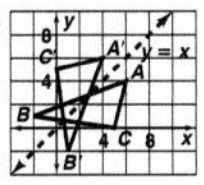

11. $A'(7, 12), B'(8, 6), C'(3, 5)$ **12.** $R'(-4, 3), S'(-6, 6), T'(-10, 8)$ **13.** $\langle -2, -1\rangle$ **14.** $\langle 11, -4\rangle$

15. **16.**
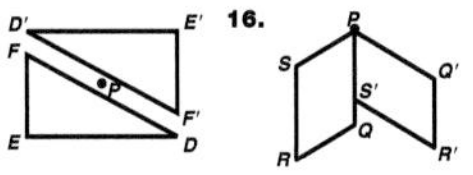

17.
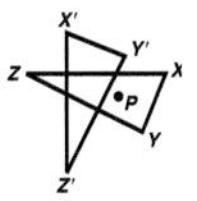

18. $(-2, 5)$ **19.** $(-3, 0)$ **20.** $(-1, -4)$ **21.** $(0, 7)$ **22.** $(8, -2)$ **23.** same; rotation **24.** opposite; reflection **25.** same; translation **26.** opposite; glide reflection **27.** same; translation **28.** opposite; glide reflection **29.** same; rotation **30.** opposite; reflection **31.** $T'(-4, -9), A'(0, -5), M'(-1, -10)$ **32.** reflectional **33.** rotational; 72°

34a.
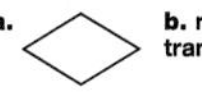
b. rotational, point, reflectional, translational, glide reflectional

35a.
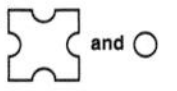
b. rotational, point, reflectional, translational, glide reflectional

36. $A'(0, 12)$ **37.** $B'(-1, 3)$ **38.** $C'(15, -20)$ **39.** $M'(-15, 20), A'(-30, -5), T'(0, 0), H'(15, 10)$ **40.** $F'(-2, 0), U'\left(\frac{5}{2}, 0\right), N'\left(-1, -\frac{5}{2}\right)$

Extra Practice

Chapter 1

1. 37, 42 **3.** 8, $\frac{8}{5}$ **7.** true **9.** true **17.** 27 **19.** 6

23.
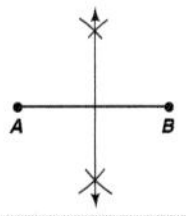

27a. 1.4 **b.** $\left(\frac{5}{2}, \frac{1}{2}\right)$ **29a.** 19.1 **b.** $\left(-\frac{1}{2}, 3\right)$ **33.** 42 in., 98 in.^{2} **35.** 3π m, $\frac{9}{4}\pi$ m^2

Chapter 2

1. If a number is one, then it is the smallest positive square. If a number is the smallest positive square, then it is one. A number is one if and only if it is the smallest positive square. **7.** No; two skew lines are a counterexample. **9.** Jorge can't buy a new car. **11.** Linda's band will win $500. **13b.** Mult. Prop. of =, Distr. Prop. **c.** Mult. Prop. of = **d.** $4c - a = 4b$ **e.** Symm. Prop. of = **15.** 15

Chapter 3

1. $m\angle 1 = 134$; Same-Side Int. △s Thm. $m\angle 2 = 46$; Alt. Int. ∠ Thm. **3.** $m\angle 1 = 58$; Alt. Int. ∠ Thm. $m\angle 2 = 122$; Same-Side Int. △s Thm. **5.** none **7.** $c \parallel d$, Conv. of Same-Side Interior △s Thm. **13.** obtuse; scalene **15.** isosceles; acute **17.** $x = 25$; $y = 19$ **19.** 65 **21.** $y - 2 = -\frac{5}{2}(x - 4)$ or $y + 3 = -\frac{5}{2}(x - 6)$ **23.** $y + 5 = -1(x - 3)$ or $y - 3 = -1(x + 5)$ **25.** ∥; same slope **27.** perp.; $m_1 \cdot m_2 = -1$

29.
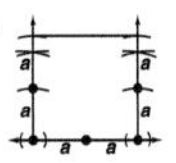

Chapter 4

1. ∠*G* **3.** ∠*T* **9.** Yes; corr. sides and corr. △s are ≅. **11.** Yes; corr. sides and corr. △s are ≅. **13.** ∠*T* ≅ ∠*S*, ∠*Y* ≅ ∠*W* and included sides $\overline{TY} \cong \overline{SW}$; ASA **15.** not possible **17.** $\overleftrightarrow{OL} \parallel \overleftrightarrow{MN}$, so ∠*OLN* ≅ ∠*MNL*. $\overline{LN} \cong \overline{LN}$ by the Reflexive Prop. of ≅. Since $\overline{LO} \cong \overline{MN}$, △*MLN* ≅ △*ONL* by SAS, and ∠*MLN* ≅ ∠*ONL* by CPCTC. **19.** $\overline{BI} \cong \overline{BI}$ by the Reflexive Prop. of ≅. Since ∠*MBI* ≅ ∠*RIB* and ∠*MIB* ≅ ∠*RBI*, △*MBI* ≅ △*RIB* by ASA, and $\overline{MB} \cong \overline{RI}$ by CPCTC. **21.** $x = 57$; $y = 66$ **23.** 6 **25.** △*RQM* ≅ △*QRS*; SSS

Chapter 5

1. $\frac{25}{7}$ **3.** 7 **5.** 5 **7.** $\frac{5}{2}$ **9.** $(1, 5)$ **11.** $(0, 0)$ **13.** ∠ bisector **15.** altitude **17a.** If two △s are not vert., then they are not ≅. **b.** If two △s are not ≅, then they are not vert. **19a.** If a car is not blue, then it has doors. **b.** If a car has doors, then it is not blue. **21.** Assume points *J*, *K*, and *L* are not collinear. **23.** Assume ▱*XYZV* is not a square. **25.** $\overline{JB}, \overline{PB}, \overline{PJ}$ **27.** $\overline{CT}, \overline{TA}, \overline{CA}$ **29.** Yes; $9 + 11 > 15$.

Chapter 6

1.
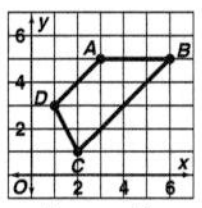

trapezoid

5. $x = 12$, $y = 84$ **7.** $x = 8$, $y = 25$ **9.** yes **11.** no **13.** square; $m\angle 1 = 45$, $m\angle 2 = 45$ **15.** ▱; $m\angle 1 = 45$, $m\angle 2 = 45$, $m\angle 3 = 80$, $m\angle 4 = 55$ **17.** $m\angle 1 = 110$, $m\angle 2 = 25$ **19.** $m\angle 1 = 110$, $m\angle 2 = 70$ **21.** $D(0, b)$; $S(a, 0)$ **23.** $D(-c, 0)$; $S(0, -b)$

Chapter 7

1. 15 ft; 10.825 ft^2 **3.** 50 ft; 143 ft^2 **5.** 15 **7.** $3\sqrt{5}$ **9.** 72 cm^2 **11.** $\frac{25}{4}\sqrt{3}$ mm^2 **13a.** 6π cm **b.** 2π cm **15a.** 18π cm **b.** $\frac{9}{2}\pi$ cm **17.** $\frac{49}{3}\pi$ ft^2 **19.** $\frac{81}{8}\pi$ cm^2 **21.** $\frac{1}{4}$ **23.** $1 - \frac{\pi}{4}$

Chapter 8

1. 10 **3.** 2 **7.** $x = \frac{80}{3}$; $y = 6$; $z = \frac{16}{3}$ **9.** $x = 30$; $y = 4$ **11.** Yes; △*QCT* ~ △*MCP* by SAS~. **13.** no **15.** $\frac{117}{10}$ **17.** 4 **23.** 3 : 4; 9 : 16

Chapter 9

1. 5.6 **3.** 11.0 **9.** 653 ft **11.** 78 ft **13a.** $\langle -49, 142\rangle, \langle 38, 47\rangle$ **b.** $\langle -11, 189\rangle$ **15a.** $\langle -54, 72\rangle, \langle -95, -33\rangle$ **b.** $\langle -149, 39\rangle$ **17.** 30.1 ft^2 **19.** 43.2 cm^2 **21.** 31.2 ft^2

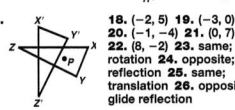

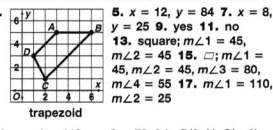

Chapter 10

1. cube **3.** cylinder

5.

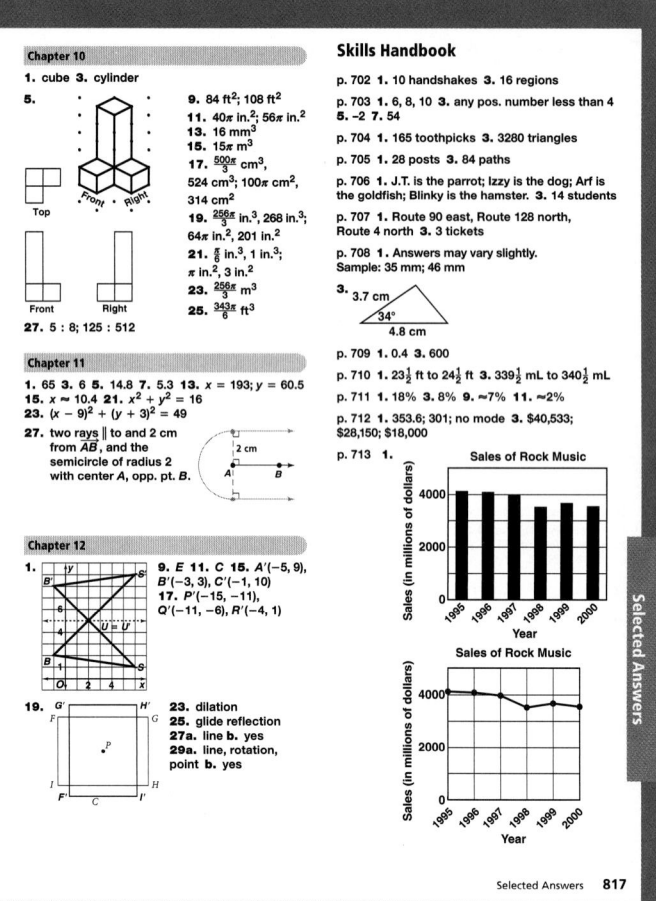

Top
Front Right
Front Right

9. 84 ft²; 108 ft²
11. 40π in.²; 56π in.²
13. 16 mm³
15. 15π m³
17. $\frac{500\pi}{3}$ cm³,
524 cm³; 100π cm²,
314 cm²
19. $\frac{256\pi}{3}$ in.³, 268 in.³;
64π in.², 201 in.²
21. $\frac{\pi}{6}$ in.³, 1 in.³;
π in.², 3 in.²
23. $\frac{256\pi}{3}$ m³
25. $\frac{343\pi}{6}$ ft³
27. 5 : 8; 125 : 512

Chapter 11

1. 65 **3.** 6 **5.** 14.8 **7.** 5.3 **13.** $x = 193; y = 60.5$
15. $x \approx 10.4$ **21.** $x^2 + y^2 = 16$
23. $(x - 9)^2 + (y + 3)^2 = 49$
27. two rays ∥ to and 2 cm from $\overline{AB}$, and the semicircle of radius 2 with center A, opp. pt. B.

Chapter 12

1.

9. E **11.** C **15.** $A'(-5, 9)$, $B'(-3, 3)$, $C'(-1, 10)$
17. $P'(-15, -11)$, $Q'(-11, -6)$, $R'(-4, 1)$

19.

23. dilation
25. glide reflection
27a. line **b.** yes
29a. line, rotation, point **b.** yes

Skills Handbook

p. 702 1. 10 handshakes **3.** 16 regions

p. 703 1. 6, 8, 10 **3.** any pos. number less than 4
5. −2 **7.** 54

p. 704 1. 165 toothpicks **3.** 3280 triangles

p. 705 1. 28 posts **3.** 84 paths

p. 706 1. J.T. is the parrot; Izzy is the dog; Arf is the goldfish; Blinky is the hamster. **3.** 14 students

p. 707 1. Route 90 east, Route 128 north, Route 4 north **3.** 3 tickets

p. 708 1. Answers may vary slightly. Sample: 35 mm; 46 mm

3. 3.7 cm
34°
4.8 cm

p. 709 1. 0.4 **3.** 600

p. 710 1. $23\frac{1}{2}$ ft to $24\frac{1}{2}$ ft **3.** $339\frac{1}{2}$ mL to $340\frac{1}{2}$ mL

p. 711 1. 18% **3.** 8% **9.** ≈7% **11.** ≈2%

p. 712 1. 353.6; 301; no mode **3.** $40,533; $28,150; $18,000

p. 713 1.

Sales of Rock Music

Sales of Rock Music

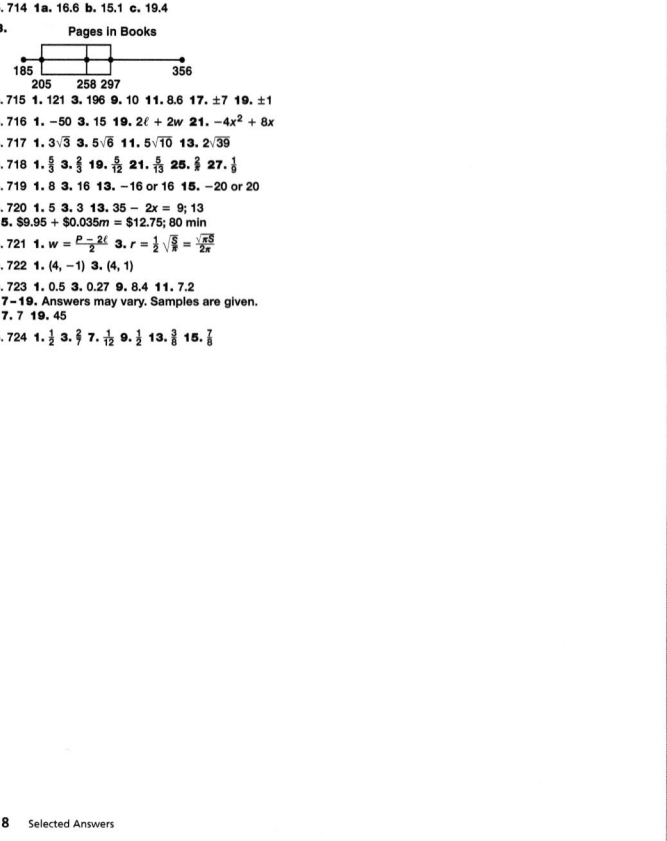

3. 8 A.M.–2 P.M.

p. 714 1a. 16.6 **b.** 15.1 **c.** 19.4

3.

Pages in Books

185 356
205 258 297

p. 715 1. 121 **3.** 196 **9.** 10 **11.** 8.6 **17.** ±7 **19.** ±1

p. 716 1. −50 **3.** 15 **19.** $2\ell + 2w$ **21.** $-4x^2 + 8x$

p. 717 1. $3\sqrt{3}$ **3.** $5\sqrt{6}$ **11.** $5\sqrt{10}$ **13.** $2\sqrt{39}$

p. 718 1. $\frac{5}{3}$ **3.** $\frac{2}{7}$ **19.** $\frac{5}{12}$ **21.** $\frac{5}{13}$ **25.** $\frac{2}{7}$ **27.** $\frac{1}{9}$

p. 719 1. 8 **3.** 16 **13.** −16 or 16 **15.** −20 or 20

p. 720 1. 5 **3.** 3 **13.** $35 - 2x = 9; 13$
15. $9.95 + 0.035m = 12.75; 80$ min

p. 721 1. $w = \frac{P - 2\ell}{2}$ **3.** $r = \frac{1}{2}\sqrt{\frac{S}{\pi}} = \frac{\sqrt{\pi S}}{2\pi}$

p. 722 1. $(4, -1)$ **3.** $(4, 1)$

p. 723 1. 0.5 **3.** 0.27 **9.** 8.4 **11.** 7.2
17–19. Answers may vary. Samples are given.
17. 7 **19.** 45

p. 724 1. $\frac{1}{2}$ **3.** $\frac{2}{7}$ **7.** $\frac{1}{12}$ **9.** $\frac{1}{2}$ **13.** $\frac{3}{8}$ **15.** $\frac{7}{8}$

CHAPTER 1

Lesson 1-1
pages 6–9   Exercises

48. a.
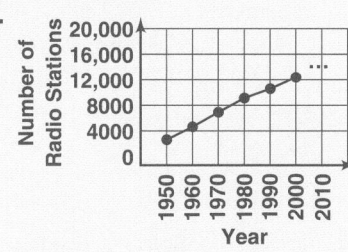

c. Answers may vary. Sample:
   Confident; the
   pattern has held for several
   decades.

Lesson 1-2
pages 13–16   Exercises

25.
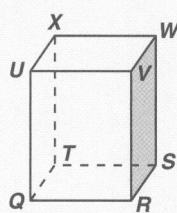

26.
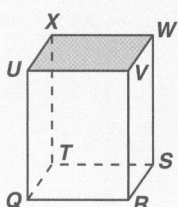

27.
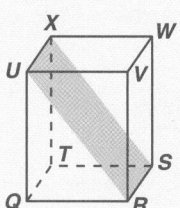

28.
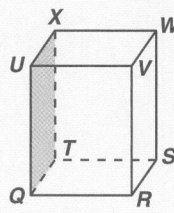

29.
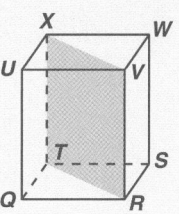

52.
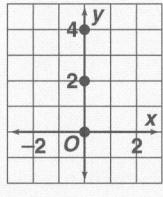

yes

53.
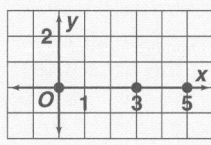

yes

54.
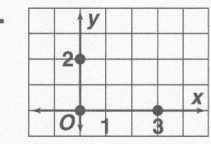

no

55.
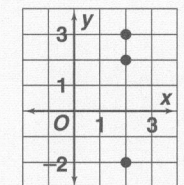

yes

56.
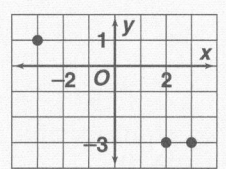

no

57.
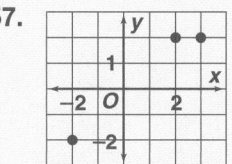

no

58.
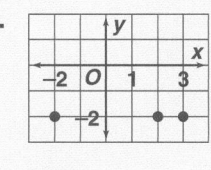

yes

59.
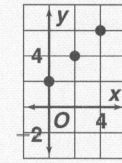

yes

73.
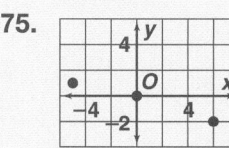

yes

74.
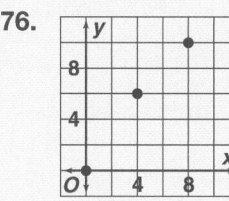

yes

75.

no

76.

no

77.

yes

Lesson 1-5
page 34   Check Skills You'll Need

1.

2.

3.

4.

5.

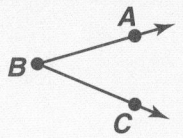

6.

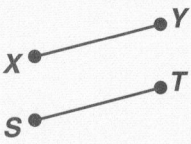

8.

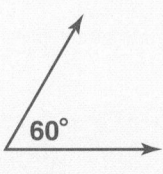

9.

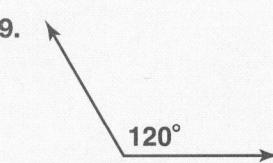

pages 37–40   Exercises

19. a–b.

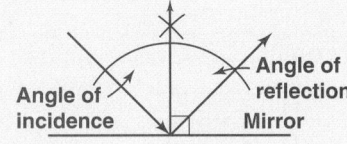

Angle of incidence   Angle of reflection   Mirror

20. Locate points *A* and *B* on a line. Then construct a ⊥ at *A* and *B* as in Exercise 16. Construct $\overline{AD}$ and $\overline{BC}$ so that $AB = AD = BC$.

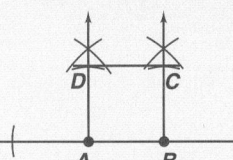

21. Explanations may vary. Samples are given.

  a. One midpt.; a midpt. divides a segment into two ≅ segments. If there were more than one midpt. the segments wouldn't be ≅.

22.

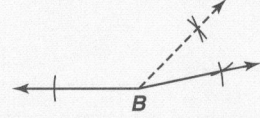

23.

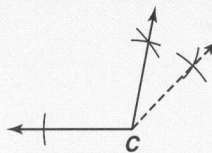

24.

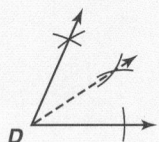

26. Open the compass to more than half the measure of the segment. Swing large arcs from the endpts. to intersect above and below the segment. Draw a line through the two pts. where the arcs intersect. The pt. where the line and segment intersect is the midpt. of the segment.

28. a.

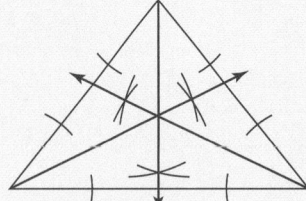

They appear to meet at one pt.

  b.

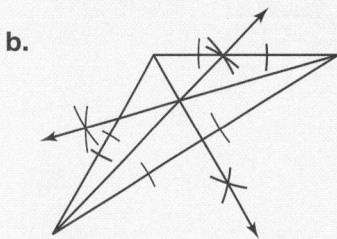

  c. The three ∠ bisectors of a △ intersect in one pt.

29.

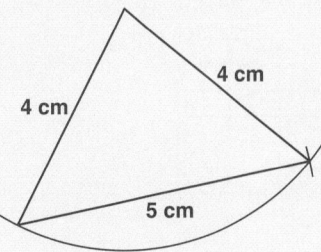

4 cm   4 cm   5 cm

30.

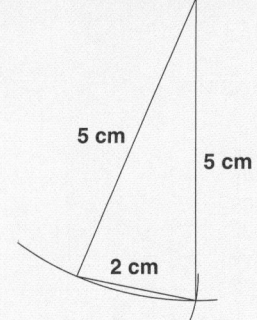

5 cm   5 cm   2 cm

34. a–c.

35. a–b.

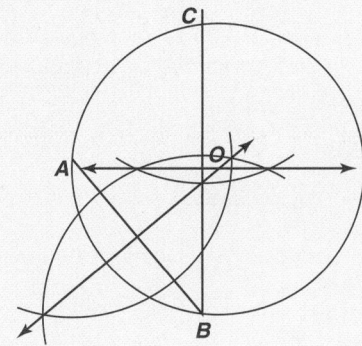

  c. Point *O* is the center of the circle.

Lesson 1-6
pages 46–49   Exercises

42.

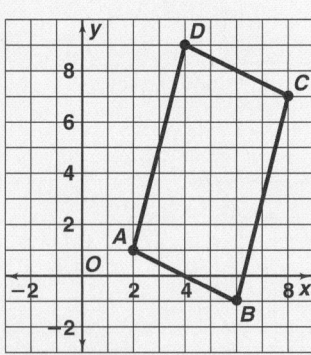

The midpts. are the same, (5, 4). The diagonals bisect each other.

Lesson 1-7
pages 55–58 Exercises

16.

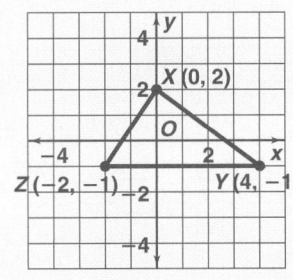

≈ 14.6 units

17.

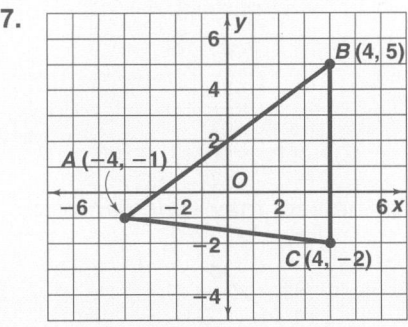

≈ 25.1 units

18.

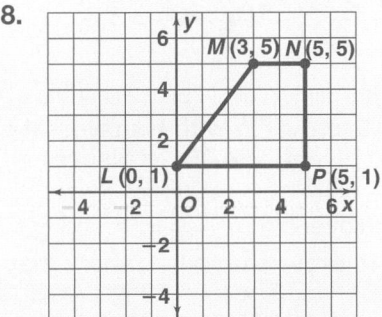

16 units

19.

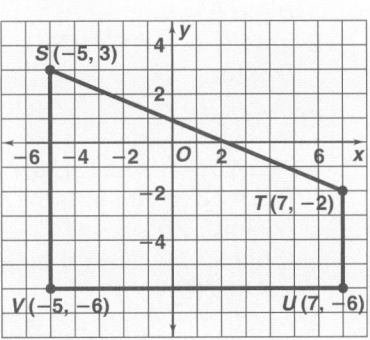

38 units

54.

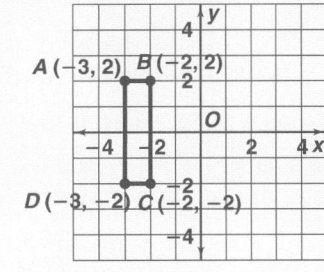

perimeter = 10 units
area = 4 units²

55.

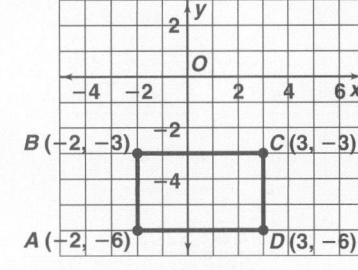

perimeter = 16 units
area = 15 units²

66. a.

base	height	area
1	98	98
2	96	192
3	94	282
⋮	⋮	⋮
24	52	1248
25	50	1250
26	48	1248
⋮	⋮	⋮
47	6	282
48	4	192
49	2	98

b.

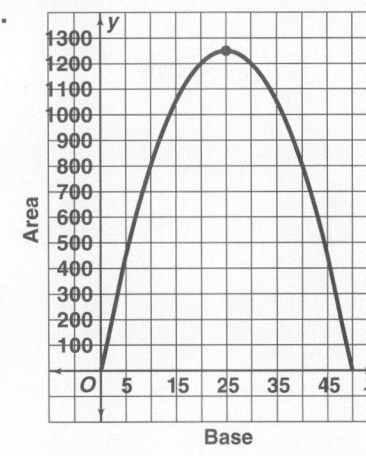

CHAPTER 2
Lesson 2-1
pages 71–74 Exercises

63. 25 statements;

$r \rightarrow s$	false
$r \rightarrow t$	true
$r \rightarrow u$	false
$r \rightarrow v$	true
$s \rightarrow r$	false
$s \rightarrow t$	false
$s \rightarrow u$	false
$s \rightarrow v$	true

Lesson 2-2
pages 78–81 Exercises

1. If two segments are congruent, then they have the same length. It is true. Two segments have the same length if and only if they are congruent.

2. If $2x - 5 = 19$, then $x = 12$. It is true. $x = 12$ if and only if $2x - 5 = 19$.

3. If a number is even, then it is divisible by 20. It is false since 4 is even but not divisible by 20.

4. If $|x| = 3$, then $x = 3$. It is false since $|-3| = 3$ also.

61.

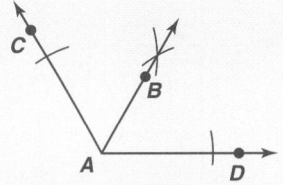

$\overrightarrow{AB}$ bisects $\angle CAD$

Lesson 2-3
page 82 Check Skills You'll Need

1. If your grades suffer, then you don't sleep enough.

2. If you must start early, then you want to arrive on time.

4. If students do not complete their homework, then they will have lower grades.

5. If two lines are perpendicular, then they meet to form right angles.

page 108 Chapter Test

18. $m\angle VNM = 62$ because vert. ⓢ are ≅. $m\angle LNV = m\angle PNM = 118$ because both ⓢ are suppl. to $\angle LNP$.

19. $\angle BCE \cong \angle DCF$ by the markings; $\angle BCF \cong \angle ECD$ by the ∠ Add. Post.

20. If a fish is a bluegill, then it is a bluish, freshwater sunfish. If a fish is a bluish, freshwater sunfish, then it is a bluegill.

page 109 Standardized Test Prep

19. Answers may vary. Sample:
[4] a correct construction; Sample:

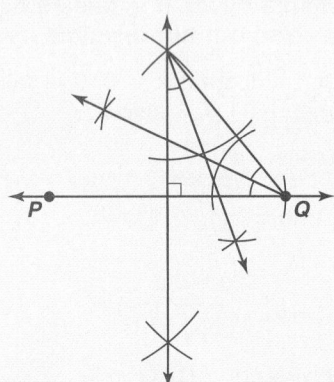

[3] correct right triangle, but only one correct angle bisector

[2] correct right triangle

[1] correctly started triangle

pages 110–111 Real-World Snapshots
Activity 2
b.

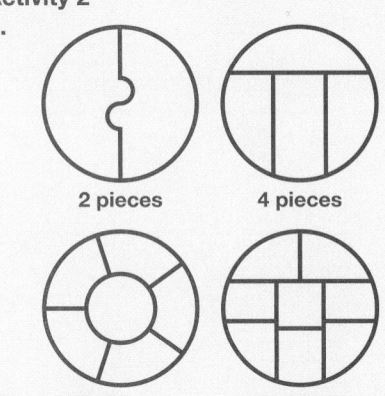

2 pieces   4 pieces

6 pieces   8 pieces

CHAPTER 3
Lesson 3-2
page 122 Check Skills You'll Need

5. If a △ has a 90° ∠, then it is a right △; true.

6. If two ⓢ are ≅, then they are vert. ⓢ; false.

pages 125–129 Exercises

46.

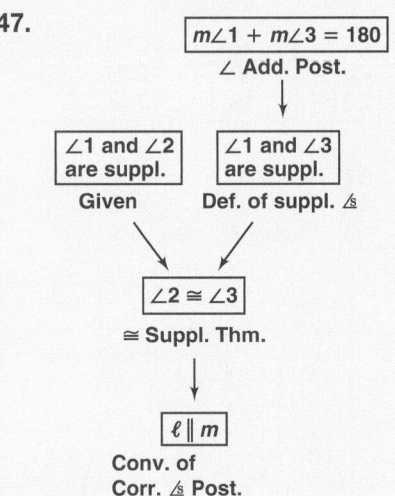

$\ell \parallel m$
Given

$\angle 12 \cong \angle 8$ $\angle 4 \cong \angle 8$
Given   Corr. ⓢ Post.

$\angle 4 \cong \angle 12$
Trans. Prop. of ≅

$j \parallel k$
Conv. of Corr. ⓢ Post.

47.

$m\angle 1 + m\angle 3 = 180$
∠ Add. Post.

$\angle 1$ and $\angle 2$ are suppl. $\angle 1$ and $\angle 3$ are suppl.
Given   Def. of suppl. ⓢ

$\angle 2 \cong \angle 3$
≅ Suppl. Thm.

$\ell \parallel m$
Conv. of Corr. ⓢ Post.

48.

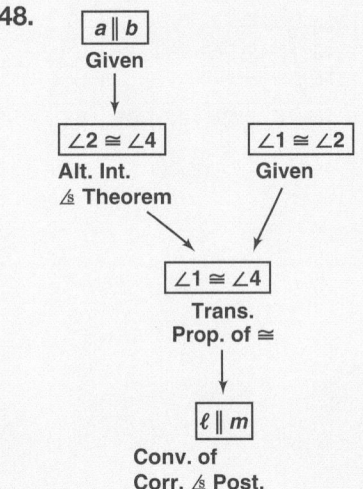

$a \parallel b$
Given

$\angle 2 \cong \angle 4$ $\angle 1 \cong \angle 2$
Alt. Int. ⓢ Theorem   Given

$\angle 1 \cong \angle 4$
Trans. Prop. of ≅

$\ell \parallel m$
Conv. of Corr. ⓢ Post.

49.

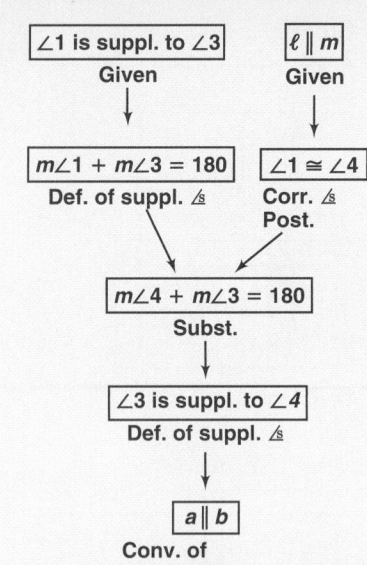

$\angle 1$ is suppl. to $\angle 3$
Given

$\ell \parallel m$
Given

$m\angle 1 + m\angle 3 = 180$
Def. of suppl. ⓢ

$\angle 1 \cong \angle 4$
Corr. ⓢ Post.

$m\angle 4 + m\angle 3 = 180$
Subst.

$\angle 3$ is suppl. to $\angle 4$
Def. of suppl. ⓢ

$a \parallel b$
Conv. of Same-Side Int. ⓢ Thm.

50. a. Answers may vary. Sample:

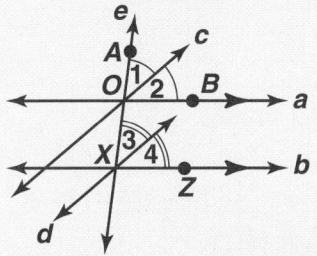

b. Given: $a \parallel b$ with transversal e, c bisects $\angle AOB$, d bisects $\angle AXZ$.

c. Prove: $c \parallel d$

d. To prove that $c \parallel d$, show that $\angle 1 \cong \angle 3$. $\angle 1 \cong \angle 3$ if $\angle AOB \cong \angle OXZ$. $\angle AOB \cong \angle OXZ$ by the Corr. ⓢ Post.

e. 1. $a \parallel b$ (Given)
   2. $\angle AOB \cong \angle AXZ$ (Corr. ⓢ Post.)
   3. $m\angle AOB = m\angle AXZ$ (Def. of ≅ ⓢ)
   4. $m\angle AOB = m\angle 1 + m\angle 2$; $m\angle AXZ = m\angle 3 + m\angle 4$ (∠ Add. Post.)
   5. c bisects $\angle AOB$; d bisects $\angle AXZ$. (Given)
   6. $m\angle 1 = m\angle 2$; $m\angle 3 = m\angle 4$ (Def. of ∠ bisector)
   7. $m\angle 1 + m\angle 2 = m\angle 3 + m\angle 4$ (Trans. Prop. of ≅)
   8. $m\angle 1 + m\angle 1 = m\angle 3 + m\angle 3$ (Subst.)
   9. $2m\angle 1 = 2m\angle 3$ (Add. Prop.)
   10. $m\angle 1 = m\angle 3$ (Div. Prop.)
   11. $c \parallel d$ (Conv. of Corr. ⓢ Post.)

55. [4] a.

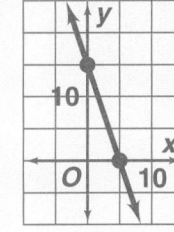

b. $m\angle 1 + m\angle 3 = 180$. If $2x - 38 + 6x + 18 = 180$, then $x = 25$. The $\angle$ measures are $2x - 38 = 12$ and 25, but $12 \neq 25$. So a can't be $\parallel$ to b.

[3] appropriate methods, but with one computational error

[2] incorrect diagram solved correctly OR correct diagram solved incorrectly

[1] correct answer (lines a and b are not $\parallel$), without work shown

Lesson 3-4
page 145   Investigation

1.

Polygon	No. of Sides	No. of Triangles	Sum of Int. $\angle$ Measures
	4	2	$2\cdot180 = 360$
	5	3	$3\cdot180 = 540$
	6	4	$4\cdot180 = 720$
	7	5	$5\cdot180 = 900$
	8	6	$6\cdot180 = 1080$

Answers may vary. Sample: The number of △ formed is two less than the number of sides. The sum of the △ increases by 180 from figure to figure.

pages 147–150   Exercises

50. Answers may vary. Sample:

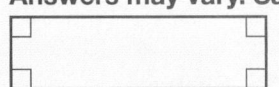

51. Answers may vary. Sample:

52. Answers may vary. Sample:

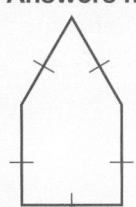

53. Answers may vary. Sample:

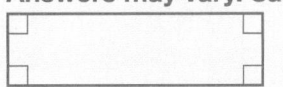

57. b.

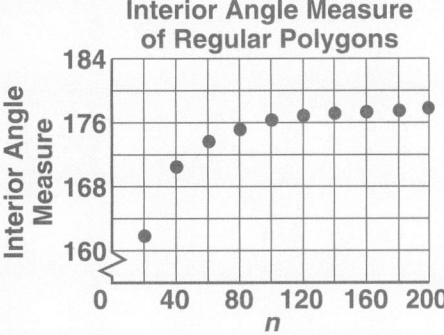

Lesson 3-5
pages 155–157   Exercises

1.

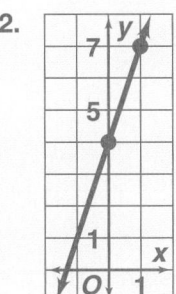

2.

3.

4.

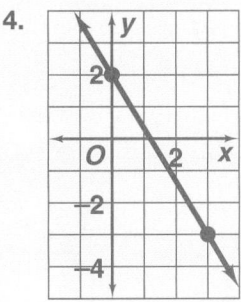

5.

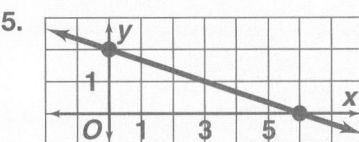

6.

7.

8.

9.

10.

11. $y = 2x + 1$

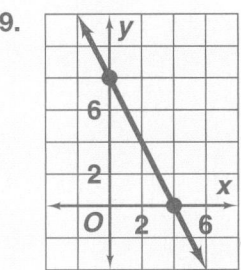

12. $y = x + 1$

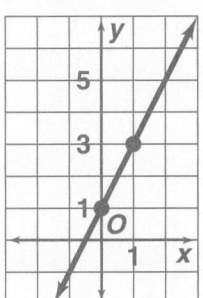

13. $y = -2x + 4$

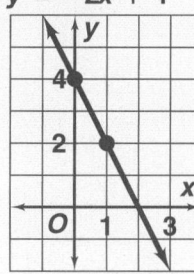

14. $y = -2x + 4$

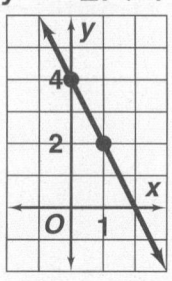

15. $y = -\frac{1}{3}x + 1$

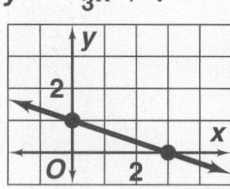

16. $y = \frac{3}{2}x - \frac{1}{4}$

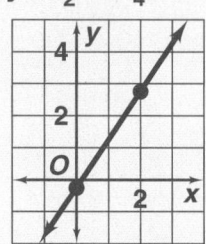

33.

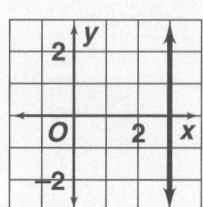

34.

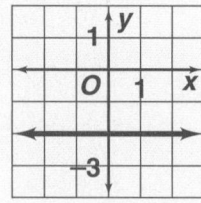

35.

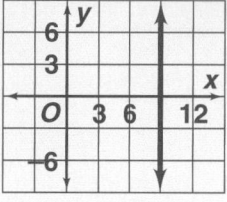

36.

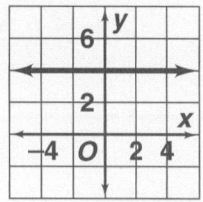

37.

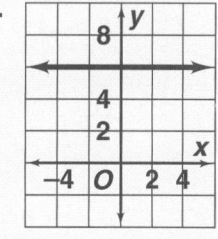

45.

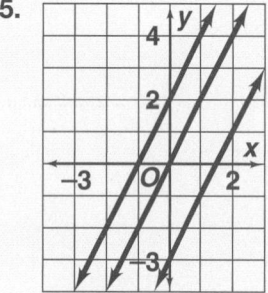

The slopes are the same, and the y-intercepts are different.

Lesson 3-7
page 165   Check Skills You'll Need

1.

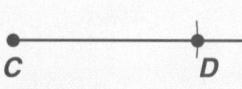

$\overline{AB} \cong \overline{CD}$

2.

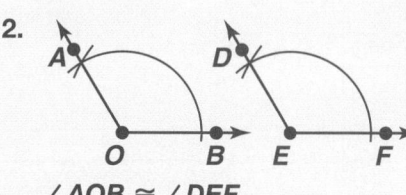

$\angle AOB \cong \angle DEF$

3.

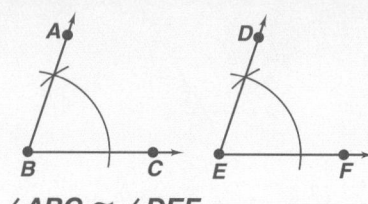

$\angle ABC \cong \angle DEF$

4.

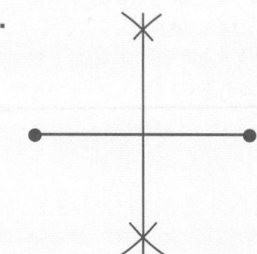

5.

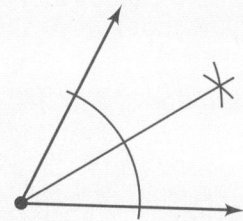

6.

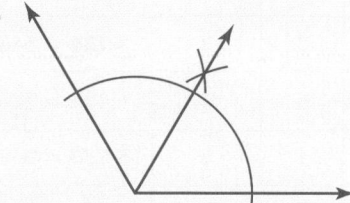

page 167   Check Understanding

4.

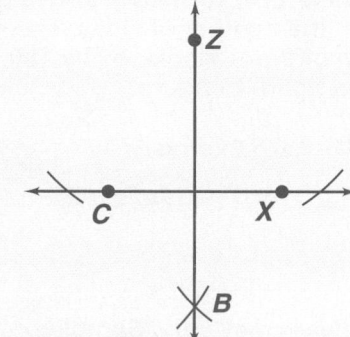

pages 168–170   Exercises

For Exercises 5–7, constructions may vary. Samples using the following segments are shown:

5.

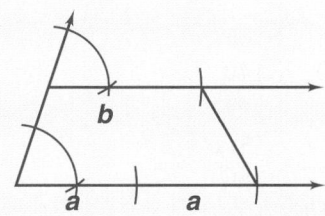

6.

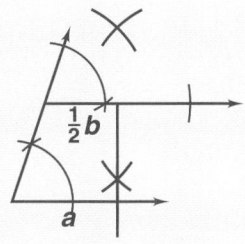

7.

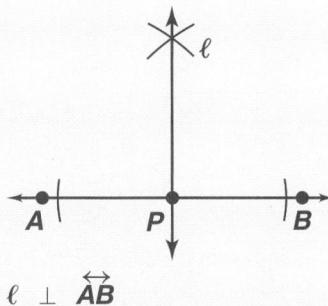

8.

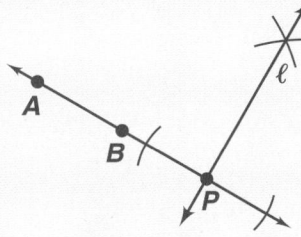

$\ell \perp \overleftrightarrow{AB}$

9.

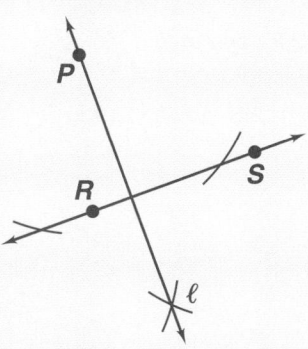

$\ell \perp \overleftrightarrow{AB}$

10.

$\ell \perp \overleftrightarrow{RS}$

11.

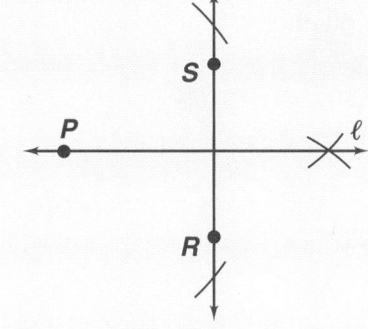

$\ell \perp \overleftrightarrow{RS}$

12.

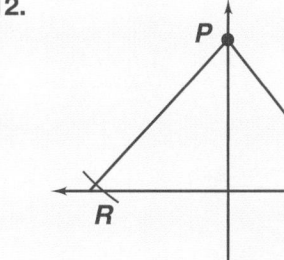

$\ell \perp \overleftrightarrow{RS}$

13.

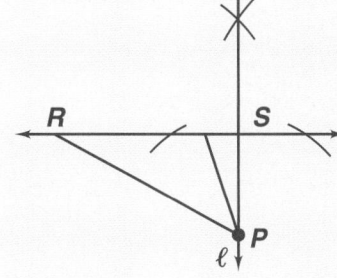

$\ell \perp \overleftrightarrow{RS}$

16. a–b.

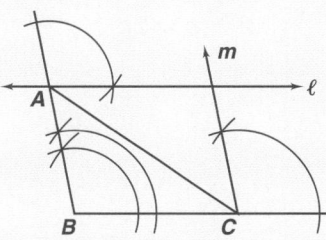

For Exercises 17–25, constructions may vary. Samples are given.

17.

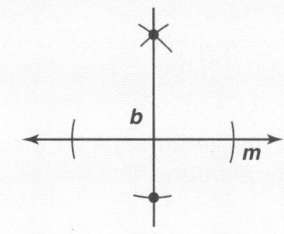

18.

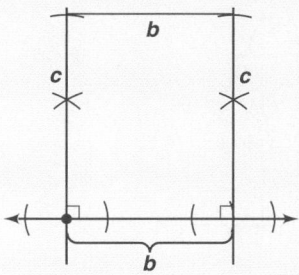

19.

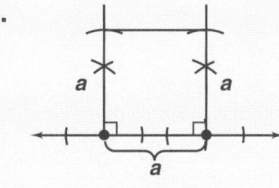

20.

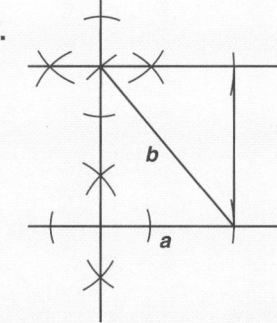

21. a.

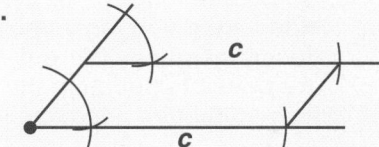

b. The sides are ‖ and ≅.

c. Check students' work.

22.

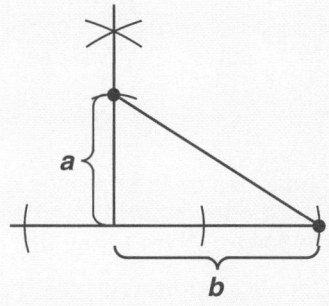

23.

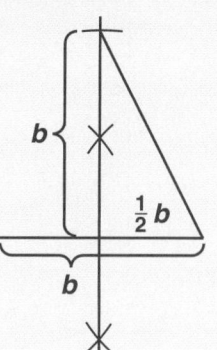

24. a.

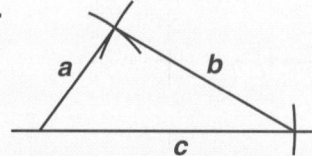

b. Answers may vary. Sample:

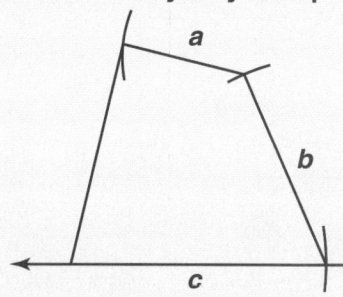

c. One; if the lengths for the 3 sides are given, only one △ is possible; many different quad. are possible because the ∡ formed by the sides can vary.

25. a–c.

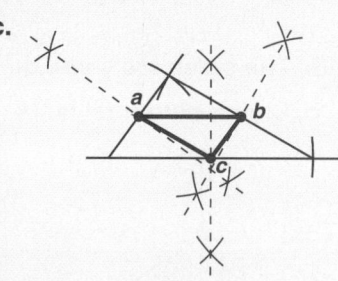

d. The sides of the smaller △ are half the length of the sides of the larger △ that they are ‖ to.

e. Check students' work.

27–28. Answers may vary. Samples are given.

27.

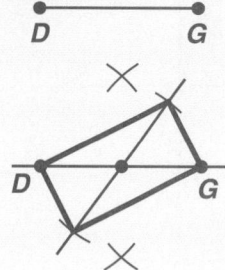

The quad. is a rectangle.

28.

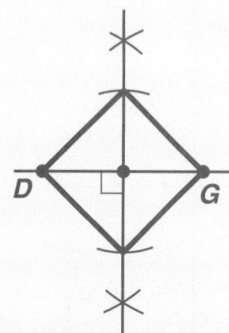

The quad. is a square.

34.

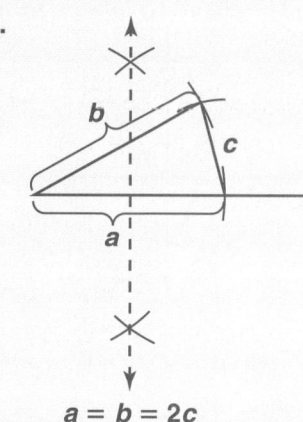

$a = b = 2c$

39. [2] a.

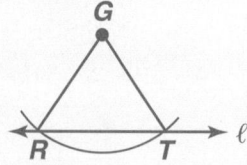

b. All points on the arc with center *G* are the same dist. from *G*, so *GR* = *GT*. The △ is isosc. because an isosc. △ must have at least two sides of the same length.

[1] incorrect sketch OR incorrect △ classification

page 171   Technology

2. c.

L1	L2
3	60
4	90
5	108
6	120
7	128.57
8	135
9	140
10	144
11	147.27
12	150
13	152.31
14	154.29
15	156
16	157.5
17	158.82
18	160
19	161.05
20	162

CHAPTER 4

Lesson 4-2
pages 189–192   Exercises

43.

```
GK bisects ∠JGM
      Given
        ↓
  ∠JGK ≅ ∠MGK
  Def. of bisect
                    → △GJK ≅ △GMK
   GJ ≅ GM                  SAS
    Given        ↗
   GK ≅ GK
 Ref. Prop. of ≅
```

Lesson 4-3
pages 195–196   Check Understanding

2. 1. ∠CAB ≅ ∠DAE;
      $\overline{AB}$ ≅ $\overline{AE}$ (Given)

   2. ∠ABC and ∠AED;
      are right ∡.   (Given)

   3. ∠ABC ≅ ∠AED
      (All right ∡ are ≅.)

   4. △ABC ≅ △AED (ASA)

3.

$\overline{RP}$ bisects $\angle SRQ$
Given

↓

$\angle SRP \cong \angle QRP$
Def. of $\angle$ bisector

$\angle S \cong \angle Q$ $\overline{RP} \cong \overline{RP}$
Given   Ref. Prop. of $\cong$

↓

$\triangle SRP \cong \triangle QRP$
AAS

Lesson 4-4
page 203   **Check Skills You'll Need**

1. $\angle J \cong \angle H$; $\angle R \cong \angle V$; $\angle C \cong \angle G$

2. $\overline{JR} \cong \overline{HV}$; $\overline{RC} \cong \overline{VG}$; $\overline{JC} \cong \overline{HG}$

3. $\angle T \cong \angle L$; $\angle I \cong \angle O$; $\angle C \cong \angle K$

4. $\overline{TI} \cong \overline{LO}$; $\overline{IC} \cong \overline{OK}$; $\overline{TC} \cong \overline{LK}$

Lesson 4-5
page 213–216   **Exercises**

43. b.

 16

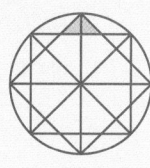 8

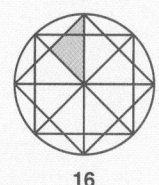 16

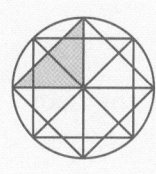 8

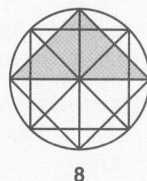 8

Lesson 4-6
pages 219–222   **Exercises**

24.

25.

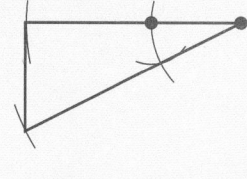

26.

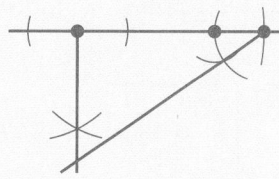

27.

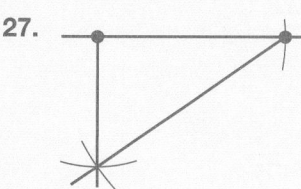

31. a.

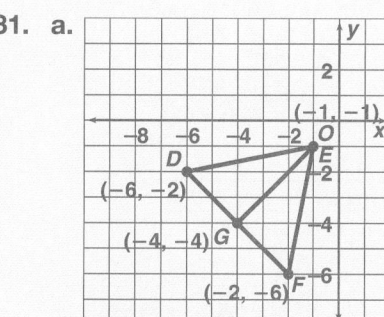

b. slope of $\overline{DG} = -1$; slope of $\overline{GF} = -1$; slope of $\overline{GE} = 1$

c. $\angle EGD$ and $\angle EGF$ are rt. $\angle$s.

e. $\triangle EGD \cong \triangle EGF$ by HL. Both $\angle$s are rt. $\angle$s, $\overline{DE} \cong \overline{FE}$, and $\overline{EG} \cong \overline{EG}$.

41. $\overline{BC} \parallel \overline{AD}$ because slope $= -1$. $\overline{BC} \perp \overline{BA}$, $\overline{BA} \perp \overline{AD}$ because product of slopes is -1.

42. If $\parallel$ lines then alt. int. $\angle$s are $\cong$.

43. If two lines are $\parallel$, then same-side int. $\angle$s are suppl.

44. Vert. $\angle$s are $\cong$.

45. If two lines are $\parallel$, then corr. $\angle$s are $\cong$.

46. If two lines are $\parallel$, then corr. $\angle$s are $\cong$.

47. If two lines are $\parallel$, then same-side int. $\angle$s are suppl.

Lesson 4-7
pages 224–226   **Check Understanding**

3. 1. $\overline{PS} \cong \overline{RS}$; $\angle PSQ \cong \angle RSQ$ (Given)

   2. $\overline{QS} \cong \overline{QS}$ (Reflexive Prop. of $\cong$)

   3. $\triangle PSQ \cong \triangle RSQ$ (SAS)

   4. $\overline{PQ} \cong \overline{RQ}$ (CPCTC)

   5. $\angle PQT \cong \angle RQT$ (CPCTC)

   6. $\overline{QT} \cong \overline{QT}$ (Reflexive Prop. of $\cong$)

   7. $\triangle PQT \cong \triangle RQT$ (SAS)

---

pages 227–230   **Exercises**

4.

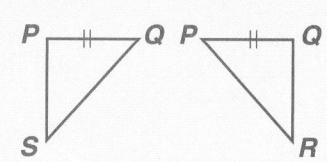

5.

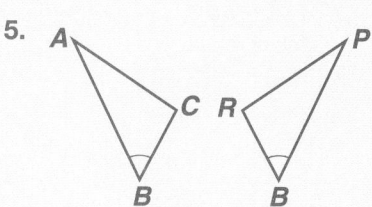

6.

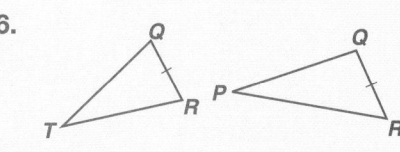

7.

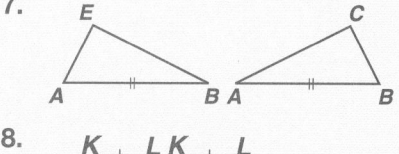

8.

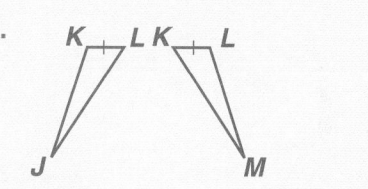

9.

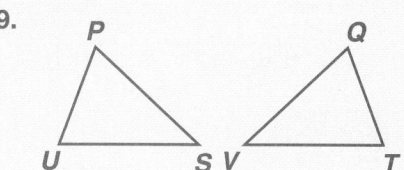

page 231   Extension

1.

E is the midpt. of $\overline{AD}$
Given

↓

$\overline{AE} \cong \overline{ED}$
Def. of midpt.

$\overline{CE} \cong \overline{BE}$ $\overline{AB} \cong \overline{DC}$
Given   Given

↓ ↓ ↓

$\triangle ABE \cong \triangle DCE$
SSS

↓

$m\angle ABE = m\angle DCE$
CPCTC

$m\angle ABC =$ $m\angle ABE +$ $m\angle EBC$
Ang. Add. Postulate

$m\angle EBC =$ $m\angle ECB$
Base $\angle$s of isosc. $\triangle$ are $\cong$

↓

$m\angle ABC = m\angle DCE + m\angle ECB$
Substitution

$m\angle DCE +$ $m\angle ECB =$ $m\angle DCB$
Ang. Add. Postulate

↓

$m\angle ABC = m\angle DCB$
Trans. Prop of =

$\overline{BC} \cong \overline{BC}$
Ref. Prop. of $\cong$

↓

$\triangle ABC \cong \triangle DCB$
SAS

↓

$\overline{AC} \cong \overline{DB}$
CPCTC

2.

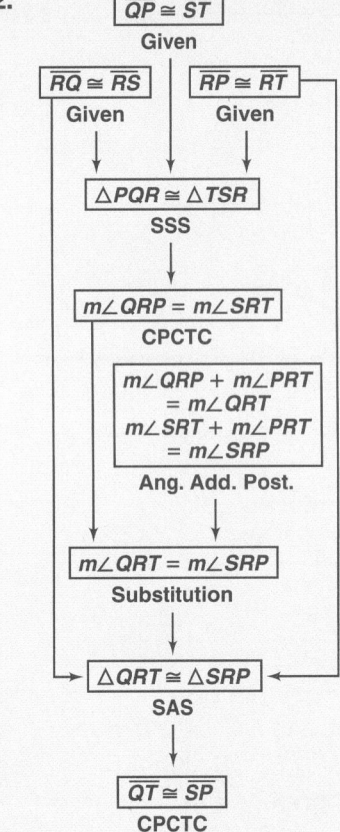

$\overline{QP} \cong \overline{ST}$
Given

$\overline{RQ} \cong \overline{RS}$ $\overline{RP} \cong \overline{RT}$
Given   Given

↓

$\triangle PQR \cong \triangle TSR$
SSS

↓

$m\angle QRP = m\angle SRT$
CPCTC

$m\angle QRP + m\angle PRT$ $= m\angle QRT$
$m\angle SRT + m\angle PRT$ $= m\angle SRP$
Ang. Add. Post.

↓

$m\angle QRT = m\angle SRP$
Substitution

↓

$\triangle QRT \cong \triangle SRP$
SAS

↓

$\overline{QT} \cong \overline{SP}$
CPCTC

page 236   Chapter Test

10.   Answers may vary. Sample:

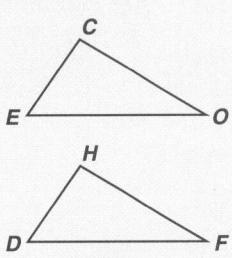

$\overline{CE} \cong \overline{HD}$; $\overline{CO} \cong \overline{HF}$;
$\overline{EO} \cong \overline{DF}$; $\angle C \cong \angle H$;
$\angle E \cong \angle D$; $\angle O \cong \angle F$

17.   Answers may vary. Sample:

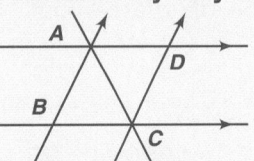

$\triangle ABC \cong \triangle CDA$

page 237   Standardized Test Prep

13.   [2]

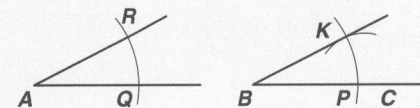

Draw $\angle A$ and draw $\overrightarrow{BC}$. Draw an arc with center A, and copy that arc with center B. Open the compass to length RQ to draw an arc with center P crossing the other arc at K. Draw $\overrightarrow{BK}$.

[1] diagram or explanation is not complete OR contains an error

14.   [2]

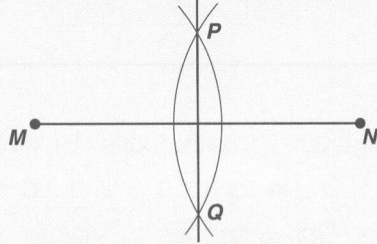

Draw arcs with the same radius using centers M and N. Label the intersections of the arcs P and Q.

Draw $\overleftrightarrow{PQ}$, which is the $\perp$ bis. of $\overline{MN}$.

[1] diagram or the explanation is not complete OR contains an error

15.   [4]

$CD = \sqrt{(5-10)^2 + (7-(-5))^2}$
$= \sqrt{25 + 144} = \sqrt{169} = 13.$

The midpt. of $\overline{CD}$ is

$\left(\dfrac{5+10}{2}, \dfrac{7+(-5)}{2}\right) = (7.5, 1).$

[3] appropriate methods, but with one computational error

[2] appropriate methods, but computational errors for both quantities

[1] no work shown

CHAPTER 5

page 240   Diagnosing Readiness

5.

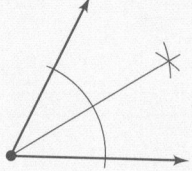

page 242   Technology

7.   The inner quad. will be a ▱. The sides of quad. YXWV are $\frac{1}{2}$ the length of the diagonals of quad. RSTU.

Lesson 5-2
page 249   Check Skills You'll Need

1.

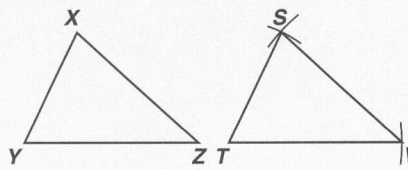

$\triangle STV \cong \triangle XYZ$

2.

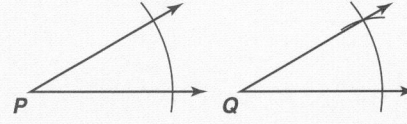

$\angle Q \cong \angle P$

3.

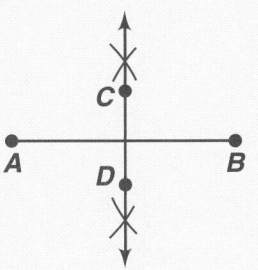

$\overleftrightarrow{CD} \perp \overline{AB}$

4.

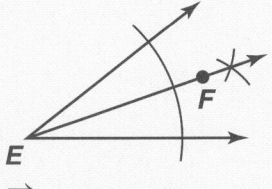

$\overrightarrow{EF}$ bisects $\angle E$

pages 251–254   Exercises

43. Answers may vary. Sample: Proof of the Conv. of the ⊥ Bis. Thm.

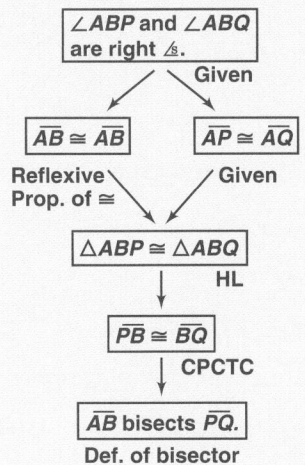

48. $\overline{BP} \perp \overrightarrow{AB}$ and $\overline{PC} \perp \overrightarrow{AC}$, thus $\angle ABP$ and $\angle ACP$ are rt. $\angle$s.

Since $\overrightarrow{AP}$ bisects $\angle BAC$, $\angle BAP \cong \angle CAP$. $\overline{AP} \cong \overline{AP}$ by the Reflexive Prop. of $\cong$. Thus $\triangle ABP \cong \triangle ACP$ by AAS and $\overline{PB} \cong \overline{PC}$ by CPCTC. Therefore, $PB = PC$.

49.

1. $\overline{SP} \perp \overrightarrow{QP}$; $\overline{SR} \perp \overrightarrow{QR}$	1. Given
2. $\angle QPS$ and $\angle QRS$ are rt. $\angle$s.	2. Def. of $\perp$
3. $\angle QPS \cong \angle QRS$	3. All rt. $\angle$s are $\cong$.
4. $SP = SR$	4. Given
5. $\overline{QS} \cong \overline{QS}$	5. Refl. Prop. of $\cong$
6. $\triangle QPS \cong \triangle QRS$	6. HL
7. $\angle PQS \cong \angle RQS$	7. CPCTC
8. $\overrightarrow{QS}$ bisects $\angle PQR$.	8. Def. of $\angle$ bis

Lesson 5-3
page 256   Check Skills You'll Need

1–2.

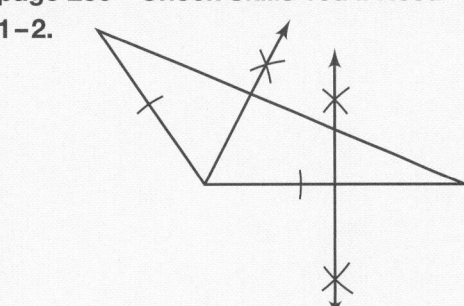

3.

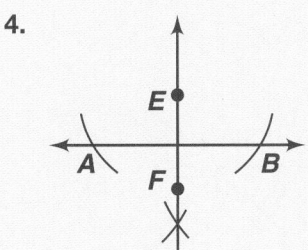

4.

pages 259–263   Exercises

41. [4]   Orthocenter–outside

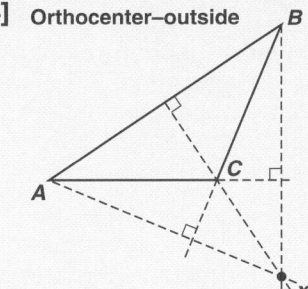

Circumcenter–outside

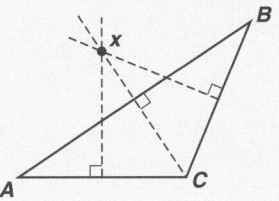

Incenter–inside

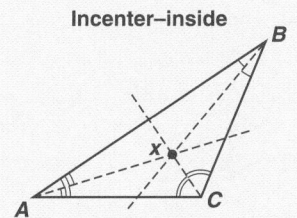

Centroid–inside

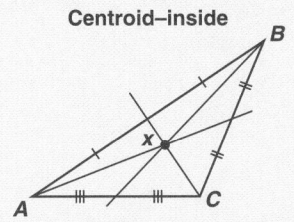

[3] one diagram partially or completely incorrect

[2] two diagrams partially or completely incorrect

[1] three diagrams partially or completely incorrect

Lesson 5-4
pages 267–270   Practice and Problem Solving

28. Angie assumed that the inverse of the statement was true, but a conditional and its inverse may not have the same truth value.

29. Assume that the driver did not apply the brakes. Then there would be no skid marks. This contradicts the fact that fresh skid marks appear. Thus the green car applied the brakes is a true statement.

30. Assume that the temperature outside is more than 32°F. Then ice would not be forming on the sidewalk. This contradicts the fact that ice is forming. Thus the statement that the temperature must be 32°F or less is true.

31. Assume that an obtuse triangle can contain a right angle. Then the sum of the measures of the obtuse angle and the right angle is more than 180. This contradicts the fact that the sum of the 3 angles of a triangle is 180. Thus the statement that an obtuse triangle cannot contain a right angle is true.

32. Assume $\overleftrightarrow{XY}$ and $\overleftrightarrow{XZ}$ are two different lines ⊥ to $\overleftrightarrow{AX}$, with Y and Z on the same side of $\overleftrightarrow{AX}$. If B is on $\overleftrightarrow{AX}$ opp. pt. A from X, then $m\angle AXY + m\angle YXZ + m\angle ZXB = 180$. But $m\angle AXY = m\angle ZXB = 90$, so $m\angle YXZ = 0$. Thus X, Y, and Z are collinear.

Lesson 5-5
page 273   Check Skills You'll Need

1.
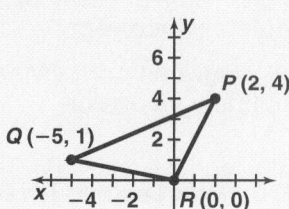
$\overline{AC}$, $\overline{BC}$, $\overline{AB}$

2.
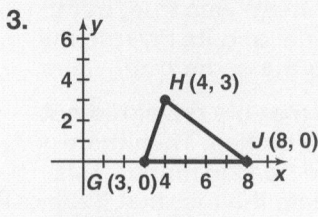
$\overline{RP}$, $\overline{RQ}$, $\overline{QP}$

3.
$\overline{GH}$, $\overline{HJ}$, $\overline{JG}$

4.
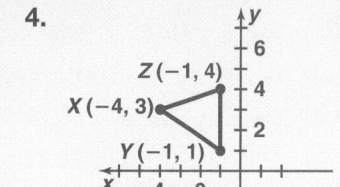
$\overline{ZY}$, $\overline{XZ}$, $\overline{XY}$

page 284   Chapter Test

4. Answers may vary.
Sample: $DE = \frac{1}{2}BC$ and $\overline{DE} \parallel \overline{BC}$ by △ Midsegment Thm.

15. Assume the obtuse ∠ is a base ∠. Then, by def. of an isosc. △, the other base ∠ must be obtuse since they are ≅. Since each ∠ would have measure greater than 90, their sum would be greater than 180. This contradicts the △ Sum Thm., so the obtuse ∠ must be the vertex ∠.

CHAPTER 6

Lesson 6-1
pages 290–293   Exercises

13. rhombus
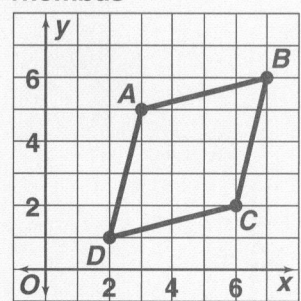

14. kite
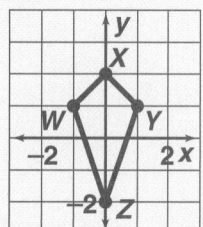

15. trapezoid
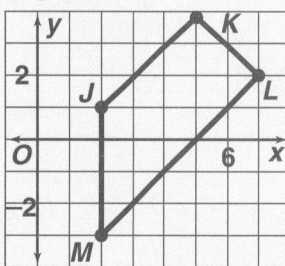

16. rectangle

17. quadrilateral
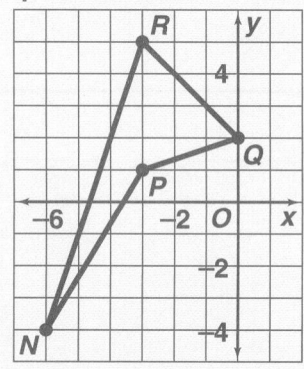

18. isosc. trapezoid
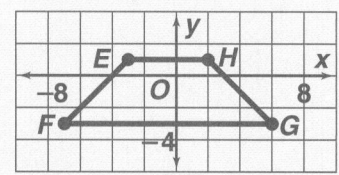

Lesson 6-2
pages 297–301   Exercises

38.
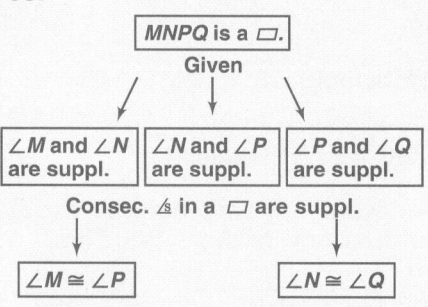

Lesson 6-3
pages 307–310   Exercises

44. [4] a. $6x = 7x - 11$; $x = 11$

   b. Yes; $m\angle ABC = m\angle CDE = 66°$.

   c. Yes; $\overline{BD} \parallel \overline{FE}$ and $\overline{BF} \parallel \overline{DE}$.

   [3] one error in calculating x

   [2] one explanation is incorrect

   [1] only part (a) answered

Lesson 6-4
pages 315–318   Exercises

24. Square; a square is both a

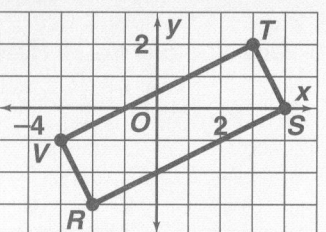

rectangle and a rhombus, so its diagonals have the properties of both.

25–34. Symbols may vary. Sample: parallelogram: ▱ rhombus: ℝ rectangle: ▭ square: 𝕊

25. ℝ, 𝕊

26. ▱, ℝ, ▭, 𝕊

27. ▱, ℝ, ▭, 𝕊

28. ▱, ℝ, ▭, 𝕊

29. ▭, 𝕊

30. ▱, ℝ, ▭, 𝕊

31. ▱, ℝ, ▭, 𝕊

32. ▭, 𝕊

33. ℝ, 𝕊

34. ℝ, 𝕊

35.

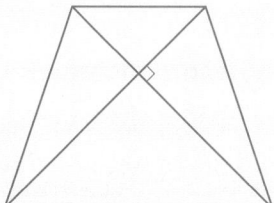

Diag. are ≅, diag. are ⊥.

36.

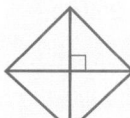

Diag. are ⊥ and ≅.

37.

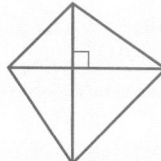

Diag. are ≅, diag. are ⊥.

38. a. Opp. sides are ≅ and ∥; diagonals bis. each other; opp. ∡ are ≅; consec. ∡ are suppl.

b. All sides are ≅; diagonals are ≅.

c. All ∡ are rt. ∡; diagonals are ⊥ bis. of each other; each diagonal bis. two ∡.

39–44. Answers may vary. Samples are given.

39. Draw diag. 1, and construct its midpt. Draw a line through the mdpt. Construct segments of length diag. 2 in opp. directions from mdpt. Then, bisect these

segments. Connect these mdpts. with the endpoints of diag. 1.

40. Construct a rt. ∠, and draw diag. 1 from its vertex. Construct the ⊥ from the opp. end of diag. 1 to a side of the rt. ∠. Repeat to other side.

41. Same as 39, but construct a ⊥ line at the midpoint of diag. 1.

42. Same as 41, except make the diagonals =.

43. Draw diag. 1. Construct a ⊥ at a pt. different than the mdpt. Construct segments on the ⊥ line of length diag. 2 in opp. directions from the pt. Then, bisect these segments. Connect these midpts. to the endpts. of diag. 1.

44. Draw an acute ∠ with the smaller diag. as a side. Construct the line ∥ to the other side through the non-vertex endpt. of the smaller diag. Draw an arc with compass set to the length of the larger diag. from the non-diag. side of the ∠, passing through the ∥ line. Draw the larger diag., and then draw the non-∥ sides of the trapezoid.

51. Square, rectangle, isosceles trapezoid, kite; drawings may vary. Samples are given:

a

52. Rhombus, ▱, trapezoid, kite; drawings may vary. Samples are given:

a   b
 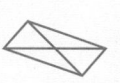  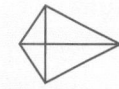

53. For $a < b$: trapezoid, isosc. trapezoid ($a > \frac{1}{2}b$), ▱, rhombus, kite; drawings may vary. Samples are given:

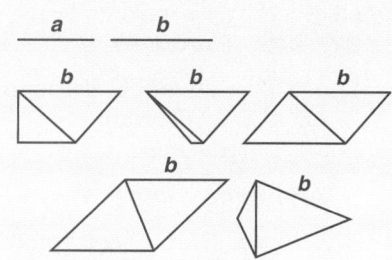

For $a > b$: trapezoid, isosc. trapezoid, ▱, rhombus ($a < 2b$), kite, rectangle, square (if $a = \sqrt{2}b$); drawings may vary. Samples are given.

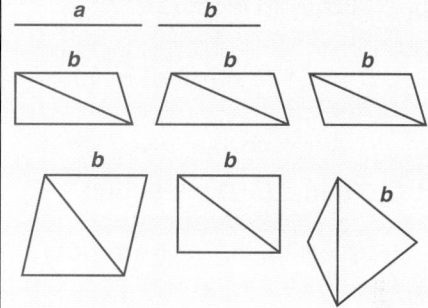

63.

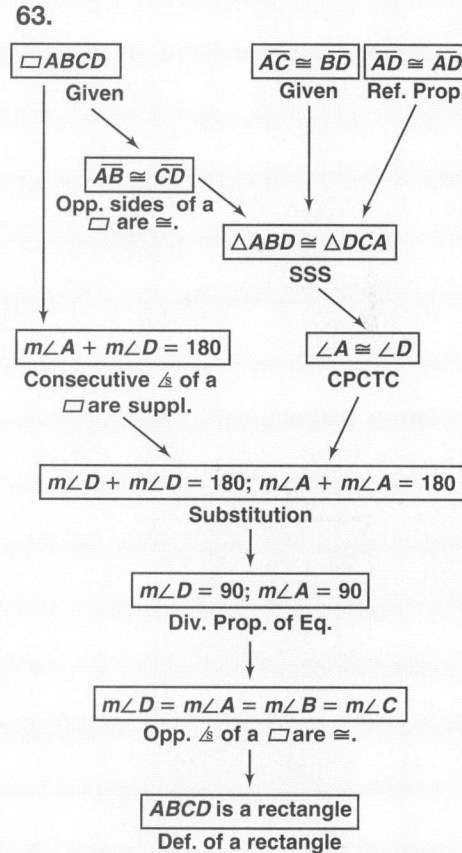

Lesson 6-5
pages 322–325 Exercises

26. 1. *ABCD* is an isosc. trapezoid, $\overline{AB} \cong \overline{DC}$. (Given)
2. Draw $\overline{AE} \parallel \overline{DC}$. (Two points determine a line.)
3. $\overline{AD} \parallel \overline{EC}$ (Def. of a trapezoid)
4. *AECD* is a ▱. (Def. of a ▱)
5. $\angle C \cong \angle 1$ (Corr. ∠ are ≅.)
6. $\overline{DC} \cong \overline{AE}$ (Opp. sides of a ▱ are ≅.)
7. $\overline{AB} \cong \overline{AE}$ (Trans. Prop. of ≅)
8. △*AEB* is an isosc. △. (Def. of an isosc. △)
9. $\angle B \cong \angle 1$ (Base ∠ of an isosc. △ are ≅.)
10. $\angle B \cong \angle C$ (Trans. Prop. of ≅)
11. ∠*B* and ∠*BAD* are suppl., ∠*C* and ∠*CDA* are suppl. (Same side int. ∠ are suppl.)
12. $\angle BAD \cong \angle CDA$ (Suppl. of ≅ ∠ are ≅.)

40. 1. $\overline{AB} \cong \overline{CB}, \overline{AD} \cong \overline{CD}$ (Given)
2. $\overline{BD} \cong \overline{BD}$ (Ref. Prop. of ≅)
3. △*ABD* ≅ △*CBD* (SSS)
4. $\angle A \cong \angle C$ (CPCTC)

Lesson 6-6
page 326 Check Skills You'll Need

1.
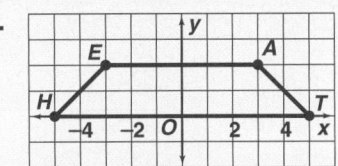
isosc. trapezoid

2.
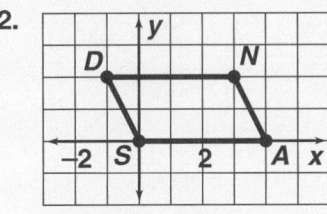
parallelogram

3.
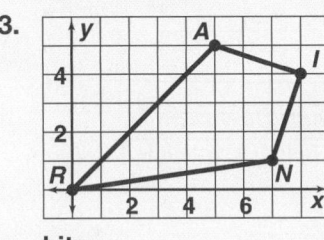
kite

4.
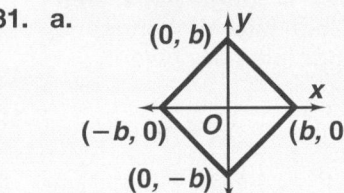
square

pages 328–331 Exercises

20. *W*(0, 2*h*); *Z*(2*b*, 0)
21. *W*(2*a*, 2*a*); *Z*(2*a*, 0)
22. *W*(−2*b*, 2*b*); *Z*(−2*b*, −2*b*)
23. *W*(0, *b*); *Z*(2*a*, 0)
24. *W*(−2*r*, 0); *Z*(0, −2*t*)
25. *W*(−2*b*, 2*c*); *Z*(0, 2*c*)
26. a. Diagonals of a rhombus are ⊥.
b. Diagonals of a ▱ that is not a rhombus are not ⊥.
27. Answers may vary. Sample: $r = 3$, $t = 2$; slopes are $\frac{2}{3}$ and $-\frac{2}{3}$; all lengths are $\sqrt{13}$; the opp. sides have the same slope, so they are $\parallel$. The 4 sides are ≅.

31. a.

$(0, b)$, $(-b, 0)$, O, $(b, 0)$, $(0, -b)$

b. $(-b, 0), (0, b), (b, 0), (0, -b)$
e. Yes, because the product of the slopes is −1.

Lesson 6-7
pages 333 Check Understanding

2. Using multiples of 2 in the coordinates for *M*, *N*, *P*, and *O* eliminates the use of fractions when finding midpoints since finding midpoints requires division by 2.

pages 333–337 Exercises

10. Answers may vary. Sample: The △ Midsegment Thm.; the segment connecting the midpts. of 2 sides of the △ is $\parallel$ to the 3rd side and half its length; you can use the Midpoint Formula and the Distance Formula to prove the statement directly.

11. a. ≅
b. midpts.
c. (−2*b*, 2*c*)
d. *L*(*b*, *a* + *c*), *M*(*b*, *c*), *N*(−*b*, *c*), *K*(−*b*, *a* + *c*)
e. 0
f. vertical lines
g. $\parallel$
h. ⊥

12–24. Answers may vary. Samples are given.

12. yes; Dist. Formula
13. yes; same slope
14. yes; prod. of slopes $= -1$
15. no; may not have intersection pt.
16. no; may need ∠ measures
17. no; may need ∠ measures
18. yes; prod. of slopes of sides of ∠*A* $= -1$
19. yes; Distance Formula
20. yes; Dist. Formula, 2 sides =
21. no; may need ∠ measures
22. yes; intersection pt. for all 3 segments
23. yes; slope of $\overline{AB}$ = slope of $\overline{BC}$
24. yes; Dist. Formula, $AB = BC = CD = AD$

35. Assume $b > a$. $a + \frac{b-a}{n}$, $a + 2\left(\frac{b-a}{n}\right)$, . . . , $a + (n-1)\left(\frac{b-a}{n}\right)$

36. Assume $b > a$; $d > c$. $\left(a + \frac{b-a}{n}, c + \frac{d-c}{n}\right)$, $\left(a + 2\left(\frac{b-a}{n}\right), c + 2\left(\frac{d-c}{n}\right)\right)$, . . . , $\left(a + (n-1)\left(\frac{b-a}{n}\right), c + (n-1)\left(\frac{d-c}{n}\right)\right)$

37. a. The △ with bases *d* and *b*, and heights *c* and *a*, respectively, have the same area. They share the small right △ with base *d* and height *c*, and the remaining areas are △ with base *c* and height (*b*−*d*). So $\frac{1}{2}ad = \frac{1}{2}bc$. Mult. both sides by 2 gives $ad = bc$.
b. The diagram shows that $\frac{a}{b} = \frac{c}{d}$, since both rep. the slope of the top segment of the △. So by (a), $ad = bc$.

40. a. $\frac{b}{c}$

b. Let a pt. on line p be (x, y). Then the eq. of p is $\frac{y - 0}{x - a} = \frac{b}{c}$, or $y = \frac{b}{c}(x - a)$

c. $x = 0$

d. When $x = 0$, $y = \frac{b}{c}(x - a) = \frac{b}{c}(-a) = -\frac{ab}{c}$. So p and q intersect at $(0, -\frac{ab}{c})$.

e. $\frac{a}{c}$

f. Let a pt. on line r be (x, y). Then the eq. of r is $\frac{y - 0}{x - b} = \frac{a}{c}$, or $y = \frac{a}{c}(x - b)$.

g. $-\frac{ab}{c} = \frac{a}{c}(0 - b)$

h. $\left(0, -\frac{ab}{c}\right)$

41. a. Horiz. lines have slope 0, and vert. lines have undef. slope. Neither could be mult. to get -1.

b. Assume the lines do not intersect. Then they have the same slope, say m. Then $m \cdot m = m^2 = -1$, which is impossible. So the lines must intersect.

c. Let the eq. for ℓ_1 be $y = \frac{b}{a}x$, and for ℓ_2 be $y = -\frac{a}{b}x$, and the origin be the int. point.

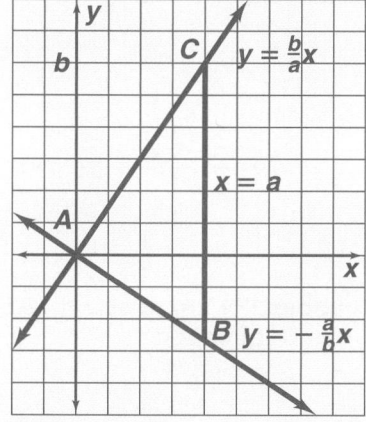

Define: $C(a, b)$, $A(0, 0)$, and $B(a, -\frac{a^2}{b})$.
Using the Distance Formula,
$AC = \sqrt{a^2 + b^2}$,
$BA = \sqrt{a^2 + \frac{a^4}{b^2}}$, and
$CB = b + \frac{a^2}{b}$. Then
$AC^2 + BA^2 = CB^2$,
and $m\angle A = 90$ by the Conv. of the Pythagorean Thm. So $\ell_1 \perp \ell_2$.

44. [2] a. $\frac{7 + a}{2} = 3$; $a = -1$
$\frac{-3 + b}{2} = 4$; $b = 11$
$(a, b) = (-1, 11)$

b.
$$\sqrt{(7 - (-1))^2 + (-3 - 11)^2}$$
$$= \sqrt{260} = 2\sqrt{65} \approx 16.12$$

[1] minor computational error OR no work shown

pages 339–341   Chapter Review

11.
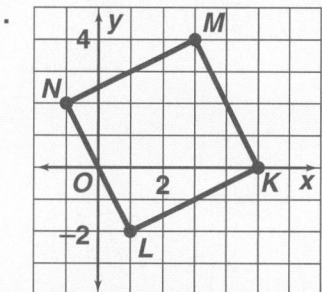

square

12.
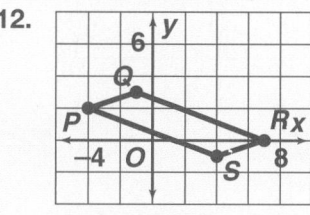

parallelogram

page 342   Chapter Test

1.
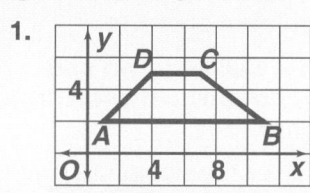

trapezoid

2.
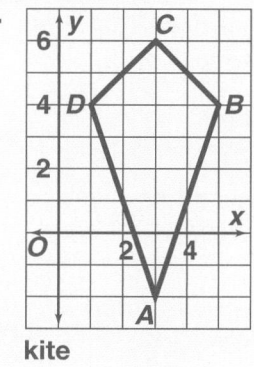

kite

3.
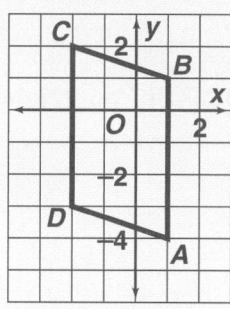

parallelogram

4. Answers may vary. Sample:
a. (0, 0), (3, 0), (3, 3), (0, 3)
b. (0, 0), (3, 0), (4, 3), (1, 3)
c. (0, 0), (5, 0), (5, 3), (0, 3)
d. (0, 0), (5, 0), (4, 3), (1, 3)

16. Answers may vary. Sample: A square has 4 ≅ sides and a kite has no opp. sides ≅.

20. x-coordinates may vary. Sample: $S(-a, -b)$, $T(-a, b)$; $(-a, 0)$; no slope

21. $S(0, 0)$, $T(b + c, d)$; $\left(\frac{b + c}{2}, \frac{d}{2}\right)$; $\frac{d}{b + c}$

pages 343   Standardized Test Prep

12. [2] $5(x - 2) = 3(x + 2)$
$5x - 10 = 3x + 6$
$2x = 16$
$x = 8$

[1] one computational error

13. [4] Answer includes any of the points (0, 8), (−4, 2), or (6, −2), and an explanation involving same slopes for opp. sides, or same side lengths using dist. formula.

[3] a correct point from a sketch

[2] an incorrect point, but correct approach with a computational error

[1] no work shown

CHAPTER 7

Lesson 7-8

pages 404–407   Exercises

30. about 5.6%

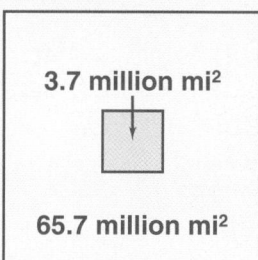

3.7 million mi²

65.7 million mi²

CHAPTER 8

Lesson 8-4
page 439   Check Skills You'll Need

9. Check students' work. Sample:

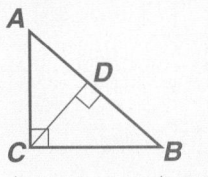

△ADC and △BCD

Lesson 8-5
pages 448–452   Exercises

51. a. A midsegment of a ▱ connects the midpts. of 2 opp. sides.

b.

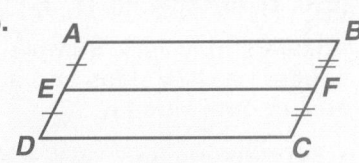

Given: ▱ABCD with $\overline{EF}$ connecting the midpts. of $\overline{AD}$ and $\overline{BC}$

Prove: $\overline{AB} \parallel \overline{EF}$; $\overline{EF} \parallel \overline{CD}$

1. ▱ABCD (Given)
2. $\overline{AE} \parallel \overline{BF}$ and $\overline{ED} \parallel \overline{FC}$ (Def. of ▱)
3. $\overline{AD} \cong \overline{BC}$ (Opp. sides of ▱ are ≅.)
4. E and F are midpts. of $\overline{AD}$ and $\overline{BC}$. (Given)
5. $AE = ED = \frac{1}{2}AD$; $BF = FC = \frac{1}{2}BC$ (Def. of midpt.)
6. $AE = BF$, $ED = FC$ (Subst.)
7. ABFE and EFCD are ▱s. (If one pair of opp. sides of a quad. is ≅ and ∥, it is a ▱.)
8. $\overline{AB} \parallel \overline{EF}$ and $\overline{EF} \parallel \overline{CD}$ (Opp. sides of a ▱ are ∥.)

c.

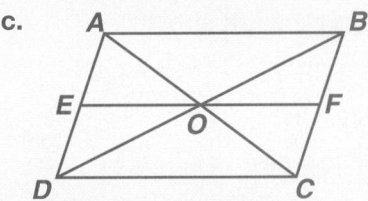

Given: ▱ABCD with midsegment $\overline{EF}$
Prove: $\overline{DO} \cong \overline{BO}$ and $\overline{AO} \cong \overline{OC}$.

1. ▱ABCD with midsegment $\overline{EF}$ (Given)

---

2. $\overline{BF} \cong \overline{FC}$ (Def. of midpt.)
3. $\frac{BO}{DO} = \frac{BF}{FC}$ (Side-Splitter Thm.)
4. $\frac{BO}{DO} = \frac{1}{1}$ ($\overline{BF} \cong \overline{FC}$)
5. $BO = DO$ (Cross-Products Prop.)
6. $\overline{BO} \cong \overline{DO}$ (Def. of ≅)
7. $\overline{AE} \cong \overline{ED}$ (Def. of midpt.)
8. $\frac{AE}{ED} = \frac{AO}{OC}$ (Side-Splitter Thm.)
9. $\frac{AO}{OC} = \frac{1}{1}$ ($\overline{AE} \cong \overline{ED}$)
10. $AO = OC$ (Cross-Products Prop.)
11. $\overline{AO} \cong \overline{OC}$ (Def. of ≅)

55. [4] a.

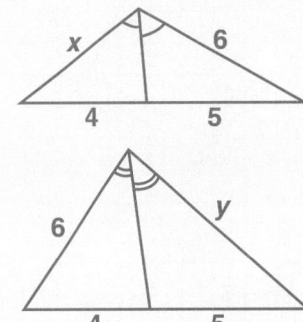

b. $\frac{x}{4} = \frac{6}{5}$
$x = 4.8$ cm
$\frac{6}{4} = \frac{y}{5}$
$y = 7.5$ cm

[3] correct drawings and proportions with one computational error

[2] one possibility drawn and done correctly OR two correct drawings

[1] one correct drawing OR one correct proportion

page 465   Standardized Test Prep

13.

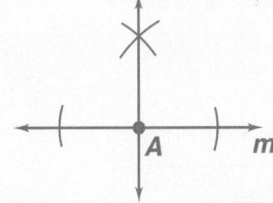

[2] ⊥ line is constructed accurately.

[1] line m with pt. A drawn and with 2 arcs marked on m at equal distances from A

CHAPTER 9

Lesson 9-3
pages 484–488   Exercises

44. [2] a.

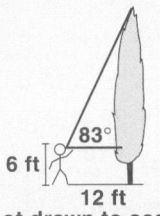

6 ft
12 ft
not drawn to scale

b. Let h represent the height of the tree.
$h = 6 + 12 \tan 83°$
$h \approx 6 + 12(8.14)$
$\approx 6 + 98$
$= 104$
The tree is about 104 ft tall.

[1] correct drawing OR correct solution without work shown

Lesson 9-4
pages 493–497   Exercises

34. a.

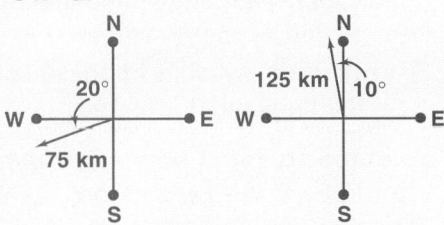

b.

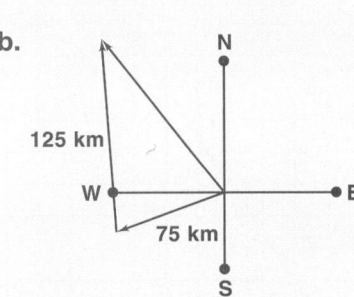

about 134 km at about 46.6° south of east

41. a.

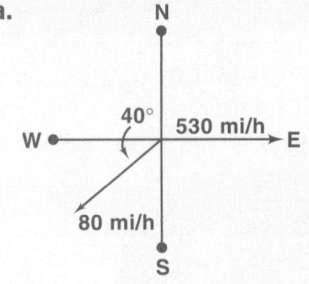

CHAPTER 10

Lesson 10-1
page 513   Check Understanding
2. Answers may vary. Sample:

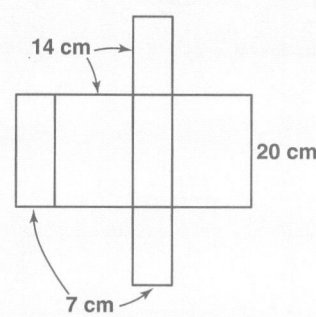

pages 514–516   Exercises
10. Answers may vary. Sample:

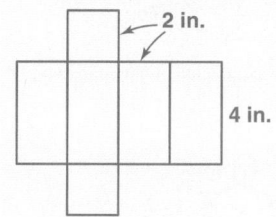

11. Answers may vary. Sample:

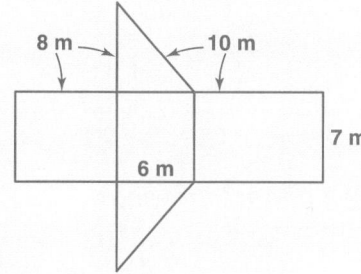

12. Answers may vary. Sample:

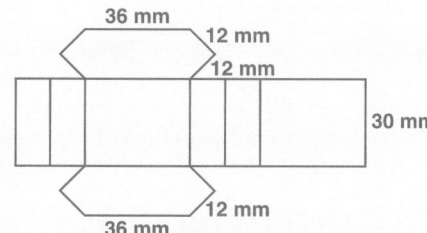

19. a–b. Answers may vary. Sample:

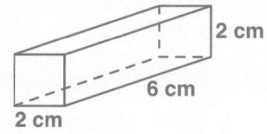

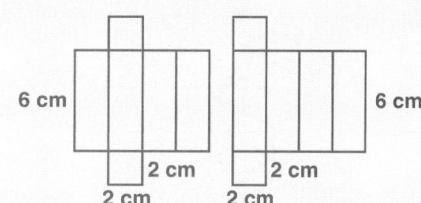

pages 519   Extension
7.

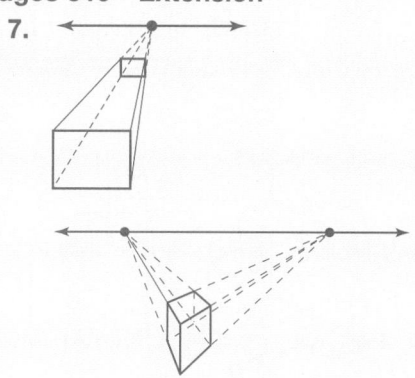

8.

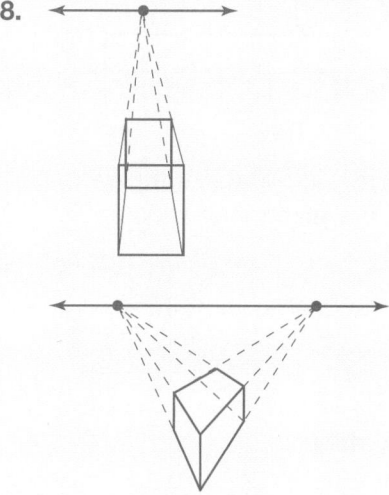

9.

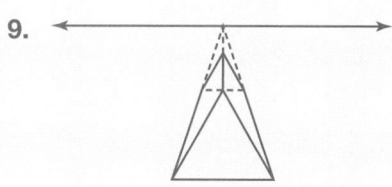

10.

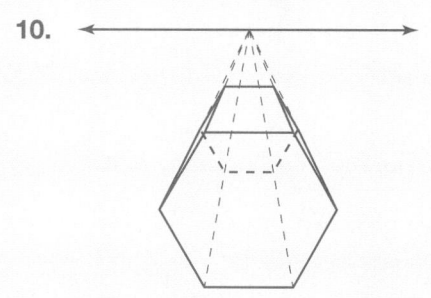

Lesson 10-2
page 520   Check Skills You'll Need
1.

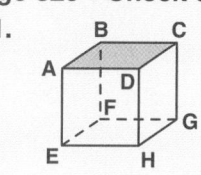

2.

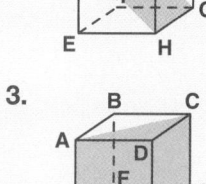

3.

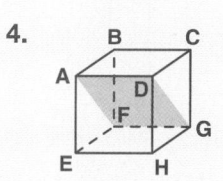

4.

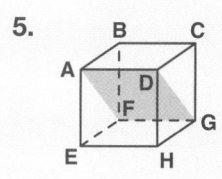

5.

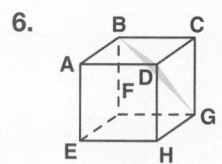

6.

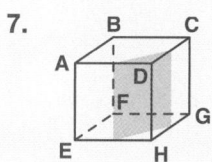

7.

pages 523–526   Exercises
7.

Front   Right   Top

10. a.

1	1	1
1	1	1

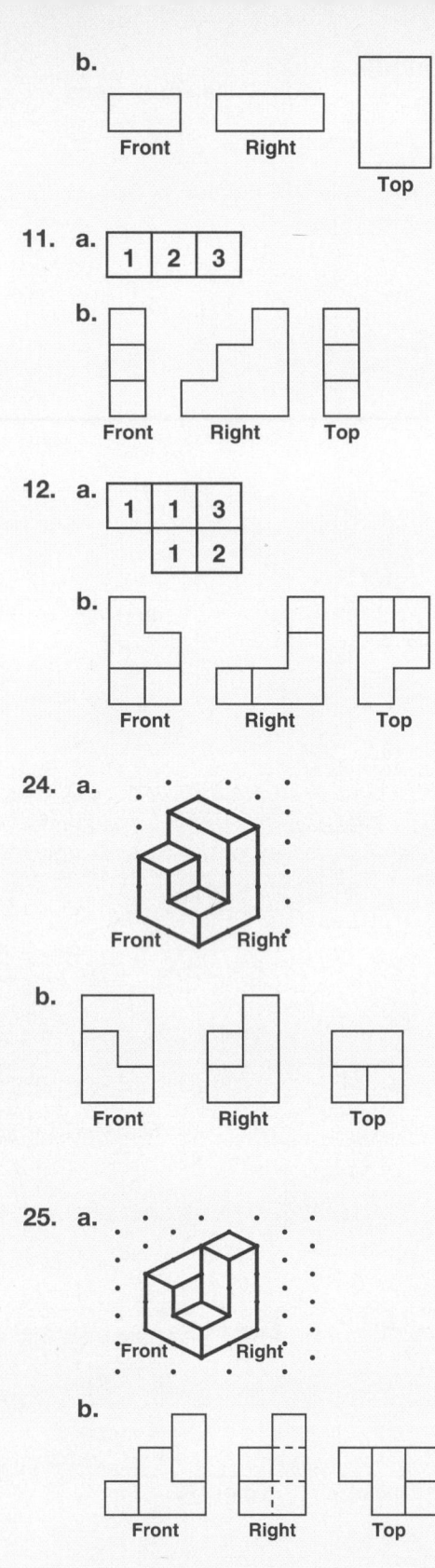

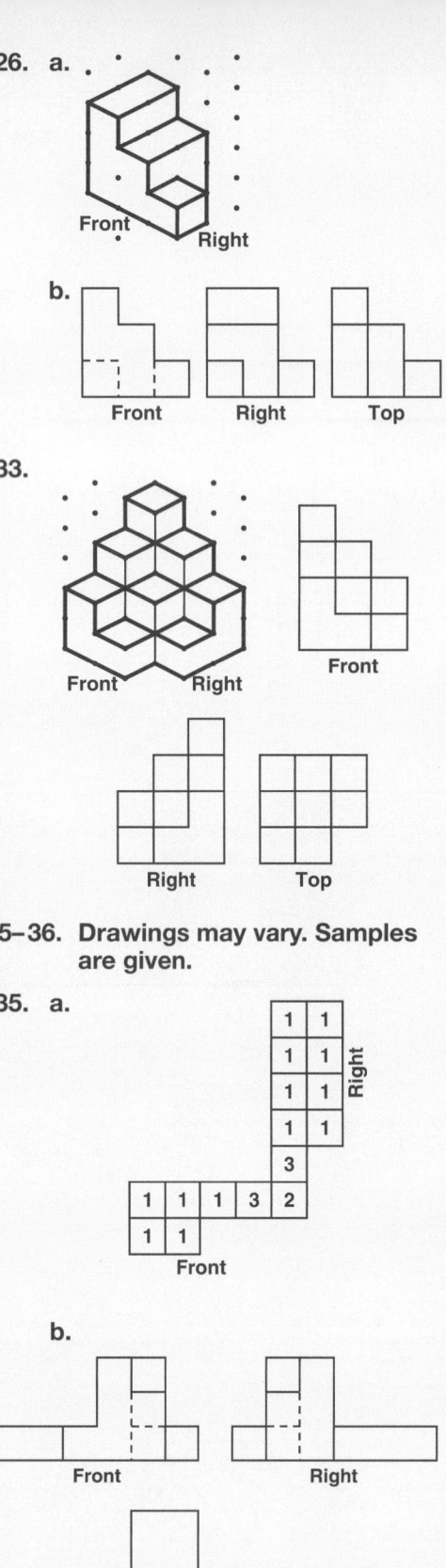

35–36. Drawings may vary. Samples are given.

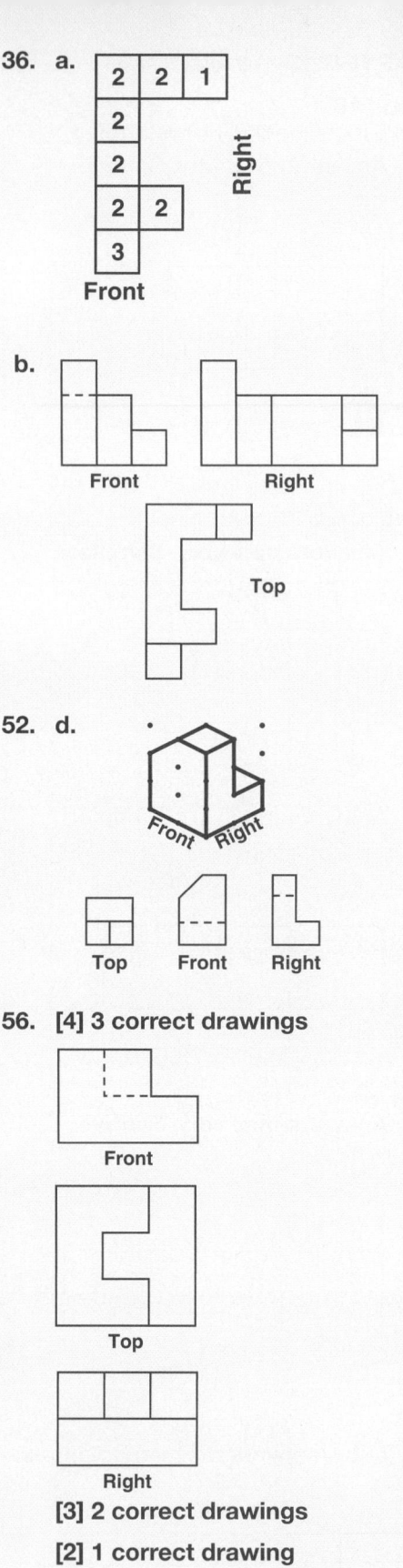

56. **[4] 3 correct drawings**

[3] 2 correct drawings

[2] 1 correct drawing

[1] 1 partially correct drawing

57. Answers may vary. Sample:

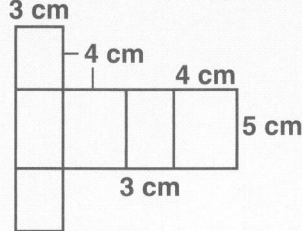

58. Answers may vary. Sample:

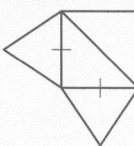

Lesson 10-8
page 566   Check Skills You'll Need

1. yes; all corr. ∠s are ≅ and corr. sides are prop.; 3:1

pages 573–575   Chapter Review

11. a.

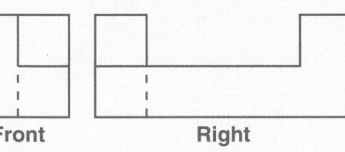

Front   Right

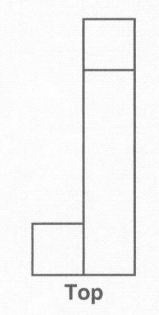

Top

b.

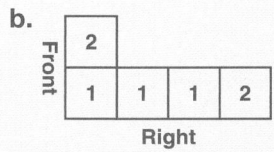

Right

16.

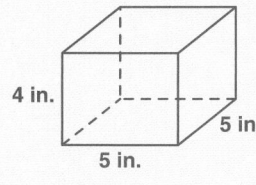

4 in.
5 in.
5 in.

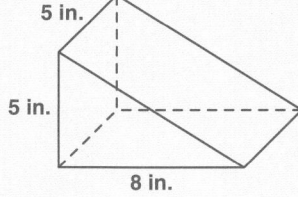

5 in.
5 in.
8 in.

---

11. [2] $C = \pi d = 12\pi$; length of $\overarc{AB}$ $= \frac{1}{4}(12\pi) = 3\pi$

[1] no work shown

12. [4] area of segment = area of sector − area of triangle = $\left(\frac{10,000\pi}{3} - 2500\sqrt{3}\right)$ m^2

[3] area of segment correct

[2] area of triangle correct

[1] no work shown

Lesson 11-1
pages 586–589   Exercises

35.

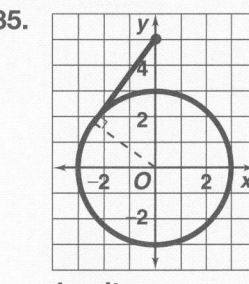

4 units

38. Assume $\overleftrightarrow{AB}$ is not tangent to $\odot O$. Then either $\overleftrightarrow{AB}$ does not intersect $\odot O$ or $\overleftrightarrow{AB}$ intersects $\odot O$ at two pts. If $\overleftrightarrow{AB}$ does not intersect $\odot O$, then P is not on $\odot O$, which contradicts $\overline{OP}$ being a radius. If $\overleftrightarrow{AB}$ intersects $\odot O$ at two pts., P and Q, then $\overline{OP}$ $\cong \overline{OQ}$ ($\cong$ radii), $\triangle OPQ$ is isosc., and $\angle OPQ \cong \angle OQP$. But $\angle OPQ$ is a rt. $\angle$, since $\overline{AB} \perp \overline{OP}$, and $\triangle OPQ$ has two rt. ∠s. This is a contradiction also, so $\overleftrightarrow{AB}$ is tangent to $\odot O$.

Lesson 11-3
pages 601–605   Exercises

44. 1. quadrilateral $ABCD$ inscribed in $\odot O$ (Given)
2. $m\angle A = \frac{1}{2}m\overarc{BCD}$ and $m\angle C = \frac{1}{2}$ $m\overarc{BAD}$ (Inscr. ∠Thm.)
3. $m\angle A + m\angle C = \frac{1}{2}m\overarc{BCD} + \frac{1}{2}$ $m\overarc{BAD}$ (Add. Prop.)
4. $m\overarc{BCD} + m\overarc{BAD} = 360$ (Entire circle = 360.)
5. $m\angle A + m\angle C = 180$ (Subst. & Mult. Prop.)
6. $\angle A$ and $\angle C$ are suppl. (Def. of suppl.)

---

7. $m\angle B = \frac{1}{2}m\overarc{ADC}$ and $m\angle D = \frac{1}{2}$ $m\overarc{ABC}$ (Inscr. ∠ Thm.)
8. $m\angle B + m\angle D = \frac{1}{2}m\overarc{ADC} + \frac{1}{2}$ $m\overarc{ABC}$ (Add. Prop.)
9. $m\overarc{ADC} + m\overarc{ABC} = 360$ (Entire circle = 360.)
10. $m\angle B + m\angle D = 180$ (Subst. and Mult. Prop.)
11. $\angle B$ and $\angle D$ are suppl. (Def. of suppl.)

Lesson 11-4
pages 611–613   Exercises

30. Given: $\overleftrightarrow{AB}$ tangent to $\odot O$ at A, $\overline{BC}$ tangent to $\odot O$ at C; Prove: $m\angle B$ $= \frac{1}{2}(360 - 2m\overarc{AC})$.
1. Construct $\overline{AC}$.
2. $m\angle A = \frac{1}{2}m\overarc{AC}$ (The measure of an ∠ formed by a tangent and a chord is half the measure of the intercepted arc.)
3. $m\angle C = \frac{1}{2}m\overarc{AC}$ (The measure of an ∠ formed by a tangent and a chord is half the measure of the intercepted arc.)
4. $m\angle B = 180 - m\angle A - m\angle C$ ($\triangle$ ∠ Sum Thm.)
5. $m\angle B = 180 - \frac{1}{2}m\overarc{AC} - \frac{1}{2}$ $m\overarc{AC}$ (Subst.)
6. $m\angle B = 180 - m\overarc{AC}$
7. $m\angle B = \frac{1}{2}(360 - 2m\overarc{AC})$ (Distr. Prop.)

Given: $\overline{BC}$ secant and $\overleftrightarrow{AB}$ tangent to $\odot O$. $\overleftrightarrow{AB}$, $\overline{BC}$ intersect at B and $\overleftrightarrow{AB}$ tangent to $\odot O$ at A. $\overline{BC}$ intersects $\odot O$ at D; Prove: $m\angle B = \frac{1}{2}(m\overarc{AC} - m\overarc{DA})$.
1. Construct $\overline{AD}$.
2. $m\angle A = \frac{1}{2}m\overarc{AD}$ (The measure of an ∠ formed by a tangent and a chord is half the measure of the intercepted arc.)
3. $m\angle ADC = \frac{1}{2}m\overarc{AC}$ (The measure of an inscribed ∠ is half the measure of its intercepted arc.)

Additional Answers

4. $m\angle B = m\angle ADC - m\angle BAD$
   (Subtr. and Ext. $\angle$ Thm.)
5. $m\angle B = \frac{1}{2}m\widehat{AC} - \frac{1}{2}m\widehat{AD}$
   (Subst.)
6. $m\angle B = \frac{1}{2}(m\widehat{AC} - m\widehat{AD})$
   (Distr. Prop.)

32. Given: a circle with tangent $\overline{TV}$ and secant $\overline{XV}$; prove: $XV \cdot YV = (TV)^2$.

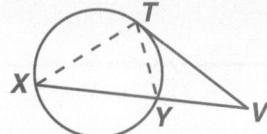

1. Construct $\overline{TX}$ and $\overline{TY}$.
2. $m\angle TXV = \frac{1}{2}m\widehat{TY}$ (The measure of an inscribed $\angle$ is half the measure of the intercepted arc.)
3. $m\angle VTY = \frac{1}{2}m\widehat{TY}$ (The measure of an $\angle$ formed by a chord and a tangent is half the measure of the intercepted arc.)
4. $m\angle TXV = m\angle VTY$ (Trans. Prop. of $=$)
5. $\angle TVY \cong \angle TVX$ (Reflexive Prop. of $\cong$)
6. $\triangle TVY \sim \triangle XVT$ (AA~)
7. $\frac{YV}{TV} = \frac{TV}{XV}$ (In similar figures, corr. sides are proport.)
8. $XV \cdot YV = TV^2$ (Prop. of Proport.)

33. Answers may vary. Sample: If the given pt. is on the circle, then a line through the given pt. can only intersect the circle tangentially or one other place. It follows that one segment has length zero, so the product of the segments is always zero.

Lesson 11-5

pages 617–620   Exercises

16. center: (−7, 5); radius: 4

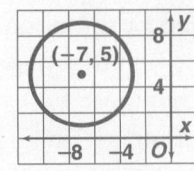

17. center: (3, −8); radius: 10

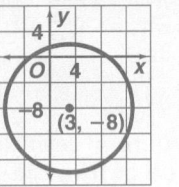

18. center: (−4, 1); radius: 5

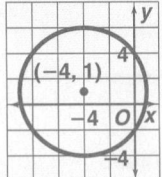

19. center: (0, 0); radius: 6

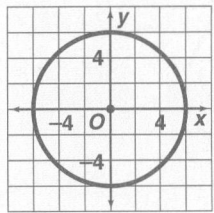

20. center: (0.3, 0); radius: 0.2

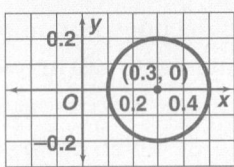

21. center: (−5, −2); radius: $4\sqrt{3}$

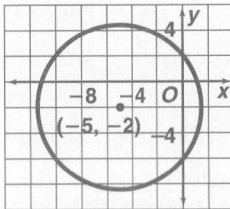

49.

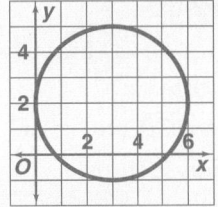

50.

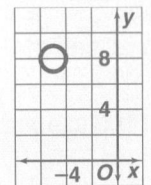

51.

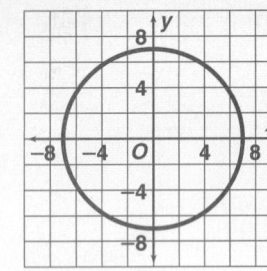

52.

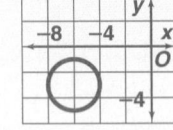

53. (3, 2); (2, 3)

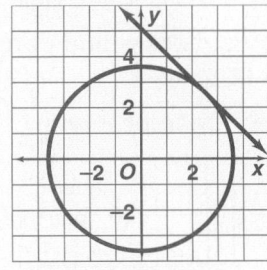

54. (4, −1); (−4, 1)

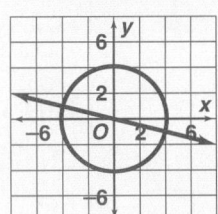

55. (2, 2); (−2, 2)

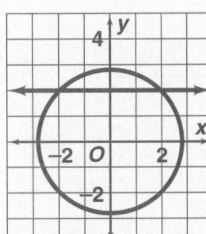

56. (2, 4)

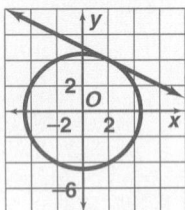

57. (−4, 4)

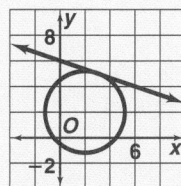

58. (3, 5)

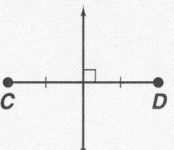

Lesson 11-6

page 621   Check Skills You'll Need

1.

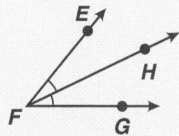

2.

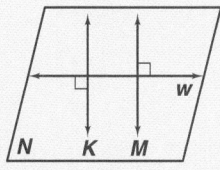

3.

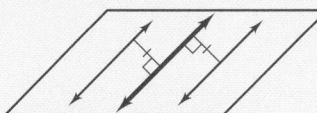

page 622   Check Understanding

3. **a.** Consider two ‖ lines in a plane. The locus is the line ‖ to and equidist. from the ‖ lines.

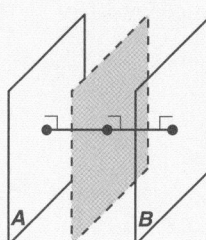

   b. Consider a segment ⊥ to both planes, with one endpoint on plane *A* and one endpoint on plane *B*. The locus is the plane ⊥ to the segment at the segment's midpt.

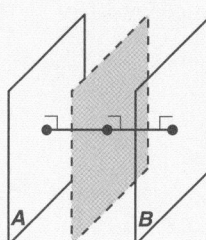

pages 623–625   Exercises

1. a circle of radius 4 cm with center *X*

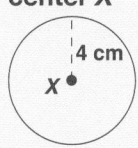

2. two distinct segments ‖ to and 2 in. from $\overleftrightarrow{UV}$, connected by two semi-circles with 2-in. radii centered at *U* and *V*

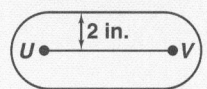

3. two distinct lines ‖ to $\overleftrightarrow{LM}$ and 3 mm from $\overleftrightarrow{LM}$

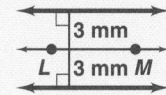

4. two circles, concentric with the original circle, of radius 2 in. and 4 in.

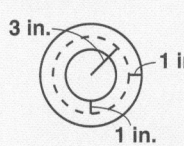

5. a line ⊥ to $\overline{PQ}$ and through the midpoint of $\overline{PQ}$

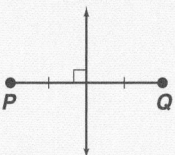

6. the ∠ bisector of ∠*ABC*

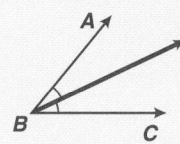

7. two ⊥ lines, meeting at the intersection of the orig. lines, making 45° ⊿ with orig. lines

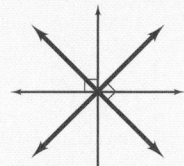

8. a circle of radius 1 cm with same center as original circle

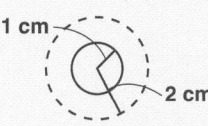

10. the pts. *M* and *N*

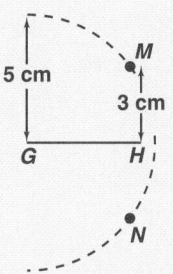

11. the single pt. *N*

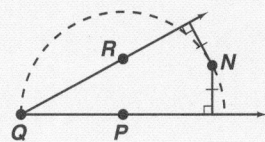

12. the center *O*

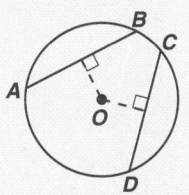

13. the pts. *B* and *D*

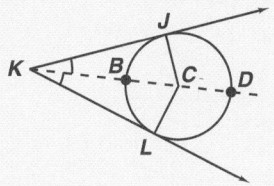

14. a sphere of radius 3 cm, centered at *F*

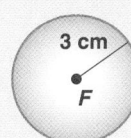

15. an endless cylinder with radius 4 cm and centerline $\overleftrightarrow{DE}$

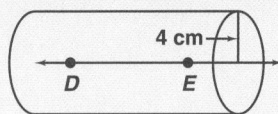

16. two planes ∥ to plane *M*, each 1 in. from *M*

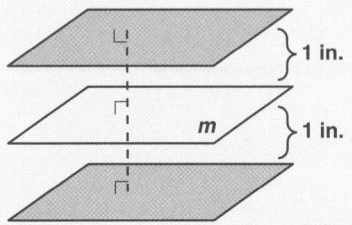

17. an endless cylinder with radius 5 mm and center ray $\overrightarrow{PQ}$ and a hemisphere of radius 5 mm centered at *P*

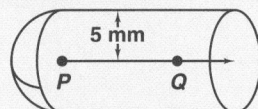

33.

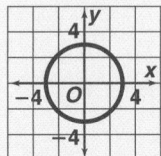

34.

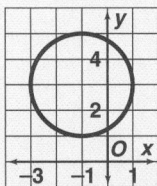

35.

36.

37.

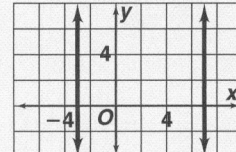
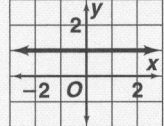

38.

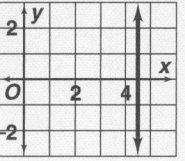

39.

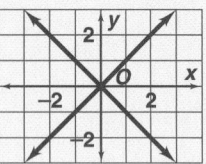

40.

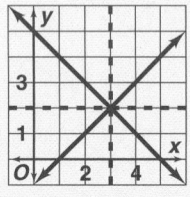

page 630   Chapter Test

6.   (4, 3); 5

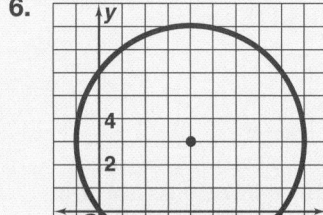

25.

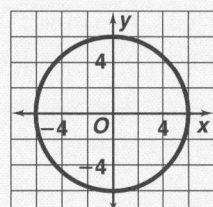

26.

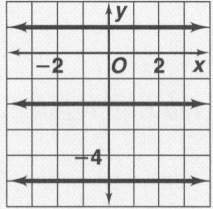

27.

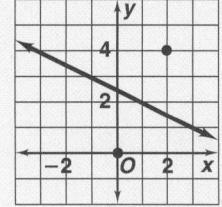

28.

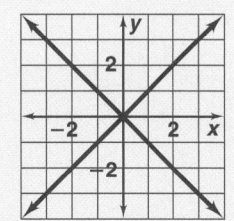

page 631   Standardized Test Prep

4. 3; a diff. rectangle is needed to contain each side of the △.

5. 1; since all four sides are ≅, only 1 rectangle is possible.

6. 2; one rectangle shares a base with a side, the other with a leg.

7. 1; since all six sides are ≅, only 1 rectangle is possible.

CHAPTER 12

Lesson 12-1
pages 636–639   Exercises

10.

11.

12.

13.

14.

15.

16.

c.

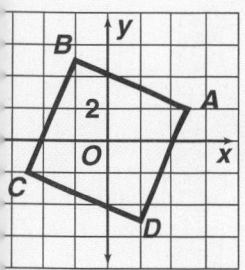

a.

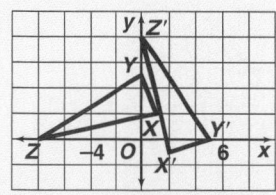

b. $X'(2, -1)$, $Y'(5, 0)$, $Z'(0, 8)$

correct amount of rotation but
mislabeled vertices

12-4

4   Check Skills You'll Need

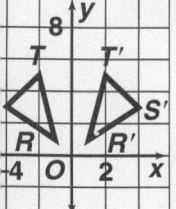

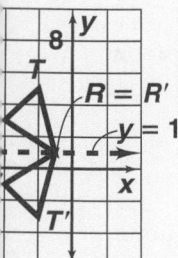

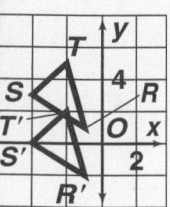

5.

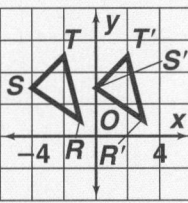

6.

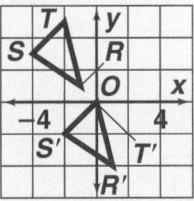

7.

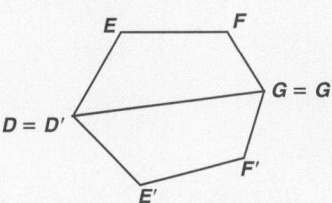

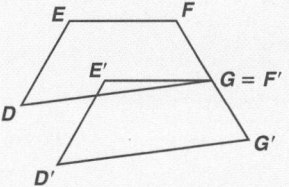

page 655   Check Understanding

2.

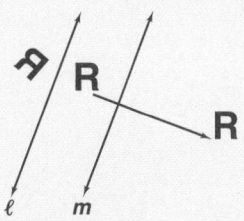

R is translated the distance and
direction shown by the arrow. The
length of the arrow is twice the
distance between ℓ and m.

3. Answers may vary. Sample:

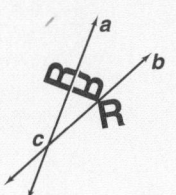

pages 657–660   Exercises

6.

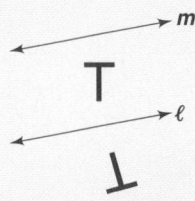

T is translated across line m twice
the distance between ℓ and m.

7.

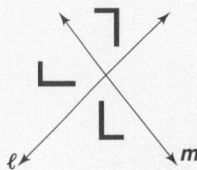

L is rotated clockwise about 180°.

8.

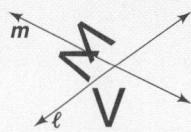

V is rotated clockwise about 145°.

9.

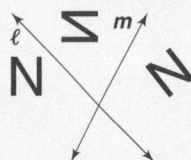

N is rotated clockwise about 160°.

10.

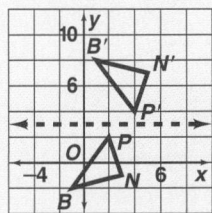

11.

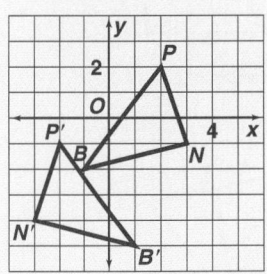

17.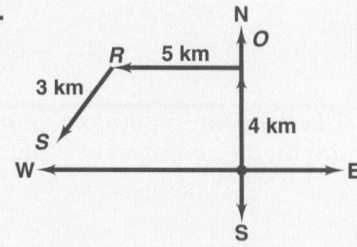

Lesson 12-2
pages 643–646   Exercises

34. a.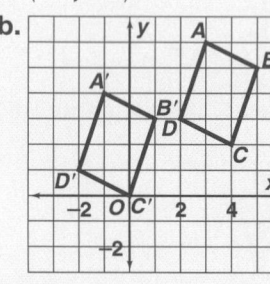

40. a. $\langle -4, -2 \rangle$

b.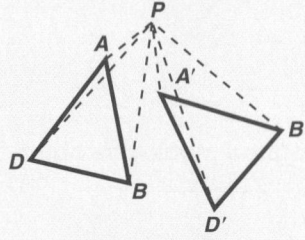

Lesson 12-3
pages 649–652   Exercises

1.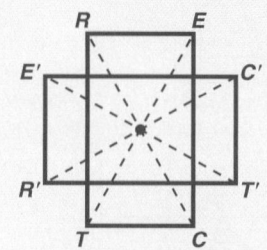

2.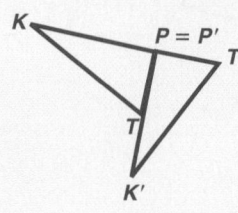

3.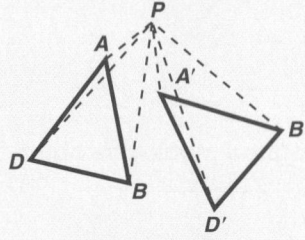

4.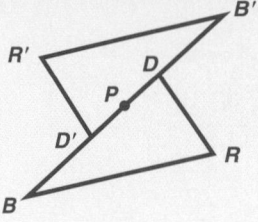

5.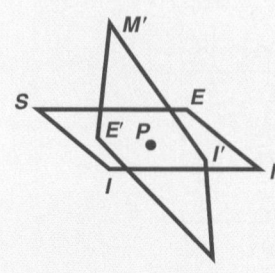

7.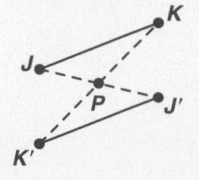

8.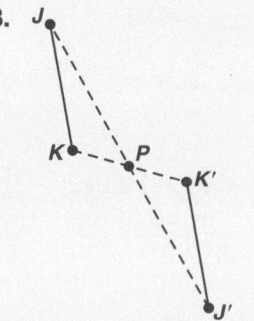

9.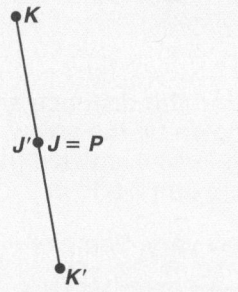

20.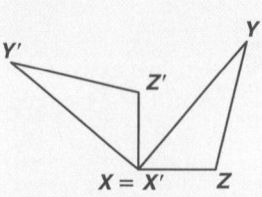

21.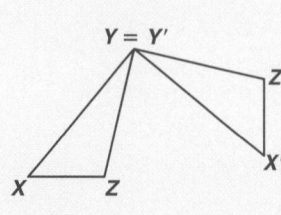

22.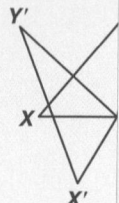

23.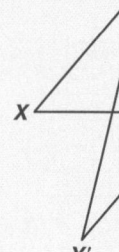

24.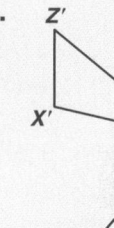

25.

31.

34. a.

39. [2

Lesson
page 6

1.

2.

3.

4.

T774

12.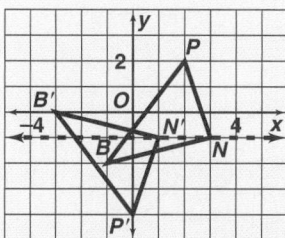

13.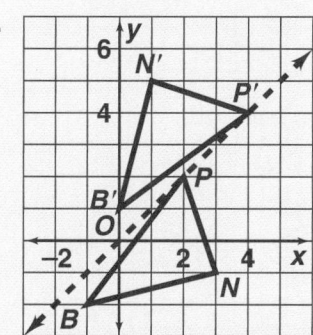

14.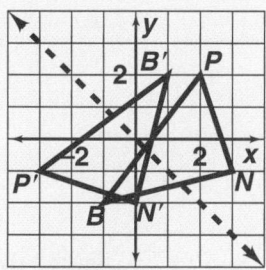

15.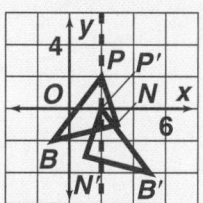

16.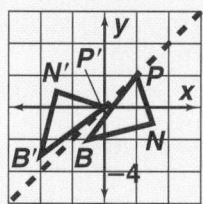

17.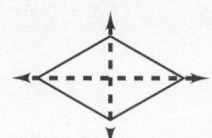

Lesson 12-5
pages 664–666   Exercises

1. line; rotational: 180°

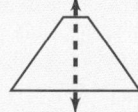

2. line

3. rotational: 90°

4. line, rotational: 60°

5. rotational: 180°

6. no symmetry

7. no symmetry

8. rotational: any angle; line: any line passing through the center

9. rotational: 60°

10. line

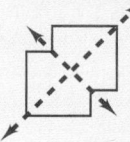

11. line, rotational: 180°

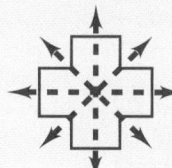

12. line, rotational: 90°

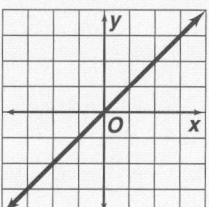

21. a.

Language	Horz. line	Vert. line	Point
English	B, C, D,E, H, I, K, O, X	A, H, I, M, O, T, U, V, W, X, Y	H, I, N, O S, X, Z
Greek	B, E, H, Θ I, K, Ξ, O, Σ, Φ, X	A, Δ, H, Θ, I, Λ, M, Ξ, O, Π, T, Υ, Φ, X, Ψ, Ω	Z, H, Θ, I, N, Ξ, O, Φ, X

41. point symmetry about any pt. on the line; reflectional in any member of the family of lines $y = -x + b$

42.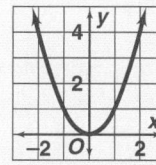

reflectional in y-axis

43.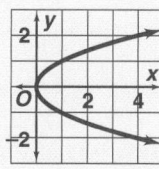

reflectional in x-axis

44.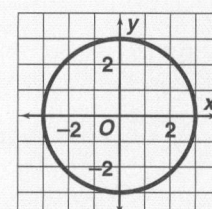

rotational symmetry of any ∠ about the origin; reflectional in any line through the origin

45.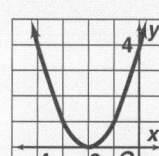

reflectional in x = −2

46.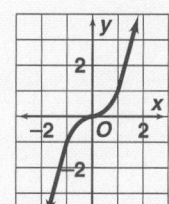

point symmetry about origin

47.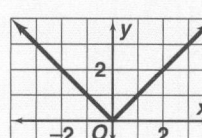

reflectional in y-axis

48.

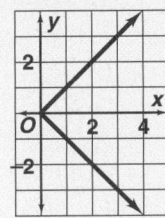

reflectional in x-axis

49–50. Answers may vary. Samples are given.

49.

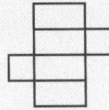 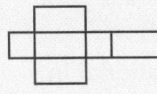

50.

Lesson 12-6
pages 670–672   Exercises

20–22. Answers may vary. Samples are given.

20.

21.

 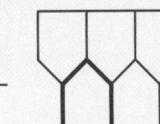

22.

 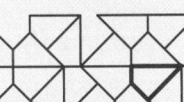

Lesson 12-7
pages 676–679   Exercises

15. $P'(6, -3)$, $Q'(6, 12)$, $R'(12, -3)$

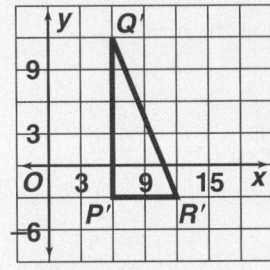

16. $P'(-50, 10)$, $Q'(-30, 30)$, $R'(10, -30)$

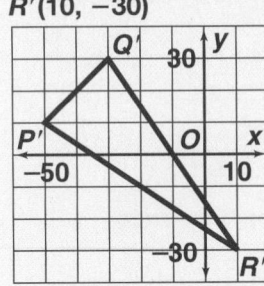

17. $P'\left(-\frac{9}{4}, 0\right)$, $Q'\left(0, \frac{9}{4}\right)$, $R'\left(\frac{3}{4}, -\frac{9}{4}\right)$

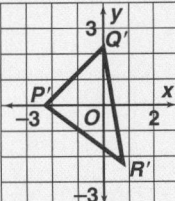

24. $A'(2, 0)$, $B'(6, 4)$, $C'(10, 2)$

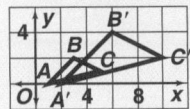

25. $A'\left(-\frac{1}{2}, -\frac{1}{2}\right)$, $B'\left(\frac{1}{4}, \frac{1}{4}\right)$, $C'\left(\frac{1}{4}, -\frac{1}{4}\right)$

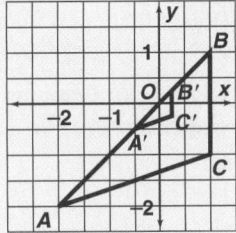

26. $A'\left(1, \frac{1}{3}\right)$, $B'(-2, -3)$, $C'(4, -1)$

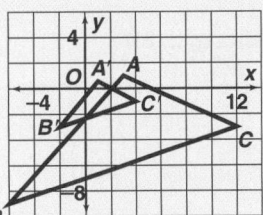

27. $A'(-10, 0)$, $B'(-20, -15)$, $C'(-15, 0)$

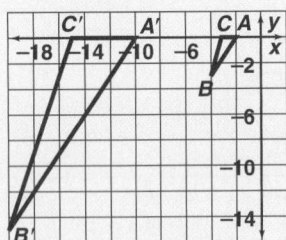

37.

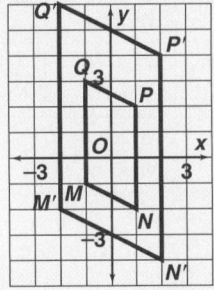

38.

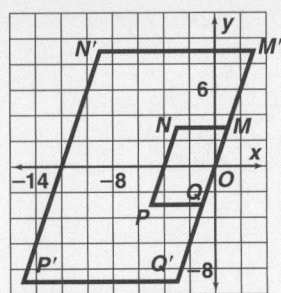

39.

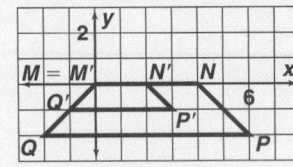

40.

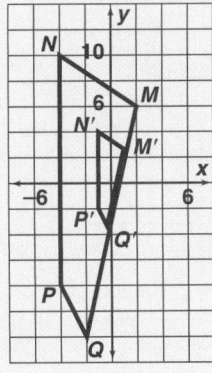

50.

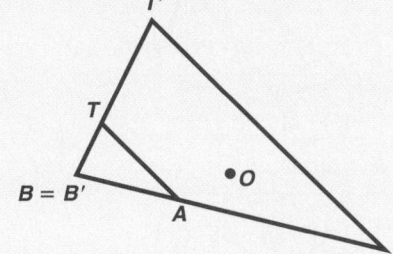

64. a., c.

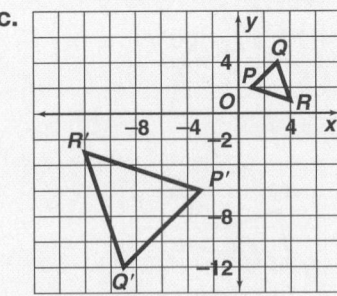

b. $P'(-3, -6)$, $Q'(-9, -12)$,
   $R'(-12, -3)$

page 684   Chapter Test

20. No; if m is not $\perp$ to $\overline{UH}$, then the reflection image of U would not be H.

21. rotational, point, reflectional, translational, glide reflectional

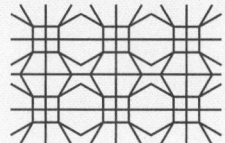

22. yes

23. yes

24. No; no part of the "K" will fit into the upper, lower, or middle angles of itself.

25. $A'(-6, 6)$, $B'(6, -6)$, $C'(9, 12)$

page 701   Extra Practice

1.

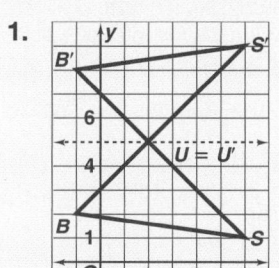

2.

3.

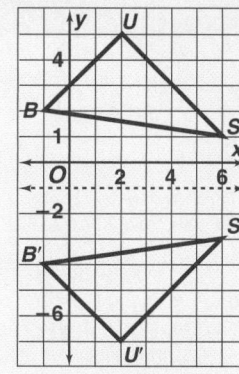

4.

5.

6.

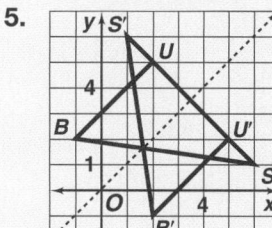

7.

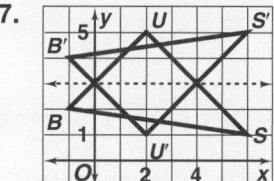

8.

Index

Index

Index

Index

Acknowledgments

STAFF CREDITS

The people who made up the *High School Mathematics* team—representing design services, editorial, editorial services, market research, marketing services, online services & multimedia development, production services, project office, and publishing processes—are listed below. **Bold type** denotes the core team members.

Leora Adler, Carolyn Artin, Stephanie Bradley, Amy D. Breaux, **Peter Brooks,** Judith Buice, Ronit Carter, **Lisa J. Clark,** Bob Cornell, Sheila DeFazio, Marian DeLollis, Jo DiGiustini, Delphine Dupee, Emily Ellen, Janet Fauser, Debby Faust, Suzanne Feliciello, Frederick Fellows, Steve Fenton, Jonathan Fisher, **Paula Foye,** Paul Frisoli, Patti Fromkin, Melissa Garcia, Jonathan Gorey, Jennifer Graham, Barbara Hardt, Daniel R. Hartjes, Richard Heater, Kerri Hoar, Jayne Holman, Karen Holtzman, Angela Husband, Kevin Jackson-Mead, Albert Jacobson, Misty-Lynn Jenese, Carolyn Lock, Diahanne Lucas, Catherine Maglio, Cheryl Mahan, Barry Maloney, Meredith Mascola, Ann McSweeney, **Eve Melnechuk,** Sandy Morris, **Cindy Noftle,** Marsha Novak, **Marie Opera,** Jill Ort, Michael Oster, Steve Ouellette, Dorothy M. Preston, Rashid Ross, Donna Russo, **Malti Sharma, Dennis Slattery,** Kathryn Smith, Lisa Smith-Ruvalcaba, Emily Soltanoff, **Deborah Sommer,** Mark Tricca, Nate Walker, Diane Walsh, **Joe Will,** Amy Winchester, Carol Zacny

COVER DESIGN
Brainworx Studio

COVER PHOTOS
Zebras, Art Wolfe/Stone/Getty Images, Inc.; **Glass Dome,** John McAnulty/Corbis.

TECHNICAL ILLUSTRATION
Network Graphics

ILLUSTRATION
Andrea G. Maginnis: 32
John Edwards: 18, 120, 182, 188, 274
JB Woolsey: 15, 76, 148, 183, 212, 315, 376, 435, 436, 482
Dennis Harms: 8, 47, 204, 205, 222, 258, 386, 457
Function through Form: 42, 250, 513, 531, 561, 643
Leo Abbett: 80, 519 All
Stephanie Bradley: 247, 525
Roberta Warshaw: 533, 545, 557
Jim Delapine: 399, 558, 559
Seymour Levy: 563
Kenneth Batelman: 443, 471, 570, 621, 624
Christine Graham: 602, 651

Roberta Warshaw: 611, 637
Peter Bollinger: 633, 688, 689
Brucie Rosch: 59, 69, 253, 636, 642
Linda Johnson: 665
Gary Torrisi: 484 all, 486
Lois Leonard Stock: 669
Ortelius Design, Inc.: 374
Gary Phillips: 28, 32

PHOTOGRAPHY
Page vii, Johnny Johnson/DRK Photo; **viii,** Andy Sacks/Stone/Getty Images, Inc.; **ix,** Peter Menzel/Stock Boston; **x,** Russ Lappa; **xi,** Timothy Hursley/SuperStock, Inc.; **xii,** Kunio Owaki/Corbis Stock Market; **xiii,** Russ Lappa; **xiv,** David Young-Wolff/PhotoEdit; **xv,** Scott T. Smith/Corbis; **xvi,** Felicia Martinez/PhotoEdit; **xvii,** Reza Estakhrian/Stone/Getty Images, Inc.; **xviii,** Roy Ooms/Masterfile Corporation.

Chapter 1: Pages 2, 3, SeaWorld; **4,** Julie Houck/Stock Boston; **6,** Brett Froomer/Image Bank/Getty Images, Inc.; **7,** Stone/Getty Images, Inc.; **9,** PhotoDisc, Inc./Getty Images, Inc.; **13,** Russ Lappa; **14,** Johnny Johnson/DRK Photo; **17,** Daryl Benson/ Masterfile Corporation; **18,** Stacy Pick/Stock Boston; **21 bl,** Dave Bartruff/Stock Boston; **21 inset,** SuperStock, Inc.; **21 tr,** Tim O'Hara/Index Stock Imagery, Inc.; **27,** Bill Nation/Corbis Sygma; **27 inset,** Chad Slattery/Stone/Getty Images, Inc.; **29,** Corbis; **31,** William Sallaz/Duomo; **32,** Cameramann/The Image Works; **35,** Jon Feingersh/Corbis Stock Market; **36,** Tim Panell/Corbis; **38 t,** ©1997 Richard Megna/ Fundamental Photographs, NYC; **38 b,** *Peanuts* reprinted by permission of United Feature Syndicate, Inc.; **40,** Dan McCoy/ Corbis Stock Market; **45,** Michael Newman/PhotoEdit; **47,** Laura Dwight/PhotoEdit; **48,** Richard Eller/Aerial Images Photography; **53,** Gail Mooney/Corbis; **56,** Hans Georg Roth/Corbis; **57,** Michael Rosenfeld/Stone/Getty Images, Inc.

Chapter 2: Pages 66, 67, Stewart Cohen/Stone/Getty Images, Inc.; **70,** Jon Chomitz; **71 t,** ©1977 NEA, Inc.; **71 bl,** AP Photo/Richard Drew; **71 br,** Tony Vaccaro/Archive Photos/Getty Images, Inc.; **73 t,** Hulton-Deutsch Collection/Corbis; **73 b,** Mug Shots/Corbis Stock Market; **77,** Richard Haynes; **79 l,** Russ Lappa; **79 r,** National Association for the Deaf; **80 l,** Andy Sacks/Stone/Getty Images, Inc.; **80 r,** C. Squared Studios/PhotoDisc, Inc./PictureQuest; **82,** Tony Freeman/PhotoEdit; **84,** InterNetwork Media/PhotoDisc, Inc./PictureQuest; **85,** Damian Strohmey/Sports Illustrated; **86 t,** Fotopic/Omni-Photo Communications, Inc.; **86 m,** *The Far Side* by John McPherson/ Dist. by Universal Press Syndicate. Reprinted with permission. All rights reserved.; **86 b,** Gregory Scott/Index Stock Imagery, Inc.; **88 l,** Courtesy of WGBH; **88 r,** ©King Collection/Retna, Ltd.; **92 l,** PhotoDisc, Inc./Getty Images, Inc.; **92 r,** Tony Freeman/PhotoEdit; **93 t,** The Granger Collection, NY; **93 m,** John Lopinot/Black Star Publishing/PictureQuest; **93 b,** Neal Preston-Andy Kent/Still Bill Productions; **97 l,** Joe Bator/ Corbis Stock Market; **97 r,** Telegraph Colour Library/FPG International/ Getty Images, Inc.; **101,** Corbis Digital Images/ PictureQuest; **102,** Paul A. Souder/Corbis; **110 hands and pan,** David Murray and Jules Selmes/Dorling Kindersley Ltd.; **110 the rest,** Dorling Kindersley Ltd.; **111 pizza cutter,** Russ Lappa; **111 grater, baking tin, mortar and pestle,** Christ Graham and Nick Nichols/Dorling Kindersley Ltd.; **111 the rest,** Dorling Kindersley Ltd.

Chapter 3: Pages 112, 113, Imtek Imagineering/Masterfile Corporation; **116 composite,** Joe Towers/Corbis Stock Market and H.P. Merten/Corbis Stock Market; **119,** Peter Menzel/Stock Boston; **122,** Gary Kufner/Corbis; **125,** Jon Chomitz; **126,** John M. Roberts/Corbis Stock Market; **127 both,** Jon Chomitz; **128,** Richard Pasley/Stock Boston; **133,** Chuck Pefley/Stone/Getty Images, Inc.; **134,** Stewart Cohen /Stone/Getty Images, Inc.; **136,** John Coletti/ The Picture Cube/Index Stock Imagery, Inc.; **137 both,** Jerry Jacka Photography; **143,** Jim Cummins/FPG International/Getty Images, Inc.; **144,** Arthur ThÈvenart/Corbis; **146,** Ken O'Donoghue; **147 l,** Russ Lappa; **147 m,** Nawrocki Stock Photo/ Picture Perfect; **147 r,** Russ Lappa; **148,** Courtesy of the Theatre in the Round Players, Inc., Minneapolis, MN; **149,** Michael Newman/ PhotoEdit; **155,** NASA; **156,** Michael Newman/PhotoEdit; **158,** Bob Daemmrich/ Stock Boston; **161,** PhotoDisc, Inc./Getty Images, Inc.; **163,** Getty Images Sport Services; **165,** Michael Newman/PhotoEdit; **167,** Addison Gallery of Art at Phillips Acadamy; **169 all,** Jon Chomitz.

Chapter 4: Pages 178, 179, Peter Willi/SuperStock, Inc.; **181,** NASA; **182,** John Elk III/Stock Boston; **184,** Richard Haynes; **185,** Hans Gregory Roth/Corbis; **187,** Tom Alexander/ Stone/Getty Images, Inc.; **189 l,** Tony Freeman Photography; **189 r,** Russ Lappa; **190 both,** Prentice Hall; **195,** Mike Greenlar Photography; **198,** Richard Haynes; **200,** Photo Researchers, Inc.; **203,** Russ Lappa; **206,** Leif Skoogfors/ Woodfin Camp & Associates; **211,** Pat O'Hara/Corbis; **214,** Fernando Serna/Department of the Air Force; **215,** Richard Hutchins/ PhotoEdit; **216,** Corbis; **218,** Tony Freeman Photography; **221,** Jeff Greenberg/ Omni-Photo Communications, Inc.; **224,** Jim Rudnick/ Corbis Stock Market; **225,** Miriam Nathan-Roberts; **226 t,** Russ Lappa; **226 b,** Walter Hodges/Stone/Getty Images, Inc.; **228,** Corbis Stock Market; **238 Isaac Newton,** Science Museum Photo Library/Dorling Kindersley Ltd.; **238 the rest,** Dorling Kindersley Ltd.; **239 cube-corner reflector,** NASA; **239 Hall of Mirrors,** Max Alexander/ Dorling Kindersley Ltd.; **239 the rest,** Dorling Kindersley Ltd.

Chapter 5: Pages 240, 241, Jeff Greenberg/PhotoEdit; **245,** Clyde Lockwood/Animals Animals/Earth Scenes; **247,** Timothy Hursley/SuperStock, Inc.; **252,** Jim Cummins/Corbis Stock Market; **265,** AP/Wide World Photos; **266,** Michael Newman/ PhotoEdit; **268,** AP/Wide World Photos; **269,** Corbis; **270,** Tom Pantages; **273,** Russ Lappa; **274,** David Young-Wolff/PhotoEdit; **277,** Dave Schiefelbein/Stone/Getty Images, Inc.; **278,** Fred Wood/Summer Productions.

Chapter 6: Pages 286, 287, Complete Sportswear; **288,** The Image Works; **291,** Photograph copyright ©1996: Whitney Museum of American Art, New York. Photography by Sheldan C. Collins; **292,** Russ Lappa; **295,** Richard Haynes; **296,** Tony Freeman/ PhotoEdit; **298, 300,** Richard Haynes; **303,** Ken O'Donoghue; **305,** Tony Freeman Photography; **306 l,** Dave Bartruff/Stock Boston; **306 r,** Mark Thayer; **307,** Russ Lappa; **308 t,** Photo of Russell W.M. and Ruth Kraus residence, S.340 in *The Architecture of Frank Lloyd Wright: A Complete Catalog,* 3rd Edition, ©2002/William Allin Storrer, PhD; **308 b,** Plan of Russell W.M. and Ruth Kraus residence, S.340 in *The Frank Lloyd Wright Companion,* ©1973/William Allin Storrer, PhD; **313,** Walter Bibikow/Index Stock Imagery, Inc.; **315,** Ron Sherman/Stone/Getty Images, Inc.; **316,** Tony Freeman Photography; **316 inset,** Russ Lappa; **320,** archivebroehandesign.com, New York; **321,** Carl Purcell/Corbis;

323, Mark E. Gibson/Visuals Unlimited; **324,** Wallace Garrison/Index Stock Imagery, Inc.; **327,** Richard Haynes; **329,** ©National Park Service, photo by Bill Hudson, Biscayne National Park; **331 both,** Geoffrey Clifford/ Woodfin Camp; **333,** SuperStock, Inc.; **336,** Kunio Owaki/Corbis Stock Market; **344–345 skater,** Index Stock Imagery, Inc./PictureQuest; **344, 345 the rest,** Dorling Kindersley Ltd.

Chapter 7: Pages 346, 347, AP Photo/NASA; **348,** Mark Thayer; **351,** Roessler/SuperStock, Inc.; **353,** Larry Lefever/Grant Heilman Photography, Inc.; **360,** Tom Tracy/FPG International/Getty Images, Inc.; **363,** The Observatories of the Carnegie Institution of Washington; **367,** Rhoda Sidney/PhotoEdit; **368,** Stephen Saks/ Index Stock Imagery, Inc./ PictureQuest; **369,** Russ Lappa; **370,** Macduff Everton/Corbis; **377,** Simon Battensby/Stone/Getty Images, Inc.; **378,** Tony Donaldson/SportsChrome-USA; **379,** The Granger Collection, NY; **381,** Photo courtesy of NidaCore; **382,** Richard Cummins/Corbis; **383,** G. Ross/FPG International/Getty Images, Inc.; **384,** F. Dewey Webster/Sovfoto/Eastfoto/PictureQuest; **387,** PhotoDisc, Inc./Getty Images, Inc.; **391,** Bill Horsman/Stock Boston; **392,** *Calvin and Hobbs* ©Watterson. Dist. by Universal Press Syndicate. Reprinted with permission. All rights reserved.; **393,** Bob Daemmrich/Stock Boston; **396,** Russ Lappa; **397,** Russ Lappa; **399,** Bill Bachmann/Photo Network/PictureQuest; **403,** David Young-Wolff/PhotoEdit; **405,** Frank Fournier/Corbis Stock Market; **406,** AP/Wide World Photos.

Chapter 8: Pages 414, 415, David Maenza /SuperStock, Inc.; **416,** both David Young-Wolff/PhotoEdit; **418,** Prentice Hall; **419,** ©AAA reprinted with permission.; **420,** Michael Dwyer/Stock Boston; **421,** NASA; **424,** Miro Vintoniv/Stock Boston; **425,** Telegraph Colour Library/FPG International/Getty Images, Inc.; **427 t,** *Peanuts* reprinted by permission of United Feature Syndicate, Inc.; **427 m,** Ralf-Finn Hestoft/Index Stock Imagery, Inc.; **427 b,** Russ Lappa; **432,** Lee Snider/Photo Images; **435,** Francis Lepine/Animals Animals/Earth Scenes; **437,** AP/Wide World Photos; **441,** Paul Chesley/Stone/Getty Images, Inc.; **443,** Kevin Miller/Stone/Getty Images, Inc.; **447,** Corbis Digital Stock; **449,** Vincent Hobbs/SuperStock, Inc.; **450,** David Woodfall/Stone/ Getty Images, Inc.; **451,** Mark Richards/PhotoEdit; **454,** Russ Lappa; **456,** David Young-Wolff/PhotoEdit; **458,** Bob Daemmrich/Stock Boston/PictureQuest; **466 both,** Dorling Kindersley Ltd.; **467 t,** Corbis Digital Stock; **467 m,** Ryan McVay/PhotoDisc, Inc./ PictureQuest; **467 bl,** Dorling Kindersley Ltd.; **467 br,** Corbis Images/PictureQuest.

Chapter 9: Pages 468, 469, Peter Hendrie/Image Bank/Getty Images, Inc.; **471,** Scott T. Smith/Corbis; **474,** Katoomba Scenic Railway; **477,** Richard Hamilton/Corbis; **479,** David Young Wolff/PhotoEdit; **481 both,** Tom Pantages; **483,** Tom Carroll Photography; **485,** The Goodyear Tire & Rubber Company; **486,** Dwayne Newton/PhotoEdit; **488,** Giulio Andreini/Liaison Agency/Getty Images, Inc.; **490,** Lowell Georgia/Corbis; **491,** Stone/Getty Images, Inc.; **492,** Bob Daemmrich/Stock Boston; **493,** William J. Weber/Visuals Unlimited; **495,** NOAA; **496,** *The Far Side* ® by Gary Larson ©1993 Farworks, Inc. All rights reserved. Used with permission; **497,** Joe Towers/ Corbis Stock Market; **499,** George Gerster/Photo Researchers, Inc.; **501,** Corbis; **502,** PhotoDisc, Inc./Getty Images, Inc.; **503,** Ralph Cowan/FPG International/Getty Images, Inc.

Chapter 10: Pages 510, 511, Dorling Kindersley Ltd.; **513,** Michael Kevin Daly/Corbis Stock Market; **515,** Breck P. Kent; **516,** PhotoDisc, Inc./Getty Images, Inc.; **520,** Mark Thayer; **521,** Barry Durand/Odyssey/Chicago; **522,** Richard Haynes;

524, Reprinted by Permission of Tribune Media Services; **525 all,** Russ Lappa; **528,** Uniphoto, Inc./Pictor International; **530,** Russ Lappa; **531,** Tony Freeman/PhotoEdit; **532,** Russ Lappa; **538,** Will & Deni McIntyre/Stone/Getty Images, Inc.; **540,** Roger Allyn Lee/SuperStock, Inc.; **542,** Michael Busselle/Corbis; **544 both,** Russ Lappa; **548,** James King-Holmes/Science Photo Library/Photo Researchers, Inc.; **551,** Ken O'Donoghue; **552,** Pictor International; **554,** Carolyn Ross/Index Stock Imagery, Inc.; **555,** John Elk/StockBoston/ PictureQuest; **556,** Phil Martin/PhotoEdit; **557,** Alan Klehr/Stone/Getty Images, Inc.; **558,** Rafael Macia/Photo Researchers, Inc.; **561 l,** Richard Hutchings/Photo Researchers, Inc.; **561 m,** Mark C. Burnett/ Photo Researchers, Inc.; **561 r,** Tony Freeman/PhotoEdit; **562,** Gene Moore/ Phototake/PictureQuest; **564,** Ken O'Donoghue; **566,** Felicia Martinez/PhotoEdit; **567,** Russ Lappa; **569,** U.S. Department of Commerce **579 t,** Dorling Kindersley Ltd.; **579 b, 467 bl,** Mick Roessler/Index Stock Imagery, Inc./PictureQuest.

Chapter 11: Pages 580, 581, Ray Ooms/Masterfile Corporation; **583,** Jose Carrillo; **584,** Patrick Ward/Corbis; **587 t,** Carl F. Romney; **587 b, 588 both,** Russ Lappa; **591,** Steve Vidler/ SuperStock, Inc.; **592,** Tony Freeman Photographs; **594,** Robert Frerck/Stone/Getty Images, Inc.; **595,** Grant Heilman Photography, Inc.; **603,** AP/Wide World Photos; **608,** Shaun Egan/Stone/Getty Images, Inc.; **610,** Carol Simowitz; **611,** Stone/Getty Images, Inc.; **613,** Rosenfeld Images Ltd./Science Photo Library/Photo Researchers, Inc.; **617,** Tony Freeman Photographs; **619,** AFP/Corbis; **622,** Reza Estakhrian/ Stone /Getty Images, Inc.; **623,** Steven E. Sutton/Duomo; **624,** Christian Grzimek/Okapia/Photo Researchers, Inc.

Chapter 12: Page 634 l, Tom Rosenthal /SuperStock, Inc.; **634 r,** Russ Lappa; **635,** Gabe Palmer/Corbis Stock Market; **638,** Seth Joel/Corbis; **641,** Adam Smith Productions/Corbis; **645,** Roy Ooms/ Masterfile Corporation; **649, 650 both,** Jerry Jacka Photography; **655,** Michael Newman/PhotoEdit; **656,** PhotoDisc, Inc./Getty Images, Inc.; **659 tl,** Viviane Moos/Corbis Stock Market; **659 bl,** Paul Jablonka/International Stock Photo; **659 tr,** Alfred Pasieka/ SPL/Photo Researchers, Inc.; **659 br,** Adam Peirport/Corbis Stock Market; **662,** Brian Parker/Tom Stack & Associates, Inc.; **663 both,** Prentice Hall; **664 l,** Andrew J. Martinez ©1993/Photo Researchers, Inc.; **664 r,** Guido Alberto Rossi/Image Bank/Getty Images, Inc.; **665 l,** Tom Salyer/ Stock Connection/PictureQuest; **665 r,** Stone/Getty Images, Inc.; **667 t,** ©1996 M.C. Escher Heirs/Cordon Art, Baarn, Holland. All rights reserved.; **667 bl,** ©2001 Cordon Art, Baarn, Holland. All rights reserved.; **667 br,** Symmetry Drawing E67 by M.C. Escher. ©2002 Cordon Art, Baarn, Holland. All rights reserved.; **668,** Syracuse Newspapers/ The Image Works; **670 tl,** Ira Kirschenbaum/Stock Boston; **670 bl,** Margaret Courtney-Clarke/Corbis; **670 tr,** Suzanne Murphy-Larronde; **670 br,** M. Angelo/Corbis; **671,** From *The Grammar of Ornament* by Owen Jones, 1856 Edition/1998 Octavo Corporation; **673,** Robert Frerck/Odyssey/Chicago; **674,** Frank T. Awbrey/Visuals Unlimited; **678,** David Young/Wolff/PhotoEdit; **683 l,** Patti Murray/ Animals Animals/Earth Scenes; **683 r,** Russ Lappa; **684 l,** Don & Pat Valenti/DRK Photo; **684 r,** Jeff Foott/DRK Photo; **689,** Stone/Getty Images, Inc.